Good Beer Guide 2002

Edited by
Roger Protz

Deputy Editor
Jill Adam

Assistant Editor
Kate Green

C D B D D C

Sponsored I

D1499230

CASK MARQUE

CAMRA
BOOKS

Campaign for Real Ale Ltd
230 Hatfield Road, St Albans,
Hertfordshire AL1 4LW

Contents

Thanks to the following at CAMRA head office: Cressida Feiler, Publications Co-ordinator, for research and progress chasing for the Breweries section; the Campaigns team of Mike Benner, Iain Loe, Louise Ashworth, Tony Jerome, Jonathan Mail, and Gayle Woodstock. The What's Brewing duo of Ted Bruning and Kim Adams. The Administration team: Kirk Winkler, Malcolm Harding, Jean Jones, Gary Fowler, Michael Green, Abi Maddocks, Rosalba La Monica and Angie Nergaard. Special thanks to Peter Feiler for work beyond the call of duty on the Breweries section. Thanks to Alan Risdon for website information. Thanks to Viv and Tina Davies of the Farmers Boy, London Road, St Albans, for allowing their pub to be used to photograph the cover.

Beer Index compiled by Jeff Evans. Extracts from books and poetry in the Guide are from A Taste of Ale, compiled by Roy Palmer, £6.95, Green Branch Press, Kencot Lodge, Kencot, Glos, GL7 3QX; tel 01367 860588; fax 01367 860765; e-mail chrisyapp@btconnect.com

Thanks to 60,000 CAMRA members who carried out research for the pubs; the Campaign's Regional Directors who co-ordinated the pub entries; CAMRA's Brewery Liaison Officers for their reports on the country's breweries; and CAMRA's National Executive for their support and enthusiasm.

The Good Beer Guide: Designed by Rob Howells. Typeset by T&O Graphics, Bungay, Suffolk. Maps by Perrott Cartographics, Machynlleth. Colour Reproduction by DDP Imaging. Printed by WS Bookwell Ltd, Finland.

Published by the Campaign for Real Ale Ltd, 230 Hatfield Road, St Albans, Herts AL1 4LW. Tel 01727 867201. Fax 01727 867670. Action Line 0845 60 30 20 8

E-mail camra@camra.org.uk   Website www.camra.org.uk
ISBN 1-85249-178-7   © Campaign for Real Ale Ltd 2001/2002

Labour of love...the unique 'union room' fermentation system at Marston's

Save Britain's Brewing Heritage

Beer lovers must act now to stop
the onward march of global brewing giants
and pub chains, says **Roger Protz**

BRITAIN'S proud brewing heritage is in mortal danger. Many of the magnificent cask-conditioned beers and their breweries listed in the Good Beer Guide could disappear unless drinkers force the government to stop further takeovers and mergers that threaten brewers' independence and drinkers' choice.

The brewing industry and pub trade have changed out of all recognition in recent years. For decades, most pubs were owned by brewers – the tied trade – while the remainder – the free trade – bought beer from regional as well as national producers. But a concerted and cynical effort by the national brewers in the 1990s to sabotage the government's Beer Orders, which attempted to improve choice by allowing tenants to buy guest beers free of the beer giants' tie, has changed the landscape. New pub groups, which are not covered by the Beer Orders, have grown rapidly and now own most of the country's pubs. A glance at the Pub Groups listing within the Guide's Breweries section shows that most of the major pub groups buy their beers almost exclusively from the global brewing

3

giants, Interbrew (Bass and Whitbread), Scottish Courage and Carlsberg-Tetley.

The listing tells only half the story. Nick Stafford, owner of Hambleton Ales, and chairman of the Society of Independent Brewers, shows graphically (pages 13 to 15) how the pub groups demand £120 discounts off barrels of beer costing £240, and then sell the beers to their tenants at the full wholesale price. Smaller brewers, who are labour intensive and pay the same extortionate levels of duty as the giants, cannot afford such deep discounts. The duopoly of global brewers and large pub companies has a stranglehold on brewing, distribution and choice. The three big brewers account for eight out of ten pints brewed in Britain; they have sweetheart deals with the pub groups; and together they have made a mockery of such concepts as competition and consumer choice.

They are not, however, omnipotent. A powerful blow was struck for beer drinkers and independent brewers in August 2001 with the defeat of a hostile takeover bid by the Pubmaster group for Wolverhampton & Dudley Breweries. W&D, which owns Banks's, Cameron's, Mansfield and Marston's, is Britain's biggest regional brewer. If it had lost to Pubmaster, then all four breweries would have been put up for sale and probably closed.

The knock-on effect could have been catastrophic. Other regional brewers, Greene King in particular, would have been in the firing line as the pub companies went on the rampage, buying and closing breweries in order to build even bigger retail estates in which to sell heavily-discounted national beer brands.

It would be naive to think that the battle to save Britain's brewing heritage is now over. With 1,700 pubs, W&D remains a tempting trophy for Pubmaster or another pub group to win. But for the moment the pub profiteers have been defeated. It is important for all who revel in the abundance of choice offered to British beer drinkers to make sure that independent brewers, from large regional companies, through family-owned firms, to small craft brewers, are allowed to survive, flourish and sell their beers unhindered by the bully-boy tactics of the pub companies and the giant global producers.

Brewers must learn the lessons of the W&D struggle. The watchwords must be 'Small is Beautiful'. W&D was warned by its friends that a dash for growth, which included buying Mansfield and Marston's in 1998, was a recipe for disaster. W&D became heavily over-stretched financially at a time of stagnating beer sales. Its greatly enlarged national pub estate made it vulnerable to attack from the voracious pub groups. It defeated Pubmaster by a whisker: the pub group won the support of 47 per cent of shareholders. At a time when large groups of shares are held by such institutions as banks, insurance companies and pension fund holders, it is difficult for companies like W&D to hang on to their independence.

Brewers who find themselves under attack should not ignore consumer power. David Thompson, the chairman of W&D, has publicly acknowledged the importance of CAMRA's help in the battle with Pubmaster. The Campaign organised petitions throughout the Midlands and also at beer festivals, and Mr Thompson believes these efforts were important in rallying individual shareholders to the group's side. W&D is still independent. Morland, which snootily rejected offers of help from CAMRA, is now closed, taken over by Greene King.

Independent brewers and beer drinkers need – and deserve – the sup port of government. Brewing is a major industry that contributes vast amounts of tax and duty to the public purse. Yet the top echelon of the industry is now in foreign hands. Interbrew is a Belgian group while Carlsberg-Tetley is a wholly-owned subsidiary of Carlsberg of Denmark. Scottish Courage is still a British-based company but, following the acquisition of Kronenbourg of France and Alken Maes of Belgium, and with Peroni of Italy in its sights, it is as much a global player as its two rivals. These massive brewing conglomerates are motivated primarily by the huge profits to be made from lager and nitro-keg 'smooth' beers. The fall in sales of cask-conditioned beer in the 1990s is due in large measure to the fact that the Big Three have turned their backs on the style in preference to nitro-keg.

There is a powerful umbilical link between the global brewers and the large pub groups. Two of the most powerful groups, Pubmaster and Unique, are controlled by foreign interests, including German and Japanese banks; Unique is wholly owned by Nomura of Japan. Whitbread sold its entire pub estate in 2001 to Morgan Grenfell, a subsidiary of Deutsche Bank of Frankfurt. The result is that the modern British brewing and pub industries are dominated by producers and retailers with no loyalty to our traditions and heritage, and no truck with the attitude of smaller brewers, who believe they have duties and responsibilties to their communities, publicans and customers. For the new beerage, profit is the driving force, and a perishable product such as cask beer is at best an irritant, at worst something to be sidelined or discarded.

We need a strategy for the brewing industry and that can come only from government. At present there is only confusion. One of New

How to get a brewery listed...

Listed buildings are ones that are officially recognised as being of special 'architectural or historic interest' and receive a greater measure of protection than others. The list is maintained by the Department for Culture, Media and Sport. Listing covers the entire building or site – outside, inside, and fixtures and fittings. It is an offence to demolish or alter a listed building without consent.

There are three categories:
Grade II, which covers some 94% of all listed buildings.
Grade II* makes up a further 4% that are considered to be of exceptional interest.
Grade I covers the remaining 2% of buildings considered to be of paramount importance to the nation.
Anyone can apply to the Department to have a building listed. The DCMS will then refer the application to English Heritage, which is the Department's official adviser.

An application must include:
● A set of photos of the site that convery an accurate impression of the architecture and internal arrangements;
● A copy of a street map marked to show where the brewery is located;
● A sketch plan showing the layout of the building.

Send applications to:
Department for Culture, Media & Sport, 2-4 Cockspur Street, London SW1Y 5DU. For futher advice, contact CAMRA on 01727 867201 or e-mail camra@camra.org.uk. This information on listing also applies to pubs: if a pub faces closure and you consider it worthy of listing, follow the steps outlined above.

Labour's first acts in 1997 was to block a proposed merger between Bass and Carlsberg-Tetley on the unarguable grounds that it was against the public interest. Yet Interbrew has been allowed to swallow both Bass and Whitbread, giving the Belgian group a 32 per cent share of the market.

A real government strategy must entail a ban on any further mergers and takeovers at the top of the industry. Interbrew's 32 per cent market share breaches government guidelines, while ScotCo hovers close to the 30 per cent level that constitutes a monopoly situation. An investigation is needed to determine whether or not both groups should be required to sell off brands and/or breweries to reduce their market shares.

The government must intervene to defend the independent, regional brewing sector, whose market share has fallen from 22 per cent to 15 per cent in a decade. The Pubmaster bid for W&D should have been blocked, on the grounds that the closure of four breweries, the loss of jobs, beer brands and reduced consumer choice were clearly against the public interest. In the event, W&D survived, but it will sell Cameron's to Castle Eden and will close Mansfield. Mansfield is a large brewery employing a substantial workforce. The government should immediately make available the funds to enable the Mansfield management to buy the plant and a small estate of pubs from W&D, and should also investigate whether European funds are available to help Mansfield.

An investigation by the Office of Fair Trading is needed into the thorny question of discounts. At present, the cosy duopoly of beer giants and pub groups effectively keeps many regional and most craft brewers out of the pub groups' estates. A level playing field is required: if discounts are to be permitted, they should be fixed at a level that will allow smaller brewers to gain access to pub groups' estates. And the benefits of discounts between brewer and pub group must be passed on to licensees so they can share in the benefits and keep beer prices down. The Good Beer Guide is not convinced, however, that discounts should exist at all. The evidence suggests that discounts distort the market, are of no benefit to licensees or drinkers, and keep beer prices artificially high.

The Beer Orders are dead and buried where the national brewers are concerned. The guest beer policy applies only to tenants of national brewers, not to managed pubs. Bass has become Six Continents, a pub retailer, Whitbread has left both brewing and pub retailing, while ScotCo has switched its pubs from tenancies to management. As Nick Stafford argues, it is now essential that the government extends the Beer Orders to the non-brewing pub groups, which should allow their tenants to buy guest beers free of the tie.

Readers of the Good Beer Guide have a role to play. Wherever possible, drink the beers made by independent brewers. They offer better value for money and, produced by craftsmen with a passion for cask beer, offer better aromas, flavours and pleasure as well. Readers can defend independent brewers against takeover and closure by attempting to list buildings of architectural and historic interest. Marston's of Burton-on-Trent is by no means safe for the future in the sometimes clumsy embrace of Wolverhampton & Dudley. One way to ensure its safety, in particular its unique 'union rooms' in which Pedigree is fermented in giant oak casks, is to have the whole site listed.

The defeat of Pubmaster means that August 2001 should mark the date when independent brewers and beer drinkers united to stand up for choice and diversity, and to safeguard our brewing heritage for future generations to enjoy.

Light my fire...Susy Smith enjoys a pint of real ale in her rural local

Thatched or despatched

Susy Smith on the continuing campaign to save rural locals

SAVE OUR COUNTRY PUBS'. Thus went the rallying cry as we launched Country Living magazine's campaign in September 2000. It would, we planned, draw attention to the demise of some of Britain's best loved and most historically important buildings where traditionalism still rules, native and stranger are united, and the ghastliness of theme pubs and slick city wine bars are left far behind.

Pubs where one can draw up a chair to the blazing log-filled inglenook or sit in the open air and revel in the beauty of Britain's glorious landscapes. Sepia pictures on the walls are likely to be genuine, and the subsidence that caused the sloping floor probably took place in the 18th century.

Our cause, we hoped, would unite each and every one of Country Living's 160,000 readers, galvanising even the most ardent teetotallers into action. For the country pub is about so much more than simply having a drink. And it matters to rural communities and town dwellers alike, albeit for different reasons.

For locals the pub is the hub of village life, a place to meet and chew the cud. It continues traditional games – shove-halfpenny, skittles and dominoes – which have, for the most part, died out elsewhere. It cements rural communities. For visitors, with a more romantic viewpoint, the country pub is as much an intrinsic element of the British countryside as safely grazing sheep and sky larks ascending.

Over the years Country Living has featured many articles celebrating the country pub and small rural breweries. One such piece by John Seymour, in September 1992, began: 'The bastions of the English village have fallen one by one. Too often the school has been closed, and the children are bussed miles away and taught city values. The church endures, but a couple of pews is all that is needed to seat the ageing congregation. Blacksmith, wheelwright, butcher, baker, carpenter and undertaker: most of these are gone. But the pub survives.'

Well, not any more it doesn't. Research by the Rural Development Commission has shown that only a third of Britain's rural parishes still have a pub. And despite tireless campaigning on the part of CAMRA and others, country pubs continue to close at a rate of six a week.

The problems for the rural publican are many: with social change being high up the list. Unreliable transport systems mean it is difficult for customers to get to their chosen hostelry. Inexpensive supermarket purchases of imported lagers make home drinking a more attractive option.

And in areas where second homes and holiday lets proliferate, any permanent population of potential drinkers will have been driven out. While other rural businesses employing local people get generous rate relief, pubs, traditionally have not. Add to this the low profit margins on beer sales and the fact that most pubs are now owned by large breweries or 'pubcos' who demand far higher returns and ruthlessly cull insufficiently profitable businesses, and it's a wonder there are any rural pubs left at all.

And when the beleaguered landlord finally decides he's had enough of all this, an enthusiastic estate agent will happily relieve him of his burden by selling it on as a private residence – for at least double the price he would get for the business. Who can blame him for selling up?

Those pubs that aren't closing are being taken over by conglomerates who, while adorning city centre bars with antique farming implements to give them a 'country feel', will take the genuine article, 'modernise' the interior and alter its sign board to something beginning with an F and Firkin or a name similarly irrelevant to its setting. The traditional name that was probably centuries old and commemorated a historical event or celebrated an aspect of the pub's locality is soon gone and forgotten.

So, we at Country Living wondered, what can be done? Well, our readers, not surprisingly, like walking in the countryside. And there's little better than a walk in the countryside we reasoned, than one with a pub at the end of it. Thus, purchasers of our September 2000 issue received a free copy of our booklet 'Short walks to country pubs'. We then officially launched our campaign with a four-page feature in our October issue and, on the basis that the best way to save country pubs is to encourage people to use them, we asked readers to nominate their favourite hostelry. We also asked them to sign our petition, which, in conjunction with CAMRA, we later used to lobby the government for 50 per cent rate relief for pubs.

In March 2001 we followed this up with a feature on the tiny craft breweries who are keeping alive Britain's wealth of regional beers. Our readers were introduced to a bevy of wonderfully named brews from Norfolk Nog and Hoop and Sneck Lifter to Isle of Skye Red Cuillin. We also invited them to join us for a spot of beer tasting and a tour of some of the country's finest independent breweries.

At around the same time we were involved in another very worthwhile project, our Enterprising Rural Women campaign. This scheme is designed to reward women who have excelled in setting up a small rural business or diversifying to help keep the family farm running. Given our ongoing interest in all things ale related, we were delighted when the judges chose, as one of our two winners, brewster Sara Barton. The word brewster – new to all of us on Country Living – is the correct term for a female brewer and originates from medieval times when making ale was a cottage industry and women brewed at the same time as they baked bread. Sara owns and runs her own craft brewery and sells distinctive real ales to almost 200 pubs across England. She plans to use her prize money to launch a range of bottled ales.

So what, at the end of all this, is the future for Britain's country pubs? The government has agreed in principle to relax the rating system although it isn't clear if this will apply universally or when it is going to come into force. Perhaps further assistance will come from the newly-formed department for Environment, Food and Rural affairs under Margaret Beckett, which will, they claim, be spearheading a major new drive on green issues and the countryside.

In the meantime it's up to all of us. The country pub is part of our heritage and as such must be saved. The best way to achieve this is to give pubs our business – as often as possible. 'Use it or lose it' must become our motto.

And if you should suddenly discover the landlord at your local has called last orders for the last time, and shut up shop, don't despair.

Country Living's ground-breaking feature on the campaign to save country pubs

And don't think there is nothing you can do about it. Take the Old Crown at Hesket Newmarket which went up for sale when the long-standing and highly-respected landlord, Jim Fearnley, retired to concentrate on the adjoining brewery. New landlords Kim and Lyn Matthews took over. However, five years later, when Jim Fearnley decided to retire altogether, Kim and Lyn felt they couldn't take on the brewery as well. They advertised it for sale in the pub and it's now owned 60 per cent by villagers and 40 per cent by regular customers. As no one can own more than one share they have guaranteed that shareholders are not in it for the money but rather for the desire to see a local asset saved.

Projects such as this can't help but foster true community spirit. And it is typical of the good old-fashioned British enterprise that in the end will probably be the saviour of our best country pubs.

Susy Smith is editor of Country Living

Dump the comfort blanket

Simon Loftus argues that regional brewers must innovate or die

A REQUEST FROM the Good Beer Guide to write an article on a strategy for saving independent brewers provokes all sorts of questions in my mind. For one thing it is clear that a number of regional brewers are doing very well, and need little help from me or anyone else. For another, it might even be fair to ask whether all brewers deserve saving – I can think of a number of dreary beers that few of us would weep for, should they disappear. And finally I doubt whether any single strategy could possibly cover the variety of independent brewers and the range of local circumstances.

Having said which, it seems clear to me that all businesses need to be well managed if they wish to survive and prosper in this increasingly

All hands and new ideas to the pumps...Simon Loftus (left) says regional brewers need fresh ideas and fresh brands to survive in the cut-throat world of modern brewing

competitive world. Regional brewers have sometimes tended to think that their problems are specific to their industry, while ignoring the basic disciplines of effective management. No company can afford to be complacent about its approach to IT, or to training, or to supply chain management, or to customer service – all of which are areas where the brewing industry has tended to fall behind the standards being set by others, which mould the expectations of customers and employees alike. Everyone needs to benchmark themselves against the standards of a wider world, looking beyond the boundaries of industry or locality.

I should personally add another key measure of business excellence, to do with corporate responsibility to the communities in which we operate and from whom we derive our livelihoods. Social and environmental issues are at the heart of the debate over sustainable development and all of us need to be involved. Partly this is a matter of crude self-interest – ensuring that our markets prosper, our customers feel warm to us – but there is also the huge boost to corporate pride which comes from doing things well, holding our heads high. That sense of motivation and passion is what separates the real drivers of future growth from the has-beens and also-rans.

Brewers depend for their survival on getting all those things right but they must also tackle the specific issues of brand management and distribution – where fundamental choices are involved which will determine the strategic direction of individual companies. Scale is key. Do you want to be a big fish in a tiny pond or a brightly-coloured fish in a larger lake? Are you happy to sell your beers through your own pubs and a few free houses in your

Down in one...a new fermenting vessel being dropped through the roof into Adnams' Southwold brewery. New vessels have boosted Adnams' production by 50 per cent.

immediate locality or do you have ambitions further afield? What are the implications of that choice, in terms of production, marketing and distribution?

There is room for plenty of niche brands, in terms of genuinely local brewers – and I see no real obstacle to the survival of micro-brewers or somewhat larger companies which operate within a tightly defined locality. But there has to be a question mark over the number of brands which a larger market can support. National distribution is dominated by a handful of supply chains and the number of major customers will continue to diminish, as pub-owning companies merge to form fewer and bigger operators. Under such circumstances it is natural for a relatively small number of regional brands to prosper, while the rest will find the market too competitive or the mechanics of building brand credibility too demanding.

Whatever the chosen scale, all breweries need to nurture their brands, even the smallest. That means distinctive product quality, consistently served – but it also means clear brand identity and visibility. There are key differences between the niche marketing of regional beers and the mechanics of a global brand, but failure to commit to brand building and brand management is one of the most obvious routes to ruin. Even within the fortress walls of his tied estate, a regional brewer's brand is vulnerable to attack – customers will simply ignore it if its competitors are doing a smarter job. In the wider world, brand management is the key to distribution as well as sales – no buyer for a retail chain of pubs will even consider stocking a product which lacks brand credibility with his customers. All of which demands a great deal of creative thinking (what is the essence of my brand?) and consistent investment in professional marketing. Companies need to be bold. Nostalgia and tradition have their place but building brands for the future demands a more radical approach, which translates such values into a classic, continuing appeal. Most independent brewers have tended to reach for the comfort blanket of their heritage rather than looking to the future.

At the point of sale much has been achieved but there is more to be done. Most beer drinkers prefer a refreshing, characterful drink to a lukewarm bowl of soup – which means that real beer should be served cool. It tastes better that way, despite the bleatings of die-hard traditionalists. Making sure that every glass is served at a consistently cool temperature is relatively simple (the technology is available) but involves investment. Brewers who fail to commit to this investment will simply lose out to more professional competitors; there is no time to waste in getting these things right. More radical, perhaps, are questions about the traditional handpump and other aspects of cellar management and dispense. Alternative approaches are available, some of which may well prove beneficial in terms of consistent quality in the glass, and nothing should be ruled out simply because it offends traditionalists. There may be better ways of doing things.

That, finally, should be the mantra for independent brewers as for all other businesses – 'Let's do things better'. The great heritage of British beers, in all its rich diversity, cannot and will not survive if we try to preserve it in aspic, a fossil of the past. Not all change is good, but good change is vital.

CAMRA has a lot to be proud of. Thirty years ago CAMRA helped reverse an apparently irresistible tide, re-creating a demand for real beer. Since then there have been effective CAMRA campaigns on all sorts of issues, fighting the closure of local breweries or local pubs, or promoting the beers that you treasure; but there have also been ill-judged initiatives, attempting to stifle positive developments by traditional brewers. Let's hope that we can move forward together, as allies in a process of change which preserves the values that we both cherish. Classic traditions live by re-invention. This should be the strategic imperative for all independent brewers, and for those who support them.

Simon Loftus is the chairman of Adnams of Southwold, Suffolk.

Getting ahead ...Nick Stafford blows the froth off small brewers' problems

Small fish to fry

Nick Stafford says small craft brewers still face major hurdles in getting their beers to market

SMALL BREWERS have been criticised for sitting on their backsides, waiting for business to come to them. But not any longer. Members of SIBA, the Society of Independent Brewers, have organised themselves into an efficient national network. The fruits of this work began to appear with the signing of a contract with the Unique Pub Co to supply selected pubs in its estate with guest beers. A trial began in July 2000 with retailers in the North-east of England, predominately in Yorkshire. The success lead to the inclusion of retailers

1 3

Cask Marque
delivering a quality promise

THE CASK MARQUE Trust – the sponsor of the CAMRA Good Beer Guide – is an accreditation scheme making awards to licensees where, through independent inspection, they have proved they can meet quality standards in serving cask beer. The award is made to the licensee and not the pub, as it is his expertise that rewards you, the customer, with the 'perfect pint'.

The scheme has been operating successfully for more than four years, it has over 2,000 award-winning licensees, and is committed to raising beer quality standards.

Pinting the way to perfection ...Felicity Atherton, licensee of the Crown at Gayton, King's Lynn, Norfolk, receives her plaque from Cask Marque director Paul Nunny (left) and Jim Louth, sales development manager of Greene King Pub Partners

Our promise to the Customer

Customers will recognise an award-winning licensee by the display of the Cask Marque plaque. This gives the customer:
● a quality guarantee that each pint of cask ale is served in perfect condition
● the opportunity to 'Try before you Buy'. All Cask Marque licensees will allow the customers a free sample before committing to purchase.
● If you are in a Cask Marque award-winning pub and the beer is, in your opinion, not up to standard, speak to the landlord and if you are still unhappy we encourage you to write to our organisation.

Who are Cask Marque licensees?

Award-winning licensees can be found by:
● The displaying of the Cask Marque plaque.
● The Cask Marque symbol alongside their entry in the Good Beer Guide. (These entries are chosen by CAMRA independent of Cask Marque.)
● Through our free regional guides available via the Cask Marque office on 01206 752212.
● By visiting our website on www.cask-marque.co.uk

Why is beer quality such an important issue?

With the price of beer today, customers quite rightly demand a quality product. Research and our own inspections have shown that all too often the quality of cask beer in the glass is less than satisfactory.

This situation is being corrected by a programme of training staff in cellar skills and investment in temperature control equipment from the cellar to the bar. Beer must be served between 11 degrees – 13 degrees C whether it be summer or winter; warm beer is insipid and lacking in refreshment, and destroys the delicate flavours for which cask beer is so renowned.

Do you want to visit a brewery?

Have you ever thought of visiting your local brewery, or seeing around breweries in other parts of the country? Cask Marque has created (with the help of its membership) a website with information on brewery tours. The website is 'http://www.visitabrewery.co.uk'

How to find out more about Cask Marque

Visit the Cask Marque website on 'http://www.cask-marque. co.uk'. You also have an opportunity to e-mail us with comments at cask-marque@mcno.com

No longer pie in the sky

Susan Nowak reports that a campaign inspired by CAMRA is revitalising pub food

IMITATION, THEY SAY, is the sincerest form of flattery. And Tom Finlay, founder of the Campaign for Real Food, is an admirer of CAMRA, and hopes his organisation can achieve similar results.

'If my campaign can do for real food what CAMRA has done for the beer drinker I'll be a happy man,' says Finlay. Appropriately, his campaign was born in a pub, while he was landlord of a Somerset freehouse, dedicated, naturally, to real ale and real food.

The main aim of the Campaign for Real Food (CARF) is to encourage pubs and restaurants to serve good, home-cooked meals prepared from

fresh ingredients, and for the public to demand nothing less when dining out.

'It's very simple. We want to bring taste back into people's lives,' says Finlay, a crusader against bought in, factory meals. 'Why is it all branding now? Why does a Cornish pasty have to be Ginster's or fish and chips Harry Ramsden's?'

Food for thought ...chef Alberto Pihno celebrates his CARF award with Carl Smith (left), licensee of Young's Guinea and Windmill pubs in London, Antony Worrall Thompson and CARF founder Tom Finlay

When he launched the campaign four years ago it was really a trade association that began through Tom getting together with like-minded publicans and restaurateurs. As it grew and attracted members from as far away as Ireland, he sold his pub to concentrate on the campaign, then had to put it on hold during a serious family illness. But in January 2001 he effectively relaunched CARF in a different form and with a powerful ally – Antony Worrall Thompson.

The TV chef and restaurateur is now the first president of CARF, which has decided to follow the example of CAMRA by throwing open its membership to the public at large.

'I'm putting my name behind it because there are such important issues here. It's like the Campaign for Real Ale which has been a fantastic campaign for a lot of pubs serving real ale. We need to do the same for food,' Worrall Thompson says.

Briefly a partner in a pub himself, he does not have the highest opinion of British pub food and believes this is an area where his campaign must concentrate. 'Pub chains hate chefs. The majority of pubs buy in ready-made food.'

Under its new colours, CARF has widened its aims and now intends to be a real campaigning organisation. Just as CAMRA has lobbied parliament over such issues as guest ales, reform of licensing hours and reducing beer tax, so CARF aims 'to be a powerful voice' promoting fresh food and forcing action on everything from GM crops to the EU red tape strangling small producers.

Says Tom Finlay: 'What we want is a voice for the ordinary people. We all have to eat, and what we eat is important. There are 600 people in the Food Standards Agency and it's just a cop out. If the government had set up an agency with teeth, as they promised, it would be different – we might not have such a massive increase in cases of food poisoning, for instance, and the foot and mouth crisis might not have reached such catastrophic levels.

'People are too reticent about complaining. Recently I had such an appalling meal in a pub that I took it back and said "You should be ashamed for serving this", and then I walked out. I didn't even ask for my money back. We have to get on our soap boxes and make the British people the biggest moaners in the world, then perhaps we'll get somewhere.'

His revamped campaign is certainly getting somewhere. After Finlay, now 70, kick started it again with £50,000 of his own money, and with Worrall Thompson promoting it through media interviews and a cookery demonstration at Olympia's Pub and Bar show, membership is growing. By May 2001, they had 50 trade members, ranging from pubs to an organic vegetable supplier, a bed and breakfast establishment serving organic breakfasts, and around 100 members of the public. They are getting three inquiries a day.

Membership of CARF costs £25 a year, which includes quarterly newsletters, discounts on meals, details of 'real food' establishments and invitations to food events. The first major event was planned for the BBC Good Food Show in November 2001.

Professional caterers can either join CARF as ordinary members or apply for full accreditation. This costs a non-returnable £150 ('we want to discourage those who are not up to scratch' says Tom Finlay) to cover the costs of a rigorous inspection of the premises, ingredients used, food preparation and meals served, then £120 a year membership. Only if it passes does it get the CARF wall plaque to display outside.

TV chef and restaurateur Antony Worrall Thompson brings his passion for good food and organic ingredients to his role as president of the Campaign for Real Food, which is as concerned about pub food as it is the restaurant versions

One of Tom Finlay's early supporters was Carl Smith, award-winning licensee of Young's Guinea and Windmill in Mayfair, a chef with the impeccable credential of being the country's official steak and kidney pie champion.

'When I saw what Tom was trying to do I wanted to join in and play an active role,' says Smith, now a director of CARF. 'There really is a crying need to encourage pubs and restaurants to prepare wholesome meals from quality ingredients in their own kitchens.'

They also see their role as educational, and want to catch them young. CARF has been pressing for the return of cookery classes, and member chefs visit schools and give lessons themselves.

In 2001, CARF awarded honorary memberships to cookery writer Henrietta Green, who compiled a directory of specialist food producers called the Farmers' Market Cookbook, Nina Planck, author of the London Farmers' Market Book, Dr Martin Caraher of Thames University's centre for food policy, a specialist on healthier eating for children, and myself as editor of CAMRA's Good Pub Food and Pub Superchefs.

For further information write to The Campaign for Real Food, 3 The Castle House, Long Street, Sherborne, Dorset, DT9 3BU, tel 01935 389497/fax 389498, e-mail carf@positivepr.co.uk, web-site www.thecarf.co.uk

BOTTLE-CONDITIONED beers are real ales in a bottle. Just as cask-conditioned beer enjoys a secondary fermentation in the cask in the pub cellar, bottle-conditioned beer does the same in the bottle, because it contains a yeast sediment and is a living product. It is not filtered; it is not pasteurised; it is not artificially carbonated.

However, researching these beers has entailed more than just popping down to the local off-licence. The vast majority of Britain's bottle-conditioned beers don't find their way into the major chains but have to be sought out in gift shops, craft and garden centres, and even farmers' markets. They are produced by micro-breweries, bottling beer on a small scale in the old tradition.

Yet it is noticeable how micro-breweries have moved beyond the stage of only bottling as an afterthought, using up left-over beer after all the casks have been filled. They have begun to recognise the merits

Overdrawn at the
bottle bank

Jeff Evans celebrates the small boom in real ale under glass

Three's a nice crowd...Peter Scholey, head brewer at Brakspear of Henley-on-Thames, parades his bottle-conditioned beers. Live Organic was first brewed for Safeway but its success has made it available in other outlets

of bottled beer per se. They see it not only as an added source of income and a means of compensating for the ever-tightening pub market, but also as a way of promoting their name.

It is also pleasantly encouraging to find larger, regional brewers, too, like Fuller's, Young's, Badger and Greene King, keeping faith with the natural bottling process. The last two are in fact new to the bottled real ale scene, and have arrived there by default, inheriting beers from breweries they closed down. But the fact that Badger has continued to bottle condition King & Barnes's Faygate Dragon and Cornucopia, and Greene King has kept faith with Morland's Hen's Tooth, deserves warm praise.

Another active regional brewery is Brakspear, which has expanded into the organic sector. Two organic beers rolled off the Brakspear bottling line almost simultaneously in spring 2001, the spicy-hopped Ted & Ben's and the gloriously Golding-rich Live Organic. Live Organic was initially exclusive to Safeway stores, indicating how the supermarket sector has now begun to take risks with bottle-conditioned beers. I say risks because the perceived wisdom is that supermarket shoppers, not being dedicated beer buffs, don't understand the concept of beer containing yeast sediment.

But as the 'real food' idea has grown, shoppers have been getting the message, and the number of bottles returned because they have 'crap in the bottom' has diminished. An excellent initiative to ram home the idea of sediment beers came when the Booths grocery chain, in the

North-west of England, launched its first own-label bottle-conditioned beer in May. Beer buyer David Smith commissioned Bateman to brew the ale and then cleverly named it 'Pour With Care', attracting shoppers with its off-the-wall name and sending them a message on how to serve the beer at the same time.

Still on the subject of the major multiples, Somerfield is now stocking a range of about eight local bottled beers in each of its stores, many being bottle-conditioned, and Bottoms Up has stood head and shoulders above the other dedicated chain off-licences with its wide range of small brewery bottles.

I've even noticed a move in the right direction in pubs. Since the guest beer law was changed in 1998 to allow tenants of national brewers' pubs to stock a guest bottle-conditioned beer, as well as a guest cask beer, the take up has been slow. I've never quite understood this. A pub that, through no fault of its tenant, has been landed with an unattractive choice of national brand draught beers can easily add a splash of colour to its shelves by stocking a tasty, distinctive bottle-conditioned ale from one of the smaller producers.

It's a no-lose situation. The landlord doesn't have to buy huge volumes (compared with cask beer), and the beer doesn't go off as quickly as cask, so if it doesn't sell through immediately, it's not a huge problem. I have been pleased, however, to hear from several publicans who have begun stocking bottled real ale in the last year. It's a trend that can only grow.

But what of the beers themselves? Frankly, there have been some staggering innovations. The Tesco Beer Challenge has thrown up three bottle-conditioned winners that deserve their success in the aisles. Hop Back's Crop Circle (fragrantly spiced with coriander) and St Austell's amazing Clouded

Gone for a Burton...after a peripatetic life in the 1990s, Worthington's White Shield, the grandaddy of India Pale Ales, is now being brewed by Museum Brewery in Burton-on-Trent, where it originated in the 19th century

Yellow (a wheat beer confection laced with vanilla, cloves and other spices) were followed by Wulfric, a premium ale subtly infused with ginger. This was produced at the Bass Museum Brewery, which, despite all the upheavals involving Interbrew, has taken a bold step forward this year. A new bottling line has been introduced there to handle the return of Worthington's White Shield to Burton upon Trent, after its sojourn at King & Barnes. The move delighted beer enthusiasts, as it kept alive one of Britain's classic bottle-conditioned beers.

Another of the classics, Prize Old Ale, is thriving in its own modest way down at Gale's in Horndean, where a new champagne-like beer called Milestones Ale at 9 per cent has been introduced. Regrettably, it looks like we have seen the last of Courage Imperial Russian Stout, as the final supplies of the most recent (1993) vintage have finally dwindled away.

However, devotees of the strong, complex Baltic stout style can console themselves with a new beer from Harveys. Imperial Extra Double Stout was first brewed (for export to the US) in 1999 and based on the meaty, nourishing beers produced by the Le Coq Brewery in Estonia, which was nationalised by the Bolsheviks in 1917. Big in vinous, fruity, roasted notes, it is now being released in Britain and makes an excellent substitute for the Courage beer. Another British classic, Thomas Hardy's Ale – while not officially deceased – is certainly fighting for its life. This world-renowned 12 per cent beer has not been brewed since 1999, thanks to the restructuring of Eldridge Pope and the sale of its brewery to a contract brewer.

On the double...Harvey's bottle-conditioned stout keeps alive the tradition of strong export stouts first brewed for the Baltic trade

The relatively small quantities needed, and the time and space occupied at the brewery by the maturing beer, means that, in the cut-throat world of contract brewing, it's not a viable option to brew it at its Dorchester home any longer. Eldridge Pope has declared that it is still looking for a brewer for the beer, and indeed has orders waiting from both Britain and the US, but there has been no progress to date.

It's a slightly disappointing note on which to end this appraisal of the bottle-conditioned beer scene, but it's heartwarming to know that, even if Hardy's Ale never resurfaces, and if we have lost Courage Imperial Russian, the bottle-conditioned beer industry can now survive these set backs. Thirty years ago, two-fifths of our bottled real ales would have been lost if these two had disappeared. Now, as regrettable as it is, their loss accounts for less than 1 per cent. With more and more breweries looking to bottle condition, and the major retailers prepared to support them, that percentage is going to appear more miniscule every year.

Jeff Evans is the author of CAMRA's Good Bottled Beer Guide.

How the Good Beer Guide is compiled

It's more than just a pub guide. We start with the quality of the beer in a pub...and then everything else falls into place

IT IS NOT HYPERBOLE to claim that the Good Beer Guide is unique. For a start, it's far more than just a pub guide. Thanks to CAMRA, with its 60,000 members, its branch structure covering the whole country, and its chain of Brewery Liaison Officers – volunteers attached to every brewery – the Guide offers in the Breweries section an annual report on the state of the industry.

Beer is the belt and braces of the Guide. Cask-conditioned real ale is a living product. It requires attention, respect, even a little love in the pub cellar to bring it to fruition. Landlords who care for cask ale need more than the 'skill' required to serve keg beer or lager, a skill confined to the ability to connect a cylinder of gas to a sealed dustbin. A cask of real ale has to be tapped, vented, checked and tasted over the course of several days to ensure it has ripened and is ready to fill your glass at the bar.

For 29 years, the Good Beer Guide has been driven by the belief that if a pub landlord cares about the quality of the beer in the cellar, then everything else – the welcome, the food, the wine, and such important considerations as the state of the toilets – will fall into line. In keg-only pubs, on the other hand, you are likely to find micro-waved food, stale sandwiches, Blue Nun and Lambrusco, and toilets that answer to the name of bogs.

In the Good Beer Guide, the term 'pub' is not a synonym for 'twee'. There are rural pubs in abundance – CAMRA has been at the forefront of the campaign to save country pubs – but even in rural areas we make every effort to choose a good cross-section of hostelries, the penny plain as well as the tuppence coloured. The real strength of the Guide is that it does not ignore pubs in towns and cities. It would be foolish to do so: while Britain's national tally of pubs – around 60,000 – has remained unchanged for a decade, there has been a shift from country to town, with many new pubs opening in urban areas in recent years. Most people live in towns and drink in town pubs. The Good Beer Guide reflects that situation by offering a wide choice of urban pubs.

The pubs in the Guide are chosen democratically. CAMRA branches monitor pubs on a regular basis. Their choice for the Guide is a result of research, discussion and often a vote at branch meetings.

Regular users of the Good Beer Guide will notice some changes to the format this year. We still offer 5,000 pubs, but 4,000 have been given longer descriptions. The aim is to provide readers with as much information as possible about each pub before you embark on your travels.

Pubs in the Guide are listed county by county in England, and by regions or local authority areas in Scotland and Wales. The Key Map on the inside back cover shows the boundaries used. Greater London and Greater Manchester are listed under L and M respectively. Each county, region or area has a location map pinpointing the pubs and also independent breweries and brew-pubs.

BEDFORDSHIRE

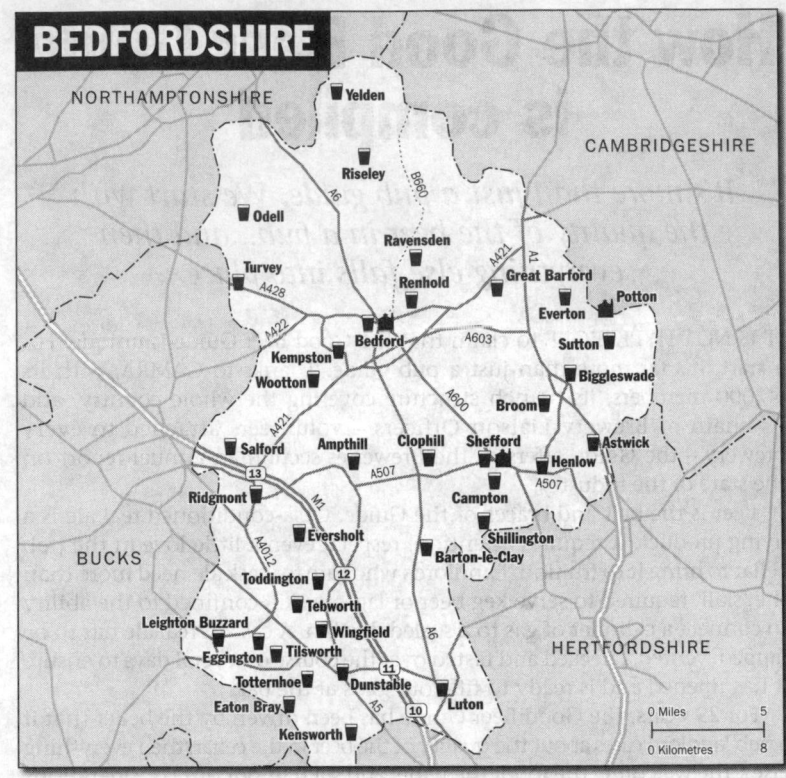

ASTWICK

Tudor Oaks
1 Taylors Road
○ 11-11; 12-3.30, 7-10.30 Sun
☎ (01462) 834133 website: www. tudoroaks.co.uk
Beer range varies Ⓗ
The Oaks is a welcoming pub and restaurant alongside the northbound A1 between Letchworth and Biggleswade. Its large, multi-beamed bar has seven handpumps serving an ever-changing selection of regional and micro-brewery beers; one is generally on sale at a reduced price. It is the only pub in the area to regularly offer real cider and perry. The restaurant offers exceptional food until late; the chef's specialities are desserts and cakes. There is an adjoining night club and motel. 🏚🌚🛏🍴◑✿P🗓

BARTON-LE-CLAY

Waggon & Horses
105 Bedford Road
○ 11.30-2.30 (3 Sat), 6-11; 12-4, 7-10.30 Sun
☎ (01582) 882011
Wells Eagle, Bombardier, seasonal beers;
guest beers Ⓗ
Village pub dating from the late 1800s, that has since been extended and refurbished. The public bar has darts and pool; the quiet main bar hosts domino matches (Thu). The restaurant serves good home-cooked food and welcomes children. Frequent winner in the brewery's garden awards for the patio. Guide Dogs for the Blind are funded by the pub and are pictured on the walls in the bar. Q🌚◑✿♣P

BEDFORD ✣

Phoenix
45 St Johns Street (A6 S of centre)
○ 11-11; 12-10.30 Sun
☎ (01234) 352862
Wells Eagle, Bombardier; guest beers Ⓗ
Welcoming local, with oodles of Irish charm, facing a large traffic island at the end of the one-way system south of the river; car access is from the northbound side. Built in 1900 and extended in the 1960s, a fine collection of historical photos is displayed in the lounge bar. Home-cooked food is served Mon-Sat, 12-2.30 and 5.30-7.30.
◑⊟≉ (St Johns) ♣P

Wellington Arms ↙
40-42 Wellington Street (off A6 N of centre)
○ 12-11; 12-10.30 Sun
☎ (01234) 308033
website: www.wellingtonarms.co.uk
Adnams Bitter; B&T Shefford Bitter, Dragonslayer;
guest beers Ⓗ
Back-street B&T pub run as a beer house, featuring beers from micro- and regional breweries on its 11 handpumps. It fields teams for traditional pub games including Northamptonshire skittles. Home-made soup and filled rolls are available Mon-Sat lunchtimes. It stocks a selection of bottled foreign beers, plus draught Budvar and Hoegaarden. North Beds CAMRA *Pub of the Year* 2000. It hosts live music most Tue and Thu and can be very busy weekend eves. Parking is difficult but a multi-storey car park is nearby. 🌚♣👣●

BIGGLESWADE

Brown Bear
29 Hitchin Street
✪ 12-3, 5-11; 11-11 Fri & Sat; 12-3, 7-10.30 Sun
☎ (01767) 316161 website: www.brownbear.org.uk
Beer range varies Ⓗ

The pub that changed the drinking map of Bedfordshire! Eight pumps serve an extensive range of micro-brewed ales. 'Never the same beer twice' is Mary's boast, so you will never find that old favourite. Festivals add to the range, plus a selection of foreign beers. The nearby station, with a good London to Peterborough junction ensures regular visits from enthusiasts. Live music means that Fri eves are very busy. Lighting verges on the gloomy but you can still see the stunning display of pump clips.
≿ ❀ ◑ ⇌ ♣ ⚲

Wheatsheaf
5 Lawrence Road (from library continue down Chestnut Ave 200 yds)
✪ 11-3.30, 7-11; 11-11 Fri & Sat; 12-10.30 Sun
☎ (01767) 222220
Greene King XX Mild, IPA Ⓗ

Small, unpretentious local, tucked well away, with a loyal, and mostly male, clientele. No frills; football and racing talk abounds, accompanied by live TV when available. No regular food service but the buffets on the cards, domino and crib nights are quite something. Weekly meat raffles and occasional trips to the races are organised. A nice beer garden hosts frequent summer barbecues. A dying breed of pub but still going strong, and a little gem!
❀ ⇌ ♣ ●

CAMPTON

White Hart
Mill Lane
✪ 12-3 (not Mon-Thu), 6.30-11 Fri; 12-11 Sat; 12-3, 7-10.30 Sun
☎ (01462) 812657
Greene King Ruddles Best Bitter, County; Hook Norton Best Bitter; Marston's Pedigree; Theakston Best Bitter; guest beers Ⓗ

Welcoming 300-year-old, Grade II listed brick and beam village pub featuring quarry-tiled floors and two inglenooks, with a wealth of bygones and memorabilia on display. The large beer garden and patio includes a well-equipped children's play area; pétanque played. No food is served, but buffets are available to order for special events. ⚏ Q ❀ ♣ P

CLOPHILL

Stone Jug
10 Back Street
(off A6 N of Flying Horse roundabout)
✪ 11-4, 6-11; 11-11 Sat; 12-10.30 Sun
☎ (01525) 860526
B&T Shefford Bitter; Courage Directors; John Smith's Bitter; guest beers Ⓗ

This back-street gem and *Guide* regular is popular with locals, and is convenient for walkers of the Greensand Ridge, but check before arriving with children. Converted to a pub in the early 20th century, from three 17th-century local stone cottages, there is a single oak-beamed, L-shaped bar, with a separate function/children's room. Excellent

home-made lunches are served 12-2 Mon-Sat. Parking can be difficult when busy.
Q ❀ ◑ ♣ P ⚲

DUNSTABLE

Victoria
69 West Street
✪ 11-11; 12-10.30 Sun
☎ (01582) 662682 e-mail: dave@victoriapub.co.uk
Beer range varies Ⓗ

Friendly, town-centre local, strong on pub games and TV sport. One bar, but a comfortable function room can be used when not booked. South Beds CAMRA *Pub of the Year* 1995-2000. The local beer, Victoria Bitter, comes from Tring and the four ever-changing guest beers from independent brewers. Including the quarterly beer festivals, over 2,000 different beers have appeared here to date. The paved patio to the rear of the pub is heated, and hosts summer barbecues. The lunches are good value. ❀ ◑ ♣

EATON BRAY

Hope & Anchor
63 Bower Lane
✪ 11-2.30, 5-11; 12-5, 7-10.30 Sun
☎ (01525) 220386
Courage Best Bitter; Vale Black Swan Dark Mild, Wychert; guest beer Ⓗ

Hospitable village pub that holds a supper licence until 1am. The comfortable bar features darts, dominoes and a juke box (that does not dominate). The restaurant is a no-smoking area serving good food at reasonable prices. The garden includes an enclosed children's play area. ❀ ◑ ♣ P

EGGINGTON

Horseshoes
High Street
✪ 11-2.30 (not Mon), 6-11; 12-10.30 Sun
☎ (01525) 210282 e-mail: a.pass@connectfree.co.uk
Theakston Best Bitter; Wadworth 6X; guest beer Ⓗ

Picture-postcard pub at the village centre. The four rooms consist of a bar with scrubbed wooden tables, much used for cards and dominoes, a snug, a restaurant and an unusual upstairs room. The building was originally three farm cottages, dating from around 1750, and has been licensed since 1850, first as the Flying Horseshoes, then the Three Horseshoes. The large garden has a lawn area that is a real suntrap in summer. The food is superb, and so popular that booking is recommended.
⚏ Q ❀ ◑ ♣ P

EVERSHOLT

Green Man
Church End
✪ 12-11; 12-10.30 Sun
☎ (01525) 280293
Draught Bass; Theakston Best Bitter; guest beers Ⓗ
The pub is situated opposite the church in

INDEPENDENT BREWERIES

B&T Shefford
Potton Potton
Wells Bedford

the centre of a village that is an amalgamation of 13 'ends' (small hamlets). It is two miles from Woburn Abbey and Safari Park. The bar has bay windows overlooking the church at one end and a pool table at the other. Food is served in the restaurant (not Sun eve), with Indian meals a speciality. The large garden sees much summer use, and features an aviary, guinea pigs and a bouncy castle for children; barbecues are accompanied by live music. An African Grey parrot can be seen from the bar. Two ever-changing guest beers come from independent brewers, and an occasional real cider is stocked.
ₐₐQ☸◐♣P

GREAT BARFORD

Golden Cross
2-4 Bedford Road (A421)
☼ 12-2, 5-11; 12-11 Sat; 12-10.30 Sun
☎ (01234) 871727
Greene King IPA; Wells Eagle; guest beers H
This traditional public house has a Cantonese restaurant attached; a take-away service is also available. The pub has a quiet lounge bar and a large public bar where traditional pub games are supplemented by entertainment, including Karaoke at weekends. A large-screen satellite TV is available for major sporting events. Up to three guest ales are stocked with the pub being a regular outlet for Potton beers, as well as other local and more distant suppliers. The management will attempt to get any beers requested. Q☸◐⊟&♣P

HENLOW

Engineers Arms
66 High Street
☼ 12-11; 12-10.30 Sun
☎ (01462) 812284 website: www.engineersarms.co.uk
Beer range varies H
This traditional two-bar village local serves an ever-changing, and always interesting, range of beers (more than 3,000 over the last six years). Mostly from micros, the range regularly features a special brewed at the Bass Museum by landlord Kevin Machin. During October there is an annual themed beer festival. The pub features live music from folk and blues through to rock most weeks. It is well decorated with brewery and sporting memorabilia. Its proximity to Henlow Grange Health Spa means it gets its fair share of celebrities enjoying their last real drink.
ₐₐQ☸⊟≠ (Arlesey) ♣

KEMPSTON

Half Moon
108 High Street
☼ 12-3, 6 (5 Fri)-11; 12-4, 7-11 Sat; 12-3, 7-11 Sun
☎ (01234) 852464
Wells Eagle, Bombardier H
Conventional, friendly local boozer with a recently renovated separate public bar and lounge. In the oldest part of the town, it is handy for pleasant walks by the River Great Ouse. The public bar has a large games area where skittles and darts are played; quiz nights are held alternate Suns. The cheerful landlord will stay open later at lunchtimes if customers are still drinking. A large

grassed area has picnic tables and children's play equipment, including swings and a rocking horse. ☸⊟♣P

KENSWORTH

Farmer's Boy ⟵
216 Common Road
☼ 11-11; 12-10.30 Sun
☎ (01582) 872207
Fuller's London Pride, ESB H
Welcoming village pub comprising a small public bar and a comfortable lounge with a separate dining area; the children's certificate covers the latter two. Note the original Mann, Crossman & Paulin leaded windows. The large garden which features a fenced-off children's play area, stages a beer festival in summer. The pub is one of the earliest venues (circa 1970) for the game of Dwyle Flunking which is still occasionally played there today. ₐₐ☸◐♣P●

LEIGHTON BUZZARD

Hunt Hotel
19 Church Road
☼ 11-2.30, 5-11; 11-11 Sat; 12-3, 7-10.30 Sun
☎ (01525) 374692
Draught Bass; Fuller's London Pride; Tetley Bitter; guest beer H
Family-owned hotel, built in 1846 to accommodate workers employed to build the London-Birmingham railway line, it was originally named the Railway Tavern. It was extended in 1886 and renamed to honour its then association with the Whaddon Chase Hunt. One of its bedrooms was regularly used by Edward, Prince of Wales, and Mrs Simpson in the 1930s. There is a restaurant, a basement conference room and a comfortable lounge bar. Apart from the ever-changing (and usually strong) guest beer, a house beer, Hunt Bitter (brewed by Tring) is also available. It hosts live music Fri eve. Good food served (not available Sun). Children are welcome in daytime. Wheelchair access is via the rear car park. ☎☸⊭◐&≠P

LUTON ✣

Bricklayers Arms
10-12 Hightown Road
☼ 12-2.30, 5-11; 12-11 Fri & Sat; 12-10.30 Sun
☎ (01582) 611017
Bateman Mild; Everards Beacon, Tiger; guest beers H
Friendly, unpretentious town pub. The basic furnishings include old casks scattered about, some from the defunct Mickles Brewery. The two ever-changing guest beers are usually sourced from micros; a good range of Belgian bottled beers is also available. Food served 12-2 Mon-Fri includes filled rolls, toasted sandwiches, ploughmans and burger with chips. A quiz is held every Mon eve and Sky TV football is shown. It can be crowded on Luton Town match days. ☸≠♣P

Two Brewers
43 Dumfries Street
☼ 12-11; 12-10.30 Sun
☎ (01582) 616008
e-mail: thetwobrewers@hotmail.com
Tring Side Pocket for a Toad, Jack o' Legs; guest beers H

Fizz warning

Some national breweries produce both cask-conditioned and 'nitro-keg' versions of their beers. Boddingtons Bitter, John Smith's Bitter, Tetley's Bitter and Worthington fall into this category. Nitro-keg beers, often promoted as 'smooth' or 'cream-flow' products, are filtered and pasteurised in the brewery, and served in pubs by a mix of applied carbon dioxide and nitrogen gases. They are bland, served extremely cold, and any hop character is lost by the use of applied gas. To add insult to injury, the keg founts that serve such beers are often topped by small dummy handpumps. As a result of lobbying by CAMRA, some producers of cask and nitro versions of the same beer now include the word 'cask' on pump clips for the genuine article. For example, both John Smith's Bitter and Tetley's Bitter now carry the word 'cask' on pump clips for the real thing. For the sake of brevity, and as the Good Beer Guide lists only cask-conditioned beers, we refer simply to John Smith's Bitter and Tetley Bitter. The Bass/Interbrew brand, Worthington, is labelled Worthington Bitter in cask form, and – bizarrely – Worthington Best Bitter in the nitro-keg version. Always choose the living rather than the dead.

Friendly, street-corner local near the Three Counties Radio building. Recently acquired by Tring Brewery as their first pub, it has been extensively refurbished without loss of character. Up to four ever-changing guest beers are available, generally from micros. The front bar has darts, the back bar has Sky Sports and a display of old football photos. A small flagged area to the rear of the pub is used for summer drinking. Acoustic music sessions are held every Thu eve – all are welcome to join in. It is popular on match days with both home and away football supporters. Regular beer festivals are held. ♨❦♣

Windmill
93 Windmill Road
🕐 10.30-11; 12-2.30, 5.30-10.30 Sun
☎ (01582) 721062
Fuller's London Pride; Young's Bitter; guest beer Ⓗ
Comfortable, friendly Victorian pub near the Vauxhall works, with one L-shaped bar featuring elegant etched windows. The ever-changing guest beer always comes from a small brewery. The current landlord is one of the longest-serving in Luton, having run the pub since 1983. Darts, dominoes, Sky Sports and regular live music all attract their followers. Good value eve meals are served Mon-Thu, and the pub opens at 9.15 Mon-Sat for breakfasts. Children are welcome at most times; a special menu is available on request. Q◖▶≠ (Airport Parkway) ♣P

Bell
Horsefair Lane
🕐 11-3, 6-11; 12-3, 7-10.30 Sun
☎ (01234) 720254
Greene King IPA, Abbot, guest beers Ⓗ
This attractive, thatched pub stands at the village centre. The garden has an aviary and leads down to the River Great Ouse, while Harrold-Odell Country Park is 300 yards down the lane. Other footpaths pass through the village, so this is an excellent place to break a walk. Although the cooking has been worthy of inclusion in *Good Pub Food*, it is first and foremost a pub with good food rather than a restaurant with good beer. ♨Q❦◖▶P

Horse & Jockey
Church End (off B660 crossroads)
🕐 12-3 (not Mon), 6-11; 12-10.30 Sun
☎ (01234) 772319
Courage Directors; Home Mild; Theakston Best Bitter Ⓗ
Traditional family-owned, village free house situated at the top of a hill, next to the church. Darts and skittles are played in the public bar, while the lounge bar, with a view towards Bedford, is used as a restaurant. Theakston's is often substituted by a guest 'supping' bitter. Fresh home-cooked food, includes a changing chalkboard menu; eve meals served Tue-Sat. It hosts occasional themed eves serving Indian, Thai and Chinese food. ♨Q❦◖▶⬳♿♣P

Three Horseshoes
42 Top End (1 mile N of A421)
🕐 11-3, 6-11; 11-11 Sat; 12-10.30 Sun
☎ (01234) 870218
Greene King XX Mild, IPA; Ruddles Best or guest beer Ⓗ
This traditional country pub boasts a large garden with a children's play area. A good choice of home-cooked food includes fresh fish and steaks (no meals Tue eve or Sun). The pub is often involved with events held on the sports field at the back. Darts and cards are played in the public bar. Occasional guest beers replace the Ruddles; this is a long-standing outlet for the dark mild. ♨Q❦◖▶⬳♿♣P

Rose & Crown ←
89 High Street (near M1 jct 13)
🕐 10.30-2.30 (12-3 Sat), 6-11; 12-3.30, 7-10.30 Sun
☎ (01525) 280245
Adnams Broadside; Wells Eagle, Bombardier, seasonal beer or guest beer Ⓗ
Attractive pub, built using locally-made bricks, and dating back some 300 years. Popular with drinkers and diners alike, the two comfortably-furnished bar areas house a collection of English sheepdog china and Rupert Bear memorabilia – note the Nutwood Ales sign on the way in from the car park. The tree-lined garden has approved facilities for camping and caravanning. Children are welcome in the

dining area. The former stables house a function/meeting room. A wide range of whiskies is available. Run by the same licensees for well over 20 years. The pub has been in every edition of this *Guide*.
✿◑ ▲P●

RISELEY

Fox & Hounds
High Street (3 miles off A6 at Sharnbrook)
✪ 11-2.30, 6.30-11; 12-3, 7-10.30 Sun
☎ (01234) 708240 e-mail: janz@tinyworld.co.uk
Wells Eagle, Bombardier; guest beers H
Extended old village inn with a reputation for good food – charcoal-grilled steaks sold by weight are a speciality (not Sat lunch). A separate room is available for special group events, but no booking is necessary for normal bar meals – meet and drink in the bar while your food is cooked; food service can, however, be busy at weekends. There is a large lawned garden and a covered patio with heating in suitable weather.
Q✿◑P●

SHEFFORD

Brewery Tap
14 North Bridge Street
✪ 11.30-11; 12-10.30 Sun
☎ (01462) 628448
B&T Shefford Mild, Shefford Bitter, seasonal beers; guest beers H
Basic, no-frills, drinkers' pub where six handpumps sell B&T beers at low prices, plus additional guests. The decor features breweriana and bottled beers. Hot pies and filled rolls are available. Formerly the Green Man, Grape Vine and Countryman, B&T took over the pub, which stands a short distance from the brewery, in 1996. Popular games include table football. Live music is staged most Fri eves. ✿♣P

SHILLINGTON

Musgrave Arms
16 Apsley End Road
✪ 12-3, 5-11; 12-11 Sat; 12-4, 7-10.30 Sun
☎ (01462) 711286
Greene King XX Mild, H **IPA, Abbot; guest beer** G
Cosy country pub boasting original Tudor beams. The raised 'public' end, with scrubbed wooden tables, is popular with domino players. The no-smoking dining

room (where children are welcome) offers good food (steak night Tue). A large garden has children's play equipment and two pétanque pitches. A *Guide* regular where the beer is served from casks whose fronts project into the bar from a cooled cellar. Try the mild.
⚞Q✿◑♣P

SUTTON

John O'Gaunt Inn
30 High Street
✪ 12-3, 7-11; 12-3, 7-11 Sun
☎ (01767) 260377
e-mail: carter-celeste@compuserve.com
Greene King IPA, Old Speckled Hen; guest beers H
Characterful village pub serving a good range of food (no meals Sun eve). The pub has a flood-lit boules pitch and Northamptonshire skittles, open to all; social evenings with a buffet can be arranged. It also has its own golf society. Occasional informal folk music sessions occur, when all are welcome; on spring and summer eves the local morris men sometimes dance in the car park. In winter you can warm yourself by an open fire and admire the village quilt in the lounge. This traditional pub, with two beamed bars, has a timeless feel to it and is very active in all village life.
⚞Q✿◑ ⊟♣P⚲

TODDINGTON

Oddfellows Arms
2 Conger Lane
✪ 12-3 (not Mon-Thu), 5-11; 12-3.30, 7-10.30 Sun
☎ (01525) 872021
website: www.oddfellowsarmstoddington.com
Adnams Bitter, Broadside; Courage Best Bitter; guest beer H
Attractive, but reputedly haunted 15th-century pub on the village green, featuring a heavily beamed and brassed L-shaped bar and a separate restaurant. Over 20 Belgian bottled beers, plus Hoegaarden White Beer on draught, are available, and all served in the correct glass. A sheltered patio area is available for *al fresco* drinking. The extensive menu offers very good value food. Beer festivals are held in spring and autumn, for which the pub remains open all day.
⚞✿◑♣●

INN BRIEF

AMPTHILL
Engine & Tender
11 Dunstable Street
11-3, 5-11; 11-11 Fri & Sat;
12-4, 7-10.30 Sun
Greene King IPA, Abbot; Ruddles Best or Draught Bass H
Friendly, one-bar pub, frequented by the local rugby club. A patio area for summer drinking. Bar snacks are served 12-2. *Cask Marque* accredited.

BEDFORD
De Parys Hotel
45 De Parys Avenue
12-11; 12-10.30 Sun
Wells Eagle; guest beers H
Comfortable hotel bar with a large garden and children's play area, a conservatory and a restaurant.

BROOM
Cock ☆
23 High Street
11-3, 6-11; 12-4, 7-10.30 Sun
Greene King IPA, Abbot H
Popular village pub with no bar; the beer is served on gravity from the cellar. The listed interior features a skittles table.

Devonshire Arms
32 Dudley Street
5.30 (4 Fri; 12 Sat)-11; 12-3, 7-10.30 Sun
Wells Eagle, Bombardier H
Flowers bedeck this attractive pub. The 'Devvy' serves good wine by the jug and Val offers food in conjunction with themed events. *Cask Marque* accredited.

EVERTON
Thornton Arms
1 Potton Road
12-3, 6-11; 12-11 Sat;
12-10.30 Sun
Wells Eagle; guest beers H/G
Village real ale pub, serving food, with an emphasis on pub games and a good community spirit.

LUTON
Globe
26 Union Street
11-11; 12-10.30 Sun
Greene King IPA; guest beers H
Street-corner local with an enclosed patio, offering two ever-changing guest ales and regular beer festivals. Good value breakfasts and lunches.

Sow & Pigs
19 Church Square
☼ 11-11; 12-10.30 Sun
☎ (01525) 873089 website: www.sowandpigs.co.uk
Greene King IPA, Abbot, seasonal beer or guest beer ⊞

19th-century commercial inn with one long, narrow bar, extensively redecorated after a fire in 1999, evidence of which can still be spotted. The dog-friendly bar (note the millennium curtains!) is heated by three real fires in winter and hosts occasional live music. The decor features assorted pigs and golfing memorabilia. No hot food, but a selection of cold platters and home-made soup are always available. An upstairs room (also available for meetings) can be booked for parties of 16-24 people, and the spread of food provided has to be seen to be believed. Overnight accommodation offers comfortable rooms at reasonable prices. The Sow has appeared in every edition of this *Guide*. ♨Q✿➟♣P●

TURVEY

Three Cranes
High Street (off A428)
☼ 11-2.30, 6-11; 12-3, 7-10.30 Sun
☎ (01234) 881305
Adnams Bitter; Courage Best Bitter, Directors; Fuller's London Pride; Hook Norton Best Bitter ⊞

Comfortable, 17th-century coaching inn serving an excellent range of food in both the bar and restaurant, with a vegetarian choice always available. The split-level bar provides inviting corners for drink and conversation. The 11-arch bridge, carrying the main road across the Great Ouse, dates from the 15th century, but the picturesque olde-worlde village was mainly a 19th-century development. Book ahead for bed and breakfast. ♨Q✿➟◑P

WINGFIELD

Plough
Tebworth Road
☼ 12-3, 5.30-11 (11-11 summer Sat); 12-4, 6-10.30 Sun
☎ (01525) 873077 e-mail: causeway@tesco.net
Adnams Bitter; Fuller's Chiswick, London Pride, ESB; seasonal beer or guest beer ⊞

Attractive, thatched village inn dating from the 17th century and licensed since 1822. Beware the low beams and entrance. The conservatory to the rear doubles as a restaurant (where children are welcome) and a function/meeting room. The bar is decorated with rural scenes featuring ploughs, and Royal Navy insignia, reflecting the landlord's past. The food is of a high standard (no meals Sun eve). Tables are set out at the front of the pub for summer drinking, and the enclosed garden to the rear has children's play equipment. The landlord was recently given Fuller's *Master Cellarman* award. ♨✿◑P

WOOTTON (HALL END)

Chequers
Hall End (from Wootton take Church Rd and keep going) OS001458
☼ 11-2.30, 5.30-11; 11-11 Sat; 12-10.30 Sun
☎ (01234) 768394
Wells Eagle; guest beers ⊞

Built as a farm in the 16th century, the Chequers retains many interesting historic features, not least the heavy beams and low ceilings that give the lounge bar its intimate atmosphere. The public bar has room for the local version of skittles, where discs or 'cheeses' are tossed at pins on the table. Food choices (not Sun eve) range from bar snacks to full restaurant meals, served in a raised part of the lounge. The large lawned garden with seats and tables is a popular venue in good weather. ♨✿◑⊟♣P

YELDEN

Chequers
High Street
☼ 12-2.30 (not Mon), 5.30-11; 12-11 Sat; 12-10.30 Sun
☎ (01933) 356383
Fuller's London Pride; ⊞ **Greene King Abbot;** ⒼＧ **Thwaites Best Bitter; guest beers** ⊞

Traditional village pub with a separate family/skittles room and a small no-smoking restaurant. The large garden offers a selection of children's play equipment. Good value bar food is available Wed-Sun (Sun meals finish at 5pm). An annual real ale festival is held over the spring bank holiday weekend. Yelden village is on the Three Shires Way walkers' route and boasts the impressive earthworks of a Norman castle looking north towards the Nene Valley. ♨☙✿◑▶Å♣●P

Mother Redcap
80 Latimer Road
11-11; 12-10.30 Sun
Greene King IPA, Abbot, Old Speckled Hen ⊞
Wood-panelled, one-bar pub with a separate games area. It offers good value lunches (not Sun) and a curry night (Wed). Sky Sports.

SALFORD
Red Lion Hotel
Wavendon Road
11-2.30, 6-11; 12-2.30, 7-10.30 Sun
Wells Eagle, Bombardier ⊞
Small country inn: enjoy the log fire in winter and garden in summer; bar and restaurant meals every day. Accommodation has four-poster beds.

TEBWORTH
Queen's Head
The Lane
11-3 (3.30 Sat), 6 (7 Sat)-11; 12-3, 7-10.30 Sun
Adnams Broadside; Ⓖ **Wells Eagle;** ⊞ **guest beer** Ⓖ
Welcoming village local with two small bars, offering good value food (not served Sun). Quiz night Thu; live music Fri. A *Guide* regular.

TILSWORTH
Anchor
1 Dunstable Road 11-11; 12-10.30 Sun
Greene King IPA, Abbot; guest beers ⊞
Welcoming village local featuring pub games, Sky Sports, lunchtime food and a large garden with a children's adventure play area. *Cask Marque* accredited.

TOTTERNHOE
Cross Keys
Castle Hill Road
11.30-3.30, 6-11; 11.30-11 Sat; 12-10.30 Sun
Greene King IPA; guest beers ⊞
Thatched, 14th-century ale house with low beams. The large garden has extensive views over the Aylesbury Vale. Good food.

> ✳ **symbol next to a main entry place name indicates there are Inn Brief entries as well.**

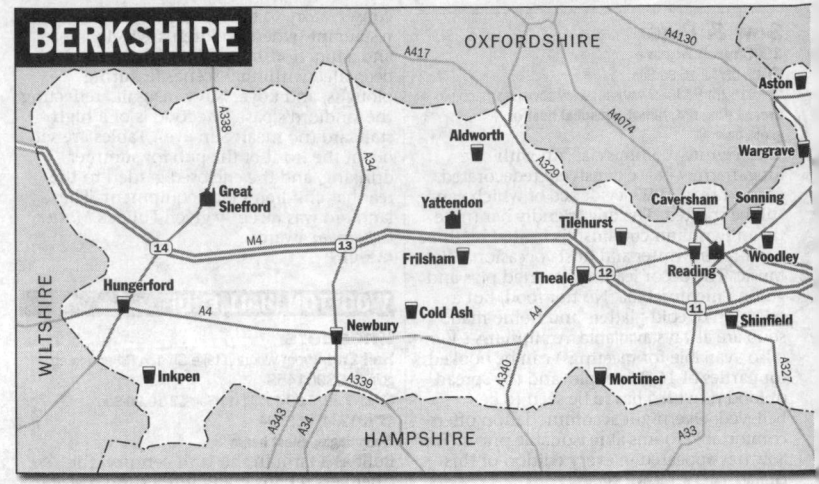

BERKSHIRE

ALDWORTH

Bell ☆ ←
Bell Lane (off B4009) OS556797
🕓 11-3, 6-11 (closed Mon); 12-3, 7-10.30 Sun
☎ (01635) 578272
Arkell's 3B, Kingsdown; Crouch Vale Best Bitter; West Berkshire Maggs Magnificent Mild; Ⓗ **guest beers** Ⓖ
Brickwork in this superb, unspoilt gem of a downland pub dates the building to the late 15th century. Run by the same family for 200 years, beer is served from a windowed hatch and drinkers can stand in the entrance passage, sit on the wall benches in the two rooms, stretch out on the seats in the enormous porch or adjourn to the lavender-filled garden by the cricket pitch. Award-winning warm filled rolls and seasonal soup or salads are offered. Old Tyler is West Berkshire's Good Old Boy rebadged. A previous CAMRA National *Pub of the Year*. 🏚Q❀◑🍽♣P⅙

ASTON

Flower Pot
Ferry Lane (off A4130)
🕓 11-3, 6-11; 12-10.30 Sun
☎ (01491) 574721
Brakspear Mild, Bitter, Special, seasonal beer Ⓗ
Hotel built in 1890 to replace an earlier inn. In rural surroundings, half a mile from Hambleden lock on the River Thames, with its own landing stage, it has been extended and refurbished to a high standard. The bare-boarded public bar complements a smart lounge and dining area warmed by a real fire. The walls bear numerous stuffed fish in glass cases. The large garden offers extensive views across fields and river to the Chiltern Hills. Good value food (not served Sunday eve). 🏚Q❀🚲◑🍽P⅙🍴

BINFIELD

Victoria Arms
Terrace Road North (B3018, N of Bracknell)
🕓 11.30-3, 6-11; 11-11 Sat; 12-10.30 Sun
☎ (01344) 483856
Fuller's Chiswick, London Pride, ESB, seasonal beer Ⓗ
On two levels around a central bar, the Victoria's name suggests its age. A dartboard

and TV feature in the lower level, while the more comfortable upper level is adorned by a large collection of beer bottles in the rafters, plus an old Simonds of Reading brewery sign. A family garden (with play area) hosts regular barbecues summer eves. A variety of basic meals are served all week, with a roast on Sunday (no food Sun eve). 10p charity fine imposed if your mobile phone rings.
🏚❀◑♣P⅙

BRACKNELL

Old Manor
High Street (opp. Met Office)
🕓 11-11; 12-10.30 Sun
☎ (01344) 304490
Courage Directors; Theakston Best Bitter; Wadworth 6X; guest beers Ⓗ
By no means a typical Wetherspoon's, situated in a former manor house, it has two bars and a multitude of drinking areas. These include the Great Hall, the costume rooms and a no-smoking/dining area in which children are welcome for meals (a special menu is available). Other features include a priest's hole dating from the Reformation era and, in the Wetherspoon's tradition, much is made of local historical associations.
Q❀◑♿♨♠P⅙●

CAVERSHAM

Prince of Wales
76 Prospect Street
🕓 11-3, 6-11; 12-11 Sat; 12-10.30 Sun
☎ (0118) 947 2267
Brakspear Bitter, Special, seasonal beers Ⓗ
The Prince of Wales' proud boast 'serving Caversham for over 100 years' is no exaggeration, for this friendly, lively local is very much at the centre of its community. The pub has three distinct, interconnected drinking areas: a bustling, basic public bar with pool table, a lounge with large-screen TV (only used for major sporting events) and a cosy, wood-panelled snug with a serving hatch. Home to an active darts team, it also

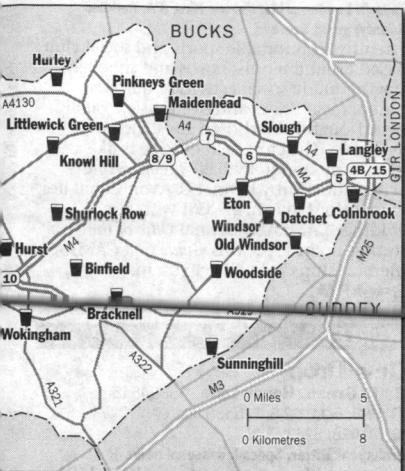

The smallest pub in a historic village; built in the 15th century this ancient inn once doubled as Colnbrook's church. It is reputed that Dick Turpin once stayed here. Original bench seating and beams help maintain a traditional pub atmosphere. The Liverpool FC-supporting publican is a qualified chef whose home-cooked food, with Indian, Chinese and Thai specialities, is particularly good value. It hosts Karaoke on Fri and regular weekend meat raffles. A splendid community local. ♨ ✿ ⋈ ◖ ♣ P

hosts occasional live music eves. Children are very welcome Sun lunchtime. ✿ ◖ ⊟ ♣ P

COLD ASH

Spotted Dog Inn ⮐
Gladstone Lane (off Cold Ash Hill)
✪ 11.30-2.30, 6.30-11; 12-3, 7-10.30 Sun
☎ (01635) 862458
Brakspear Bitter; Fuller's London Pride; guest beers Ⓗ
Fine example of a rural pub, serving a large village community. The small bar to the left of the entrance is set aside as a restaurant; the Talbot Bar is a large saloon, where oak beams, sensitive lighting and horse brasses enhance the welcome. The room is lightly partitioned to provide a quieter area away from the bar. Another smaller area, with wood panelling and slate floor tiles, houses the dartboard and tables for card games. ♨ ✿ ◖ ♣ P

COLNBROOK

Ostrich ⮐
High Street
✪ 11-3, 5.30-11; 11-11 Fri; 12-3, 6.30-10.30 Sun
☎ (01753) 682628
Draught Bass; Courage Directors; Wells Bombardier Ⓗ
Reputedly the third oldest pub in England, there has been a pub on this site since the 11th century. Most of the current building dates from the 15th century, but some older parts remain. Although the main bar has been modernised, the original beams and timbers are still visible. The infamous 16th-century publican Mr. Jarman plied guests with wine and then opened a trap door, tilting their beds and dropping them into a cauldron of boiling oil. Unsurprisingly the pub is haunted (free tours available). The extensive menu includes ostrich steaks. ♨ ✿ ◖ P

Red Lion
High Street
✪ 12-11; 12-10.30 Sun
☎ (01753) 681224
Ushers Best Bitter, Founders Ale; guest beer Ⓗ

DATCHET

Royal Stag
The Green
✪ 11-11; 12-10.30 Sun
☎ (01753) 584231
Ind Coope Burton Ale; Marston's Pedigree; Tetley Bitter; guest beer Ⓗ
A pillared porchway and heavy oak door open on to an old coaching inn that has been an ale house since the mid-17th century. One side of the building is Elizabethan. Originally called Five Bells, then High Flyer, the present name was adopted in 1857. The comfortable lounge is partially clad with antique wooden champagne crates. The ghostly print of a child's hand appears on the window overlooking the churchyard. Although run by Bass Retail, the pub is owned by the Bridge House Trust, whose profits go towards the upkeep of the village. No food Sun eve. ♨ ◖ ⊟ ⇌ ♣ ⬤ P

ETON ✣

New College
55 High Street
✪ 11-11; 12-10.30 Sun
☎ (01753) 865516
e-mail: the.newcollege@care4p-ee.net
Badger K&B Sussex, Best, Tanglefoot, seasonal beers Ⓗ
The former College Arms was taken over, renovated and renamed by Hall & Woodhouse three years ago, freeing Eton of its one keg-only outlet. The large, open-plan bar was changed to a comfortable multi-sectioned drinking area by the judicious use of wood panelling, and it has a pleasantly intimate feel. Open at 10am summer weekends for tea and coffee, children are welcome in the dining area until early eve. An innovative menu and an annual mini beer festival (Aug) add to its appeal. Parking is difficult.
✿ ◖ ⇌ (Windsor & Eton Riverside) ⧼ ⬤

Waterman's Arms
Brocas Street (near Windsor Bridge)
✪ 11-2.30, 6-11 (may vary); 12-3, 7-10.30 Sun
☎ (01753) 861001
Brakspear Bitter; Courage Best Bitter, Directors; Greene King IPA, Abbot; Wadworth 6X Ⓗ
Friendly free house between the High Street and the Thames. Boating memorabilia abounds, particularly in the no-smoking

INDEPENDENT BREWERIES

Butts Great Shefford
Reading Lion Reading
West Berkshire Yattendon

33

room, and the pub is home to the local Dragon boat team. Built circa 1542, but only a hostelry since the mid-19th century, it previously served as a workhouse and a mortuary. Its ongoing popularity among locals and tourists alike is fully justified and has lead to its regular inclusion in this *Guide*. An extensive menu is served in both the bar and conservatory (no food Sun eve). The beer range may vary. Parking is difficult. ♨✿◑▶➤ (Windsor & Eton Riverside/Central) ♣⌇

FRILSHAM

Pot Kiln ☆ ⟨⟨

On Yattendon-Bucklebury road (ignore signs to Frilsham) OS553732

☼ 12-2.30 (not Tue), 6.30-11; 12-3, 7-10.30 Sun
☎ (01635) 201366 website: www.real-ale-guide.co.uk

Arkell's 3B; Greene King Morland Original; West Berkshire Brick Kiln Bitter, Gold Star, seasonal beers Ⓗ

An isolated rural gem, whose fine garden overlooks peaceful meadows and woodlands with plenty of attractive walking nearby. It was once a private beer house for thirsty kiln workers; since going 'public' in the 1920s, it has only had two owners. The three small bar rooms still appear unspoilt with wooden floors and benches. Summer weekends can be very busy, with delays for food and drink, but in this determinedly old-fashioned pub good conversation seems more important than ringing tills. West Berkshire Brewery is a separate business with a brewhouse on site, Brick Kiln Bitter is only available here. No eve meals Tue. ♨Q✿◑▶⊟♣P⌇

HUNGERFORD

Hungerford Club
1 The Croft (off Church St)
☼ 12-3 (not Mon-Fri), 7-11; 12-3, 7-10.30 Sun
☎ (01488) 682357

Fuller's London pride, Greene King IPA, Ruddles County; guest beers Ⓗ

Friendly, comfortable sports and social club based around tennis, bowls and snooker, staging many social activities: quizzes, bingo, meat draws and live music. Usually two thoughtfully chosen guest ales are available. The croft field outside is like a pleasantly tranquil village green, while across the nearby Kennet & Avon Canal lies Hungerford Marsh, an SSSI with rare wildlife. CAMRA's national *Club of the Year* runner up in 1999, this *Guide* or a CAMRA membership card will get you in. ✿➤♣P●

HURLEY

Dew Drop
Batts Green, Honey Lane OS824815
☼ 12-3, 6-11; 12-3, 7-10.30 Sun
☎ (01628) 824327

Brakspear Bitter, Special, seasonal beers Ⓗ

Converted from farm cottages about 150 years ago, this small pub, in the midst of Ashley Hill Woods, is a hidden gem, popular with walkers and horse riders (a 'boot corner' is provided for muddy wellies). Recent renovations that extended the bar area into what was previously the kitchen have maintained the cosy, log fire charm of the original layout. Home-cooked food and a large garden add to the appeal. The publican advertises the pub as having 'a rustic landlord and eccentric beams'. No food Sun eve. ♨Q✿◑▶▲♣P

HURST

Green Man
Hinton Road (off A321; Wokingham-Twyford road)
☼ 11-3, 5.30-11; 12-3, 7-10.30
(extended hours summer) Sun
☎ (0118) 934 2599

Brakspear Bitter, Special, seasonal beers Ⓗ

Superb 17th-century oak-beamed pub

INN BRIEF

ETON
Hogshead
77 High Street
12-11; 12-10.30 Sun
Boddingtons Bitter; Brakspear Bitter; Fuller's London Pride; Marston's Pedigree; Wadworth 6X; guest beers Ⓗ
Old pub in typical Hogshead style, hosting a summer beer festival and barbecues. It can get very crowded, especially in the tourist season.

KNOWL HILL
Old Devil
Bath Road
11-11; 12-10.30 Sun
Badger K&B Sussex, IPA, Best, Tanglefoot, seasonal beers Ⓗ
A comfortable roadside pub with a family-friendly garden, handy for nearby golf club and woodland walks. *Cask Marque* accredited.

PINKNEYS GREEN
Stag & Hounds
1 Lee Lane
(1/2 mile along Pinkneys Drive from A308)
11-3.30, 6-11; 11-11 Fri & Sat;
12-10.30 Sun
Brakspear Bitter; Fuller's London Pride; Marston's Pedigree; guest beer Ⓗ
Rural pub with a skittle alley and large garden. Limited parking.

READING
Back of Beyond
104-109 Kings Road
10-11; 12-10.30 Sun
Courage Best Bitter; Fuller's London Pride; Shepherd Neame Spitfire; Theakston Best Bitter; guest beers Ⓗ
Large pub with usual Wetherspoon's format on the eastern side of town. By the Kennet & Avon Canal.

WINDSOR
Three Elms
192 Clarence Road, Clewer
11-11; 12-10.30 Sun
Greene King Morland Original, Triumph, Ruddles County Ⓗ
Community local in a western suburb with three main areas, hosting live music Sat. Home-made weekday lunches served.

WOKINGHAM
Broad Street Tavern
29 Broad Street
11-11; 12-10.30 Sun
Wadworth IPA, 6X, seasonal beers; Ⓗ **guest beers** Ⓗ/Ⓖ
Large, multi-roomed town-centre pub, unusually converted from a wine bar. It holds occasional beer festivals. *Cask Marque* accredited.

Metropolitan
56 Rose Street
11-11; 12-10.30 Sun
Greene King IPA; Ruddles Best, Morland Original Ⓗ
Rose Street is a wide thoroughfare with many ancient buildings, including this traditional local.

Check it out

Pubs in the Good Beer Guide may change ownership and the facilities listed could alter. If a visit to a pub in the guide involves a lengthy journey, it is advisable to check before leaving that full meals, family facilities, accommodation or camping sites are still available.

tucked down a side road where rural views make it the perfect place for a meal and a pint. Dining areas are provided for smokers and non-smokers, with fish dishes a favourite and specials shown on a blackboard. Although food is important, this is also a place for a good pint in good company. The garden is very attractive, with hanging baskets and flower beds in summer, and a heated patio area. Children have a play area and are welcome inside until 8.30pm. 🏠Q🌲🕽🍴🅿✠

INKPEN

Crown & Garter

Great Common (follow signs to Inkpen Common) OS378638

🕐 12-3 (not Mon or Tue); 6.30 (6 Fri & Sat)-11; 12-3, 7-10.30 Sun

☎ (01488) 665325 website: www.crownandgarter.com

Archers Village, West Berkshire Good Old Boy, seasonal beers; guest beers Ⓗ

Set in a beautiful rambling village below scenic downland – right under the famous double gibbet on Inkpen Beacon – this pub was rejuvenated by dynamic new owners after facing closure in 1998. The bistro-type decor, oriental features and new en-suite bedrooms set around a landscaped courtyard should not mislead you – this is still very much a village local. A small converted smithy serves as a skittle alley-cum-function room. The excellent food is home-made and imaginative, while summer barbecues are popular. No meals Sun eve.

🏠🌲🛏🕽🍴🅿

Swan

Craven Road, Lower Green
(3 miles from Hungerford) OS359643

🕐 11-2.30, 7-11 (11-11 summer Sat); 12-3, 7-10.30 (12-10.30 summer) Sun

☎ (01488) 668326

website: www.theswaninn-organics.co.uk

Butts Bitter; Hook Norton Mild, Best Bitter; guest beers Ⓗ

After closure in 1999, this 16th-century inn has been extensively but sympathetically renovated by a local organic beef farmer, who added 10 guest rooms, two dining areas, a games room and an organic shop. Still, however, a village pub with a lively local trade, it is ideally situated for walkers, cyclists and tourists from the beautiful Combe Hills. The carefully chosen menu uses mostly organic ingredients. One guest ale is often organic, as are many of the bottled beers and wines. Local CAMRA *Pub of the Year* 2000.

🏠🌲🛏🕽🍴🅿✠

LANGLEY

Red Lion

1 St Marys Road

🕐 11-11; 12-10.30 Sun

☎ (01753) 582235

Greene King IPA, Abbot, Old Speckled Hen; guest beer Ⓗ

Over 600 years old, this pub's history is inextricably linked with that of the church opposite. As a brewhouse in its early years it produced the church's Whitsun ale. Where the ladies' toilet now stands was once the mortuary and coffin maker's workshop. Nowadays it often seems to function as the church hall's canteen. After many years disuse, the splendid inglenook will be operational again soon. Home-cooked specials help the publican's aim of making the Red Lion a country pub in the town. 🌲🕽🛏🅿✠

LITTLEWICK GREEN

Cricketers

Coronation Road (off A4)

🕐 11-11; 12-10.30 Sun

☎ (01628) 822888

Brakspear Bitter; Fuller's London Pride; guest beers Ⓗ

Old-fashioned country pub, overlooking the green and cricket pitch in a pretty village. As might be expected there is a sporting theme to the decor; note also the factory clock in the main bar. A friendly atmosphere and, in winter, a welcoming open fire help make this inn popular with locals and visitors alike; it is handy for the nearby business park. An extensive menu of home-cooked food and good value accommodation (four rooms) complete the facilities here. 🏠🌲🛏🕽🍴🅿

MAIDENHEAD

Hand & Flowers

15 Queen Street

🕐 11.30-11; 7-10.30 Sun

☎ (01628) 623800

Brakspear Bitter, Special, seasonal beers Ⓗ

This small town-centre pub's major refurbishment three years ago happily retained its atmosphere, to which Hooper, the landlady's green parrot, contributes. There are tall tables and standing room at the front of the uncarpeted bar and more traditional seating further in; the far end boasts a cosy fire. The emphasis on wine has not detracted from the quality or quantity of beer served. It is often crowded, especially eves, with a mainly thirty-something clientele. A limited menu is served weekday lunchtime. 🕽≉

Vine

20 Market Street

🕐 11-11; 12-10.30 Sun

☎ (01628) 782112

Brakspear Bitter, Special, seasonal beers Ⓗ

Attractive, older-style pub, set right in the town centre amidst offices and shops, this friendly local is a pleasant retreat from the surrounding hubbub. A feature of the Vine is its collection of spirit and liqueur miniatures, carefully displayed in cabinets. The extensive menu offers mostly traditional pub grub, and plentiful tables inside and out makes eating in comfort easy at all but the very busiest of periods. The resident dart teams are active in the local leagues. 🌲🕽≉🍴●

MORTIMER

Turner's Arms

West End Road

(between Mortimer West End and the Common)

🕐 11.30-3, 5 (6 Sat)-11; 12-3, 7-10.30 Sun

☎ (0118) 933 2961

Brakspear Mild, Bitter, Special, seasonal beers ⊞
Three 19th-century cottages (including the wood turner's dwelling), have been knocked together to form a fine roadside pub: one cottage is the restaurant, one the long bar and the third houses a quieter snug. Although half a mile from the village centre, the locals, a hardy lot, are usually propping up the bar. The pub offers a varied menu, with grills and fish to the fore; specials might include local pheasant and it hosts popular themed food eves. Note the original GWR boardroom chairman's seat and a throne made for the stage production of *The Lion, The Witch and the Wardrobe*.
ﬔQ✿❍P

NEWBURY

Hogshead
1-3 Wharf Street
✪ 12-11; 12-10.30 Sun
☎ (01635) 569895
e-mail: newbury.hogshead@whitbread.co.uk
Brakspear Special; Butts Barbus Barbus; Fuller's London Pride; Greene King Abbot; Taylor Landlord; Wadworth 6X ⊞
Spacious open-plan, town-centre pub, just off the market place, whose interior displays posters dating from when the building was used as auction rooms. A small terrace overlooks the Kennet & Avon Canal. Between six and 12 regular beers are available, including the locally-brewed Butts beer, plus up to six guest ales per week. It stocks a good range of bottled Belgian beers and Hoegaarden on draught. Food is served all day, until 9pm (8pm Fri and Sat).
ﬔ✿❍ঌ⧖❧

Lion
39 West Street
✪ 12-2.30, 5-11; 12-11 Sat
(may close 2.30-4 if no sport on TV);
12-10.30 Sun
☎ (01635) 528468
Badger Tanglefoot; Wadworth IPA, 6X, JCB, seasonal beers ⊞
Mid-1980s pub, just off the main shopping street, built on the site of a popular old pub of the same name. The original L-shaped layout has been modified in recent years, resulting in an island bar, with a snug area now given over to pool. Old musical instruments provide decor above the booth seating to the front, while to the rear old, cushioned benches and large 'kitchen' tables dominate. Office workers bring regular trade at lunchtime and early eves. Sports fans congregate for live TV events (especially soccer).
✿❍ঌ⧖❀

Monument
57 Northbrook Street
(near clock tower)
✪ 11-11; 12-10.30 Sun
☎ (01635) 41964
website: www.themonument.freeserve.co.uk
Butts Bitter, Barbus Barbus; Gale's HSB; Greene King Old Speckled Hen; Theakston Old Peculier; guest beers ⊞
Historic Berkshire brewery photos line the walls of this noisily busy town-centre

boozer. Part of the Tap & Spile chain, the low-ceilinged 16th-century building has three small, partitioned areas, two showing MTV or sport TV, while the third has table football. Regular darts (Mon), pub games (Tue), live blues or folk (Wed) and stand-up comedy (Thu), are complemented by free pinball, playstation and web access. Sun roasts are excellent value at Butts Brewery's only regular Newbury outlet.
✿❍⧖♣❧✂

OLD WINDSOR

Jolly Gardeners
92 St Lukes Road
(B3021)
✪ 11-11; 12-10.30 Sun
☎ (01753) 740893
Ansells Mild; Courage Best Bitter; Ushers Best Bitter ⊞
Genuine community local, the single horseshoe-shaped bar keeps the atmosphere of its original two bars, with one end dominated by darts, TV and sport, and the other providing a more lounge-type feel. While the beer range may be subject to change, mild is a fixture – unusual in this part of the country. The publicans' aim to maintain a traditional pub in the village is as successful as it is laudable; please, use your mobile phone outside.
✿P

READING ✣

3B's Café Bar
Town Hall, Blagrave Street
✪ 11-11; closed Sun
☎ (0118) 939 9803
Beer range varies ⊞
The 3B's, named after Reading's famous trades (beer, bulbs and biscuits – now all defunct) is situated in the old Town Hall. It is a cosmopolitan café-bar, serving the whole community during the day, while a mainly younger crowd enjoys regular live music and jam sessions eves. Real ale is a major feature, with four handpumps serving an ever-changing range of beers, including local micro-breweries' beers (fairly rare in Reading). The one-price beer policy makes the stronger brews good value. A no-smoking area operates from 10–6.
✿❍ঌ⧖✂

Bugle
144 Friar Street
✪ 10-11; 12-7 Sun
☎ (0118) 957 3514
Courage Best Bitter ⊞
The last surviving 'real pub' in Friar Street, the Bugle is a two-bar gem, surrounded by café-bars, mega-pubs and the like. With a busy front public bar and a more comfortable lounge at the rear, the pub attracts shoppers and workers at lunchtime and locals eves. It is also rare in that it is a tenanted pub, with no food and only one cask beer.
⬒⧖

Butler
89-91 Chatham Street
✪ 11-11; 12-3, 7-10.30 Sun
☎ (0118) 939 1635

Fuller's Chiswick, London Pride, ESB, seasonal beers; guest beers ⊞

Butler & Sons were a firm of Victorian wine merchants who sold imported wines under the 'Old Reading Abbey' trade mark. Their premises were acquired by Fuller's in the late 1970s, as their first pub in Reading, and the present landlord is the son of the original tenant for the Chiswick Brewery. The Butler has a look of a Victorian establishment and is a welcome refuge from the hustle and bustle of the town centre. No food Sun eve.

🏨⊛◑≢P

Eldon Arms
19 Eldon Terrace
(off Eldon Road)
✪ 10.30-3, 5.30-11; 12-3, 7-10.30 Sun
☎ (0118) 957 3857
Badger Tanglefoot; Wadworth IPA, 6X, seasonal beers ⊞

Quiet back-street pub in a residential area only 10 minutes' walk from the town centre. Wadworth's first and only Reading pub is run by the town's longest-serving tenants in a real ale pub. It retains two distinct bars with a large public bar to the left and a smaller, plusher lounge, separated by the former jug and bottle hatch. It hosts regular live music nights.

Q🗗♣

Hobgoblin
2 Broad Street
(opp. entrance to Oracle Shopping Mall)
✪ 11-11; 12-10.30 Sun
☎ (0118) 950 8119
Beer range varies ⊞

The London Tavern was acquired by Wychwood in 1993 and renamed the following year. Mock gaslamps in the front window provide a welcoming feel. The pub is a somewhat eccentric shape, with an upper level housing small alcoves connected to the main bar by a narrow passage. Usually three Wychwood beers are supplemented by five ever-changing guests, mainly from small independent breweries; pump clips from some of the 3,000 guest beers served over the years are displayed. A popular quiz is stage Mon eve.

≢▲

Hop Leaf
163-165 Southampton Street
(A33 one-way system)
✪ 12-2 (not Mon or Tue), 4-11; 12-11 Sat; 12-10.30 Sun
☎ (0118) 967 2330
Hop Back GFB, Best Bitter, Entire Stout, Thunderstorm, Summer Lightning, seasonal beers; guest beers ⊞

Former Simonds house – hence the name, acquired by Hop Back as their third tied house and reopened in 1995. The pub incorporates a small brewhouse using original plant from the Wyndham Arms, Salisbury. These beers are marketed under Reading Lion brand, commemorating the famous lion sculpted by a member of the Simonds family. Although very popular with real ale enthusiasts, the pub is also a genuine community local, fielding darts and cribbage teams; bar billiards is also popular.

🎀⊛♣✂

Magpie & Parrot
Arborfield Road (A327 just S of village)
✪ 12-7; 12-3 Sun
☎ (0118) 988 4130
Fuller's London Pride ⊞

An intimate snug bar, in the annexe of a former Simonds pub of the same name, it forms part of a small garden centre – the price list at the bar includes plants, as well as beverages. The walls abound with artefacts, some with an aeronautical theme. The garden is an ornithologist's paradise and sheep graze in the adjacent meadow. The 144 bus stops conveniently outside the pub. 🏨Q⊛&♣P

White Hart
The Street (off Straight Mile, B3018)
✪ 12-2.30, 7-11; 12-3, 7-10.30 Sun
☎ (0118) 934 3301 e-mail: white@hart5.co.uk
Brakspear bitter; Fuller's London Pride; Wadworth 6X; guest beer (occasional) ⊞

This rural gem, tucked away in a small village, is run by a landlord who has chalked up a quarter of a century of service. A large fireplace is a central feature, spanning both drinking areas, which are decorated with pub memorabilia. Remnants of the former and much-lamented Wethered's Brewery remain. Eve meal times are variable.

Q⊛◑P🏠

Rose & Crown
312 High Street (E end)
✪ 11-11; 12-10.30 Sun
☎ (01753) 521114
Beer range varies ⊞

Excellent,17th-century hostelry, first licensed 1820, this genuine, privately-owned free house offers at least two ales, often from unusual breweries and hosts a mini beer festival in summer. The smallest and, despite Fri eve Karaoke, most traditional pub in the High Street, its two bars are popular with postal workers from the nearby sorting office and those who prefer to avoid the 'disco and doorstaff' venues prevalent in this part of town. There is a small patio area out front. Sun lunch served. ⊛≢

Wheatsheaf
15 Albert Street, Upton
✪ 11-11; 12-10.30 Sun
☎ (01753) 522019
Fuller's Chiswick, London Pride, ESB, seasonal beers ⊞

Formerly a bakery, this comfortable one-bar pub was licensed in 1897. Away from the town centre, it is effectively Upton's 'village local', one of the few traditional pubs left in Slough. The bar features a working red telephone box. Home-made pies cooked with beer are a speciality. The heated, covered garden contains a pool table. It hosts occasional live music and regular quizzes; constant TV does not detract from the atmosphere. Horticultural implements and musical instruments adorn the walls.
⊛◑●

SONNING

Bull
High Street (off B478)
🌣 11-3, 5.30-11; 12-3, 7-10.30
(12-10.30 summer) Sun
☎ (0118) 969 3901
Gale's Butser, GB, HSB, seasonal beers ℍ
Up-market oak-beamed historic inn bedecked with hanging baskets in summer. Its proximity to the Thames makes it popular with walkers and river folk, however, smart casual dress is the norm here. Food is in the higher price bracket in keeping with the pub's image; there is a dining area as well as a bar for drinkers only. The manager has been a finalist in the *Innkeeper of the Year* contest. A pleasant patio and garden add to its appeal.
🏠Q❀🛏🌣🍴🍺●

SUNNINGHILL

Duke's Head
Upper Village Road (near B3020) OS936680
🌣 11-11; 12-10.30 Sun
☎ (01344) 626949
Greene King IPA, Abbot, seasonal beers; guest beers ℍ
Friendly local, hidden in a village backstreet, comprising three distinct drinking areas that can become lively at times, especially weekends. The family/no-smoking room can be set aside for diners at busy times. An interesting menu features Thai food as a speciality, except Sun when a traditional lunch is on offer. Thai take-aways are available and orders can be placed by fax (01344 873066). 🌣❀🍴P✂

THEALE

Fox & Hounds
Station Road, Sunnyside (1 mile S of station, across canal)
🌣 11-3.30, 5-11; 12-3.30, 7-10.30 Sun
☎ (0118) 930 2295
Badger Tanglefoot; Draught Bass; Wadworth IPA, 6X, Farmers Glory; guest beers ℍ
Wadworth's pub which has tried to retain an olde-worlde charm and character with oak beams and a blazing log fire in winter. It has one long bar, with a tiled area at one end, but there is also an area for food. As well as a garden there is a children's outside play area. It is handy for motorway travellers (junction 12, M4) who want a change from service station food. Q❀🍴P

TILEHURST

Butcher's Arms
9 Lower Armour Road
🌣 11-3, 6-11; 12-3, 7-10.30 Sun
☎ (0118) 942 4313
Archers Best Bitter; Flowers IPA ℍ
Genuine, two-bar pub, the Butcher's Arms assures visitors of a friendly welcome from staff and regulars alike. It stands near the top of Armour Hill, on the flanks of which stood the tileworks, reputedly of Roman origin, that gave Tilehurst its name. To find the pub, take Kentwood Hill from Tilehurst station and then right into Armour Hill, or get off a No. 17 bus at Norcot Hill and take the second right turning off Armour Road.
❀🛏♿♣P

WARGRAVE

Bull
High Street (A321)
🌣 11-3, 6-11; 12-4, 7-10.30 Sun
☎ (0118) 940 3120
Brakspear Bitter, Special, seasonal beers ℍ
Attractive, spacious, unspoilt 17th-century inn on a village-centre crossroads. With exposed beams, horse brasses and a huge log fire in winter, and good road, rail and bus connections, it is an ideal place to stay when visiting the Thames Valley. The multi-area layout caters for both drinkers and diners, enjoying the appetising selection of home-cooked food prepared by a first-class chef. A terrace and large enclosed garden offers a safe environment for families. 🏠Q❀🛏🍴🍺

WINDSOR ✤

Mitre
Oxford Road
🌣 11-11; 12-10.30 Sun
☎ (01753) 862510 website: www.mitrewindsor.co.uk
Brakspear Bitter; Fuller's London Pride ℍ
The 200-year-old-plus Mitre is the last remaining pub of the 11 that once graced Oxford Road. This comfortable community local has over 20 teams based here, varying from crib to clay pigeon shooting, and from hockey to darts. Although not in the tourist area, the many local B&Bs ensure plenty of visitors. The menu, featuring home-cooked fare, is available Mon–Sat. There is big-screen TV for sports events; quizzes alternate Suns and a pool room.
🍴🍺 (Windsor & Central) ♣✂

Vansittart Arms
105 Vansittart Road
🌣 11-11; 12-10.30 Sun ☎ (01753) 865988
Fuller's London Pride, ESB, seasonal beers ℍ
In a side street, west of the town centre, near Windsor Boys' School and the A308, this excellent old pub has welcoming coal fires in winter and its patio garden is popular in summer. The home-cooked food leads to this multi-sectioned bar often being crowded at mealtimes. The long-standing publican's cellarmanship has ensured entry in this *Guide* for many years, and a local CAMRA *Pub of the Year* award.
🏠❀🍴🍺 (Windsor & Central) P

WOKINGHAM ✤

Crooked Billet
Honey Hill, Wokingham Without
(off Nine Mile Ride) OS826667
🌣 11-11; 12-10.30 Sun
☎ (0118) 978 0438
Brakspear Bitter, Special, seasonal beers ℍ
Delightful weatherboarded country pub, just south-east of the centre. The bar area maintains a traditional image with a snug at one end, exposed beams and a welcoming fire in winter. Home-cooked favourites such as lamb and apricot pie, Cumberland sausage and Sun roasts are served in the no-smoking dining room (booking advised) where children are welcome. The pleasant garden is also popular in summer with families, as well as cyclists and ramblers from nearby Finchampstead Ridges (NT).
🏠Q❀🍴♿♣P

Red Lion
25 Market Place
✪ 11-3, 5.30-11; 12-3, 7-10.30 Sun
☎ (0118) 978 0319
Brakspear Bitter, Special Ⓗ
Characterful, two-bar pub retaining parts of the original interior and displaying a fascinating collection of bric-à-brac and old prints. It overlooks the market place with its eccentric Victorian town hall, and provides a pleasant retreat from shopping in the 700-year-old town. Meals are provided in the excellent Thai restaurant upstairs, which does not interfere with the ambience of the pub. Q◖▸⇌

Inn on the Park
Woodford Park, Haddon Drive
✪ 11-3, 6-11; 11-11 Fri & Sat; 12-10.30 Sun
☎ (0118) 969 0356
website: www.inn-on-the-park.co.uk
Brakspear Bitter, Special; Fuller's London Pride; guest beers Ⓗ
Fairly large bar within a sports and community centre, owned by the Town Council, unusual for its kind in having a good range of beer from Brakspear's and

interesting guest beers. The bar is entered through a reception area where details of sporting groups and other local activities are displayed. It is a good venue for families as a play area and paddling pool adjoins the outside drinking area.
❀◖&P

Duke of Edinburgh
Woodside Road (off A332)
✪ 11-3, 5-11; 11-11 Fri & Sat; 12-10.30 (6 winter) Sun
☎ (01344) 882736
Arkells 2B, 3B, Kingsdown, seasonal beers Ⓗ
This Windsor Estates building reveals high ceilings and luxurious furnishings with armchairs, settees and a variety of tables. It has three main bar areas and a restaurant. The sports bar, with its wide-screen TV, fruit machine and football memorabilia, contrasts with the remainder of the pub which is festooned with dried hops and hand-painted literary 'quips'. The corner garden is a big draw to summer visitors, especially when Windsor Park and Ascot Racecourse events are scheduled.
♨❀◖▸P

Magpie and Stump

This favoured tavern, sacred to the evening orgies of Mr Lowten and his companions, was what ordinary people would designate a public-house. That the landlord was a man of money-making turn was sufficiently testified by the fact of a small bulkhead beneath the tap-room window, in size and shape not unlike a sedan-chair, being underlet to a mender of shoes; and that he was a being of philanthropic mind was evident from the protection he afforded to a pieman, who vended his delicacies without fear of interruption on the very door-step.

In the lower windows, which were decorated with curtains of a saffron hue, dangled two or three printed cards bearing reference to Devonshire cider and Dantzig [sic] spruce, while a large blackboard announcing in white letters to an enlightened public, that there were 500,000 barrels of double stout in the cellars of the establishment, left the mind in a not unpleasing state of doubt and uncertainty as to the precise direction in the bowels of the earth, in which this mighty cavern might be supposed to extend.

Charles Dickens, *The Pickwick Papers*, 1837. The Magpie and Stump, London EC4, stands opposite the Old Bailey courts, and also featured in the TV series Rumpole. Danzig beer was flavoured with spruce cones and twigs.

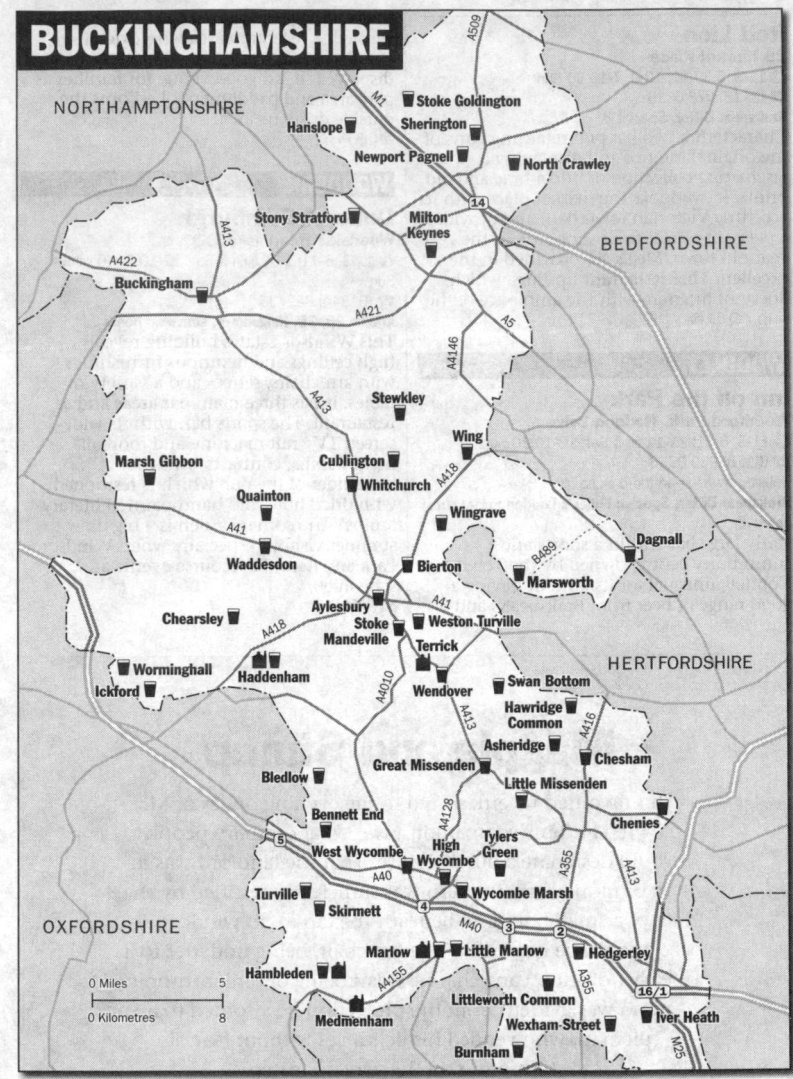

BUCKINGHAMSHIRE

NORTHAMPTONSHIRE

BEDFORDSHIRE

HERTFORDSHIRE

OXFORDSHIRE

Stoke Goldington
Sherington
Hanslope
Newport Pagnell
North Crawley
Stony Stratford
Milton Keynes
Buckingham
Stewkley
Wing
Marsh Gibbon
Cublington
Whitchurch
Quainton
Wingrave
Waddesdon
Bierton
Dagnall
Marsworth
Chearsley
Aylesbury
Weston Turville
Stoke Mandeville
Terrick
Worminghall
Haddenham
Wendover
Swan Bottom
Ickford
Hawridge Common
Asheridge
Chesham
Bledlow
Great Missenden
Little Missenden
Bennett End
Chenies
West Wycombe
Tylers Green
High Wycombe
Turville
Skirmett
Wycombe Marsh
Hambleden
Marlow
Little Marlow
Hedgerley
Medmenham
Littleworth Common
Wexham Street
Iver Heath
Burnham

0 Miles 5
0 Kilometres 8

ASHERIDGE

Blue Ball
12-2.30; 12-11 Fri & Sat; 12-10.30 Sun
☎ (01494) 758263 website: www.blueball.org
Fuller's London Pride; Greene King IPA; guest beer Ⓗ
Asheridge (not to be confused with Ashridge, 6 miles away near Berkhamsted) is a small farming hamlet two miles up a tiny lane above Chesham surrounded by beech trees and old hedgerows. At first glance, the Blue Ball is an unremarkable, converted farmhouse with a large garden and rear field used by groups for camping (booking in advance). However the landlord and his family work hard to make their beer festival (early June) exceptional. It not only offers 30 interesting ales, but music, food, camping, dragsters, the Sealed Knot and many other forms of entertainment. Only a taxi ride from the end of the London tube, you will experience a true English rural welcome. ♨Q❀◑ ÅP

AYLESBURY

Queen's Head
1 Temple Square
11.30-3, 5.30-11; 11.30-11 Fri; 11.30-5, 7-11 Sat; 12-5, 7-10.30 Sun
☎ (01296) 415484
Adnams Bitter; Draught Bass; Courage Directors; Flowers IPA Ⓗ
Village pub at the heart of town, close to the Roald Dahl Museum. Very friendly, and popular with local business people (especially lunchtime), this pub offers a traditional atmosphere with no juke boxes or fruit machines. There are oak beams throughout, from which hang a collection of jugs in the back bar. An open fire warms the front bar and a small outdoor drinking area is at the rear. Daily specials complement the Thai food on offer eves. It stages jam sessions or a local band Sun eve.
♨Q❀⇔◑❋

BIERTON

Bell
191 Aylesbury Road
☼ 11-3, 6-11 (11-11 winter Sat); 12-3, 7-10.30 Sun
☎ (01296) 436055
Fuller's Chiswick, London Pride, ESB, seasonal beers; guest beer Ⓗ
Small two-roomed pub drawing its custom from the village and Aylesbury, two miles away. A guest beer from an independent brewer changes monthly. Live music eves are held alternate Suns – generally rock 'n' roll, rockabilly or blues. Food is always available except on music nights and the pub opens all day during the football season. Parking and outdoor drinking space are somewhat limited. ⌂◑♣P

BLEDLOW

Lions of Bledlow
Church End (off B4009, Chinnor-Princes Risborough Road) OS776020
☼ 11-3, 6-11; 12-3, 7-10.30 Sun
☎ (01844) 343345
Courage Bitter; Wadworth 6X; guest beers Ⓗ
Rambling, unspoilt, 16th-century pub replete with beams and inglenooks, and a particularly large log fire in the main bar. It comprises a games room, restaurant and a large bar, where a good range of food is available from blackboard menus. The extensive rear garden gets busy in summer with walkers and families; tables at the front of the pub enjoy a picturesque setting at the junction of footpaths and bridleways. Children are welcome. ▒Q⌂◑P

BURNHAM

Bee
1 Britwell Road
☼ 12-3, 6-11; 12-11 Sat; 12-10.30 Sun
☎ (01628) 602827
Brakspear Bitter, Special, seasonal beers Ⓗ
Comfortable, cosy hostelry at the north end of Burnham High Street. Previously known as the Crispin, the name was changed after it was taken over and refurbished by Brakspear's Brewery in the late 1990s. The inverted L-shaped bar is often busy, especially at weekends. All Brakspear's seasonal beers appear here in their turn. Good food is served.
⌂◑P

CHEARSLEY

Bell
The Green
☼ 12-2.30 (not Mon), 6-11; 12-3, 7-10.30 Sun
☎ (01844) 208077
Fuller's Chiswick, London Pride, ESB, seasonal beers Ⓗ
Traditional, thatched country pub by the village green, famous for its excellent range of food at reasonable prices: bar snacks, an *à la carte* menu and Sun lunches are all available, together with vegetarian and children's selections. Eve meals are served Tue-Sat. Its comfortable atmosphere is enhanced by open fires in winter. It has a large safe garden with a play area. Aylesbury Vale Council's *Best Village Pub* winner for 1998 and 2000.
▒Q⌂◑♣P●

CHENIES

Red Lion
Off A404, between Chorleywood and Little Chalfont
☼ 11-2, 5.30-11; 12-3, 7-10.30 Sun
☎ (01923) 282722
Benskins Bitter; Vale Notley Ale; Wadworth 6X Ⓗ
In the over-priced south, a genuine free house dedicated to serving high quality food and beer is rare, but here food is prepared to order (no chips and no booking) and four local beers are always available; Lion Pride is brewed for the pub by Rebellion. Chenies is a small village near the Chess Valley Walk and the Chenies Manor gardens are often open to the public. The small rear snug is deliberately spartan, with bare floorboards and painted walls; the front bar is very comfortable, displaying leonine artefacts and old Chenies postcards.
Q⌂◑P

DAGNALL

Golden Rule
Main Road (A4146)
☼ 11.30-3, 5.30-11; 12-3, 7-10.30 Sun
☎ (01442) 843227
Adnams Bitter; Fuller's London Pride, ESB; Ⓗ **guest beers** Ⓗ/Ⓖ
Handy for Whipsnade Zoo and Dunstable Downs, the Golden Rule is an ex-sweetshop that is now two separate businesses within the one small building. A popular 28-seat restaurant occupies one side of the bar, where the chef runs his own business (booking necessary). On the other side, at least seven real ales are always available from the cellar or the eight-barrel rack which is water-cooled; Olden Grule is a house beer from Tring. This true free house runs four beer festivals a year.
Q⌂◑♣P

GREAT MISSENDEN

Cross Keys
40 High Street
☼ 11-3, 5-11; 12-3, 7-10.30 Sun
☎ (01494) 865373
Fuller's Chiswick, London Pride, ESB, seasonal beers Ⓗ
Quality Fuller's house at the heart of a commuter-belt village (on the Marylebone-Aylesbury line). Although the building is over 400 years old, the current layout is unusual, with a restaurant in the old lounge bar. The bar is long and winding with two distinct areas: the front has a huge inglenook and wooden settles against the walls, the rear is stone-flagged and narrow. Local pictures, mirrors, brasses and, unusually, skis abound, as does village gossip.
Q⌂◑♿⇌P

INDEPENDENT BREWER

Chiltern Terrick
Old Luxters Hambleden
Rebellion Marlow
Trueman's Medmenham **41**
Vale Haddenham

HADDENHAM

King's Head
52 High Street
✪ 12-2.30, 5-11; 12-11 Fri & Sat; 12-10.30 Sun
☎ (01844) 291391
Adnams Bitter; Fuller's London Pride; Ⓖ Greene King IPA, Ⓗ Abbot Ⓖ
Thriving, traditional pub in the old part of town. It has two entrances, one is on Townside. The pub dates back to the 16th century, but part of it was burnt down in the 18th century when the minister, who ran the pub at the time, left a candle burning when he went to hold an evening service. The patio drinking area can be a suntrap. It hosts occasional music eves, and Sky Sports are screened. ▨Q❀◖◗⧄♣P

Red Lion
Church End
✪ 11.30-3, 5.30-11; 11-11 Sat; 12-10.30 Sun
☎ (01844) 291606
Adnams Bitter; Ansells Mild; Marston's Pedigree; Young's Bitter Ⓗ
Friendly pub at the southerly end of the village, looking out on to the green, church and duckpond. Built in 1939, it replaced an existing 17th-century Wychert-built pub. Unaltered since it was opened, it retains its polished oak floor and original tables. There have only been four licensees since 1939; the landlord is due to celebrate 30 years in the pub in 2002. It fields thriving darts, crib, domino and quiz teams, and pool is popular. ▨Q❀⋈◖◗⧄♣P

HAMBLEDEN

Stag & Huntsman
(1 mile N of A4155) OS785866
✪ 11-2.30 (3 Sat), 6-11; 12-3, 7-10.30 Sun
☎ (01491) 571227 website: stag&huntsman.com
Brakspear Bitter; Wadworth 6X; guest beers Ⓗ
Unspoilt, characterful, local gem, in a picturesque brick and flint NT village, the pub boasts an L-shaped rear lounge, a small, front, curtained hideaway and the locals' public bar (only accessible from a side entrance). A dining room offers restaurant facilities, and an extensive bar menu is available throughout the three bars. The weekly changing guest beer often favours the landlord's native west country. ▨❀⋈◖◗ ⧄♣P

HANSLOPE

Globe
50 Hartwell Road (Longstreet Village is between Hanslope and Hartwell on unclassified road)
✪ 12-2.30 (not Tue), 6-11; 12-3, 7-10.30 Sun
☎ (01908) 510336
Banks's Bitter, Ⓗ/Ⓟ guest beers Ⓗ
This classic country pub has twice won awards for the excellence of its ale. In a mixed commuting and farming village, it has a community-focused public bar and games room, contrasting with a quiet lounge and no-smoking restaurant, nicely decorated in country style, where excellent, good value meals are served (booking essential). There is also a bar menu (no eve meals Tue or Sun). A pleasant garden contains a well-equipped children's play area. One of Wolverhampton & Dudley group's seasonal beers is usually stocked at this former local CAMRA *Pub of the Year*.
Q❀◖◗ ⧄Pⓣ

HAWRIDGE COMMON

Full Moon
Cholesbury Lane OS936069
✪ 12-3, 5.30-11; 11-11 Sat; 12-4, 7-10.30 (12-10.30 summer) Sun
☎ (01494) 758959
Draught Bass; Boddingtons Bitter; Fuller's London Pride; guest beers Ⓗ
This classic Chilterns country pub is pretty near perfect – with a cricket pitch out front, (private) windmill to the rear, garden, patio, paddock (with hitching-rails for horses), two restaurants (one no-smoking) and a huge fire. Above all, this 400-year-old inn has a genuine, low-beamed, stone-flagged main bar with up to six real ales. At the top of a quiet village, hidden away between Chesham, Wendover and Tring it is always buzzing, with locals and visitors alike. ⮑❀◖◗⧄P

HEDGERLEY

White Horse
Village Lane OS969874
✪ 11-2.30, 5.30-11; 11-11 Sat; 12-10.30 Sun
☎ (01753) 643225
Greene King IPA; guest beers Ⓗ/Ⓖ
Picturesque, 15th-century free house run by the same family since 1979. The small

INN BRIEF

BENNETT END

Three Horseshoes Inn
Bennett End Road, Radnage
12-2.30, 7-11; closed Mon;
12-2.30 (closed eve) Sun
Brakspear Bitter; Flowers Original Ⓗ
Fine old country pub in splendid Chilterns countryside, with cosy bars. Note the red telephone box in the duckpond.

BUCKINGHAM

Whale
Market Hill
✪; 12-10.30 Sun
Chiswick,
Pride, ESB Ⓗ
...al, town-centre pub with
...l gaslights. This friendly
... split-level bar with
... Sun 1-3pm. Rooms

CHESHAM

Last Post
77 The Broadway
11-11; 12-10.30 Sun
**Boddingtons Bitter;
Courage Directors; Theakston Best Bitter;
guest beers Ⓗ**
Typical Wetherspoon's conversion of the small, town-centre ex-Post Office, into a pub popular with all ages. Food serves all day.

Queen's Head
116 Church Street
12-2.30, 5-11; 12-11 Sat; 12-10.30 Sun
**Brakspear Bitter; Fuller's London Pride,
ESB, seasonal beers Ⓗ**
Traditional old town pub, sympathetically refurbished by Fuller's. Thai food is served Mon-Sat.

CUBLINGTON

Unicorn
High Street
5.30 (5 Sat)-11; 12.30-9 Sun
**Brakspear Bitter; Shepherd Neame
Spitfire; Vale Wychert; guest beer
(summer) Ⓗ**
Superb, low-beamed family-run country local with open fires at either end, unspoilt by the intrusion of food – there isn't any.

IVER HEATH

Stag & Hounds
Church Road (A412)
11-11; 12-10.30 Sun
**Draught Bass; Courage Best Bitter;
Fuller's London Pride Ⓗ**
Reputedly the first of this name, this 19th-century busy local and focus of the community has a distinctive L-shaped bar.

public bar boasts a stone floor and inglenook while the more spacious lounge is decorated with old photos of the village. Always at least six ales are on tap, plus a good selection of bottled beers. An annual beer festival is held in a marquee in the extensive garden (Whitsun) and barbecues are a regular bank holiday feature. Truly a gem, not to be missed. ⚏Q✿◑⊟♣♠P

HIGH WYCOMBE

Bird in Hand
81 West Wycombe Road (A40, W of town)
✪ 11-3.30, 5.30-11; 11-11 Fri & Sat; 12-10.30 Sun
☎ (01494) 523502
Courage Best Bitter, Directors; Vale Notley Ale Ⓗ
Built in 1932 on the foundations of an earlier Bird in Hand, this family-run pub was knocked through into one long room several years ago. It retains the wood panelling that was once very typical of the area, but is now rare. As it is not on town pub-circuit runs, it escapes rowdiness but, nevertheless, it is lively enough. No food Sun eve. ⚏◪◑♣P

Rose & Crown
Desborough Road
✪ 12-3, 5-11; 12-11 Fri & Sat; 12-10.30 Sun
☎ (01494) 527982
Brakspear Bitter; Courage Best Bitter; Fuller's London Pride; Wells Bombardier; Young's Bitter; guest beers Ⓗ
L-shaped pub, boasting double doors with a fine set of Rose and Crown stained glass motifs. Its office lunchtime trade (no food weekends) contrasts with eves when dominoes, crib and darts matches are regularly played. Two TV sets (satellite/terrestrial) are usually tuned to sport. A Labrador and two Rottweilers are kept in the rear of the pub. Rebellion beers are a speciality – not to be missed. It is near a busy shopping area, west of the centre, handy for the bus station and is to remain under the western development scheme. ⚏◑≋♣

ICKFORD

Rising Sun
36 Worminghall Road
✪ 12-3 (not Mon), 5-11; 12-11 Sat; 12-10.30 Sun
☎ (01844) 339238 e-mail: honour-paul@hotmail.com

Hancock's HB; Marston's Pedigree; Wadworth 6X; guest beer Ⓗ
Friendly village local, parts of which date back to the 15th century. Although food is on offer, it in no way dominates the pub, and accounts for a small percentage of the turnover. Very active in local leagues for darts, crib, pool and quizzes, an Aunt Sally provides amusement in summer. The pub is known locally as the Woodcutter's Arms because the landlord is a forestry contractor. ⚏Q✿◑♣P

LITTLE MARLOW

King's Head
Church Road OS872882
✪ 11-3, 5.30-11; 11-11 Fri & Sat; 12-10.30 Sun
☎ (01628) 484407
Brakspear Bitter; Fuller's London Pride; Taylor Landlord; guest beers Ⓗ
Village pub of great character, dating from the 14th century, where fine ale and varied, home-cooked meals take centre stage. The L-shaped bar serves up to six ales in a pleasant atmosphere. Families are welcome throughout the pub and the large rear garden offers a secluded summer haven. Wheelchair WC. ⚏Q✿◑♿♣P⌇

LITTLE MISSENDEN

Crown
Off A413
✪ 11-2.30, 6-11; 12-3, 7-10.30 Sun
☎ (01494) 862571
Adnams Bitter; Brakspear Special; Marston's Pedigree; guest beers Ⓗ
At the old Amersham end of this quiet village next to the River Misbourne, the Crown is a small pub with a large following, providing the basics of good ale and fine food in friendly surroundings, to a very high standard. In the How family for nearly 100 years, it has a genuine Chilterns atmosphere, with a stone-flagged floor at one end and oak panelling at the other of the single small room. No food Sun. ⚏Q✿◑♣P

LITTLEWORTH COMMON

Blackwood Arms
Common Lane OS935861
✪ 11-2.30, 5-11; 12-11 Sat; 12-10.30 Sun

MARLOW
Hogshead
82-84 High Street
11-11; 12-10.30 Sun
Boddingtons Bitter; Brakspear Bitter; Marston's Pedigree; guest beers Ⓗ
Large, popular ale house on the site of the former Wethered Brewery. It offers 10 real ales, Biddenden cider and food every day.

Prince of Wales
Mill Road
11-11; 12-10.30 Sun
Brakspear Bitter; Fuller's London Pride; guest beer Ⓗ
Friendly, street-corner local with connecting bars and dining area (families welcome). Meals served Mon-Fri lunch and eve.

SKIRMETT
Frog
11.30-3, 6.30 (6 Fri & Sat)-11; 12-4, 7-10.30 (12-10.30 summer) Sun
Brakspear Bitter; Fuller's London Pride; guest beers Ⓗ
300 years old, this free house and restaurant also offers high quality accommodation with fine views across beautiful countryside. *Cask Marque* accredited.

STEWKLEY
Swan
High Street North
12-3 (not winter Tue), 5.30-11; 12-4, 7-10.30 (12-10.30 summer) Sun
Draught Bass; Courage Best Bitter, Directors Ⓗ
Fine Georgian village pub, enjoying a good atmosphere in its old beamed bars and dining area.

STOKE MANDEVILLE
Bull
5 Risborough Road
12-3, 5.30-11; 12-11 Sat; 12-10.30 Sun
Draught Bass; Fuller's London Pride; Tetley Bitter Ⓗ
Small village local with two contrasting bars, well served by public transport. Ample garden. Lunches served.

> ✳ symbol next to a main entry place name indicates there are Inn Brief entries as well.

☎ (01753) 642169
Beer range varies Ⓗ
Allegedly named after one of Nelson's admirals at the Battle of Trafalgar, this small, 18th-century building in idyllic woodland, is something of a local institution. A free house, that has appeared in the *Guinness Book of Records* for its number of ever-changing real ales, it regularly hosts themed festivals of unusual beers. The landlord aims to achieve 'a continuous real ale festival'. A great place for exploring Burnham Beeches – some of the footpaths start at the car park. Good home-cooked food is served.
ﬔQ❀◑➠P

Jolly Woodman
Littleworth Road OS934865
✪ 11-11; 12-10.30 Sun
☎ (01753) 644350
Brakspear Bitter; Flowers Original; Vale Black Swan Dark Mild; guest beers Ⓗ
On the edge of Burnham Beeches, this country pub was originally three 16th-century cottages. Now a listed building, its long single bar features a rowing boat hanging from the central beams, agricultural and woodcutting implements, and a large collection of beer bottles. The open interior has a large central section with a stove, a raised end, and a no-smoking area. In winter two real fires add cosiness to comfort. A fine garden and good food add to its appeal. A rare outlet for mild locally.
ﬔQ❀◑P✂

MARLOW ✣

Carpenters Arms
15 Spittal Street
✪ 11-11; 12-10.30 Sun
☎ (01628) 473649
Morrells Oxford Blue, Varsity Ⓗ
Genuine workingman's local, the only one left in the town (acquired by Morrells in 1992) which buzzes with lively conversation and debate. The decor includes old carpentry tools, and matchboxes on the ceiling. Try the landlady's de-luxe sandwiches. It fields both darts and soccer teams, and live Sky football fixtures are shown on the big screen for the keen footie fans in the bar. A meat raffle is a regular event.
ﬔQ❀≠♣

Crown & Anchor
45 Oxford Road
✪ 12-2.30, 5-11; 11-11 Sat; 12-10.30 Sun
☎ (01628) 891161 website: www.crown@anchor.co.uk
Trueman's Best, Tipple; guest beers Ⓗ
Home of, and sole outlet for, Sam Trueman's beers, this 18th-century roadside pub has gone from strength to strength. Constantly changing guest beers (and a guest cider) satisfy the strong local contingent of beer connoisseurs. Regular crib (Mon) and quizzes (Wed) are supplemented by live music and jam sessions Fri and Sat, plus dinner date theme nights. A heated enclosed patio is used on winter music nights when the bar is full. A mini-beer festival is held at Christmas. No food Mon eve.
ﬔ❀❀◑&♣➠

MARSH GIBBON

Greyhound
West Edge
✪ 12-3.30, 6-11 (closed Mon); 12-4, 7-10.30 Sun
☎ (01869) 277365
Fuller's London Pride; Greene King IPA, Abbot; Ⓗ
Country pub in a quiet *Domesday* village. A listed building, with 17th-century brickwork, it was rebuilt after a fire in 1740. It has an oak-beamed interior, a wood-panelled bar, two drinking areas and a restaurant; bar seating is on comfortable benches and stools and there is a wood-burning fire in the main bar area. Historical documents, bills and receipts dating back to 1813 are displayed. The Greyhound specialises in Thai food, freshly prepared to order (book weekend eves). ﬔQ❀◑P⊟

MARSWORTH

Red Lion
90 Vicarage Road (off B489, by canal bridge 130) OS919147
✪ 11-3, 6-11; 12-3, 7-10.30 Sun
☎ (01296) 668366
Fuller's London Pride; Vale Notley Ale; guest beers Ⓗ
Marsworth Junction is where the Aylesbury arm of the Grand Union Canal joins the main waterway and this village, near Tring, is dominated by the hire, sale and repair of canal boats. Free moorings are available close to the 400-year-old Red Lion. It has three distinct drinking areas and a large garden that plays host to open-air theatre on summer eves. In winter, there may be skittles or simply 'Wild' Willy Barratt amusing himself on the piano – it's that kind of pub. ﬔQ☎◑⊟&♣➠P

MILTON KEYNES

Cross Keys
34 Newport Road, Woolstone
✪ 12-11; 12-10.30 Sun
☎ (01908) 679404
Wells Eagle, Bombardier Ⓗ
16th-century thatched pub in Woolstone Village, just two minutes' walk from bridge No. 84 on the Grand Union Canal. Two bars, both have exposed beams and there is an inglenook in the lounge. Darts, dominoes and cards are played in the Village Bar which also has a fruit machine, TV and piano. Children are welcome in the lounge bar and there is a play area in the garden. Good quality home-cooked food is served in both bars lunchtime and Wed-Sat eves. ❀◑⊟♣P

Moon under Water
10 Avebury Boulevard
✪ 11-11; 12-10.30 Sun
☎ (01908) 528854
Courage Directors; Shepherd Neame Spitfire; Theakston Best Bitter, Old Peculier; Wadworth 6X; guest beers Ⓗ
Very busy city-centre Wetherspoon's, situated in the new X-scape Complex where amenities include a snow-dome, multi-screen cinema and bowling alley. One large, serpentine bar boasts striking modern decor and lighting. There are two no-smoking areas, one by the front entrance, with easy wheelchair access, and one on the raised area towards the rear of the pub. The glass

South Kensington
    Science Museum Exit

Exhibition Road.
    Science Museum Entrance

South Kensington
    Science Museum Exit
Exhibition Road
    Science Museum Entrance

frontage can be opened fully in summer on to a large patio area with wooden tables, chairs and parasols. Food is served all day.
Q ✿🐕🅞♿≠P✗🎵●

Nag's Head
30 High Street, Great Linford (follow signs to Gt Linford off Marsh Drive)
☼ 12-2.30, 5.30-11; 12-11 Thu-Sat; 12-10.30 Sun
☎ (01908) 607449
Friary Meux Bitter ⒣

Wonderfully unspoilt mid-16th-century thatched pub in an old village on the edge of the new city. The lively public bar has TV and traditional games, a quieter low-beamed lounge boasts a magnificent inglenook. The formerly agricultural village of Great Linford has kept its charm, and the lounge displays framed photographs of bucolic locals from bygone days. Part of a group of historic buildings near the Grand Union Canal, train buffs may be interested to know that pioneer locomotive builder Edward Bury lived next door. Other cask ales are served with cask breathers.
🏚Q✿🅞🅞P

Wetherspoon's
201 Midsummer Boulevard
☼ 11-11; 12-10.30 Sun
☎ (01908) 606074
Courage Directors; Shepherd Neame Spitfire; Theakston Best Bitter; Wadworth 6X; guest beers ⒣

Cavernous Wetherspoon's dating from 1995, rather than a venerable conversion. This striking glass pavilion with a wavy roof, is situated in the business district, near the station. The usual great value food, cheap prices and superb quality cask ale make this the area's most prominent beer outlet by far. The large no-smoking area is particularly welcome. It can get very busy Fri and Sat eves and when offices disgorge. It generally offers two or three guests from small independents and twice-yearly beer festivals. Q✿🅞🅞♿≠✗●

Cannon
50 High Street
☼ 11-11; 12-10.30 Sun
☎ (01908) 211495
Draught Bass; M&B Brew XI; guest beers ⒣

This partially-listed building was also the site of the last local brewery. The oldest parts of the structure date from the 15th century but the Cannon has only been a pub since Victorian times. It features military memorabilia at one end, together with a stoutly individualistic juke box and, although essentially one room, it divides into three distinct areas. The guest beers are often from Bass Museum. A live acoustic/roots jam session happens Wed. Several languages (including Flemish) spoken. 🏚♣🍺P

Cock
16 High Street
☼ 12-3, 6-11; 12-11 Sat; 12-11 Sun
☎ (01234) 391222 e-mail: terrypubmaster@aol.com
Wells Eagle, Bombardier; guest beers ⒣

Village pub in the shadow of a large Pevsner-lauded church. A small, tidy public

bar contrasts with a much larger lounge, decorated with many bottles and plates, as well as numerous paintings (the work of a former landlord). The pub's proximity to Cranfield University explains the cosmopolitan feel, quite unexpected in this rural setting. There is some evidence of an inn on the site going back to the 11th century. Children are welcome in the 'Cockpit'. No eve meals Sun.
🏚🐄✿🅞🅞♣P●

White Hart
4 The Strand
☼ 12-2 (not Thu; 3 Sat), 7 (5.30 Mon)-11; 12-3, 7-10.30 Sun
☎ (01296) 655234
Adnams Bitter; Benskins Bitter; guest beer ⒣

The pretty village of Quainton has a windmill at the top of the green and the famous Buckinghamshire Railway Centre as its tourist attraction. The White Hart, an unpretentious 1930s pub, draws most of its custom from the village, together with some passing trade, perhaps visiting Claydon House or Waddesdon Manor (both NT). 'Cheap and cheerful' bar meals are served (not Thu). The landlord is lovingly restoring a vintage double-decker bus (a Lincolnshire Road Car, 1960) in the car park.
🏚✿🚅🅞♣P

White Hart
1 Gun Lane
☼ 12-11; 12-4, 7-10.30 Sun
☎ (01908) 611953
Fuller's London Pride; Vale Wychert; Young's Bitter; guest beers ⒣

Splendid old village local, sold as a private house in 1995, but saved and preserved as a pub by community action after a public outcry. Gratifyingly, this support continues and it is a genuine focus for local life, as well as welcoming visitors. Although not large, there are three distinct areas, one for dining, where a very varied menu of home-cooked food (including tapas), is offered. One of the outbuildings now provides accommodation. A beer and sausage fest is held May bank holiday. Parking can be tricky. Boules played.
🏚Q✿🚅🅞♣P

Lamb
20 High Street
☼ 12-3, 5-11; 12-11 Fri & Sat; 12-10.30 Sun
☎ (01908) 551233
Hook Norton Best Bitter; guest beers ⒣

Recently improved village local on the main road, run by an enthusiastic and ambitious management. A comfortable and welcoming bar, with a snug at the rear, is complemented by a dining area. Belgian bottled beers are available. The large garden hosts a summer beer festival. There are two pub dogs; one dafter than the other. The main bar area houses a skittle alley.
🏚✿🅞♣🍺P✗

STONY STRATFORD

Bull Hotel & Vaults Bar
64 High Street
✪ 12-11; 12-10.30 Sun
☎ (01908) 567104
Draught Bass; Benskins Bitter; Fuller's London Pride; guest beers Ⓗ

The Bull's lounge bar has a warm 17th-century feel, with wooden floors and five handpumps. Next door, the Vaults Bar, which at one time was an antique shop, boasts a stone floor and seven handpumps. A disastrous fire started at the Bull Hotel in 1742, burning down one side of the town (146 houses) and the church of St Mary Magdalene. Legend has it that visitors from the Cock hotel told stories at this old coaching inn, giving rise to the expression 'cock and bull story'. ▲Q✿❀◑◐♣P

Fox & Hounds
87 High Street
✪ 12-11; 12-10.30 Sun
☎ (01908) 563307 website: www.stonystratford.co.uk
Adnams Broadside; Draught Bass; Smiles Best; guest beers Ⓗ

17th-century, two-bar pub, in an old coaching town. This local CAMRA *Pub of the Year* 1998 always serves a good range of real ales from small brewers. It is one of the best live music venues around for blues, folk and jazz, especially Thu and Sat eves (the first Tue each month is an open session). It also hosts monthly exotic food eves. Northants skittles is played. No smoking in the lounge when food is served. Q✿◑♣P

SWAN BOTTOM

Old Swan
Kingswood, The Lee OS902055
✪ 12-3, 6-11; 12-11 Sat; closed Mon; 12-10.30 Sun
☎ (01494) 837239
Adnams Bitter; Brakspear Bitter; Fuller's London Pride; guest beer Ⓗ

16th-century inn beside the Chiltern Way Walk, close to the quiet, but affluent village of The Lee, and Wendover Woods. This typical Chilterns country pub features low beams, stone-flagged floors, settles and a large real fire. Home-prepared food is cooked to order (food at weekends; no food Sun eve) it has a very friendly atmosphere where all are welcome (dogs must be kept on a lead). Its two acres of gardens are very tranquil on hot summer's days. ▲Q✿◑⅙P

TURVILLE

Bull & Butcher
(off M40 jct 5, through Ibstone) OS768911
✪ 11-3, 6 (6.30 Sat)-11; 12-5, 7-10.30 Sun
☎ (01491) 638283 website: www.bullandbutcher.com
Brakspear 2.5 Bitter, Mild, Bitter, Old, Special, Coniston Bluebird, seasonal beers Ⓗ

Set in an unspoilt village in a beautiful Chiltern valley, with a pretty garden, this charming, 16th-century timbered pub has open log fires and now incorporates, in the recent bar extension, a table set over an old 50-ft well. Over 35 wines are sold by the glass and the excellent *à la carte* menu is reasonably price (booking recommended; no meals Sun eve). Bounds cider is served straight from the cask. ▲Q✿◑♣P⅞

TYLERS GREEN

Horse & Jockey
Church Road
✪ 12-2.30, 5.30-11; 12-3, 7-10.30 Sun
☎ (01494) 815963
Adnams Broadside; Brakspear Bitter; Greene King Abbot; Tetley Bitter; guest beer Ⓗ

Nothing much changes at the Horse & Jockey. A warm welcome and good beer – who would want to change that? Food is now a major factor but it retains aspects of the traditional village boozer it once was. It looks a little lost as a village pub in an increasingly commuter belt; but it survives well. Located in the older part of the village near an interesting church, Tylers Green tends to be dominated by the smaller village of Penn nearby, because of the latter's historic links with America. ▲✿◑♣P

WADDESDON

Lion
78 High Street
✪ 12-2.30, 5.30-11; 12-3.30, 7-10.30 Sun
☎ (01296) 651227
Draught Bass; Fuller's ESB; guest beer Ⓗ

Waddesdon Manor is one of the National Trust's top attractions; the nearby Lion offers an excellent range of food (booking advisable). The bar and dining area is deceptively large with big comfortable tables. The landlord and chef, Jean-Marie Decrette, comes from Normandy and offers a varied menu including a choice of over 30 main courses (not by any means all French) including daily specials. The menus change according to season, meals are reasonably priced and the portions generous. However, good food cannot be hurried and an hour will not be enough for lunch. No food Sun eve. Q✿◑♣P⅞

WENDOVER

End of the World
World's End (Aylesbury road, 1 mile from Wendover)
✪ 11.30-2.30, 5.30-11 (12-11 summer); closed Mon; 12-10.30 Sun
☎ (01296) 622299
Brakspear Bitter; guest beers Ⓗ

Popular bar and restaurant opposite a garden centre. Formerly called the Swan, it dates back over 350 years and boasts some original timbers. Four real ales are always available, with one sold at a very popular reduced price. With seating for 80 in the three restaurant areas and a further 40 in the bar, there is plenty of space to enjoy the wide range of food (mainly English cuisine) with fresh fish and daily specials, all prepared on the premises by a team of chefs. ✿◑❀P☖

WEST WYCOMBE

George & Dragon
High Street (A40)
✪ 11-2.30 (3 Sat), 5.30-11; 12-3, 7-10.30 Sun
☎ (01494) 464414
Courage Directors; Fuller's London Pride; Wells Bombardier; guest beers Ⓗ

Rustic, oak-beamed 18th-century inn, NT-owned (as is most of the village) with an entrance via a narrow, uneven cobbled

surface and archway leading to a courtyard containing kitchens (good food), plus a vintners run by the tenants. Two bedrooms have four-poster beds. The garden has children's play equipment. A pigeon loft from coaching days despatched messages to Oxford and London with details of coach departures. West Wycombe Park and House (NT) stand behind the village; the famous Hellfire caves, mausoleum and church with golden ball on top can also be visited.
🏚Q🛏♿⌂🍴◑P⅂

WESTON TURVILLE

Chequers
35 Church Lane (parallel to B4544)
🍺 12-3 (not Mon), 6-11; 12-3, 7-10.30 Sun
☎ (01296) 613298

Adnams Bitter; Fuller's London Pride; Young's Special Ⓗ

The cosy stone-flagged main bar and adjoining *à la carte* restaurant in a converted barn blend easily into this olde-worlde part of the village. The pub name dates from 1768, after the board games that were played here. Bar meals are served Tue-Sat lunchtime, otherwise the main bar's ambience is only spoilt by the unnecessary piped muzak. Paintings by local artists are for sale. A second bar, in a sunken area, leads to the restaurant (meals served Tue-Sat and Sun lunch) where beers may differ from those in the main bar. 🏚❀◑P

WEXHAM STREET

Plough
Wexham Street, Stoke Poges
🍺 11-11; 12-10.30 Sun
☎ (01753) 662613

Courage Best Bitter; Fuller's London Pride; Young's Special; guest beers Ⓗ

Originally three cottages dating back to the 1700s, the frontage is listed and the bar has a low-beamed ceiling. The two guest beers are from the Carlsberg-Tetley portfolio. The publican strongly promotes real ale with 'Meet the Brewer' eves and other events. Good value, home-cooked food is served in a dining area warmed by two real fires. The large rear function/family room, originally the stables, has recently been refurbished. Roadside tables provide outdoor drinking.
🏚Q🛏❀◑♣P

WHITCHURCH

White Swan
10 High Street
🍺 11-11; 12-3, 7-10.30 Sun
☎ (01296) 641228

Fuller's Chiswick, London Pride, ESB, seasonal beers Ⓗ

Attractive, part-thatched 16th-century pub with an intimate atmosphere. It has a huge mature garden and distinctive wood panelling in the lounge bar. Good value food is available (except Sun eve) with daily specials (Tue-Sun) and occasional food theme nights. You can eat in either of the bars or the small, no-smoking dining room. The landlord is *Fuller's Master Cellarman No. 22* and has several appearances in this *Guide* to his credit at this and other pubs in the county.
🏚Q❀◑🍴♣P

WING

Cock
26 High Street
🍺 11.30-3, 6-11; 12-3, 7-10.30 Sun
☎ (01296) 688214

Courage Directors; Webster's Yorkshire Bitter; guest beers Ⓗ

This former coaching inn should appeal to most tastes. Four of its six real ales come from independent or micro-breweries, often rarely seen in this area, making it something of a mecca for local beer drinkers. Mini beer festivals are occasionally held. The bar has three main drinking areas, one with a dartboard. The large carvery restaurant can get very busy at weekends. The car park is spacious but beware the narrow entrance. 🏚Q❀◑♣P

WINGRAVE

Rose & Crown
The Green
🍺 11.30-3, 5.30-11; 11.30-11 Sat; 12-10.30 Sun
☎ (01296) 681257

Flowers IPA; Fuller's London Pride; Greene King IPA; guest beer Ⓗ

Built in the early 17th century, this traditional village pub has retained its three bars. It has a stone-flagged public bar, complete with dartboard and real fire, a small snug in the middle and a large lounge (with a library) at the other end. A dining area, an ample family/function room and a garden overlooking the village recreation ground complete the picture. Beer festivals are held every Sept and on special occasions. 🏚🛏❀◑🍴♣P🍴●

WORMINGHALL

Clifden Arms
75 Clifden Road OS640083
🍺 12-2.30 (3 Sat), 6-11; 12-4, 7.30-10.30 Sun
☎ (01844) 339273

Adnams Broadside; Brakspear Bitter; Hook Norton Best Bitter; guest beer Ⓗ

Off the beaten track between Oxford and Thame, this really is a hidden gem. A picturesque village local with two bar areas featuring beams, and local memorabilia; the restaurant area serves a wide choice of meals and snacks, including vegetarian and children's options. Specials include curry nights (Thu) and take-away fish and chips. The extensive secluded garden features the local game of Aunt Sally. Bar billiards is also played at this local CAMRA *Pub of the Year* 2001. 🏚❀◑🍴♣P

WYCOMBE MARSH

General Havelock
114 Kings Mead Road
🍺 12-2.30, 5.30-11; 11-11 Fri & Sat; 12-10.30 Sun
☎ (01494) 520391

Fuller's Chiswick, London Pride, ESB, seasonal beer Ⓗ

Imposing building on a quiet road that runs parallel, and to the south of the A40. This smart pub has what could be called an extended-family atmosphere. It has been run by the same landlord since it was acquired by Fuller's and it The dry ski slope is nearby as is a sports field where rugby, cricket and netball are played. Eve meals served Fri and Sat. 🏚❀◑♣P

CAMBRIDGESHIRE

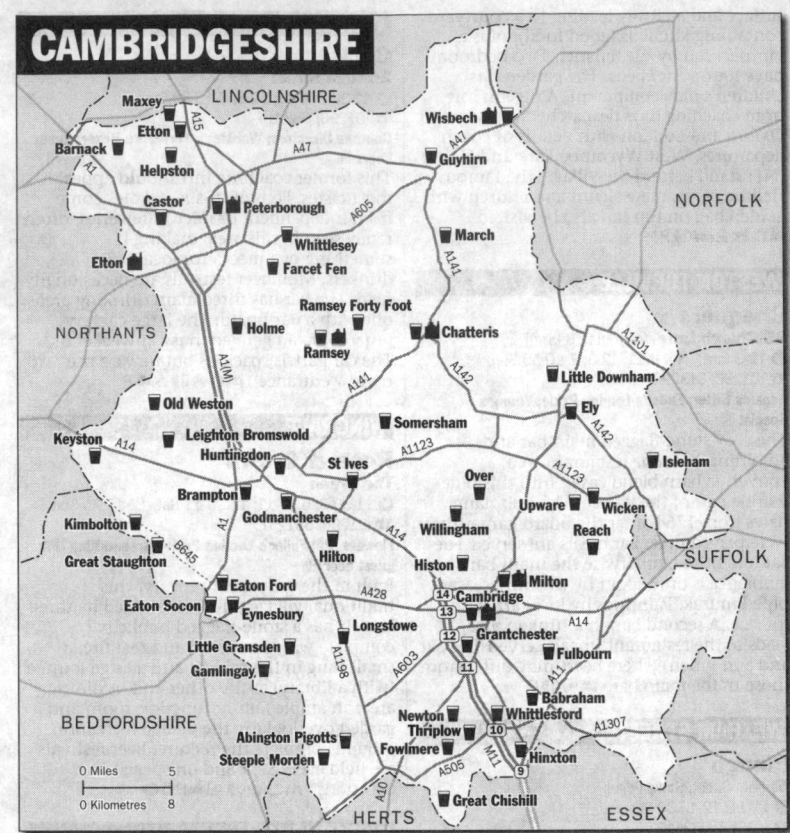

Pig & Abbot
High Street (off A505 towards Litlington)
OS306444
☼ 12-3, 6-11; 12-11 Sat; 12-10.30 Sun
☎ (01763) 853515
Adnams Bitter; City of Cambridge True Blue; guest beers Ⓗ
The only pub in this small, deeply rural South Cambs village. Formerly known by the geriatric name of Darby & Joan, new owners attempted to bring the pub up to date with a more striking name, it failed, the pub closed, but was luckily saved by a village buyout in 1997. Deceptively large for a village local, it features a comfortable restaurant and well-appointed lounge bar where a large inglenook holds a wood-burning stove. An imaginative menu includes blackboard specials. A good range of beers is always on tap.
ᐃQ☸◐P

BABRAHAM

George Inn
High Street
☼ 12-2.30, 6-11; 12-3, 7-10.30 Sun
☎ (01223) 832204
Greene King IPA, Ruddles County, Abbot; guest beers Ⓗ
Early 18th-century coaching inn: a comfortable, beamed, one-bar pub with a dining room, popular with biotechnology companies' staff beginning to spread into local villages. Old photographs, cigarette cards and uncluttered bric-à-brac abound in the bar; the dining room decor features a number of different Georges. It is renowned for its food, including the 'Pudding Lovers' Club' every Wed, for traditional English puds. The village football and cricket clubs meet here Sun lunch. Morris dancers make regular summer appearances.
ᐃQ☸◐

BARNACK

Millstone
Millstone Lane (back street between 'Hills and Hollows' and Main St)
☼ 11.30-2.30, 5.30 (6 Sat)-11; 12-4, 7-10.30 Sun
☎ (01780) 740296
Adnams Bitter; Everards Tiger, Original; guest beer Ⓗ
Now the only pub in the village, the Millstone still caters well for drinkers, although food is now a major part of its trade (no food Sun eve). Winner of numerous awards for beer quality, cellarmanship and food, the landlord is now in his 17th year here, boasting a *Guide* entry for much of that time. The village is home to the 'Hills and Holes', an ancient quarry where the stone for Peterborough Cathedral was extracted. The site is now a nature reserve and provides a pleasant local walk.
Q☸◐ఉP⊬●

BRAMPTON

Grange Hotel
115 High Street
☼ 11-3, 6-11; 11-11 Fri & Sat; 12-4, 7-10.30 Sun
☎ (01480) 459516
website: www.grangehotelbrampton.co.uk
City of Cambridge Hobson's Choice; Greene King IPA; guest beer Ⓗ

Stylish bar in an elegantly-refurbished small hotel. The new proprietors are developing a reputation for good food, wine and beer following their move from the Old Bridge Hotel in Huntingdon. Built as a private residence in 1773, and used as a girls' school in the early 19th century, the building was requisitioned by the RAF at the outbreak of WWII, and used as the HQ of the American Eighth Air Force, only becoming a hotel in 1981. Sun eve meals for residents only. Q❀⇔◑⅁P⅄

CAMBRIDGE ❄

Bird in Hand
73 Newmarket Road
☼ 12-2.30, 5-11; 12-11 Fri & Sat; 12-10.30 Sun
☎ (01223) 351919
website: www.bird-in-hand.fsnet.co.uk
Greene King XX Mild, IPA, Abbot, Old Speckled Hen; guest beers Ⓗ

Characterful early 20th-century one-bar pub, where extensive menu of freshly-cooked food is prepared from local ingredients. It specialises in Gujarati food (Sat) and Baltis (Sun eve). Popular quiz on Thu eves. Games include shove-ha'penny. Local artists' work is exhibited on the walls and the walled garden is a pleasant addition. ♨❀◑♣

Cambridge Blue
85-87 Gwydir Street (off Mill Rd)
☼ 12-2.30, 5.30-11; 12-3, 6-11 Fri & Sat; 12-3, 6-10.30 Sun
☎ (01223) 361382
e-mail: cambridgeblue@fsbdial.co.uk
Beer range varies Ⓗ

One of the very few completely no-smoking pubs, it stocks a fine array of beers. City of Cambridge Hobson's Choice and Woodforde's Wherry are frequently stocked, alongside beers from small independent breweries all over Britain. Imported German draught lager and Hoegaarden plus a good selection of wines add choice. Real food is available every session. In summer the large garden is very popular. The pub boasts its own rowing club, inspiring much of the decor. ♨Q❧❀◑⇌♣♨⅄●

Castle Inn
38 Castle Street
☼ 11.30-3, 5-(6 Sat)-11; 12-3, 7-10.30 Sun
☎ (01223) 353194
Adnams Bitter, Fisherman, Broadside; Fuller's London Pride; Marston's Pedigree; guest beers Ⓗ

Adnams' western flagship is a textbook example of sensitive pub renovation. The ground floor has five distinct drinking areas, with three more upstairs. The suntrap patio garden is bordered by the mound of the long-gone Cambridge Castle. Nine real ales are usually available, with beers from regional brewers complementing Adnams' own products and excellent food is served. The landlord has an illustrious past as a rock drummer, including a spell as Barry Wom in Beatles spoof band, The Rutles. ♨❀◑♣⅄

Champion of the Thames
68 King Street
☼ 11-11; 12-10.30 Sun
☎ (01223) 352043
Greene King IPA, Ⓗ Abbot; Ⓖ Ruddles County; guest beer Ⓗ

Traditional pub, full of character, which is something increasingly hard to find these days in a town centre full of beer barns. As the name suggests, it bears a boating theme, with marvellous etched glass windows depicting 'The Champ'. Prints of boat races and Cambridge life, feature in a lovely wood-panelled pair of bars with some nice nooks and corners and comfortable leather-upholstered benches. Popular with both students and locals, the atmosphere is always convivial; live music most Tue eves. ♨Q♣

Elm Tree
Orchard Street (behind Parkside School)
☼ 12-2.30, 4-11; 12-11 Sat; 12-10.30 Sun
☎ (01223) 363005
Adnams Broadside; Wells Eagle, Bombardier; guest beers Ⓗ

Very relaxing pub where a mellow ambience prevails. Live jazz on Mon as well as Thu and Sun, recorded jazz is often playing quietly while drinkers play board games from the large selection next to the fish tank. It is a haven for de-stressing. Major sports events are shown on TV – without the big bar lager element. The guest beers change regularly and may include Badger Tanglefoot or Manchester brews from JW Lees. ❀♣

Empress
72 Thoday Street
☼ 11.30-2.30, 6.30-11; 12-2.30, 7-10.30 Sun
☎ (01223) 247236
Castle Eden Ale; Marston's Pedigree; Taylor Landlord; guest beers Ⓗ

Unpretentious, back-street local which proves that if you get the basics spot on – ace beer in a welcoming atmosphere – then you do not need to offer food to attract the crowds. The interior has been extended over the years but the original public and lounge bar areas remain intact within the open-plan layout. The only regular outlet for Taylor's Landlord in the city, this part of Cambridge 'over the bridge' is short of good pubs, so thank heavens for the Empress. Q❀⊟⇌♨

Kingston Arms
33 Kingston Street (off Mill Rd)
☼ 12-2.30 (not Mon); 5-11; 12-11 Sat; 12-3.30, 7-10.30 Sun
☎ (01223) 319414

INDEPENDENT BREWERIES

City of Cambridge Cambridge
Elgood's Wisbech
Fenland Chatteris
Milton Milton
Oakham Peterborough
Payn Ramsey
Rockingham Ales Elton

Lidstone Rowley Mild, Lucky Punter, Bookies Revenge, Rawalpindi IPA, Old Ale; guest beers H

Transformed by Lidstones Brewery from a sleazy dive into a cracking little local, it was voted Cambridge CAMRA *Pub of the Year* 2001. The fabulous products of Lidstones themselves are accompanied by a generous selection of other micro-brewery beers. Booking is advisable for the freshly-cooked food which has gained an enviable reputation. Exhibitions by local photographers often adorn the walls. The secluded garden is an asset.

🏮Q❀◖❙🚄

Live & Let Live
40 Mawson Road
(200 yds from Mill Rd)

❂ 11.30-2.30; 5.30-11; 11.30-2.30, 6-11 Sat; 12-2, 7-10.30 Sun

☎ (01223) 460261 e-mail: liveandletlive@aol.com

Adnams Bitter; Bateman Mild; B&T Shefford Bitter; Everards Tiger; Nethergate Umbel Ale; guest beers H

There has been a pub here since the mid-19th century; the name supposedly resulted from a protest by an early landlord against the Beer Act. Nowadays it is a friendly back-street local with modern wood panelling and gas lighting enhancing a pleasant atmosphere. Hugely popular with students and locals alike, it offers an ever-changing range of guest beers and good home-cooked food. It has a pleasant snug bar and hosts live music Sun eve.

Q◖❙🚄♣✦●

Portland Arms
129 Chesterton Road

❂ 12-11; 12-10.30 Sun

☎ (01223) 357268 website: www.come.to/theportland

Greene King XX Mild, IPA, Triumph, Abbot, seasonal beers; guest beers H

Virtually unaltered example of an inter-war 'improved public house' under the ownership of Barclay & Perkins, then Greene King. The panelled lounge is especially fine. The back-room stages live music most eves, and plays host to both Cambridge folk clubs. The public bar space has been returned almost to its original state, except for the colour scheme and the addition of Internet access. Good value food is served at this CAMRA *Pub of the Year* 2000; Eve meals available Wed–Sat.

🏮❀◖❙🗗♣✂

St Radegund
129 King Street

❂ 5 (12 Sat)-11; 12-2, 6-10.30 Sun

☎ (01223) 311794

Bateman XB; Fuller's London Pride; Shepherd Neame Spitfire H

Small in size but great in character, this is one of Cambridge's true freehouses, named after a 16th-century Queen of France, who founded a priory on the site of nearby Jesus College. The pub reveals much of interest, including a collection of ties and an array of reference books; elsewhere an invitation to join the Vera Lynn Club (Fri) or participate in the King Street Run. Messages from customers are pinned around the bar. Background jazz music does not intrude and neither should your mobile phone. The TV is only switched on for rugby and cricket.

CASTOR
Royal Oak
24 Peterborough Road (old A47, W of Peterborough)

❂ 12-3, 5-11; 12-11 Sat; 12-10.30 Sun

☎ (01733) 380217

Ind Coope Burton Ale; Tetley Bitter; guest beers H

Picture postcard, 17th-century thatched pub with three bars. It stood formerly on the main A47, but is now bypassed, along with the rest of the village. The front patio is now used much more in warmer weather, due to minimal intrusion from passing traffic. As in many villages a church and school are close by. Lunches are served Tue–Sat. Pétanque is played. 🏮Q❀◖❙🗗♣P

CHATTERIS
Walk the Dog
34 Bridge Street

❂ 12-2.30 (not Tue), 6.30-11; 12-2.30, 7-10.30 Sun

☎ (01354) 693695

Adnams Bitter; Courage Best Bitter; guest beer H

On the edge of a fenland town, this pub is a justly popular local, and is a recent winner of a local CAMRA *Gold Award* for its beer quality and choice. The pub has the usual choice of games to complement more unusual ones such as Scrabble and Chess. Quiz night is Sun.

🏮Q❀♣P🗗●

INN BRIEF

CAMBRIDGE

Alma
26 Russell Court
11-3, 6-11; 11-11 Wed-Sat; 12-10.30 Sun

Ridleys IPA, Rumpus, Old Bob, seasonal beers H

Spacious, well-modernised pub where unusual decor includes piranhas in a phone box! Strong emphasis on music; food all sessions.

Grapes
19 Histon Road
12-2.30, 5.30-11; 11-11 Sat; 12-3, 7-10.30 Sun

Greene King IPA, Ruddles County, Abbot, Old Speckled Hen; guest beers H

Smart, open-plan, community pub where the food is good, cheap and plentiful.

Wrestlers
337 Newmarket Road
12-3, 5-11; closed Sun

Adnams Broadside; Badger Tanglefoot; Greene King Old Speckled Hen; Wells Eagle, Bombardier; guest beer H

Bustling, friendly pub staging live music Thu, Fri and Sat. Superb Thai food is cooked to order. *Cask Marque* accredited.

EATON FORD

Barley Mow
27 Crosshall Road
11.30-3, 5.30-11; 11.30-11 Fri & Sat; 12-10.30 Sun

Greene King IPA, Abbot; guest beers H

Friendly, one-bar community pub.

ETTON

Golden Pheasant
1 Main Road
12-3, 6-11 (11-11 summer Sat); 12-10.30 Sun

Beer range varies H

Imposing former Georgian rectory: one large bar, a garden with family facilities and a no-smoking restaurant. Always four real ales on tap.

FOWLMERE

Chequers
High Street
11.30-2.30, 6.30-11; 12-3, 7-10.30 Sun

Adnams Bitter; guest beer H

Upmarket, food-orientated, 16th-century coaching inn. Drinkers will feel most comfortable in the low-level area to the left of the bar.

EATON SOCON

Bell
37 Great North Road
✪ 12-2.30, 5-11; 12-3, 7-11 Sat; 12-8 Sun
☎ (01480) 212274
website: www.thebell-eatonsocon.co.uk
Adnams Broadside; Wells Eagle; guest beers Ⓗ ♣
The Bell is a purpose-built 20th-century roadhouse, with a single bar divided into three drinking areas. There has been a pub on this site for over 300 years. The name stems from the premature delivery of the church bells when the tower of the nearby St Mary's was rebuilt and the bells were stored in the farm opposite. The Bell offers traditional home-cooked food on a constantly changing blackboard menu. To the rear is a large, family-friendly garden with a variety of games. Q⛲◑♣P

ELY

Fountain
1 Silver Street
✪ 5-11; 12-2, 6-11 Sat; 12-2, 7-10.30 Sun
☎ (01353) 663122
Adnams Bitter, Broadside (winter)**; Fuller's London Pride; guest beer** Ⓗ
Handy for the cathedral and station, this intriguing pub with its wood floor and real fire is worth seeking out. In the decor, an antler rack, buffalo horns and stuffed animals compete with pictures of the King's School and militaria. Children are welcome at all times, although the pub is usually very busy after 8.30 most eves. The atmosphere is most relaxing and, once settled, you will not want to leave. Adnams' Regatta replaces the Broadside in summer.
⚌Q⌂⛲≠

Prince Albert
62 Silver Street
✪ 11-3 (3.30 Thu-Sat), 6.30-11; 12-3.30, 7-10.30 Sun
☎ (01353) 663494
Greene King XX Mild, IPA, Triumph, Abbot; guest beer Ⓗ
Town-centre local where you can take your own food into the lovely back garden as long as you buy a drink. Books are for sale in the bar. Do not miss this classic pub, which is a rare regular outlet for mild. No meals served Sun. Q⛲◑≠

West End House
16 West End
✪ 11.30-2.30, 6-11; 12-2, 7-10.30 Sun
☎ (01353) 662907
Adnams Bitter; Courage Directors; Greene King IPA; Marston's Pedigree; Webster's Yorkshire Bitter Ⓗ
This multi-roomed pub has a very welcoming feel. Many pictures of bygone Ely and the surrounding area adorn the walls. The large open fireplace at one end of the split bar is very much appreciated in the winter months and there is a concrete patio area for the summer. The ceiling is quite low in places, so mind your head. ⚌⛲≠

EYNESBURY

Chequers
St Mary's Street
✪ 10.30-2.30, 7-11; 12-2 (closed eve) Sun
☎ (01480) 472116
website: www.cambs.com/chequers/
Beer range varies Ⓗ
This 16th-century inn may be the oldest house in Eynesbury. Many additions and much restoration over the years have extended and enlarged the inn. Manor courts were held here in the 18th century and a wealth of beams and wood panelling give it olde-worlde charm. There is a comfortable lounge bar with areas set aside for dining. A long-term commitment to excellent food has ensured the pub has featured in many guide books. ⚌Q⛲◑P

FARCET FEN

Plough
Milk and Water Drove, Ramsey Road (B1095, 2 miles S of A605 jct)
✪ 11-3 (not Mon-Fri), 5.30 (6 Fri, 12 Sat)-11; 12-10.30 Sun
☎ (01733) 844307
website: www.members.tripod.co.uk/ploughfarcet
Oakham JHB; John Smith's Bitter; guest beers Ⓗ
This white-painted pub on the windswept fen road between Peterborough and Ramsey is a local success story. Renowned for its quality, reasonably-priced food and extensive array of real ales, this local CAMRA *Gold Award-winner* has become a magnet for beer and food lovers from miles around. Since the present landlord arrived four years ago, the public bar has been reinstated and the interior refurbished to a high standard. The extensive outdoor area has uninterrupted views of the Fens with wonderful sunsets. ⚌Q⛲◑⊞♿♣♠P▯

FULBOURN

Six Bells
9 High Street
✪ 11.30-2.30, 6-11; 12-11 Sat; 12-10.30 Sun
☎ (01223) 880244
Adnams Bitter; Flowers IPA; Ind Coope Burton Ale; Tolly Cobbold Mild; guest beer Ⓗ
Traditional, friendly village local with cosy corners. A good, varied menu of home-cooked food is served in the restaurant. It hosts live jazz twice monthly, with dancing and dining. The three bars offer a warm, comfortable atmosphere enhanced by real fires and a wide selection of real ales. A quiz is staged and games are played in one of the bars. Outside is a large garden and patio.
⚌Q⌂⛲◑⊞♿♠P

GAMLINGAY

Cock
25 Church Street
✪ 11.30-3, 5.30-11; 11.30-11 Sat; 12-4, 7-10.30 Sun
☎ (01767) 650255
Greene King IPA, Abbot; guest beers Ⓗ
This 400-year-old pub is the only survivor of the great fire of Gamlingay that destroyed most of the village in 1660. It boasts many beams and a large inglenook. Excellent, good value meals are available – the restaurant is accessed through the lounge bar. The public bar caters for the sports fans, but you should look around and spot the collection of cocks. A well-stocked patio area leads to the garden, which caters well for young children with play equipment plus a menagerie. ⚌⌂⛲◑⊞♣P

GODMANCHESTER

Exhibition
London Road
☼ 11.30-3, 5.30-11; 11.30-11 Fri & Sat;
12-10.30 Sun
☎ (01480) 459134
Greene King IPA; guest beers Ⓗ
Spacious two-bar pub, leased by a local restaurateur who has introduced bistro-style dining. There is a large dining room and a busy lounge bar where good food is also served on candlelit tables. This bar features some unusual mock-ups of Victorian shop fronts around its walls, retained from a previous refurbishment. The licensee owns steam traction engines and the pub hosts an annual 'steam-up' (Oct). The food is of high quality and includes a range of tasty sandwiches at lunchtimes. ✿◖▶P

GRANTCHESTER

Blue Ball Inn
57 Broadway
☼ 11.30-3, 6-11; 12-3, 7-10.30 Sun
☎ (01223) 840679 e-mail: john.roos@ntlworld.com
Greene King IPA, Abbot Ⓗ
There has been a Blue Ball in Grantchester since the mid-18th century; the present pub dates from the end of the 19th century. It is small, with two rooms and only five tables. Photographs of the pub and village decorate the walls, along with a complete list of landlords since 1767. The Blue Ball was a hot-air balloon flown from Trinity Hall Farm to Wickhambrook (Suffolk) in 1785. Food is available, although booking is advised (especially Sun lunch); no food Sun eve or Mon. Children are discouraged. ▲Q✿▷◖▶♣

HELPSTON

Bluebell
10 Woodgate
(200 yds S off B1443 at central crossroads)
☼ 11-12, 5-11; 11-3, 6-11 Sat; 12-4, 7-10.30 Sun
☎ (01733) 252394
Bateman XB; John Smith's Bitter; guest beers Ⓗ
This CAMRA-award winning traditional village ale house retains much of its rural charm, appealing to locals and visitors alike. A collection of teapots and Toby jugs decorate the wood-panelled lounge while a log fire keeps the atmosphere cosy in winter. Look out for the old parish chest by the fireplace. The village was the birthplace of 'the peasant poet', John Clare, in 1793. An annual festival is held in his honour (July) when the Bluebell hosts poetry readings, folk singing and morris dancing. A beer festival is also staged in June. Sun lunch is served. ▲Q✿▣♣♠P●

HILTON

Prince of Wales
Potton Road
☼ 11 (12 winter)-2.30 (3 Sat; not Mon), 6 (7 winter Sat)-11; 12-3, 7-10.30 Sun
☎ (01480) 830257
Adnams Bitter; Elgood's Black Dog Mild; guest beer (occasional) Ⓗ
Popular local on the main road through this stylish village, well known for its historic

turf maze. There is a small public bar, a larger lounge bar with an impressive log fire and smart, comfortable furnishings and a rear plush lounge. The high quality en-suite accommodation is well-used by business travellers. Another big attraction is good food, including home-made pies (no food Mon or winter Sun eve). This is a rare local outlet for cask mild ale, the award-winning Black Dog from local brewers, Elgood's. ▲✿�’◖▶▣P

HINXTON

Red Lion
High Street
☼ 11-2.30, 6-11; 12-2.30, 7-10.30 Sun
☎ (01799) 530601
Adnams Bitter; Greene King IPA; Woodforde's Wherry; guest beer Ⓗ
Popular 16th-century coaching inn with a compartmented L-shaped bar; note the unusual polished copper doorsteps. There is a big emphasis on food here – the dining room extension deservedly won an award for its sympathetic design, with much original brickwork and punctuated throughout by fine old clocks, horse brasses and stuffed animals. The garden is home to more animated pets, including a horse. The pub fields a cricket team and cribbage is popular (Wed). Morris men visit each June, as do passing participants in the annual London–Cambridge cycle ride. ▲Q◖▶♣P⊁

HISTON

Red Lion
27 High Street
☼ 11.30-3, 5 (4 Fri)-11; 11.30-11 Sat; 12-6, 7-10.30 Sun
☎ (01223) 564437
Bateman Mild; Everards Beacon, Tiger; Oakham Bishops Farewell; guest beers Ⓗ
A two-bar free house, comprising a quiet lounge, where food is served and a more boisterous public bar that displays a fine collection of bottled beers in wall cabinets. Both bars have a wide range of breweriana, including old pub signs and water jugs, plus photographs of the pub's cricket team. It stages two beer festivals each year: an Easter 'aperitif' and the main event in early Sept with a marquee in the garden and live entertainment each eve. A range of Belgian bottled beers is always stocked. An anti-mobile phone policy is upheld. ▲Q✿◖▣♣P

HOLME

Admiral Wells
41 Station Road
☼ 12-2.30, 5-11; 12-11 Sat; 12-10.30 Sun
☎ (01487) 831214
Oakham JHB; Woodforde's Wherry; guest beers Ⓗ
This Victorian yellow-brick pub is reputedly the lowest pub in Britain. The surrounding area was reclaimed in the 19th century from one of the largest inland lakes in the country and the Fens have been sinking ever since. The bar is divided into three drinking areas alongside a dining room and conservatory. The rear garden provides a tree-shaded haven. It is named after Admiral Thomas Wells, a pall bearer at

Nelson's funeral. Up to five guest beers are stocked. 🏛️🕸️◑🍴♣️P⏸

HUNTINGDON

Old Bridge Hotel
1 High Street
🕐 11-11; 12-10.30 Sun
☎ (01480) 424300
e-mail: oldbridge@huntsbridge.co.uk
Adnams Bitter; guest beers Ⓗ

Sumptuous splendour is provided in this handsome hotel bar with a relaxing environment for local beer drinkers, residents and diners. The 18th-century building was once a private bank and sits alongside the River Great Ouse in the birthplace of Oliver Cromwell. The food and wine is stylish and imaginative, and served in a relaxed atmosphere on the terrace or in the more formal dining room.
🏛️Q🕸️🛏️◑P⏺

ISLEHAM

Merry Monk
30 West Street
🕐 12-3, 7-11; 12-4, 7-10.30 Sun
☎ (01638) 780900
Castle Eden Ale; Flowers IPA Ⓗ

Formerly the Red Lion, the name was changed to stress the pub's position close to a priory. Built in the mid-17th century as four cottages, the yellow-painted pub has a beamed interior with clunch (the local soil) on the walls. There are three distinct areas, with eating in the lounge, though food can be served in the public area when busy. The bar is decorated with hops and there are two open fires. Food ranges from a ploughmans to pasta, fish and vegetarian dishes, with a roast on Sun. Food is not served Mon unless a group books in advance. A spacious garden has children's play equipment. 🏛️🕸️◑ ⊟P

KEYSTON

Pheasant
Village Loop (off A14)
🕐 12-3, 6-11; 12-3, 7-10.30 Sun
☎ (01832) 710241
Adnams Bitter; guest beer Ⓗ

A series of thatched cottages in an idyllic setting, the Pheasant has a number of open-plan rooms featuring oak beams and farm implements. The main bar is a lounge drinking area with a large fireplace. There are three dining areas, two are informal with simple wooden furniture, plus the Red Room restaurant. A constantly changing range of real ales is drawn from local micro-breweries and independents. A range of Belgian beers is also stocked. The food is modern with an emphasis on Mediterranean cuisine. 🏛️Q🎒🕸️◑P⏸

KIMBOLTON

New Sun
20 High Street
🕐 11-2.30, 6-11; 11.30-2.30, 6.30-11 Sat; 12-10.30 Sun
☎ (01480) 860052 e-mail: newsuninn@supanet.com
Greene King Old Speckled Hen; Wells Eagle, Bombardier Ⓗ

Impressive Georgian-fronted building that

opens into a comfortable lounge with exposed beams, sofas and a fireplace. The door to the left leads to a formal dining room and the passage in front to the main bar with tiled floor. A second dining area leads to a patio housing potted plants. Food includes an *à la carte* restaurant menu with an extensive wine list, and a constantly changing blackboard of traditional pub food. All the food is home made. Eve meals are served Tue–Sat.
🏛️🎒🕸️◑

LEIGHTON BROMSWOLD

Green Man
37 The Avenue (off A14, W of Huntingdon)
🕐 12-3 (not Mon-Thu), 7-11 (not Mon); 12-3, 7-10.30 Sun
☎ (01480) 890238
Nethergate IPA; Ⓖ **guest beers** Ⓗ

First licensed in 1650 as a farm-cum-brew-pub, the brewhouse was active until the beginning of the 20th century. The large beamed lounge bar is divided into a variety of areas: to the left is a comfortable dining area, and to the right is a skittle alley leading to a family room. It sports a vast array of pub memorabilia (jugs, bottles, mirrors and rare brewery signs) and a collection of signed Giles cartoons. An extensive range of real ales is complemented by a wide range of Belgian beers.
🎒🕸️◑♣️P

LITTLE DOWNHAM

Plough
106 Main Street
🕐 12-3 (not Mon), 7-11; 12-3, 7-10.30 Sun
☎ (01353) 698297
Greene King IPA Ⓗ

Traditional Fenland village pub, five minutes' drive down the A10 from the centre of Ely which is worth a detour for the cathedral and other attractions. Good food is served here (no meals Sun lunch), but this is first and foremost a drinkers' pub.
🏛️Q🕸️◑P

LITTLE GRANSDEN

Chequers
71 Main Street
🕐 12-2.30, 5-11; 11-11 Sat; 12-3, 7-10.30 Sun
☎ (01767) 677348
Adnams Bitter; guest beers Ⓗ

Run by the same family for the last 50 years, its history has been well researched and documented by the landlord, and provides interesting reading. While retaining an excellent basic public bar, a comfortable lounge has been added. The landlord has devised a secret weapon to stop people hanging around in front of the bar in winter; you will find out if you linger too long. There is always an interesting guest beer at this local CAMRA *Pub of the Year* 2001. 🏛️🎒🕸️⊟♣️P

LONGSTOWE

Red House
Old North Road
🕐 12-3 (not Mon), 5.30-11; 12-3, 5.30-11 Sun
☎ (01954) 718480

Greene King IPA; guest beers ⊞
On the main road, about a mile south of the village, this enterprising free house offers a choice of drinking areas. The space fronting the bar is tiled and simply furnished, while to the right, the room is dominated by a fine brick fireplace. Steps lead down to a further room with armchairs and settees. A spacious restaurant serves home-cooked traditional English food. The two changing guest beers often include a brew from the nearby Potton Brewery.
🏨❀✿◑◗♣P⤝

Rose & Crown
41 St Peters Road (B1099, off old A141)
🕒 12-2.30 (not Wed; 12-3 Sat), 7-11; 12-3, 7-10.30 Sun
☎ (01354) 652879
Fuller's London Pride; guest beers ⊞
Traditional, two-roomed local where one bar is for non-smokers. A collection of over 100 whiskies and about 1,000 real ales offered so far, make this an attractive proposition for visitors to this large Cambridgeshire town. One of the few pubs in the area to receive a local CAMRA *Gold Award,* it always stocks a guest mild and a cask cider that change fortnightly. Meals are served Thu–Sat.
Q❀◑◗⊟♿♣◆P⤝

Bluebell
37-39 High Street
🕒 5.30-11; 12-4.30, 7-11 Sat; 12-5, 7-10.30 Sun
☎ (01778) 348182
Everards Tiger; Fuller's London Pride; guest beers ⊞
This ancient stone pub converted to real ale several years ago and has since gone from strength to strength. Built in the 16th century, possibly as a grain-store, the Bluebell retains many period features, including the double-hinged front door used to facilitate beer deliveries when barrels were substantially bigger than they are today. There is a shove-ha'penny board and some 35 different whiskies are on sale here.
🏨Q❀⊟♿▲♣P⤝⛉

Waggon & Horses
39 High Street
🕒 12-2.30, 5-11; 12-4, 6-11 Sat; 12-3, 7-10.30 Sun
☎ (01223) 860313 e-mail:
winningtons.waggon@ntlworld.com
Elgood's Black Dog Mild, Cambridge, Pageant Ale, Greyhound Strong; guest beers ⊞
Elgood's first acquisition for 55 years, this imposing mock-Tudor one-roomed pub boasts a large collection of hats. The sizeable garden houses chickens and is safe for children. Games include bar billiards and pétanque and a popular quiz is staged Wed. Baltis are the speciality Thu eve, but all meals represent good choice and value. The cider is from Cassels.
🏨❀◑◗♣◆P

Queen's Head
Fowlmere Road
🕒 11.30-2.30, 6-11; 12-2.30, 7-10.30 Sun
☎ (01223) 870436
Adnams Bitter, Broadside, seasonal beers Ⓖ
Unchanging gem: a village local that has appeared in every edition of this *Guide.* Just 18 landlords have presided here since 1729. The traditional public bar has wooden benches, a high-backed settle, tiled floor and the comforting tick of a large old clock. Squeezing past the piano into the games annexe you can enjoy shove-ha'penny and Devil Among the Tailors, among others. The cosy saloon features a roaring fire and built-in seating. Simple, satisfying food is freshly prepared to order. The outdoor drinking area extends to the green opposite.
🏨Q❀◑◗⊟▲♣◆P⤝

GREAT CHISHILL
Pheasant
24 Heydon Road
12-3, 6-11; 11-11 Sat; 12-10.30 Sun
Adnams Bitter; Greene King IPA; guest beers ⊞
Unspoilt, peaceful, friendly free house with an outstanding garden. Bar snacks and meals all sessions. Annual beer festival (July).

GREAT STAUGHTON
White Hart
56 The Highway
12-2, 5-11; 12-3, 7-11 Sat; 12-3, 7-11 Sun
Bateman XB, XXXB, seasonal beers ⊞
Village local, styled as a coaching inn with a large games room and restaurant.

GUYHIRN
Oliver Twist
High Road
11.30-2.30, 6-11; 12-2.30, 6-10.30 Sun
Elgood's Black Dog Mild; Everards Tiger; guest beers ⊞
Comfortable free house, with a busy food trade, situated on the river bank towards Wisbech St Mary. *Cask Marque* accredited.

PETERBOROUGH
Blue Bell
Welland Road, Dogsthorpe
11-2.30 (11.30-3 Sat), 6-11; 12-3, 7-10.30 Sun
Elgood's Black Dog Mild, Cambridge, Greyhound Strong, seasonal beers; guest beer ⊞
Peterborough's oldest pub: two large rooms with a tiny snug bar, a large patio and children's play area. Weekday lunches served.

Fitzwilliams
5 Fitzwilliam Street
11-11 (closed Mon); 12-10.30 Sun
Adnams Bitter; Draught Bass; guest beer ⊞
Pleasant bar/restaurant next to the library, offering excellent food.

THRIPLOW
Green Man
2 Lower Street
12-2.30, 6-11; 12-10.30 Sun
Beer range varies ⊞
Comfortably-appointed two-roomed pub offering excellent food and three constantly changing beers from independent breweries.

WHITTLESEY
Hero of Aliwal
75 Church Street
11-3 (not Mon), 7-11; 12-3, 7-10.30 Sun
Adnams Bitter; guest beers ⊞
Comfortable bar, plus a dining room (meals served daily). B&B available and boat moorings nearby.

WICKEN
Maid's Head
12 High Street
11.30-3, 6.30-11; 12-3, 7-10.30 Sun
Greene King IPA, Ruddles Best; guest beers ⊞
Traditional village pub opened in 1579, apparently haunted by a ghost of an old lady. It serves good food daily. Children always welcome.

❀ **symbol next to a main entry place name indicates there are Inn Brief entries as well.**

OLD WESTON

Swan

Main Street (B660, off A14)
⏲ 6.30-11; 12-3, 7-11 Sat; 12-3, 7-10.30 Sun
☎ (01832) 293400 e-mail: westonswan@aol.com
Adnams Bitter, Broadside; Greene King Abbot; Taylor Landlord Ⓗ
16th-century beamed village pub, with a central bar area, a dining area and a games area offering hooded skittles, darts and pool. The central bar has a large inglenook. The pub started life as two private houses that have since been merged, and the building has grown over the years. At the turn of the century the pub had its own brewery. In the 1950s and 60s it was known as the Mucky Duck, due to the barmaids' risqué attire. A varied menu of home-cooked traditional pub food includes good puddings (Wed–Sat eves and Sun lunch).
ጰQ❀◗⅄♣P

OVER

Admiral Vernon

31 High Street
⏲ 12-2, 6-11; 11-11 Sat; 12-10.30 Sun
☎ (01954) 230300
Wells Eagle, Bombardier; guest beer Ⓗ
Splendidly down-to-earth village local. The front door leads into a split-level room; the upper area is dominated by a pool table while the lower is where the serious drinkers and locals congregate. The lounge is simply, but comfortably, furnished. Above the bar is a growing collection of photos showing customers disporting themselves. Admiral Vernon was an 18th-century naval hero who gained notoriety by watering down the sailors' rum – no danger of such dastardly practices here.
❀◖◗♣▯

PETERBOROUGH ❊

Bogart's

17 North Street
⏲ 11-11; 12-10.30 Sun
☎ (01733) 703599
Bateman XXXB; Fuller's London Pride; Oakham JHB; guest beers Ⓗ
Originally the Ostrich, then a home-brew shop, it is now a small single-roomed bar, with a Humphrey Bogart theme. The nearest thing to a street-corner local in the city centre, it enjoys a good regular following. A cosy suntrap courtyard is at the rear of the building. A few minutes' walk from the north entrance of Queensgate Shopping Centre it is also handy for the bus station.
❀◖

Brewery Tap

80 Westgate (near bus and rail stations)
⏲ 12-11 (1.30am Fri & Sat); 12-10.30 Sun
☎ (01733) 358500
Oakham JHB, seasonal beers; guest beer Ⓗ
Largest brewpub in Europe, housed in a distinctive 1930s building, once a Labour Exchange; Oakham Brewery can be observed through large windows. The bar's modern design incorporates some brewing artefacts, and a mezzanine area. Excellent authentic Thai food is served. One wall is adorned with the many awards bestowed on the ales; White Dwarf was East Anglian *Beer of the Year* 2000. Entertainment and a late licence Fri and Sat means door controls and an entrance charge after 10.30pm.
◖◗⇌

Charters

Town Bridge (steps down off W side of Town Bridge)
⏲ 12-11; 12-10.30 Sun
☎ (01733) 315700
Draught Bass; Everards Tiger; Fuller's London Pride; Oakham JHB; guest beers Ⓗ
Moored on the River Nene, Charters is a converted Dutch grain barge circa 1907. It was sailed across the North Sea in 1992 and literally sunk to get under Town Bridge. The bar bears a nautical theme, with a weekend restaurant on the upper deck. Moorings are available, and a lovely garden gives a surprisingly peaceful hideaway considering the proximity of shopping centres. Restricted entry applies on football match days. Nene Valley Railway and Railworld are accessible via the river footpath.
❀◖◗⇌

Cherry Tree

9-11 Oundle Road (old A605 S of centre, near football ground)
⏲ 12-2.30, 6-11; 12-11 Sat; 12-10.30 Sun
☎ (01733) 703495 website: www.cherrytreeinn.co.uk
Adnams Broadside; Draught Bass; Marston's Pedigree; Tetley Bitter; guest beer Ⓗ
Open-plan three-roomed community local with a recently added meeting/function room in a converted barn. The pub hosts fundraising events for charity and local causes. Activities range from crib, dominoes and quizzes to regular live music. The meals represent excellent value for money. The newly landscaped garden area with children's playthings affords good views of passing trains; Nene Valley Railway and Railworld are about five minutes' walk away.
ጰ❀◖◗P

College Arms

40 Broadway (opp. Bayard Place)
⏲ 10-11; 12-10.30 Sun
☎ (01733) 319745
Courage Directors; Theakston Best Bitter; guest beers Ⓗ
Typical Wetherspoon's outlet, converted from Peterborough Technical College, it sells guest beers, well-priced national brands and good value food. A little soulless for lone drinkers, but a popular meeting place, it gets busy Fri and Sat eves when door controls operate. Pictures of old Peterborough adorn the walls. The toilets are up three flights of stairs. It holds occasional beer festivals and has a small garden at the rear.
Q❀◖◗P●

Eight Bells

211 Lincoln Road
⏲ 11-11; 12-10.30 Sun
☎ (01733) 564653
Draught Bass; guest beer Ⓗ
Recent convert to real ales, this vibrant two-roomed local offers superb Irish hospitality. It fields crib, darts and pool teams, and hosts occasional live music or Irish singers; an Irish folk dancing team performs Tue eve. The well-documented pub ghost must

be a real ale fan as it turns off the gas cylinders! Look for the large print of Peterborough city centre circa 1962. The car park houses a new gravelled patio area. Children are welcome in the lounge until 6pm. Plenty of places to eat nearby.
爱母齿蛱P

Hand & Heart ☆
12 Highbury Street
🕐 11-11; 12-10.30 Sun
☎ (01733) 569463
Courage Directors; John Smith's Bitter, Magnet; guest beers Ⓗ

Superb, unspoilt drinking pub, boasting a black and white tiled entrance, a drinking corridor, public bar and a smoke room with a serving hatch. Rare to find an almost intact 1930s interior, this is Peterborough's best example. Note, too, the Warwicks Brewery windows. Eve meals finish early, but you can always eat at one of the many local restaurants, offering a variety of ethnic cuisines, before moving on to the Eight Bells just a few yards away. ⚲Q爱ⓄⒹ母蛱

RAMSEY

Jolly Sailor
43 Great Whyte
🕐 11-3, 5.30 (6 Sat)-11; 12-3.30, 7-10.30 Sun
☎ (01487) 813388 e-mail: jollymichael@barclays.net
Adnams Bitter; Greene King Abbot; Tetley Bitter; Wells Bombardier; guest beers Ⓗ

Grade II listed building where several bars and a clutch of handpumps make it one of the highlights of this small Fenland town. Situated on the main road in the town centre makes it easy to spot, except Sat, when it is obscured by the busy market. The small front bar (snug) provides a cosy haven from the rigours of shopping; the side bar boasts a real fire. The main street outside, called Great Whyte, was once a river. The ruins of the local abbey are one of the area's attractions.
⚲Q爱蛱P

RAMSEY FORTY FOOT

George Inn
1 Ramsey Road (B1096, 3 miles NE of Ramsey)
🕐 12-4, 6-11; 12-4, 7-10.30 Sun
☎ (01487) 812775
John Smith's Bitter; guest beers Ⓗ

On one of the many drainage channels or Drains used to reclaim the Fens in the 19th century, this award-winning village local provides an ideal stopping-off point for travellers in cars or boats (moorings 50 yards away). The pub is divided into three bars, one of which is a family/pool room. The main bar features an inglenook which, accompanied by the excellent home-cooked food, should keep you warm and contented. A CC Club-registered site is behind the pub.
⚲Q㞢爱ⓄⒹ母齿Å蛱P

REACH

Dyke's End
8 Fair Green Reach
🕐 12-3, 6-11; 12-3, 7-10.30 Sun
☎ (01638) 743816
Adnams Bitter; Greene King IPA; Woodforde's Wherry; guest beers Ⓗ

Saved from closure in 1999, when villagers clubbed together to buy it, the Dyke's End has since gone from strength to strength. First and foremost a pub, with a cosy L-shaped bar and fine selection of ales, it has also developed a brilliant reputation for food. You can eat in the upstairs restaurant (booking advisable) or have bar snacks downstairs. Local artists exhibit their works on the walls. The nominal dyke is the Devil's Dyke, a Dark Ages boundary or defence ditch that stretches for miles.
⚲㞢爱ⓄⒹ齿蛱P✗

ST IVES

Royal Oak
13 Crown Street
🕐 11-11; 12-10.30 Sun
☎ (01480) 462586
Marston's Pedigree; Tetley Bitter; guest beers Ⓗ

Busy Festival Ale House, one of a number of historic listed pubs in the town, whose most famous inhabitant was Oliver Cromwell. Despite the date 1502 over the door, most of the building is 18th century. The room layout and character was happily preserved in a sensitive renovation in the 1990s. A constantly changing range of four guest beers keeps the customers happy; quizzes (Thu), card nights and satellite TV are also provided. Curries are served Mon–Thu eves, plus a full daily lunch menu.
爱ⓄⒹ蛱P●

SOMERSHAM

Windmill
St Ives Road (1 mile from Somersham, towards St Ives)
🕐 11.30-2.30, 5.30 (6 Sat)-11; 12-3, 7-10.30 Sun
☎ (01487) 840328
Greene King IPA, Abbot, Old Speckled Hen Ⓗ

Popular Greene King pub, just outside the village. The original small cosy public bar has thankfully survived renovations which have extended the pub into two adjacent cottages, creating an ample dining area and an enlarged lounge bar. Food includes Mexican and lobster dishes as well as plainer fare, and themed nights such as curries (Wed); no food Sun eve which is quiz night. Occasional fantasy rôle play eves and themed weekends are staged. It is reputedly haunted by the last locally-hanged arsonist, Tom Savage. 爱ⓄⒹP●

STEEPLE MORDEN

Waggon & Horses
19 Church Street
🕐 12-3, 7-11; 12-11 Sat; 12-10.30 Sun
☎ (01763) 852829
Greene King XX Mild, IPA; guest beer (summer) Ⓗ

Deep in the heart of South Cambridgeshire's rambling countryside, this traditional 300-year-old village pub provides a welcoming retreat. Your thirst can be slaked with an excellent pint of the rare XX Mild. The tile floored public bar, complete with pool table, leads to a cosy lounge boasting a large inglenook (children welcome). A CC Club-registered site at the rear of the pub must be booked. Pétanque is played. Look out for the former WWII American Air Force base memorial close by.
⚲㞢爱母Å蛱P

Drinking in Moderation

Perhaps the workman spends, night after night, more than he should on beer. Let us remember, if he needs excuse, that his employers have found him no better place and no better amusement than to sit in a tavern, drink beer (generally in moderation), and talk and smoke tobacco. Why not? A respectable tavern is a very harmless place; the society which meets there is the society of the workman; it is his life; without it he might as well have been a factory hand of the good old time – such as hands were forty years ago; and then he should have made but two journeys a day — one from bed to mill, and the other from mill to bed.

Walter Besant, *As We Are and As We May Be,* 1903

UPWARE

Five Miles from Anywhere Inn

Old School Lane (2 miles off A1123, between Wicken and Stretham)

✪ closed Mon; 11-3, 7-11 (midnight Wed; 2am Fri); 11-2am Sat; 12-10.30 Sun

☎ (01353) 721654 website: www.fivemiles.co.uk

City of Cambridge IPA, Hobson's Choice; guest beers Ⓗ

Unusual pub that successfully caters for many different types of customer; depending on the time of day you will encounter here all ages; walkers, boaters and families with children. Outside, almost four acres of grounds include a fully-equipped children's play area, extensive moorings and a heated terrace for dining. Children love the bouncy castle in summer. It hosts live entertainment Fri and Sat eves and monthly jazz (Sun lunchtime). The lounge bar stocks a varying choice of real ales, the public has a large-screen TV. Children's certificate. ✪◑➁➄P

WHITTLESEY ✤

Bricklayers Arms

9 Station road (B1093, 200 yds S of market place)

✪ 11-4, 7-11; 12-4, 7-10.30 Sun

☎ (01733) 202593

John Smith's Bitter; guest beer Ⓗ

Friendly Fenland town local, providing the best in real ale in a no-nonsense atmosphere comprising a comfortable, cosy lounge and a public bar. Outside, the large grassed area is used for camping and caravanning, as well as for drinking. The pub is the HQ for the Straw Bear Festival (Jan) which sees the town beseiged by morris men and a man dressed up as a giant haystack. Wheelchair access is via the garden door. ✪◑➁➄Å➚♣P➘

WHITTLESFORD

Bees in the Wall

36 North Road

✪ 12-2.30, 6-11; 12-11 Sat; 12-10.30 Sun

☎ (01223) 834289

Badger Best; Taylor Landlord; guest beers Ⓗ

Two-bar pub, on the northern edge of the village, that actually *does* have bees in its wall. The public bar oozes character, especially when the fire is blazing. The long lounge bar opens on to a huge garden paddock with plenty of tables. The two guest beers change every week and there is always something interesting on offer. ➃Q➁◑➁♣P

WILLINGHAM

Three Tuns

43 Church Street

✪ 12 (11 Sat)-3, 5-11; 12-3, 7-10.30 Sun

☎ (01954) 203243 website: www.the-three-tuns.com

Greene King XX Mild, IPA, Ⓗ **Abbot; guest beer** Ⓖ

Classic village pub, in this *Guide* for over 20 years. The small, comfy lounge doubles as a dining area while the simply-appointed public bar is popular for dominoes and darts. This is a true community local where farmworkers, company directors and village elders all get on famously together; visitors also find a warm welcome. Attractions include the varied, changing menu, the large garden and the rare XX Mild. No meals served Sun eve or Mon. ✪◑➁➄♣P●

WISBECH

Rose Tavern

53 North Brink (follow north bank of river, past Elgood's)

✪ 12-3, 6-11; 12-3, 7-10.30 Sun

☎ (01945) 588335

Adnams Broadside; Fuller's London Pride; Woodforde's Wherry; Ⓗ **guest beers** Ⓗ/Ⓖ

This small, unassuming, town pub is the closest pub to Elgood's Brewery and can be found on the north bank of the River Nene. Popular with sporting teams, it has been known to offer nine different beers at the weekend. The National Trust's Peckover House, only a short walk away, is worth a visit. ➃Q➁♣

CHESHIRE

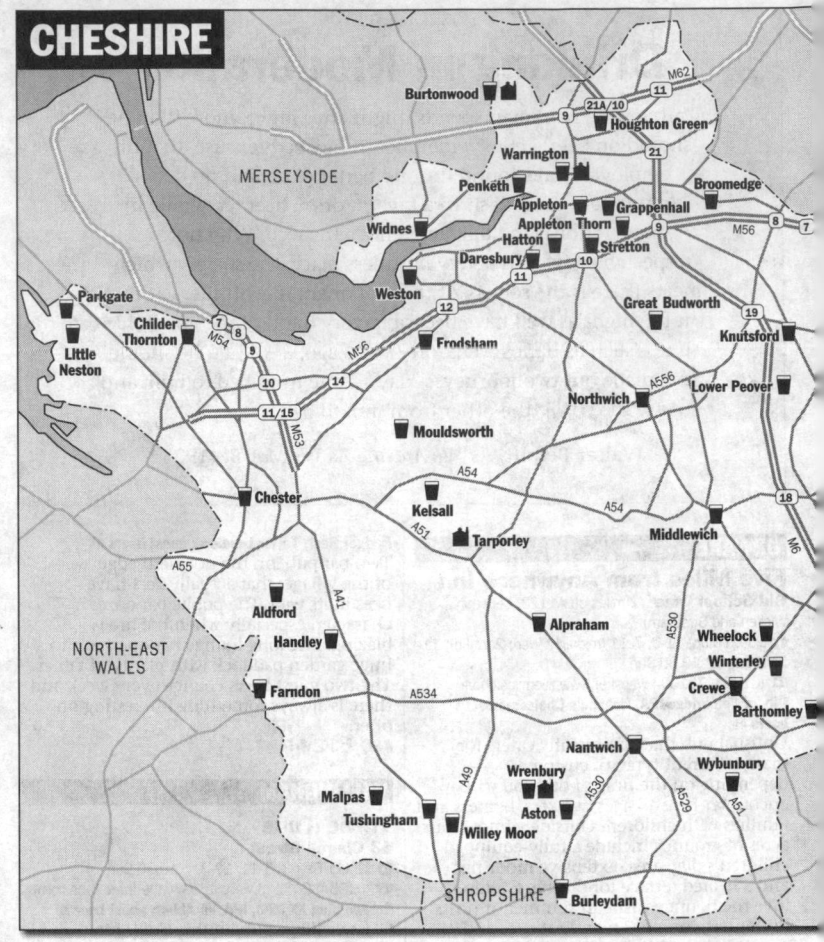

ALDFORD

Grosvenor Arms
Chester Road (B5130)
🕐 11.30-11; 12-10.30 Sun
☎ (01244) 620228
e-mail: grosvenor.arms@brunningandprice.co.uk
Bateman XB; Caledonian Deuchars IPA; Flowers IPA; guest beers ⊞

Families are welcome at this Victorian pub, run as a free house by a small pub company. The interior is large and open plan, but with comfortable and quiet areas in which to relax. Bare boards and old wooden furniture create a homely, friendly atmosphere. The walls display old prints and adverts. An emphasis on food, with a justified reputation, attracts large numbers. Menus are on blackboards; Sun lunch is popular. There is a conservatory and a garden with seats. A good choice of malt whiskies, Irish whiskies and Bourbons is stocked. ▲Q❀◑❤P

ALPRAHAM

Travellers Rest ☆
Chester Road (A51)
🕐 12-3 (not Mon-Fri), 6.15-11; 12-3, 7-10.30 Sun
☎ (01829) 260523

Bateman Mild; Marston's Pedigree; Tetley Bitter ⊞
Close to the canal (Bunbury lock), this family-owned rural local is in a 1960s timewarp; winner of many CAMRA awards. A large bowling green stands at the rear. The bar is divided by a wall separating two rooms, one of which is completely independent of the rest of the pub, the other is its heart and soul, where many regulars sit in favourite seats. To the rear is a darts room notable for its unusual 1960s furniture. Dominoes played, particularly Tue eve. Children are not welcome. Toilets are outside. Q❀♣P

ALSAGER

Mere
58 Crewe Road (B4077)
🕐 11-11; 12-10.30 Sun
☎ (01270) 882019
Flowers IPA; guest beers ⊞

Traditional, town-centre pub opposite the beautiful Northholme Gardens and Alsager Mere. An excellent range of beers includes five guest beers, rotating weekly; a monthly list and week's description board is displayed by the bar. Themed memorabilia decorate the walls, along with details of the pub's past 110 years of licensees. Tue is live

GTR MANCHESTER

Disley

Handforth

Mobberley

Kettleshulme

DERBYSHIRE

A537

A538

A23

Bollington

Prestbury

Rainow

Higher Hurdsfield

Peover Heath

Macclesfield

A535

A537

A54

Gawsworth

A536

A523

Higher Sutton

Swettenham

A50

A54

Congleton

17

Astbury

Rode Heath

Alsager

STAFFORDSHIRE

16

0 Miles   5

0 Kilometres   8

music night and themed days are a regular occurrence. It serves as a base for local sports teams and has a large-screen satellite TV in the bar, plus a games room with TV and pool. Hot snacks are served all day.

🌞🚲♣P

APPLETON

Birchdale Hotel
Birchdale Road (off A49 at London Bridge)
☼ 6 (8.30 Fri & Sat)-11; 8.30-11 Sun
☎ (01925) 263662 e-mail: roger@birchdalehotel.co.uk
Taylor Landlord; guest beers Ⓗ
Off the beaten track, in a village on the outskirts of Warrington, this quiet, unspoilt hotel is located within 100 yards of Delamere Way and the Bridgewater Canal – ideal for walkers and cyclists. Built in mock-Tudor style during the early 1800s, it features a large, comfortable split-level lounge, a small games room and extensive rear gardens. Traditional home-cooked food is served Mon-Thu, 6.30-8, with peppered steak a speciality. A friendly welcome is extended to both residents and non-residents. It stands on the Warrington-Northwich bus route.
Q🌞🛏♪♣P🗂

APPLETON THORN

Appleton Thorn Village Hall
Stretton Road
(B5356)
☼ 8.30-11 (not Mon-Wed); 8.30-10.30 Sun
☎ (01925) 261187
Beer range varies Ⓗ
Former school, now a thriving village hall offering an ever-changing range of seven beers from regional and micro-breweries. The attractive sandstone building houses a small, comfortable lounge and a larger hall with TV and darts, leading on to a small pool room. There is a garden area and bowling green to the rear. Home to various societies, this former CAMRA *Club of the Year* (1995) holds a popular beer festival every Oct. It also opens on the first and third Sun of the month from 12-3. A bus service from Warrington runs on Fri and Sat.
Q🌞♿P🗂

ASTBURY

Egerton Arms
Astbury Congleton (Signed on the A34)
☼ 11.30-11; 12-3, 7-10.30 Sun
☎ (01260) 273946 website: www.egertonarms.com
Robinson's Best Bitter, Frederics, Old Tom (occasional) Ⓗ
A 15th-century country village inn, across the road from the stunning parish church. The interior of the inn is spacious, and so relaxed you wonder why you do not visit more often. An extensive, imaginative bar menu offers unusual specials. There are six bedrooms and a restaurant. The garden is a haven for families being well equipped, well maintained and fenced off.
🛏Q🍴🌞🛏◖♪P🗂

ASTON

Bhurtpore Inn
Wrenbury Road (off A530)
☼ 12-2.30 (3 Sat), 6.30-11; 12-3, 7-10.30 Sun
☎ (01270) 780917
Hanby Drawwell; guest beers Ⓗ
Enterprising free house returned to family ownership, decorated with photographs of local interest, and of Bhurtpore in India (the local landowner, Lord Combermere, secured a victory there in 1825). Up to 10 beers are available on handpump (including a mild) plus an extensive range of Belgian beers and malt whiskies. The restaurant offers a good choice of meals, including curries. It attracts custom from a wide area; locals favour the back bar. It hosts an annual beer festival, for which main line trains may be specially arranged to stop.
🛏Q🌞◖ 🚆(Wrenbury) ♣●P🗂

INDEPENDENT BREWERIES

Beartown Congleton
Burtonwood Burtonwood
Coach House Warrington
Paradise Wrenbury
Sarah's Hop House Warrington
Storm Macclesfield
Weetwood Tarporley

BARTHOMLEY

White Lion ☆
Audley Road (1½ miles from M6 jct 16)
✪ 11.30 (5 Thu)-11; 12-10.30 Sun
☎ (01270) 882242
website: www.whitelion-barthomley.co.uk
Burtonwood Bitter, Top Hat; guest beer Ⓗ
This popular black and white thatched
Tudor cottage has been serving ales since
1614. Nestling at the centre of the small
rural village of Barthomley, its main bar and
two side rooms have low-beamed ceilings
and leaded glass windows. The walls bear
pictures of old Barthomley and
documentation of previous licensees. In
summer, bench tables on the pub's
cobblestone front and side prove very
popular, attracting passing walkers, cyclists
and motorcyclists. Children are allowed in
the side rooms until 9pm. ⚏Q⛺❀◐♣P

BOLLINGTON ❖

Poachers Inn
95 Ingersley Road
✪ 12-2, 5.30 (7 Sat)-11; 12-2.30, 7-10.30 Sun
☎ (01625) 572086
website: www.poachersinbollington.co.uk
Boddingtons Bitter; Taylor Landlord; guest beers Ⓗ
Genuine free house offering a warm,
intimate atmosphere. Gradually converted
from five terraced cottages, starting in 1908,
it now comprises a single room pub, plus a
no-smoking restaurant, which enjoys an
excellent reputation for good quality home-
prepared food at reasonable prices. Adjacent
to attractive countryside and several good
walks, it is within sight of the Peak District
National Park and only a few hundred yards
from the Gritstone Trail walk from Lyme
Park to Mow Cop. One of the guest beers is
often from the local brewery, Storm
Brewing. ⚏❀◐P

BROOMEDGE

Barn Owl
Agden Wharf, Warrington Lane (Off A56
Altrincham-Lymm road) OS707872
✪ 11-11; 12-10.30 Sun
☎ (01925) 752020
Marston's Bitter, Pedigree; guest beer Ⓗ
Open-plan pub in a converted boatyard
building whose main room overlooks the
Bridgewater Canal, with boaters and
waterfowl in full view. Popular with canal-
based tourists, local cruising clubs also
regularly use the pub. For walkers on the
opposite towpath, the ringing of a bell
summons the ferry from the pub. Good
food, including home-made Sun lunches,
and a children's certificate make it popular
with diners, and despite the rural location it
enjoys a thriving local trade. It hosts live
music Sat and a quiz Thu. Drivers pay £1 for
their first coke or lemonade, with free top-
ups. ❀◐&♣P

Jolly Thresher
Higher Lane (A56/B5159 jct)
✪ 11-3, 5.30-11; 11.30-11 Sat; 12-10.30 Sun
☎ (01925) 752265 e-mail:jollythresher@aol.com
Hydes Mild, Bitter, Jekyll's Gold, seasonal beer Ⓗ
Well-established, large, roadside pub where
a recent refurbishment has extended the
already popular restaurant with its good

quality and value food. A large open-plan
drinking area greets you on entering, with a
small snug to the rear of the bar. There is a
bowling green behind the pub where the
local team plays. The name refers to a
former landlord who hid in fields to avoid
paying his taxes to the local Trafford estate.
⚏❀◐&♣P

BURLEYDAM

Combermere Arms
Whitchurch Road On A525, opp. Dodd's Green
Lane, 5 miles W of Audlem
✪ 12-11; 12-10.30 Sun
☎ (01948) 871223
Draught Bass; guest beers Ⓗ
Friendly, welcoming, family-run free house
whose history can be traced back to the
mid-16th century, coinciding with the
Dissolution of the Monasteries, including
the nearby Combermere Abbey. The name
derives from the first Lord Combermere, Sir
George Cotton, granted the abbey and
lands by Henry VIII. His heraldic crest may
be seen inside the front door. King Billy
passed by on his way to the Battle of the
Boyne (1690) and the Duke of Wellington
and the Empress of Austria were regular
visitors to Combermere Abbey. Today it is a
much appreciated haven for locals, cyclists,
walkers and families, serving excellent
home-prepared food at sensible prices (until
7.30pm). South Cheshire CAMRA *Pub of the
Year* 2001. ⚏Q⛺❀◐♣P✄

BURTONWOOD

Bridge Inn
Phipps Lane
✪ 11.30-11; 12-10.30 Sun
☎ (01925) 225709
Burtonwood Bitter Ⓗ
This community pub with its own bowling
green in the village centre acts as a base for
several local sports teams (bowls, rugby
league, ladies' rounders, golf, football). The
small outside drinking area has a children's
slide. An island bar serves two rooms: one
with large TV screen, dartboard and
mementos of the licensee's RL playing days;
the other a lounge displaying pictures of old
Burtonwood, where a singer entertains Sat
eves. Another room has a pool table and
Burtonwood Brewery memorabilia –
children are permitted here and in the
conservatory. Weekday lunches served.
❀◐♣P

CHESTER ❖

Albion Inn
Park Street (close to the Newgate)
✪ 11.30-3, 5 (6 Sat)-11; 12-3, 7-10.30 Sun
☎ (01244) 340345 e-mail:
mike@albioninn.freeserve.uk
Greenalls Bitter; Taylor Landlord; guest beers Ⓗ
This classic Victorian street-corner pub is
situated within the city walls, and has a
strong local following. The pub celebrates
all things English and this is reflected in the
food menu – no chips, no foil packages, just
good local produce. It has retained the
traditional three-room layout of vault, snug
and lounge; a Victorian cast-iron fireplace is
complemented by the William Morris
wallpaper. The landlord's passion, the Great

War, is reflected in the artefacts and pictures, along with posters and enamelled signs of that period. Various events are held throughout the year to commemorate WW1. If travelling phone to confirm opening times. ⚠Q◑▶

Duttons
10-12 Godstall Lane (access from St Werburgh St or Eastgate St Row)
☼ 11-11; 12-10.30 Sun
☎ (01244) 403010
Lees Bitter, seasonal beers Ⓗ
An interesting blend of ancient and modern, this bar features old wood panelling, wooden furniture and a polished metal bar top. A comfortable, relaxing area has armchairs and coffee tables. There is an emphasis on good food, and coffee is popular during the day. Duttons was a wine merchants in these premises until its conversion to a pub. Historic Godstall Lane, which runs from opposite the cathedral to one of the famous Chester 'rows', is pedestrian only, which allows tables and chairs for outside drinking. Can get busy at weekends. ❀◑▶♿

Mill Hotel ←
Milton Street
☼ 11-11; 12-10.30 Sun
☎ (01244) 350035 e-mail: reservations@millhotel.com
Cains Bitter; Theakston Cool Cask; Weetwood Best Bitter; Wells Eagle; guest beers Ⓗ
Quite rightly, cask ale aficionados from all over the region flock to this canalside hotel. While many pubs have tried the guest ale route and failed, the consistent top quality of the 16 beers has reaped rewards (and awards) here, including national winner, 2001 of the *Food Safety* and *Hygiene* award. Converted from a Victorian corn mill it features pitch pine beams. There is an *à la carte* restaurant and you can dine in the hotel's own canal boat. The bar has a very popular 'beer of the week' policy with ales recommended by the customers.
❀⚠◑♿▬P✄

Talbot
33 Walter Street, Newtown (near Leisure Centre)
☼ 11-11; 11-5, 7-11 Sat; 12-5, 7-10.30 Sun
☎ (01244) 317901
Burtonwood Bitter Ⓗ
Situated close to the city fire station in an area of terraced housing, the Talbot may prove tricky to find. It is well worth making the effort, however, especially for devotees of the traditional back-street boozer. A friendly welcome is assured for all, but this is a pub that takes pride in serving its local community. The main bar contains a bagatelle table but with its low ceilings and confined space this room is dominated by conversation. A more spacious second room holds a pool table. Visitors should note the eclectic juke box, historic pictures of Chester and quirky porcine collection.
◖≈♣

Union Vaults
44 Egerton Street (near Mill Hotel)
☼ 11-11; 12-10.30 Sun
☎ (01244) 322170
Plassey Bitter; guest beer Ⓗ
Welcoming, conversational street-corner local that attracts a loyal clientele of all ages. A simple main bar offers satellite TV and bagatelle, and leads through to a quieter, more comfortable drinking area on an upper tier. It hosts folk music most Sun eves. On a busy weekend night it can boast one of the best traditional pub atmospheres in Chester. Situated near the canal, this is the city's only regular outlet for locally-brewed Plassey.
≈♣

White Lion
New Road (off A41)
☼ 11.30-11; 12-10.30 Sun
☎ (0151) 339 3402
Thwaites Mild, Bitter Ⓗ
Small, friendly, country pub on the outskirts of Ellesmere Port, this former regional CAMRA *Pub of the Year* is popular with all sections of the community. It was extensively refurbished in 1999 to create an extra small lounge from part of the kitchen and reveal an original brick fireplace in the bar. It is handy for the Boat Museum and Cheshire Oaks, Europe's largest designer outlet. Popular with families who are welcome in the small snug at lunchtime and who spill out into the garden in summer. Good value lunches – try the home-made chicken tikka (no meals Sun).
⚠Q❀◑P

Beartown Tap
18 Willow Street (A54 Buxton Road)
☼ 12-2, 4-11; 12-11 Fri & Sat; 12-10.30 Sun
☎ (01260) 270990
website: www.beartownbrewery.co.uk
Beartown Bear Ass, Kodiak Gold, Bearskinful, Polar Eclipse, Black Bear; guest beer Ⓗ
First pub owned by Beartown Brewery, the ideal spot to sample the full Beartown range, plus a guest beer. One Belgian beer is always on draught, plus a changing selection of Belgian bottled beers. The pub has three rooms and one bar, with a function room upstairs. Bare floorboards by the bar give way to more comfortable seating in the other rooms. Real cider changes on a regular basis. No fruit machines or music spoil the atmosphere of this pub. Street parking is possible nearby.
⚠Q≈♣◐✄

Congleton Leisure Centre
Worral Street (by Congleton Park)
☼ 10-1 (not Mon), 7-11 (9.30 Sat); closed lunch, 8-10.30 Sun
☎ (01260) 271552
Beer range varies Ⓗ
It is very rare to find a municipally-owned leisure centre selling not only good real ale, but an ever-changing choice of three at any one time. The building is a typically bland, modern public structure, but great efforts have been expended to create a pub atmosphere in the bar – the walls are adorned with brewery posters and beermats, and it has a snug feel. By contrast, the no-smoking/family room/meeting room is a little sterile. The bar is open to all, even if you do not use the sporting facilities.
Q♿♿≈P✄

Queen's Head

Park Lane (opp. station, at bridge 75 of Macclesfield Canal))
⏲ 11-11; 12-10.30 Sun
☎ (01260) 272546
Ansells Mild; Greene King Abbot; Tetley Bitter; Wadworth 6X; guest beer Ⓗ
Canalside pub with its own moorings, popular with locals and the canal trade. The very large garden has a children's play area and stages occasional outdoor events in summer. The pub was originally built for the railway trade, but has enjoyed something of a revival in recent years under the current landlord. One room has a pool table; food is served in a separate area at the back, mostly home cooked, and there is a changing specials board. Guest beers are frequently from local breweries.
❀⇆◑⇌♣P

Wharf

121 Canal Road (near Dog Lane aqueduct)
⏲ 11-11; 12-10.30 Sun
☎ (01260) 272809
Greenalls Mild, Bitter; guest beer Ⓗ
Smart, friendly pub on the outskirts of town, offering fresh home-cooked food from a very varied menu. The large garden has a children's play area. The guest ale is constantly changing. The pub stands 50 yards from the Cheshire Ring Canal and is very popular with canal users in summer.
❀◑⇌♣P

CREWE ❋

Borough Arms

33 Earle Street (on bridge; entrance via Thomas St)
⏲ 7 (3 Fri)-11; 12-4, 7-11 Sat; 12-4, 7-10.30 Sun
☎ (01270) 254999
Beer range varies Ⓗ
Town-centre, genuine free house offering a staggering list of ever-changing beers from small and micro-brewers. It is a haven for the real ale connoisseur and much appreciated by regulars. Late Victorian in origin, built on a railway bridge, with views over the Liverpool line, it was an Allsopps' pub until 1902, (see the evidence on the west gable). Only when bought by the present licensee did it revert to its original name. Belgian dark, fruit and blonde beers are always on tap, alongside 50-plus bottled varieties and a changing cider from small producers. Definitely worth the detour; a micro-brewery is in the pipeline. Q❀⇌●⚟

DARESBURY

Ring o'Bells

Old Chester Road (off M56, 1/2 mile N of jct 11)
⏲ 11.30-11; 12-10.30 Sun
☎ (01925) 740256
Boddingtons Bitter; Cains Bitter; Greenalls Mild, Bitter; guest beer Ⓗ
This multi-roomed pub in the heart of Daresbury is well known in the local area for both good food and great beer. Bookings are recommended for meals; children are welcome all day in the dining areas. The pub dates back to the 18th century, and the extensive beer gardens offer a superb view of the local church across the way, where Lewis Carroll's father was the vicar; related memorabilia is prominently displayed, notably mosaics. ♨Q❀◑♿♣P

DISLEY

Albert

75 Buxton Road (A6)
⏲ 4 (2 Fri; 12 Sat)-11; 12-10.30 Sun
☎ (01663) 764552
Camerons Strongarm; Tetley Bitter; guest beers (occasional) Ⓗ
This small, but imposing, red-brick pub was built around 1900 and stands alongside the busy A6 a short distance from the village centre. Inside this community pub are four separate drinking areas surrounding the bar; one houses a pool table. Frequented mainly by locals of mixed ages, it is also used as a base by the Disley Football Club. A large retractable Sky TV screen dominates the two front bar areas but is only used for important sporting events. The Peak Forest Canal is a short distance away, and the Goyt Way, a half-mile or so walk. ♨❀⇌♣

FARNDON

Farndon Arms

High Street
⏲ 11.30-3, 5-11; 12-3, 7-10.30 Sun
☎ (01829) 270570 website: www.farndonarms.com
Worthington Bitter; guest beers Ⓗ
Close to the River Dee and the Welsh border lies this 16th-century coaching inn featuring a striking mock-Tudor façade and a large heraldic sign. Behind the porch with its burgeoning yukka plants is a comfortable

INN BRIEF

BOLLINGTON

Queen's Arms
40 High Street
2 (12 Fri & Sat)-11; 12-10.30 Sun
Robinson's Hatters Mild, Best Bitter Ⓗ
Solidly built, stone pub that has been modernised but remains comfortable and friendly. Close to canal and White Nancy footpaths.

CHESTER

Ship Victory
47 George Street
12 (11 Sat)-11; 12-10.30 Sun
Tetley Bitter, guest beer Ⓗ
Small local with a strong community focus. Spared from 1960s city development, it now stands isolated in a pay and display car park.

CREWE

Monkey
141 West Street
11-11; 12-10.30 Sun
Eccleshall Slaters Bitter, Slaters Premium, Slaters Supreme; guest beers Ⓗ
The brewery's second tied house, opened in 1999, an open-plan street-corner pub.

GAWSWORTH

Harrington Arms ☆
Church Lane
12-3, 6-11; 12-3, 7-10.30 Sun
Robinson's Hatters Mild, Best Bitter Ⓗ
Old coaching inn, in the same family for over 100 years, and part of a working farm. Totally unspoilt, worth seeking out.

GRAPPENHALL

Ram's Head
Church Lane
12-3, 5-11; 12-11 Sat & summer; 12-10.30 Sun
Boddingtons Bitter; Greenalls Bitter; Marston's Pedigree Ⓗ
Village local where the main lounge is split into two; it stands in a cobbled street. Emphasis on food service, with generous portions.

HANDLEY

Calvelly Arms
Whitchurch Road
12-3, 6-11; 12-4, 7-10.30 Sun
Boddingtons Bitter; guest beer Ⓗ
Pleasant inn, just off the A41, runner-up in the *Cheshire Life Pub Food of the Year* contest.

modernised interior where etched windows reveal its former name – the Raven. Sofas, a small library, local prints of a bygone era, horse brasses and a real fire add to the ambience. A pool table and discreetly located TV cater for those not content with simple conversation, while there's a cosmopolitan menu for the hungry. Acoustic jam sessions are held on Tue.

♨ ⚅ ✿ ⊨ ◖ ♣ P

Greyhound
High Street

✿ 5-11; 11-11 Sat, 12-10.30 Sun
☎ (01829) 270244
Greenalls Mild, Bitter; guest beers Ⓗ

The Greyhound is one of three pubs in this pleasant border village. On entering the pub you will find it divided into three distinct areas; one acts as the dining area with a real log fire and pictures and maps of old Farndon and Chester. A very good selection of food is served – curry night on Thu is popular. Accommodation is competitively priced. ♨ ✿ ⊨ ◖ ♣ P

Helter Skelter ⬅
31 Church Street

✿ 11-11; 12-10.30 Sun
☎ (01928) 733361
Weetwood Best Bitter; guest beers Ⓗ

Built about 1870 as two cottages, the pub was named after a visitor attraction on Frodsham Hill (until 1977). This local CAMRA *Pub of the Year* 2000 offers five rotating guest beers, a locally-brewed house bitter and a selection of imported bottled beers. Centrally located, the large single bar area, which can be crowded on Fri and Sat eves, is surrounded by high captain's chairs, stools and bench seating. Food is freshly prepared from an interesting bar menu. Sun meals are served 12-4; eve meals Mon-Sat finish at 8pm. Real ale memorabilia posters and signs are an attractive feature. ◖ ⇌ ♣ ⊟

Netherton Hall
Chester Road (A56 1 mile W of town)

✿ 12-11; 12-10.30 Sun
☎ (01928) 732342
Draught Bass; Greene King Abbot; Jennings Bitter; Taylor Landlord; guest beer Ⓗ

Old photographs of this former manor home of the Netherton family line the walls, with prominent signs indicating the

original rooms. A cast-iron fireplace and old dentist's chair are noteworthy items in a lounge area frequented eves by diners not booked into the separate dining room/old library. A notice board from 1812 records the 'List of tolls for the Chester to Frodsham Road'. Highly recommended for its extensive food choice, chalked on a blackboard. Live music is featured Sun eves. ✿ ◖ P

Queen's Head
92 Main Street

✿ 11.30-3, 7 (5 Tue-Wed)-11; 11-11 Thu-Sat; 12-10.30 Sun
☎ (01928) 733289
Greenalls Mild, Bitter; guest beers Ⓗ

Built in 1550 this main street, bay-fronted pub was named the King's Head until the reign of Queen Victoria. During the late 18th century in an upstairs room, known as the Court Lete, murderers could be sentenced to death at the gallows behind the pub. Local CAMRA *Pub of the Year* 1999, the open bar area offers a friendly atmosphere away from the traditional games room. A folk club meets in the stables on Fri and Sun eves. Busy on Thu market days when food is served outside the usual 12-2 weekday times, one or two guest beers are available at most times, especially weekends. ◖ ⇌ ♣ P

Grappenhall Community Centre
Bellhouse Farm, Bellhouse Lane (off A50)

✿ 7 (2 Sat)-11; 2-10.30 Sun
☎ (01925) 268633 e-mail: gyca@freenet.co.uk
Greene King Ruddles Best; guest beers Ⓗ

Converted from an old farmhouse and barn over a quarter of a century ago, this large private club and social centre supports a wide range of groups and activities. A central bar area serves a games/family room, where pool and darts are played, and which hosts a Wed quiz; a large comfortable lounge with a no-smoking section at one end; and the function room in the old barn, which is also the venue for the beer festival in April. Situated near Grappenhall village and the Bridgewater Canal, a CAMRA membership card gains admission.
⚅ ♿ ♣ P ✂

HOUGHTON GREEN
Millhouse
Ballater Drive
12-11; 12-10.30 Sun
Holt Mild, Bitter Ⓗ
Large, open-plan pub, with lounge and bar areas; built in the late 1980s to cater for new housing estates.

KNUTSFORD
Builders Arms
63 Mobberley Road
11-11; 12-10.30 Sun
Banks's Original, Bitter; Marston's Bitter Ⓗ
Cosy, unspoilt two-roomed pub with a garden on the edge of town; it enjoys a wonderful ambience. Weekday lunches.

LITTLE NESTON
Harp Inn
19 Quayside
12-11; 12-10.30 Sun
Taylor Landlord; Whitbread Trophy; guest beers Ⓗ
Delightful, two-roomed, ex-miners' pub served by one bar. The superb public bar has a real fire and low beams. A gem.

MACCLESFIELD
Boarhound
37 Brook Street
12-11; 12-10.30 Sun
Robinson's Hatters Mild, Best Bitter Ⓗ
Popular local on the 'Silk Road', with a large, well-used function room upstairs. Most pub games played.

MALPAS
Crown Hotel
Old Hall Street
11.30-11; 12-10.30 Sun
Weetwood Eastgate Ale; guest beer Ⓗ
Oasis of cask beer in a pleasant farming town, hosting Karaoke eves Thu and Sat. Meals and accommodation are available.

MIDDLEWICH
Big Lock
Webbs Lane (by lock 75 on Trent-Mersey Canal)
11-11; 12-10.30 Sun
Black Sheep Best Bitter; Greene King Abbot; Whitbread Trophy; guest beers Ⓗ
Large, canalside pub with a lounge bar, restaurant and a games room. Beartown beers are often available.

Parr Arms
Church Lane

✪ 12-3, 5.30-11; 12-11 Sat; 12-10.30 Sun
☎ (01925) 267393

Boddingtons Bitter; Castle Eden Ale; Greenalls Bitter; Marston's Pedigree; guest beer (occasional) Ⓗ

Winning Inn Partnership's *Catering Pub of the Year* 2000 indicates that food service is very important to this traditional village pub. It stands next to the church in a picturesque cobbled street with outdoor seating. (Beware: no waiting allowed in street but no yellow lines). Inside, a central bar serves two lounges (one no-smoking), and a public bar. Furnishings in the lounge bars are in country style, while the public bar features Rugby League memorabilia (the landlord was a player). The Bridgewater Canal is just a few hundred yards from the front door. ✿◑Ɑ➳♣P⅟

GREAT BUDWORTH

George & Dragon
High Street (off A559 Northwich-Warrington road)

✪ 11.30-3, 6-11; 11.30-11 Fri & Sat; 12-10.30 Sun
☎ (01606) 891317 website: www.georgegb.fsnet.co.uk

Tetley Bitter; guest beers Ⓗ

This comfortable pub is set in one of Cheshire's most attractive villages. Usually private transport is needed, but a pub bus circulates on Fri and Sat eves. A large public bar, with pool and table football, welcomes dogs. A cosy front lounge serves good food at fair prices. A blackboard describes the guest beers, which constantly change. The upstairs restaurant welcomes children. The staff are friendly and helpful; a plaque from an American war veteran who recuperated here testifies to this. Look out for Eric the cat, and note the elegant pub sign. Q✿◑Ɑ♣➳P⅟

HANDFORTH

Railway
Station Road

✪ 12-3.30, 5.30-11; 12-3.30, 7-10.30 Sun
☎ (01625) 523472

Robinson's Hatters Mild, Best Bitter, seasonal beers (summer) Ⓗ

Large, multi-roomed 100-year-old pub facing the station. In winter it is a rare outlet for handpulled Robinson's Old Tom. The pub is frequented by a good cross-section of people and seems always to be busy and welcoming, with a pleasant array of plants and flowers. The no-smoking room at the back of the pub has no piped music. Lunches which range from snacks to full meals, including vegetarian options, are served Mon-Sat. Bandleader Syd Lawrence was a previous landlord; the current incumbent has won a local gardening prize for the last three years. Q➳✿◑Ɑ➳♣P⅟

HATTON

Hatton Arms
Hatton Lane (1 mile from A49/B5356 jct, near M56 jct 10)

✪ 11.30 (11 Sat)-11; 12-10.30 Sun
☎ (01925) 730314

Greenalls Mild, Bitter; Marston's Pedigree; Theakston Best Bitter Ⓗ

The character of this attractive 17th-century village inn has been enhanced by the addition of a restaurant. Other rooms include a quiet lounge, tap/games room and an open bar with low-beamed ceilings. Being close to Delamere Way, other trails and relatively quiet roads, it is usual to find cyclists and walkers here, especially in summer. The large garden has picnic tables. An excellent selection of food includes specials (no meals Mon eve). ⌂Q✿➳◑➳♣P

HIGHER HURDSFIELD

George & Dragon
61 Rainow Road

✪ 12-3 (not Mon), 7 (5 Fri)-11; 12-10.30 Sun
☎ (01625) 424300

Courage Directors; guest beers Ⓗ

Small, friendly, free house on the Whaley Bridge road out of Macclesfield, set back off the road with outside tables, near a bus stop. Bult of local stone, part of the pub is reputed to be 400 years old and was once a school for young ladies. This is a true community pub with a welcoming atmosphere. The main part of the pub is split into three: the inviting bar area to the left boasts a display of pump clips behind the bar; there is also a pool room and a snug. The two guest beers are often local brews. ✿◑♣P

HIGHER SUTTON

Hanging Gate
Meg Lane

✪ 12-3, 7 (5.30 Fri)-11; 12-11 Sat; 12-10.30 Sun
☎ (01260) 252238 e-mail: rebecca.m@tinyworld.co.uk

Hydes Bitter, Jekyll's Gold, seasonal beers Ⓗ

An unusual building, dating from 1621, built on the hillside with small rooms on three levels going down the hill; the lowest room affords a wide panorama of the hills and the Cheshire Plain, stretching to the Welsh mountains. Despite its exposed position, inside it is cosy and welcoming with blazing fires in winter. A family-run pub, it is popular with diners, with a well-deserved reputation for its fresh home-cooked food. This local CAMRA *Pub of the Year* 2000 is a rare outlet for Hydes in the area. ⌂Q➳✿◑P⅟

KELSALL

Morris Dancer
Chester Road (from A54 follow signs for Kelsall Village)

✪ 11-11; 12-10.30 Sun
☎ 01829 751291

Theakston Best Bitter; guest beers Ⓗ

Old village pub that has been extended, without losing its character: beams, oak settles and bare wooden floors create a relaxing, friendly and traditional atmosphere. Very much the centre of the village, both geographically and socially, this pub acts as a meeting place for local clubs and societies. It hosts a quiz (Wed) and occasional live entertainment. Facilities include a restaurant serving local produce. A beer festival is held in April and a folk festival on Whit weekend. Beers from local brewery Weetwood are featured as guests. Live football, via satellite, is shown in the bar on Sat. ⌂Q✿◑▲♣P

KETTLESHULME

Swan

Macclesfield Road (B5470)
☼ 12 (5.30 Mon)-11; 12-10.30 Sun
☎ 01663 732943
Thwaites Bitter; guest beers Ⓗ

15th-century white-walled pub nestling alongside the B5470. The classic interior of this small country inn features original timber posts and beams. The cosy bar area includes settles close to a real fire with stone chimney breast; a small side room with a second real fire completes the drinking areas. Lunches consist of bar snacks and meals (try one of the landlord's chilli-pickled eggs if you dare). Families and hikers are welcome. Three ever-changing guest beers are available. This picturesque Peak District National Park village is surrounded by excellent walking country. No food Mon. ▲☎️🌜🏵🗘♣️👄P

KNUTSFORD ❖

Cross Keys

52 King Street
☼ 11.30-3, 5.30 (7 Sat)-11; 12-3, 7-10.30 Sun
☎ (01565) 750404 website: www.hotel.knutsford.co.uk
Boddingtons Bitter; Taylor Landlord; guest beers Ⓗ

Largely rebuilt in 1909, this former 18th-century coaching inn is set on Knutsford's attractive and popular 'Bottom Street'. A glass and wood screen separates the lounge from the vault with its pool table and TV. Bar meals can be had at lunchtimes, while the restaurant, reached by a barrel-vaulted tunnel, opens Tue-Sat eves. The fine choice of cask ales sets the Cross Keys apart: a gleaming bank of polished brass handpumps features three constantly changing guest beers. Real cider appears on occasion. 🛏🗘️🍺🚯👄P🍴

LOWER PEOVER

Crown

Crown Lane (B5081, off the A50 S of Knutsford))
☼ 11.30-3, 5.30-11; 12-3, 7-10.30 Sun
☎ (01565) 722074
Boddingtons Bitter; Flowers IPA; Greene King Old Speckled Hen; Taylor Landlord; guest beer Ⓗ

Homely 17th-century country inn, with cobbled frontage, flower tubs and hanging baskets. Three rooms cluster around a central bar; the first is a gem, with benches, scrubbed tables and a well-used dartboard creating a timeless feel. Low ceilings, beams and brasses abound. The smart front room is used mainly by diners. An annual gooseberry competition is held on the last Sat in July. The guest beer is usually from one of Cheshire's independent brewers, typically Weetwood. ▲🏵🗘️♣️P

MACCLESFIELD ❖

Baths

40 Green Street (off A537, behind station)
☼ 12-5 (not Mon-Fri), 6.30-11; 12-4, 7-10.30 Sun
Banks's Original, Bitter; Boddingtons Bitter; Mansfield Bitter Ⓗ

Small but thriving local, part of a row of terraced houses, just 10 minutes' walk up the hill from the station (turn left out of the forecourt). A local bowling green inspired its original name, then it was renamed after the (now closed) public baths. There is a traditional cosy lounge and a large, much-used games room, as well as the small bar area. On the bar wall is the original indenture of the pub, dated 1890 and complete with wax seals. 🍺➡♣️

British Flag

42 Coare Street
☼ 7 (4 Sat)-11; 12-3, 7.30-10.30 Sun
☎ (01625) 425500
Robinson's Hatters Mild, Best Bitter, Ⓟ **Old Tom** (winter) Ⓖ

This is an old-fashioned and friendly town local, where four rooms surround a central bar. Pub games are popular; with skittles in one room, darts and pool in another; there is also a large screen TV for sport. In the 1860s the pub boasted ginger beer manufacturing. It had a reputation as the neighbouring King's School local, being frequented by its staff.
➡♣️

George & Dragon

21-23 Sunderland Street
☼ 11-4 (3 Tue & Wed), 5.30-11; 11-11 Fri; 11-5, 7-11 Sat; 12-3, 7-10.30 Sun
☎ (01625) 421898
Robinson's Hatters Mild, Best Bitter Ⓟ

Conveniently located for both bus and rail stations, this friendly local boasts a good range of pub games – bar skittles, darts, dominoes, pool and cards are all played. The interior is essentially open plan, however it still manages to give the impression of separate drinking areas. So consistent has been the quality of the beer in this pub that the local CAMRA branch presented the landlord with an award for appearing in 10 editions of this *Guide*.
🏵🗘️➡🍴

Railway View

Byrons Lane (off London Rd, off A523, at lights on Langley-Wincle road)
☼ 12-3 (not Mon-Thu), 6-11; 12-3, 7-10.30 Sun
☎ (01625) 423657
Boddingtons Bitter; Cains Mild; guest beers Ⓗ

Very pleasant pub, 100 yards from the main London road. The beer range includes a house beer from Coach House, and four changing guests from around the country. Home-made food is always available, with a good selection of tasty pies. This is a pub that is well worth looking out for. Mon eve features beer at a reduced price.
▲🏵🗘️➡♣️

Waters Green Tavern

96 Waters Green
☼ 11.30 (11 Sat)-3, 5.30 (7 Sat)-11; closed lunch; 7-10.30 Sun
☎ (01625) 422653
Lees Bitter; Taylor Landlord; guest beers Ⓗ

Close to the bus and rail stations, this pleasant town pub originally had three storeys; the half-timbered front is false. Traditional home-cooked food is served. Slightly opened out to give three areas and a pool room to the rear, the long bar to the left stocks seasonals and more unusual beers – up to five guests – often including some from north of the border. This local CAMRA *Pub of the Year* 1999 fields thriving darts, pool and quiz teams.
▲🗘️➡♣️

MOULDSWORTH

Goshawk
1 Station Road
☼ 12-3, 5.30-11; 12-11 Sat; 12-10.30 Sun
☎ (01928) 740302
Greenalls Mild, Bitter; guest beer Ⓗ
This large red-brick former coach house is conveniently located for the Mouldsworth Motor Museum and walks in Delamere Forest. Formerly the station hotel, the pub hosts various society meetings and business conferences and consists of a public bar, games room, a restaurant plus two plush lounges – one with a fireplace. Additional features include a floodlit bowling green and a children's play area that resembles an assault course. ♨Q♿☕◑⊟Å➔♣P⌿

NANTWICH ✣

Black Lion
Welsh Row
☼ 3 (12 Fri & Sat)-11; 12-10.30 Sun
☎ (01270) 628711
Weetwood Best Bitter, Old Dog; Hanby Rainbow Chaser Ⓗ
Small, timber-framed black and white pub, with the date 1664 carved above the door. Three small rooms downstairs are lit by candles; upstairs there are two sitting rooms – the front room has a TV, and is sometimes used by societies for meetings. Chess is played every eve, and you can easily get a game; Tue eve is for jamming (bring your instrument); Wed is charity quiz night (bring your own team). This is a friendly pub where conversation predominates. At the side is a small paved garden. A Titanic beer is usually stocked. ♨Q☕♣♨

PARKGATE

Red Lion
The Parade
☼ 12-2.30, 5-11; 12-11 Fri, Sat & summer; 12-10.30 Sun
☎ (0151) 336 1548
Adnams Bitter; Ind Coope Burton Ale; Tetley Bitter Ⓗ
Wirral CAMRA *Pub of the Year* 1996, this traditional lounge and bar offers superb views across the Dee estuary to the Welsh hills. The local marsh is famous for birdlife and attracts many visitors. Parkgate is also famous for ice cream. Local numbers are swelled by many walkers off the Wirral Way and promenading day trippers. The lounge pictures show stormy evidence of bygone years and Dee high tides; the bar is guarded by Nelson the parrot. No food Sun. Q◑⊟♣

PENKETH

Ferry Tavern
Station Road (off Tannery Lane, off A562, follow signs to Fiddlers Ferry Yacht Haven)
☼ 12-3, 5.30-11; 12-11 Sat & summer; 12-10.30 Sun
☎ (01925) 791117
Boddingtons Bitter; Courage Directors; Wells Bombardier; guest beers Ⓗ
The site dates back to 1160 as a ferry crossing point across the Mersey. Located between the river and now disused Sankey-St Helens Canal, access to the pub from the car park is by crossing a railway line. Six handpumps in bar area are complemented by over 300 whiskies. Home-made food is served Mon-Sat in either bar area or upstairs in the more formal surroundings of the small no-smoking restaurant. Children are allowed until 8.30pm and will enjoy playing the large, old-fashioned table football. ♨Q☕◑⊟♣P

PEOVER HEATH

Dog Inn
Well Bank Lane (off A50 at the whipping stocks)
☼ 11.30-3, 5 (5.30 Sat)-11; 12-10.30 Sun
☎ (01625) 861421
website: www.info@thedoginncheshire.co.uk
Hydes Bitter; Moorhouses Black Cat; Weetwood Best Bitter, Old Dog Ⓗ
This comfortable rambling pub, set on a quiet lane and converted from a row of 18th-century cottages, justifiably features in CAMRA's *Good Pub Food* and *Room at the Inn* (booking is advisable). It has a tap room with pool and darts, a lounge bar warmed by a real fire and an extensive restaurant, using local produce. Beams, dried flowers and photos of old village life add interest. Around the benches on the patio is a splendid array of flower tubs and hanging baskets. ♨Q☕♿◑⊟♿♣P⌿

PRESTBURY

Admiral Rodney
New Road
☼ 11-3, 5-11; 11-11 Fri & Sat; 12-10.30 Sun
☎ (01625) 828078
Robinson's Hatters Mild, Best Bitter Ⓗ
Situated at the village centre less than five minutes' walk downhill from the station, this Grade II listed building dates back to 1730 and has been owned by Robinson's since 1939. The pub is named after a British naval officer who was a contemporary of Nelson. Close to the bar is a history of the Admiral himself and a list of every landlord of the pub. The interior is divided into cosy drinking areas, with no juke box or pool table. Some of the furniture is made from old beer barrels. Q☕◑➔P

RAINOW

Highwayman
Whaley Bridge Road (B5470, 1 mile N of village centre)
☼ 12-2.30, 7-11; 12-3, 7-10.30 Sun
☎ (01625) 573245
Thwaites Bitter Ⓗ
Remote pub, providing a warm welcome, and panoramic views over Manchester. A Black Horse on one exterior wall is visible for miles; inside is a maze of connecting rooms, three with blazing open fires. Known locally as 'the Patch', it was once the Blacksmith's Arms, reflecting the changing of horses on the Nantwich-Buxton salt trail. It now commemorates a local highwayman, Pymm, who could see travellers for miles around from a nearby vantage point, Pymm's Chair. The pub serves Mexican and Indian meals as well as traditional home-cooked food. ♨Q☕◑➔P

RODE HEATH

Royal Oak
41 Sandbach Road
☼ 12-11; 12-10.30 Sun ☎ (01270) 875670

Draught Bass; Greene King Abbot; Tetley Dark Mild, Bitter; Titanic Premium; guest beer Ⓗ

Known for miles around for its good food and beer, this village pub has a main dining room plus a small private room seating up to eight; a children's menu, high chairs and baby changing facilities are all available. Meals are served all day, but popularity makes booking advisable. Special food promotions feature Mon-Thu eves, pensioners' specials 12-4 weekdays and 'happy hour' Mon-Fri 5.30-6.30 on Bass and Titanic. Beer festivals are held Easter weekend and Aug bank holiday. The garden has a children's play area. Two large screen satellite TVs, a pool table and darts add to its appeal. Within easy reach of the canal, it was recently recommended in a book called *Walking on Water*. ✿◑🍴⅍♣P⊁

STRETTON

Ring o' Bells
Northwich Road, Lower Stretton
(A559, off M56 jct 10)
✪ 12-3, 5.30 (7 Sat)-11; 12-3, 7-10.30 Sun
☎ (01925) 730556
Greenalls Mild, Bitter; guest beer Ⓗ

Originally a row of cottages that included a vet's practice this friendly and comfortable country local offers lively conversation in the main room/bar area but has two quieter side rooms. Sewing machine tables abound with a collection of local views in the back snug. Social and sporting events, including a boules league, are well publicised. The one guest beer typically changes three times a week from a monthly choice. A small patio garden with benches adjoins the rear car park. 🏚Q✿P

SWETTENHAM

Swettenham Arms
Behind the church
✪ 11-3, 6-11; 12-4, 7-10.30 Sun
☎ (01477) 571284 website: www.cheshireinns.co.uk
Beartown Bearskinful; Hydes Bitter; Jennings Bitter; Moorhouses Black Cat Ⓗ

Following the signs for Swettenham will take you down a long country lane, which terminates in the village. Hidden behind the church is an enormous car park with pub attached. The Swettenham Arms is an upmarket, award-winning country pub, and a family-run free house. The building is long and thin, composed of four areas, of which one is mainly for eating. Exposed beams, real fires, and many equine pictures give a relaxed and comfortable ambience. A new, large function suite is now open. 🏚✿◑P⊁

TUSHINGHAM

Blue Bell Inn
Signed Bell 'o t'Hill from A41, 4 miles N of Whitchurch
OS523454
✪ 12-3, 6-11; 12-3, 7-10.30 Sun
☎ (01948) 662172 e-mail: patgage@btinternet.com
Hanby Drawwell; guest beers Ⓗ

This part-14th-century, timber-framed pub positively exudes atmosphere. Floodlit and imposing on the outside, access is via a cobbled frontage and two hefty oak doors. While the back rooms are the domain of diners and escapees from a veritable menagerie of domestic animals, the real character lies in the bar adorned with bells and thematically arranged horse brasses. Here, presided over by an offbeat American landlord, visitors swiftly become engaged in genial conversation. The eerie display of Civil War artefacts adds credence to the tales of poltergeists. 🏚Q✿◑🛆♣P

WARRINGTON ✣

Bull's Head
33 Church Street
✪ 12-11; 12-10.30 Sun
☎ (01925) 635680
Cains Bitter; Courage Directors; Greenalls Mild, Bitter; guest beer Ⓗ

Attractive, rambling, 17th-century building, converted from a row of cottages, it is now a thriving community pub. The modest frontage conceals a warren of rooms including a lounge area to the front, a bar area with pool table and two quieter rooms to the rear. At the back is a large function room as well as a bowling green. It is not surprising that the pub is home to many sports clubs. A welcome haven from the bustle of the redeveloped town centre. ✿◑⅍≠ (Central) ♣

Wilkies
25 Church Street   (A49, 500 yds from centre)
✪ 2 (12 Fri & Sat)-11; 12-10.30 Sun
☎ (01925) 416564
e-mail: john@wilkiestavern.freeserve.co.uk
Beer range varies Ⓗ

The only genuine free house in Warrington: a single room bar with an Irish theme. A continually changing range of five beers is invariably sourced from smaller/micro-breweries. Two beer festivals, at Easter and early December, held in the rear courtyard, usually feature new breweries. Sky TV on a big screen makes the pub especially popular at the weekend when live Rugby League or football are shown. Real cider is served at festivals and occasionally in winter. ≠ (Central) ♣ 🍸

WESTON

Prospect
70 Weston Road
✪ 11-11; 12-10.30 Sun
☎ (01928) 561280
Greenalls Mild, Bitter: Young's Special; guest beer Ⓗ

This little gem at the heart of the village has been sympathetically refurbished to 1920s style. It has a vault where darts and pool are played. Recently listed as the fifth Best Folk Venue in the UK by *The Times,* folk nights take place every Mon eve, with bands coming from as far afield as the United States and from all over Britain. Points of particular interest are the original Greenalls etched window, and a wide selection of local photographs. The pub is well known locally for its superb food. 🏚Q✿◑🛆P

WHEELOCK

Cheshire Cheese
466 Crewe Road
✪ 12-11; 12-10.30 Sun
☎ (01270) 760319
Hydes Bitter, Jekyll's Gold, seasonal beers Ⓗ

Well-known pub whose frontage, just

below road-level, shows the bulding's age as an inn servicing the nearby canal. Inside, there is an upper lounge with a warming coal fire and two snug window alcoves, and a lower more open area with a dartboard. It is often quite full with locals, but is friendly to all, supporting darts and quiz teams. In summer, the large garden with slide, tables and covered area is an attractive feature. Popular with boaters, breakfasts and take-away meals are available.
ₐₐ⊛◐♣

WIDNES

Horse & Jockey
18 Birchfield Road (300 yds S of station)
🟢 11-11; 12-10.30 Sun
☎ (0151) 420 29966
Greenalls Bitter; Tetley Bitter; guest beer Ⓗ
A warm welcome is guaranteed at this local CAMRA *Pub of the Year* 2001. This cosy, one-roomed pub, close to the town centre, benefits from excellent links to train and bus services. Over a century old, it backs on to a park and has a large, fully enclosed garden with a children's play area. It is much favoured by the local community and is free from a juke box. The guest beer changes weekly.
⊛≒P

WILLEY MOOR

Willey Moor Lock Tavern
Tarporley Road (300 yds off A49) OS534452
🟢 12-2.30 (3 summer), 6-11; 7-10.30 Sun
☎ (01948) 663274 e-mail:
gilkes@willeymoor.fsnet.co.uk
Theakston Best Bitter; guest beers Ⓗ
Approached via a driveway guarded by unforgiving sleeping policemen, this attractive, red brick and whitewashed, ex-lock keeper's cottage is only accessible by crossing the Llangollen Canal. Served by one bar, there are several drinking areas featuring paintings of canal life by A R Oliver, an extensive collection of Toby jugs and teapots. Overseen by a *Grand Master Cellarman,* extra ales are stocked in the summer to cater for the seasonal influx of boaters as well as walkers from the Sandstone Trail. The large garden is particularly popular.
ₐₐ⊛◐P

WRENBURY

Cotton Arms
Cholmondley Road
🟢 12-3, 6-11; 12-11 Sat; 12-10.30 Sun
☎ (01270) 780377 e-mail:
hatton@cottonarms.freeserve.com
Greenalls Bitter; guest beer Ⓗ
Pleasant roadside pub at the end of the village. The vaults bar is a basic locals' room, while the large lounge has an emphasis on food. The lounge is on two levels, the upper level is no-smoking and is usually set out for meals. The lower level can also be set for meals, but drinkers are welcome. At the rear is a bowling green (fee payable) and beyond that a camping ground that backs on to the canal.
ₐₐ⊛◐⊟≒▲≒♣P

Dusty Miller
Cholmondley Road
🟢 11-3 (not winter Mon), 6.30-11; 12-3, 7-10.30 Sun
☎ (01270) 780537
Robinson's Hatters Mild *or* Old Tom, Best Bitter, seasonal beers Ⓗ
Converted from a mill, the pub straddles the River Weaver, alongside the Llangollen Canal, overlooking one of the lifting bridges typical of this waterway. The main room has large floor-to-ceiling windows looking on to the canal. The upstairs function room is divided by roof beams, and the floor is still marked out as it was when used to store grain. This is used as an extra dining room at weekends. Outside, benches line the towpath, and the garden is beside the river.
⊛▲♣P⅄

WYBUNBURY

Swan
2 Main Road (B5071)
🟢 12-11; 12-10.30 Sun ☎ (01270) 841280
Greene King Abbot; Jennings Mild, Bitter, Cumberland Ale; Cocker Hoop, Sneck Lifter; guest beer (summer) Ⓗ
Spacious village inn, bow-fronted with low, beamed ceilings, acquired by Jennings in 1999. Popular with diners, it offers a special two-course lunch, Tue-Sat and a choice of roasts, Sun (12-8). The bar boasts a piano, seldom-played, and a keen darts following. It stands adjacent to a leaning tower, all that remains of the original parish church, a prominent local landmark. ₐₐQ⊛⊠◐♣P

INN BRIEF

MOBBERLEY
Bull's Head
Mill Lane
11.30-11; 12-10.30 Sun
Boddingtons Bitter; Tetley Bitter; guest beers Ⓗ
Traditional country local with a bowling green and good food. It hosts occasional beer festivals and music. Two guest beers, one is often local.

> ✳ **symbol next to a main entry place name indicates there are Inn Brief entries as well.**

NANTWICH
Peacock
221 Crewe Road, Willaston (A534/A500 jct)
11-11; 12-10.30 Sun
Courage Directors; Greenalls Bitter; guest beers Ⓗ
Miller's Kitchen pub on the outskirts of town. A changing guest beer from independent breweries. Families welcome.

NORTHWICH
Freemasons
43 Castle Street
11-11; 12-10.30 Sun
Webster's Yorkshire Bitter; guest beers Ⓗ
Unassuming town pub, dating back to the mid 1860s, which has resisted 'improvements' and remains cosy and welcoming.

WARRINGTON
Lower Angel
27 Buttermarket Street
11-11; 12-10.30 Sun
Ind Coope Burton Ale; Tetley Dark Mild, Bitter; guest beers Ⓗ
Traditional two-roomed pub retaining its Walkers' identity in the windows.

WINTERLEY
Foresters Arms
473 Crewe Road
Marston's Pedigree; Weetwood Old Dog Ⓗ
Cosy, low-beamed village pub serving good value lunches. The unusual garden boasts a small dovecot and a classic tractor.

CAMRA's National Inventory
of Pubs Interiors of Outstanding Historic Interest

Most pub interiors have been radically altered in the past two or three decades, and many of them ruined thanks to theming, modernising and other 'improvements'. The following list, the product of ten years' work by CAMRA, identifies those pubs that retain the most complete and important historic interiors in the country. They form a very diverse group, ranging from tiny country pubs and now rare, basic back-street locals, to ornate drinking palaces in major cities. Most, though not all, sell real ale.

The chief criterion for inclusion is that an interior is very largely as it was before the Second World War. In some cases we have accepted a certain amount of change provided the essential historic character of the pub has been kept. Inclusion on the list does not mean a pub is safe. The retirement or death of the owner may lead to closure of small pubs while drastic and sometimes appallingly insensitive changes still affect important urban examples. So, make the most of these pubs. We hope they will be around for a long time to come. But some may not.

Where known we have given a warning on restricted hours. Fuller information and descriptions of the pubs can be found on the CAMRA website along with photographs.

ENGLAND

Bedfordshire
Broom: Cock. Multi-room village pub: no counter.
Luton: Painters Arms, 79 High Town Road. 1913. Excellent tiling and a rare off-sales snug.

Berkshire
Aldworth: Bell. One of the great rural classics: c.1930s servery: outdoor gents.
Frilsham: Pot Kiln. Three-room country pub in attractive surroundings.

Cambridgeshire
Peterborough: Hand & Heart, Highbury Street. 1930s side-street pub.

Cheshire
Alpraham: Travellers Rest. Little changed since 1937: four small rooms, bowling green: closed weekday lunchtimes.
Barthomley: White Lion. Half-timbered and thatched: three contrasting rooms, 17th-century panelling.
Bollington: Holly Bush, Palmerston Street. 1930s brewers' Tudor with original interior.
Gawsworth: Harrington Arms. Part of a working farm: three-rooms.
Macclesfield: Castle, Churchwallgate. Multi-room town pub: fine snug: decorated ceiling.
Stockton Heath: Red Lion, London Road. 200-years old: six rooms.
Wheelock: Commercial. Built 1805 refitted in and unaltered since c.1930.

Cornwall
Falmouth: Seven Stars, The Moor. Two rooms, marble counter: casks behind the servery.

Cumbria
Broughton Mills: Blacksmiths Arms. Delightful, multi-room country pub.
Carlisle: Cumberland Inn, Botchergate. 1929-30: least altered of the pubs built in Carlisle under nationalisation by architect Harry Redfern.

Derbyshire
Brassington: Olde Gate Inne. Smart village pub in a 17th-century building.
Derby: Old Dolphin, Queen Street. Inter-war refurnishing in a late 16th-century pub: four rooms including tiny panelled snug.
Elton: Duke of York. Simple three-room village pub. Opens c.8.30 p.m.
Kirk Ireton: Barley Mow. Three-room pub in a Jacobean building.
Wardlow Mires: Three Stags Heads. Formerly

doubled as a farm; flagstoned bar with huge stone fireplace. Restricted hours.

Devon
Drewsteignton: Drewe Arms. Classic village pub with no bar counter; four rooms.
Holsworthy: Kings Arms, Fore Street. Rebuilt 1902. Four rooms including a small snug.
Luppitt: Luppitt Inn. Basic two-room farmhouse pub: casks stillaged behind the bar. Mon-Sat evenings only.
Topsham: Bridge. Scarcely changed since Victorian times except the malthouse is now a lounge. Much old woodwork.
Widecombe-in-the-Moor: Rugglestone Inn. SE of the centre: charming small country pub

Dorset
Pamphill: Vine. Small village pub on two levels in salubrious estate setting. Tiny bar.
Worth Matravers: Square & Compass. A country classic: two rooms: no counter.

County Durham
Durham: Shakespeare, 63 Saddler Street. Small early 19th-century narrow town pub with tiny snug.
Durham: Victoria, 86 Hallgarth Street. Intact layout and fittings of 1899 including screened 'family dept' (off-sales).

Gloucestershire & Bristol
Ampney St Peter: Red Lion. 300-year old two-room cottage pub. No counter. Closed weekday lunchtimes.
Bristol: Kings Head, 60 Victoria Street. Superb counter and bar back, c.1865. Interesting snug inserted later.
Duntisbourne Abbots: Five Mile House. Two classic old rooms: settles.
Purton: Berkeley Arms. Two rooms, huge settle, hatch service and big open fire
Willsbridge: Queens Head. Three-room pub in a 17th to 18th-century building. Plain public bar.

Hampshire
Steep: Harrow. Unspoilt two-roomed village pub: hatchway service.

Herefordshire
Kington: Olde Tavern, 22 Victoria Road. Beautifully-preserved Victorian pub. Vast settle. Closed weekday lunchtimes.
Leintwardine: Sun Inn. Essentially a private house with a public room. Beer fetched from the kitchen. Closed weekday lunchtimes.

Continued on page 105

CORNWALL

ALBASTON

Queen's Head

S of A390 above Gunnislake
☼ 11.30-3, 6-11; 12-3, 7-10.30 Sun
☎ (01822) 832482
Courage Best Bitter; guest beers Ⓗ
Pleasant, two-bar local, run by the same
family for 40 years. Of particular note are
the interesting old photos on the walls, a
small mineral collection and tinplate
railway items. It hosts occasional live music.
The nearby branch line runs to Plymouth
until late eve. 🏚Q❀⬥❀P

ALTARNUN

Rising Sun

1 mile N of the village
☼ 11-3, 6-11 (11-11 Sat & summer); 12-10.30 Sun
☎ (01566) 86332
Beer range varies Ⓗ

Converted from a 16th-century farmhouse,
this excellent rural pub retains many
original features including slate and
wooden floors, and beamed ceilings. The
front wall collapsed when a previous
landlord dug out the cellar. It generally
offers four constantly varied ales, with five
at weekends and up to six in summer. Two
small rooms lead off the main bar. Camping
is possible in the pub grounds.
🏚Q❀❀⬥❀◑▲♣P

BLISLAND

Blisland Inn

The Green
☼ 11.30-11; 12-10.30 Sun
☎ (01208) 850739
Beer range varies Ⓗ /Ⓖ
CAMRA's national *Pub of the Year* 2001 is a
friendly, rural community pub on the only
village green in Cornwall. Out of around six

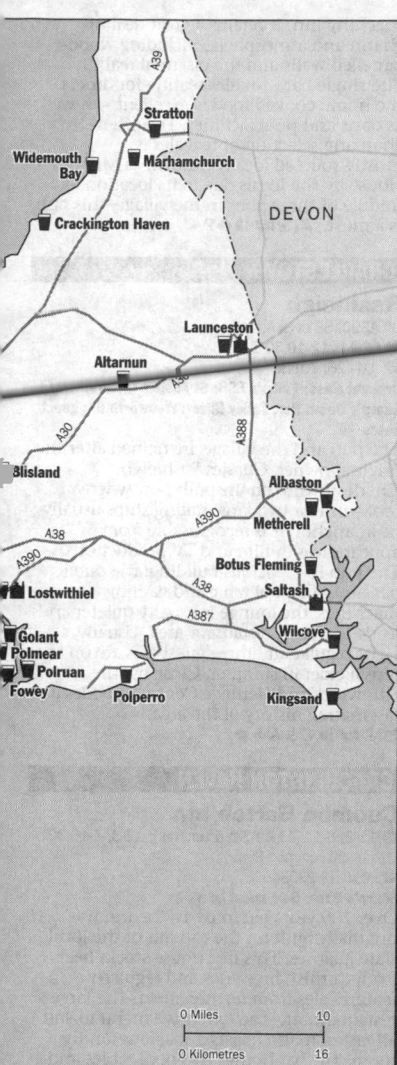

line in summer. Late evening buses also stop nearby. Q ♿ ⛱ ⌖ ◑ ♣

Mason's Arms
5-9 Higher Bore Street (near Town Wall, on Lanivet road)
🕐 11-11; 12-10.30 Sun
☎ (01208) 72607
Sharp's Cornish Coaster; Taylor Landlord; guest beers Ⓗ
Dating from before Napoleonic times, this pub claims to be the oldest licensed premises in town. The lively, slate-flagged public bar provides games and supports a league-level quiz team. The lounge is quieter and preferred by locals seeking a relaxed pint. Traditional bar meals are available at lunchtime. This friendly pub is on the edge of the town and thus too far out for the pub crawl 'circuit'. ♨ Q ⛱ ◑ ♣ P

BOTUS FLEMING

Rising Sun
$1/2$ mile off A388, near Saltash
🕐 12-4 (not Mon or Thu), 6-11; 12-11 Sat; 12-10.30 Sun
☎ (01752) 842792
Draught Bass; Worthington Bitter; guest beers Ⓗ
Rural gem near Saltash, tucked away off the beaten track, in a small, quiet village. Unaltered for some 40 years, the pub has low ceilings and well-trodden wood floors, while the traditional outside toilets are rather primitive. It boasts a boules piste. No food is served. Buses, including an evening service, stop on the A388, about 20 minutes' walk away. ♨ ⛱ ♠ ♣ P

BREA

Brea Inn
Higher Brea (S of railway, near Pool Ind. Estate) OS666403
🕐 12-2.30 (not Mon), 7 (6.30 Sat)-11; 12-3.30, 7-10.30 Sun
☎ (01209) 713706
Boddingtons Bitter; Flowers IPA; Sharp's Doom Bar Ⓗ
Small, split-level, 18th-century pub with a single bar on the lower level, and a dining area above. This old granite pub, set in the thick of the mining district, was once a mine captain's house before becoming a miners' ale house. It has been sympathetically modernised and serves good value food, based on fresh local produce (booking for eve meals is strongly advised). There is no food Mon, or Tue and Sun eves. Tom is the resident ghost. ♨ Q ⛱ ⌖ ◑ ♠ P

ever-varying real ales, at least two come from Cornish brewers; the landlord has clocked up around 1,500 different ales so far. The cider varies. Excellent food is based on local produce (booking is recommended for full meals). An iguana keeps a watchful eye over the family room.
♨ Q ♿ ⛱ ◑ ♣ ♠ P 🏠

BODMIN

George & Dragon
3 St Nicholas Street (behind Shire House)
🕐 11-11; 12-10.30 Sun
☎ (01208) 72514
St Austell XXXX Mild, Tinners, HSD Ⓗ
Small, single-bar local with a welcoming atmosphere, on the edge of the town centre. Home-cooked meals are available at reasonable prices. This comfortable pub is close to the preserved Bodmin & Wenford steam railway, which connects to the main

INDEPENDENT BREWERIES

Bird in Hand Hayle
Blackawton Saltash
Blue Anchor Helston
Driftwood St. Agnes
Keltek Lostwithiel
Organic Cury Cross Lanes
Redruth Redruth
Ring O'Bells Launceston
St Austell St Austell
Sharp's Rock
Skinner's Truro
Ventonwyn Grampound Road

BREAGE

Queen's Arms Inn
By church, just off A394
- 11.30-2.30, 6.30-11; 12-10.30 Sun
- ☎ (01326) 573485
website: www.thequeensarmsinn.co.uk
Draught Bass; Flowers Original; Sharp's Doom Bar; guest beers Ⓗ

Lively village local in the shadow of the church. One long bar boasts an open fire at each end and a games area round the corner. The dining room is no-smoking. Note the large collection of plates hanging from the beams. In summer, tables are put outside on grass and tarmac, with more across the lane in a safe play area – families with children are very welcome. A wide range of food is available; last orders 9pm. It hosts jazz (swing) on Thu eve.
🏛❀☕◑♣♨P

BRIDGE

Bridge Inn
On B3300, just over a mile from Portreath
- 11-3, 6-11 (11-11 summer); 12-3, 7-10.30 Sun
- ☎ (01209) 842532
website: www.downourlocal.com/thebridgeinn
Flowers IPA; guest beer Ⓗ

18th-century traditional Cornish granite inn, reputedly haunted. Ghosts aside, the atmosphere in the L-shaped bar is warm and friendly, where fun is the byword; activities include an annual beer festival. An ever-changing beer menu provides variety for the regulars; a second guest appears in summer. Home cooking is a speciality. The picturesque riverside garden is home to a dovecote and boules piste. The nearby old Portreath tram road provides a delightful coast-to-coast walk through Cornish mining history.
Q❀☕◑&Å♣♨P

BUGLE

Bugle Inn
57 Fore Street
- 11-11; 12-10.30 Sun
- ☎ (01726) 850307
St Austell IPA, Tinners, Tribute Ⓗ

The village and pub name were apparently derived from the bugle played as stagecoaches passed through this area. Now situated in the heart of china clay country at the village centre; many of the locals are associated with this industry. Recently, the pub has benefited from visitors to the nearby Eden Project. The pub is a comfortable, friendly house, ideally situated for visitors touring central Cornwall. Sunday lunches are very popular (booking advised). It gets very busy on the day of the annual Silver Band Festival in June.
🏛Q❀☕◑&Å≈♣P●

CHACEWATER

Britannia Inn
Fore Street
- 5 (11 Sat & summer)-11; 12-10.30 Sun
- ☎ (01872) 560362
Skinners Betty Stogs Bitter, Cornish Knocker; Wadworth 6X Ⓗ

Although much has changed at this former coaching inn, it retains a great deal of charm and atmosphere, including wood-panelled walls and the essential real fire. The single bar provides seating for diners – the home-cooked food is excellent – as well as darts and pool facilities. The often-changing selection of real ales is mostly sourced locally. Known as Middle House by the locals due to its location as middle of three pubs in the village, this pub is a must. 🏛❀☕◑♣P

CHARLESTOWN

Rashleigh
Off A390, SE of St Austell
- 11-11; 12-10.30 Sun
- ☎ (01726) 73635
Draught Bass; Fuller's ESB; St Austell Tinners; Sharp's Doom Bar; Tetley Bitter; Wadworth 6X; guest beers Ⓗ

The pub and the village are named after the original owner, Charles Rashleigh. Charlestown is an unspoilt port where today one or two large sailing ships usually lie at anchor. It is recognisable from appearances in film and TV productions. The pub is a spacious building: the public bar houses a pool table and gaming machines; the lounge is usually quieter and leads to a large restaurant area. Usually eight regular and three guest ales are on tap, plus a cider in summer. Close by, the Shipwreck and Heritage Centre provides a fascinating history of the area.
🛏❀☕◑&Å♣♨

CRACKINGTON HAVEN

Coombe Barton Inn
- 11-3, 6-11 (11-11 Sat & summer); 12-3, 7-10.30 (12-10.30 summer) Sun
- ☎ (01840) 230345
Sharp's Doom Bar; guest beers Ⓗ

Over 200 years old in parts, the inn was originally built for the captain of the local slate quarries. This free house stocks beers from Cornish breweries and regularly features ales from further afield. The large restaurant offers an extensive menu to suit all tastes. It also boasts a spacious family room. The bar houses two pool tables and enjoys a good view over the beach and out to sea. 🛏❀☕◑Å♣P

CRANTOCK

Old Albion
Langurroc Road
- 12-11; 12-10.30 Sun
- ☎ (01637) 830243
Courage Best Bitter; John Smith's Bitter; Skinner's Betty Stogs Bitter; guest beer Ⓗ

This idyllic part-thatched pub was once a tearoom when all pubs in the village were closed following a Methodist campaign. Named after the last man-o-war to be built on the banks of the local River Gannel, the pub claims a long history of harbouring smuggling gangs, with secret tunnels to the nearby church and beach. A good range of real ales is stocked to wash down good value food from a varied menu; the food choice is more extensive in summer when cider is also sold. Nearby camping/caravan sites, hotels and B&Bs increase the seasonal trade.
🏛🛏❀◑Å♨P

CROWLAS

Star Inn
On A30 near Penzance
🕏 11-11; 12-10.30 Sun
☎ (01736) 740375
Beer range varies H

Friendly, spacious old pub which is becoming a local mecca for real ale. Run by an ex-Cotleigh brewer, who buys the beer from a wide variety of sources, it is normal to find five or six ales that change rapidly. His plans include the installation of a brewing plant. Try the local pubs in the daytime, and the Star at night – a good bus service (running until late eve) passes the door. 🗚Q🕏❀🖼️♠️♣P

CROWNTOWN

Crown Inn
On B3303 Helston-Camborne road
🕏 12-2.30, 6-11; 12-3, 7-10.30 Sun
☎ (01326) 565538
Skinner's Betty Stogs Bitter, seasonal beer; Theakston Old Peculier, guest beers G

Large, friendly old granite free house with a restaurant and garden. The single, but spacious bar includes several distinct drinking areas and a space for the pool table. This is a community pub where conversation dominates, although occasional live entertainment is staged. The Skinner's beers are the staples, and may vary from time to time, supplemented by two ever-changing guests. Unusually, the ales are dispensed by gravity in the cellar despite the array of handpumps on the bar. A limited bus service passes the door.
Q🕏◑♣P

FALMOUTH

Seven Stars ☆
The Moor
🕏 11-3, 6-11; 12-3, 7-10.30 Sun
☎ (01326) 312111
Draught Bass; Sharp's Eden Ale; Skinner's Cornish Knocker G

A priest runs this unspoilt, timeless old town-centre pub which has a busy, if narrow, tap room and a quiet snug at the back; the old 'bottle and jug' still exists for outside drinkers. Bass is ever-present, but the Sharp's and Skinner's beers are changed from time to time. Note the old clock on the shelf permanently proclaims the time as GMT; mobile phones are banned here. Late eve buses leave nearby. Q🕏🖳≠ (Town)

FLUSHING

Royal Standard
St Peters Hill (off A393 at Penryn)
🕏 11-2.30 (3 Fri & Sat); 6.30-11 (varies winter); 12-3, 7-10.30 (varies winter) Sun
☎ (01326) 374250
Draught Bass; Sharp's Cornish Coaster, Doom Bar H

Friendly local pub, run by the present landlord for over 30 years. Home-made pasties and apple pies are specialities on the menu. Fine views of Falmouth and the Penryn River can be enjoyed from the front patio. Drivers beware of swans in the road nearby. The pub is accessible from Falmouth by foot ferry across the creek.
🗚❀◑♣

FOWEY

Galleon
12 Fore Street (near Town Quay)
🕏 11-11; 12-10.30 Sun
☎ (01726) 833014
Draught Bass; Flowers IPA; Sharp's Cornish Coaster; guest beers (summer) H

This one-time, run-down Courage pub has been sympathetically refurbished by new owners. Now a completely free house, it boasts a wide range of bar food, with fish a speciality. The bar area has new timbered ceilings, modern toilets and light American ash bar furniture. This blends in with the original tiled floor and repointed walls. The highlight of this pub is the fine river view from the back patio. Live music is performed Sunday lunch.
🗚🖙❀🖼️◑👶♣

HELSTON

Blue Anchor
50 Coinagehall Street
🕏 11-11; 12-10.30 Sun
☎ (01326) 562821
Blue Anchor Middle, Special, seasonal beer H

Rambling, unspoilt 15th-century building under a thatched roof, with its own brewery at the rear. A garden and accommodation have recently been added for good measure. There are no distracting bandits or juke box, only good conversation in the two small bars. An indoor skittle alley at the back has its own bar (used for group functions). The pub enjoys good bus connections with other West Cornwall towns until late eve; one service connects with mainline trains at Redruth. Good home-cooked food is served.
🗚Q🖙❀🖼️◑🖳♣

HOLYWELL BAY

St Piran's Inn
🕏 11 (7 winter)-11; 12-10.30 Sun
☎ (01637) 830205 e-mail: stpirans@btinternet.com
St Austell Tribute; Skinner's Cornish Knocker, Organic Serpentine; guest beers H

Almost on the golden sands of a picturesque bay, this free house keeps up to four real ales, including at least one local brew; the choice varies throughout the year. Good value meals are available more widely in the tourist season, when there may be a refundable charge for the car park, to avoid beachgoers using it and not the pub. Landlord has a habit of renaming beers and producing his own pump clip designs. Many camping/caravan sites and self-catering holiday accommodation are close by; the army training camp at Penhale occasionally boosts trade, too.
🗚Q🖙❀◑ÅP

KINGSAND

Rising Sun
The Green
🕏 12-11; 12-10.30 Sun
☎ (01752) 822840
Draught Bass; Courage Best Bitter; John Smith's Bitter; guest beer H

Cosy village inn which is at once both popular and quiet. The pub was once the Customs & Excise house in this village of narrow streets, close to the coastal footpath. Parking is limited to just four cars. The excellent locally-produced food may include crab dishes and the famous half-yard of sausage. Occasional live entertainment is staged, especially Fri.

🏠Q❀🛏🕪♣P

LANLIVERY

Crown Inn
Off A390, 2 miles W of Lostwithiel
☼ 11-3, 6-11; 12-3, 6-10.30 Sun
☎ (01208) 872707
Sharp's Doom Bar, Eden Ale 🅗

Picturesque 12th-century inn at the village centre. Lanlivery is a remote village, but only a mile from the main road and within easy reach of Lostwithiel, Fowey, Bodmin and St Austell. The building reopened as a pub in the 1970s, having been a private house for the previous 60 years. The long farmhouse-style building has the main bar at one end, together with a snug, plus a comfortable lounge area with inglenook and a restaurant. The house beer by Sharp's is Crown Inn Glory.

🏠Q❀🛏🕪 🖺🕭♣P

LANNER

Lanner Inn
The Square (A393 Redruth-Falmouth road)
☼ 12-3, 4.30-11; 12-11 Fri & Sat; 12-3, 7-10.30 Sun
☎ (01209) 215611 e-mail: lannerinn@aol.com
Sharp's Cornish Coaster, Doom Bar; guest beers 🅗

Busy, if small, community pub whose landlord varies the guest beer regularly on the advice of his locals. An extra gravity-dispensed beer may appear on the bar on special occasions. Food is confined to simple bar fare; the emphasis is on real ale, conversation, and games such as darts, euchre, pool and dominoes. A delightful orchard doubles as the garden and children's play area in summer; the pub also boasts a boules piste, common locally. Nearby buses run to Truro and Camborne until late eve. The accommodation represents good value.

🏠Q❀🛏♣P

LAUNCESTON

Bakers Arms
Southgate Street
☼ 11-11; 12-10.30 Sun
☎ (01566) 772510
Courage Directors; John Smith's Bitter; guest beers 🅗

Popular town pub, situated close to the historic Southgate arch. The lounge is cosy, while the public bar is games oriented. One or two guest ales are regularly varied, and the pub hosts mini beer festivals. Good value home-cooked lunches are served. Parking is in the public car park at Race Hill (100 yards). The pub is close to the route of two 30-mile recreational walks: the Two Castles Way (Okehampton), and Tamar Valley Discovery Trail (Plymouth).

🏠🛏🕭🕭🖺♣

LONG ROCK

Mexico Inn
Gladstone Terrace (signed at A30/A394 roundabout)
☼ 11.30-2.30, 5-11; 12-3, 5-10.30 Sun
☎ (01736) 710625
Marston's Pedigree; Sharp's Eden Ale; Skinner's Cornish Knocker 🅗

Typical Cornish pub, once part of a mine, dating from 1799 with bare granite walls and beams inside. Meals may be taken in the bar (smoking) or the restaurant area (no-smoking). Beers change little during the quieter winter months, but guest beers become frequent in the busier summer months. An enclosed patio area stands next to the small car park at the rear. Although it cannot be seen from the pub, the beach is only about 50 yards away.

🏠Q❀🕭🖺♣AP

INN BRIEF

EDMONTON
Quarryman
12-11; 12-10.30 Sun
Beer range varies 🅗
Family-friendly, food-oriented country pub stocking up to four real ales, usually with one each from Sharp's and Skinner's.

GOLANT
Fisherman's Arms
Water Lane
12-3, 6-11; 12 (11 summer)-11 Sat; 12-10.30 Sun
Courage Best Bitter; Ushers Best Bitter; guest beer (summer) 🅗
Waterside pub, in a delightful river setting where various pub games include boules. Home-cooked food.

PADSTOW
Golden Lion Inn
Lanadwell Street
11-3, 6.30-11 (11-11 summer);
12-3, 7-10.30 Sun
Draught Bass; guest beer 🅗
Padstow's oldest pub, well over 400 years old, home of the May Day Red 'Oss. The guest beers are regularly changed.

PAR
Par Inn
2 Harbour Road
11-11; 12-10.30 Sun
St Austell Tinners, seasonal beer 🅗
Unpretentious, friendly drinkers' pub near the harbour.

PENZANCE
Alexandra Inn
Alexandra Road
11.30-2.30, 5.30-11; 11-11 Sat (may vary in summer); 12-10.30 Sun
Draught Bass; Courage Directors 🅗
Sympathetically modernised free house near the promenade. Pirate's Pride is a house beer from Skinner's. Good food.

PERRANWELL
Royal Oak
Perranwell Station
11-3, 6-11 (may vary summer); 12-10.30 Sun
Draught Bass; Flowers IPA; guest beer 🅗
Small, friendly cottage pub, dating from the 18th century, now a free house specialising in excellent food.

POLMEAR
Ship Inn
Polmear Hill
11.30-3, 6-11; 11-11 Sat; 12-10.30 Sun
Draught Bass; Marston's Pedigree; Sharp's Doom Bar; guest beers 🅗
Near Par beach, the pub is ideal for families visiting in summer, but reverts to a local in winter.

POLRUAN
Lugger
The Quay
11-3, 6-11; (11-11 summer); 12-10.30 Sun
St Austell Tinner's, HSD (summer), **seasonal beer** 🅗
Fine, friendly riverside, two-bar pub, with nautical decor, reached by foot ferry from Fowey. *Cask Marque* accredited.

QUINTRELL DOWNS
Two Clomes
East Road
12-3, 7-11; (12-11 summer); 12-3, 7-10.30 (12-10.30 summer) Sun
Sharp's Doom Bar; guest beers 🅗
Old free house named after its clome ovens by the fireplace. The guest beers are constantly varied.

LOSTWITHIEL

Royal Oak
Duke Street
☼ 11-11; 12-10.30 Sun
☎ (01208) 872552
Draught Bass; Fuller's London Pride; Marston's Pedigree; Sharp's Own; guest beer Ⓗ
The Royal Oak is situated just off the main road in Lostwithiel, which was the old capital of Cornwall. It is a busy, friendly 13th-century inn, very well known for its good food. It has a traditional stone-floored bar and a comfortable lounge, leading to the restaurant. It specialises in guest beers from small independent breweries and stocks a fine selection of bottled beers. Reputedly a tunnel runs from the cellar to the dungeons of Restormel Castle, which may have been used as a smuggling route.
Q ❀ ☎ ◑ ⊕ ♨ Å ⇌ ♣ P

LUDGVAN

White Hart
Signed at Crowlas on A30
☼ 11-2.30, 6-11; 12-3, 7-10.30 Sun
☎ (01736) 740574
Draught Bass; Flowers IPA; Marston's Pedigree Ⓗ
Uneven floors reflect the age of this pub and the wooden panels and partitions, together with the varied furniture and photographs, create an authentic atmosphere. Sharing a car park with the church, this renowned pub serves food of high quality and good value, with much of the produce coming from local sources (no meals Mon eve in winter). Two large wood-burning stoves keep it warm throughout.
▲ Q ❀ ◑ ♣ P ⌇

MALPAS

Heron Inn
From A390 in Truro, take road signed Malpas, next to Radio Cornwall OS843426
☼ 11 (11.30 winter)-2.30, 6-11; 11-2.30, 6-10.30 Sun
☎ (01872) 272773
St Austell IPA, Tribute, seasonal beer Ⓗ
This picturesque village pub, just outside Truro, can be reached by river or road. Set above the road, it benefits from wonderful views over Truro River and surrounding woodland. The terrace outside is a popular place for a drink. The interior's natural slate and oak combine with a blue colour scheme, enhanced by artefacts from local artists and craftsmen. A good menu is supplemented by a specials board, all home-cooked. Children are welcome. ❀ ◑ P ●

MARHAMCHURCH

Buller's Arms
☼ 11-3, 6-11; 11-11 Sat & summer; 12-10.30 Sun
☎ (01288) 361277
Fuller's London Pride; Sharp's Own or Eden Ale; guest beers Ⓗ
Popular village pub with a large, dimly-lit, L-shaped bar of beamed ceilings and a slate flagstoned floor. The bar is well-appointed with wooden settles, the games area having the extra comfort of padded settles. It enjoys a reputation for good food, and features regular live entertainment, particularly Sat eve. Function room is large

enough to cater for weddings and conferences. ▲ ❀ ☎ ◑ ♣ P

METHERELL

Carpenters Arms
Lower Metherell (off A390, near Callington)
☼ 12-3, 7 (6.30 summer)-11; 12-3, 7-10.30 Sun
☎ (01579) 350242
Sharp's Cornish Coaster; Summerskills Best Bitter; guest beers (summer) Ⓗ
Comfortable, 15th-century pub with worn and highly polished slate flagstoned floor and exposed stone walls. There is a spacious lounge and dining area where a varied menu offers a wide range including vegetarian options; fish a speciality. Outside seating is on the front terrace; the lounge is a no-smoking area. ▲ Q ❀ ☎ ◑ ⊕ ♣ P ⌇

MEVAGISSEY

Fountain Inn
3 Cliff Street
☼ 11-11; 12-10.30 Sun
☎ (01726) 842320
St Austell Tinners, HSD Ⓗ
Friendly, two-bar 15th-century inn with slate floors, stone walls, old photographs and low beams – the tunnel to the side door is particularly low. The Cornish landlord was a local fisherman, and has run the pub for many years. The Smugglers' Bar still bears signs of the pilchard press that was once housed here; a glass plate in the floor covers the pit where the fish oil was caught and which doubled as a store for contraband. Regular buses (including eves) run to St Austell. ▲ Q ☎ ◑ ⊕ Å ♣

MOUNT HAWKE

Old School Pub
W of B3277
☼ 7-11 (midnight Fri & Sat); 12-3, 7-10.30 Sun
☎ (01209) 891158 e-mail: dawsonron@hotmail.com
Tetley Bitter; guest beer Ⓗ
This family-run free house, formerly the village school, is the centre for community activities. With teams in all pub games leagues, there is always something happening. Outside, the building remains unchanged. The spacious bar, with a no-smoking area, has comfortable seating. A dining room, skittle alley and function room complete the accommodation; bric-à-brac is a feature of the decor. Excellent value meals include fish caught by the landlord. Close to the coast, it is a popular watering-hole for tourists and locals alike. A second guest beer is stocked in summer.
Q ⅍ ❀ ◗ Å ♣ P ⌇

MYLOR BRIDGE

Lemon Arms
Off A393 at Penryn
☼ 11-3, 6-11; 12-3, 7-10.30 Sun
☎ (01326) 373666
St Austell Tinners, Tribute, HSD Ⓗ
Friendly, one-bar. village-centre pub, frequented by local sports teams. Good, home-cooked food is available, and families with children are made welcome. The real ales are always from the St Austell Brewery but the range may vary from time to time. There is a patio for summer drinking. This is

a particularly picturesque part of Cornwall with plenty to interest visitors, including NT Gardens within a short drive.
🏚⊛◑♣P●

NEWBRIDGE

Fountain Inn
On A3076 Penzance-St Just road
☼ 11-11 (11-2, 6-11 winter Mon); 12-10.30 Sun
☎ (017360) 364075
St Austell IPA, Ⓗ Tinners, Ⓖ Tribute, Ⓗ HSD, Ⓖ seasonal beers Ⓗ
Lovely old inn set in a quiet hamlet. This Grade II listed building has solid stone walls and a flagstoned floor; the carpeted lounge area boasts an enormous granite fireplace. Some tables are formed from old casks with disused dartboards as tops. Keen licensees have transformed this pub, the only one left in the parish, which was recently threatened with closure. Cornish language lessons are held here, and it is popular for good quality meals. Children are welcome. A good bus service passes the door.
🏚Q⊛◑♣P

NEWQUAY

Skinner's Ale House
58 East Street
☼ 12-11; 12-10.30 Sun
☎ (01637) 876391
Skinner's Betty Stogs Bitter, Cornish Knocker, Blonde; Ⓗ **guest beers** (occasional) Ⓖ
Real ale haven among the theme bars of this boisterous seaside town. Furbished also on an old ale house 'theme', peanut shells on the floor provide the 'sawdust'. Free peanuts from the barrel act as a taster for more substantial meals. Goofy is a house beer and all test brews are tried out first in this, Skinner's only tied house. Two beer festivals are normally held each year, when guest micros' products are racked on gravity dispense. Live music is staged most Fri and Sat eves. Be ready to talk surfing. ◑⇌

PENDEEN

North Inn
On B3306, St Just-St Ives road
☼ 12-11; 12-10.30 Sun
☎ (01736) 788417
website: www.cornwall-online.co.uk/north-inn
St Austell IPA, Tinners, Tribute, HSD Ⓗ
Local in an ex-mining village. The single large room is decorated with artefacts from nearby Geevor, the last working mine to be closed in the Pendeen area and now a mining museum where visitors are taken on a fascinating underground tour. The inn is in an area of outstanding natural beauty, with nearby cliffs and good walking. One of the ales may be replaced by a seasonal brew. No food Mon. Buses between Penzance and St Just pass nearby until late eve.
🏚Q⊛⇌◑♣P

PHILLACK

Bucket of Blood
14 Churchtown Road (off A30 near Loggans Moor)
☼ 12-2.30 (3 Sat), 6-11; 12-4, 7-10.30 Sun
☎ (01736) 752378
St Austell IPA, HSD, seasonal beer Ⓗ

Mind your head – the beams are very low in this friendly old pub near the sand dunes of Hayle Towans. The name is linked to a gory legend involving the pub's well – read the explanation near the door. The seasonal beer, or another from the St Austell list, is not always available, and depends on demand in an area where business is highly seasonal. Mainly a local where food is not a winter priority (served Thu–Sat eve), lunches are a summer feature, when meals are served both sessions, Tue–Sat.
🏚⇋⊛◑⊟♣P●

PIECE

Countryman
On Four Lanes-Pool road OS679398
☼ 11-11; 12-10.30 Sun
☎ (01209) 215960
Courage Best Bitter; Greene King Old Speckled Hen; Sharp's Own; Theakston Old Peculier Ⓗ
Lively country pub, high above Redruth in former mining country, it was once a 'Count House' for the nearby copper mines. It stocks a varying Skinner's beer that may be a seasonal brew; the house beer, from Sharp's, is called No-Name, as nobody could think of one in a 'Name the Beer' competition. There is some form of entertainment every night, as well as Sun lunchtime. Food is served all day. Buses to local towns pass the door until late eve.
🏚⊛◑⊟♣P

POLGOOTH

Polgooth Inn
Two miles S of St Austell OS998501
☼ 11-3, 6-11; 12-3, 6-10.30 Sun
☎ (01726) 74089
St Austell Tinners, Tribute, HSD Ⓗ
Large, well modernised village local, warmed by a welcome log fire in winter, set in secluded rural valley. The bar, which is an unusual W-shape, may feature one of St Austell's seasonal ales in place of one of the regulars. The food servery operates daily (last eve orders 10pm) and there is a dining room. Families and dogs are welcome – there is an outdoor playground for children. Accessible by bus from St Austell at lunchtime, extra buses (including eves) pass London Apprentice, 15 minutes' walk down the wooded valley.
🏚Q⇋⊛◑♣P●

POLKERRIS

Rashleigh Inn
Signed off A3082, between Par and Fowey
☼ 11-11; 12-3, 6.30-10.30 (12-10.30 summer) Sun
☎ (01726) 813991
Draught Bass; Ⓗ **St Austell HSD;** Ⓖ **Sharp's Doom Bar; guest beers** Ⓗ
Excellent pub situated down a steep wooded valley and bordering an isolated beach, affording fine views of St Austell and Mevagissey Bays. The guest beers are constantly varied. The split-level restaurant is highly recommended, and the à la carte menu caters for vegetarians. Children are allowed in the saloon bar dining area. This pub is well worth finding, winter or summer, when the patio comes into use.
🏚Q⊛◑♣P

POLPERRO

Blue Peter Inn
The Quay

⚙ 11-11; 12-10.30 Sun
☎ (01503) 272743

St Austell Tinners, HSD; Sharp's Doom Bar; guest beer Ⓗ

Named after a naval flag, this friendly, small, dimly-lit pub on the coastal path is reached by steps up from the harbour. Originally two fisherman's cottages, it has bare boards and interesting corners, and boasts the only sea view from a pub in town. It stocks Haye Farm cider, and a second guest ale appears in summer; the pub tends to support local breweries. Live music is performed Sat eve and lunchtime. No food, but you may take in your own sandwiches. 🏮🍽️🐾🌸

REDRUTH

Tricky Dickie's
Tolgus Mount (signed NW off old Redruth bypass, A3047) OS686427

⚙ 11-3, 6-11; 11-11 Fri & Sat; 12-10.30 Sun
☎ (01209) 219292 website: www.trickydickies.co.uk

Sharp's Own; guest beer Ⓗ

Imaginatively converted former tin mine smithy with a lively atmosphere. One large bar is partitioned into areas, with a small no-smoking room behind the bar. Good value fresh food and a varied selection of wines complement the beers, which include a second Sharp's brew. A partly-covered patio is used for barbecues in summer. The accommodation block is across the car park from the bar, and there is a squash court and fitness centre next door. It hosts jazz (Tue) and other music Thu eve (late licence). Children are welcome. 🌸🚌🍺🅿️✗

ST AGNES

Driftwood Spars Hotel
Trevaunance Cove

⚙ 11-11 (midnight Fri & Sat); 12-10.30 Sun
☎ (01872) 552428 website: www.driftwoodspars.com

Draught Bass; Driftwood Cuckoo Ale; St Austell HSD; Sharp's Own; Tetley Bitter; guest beers Ⓗ

Former 17th-century mine warehouse and sail loft, now a fine family-run hotel with a micro-brewery. Built of granite, slate and enormous ships' spars, the three-bar

interior, with beamed ceilings, leaded light windows and granite fireplaces, is cosy and atmospheric. Just off the seashore, the nautical decor features a fine collection of ships' clocks and a 'wreckers' tunnel. Popular with locals and tourists, it enjoys easy access for surfing and cliff walks. An extensive menu offers excellent meals. Weekend entertainment includes live theatre and music. 🏮Q🐾🌸🍺🍽️🅿️

ST AUSTELL

Western Inn
West Hill

⚙ 12-3, 5-11; 12-11 Sat; 12-10.30 Sun
☎ (01726) 72797

St Austell Tinners, HSD, seasonal beers Ⓗ

This property was obtained by St Austell Brewery when it acquired six pubs from the Treluswell Brewing Company of Penryn in 1943. Until the late 1960s it was a classic pub with many back rooms and a snug; the present layout consists of a single bar, with a dining area at one end, and a raised platform at the other for games, including pool and darts. The bar counter and pews were obtained from a chapel in Lostwithiel. 🏮🌸🍺🍽️🐾

ST IVES

Western Hotel ←
Gabriel Steet

⚙ 11-11; 12-10.30 Sun
☎ (01736) 795277

St Austell Tribute, HSD, seasonal beer Ⓗ

Town-centre granite hotel with two cosy real ale bars: the Kettle & Wink below pavement level effectively functions as the 'public', favoured by locals, while the upstairs saloon opens in summer and at busy holiday weekends. A fourth real ale from St Austell appears during summer. This is the town's main venue for live entertainment, especially jazz and folk music. No food eves except the Sunday carvery (6-8). 🏮Q🐾🍺🍽️👣🌸🐾

ST JUST-IN-PENWITH

Star Inn
1 Fore Street

⚙ 11-11; 12-10.30 Sun
☎ (01736) 788767

INN BRIEF

RESTRONGUET CREEK

Pandora Inn
End of Restronguet Hill
12-2.30, 7-11 (11-11 summer); 12 (11 summer)-11 Sat; 12-10.30 Sun

Draught Bass; St Austell IPA, Tinners, Tribute, HSD Ⓗ

13th-century thatched waterside pub – accessible by both road and water. Snacks in the bar, à la carte restaurant upstairs.

ST EWE

Crown Inn
12-2.30, 6-11; 12-2.30, 7-10.30 Sun

St Austell Tinners, HSD, seasonal beer Ⓗ

Unspoilt pub in a pretty Cornish village with slate-flagged floors and a restaurant on an upper level. *Cask Marque* accredited.

STICKER

Hewas Inn
Fore Street
11-3, 6-11; 12-10.30 Sun

St Austell IPA, Tinners, Tribute Ⓗ

Large village pub, popular with locals and visitors. Good food is well priced; children welcome. *Cask Marque* accredited.

STRATTON

King's Arms
Maiden Street
12-2.30, 6.30-11; 12-11 Fri & Sat; 12-10.30 Sun

Exmoor Ale; Sharp's Doom Bar, Own; guest beers Ⓗ

Slate-flagged, 17th-century coaching inn, in an ancient market town, stocking two guest ales, plus a draught cider in summer.

TRURO

Rising Sun
Mitchell Hill
12-2.30, 5-11; 11-11 Sat; 12-3, 7-10.30 Sun

Draught Bass; Ⓗ **Boddingtons Bitter;** Ⓟ **Sharp's Doom Bar,** Ⓗ **Own; guest beer** Ⓖ

Local on the edge of the city centre, 10 minutes' walk from shops and buses. No food Sun eve.

> ❋ symbol next to a main entry place name indicates there are Inn Brief entries as well.

St Austell XXXX Mild, ⒽTinners, ⒼTribute, Ⓗ
HSD, Ⓖseasonal beers Ⓗ

Popular, 18th-century granite inn, a reputed
lodging of John Wesley. The beamed,
atmospheric bar is full of interest, recalling a
long association with tin mining; it is
comfortable, with an open fire, slate floor
and varying styles of wooden seating.
Centre of the local folk music scene,
reflecting the character of the area,
singalongs are guaranteed most eves;
traditional games also thrive. Food is
limited to substantial bar snacks. In this
drinkers' pub, local tipplers will always
provide a yarn or two.
🏚Q☮🛏◖◗🅰♣♠

ST MABYN

St Mabyn Inn
Churchtown
✪ 11-3, 5-11; 12-3, 6-10.30 Sun
☎ (01208) 841266
Draught Bass; John Smith's Bitter; guest beer Ⓗ

Attractive, 15th-century village pub next to
the church, with friendly locals and a huge
welcoming log fire in winter. The pub is
very much central to community life, and
the guest ale usually comes from one of the
Cornish brewers. The pub is known for
good food, and provides a wide range of
meals, freshly cooked from local produce.
🏚Q☮◖◗🖵♣P

ST TUDY

Cornish Arms
✪ 12-3, 6.30-11; 12-4, 7-10.30 Sun
☎ (01208) 850656
Draught Bass; St Austell XXXX Mild; guest beer
(summer) Ⓗ

16th-century village pub with beamed
ceilings and a classic slate floor in the bar. It
has a games area and several other rooms,
including a restaurant where an imaginative
menu uses local produce. Bar meals and

takeaways are also available. The guest beer
is restricted to an occasional summer
offering. The pub is family-friendly, having
a tailor-made children's room and a large
garden.
Q🛏🕸◖◗♿♣♠P🖵

SPARNON GATE

Cornish Arms
Near Redruth, on old Portreath road
✪ 12-3, 6-11; 12-3, 7-10.30 Sun
☎ (01209) 216407
Sharp's Doom Bar, ⒼOwn; Ⓗ guest beer
(occasional) Ⓖ

Friendly, out-of-town local in the old
tradition, on the original Portreath road
from Redruth. Its location in the former
mining district is commemorated by old tin
and copper mining artefacts and pictures.
Of the two bars, the larger is favoured by
the locals eves, with a welcoming fire in
winter. The guest beer appears
intermittently, during the summer. Both
the beer and the home-cooked food
represent excellent value; meals are
prepared by the landlady. It fields a keen
euchre team.
🏚Q🕸◖◗♣P

STITHIANS

Seven Stars Inn
Church Road
✪ 12-2 (2.30 summer), 7 (6 Fri)-11; 11-11 Sat; 12-3,
7-10.30 Sun
☎ (01209) 860003
Sharp's Doom Bar or Skinner's Betty Stogs Bitter;
guest beers Ⓗ

Lively village local used by a good cross-
section of the community, where euchre is
enthusiastically played (league match night
is Thu). One or two guest beers are regularly
varied by the landlord while occasional
mini-beer festivals feature up to 12 ales not
normally found in Cornwall. The original

The Maypole

All bars are snug places, but the Maypole's was the very
snuggest, cosiest, and completest bar, that ever the wit of man
devised. Such amazing bottles in old oaken pigeon-holes; such
gleaming tankards dangling from pegs at about the same
inclination as thirsty men would hold them to their lips; such
sturdy little Dutch kegs ranged in rows on shelves;...such
closets, such presses, such drawers full of pipes, such places for
putting away in hollow window-seats, all crammed to the
throat with eatables, drinkables, or savoury condiments; lastly,
and to crown all, as typical of the immense resources of the
establishment, and its defiance to all visitors to cut and come
again, such a stupendous cheese.

Charles Dickens, *Barnaby Rudge,* 1841. The model for the
Maypole is the King's Head, Chigwell, Essex.

bar and lounge have been opened out to form one drinking area, while a more modern extension houses the pool table. Good bus services (including eves) run to local towns. ⚌Q❀◐♣

TREBELLAN

Smugglers' Den Inn
Off A3075 towards Cubert then signed
✪ 12-2.30 (not winter Mon-Wed), 6-11 (11-11 summer); 12-10.30 Sun
☎ (01637) 830209
website: www.smugglers-den-inn.co.uk
Beer range varies Ⓗ/Ⓖ
Tucked down a steep narrow lane, this 40-year-old thatched inn boasts an Elizabethan courtyard, as well as a garden. The popular no-smoking restaurant serves daily specials. The large fireplace is a popular focal point in the winter. The friendly owners offer a varying range of ales, with mainstays from St Austell, Skinner's and Sharp's; Callestick Farm cider is available in summer. An Ale and Pie Festival is becoming a regular feature every April. ⚌☕❀◐Å♣P

TRURO ✳

City Inn
Pydar Street (B3284, Perranporth road)
✪ 11-11; 12-10.30 Sun
☎ (01872) 272623
Courage Best Bitter; Sharp's Doom Bar; Skinner's Betty Stogs Bitter; guest beer Ⓗ
This busy two-bar community pub, away from the shopping centre, is popular with local residents. The Skinner's ales are regularly varied as is the guest beer; Haye Farm cider is also usually on offer under gravity dispense. The comfortable lounge has several drinking corners and sports a collection of water jugs, while the public bar is more spartan and games-oriented. The large garden is a suntrap. The pub is about 10 minutes' walk from the main bus services, and 15 minutes from the station. ❀☕◐ᵇ⇌♣●

TYWARDREATH

New Inn
Fore Street
✪ 12-4, 6-11; 12-4, 7-10.30 Sun
☎ (01726) 813901
Draught Bass; Ⓖ **St Austell Tinners, Tribute,** Ⓗ **seasonal beer** (summer) Ⓖ
This classic local has featured in every edition of this *Guide*, and is the hub of village life. Many functions are held in the large, secluded garden. The building dates from 1752 and was originally owned by the Rashleigh family; St Austell Brewery acquired it in 1932. The unusual situation of Draught Bass being sold in a St Austell house has been a right for many years. There is a games/children's room. Snacks are available at most times. Parking is limited. ⚌Q☕❀☕ᵇÅ⇌ (Par) ♣●P

WENDRON

New Inn
On B3297 Helston-Redruth road
✪ 12-3, 7 (6 Fri & Sat)-11 (11-11 summer); 12-3, 7-10.30)12-10.30 summer) Sun
☎ (01326) 572683

Draught Bass; Skinner's Cornish Knocker; guest beers Ⓗ
Stone country pub on the main Redruth–Helston road, with two bars displaying fine collection of brassware; the back bar doubles as a restaurant. The licensees are keen real ale fans and vary the choice of two guest beers regularly, although the Bass and Cornish Knocker are likely to remain fixtures. Food includes daily 'specials', with a roast lunch on Sun. Summer opening starts at Easter. Bus service T34 passes the door and connects with trains at Redruth.
Q◐P

WIDEMOUTH BAY

Bay View Inn
Marine Drive
✪ 11-3, 6-11 (11-11 summer); 12-3, 6-10.30 (12-10.30 summer) Sun
☎ (01288) 361273
Sharp's Doom Bar, Own; guest beers Ⓗ
This small, friendly pub enjoys a lovely position, providing unrivalled views over a popular surfing beach and the bay. The interior is being covered by a growing collection of beer mats, pumpclips and bar towels, not to mention the frogs. A house beer, Kitch's Klassic is brewed by Skinner's, and is named after the owner, while the single guest ale increases to two during the summer. ☕❀☕◐Å♣P

WILCOVE

Wilcove Inn
Off A374, 2 miles from Torpoint Ferry
✪ 12-3, 6.30-11 (may vary summer); 12-10.30 Sun
☎ (01752) 812381
Draught Bass; guest beer (summer) Ⓗ
Traditional, friendly, country village pub, tucked away beside a secluded creek off the River Tamar. The guest beer is usually local. Children are welcome at this community-oriented pub that supports pool and darts teams and hosts an annual regatta centred around a canoe race. On fine days, enjoy the palm trees in the garden and river views. The pub is handy for woodland walks around nearby Anthony House. Beware, though, the spring tides that flood the road and car park at times.
⚌☕❀◐♣P

ZELAH

Hawkins Arms
High Road (off A30)
✪ 11-3, 6-11; 12-4, 7-10.30 Sun
☎ (01872) 540339
Draught Bass; Tetley Bitter; guest beers Ⓗ
Although alphabetically the last recommendation in the county, this unspoilt village pub should be first on your list for good quality real ale complemented by a varied menu and a few rooms available for B&B. The guest beers constantly change while local brewery, Skinner's, produces a special blend called Old Zelah Mist. The Bass and Weston's Old Rosie cider are served straight from the cask, although handpumps display their clips. Easy access, just off the main A30, makes this village pub an ideal halt while touring the area.
⚌Q☕❀☕◐⬤♣●Pᵀ

CUMBRIA

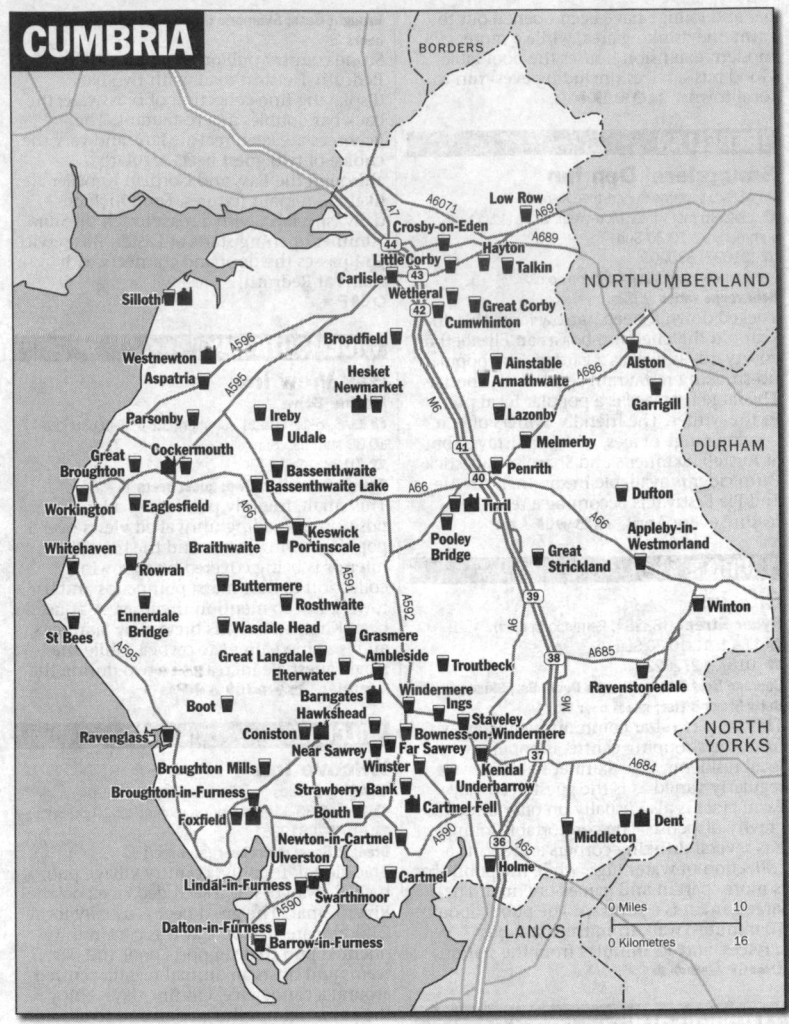

AINSTABLE

New Crown Inn

⊕ 12-2 (not Mon-Thu), 6-11; 12-2, 6-10.30 Sun
☎ (01768) 896273 website: www.newcrowninn.co.uk
Tetley Bitter; guest beers Ⓗ

Located above the Eden Valley, the pub dates back to around 1700. Originally a drovers' inn with attached stables, over the years several alterations have been made to the building, with the stables becoming the kitchen and a cottage becoming the dining room. There is a fine oak bar, with a slate floor and a wood-burning stove in the public area. Opposite the pub is the Millennium Green. ♨Q✿☎⊨◑&♣P

ALSTON

Angel Inn

Front Street
⊕ 11-4, 7-11 (closed Tue eve); 12-3, 7-10.30 Sun
☎ (01434) 381363
Boddingtons Bitter; Flowers IPA Ⓗ

Alston's Town Hall until the late 1800s, when a new building was opened, it was soon converted into a pub serving miners and the many people who visit this, the highest market town in England. It enjoys the support of the local community, and fields a successful darts team. Sympathetically modernised, it provides three distinct areas: the main one has a large open fire which is lit on cool summer's days if needed. It is convenient for visiting the narrow gauge railway or walking the Pennines. ♨✿⊨◑♣P

AMBLESIDE

Golden Rule

Smithy Brow
⊕ 11-11; 12-10.30 Sun
☎ (015394) 32257
Robinson's Hatters Mild, Hartleys XB, Best Bitter, Frederics, seasonal beers Ⓗ

Traditional pub in all respects – no juke box, piped music, pool or meals – just conversation, plus well-filled butties and pork pies. The bar area connects three other rooms, all displaying interesting pictures and trophies. One room has darts and a quiet games machine; another, down a couple of steps, has an Internet facility in a cubicle; the rear room has a TV. A sheltered rear patio acts as a suntrap in summer. Start the Fairfield Horseshoe walk here, or even better, aim for the finish. ⚐Q☭♣

Queen's Hotel
Market Place
☼ 11-11; 12-10.30 Sun
☎ (015394) 32206
Jennings Bitter; Tetley Bitter; guest beers Ⓗ

Central hotel in a popular Lake District location. The accent here is on the quality and variety of the guest beers, sourced from near and far. As a result, it attracts a regular following of locals and visiting real ale enthusiasts. Food is served all day; there is a dining room and an à la carte restaurant open eves (both no-smoking). The (no-smoking) cellar area houses a pool table and various alcoves. The patio at the rear is sheltered by a large tree, but beware of the birds. ⚐☭⚑◑⚊●

ARMATHWAITE

Fox & Pheasant
☼ 12-3, 6-11; 12-11 Sat; 12-11 Sun
☎ (016974) 72400
e-mail: fox.pheasant@dial.pipex.com
Jennings Mild, Bitter, Sneck Lifter; guest beers Ⓗ

Close to the River Eden, this former coaching inn, with attached stables, was originally the Red Lion Hotel. The stables have been converted into a bar area, preserving the old stalls which now act as seating dividers. There are three main rooms with two bars, linked to the original hotel. The public bar area, with a sandstone-flagged floor, a fine stone fireplace and exposed beams, displays old pictures of the hotel. Excellent food is served (booking advisable at weekends). ⚐Q☭◑⚑⚊♣P●

BARROW-IN-FURNESS

Cross Keys
Preston Street (behind Debenham's)
☼ 11-11; 12-10.30 Sun
☎ (01229) 828447
Barngates Tag Lag; Theakston Best Bitter, Cool Cask; guest beer Ⓗ

This lively, popular oasis of cask beer in a nitro-keg desert is a magnet for those seeking a guest beer in the neighbourhood. It can be noisy and very busy at weekends and on games nights. The public bar and lounge are served from one central bar (due to undergo considerable alteration at the time of survey). ⚑☭⚊♣

BASSENTHWAITE

Sun Inn
Turn off A591 by Castle Inn, signed Bassenthwaite Village
☼ 12-3 (not winter), 6-11 (12-11 summer Sat); 12 (6 winter)-10.30 Sun
☎ (017687) 70252
Jennings Mild, Bitter, Cumberland Ale, Sneck Lifter Ⓗ

Comfortable, large, single-bar inn situated between Skiddaw and Bassenthwaite Lake, well worth a detour from the main road. It offers an excellent range of Jennings beers. The pub has recently been refurbished and has full wheelchair access (including WC).

The Penrith–Workington bus stops at the lane end, about half a mile away, every two hours. Pool and darts are played. ⚐◑☭P●

BASSENTHWAITE LAKE

Pheasant
Just off A66, at W end of lake
☼ 11-2.30, 5.30-10.30; 12-2.30, 6-10.30 Sun
☎ (017687) 76234 website: www.the_pheasant.co.uk
Draught Bass; Jennings Cumberland Ale; Theakston Best Bitter Ⓗ

Lovely old coaching inn, surrounded by 60 acres of gardens and natural woodlands. The public bar has remained unchanged for many years; successive coats of varnish on the walls have culminated in an antique brown glow. The gardens are a joy to sit in on a hot summer's day, and just far enough off the A66 to escape noise pollution. This bar is a must for all visitors to the northern lakes, but children are not welcome in the public bar. The Penrith–Workington bus stops nearby. Q☭⚑◑P●

BOOT

Brook House Inn
½ mile from R&ER terminus OS176008
☼ 11-11; 12-10.30 Sun
☎ (019467) 23288 website: www.brookhouseinn.co.uk
Taylor Landlord; Theakston Best Bitter; guest beers Ⓗ

Family-run free house where the guest beers are mainly from Cumbrian breweries. The bar is comfortable and friendly, with the welcoming log-burning stove lit in winter. A no-smoking room has a children's certificate. A small patio drinking area extends to the front and side of the pub. Eskdale is a popular tourist destination, with beautiful scenery, and the remains of Roman Hardknott Fort just up the road. The restaurant opens eves, but food is served all day. ⚐Q☜☭⚑◑À⚞(Dalegarth R&ER) ♣P⚊

Burnmoor Inn
¾ mile from R&ER terminus OS176011
☼ 11-11; 12-10.30 Sun
☎ (019467) 23224 website: www.burnmoor.co.uk
Black Sheep Best Bitter; Jennings Bitter, Cumberland Ale Ⓗ

This nine-bedroomed inn dates from 1578. Meals are served in the bar or garden all day and eves in the restaurant; the menu includes some Cumbrian specialities. The large garden houses a children's mini-assault course. The guest beer comes from Barngates. All rooms are en-suite and two two-bedroomed self-catering cottages are available in the village, opposite the inn,

INDEPENDENT BREWERIES

Barngates Barngates
Coniston Coniston
Dent Dent
Derwent Silloth
Foxfield Foxfield
Hesket Newmarket Hesket Newmarket
Jennings Cockermouth
Strawberry Bank Cartmel Fell
Tirril Tirril
Yates Westnewton

which is situated near a working watermill in a picturesque valley.
🏚Q🏵🚲❀◐ Å⇌ (Dalegarth R&ER) ♣P

BOUTH

White Hart Inn
Off A590, 6 miles NE of Ulverston
🕐 12-2, 6-11; 12-11 Sat; 12-10.30 Sun
☎ (01229) 861229 website: www.whitehartbouth.co.uk
Black Sheep Best Bitter; Boddingtons Bitter; Jennings Cumberland Ale; Tetley Bitter; guest beers 🅷
Beamed country village inn on the edge of the Lake District, five miles from the centre of Grizedale Forest with its good walking routes. The village often wins *Best Kept Village* awards and boasts a good play area on the green. The pub displays old Lakeland photos and paintings and hunting memorabilia. It has a games room, an upstairs dining room and a patio that gets very busy in summer with diners, drinkers and families. A good choice of food offers good value. A mild or a dark beer often features in the excellent range of guest beers. 🏚Q☸🏵🚲◐Å♣P

BOWNESS-ON-WINDERMERE

Village Inn
Lake Road
🕐 11-11; 12-10.30 Sun
☎ (015394) 43731 e-mail: villageinns@hotmail.com
Black Sheep Best Bitter; Boddingtons Bitter; Castle Eden Ale; Jennings Cumberland Ale; guest beers 🅷
At the centre of a very popular Lakeside holiday resort, this is a lively pub with games machines, TV and bar meals at one end, plus a restaurant at the other (same menu but served until 10pm). Built as the manse to the parish church opposite, it later became the St Martins Hotel. It now offers a welcome choice of guest beers, often from local micros, in a location largely dominated by brewery tied outlets. The paved patio is an ideal spot for watching the

world go by; the piers for steamer trips on Windermere are nearby.
🏵◐&P

BRAITHWAITE

Coledale Inn
Above village, just off Whinlatter Road
🕐 11-11; 12-10.30 Sun
☎ (017687) 78272 website: www.s_h_systems.co.uk
Jennings Bitter; Theakston Best Bitter; Yates Bitter; guest beer (summer) 🅷
Busy country inn near to the beautiful Newlands Valley. Built in 1824, as a wool mill, it then became a pencil mill. Nearby is an extremely popular camping and caravan site from which the bar draws a healthy trade. The Georgian bar in the Coledale dates from 1824, and the Victorian bar from 1899. It is now the sole outlet for the superb Yates Bitter in the Keswick area, but note that the four real ales are spread between the two bars. The Penrith-Workington bus stops in the village every two hours.
🏚☸🚲◐🍴Å♣P✄

BROADFIELD

Crown Inn
4 miles S of Carlisle Racecourse
🕐 12-3 (not Tue), 6.30-11; 12-3, 7-10.30 Sun
☎ (016974) 73467
Theakston Best Bitter; guest beer 🅷
Although only six miles outside Carlisle, this is a true country community pub, in the midst of rural Cumbria. It has been recently extended to provide restaurant meals of excellent quality; bar food is of the same high quality and a friendly welcome is assured. Eve meals are only served in the restaurant and must be booked in advance. The pub has a small patio for summer drinking.
🏚Q🏵🚲◐&P

INN BRIEF

APPLEBY-IN-WESTMORLAND
Golden Ball
4 High Weind
12-11;
12-10.30 Sun
Jennings Bitter; Cumberland Ale 🅷
An endangered species – the unspoilt 'back-street boozer': two rooms and a central servery, with a quiet juke box in the bar.

ASPATRIA
Fox & Hounds
King Street
11-11;
12-10.30 Sun
Jennings Mild, Bitter 🅷
Busy community pub in a building dating back to the 1800s. The mild is always available.

BROUGHTON MILLS
Blacksmith's Arms ☆
11-11;
11-10.30 Sun
Jennings Bitter, Cumberland Ale; guest beers 🅷
Unspoilt pub: a tiny bar with a real fire and three other rooms, serving a large selection of bottled beers, plus cider in summer.

CARLISLE
Woodrow Wilson
48 Botchergate
11-11; 12-10.30 Sun
Derwent Bitter; Shepherd Neame Spitfire; Theakston Best Bitter; Thwaites Mild; guest beers 🅷
Wetherspoon's pub in a former Co-op, five minutes' walk from the station, offering the biggest range of real ales in Carslisle. *Cask Marque* accredited.

EAGLESFIELD
Black Cock
8 (7 Sat & summer-11); 7-11 Sun
Jennings Bitter 🅷
The village local has remained unchanged for many years; real beams, oak panels and gleaming brassware make it worth seeking out. West Cumbria *Pub of the Season* summer 2001.

HAWKSHEAD
King's Arms Hotel
The Square
11-11; 12-10.30 Sun
Black Sheep Best Bitter; Coniston Bluebird; Tetley Bitter; guest beers 🅷
Traditional pub in a typical Lakeland village with oak beams, an open fire and an unusual collection of glasses.

HOLME
Smithy Inn
Milnthorpe Road
11-2.30 (may extend), 6-11; 11-11 Sat; 12-10.30 Sun
Thwaites Bitter, Daniel's Hammer 🅷
Well-appointed, village-centre pub with a spacious bar area and a dining section. A good garden houses play equipment.

KENDAL
Ring o'Bells
39 Kirkland
12-3 (may vary Tue), 6-11; 12-3, 7-10.30 Sun
Draught Bass; Tetley Bitter; Worthington Bitter; guest beer 🅷
Standing on consecrated ground, this cosy pub has a tiny snug next to the front bar. Good value meals are served in the rear lounge.

LAZONBY
Joiners Arms
12-3.30, 7-11;
12-3.30, 7-10.30 Sun
Boddingtons Bitter; guest beers 🅷
Close to the Settle and Carlisle Railway, this friendly local enjoys a cosy atmosphere.

BROUGHTON-IN-FURNESS

Manor Arms
The Square
☼ 12-11; 12-10.30 Sun
☎ (01229) 716286
Coniston Bluebird; Taylor Landlord; Yates Bitter; guest beers Ⓗ

At the centre of local life, this free house stocks up to seven real ales at any one time, plus a range of continental bottled beers and Liefmans Kriek on tap; cider is occasionally available. Large enough to boast a games room for darts and pool, the pub still provides intimacy by virtue of its three sectional layout. The atmosphere is enhanced by original features such as the 18th-century fire basket that is put to good use in winter. ♨Q⇘⊲◑♣♠☗

BUTTERMERE

Bridge Hotel
On B5289
☼ 10-11; 12-10.30 Sun
☎ (017687) 70252 website: www. bridge-hotel.com
Black Sheep Best Bitter; Flowers IPA; Theakston Old Peculier Ⓗ

Popular walkers' pub in a village, nestling in a valley between Crummock Water and Buttermere. Both the bar areas afford views out over the fells. The original building dates back to the 18th century. It can be very busy in summer but is well worth a visit. A circular bus service from Keswick runs four times a day in each direction during the summer season. Q⇘⊲◑P

CARLISLE ❊

Carlisle Rugby Club
Warwick Road (A69, by Carlisle United FC ground)
☼ 7 (5.30 Fri; 6 Sat)-11 (1-11 Sat in football season); 12-3, 7-10.30 Sun
☎ (01228) 521300
Tetley Bitter; Yates Bitter; guest beer Ⓗ

Stalwart supporter of real ale, Carlisle Rugby Club was formed in 1873, kicking-off straight into the record books – the club's first match was against Langholm and is claimed to be the earliest international club fixture. It has become an annual New Year's Day event. The present clubhouse was opened in 1959, and has had a number of international players. Its cosy lounge and large bar often becomes crowded when neighbours Carlisle Utd are at home. Show this *Guide* or CAMRA membership card to be signed in. ♨⚲❀♣P

Gosling Bridge
Kingstown Road (A7, 3 miles N of centre)
☼ 11-11; 12-10.30 Sun
☎ (01228) 515294
Marston's Pedigree; Theakston Best Bitter; guest beers Ⓗ

Modern pub, on the road to Scotland, that has established a strong following from local residents who appreciate the ever-changing guest ales. It serves meals all day and is a very popular stopping-off point for people travelling through town to have a meal in the very light, airy and pleasant dining areas. There is plenty of outdoor seating. It won local CAMRA's spring 2001 *Pub of the Season* award.
♨❀⇘⊲◑P⅌

Howard Arms
107 Lowther Street (next to Lanes shopping centre)
☼ 11-11; 12-3, 7-10.30 Sun
☎ (01228) 532926
Theakston Best Bitter, Cool Cask; Ⓗ

This popular, city-centre pub, with several small rooms, is a regular *Guide* entry. Like all Carlisle pubs over 30 years old, the Howard Arms is an ex-State Management Scheme pub, and has changed little in character since those days. The city's late-lamented theatre stood opposite the pub, which boasted Charlie Chaplin, Laurel and Hardy and other music hall legends among its customers. Old photos and posters on the walls are reminders of its theatrical links. Note the superb tiled exterior. No food Sun. ❀⊲≢

Near Boot
Whiteclosegate (B6264, 1½ miles NE of centre)
☼ 11-11; 12-10.30 Sun
☎ (01228) 529547
Theakston Best Bitter; guest beers Ⓗ

Friendly, 18th-century coaching inn whose unusual name derives from the near-side boot when riding out of Carlisle. The inn was redesigned by Carlisle State Brewery architect, Harry Redfern. Alas the bowling green is now only used as a garden, but it affords excellent views over the city and the Caldbeck Fells. Internally, the pub is due for refurbishment into one room; check before travelling in case of temporary closure. The guest beers often feature Cumbrian breweries. Bus service 84 from the city-centre bus station stops nearby.
♨❀⊲◑⊟♣P

CARTMEL

King's Arms
The Square
☼ 11-11; 12-10.30 Sun
☎ (015395) 36220
Beer range varies Ⓗ

Cartmel is one of south Lakeland's oldest villages, with a monastic history dating back to 1188. Occupying an unrivalled position in the old market square, the King's Arms boasts a cobbled beer garden and a riverside dining room, with views of the 12th-century priory across the River Eea. The bar serves several spacious drinking areas which are distinct but not completely separate. They are cosy and inviting, but not isolated from the ambience of this often busy, traditional inn. Cider is stocked in summer. ♨⚲❀⊲◑♣♠

COCKERMOUTH

Bitter End
15 Kirkgate (off market place)
☼ 12-2.30 (11.30-3 Fri & Sat), 6-11 (11-11 summer Sat); 12-3, 7-10.30 Sun
☎ (01900) 828993 website: www.bitterend.co.uk
Jennings Bitter, Cumberland Ale, seasonal beers; Yates Bitter; guest beers Ⓗ

Within 50 yards of two big car parks, this pub won an award from the local Civic Trust for its renovation. It is next door to the Kirkgate Centre which stages films, plays and exhibitions. Cumbria CAMRA *Pub of the Year* 2000 and local 1999 and 2000 award winner, it also offers some 20 foreign bottled beers. It supports the local mountain rescue team, serving a special Call Out bitter in 2000 to raise funds. Children are welcome. 🏚◖▲●

Bush Hotel
Main Street
☼ 11-11; 12-10.30 Sun
☎ (01900) 822064
Jennings Bitter, Cumberland Ale, Sneck Lifter, seasonal beers; guest beers Ⓗ

Friendly pub right in the town centre. Late 18th century in origin, with exposed beams in the front bar, it has an open fire in each of the two bars. It stocks the fullest range of Jennings beers in town. There is ample parking 75 yards away in Lowther Went. Tue is public quiz night. Walkers note that soup and sandwiches are available in the afternoons from 2.30–6; Home-cooked lunches are served 12–2 daily.
🏚◖▲●

CONISTON

Sun Inn
Up the hill from the bridge
☼ 11-11; 12-10.30 Sun
☎ (015394) 41248
website: www.smoothhound.co.uk/hotel/sun
Black Sheep Best Bitter; Coniston Bluebird; Moorhouses Black Cat; guest beers Ⓗ

This inn is over 400 years old and continuing work is revealing many original features, including flagged floors, a beamed ceiling and a beautiful old range in the fireplace. A single bar serves three drinking areas, each with its own distinctive appeal. The hotel was added in 1902 to overlook the surrounding countryside and spectacular mountains; the east-facing restaurant affords views over the village and beyond to the lake and Yewdale Crags. Donald Campbell stayed here during his later attempts at the water speed record. At the junction of three footpaths, including the Walna Scar road, the Sun Inn is an ideal halt for scenic walks.
🏚❀⌂◖▲♣P✂

CROSBY-ON-EDEN

Stag Inn
Off A689, E of Carlisle
☼ 12-3, 6-11; 12-3, 6.30-10.30 Sun
☎ (01228) 573210
Jennings Mild, Bitter, Cumberland Ale, Sneck Lifter Ⓗ

Renowned locally for its good food, this pub is at the centre of what is now a peaceful village, due to a bypass having been built. Four small rooms off a central bar area provide a variety of different atmospheres; of note are the low-beamed ceilings and stone-flagged floors. Upstairs is a spacious restaurant, serving a full à la carte menu. On a warm day, enjoy a drink in the beer garden with views of the distant Pennines.
❀◖♣P

CUMWHINTON

Lowther Arms
Off A6, S of Carlisle
☼ 12-2, 5.30-11; 12-11 Sat; 12-3, 6-10.30 Sun
☎ (01228) 560905
Jennings Cumberland Ale Ⓗ

Ex-State Management pub, on the edge of the village, it is the only surviving pub out of three that once served the village. A small terraced outdoor drinking area leads to the car park which used to be an orchard. The pub was extended during 1998/99 and good use was made of the local stone inside to blend the original part of the pub with the new area. Popular with all ages, it offers good value meals. Note the large Jennings Brewery mirror.
❀⌂◖ﾟ♣P

DALTON-IN-FURNESS

Black Dog Inn
Holmes Green, Broughton Road (follow signs for Wildlife Park, 1/2 mile further on) OS233761
☼ 5 (11 Wed-Sat)-11; 12-10.30 Sun
☎ (01229) 462561
e-mail: jack@blackdoginn.freeserve.co.uk
Beer range varies Ⓗ

After standing neglected for years, this pub has become an established member of the Furness real ale scene. Local CAMRA *Pub of the Year* 1998/99, it has won various other awards. With at least six ales and up to six ciders/perries to choose from, this snug country local offers accommodation for walkers and tourists. A central bar serves the split-level interior that boasts exposed beams and tiled floors; the no-smoking family room doubles as a meeting room. Outside the pub has two seating areas, one by a small stream. The menu features local lobster, rabbit and sausages.
🏚Q🐾❀⌂◖♣●P✂🛏

Red Lion
5 Market Street
☼ 7 (12 Fri & Sat)-11; 12-10.30 Sun
☎ (01229) 467914
website: www.dalton-in-furness.org.uk/red-lion
Coniston Bluebird; guest beers Ⓗ

This low-ceilinged, double-fronted pub is on the main road, down the hill from Dalton Castle. Dating from 1647, the pub combines a handy town local, with a country pub feel, enhanced by the black wood beams and huge fireplace. Local beers take pride of place on the single bar serving the main room and the games area at the rear. The 42-seat restaurant doubles as a function room. Very popular at weekends, it can also get busy midweek.
🏚❀⌂◖≋♣♠

DENT

Sun Inn
Main Street
☼ 11-2.30, 7-11; 11-11 Sat & summer, 12-10.30 Sun
☎ (015396) 25208
Dent Bitter, T'Owd Tup, Kamikaze, seasonal beer Ⓗ

Superb example of an unspoilt pub in a picturesque Dales village. The whitewashed frontage on to the cobbled street is popular with photographers and artists. Inside, the traditional decor exudes real atmosphere. A side room is for non-smokers and the games room has a juke box, pool, etc. The Dent Brewery is a couple of miles along the valley towards Dent Station. Note: opening hours may be restricted in winter. The George & Dragon, only a step away, also Dent-owned, is usually open if the Sun is closed.
🏚Q❀⌂◖▲♣P✂

DUFTON

Stag Inn

☻ 12-3 (not winter Mon), 6-11; 12-11 Sat & summer; 12-10.30 Sun
☎ (017683) 51608

Black Sheep Best Bitter; Castle Eden Ale; Flowers IPA (summer)**; guest beers** Ⓗ

Note: the front door opens outwards! Once inside, this Pennine village pub, expanded from the original 'front room' drinking house, has a bar area with country pursuits decor, a fully operational kitchen range and a section for dining. Another bar (families welcome) to the right overlooks the rear garden. It acts as a centre for the lively social life of the community and a welcome stopping-off point for thirsty Pennine Way walkers. ▲Q❀⇔◑▲♣P

ELTERWATER

Britannia Inn

☻ 11-11; 12-10.30 Sun
☎ (015394) 37201 website: www.britinn.co.uk

Coniston Bluebird; Dent Aviator; Jennings Bitter; guest beers Ⓗ

Popular pub in an area of outstanding natural beauty. The bar area has plenty of tables and benches. The no-smoking dining room (booking advised eves) and back room are reached via a lobby with a rocking chair. No loudspeakers, pool, TV or machines will be found in this interesting old building. A multi-level paved patio overlooks the village green – often pressed into service as an overspill drinking area. An afternoon snack menu and guest beers from less well-known breweries complete the picture.
▲Q❀⇔◑▲

ENNERDALE BRIDGE

Shepherds Arms

Ennerdale Bridge

☻ 11-11; 12-10.30 Sun
☎ (01946) 861249
website: www.shepherdsarmshotel.co.uk

Courage Directors; Jennings Bitter; Theakston XB; guest beer Ⓗ

This inn has established a reputation for its beer and good food in five years under the aegis of the current landlord. Often busy in summer, as this small Lakeland village stands on Wainwright's Coast-to-Coast walk. Traditional live music is often performed at weekends out of season. A single bar serves the split-level room. The Cockermouth–Cleator Moor bus service runs through the village. ▲❀⇔◑▲P

FAR SAWREY

Claife Crier Bar (Sawrey Hotel)

On B5285, between Hawkshead and the ferry
☻ 11-11; 12-10.30 Sun
☎ (015394) 43425

Black Sheep Best Bitter; Jennings Cumberland Ale; Theakston Best Bitter Ⓗ

Characterful bar, named after the ghost of Claife Heights (a local hill) in a converted byre, complete with original features such as mangers and water troughs, it is not apparent at all from the drinkers' point of view that the bar is actually part of a large hotel, as prices are not inflated. The seating, in stalls once inhabited by cattle, provides privacy for small groups and adds to the overall character of a very distinctive pub. This quiet, intimate hostelry is well worth a visit.
Q⇔◑▣

FOXFIELD

Prince of Wales

(opp. station, on A595)
☻ 5 (12 Fri & Sat)-11; 12-10.30 Sun
☎ (01229) 716238

Beer range varies Ⓗ

Comfortable, friendly country pub. A dartboard and board games are available plus a good selection of general magazines for browsers. Home to Foxfield micro-brewery and main outlet for Tigertops beers, it offers a very varied rotation of guest beers; a mild is always available and it keeps a wide selection of bottled continental beers. Speciality beer weekends are arranged and themed mini beer festivals occur at regular intervals. A haven for serious beer sampling with a friendly, knowledgeable landlord.
▲Q⇔≠♣P▣

GARRIGILL

George & Dragon Inn

4 Miles S of Alston, off B6277
☻ 12-3, 7-11; 12-3, 7-10.30 Sun
☎ (01434) 381293 website: www.cumbria1st.com

Castle Eden Ale; Flowers IPA; Marston's Pedigree Ⓗ

The focal point of a small village high in the Pennines. Built in the 17th century as a coaching inn, it served the local lead and zinc mining community, but now welcomes visitors who are following the Pennine Way and Coast-to-Coast cycle and walking routes. The bar is notable for its large open fireplace which boasts a roaring log fire. Over the bar, the large original hinged cover has eight glass panels with very nice drawings depicting Ritson's *The Rights of the Dragon*. No meals Tue eve.
▲❀⇔◑♣

GRASMERE

Travellers Rest

1/2 mile N of village on A591
☻ 11-11; 12-10.30 Sun
☎ (015394) 35604 website: www.lakelandinns.com

Jennings Bitter, Cumberland Ale, Sneck Lifter; guest beer Ⓗ

The flagged bar area here may be small, but it sports a fine fire in winter. Up a few steps is a games room/lounge. To the right are two dining areas (one no-smoking) where good value meals are served – all day in summer. The patio commands splendid mountain views and even has a coin-operated telescope for greater detail. It is a popular stop on the nearby Coast-to-Coast walk. The King's Arms at Thirlspot (some six miles north) is in the same ownership and also worth a visit.
▲Q❀⇔◑♣P●

GREAT BROUGHTON

Punchbowl

19 Main Street (off A66)
☻ 11.30-4.30 (not Mon), 7-11; (11.30-11 summer); 12-5, 7-10.30 Sun
☎ (01900) 824708

85

Jennings Bitter; guest beers (summer) Ⓗ
The Punchbowl started as a small coaching inn in the 1600s and in more recent times was part of the Carlisle State Management Scheme. It is now owned by its licensees who continue to sell Jennings Bitter, supplemented by guest beers from Easter onwards. The tiny bar area is cosy, with beams, low ceiling and a real fire in winter. It is a thriving community pub, where visitors are always made welcome. A regular bus service through the village runs between Workington and Cockermouth until early eve.
🏰♣P

GREAT CORBY

Corby Bridge Inn
Off A69, E of Carlisle
✪ 12-11; 12-10.30 Sun
☎ (01228) 560221
Thwaites Mild, Bitter; guest beer Ⓗ
Grade II listed building, of architectural and historic significance, sited alongside the Carlisle–Newcastle railway line. Three open-plan rooms together provide a large area for functions and special gourmet food nights. No food is served Mon. Local CAMRA *Pub of the Season* 2000.
🏰Q❀🛏◑≠ (Wetheral) ♣P

GREAT LANGDALE

Old Dungeon Ghyll
✪ 11-11; 12-10.30 Sun
☎ (014394) 37272 website: www.odg.co.uk
Jennings Cumberland Ale; Theakston Cool Cask, Old Peculier; Yates Bitter; guest beers Ⓗ
Quintessential basic bar for climbers and walkers with its hard benches and floor: wet clothes steaming by the kitchen range, talk of mountain adventures and impromptu music-making are the norm here. A Black Sheep beer is stocked and soup is usually available, when the good honest mealtime pub grub is not. The adjacent hotel has a more formal bar for residents and diners (booking essential). The surrounding fells provide one of the most dramatic backdrops and impressive climbing routes in Lakeland.
🏰Q❀🛏◑▲♣♠PⒽ●

GREAT STRICKLAND

Strickland Arms
✪ 12-3 (not Wed), 6-11; 12-10.30 Sun
☎ (01931) 712238
Black Sheep Best Bitter; Greene King Old Speckled Hen; Ind Coope Burton Ale; Jennings Cumberland Ale; Tetley Bitter; guest beer Ⓗ
Traditional, two-bar village local with an area for pool and darts. No machines or juke box – just gentle classical music, although a spontaneous celebratory sing-song is not unknown. The rear lounge displays collections of jugs and miniature dolls. Good value meals, using fresh produce from local suppliers, are prepared upstairs and descend via a dumb waiter. A snack menu is available from 9pm until closing time (not Wed). The large, safe garden with children's play area is to the rear.
🏰❀🛏◑▲♣PⒽ

HAWKSHEAD ❖

Sun Inn
Main Street
✪ 11-11; 12-10.30 Sun
☎ (015394) 36236
Black Sheep Best Bitter; Greene King Old Speckled Hen; guest beers Ⓗ
Good village pub, well used by locals and tourists alike. It has a good rotation of guest ales. An open fire, pool and darts feature on the upper level of this split-level house. It has a quarry-tiled floor and table tops, with plentiful tables and comfortable chairs. This very welcoming pub is well worth a visit, but it can become hectic in summer with tourists, but all pubs in this village are well worth a visit. ❀🛏◑▲

HAYTON

Lane End Inn
On A69, 2 miles E of Brampton
✪ 11-11; 12-10.30 Sun
☎ (01228) 670674
Jennings Bitter, Cumberland Ale, Cocker Hoop, seasonal beers Ⓗ
Originally a coaching inn on the main road between Newcastle and Carlisle, its stables still survive. Carlisle's pubs were nationalised, due to the high levels of drunkenness in WWI, and this inn was the first free house outside the State Management Scheme, when travelling east from the city. It is now a popular Jennings-managed house, serving food all day from a very extensive menu. Beware, the low beam just inside the front door catches many tall people out. 🏰❀❀◑P⌇

HESKET NEWMARKET

Old Crown ←
1 mile SE of Caldbeck
✪ 12-3 (not Mon), 5.30-11; 12-11 Sat; 12-3, 7-10.30 Sun
☎ (0169 74) 78288
Hesket Newmarket Great Cockup Porter, Blencathra Bitter, Skiddaw Special Bitter, Doris's 90th Birthday, Catbells Pale Ale, Old Carrock Strong Ale Ⓗ
On the edge of the Calbeck Fells, the northernmost part of the Lake District, this superb pub lies at the heart of a peaceful village. It serves as the tap for Hesket Newmarket Brewery, which is in a converted barn at the rear. The pub is very popular with the local community, who formed a co-operative to buy the brewery when it was sold in 1999 by its founder, Jim Fearnley. It is renowned for its curries. The rooms may be small but the welcome is always large at this local CAMRA *Pub of the Year* 2000. 🏰Q❀◑▲♣♠

INGS

Watermill Inn ←
✪ 12-2.30, 6-11; 12-3, 6-10.30 Sun
☎ (01539) 821309
website: www.watermill-inn.demon.co.uk
Black Sheep Special; Coniston Bluebird; Jennings Bitter; Lees Moonraker; Theakston Old Peculier; guest beers Ⓗ
Originally a timber mill, then a guest house but, since 1990, an award-winning, family-run pub offering a wide selection of guest beers. No loudspeakers, machines, pool or

TV; conversation is the order of the day here. The right-hand bar (partly no-smoking) is popular with families and diners. The other bar attracts locals, regular visitors, dog owners (dogs are fed and watered) and diners. The cellar can be viewed via a cartwheel-shaped window. Runner-up in national CAMRA's *Pub of the Year* 1999 awards.
🏛Q🎄🏵🚪⬧👶♣🅿✂●

IREBY

Lion
The Square
☼ 6-11; 12-3, 7-10.30 Sun
☎ (0169 73) 71133

Greene King Abbot; Marston's Pedigree; Tetley Bitter; guest beers Ⓗ
The pub stands in the centre of what most people would class as a village, however Ireby is a town – the medieval market cross giving it this status. Inside the pub you will find much wood, including the bar (from a pub in Leeds), panelling from local chapels, bare boards in the bar area, and fine exposed beams. There is a pool room, and a quiz night is held fortnightly, alternating with a locals' music night. 🏛Q🏵🍴👶♣

KENDAL ✤

Burgundys
19 Lowther Street
☼ 11-3 (not Mon-Wed), 6.30-11 (not Mon); 7-10.30 Sun
☎ (01539) 733803
website: www.burgundyswinebar.com
Beer range varies Ⓗ
Formerly part of a tobacco warehouse, now a multi-level, bistro-style bar with a constantly changing choice of real ales. It also offers an above-average range of draught and bottled continental lagers and hosts a Cumbrian challenge micro-beer festival each spring where the winning beer is chosen by a tasting panel and customers. Eve meals are available by prior arrangement. No juke box or pool, the TV is only used for special occasions. ◖≢●

Castle Inn
13 Castle Street
☼ 11.30 (Sat 11)-11; 12-10.30 Sun
☎ (01539) 729983
Jennings Bitter; Tetley Bitter; guest beer Ⓗ
Popular, 18th-century pub on the fringe of the town centre, serving exceptional value lunches to office staff. By night and at weekends it becomes a busy community pub, hosting quizzes and other events. The lounge boasts an impressive tropical fish tank. The bar, with a TV, features a wall-mounted etched Dutton's Brewery window; the raised games area houses a pool table. A beer from Dent is usually on tap. ◖≢♣

KESWICK

George Hotel
3 St John's Street (near Moot Hall)
☼ 11-11; 12-10.30 Sun
☎ (017687) 72076
Jennings Bitter, Cumberland Ale, Cocker Hoop, Sneck Lifter Ⓗ
Right in the centre of Keswick stands this impressive former coaching inn, carefully

restored to its former glory. Beloved of discerning drinkers and those in search of a quiet pint, the bar features all that is best in the English pub. Great cask-conditioned beers from the local brewery can be enjoyed in intimate surroundings. Traditional food, with a modern twist, is prepared with care and beautifully presented in the comfortable atmospheric dining room or the cosy bar areas. 🏛🚪◖🅿●

LITTLE CORBY

Haywain
(off A69, E of Carlisle)
☼ 7 (6 Fri; 11 Sat)-11; 12-10.30 Sun
☎ (01228) 560598
Robinson's Best Bitter, seasonal beers Ⓗ
The only pub in the area that escaped State Management control, it lies close to the River Eden. Once called the Plough, this recently altered village pub with its new, larger bar area decorated with stained glass, has not lost any of its character. The bar area features a stone-flagged floor, bar stools made from old tractor seats, hunting pictures and a very large mirror above the fireplace with its new fake fire. The car park is a short walk from the pub. Meals served at weekends. Q◖👶♣🅿

MELMERBY

Shepherds' Inn
☼ 10.30-3, 6-11; 12-3, 7-10.30 Sun
☎ (0870) 7453383 website: www.shepherdsinn.net
Dent T'Owd Tup; Jennings Cumberland Ale; guest beers Ⓗ
Built in 1789, this fine pub is located at the village centre. An attached barn has been converted into a bar area, creating two split-level rooms, one with a raised pool table area. Both rooms enjoy a relaxed atmosphere, with fine oak beams in the barn and a stone-flagged floor. It serves excellent food and was a previous *Cheeseboard Pub of the Year*. A collection of pub mirrors adorns the high wall in the barn. 🏛Q🏵◖🍴👶♣🅿🍴●

MIDDLETON

Swan Inn
On A683
☼ 11-2.30, 6-11; 11-11 Sat; 12-10.30 Sun
☎ (015242) 76223 website: www.theswaninn.com
Black Sheep Best Bitter; guest beers Ⓗ
16th-century inn, retaining many original features. The bar area displays a board with an impressive list of recent and forthcoming beers, with a mild often taking pride of place. There is a games room/lounge to the left and a cosy dining room, with a fine kitchen range to the right. The large, lawned garden at the front extends up to the road. The surrounding countryside is one of the most picturesque stretches of the Lune Valley. 🏛🏵🚪🍴♣🅿

NEAR SAWREY

Tower Bank Arms Hotel
Off B5285 OS370956
☼ 12-3, 6-11; 12-3, 6-10.30 Sun
☎ (015394) 36334
Theakston Best Bitter, Cool Cask, Old Peculier; guest beers Ⓗ

Large country pub (which featured in *Jemima Puddle Duck*) with a dining area. The bar area, with its extremely comfortable seats, is a gallery of signed photographs of the many celebrities who have stayed here over the years. The guest beers tend to be weird and wonderful – many from unfamiliar micro-breweries, which are mostly excellent. A large selection of bottled continental beers is also stocked. The atmosphere is great – typical of a local pub in this part of the Lake District. ▲Q✿✎◑

NEWTON-IN-CARTMEL

Crown Inn
Off A590 at High Newton Village
✪ 12-2.30, 6-11 (12-11 summer); 12-10.30 Sun
☎ (015395) 31793
website: www.thecrowninn.lakeland.com
Theakston Cool Cask; Yates seasonal beers; guest beers Ⓗ

17th-century coaching inn, in beautiful south Lakeland surroundings, three miles from Lake Windermere. It boasts flagged floors, a huge fireplace and an oak-beamed ceiling. The inn is the only survivor of three in the village, and not much has changed here since the last coach came by. A split-level bar serves both the distinctive upper and lower rooms; there is also a pool room. Reputed to be haunted by Henry, who presides over the inn from his favourite chair. The ghost, for reasons best known to himself, only ever presents himself to women. ▲✿✎◑♣P

PARSONBY

Horse & Jockey Inn
On B5301
✪ 11-11; 10.30-10.30 Sun
☎ (016973) 20482
website: www.horseandjockeypub.co.uk
Jennings Mild, Bitter Ⓗ

Cosy 200-year-old roadside pub between Aspatria and Cockermouth. It features a large open stone fireplace, low ceilings and heavy oak beams. There is a pool table and a dining area where food is served daily, 12–9, including vegetarian options and curries as well as old favourites. The licensees have a large collection of pigs in ornamental and pictorial form displayed around the bar, which also boasts several pub mirrors. ▲✿◑♣P

PENRITH ✳

Agricultural Hotel
Castlegate (by station)
✪ 11-11; 12-10.30 Sun
☎ (01768) 862622
Jennings Mild, Bitter, Cumberland Ale, Cocker Hoop; Sneck Lifter Ⓗ

Comfortable pub, close to the railway station, and a short uphill walk from the town centre. The Aggie (as it is known locally) has a friendly atmosphere and provides a good range of home-cooked meals. Part of the dining area is set aside for non-smokers and can be used by drinkers preferring a smoke-free environment outside meal times. The pub is just a stone's throw from the ruins of Penrith Castle, which remain as testimony to the turbulent history of the border counties and are worth a visit. ✿✎◑≿⇌P✗●

POOLEY BRIDGE

Sun Inn
✪ 12-11; 12-10.30 Sun
☎ (017684) 86205
Jennings Bitter, Cumberland Ale, Cocker Hoop, Sneck Lifter, seasonal beers Ⓗ

Split-level local at the centre of this popular north Lakes village. The panelled upper bar is no-smoking and has a good fire in winter. The lower bar offers pool in winter and has a TV. Dogs are welcome in both bars and in the guest accommodation. Good value meals are served in both bars and in the no-smoking (dog-free) dining room. A large lawned garden extends to the side and rear. The pier, for summer steamer trips on Ullswater, is a short walk away. ▲✿✎◑⊟≿♣P✗●

PORTINSCALE

Farmers Arms
Off A66, 1 mile W of Keswick
✪ 11-3, 6-11; 12-3, 7-10.30 Sun
☎ (017687) 73442
Jennings Bitter, Cumberland Ale; guest beer Ⓗ
Cosy pub, five minutes' walk from the Nichol End landing stage of the Keswick Launch Company, whose wooden craft carry passengers around Derwentwater. As in most Lakeland pubs, locals and tourists intermingle, along with their respective dogs. The landlord also rents out a spacious

INN BRIEF

LINDALL-IN-FURNESS
Railway Inn
6 London Road
2-11; 2-10.30 Sun
Caledonian Deuchars IPA; John Smith's Bitter; guest beer (occasional) Ⓗ
Friendly village local, with a real fire. Pool and darts can be played. Probably the best pint of Deuchars in the area.

LOW ROW
Railway Inn
12-3, 5.30-11;
12-3, 6.30-10.30 Sun
Thwaites Reward; guest beer Ⓗ
Nestling out of sight of the main road, but not the railway, this quiet pub is well worth visiting, for both food and drink.

PENRITH
Miner's Arms
27 Southend Road
11-11 (12-3.30, 7-11 winter); 12-10.30 (12-3.30, 7-10.30 winter) Sun
Bateman XB; Brains SA; guest beer (summer) Ⓗ
One-roomed pub on the fringe of the town centre, hosting regular live music on Sat.

RAVENGLASS
Ratty Arms
11-3, 5.30-11; 11-11 Sat & summer;
12-10.30 Sun
Greene King Ruddles Best; Jennings Bitter; Theakston Best Bitter; guest beer Ⓗ
The old Furness Station building, owned by R&ER Preservation Society, it stands next to the main line station. Meals all day.

RAVENSTONEDALE
Black Swan Hotel
11-3, 6-11; 11-11 Fri & Sat;
12-10.30 Sun
Black Sheep Best Bitter; Dent Bitter; John Smith's Bitter; guest beers Ⓗ
Comfortable hotel with a locals' bar, lounge and a well-appointed dining room. Wheelchair access to ground-floor bedrooms.

SWARTHMOOR
Miner's Arms
Fox Street
11.30-2.30 (5 Sat), 6-11; 12-3,
7-10.30 Sun
Thwaites Mild, Bitter; guest beers Ⓗ
Small, single-roomed local serving guest beers usually of Cumbrian origin.

self-catering house near the pub. The Farmers is now the only pub in a village that once supported several, and this old, unassuming local is worth a visit.

🚶🏠🍴▶🚗♣

ROSTHWAITE

Scafell Hotel

From Keswick go S on B5289 towards Borrowdale OS259149

☼ 11-11; 12-10.30 Sun

☎ (017687) 77208 website: www.scafell.co.uk

Theakston Best Bitter, XB, Old Peculier; guest beer (summer) Ⓗ

Situated in the breathtakingly beautiful Borrowdale Valley, this hostelry, with its lively public bar, is perfectly situated for hillwalkers, climbers or just plain tourists. The owner is a keen fellrunner and the annual Borrowdale Race starts in the paddock opposite the hotel (first Sat in Aug). The riverside bar is spacious; families and pets are welcome in what can be an incredibly busy place in season. Nearby is Seathwaite Farm which suffers the highest rainfall in England. A regular bus service runs from Keswick. **🚶🏠🍴◀🚗▶AP**

ROWRAH

Stork

Rowrah Road

☼ 12-2, 6-11; 11-11 Sat & summer; 12-10.30 Sun

☎ (01946) 861213

e-mail: stork/hotel/@/hotels/active//bookinguk

Jennings Bitter; guest beers Ⓗ

Traditional Cumbrian village pub where the bar talk is general and inclusive. A stone floor, warm fire in winter and beer that has earned a long history of Guide entries, make the Stork well worth the tourist's visit. Close to the Coast-to-Coast walk, it is also geared up for overnight stays for walkers and visitors to the nearby go-karting track. There is a paved area outside for summer drinks and a tiny car park with just three spaces.

🚶Q🍴🏠◀▶AP

ST BEES

Queen's Hotel

Main Street

☼ 12-3, 5.30-11; 12-3, 7-11 Sun

☎ (01946) 822287 website: www.queenshotelstbees.co.uk

Jennings Bitter; Yates Bitter; guest beers (summer) Ⓗ

Large 17th-century pub and hotel in the middle of the village, replete with low beams, cosy rooms and log fires. In summer, customers can eat and drink in the garden or the no-smoking conservatory. Locals at the bar are a source of good conversation and local knowledge. This picturesque village, home to a medieval priory and a 400-year-old public school, stands at the start of the Coast-to-Coast walk to Robin Hood's Bay. The menu includes local Cumberland sausage (no lunches Tue, or eve meals Sun).

🚶Q🍴🏠◀▶🚗▶P✦

SILLOTH

Golf Hotel

Criffel Street (B5305)

☼ 10-2, 6-11; 10-11 Sat; 10-11 Sun

☎ (016973) 31438

e-mail: golf.hotel@virgin.net

Derwent Bitter; guest beers (summer) Ⓗ

This 22-bedroom Victorian hotel has a comfortable spacious lounge with a small bar in the corner. The dining room offers a good selection of traditional dishes. The summer guest beers are from the local Derwent Brewery. The building affords a pleasant view over the green and is about 200 yards from the Solway Coast. The various rooms display pictures of old Silloth; all are mobile phone-free zones. Pool and snooker played. A bus service to Carlisle runs until early eve.

Q🍴◀▶A♣

STAVELEY

Eagle & Child

Kendal Road

☼ 11-11; 12-10.30 Sun

☎ (01539) 821320

website: www.eaglechildinn.co.uk

Black Sheep Best Bitter, Special; Coniston Bluebird; guest beers Ⓗ

The recently refurbished ground floor of this Victorian inn has a U-shaped area with the bar at one end and the other set out for dining. Guest beers are usually from local micro-breweries. A secluded garden to the rear is complemented by another, next to the River Kent, across the road. Staveley, now bypassed from the

WETHERAL

Wheatsheaf

12-2.30, 5-11; 12-11 Fri, Sat & summer; 12-11 Sun

Greenalls Bitter; Marston's Pedigree Ⓗ

Village local serving good food. The village is on the banks of the River Eden, excellent for fishing and walking.

WHITEHAVEN

Welsh Arms

22 Tangier Street

11-11; 2-10.30 Sun

Robinson's Old Stockport Bitter, Hartleys XB, seasonal beers Ⓗ

Family-run pub, near the newly refurbished harbourside and promenade, and rail and bus stations. Meals lunch and eve (not Sun).

WINDERMERE

Elleray Hotel

2-6 Cross Street

11-11; 12-10.30 Sun

Beer range varies Ⓗ

Two-bar hotel with a dining room. Guest beers usually include one from a local micro-brewery. Close to train and bus services.

WORKINGTON

George IV

Stanley Street

11-11;
12-3, 7-10.30 Sun

Jennings Bitter Ⓗ

Cosy, harbourside pub in old part of town, regenerated in recent years. Handy for the station, rugby and football grounds.

main road into Lakeland, is handy for the Kentmere Valley, with many good walks, and the Dales long distance path.
♛❀⇌◑▲≠♣●P

STRAWBERRY BANK

Mason's Arms

Off A592 OS413895
✪ 11.30-3, 6-11; 11-11 Fri & Sat; 12-10.30 Sun
☎ (015395) 68486 website: www.masonsarms.uk.com
Beer range varies Ⓗ
Extremely popular south Lakeland inn where the single bar serves several distinct drinking and eating areas. The inn's micro-brewery produces bottled Damson beer, flavoured with the produce of the Lyth Valley, which the inn overlooks. It is also renowned for its home-cooked food and has featured in several TV and radio programmes; the menu includes an extensive selection of vegetarian dishes. Cider is stocked in summer. From the garden, the view over the valley towards Morecambe Bay can be quite breathtaking.
♛❀⇌◑♿▲♣●P

TALKIN

Blacksmith's Arms

Two miles S of Brampton, off A69
✪ 12-3, 6-11; 12-3, 6.30-10.30 Sun
☎ (016977) 3452
Black Sheep Best Bitter; Boddingtons Bitter; Tetley Bitter Ⓗ
Opened in the 17th century as the village smithy, it gradually expanded to include a forge and started serving refreshments to waiting customers. It became a very popular pub with coal miners and stone quarrymen. When Lady Caroline Howard closed all the pubs on her estate, as part of the Temperance Movement, her miners used to hire a bus at weekends to bring them here. It is now a spacious free house at the heart of a quiet village on the edge of the Pennines, near Hadrian's Wall.
♛❀⇌◑♿♣P⚟

Choosing Pubs

CAMRA members and branches choose the pubs listed in the Good Beer Guide. There is no payment for entry, and pubs are inspected on a regular basis by personal visits; publicans are not sent a questionnaire once a year, as is the case with some pub guides. CAMRA branches monitor all the pubs in their areas, and the choice of pubs for the guide is often the result of democratic vote at branch meetings. However, recommendations from readers are welcomed and will be passed on to the relevant branch: write to Good Beer Guide, CAMRA, 230 Hatfield Road, St Albans, AL1 4LW; or send an e-mail to camra@camra.org.uk.

TIRRIL

Queen's Head Inn

✪ 12-3, 6-11; 12-11 Sat ; 12-10.30 Sun
☎ (01768) 863219 website: www.queensheadinn.co.uk
Tirril John Bewsher's Best Bitter, Charles Gough's Old Faithful; Thomas Slee's Academy Ale; guest beers Ⓗ
This attractive village inn boasts an award-winning fireplace in the front bar; a pool table and juke box are housed in the one at the rear. Further back is the tiny Tirril Brewery (although this may be moving to larger premises nearby). Ask about the derivation of the beer names. A lunchtime snack menu complements the good quality meals, served in both bars and the multi-level, no-smoking dining room. It hosts a weekend Cumbrian beer and sausage festival (mid Aug).
♛❀⇌◑⊟♣P●

TROUTBECK

Mortal Man

✪ 12-11; 12-10.30 Sun
☎ (015394) 33193
website: www.mortal-man-inns.co.uk/mortalman
Jennings Cumberland Ale; Theakston Best Bitter; guest beer Ⓗ
The comfortable tap room welcomes walkers in boots with their dogs. The adjoining lounges are furnished in the style of a country house and command fine views. Bar meals are served all day, changing to an eve menu at 6pm. The *à la carte* (no-smoking) dining room, open at 7pm, benefits from views extending down the valley to Windermere. Of the two gardens, one is sheltered by the building, the other is across the lane by the car park. Troutbeck makes an ideal (quieter) centre from which to explore Lakeland.
♛Q❀⇌◑♿▲♣P⚟

ULDALE

Snooty Fox

✪ 12-2, 6.30-11, 12-2, 6.30-10.30 Sun
☎ (016973) 71479
Black Sheep Special; Theakston Best Bitter Ⓗ
The building became a pub in the late 1860s, and was originally called the George & Dragon; it was sold to the Workington Brewery in 1940. Following a period of closure in the 1980s, the pub's name changed to the Snooty Fox. One large bar joins the lounge and bar rooms; the dining room upholds a no-smoking policy. The oak beams date from before 1700. Several old framed maps can be

found around the walls. The house beer, Uldale, is brewed by local Hesket Newmarket Brewery.

🏠Q🅿️🍴◑ ⏚♿♣P

ULVERSTON

Farmers Arms
Market Place
🕐 10-11; 11-12.30 Sun
☎ (01229) 584469
website: www.farmersulv.freeserve.co.uk
Theakston Best Bitter; guest beers Ⓗ
Town-centre pub, popular with all ages. The building, totally modernised, extends back into a dining-cum-lounge area. The original fireplace has been retained and enhances the bar area, overlooking the market (Thu and Sat). Coffee and soft drinks only are served before 10.30 (12 Sun). Daily newspapers help create a relaxing environment during the day. It gets very busy eves, especially at weekends, with a popular quiz (Tue). It offers an extensive range of food and wines and normally three guest beers are on tap. Children are welcome until 9pm.

🏠🅿️◑Å⇌

Stan Laurel Inn
31 The Ellers
🕐 12-3 (not winter), 7-11; 12-3, 7-10.30 Sun
☎ (01229) 582814
Tetley Dark Mild, Bitter; guest beers Ⓗ
Comfortable local where good conversation is guaranteed. As the name suggests, Laurel and Hardy memorabilia abound; Stan Laurel was born in Ulverston and the town boasts a Laurel and Hardy Museum. Due to its connections, it attracts fans from all over the world, particularly on carnival day (first Sat in July) when they join in the town parade before descending on the Stan for an afternoon of lively entertainment. The pub's three rooms play host to many community group meetings, including the Furness morris men (Fri eve).

🅿️🍴⏚Å⇌♣P

UNDERBARROW

Punchbowl Inn
🕐 12-3.30 (not Tue), 6-11; 12-4, 7-10.30 Sun
☎ (015395) 68234
Draught Bass; Jennings Cumberland Ale; guest beer Ⓗ
The tiny bar counter is set in a spacious room, full of interest: part of a priest's-hole can be glimpsed behind the bar; a spice cupboard beside the fireplace, heavy ceiling beams and lots of wall-mounted artefacts complete the picture. An adjacent room has further seating and dining space, serving good value meals, especially the fresh fish on Fri eve. Up a few steps is a games room. It is near a good walking and birdwatching area, and the market town of Kendal is a short drive away 🏠🅿️◑♣P

WASDALE HEAD

Wasdale Head Inn
At head of valley OS187088
🕐 11-11 (10 winter); 12-10.30 (10 winter) Sun
☎ (019467) 26229 website: www.wasdale.com
Derwent Bitter; Jennings Mild, Cumberland Ale; Yates

Bitter; guest beer Ⓗ
Dramatically located at the head of Wasdale, the inn is surrounded by England's tallest mountains and next to its deepest lake. Inside, see the many photographs of early rock climbs in the area. A single bar serves a main slate-floored room and two adjoining rooms. Ritson's Bar is named after Will Ritson, a fellsman and raconteur who won the first-ever *World's Biggest Liar* competition. Hearty food is served (no chips) The inn holds occasional beer festivals when the emphasis is on Cumbrian beers, as in the choice of guest ales. Q🅿️🍴◑ ⏚Å♣P⇱⏚

WHITEHAVEN ✳

John Paul Jones
Strand Street
🕐 12-11 (1am Fri & Sat); 12-10.30 Sun
☎ (01946) 690916
Theakston Cool Cask; guest beers Ⓗ
Warm, welcoming pub, close to the marina and historic port. It is themed on an 18th-century sailing ship, and relates the history of John Paul Jones, the founder of the US Navy. Home-made meals are served daily from 12–2.30 and 6–8 during the summer season. Tues is general knowledge quiz night and live music is performed by local bands Fri. It gets very busy at weekends.
◑♿⇌

WINSTER

Brown Horse Inn
On A5074
🕐 11-2.30, 5.30-11; 11-11 Sat & summer; 12-10.30 Sun
☎ (015394) 43443 website: www.thebrownhorse.com
Black Sheep Best Bitter; Jennings Bitter, Cumberland Ale; guest beer Ⓗ
There is an equally warm welcome here for those who (with or without a dog) come to enjoy a drink or game of darts at one end of the bar area, as for those having an above-average quality meal at the other. No juke box, pool or machines invade here, just quiet background music and a box of children's toys. The no-smoking dining room can be hired for functions (licensed until midnight). The Winster Valley is a quiet, unspoilt area, yet is close to the bustle of Bowness.
🏠🅿️◑♣P●

WINTON

Bay Horse Inn
Just off A685
🕐 12-3 (not Tue or weekdays Nov-Easter), 7-11; 12-3, 7-10.30 Sun
☎ (017683) 71451
Black Sheep Best Bitter; Theakston Cool Cask; guest beers Ⓗ
Overlooking the village green, this friendly local dates from the late 1600s. The bar counter serves both a stone-flagged public bar and a dining area. A sign requests customers to switch off mobile phones. A raised games room at the rear is used for pool, music and other activities. A leaflet is available, detailing an interesting circular walk from the pub. Nearby Kirkby Stephen hosts an annual vintage bus rally.
🏠Q🅿️◑ ⏚♣P

DERBYSHIRE

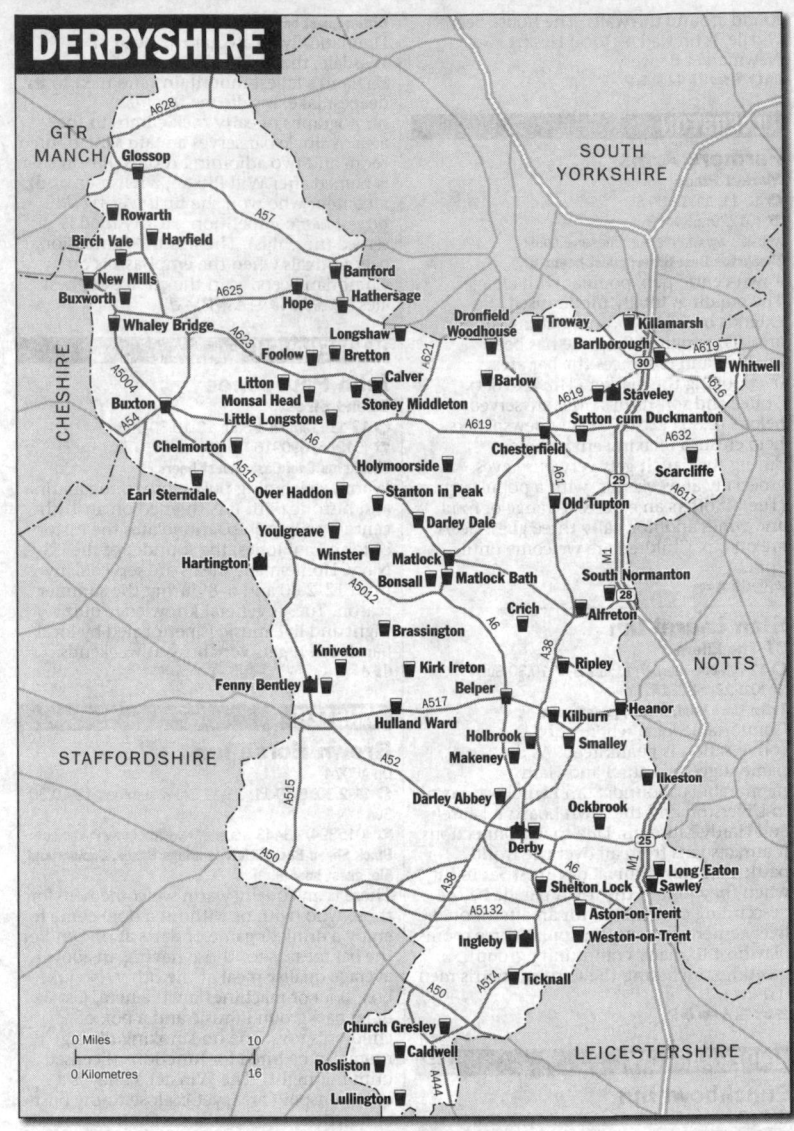

Victoria Inn

80 Nottingham Road (B600)
⏰ 1 (12 Sat)-11; 12-10.30 Sun
☎ (01773) 520156
Beer range varies Ⓗ

Extensively refurbished, busy, two-roomed local, with a friendly atmosphere. An illuminated aquarium is a feature of the lounge, while the pub bar bears pump clips of previous beers on the beams and Sky TV. The guest beers change regularly and often come from local micro-breweries; it hosts a summer beer festival. Near the town centre, car parking is difficult. An outdoor yard for drinking and long alley skittles is lit.

Q✿🏠🚃♣

Malt Shovel

The Green (off Derby Rd)
⏰ 11-11; 12-10.30 Sun
☎ (01332) 792256 e-mail: maltshovel@talk21.com
Draught Bass; Fuller's London Pride; Marston's Pedigree; Wells Bombardier; guest beer Ⓗ

The brewer's Tudor exterior marks this as a latecomer among the hand-made bricks of the surrounding buildings. Even if you prefer the quieter atmosphere of the lounge bar, it is worth visiting the public bar to admire the unspoilt oak panelling. An experiment with Tapster's Choice has settled as a range of local favourites, plus a guest beer, probably from Church End. Reading matter is provided among a collection of copper, brass and horse tack, in the English country pub idiom. Regular buses run from Derby. 🏚✿🍺🏠♣P

BELPER

Queen's Head
29 Chesterfield Road
☼ 12-11; 12-10.30 Sun
☎ (01773) 825525 website: www.thequeenshead.net
Greene King IPA; Ind Coope Burton Ale; Tetley Bitter; guest beers Ⓗ
Popular, multi-roomed local about half a mile from the town centre, on a bus route, with street parking close by. Regular guest beers are offered, alongside old favourites. With a real fire in the bar area, It has no juke box, but a variety of games, and hosts weekend entertainment (usually blues or folk based). Regular themed beer festivals showcase beers from near and far. An attractive patio affords pleasant views of the surrounding town and countryside.
🏚Q✿⬚≠♣

BIRCH VALE

Vine
Hayfield Road (A6015)
☼ 12-3, 6-11; 12-3, 6-10.30 Sun
☎ (01663) 741021
Robinson's Hatters Mild, Best Bitter Ⓗ
Stone roadside pub, conveniently situated for the Peak District. Of the four drinking areas, one houses a pool table, the other three can all accommodate diners. The bar area benefits from views across the Sett Valley. The menu includes good value traditional English fare, international dishes, children's choices and pensioners' lunches. With three twin-bedded rooms (one en-suite), just off the Sett Valley Trail, the pub makes a good base for walking or touring. 🏚⛺🛏◑♣P

BONSALL

Barley Mow
The Dale (off the Via Gellia, A5012)
☼ 6 (12 Sat)-11; 12-10.30 Sun
☎ (01629) 825685 website: www.thebarley.com
Whim Hartington Bitter; guest beers
Up the hill from the main village, the Barley Mow is pushed back from the road into the rocks from which the cellar and secret room were hewn back in the 17th century. This small pub makes incredible use of a limited space. The best-seller *Pastures Nouveaux* by Wendy Holden is about life in Bonsall and features this friendly local. The pool room has only enough room for players, so on league nights the teams have to watch the match on CCTV in the bar. Watch out for the landlord's organised walks, boules in the car park and world championship hen racing (Aug).
🏚✿◑▲♣P

King's Head
62 Yeoman Street
☼ 12-2.30 (not Mon), 6-11; 12-3, 6-10.30 Sun
☎ (01629) 822703
Bateman Mild, XB, seasonal beers Ⓗ
In the centre of Bonsall next to the Market Cross (the tallest in Derbyshire) stands the furthest-flung Bateman's pub, the King's Head. This traditional, two-roomed stone pub, dating from 1677, has a warm, welcoming, wood-panelled interior, displaying a large collection of pickle jars on a Delft shelf and many old photographs of local sports teams. Bonsall and the landlord have been in the national press for UFO-sighting – nothing to do with the strength of the beer!
🏚✿◑P

BRASSINGTON

Olde Gate Inn ☆
Well Street (off A5023, between Ashbourne and Wirksworth)
☼ 12-2.30, 6-11; 12-3, 7-10.30 Sun
☎ (01629) 540448
Marston's Pedigree, seasonal beers Ⓗ
Family-run, ivy-clad village pub built in 1616; reputedly haunted and Grade II listed, it featured on Carlton TV's *Heart of the Country*. With three real fires including a black-leaded range in the main bar, it has been a Homefire *Real Fire Pub of the Year* winner. Gleaming copper pots and utensils hang around the fire, and oak beams abound. No children under 10 allowed. An extensive menu offers home-cooked dishes (no meals Mon eve). Local attraction Carsington Water nearby is worth a visit.
🏚Q✿◑⅄♣P⅄⊟

BRETTON

Barrel Inn
OS201779
☼ 11-3, 6-11; 11-11 Sat & summer; 12-10.30 Sun
☎ (01433) 630856
Greene King Abbot; Marston's Pedigree; Tetley Bitter; guest beers Ⓗ
Inn dated 1597, which became a landmark on the 18th-century turnpike from Sheffield to Buxton. Although the modern major road network has bypassed it, it is now popular with walkers, not least because of its spectacular position on a gritstone edge, with a view reputed to embrace five counties on a clear day. There is one long bar with an L-shaped extension, well decorated with local photographs and paintings. Performers of Irish folk music congregate Wed eve. There is a youth hostel nearby.
🏚🛏✿◑▲P

BUXTON ✿

Bakers Arms
26 West Road
☼ 12-2, 6 (4 Fri; 7 Sat)-11; 12-3, 7-10.30 Sun
☎ (01298) 24404 e-mail: markatbakers@aol.com
Greene King Abbot; Tetley Bitter; guest beers Ⓗ
Small, two-roomed, friendly local, very popular with members of sporting clubs, whose large trophy collection is on display here. There is just enough room to play darts next to the bar. An ever-changing selection of guest beers includes a regular guest from Kelham Island. A patio is available for outdoor drinking in fine weather. ✿▲≠P

INDEPENDENT BREWERIES

Brunswick Derby
Leatherbritches Fenny Bentley
Lichfield Ingleby
Lloyds Ingleby
Townes Staveley
Whim Hartington

Ramsey's Bar (Buckingham Hotel)
1 Burlington Road
⚙ 12-2, 6-11; 12-3, 6-10.30 Sun
☎ (01298) 70481
Theakston Cool Cask; Wells Bombardier; guest beers Ⓗ
Large public bar and restaurant, part of the Buckingham Hotel, the bar's name comes from the fact that No. 1 Burlington Road was the home of local artist George Ramsey in the early part of the last century; his engraved signature is to be found on one of the bar windows. With four guest beers on tap permanently, this bar is proving very popular. A wide choice of food ranges from simple bar meals to a full restaurant menu, and a carvery serving a good selection of meats. Q ⚘ 🐾 ◁ ◑ 𝐀 ⇌ P

BUXWORTH

Navigation
Brookside Road (off B6062 by canal basin)
⚙ 11-11; 12-10.30 Sun
☎ (01663) 732072
Marston's Pedigree; Taylor Landlord; Webster's Yorkshire Bitter; guest beer Ⓗ
Excellent, multi-roomed 18th-century pub, with an extensive restaurant. Partially stone-flagged, it stands alongside Britain's only remaining canal/tramway interchange. The tramway was the old Peak Forest tramway, long since defunct. The canal basin, however, part of the Peak Forest Canal, has happily been restored and opened again to boats. Walkers are welcome and there is a particularly nice outdoor drinking area. Cider is stocked in summer.
🐾 🛏 🐾 ◁ ◑ 🍴 ◆ P

CALDWELL

Royal Oak Inn
Main Street
⚙ 11.30-11; 11.30-10.30 Sun
☎ (01283) 761486
Marston's Pedigree; guest beers Ⓗ
Serving a village of some 50 dwellings, this cosy pub has a devoted clientele, not all of whom are local. A little off the beaten track, it is popular with walkers and cyclists. There is a small bar and lounge, with a slightly elevated balcony area. The pub's varying guest beers are often suggested by the regulars. Meals are served, but often nibbles

are provided, although, at quiet times, these tend to attract the attention of the owner's two Labradors. 🐾 🛏 ◆ ♣

CALVER

Bridge Inn
On A623
⚙ 11.30-3 (3.30 Sat), 5.30-11; 12-3.30, 7-10.30 Sun
☎ (01433) 630415
Hardys & Hansons Best Bitter, Classic, seasonal beers; guest beer Ⓗ
This pub was bought from Stones by Hardys & Hansons in the 1980s, but retained the same landlord who still presides. The stone village inn enjoys a strong local trade but welcomes visitors. There are two cosy lounges, one housing a collection of local guide books for perusal, and the other a large collection of antique fire-fighting equipment. The pleasant garden, on the bank of the River Derwent, faces the newly-restored Calver Mill. No food is served Mon eve or winter Sun eve. 🐾 Q ⚘ ◁ ◑ ♿ 𝐀 P 🍴 🛏

CHELMORTON

Church Inn
Main Street
⚙ 12-3.30, 7-11 (12-11 summer Sat); 12-3.30, 7-10.30 (12-10.30 summer) Sun
☎ (01298) 85319
Adnams Bitter; Marston's Bitter, Pedigree; guest beer Ⓗ
Set in beautiful surroundings, opposite the church, this traditional village pub caters for both locals and walkers alike. Even though the main room is laid out with dining tables and good home-cooked food is on offer, a cosy atmosphere is still maintained, enhanced by a low ceiling and real fire, and the pub is run primarily as a local. Quiz nights are hosted. Parking is possible on the dead-end road outside the pub. 🐾 Q ⚘ ◁ ◑

CHESTERFIELD

Boythorpe
77 Boythorpe Road
⚙ 12-11; 12-10.30 Sun
☎ (01246) 235280
Hardys & Hansons Best Mild, Best Bitter, Classic, seasonal beers Ⓗ
Spacious local off the town centre, on the Matlock road; as well as drawing local and

INN BRIEF

BAMFORD
Angler's Rest
Taggs Knoll
12-3, 6-11; 12-11 Sat; 12-10.30 Sun
Banks's Bitter; Mansfield Cask Ale; Marston's Pedigree Ⓗ
Village local, renovated in open-plan style with high-backed pews and a dining area.

BARLBOROUGH
Rose & Crown
High Street
12-3, 6-11; 12-3.30, 7-10.30 Sun
Hardys & Hansons Best Bitter, seasonal beers Ⓗ
Comfortable village pub set behind a historic cross. Lunches served Tue-Sun; eve meals Wed-Sat. Close to M1 junction 30.

BARLOW
Hare & Hounds Inn
Commonside Road
11-11; 12-10.30 Sun
Draught Bass; Stones Bitter Ⓗ
Off the main Barlow road, this cosy three-roomed local affords panoramic views across the valley. Home-made local cheese and gammon are for sale.

BUXTON
Duke of York
123 St John's Road, Burbage
11-11; 12-10.30 Sun
Draught Bass; Tetley Mild, Bitter; guest beers Ⓗ
Two-roomed local, served by an open-plan central bar. Good, home-cooked food is served all day; walkers welcome.

BARLOW

Eagle
The Market Place
11-11; 12-10.30 Sun
Hydes Bitter, Jekyll's Gold Ⓗ
Large, busy, town-centre pub. Recently taken over and refurbished by Hydes. Three distinct areas include a public bar.

CHURCH GRESLEY
Rising Sun
77 Church Street
11.30 (12 Fri)-11; 12-10.30 Sun
Draught Bass; Marston's Pedigree; guest beer Ⓗ
One of the last pubs to be built for Bass with stables; a comfortable bar with a snug.

business trade, it is an excellent venue for sports enthusiasts. Sponsors Chesterfield ladies' football team and football teams from the nearby Royal Mail offices and also fields its own ladies' netball team. To the rear is a pleasant garden and a crown bowling green where matches are played by the pub's teams most eves throughout the summer. A big-screen TV shows important sporting events in one bar. ⬧❀◖&♣P◻●

Derby Tup
387 Sheffield Road, Whittington Moor
⊘ 11.30-3, 5-11; 11.30-11 Wed-Sat; 12-4, 7-10.30 Sun
☎ (01246) 454316
Black Sheep Best Bitter; Greene King Abbot; Taylor Landlord; Theakston Old Peculier; Whim Hartington Bitter; guest beers ⊞
Friendly, ever-popular street-corner local, this long-standing *Guide* entry was Chesterfield CAMRA *Pub of the Year* 2001. At least four guest beers are available at all times, many from micros, as well as a broad selection of well-known names from all over the country. A selection of bottled Belgian beers, draught Hoegaarden Wit and Weston's cider add choice. A good range of food includes vegetarian options (eve meals end 7.30pm) with speciality food nights, brewery nights, a Sun quiz and occasional live music, the Tup caters for everyone.
Q◖❙ᵍ♣ ⊛⌀◻

Market
95 New Square (opp. Market Hall)
⊘ 11-11; 7.30-10.30 Sun
☎ (01246) 273641
Greene King Abbot; Ind Coope Burton Ale; Marston's Pedigree; Tetley Bitter; guest beer ⊞
Carlsberg-Tetley Festival Ale House, it overlooks the smaller of the town's two market places. The unplastered walls are adorned with pub and brewery memorabilia. Originally a two-roomed pub, now opened into an L-shape, it retains the original central bar dating from the 1960s. Five regular guest beers offer an impressive changing range, from micros to long-established breweries. It hosts a monthly wine tasting club and folk club (second Tue). ❀◖≉●

Rutland
16 Stephenson Place
⊘ 11-11; 12-10.30 Sun
☎ (01246) 205857

Boddingtons Bitter; Castle Eden Ale; Greene King Abbot; Marston's Pedigree; ⊞ guest beers ⊞/Ⓖ
Refurbished to the Hogshead Ale House theme, six guest beers are always available, two on gravity. Regular mini beer festivals are held with a selection of up to 13 beers. The original pub was drastically reduced in size early last century but the Hogshead conversion incorporated the adjoining former vicarage. In the shadow of the famous crooked spire of St Mary's and All Saints, it is separated only by a walkway from the rear of the 12th-century church. The dining area maintains a no-smoking policy. ❀◖≉●

Victoria Inn
21-23 Victoria Street West, Brampton
⊘ 12-4, 7-11; 12-4, 7-10.30 Sun
☎ (01246) 273832
Stones Bitter; Tetley Bitter; guest beers ⊞
Friendly, traditional local, retaining a two-roomed layout, this recent CAMRA *Pub of the Season* keeps three guest beers, two of which, Adnams Bitter and Camerons Strongarm, are regulars. A charity quiz night is held every Mon and a charity walk is held Aug bank holiday, with an all-day barbecue. A selection of local produce is always on sale, including eggs, cheese and pickled onions. Although only 100 yards off the main road to Baslow (and Chatsworth House), the pub is not easy to spot.
⬧❀ᵍ♣P

Cliff Inn
Cromford Road (near Tramway Museum)
⊘ 11.30-3, 6-11; 12-4, 6-10.30 Sun
☎ (01773) 852444
Hardys & Hansons Best Mild, Best Bitter, seasonal beers ⊞
Run by the Calladines since 1974, the Cliff has appeared in most editions of this *Guide* since. A compact stone pub with two public rooms, it stands next to the National Tramway Museum. The lounge is dominated by a large landscape executed by a friend of the licensee; it depicts the former homes of two local heroines, Florence Nightingale and Ellen MacArthur. The garden offers a wonderful view over the Derwent Valley where the dreamy sight of the sun setting is pure pleasure on a summer's eve. ⚲Q❀◖ᵍ▱♣P

DARLEY DALE
Church Inn
Church Road
12-3.30 (not Mon or Tue), 5.30-11; 12-11 Fri & Sat; 12-3, 7-10.30 Sun
Hardys & Hansons Best Bitter, seasonal beers ⊞
Cosy, 17th-century inn, set in a traditional Peak District village. The Peak rail line runs past the door.

FENNY BENTLEY
Coach & Horses
On A515
11-3, 5-11; 11-11 Sat; 12-10.30 Sun
Marston's Pedigree; guest beers ⊞
Family-run pub, the former Black Bull Brewery tap, serving up to three guest beers in tourist season.

FOOLOW
Bull's Head Inn
12-3 (not Mon), 6.30-11; 12-3, 7-10.30 Sun
Black Sheep Best Bitter; Marston's Pedigree; guest beer ⊞
Smart pub in an attractive limestone village; the stone-flagged bar area separates the restaurant and drinking areas.

HEANOR
Ray's Arms
52 Ray Street
2 (12 Fri & Sat)-11; 12-10.30 Sun
Banks's Original, Bitter; Marston's Pedigree ⊞
Large, multi-roomed, back-street pub, with open-plan Victorian rooms, a games room and upstairs function room.

INGLEBY
John Thompson Inn
10.30-2.30, 7-11; 12-2.30, 7-10.30 Sun
Ind Coope Burton Ale; Lloyds JTS XXX, seasonal beers; Tetley Bitter ⊞
Well situated, near the River Trent, the home of Derbyshire's brewery revival in 1977; try the porter.

KNIVETON
Red Lion
Wirksworth Road
12-2.30, 7-11; 12-2.30, 7-10.30 Sun
Burton Bridge Bitter; guest beers ⊞
Friendly village local, with an outdoor skittle alley, and well-known locally for its unusual range of vegetarian food, served daily.

DARLEY ABBEY

Abbey

Darley Street (on riverside)
☼ 11.30-2.30, 6-11; 12-11Sat; 12-10.30 Sun
☎ (01332) 558297
Samuel Smith OBB Ⓗ

This erstwhile guesthouse is all that survives of the Augustinian Abbey of St Mary de Pratis, the most powerful abbey in middle England before the Dissolution. Rescued from long neglect in 1978, it won the architect a national award for its sympathetic conversion to present use. Friar Tuck himself would feel quite at home in here. Do not miss the upper floor, reached via a stone staircase. At the heart of a charming conservation area, the abbey is a pleasant walk from the Furnace pub (see Derby) across Darley Park. ▲Q✿◑ⅅ♣P

DERBY

Alexandra Hotel

203 Siddals Road (by station)
☼ 11-11; 12-3, 7-10.30 Sun
☎ (01332) 293993
Bateman XB; Draught Bass; Hook Norton Best Bitter; Taylor Landlord; guest beers Ⓗ

Not so long ago, the end wall boasted a big sign advertising Zacharia Smith's Shardlow Ales, but both the sign and brewery have slipped into history. Long a Shipstone's house, then Bateman's, now Tynemill, it has become a champion of micro-breweries, like its neighbour, the Brunswick. Named after the popular Queen of Edward VII, it is steeped in railway memorabilia. As well as its ever-changing range of British beers it offers a good choice of continental brews, malt whiskies and country wines. Meals and accommodation represent good value.
Q✿☒◑ⅅ&≠♣●P⅄

Brunswick Inn

1 Railway Terrace (by station)
☼ 11-11; 12-10.30 sun
☎ (01332) 290677
Brunswick Triple Hop, Second Brew, Railway Porter; Sarah Hughes Dark Ruby; Taylor Landlord Ⓗ **guest beers** Ⓗ/Ⓖ

The world's first railway inn was built by the Midland Railway as the centrepiece of the railway village, now a conservation area. Then, as now, it had its own brewhouse and several distinct rooms, but no bars; all the ale was served by pot-boys. It was acquired by Hardys & Hansons in 1947 and run by them until 1974, when it closed and fell into dereliction. Rescued and restored by the Derbyshire Historic Buildings Trust, it was reopened in 1987 to become one of the best-known free houses in the country, and a champion of small brewers.
Q☎✿◑ⅅ&≠♣●⅄

Captain Blake

Agard Street (off Friargate)
☼ 11.30-2.30, 5-11; 11-11 Sat; 12-4, 7-10.30 Sun
☎ (01332) 295284
Adnams Bitter; Draught Bass; Marston's Pedigree Ⓗ

Standing beside Markeaton Brook in Derby's west end, this former home-brew house was originally the Golden Eagle, renamed after its latest make-over to honour a local youth leader. Rather dwarfed nowadays by neighbouring student

residences and the Inland Revenue building opposite, the interior divides into several discrete seating areas, though a knot of regulars rallies at the bar. Pleasantly lit, it could not be more removed from the roughhouse that was once the Golden Eagle. One of only two places in Derby to be sure of Adnams. ✿◑▶

Crompton Tavern

Crompton Street
☼ 11-11; 12-10.30 Sun
☎ (01332) 292259
Banks's Bitter; Marston's Pedigree; Taylor Landlord; guest beers Ⓗ

In a cul-de-sac off Green Lane, picked out at night by fairy lights, two front doors open on to different sides of the same bar, with lower-level areas on either side; one is occupied by a pool table. The walls of the cheery interior serve as a free gallery for local artists. It used to provide digs for travelling theatricals, and it was just around the corner at the Grand Theatre that the very first performance of Bram Stoker's *Dracula* was staged in 1924. ▲✿♣

Duke of Clarence

87 Mansfield Road (near Chester Green)
☼ 12-11; 12-4, 7-10.30 Sun
☎ (01332) 346882
Hardys & Hansons Best Mild, Best Bitter, seasonal beers Ⓗ

Named after the first Duke of Clarence (William IV), this unpretentious roadside local stands close to the site of a Roman encampment, now marked only by street names. The older part (with crooked upper windows) was a farmhouse, before the area was built up, and later extended to make a music room. The rather cramped bar is given exotic interest by a tankful of piranhas. A brass marker on the bar counter shows the height of the flood in 1965 when the nearby Derwent burst its banks. One of the rare good mild houses in Derby.
Q✿☒&♣P

Falstaff

74 Silverhill Road, Normanton
☼ 12-11; 12-10.30 Sun
☎ (01332) 342902
Greene King Abbot; Marston's Pedigree; guest beers Ⓗ

Known locally as the Folly, this was built as a latter-day coaching inn for Pountain, Girardot & Forman (see the terracotta monogram outside), before the surrounding area was built up, closing it in. Formerly an Allied house, it was for many years keg-only until acquired by an enthusiastic publican (now retired). The curved bar is flanked on one side by a small lounge and on the other by a games room. Frequented by 'new-agers', students and locals, a brew-house opened and closed in the space of a year, but may yet be revived.
▲Q✿☒♣

Flowerpot

25 King Street
☼ 11-11; 12-10.30 Sun
☎ (01332) 204955
Draught Bass; Ⓖ Marston's Pedigree; Ⓗ **guest beers** Ⓗ/Ⓖ

Just up from the cathedral, this is one of the pubs that spearheaded Derby's free trade expansion in the 1990s, to become a showcase for small breweries. Much expanded from its original premises, it reaches far back and divides into several interlinking rooms, the furthest providing the stage for a lively gig scene. Note the glass cellar wall, revealing row on row of stillaged firkins (up to two dozen), all gravity dispensed. The patio is fringed with flowering cherry trees in spring. There is a car park opposite. Q❀◖❶❃⌖♠

Friargate
114 Friargate
✪ 11-11; 7-10.30 Sun
☎ (01332) 297065
Draught Bass; Marston's Pedigree; Ⓖ Oakham JHB; Whim Arbor Light, Hartington IPA; Ⓗ guest beers Ⓗ/Ⓖ
Close to the site of a Dominican friary, in one of Derby's older streets, this attractive Victorian free house replaced a much older, timber-framed ale house called the Sun. It stands almost opposite the deconsecrated church where Doctor Johnson married Tetty Porter in 1736; further up is the old county gaol (now a museum) where 'England's last revolutionaries' were hanged and beheaded in 1817. A changing guest range frequently includes Rooster's. It hosts live music (most Wed). Several good restaurants are nearby, but parking is difficult. ◖❃P

Furnace
Duke Street
✪ 11-11; 12-3, 6.30-10.30 Sun
☎ (01332) 331563
Hardys & Hansons Best Mild, Best Bitter, Classic, seasonal beers Ⓗ
Just off old St Mary's Bridge, with its 15th-century bridge chapel, the Furnace stands on the west bank of the Derwent at the edge of Darley Park, faced by a cliff-like block of flats. The name preserves a connection with Handyside's Britannia foundry, to which it once belonged. Scenes of contemporary Derby decorate the walls and bar top. Unlike the historic Abbey across the park, it is the pubby atmosphere rather than the building that gives this local boozer its appeal, with a well-used dartboard and juke box. It hosts Karaoke weekend eves.
❀❃♠P

Old Dolphin ☆
5 Queen Street
✪ 10.30 (9am for breakfast)-11; 12-10.30 Sun
☎ (01332) 267711
Adnams Bitter, Draught Bass; Black Sheep Special; Caledonian Deuchars IPA; Fuller's London Pride; Greene King Abbot; guest beers Ⓗ
The most picturesque and oldest pub in the city centre, though much restored latterly. The old sign depicts a scaly, green-eyed fish, the pre-Reformation symbol of Christianity, consistent with the date (1530) which it shares with the gothic tower close by. The beamed interior comprises a bar, snug, upper and lower lounges and an upstairs steak bar (6–midnight and breakfast). The extensive patio is decked with flowers and illuminated in summer. An equestrian statue of Bonnie Prince Charlie (this was as far as he got) stands on Cathedral Green at the rear. An annual beer festival is held in July. ⌖Q❀◖❶❃♠P

Rowditch Inn
246 Uttoxeter New Road (1 mile from centre)
✪ 12-2 (not Mon-Wed), 7-11; 12-2, 7-10.30 Sun
☎ (01332) 343123
Hardys & Hansons Best Bitter, Classic, seasonal beers; Marston's Pedigree; guest beers Ⓗ
On the borough's ancient boundary, that was marked by a defensive dyke or rough ditch (whence Rowditch), this plain-fronted, but welcoming roadside pub has an unexpectedly deep interior. The cluttered bar always offers a tempting ale choice. The vaulted cellar bar is a pleasant surprise, but is not always open. At the start of the last century this was one of a thousand houses owned by Strettons, by far the biggest brewer in Derbyshire, swallowed by Allsopps in 1927, when brewing was transferred to Burton. Local CAMRA *City Pub of the Year* 2001. ⌖❀♠⌖

Smithfield
Meadow Road
✪ 11-11; 12-10.30 (12-3, 7-10.30 winter) Sun
☎ (01332) 370429
Draught Bass; Oakham JHB, Bishop's Farewell; Whim Arbor Light, Hartington IPA; guest beers Ⓗ
Formerly leased to Offilers, now free, this bow-fronted riverside pub was built to serve the old cattle market by the cattle market bridge. Both bridge and market are now gone, leaving the 'Smithy' in a bit of a backwater, but only just downriver from the market place. The handpulls in the bar frequently dispense Derbyshire and Rooster's beers. The back room bears a stone fireplace and motley collection of wooden settles; the side room has big board games and giant-sized dominoes, but no children are allowed after 9pm. A pleasant outlook over the river can be enjoyed from outside seating. ⌖❃❀◖❶♠P

Station Inn
Midland Road
✪ 11.30-2.30, 5 (7 Sat)-11; 11.30-11 Fri; 12-3, 7-10.30 Sun
☎ (01332) 608014
Draught Bass; Ⓖ Marston's Pedigree Ⓗ
This modest, but elaborately-fronted pub was named after the Midland Railway's classical station nearby, replaced in 1983 by the present functional, but uninspiring edifice. The pub, however, retains a traditional bar with panelled counter, cast iron foot rail and quarry-tiled floor; many cellar awards attest to the skill of the well-established licensee. In the pool room is a prominent portrait of 'Hurricane' Higgins, and a gleaming row of trophies. Bar room conversation is punctuated with the shrill whistle of the pub cockatiel. The Sun lunches are good value. ◖❶❖♠❒

Jolly Farmer
Pentland Road (off B6056)
✪ 12-11; 12-10.30 Sun
☎ (01246) 418018
Marston's Pedigree; John Smith's Bitter, Magnet; Taylor Landlord; Tetley Bitter; guest beers Ⓗ
Built by the lamented former Nottingham brewers Shipstone's, this pub opened in 1976 as the Gorsey Brigg. It later became a Greenalls ale house, renovated in

farmhouse style – open plan with many alcoves. Further changes of ownership have occurred, but the manager is keen to keep as large a range of beers as he can. There is a glass-fronted cellar behind the bar and no lager or keg fonts are visible. The pub, serving a large private housing estate, is well supported by local residents. No eve meals Sun. ❀◑❿❧♣♣

Quiet Woman
Off B5053
❀ 12-4, 7-11; 12-3, 7-10.30 Sun
☎ (01298) 83211
Adnams Bitter; Mansfield Dark Mild; Marston's Bitter, Pedigree; guest beer Ⓗ
This unspoilt local is set at the heart of the Peak District National Park, opposite the village church and green. The low-beamed room has a real fire and a small bar; one of the beams displays Marston's pump clips from long-lost beers. Two dominoes tables are in the main bar, and there is a separate games room. Basic lunchtime snacks, local cheeses, fresh eggs and traditional pork pies can be purchased from the bar. Walkers are welcome. Live folk music is performed every Sun. ㎫Q❀♣♣P

Bentley Brook Inn
On A515
❀ 11-11; 12-10.30 Sun
☎ (01335) 350278
Marston's Pedigree; guest beers Ⓗ
Roadside pub combining the elegance of a modest country house, with the friendliness of a family-run hotel, and the added attraction of Leatherbritches Brewery. Beyond the gateway to Dovedale, it gives ideal access to local scenery. The revitalised range expands for the summer season; the choice at the bar varies but always includes beers from Leatherbritches. At least two real ciders are always available. A pleasant outdoor terrace overlooks an extensive garden where regular 'blues & booze' festivals are held in a marquee; it also has a skittle alley.
㎫☎❀☒◑❧▲♣♣▶P✄

Bull's Head
102 Church Street, Old Glossop
❀ 2 (12 Sat)-11; 12-10.30 Sun
☎ (01457) 853291
Robinson's Old Stockport, Best Bitter Ⓗ
16th-century roadside pub in the quiet, old part of town at the foot of the Pennines. Renowned for its Indian balti cuisine, meals are now served in a recently-extended dining room. The pub boasts a good, traditional, northern style tap room. It can be reached by a pleasant walk through Manor Park, from the town centre, as well as by road. ☎❀◑❧♣

Crown Inn ⬸
142 Victoria Street
❀ 5 (12 Fri & Sat)-11; 12-10.30 Sun
☎ (01457) 862824
Samuel Smith OBB Ⓗ
Friendly local, in the Whitfield area of

town, where a central curved bar serves two small snugs, a bar area and a large games room. Built at the end of a terrace in 1846, it has been a Sam Smith's house since 1977 – the only one in the entire High Peak. Old pictures of Glossop feature in the bar area. The Crown is testament to the fact that pubs do not need to have their interiors ruined to be a popular and pleasant place in which to drink; a fine example of the type of local that is sadly disappearing.
㎫Q❀☒♣♣✄

Friendship
3 Arundel Street
❀ 4 (3 Fri; 12 Sat)-11; 12-3, 7-10.30 Sun
☎ (01457) 855277
Robinson's Hatters Mild, Best Bitter, seasonal beers Ⓗ
Street-corner local run by a committed licensee who has recently made sympathetic refurbishments that have not spoilt the pub's character. A semi-circular bar and a wood-panelled interior are attractive features of the open-plan lounge. A corner is dedicated to the local cricket enthusiasts who frequent the pub, along with those from Glossop FC, also close by. The back tap room is served by a hatch. Up to 30 malt whiskies are sold. Families with children are welcome until 8pm. Note the impressive lamp over the front door, circa 1900. ㎫☒❧♣

Old Gloveworks
Riverside Mill, George Street
❀ 12-11 (may shut in early eve Mon-Wed in winter); 12-10.30 Sun
☎ (01457) 858432
John Smith's Bitter; Theakston Cool Cask; guest beers Ⓗ
Converted mill, previously a wine bar, affording elevated views over Glossop Brook. Entertainment includes local bands (Thu), discos (Fri and Sat) and Sun cabaret (from 3.30pm). Four ever-changing guest beers are stocked. A discretionary age limit of 25 upwards is imposed by the landlord, a licence extension until midnight Fri and Sat applies to those in by 10.45pm. Outside, enjoy the riverside patio and roof terrace. Weekday lunches served. ❀◑⇌P

Star Inn Ale House
2 Howard Street
❀ 11-11; 12-10.30 Sun
☎ (01457) 853072
Boddingtons Bitter; Taylor Landlord; guest beers Ⓗ
Highly regarded ale house, selling 12–15 guest beers each week. Bare floorboards and the back tap room, served by a hatch, create an authentic atmosphere. Background music does not intrude on conversation. Built in 1837, it became a Boddingtons house in 1889 and remained so until acquired by Greenalls in 1993. Local tastes ensure that only rarely is a dark beer on sale, but Pictish and Phoenix beers frequently appear. Handy for buses, it stands opposite the rail station. ♣⇌♣P

Little John Hotel
Station Road (B6001)
❀ 11-11; 12-10.30 Sun
☎ (01433) 650225

Beer range varies Ⓗ

Large, stone former Whitbread pub, now a free house, serving an ever-changing range of real ales; expect a choice of around six at any one time. The home-cooked food is renowned for the generosity of its helpings (meals served all day Sat and Sun). Accommodation is available in the pub and also in new holiday cottages built behind the car park. One long bar serves several areas; the games area has a bar billiards table dating from 1902. Usual activities are folk (Sun), Karaoke (Tue), quiz (Wed) and bingo (Fri).
♨Q✦◑占⇌♣☀⌘

Scotsman's Pack
School Lane
✪ 11.30-3, 6-11; 11.30-11 Sat; 12-10.30 Sun
☎ (01433) 650253

Burtonwood Bitter, Top Hat, guest beers Ⓗ
This comfortable village pub, built by Hope & Anchor about 100 years ago, was acquired by Burtonwood in the 1980s, and has become their flagship pub in the area. Three lounge areas are served by a central bar. Well known for meals (all day Sat and Sun), it is popular with locals and visitors. It hosts monthly jazz (first Mon) and a weekly quiz (Thu). Little John is reputedly buried in the nearby churchyard, and the pub displays details of the legend. High quality accommodation.
Q❀✦◑Å⇌♣P⌘

HAYFIELD

Royal Hotel
Market Street
✪ 11-3, 6-11; 11-11 Fri & Sat; 12-10.30 Sun
☎ (01663) 742721

Marston's Pedigree; Tetley Bitter; guest beers Ⓗ
Imposing stone pub entirely in keeping with its surrounding environment in an attractive Peak District village, this former vicarage stands near the church and cricket ground. The River Sett in front of the pub flows down from Kinder Scout. The traditional interior boasts original oak panels and pews, which, aided by real fires, give a pleasant, relaxing atmosphere. The pub usually holds a beer festival early Oct.
♨Q➴❀✦◑占ÅP⌘

HOLBROOK

Dead Poets Inn
Chapel Street
✪ 12-2.30, 5-11; 12-11 Fri & Sat; 12-10.30 Sun
☎ (01332) 780301

Greene King Abbot; Marston's Pedigree; Ⓖ **Wells Bombardier; guest beers** Ⓗ
Remarkable transformation from an ailing Allied house to a thriving free house, attracting drinkers from outside the village. Built in 1800, the high-backed pews, stone-flagged floors and the exposure of a previously hidden inglenook combine to create a medieval atmosphere. The licensee, a former coffin maker, believed that many of our famous poets gained inspiration for their work from atmospheric taverns such as this; poetry readings are held monthly (first Tue). The pub's growing reputation was crowned by the local CAMRA *Pub of the Year* award 1999. A house beer is brewed by Brunswick. ♨❀◑♣P

Wheel Inn
14 Chapel Street
✪ 12-2.30 (not Mon), 6.30-11, 11.30-11 Sun; 12-3, 7-10.30 Sun
☎ (01332) 880006

Courage Directors; Marston's Pedigree; Theakston Cool Cask, Old Peculier; Ⓗ **Whim Hartington Bitter;** Ⓖ **guest beers** Ⓗ/Ⓖ
Warm, 18th-century pub with a brewer's Tudor frontage, and much altered inside. The restaurant area offers a good range of reasonably priced home-cooked food (not served Sun eve or Mon). The patio and award-winning garden are a joy to behold in summer. Two beer festivals a year are held and up to 40 single malt whiskies are stocked. The house beer is from an undisclosed source. This *Guide* regular is in an exceptional village for real ale enthusiasts, with a decent bus service from Derby. ♨❀◑

HOLYMOORSIDE

Lamb Inn
16 Loads Road
✪ 12-3 (not Mon-Fri), 7-11; 12-3, 7-10.30 Sun
☎ (01246) 566167 e-mail: pgoucher@rd+.net

Home Bitter; guest beers Ⓗ
Cosy, two-roomed pub in a village close to the Peak District National Park, warmed by a real fire in one room. The holder of numerous CAMRA awards, it keeps up to six guest ales. A pleasant outdoor drinking area, is ideal for summer eves (note that the pub is closed lunchtime except at weekends). ♨Q❀♣P

HOPE

Cheshire Cheese
Edale Road
✪ 12-3, 6-11; 12-11 Sat; 12-4, 6-10.30 Sun
☎ (01433) 620381

Barnsley Bitter; Black Sheep Best Bitter; Whim Hartington Bitter; guest beer Ⓗ
This 16th-century inn has been a free house for a long time, but has not had such an enterprising range of beers until taken over by its present owner (formerly the cellar manager). The pub is small, with three cosy rooms, one of which is at a lower level than the other two. It is ideally situated, in the heart of walking country on the edge of the village, but also draws a faithful local trade. The car park is small and the road outside narrow – so it is best approached on foot. ♨Q❀✦◑ÅP

HULLAND WARD

Black Horse Inn
On A517, halfway between Ashbourne and Belper
✪ 12-2.30, 6-11; 12-3, 7-10.30 Sun
☎ (01335) 370206

Draught Bass; Marston's Pedigree; guest beers Ⓗ
This traditional 300-year-old country inn stands in an elevated village, in some of the most picturesque country outside the Peak, close to Carsington Water. It is noted for its two rotating guest ales, four-poster accommodation, bar billiards, and mind-bending bar puzzles (solutions given on donation to charity). The split-level, multi-roomed drinking area, with low-beamed ceilings and quarry-tiled floor, is served by a

central bar. An extensive bar menu, with a wide vegetarian selection (takeaways available) is complemented by a popular Sun carvery in the restaurant.
❀⇔◑❿♣P✂●

ILKESTON

Dewdrop Inn
Station Street (off A609, by railway bridge)
❀ 11.30-3 (not Sat), 7-11; 12-4.30, 7-10.30 Sun
☎ (0115) 932 9684 website: www.eggpie.com
Draught Bass; Taylor Best Bitter; Whim Hartington IPA; guest beers Ⓗ
Built in 1884 on the Lord Middleton estate, the Dewdrop had several brewery owners before becoming a free house in 1992, winning CAMRA's regional *Pub of the Year* award five years later. The three-roomed pub contains a public bar, lounge (with roaring fire most of the year) and a family room. It stocks over 50 malt whiskies, a house beer from Broadstone and an occasional cider. The patio is used for long alley skittles. It hosts annual beer festivals and regular cheese and wine eves.
▥Q⛄❀⇔♣♠

Durham Ox
25 Durham Street
❀ 11-11; 12-10.30 Sun
☎ (0115) 932 4570
Draught Bass; Ⓖ **Greene King IPA;** Ⓗ **guest beers** Ⓗ/Ⓖ
This typical, back-street local, dating back to 1760, was originally a prison with a network of tunnels, becoming a pub in the 19th century. The cosy, open-plan interior is divided into four distinct drinking areas, one with wooden settles, a real fire and old pictures from the coal mining era. Another area houses the TV, pool table and juke box. Regulars enjoy darts, dominoes, cribbage and long alley skittles. The licensees run occasional beer trips and always stock at least two guest beers. ▥♣▯

KILBURN

Travellers Rest
114 Chapel Street (1 mile off B6179, at toll-bar traffic lights)
❀ 12-4 (not Mon-Thu), 5.30-11; 12-4, 7-10.30 Sun
☎ (01332) 880108
Greene King Abbot; Ind Coope Burton Ale; Robinson's Best Bitter; Tetley Bitter Ⓗ
Traditional, friendly two-roomed village pub in a former mining area. Known locally as Mamma's after a previous landlady, it enjoys a good standing in several pub games leagues. The small garden houses an open skittle alley. It sells snacks and the local chippie is opposite. The selection of beers is unusual for the area. John Flamsteed, the first Astronomer Royal, was born in Denby village, a mile away.
▥❀⇔♣P

KILLAMARSH

Angel Inn
127 Rotherham Road, Norwood End (A618)
❀ 12-2.30, 4-11; 12-3, 7-10.30 Sun
☎ (0114) 248 5607
Greene King Old Speckled Hen; guest beers Ⓗ
Formerly the Norwood Hall, this pub dates back at least to the 17th century and parts

of the original building survive. It is close to the Chesterfield Canal and a pit (in the event of fatal mining accident, the pub's cellars were used as a mortuary). It is also near the Rother Valley Country Park. The present pub comprises a large open-plan lounge, on two levels, with an L-shaped bar and a games area, with pool table, at one end. No food Sun. ❀◑P✂

KIRK IRETON

Barley Mow ☆
Main Street
❀ 12-2, 7-11; 12-2, 7-10.30 Sun
☎ (01335) 370306
Hook Norton Old Hooky; Marston's Pedigree; guest beers Ⓖ
Tall, gabled Jacobean building, an archetypal country village pub of low-beamed ceilings, quarry-tiled floors, slate-topped tables and bench seating. No music, gaming machines, chintzy covers or excess luxury here. Once your beer has been served, straight from the barrels behind the bar, or via a jug from the cellar, you may choose to drink by the fire in the front bar or retire to the back room or parlour. In summer, drinkers spill out into the garden which boasts a sundial.
▥Q❀⇔⌂♣♠

LITTLE LONGSTONE

Packhorse Inn
Main Street
❀ 11.30-3 , 5 (6 Sat)-11; 12-10.30 Sun
☎ (01629) 640471 e-mail: packhorseinn2@aol.com
Marston's Bitter, Pedigree Ⓗ
Genuine village local, a pub since 1787, it has retained many original features. Located where the Monsal Trail emerges from fields on to the minor road leading to Monsal Head, it is popular with walkers, but also enjoys a local trade. Three small rooms are nicely decorated, but at busy times in fine weather it is possible to escape out the back to the garden, up a flight of steps. Live folk music is performed Wed eve – singers and players are welcome. ▥Q❀◑⌂♣

LITTON

Red Lion
Main Street
❀ 12-3, 6-11; 12-11 Sat; 12-10.30 Sun
☎ (01298) 871458 website: www.littonvillage.co.uk
Oakwell Barnsley Bitter; Tetley Bitter; guest beers Ⓗ
Gem of a local, now the hub of village life in the traditional way, but until recently it had become more of a restaurant under previous ownership. It faces south across a village green, complete with stocks. Three small rooms surround a huge open fireplace and a bit more space is created by the unusual sliding door leading into the pub. Two guest beers are usually available, often including Jennings Cumberland Ale and other beers from Oakwell Brewery. No food Sun eve. ▥Q❀◑⌂♣P✂

LONG EATON

Hole in the Wall
Regent Street
❀ 10.30-3.30, 5.30-11; 10.30-11 Fri & Sat; 12-4.30, 7-10.30 Sun

☎ (0115) 973 4920 e-mail: hiw.pub@ntlworld.com
Castle Rock Hemlock; Courage Directors; John Smith's Bitter; guest beers Ⓗ

This CAMRA award-winning, town-centre boozer has two rooms, plus a small serving hatch area. Popular with all ages who support local rugby, football and hockey teams, it is also strong on traditional pub games. Both rooms display large collections of bottles, stoneware and other breweriana. An enclosed patio houses long alley skittles and hosts regular barbecues in summer. Its ever-changing guest beer policy champions local micro-breweries, Castle Rock being a particular favourite. Bar snacks available; pay and display parking opposite. ☼⛟P

LONGSHAW

Grouse Inn
On A625 OS258779
✪ 12-3, 6-11; 12-11 Sat; 12-10.30 Sun
☎ (01433) 630423
Banks's Bitter; Marston's Pedigree; guest beer Ⓗ

Isolated moorland pub, originally thought to have been converted from a farmhouse to slake the thirsts of men building the nearby Totley tunnel. A long-standing free house, in the same family since 1965, its front lounge is cosy and decorated with photographs of local gritstone edges. Behind is the more basic tap room, which doubles as a function room and leads to a conservatory. The pub is particularly convenient for walkers. No eve meals are served Mon or Tue. The guest beer is from Banks's guest list. ⛺Q⛟❀◑⛟♣P⛟

LULLINGTON

Colvile Arms
Main Street
✪ 12-2 (not Mon-Fri), 7-11; 12-3, 7-10.30 Sun
☎ (01827) 373212
Draught Bass; Marston's Pedigree; guest beer Ⓗ

This 18th-century free house is situated at the heart of a hamlet of 130 people. The lounge, formerly two cottages, offers comfortable red velour seating around the walls. The second, central lounge encourages good conversation; while the snug, with its high-backed settles reminds visitors of earlier times. Three quiz teams and the local cricket team meet here regularly and traditional games are played in the snug. Outside there is a bowling green, garden and ample car park. ⛺❀♣P

MAKENEY

Holly Bush Inn
Holly Bush Lane OS352447
✪ 12-3, 5-11; 12-11 Fri & Sat; 12-10.30 Sun
☎ (01332) 841729
Brains Dark; Ⓗ **Greene King Ruddles County; Marston's Pedigree;** Ⓖ **guest beers** Ⓗ

Grade II listed, and once a farmhouse with its own brewery on the Strutt estate, this late 17th-century, former Offilers house positively oozes character. It stood on the Derby Turnpike before the Strutts opened the valley route in 1818; Dick Turpin is known to have drunk here. The enclosed wooden snug is sandwiched between two bars. Little changes here, least of all the licensees (only two families have run the pub since 1939). Spring and autumn beer festivals add to the usual range of up to five guest beers. ⛺Q⛟❀⛟P

MATLOCK ✲

Boat House Inn
110 Dale Road (A6 to Matlock Bath)
✪ 12-11; 12-10.30 Sun
☎ (01629) 583776
Hardys & Hansons Best Mild, Best Bitter, Classic, seasonal beers Ⓗ

Prominent two-roomed Dales pub on the main road between Matlock and the tourist magnet of Matlock Bath. Full of character, it features a cosy bar area, low-beamed ceilings and a real fire in winter. It can be relied upon to serve the full Kimberley range of cask ales, including the mild and seasonal beers when available. An extensive menu, with seafood a particular speciality, is served in the dining area. ⛺Q⛟❀◑⛟⛟P⛟

Crown
Crown Square
✪ 11-11; 12-10.30 Sun
☎ (01629) 580991
Courage Directors; Marston's Pedigree; Shepherd Neame Spitfire; Theakston Best Bitter, Old Peculier; guest beers Ⓗ

Modern Wetherspoon's pub built on the site of two shops. Busy at midday with shoppers, local workers and tourists, it changes character at night and becomes more of a young person's pub. It has an extensive no-smoking area and serves food all day. Convenient for both bus and railway stations, it is also handy for the market. ◑🅰●

MATLOCK BATH

Princess Victoria
South Parade
✪ 12-11; 12-10.30 Sun
☎ (01629) 57462
Greene King Abbot; Marston's Pedigree; Taylor Landlord; Wells Bombardier Ⓗ

Grade II listed building, it originally formed part of a terrace of hotels, built in the 18th century for visitors to this fashionable spa town. The cellar backs on to caves in the rocks where the thermal spring water is constantly running. Since ceasing business as a hotel, the property has had several uses, including selling Blue John gifts, and as a restaurant. The pub name is a reminder that Queen Victoria spent time in Matlock Bath as a young girl. ⛺◑≠

MONSAL HEAD

Monsal Head Hotel
On B6465
✪ 11-11; 12-10.30 Sun
☎ (01629) 640250 website: www.monsalhead.com
Courage Directors; Marston's Pedigree; Taylor Landlord; Theakston Best Bitter, Old Peculier; Whim Hartington Bitter Ⓗ

The hotel owes its existence to the now-closed Derby–Manchester railway line which plunged into a tunnel underneath here, before emerging on to a viaduct (now open to walkers) over the River Wye. Monsal Head remains a popular beauty spot for motorists. The real ale range is kept in the Stable Bar, to the rear, retaining the original floor and decorated appropriately. A house beer is brewed by Lloyds. The car park is small, but adjoins a much larger public car park. ⚫Q❀✍⬥◗Å♣◆P

NEW MILLS ✿

Pack Horse

Mellor Road (1 mile from centre)
✪ 12-3, 5-11; 12-11 Sat; 12-10.30 Sun
☎ (01663) 742365
Tetley Bitter; guest beers Ⓗ

Stone-built, in keeping with the farmhouses dotted around the surrounding countryside, this pub nestles in a fold of the back road from New Mills to Mellor and Marple Bridge. Its hillside position affords good views up the valley to Hayfield and Kinder Scout beyond, and south over Ollersett Moor to Chinley. A comfortable, well-appointed single room serves good quality meals until late. Catering for all tastes, it is a friendly, relaxing place in which to drink and dine.
⚫Q❀✍◗P

OCKBROOK ✿

Royal Oak

Green Lane (off A52, follow Ilkeston signs)
✪ 11.30-2.30, 6.30-11; 12-2.30, 7-10.30 Sun
☎ (01332) 662378
Draught Bass; guest beers Ⓗ

Set well back from the road, across a cobbled courtyard, this fine pub was CAMRA East Midlands *Pub of the Year* 2000. In the same family since the 1950s, and little changed, its every aspect speaks of good, old-fashioned values; no dizzy lights or thumping music intrude here. Each room bears a different character, the newest being the Assemby Room where German POWs used to assemble before being set to work on neighbouring farms. Now it is the meeting place for, among others, local morris men and the Morris Minor Club. It hosts an annual beer festival (Oct).
Q❀◗♦♣P⚟

OLD TUPTON

Royal Oak

Derby Road (A61, 3 miles S of Chesterfield)
✪ 12-11; 12-10.30 Sun
☎ (01246) 862180
Home Bitter; John Smith's Bitter, Magnet; Theakston Old Peculier; Wells Bombardier; guest beers Ⓗ

Set on a roundabout on the main Chesterfield–Derby road, this 200-year-old brick free house has recently been sympathetically refurbished. The interior, although open plan, still has four distinct areas: a games room, tap room, snug and best room. These are complemented outside by a well-equipped children's play area, boules court and skittle alley. Watch out for annual beer festivals at this atmospheric local that extends a big welcome to travellers and walkers. Saxon cider is stocked.
⚫❀◗Å♣◆P◨●

OVER HADDON

Lathkil Hotel

From Bakewell, take B5055 for 1 mile, follow signs
OSSK206665
✪ 11.30-3, 7-11 (11-11 summer Sat); 12-4, 7-10.30 (12-10.30 summer) Sun
☎ (01629) 812501 website: www.lathkil.co.uk
Wells Bombardier; Whim Hartington Bitter; guest beer Ⓗ

Free house in an idyllic setting, benefiting from spectacular views across the picturesque Lathkil Dale Nature Reserve. The bar features fine oak panelling and a welcoming real fire, much appreciated by walkers who stop for a decent pint and a bite to eat. A must for any lovers of real ale, the Lathkil usually stocks two guest beers. The dining room offers quality food and an extensive specials board applies to diners in the bar, too. Superior accommodation is also available. The children's room opens lunchtime only.
⚫Q☎❀✍◗♣P◨

ROWARTH

Little Mill Inn

(signed off Siloh Road)
✪ 11-11; 12-10.30 Sun
☎ (01663) 743178
Banks's Bitter; Camerons Strongarm; Marston's Pedigree; guest beer Ⓗ

Spacious pub of character, with a history that tells a tale, originally a candlewick mill. It features a fully working waterwheel, commissioned and installed by the landlord. A large open area at the front of the pub provides a garden and adventure playground. A huge log fire dominates the lounge. Home-cooked food is served all day.
⚫Q☎❀✍◗⬥ÅP◨

INN BRIEF

MATLOCK

Duke William
91 Church Street
12 (5 Mon)-11;
12-10.30 Sun
Banks's Bitter; Mansfield Dark Mild; Marston's Pedigree, seasonal beers Ⓗ
Popular community pub that welcomes walkers.

Thorn Tree Inn
48 Jackson Road
12-2.30 (not Mon or Tue), 7-11; 12-10.30 Sun
Draught Bass; Black Sheep Best Bitter; guest beer Ⓗ
Two-roomed, back-street basic pub with a paved drinking area commanding a wonderful view. Snacks available.

NEW MILLS

Beehive
67 Albion Road
5-11; 4-10.30 Sun
Boddingtons Bitter; guest beers Ⓗ
Former tollhouse, now a superb place to drink, with beer downstairs and an Indian restaurant upstairs.

OCKBROOK

White Swan
19 Church Street
11-2.30, 7-11; 12-3, 7-10.30 Sun
Ind Coope Burton Ale; Marston's Pedigree; guest beer Ⓗ
Opposite end of the village from the Royal Oak (see listing), tucked away in leafy seclusion, a low-ceilinged lounge and cell-sized bar.

RIPLEY

Rose & Crown
23 Nottingham Road
12-4 (not Mon-Fri), 7-11;
12-3, 7-10.30 Sun
Bateman XB, XXXB; guest beers Ⓗ
Two-roomed local with a friendly atmosphere; TV in the bar and a skittle alley outside.

ROSLISTON

Bull's Head
19 Burton Road
12-3, 7-11; 12-3, 7-10.30 Sun
Draught Bass; Marston's Pedigree Ⓗ
Friendly, comfortable, 19th-century village pub serving meals at lunchtimes, including a traditional Sun roast.

SAWLEY

Harringtons Arms
392 Tamworth Road
(B6540, opp. church)
☺ 11-11; 12-10.30 Sun
☎ (0115) 973 2614
Hardys & Hansons Best Bitter, Classic, seasonal beers Ⓗ

Former coaching inn on a bend of the River Trent, this managed house has traditional decor throughout, with panelled walls, low-beamed ceilings and a large open-plan area of two distinct sections (both with open fires). It serves a range of freshly-cooked international dishes in the restaurant area, but the bar menu is just as good, with a continually changing blackboard menu and a good selection of wine. It hosts regular food-based theme nights (English, Greek and Thai) and an annual beer festival (Aug).
🏛🏵◑ᵹ≉(Long Eaton) P⊁●

SCARCLIFFE

Horse & Groom
Rotherham Road (B6417)
☺ 12-4, 6-11; 12-3, 7-10.30 Sun
☎ (01246) 823152
Draught Bass; Greene King Abbot; Mansfield Cask Ale; Stones Bitter; Theakston Best Bitter; guest beers Ⓗ

Free house standing at the crossroads at the top of the village. It is somewhat of a rarity in that it does not serve meals and eschews electronic slot machines – a proper pub offering good conversation. It has no family room, but there is a covered verandah at the rear, with a barrel water feature. Dark wood-panelled seats, a copper-topped bar and hunting scenes characterise the bar. The landlord has won an award for his Stones Bitter and keeps an extremely good selection of malt whiskies.
Q🏵ᵹ♣P

SMALLEY

Bell Inn
35 Main Road
☺ 11.30-3, 5-11; 11-11 Sat; 12-10.30 Sun
☎ (01332) 880635
Adnams Broadside; Glentworth Dizzy Blonde; Mallard Duckling; Marston's Pedigree; Whim Hartington Bitter; guest beers Ⓗ

Popular 150-year-old, two-roomed local, a firm champion of local micro-breweries; the Dizzy Blonde is said to have been especially chosen to reflect the landlady's character. The cellarman is the previous licensee – the pub has been a *Guide* regular for some years. Much historical and brewing memorabilia adorn the walls. The excellent value home-cooked food includes a range of curries. An adjoining stable block has been converted to three apartments offering year-round accommodation; Shipley Country Park is a local attraction.
🏛Q🏵🛏◑ᵹᵹP

SOUTH NORMANTON ❖

Clock Inn
107 Market Street
☺ 11-11; 12-10.30 Sun
☎ (01773) 811396 website: www.theclockinn.co.uk
Marston's Bitter; Shepherd Neame Spitfire; guest beers Ⓗ

Extensively refurbished, family-run free house, the pub's own jazz band – the Clock Inn All Stars – play Mon eve. It stages themed nights for folk music and blues (Fri) while Sat eve showcases 60s to 80s music and Sun is 'Rock'n'Roll Nite'. Excellent home-cooked food, in generous helpings, is available all day, including daily specials. This local CAMRA *Pub of the Season* operates a driver-friendly soft drinks pricing policy. The pub has two rooms – a tap room and quiet lounge bar which is completely no-smoking.
Q🏵◑ᵹ♣P⊁

STANTON IN PEAK

Flying Childers
Main Road
☺ 12-2 (3 Sat; not Mon), 7-11; 12-3, 7-10.30 Sun
☎ (01629) 636333
Bateman XB; guest beer Ⓗ

Created out of four cottages in the 18th century, this free house stocks changing guest beers from a range of brewers, including Bass, Fuller's, Marston's and Whim. The cosy, timeless bar offers a real fire, wooden settles and beams, while the lounge has leather seating – both rooms are adorned with copious brass. Cobs and sandwiches are available lunchtime. Handy for walkers exploring the magical Stanton Moor, the pub name commemorates the fourth Duke of Devonshire's favoured racehorse.
🏛Q🏵ᵹ▲♣P

SHELTON LOCK
New Bridge Inn
262 Chellaston Road
11-3, 5-11; 11-11 Fri & Sat; 12-10.30 Sun
Banks's Original; Marston's Pedigree Ⓗ
Roadside pub, its traditional bar and lounge are a hub of local activity, particularly the huge fishing club.

SOUTH NORMANTON
Boundary
Lea Vale, Broadmeadows
12-3, 5-11; 12-11 Fri & Sat; 12-10.30 Sun
Draught Bass; Bateman XXB; Fuller's London Pride; Mansfield Cask Ale; Young's Special; guest beers Ⓗ
Large estate pub with food, accommodation, children's play areas and a guest beer club – customers choose the beers.

STONEY MIDDLETON
Moon Inn
Town End
12-2.30, 6-11; 12-11 Sat; 12-3, 7-10.30 Sun
Stones Bitter; guest beer Ⓗ
Cosy, low-ceilinged pub in a quarrying village.

TICKNALL
Staff of Life
Ashby Road
11.30-2.30, 6.30-11; 12-2.30, 6.30-10.30 Sun
Taylor Landlord; Marston's Pedigree; guest beers Ⓗ /Ⓖ
Convenient stop near Calke Abbey. Ask for gravity dispense. Good food is served daily. *Cask Marque* accredited.

STAVELEY

Speedwell Inn
Lowgates
⊛ 6 (5 Fri & Sat)-11; 5-10.30 Sun
☎ (01246) 472252
Townes Sunshine, Golden Bud, Speedwell Bitter, Best Lockoford Bitter, seasonal beers; guest beers ℍ
Visitors who enjoy good beer in simple surroundings will love this pub. Situated in a former coal mining village on the main A619, this ex-John Smith's house, closed in 1995 and became the home of Townes Brewery in 1998. The comfortable, local was voted Chesterfield CAMRA *Pub of the Year* 2000, after only reopening to the public in Nov 1999. An annual beer festival is held (Dec) with up to 25 beers on offer. Saxon cider is sold. Q♣♠P⦸⊟

SUTTON CUM DUCKMANTON

Arkwright Arms
Chesterfield Road (A632, between Chesterfield and Bolsover)
⊛ 11-11; 12-10.30 Sun
☎ (01246) 232053 website: www.arkers.co.uk
Marston's Pedigree; guest beers ℍ
Friendly, traditional free house where four guest ales are usually on offer. It has a separate restaurant but eve meals are only served Fri and Sat. A beer festival is held every Easter. ♨Q⊛◑∅♣♠P

TROWAY

Gate Inn
Main Road
⊛ 12-3, 7-11; 12-3, 7-10.30 Sun
☎ (01246) 413280
Burtonwood, Top Hat; guest beer ℍ
Relax and soak up the charm of this small, friendly pub in good walking country on the south side of the Moss Valley. Burtonwood's monthly guest beer policy adds welcome variety to the range available. There is usually a dog or two sprawled in front of the fire in the bar, keeping a watchful eye open for the resident cats, while ducks have their own miniscule pond in the well-tended garden. The annual marrow contest (Oct) provides much entertainment, especially in the 'Best Dressed' class. ♨Q⊛∅♣♠P⊟

WESTON-ON-TRENT

Coopers Arms
Weston Hall (signed off main road)
⊛ 11-11; 12-10.30 Sun
☎ (01332) 690002 website: www.coopers-arms.co.uk
Draught Bass; Marston's Pedigree; ℍ **guest beer** ⒼB
Pub in a 17th-century 'skyscraper', visible from several miles around and commanding impressive views over a picturesque landscape. The ground floor is used for conferences and weddings. The basement houses a popular carvery and the all-important bar with a drinkers' corner. It is a frequent *Publican* award-winner, including *Free House of the Year* 2000. The recent arrival of a guest beer on cooled gravity dispense is most welcome. The house was used as a Parliamentarian garrison during the Civil War; the former moat has been converted into a lake (fishing tickets available). ♨Q⊛◑P

WHALEY BRIDGE

Shepherd's Arms
7 Old Road
⊛ 12-11; 12-10.30 Sun
☎ (01663) 732840
Banks's Original; Marston's Bitter, Pedigree ℍ
Attractive whitewashed building in the centre of Whaley Bridge, overlooking the A6, close to the station and the notable architecture of the Peak Forest Canal terminus basin. This is an ageless local of the type that are sadly disappearing. Its interesting layout includes a quiet, comfortable lounge; however the pub's pride and joy is the traditional tap room. ♨Q⊛◑⇌♣P

WHITWELL

Mallet & Chisel
Hillside
⊛ 12-3, 5.30-11; 11-11 Sat; 12-10.30 Sun
☎ (01909) 720343
Mansfield Dark Mild, Riding Bitter; Tetley Bitter; guest beer ℍ
Hidden away in a picturesque and historic village, this pub was originally known as the Mallet & Tool, and until 1867 it held a beer house licence. Four real ales can be enjoyed in this comfortable, friendly local, enhanced by two real fires and exposed beams. Good value home-cooked food is another attraction, making this unspoilt pub well worth seeking out.
♨⊛◑⇌♣P

WINSTER

Old Bowling Green ⟵
East Bank (off B5057 at old market hall, NT)
⊛ 6 (12 Sat)-11; 12-10.30 Sun
☎ (01629) 650219 website: www.bowling_green.co.uk
Black Sheep Best Bitter; Whim Hartington Bitter; guest beers ℍ
Free house, built in 1472, this unusual cruck construction is the oldest in the village, comprising a lounge with real fire and parlour bars, conservatory/family room, an upstairs dining room for larger parties and an outside drinking area. The attention to detail is impressive – from the fine original pictures to the splendid ladies' loo – creating a comfortable, quiet and smoke-free environment. Fresh, varied, good quality food is served 6–9 and weekend lunchtimes (booking recommended).
♨Q☎⊛◑♿♠P⦸

YOULGREAVE

George Hotel
Church Street
⊛ 11-11; 12-10.30 Sun
☎ (01629) 636292
John Smith's Bitter; Theakston Mild; guest beers ℍ
Award-winning, 17th-century village pub with accommodation, overlooked by a magnificent 12th-century church. Situated on the Limestone Way, this village is popular with walkers, who are welcome at the George. The friendly three-roomed pub was formerly known as the Pig o' Lead, highlighting the historical importance of mining to the community. The menu specialises in game dishes.
Q⊛≏◑⊟♠P

CAMRA's National Inventory
of Pubs Interiors of Outstanding Historic Interest

Kent

Broadstairs: Neptune's Hall, Harbour Street. Last-remaining unspoilt fishermen's pub in the area: three rooms (was five). Good bar back.
Cowden Pound: Queens Arms. Victorian roadside pub with original fittings.
Ightham Common: Old House. Part 17th-, part 19th-century cottages with two public rooms. Restricted hours.
Snargate: Red Lion. Quaint rural village pub in same family since 1911: white marble bar top: casks behind the bar.

Lancashire

Great Harwood: Victoria, St John's Street. Edwardian pub: superb tiling, five-rooms and counter screens
Preston: Black Horse, 166 Friargate. 1898. Superb fittings including ceramic bar counter.

Leicestershire

Medbourne: Horse & Trumpet. Basic village pub. Closed at time of going to press

Greater London

Central

EC1 Hatton Garden: Olde Mitre, Ely Court, Ely Place. Tucked-away late 18th-century pub with 1930s panelled interior. Closed weekends.
EC4 Blackfriars: Black Friar, 174 Queen Victoria Street. c.1875 pub given a unique Art Nouveau makeover in 1905. Magnificently appointed. Closed weekends.
WC1 Holborn: Cittie of York, 22 High Holborn. 1923-4. Medieval-style baronial hall lounge with 10 drinking booths, enormous casks and high-level walkway. Closed Sun.
WC1 Holborn: Princess Louise, 208 High Holborn. Built 1872 and magnificently refitted 1891. Lavish gents' toilets.
WC2 Covent Garden: Lamb & Flag, Rose Street. 18th-century building, Victorian fittings.
WC2 Covent Garden: Salisbury, St Martin's Lane. c.1899 retaining fine woodwork and glass.

North

N4 Finsbury Park: Salisbury, 1 Grand Parade, Green Lanes. Sumptuous pub of 1898-9: billiard room with impressive skylight.

North-West

NW3 Hampstead: Holly Bush, Holly Mount. Tucked-away pub with number of rooms.
NW6 Kilburn: Black Lion, 274 Kilburn High Road. 1898 with spacious layout and fine fittings.
NW8 St John's Wood: Crocker's Folly, Aberdeen Place. Grand pub of 1898: superb fittings. Restaurant originally the billiard hall.

South-East

SE21 Dulwich: Crown & Greyhound, Dulwich Village. Imposing pub of c.1900 with good fittings.

South-West

SW1 St James: Red Lion, Duke of York Street. Small in scale but opulently fitted c.1900. Closed Sun.

West

W1 Marylebone: Barley Mow, Dorset Street. Victorian bar fittings: two unique, tiny drinking boxes. Closed Sun.
W1 Soho: Argyll Arms, Argyll Street. Remodelled c.1895: still retains three small bars and stunning display of glass and mahogany.
W9 Maida Vale: Prince Alfred, Formosa Street. Supreme example of a multi-partitioned Victorian pub interior: an amazing survivor.
W9 Maida Vale: Warrington Hotel, 93 Warrington Crescent. Spectacularly appointed pub of c.1900 (the garish paintings are modern).

Greater Manchester

Altrincham: Railway, 153 Manchester Road. Small Victorian pub with simply appointed rooms.
Bolton: Howcroft, Clarence Court. Victorian pub with unusual layout and bowling green.
Eccles: Grapes, 439 Liverpool Road, Peel Green. 1903. Fine woodwork, glass etc.
Eccles: Lamb, 33 Regent Street. 1906. Splendid array of fittings. Billiard room.
Eccles: Royal Oak, Barton Lane. Red brick and terracotta pub of 1904 with excellent fittings. Intact outdoor department and stables.
Gorton: Plough, 927 Hyde Road. 1893 remodelling with impressive fittings. Four rooms.
Heaton Norris: Nursery Inn, Green Lane. 1939. Three rooms, panelling and own bowling green.

Manchester

City centre: Briton's Protection, Great Bridgewater Street. Good c.1930 interior and several rooms: restricted weekend hours.
City centre: Circus Tavern, 86 Portland Street. Tiny two-room pub: no lager or wine. Closed Sundays.
City centre: Hare & Hounds, 46 Shudehill. Intact c.1930 interior: two rooms and drinking lobby.
City centre: Mr Thomas's, 52 Cross Street. Tall narrow luncheon bar of 1901 with much tiling. Closed Sun.
City centre: Peveril of the Peak, Great Bridgewater Street. Remodelled c.1900 with colourful exterior tiling, three rooms and a drinking lobby. Restricted weekend hours.
Mossley: Colliers Arms, Broadcarr Lane. Basic pub in 18th-century building. Restricted hours.
Rochdale: Cemetery Hotel, 470 Bury Road. c.1900. Carefully preserved with very contrasting rooms: good Art Nouveau tiling.
Salford: Coach & Horses, 350 Eccles New Road.1920s but with Victorian-style planning. Stalybridge
Salford: Grosvenor, Grosvenor Street. 1930s remodelling. Huge drinking lobby with three small rooms leading off.
Salford: Station Buffet. 1885. Rare, genuine 1880s Victorian railway buffet bar.
Stockport: Alexandra, 195 Northgate Road, Edgeley. Intact five-roomed pub of 1911; rich fittings.
Stockport: Arden Arms, Millgate. Victorian gem with access to snug through the bar.
Stockport: Bishop Blaize, Lower Hillgate. Refitting of c.1930 in early 19th-century terrace; interesting layout.
Stockport: Queen's Head, Little Underbank. Simple Victorian fittings. Rare spirit taps.
Stockport: Swan with Two Necks, Princes Street. Beautifully preserved c.1930 layout and fittings.
Wigan: Springfield Hotel, Springfield Road. Large red brick and terracotta 1903 pub.

Continued on page 143

DEVON

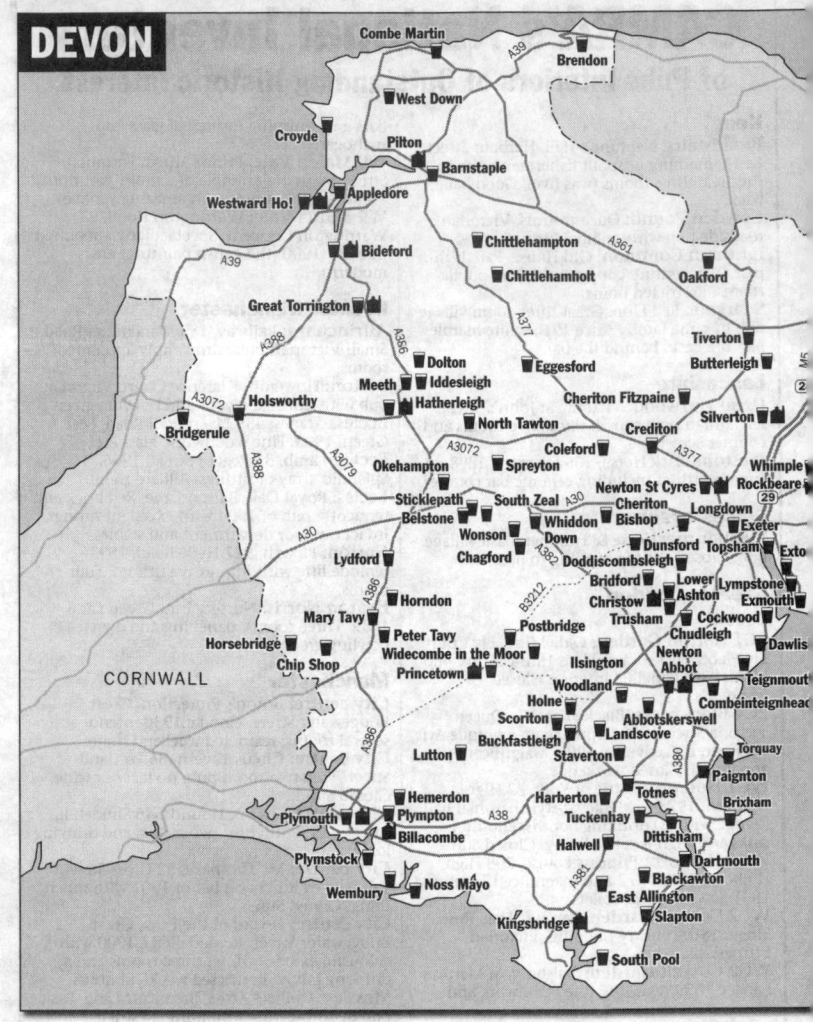

ABBOTSKERSWELL ✤

Court Farm Inn
Wilton Way
✪ 11-11; 12-10.30 Sun
☎ (01626) 361866
Draught Bass; ⒢ Flowers IPA; Fuller's London Pride; Wadworth 6X; guest beer ⒣
Impressive, characterful 17th-century Devon longhouse in the heart of the historic village. It was converted to a pub in 1972. It is an olde-worlde pub of old beams, wooden pews, brasses, great open fireplaces and a stone-flagged floor. It has extensive grounds with a play area outside. A varied menu features good quality dishes from around the world. Families with children are catered for and made most welcome. There is a large parking area at the front of the pub. ♨⚘⏣⊟♣P

APPLEDORE

Beaver Inn
Irsha Street (take A386 N from Bideford)
✪ 11-3.30, 6-11; 11.30-11 Sat; 12-10.30 Sun
☎ (01237) 474822
Draught Bass; guest beers ⒣
The Beaver has a fairly modern interior, with a raised area, where food is usually served, overlooking the estuary. The pub name results from an association with the fur trade in the early part of the last century. A games room houses pool and darts. The two guest beers always come from local breweries and the cider is Ostler's. After sampling the real ales why not try one of the large collection of whiskies from around the world? ♨⚘⏣▲♣⚘

Coach & Horses
5 Market Street (take A386 N from Bideford)
✪ 12-11; 12-10.30 Sun
☎ (01237) 474470
Fuller's London Pride; Marston's Pedigree; Wells Bombardier; guest beer ⒣
Friendly establishment, with a selection of five real ales to choose from. A real fire warms the bar and the games area can be serviced from its own section of the bar. The pub dates from the 17th century and

food, from a menu usually chalked on a blackboard. ♨ Q ◖ ⅃ & ♣ ♠ P

AXMOUTH

Ship Inn
Church Street
🕐 11-2.30, 6-11; 12-3, 7-10.30 Sun
☎ (01297) 21838
website: www.axmouth.uk.com/shipinn
Draught Bass; Otter Bitter Ale Ⓗ
This creeper-clad village pub was rebuilt in 1880 after a fire destroyed the original 10th-century building. Joint licensee, Christopher Chapman, is the son of the first TV 'super cook', Fanny Craddock. The public bar, known as the Guinness Bar, displays a collection of memorabilia, while the restaurant features costumed dolls from around the world. The decked garden area provides a home to convalescing owls. The skittle alley, in a separate building, doubles as a children's room when not in use. The Ship has been in every edition of this *Guide*. Q ⅍ ❀ ◖ ⊟ & Å ♣ P

BARNSTAPLE

Check Inn
14 Castle Street
🕐 11-11; 12-10.30 Sun
☎ (01271) 375964
Beer range varies Ⓗ/Ⓖ
North Devon CAMRA's *Pub of the Year* 1998 and 2001, this friendly town-centre house has put real ale on the map in Barnstaple. The landlord's enthusiasm is reflected in the constantly changing range of beers. The latest CAMRA award was celebrated with a specially-commissioned beer called, of course, Pub of the Year, brewed at Barnstaple's Barum Brewery. The Check supports countless pub sports teams and has welcomed several top darts players for charity matches. ☕ ≉ ♣ ♠

Reform Inn
Reform Street, Pilton
🕐 11.30-11; 12-10.30 Sun
☎ (01271) 323164 website: www.barumbrewery.co.uk
Beer range varies Ⓗ/Ⓖ
Welcome return to the *Guide* for the Reform, whose beers, of varying strengths, come from the Barum Brewery situated behind the pub. Fuller's has been known to

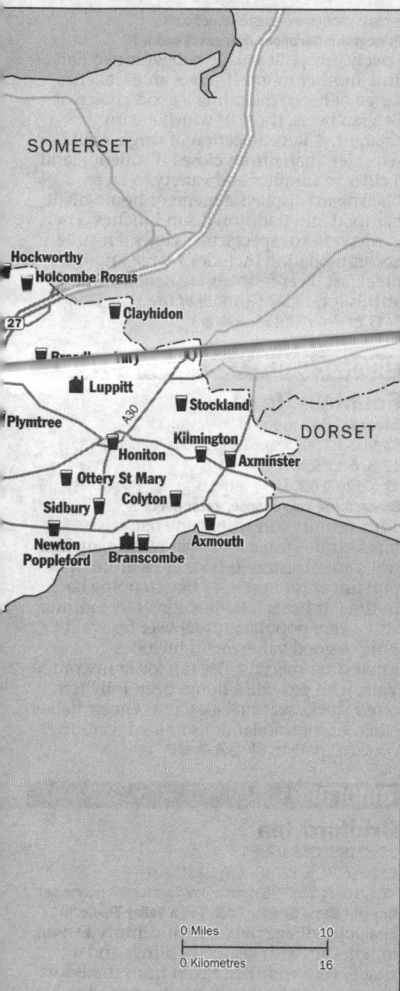

SOMERSET

Hockworthy
Holcombe Rogus
27
Clayhidon
Luppitt
Plymtree
Stockland
DORSET
Honiton
Kilmington
Ottery St Mary
Axminster
Sidbury
Colyton
Newton
Poppleford
Branscombe
Axmouth

0 Miles 10
0 Kilometres 16

was, according to legend, a favourite with the local smugglers. It hosts monthly food theme nights and quizzes; A traditional association with music is continued with Irish, folk and jazz nights. Camping is possible at nearby Knapp House. ♨ ❀ ◖ Å ♣

AXMINSTER

Red Lion Inn
Lyme Street
🕐 11-2.30, 7-11; 11-11 Thu-Sat; 12-2.30, 7-10.30 Sun
☎ (01297) 32016
website: www.axminster.uk.net-redlion
Branscombe Vale BVB; Otter Bitter; Tetley Bitter; guest beer Ⓗ
Welcoming town pub, at the eastern end of this lovely historic town, with a large car park opposite. Axminster is renowned for its world-famous carpets; it has a weekly cattle market and also holds an annual horticultural show (June). The landlord always serves four real ales, and his pub is extremely popular with the locals. The dining area serves good value home-cooked

INDEPENDENT BREWERIES

Barum Pilton
Beer Engine Newton St Cyres
Blewitts Kingsbridge
Branscombe Vale Branscombe
Clearwater Great Torrington
Country Life Westward Ho!
Exe Valley Silverton
Jollyboat Bideford
Otter Luppitt
Points West Plymouth
Princetown Princetown
Scattor Rock Christow
Summerskills Billacombe
Sutton Plymouth
Tally Ho! Hatherleigh
Teignworthy Newton Abbot

supply the occasional guest. The pub is divided into two bars, one with a pool table, the other with a fire, providing a more conversational atmosphere. It normally hosts two beer festivals a year, one of them providing a focus for Pilton's annual Green Man pageant. Q ≈ ♣

BELSTONE

Tors

OS619935

⚙ 11-2.30, 6-11 (11-11 summer); 12-3.30, 7-10.30 (12-10.30 summer) Sun

☎ (01837) 840689

Sharp's Doom Bar; guest beers Ⓗ

The Tors is a large granite building, next to the church in an unspoilt North Dartmoor village near Okehampton. The long, single bar acts as a friendly local while also catering for the many walkers who come to enjoy the open moorland, as well as the river valleys leading to the moor. The Tarka Trail passes through the village and pony trekking is also available nearby. Although the beer range varies regularly, the accent is on West Country products. Gray's cider is stocked in summer. 🏨 ▷ ✿ ⋈ ◑ ♣ ●

BIDEFORD

King's Arms

The Quay

⚙ 11-11; 12-10.30 Sun

☎ (01237) 475196

Beer range varies Ⓗ

In a town with a reputation for its nightlife, the King's Arms is a real ale oasis in Bideford's desert of keg. The tables have been moved from the main bar area to create more space in this busy pub, the only one on the town's river front. Low ceilings and exposed beams reveal its true age of some 350 years. Although popular with the younger crowd eves and weekends, it draws a good crowd all day and enjoys a lively atmosphere. The house beer is brewed by Clearwater. 🏨 ◁ ◑ ♣ ●

BLACKAWTON

George Inn ◁

Main Street (1 mile off A3122) OS805509

⚙ 12-2.30 (not Mon), 7-11; 12-3, 7-10.30 Sun

☎ (01803) 712342

e-mail: georgeinn@bushinternet.com

Princetown Dartmoor IPA; guest beers Ⓗ

Lovely, unspoilt village pub with two bars and another room. It serves an excellent range of beers, including a good choice of Belgian beers, three of which are on draught. A large selection of single malt whiskies, many from closed distilleries, and a cider in summer add variety. A large blackboard displays a menu of home-made bar food and traditional Sun lunches. The garden affords spectacular views. En-suite accommodation includes a large English breakfast. Beer festivals are held in summer at this local CAMRA *Pub of the Year* 1999. 🏨 Q ▷ ⊠ ✿ ◑ ◑ ⊟ ⌂ ♣ ● P

BRANSCOMBE

Fountain Head

Street (western end of linear village)

⚙ 11.30-2.30 (3 summer), 6.30 (6 summer)-11; 12-3, 6-11 Sun

☎ (01297) 680359

Branscombe Vale Branoc, guest beers Ⓗ

14th-century inn where one bar was a blacksmith's forge. Original wood-panelled walls and flagstoned floor are features in a pub full of interest – it's like stepping back in time. It hosts folk music eves in summer and a very popular annual beer festival in June. A good value menu includes interesting specials. The tap for Branscombe Vale, who provide a house beer, Jolly Jeff, it often stocks seasonal ales, plus Green Valley cider. Accommodation is in a self-catering cottage. 🏨 Q ▷ ◑ ⊟ ⌂ ♣ ● P

BRIDFORD

Bridford Inn

Off B3193 OS815864

⚙ 12-2.30, 6-11; 12-3, 7-10.30 Sun

☎ (01647) 252436 e-mail: david.gervers@lineone.net

Draught Bass; Scattor Rock Teign Valley Tipple Ⓗ

Spacious village pub, a 17th-century Devon longhouse, with beamed ceilings and a single, very wide bar, taken from the Boots pharmacy in Exeter. It was converted to a pub in 1968 with an open-plan seating area for drinkers and diners, plus an area for children, a snug and a meeting room. The large fireplace houses a wood-burning stove and a bread oven. The Bridford Jack house beer is brewed by Scattor Rock Brewery, using hops grown in the pub grounds. A

INN BRIEF

ABBOTSKERSWELL

Two Mile Oak

Totnes Road

11-11; 12-10.30 Sun

Draught Bass; Flowers IPA; Fuller's London Pride; Greene King Abbot Ⓖ

Ancient coaching house: a superb public bar and a lounge bar with dining area where excellent food is served.

BRENDON

Rockford Inn

12-11; 12-10.30 Sun; hours vary winter

Cotleigh Tawny, Barn Owl Ⓗ

Riverside pub in a stunning wooded valley of Exmoor, an excellent walking area.

BRIXHAM

Blue Anchor

83 Fore Street

11-11; 12-3, 7-10.30 Sun

Dartmoor Best Bitter; Greene King Abbot Ⓐ

16th-century harbourside pub that has served as a sail loft and a chapel; a cosy main bar and a small dining area.

CHITTLEHAMHOLT

Exeter Inn

11.30-2.30, 7-11 (11-11 summer); 12-3, 7-10.30 Sun

Dartmoor Best Bitter; Greene King Abbot Ⓗ

Fine village pub with a tradition of serving good food and fine beer. The interior boasts original beams. B&B available.

COCKWOOD

Anchor Inn

11-11;

12-10.30 Sun

Flowers Original; Fuller's London Pride; Greene King Abbot; Marston's Pedigree; Wadworth 6X Ⓗ

16th-century ex-seamens' mission with a friendly ghost. Low beams, flagged floors and settles feature at the CAMRA *Best UK Food Pub* 2000.

DAWLISH

Laffin Pig

1 Commercial Road

11-11;

12-10.30 Sun

Draught Bass; Flowers IPA; guest beers Ⓖ

Busy, no-frills, town-centre pub with a lively atmosphere.

good selection of food caters for all tastes. Cider in summer varies. Dogs welcome.

🏠 Q 🛏 ✿ 🍴 ◁◐ ♣ ♠ P

BRIDGERULE

Bridge Inn

Take A39 Bideford-Bude, then B3254

☻ 12-2 (not Mon-Fri), 6.30-11; 12-3, 7-10.30 Sun

☎ (01288) 381316

Flowers Original; guest beer Ⓗ

Delightful village pub where a real fire greets the winter visitor, set in a fireplace in the middle of the main bar. Good value snacks are served in one bar; ask for children's portions of meals if required. As with all traditional village pubs, the Bridge is a focal point for the community. It also enjoys a good summer trade from visitors who want to get away from the coast, and may open weekday lunchtimes in summer – phone to check. There is an aviary at the rear of the pub.

🏠 ✿ ◁◐ ♣ P

BROADHEMBURY

Drewe Arms

☻ 11-3, 6-11; 12-3 (closed eve) Sun

☎ (01404) 841267

Otter Bitter, Bright, Ale, Head Ⓖ

Picturesque, relatively unspoilt, thatched Grade II listed inn, set in a village of cob and thatched cottages, owned by the Drewe family of Castle Drogo in the Teign Valley, since early in the 20th century. Predominantly a food pub, the restaurant specialises in fish dishes (booking essential) and it has won numerous awards. The old-fashioned public bar is very small and displays cinema memorabilia, while the main bar houses various wicker items. The beers are served direct from barrels, housed in the walls. Q ✿ ◁◐ 🍴♣ P

BUCKFASTLEIGH

White Hart

2 Plymouth Road

☻ 12-2.30 (not Mon), 5.30 (6 Mon)-11; 12 (6 Mon)-11 summer; 12-3.30, 7-10.30 Sun

☎ (01364) 642337

website: www.onlinepubguide.com/the-white-hart/buckfastleigh/index

Greene King Abbot; Teignworthy Beachcomber; guest beer Ⓗ

Pleasant pub with a single, open-plan bar area, a dining area, plus a restaurant that is not open all year round. Outside, a large courtyard provides additional seating and summer barbecues. The house beer is brewed in Teignworthy. The guest beers are varied and come from all over the country, there is always one on tap. A good range of fresh, home-cooked food is available. Sam's dry cider is served.

🏠 🛏 ✿ ◁◐ ♣ ♠ 🍴

BUTTERLEIGH

Butterleigh Inn

☻ 12-2.30, 6 (5 Fri)-11; 12-3, 7-10.30 Sun

🍴 (01884) 855407

website: www.thebutterleighinn.co.uk

Cotleigh Tawny, Barn Owl, Old Buzzard; guest beers (occasional) Ⓗ

This is what a country pub should be; in a charming spot, set back from the road, this splendid 400-year-old Devon cob building is full of character with different rooms, including a snug, main bar and an adjoining lounge/dining area. The open fire in an ancient fireplace helps make it very welcoming. In summer, enjoy the attractive, secluded garden and views of the surrounding rolling hills. The Old Buzzard is replaced in summer by a guest ale from another local brewery.

🏠 Q 🛏 ◁◐ ♿ ♣ ♠ P

CHAGFORD

Bullers Arms

7 Mill Street

☻ 11-3, 6-11; 11-11 Sat & summer; 12-10.30 Sun

☎ (01647) 432348

website: guestbeds.com/details/bullersarms

Draught Bass; Sharp's Doom Bar; guest beer Ⓗ

Friendly community pub, popular with the locals, situated just off the square in this small market town on the edge of Dartmoor. Parts of the inn date back to the 17th century, although changes over the years have brought about a much more spacious bar area. The pub fields darts and chess teams, and its location also makes it popular with walkers. The present owners have recently refurbished the guest rooms and restaurant; B&B is reasonably priced and meals are also available as takeaways – try the speciality curries.

🛏 ✿ ◁◐ ♣

South Devon Inn
Strand Hill
11.30-11; 12-10.30 Sun
Draught Bass; Wells Bombardier; guest beer Ⓗ
Around 300 years old, this former coaching inn has one bar out in converted stables. Recently updated lounge. Good food; B&B.

EXETER

Welcome Inn
Haven Banks
12-2.30, 7-11; 12-3, 7-11 Sat; 12-3, 7-10.30 Sun
Beer varies Ⓗ
200 years old, this aptly-named, canalside pub has gas lighting and flagged floors. A single handpump generally serves micro-brewery beers.

EXTON

Puffing Billy
Station Lane
11.30-3, 5.30-11; 12-2, 7-10.30 Sun
Exe Valley Dob's Best Bitter; Otter Ale; guest beers (summer) Ⓖ
16th-century, modernised pub with views over the Exe estuary. Good food on a *Nouvelle Cuisine* menu, specialising in fish.

GREAT TORRINGTON

Torridge Inn
1 Mill Street
12-3, 6-11; 12-3, 6-10.30 Sun
St Austell HSD; guest beer Ⓗ
17th-century thatched inn, with a garden overlooking the River Torridge: a single bar and a good value restaurant. B&B available.

HONITON

Three Tuns
113 High Street
11-11; 12-4, 7-10.30 Sun
Draught Bass Ⓗ
Busy, two-bar town pub with skittles/function room. The lounge bar boasts numerous brass artefacts.

LANDSCOVE

Live & Let Live
12-2.30, 6.30-11; 12-3, 7-10.30 Sun
Draught Bass; Princetown Dartmoor IPA; guest beer Ⓗ
Typical small village pub with an L-shaped bar, beamed ceilings and a small walled garden. A real cider is stocked and food served.

CHERITON BISHOP

Old Thatch Inn

Just off A30 from Exeter

✪ 11.30-3, 6-11; 12-3, 7-10.30 Sun

☎ (01647) 24204 e-mail: oldthatchinn@aol.com

Branscombe Vale Branoc; Otter Ale; guest beer Ⓗ

Large 16th-century thatched free house, on the north-eastern edge of Dartmoor, with beamed ceilings. The pub is multi-level with a small bar area, and a larger area beyond the stone fireplace, plus a no-smoking room. The three ales all come from independent breweries and usually at least two are from the South West. A varied selection of food is available from the *à la carte* menu. En-suite accommodation is also available. An annual beer festival is held in May. ♨◬☺✿◁◑♣♠P✄

CHERITON FITZPAINE

Ring of Bells

The Hayes (behind the church)

✪ 12-3 (not Mon-Thu or winter Fri-Sat), 6-11; 12-3, 7-10.30 Sun

☎ (01363) 866374

Cotleigh Tawny; Exe Valley Dob's Best Bitter; Dartmoor Best Bitter; guest beer (occasional) Ⓗ

14th-century thatched inn, with a central bar and a restaurant. The wood-burner, together with log fires, ensures a welcoming environment. A varied bar/restaurant menu is prepared by a resident chef. Skittles are played in an adjoining barn and a boules court is available in the enclosed garden, which also has ancient bee boles in a south-facing wall. It hosts many events in the annual Crediton Folk Festival staged in the village in spring. The guest accommodation has en-suite facilities. ♨◬☺◁◑♣P

CHIP SHOP

Chip Shop Inn

Off A384, 3 miles W of Tavistock OS437751

✪ 12-2.30, 5-11; 12-10.30 Sun

☎ (01822) 832322

Draught Bass; Sharp's Doom Bar; guest beers Ⓗ

This remote, popular pub offers a friendly welcome to visitors and locals alike. Chip Shop was once a busy mining village where the miners exchanged their wages of company-issued chips for goods. The L-shaped bar boasts a large collection of mirrors. The skittle alley is often in demand and supports two teams. The garden has a children's play house. The pub is dog-friendly. ♨Q☺◁◑♠P

CHITTLEHAMPTON

Bell Inn ←

The Square (take B3227 from South Molton, A361 or from A377)

✪ 11-3, 7-10.30; 11-11 Sat; 12-3, 7-10.30 Sun

☎ (01769) 540368

Draught Bass; Fuller's London Pride; Ⓗ **guest beers** Ⓖ

The only pub remaining in a village which at the beginning of the 20th century had at least six public houses and a brewery. You are assured of a warm welcome and a fine selection of ales either on handpump or gravity dispense. There is much local activity here, particularly in the cricket season. A small restaurant area serving an excellent menu makes this a pub well worth visiting. Cider is stocked in summer. ●

CHUDLEIGH

Bishop Lacy

Fore Street (signed off the A38)

✪ 11-11; 12-10.30 Sun

☎ (01626) 854585

e-mail: thebishoplacyinn@btinternet.com

Fuller's London Pride; Princetown Jail Ale; Skinner's Cornish Knocker; Ⓖ **Theakston XB;** Ⓗ **guest beers** Ⓖ

Grade II listed, 14th-century former church house, now a bustling local, it has built up a reputation for serving a good selection of ales, mostly on gravity. The pub has two bars, both warmed by open fires. Home-cooked food is served in a no-smoking restaurant area. Beer festivals are a regular event at this local CAMRA *Pub of the Year* 2000 and regional winner in 1998. The house beer comes from Branscombe Vale. Children and dogs are welcome. ♨Q☺◑♣♠P

CLAYHIDON

Half Moon Inn

✪ 12-2.30 (3 Sat), 7-11 (closed Mon); 12-3 (closed eve) Sun

☎ (01823) 680291

Cotleigh Tawny; guest beers Ⓗ

Set in the Blackdown Hills, near the Somerset border, the inn benefits from outstanding views over the Culm Valley, and is very popular with locals and visitors to the hills. A traditional country inn, it is noted locally for its varied range of reasonably priced meals in both the bar and restaurant area. The Half Moon is believed to have originated as a cottage, built by stone masons for their use while building the church; in the 18th century the building was known as the Church House. ♨Q☺◑♣●P

COLEFORD

New Inn

✪ 12-2, 7-11; 12-2.30, 7-10.30 Sun

☎ (01363) 84242 website: www.reallyreal.com

Badger Best; guest beers Ⓗ

Spacious, 13th-century Grade II listed country pub with everything you would expect – thatched roof, exposed beams, copper artefacts, brasses and a wood fire. The pub is open plan but manages a more intimate atmosphere. Food is dominant, with a varied menu produced by two resident chefs, from mostly local ingredients. The garden is delightfully situated by the River Coleford. Accommodation is offered, but be prepared to share it with Sebastian, the resident ghost, who was a monk. ♨Q☺✿◑♣●P

COLYTON

Gerrard Arms

Rosemary Lane

✪ 11-2.30 (3 Sat), 6-11; 12-3, 7-10.30 Sun

☎ (01297) 552588 website: www.colyweb.co.uk

Draught Bass; Ⓗ **Branscombe Vale Branoc,** Ⓖ **Quay, Harbour Master; guest beer** Ⓗ

Small, one-bar pub in this delightful little town of narrow streets and lovely old cottages. The pub can be accessed by foot from the town square and through the churchyard. It is possible to take the tramway from Seaton to Colyton in summer, with a short walk from the junction. Extremely popular with locals, it has a well-used skittle alley at the rear, also a spacious garden for families. The home-made food is very good value and a traditional roast is served Sun. ⌂⌂⊕⌂⌂⊕♣

COMBEINTEIGNHEAD

Wild Goose

Between Newton Abbot and Shaldon, S of Teign estuary
✪ 11.30-3, 6.30-11; 12-3, 7-10.30 Sun
☎ (01626) 872241
Beer range varies Ⓗ

17th-century free house, in a small quiet village, commanding a superb position overlooking the River Teign. The pub has a long single bar with a number of seating areas for drinkers away from the bar area. It serves six ever-changing real ales which are sourced from independent breweries. There is a dining area at the rear of the bar, where excellent, home-cooked food is served. Plenty of character and a wonderful community feel are added attractions. ⌂Q⌂⊕⌂⌂♣P

COMBE MARTIN

Castle Inn

High Street (near town hall/fire station)
✪ 12-11; 12-10.30
☎ (01271) 883706 website: www.thecastleinn.com
Draught Bass; Worthington Bitter; guest beers Ⓗ

Absolute beer drinkers' paradise, with guest ales sourced from all over the UK. After a sympathetic refurbishment, it is still a one-roomed bar where bare floorboards, railway sleepers and a real fire create a picture of a pub from times past. A sound-proofed restaurant is attached to the bar, serving fine meals, based solely on local produce (no food Tue lunchtime). Skittles, pool and darts can all be played here. ⌂⌂⌂⊕⌂⌂♣P

London Inn

Leigh Road
✪ 11-4, 6.30-11; 11-11 Sat & summer; 12-4, 7-10.30 (12-10.30 summer) Sun
☎ (01271) 883409 website: www.london-inn.co.uk
Greene King Abbot; Wadworth 6X; guest beer Ⓗ

Cosy public bar, with real fire at one end. This old coaching inn borders the Exmoor National Park and benefits from a delightful and extensive south-facing riverside garden. Games include skittles and pool. An additional beer from the Clearwater Brewery is normally on tap. ⌂Q⌂⌂⊕⌂⌂♣P

CREDITON

Crediton Inn

28a Mill Street (opp. Somerfield on main Tiverton Road)
✪ 11-11; 12-2, 7-10.30 Sun
☎ (01363) 772882 website: www.crediton-inn.co.uk
Draught Bass; Sharp's Doom Bar; guest beers Ⓗ

Friendly free house, just off the town centre, known locally as the Kirton Inn. Four ales are always available and the two guests are often from south-western independents. A modest menu of good value cooked meals is available. The pub runs its own angling club and has a skittle alley. Occasional quiz or theme nights are held. This is a real gem – but do not get tempted by the chilli sherry! ⌂Q⌂⌂⊕⌂⌂⌂♣⌂♣P⌂⌂⌂

CROYDE

Thatched Barn Inn

14 Hobbs Hill
✪ 11-11; 12-10.30 Sun
☎ (01271) 890349 website: www.thethatch.com
Barum Original; Draught Bass; St Austell HSD Ⓗ

Outstandingly popular pub frequented by a broad spectrum of customers, including, in season, surfers tuckered out from catching waves at the nearby famous Croyde beach. Having started out as a late-medieval barn, it was converted to a pub in 1978, retaining much of the original structure. The pub is a fair size, but sympathetic divisions of space and soft lighting afford it an atmosphere of intimacy normally enjoyed by much smaller venues. Happily, the renowned food trade is managed skilfully enough for the diners not to usurp the drinkers. ⌂⌂⌂⌂♣P

DARTMOUTH

Cherub Inn

13 Higher Street
✪ 11-2.30, 5.30-11 (11-11 summer); 12-10.30 Sun
☎ (01803) 832571 website: www.the-cherub.co.uk
Beer range varies Ⓗ

This half-timbered Grade II listed building is reputed to be the oldest in Dartmouth; originally a wool merchant's house, it became an inn and restaurant in 1972, taking its name from a boat built to carry wool. The small, cosy, oak-beamed bar has a welcoming atmosphere and a good reputation for bar food. Climb the twisted spiral staircase to the small restaurant which is famous for local fish. The house beer is brewed by Summerskills and three other guest beers change monthly (two in winter). ⌂Q⌂⊕

Windjammer Inn

23 Victoria Road
✪ 11-3, 5.15-11; 12-3, 6-10.30 Sun
☎ (01803) 832228
Draught Bass; Princetown Dartmoor IPA; guest beer Ⓗ

The straight-forward town pub exterior conceals a single large bar area, furnished in light coloured woods and bearing a nautical theme: the latest yachting headlines are chalked up for your information. The pub has a growing reputation for good, reasonably priced food. The two regular beers are supplemented by an ever-changing guest beer chosen from an extensive list. It is convenient for the market square. ⌂Q⊕

DITTISHAM

Red Lion Inn

The Level
(signed off A3122, Totnes-Dartmouth road) OS861552
✪ 11-2.30 (3 Sat), 6-11; 12-3, 7-10.30 Sun
☎ (01803) 722235
e-mail: bazredlion@madasafish.com
Butcombe Bitter; Palmers IPA; guest beers Ⓗ

Set in the heart of one of Devon's most

tranquil villages, the Red Lion has been offering generous hospitality since 1750, starting as a coaching house. The dining room serves good food, using local fresh fish and produce, cooked to order. Superior guest accommodation is provided in six en-suite rooms plus two cottages in the grounds. The single bar, with open fires, admits dogs on leads. There is a children's room and patio garden. Heron Valley cider is stocked in summer.

▲Q☜☼☒⛱◗ Å♣ P

DODDISCOMBSLEIGH

Nobody Inn

☼ 12-2.30, 6-11; 12-3, 7-10.30 Sun
☎ (01647) 252394 e-mail: inn.nobody@virgin.net
Draught Bass; Ⓗ guest beers Ⓗ /Ⓖ
This 16th-century inn is a real gem. The bar area boasts exposed beams, flagged floors, wooden furniture, brass and copper artefacts, decorative firearms, a large open fire and subdued lighting. The Branscombe Vale house beer and two guest ales are complemented by Heron Valley and Brimblecombe's cider, plus over 250 whiskies and a staggering choice of over 800 wines. It also offers around 40 West County cheeses (mainly from Devon) as well as good quality food. The olde-worlde accommodation is very popular – book 15 weeks in advance to avoid disappointment.

▲Q☼☒⛱◗♣ P

DOLTON

Union Inn

Fore Street (B3217, off A3124 at Dolton Beacon)
☼ 12-2.30, 6-11 (closed Wed); 12-2.30, 7-10.30 Sun
☎ (01805) 804633 e-mail: union.inn@eclipse.co.uk
St Austell HSB; guest beer Ⓗ
Originally a cob-walled Devon longhouse, converted to a hotel during Georgian times, the Union has one main bar and an airy comfortable lounge, with a restaurant on the far left. The bar is full of horse tack and brasses, and is a meeting place for the local farming community. Many places of interest nearby include the Halsdon Nature Reserve and Stafford Moor fishing lake – bring a fish back to the pub and it will be cooked for you. The guest ale is normally local.

▲Q☼☒⛱◗Å♣P

DUNSFORD

Royal Oak

7 miles W of Exeter on road to Moretonhampstead
☼ 12-2.30, 6.30 (Mon 7)-11; 12-2.30, 7-10.30 Sun
☎ (01647) 252256 website: www.troid.co.uk
Dartmoor Best Bitter; Greene King Abbot; Princetown Jail Ale; Sharp's Own; guest beers Ⓗ
Popular local on the edge of Dartmoor; the single bar in Victorian style keeps a selection of board games and some toys for children (however, under 14s are not allowed in bar). Pool and bar billiards are also played. A varied menu of home-cooked food at sensible prices is served in the dining area. Beer festivals, featuring 12 different ales, are held spring and autumn; other weekly events are fish and chip night (Tue), charity quiz night (Thu) and mystery ale at £1 a pint (Fri).

▲Q☼☒⛱◗♣◖P⚲

EAST ALLINGTON

Fortescue Arms

Follow sign off A381, Totnes-Kingsbridge road
☼ 11-2.30, 6-11 (11-11 summer); 12-3, 7-10.30 (12-10.30 summer) Sun
☎ (01548) 521215
website: www.webmachine.co.uk/fortescue
Palmers IPA; Princetown Dartmoor IPA; guest beer Ⓗ
The Fortescue is an olde-worlde village pub, offering fine ales, superb cuisine, open fires, candlelit tables and a warm welcome. Lovingly restored to a high standard with original Victorian fittings, furniture, mirrors and stone-flagged floors, the atmosphere is reminiscent of a bygone era. A few miles from Kingsbridge, it is just a short drive away from the many historic and beautiful highlights of South Devon, making it an ideal base from which to explore the area. Lunches are served Wed–Sun; take-away meals are available. ▲Q☼⛱◗♦Å♣◖P

EGGESFORD

Eggesford Country Hotel

On A377, near station
☼ 11-11; 12-10.30 Sun
☎ (01769) 580345 website: www.eggesfordhotel.co.uk
Cotleigh Tawny; guest beers Ⓗ
Family-run hotel, set in the beautiful Taw Valley, with 10 acres of gardens and lovely river walks. A cheery welcome awaits at the Fox and Hounds Bar, where guest ales tend to be local brews and paintings reflect the owner's interest in steam trains. It is popular with fishermen during the season, so salmon and trout appear regularly on the extensive home-cooked menu. It is still the haunt of local farmers; the grounds were the old village cattle market. A beer festival is held annually (Aug).

▲☜☼⛱◗♦≈♣◖P

EXETER ✼

Double Locks Hotel

Canal Banks (follow lane from Marsh Barton Trading Estate) OS933901
☼ 11-11; 12-10.30 Sun
☎ (01392) 256947
Adnams Broadside; Branscombe Vale Branoc; Everards Original; Ⓖ Smiles Best, Heritage; Young's Special Ⓗ
The Double Locks Hotel overlooks Exeter's historic canal. There is an extensive outdoor area and a family room. It is popular with walkers and canoeists; dogs are welcome. The hotel can be approached on foot from the swing bridge at Countess Weir but vehicles must approach via Marsh Barton Trading Estate, over a narrow bridge. A wide range of meals and snacks is served all day; the beer range varies. Frequently live music is staged and the pub has a relaxed, informal, somewhat eccentric atmosphere.

▲☜☼◗P●

Great Western Hotel

St David's Station Approach
☼ 11-11; 12-10.30 Sun
☎ (01392) 274039
website: www.greatwesternhotel.co.uk
Adnams Bitter, Broadside; Draught Bass; Fuller's London Pride; guest beers Ⓗ
Hotel built to serve Brunel's St David's Station; its Loco Bar is a mecca for real ale

enthusiasts and railway buffs alike. This split-level bar, local CAMRA *Pub of the Year* 2000, serves 12 real ales at the weekend. The guest beer range is constantly changing as 30-plus casks are drunk each week. The emphasis is on local beers but expect the unexpected. The August beer festival offers 150 beers. Excellent food, in generous portions, is served in the bar, and also in the hotel's Brunel Restaurant.
🕮🖂◑🏺 (St David's) P

Royal Oak
81 Fore Street, Heavitree
🕒 11-3, 6-11; 11-11 Fri; 11-3.30, 7-11 Sat; 12-3, 7-10.30 Sun
☎ (01392) 254121
Draught Bass; Castle Eden Bitter; Flowers IPA; Otter Ale Ⓗ

Cob-walled, 14th-century ex-manor house, with the only fully thatched roof in the city; a single bar, with separate rooms on different levels. It is full of vintage weapons and other curios, including handpumps fashioned from old French bayonet handles, and a cell door from Dartmoor Prison. Home-cooked food is served. Smoking restrictions apply lunchtime in the snug. A popular quiz is held (Wed) and the community feel is furthered by two darts teams, Sun eve card schools and clay pigeon and pheasant shoot syndicates that meet regularly. Q🌑🕮◑♣½

Well House
16-17 Cathedral Yard
🕒 11-11; 12-2, 7-10.30 Sun
☎ (01392) 319953
Draught Bass; guest beers Ⓗ

The Well House on the cathedral green is a city-centre pub with a large front window overlooking the cathedral. At lunchtime, several tables are usually laid-up to serve meals. A wide range of beers changes on a frequent basis. Under the pub, a historic cellar is open for view (on request) and houses a skeleton in a glass case. The Well House can get busy at times; it is very popular with thirsty shoppers as it is only a few minutes' walk from the High Street.
◑🏺 (Central)

Bicton Inn
5 Bicton Street
🕒 11-11; 12-10.30 Sun
☎ (01395) 272589 e-mail: bicton@lineone.net
Draught Bass; Branscombe Vale Branoc; guest beer Ⓗ

Friendly, traditional, unpretentious corner pub near Trinity Church, popular with locals. The main room is supplemented by a pool room; cards, dominoes and darts are also played. A good value set meal is served weekday lunchtimes (12–2pm). No other food is available. ◑🏺♣

Grove
The Esplanade
🕒 11-11; 12-10.30 Sun
☎ (01395) 272101
Draught Bass; Brakspear Special; Flowers Original; Greene King Abbot; Wadworth 6X; guest beer Ⓗ

Large seafront pub, popular with locals. The upstairs (no-smoking) dining room affords panoramic views across the sea

and Exe estuary. Good food is also served in the bar. It hosts live music Fri eve, and a quiz night (Thu); occasional beer festivals are held in winter. Families are welcome, and the large garden is popular in summer when a bouncy castle is erected by the play area. Parking is limited. Wheelchair WC. 🕮◑♿♣🏺P

Powder Monkey
2-2A The Parade
🕒 11-11; 12-10.30 Sun
☎ (01395) 280090
Courage Directors; Shepherd Neame Spitfire; Theakston Best Bitter; Wadworth 6X; guest beers Ⓗ

Wetherspoon's town centre pub, named after local Nancy Perriam, who was a powder monkey (naval slang for young boys – normally – who filled shells and cartridges). Nine cask ales are stocked, including five guests, of which one or two are always from local brewers. The patio (with heaters) is popular in the summer. The pub appeals to a wide range of ages, but particularly attracts young people eves. Meals are served all day, until 10pm (9.30 Sun). 🕮Q🕮◑🏺½●

Black Horse Inn
High Street
🕒 11-3, 6-11; 11-11 Sat; 12-4, 7-10.30 Sun
☎ (01805) 622121
Courage Best Bitter, Directors; John Smith's Bitter; guest beer Ⓗ

16th-century coaching inn at the centre of a town used by Hopton and Fairfax during the Civil War Battle of Torrington in 1646. Although it has seen some alteration, the inn still retains its character. The entrance is part cobbled, part brick-tiled, with the bar on the left and lounge on the right, behind a black oak wall panel. The bar is a meeting place for many local groups; its ceiling is decorated with pump clips from guest ales (from independent breweries). The large restaurant at the rear stages theme nights.
🕮🖂◑♣

Old Inn
From Totnes, take A381 towards Kingsbridge
🕒 11-3, 6-11; 12-3, 6-10.30 Sun
☎ (01803) 712329
website: www.the-old-inn.freeserve.co.uk
RCH PG Steam (winter), East Street Cream; guest beer (summer) Ⓗ

Friendly, family-run roadside pub with a warm village atmosphere, situated next to the beautiful Norman church. The pub is so named as it stands on a site that has been occupied by an inn since 1104; the present building dates from 1874. There is a single bar, with seating and dining tables. The no-smoking dining room serves excellent food at reasonable prices with oriental food a speciality. En-suite accommodation is available. Cider is stocked in summer.
🕮Q🌑🕮◑♣●P½

Church House Inn
(off main Totnes-Kingsbridge road)
🕒 12-3, 6-11; 12-3.30, 7-10.30 Sun

☎ (01803) 863707
Draught Bass; Wells Bombardier; guest beers Ⓗ
Friendly, 12th-century pub, originally built to house the masons working on the church. It later became a chantry house for monks. In 1327 the abbot handed the property over to the poor and in 1950 it passed out of the church's hands. A Tudor window frame and latticed window containing panes of 13th century hand-made glass remain. Heavy beams and a flagstoned floor feature in the bar and dining area; there is also a family room. An extensive range of excellent food is available. ▲Q☺৬⊨ⅅ●P⅍

HATHERLEIGH

Tally Ho! Country Inn & Brewery
14 Market Street
☺ 11-3, 6-11; 12-3, 7-10.30 Sun
☎ (01837) 810306
Tally Ho! Market Ale, Tarka's Tipple, Nutters; guest beer (occasional) Ⓗ
A brewery was first established at this site in 1790, but was destroyed by fire in 1806. Brewing recommenced in 1824, but ceased again early in the last century. The brewery has recently undergone another refurbishment and prides itself on using no sugars, extracts or preservatives in its beer. The pub itself is situated in the centre of the market town and comprises a single bar and a small restaurant.
▲Q☺⊨ⅅ♣●P

HEMERDON

Miners Arms
☺ 11-2.30, 5.30-11; 12-3, 7-10.30 Sun
☎ (01752) 343252
Draught Bass; Ⓗ/Ⓖ **Sutton X&B;** Ⓗ/Ⓟ **Ushers Best Bitter; guest beer** Ⓗ
Completely unspoilt and friendly village pub that has been run by the same family since 1870. The main bar, complete with beams, a flagstoned floor and a large open fire, displays many mementos from the days when the area had mining interests. The second drinking area is smaller, but has a window overlooking the owner's superb garden; another area features a genuine well, discovered during renovations. The pub stands on a hill and commands a good view of Plymouth, especially at night when the city is lit up.
▲Q☺₷♣P

HOCKWORTHY

Staplecross Inn
☺ 12-3 (not Mon-Fri), 6.30-11; 12-3, 6.30-10.30 Sun
☎ (01398) 361374
Cotleigh Tawny, Barn Owl; guest beers Ⓗ
On the border with Somerset, this attractive building (circa 1600) has been used as a public house since the early 1700s. Totally unspoilt, it comprises two bars; one with quarry tiles, the other is a carpeted lounge area. It is frequented mainly by the locals, as its rural location does not attract a lot of passing trade. Cider is stocked in summer. The car park is the venue for an annual skittles tournament (Aug) and the pub hosts a Harvest Home celebration each October.
▲Q☺ⅅ₷ẞ▲♣●P

HOLCOMBE ROGUS

Prince of Wales
☺ 12-3 (not Mon-Thu, Oct-Mar), 6.30-11; 12-3, 7-10.30 Sun
☎ (01823) 672070
Cotleigh Tawny; Otter Bitter; guest beers Ⓗ
Pleasant 17th-century country pub, not far from the Grand Western Canal, which is popular with cyclists and walkers. Its unusual cash register handpumps were lovingly restored by Cotleigh Brewery when they owned the pub. The guest beers change regularly; cider is sold in summer. A large restaurant area offers home-cooked food (including vegetarian options) or you can relax in the pleasant lounge area by the log-burning stove. A skittle alley, pool and darts areas and an attractive walled garden complete the picture. ▲Q☺ⅅ♣●P

HOLNE

Church House Inn
OS706696
☺ 12-3, 7-11; 12-3, 7-10.30 Sun
☎ (01364) 631208
website: www.churchhouse-holne.co.uk
Butcombe Bitter, Gold; Palmers IPA, 200 Ⓗ
Grade II listed, 14th-century inn in the centre of a village in the Dartmoor National Park. The pub has two bars, one leading to the dining area, and the other just for drinkers. Excellent fresh food is cooked to order from local ingredients. Families with children, dogs and walkers are all most welcome. Accommodation available, with some rooms en-suite. A good selection of beers, wines and spirits is complemented by Gray's cider. ▲Q₷⊨ⅅ▲●

HOLSWORTHY

Kings Arms ☆
The Square
☺ 11-11; 12-3, 7-10.30 Sun
☎ (01409) 253517
Draught Bass; Sharp's Doom Bar Ⓗ
This 17th-century inn houses three bars and has entrances off two streets, resulting in two postal codes. Whichever way you enter, you are certain of a warm welcome and fine ale. The snug and public bars are separated by a snob screen – an original feature. The pub displays much noteworthy pub and beer memorabilia; the pictures are of particular interest. ▲Q

HORNDON

Elephant's Nest
1½ miles E of Mary Tavy (A386) follow signs
OS517800
☺ 11.30-2.30, 6.30-11; 12-2.30, 7-10.30 Sun
☎ (01822) 810273
website: www.elephantsnestinn.co.uk
Boddingtons Bitter; Palmers IPA; St Austell HSD; guest beers Ⓗ
This picturesque, 16th-century pub takes its name from a former landlord's beard! It offers superb moorland views from the large garden. The traditionally-appointed bar features many elephant items, including mural, figures, curios and the word 'elephant' spelt out in many languages on the ceiling beams. The bar is supplemented by a further two rooms suitable for children.

Local CAMRA *Pub of the Year* 1996, it supports a pony club and cricket and darts teams. ⚐Q⚑☉⚌♣☙P

HORSEBRIDGE

Royal Inn

Between B3362 and A388
☼ 12-3, 7-11; 12-3, 7-10.30 Sun
☎ (01822) 870214 website: www.royalinn.co.uk
Draught Bass; Sharp's Doom Bar; guest beers Ⓗ
The inn stands on the banks of the River Tamar by a historic bridge linking Devon with Cornwall. Monks built the bridge and the pub – originally as a nunnery, which gives the building its character. In an acre of ground, its terraced garden is full of flowers in summer. The main bar is traditional, with hops and horse brasses; a second room is no-smoking. Up to six guest ales are stocked in summer. ⚐Q☉⚌♣☙P⚲

IDDESLEIGH

Duke of York

On B3217, N of Okehampton
☼ 11-11; 12-10.30 Sun
☎ (01837) 810253
Adnams Broadside; Cotleigh Tawny; guest beers Ⓖ
Dating back to the 14th century, the Duke was originally four cottages built to accommodate the craftsmen working on the church. Despite its rural location, this is at times a bustling place. Food is available all day, much of it based on produce from the landlord's farm and market garden. Big open fires dominate the single bar and dining room, popular with locals and visitors alike. Children and dogs are welcome in the pub, horses are asked to wait outside. ⚐Q☉⚟⚌♣☙

ILSINGTON

Carpenter's Arms

OS786761
☼ 11-3 (12-2.30 winter), 6-11; 12-3, 7-10.30 Sun
☎ (01364) 661215
Draught Bass; Ⓗ **Flowers IPA** Ⓖ
Typical old local, with a friendly atmosphere, used mainly by local farmers and villagers. At the village centre, next to the school, it became a pub in the early 1800s and has a single, curved L-shaped bar with an open-plan area, and a family area away from the bar. Lovely open fires are lit in winter. Food, all home cooked, includes Sunday roasts. Its main real ale is served on gravity. ⚐Q☉♣♧♣

KILMINGTON

New Inn

The Hill
☼ 11-2.30 (3 summer), 6-11; 12-3, 7-10.30 Sun
☎ (01297) 33376
Palmers BB, Dorset Gold, IPA Ⓗ
This 14th-century Devon longhouse is situated in a delightful village, just off the A35 and has appeared in every edition of this *Guide*. Full of character, and very popular with the locals, it has a well-used skittle alley at the rear. In summer the lovely, well-kept gardens are popular with families and an aviary adds interest. Good value, home-cooked food is served in the dining area. ⚐Q☉⚌⚟⚃⚄P

LONGDOWN

Lamb Inn

On B3212, 2 miles from Exeter towards Mortenhampstead
☼ 12-2.30, 6-11; (11-11 summer); 12-2.30, 7-10.30 (12-10.30 summer) Sun
☎ (01392) 811711
Greene King Abbot; Otter Bitter; Princetown Jail Ale Ⓗ
Substantial stone building in a small village amid rolling hillside, opened-out inside into one area; part is set aside as a popular, no-smoking restaurant. The main area, served from a central bar, finished with a light oak bartop, is carpeted and furnished with comfortable settees, chesterfield, and plenty of bar stools. Dogs are welcome in the village bar, and a small corner is allocated for well-behaved children. Blackboards list events, including two weekend beer festivals per year. ⚐Q☉⚌♣P

LOWER ASHTON

Manor Inn

Just off B3193
☼ 12-2, 6 (6.30 Sat)-11; closed Mon; 12-2.30, 7-10.30 Sun
☎ (01647) 252304
e-mail: manor_ashton@compuserve.com
Princetown Jail Ale; RCH Pitchfork; Teignworthy Reel Ale; guest beers Ⓗ
True country gem in a tiny Teign Valley hamlet boasting outstanding views towards the Dartmoor National Park. This two-bar pub offers a friendly atmosphere with a good choice of beers (four guests in summer, reducing to one in winter). Excellent, reasonably priced home-cooked food is listed on a blackboard menu. There is a lovely garden for families to enjoy. This local CAMRA *Pub of the Year* 1998 was a previous regional winner. ⚐Q☉⚌⚟⚄♣☙P

LUTTON

Mountain Inn

Old Church Lane (off Plympton-Cornwood road)
OS596594
☼ 11-2.30, 7 (6 Thu-Sat & summer)-11; 12-3, 7-10.30 Sun
☎ (01752) 837247
Sutton XSB; guest beer Ⓗ
Traditional village pub nestling at the edge of Dartmoor; popular with locals and visitors alike, it is frequented by horse riders. The house beer is brewed by Summerskills; cider is stocked in summer. The interior is distinctive with cob walls and a large fireplace. The pub name is a corruption of a local landowner's name, Montain. Boules is played in summer and it is convenient for Sparkwell Wildlife Park. ⚐Q☉⚌⚄♣P

LYDFORD

Mucky Duck Inn

Next to White Lady Falls, Lydford Gorge
☼ 11-3, 6.30-11 (winter varies); 12-3, 7-10.30 Sun
☎ (01822) 820208
Sharp's Cornish Coaster; guest beers Ⓗ
The duck theme was revived when the present licensee acquired this 170-year-old property in 1993. It has been completely

refurbished and now features an attractive bar with a display of hundreds of ducks of all varieties (and a lone leprechaun). 1960s music and a relaxed atmosphere are the norm. The pub has a skittle alley and an unfenced garden by the car park. Guest accommodation is in four newly-renovated holiday flats. ♨Q☼❀⌂◑♣✿P

LYMPSTONE

Redwing
Church Road
✪ 11.30-3, 6-11; 11.30-11 Sat; 12-10.30 Sun
☎ (01395) 222156
Greene King Abbot; Ushers Best Bitter; Wells Bombardier; guest beer ⑭
Friendly, lively village pub in picturesque estuary village. It is renowned for excellent home-cooked meals, based on local produce and hosts occasional specialist eves (no food Sun eve). Thatcher's cider is sold. Live music is staged Fri and Tue eves and a quiz night, Mon. It is the HQ of East Devon's Hockey Club, fielding four teams. Q❀◑⌸≒♣✿P

MARY TAVY

Mary Tavy Inn
Lane Head (A386)
✪ 11.45-3, 6-11; 12-3, 7-10.30 Sun
☎ (01822) 810326
Draught Bass; St Austell Tribute; guest beer ⑭
Jim Hawkins, the son of a blacksmith, who ran the adjacent former smithy, is said to haunt the Mary Tavy Inn. Do not let that deter you from visiting this pub on the edge of Dartmoor, which in fact is cosy and friendly. Its bar and lounge are supplemented by a conservatory and dining room, where children are welcome. Good views can be enjoyed from the garden. Sam's cider is stocked.
♨Q☼❀⌂◑Å♣✿P

NEWTON ABBOT

Dartmouth Inn
63 East Street (opp. hospital)
✪ 12-3, 4.30-11; (12-11 Fri, Sat & summer); 12-10.30 Sun
☎ (01626) 353451
RCH East Street Cream; ⑭ **guest beers** ⑭/Ⓖ
Three-roomed pub, with a cosy feel, especially when the real log fire is blazing away in the cold nights of winter. During the summer, the small beer garden is a suntrap, hosting occasional barbecues (Sun). The excellent beer range comes mostly from south-western micro-breweries, with a second guest beer available on gravity at busier times. Sam's dry cider and bottle-conditioned RCH East Street Cream are also available. Children are welcome until 7pm. Bar skittles played. ♨☼❀◑≒♣✿

Golden Lion
4 Market Street (near the library)
✪ 11-2.30, 5.30-11; 11-4, 6-11 Sat; 12-3, 7-10.30 Sun
☎ (01626) 367062
Teignworthy Reel Ale; guest beers ⑭
A pub has been on this site since 1628 but only as the Golden Lion since 1722. The garden once housed the stables and is now used as the venue for occasional beer festivals. The single bar, friendly pub has

two rooms, one for games. Lunches, served until 1.45 (not Sun), are good value. The pub was one of the first to sell beer from the local Teignworthy Brewery and the Reel Ale has been popular ever since. All beers in the pub's excellent range are very reasonably priced. Local CAMRA runner-up in the *Pub of the Year* awards 2000. ❀◑≒♣P

NEWTON POPPLEFORD

Cannon Inn
High Street
✪ 11-2.30, 5.30-11; 12-3, 7-10.30 Sun
☎ (01395) 568266
Ringwood Best Bitter, seasonal beers; guest beers Ⓖ
Dating back to the 1500s, this hotel and former coaching house is full of character – its two bars are crammed full of pictures and knick-knacks, even a rowing boat suspended from the lounge bar ceiling. Open fires, a friendly atmosphere, great food and local cider make it worth a visit. Skittles and darts teams play during the week and a folk group performs Wed eve. A pool room and extensive large, safe gardens complete the picture. ♨Q❀⌂◑⌸♣✿P

NEWTON ST CYRES

Beer Engine
Turn off A377
✪ 11-11; 12-10.30 Sun
☎ (01392) 851282 e-mail: peterbrew@aow.com
Beer Engine Rail Ale, Piston Bitter, Sleeper Heavy, seasonal beers ⑭
Built as a railway hotel, the pub is now home to Devon's oldest brewery (following the sale and relocation of Blackawton), having opened in 1983. The single room has bar and eating areas (children encouraged); the bar is decorated with hops and artwork, including the original Beer Engine pub sign. 'Real' food includes a popular range of sausages. The brewery can be viewed on the lower level of the pub. A well-stocked garden is adjacent to the railway line – hold on to your pints when the trains pass! Note: all real ales are normally served with sparklers (brewer's policy) but will be removed on request. ♨Q❀◑Å♣✿P⑰

NORTH TAWTON

Railway Inn
Whiddon Down Road (A3124, 1 mile S of North Tawton) OS666001
✪ 12-2 (not Tue or Thu), 6-11; 12-3, 7-10.30 Sun
☎ (01837) 82789
Teignworthy Reel Ale; guest beers ⑭
Set in a rural location, the Railway is a friendly, single-bar local that is part of a working farm. The pub stands next to the former North Tawton Station (closed 1971), which it predates, and the bar decor includes railway memorabilia and old photos of the station. The beer range, although changing regularly, is generally West Country based, as is the cider stocked in summer. The pub has both a dining room and a games room. ♨❀⌂◑Å♣✿P

NOSS MAYO

Ship Inn
✪ 11-11; 12-10.30 Sun

☎ (01752) 872387 e-mail: ship@brunning.host.co.uk
Exmoor Gold, Shepherd Neame Spitfire; Summerskills Tamar; guest beers Ⓗ

Superb waterside pub in a yachting village in the South Hams. The pub was refurbished in 2000 and made brighter, but it has still kept its original character. There is space at the bar for those who prefer to stand, and plenty of cosy seating areas on the floors. It has a small family room. Daily newspapers and magazines are available to those who tire of watching the boats on the river. Bottled organic cider from Heron Valley is sold. 🏚🍴🕭🚽 ♿ ♣ ⬤ ⅀

OAKFORD

Red Lion
Rookery Hill (off A396)
☉ 11.30 (12 winter)-2.30, 6.30-11 (closed winter Mon); 12-3, 7-10.30 Sun
☎ (01398) 351219 website: www.redlion-oakford.co.uk
Juwards Bitter; guest beer Ⓗ

A warm welcome awaits at this 17th-century ex-coaching inn between Tiverton and Dulverton, in a small Exe Valley village – an area of outstanding natural beauty. Juwards in Somerset provides the regular ale, supplemented by a guest most weeks, in the large single bar. The food is all home-cooked, featuring Exe Valley trout and meat from Somerset. The restaurant area is no-smoking. Close to Exmoor for visitors and walkers, the accommodation here consists of three en-suite rooms; one has a four-poster bed. 🏚Q🕭🛏🚽⬤♣P

OKEHAMPTON

Plymouth Inn
26 West Street
☉ 12-3, 7-11; 12-11 Sat; 12-10.30 Sun
☎ (01837) 53633 e-mail: geoffgoatherd@aol.com
Beer range varies Ⓖ

16th-century former coaching inn, near the bridge over the West Uckment River, at the western end of town. The Plymouth is a friendly pub that brings the welcome and atmosphere of a village pub to an old market town. Walking and cycling groups are informally organised in summer, and two beer festivals are held (normally May and Nov). The constantly changing beer range places the accent on West Country breweries. Occasional live music is performed in the bar, usually acoustic, and sometimes impromptu. 🚽🕭⬤♣⅀

OTTERY ST MARY

King's Arms Hotel
Gold Street
☉ 11-2.30, 6-11; 11-11 Sat; 12-10.30 Sun
☎ (01404) 812486
Branscombe Vale Branoc, seasonal beers; Otter Ale; guest beers Ⓗ

Traditional hotel-style public bar, popular with locals, usually stocking a wide selection of local beers and staging an ale festival in early summer (14 ales in the 2000 festival). Live entertainment includes bands (Fri eve) and Karaoke (Sun eve). Children are welcome in the restaurant area; a wide-screen TV, juke box and fruit machines can be found in the bar; the pool table has its own room, as does the skittle alley.
🚽🕭♣P🛏

PAIGNTON

Devonport Arms
42 Elmbank Road (behind the zoo)
☉ 11-11; 12-10.30 Sun
☎ (01803) 558322
Courage Best Bitter; John Smith's Bitter; guest beers Ⓗ

This unpretentious corner pub was built in the 1930s and remains largely unaltered; the embodiment of a traditional boozer. Multi-roomed, it has a large bar with wide-screen TV, a small family room and a lounge bar. A varied list of guest beers and a welcoming staff enhance this pub, used mainly by locals. A skittle team plays in an alley in the barn behind the pub. Well-prepared basic food of excellent value is served lunchtime Mon–Sat and Thu–Sat eves.
🏚Q🕭🚽⬤🕭P

Isaac Merritt
54-58 Torquay Road
☉ 11-11; 12-10.30 Sun
☎ (01803) 556066
Draught Bass; Courage Directors; Exmoor Gold or Stag; guest beers Ⓗ

Busy town-centre alehouse on the main road. Popular with all ages, its comfortable, friendly atmosphere is enhanced by cosy, seated alcoves. Accessible to wheelchair-users, there is a designated ground-floor WC. This excellent Wetherspoon's outlet is developing a growing reputation for its excellent quality and ever-changing list of guest beers from all over the country. Superb value meals are available all day. The pub is fully air conditioned, with patio door frontage which is opened up in warm weather. Local CAMRA *Pub of the Year* 2001. Q🕭🚽♿⬤♣⅀

PETER TAVY

Peter Tavy Inn
Off B386
☉ 12-3, 6 (6.30 winter)-11; 12-3, 7-11 Sun
☎ (01822) 810348 e-mail: petertavy@virgin.net
Badger Best; Draught Bass; Princetown Jail Ale; Summerskills Tamar; guest beer Ⓗ

Very friendly, 15th-century pub with loads of character, in an old village on Dartmoor. There is one central bar area boasting granite floors and huge beams. An old watchkeeper's window in the pub is said to be part of the beacon system to warn of trouble from the sea. Luscombe's cider is sold. The pub has a patio and garden for fine weather. Meals, including vegetarian and children's choices, are of excellent quality.
🏚🕭🚽⬤Å⬤P⅀

PLYMOUTH

Britannia
3 Wolsely Road, Milehouse
☉ 11-11; 12-10.30 Sun
☎ (01752) 607596
Courage Directors; Shepherd Neame Spitfire; Theakston Best Bitter, Old Peculier; Wadworth 6X; guest beers Ⓗ

Typical Wetherspoon's conversion from a run-down Edwardian pub into one that has atmosphere and is busy at most times. Three miles from the centre, it

can truly be called a community pub, attracting mostly regular locals. It stands by a very busy road junction, near the Mayflower Sports Centre and swimming pool in Plymouth's largest public park, a large oasis of green within the city. The pub sponsors a player from nearby Plymouth Argyle and admits football supporters on match days, when the atmosphere always remains good humoured.
🏠Q☜☆◑🏮 🚃(North Rd) 🍴✗●

Butchers Arms
160 Cremyll Street, Stonehouse
🕐 1-11; 12-3, 7-10.30 Sun
☎ (01752) 660510
Courage Best Bitter; guest beer 🅗

This small, cosy, single bar local has been recently renovated. It stands near the Grade I listed King William victualling yard that used to supply the Royal Navy; now closed, its future use is undetermined. Also nearby is Cremyll ferry (foot passenger ferry to Cornwall), Mount Edgecombe Park and Devil's Point – the narrowest point on the Tamar River and a good spot for watching the ship traffic in and out of Devonport's naval base. The pub has an enclosed garden that is safe for children. A varied cider is stocked in summer. Q☆◑♣🍴

Clifton
35 Clifton Street, Greenbank
🕐 5 (12 Fri & Sat)-11; 12-10.30 Sun
☎ (01752) 266563
Draught Bass; Worthington Bitter; guest beers 🅗

Clifton Classic is the house beer brewed by Summerskills for this spacious back-street pub near the city centre. Warm and friendly, the pub fields many competitive teams. Ignore the large clock – it is only correct twice a day. The Clifton was once considered the luckiest pub in Britain as it numbered no less than three National Lottery millionaires among its regulars.
&🚃(North Rd) ♣

Compton Inn
77 Priory Road, Lower Compton
🕐 12-2.30, 6-11; 12-11 Sat; 12-10.30 Sun
☎ (01752) 266962
Draught Bass; Courage Best Bitter, Directors 🅗

Styled as a village inn, this local is in a residential area of Plymouth. Situated in a narrow back road, parking can be a problem. The single, large carpeted bar is comfortable and has an area set aside for games. The TV is always tuned to sports broadcasts – rugby is the favourite. An upstairs room houses a pool table and doubles as a family area. ☜◑♣

Dolphin ⇐
The Barbican (opp. Dartington Glass)
🕐 10-11; 12-10.30 Sun
☎ (01752) 660876
Draught Bass 🅖

The only remaining unspoilt pub in the historic Barbican, opposite the old fish market, drawing customers from all walks of life. Note the numerous portraits of the landlord painted by famous artists. The Tollpuddle Martyrs stayed here on their return from Australia. The windows are the original local Octagon Brewery windows; Octagon was sold to Plymouth Breweries, which in turn was bought by Courage. The

pub ended up with Punch Taverns. It is within walking distance of the National Aquarium and Mayflower Steps. 🏠Q

Hogshead
9-11 Mutley Plain
🕐 11-11; 12-10.30 Sun
☎ (01752) 256936
Boddingtons Bitter; Sutton XSB, Comfort; 🅗 **guest beers** 🅗/🅖

Completely refurbished since last year, this single-bar but extensive Hogshead has been transformed by soft furnishings, a bright paint scheme and modern lighting. A popular meeting place for younger drinkers, particularly students, it is liable to be very busy at weekends. The large-screen TV shows major sporting events. It stocks a rotating range of guest beers.
◑&🚃(North Rd) ✗

Hogshead
12-14 Royal Parade
🕐 11-11; 12-10.30 Sun
☎ (01752) 260442
Badger Tanglefoot; Boddingtons Bitter; Sutton XSB, Comfort; guest beers 🅗

Brightly decorated, city-centre pub situated opposite St Andrew's Church. Modern furnishing include upholsted seating and fine tables. A converted bank, it has large windows facing on to the street. The single large bar is popular with office staff and numerous shoppers during the day; younger drinkers take over eves and it can get very busy at weekends.
◑🚃(North Rd) ✗

Lounge ⟋
7 Stopford Place, Stoke
🕐 11-2.30, 7-11; 12-2.30, 7-10.30 Sun
☎ (01752) 561330
Draught Bass; guest beer 🅖

A gem of an urban pub in a back street leading to Devonport Park; comfortable and old-fashioned, it is like drinking in someone's home. The licensee and locals are friendly and a pint of gravity-dispensed Bass is a rare treat. Although hidden away, it is worth seeking out. There is an emphasis on food at lunchtimes, which is very popular with the local retired population.
🏠Q◑🚃(Devonport)

Prince Maurice
3 Church Hill, Eggbuckland
🕐 11-3, 7 (6 Fri)-11; 11-11 Sat; 12-3, 7-10.30 Sun
☎ (01752) 771515
Badger Tanglefoot; Draught Bass; Courage Best Bitter; Summerskills Best Bitter, guest beers 🅗

Near the 14th-century church in an Anglo-Saxon settlement, now part of Plymouth, the pub was built in the 16th century. It no doubt served the Royalist troops preparing their attack on Parliamentary Plymouth in the Civil War (the house beer brewed by Summerskills is called Royale). Real fires in both bars provide a welcoming atmosphere; in summer, you can sit outside and look over the old village green. Ten beers are always available at Plymouth CAMRA's *Pub of the Year 2000*; a cider (varies) is stocked in summer. 🏠☆⊟♣🍴P

Royal Albert Inn
930 Wolseley Road, Saltash Road, St Budeaux (under Tamar bridge)

❂ 10.30-11.30, 12-10.30 Sun
☎ (01752) 361108
Draught Bass; Courage Best Bitter; guest beers Ⓗ
Small, friendly pub owned by the current landlords for the last 10 years, it is frequented by locals and visitors alike. Situated practically under the Tamar Bridge, the garden (across the road) has views across the river to Cornwall. The pub features many maritime artefacts and memorabilia. The kitchen, which provides home-cooked fare, has been awarded the City Council's *'Eat'* award for the last nine years. ❀◑⭢(St Budeaux) ♣P

Sippers
18 Millbay Road, Millbay
☙ 11-11; 12-10.30 Sun
☎ (01752) 670668
Boddingtons Bitter; Flowers Original; Fuller's London Pride; Marston's Pedigree; Wadworth 6X; guest beer Ⓗ
This corner pub has one main bar, with a slate floor but seating areas upstairs and a more intriguing subterranean area. It is the nearest real ale outlet to Plymouth Pavilions conference/entertainment centre (car park can be used free of charge eves). It stands almost at the entrance to Millbay Docks where the Roscoff ferry departs for France. It is about 500 yards from the city centre, on the road to uncrowded West Hoe. The beers may change at this former Whitbread tied house. ❀◑●

Thistle Park Tavern
32 Commercial Road, Coxside (between Aquarium and Warner leisure complex)
❂ 11-1am; 12-10.30 Sun
☎ (01752) 204890
e-mail: suttonbrewery@xsb42.forreg.co.uk
Sutton Plymouth Pride, XSB, Wild Blonde, Comfort, Pandamonium, seasonal beers; guest beers Ⓗ
This friendly, basic pub, drawing a mixed clientele, can be reached by foot, via a swing bridge from the historic Barbican. It has bare floorboards and an air of a village pub within the city. The tap for Sutton Brewery, it stocks a good range of their beers. The licensee is a South African, so Biltong is available. Note the late licence until 1am Mon–Sat. 'Lunches' are served until 5pm. Pavement tables are available in fine weather. ❀◑♣

London Inn
Church Road
❂ 11-11; 12-10.30 Sun
☎ (01752) 337025
Courage Best Bitter; Greene King Ruddles County; guest beers Ⓗ
Friendly two-bar pub situated in an area of historic interest. Note the collection of naval memorabilia in the lounge, which is usually quiet. It hosts regular food theme nights, focusing on international cuisine, such as Indian or Italian. The garden is opposite the pub, across the road.
⚌Q❀◑⍌♣P

Boringdon Arms
Boringdon Terrace, Turnchapel
❂ 11-11; 12-10.30 Sun
☎ (01752) 402053 website: www.bori.co.uk
Butcombe Bitter; Oakham JHB; RCH Pitchfork;

Summerskills Best Bitter; guest beers Ⓗ
Terraced pub in a waterside village in a conservation area, on a coastal footpath, popular with locals. It is fairly basic but bare floorboards and a real fire help create a good atmosphere. Maritime decor includes many ship's plaques and charts on display around the bar. Beer festivals are staged every odd-numbered month (last weekend). It has twice been Plymouth CAMRA's *Pub of the Year*. A water taxi runs from the Barbican to the Mounthatten pub (five minutes' walk). An occasional cider (make varies) is stocked; good value food includes famous home-made pies. The rear garden is entirely enclosed by rock walls.
⚌Q❀⌂◑⍌♣●

New Inn
Boringdon Road, Turnchapel
❂ 12-3 (not Mon-Thu), 6-11; 12-11 Sat; 12-10.30 Sun
☎ (01752) 402765
Draught Bass; Princetown Jail Ale; Sharpe's Doom Bar; guest beers Ⓗ
This friendly, 18th-century pub, on the waterside, affords excellent views across to Plymouth's Barbican area. A water taxi from the Barbican links to the south-west coastal footpath which passes the New Inn. The pub has expanded over the years, taking in a bakery and a butcher's shop on either side. The food is good quality and the guest bedrooms are all en-suite. ⚌Q⌂◑♣

Blacksmith's Arms
3 miles S of Dulford, on A373
❂ 12-2.30 (closed Mon; 12-3 Sat), 6 (5 Fri)-11; 12-3, 7-10.30 Sun
☎ (01884) 277474
website: www.eclipse.co.uk/plymtree/index.htm
Exe Valley Dob's Best Bitter; O'Hanlons Red Ale; guest beers Ⓗ
18th-century, popular village pub, with a reputation for good quality food, the ingredients for which are sourced locally wherever possible; a children's menu is available. It hosts occasional live music and quiz nights; skittles (five teams) and boules are also played. From easy chairs around the log burner, admire the oak-beamed interior, decorated with blacksmith's tools, diving memorabilia and a collection of deer antlers. In summer this friendly local plays host to local and touring cricket sides and stages a mini-beer festival. ⚌❀◑♣P

Warren House Inn
On B3212, to Mortonhampstead
❂ winter 11-3, 6-11, (11-11 Fri, Sat & summer); 12-3, 6-10.30 (12-10.30 summer) Sun
☎ (01822) 880208
Badger Tanglefoot; Butcombe Bitter; guest beers Ⓗ
Third highest pub in England, isolated high on Dartmoor; a welcome haven for both walkers and visitors. The interior boasts exposed beams and wood-panelled walls, complemented by rustic wooden benches and tables. A log fire is said to have been burning continuously since 1845. There is a large family room and also tables outside affording breathtaking views over the moors. Countryman cider is stocked.
⚌Q⛺❀◑Å♣●P

PRINCETOWN

Plume of Feathers Inn
The Square (opp. visitors centre)
◷ 11-11; 12-10.30 Sun
☎ (01822) 890240
Draught Bass; Princetown Jail Ale ⊞
Princetown's oldest building (1785) features copper bars, slate floors and granite walls. A busy pub, used by locals and visitors, particularly walkers. Dormitory accommodation is available in a bunkhouse and the pub has its own campsite. It has very good facilities for the disabled. Most of Princetown is owned by the Duke of Cornwall (Prince of Wales); the pub name is derived from his insignia. The restaurant doubles as a family room. The cider varies.
🏨🛏🏱🛌⌕🍴🚻♣♠P

SCORITON

Tradesman's Arms
On Holne road OS704684
◷ 11-2.30, 6.30-11 (closed winter Mon; 11-11 summer); 12-2.30, 7-10.30 (not winter eve) Sun
☎ (01364) 631206
website: www.thetradesmansarms.com
Draught Bass; Princetown Dartmoor IPA, Jail Ale ⊞
17th-century village pub, originally an ale house, built for the tin miners, now a single bar with an open-plan bar area and a dining alcove, plus a family room. A friendly atmosphere is enhanced by a quiz night (Thu), folk night (Fri) and jazz on Sun lunchtime; look out for the monthly 'mystery beer' on a fourth handpump. No keg or creamflow bitters are stocked, but there is good quality and choice of food and wines, plus over 30 malt whiskies.
🏨Q🛏🏱⌕P

SIDBURY

Red Lion
Fore Street
◷ 11.30-2.30, 5-11; 11-11 Sat; 12-10.30 Sun
☎ (01395) 597313
Ringwood Best Bitter; guest beers ⊞
Popular, 400-year-old pub opposite the church, full of character in its cosy, beamed bars. It hosts a beer festival each Easter and regular music and quiz nights. From the front, you can see the pub used to be a coaching inn – go under the archway into a large sheltered patio area, great for an *al fresco* supper. Darts and skittles teams compete weekly; also euchre is played here. The licensee offers interesting guest ales and will try to get a favourite brew if you ask.
Q🏱🏠⌕♣♠

SILVERTON

Lamb Inn
Fore Street
◷ 11-2.30, 6-11; 11-11 Sat; 12-10.30 Sun
☎ (01392) 860272 website: www.lamb-inn.com
Draught Bass; Exe Valley Dob's Best Bitter; ⊞
guest beers Ⓖ
Family-run village pub of stone floors, stripped timber and old pine tables and chairs. Most ales are served from a temperature-controlled stillage behind the bar. A recently-built function room houses a skittle alley with its own bar. Good value

home-cooked food includes a specials board which always features a vegetarian option; monthly steak nights are held (low prices). Village organisations, such as bell-ringers and short mat bowlers, use the pub as a meeting place.
🏨◑⌕🛌♣✂

SLAPTON

Queen's Arms
Signed off A379
◷ 12-3, 6-11; 12-3, 7-10.30 Sun
☎ (01548) 580800
website: www.slapton.org/queensarms
Princetown Dartmoor IPA; guest beers ⊞
One of the famous free houses of south Devon; a single bar with a traditional atmosphere and a large open fire. The IPA is the mainstay of the cask ales, with up to three guest beers available, depending on the time of year. A full menu tends towards the traditional, with the chef's home-made pies a speciality (takeaways available). See the many old photos of the area, including the wartime evacuation. Peaceful, secluded walled gardens and a patio add to its appeal. Children (and dogs) are welcome.
🏨Q🏱◑⌕P

SOUTH POOL

Millbrook Inn
Off A379 at Chillington, E of Kingsbridge OS776402
◷ 12-2.30, 6-11; 12-3, 7-10.30 Sun
☎ (01548) 531581 website: www.millbrookinn.co.uk
Draught Bass; Ⓖ **Fuller's London Pride; Wadworth 6X**
(summer); **guest beer** ⊞
The Millbrook is situated at the head of the Salcombe estuary in the picturesque village of South Pool. The main section of the pub dates back to the early 17th century, with the top bar (children welcome) added later. The pub is busy in the summer months, with most of its trade coming from boaters and walkers. It is well known for its crab sandwiches and Aylesbury ducks. No Sun eve meals are served Jan–March. Note no debit or credit cards accepted.
🏨Q🏱◑🛌⌕♣

SOUTH ZEAL

Oxenham Arms
◷ 11-2.30, 6-11; 12-2.30, 7-10.30 Sun
☎ (01837) 840244 website: www.hoteldevon.net
Princetown Dartmoor IPA; Ⓖ **guest beer** ⊞
First licensed in 1477, the Oxenham Arms was described by one novelist as the 'stateliest and most ancient abode in the hamlet', still a fair description, although the hamlet has now grown into a village. Thought to have been built by monks in the 12th century, it has the unspoilt atmosphere of an old country inn, with low beams, stone-flagged floors, open fires and mullioned windows. A visit to the small lounge behind the bar will reveal even more ancient roots as the monastic builders incorporated a prehistoric standing stone in the wall. 🏨Q🛏🏱🛌◑⌕♣P

SPREYTON

Tom Cobley Tavern
◷ 12-2, 6-11 (closed Mon); 12-3, 7-10.30 Sun
☎ (01647) 231314

Draught Bass; Cotleigh Tawny; guest beer (occasional) Ⓗ
Small inn, close to Dartmoor National Park, licensed since 1589. The main bar, welcomes drinkers, darts players and diners. To the rear is a designated dining area and an adjoining room where table tennis can be played, or an indoor barbecue arranged around the purpose-built fireplace. It leads to the lovely garden, with fine country views. Spreyton is the village from where Tom Cobley – a local landowner and his friends left to visit Widecombe Fair, as immortalised in the song. Good home-cooked food includes monthly curry nights (book). ♨Q⦰❀⇗◑♣♠

STICKLEPATH

Devonshire Inn
☼ 11-11 (11-3, 5-11 winter); 12-3, 7-10.30 Sun
☎ (01837) 840626
Draught Bass; St Austell Tinners, HSD, seasonal beers Ⓖ
At the end of what was originally a terrace of Elizabethan cottages, in this north Dartmoor village, the Devonshire is an unspoilt thatched local, with low ceilings and a large open fire. A leat running past the back wall of the pub helps to cool the stillage for the gravity-dispensed beers, as well as powering the waterwheels of the nearby Finch Foundry Museum (NT). The Exeter–Okehampton bus service stops outside and a number of footpaths access the Dartmoor countryside nearby.
♨Q⦰Å♣P

STOCKLAND

King's Arms
☼ 12-3, 6.30-11; 12-3, 6.30-10.30 Sun
☎ (01404) 881361 website: www.kingsarms.net
Courage Directors; Exmoor Ale, Gold; Otter Ale Ⓗ
Large pub in a delightful village in the Blackdown Hills. The spacious public bar, favoured by locals, leads through to a

smaller lounge and a well-used skittle alley. The pub is well known for its excellent food, with the menu displayed on a blackboard in the Cotley restaurant bar (and explained in full by the landlord); booking is essential in summer. There is also a no-smoking restaurant. Folk eves are held regularly. Harper's dry cider is stocked in summer. ♨Q⦰❀◑ ⊟♿♣♠P

TEIGNMOUTH ✣

Golden Lion
85 Bitton Park Road (A379)
☼ 12-4, 6-11; 12-4, 7-10.30 Sun
☎ (01626) 776116
Beer range varies Ⓗ
Friendly, welcoming, typical two-bar pub, overlooking the docks. There is a cosy L-shaped lounge bar with beamed ceilings and a larger public bar with an L-shaped bar and a pool table. Three ever-changing real ales are served on handpump at very reasonable prices. There is limited parking at the front of the pub. ⊟⇌♣P

TIVERTON ✣

White Ball
Bridge Street (behind Westexe South car park)
☼ 11-11; 12-10.30 Sun
☎ (01884) 251525
Courage Directors; Exmoor Stag; Theakston Best Bitter; Wadworth 6X; guest beers Ⓗ
Cosy town pub with a friendly atmosphere, a large log fire and genuine beams enhanced by soft lighting and an absence of music. The lovely garden has decking overlooking the river. Beer festivals are held in spring and at Hallowe'en. A variety of meals are served throughout the day, with weekly promotions on curries and grills. The seating areas are cosy, spacious and comfortable; special attention is paid to no-smoking areas. Children are welcome in the garden, but the bar is strictly for over 18s. ♨Q⦰◑✂●

INN BRIEF

MEETH
Bull & Dragon
11-3, 6-11;
12-3, 7-10.30 Sun
Adnams Broadside; guest beer Ⓗ
Ancient thatched village inn with a bar, games and restaurant. B&B available.

ROCKBEARE
Jack-in-the-Green
11-2.30 (3 Fri & Sat), 6-11;
12-10.30 Sun
Draught Bass; Cotleigh Tawny; Otter Ale; guest beer Ⓗ
Large, food-dominated, traditional beamed and timbered, roadside pub (on old A30). Extensive, imaginative menus make it very popular.

STAVERTON
Sea Trout Inn
11-3, 6-11 (11-11 summer Fri & Sat);
12-3, 7-10.30 (12-10.30 summer) Sun
Palmers Dorset Gold, IPA, 200 Ⓗ
15th-century pub, with two bars and a restaurant, near the River Dart and the preserved steam railway. Good food and accommodation.

TEIGNMOUTH
Blue Anchor
Teign Street
11-11, 12-10.30 Sun
Adnams Broadside; Greene King Abbot; guest beers Ⓗ
Small local near the docks: a single bar with pool table and darts, stocking up to six real ales; full of character and local charm.

TIVERTON
Racehorse
Wellbrook Street
11-11.30, 12-10.30 Sun
Draught Bass; Courage Best Bitter; Greene King IPA; Wychwood Hobgoblin Ⓗ
Vibrant local in a terrace, close to Heathcoat's Mill. You must visit the rear garden and see the mini-zoo!

TOTNES
Kingsbridge Inn
9 Leechwell Street
11.30-3, 6-11; 12-3, 7-10.30 Sun
Draught Bass; Cotleigh Tawny; Redruth Cornish Rebellion; Theakston Old Peculier; guest beer Ⓗ
Friendly pub: a comfortable, subtly-lit bar with alcoves and a low ceiling, plus a dining area.

TRUSHAM
Cridford Inn
9 Leechwell Street
11.30-3, 6.30-11; 12-4, 7-10.30 Sun
Scattor Rock Teign Valley Tipple; guest beer Ⓗ
13th-century Devon longhouse that became a pub in 1983. Stained glass windows and old church pews add character. Food and accommodation available.

WESTWARD HO!
Nelson Inn
5 Nelson Road
11-11; 12-11 Sun
Fuller's London Pride; guest beer Ⓗ
Originally a house, it has a dining area and large TV for sport. A second guest beer is stocked in summer. B&B.

WONSON
Northmore Arms
5 Nelson Road
11-11; 12-10.30 Sun
Adnams Broadside; Cotleigh Tawny; Exe Valley Dob's Best Bitter Ⓖ
Traditional country local on the northern edge of Dartmoor, ideally situated for walkers, with good accommodation. Bar food.

TOPSHAM

Bridge Inn
Bridge Hill
✪ 12-2, 6-10.30 (11 Fri & Sat); 12-2, 7-10.30 Sun
☎ (01392) 873862 website: www.cheffers.co.uk
Adnams Broadside; Branscombe Vale Branoc; guest beers Ⓖ

Traditional unspoilt inn, free from juke boxes or fruit machines, serving a good selection of ales including some regular local brews, such as Branscombe's Branoc, but the beer list varies. This 15th-century Grade II listed pub has been in the same family for over 100 years. Home-made soup and ploughmans are usually available. Popular with locals and visitors, particularly since the Queen visited this inn. Benches on a grassy area outside the pub are used for summer drinking.
🏚Q❀≈P

Lighter Inn
The Quay, Fore Street
✪ 11-11; 12-10.30 Sun
☎ (01392) 875439
Badger Best, Tanglefoot, seasonal beers Ⓗ

This building was once the town's custom house but now it is Hall & Woodhouse's most westerly pub. The years have seen quite a few refurbishments, with the current layout being comfortable and pleasant, offering a choice of drinking areas; the inevitable nautical theme is subdued. Take your drink on to the quayside and enjoy the views across the River Exe. The menu usually features interesting specials, the house speciality being (naturally) fresh fish. Quiz nights are held every other Thu.
🎕❀◑♿≈✿●

TORQUAY

Crown & Sceptre
2 Petitor Rd, St Marychurch
✪ 11-3 (4 Sat), 5.30 (6.30 Sat)-11; 12-3, 7-10.30 Sun
☎ (01803) 328290
Draught Bass; Courage Best Bitter, Directors; Greene King Old Speckled Hen; Wadworth 6X; Wychwood Hobgoblin; Ⓗ **guest beers** Ⓗ/Ⓖ

This 200-year-old stone coaching house will not only give you a good time in a friendly atmosphere, but also a sense of belonging. The same landlord and some of the locals have been there for over 20 years and the pub has been listed in this *Guide* for all of them. A full menu is served lunchtime and snacks on request at any time (no food Sun). It stages a folk night (Thu) and monthly jazz (second Sunday afternoon). Children (and dogs) are welcome. Beer is expensive.
🏚Q❀◑🍴♣P

TUCKENHAY

Maltsters Arms
Bow Creek (signed from A381, Totnes-Kingsbridge road)
✪ 11-11; 12-10.30 Sun
☎ (01803) 732350 website: www.tuckenhay.com
Princetown Dartmoor IPA; guest beers Ⓗ

Marvellous waterside pub overlooking the peaceful, wooden Bow Creek, where tables

by the water, and moorings are available. The pub has a narrow main bar, linking two other cosy rooms; the snug with an open fire and another room with red-painted seats and kitchen chairs on a wooden floor. The restaurant area offers excellent food; barbecues and live music are hosted outside in summer. Good quality accommodation is available (10% discount to card-carrying CAMRA members), but the beer is expensive. Heron Valley cider is sold in summer.
🏚Q🛏❀🍴◑♣✿P

WEMBURY

Odd Wheel
Knighton Road
✪ 12-3, 6.30-11; 12-11 Sat, 12-4, 7 10.30 Sun
☎ (01752) 862287
Boddingtons Bitter; Courage Best Bitter; Princetown Jail Ale; Scattor Rock Scatter Brain; Skinner's Coast Liner; Sutton XSB Ⓖ

Friendly, traditional, two-bar pub inside the South Hams, but on a regular bus route from Plymouth. It comprises a large lounge, with comfortable seating and a public bar with a real fire. The pub runs its own golf society and is the meeting place for many sporting teams. It makes a good start, or finishing point for a coastal walk.
🏚❀◑🍴♣P

WEST DOWN

Crown
The Square
✪ 12-3, 7-11; 12-3, 7-10.30 Sun
☎ (01271) 862790
Barum Original; Wadworth 6X Ⓗ

Genuine locals' local; this charming rural inn, in the village square, enjoys the support of the many pub teams that play there, and is also frequently filled with the lively, village panto rehearsal crowd. The small, recently revamped dining area, provides an intimate candlelit environment, a perfect foil for the brilliant, and deservedly popular food. In summer, take your drinks outside to sit and enjoy one of the loveliest pub gardens you are ever likely to find. Overall, a real gem.　🏚Q❀◑♠♣P

WESTWARD HO! ☼

Pig on the Hill
Pusehill (off A39, Bideford-Abbotsham road)
✪ 12-3, 6 (6.30 winter)-11; 12-3, 7-10.30 Sun
☎ (01237) 425889
website: www.pigonthehill.co.uk
Country Life Old Appledore, Golden Pig; Ind Coope Burton Ale; guest beer (occasional) Ⓗ

This converted farm is home to the Country Life Brewery. The brewing process can be observed through a large window at the far end of the restaurant. The intimate bar is decorated with pictures and figurines of all things porcine. Q🛏❀🍴◑♠♣✿P

WHIDDON DOWN

Post Inn
Exeter Road (on old main road, near A30 Whiddon Down services)
✪ 11-11; 12-10.30 Sun
☎ (01647) 231242
Beer range varies Ⓗ

Built in the 16th century as the post office on the old coaching road to the West, the Post is a pleasantly refurbished country pub, handy for the A30 and keen to cater for the modern traveller (meals served 11–11). The central bar serves three rooms, with the two side rooms, although generally laid out for diners, available for non-smoking drinkers. The ales follow a West Country theme, while the cider is from a local maker.
🏚️✿◑♠♣P⚲

WHIMPLE

New Fountain Inn
Church Road
🕐 12-2.30, 6.30-11; 12-3, 7-10.30 Sun
☎ (01404) 822350
Branscombe Vale Branoc; Teignworthy Reel Ale; guest beers Ⓗ/Ⓖ
Very friendly local in a delightful village with access from the old A30 or by train (the station, within walking distance, links Whimple to the Exeter–London line). During the year, various special events take place, including wassailing with morris dancers visiting and regular charity quizzes. The home-cooked food is extremely good and varied, with very reasonable prices. The landlord always supplies local ales and now stocks beer from the nearest brewery, O'Hanlon's.
🏚️Q✿◑♣⚞≈♣P

Ruggiestone Inn ☆
¼ mile S of village centre OS721766
🕐 11-2.30 (3 Sat), 7 (6 summer)-11; 12-3,

7 (6 summer)-10.30 Sun
☎ (01364) 621327 website: www.rugglestone.f9.co.uk
Draught Bass; Butcombe Bitter Ⓖ
Unspoilt, cosy pub in a splendid Dartmoor setting where a small bar area has some seating and a stone floor, while the lounge area boasts an open fire. The pub is named after a local 'logan' stone. Children under 14 are not allowed inside, but across the stream is a large grassed seating area with a shelter for use in bad weather. A selection of home-cooked food is available. The pub's car park is just down the lane. The beer is served via gravity dispense, from a small serving hatch.
🏚️Q✿◑♠⚞

WOODLAND

Rising Sun
Signed from the Plymouth-bound A38
🕐 11-3 (not Mon), 6-11 (not winter Mon); 12-3, 7-10.30 Sun
☎ (01364) 652544
website: www.risingsunwoodland.co.uk
Princetown Jail Ale; guest beers Ⓗ
Lovely rural free house in beautiful countryside between Torbay and Dartmoor comprising a long single bar and a large open-plan drinking and dining area, where small screens offer some privacy. An additional children's area is off the main bar. Outside, extensive grounds include seating at the front and a children's play area. The pub serves an excellent range of home-made food and is well known for its pies. Note the large collection of keys hanging from the ceiling in the bar area.
🏚️Q⚞✿☙◑♠P⚲

Fishy business

CAMRA and the Good Beer Guide probably receive more enquiries concerning beers suitable for vegetarians and vegans than any other subject. Brewers use isinglass to 'fine' or clear cask-conditioned beers of yeast. Isinglass is made from the swim bladders of the sturgeon. Its use dates from the 18th century and it is high time that the brewing industry found a better method, especially as the sturgeon is in danger of being fished to extinction as a result of the demand for caviar. Irish moss is used to clarify the 'hopped wort' in the brewing copper prior to fermentation, and, along with other natural plants and herbs, could be a substitute for isinglass. The problem is that publicans are under intense pressure to serve and empty casks as fast as possible, and isinglass works more quickly than other clearing agents. However, by the time a cask of beer has 'dropped bright' in a pub cellar, isinglass, dead yeast cells and other detritus will have settled in the belly of the cask, and will not be served in the glass along with the beer. Most producers of bottle-conditioned beers also use isinglass, though a few do use Irish moss or other forms of what are called 'auxiliary finings'. As a small step forward, it would be useful if brewers indicated on bottle labels whether or not they use isinglass. Better still, the industry should look at less environmentally harmful methods of clearing both cask- and bottle-conditioned beers.

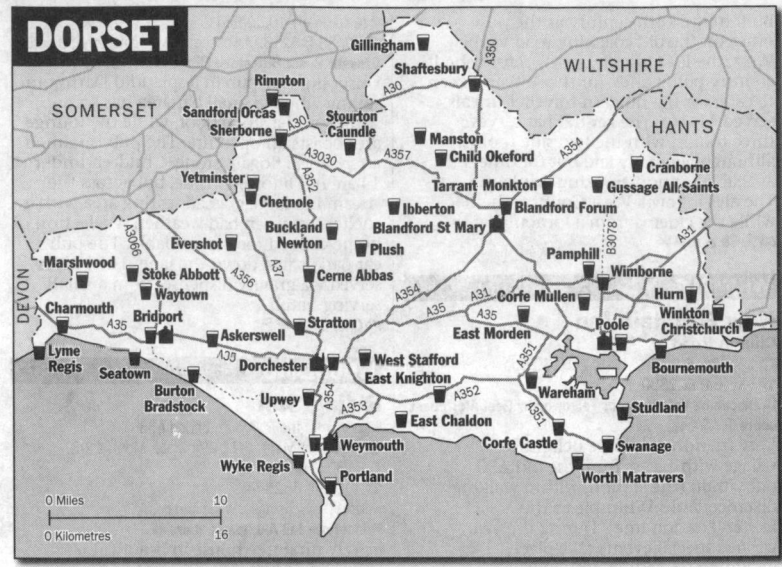

DORSET

ASKERSWELL

Spyway

1/2 mile N of village, N of A35

☼ 11.30-2.30, 6-11; 12-3, 7-10.30 Sun

☎ (01308) 485250

Adnams Bitter; Branscombe Vale Branoc; Greene King IPA, Abbot Ⓗ

Situated above the village on an old road called Spyway, this smugglers' inn dates from 1600. The south-facing garden provides stunning views of the surrounding countryside, which, with its numerous walks, featured in the film of *Far from the Madding Crowd*. Inside is a comfortable lounge, a dining room and cosy, beamed bar, with open fire and settles where a ghost of a young, Victorian woman has been detected. The interesting menu (not served Sun eve or Mon) uses local farm produce and fish from West Bay. ♨Q🏠🐕🍴◖◗P

BOURNEMOUTH

Goat & Tricycle

27-29 West Hill Road (off Poole Hill)

☼ 12-3, 6-11; 12-3, 7-10.30 Sun

☎ (01202) 314220

e-mail: daveandwendy@the
goatandtricyclefreeserve.co.uk

Wadworth IPA, 6X, JCB, seasonal beers; guest beers Ⓗ

Traditional and comfortable, the Goat was formerly two small adjacent pubs, the Pembroke Arms and Pembroke Shades. It stands just far enough from the town centre to avoid the clubbing crowd who have forced some Bournemouth pubs to become trendy bars. Eight real ales are on offer, with the guest ales often featuring Tom's Tipple from the Red Shoot brew-pub in the New Forest. A courtyard filled with hanging baskets makes a very pleasant drinking space. ♨Q🏠🐕◖◗♿🌸●

Porterhouse

113 Poole Road, Westbourne

☼ 11-11; 12-10.30 Sun

☎ (01202) 768586

Ringwood Best Bitter, True Glory, Fortyniner, Old Thumper, seasonal beers; guest beer Ⓗ

Winner of local CAMRA's *Pub of the Year* award five times in seven years, including joint winner in 2000, this superb pub is one of four owned by Ringwood Brewery. Recently redecorated, this local offers the complete range of Ringwood beers plus usually one guest ale, and a traditional cider. Food, served Mon–Sat, is basic but good value. There are no fruit machines or loud music (none required), only the sound of conversation. A proper pub; but watch out for the ghost. Q◖◗⇌(Branksome) 🌸●●

Shoulder of Mutton

1010 Ringwood Road, Bearwood (400 yds from Clock Garage, via slip road)

☼ 12-2.30, 6-11; 12-4.30, 7-11 Sat; 12-3.30, 7-10.30 Sun

☎ (01202) 573344

Flowers Original; guest beer Ⓗ

The third oldest pub in Bournemouth, this beautiful, two-roomed inn has a comfortable L-shaped lounge displaying pictures of old Longham and Bearwood and, of course, sheep. The public bar is basically furnished and houses a dartboard. Outside is a good-sized, well-equipped children's play area and a large car park. Food is only served on special occasions. If travelling by car do not miss the slip road by the Clock Garage. 🌸🐕🌸P

Sir Percy Florence Shelley

673-675 Christchurch Road, Boscombe

☼ 11-11; 11-10.30 Sun

☎ (01202) 300197

Courage Directors; Ringwood Old Thumper; Theakston Best Bitter; guest beers Ⓗ

Atmospheric Wetherspoon's local whose interior walls reflect the building's early life as a theatre, staging acts such as Laurel and Hardy. Pictures also show the Boscombe area in the 19th and 20th centuries, along with a brief history of the Shelley family. An extensive area of polished floorboards in front of the bar is complemented by a raised no-smoking section and seating booths at the rear, leading to a quiet courtyard. It offers regularly changing guest ales at low prices, with good value food all day until 10pm. It hosts beer festivals in spring and autumn. ✿◑&≋ (Pokesdown) ●

BRIDPORT ✤

Hope & Anchor
13 St Michaels Lane
✪ 11-11; 11-10.30 Sun
☎ (01308) 422160 website: www.shecan.com
Beer range varies Ⓗ

Unspoilt back-street local serving wide cross-section of community – doctors, bankers, bikers and retired folk all co-exist, presided over by a welcoming landlady. It hosts live, mainly blues music, Sun lunchtime and most Fri and Sat eves. An ever-changing selection of three real ales, usually from West Country brewers, is supplemented by occasional beer festivals in summer. There is always a strong beer available. Three ciders are also served from Taunton, Burrow Hill and Cheddar Valley. The bus station and municipal car park are next door. ♨✿♣●

King Charles Tavern
114 St Andrews Road
✪ 11-2.30, 6-11; 12-2.30, 7-10.30 Sun
☎ (01308) 422833
Draught Bass; guest beer Ⓗ

Unpretentious free house on the outskirts of town, catering for a mainly local trade. The small bar has a games area and adjacent restaurant. A skittle alley is in the adjoining building. The pub can be busy at weekends when teams play. Decor includes replica weaponry and pictures of the long-closed Bridport Station that stood nearby. Booking is advised for the popular Sun lunch. A guest ale, usually from Oakhill or Tisbury, is competitively priced. ☎◑♣

BUCKLAND NEWTON

Gaggle of Geese
E of village, 600 yds from B3143
✪ 12-2.30, 6.30-11; 12-3, 7-10.30 Sun
☎ (01300) 345249
Badger Best; Ringwood Best Bitter, Fortyniner; guest beer (summer) Ⓗ

Large village pub at the top of the Piddle Valley. As well as several drinking areas there is a dining area where an extensive menu, including home-made curries and pasta, can be enjoyed. The bar now boasts a computer, with internet access, available to customers. Popular with ramblers and cyclists, it hosts a goose auction in May and Sept. The adjacent caravan site is also run from the pub. The guest beer is normally from Oakhill or Butcombe. ♨✿◑♣P

BURTON BRADSTOCK

Anchor
High Street
✪ 11-3, 6-11; 12-3, 7-10.30 Sun
☎ (01308) 897228 website: www.westcountry.net
Draught Bass; Ushers Best Bitter; Wadworth 6X Ⓗ

The oldest pub in this coastal village boasts unusual, eye-catching windows. The large public bar used to be a stable, hence the

many country artefacts adorning the walls. Games include table skittles and a bar billiards table, a rarity in the county. Deserved winners of Usher's *Best Food Pub* award, vegetarian and vegan choices are available along with local fish, scallops and game (only roasts are served Sun lunchtime); booking is recommended. A large choice of speciality malt whiskies add to its attraction. Q◑⊟&λ♣●P

CHETNOLE

Chetnole Inn
1 mile E of A37
✪ 11-2.30, 6-11; 12-3, 7-10.30 Sun
☎ (01935) 872337 website: www.chetnoleinn.co.uk
Branscombe Vale Branoc; Butcombe Bitter; Palmers IPA; guest beers Ⓗ

This classic village pub, opposite the church, in unspoilt countryside, is the centre of activities in the community. Chetnole Halt lies on the Weymouth–Bristol line so, for an idyllic day out, take the train and the village is a 20-minute stroll along country lanes. The public bar, warmed by a blazing fire, has a skittle alley behind. Excellent food is served in the lounge, restaurant or garden. Two guest beers are provided by West Country brewers, with the Easter weekend hosting the annual beer festival (open all day). ♨Q✿◑⊟≋ (Chetnole Halt) ♣

CHILD OKEFORD

Saxon Inn
Gold Hill
✪ 11.30-2.30 (3 Sat), 7-11; 12-3, 7-10.30 Sun
☎ (01258) 860310
Butcombe Bitter; guest beer Ⓗ

Set back off the road, this welcoming pub fully deserves its local CAMRA *Pub of the Season* award. Walk into a cosy bar with a real fire; pause at the bar for your beer, then continue up the steps into the lounge area. Among the many old maps and local photographs, see those showing the making and hanging of the pub sign. Food is cooked to order (no eve meals Tue or Sun). With a large, attractive garden, this is definitely a place to relax. ♨Q☎✿◑&λ♣P

CHRISTCHURCH

Olde George Inn
2A Castle Street
✪ 11-11; 12-10.30 Sun
☎ (01202) 479383
Brains Dark; Hampshire Strong's Best Bitter; Ringwood Fortyniner; guest beers Ⓗ

Historically exciting coaching inn, over 600 years old, comprising two low-ceilinged rooms; one has an area dedicated to diners (try the excellent summer menu). The courtyard, where children are welcome, has heating and houses the Barn Bar, hosting

INDEPENDENT BREWERIES	
Badger	Blandford St. Mary
Goldfinch	Dorchester
Thomas Hardy	Dorchester
Palmers	Bridport
Poole	Poole
Quay	Weymouth

live jazz (Thu eve) and folk and Irish rock (Fri eve) free of charge. Two ciders are normally on tap. New owners have improved many aspects of this pub: ale, food and music. ☙❀◑▮ ☞

Railway Hotel
2 Stour Road (opp. station)
◒ 11-11; 12-3.30, 7.30-10.30 Sun
☎ (01202) 484180
Flowers Original; Ringwood Best Bitter; guest beer (occasional) Ⓗ

Two-bar corner pub, built in an unusual late Victorian style, with a tower feature at the front. The public bar has a dartboard, shove-ha'penny board and a fruit machine, but no handpumps as the real ales are served from the lounge bar at the rear. This is an unusual wedge-shaped room, with comfortable settles around the walls. Both bars display railway pictures, models and artefacts. This friendly, family-run local has won awards for its cellar and hanging baskets. Ringing mobile phones incur a fine.
🏨❀⌸≈♣P

CRANBORNE

Sheaf of Arrows
4 The Square
◒ 11-11; 12-10.30 Sun
☎ (01725) 517456
Draught Bass; Ringwood Best Bitter; guest beer Ⓗ

Set in the middle of Cranborne, the pub comprises a large, friendly locals' public bar with pool table, darts and TV, a smaller, snug lounge bar and a function room-cum-skittle alley. Well-behaved, accompanied children are allowed in the lounge bar and function room for meals. Regular themed food eves feature Chinese and Indian meals. Like many country pubs, it is popular at weekend lunchtimes with cyclists and walkers; takeaways are also available. The annual beer festival showcases over 30 ales.
🏨Q❀⌸◑⌸▮♣

DORCHESTER

Blue Raddle
8 Church Street
◒ 11.30-3, 7-11; 12-3, 7-10.30 Sun
☎ (01305) 267762
Greene King Abbot; Sharp's Cornish Coaster; guest beers Ⓗ

This warm, friendly town-centre free house, frequently serves beers from West Country micro-breweries such as RCH, Hop Back and Oakham. Two of the most realistic flame-effect gas fires imaginable are often mistaken for the real thing. The public lounge-style bar displays rather lewd and suggestive paintings on the walls. The menu often includes various game dishes but vegetarians are also well catered for. Check out the unusual pub sign; the Cerne Giant is on one side in the background, but omitted on the other. Q◑&≈ (South/West)

Tom Brown's
47 High East Street
◒ 11-11; 11-3, 5.30-11 Tue & Wed; 12-4, 7-10.30 Sun
☎ (01305) 264020
Goldfinch Tom Brown, Midnight Sun Special, Flashman's Clout (occasional), **Midnight Blinder** Ⓗ

Home of the Goldfinch Brewery, near the lower end of the main thoroughfare, the bar takes the form of an old public bar with bare floorboards and plain wooden tables and chairs. Conversation rules in this friendly pub, only occasionally disturbed by the ancient juke box. The brewery is situated to the rear of the building in what used to be a night club. Three Goldfinch beers are always available, Flashman's Clout only making infrequent appearances nowadays. ⌸◑&≈ (South/West) ♣

EAST CHALDON

Sailor's Return
1 mile S of A352 OS791834
◒ 11-2.30, 6-11; 12-2.30, 7-10.30 Sun
☎ (01305) 853847
Beer range varies Ⓗ

Accessed via a single track road, this thatched inn stands on the fringe of a small hamlet. Sympathetically extended over the years, it is extremely popular with diners and drinkers, and can get busy on summer weekends. The Dorset Coastal Path lies a mile to the south and the pub provides a welcome refreshment stop for ramblers. Excellent food, in generous portions, dominates the numerous flagstoned rooms while the main bar retains the air of a local. Five ever-changing ales are served; tented beer festival on the late spring bank holiday offers local brews. Q❀◑♣☞P

INN BRIEF

BLANDFORD FORUM
Damory Oak Inn
Damory Court Street
11-11;
12-10.30 Sun
Badger Best, Tanglefoot Ⓗ
Heavily into sport, this pub has TV and many traditional games.

BRIDPORT
Greyhound
2 East Street
11-11; 11-11 Sun
Courage Directors; Elgood's Greyhound Strong; Theakston Best Bitter; Wadworth 6X; guest beers Ⓗ
Deservedly popular Wetherspoon's house, offering unusual guest ales. Very busy eves, it has a no-smoking area. *Cask Marque* accredited.

CERNE ABBAS
Royal Oak
23 Long Street
11-3, 6-11;
12-3, 7-10.30 Sun
Butcombe Bitter; Greene King Old Speckled Hen; Wadworth IPA, 6X Ⓗ
Built in 1540, this stone-walled thatched pub has three rooms with flagged floors and low beams.

CHARMOUTH
Royal Oak
The Street
12-4, 7-11;
12-4, 7-10.30 Sun
Palmers BB, IPA, 200 Ⓗ
Cosy, two-bar village pub, popular with walkers and locals. Noted for arranging an annual Xmas day swim. Limited food.

CORFE CASTLE
Greyhound Inn
The Square
11-11; 12-10.30 Sun
Beer range varies Ⓗ
This 17th-century coaching inn nestles in the shadows of famous ruins. It has many nooks and crannies and a superb range of food.

CORFE MULLEN
Coventry Arms
Mill Street
11-3, 5.30-11; 11-11 Fri & Sat;
12-10.30 Sun
Courage Directors; Marston's Pedigree; Ringwood Best Bitter, Fortyniner; guest beers Ⓖ
Built in 1426, this traditional pub keeps barrels on stillage behind the bar. Riverside garden and excellent food add to its appeal.

EAST MORDEN

Cock & Bottle

On B3075, off A35 near Wareham

○ 11-3, 6-11; 12-3, 7 10.30 Sun

☎ (01929) 459238

Badger K&B Sussex, Best, Tanglefoot Ⓗ

Traditional village pub unspoilt by development. An open fire is a main feature in the warm public bar. The pub is well used by locals and attracts a lot of custom for its meals served in the cosy dining area. The garden is well situated for the summer as the village is off the main road. Wheelchair access is excellent, with a designated WC.

▲▲❀◑ 🐾&♣P

GILLINGHAM

Buffalo

Lydfords Lane, Wyke

(150 yds from B3081, Wincanton road)

○ 12-2.30, 5.30-11; 12-3, 7-11 Sat; 12-3, 7-10.30 Sun

☎ (01747) 823759

K&B Badger Sussex, Best Ⓗ

Definitely a rural pub down a quiet lane, but standing on the outskirts of this fast-growing town. A single bar serves two areas, whose flagged floors, open fire and exposed beams provide country inn character. In one area the ceiling is adorned with a fine selection of jugs, while the other boasts ornate plasterwork. Simple home-cooked food is served Mon–Sat, mainly lunchtimes. Darts and quiz nights are popular, as is the occasional music night around the piano. From the benches and tables outside the front you can see the old Matthews brewery tower.

▲▲Q❀◑♣P

Phoenix

High Street

○ 10-2.30 (3 Sat), 7-11; 12-3, 7-10.30 Sun

☎ (01747) 823277

Badger K&B Sussex, Best, seasonal beers Ⓗ

Interesting, town-centre, single-bar pub, originally part of a handsome 18th-century coaching inn that has sadly been broken up into various other businesses; these include a cake shop and an unobtrusive Tandoori restaurant. Friendly and welcoming to visitors, its landlord is a great conversationalist. The bar has an extensive display of pub bric-à-brac. Outside there is a quiet patio on the old town square, now almost entirely free of traffic. Diners will appreciate the efficient air filtration system.

▲▲❀◑ Å⇌♣🗕●

GUSSAGE ALL SAINTS

Drovers' Inn

○ 11.45-2.30 (11-3 Sat). 6-11; 12-3, 7-10.30 Sun

☎ (01258) 840084

Ringwood Best Bitter, True Glory, XXXX Porter, Fortyniner, Old Thumper Ⓗ

This lovely 17th-century rural pub was sold for development into a private residence, but after being totally gutted, planning permission was refused and it was bought by Ringwood who turned it back into a nice, cosy pub. The large single bar has a side room for darts. The big garden benefits from wonderful views. Excellent food is

served every day and it can get very busy at weekends; popular with walkers.

▲▲Q❀◑▶♣♦P

HURN

Avon Causeway Hotel

Through Hurn village, sharp left from B3073 bridge

○ 11.30-11; 12-10.30 Sun

☎ (01202) 482714 website: www.avoncauseway.co.uk

Red Shoot Forest Gold; Tom's Tipple; Ringwood Old Thumper; Wadworth IPA, 6X, JCB, Ⓗ

Originally Hurn Station, the building has been greatly enlarged to what is now a comfortable 12-roomed hotel, including a four-poster bridal suite. The large pub comprises two bar areas, a public with oak floor, and a lounge with a fully accessible family area leading to the garden and carvery. See the numerous railway mementos, as well as the Pullman carriage by the platform, now the Orient Restaurant, where Murder Mystery eves are staged in opulent surroundings. Wheelchair WC.

Q ⛟❀🖂◑ 🐾&AP✁●

IBBERTON

Crown

Church Lane (4 miles SW of A357) OS788077

○ 12-2.30, 7-11; 12-2.30, 7-10.30 Sun

☎ (01258) 817440

M&B Brew XI; guest beer Ⓗ

Lovely example of an idyllic country pub, surrounded by the breathtaking scenery of Bulbarrow Hill, it is a natural choice for walkers. Although lacking separate bars, there are defined areas. Open the massive door and step on to the original flagstone floor with an inglenook. Photographs of bygone village life are displayed and a dartboard is tucked away. There is an equally cosy, but more formal area, to the left. The attractive garden has a small stream running through it. Well-behaved, accompanied children are welcome.

▲▲Q❀◑&♣♦P

LYME REGIS

Nag's Head

Silver Street

○ 11-3, 6-11; 10-11 Fri & Sat; 12-10.30 Sun

☎ (01297) 442312

Beer range varies Ⓗ

Fine brick and flint coaching inn, well worth the effort to find. Situated above the town, it commands superb views across Lyme Bay to Portland Bill. This large local has two linked bars, a lower-level pool room, a good-sized garden and a renowned first-floor restaurant, famous for its 'Tipsy Cod' speciality. The house beer, at 3.6% ABV, is brewed by Quay Brewery in nearby Weymouth. The Channel Islander landlord is hoping soon to become a mainland outlet for Guernsey cask ales. ▲▲Q❀🖂◑♣P

Volunteer

31 Broad Street

○ 11-11; 12-10.30 Sun

☎ (01297) 442214

Draught Bass; Otter Ale; guest beer Ⓗ

Double-fronted, pebble-dashed inn where the house beer, Donegal, brewed by Branscombe Vale, indicates the origin of the cheerful landlord, a popular publican in

Lyme for over 30 years. The single, low-beamed, timber and stone-clad bar boasts an old-fashioned kitchen range. The dining room serves a comprehensive menu. The pub name alludes to the Volunteer Regiment, founded in 1794 to combat threat of a French invasion, but the pub is older than this, as is suggested by the occasional sighting of three card-playing Cavalier ghosts. ⚑Q◖♣

MANSTON

Plough
Shaftesbury Road (B3091 2½ miles NE of Sturminster Newton)
✪ 11.30-2.30, 6.30-11; 12-3, 7-10.30 Sun
☎ (01258) 472484
Beer range varies Ⓗ/Ⓖ
Prominently sited on a bend in the Shaftesbury–Sturminster road, this now popular village pub was rescued from oblivion barely four years ago. The selection of changing guest ales contributed to the Plough winning the *Pub of the Year* from local CAMRA. One single bar caters for drinkers and diners alike; note the curious plasterwork which is said to contain fertility symbols. The garden's pétanque pitch is a summer attraction, as is the beerfest held in a marquee (usually late July).
⚑❀◖♿♣P

MARSHWOOD

Bottle
On B3165, close to Devon border OS376997
✪ 12-3, 6.30-11; (closed winter Mon); 12-3, 7-10.30 Sun
☎ (01297) 678254
Otter Bitter; guest beers Ⓗ
This thatched country inn enthusiastically embraces the provision of natural products, with organic beer, food, wine and even organic cola available. The wholesome menu includes vegetarian and vegan choices, as well as locally-reared GM-free beef and pork. A single bar serves two small rooms (one no-smoking) with a family room and skittle alley leading to a large garden overlooking Marshwood Vale. Of the two guest beers one is usually from Quay Brewery in Weymouth. The pub hosts a nettle-eating competition in June – organic of course!
Q❀◖♣P♿

PAMPHILL

Vine Inn ☆
Vine Hill (off B3082)
✪ 11-2.30, 7-11; 12-3, 7-10.30 Sun
☎ (01202) 882259
Beer range varies Ⓗ
This unspoilt inn was built as a bake house, 200 years ago, near Kingston Lacy House, both now owned by the National Trust. A true free house, it serves real ale from many small breweries by handpump and gravity in oversized glasses. Run by the same family for three generations, it has two small bars with a games room upstairs. A large garden with plenty of seating is very popular with walkers and cyclists alike. Sandwiches and ploughmans are available at lunchtime at this local CAMRA *Rural Pub of the Year*.
Q❀🡤♣♣P🡧

PLUSH

Brace of Pheasants
1½ miles off B3143 OS715024
✪ 12-2.30, 7-11; 12-3, 7-10.30 Sun
☎ (01300) 348357 e-mail:
geoffreyknights@braceofpheasants.freeserve.co.uk
Fuller's London Pride; Tisbury Stonehenge; guest beer Ⓖ
Negotiating the narrow, twisting access road is a small inconvenience compared to the reward awaiting here. Originally a row of 16th-century cottages, this heavily beamed, thatched inn serves real ale by gravity from a stillage behind the bar, with not a keg font in sight. Cider is available in summer. Solid comfortable seating, an open fire and inglenook complete the picture. The restaurant has an excellent reputation, using local produce whenever possible (booking is advised). Note the unusual pub sign: two stuffed pheasants in an illuminated glass case.
⚑Q🡥❀🡤◖♣♣P♿🡧

POOLE

Bermuda Triangle
10 Parr Street, Lower Parkstone
✪ 12-2.30, 5.30-11; 12-11 Sat; 12-10.30 Sun
☎ (01202) 748087
Beer range varies Ⓗ
From Ashtley Cross walk along Parr Street toward St Peter's Church on the left; look up at the roofs, when you see a rowing boat and lifebuoy you have arrived at the Bermuda Triangle. Above the small bar area is a canopy with notice boards listing the four ever-changing cask beers. Peruse the fascinating old photos, maps and news cuttings detailing the Triangle mystery. A wood-panelled extension has increased the seating area of this free house that stocks a small but interesting imported bottled beer selection. ◖🚄(Parkstone)

Blue Boar
29 Market Close
✪ 11-3, 5 (6 Sat)-11; 12-3, 7-10.30 Sun
☎ (01202) 682247
Cottage Southern Bitter; Courage Best Bitter; Directors; guest beers Ⓗ
Former merchant's house dating back to 1750, in the old part of Poole, it bears a nautical feel. Numerous historical items hang on the walls and pillars, with brief information on each. The cellar bar admits children at lunchtime and hosts live music Wed and Fri. Two guest beers are rotated regularly. Just off the High Street, this pub is a welcome retreat. ◖🚄

Branksome Railway Hotel
429 Poole Road, Branksome
✪ 11-11; 12-10.30 Sun
☎ (01202) 769555 e-mail:
branksomerailway@eurolinkltd
Fuller's London Pride; Hampshire Strong's Best Bitter; guest beer Ⓗ
Imposing, late Victorian coaching inn which had stables and staff quarters to serve rail passengers. After years of decline it has recently been extensively refurbished to provide six en-suite bedrooms and a restaurant. The drinking area is now one large bar divided into three distinct areas, all high-ceilinged with long windows. One

area houses a pool table, the second is a smaller, quiet seating area and the main, comfortable lounge overlooks the railway line. It opens at 9am for breakfast. The guest beer is often popular, drawn from small southern breweries such as Hop Back or Cottage. 🖤◑🍺⇌ (Branksome) **P**

Brewhouse
68 High Street
🕐 11-11; 11-5, 6-11 Sat; 12-10.30 Sun
☎ (01202) 685288
Poole Bitter, Bosun Ⓗ
Home of Poole Brewery, a good, basic old town local in the main High Street. It has one bar, but on split levels: the drinking area is below, with two pool tables slightly raised. The Poole Brewery logo is displayed between the two levels, and it sells the lowest-priced beer in the area and house beers are occasionally on tap. ⇌♣

Bricklayers
41 Parr Street, Lower Parkstone
🕐 12-2.30, 5-11; 12-4, 6-11 Sat; 12-4, 7-10.30 Sun
☎ (01202) 740304
Hop Back Summer Lightning; Ringwood Best Bitter, Fortyniner Ⓗ
Lovely free house, this local has a large, comfortable lounge which is a very pleasant place for a drink; in winter a real fire is usually blazing, while in summer there is a secluded garden at the rear. Food is served daily at lunchtime, the menu supplemented by a specials board of reasonably priced dishes, plus a Sun roast. A function room is available for hire. 🖤❀◑⇌ (Parkstone)

Hogshead
382 Ashley Road, Parkstone
🕐 11-11; 12-10.30 Sun
☎ (01202) 740596
Boddingtons Bitter; Flowers Original; Marston's Pedigree; guest beers Ⓗ/Ⓖ
This single bar, part of the Whitbread chain of Hogsheads, was converted from a former Co-operative clothes and homeware store. The largely wooden interior features stone floors, with seating on two levels and a large open fire at one end. Very popular with shoppers during the day, it becomes lively at weekends when the policy is to turn the music up loud. It keeps five real ales on handpump at all times, with four casks on stillage behind the bar (two available at a time). Food is served daily until 9pm. 🖤◑🚹♣**P**

Queen Mary
West Street
🕐 11-3, 6-11; 12-3, 6-10.30 Sun
☎ (01202) 661701
Beer range varies Ⓗ
Cosy, quiet pub, but it hosts the occasional live band, so if you want to have a peaceful visit ring first to check. Only two minutes' from the High Street, it is well worth taking the trouble to find it. Pleasantly decorated and gleaming with polish, it is a haven from the town's bustle. Quality home-made food, including a vegetarian selection, represents good value. 🖤❀◑⇌🚹**P**

Royal Oak & Gas Tavern
25 Skinner Street
🕐 11-11; 12-10.30 Sun
☎ (01202) 672022 e-mail: amuspratt@aol.com

Hampshire Strong's Best Bitter; Ringwood Fortyniner Ⓗ
Traditional, back-street pub, dating back to 1798 where many original features still remain. Pictures of old Poole hang on wood-panelled walls, which, together with a part-wood, part-carpeted floor, provide a warm, welcoming feel. Close to Poole Quay, it boasts a pleasant, enclosed garden you would not expect to find in the back streets of Poole. The function room has space for up to 100 people. ❀♣

George Inn
133 Reforne, Easton
🕐 11-11; 12-10.30 Sun
☎ (01305) 820011
Ringwood Fortyniner; Worthington Bitter Ⓗ
Oldest pub on the island (17th century) it has a feel of two pubs in one. The original bar, with what could easily be the original tables and a ceiling supported by beams from long-gone sailing ships, is usually full of Portland characters; a place for conversation. In contrast, the larger Quarr Bar, a sympathetic recent addition, features live bands (Sat eve). The menu is unpretentious but wholesome, with large portions. Idyllically located across from the cricket ground, many a summer's eve can be spent leaning on the stone boundary wall. The beer range may vary. 🖤❀◑♣♣

White Post Inn
On B3148, N of Sherborne OS603206
🕐 12-3, 6.30-11; 12-3, 7-10.30 Sun
☎ (01935) 850171
Butcombe Bitter; Greene King IPA Ⓗ
Genuine free house straddling the Somerset border – it is possible to drink in both counties – a fact discovered by a previous landlord when he received two rate demands. Great play used to be made of ushering customers to the legal side in early days when closing times differed. The extensive menu offers excellent value; the cider is from Bridge Farm. The pub is on a hill, affording pleasant views across the countryside towards Yeovil. Games include Shut the Box. Children are admitted but a firm disciplinary code exists.
Q❀◑🚹♣♣**P**⌀

Mitre Inn
N of Sherborne, signed from B3148 OS626205
🕐 11.30-2.30, 7-11; 12-3, 7-10.30 Sun
☎ (01963) 220271
Greene King IPA, Abbot; Wadworth 6X Ⓗ
Entering the Mitre (mind your head) is to experience a pub that really knows its role in life. The welcome is warm, the home-cooked food excellent, the seating comfortable (armchairs in the bar) and the beer in top condition. Flagged floors extend from the bar area to the dining room; well-behaved children are welcome. Outside is an elevated garden. There is no food Mon eve – skittle night. B&B accommodation is available at this village pub near the Somerset border.
🖤**Q**❀🖤◑🚹♣**P**

SEATOWN

Anchor
Turn S off A35 in Chideock
⊙ 12-3, 6-11; (12-11 summer); 12-3, 7-10.30 Sun
☎ (01297) 489215
Palmers BB, (summer) Ⓖ **Dorset Gold, IPA, 200** Ⓗ
This comfortable inn, situated nearly on the beach, is considered by many to serve the best Palmers' in the area. Reached by a single track road from Chideock, or by foot along the Dorset Coastal Path, the pub is popular with tourists and local walkers alike. Public parking is available opposite. Occasional live jazz groups feature at weekends. Opening times may vary depending on sea conditions and the season – phone beforehand it travelling far.
🏨Q⊛🍴🚆⊙▲♣♠

SHAFTESBURY ❈

Ship Inn
Bleke Street
⊙ 11-3, 5-11; 11-11 Thu-Sat; 12-10.30 Sun
☎ (01747) 853219
Badger Best, Tanglefoot, seasonal beers Ⓗ
This 16th-century building was once a doctor's surgery, complete with dispensary. It is now a multi-roomed town pub with a single bar where King & Barnes ales and those from the Gribble Inn brew-pub are often available. The Ship, with exposed beams, sloping everything, and a nautical feel, is very popular with locals. Seek out the tiny snug with its cosy open fire. Excellent home-produced food is reasonably priced. Play pétanque in the garden in summer. It hosts monthly folk music nights (last Sun). Note the pillory by the front door.
🏨⊛⊙♣♠♠●

SHERBORNE ❈

Britannia
Westbury
⊙ 11-2.30, 6-11; 12-3, 7-10.30 Sun
☎ (01935) 813300
e-mail: ian@britannia-sherborne.fsnet.co.uk
Beer range varies Ⓗ
300-year-old inn, close to the Abbey, believed to be the oldest (and cheapest) in town, it is slowly being sympathetically refurbished by the family owners. Collections of model cars, brewing equipment and other artefacts adorn the walls. Normally five real ales, usually include one from Ringwood, with the others from the south-west or Wales. Cider comes from Thatcher's. Inch's or Denning's. Classical music or jazz provides the background in the lounge with rock (not deafening) in the public bar. Home-made bread is used in the sandwiches and ploughmans.
⊛🍴⊙⊙🚆♣♠♠P

Skippers
1 Terrace View, Horsecastles
⊙ 11-2.30, 5.30 (6 Sat)-11; 12-2, 7-10.30 Sun
☎ (01935) 812753 e-mail: chrisfrowde@lineone.net
Butcombe Bitter; Wadworth IPA, 6X, JCB, seasonal beers Ⓗ
Large bar with two linked but separate dining areas; deservedly very popular for its food, two chefs produce an extensive and ever-changing menu. A broad clientele includes parents of pupils from the two independent schools nearby, as well as locals. Note the collections of walking sticks and ornamental pigs. On the walls photographs of nearby Yeovilton Naval Air Base mingle with cartoons after the style of Heath Robinson. ⊛⊙P

STOKE ABBOTT

New Inn
⊙ 11-2.30, 6-11; 12-3, 7-10.30 Sun
☎ (01308) 868333
Palmers Dorset Gold, IPA, 200 Ⓗ
Comfortable 17th-century country inn in the middle of a picturesque village. The licensees offer good quality home-cooked food which means the bar can get busy with diners in the tourist season. The bar's

INN BRIEF

EAST KNIGHTON
Countryman
Blacknoll Lane
11-3, 6-11; 12-3, 7-10.30 Sun
Courage Best Bitter, Directors; Ringwood Best Bitter, Old Thumper; John Smith's Bitter; Wadworth 6X Ⓗ
Country pub just off the main road with a restaurant, children's room and a large bar.

EVERSHOT
Acorn
28 Fore Street
11.30-2.30, 6.30-11; 12-3, 7-10.30 Sun
Butcombe Bitter; Fuller's London Pride; guest beer Ⓗ
17th-century coaching inn of immense character. Children are welcome in the Village Bar.

SHAFTESBURY
Olde Two Brewers
24 St James Street
11-3, 6-11; 12-3, 7-10.30 Sun
Courage Best Bitter, Directors; Theakston XB; guest beers Ⓗ
Popular local, and tourist pub of many drinking areas and a garden, at foot of famous Gold Hill (good views). Excellent home-cooked food.

SHERBORNE
Digby Tap
Cooks Lane
11-2.30, 5.30-11;
12-2.30, 7-10.30 Sun
Exmoor Ale; guest beers Ⓗ
Lively, long-established free house, close to the abbey and station, with flagged floors and cosy corners.

SWANAGE
Red Lion
High Street
11-11; 12-10.30 Sun
Fuller's London Pride; Greene King Old Speckled Hen; Hampshire Strong's Best Bitter; Ringwood Best Bitter Ⓖ
Traditional, busy-two bar pub, near the beach and Swanage steam railway.

WAREHAM
Duke of Wellington
7 East Street
11-11; 12-10.30 Sun
Fuller's London Pride; Ringwood XXXX Porter Ⓗ
Friendly pub, with a large patio, excellent for food (served all day in summer). Beer range may vary.

WEST STAFFORD
Wise Man
11-3, 6-11; 12-3, 7-10.30 Sun
Ringwood Fortyniner Ⓗ
400-year-old thatched pub, draped in ivy, that has retained a lounge and public bar.

WINKTON
Fisherman's Haunt
Salisbury Road
10.30-2.30, 5-11; 10.30-11 Sat;
12-10.30 Sun
Draught Bass; Gale's HSB; Ringwood Fortyniner Ⓗ
Spacious, multi-roomed, 17th-century pub and restaurant serving food at all sessions. *Cask Marque* accredited.

> ❈ symbol next to a main entry place name indicates there are Inn Brief entries as well.

unusual thatched 'roof' reflects the thatch covering the building. An impressive fireplace means that this pub is never cold. It makes a good stopping-point for walkers on the ancient lanes and bridleways that criss-cross this part of the county.
ᴹᴬQ✿☕⌂◑⅃♿♣P

STOURTON CAUNDLE

Trooper
☼ 12-3; 7-11; 12-2.30, 7-10.30 Sun
☎ (01963) 362405
Sharp's Doom Bar; guest beers Ⓗ
Idyllically situated beside a brook, the Trooper is a real gem. Village social life is centred on the cosy public bar which is festooned with country memorabilia, providing a foretaste of the landlord's pride and joy, his countryside museum. It displays items he collected in his previous career as a professional shepherd. The museum doubles as a skittle alley, and is used for monthly folk nights (third Tue). Food is unpretentiously satisfying; the guest ales are usually selected by the regulars. Free camping behind the pub. Q☎✿◑⅃♿Å♣♠P

STRATTON

Saxon Inn
Dorchester Road (off A37, 2 miles N of Dorchester)
☼ 11-3; 6-11; 12-3, 7-10.30 Sun
☎ (01305) 260020
Fuller's London Pride; Greene King Abbot; Palmers IPA Ⓗ
A rarity in these modern times, a brand-new country pub, not a bank conversion or town wine bar, but a purpose-built, thatched hostelry which opened as recently as Easter 2001. It features flagged floors, a real fire and good food. Enthusiastically embraced by villagers and tourists alike, it is presided over by an experienced ex-Palmers landlord whose previous pub regularly featured in this *Guide*. This is no transient, trendy pub but one that is destined to mature and acquire great character with time. The house beer is re-badged Palmers Dorset Gold. ᴹᴬ✿◑♿P

STUDLAND

Bankes Arms
☼ 11-11; 12-10.30 Sun
☎ (01929) 450225
Beer range varies Ⓗ
This traditional Purbeck stone inn occupies an enviable position overlooking Studland Bay with views across the water to Bournemouth. Eight real ales, constantly changing, are sourced from small and regional breweries. Local CAMRA's joint *Pub of the Year* 2000, it hosts an Irish festival in spring and a beer festival (Aug) in a marquee, with 50 ales. Superb food is served – the menu chalked on blackboards, with many specials. As with many pubs on the Purbecks, it can be busy at weekends.
ᴹᴬ✿☕⌂◑♣♠P

TARRANT MONKTON

Langton Arms
Off A354
☼ 11.30-11; 12-10.30 Sun
☎ (01258) 830225
Beer range varies Ⓗ
17th-century country pub set in a pretty village, offering at least four, ever-changing guest beers. The public bar houses a pool table and dartboard; the lounge bar is pleasant and airy with a beamed ceiling. A restaurant-cum-function room, with a conservatory, serves excellent food at all times and is becoming very popular for wedding receptions. An annual beer festival showcases 30-plus beers. The large garden has a children's play area. Well-behaved dogs are allowed.
ᴹᴬQ✿☕⌂◑⅃♿♣⚲●

UPWEY

Royal Standard
700 Dorchester Road
☼ 11-3, 6-11; 12-10.30 Sun
☎ (01305) 812558
Archers Village; guest beers Ⓗ
The first pub encountered on the main road into the borough is a genuine two-bar establishment selling two guest beers. The lounge reflects the landlord's interest in railways with pictures and models, while he often passes quieter periods constructing his next project on the bar. Outside, at the rear, an aviary houses a magnificent eagle owl, about which the licensee is as passionate as he is about vintage motor cycles. Beware the fine, should your mobile ring in the public bar. ᴹᴬQ✿⌂≠♣P

WAYTOWN

Hare & Hounds
☼ 11.30-3, 6.30-11; 12-3, 7-10.30 Sun
☎ (01308) 488203
Palmers Dorset Gold, IPA Ⓖ
Unspoilt country pub offering, unusually, Palmers' ale on gravity dispense. A single counter serves two drinking areas. Tucked away in a small hamlet, best reached from the Netherbury end, this pub is a true local to the surrounding community. The garden offers superb views and it makes an excellent stopping-place for the many walks that you can take in one of the prettiest parts of west Dorset. No food is served Sun eve or winter Mon. Taunton cider is stocked.
ᴹᴬQ✿◑♿Å♠P

WEYMOUTH

Boot
High West Street (behind fire station)
☼ 11-11; 12-10.30 Sun
☎ (01305) 770327
Ringwood Best Bitter, True Glory, Fortyniner, Old Thumper; guest beers; seasonal beers Ⓗ
Probably Weymouth's oldest pub, it can be difficult to find, tucked in behind the fire station. Bought by Ringwood Brewery from Greenalls in 1999 as only their third tied house, this small hostelry just oozes welcome. The single wood-floored bar area gives way at each end to rooms with comfortable seating and warming fires. The landlord complements the excellent beer range with his personal choice of weekly guest beers and Cheddar Valley cider. Tasty bar food includes proper pork pies, sausages and pickles. A true pub, where conversation rules. ᴹᴬQ✿◑≠♣●

Weatherbury

7 Carlton Road North
✪ 11-11; 12-10.30 Sun
☎ (01305) 786040
e-mail dave@theweatherbury.demon.co.uk
Draught Bass; Fuller's London Pride; guest beers Ⓗ
Large corner pub in a residential area on the north side of town, near the beach – in summer the small patio can be a suntrap. The three ever-changing guest beers tend to come from a portfolio of small, established breweries; a popular beer festival is held in July. The interior is open plan with a pool table dominating one end, plus a small side room, for meetings or families. The menu is varied without being over-elaborate 'Happy hours' feature in the late afternoon.
✿⇔◗⓿ዿ⇌♣P

WIMBORNE

Cricketers

Park Lane
✪ 11-11; 12-10.30 Sun
☎ (01202) 882846
Marston's Pedigree; Ringwood Best Bitter, Fortyniner; guest beers Ⓗ
Busy (especially at weekends) but welcoming, town-centre pub bearing a cricketing theme; the garden overlooks the town cricket pitch. The large single bar has a pool table one end with a comfortable area at the other. RATS, the Real Ale Tasting Society meets every Mon and Thu; members can buy beer at a discount. A beer festival is held in the summer and two guest beers are always available.
🏚✿◗♣●

Crown & Anchor

6 Wimborne Road
(next to Walford Bridge)
✪ 11-2, 6-11; 12-3, 7-10.30 Sun
☎ (01202) 841405
Badger Best, seasonal beers Ⓗ
No more than a 10-minute walk from the town centre, this recently redecorated pub has kept its charm and is one of the finest outlets for Badger beers in East Dorset. This friendly local, with a garden alongside the River Allen, stands close to Walford Mill Craft Centre. The pub comprises a one-roomed, L-shaped lounge, with no loud music. It serves good value lunches.
🏚Q✿◗AP●

WINKTON ✤

Lamb Inn

Burley Road (off B3347)
✪ 11-3, 5-11 (11-11 summer Sat); 12-10.30 Sun
☎ (01425) 672427
Fuller's London Pride; Ringwood Best Bitter; guest beers Ⓗ
This pub sits a little aloof from the rest of the village, looking out over fields. Retaining two bars, the public has a real fire and a piano, plus a dartboard. The comfortable lounge offers an interesting menu, much of which is displayed on a large blackboard (children welcome if eating). Come on Wed eve for the Curry Club and trad jazz. The restaurant has its own Sun lunch menu. The garden has tables and a children's play area.
🏚✿◗ 🞰♣P

WORTH MATRAVERS

Square & Compass ☆

Off B3069 OS974777
✪ 12-3, 6-11; 12-11 Sat;
12-3, 7-10.30 (not winter eve) Sun
☎ (01929) 439229
Badger Tanglefoot; Ringwood Best Bitter; guest beers Ⓖ
Magnificent stone inn, where two serving hatches, flagstoned floors, wooden tables and settles, and a rare drinking corridor are crowned by views of medieval field systems and the sea. It was granted a licence in the early 18th century and has hardly changed since. Run by the Newman family since 1907, it has featured in every edition of this *Guide*. This ancient, magical place stands apart from the rest, a world away from the ravages of modernisation; a true bastion of the Purbecks, surrounded not only by superb coastal scenery but also timeless bucolic peace. It holds a beer festival (Oct) and a cider festival (Dec). Ring the landlord for camping. 🏚Q✿▲♣●

WYKE REGIS

Wyke Smugglers

76 Portland Road
✪ 11-2.30, 6-11; 12-3, 7-10.30 Sun
☎ (01305) 760010
Beer range varies Ⓗ
Large community pub in a residential area on the main road to Portland, specialising in team games: soccer, darts, skittles and even water polo. Although open plan, two distinct areas give an impression of lounge and public bars. Two or three beers are selected from Inn Partnership's guest list, but this choice may not be available midweek when the pub is quiet; it builds to the full range at weekends, when there is a disco (Fri and Sat). Children are not encouraged in the pub itself, but are welcome on the patio. ✿ዿ♣P

YETMINSTER

White Hart

High Street
✪ 11.30-2.30, 7-11; 12-3, 7-10.30 Sun
☎ (01935) 872338
Greene King IPA; guest beers Ⓗ
This is good walking country and ramblers are well served by this 400-year-old thatched inn at the village centre, within 10 minutes' stroll of the railway halt. A genuine two-bar pub, the convival public bar is basically furnished and caters for pub games. An imaginative menu, including vegetarian dishes, is served in the more comfortable lounge area. Accommodation is in an adjoining converted barn. The skittle alley, quite lively on games nights, has its own bar. The garden has a play area for children. Q⇔◗⓿ 🞰ዿ⇌♣P

Guide site

Keep your copy of the Good Beer Guide up-to-date by contacting the CAMRA website where you will find information about changes to pubs and breweries
www.camra.org.uk/gbg

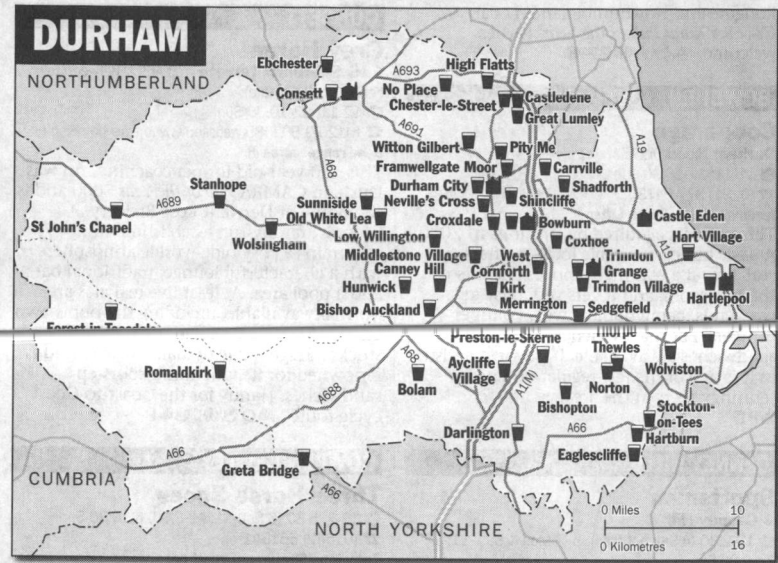

DURHAM

Co Durham incorporates part of the former county of Cleveland

AYCLIFFE VILLAGE

County

13 The Green (off A167)
🕐 12-3, 5.30-11; 12-3, 7-11 Sun
☎ (01325) 312273 website: www.the-county.co.uk
John Smith's Magnet; Wells Bombardier; guest beers Ⓗ

Overlooking the broad village green, this pub is verging on being a fully-fledged restaurant, but four prominent handpumps demonstrate chef/landlord Andrew Brown's commitment to good beer as well as fine food. He was Raymond Blanc's first scholar, and in 2000 earned fame by hosting a supper here for Tony Blair and President Jacques Chirac of France. The space is cleverly divided into various linked bar and dining areas, unified by bright modern decor throughout: pine furniture, tiled floors and white-painted walls complement older features such as beams and fireplaces housing stoves. Advisable to book for meals at weekends (no bar food Sun eve).
🏮🏵️◑P

BISHOP AUCKLAND

Newton Cap

Newton Cap Bank (200 yds from bus station)
🕐 12-4 (not Tue), 7-11; 12-3, 7-11 Sun
☎ (01328) 605445
John Smith's Bitter; guest beer Ⓗ

Friendly, traditional workingmen's (and women's) pub in a town dominated by young music pubs. The bus station nearby runs services to all parts of the area. If the bar is not too busy try your hand and eye at a game of Ringo – it's not as easy as it looks. Now a Castle Eden pub, it often offers seasonal and special brews from this brewery, at very reasonable prices, but is not now permitted to stock Camerons Strongarm despite a previous high demand.
🍺🔁♣♠

Tut 'n' Shive

68 Newgate Street (main shopping street)
🕐 11-11; 12-10.30 Sun
☎ (01388) 603252
Beer range varies Ⓗ

Busy, town-centre house, a circuit pub at weekends, but it is quieter early in the week. It stages live music most Thu eves. Up to four cask ales are on offer, with Black Sheep regularly represented, and some very rare brands for this area. A typical Tut'n'Shive, the split-level decor is somewhat unusual, displaying a fine collection of beer mats on the ceiling and walls. Handy for the bus station, shops, banks and tourist information (Town Hall), there is a market twice a week. No food Sun.
◑🔁P

BOLAM

Countryman

Dunwell Lane (off B6275)
🕐 12-2 (not Mon), 6-11; 12-2, 7-10.30 Sun
☎ (01388) 834577
Black Sheep Best Bitter; guest beers Ⓗ

Tucked away in a small Tees valley escarpment village just off Dere Street Roman road, this is a treat for lovers of good food and beer. The whitewashed pub (once the Shoulder of Mutton) was redesigned long ago into an interlinked bar, lounge and restaurant but the quality has improved more recently with the current licensees. The food is prepared by a chef and is of a high standard. Guest ales come mainly from small breweries, including

INDEPENDENT BREWERIES

Camerons Hartlepool
Castle Eden Castle Eden
Derwent Rose Consett
Durham Bowburn
Trimdon Trimdon Grange

Rudgate and Northumberland. Local CAMRA *Rural Pub of the Year*. Parties welcome. ♨☼✿●①Ρ⊁●

BOWBURN

Cooperage
Durham Road (A177)
☼ 11-11; 12-10.30 Sun
☎ (0191) 377 9473
Jennings Bitter, Sneck Lifter Ⓗ

This pub was acquired by Jennings in 2000. A basic but comfortable local, it offers two real ales, at a reasonable price. There is just the one room, and it gets very busy at weekends, being popular with younger drinkers. Bar snacks such as toasted sandwiches are available. It is worth a visit as it is one of the few regular outlets for Jennings beers in the area.
♣Ρ⊟

CANNEY HILL

Sportsman
4 Canney Hill
☼ 12-2.30 (4 Sat; not Mon), 5 (7 Mon & Sat)-11; 12-4, 7-10.30 Sun
☎ (01388) 603847
Camerons Strongarm; guest beer Ⓗ

Situated on the A689 on the edge of Bishop Auckland, the Sportsman is a popular and well-known pub, renowned for an excellent pint of Strongarm and good meals (booking advisable for Sun lunch). The pub has benefited from a recent extension and now comprises a bar, snug and a dining area. Well worth a visit.
♨Q✿①●⊞♣Ρ⊟

CASTLEDENE

Smith's Arms
Brecon Hill (over Lumley new bridge, past golf course, left after roundabout)
☼ 4 (12 Sat)-11; 12-5, 7-10.30 Sun
☎ (0191) 385 6915
Black Sheep Best Bitter; Courage Directors; guest beer Ⓗ

Popular country pub, on the edge of Brecon Woods. It has a small, friendly traditional bar which is warmed by a Yorkshire range in winter. There is a comfortable lounge and a games room with a pool table. Coffee and snacks are always offered, and on a Sun lunchtime a variety of cheeses, patés, crackers and toast are available free on the bar, as well as plates of Yorkshire puddings. An upstairs restaurant was due to open summer 2001.
♨Q⊞♣Ρ⊟

CHESTER-LE-STREET

Butchers Arms
Middle Chare (off Front St)
☼ 11-3, 6.30-11; 12-3, 7-10.30 Sun
☎ (0191) 338 3605
Camerons Bitter; Marston's Pedigree Ⓗ

Traditional one-roomed town pub. It offers a pleasant atmosphere, but can be busy at mealtimes. It has the unhappy distinction of being the town centre's only surviving real ale outlet. Handy for travellers on the A1(M), Chester-le-Street is home of Durham's County Cricket ground.
①♣

CONSETT

Grey Horse
115 Sherburn Terrace (off A692, between town centre and Leadgate)
☼ 12-11; 12-10.30 Sun
☎ (01207) 502585 website: www.thegreyhorse.co.uk
Beer range varies Ⓗ

This 150-year-old former coaching inn was Durham CAMRA *Pub of the Year* 2000 and is the home of Derwent Rose Brewery. A friendly, family-run establishment, it maintains a cosy olde-worlde atmosphere with a characterful lounge, traditional bar and a pool area. At least five real ales are normally available, including the pub's own C2C brew. An annual beer festival is held. It stocks a huge range of malt whiskies and is renowned for its lunchtime doorstep sandwiches. Handy for the Coast-to-Coast cycle route. ♨Q☼✿①⊞♣Ρ

COWPEN BEWLEY

Three Horse Shoes
☼ 12-2, 5.30 (6 Sat)-11; 12-3.30, 6-10.30 Sun
☎ (01642) 561541
Camerons Strongarm; guest beer Ⓗ

Homely village local, at the west end of the green. There has been a pub on this site for hundreds of years, which was once owned by the Prince Bishops of Durham and mentioned in the *Domesday Book*. The present building dates from 1955 and consists of two rooms off a long corridor. The guest beer in the two rooms is often different (from the Tapster's Choice range). An extensive à la carte menu is served, the comfortable back room being more popular for diners and the front bar for serious drinkers. ♨✿①⊞&♣Ρ

COXHOE

Black Horse Hotel
Station Road East (off A177)
☼ 12-2.30 (3 Sat; not Mon-Thu), 7-11; 12-3, 7-10.30 Sun
☎ (0191) 377 9574
Camerons Bitter, Strongarm Ⓗ

Detached Victorian pub, built on the site of Coxhoe pottery. It overlooks open countryside and is a very comfortable local. There is a lounge with a dining area (bookable for private parties), serving wonderful home-cooked meals prepared by the landlady. The bar leads into a pool room. A meeting room upstairs holds 60 people. The hotel has five guest rooms, one is a family room. A paved area has seats for outside drinking. ✿✉①⊞Ρ

CROXDALE

Daleside Arms
Front Street (B6288 3 miles S of Durham, off A167)
☼ 12-2.30 (3 Sat; not Mon-Thu), 7-11; 12-3, 7-10.30 Sun
☎ (01388) 814165
e-mail: daleside@croxdale94.fsnet.co.uk
Beer range varies Ⓗ

Local CAMRA *Pub of the Year* 2001, this pub has gained a reputation for its interesting choice of guest ales from independent brewers, both near and far, including Caledonian, Mordue and Northumberland.

A folk club is held every Tue eve. The cosy public bar, to the right of the main doors, is supplemented by a sizeable eating area which serves good quality home-made food Thu, Fri and Sat eves; Sun lunches are also available (booking essential). A welcome return to the *Guide* for this gem of a pub.
Q ⋈ ♠ ▮ ⊟ ♿ ♣ P ▯

DARLINGTON

Binns Department Store (off-licence)
1-7 High Row
☼ 9-5.30 (6 Sat); 11-5 Sun
☎ (01325) 462606

House of Fraser department store with a commodiously stocked bottled beer section in the basement. Over 350 quality beers to take away, including dozens of British and Belgian bottle-conditioned ales. It also sells a good selection of special glasses. Regular tasting sessions are held on the first Sat of every month and at some other times, often hosted by brewers. It was highly commended in the British Guild of Beer Writers *Take Home Beer Awards* 2000. ☞

Number Twenty-2
22 Coniscliffe Road
☼ 11-11; closed Sun
☎ (01325) 354590
Hambleton Nightmare; Ind Coope Burton Ale; Village White Boar, Bull, Old Raby; guest beers ℍ

Extremely popular 'ale house and canteen' with true class and a rare passion for cask ale, winner of numerous local, regional and national CAMRA awards since being created within a former shop and restaurant in the mid-1990s. Huge curved windows and a high ceiling give an airy spaciousness, even when packed. The clientele are a cut (and generation) above the usual town-centre circuit-goers. Twelve handpumps serve beers mainly from small independent brewers; this is the home pub of Village Brewer beers, commissioned from Hambleton. It also stocks Liefmans Frambozen and Erdinger Weissbier on draught. Pity about the Sun closure.
Q ▮ ☞ ▯ ●

Old Yard Tapas Bar
98 Bondgate
☼ 11-11; 12-10.30 Sun
☎ (01325) 467385 website: www.tapasbar.co.uk
John Smith's Magnet; Theakston Cool Cask; guest beers ℍ

Small, but busy, town-centre bar, with a Mediterranean theme, offering three regularly changing guest ales. The two-storey seating areas cater for those wishing to partake of the excellent Spanish and Greek fare. The extensive menu is supplemented by lunchtime specials. Regular theme nights are organised for small and large parties alike, with live *bouzouki*, plate-smashing, belly-dancing, flamenco and salsa. A large public car park is within 50 yards. ♣ ❀ ▮ ☞

Tap & Spile
99 Bondgate
☼ 11.30-11 (midnight Fri & Sat); 12-10.30 Sun
☎ (01325) 381679
Theakston Cool Cask; guest beers ℍ

The name's the same, but inside the arrangement is quite different from when this was one of the country's first themed real ale houses. A refurbishment was long overdue, but the layout and furnishings provided by new owners Enterprise Inns are altogether more mainstream. Handpulled beers no longer dominate the bar and the range of guest beers is less adventurous, but the choice of up to four guests is still good by most standards. It hosts live bands Fri and Sat and impromptu music sessions Sun. A large-screen TV is used for sporting events. Children welcome at sensible hours.
▮ ☞ ♣ ♿ ▯

DURHAM CITY

Colpitts
Hawthorne Terrace (A690 near bus station)
☼ 12-11; 12-10.30 Sun
☎ (0191) 386 9913
Samuel Smith OBB ℍ

Real, old-style boozer, with cheapest pub prices for miles around. It gets busy from early eve most days in the small lounge, side pool room and larger bar. Very popular with locals and students, it hosts live music Mon eve. With its basic decor, it is plain and unpretentious. Handy for public transport, being within walking distance of the train and bus stations. ♨ Q ⊟ ☞ ♣

Court Inn
Court Lane
☼ 11-11; 12-10.30 Sun
☎ (0191) 384 7350
Draught Bass; Greene King Ruddles County; Young's Special ℍ

Standing next to the Crown Court and prison, the pub affords an imposing view looking westwards towards the cathedral. The comfortable, well-appointed bar has a congenial atmosphere. A larger area with tables is used by drinkers and diners. A wide range of good quality bar snacks and meals is sold throughout the day. It is popular with locals, students and tourists. Look out for the crouched figures supporting the ceiling. ❀ ▮ ▯ ♿

Dun Cow
37 Old Elvet
☼ 11-11; 12-4, 7.30-10.30 (12-10.30 summer) Sun
☎ (0191) 386 9219 website: theduncow.com
Boddingtons Bitter; Castle Eden Ale; guest beers ℍ

Historic, characterful pub situated opposite the Crown Court and prison. The intimate snug (entered via a sliding door off a passageway) is popular with town-centre workers and locals. The passageway continues to the rear of the pub to a larger lounge. Well patronised by students, its congenial atmosphere attracts all ages. It reputedly has the highest sales of Castle Eden Ale in the country. The guest beers often come from the same brewery. Good value snacks are sold at lunchtime. Q ▮ ⊟ ♣

Garden House
North Road (off A691)
☼ 11-11; 12-10.30 Sun
☎ (0191) 384 3460
Jennings Bitter; guest beers (occasional) ℍ

In the style of a country inn, this pub is on different levels with a modern conservatory extension housing a restaurant. It has retained few original features and has suffered from much alteration. Convenient for County Hall, the Durham Light Infantry Museum and Art Gallery, it displays an interesting collection of old photographs of the city. Frequented by office workers and locals, it offers a wide range of above-average bar snacks and meals, but the food tends to be expensive. ⊛⇔◁◑➥P

Half Moon
New Elvet (opp. Royal County Hotel)
◷ 11-11; 12-10.30 Sun
☎ (0191) 386 4528
Draught Bass; Worthington Bitter; guest beer Ⓗ
The Half Moon occupies a splendid position by the River Wear, which itself allows wonderful meandering walks and superb views of Durham's magnificent cathedral. This classic inn has a listed interior; its back bar is particularly noteworthy. It attracts a good mix of business people, students and locals, and is handy for the town centre and market place. The guest beers come from Durham Brewery. Sandwiches are available at lunchtime.
⊛&➥

Hogshead
58 Saddler Street (between market place and Cathedral)
◷ 11-11; 12-10.30 Sun
☎ (0191) 386 9550
Black Sheep Best Bitter; Boddingtons Bitter; Castle Eden Ale; Wadworth 6X; guest beers Ⓗ/Ⓖ
Typical Hogshead, one of the smallest pubs in the chain, it offers up to eight beers and has featured over 300 guest ales since opening in Nov 1997. A basic wooden decor greets the visitor. The pub is popular eves with both students and locals, and can be very noisy. An enterprising manager tries to place an emphasis on new and interesting guest beers as well as regularly featuring Caledonian 80/-, Deuchars IPA and Fuller's London Pride on rotation; however city-centre prices apply. Wheelchair WC available.
◁&➥●

Old Elm Tree
12 Crossgate
◷ 12-3, 6-11; 12-11 Sat; 12-3, 7-10.30 Sun
☎ (0191) 386 4621
Adnams Bitter; Draught Bass; Camerons Strongarm; Tetley Bitter; guest beers Ⓗ
Old coaching inn, incorporating the original elm tree in the wall. This cosy, city-centre pub attracts a wide clientele, including students and locals. It hosts live folk music Tue and a quiz night Wed. Within easy walking distance of the city centre, rail and bus stations, it offers B&B accommodation. A good atmosphere is enhanced by friendly staff. The outside drinking area is simply a bench on the pavement. Q⇔➥♣P

Swan & 3 Cygnets
Elvet Bridge
◷ 11-11; 12-10.30 Sun
☎ (0191) 384 0242
Samuel Smith OBB Ⓗ
Once a shop, this 19th-century building was converted to a pub by Sam Smith's about 10 years ago, and sells the cheapest pint in the city centre. It is ideally situated for tourists, near the ancient heart of the city, now designated a World Heritage site with its fine cathedral and castle. Tables out on the terrace and by the river afford splendid views. The main shops and market are just two minutes' walk away. ⊛◁➥⊬

Victoria ☆
86 Hallgarth Street
◷ 11-3, 6-11; 12-2, 6-10.30 Sun
☎ (0191) 386 5269
McEwan 80/-; Marston's Pedigree; Theakston Best Bitter; guest beers Ⓗ
The Victoria is a gem of a pub, and it now has listed status. A cosy three-roomed house, it offers a good choice of real ales in a very friendly environment. Entering the impressive bar is like stepping back in time, and it is well worth going into the snug, with its own serving hatch and original bell

---

INN BRIEF

BISHOPTON
Talbot
The Green
12-3, 5.30-11 (11-11 Sat); 12-3, 6.30-10.30 Sun
Camerons Strongarm; guest beer (occasional) Ⓗ
Cosy village local, with a strong emphasis on meals. Upstairs restaurant.

CARRVILLE
Grange Inn
High Street
11-11; 12-10.30 Sun
Castle Eden Ale; Nimmo's XXXX; guest beer Ⓗ
Basic, but comfortable, High Street pub. As part of the Castle Eden estate, real ale has returned to this pub.

FRAMWELLGATE MOOR
Salutation
Wells Bombardier Ⓗ
The third Enterprise Inns-owned pub in Framwellgate Moor, with a food emphasis. Busy and comfortable, but a guest beer would be appreciated.

HART VILLAGE
White Hart Inn
11.30-3.30 (5.30 Sat), 7-11; 12-5.30, 7-10.30 Sun
Greene King Abbot Ⓗ
Classic picturesque two-roomed pub displaying old village photographs. Traditional home-cooked lunches available.

HARTLEPOOL
Knights
25-27 Church Square
11.30-3, 5-11; 12-11 Fri & Sat; 12-10.30 Sun
Black Sheep Best Bitter; Tetley Bitter; Worthington Bitter; guest beer Ⓗ
Near the historic quay and museum; sympathetically converted from a grocer's shop, retaining bare wood floors. Lunches served.

HIGH FLATTS
Plough Inn
11-11; 11-10.30 Sun
Black Sheep Special; Wadworth 6X Ⓗ
Spacious out-of-town pub, near farmland. New landlords are working hard to establish this hostelry.

SHADFORTH
Plough
South Side
7 (11 Sat)-11; 12-3, 7-10.30 Sun
Beer range varies Ⓗ
Cosy village pub, stocking one or two rotating guest beers. Small traditional bar and a larger lounge. No food.

STOCKTON-ON-TEES
Mitre
Harrowgate Lane
11-11; 12-10.30 Sun
Black Sheep Best Bitter; Castle Eden Ale; Tetley Bitter; guest beers Ⓗ
Built in the 1960s, now a Beefeater Restaurant with an emphasis on real ale. Meals served all day.

WITTON GILBERT
White Tun
Sacriston Lane
12-3 (not Mon-Wed), 7-11; 12-10.30 Sun
Castle Eden Bitter, Nimmo's XXXX; guest beer Ⓗ
Estate pub with a spacious lounge and a smaller bar. Lunches served when open; extensive eve menu served 7-9.

pushes that were used to summon the bar staff. The pub is a credit to Mike Webster, who has ensured that it has retained its character. The accommodation is brilliant too. Toasted sandwiches are available at lunchtime. ⌂Q✿☎⊖&

Woodman Inn
23 Gilesgate
✿ 12.30-11; 12-10.30 Sun
☎ (0191) 386 7500
Beer range varies Ⓗ
Local pub that enjoys busy eve trade, attracting lots of students. It offers more than 40 different real ales per year, showcasing local breweries. Four beers are on tap at any one time and are changed weekly. It also hosts an annual beer festival in May. It is well worth the five-minute walk uphill along Claypath from the market place to visit this pub.
⌂Q✿☎⊖&≋♣♠P⅍⊟

EAGLESCLIFFE

Blue Bell
663 Yarm Road
✿ 11-11; 12-10.30 Sun
☎ (01642) 780358
Courage Directors; Taylor Landlord; guest beers Ⓗ
On the north bank of the River Tees, the recent rebuild of this old roadhouse has transformed it beyond recognition. It stands beside a much-altered and widened stone bridge, built on the orders of William Skirlaw, Bishop of Durham, in order to collect tolls from people and goods passing from Durham into the North Riding of Yorkshire. Now part of Scottish Courage's JT Barras chain, it places a strong emphasis on food. However, it does feature a good range of real ales not often found in the area, including guests from independents.
✿⊖&♣P

EBCHESTER

Derwent Walk
On B6309, Leadgate road
✿ 12-3, 6-11; 12-11 Fri & Sat; 12-10.30 Sun
☎ (01207) 560347
Jennings Bitter, Cumberland Ale, Cocker Hoop, Sneck Lifter; guest beers Ⓗ
This friendly pub, popular with locals and walkers alike, has gained a good reputation for both the quality of its beer and home-cooked food. Indeed, *Cask Marque* accreditation was recently awarded, and well deserved it is too. The four regular Jennings beers are usually supplemented by two guest beers. The wood flooring and memorabilia above the bar give the pub an olde-worlde feel; enjoy the views across the Derwent Valley. Q✿⊖&P⊟●

FOREST IN TEESDALE

High Force Hotel
✿ 11-3, 7-11 (11-11 summer); 7 (12 summer)-10.30 Sun
☎ (01388) 622222
High Force Teesdale Bitter, Forest XB, Cauldron Snout Ⓗ
Small, unpretentious, 19th-century residential hotel, popular with walkers and visitors to England's highest and most spectacular waterfall, High Force, secreted in

woods just opposite. The stepped, two-roomed public bar is simply furnished and has a preponderance of panelling, exposed stone and well-used open fires – snow comes early 1,060 feet up in the Pennines. A former stable behind the hotel became home to the pint-sized High Force Brewery in November 1995 but due to the many pressures on the licensees' time the frequency of brewing is due to be reduced as the *Guide* goes to press, with Darwin taking over production of the draught brands.
⌂✿☎⊖♣P

FRAMWELLGATE MOOR ❋

Tap & Spile
27 Front Street (off A167 bypass, 1½ miles from Durham centre)
✿ 11.30-3 , 6 (5 Fri)-11; 12-3, 7-10.30 Sun
☎ (0191) 386 5451
Beer range varies Ⓗ
This continues to be a must for devotees of fine real ales, offering a brilliant, constantly changing choice of guest ales, despite Enterprise Inns' restrictive guest beer policy. This basic, but comfortable, pub is divided into four rooms: a front bar, a rear no-smoking lounge bar, a games room and a family room. It featured its 1,000th guest ale during 2000 and is continuing to add to its total. The cider is Weston's Old Rosie.
Q☎&♣♠⅍

GREAT LUMLEY

Old England
Front Street
✿ 11-11; 12-10.30 Sun
☎ (0191) 388 5257
Beer range varies Ⓗ
Large village pub, whose busy bar is popular with younger drinkers, containing a pool table, dartboard, TV and juke box. The spacious, comfortable lounge is quieter and attracts older drinkers and diners. Meals are also served in the no-smoking area (lunches Fri–Sun; eve meals Mon–Sat). The lounge is split level and divided into smaller areas by wood and coloured glass panels. A popular quiz is held Thu eve. A wide range of guest ales, with usually three on tap, includes beers from small local breweries in Northumberland and Durham.
Q⊖&♣P

GRETA BRIDGE

Morritt Arms Hotel
✿ 11-11; 12-10.30 Sun
☎ (01833) 627232
Black Sheep Best Bitter; Castle Eden Conciliation Ale; Taylor Landlord; Tetley Bitter Ⓗ
Classically proportioned and staunchly traditional country house hotel, in a fine setting, secluded from the roar of the nearby A66. It boasts strong connections with Sir Walter Scott and Charles Dickens, who visited the area when researching *Nicholas Nickleby*. The main bar has a fine open fireplace but it is the whimsical Dickensian murals by the noted 'Guinness artist' John Gilroy which dominate. Licensed for civil weddings, it has fine gardens. The detached Sir Walter Scott Bar, beneath a 1960s Watneys sign, is as plain as the hotel is plush, catering mainly for locals

(open from 8pm); it generally stocks just one cask beer. ♨Q❀❄◑O◕♣P

HARTBURN

Masham Hotel
87 Hartburn Village
❂ 11-11; 12-3, 7-10.30 Sun
☎ (01642) 580414
Draught Bass; Black Sheep Special Ⓗ
Fine, unspoilt, terraced pub set in a leafy tree-lined village street. Its origins as a private house are discernible with several small drinking rooms opening off a central bar and corridor. To the rear is a large garden and paved area where barbecues take place regularly in summer. The pub hosts live music at least once a month, often with an Irish theme. The pub has a strong local following, while also attracting drinkers from a wider area. No meals served Sat eve or Sun.
Q❀◑O◕♣P✟

HARTLEPOOL ❖

Causeway
Vicarage Gardens, Stranton
❂ 11-11; 12-10.30 Sun
☎ (01429) 273954
Camerons Bitter, Strongarm; Mansfield Bitter; guest beers Ⓗ
One of two Camerons' pubs adjacent to the brewery, this one has always been regarded as the tap. Behind a magnificent red-brick frontage can be found a sizeable public bar and two snugs (one of them no-smoking), both served by a hatch in the passage. The pub became a Tap & Spile for a time, before reverting to brewery ownership. Guest beers are currently from the W&D Festival Ales range. The licensee is a keen musician and hosts regular live music eves.
Q◑O◕♣✁✟

Jackson Arms
Tower Street
❂ 12-11; 12-10.30 Sun
☎ (01429) 862413
Draught Bass; guest beers Ⓗ
Two-roomed, traditional pub in an old part of town, named in memory of one of Hartlepool's founding fathers and benefactors, Ralph Ward Jackson. Just a stone's throw from the recently revitalised Church Street area and the new marina, it is close to Christchurch Art Gallery. Three ever-changing guest ales are brought in each week, from all over the country. The second generation licensee continues to promote real ales, as demonstrated by the hundred or so pump clips above the bar.
◕≄

Nursery
Hopps Street
❂ 12-11; 11.30-11 Sat; 12-10.30 Sun
☎ (01429) 268994
Camerons Strongarm Ⓗ
Built in the 1880s on the site of the Mary Willett Excursionists Day Nursery Gardens (hence the name!), this classic street-corner pub, enjoying a strong local patonage, situated on the outskirts of town, is well worth searching out. Recent winner of Camerons' *Best Kept Cellar* award, the pub has a music room that hosts regular band

and folk club nights. Old photographs of the town adorn the walls of a pub that supports its own pigeon club, as well as a local Sun football team. ❀◕P✟

HUNWICK

Quarryburn
1 Helmington Square (B6286)
❂ 12-2.30 (not Wed), 5.30 (7 Wed)-11; 12-11 Sat; 12-10.30 Sun
☎ (01388) 607236 e-mail: keithdufton@hotmail.com
Banks's Original; Camerons Strongarm Ⓗ
Around 200 years old, the pub's dining room displays a collection of theatrical memorabilia and an original Friary Meux mirror adorns one of the bar walls. The pub dog has a habit of barking at those who do not buy a drink, and a ghost can sometimes be heard treading the upstairs floorboards at night. Conveniently situated for buses on the Bishop Auckland–Willington route, it is well worth a detour to sample a very fine pint of Banks's. Lunches served at weekends; eve meals Mon–Sat. ♨Q◑A♣

KIRK MERRINGTON

Half Moon
Crowther Place (2 miles W of Ferryhill on B6288)
❂ 11.30-11; 12-10.30 Sun
☎ (01388) 811598
website: www.britnett.com/thehalfmoon
Beer range varies Ⓗ
This one-roomed village local is popular with all ages. A friendly landlady and a roaring coal fire ensure a warm welcome. Regular guest beers come from Daleside Brewery in Yorkshire as well as the more local Durham Brewery. No eve meals Sun. The local churchyard is quite ancient and worth a visit, although it was the scene of a murder some years ago, so not everyone would want to venture in. ♨◑P

LOW WILLINGTON

Black Horse Inn
42 Low Willington (A690, Durham road)
❂ 7 (12 Sat)-11; 12-10.30 Sun
☎ (01388) 746340
Beer range varies Ⓗ
Very friendly pub on the edge of a town that is a real ale desert. Two fine beers are always available here, with some interesting surprises from time to time, complemented by a range of around a dozen malt whiskies. Situated near Roman roads and encampments, the house is reputedly haunted by a Roman soldier who rearranges newly-laid beer mats and table decorations. It lies on the X46 bus route from Durham to Crook; the No. 108 from Bishop Auckland stops at the door of this local CAMRA *Pub of the Year* 2000. Q❀◕A♣P✟

MIDDLESTONE VILLAGE

Ship Inn
Low Road
❂ 5 (12 Fri & Sat)-11; 12-10.30 Sun
☎ (01388) 810904
Camerons Strongarm; guest beers Ⓗ
Superb, friendly, country pub, where a wide range of cask ales always includes a beer from both Daleside and Durham, plus two guests, often from Mordue, Ashvine or

Darwin. Set in beautiful countryside in a small rural village, the locals are friendly. Quiz night is Wed; games include Toad in the Hole and bar skittles. Weekend lunches served; eve meals Thu-Sat. It is said to be haunted by a ghost (believed to be Lord Eden) who makes regular appearances. Local CAMRA *Pub of the Year* 2001.
🏚Q❀◑♣P🍺

NEVILLE'S CROSS

Neville's Cross Free House
Neville's Cross complex, Darlington Road
✪ 12-3, 6-11; 12-11 Sat; 12-10.30 Sun
☎ (0191) 375 7707
website: www.the-neville-complex.co.uk
Castle Eden Bitter, Banner Bitter; Theakston Cool Cask; guest beers ⒣
The former Neville's Cross Hotel has been transformed by new private owners into a complex, incorporating a free house. Created at some expense, the complex features a mix of architectural styles. The gothic-style bar offers three regularly changing guest beers. Popular with younger drinkers, it is worth visiting for its unusual surroundings; it must be one of the few bars with new stained glass (commemorating the Battle of Neville's Cross). You may also wish to try the Departure Lounge cocktail bar or the Copper Dome Restaurant. ◑🍴&♿P

NO PLACE

Beamish Mary Inn
Front Street (600 yds off A693)
✪ 12-11; 12-10.30 Sun
☎ (0191) 370 0237
Black Sheep Best Bitter; Courage Directors; Theakston Cool Cask; Old Peculier; guest beers ⒣
While the pub has been tidied in recent years, its design and furnishings must be experienced to be appreciated. It enjoys good local support and is well worth a visit, especially in February for the annual beer festival. It offers a good combination of above-average food and live music. It stocks a wide range of guest ales, as well as house beers from Big Lamp. It is just a mile from the outstanding Beamish Open Air Museum where the on-site real ale pub was rebuilt from its original home in Bishop Auckland.
🏚Q❀🛏◑🍴

NORTON

Unicorn
High Street
✪ 12-3.30, 5.30-11; 11-11 Fri & Sat; 12-4, 7-10.30 Sun
☎ (01642) 643364
John Smith's Magnet ⒣
Atmospheric gem that enjoys (deservedly) a near-fanatical following. The fact that the pub has survived in its near-original layout owes as much to the customers as the sympathetic landlady. A great furore was caused when a well-meaning brewery wanted to box in a steel beam with 'Dorman long steel' cast into it. No need to be ashamed of local craftsmen is there? It has a tiny bar and a corridor with several rooms served from a hatchway. Keg John Smith's Magnet is also available, so don't forget to ask for cask. Local CAMRA *Pub of the Season* 2001. Q☎❀◑🍴&♣

OLD WHITE LEA

Dun Cow (Cow's Tail)
Turn left at Royal George, then 1 mile
✪ 7-11 Wed, Fri & Sat; 7-10.30 Sun
☎ (01388) 762714
Darwin Evolution ⒣
This traditional rural pub has hardly altered since the present family took it over in the early 19th century. Although well off the beaten track, it is well worth seeking out. A fine collection of mugs and drinking utensils feature in the bar, while local brewing memorabilia adorn the front room, which is virtually unchanged since first licensed in 1830. It will open at other times with prior notice; other Darwin beers for group visits can be arranged. Best to phone before making a special trip.
🏚Q❀🍴P✂

PITY ME

Lambton Hounds
62 Front Street (off A167 roundabout, 2 miles N of Durham)
✪ 11-11; 12-10.30 Sun
☎ (0191) 386 4742
Marston's Pedigree; guest beers ⒣
250-year-old coaching inn, this former Vaux house continues to serve its real ales in excellent condition, despite the choice of beers having been rationalised by Enterprise Inns. This is a very warm and friendly pub and refurbishment has created a very pleasant drinking and eating environment. Food is superb, with a very experienced chef in charge of the kitchen. Check out the bar which originates from the *Titanic's* sister ship, the *Olympic*.
Q☎❀🍴◑🍴&♣P

PRESTON-LE-SKERNE

Blacksmith's Arms
Ricknall Lane (1 mile E of A167, off Gt Stainton road)
✪ 12-3, 6.30-11 (12-11 high summer); 12 (6.30 winter)-10.30 Sun
☎ (01325) 314873
website: www.blacksmithsarms.co.uk
Theakston Cool Cask; guest beers ⒣
Long, narrow, family-run free house standing by itself and offering an unusual combination of pub, nursery and more. The bar and lounge are separated by a long corridor. The beamed lounge is in 'farmhouse kitchen' style, complete with a Welsh dresser. Up to three guest ales are available along with home-cooked meals. Musicians are invited to come along for impromptu sessions Sun eve. The plants and vegetables are for sale; hens, ducks and guinea fowl roam free in the garden, and there is even a helicopter landing pad.
❀◑🍴♣P

ROMALDKIRK

Kirk Inn
The Green
✪ 12-2.30 (not Mon-Wed), 6-11; 12-3, 7-10.30 Sun
☎ (01833) 650260
Boddingtons Bitter; Fuller's London Pride; guest beers ⒣
Welcoming, family-run pub built in 1745 overlooking the large, attractive village

green. The cosy single room doubles as the village Post Office before lunchtime, but it is almost impossible to detect this at other times. Fine home-cooked food appears from the labyrinthine kitchen area; lunches are served Fri–Sun, eve meals Mon and Wed–Sat. Sun lunches popular – best to book.

🏠🕷️🕽️♣P

ST JOHN'S CHAPEL

Blue Bell Inn
12 Hood Street
🕓 5 (11 Sat)-11; 12.30-3; 6.30-10.30 Sun
☎ (01388) 537256
Tetley Bitter Ⓗ

Traditional pub and one of the region's very few outlets for cask-conditioned cider (Addlestone's). A fine collection of curios adorns the bar walls; you may be able to try some of the rarer items! Convenient for fell-walkers and cyclists, it is near the Kilhope Lead Mining Museum. The scenery is deserving of the title 'England's Last Wilderness' but the weather can be unpredictable in winter and spring. Served by the No. 101 bus from Stanhope, but check return times before travelling. 🅰️♣🕽️

SEDGEFIELD

Ceddesfield Hall
Sedgefield Community Association, Rectory Row
🕓 7.30-10.30; 8-11 Sat; 8-11 Sun

☎ (01740) 620341
Beer range varies Ⓗ

Run by volunteers of the Sedgefield Community Association, the building, dating from the 1750s, was the rectory and is set in seven acres of grounds. It is now used for a wide range of activities, everything from Bonsai to squash. There is a friendly small bar, large lounge and function room, serving excellent cheap beer (40–50 different beers every year). A beer festival is held the first weekend in July, usually with at least 10 beers. CAMRA *Club of the Year* 1999, the resident ghost is known as 'the pickled parson'.
Q🕷️🕽️🅿️

Hardwick Arms Hotel
North End
🕓 11-11; 12-10.30 Sun
☎ (01740) 620218
Jennings Bitter, Cumberland Ale Ⓗ

18th-century coaching inn in Tony Blair's constituency, on the old York to Edinburgh route, it is now very popular with the locals. This is a lively establishment hosting entertainment most eves. It has one large L-shaped bar that is plain, but very comfortable, plus a no-smoking restaurant.
🛏️🕽️♣P

SHINCLIFFE

Rose Tree
Low Road West
(A177, 1½ miles from Durham centre)

The Origins of Porter

Once the pride of the great London breweries, porter is today an almost obsolete term. Porter was a dark beer intermediate in style between ale and stout. The origin of the name is obscure but the beer seems to have been first brewed early in the 18th century in response to a demand, perhaps by market porters, for 'half and half' – a blend of ale and beer, or for 'three threads', a mixture of ale, beer and the weak 'twopenny'.

When thus brewed 'entire' it was no doubt darkened to distinguish it from unblended beers. It held its place as the major product of many breweries for a century or more, but its popularity waned as the taste for ales increased and the stouts grew stouter.

Porter finally expired when increasing taxation reduced the stouts to the gravity of the erstwhile porter, and the porter to a pale shadow of its old robust self. With its expiry, cooper, which was a mixture of stout and porter, likewise disappeared.

Booklet on the history of Whitbread's Brewery, 1951. The revival of interest in porter in both Britain and the US suggests the style has outlived Whitbread.

✪ 11-11; 12-10.30 Sun
☎ (0191) 386 8512
Draught Bass; Castle Eden Bitter; Greene King Old Speckled Hen; Marston's Pedigree Ⓗ
Friendly, cosy, pub whose hosts and staff always seem eager to please. Situated by the River Wear, it is a popular venue for good meals. Families are well provided for, with an enclosed children's play area next to the attractive, heated patio outside the front. It says much for the hard work and enthusiasm of the hosts that the fine standard of service was quickly restored after the premises were severely flooded in October 2000. Q ⌨ ❀ ◖ ◗ ⊟ P

Seven Stars
High Street North (A177, 1¾ miles S of Durham)
✪ 12-11; 12-10.30 Sun
☎ (0191) 384 8454 website: www.sevenstarsinn.co.uk
Courage Directors; Marston's Pedigree; Theakston Best Bitter; guest beers Ⓗ
This warm, friendly olde-worlde coaching inn, at the edge of a quaint picturesque village, boasts a varied and imaginative food menu. Well worth a visit in its own right, it is also within easy reach of attractive countryside and many places of interest, not least the historic city of Durham with its castle, cathedral and many good pubs. To the north, a visit to Beamish Open Air Museum could well take up a whole day, so the B&B on offer here could prove useful.
Q ❀ ☎ ◖ ◗ ⊟ ●

STANHOPE

Queen's Head
Front Street
✪ 11-11 (may vary winter); 12-10.30 Sun
☎ (01388) 528160
Beer range varies Ⓗ
Stone pub on three floors, dating from the early 19th century. Popular with locals, it is a good base for walkers and cyclists, providing an overnight stop for the Coast-to-Coast (C2C) cycle route and visitors to the outstanding local fells. The second bar has been converted to a dining room, so the remaining bar can become congested at busy times. The beer range can be restricted in winter but up to three cask ales are stocked in summer, usually including Theakston XB. The 101 bus from Crook and Bishop Auckland stops at the door.
Q ☎ ◖ ◗ ♠ ♣

STOCKTON-ON-TEES ❉

Fitzgeralds
High Street
✪ 11.30-3 (3.30 Fri; 4 Sat), 6.30-11; 7-10.30 Sun
☎ (01642) 678220
Draught Bass; Taylor Landlord; guest beers Ⓗ
The fine stone frontage of this pub, with its granite pillars looks far too grandiose for a pub, and indeed it was originally a gentlemen's club with an upstairs billiards room, but became a pub many years ago. A central bar serves a split-level drinking area featuring typical woodwork salvaged from long-demolished pubs. The bar-back pays tribute to the wide range of guest beers featured during the recent past. Recently sold by Sir John Fitzgerald & Co, the new owners have promised to continue offering a wide range of real ales. Q ◗ ♣ ♠

Sun
Knowles Street
✪ 11-11; 12-10.30 Sun
☎ (01642) 623921
Draught Bass Ⓗ
Undoubtedly the most popular pub in town, for many years the Sun has enjoyed the largest sales of Bass in the country, a fact which comes as no surprise to those who travel from far and near to drink it. The pub sells no other ale, very little lager, and watching the bar staff pull 'bankers' (half pints with large heads to be topped up a few minutes later) is an education and entertainment. This serving method is an old-established tradition designed to provide quick service at busy times. A large function room at the rear hosts a weekly folk club.
⊟ ≈

Thomas Sheraton
4 Bridge Road
✪ 11-11; 12-10.30 Sun
☎ (01642) 606134
Boddingtons Bitter; Courage Directors; Theakston Best Bitter; Worthington Bitter; guest beers Ⓗ
Superb conversion by Wetherspoon's of a former county court building. A large central bar serves several drinking areas. A fine staircase leads to a gallery with seats and tables, and gives access to a roof garden in summer; the no-smoking area houses an extensive library. The food and beer range are typical of Wetherspoon's, with some guest ales coming from unusual sources. The food is cheap and plentiful, and the pub attracts a wide range of customers, from teenagers to pensioners.
Q ❀ ◖ ◗ ♿ ≈ (Thornaby) ⚭ ●

THORPE THEWLES

Hamilton Russell Arms
Bank Terrace
✪ 12-11; 12-10.30 Sun;
☎ (01740) 630757 website: www.hamiltonrussell.co.uk
Courage Directors; John Smith's Magnet; Wells Bombardier; guest beer Ⓗ
Historic pub overlooking a picturesque village green. Originally part of the estate of the Marchioness of Londonderry, it was named after the 1928 marriage of Gustavson Hamilton to Emma Russell. Much extended over the years, and recently refurbished to provide an open-plan interior, it has retained the snug and a games room, alongside several distinct drinking areas, including a large space for no-smokers. Real fires, a cheery staff and south-facing garden add to its appeal. An extensive, much-praised menu, with fish and vegetarian options, is available all day. Wheelchair WC.
🛏 ❀ ◖ ◗ ⊟ P ⚭

TRIMDON GRANGE

Dovecote Inn
Salters Lane (B1278)
✪ 7 (12 Fri & Sat)-11; 12-10.30 Sun
☎ (01419) 880967
Trimdon Busty Bitter; guest beer Ⓗ
Built originally for the local pit and coke oven workers, now a traditional welcoming

one-roomed village local, the owner, Steve, is a real ale enthusiast running his own brewery, Trimdon Cask Ales. Currently brewed are Busty Bitter, Harvey Bitter and Pitprop; the first two are named after coal seams. Usual pub games are available, but be warned – avoid playing the landlord at pool. ♨◖❶

TRIMDON VILLAGE

Bird in Hand
Salters Lane (B1278, Fishburn road)
☼ 11-11; 12-3, 7-11 Mon; 12-10.30 Sun
☎ (01429) 880391 e-mail: nsteggall@aol.com
Black Sheep Best Bitter; guest beers Ⓗ
Large, friendly local dating from the 1950s on the very edge of the village, overlooking open country. It has a central serving area, with a bar at one side and a large lounge/restaurant at the other. Normally stocking three guests, the landlord is very committed to promoting real ale and stages six themed beer weekends a year. He also hosts old fashioned pub games nights, an Aug bank holiday 'Battle of the Bands' (rock and blues), and regular live entertainment. Inches cider is sometimes available.
🏠❀◖⊟♣P

WEST CORNFORTH

Square & Compass
7 The Green
☼ 7.30 (11 Sat)-11; 12-10.30 Sun
☎ (01740) 654606
Beer range varies Ⓗ
Traditional village pub, occupying a commanding position at the top of the hill, overlooking the green, which is the oldest part of Cornforth. Well refurbished, the pub owes its name to a former connection with Freemasonry. A genuine free house the Square normally has two handpulled beers on tap usually from Clark's in Yorkshire and Durham Brewery. It stages a quiz on Thu eve and live entertainment Sat. The real log fire is very welcome in winter.
♨❀P

WITTON GILBERT ❄

Glendenning Arms
Front Street (off A691, Consett Road)
☼ 4 (12 Fri & Sat)-11; 12-10.30 Sun
☎ (0191) 371 0316
Draught Bass; Boddingtons Bitter; Tetley Bitter; Worthington Bitter Ⓗ
Warm, friendly village pub with a bar and lounge. It used to feature racing memorabilia when owned by Vaux, but is currently undergoing minor refurbishment to add small table dividers in the bar. It appeared for 19 straight years in this *Guide* until 1995. Unspoilt and comfortable, it is popular with locals. Note the old Vaux handpulls from the 1970s in the bar; the lounge is cosy; both rooms have open fires. Outside seating is provided in the car park.
♨Q❀⊟♣P

Travellers Rest
Front Street (A691, Consett road, 2 miles from Durham centre)
☼ 11.30-3, 6.30-11; 11-11 Fri & Sat; 12-10.30 Sun
☎ (0191) 3710458 e-mail: travellersrest@barclays.net
Courage Directors; Greene King Ruddles County, Old

Speckled Hen; McEwan 80/-; Theakston Best Bitter; guest beers Ⓗ
Very popular, country-style inn with four rooms, including a conservatory and split-level no-smoking room, both of which are popular with families. A regular *Guide* entry, this pub offers a large variety of meals to suit most tastes. Served in the bar or restaurant, the menu changes with the seasons. The interior is largely unaltered; the style is contemporary and comfortable. Two guest beers are normally available. Boules is played in summer.
♨Q🍴❀⛱◖⊟♣✍

WOLSINGHAM

Mill Race Hotel
West End (A689)
☼ 11-11; 12-10.30 Sun
☎ (01388) 526551
McEwan 80/-; guest beers Ⓗ
This imposing 1920s building retains many of the architectural features of the period, including iron-framed windows. A very friendly local on the edge of the village, it offers excellent meals and good quality accommodation. It is ideally situated for walks, both around the historic village or further afield on the moors and fells, and the long distance Wear Valley Way footpath. The area is also excellent cycling terrain. The No. 101 bus from Crook and Bishop Auckland stops nearby.
♨Q🍴❀⛱◖⊟▲♣P

WOLVISTON

Ship Inn
50 High Street
☼ 12-3, 6-11; 12-3, 7-10.30 Sun
☎ (01740) 644420
Black Sheep Best Bitter; guest beer Ⓗ
At the north end of the village, the Ship dates from the 1800s and was originally a coaching inn. The present building, however, dates from the early 1900s, although the original stables can still be seen to the rear. The pub has a homely atmosphere, with a no-smoking area supplemented by a good ventilation system. All the food is freshly prepared and, as the landlady says, 'there are no microwave "pings" in my kitchen'. The guest beer comes mainly from independent breweries. Local CAMRA *Pub of the Season* 2000.
❀◖♣P✍

Check it out

Pubs in the Good Beer Guide may change ownership and the facilities listed could alter. If a visit to a pub in the guide involves a lengthy journey, it is advisable to check before leaving that full meals, family facilities, accommodation or camping sites are still available.

CAMRA's National Inventory
of Pubs Interiors of Outstanding Historic Interest

Merseyside

Birkenhead: Stork Hotel, Price Street. Remodelled c.1900: fine tiling and screens.
Liverpool: Lion, Moorfields. Remodelled c.1900: bell-pushes in 'Newsroom' still in use. Closed Sun.
Liverpool: Philharmonic, Hope Street 1898-1900. The palatial layout and sumptuous fittings make this the most spectacular pub in England. Don't miss the gents'.
Liverpool: Prince Arthur, 93 Rice Lane, Walton. Mid 19th-century pub remodelled c.1905. Good fittings.
Liverpool: Vines, Lime Street. 1907. Splendid interior with copper fireplaces, plasterwork, panelling and stained glass dome.
Lydiate: Scotch Piper. Mid 16th-century timber-framed building. Three small rooms.

Norfolk

Warham: Three Horseshoes. Trace the growth from a small 19th-century pub (right) through to the 1930s room.

Northumberland

Berwick-upon-Tweed: Free Trade, Castlegate. Complete Victorian interior. Interesting layout. Closed lunchtimes.
Netherton: Star Inn. Single public room in former hotel, unchanged for 100 years Limited hours.

Nottinghamshire

Arnold: Vale Hotel, Thackeray's Lane, Woodthorpe. Substantial 1930s roadhouse with Art Deco details.
Nottingham: Olde Trip to Jerusalem, Brewhouse Yard, Castle Road. Remarkable pub with old rooms on two levels, some hewn-out of the Castle Rock
West Bridgford: Test Match Hotel, Gordon Square. 1938. Superb interior: two-storey high lounge bar: original Art Deco-style fittings. Don't miss the public (left) and cocktail (upstairs) bars.

Oxfordshire

Bix: Fox. 1936. England's best and most intact surviving roadhouse.
Christmas Common: Fox & Hounds. Three-room country pub, could alter, visit now.
Steventon: North Star. Wonderful village pub in 16th-century building: high-backed benches form a drinking area: no bar counter.
Stoke Lyne: Peyton Arms. Simple, unspoilt rural pub.
Stoke Row: Crooked Billet. Smart eatery but retaining two old rooms.
Stoke Talmage: Red Lion. Attached to a farm: two rooms and former off-sales. Closed most lunchtimes.
Wantage: Shoulder of Mutton, 38 Wallingford Street. Small town pub: unusual layout.

Shropshire

Halfway House: Seven Stars. Unique tiny beerhouse alongside larger modernised pub. No bar, no smoking, no spirits, no wine. Rear room used if busy.
Selattyn: Cross Keys. Four-roomed village pub that until 1994 doubled as the village shop.

Shrewsbury: Loggerheads, Church Street. Rambling four-room interior in 18th-century building.
Whitchurch: Plume of Feathers, Bark Hill. Late-Victorian: five rooms refurbished in the 1930s.

Somerset

Appley: Globe. Multi-room village pub.
Bath Appley: Old Green Tree, Green Street. Three inter-war panelled rooms in a Georgian terrace.
Appley: Star, The Vineyards. Wonderful four-room 1936 interior in a Georgian terrace.
Crowcombe: Carew Arms. Village pub with stone-flagged floor: skittles bar.
Faulkland: Tucker's Grave Inn. No counter, superb tap room and small lounge bar.
Midsomer Norton: White Hart. Victorian multi-room town pub.
Witham Friary: Seymour Arms. c.1866. Splendid servery with glazed screens, stone floored bar and basic lounge with hatch service.

Staffordshire

Tunstall: Vine, Naylor Street, Pitts Hill. Rare survival of a Victorian back-street local. Closed weekday lunchtimes.

Suffolk

Brent Eleigh: Cock. 15th-century thatched building with two small bars.
Bury St Edmunds: Nutshell. Britain's smallest pub, only 4.8m x 2.3m internally: 6-day licence.
Ipswich: Margaret Catchpole, Cliff Lane. 1936: probably the best inter-war pub in Britain for a combination of quality and completeness.
Laxfield: King's Head ('Low House'). 16th-century thatched pub: high Victorian settles form a drinking area: four rooms in all.
Pin Mill: Butt & Oyster. Characterful 17th-century riverside pub, high settles.

East Sussex

Firle: Ram. Popular village pub. Three rooms including former Georgian court room.
Hadlow Down: New Inn. Classic unspoilt rural pub built 1885. Former hotel.

West Sussex

The Haven: Blue Ship. Hard-to-find, four-room country pub.

Tyne & Wear

Newcastle upon Tyne: Crown Posada, 31 Side.1880 splendid narrow pub with snug at front and fine stained glass.

Warwickshire

Five Ways: Case is Altered. 300-year-old, three-room cottage pub.
Long Itchington: Buck & Bell. Victorian layout and fittings: currently closed.

Continued on page 196

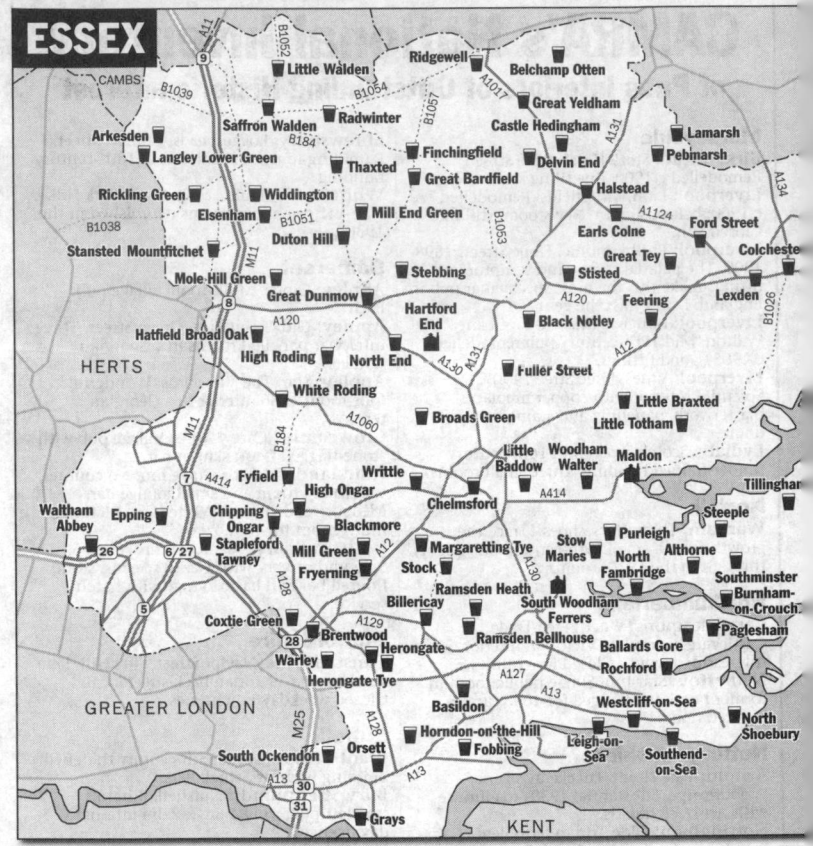

ESSEX

AINGERS GREEN

Royal Fusilier
Aingers Green Road (1 mile S of Gt. Bentley)
OS119204
☼ 11-2.30 (3.30 Sat), 5.30-11; 12-4, 7-10.30 Sun
☎ (01206) 250001
Greene King IPA; guest beers Ⓗ
New signposts now point the way to
Aingers Green and therefore this rural pub
is much easier to locate. It is now being run
by the third generation of the same family.
In its early days it was simply an ale house
but has for a long time catered for all
customers, young and old. The MG Club
now holds its meetings on Fri. A warm
welcome is always guaranteed. ♨Q✿♣P

ALTHORNE

Huntsman & Hounds
Green Lane (off B1018) OS906004
☼ 12-3, 5-11; 12-11 Sat; 12-10.30 Sun
☎ (01621) 740387
Greene King IPA; guest beers Ⓗ
Very attractive, part-thatched Gray's pub
with extensive gardens. The pub is
especially popular with campers; facilities
for tents and caravans (power and water
supplies) are available in the large
neighbouring field. This field can be booked
for functions as can the new barbecue area.
Overall this is a delightful, picture-postcard
pub. ♨Q✿◑▲♣P

ARKESDEN

Axe & Compasses
(opp. Post Office, 2 miles N of B1038) OS483344
☼ 11.30-2.30, 6-11; 12-3, 7-10.30 Sun
☎ (01799) 550272
Greene King IPA, Ruddles Best, Old Speckled Hen Ⓗ
Thatched, 17th-century local with
public bar and restaurant serving
award-winning food. Bar snacks and
excellent meals are offered. Enjoy the
friendly atmosphere and the beautiful
setting. This friendly community pub is at
the centre of the village. Note the wealth of
memorabilia.
♨Q✿◑ ⊞♣P●

BALLARDS GORE

Shepherd & Dog
Gore Road (2½ miles from Rochford, between
Stambridge & Paglesham)
☼ 12-3, 6-11; 12-10.30 Sun
☎ (01702) 258279 website: www.shepndog.com
Beer range varies Ⓗ
Welcoming, traditional pub in a rural
setting close to Rochford. Normally three
beers are stocked from independent and
small breweries in the comfortable and
child-free bar – just the place to relax for a
quiet drink and civilised conversation.
Meals are available in the bar or separate
restaurant. There is a pleasant garden with
summer barbecues and garden parties

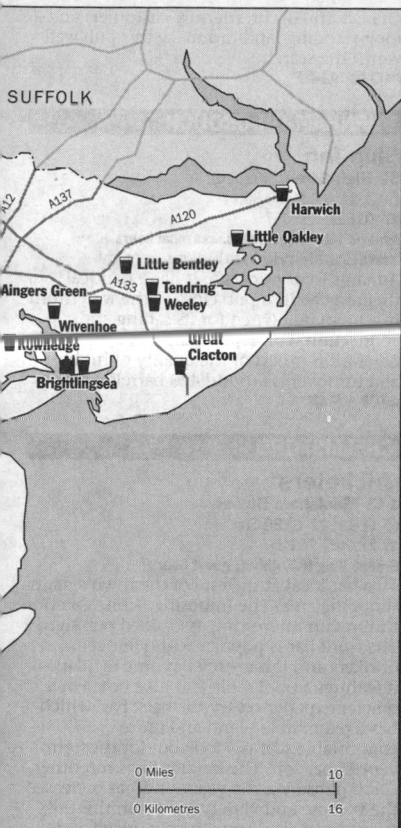

SUFFOLK

Harwich

Little Oakley

Little Bentley

Aingers Green

Tendring
Weeley

Wivenhoe

Rowhedge

Great
Clacton

Brightlingsea

0 Miles   10
0 Kilometres   16

BILLERICAY ❄

Coach & Horses
36 Chapel Street (off High St, 300 yds S of railway)
✪ 10-11; 12-3.30, 7-10.30 Sun
☎ (01277) 622963

Adnams Bitter; Greene King IPA, Abbot; guest beer Ⓗ
Friendly town local with the emphasis on
good beer and conversation. This Gray's
house is close to the High Street but far
enough away to appeal to those who enjoy
a drink in a real pub with no gimmicks and
no live music. It is on the site of the tap
room of the Crown brewery, a one-time
coaching inn. The single bar is adorned
with many photographs and prints plus
impressive collections of jugs and
elephants. Good value snacks and meals
(not served on Mon, Tue or Sat eves or all
day Sun). ⚄ ❀ ◑ ⇌ ♣ P

BLACKMORE

Leather Bottle
Horse Fayre Green
✪ 11-11; 12-10.30 Sun
☎ (01277) 821891

Adnams Bitter; Ridleys IPA; guest beers Ⓗ
Situated in the attractive village of
Blackmore, the pub faces a small green.
Rebuilt in mock-Tudor style, it boasts two
bars, one mainly given over to food, the
other remaining a comfortable blend of
public/saloon. It also benefits from a large
garden with a roofed patio area; children's
toys and further seating are provided at the
front. A back room houses a pool table.
Events include a beer festival at Easter, live
music and speciality eves. Weston's Old
Rosie cider is stocked. Limited parking.
⚄ ❀ ◑ ♣ P ●

BLACK NOTLEY

Vine Inn
105 The Street
✪ 12-2.30 (not Mon), 6.30-11; 12-3.30, 7-10.30 Sun
☎ (01376) 324269

Adnams Bitter or Ridleys IPA; guest beers Ⓗ
This pub is 15 minutes' walk from Cressing
railway station, and worth the effort. It is a
two-roomed village local that can trace its
history as a pub back to 1640. There is a
restaurant area at the far end of the long
main room and a pool table in the smaller
room. Three guest beers are usually
available with 217 different beers served in
the past year. Good, home-made food
includes a regularly changing special pie
menu and the Essex Huffer – a large,
generously filled bap. An annual beer
festival is held in late March. ❀ ◑ ♣ P

BRENTWOOD

Swan (Hogshead)
123 High Street (A1023)
✪ 11-11; 12-10.30 Sun
☎ (01277) 211848

organised. Popular with walkers and
cyclists, the pub was built around 1940 and
was thatched until a fire in the late 1960s.
The handpumps may be fitted with
sparklers which the staff are happy to
remove on request. Real cider is served in
summer.
Q ❀ ◑ & ♣ P

BELCHAMP OTTEN

Red Lion
Fowes Lane OS799415
✪ 12-3 (not Mon-Fri), 7-11 Sat; 12-3, 7-10.30 Sun
☎ (01787) 277537
website: www.5-parishes-millennium.fsnet.co.uk/redlion

Greene King IPA; guest beer Ⓗ
Village local with a friendly atmosphere
and some of the best-kept IPA in the
area. Signposted off the village main street
down a narrow no-through road
overlooking Beauchamp (beautiful
fields), this quiet pub is free from
music and machines with an open fire
in winter and a patio to the front and
rear for the better weather. Popular
with cyclists, walkers and locals, families
are also welcome. The pub offers a good-
value bar menu of tasty, home-cooked
food including specialities such as
gammon and pies. Food is served at
all eve sessions and weekend
lunchtimes.
⚄ Q ᴥ ❀ ◑ ▲ ♣ P ⊬

INDEPENDENT BREWERIES

Crouch Vale South Woodham Ferrers
Mighty Oak Maldon
Railway Tavern Brightlingsea
Ridleys Hartford End

Boddingtons Bitter; Mighty Oak Burntwood; Wadworth 6X; Young's Special; guest beers Ⓗ
15th-century pub that, despite refurbishment, retains much of its wood panelling. It has a small patio at the rear. The gravity dispense has gone, but a wide and varied range of real ales is stocked including some from micro-breweries. Some interesting photographs of old Brentwood adorn the pub.
🏛Q🕸🍺≢

BRIGHTLINGSEA

Railway Tavern
58 Station Road (B1029)
✪ 5 (3 Fri; 12 Sat)-11; 12-10.30 Sun
☎ (01206) 302581
Crouch Vale Best Bitter; guest beers Ⓗ
The only brewery in the Tendring peninsula but its fame has spread to the United States; alas the beer is not in bottles so the request was not fulfilled. The brewery is now in its fourth year and produces four barrels a month. Its Crab and Winkle mild won the mild class at the Ipswich beer festival. Also brewed are Sprat and Oyster Bitter and Bladderack Stout. A cider festival is held in May. The pub still has all the hallmarks of the old station waiting rooms and there are two bars. The front bar is always alive with conversation. There is a small, enclosed garden.
🏛Q🌀🕸♣🍺

BROADS GREEN

Walnut Tree
Turn off A130 for Great Waltham, take next left
OSTL694125
✪ 11.30-2.30, 6.30-11; 12-2.30, 6.30-10.30 Sun
☎ (01245) 360222
Ridleys IPA Ⓖ
Unspoilt Victorian pub on an isolated village green. There is a narrow servery, with seating for five or six people and a wood-panelled public bar with a real fire. Here you will find some old Ridleys posters and a cabinet display of model vans, mainly with brewery designs. Lunchtime food is served Mon-Sat. The saloon has plusher seating and a collection of wall-mounted plates showing military aircraft. Look out for the old, wooden Ridleys cask. Genuine,

characterful decor, friendly customers and a long-standing landlord make this pub well worth the search.
🏛Q🕸🍺◁♣P

BURNHAM-ON-CROUCH

Ship Inn
52 High Street (B1010)
✪ 11-11; 12-10.30 Sun
☎ (01621) 785057
Adnams Bitter, Broadside, seasonal beers Ⓗ
Traditional-style local taken over by Adnams four years ago. It has a nautical theme as befits a pub close to the waterfront in a town renowned for its sailing and connection with Ellen MacArthur. The landlord is proud of the quality of his beer and turnover is around 420 barrels a year.
🍴◁▷⅙P●

CHELMSFORD ☸

Cricketers
143 Moulsham Street
✪ 11-11; 12-10.30 Sun
☎ (01245) 261157
Greene King IPA, Abbot; guest beer Ⓗ
Two-bar local at the end of the town's main shopping area. The imposing, white exterior features an interesting, two-sided pub sign. The front bar is popular with younger drinkers and interesting daytime regulars – it features a pool table and juke box. For a quieter experience, try the back bar, which has a reasonable piano and more comfortable seating; look out for the 'retro-veneer' bar top! The landlord has run other Guide pubs over the years, and has increased the volume and variety of beer in this pub. Guest beers are competitively priced and come from small and medium-sized brewers all over the country. Lunchtime food served Sun–Fri. Q🕸◁▷⅙♣

Endeavour
351 Springfield Road
✪ 11-11; 12-2.30, 7-10.30 Sun
☎ (01245) 257717
Adnams Bitter; Greene King XX Mild, IPA; guest beers Ⓗ
Friendly and quiet pub where the only sound is the buzz of conversation. It was built in 1810 and has been a pub since

INN BRIEF

BASILDON
Moon on the Square
1-11 Market Square
11-11; 12-10.30 Sun
Courage Directors; Ridleys Old Bob; Shepherd Neame Spitfire; Theakston Best Bitter; guest beers Ⓗ
Attractive Wetherspoon's, once a bakery. One large bar which can get very busy at lunchtime on market days. Cask Marque accredited.

BILLERICAY
Blue Boar
39 High Street
11-11; 12-10.30 Sun
Courage Directors; Greene King IPA, Abbot; Shepherd Neame Spitfire; Theakston Best Bitter; guest beers Ⓗ
New Wetherspoon's pub on the site of former Co-op supermarket. Single, large bar. Cask Marque accredited.

CASTLE HEDINGHAM
Wheatsheaf
2 Queen Street
12-2.30, 5-11; 12-11 Sat;
12-10.30 Sun
Greene King IPA, Old Speckled Hen; guest beer Ⓗ
Grade I listed 15th-century building. Welcoming atmosphere.

CHELMSFORD
Original Plough
28 Duke Street
11-11;
12-10.30 Sun
Adnams Bitter; Ind Coope Burton Ale; Tetley Bitter; guest beers Ⓗ
Large, open-plan pub with varied guest beers. Popular with young drinkers, beer enthusiasts and commuters; next to railway station.

COLCHESTER
King's Arms (Hogshead)
61-63 Crouch Street
11-11;
12-10.30 Sun
Adnams Bitter; Mighty Oak Burntwood; guest beer Ⓗ/Ⓖ
This sizeable ale house serves up to 10 well-kept real ales. Can be very busy, especially Thu-Sun eves. Holds own mini festivals on bank holidays.

Robin Hood
45 Osborne Street
11-11;
12-10.30 Sun
Tolly Cobbold Bitter, seasonal beer; guest beer (occasional) Ⓗ
Town-centre pub brought back to life by present landlord.

1844. One of the few outlets for Greene King Mild in the area, it serves up to three guest beers from the much-improved Gray's guest list. Good home-cooked food is offered daily (not Sun eve) with special themed menus every 4–6 weeks (booking is essential). Several charities, including guide dogs for the blind and the RNLI, are supported. The charity box awaits transgressors of the 'no mobile phones' rule. ᴁQ◑⊕♣⅄

Queen's Head
30 Lower Anchor Street (near cricket ground)
✪ 12 (11 Sat)-11; 12-10.30 Sun
☎ (01245) 265181

Crouch Vale Brewers Gold, Best Bitter; guest beers Ⓗ
An award-winning, back-street, Victorian gem, it survived the wartime bombing that destroyed many nearby houses. Now Crouch Vale's second tied house, it boasts eight handpumps, usually offering five guest ales. Mild is always available, as is another dark beer. This friendly, welcoming pub has no machines or piped music, although major sporting events are often shown on the TV. The station is five minutes' walk through the park behind Essex County Cricket ground. The recent refurbishment will be a pleasant surprise to those who remember the pub from its days as 'The Partners'. Annual beer festival hosted in autumn. Lunchtime food served Mon–Fri. Local CAMRA *Pub of the Year* 2001.
ᴁQ❀◑≠♣●P

Riverside Inn
Victoria Road (near Riverside Ice and Leisure centre)
✪ 11-11; 12-10.30 Sun
☎ (01245) 266881

Young's Bitter, Triple A, Special, Winter Warmer Ⓗ
Expensive Young's pub in a converted 16th-century mill. The building is listed, and the front part features authentic beams and parts of the original mill workings. The conservatory, which affords good views of the river Chelmer and award-winning garden, is a modern addition but in keeping with the original building. The full range of Young's beers is currently served (including seasonals), but some may be replaced by Smiles ales in the near future. The small upstairs restaurant-bar is open in the eve, but diners are welcome downstairs at all times. Very good food available all day. ❀≠◑≠⅄

CHIPPING ONGAR

Cock Tavern
218 High Street (opp. Budworth Hall, A128)
✪ 11-3, 5.30-11; 11-11 Fri & Sat; 12-3, 7-10.30 Sun
☎ (01277) 362615

Greene King IPA, Abbot; Shepherd Neame Spitfire Ⓗ
400-year old locals' pub. Wooden beams, traditional jugs, tankards and plates add character. The saloon bar has a seating area separated into booths and plenty of standing space in front of the imposing fireplace. There is a welcoming, friendly atmosphere. Lunchtime meals are served wth a limited vegetarian selection. ᴁ◑

COLCHESTER ❄

Bricklayers
27 Bergholt Road (close to station, between A134 and B1508)
✪ 11-3, 5.30-11; 11-11 Sat; 12-3, 7-10.30 Sun
☎ (01206) 852008

Adnams Bitter, Fisherman, Broadside; guest beers Ⓗ
Flagship Adnams town pub with two bars, one with split levels. Good value bar food is available every day at lunchtimes. Very popular lunches, with always a vegetarian option. In addition to the regular Adnams range, their seasonal beers augment the choice together with a changing selection of guest beers. Experienced, friendly staff offer a warm welcome to locals and visitors alike. The landlord proudly displays numerous CAMRA awards won in past years, including local *Pub of the Year*. Although more than a mile from the town centre, frequent buses ensure easy access. Proximity to the station makes rail 'stop-over' visits an attractive option. ❀◑⊕≠(North) ♣P●

Dragoon
82 Butt Road (on B1026, 100 yds from police station)
✪ 11.30-3, 5-11 Fri; 11-11 Sat; 12-10.30 Sun
☎ (01206) 573464

Adnams Bitter, seasonal beers; Everards Tiger; guest beer Ⓗ
Single-bar pub, complete with its own ghost, the grey lady. Comprises a lounge

GREAT BARDFIELD
Bell
Dunmow Road
11-3;
12-10.30 Sun
Greene King XX Mild, IPA, Abbot; Shepherd Neame Spitfire Ⓗ
Cosy, friendly two-bar local in centre of village. Open fire in saloon. Meals served lunchtime and eve until 9.30pm.

GREAT DUNMOW
Kicking Dickey
Ongar Road
11-3, 6-11;
12-3, 7-10.30 Sun
Greene King IPA; guest beers Ⓗ
One-bar pub with separate dining room. It offers accommodation and caters for local residents and businesses. Good selection of food.

HORNDON-ON-THE-HILL
Bell Inn
High Road
11-2.30 (3 Sat), 6 (5.30 Sat)-11;
12-4, 7-10.30 Sun
Draught Bass; guest beers Ⓗ/Ⓖ
Popular, 15th-century coaching inn with a highly acclaimed restaurant. Up to four regularly changing guest beers stocked.

LEIGH-ON-SEA
Crooked Billet
51 High Street, Old Leigh
12-3, 6-11; 12-11 Sat & summer;
12-10.30 Sun
Adnams Bitter; Draught Bass; Greene King IPA; Ind Coope Burton Ale Ⓗ
Historic old town pub, popular with day trippers and locals. Food served Mon-Sat lunch only.

Sarah Moore
57-59 Elm Road
11-11; 12-10.30 Sun
Boddingtons Bitter; Wells Bombardier; guest beers Ⓗ
Bright, airy bar recently converted from a club. Named after a fabled local sea witch. It has a good selection of food and ales. *Cask Marque* accredited.

LEXDEN
Crown
235 Lexden Road
11.30-3, 6-11; 11.30-11 Sat;
12-3, 7-10.30 Sun
Beer range varies Ⓗ
Welcoming, friendly pub on split-level site with small dining annexe. Larger room is ideal for meetings. Easy access to local parks.

area at one end and public bar with pool table, dartboard and large-screen TV (showing live football) at the other. A favourite with football fans on match days when an awesome chilli is served. The menu includes other hot, spicy dishes. Eve meals are served Fri, Sat, and match nights. The garden is a suntrap. ⊛◑♣

Foresters Arms
2 Castle Road (just off East Hill, near A1232)
✪ 11-11; 12-10.30 Sun
☎ (01206) 542646
Adnams Bitter, Broadside; guest beer (occasional) ⒣
Pleasant pub with a single bar in a quiet back street close to the centre; it has the feel of a country pub in town. Excellent home-cooked food served daily, including Sun lunches. Two minutes' walk from the town's castle and park. The outside drinking area is ideal on warmer days.
⊛◑⇌(Town) ⌷

Hospital Arms
123-125 Crouch Street (opp. hospital, near A1124)
✪ 11-2.30, 5-11; 11-11 Sat; 12-3, 7-10.30 Sun
☎ (01206) 573572
Adnams Bitter, Broadside, seasonal beer; Everards Tiger; Fuller's London Pride; guest beer ⒣
This Grade II listed former almshouse is also known by locals as 'Ward Nine'. The hospital across the road only has eight wards. Despite many alterations, this pub has retained its character with several different drinking areas. This is helped by the fact that there is no pool, darts or juke box. This is a drinkers' pub and when outside the smell of the curry house next door is a deadly combination. Be warned the Broadside has claws! ♨⊛◑

Odd One Out
28 Mersea Road (B1025)
✪ 4 (11 Fri & Sat)-11; 12.30-10.30 Sun
☎ (01206) 578140
Archers Best Bitter; guest beers ⒣
Small, friendly local, this genuine free house has six frequently changing guest beers and three ciders (Crones, Rich's Medium and Thatcher's) on offer at extremely reasonable prices. Beers may include a mild or a porter, and always two or three stronger ales, for example Mauldon's Suffolk Comfort and Tolly Cobbold Old Strong. There is also a wide range of single malts to choose from. A strong community atmosphere means that the pub fields two cricket teams, and is a meeting place for such diverse groups as the Socialist Workers Party and Colchester Re-enactment Society (English Civil War, etc). Local CAMRA *Pub of the Year* 1999.
♨Q⊛⇌(Town) ♦⌿

Rose & Crown Hotel
51 East Street (A137, adjacent to railway level crossing)
✪ 11-2.30, 6-11; 12-3, 6.30-10.30 Sun
☎ (01206) 866677 website: www.rose-and-crown.com
Adnams Broadside; Tetley Bitter ⒣
The oldest inn in Britain's oldest recorded town. The single bar on two levels welcomes hotel guests and locals alike. The good-value bar menu has an emphasis on quality fish. The permanent house bitter is supplied by a regional brewer. Sparklers are removed on request

and with a good grace. Easy 15 minutes' walk downhill from the Norman castle in the town centre. Good bus services back uphill into town. The hotel is a convenient staging post for ferry passengers travelling via nearby Harwich. Colchester's Roman town walls are still mostly intact and close to the hotel. ♨⇋◑P

COXTIE GREEN

White Horse
173 Coxtie Green Road (1 mile W of A128)
✪ 11.30-11; 12-10.30 Sun
☎ (01277) 372410
Adnams Bitter; Fuller's London Pride; guest beers ⒣
CAMRA's local *Pub of the Year* 2001. An excellent two-bar hostelry with a comfortable saloon and a more basic public bar. The extensive garden has children's apparatus and an outside bar in summer. The annual beer festival in July is eagerly awaited, and there is a mini-fest at Easter. No food Sun, eve meals served Thu–Sat.
Q⊛◑⊟♿P

DELVIN END

Bottle Hall
Toppesfield Road (from Sible Hedingham, take Rectory Road for 1½ miles) OS756353
✪ 5-11; 12-10.30 Sun
☎ (01787) 462405
Greene King IPA; guest beer Ⓖ
Although difficult to find, this remote rural pub is well worth discovering. It is a cosy, restored, very old former blacksmith's. The name comes from two windows which were blocked up with bottles to avoid window tax. A small but interesting range of gravity-fed beer is always available. Popular with cyclists, walkers and locals, families are also welcome. The pub offers a good menu of reasonably priced, home-cooked food in generous portions which can be eaten in the bar or restaurant. Food is served every eve and all day Sun. ♨Q♿⊛◑P

DUTON HILL

Three Horseshoes
Off B184, Thaxted Road OS606268
✪ 12-2.30; not Wed, 3 Sat, 6-11; 12-3, 7-10.30 Sun
☎ (01371) 870681
Adnams Bitter; guest beers ⒣
Cosy village local where families are welcome. Open air theatre is staged in the amphitheatre one weekend in July and an annual beer festival is held on spring bank holiday weekend. Interesting collection of breweriana and other artefacts. Splendid views over open farmland to Chelmer valley. Unpretentious pub food, it is definitely a village pub not a restaurant. A large wild pond is home to frogs and newts. Meals are served Fri–Tue. There is a millennium beacon in the garden.
♨Q♿⊛◑♿Å♣P

EARLS COLNE

Bird in Hand
Coggeshall Road (B1024 at America Road jct)
✪ 12-2, 6-11; 12-2 (closed eve) Sun
☎ (01787) 222557
Ridleys IPA, Old Bob or guest beer ⒣

Traditional, two-bar pub about 1¹/₂ miles from the town centre. It stands in delightful open countryside offering a number of footpaths; ideal for pleasant pre- or post-ale walks. This country pub is close to a former US air base, wartime pictures feature in the saloon bar; guest beers are supplied by Ridleys. Pool, darts, crib, shove-ha'penny and dominoes are played. ⚖Q❀◑⊟&♣P

ELSENHAM

Crown
The Cross (B1051)
☼ 11-2.30, 6-11; 12-2.30, 7-10.30 Sun
☎ (01279) 812827 e-mail: ian@igood.fsnet.co.uk

Crouch Vale Woodham IPA; guest beers ⊞
Deservedly popular village pub, the building dates from about 1631, and has been used as a pub since 1762. The typical Essex pargetting on the frontage is matched inside by the oak-beamed interior and the inglenook. The pub is central to much village life, particularly the local cricket club. It enjoys an established reputation for imaginative food (not served Sun eve). ⚖❀◑⊟♣P

EPPING

Forest Gate
111 Bell Common (off B1393, Ivy Chimneys Road) OS451011
☼ 10-3, 5.30-11; 12-3, 7-10.30 Sun
☎ (01992) 572312
Adnams Bitter, ⊞ **Broadside,** ⊞ **Ridleys IPA,** ⊞ **Woodforde's Wherry** ⊞
Timeless 17th-century country free house, owned and run by the same family for many years. Situated on the edge of Epping Forest, it is popular with walkers. Well-behaved dogs are welcomed. Specialising in real ale, there are no frills, juke box, music or fruit machines. Snacks are available lunchtime and eve. A renowned turkey broth is sold (Oct–May). There is a large, lawned drinking area at the front of the building. Bulmers traditional cider is sold. ⚖Q❀◑♠P

FEERING

Sun Inn
3 Feering Hill (B1024)
☼ 11-3, 6-11; 12-3, 6-10.30 Sun
☎ (01376) 570442
Beer range varies ⊞
This fine pub was formerly a Tudor mansion featuring many carved beams and two blazing log fires in the winter months. It stocks six ever-changing real ales, many from micro-breweries (frequently in excess of 20 beers in a week). Real food that comes in hearty portions is offered. The menu is imaginative and often includes unusual dishes such as kangeroo, ostrich and BOG pie in this local CAMRA *Pub of the Year* 1998. Camping is possible by prior arrangement. ⚖❀◑&▲⇄(Kelvedon) ♣♠P

FINCHINGFIELD

Red Lion
6 Church Hill (B1053)
☼ 11.30-11; 12-10.30 Sun
☎ (01371) 810400
website: www.red-lion-finchingfield.com

Ridleys IPA, Old Bob, seasonal beers ⊞
Located close to the duckpond at the centre of one of the most picturesque villages in Essex, the Red Lion lies opposite the church and Guildhall. An attractive old building on several levels, the main bar is cosy and heavily beamed, with a log fire. The airy restaurant, a later addition, may also be used when not busy by drinkers preferring a no-smoking environment. Ridleys seasonal beers are usually available. The landlord is also enthusiastic about food. A wide range of snacks and home-cooked meals is served in the bar or the restaurant. ⚖❀⋈◑♣P

FOBBING

White Lion
High Road (on B1420, follow high road from A13 Five Bells jct)
☼ 12-3, 5.30-11; 12-11 Fri & Sat; 12-10.30 Sun
☎ (01375) 673281
Greene King IPA, Old Speckled Hen; guest beers ⊞
Historic 14th-century country inn set in a quiet village location, with a warm, friendly atmosphere. There are pleasant soft furnishings, lots of horse brasses and several photographs of the village and historical events. Good home-made food with vegetarian options. On August bank holiday Sun there is an annual cricket match between the gentlemen and the players, followed by a village barbecue and disco. Fobbing is well-known for two revolts, the first in 1381 by peasants, the second was a bit later for that good old poll tax saga. ⚖Q☎❀⋈◑&▲♣♠P✕🚻

FORD STREET (ALDHAM)

Coopers Arms
Ford Street (A1124, 3 miles W of Colchester, formerly A604)
☼ 12-2.30, 5 (7 Mon, Thu & Sat)-11 Tue, Wed & Fri; 7-11; 12-3, 7-10.30 Sun
☎ (01206) 241177
Greene King IPA; Woodforde's Wherry; guest beers ⊞
Originally known as the King's Arms, this 16th-century pub offers a friendly welcome with a front bar serving up to five beers on handpump. Relax in comfortable leather sofas and armchairs before dining in the restaurant serving 'proper' food, including a good choice for vegetarians. The pub also hosts a fishing club with a local venue. Q◑P

FRYERNING

Woolpack
Mill Green Road OSTL640002
☼ 11.30-3, 6-11; 12-4, 6-10.30 Sun
☎ (01277) 352189
Adnams Bitter, Broadside; Hancock's HB; guest beer ⊞
While this small two-roomed country pub is justifiably popular for its food, it's also worth a visit for the beer. It's been a pub since 1848 and is haunted by a female ghost, who has been seen by the landlady. The guest beer changes regularly but you may well find it's from the Mighty Oak Brewery. Extensive menu of regulars and daily changing specials, the house speciality is a complete roast for four, carved at the table, available with a day's notice. Examine the toilet seats on the walls closely. ⚖Q❀◑P

FULLER STREET

Square & Compass

Turn off A137 at St Anne's Castle – second left
OSTL748161

⚙ 11.30-3, 7 (6.30 summer)-11; 12-3, 7-10.30 Sun

☎ (01245) 367477

Nethergate Suffolk County; Ridleys IPA Ⓖ

A country pub for country people, hidden away in a rural oasis between Chelmsford and Braintree. The pub has been greatly expanded in recent years, but retains its authentic character, with a vast collection of taxidermy, local agricultural tools and photographs of historical farming practices. The excellent food is all 'real', even down to the bread and condiments. Seasonal game and local produce feature heavily, and meals are available every lunchtime and eve. The pub is popular with ramblers, and on-site camping is free if you make use of the pub. A function room is available for large parties.

🏚Q⚙◖🍴🍺▲♣P

FYFIELD

Queen's Head

Queens Street (off B184)

⚙ 11-3, 6-11; 11-11 Sat; 12-3, 7-10.30 Sun

☎ (01277) 899231

Adnams Bitter, Broadside; guest beers Ⓗ

Busy, 500-year-old country pub with a beamed ceiling and wooden floor around the bar (mind the step from road entrance). The River Roding runs through the rear garden. Good food is available at lunchtime (tends to get very crowded). The three guest beers come from independent breweries. A great deal of money has been spent on the cellar without any increase in the price of the beer.

🏚⚙◖P

GRAYS

Grays Athletic FC

Bridge Road

⚙ 5 (3 Thu; 12 Fri & Sat)-11; 12-3, 7-10.30 Sun

☎ (01375) 377753

Greene King IPA; guest beers Ⓗ

The social club of the Grays Athletic Football Club admits card-carrying CAMRA members, or bearers of this *Guide*. The bar overlooks an indoor five-a-side football pitch. TV sports are shown on a large screen. There are usually two guest beers available, often of a higher strength – 5% to 7% ABV is not uncommon. Limited parking. �♣P

Theobald Arms

King's Walk

⚙ 10.30-3, 5-11; 10.30-11 Fri & Sat; 12-10.30 Sun

☎ (01375) 372253

Courage Best Bitter; guest beers Ⓗ

Traditional, family-run, two-bar pub located in an area that has been cleared for redevelopment – opposite is the recently refurbished Grays town wharf fronting on to the River Thames. Three constantly changing guest beers are available. The pub has several darts teams and the public bar features an unusual revolving, round pool table. There are outdoor drinking areas for both the public and saloon bars. An annual beer festival is held in June with one of the

former stables at the rear converted into a bar. Excellent value food is served weekday lunchtimes. ⚙◖🍺&�♣P

GREAT CLACTON

Plough

1 North Road (near B1032)

⚙ 11-11; 12-10.30 Sun

☎ (01255) 429998

Greene King IPA; Tetley Bitter; guest beers Ⓗ

This pub and the local church must be the oldest buildings in this village on the outskirts of Clacton. The two bars cater for two different types of customer. Youngsters congregate in the larger of the two bars, particularly at weekends when local bands perform. The smaller bar was once two rooms and caters for the more garrulous members of the community. Guest beers are making a welcome reappearance. How refreshing to hear that every good pub should have a mild! Parking available in the Queen's Head car park.

🏚⚙♣P

GREAT DUNMOW ❖

Boar's Head

37 High Street

⚙ 11-11; 12-10.30 Sun

☎ (01371) 873630

Brakspear Bitter; Marston's Pedigree; Young's Bitter Ⓗ

Fine, town-centre traditional pub on the corner of the entrance to the busy main public car park. Low ceilings, beams, pictures of old Dunmow and a tropical fish tank feature in this 17th-century pub. It is a timber-framed, lathe and plaster building, useful as it bends when local delivery lorries 'bump it' while negotiating the tight corner! Lively atmosphere eves and weekends, quieter at lunchtimes. Mainly a locals' pub but some passing trade and a stop-off for commuters. There is a temperature-controlled cellar and the house cigarette lighters bear the motto 'a little pub with a big atmosphere'.

⚙◖♣P

GREAT TEY

Chequers

The Street (1½ miles N of A120)

⚙ 11.30-3, 6.30-11; 12-4, 7-10.30 Sun

☎ (01206) 210814

Greene King XX Mild, IPA, Abbot; guest beers Ⓗ

16th-century beamed pub offers a warm welcome in the heart of the village. Popular with locals, the range of beers includes a regular mild and guest beers. The large restaurant offers a good choice of food, or relax in the bar and play pub games by the fire. ⚙◖🍺♣P✂●

GREAT YELDHAM

Waggon & Horses

High Street (A1017)

⚙ 11-11; 12-10.30 Sun

☎ (01787) 237936

website: www.waggonandhorses.net

Greene King IPA, Abbot; guest beer Ⓗ

16th-century inn, standing on the main road in the centre of the village. Well-kept house ales are accompanied by guest beers from several brewers from the eastern region, including nearby Nethergate. A popular village pub serving a range of traditional bar food, all day at weekends. B&B is available in a newly-built annexe. You can be sure of a friendly welcome. Pub games such as shove-ha'penny are played. ❀❀◖◗⬧♣P

White Hart
Poole Street (A1017)
🕑 11-3, 6-11; 12-3, 7-10.30 Sun
☎ (01787) 237250 e-mail: wjdicken@hotmail.com
Adnams Bitter; guest beers Ⓗ
Imposing coaching inn on the edge of the village by a small bridge, built in 1505.

Known for many years for excellent cuisine, it is now building a reputation for its range of beers. Guest ales come from a number of local breweries as well as from around the country and are always changing. Interesting selection of bottled beers also offered. Savour a drink in front of the open log fire, or on the patio overlooking the river and extensive gardens. The restaurant serves a full *à la carte* menu, while traditional home-cooked bar meals are served every day.
🚪Q❀❀◖◗P

HALSTEAD

Dog Inn
37 Hedingham Road (A1124)
🕑 11-3 (not Mon), 5-11; 12-4, 7-10.30 Sun
☎ (01787) 477774
Adnams Bitter; Mauldons Moletrap; guest beers Ⓗ
Conversation rules in this popular two-bar pub close to Halstead's busy high street. Although well-used by locals you will not feel out of place here. Join in the conversation or just sit and enjoy the friendly banter. The comfortable bar is beamed with seating arranged around tables. Guest ales usually come from local independent brewers. Meals are served weekdays only. Food and en-suite accommodation are both reasonably priced. Visitors from Colchester can make use of the late night bus service that runs Mon–Sat. Take care leaving the car park as the exit is on a blind bend.
🚪❀❀◖◗♣P

HARWICH

Hanover Inn
65 Church Street
🕑 10.30-2.30, 6.30-11; 12-4, 7-10.30 Sun
☎ (01255) 502927
website: www.hanover-inn-harwich.co.uk
Greene King IPA; Tolly Cobbold Mild, Old Strong; guest beer Ⓗ
Harwich once claimed that it had more pubs per square mile than any other town. The Hanover is now one of only a handful but offers a warm, local welcome with a cosy and (genuinely) nautically-themed front bar. Strong links with Tolly Cobbold are on display and the present owners provide a welcome outlet for the Suffolk brewer. Tolly Mild is available and the Old Strong (seasonal) is always excellent. An ideal base to explore the area, the pub offers accommodation as well as meeting and conference facilities.
🚪🛏≠ (Town) ♣

HATFIELD BROAD OAK

Cock Inn
High Street (B183) OS547166
🕑 12-3, 6-11; 12-3, 7-10.30 Sun
☎ (01279) 718306
Adnams Bitter; Fuller's London Pride; guest beers Ⓗ
An arched gateway leads to this interesting bare-boarded pub in a pretty, rural village. It has one large main bar with a smaller bar attached. Several other rooms are available for meetings by prior arrangement. Bar billiards is played in the main bar. In addition to the regular beers, at least one guest is normally sold, selected from a small independent brewery. The food is of a high standard and includes many unusual choices (no food Sun eve). Customers here represent the wide cross-section of village life. 🚪Q❀◖◗♣P

HERONGATE

Green Man
11 Cricketers Lane (near A128)
🕑 11-11; 12-10.30 Sun
☎ (01277) 810292
Draught Bass; Greene King IPA; Ind Coope Burton Ale; Tetley Bitter; Young's Bitter; Ⓗ **guest beers** Ⓖ
The Green Man is located in a small lane just off the A128. A comfortable main bar area has several small, intimate rooms set back. There are varying guest beers served straight from the cask behind the bar (cooling jackets are used). Adnams Bitter is another regular beer stocked. Occasional beer festivals are hosted in the back room. This local CAMRA *Pub of the Year* 1999 has a children's play area in the garden. Games are available on request and regular quizzes held. 🚪Q⬧❀◖◗⬧✦●

HERONGATE TYE

Old Dog Inn
Billericay Road (1 mile E of A128) OS641910
🕑 11-2.30, 6-11; 12-3, 7-10.30 Sun
☎ (01277) 810337
Greene King Abbot; Ⓖ **Mighty Oak Burntwood; Ridleys IPA;** Ⓗ **guest beers** Ⓖ
Friendly country local with low beams, horse brasses and pump clips adorning the ceiling. Popular for its large selection of real ales, served straight from the cask (cooling jackets are used); beers from independent and micro-breweries include Mauldons and Mighty Oak. The attractive new restaurant serves home-cooked food. ❀◖◗♣●P

HIGH ONGAR

Foresters Arms
The Street (near A414)
🕑 11 (5 Mon)-11; 12-10.30 Sun
☎ (01277) 363626
Adnams Bitter, Broadside; Greene King IPA; guest beer Ⓗ
Small pub with half the area given over to food. Fresh fish is served Thu–Sat. No food served on Mon. There are different lunch and eve menus but a limited vegetarian selection. Eve meals finish at 8.30pm. This family-fun local has a friendly landlord and olde-worlde decor. Mainly hanging horsebrass-style decorations and signs of a mishmash of repairs and renovations give the place a lived-in, homely feel. ❀◖◗▲P●

HIGH RODING

Black Lion
3 The High Street (B184, S of Great Dunmow)
✪ 12-3, 6-11; 12-11 Sat; 12-10.30 Sun
☎ (01371) 872847 website: www.theblacklioninn.co.uk
Ridleys IPA, ESX, Ⓗ Rumpus; guest beer Ⓖ

Built some time in the mid-1400s, this beautiful, timber-framed building is one of the three oldest pubs in Essex. There is a separate dining room for up to 24 people, available for private functions. The food specialises in fish delivered daily from Norfolk. After the death of the previous landlord (who was in the pub for over 20 years) it's nice to see the pub still in business, unlike the trend for closing or converting country pubs into houses.
⚲Q⊃❀⋈◑⊟♣P

HORNDON-ON-THE-HILL ❀

Swan
121 High Road
✪ 11-3 (4.30 Sat); 12-4.30, 7-10.30 Sun
☎ (01375) 640617
Adnams Bitter; guest beers Ⓗ

This welcoming 400-year-old coaching inn, looks surprisingly fresh and lively. There are two separate bars connected at the front and back of the pub. Hops hang from the exposed beams, some sporting memorabilia appears on the walls and the bar top is covered with pre-decimal coins. A separate no-smoking area is a bonus. Excellent live folk music on a Sun eve (from 8.30pm) where, if you feel like getting up and singing, you are more than welcome.
⚲Q❀◑⊟♿▲♣P⊬

LAMARSH

Lamarsh Lion
Bures Road (1½ miles NW of Bures) OS892355
✪ 11-3, 6-11; 12-3, 7-10.30 Sun
☎ (01787) 227918
Beer range varies Ⓗ

16th-century free house with a wealth of beams and stunning views across the Stour Valley. Friendly locals mix with cyclists and walkers – the Stour Valley and St Edmund Way footpaths conveniently pass the door. Three beers change regularly with a Nethergate beer often available. Some of the furnishings came from an old church and the unusual bar is worthy of an after inspection. Reasonably priced home-made food can be enjoyed in a separate restaurant area (not served Sun eve unless booked). En-suite accommodation provides an ideal base for exploring the attractive towns and villages nearby. ⚲⚭⋈◑ ♣P

LANGLEY LOWER GREEN

Bull
Turn off B1038 at Clavering
✪ 12-2.30, 6-11; 12-3, 7-10.30 Sun
☎ (01279) 777307
Greene King IPA, Old Speckled Hen Ⓗ

Lovely Victorian village local which has little passing trade. Welcoming pub with pool table in the public bar. Pub games such as penny-in-the-hole are played here. There is no menu but food can be arranged in advance. In winter home-made soup is available. This pub is very isolated, set in

beautiful countryside and can be reached down small minor roads.
⚲Q❀⋈⊟♣P

LEIGH-ON-SEA ❀

Broker
213-217 Leigh Road
✪ 11-3, 6 (5.30 Fri & Sat)-11; 12-4, 7-10.30 Sun
☎ (01702) 471932
website: www.brokerfreehouse.co.uk
Shepherd Neame Spitfire; Tolly Cobbold Original; guest beers Ⓗ

Friendly, family-run free house which has featured in this *Guide* since it opened in 1993. Two ever-changing guest beers are offered in addition to the two regular ales. It is a comfortable pub with a small garden at the rear. Children are welcome until 7.30pm in a sectioned-off, no-smoking area of the bar. Enjoy the entertainment on Sun eve, either live music or a quiz. This community local organises many charity fundraising events and has a football team, golf society, crib league and investment club. Bar and restaurant meals are available lunchtimes (Mon–Sat) and eves (Thu-Sat).
❀◑⇌(Chalkwell)

Elms
1060 London Road (A13)
✪ 10-11; 12-10.30 Sun
☎ (01702) 474687
Courage Best Bitter; Directors; Shepherd Neame Spitfire; Theakston Best Bitter; guest beers Ⓗ

Large, busy roadhouse pub on the A13. The name originates from the farmhouse which previously occupied the site. The pub had been closed for a time, but was rescued by Wetherspoon's. The refurbishment has created a large, comfortable pub with many alcoves providing seating. There is a large garden to the front with a deep hedge to reduce the noise from the busy road. The pub has many interesting photographs and pictures recalling past local inhabitants, the history of Leigh and of the old town. Food is available 11–10 (Mon–Sat) and 12–9.30 (Sun). Q❀◑P⊬●

LITTLE BADDOW

Rodney
North Hill (off A414 into Little Baddow past Post Office on left) OS778080
✪ 11.30-2.30 (3 Sat), 6-11; 12-10.30 Sun
☎ (01245) 222385
Greene King IPA, Old Speckled Hen; guest beer Ⓗ

Built in 1650 as a farmhouse, this well-maintained pub has been the site of a brewery, baker's and a grocer's shop as well as trading since the early 1800s as the Rodney. It takes its name from an inn further up the hill. This two-roomed, beamed pub with its numerous brasses, posters and seafaring prints has two regular ales and a frequently-changing guest beer. The extensive menu is all home-made, dining is in a compact and comfortable environment. Q❀◑⊟▲♣P

LITTLE BRAXTED

Green Man
Kelvedon Road (1½ miles SE of village)
OS849130

◑ 11-3, 6-11; 12-3, 7-10.30 Sun
☎ (01621) 891659
Ridleys IPA, ESX, Old Bob Ⓗ
This delightful pub offers a mixture of cosy, beamed saloon bar, basic public bar and secluded garden – take your pick! A very attractive setting, especially in spring. The food is good value with an extensive menu; the pub is renowned for the size of the sandwiches. Note the interesting collection of model vehicles in the public bar, the unusual handpumps in the saloon bar and collection of wooden hop shovels. Has it got a ghost?
ᴁQ❀◑▣♣P

LITTLE OAKLEY

Olde Cherry Tree
Clacton Road
◑ 11-2.30, 5-11; 12-3, 7-10.30 Sun
☎ (01255) 880333 website: www.cherrytreepub.com
Adnams Bitter, Broadside; Fuller's London Pride; Wells Eagle; guest beers Ⓗ
This historic pub once fronted a large cherry orchard and now stands on the picturesque Harwich to Clacton road. Sporting four regular real ales plus a constantly changing guest, the pub has become a haven for those who enjoy the excellent beer and superb home-cooked food. The good-sized main bar is separated from the dining area by the award-winning open fire. The pub has won a host of awards including local CAMRA *Pub of the Year* for the past two years. A beer festival and hog roast is a regular feature in June.
ᴁ❀◑♣PⒻ●

LITTLE TOTHAM

Swan
School Road (2 miles SE of B1022)
◑ 11-11; 12-10.30 Sun
☎ (01621) 892689
website: www.theswanpublichouse.co.uk
Adnams Bitter; Crouch Vale Brewers Gold; Iceni Fine Soft Day; Mighty Oak IPA; guest beers Ⓖ
Friendly, 16th-century pub near the village green with a constantly changing range of guest beers on gravity, plus a cider and perry. There are authentic beams and a pleasant patio, lounge bar and separate, traditional public bar with bar billiards. The restaurant serves a good range of home-

cooked traditional English meat and seafood dishes. A diary of pub development and village activities since 1996 is available in bar. Hosts a beer festival in June (9th–17th). Essex CAMRA *Pub of the Year* 1999 and 2000. No food Sun night or Mon. Muddy boots and dogs welcome. Free soft drinks for drivers bringing in three drinkers. Award-winning website.
ᴁ❀◑▣♣▲♣Pⓣ

LITTLE WALDEN

Crown
On B1052, 2 miles NE Saffron Walden
◑ 11.30-2.30, 6-11; 12-10.30 Sun
☎ (01799) 522475
City of Cambridge Boathouse Bitter, Hobson's Choice; Greene King Abbot; guest beers Ⓖ
Delightful, 18th-century beamed country pub featuring a large inglenook and offering an extensive menu. Racked cask stillage is used for dispensing an excellent selection of real ales. There is a large car park, a pleasant garden and patio. Enjoy many interesting walks in the area. This quiet country hamlet pub attracts a lot of local characters and business folk from Saffron Walden. It is used for local club meetings and offers a welcoming atmosphere. ᴁQ❥❀◑♣P

MARGARETTING TYE

White Hart
Swan Lane (between Stock, Galleywood and Margaretting)
◑ 11.30-3, 6-11; 12-10.30 Sun
☎ (01277) 840478 website: www.thewhitehart.uk.com
Adnams Bitter, Broadside; Mighty Oak IPA; Ⓗ **Ridleys Old Bob; guest beers** Ⓗ/Ⓖ
This single bar with beamed interior is set amid farmland close to central Chelmsford. It is sometimes referred to as Tigers Islands after the 19th-century railway workers' bare-knuckle fights. It is a genuine free house offering regular beers plus a vigorous guest beer policy. The restaurant in the conservatory serves home-made daily specials plus an extensive bar snack menu. The beer garden with large children's play area and pets corner make it a popular place for families. Darts and cribbage teams play regularly. The pub's four-day beer festival takes place in a marquee in mid-June.
ᴁ❥❀◑よ♣♣P⚥

INN BRIEF

LITTLE BENTLEY
Bricklayers Arms
Rectory Road
12-3, 6.30-11; 12-4, 7-10.30 Sun
Greene King IPA, Ruddles Best Ⓗ
Typical village green pub, full of character. There are two bars and the restaurant serves excellent food.

NORTH END
Butcher's Arms
Dunmow Road
12-3, 6-11; 11-11 Sat; 12-10.30 Sun
Ridleys IPA, ESX, Old Bob, seasonal beer Ⓗ
500-year-old country pub offering traditional food. The award-winning garden hosts family fundays on bank holidays.

NORTH FAMBRIDGE
Ferry Boat Inn
Ferry Road
12 (11 Sat & summer)-3, 7 (6.30 Sat & summer)-11; 12-4, 7-10.30 (12-10.30 summer) Sun
Shepherd Neame Master Brew Bitter, Spitfire Ⓗ
An attractive riverside pub with flagstone floor in the bar. Very popular in the summer.

RIDGEWELL
White Horse
Mill Road
11-3, 6-11; 12-3, 7-10.30 Sun
Adnams Bitter; Ridleys Bitter, Old Bob; guest beer Ⓗ
Large, low-ceilinged 17th-century village local. Large restaurant and good range of bar snacks.

SAFFRON WALDEN
Axe
60 Ashdon Road
12-2.30, 6-11; 12-10.30 Sun
Beer range varies Ⓗ
Popular, town local with a wealth of Victoriana and military memorabilia. Award-winning garden and boules competitions. *Cask Marque* accredited.

King's Arms
Market Hill
11-4, 5-11; 11-11 Fri & Sat; 12-5, 7-10.30 Sun
Draught Bass; Greene King IPA Ⓗ
16th-century pub near market square called the Plough, renamed King's Arms at restoration of monarchy. Log fires create a cosy atmosphere.

MILL END GREEN

Green Man

1 mile E of B184, near Great Dunmow OS619260
☼ 12-3, 7 (6 summer)-11; 12-11 Sat; 12-5,
7-10.30 Sun
☎ (01371) 870286

Adnams Bitter; Greene King IPA; Ridleys IPA Ⓗ
Very pleasant, 15th-century rural pub on a
quiet country road with good views over
open farmland. The original thatched roof
was destroyed by fire in 1979 and
subsequently replaced with a tiled roof. The
interior features oak studwork and low
beams; the cosy bar has padded settles. The
main bar, also with settle seating, adjoins
the dining area. The central open fireplace
is controlled by an adjustable smoke hood.
Enjoy the excellent large garden which has
a pond (mesh-covered) and its own tennis
court. The two chefs are the licensees and
also keep the cellar in good order. Good
mixtures of traditional and imaginative
meals, all home-prepared using fresh
produce. ▲✿✿✍◖P

MILL GREEN

Viper

Mill Green Road OS641018
☼ 12-3, 6-11; 12-3, 7-10.30 Sun
☎ (01277) 352010

Ridleys IPA; guest beers Ⓗ/Ⓖ
The only Viper in the country, this
unspoilt, three-roomed pub is set in
woodland. Popular with walkers, it has a
wood-panelled public bar and snug and a
comfortable lounge. Three or four guest
beers are available, usually from micro-
breweries and often featuring a beer from
the local Mighty Oak Brewery. Good pub
lunches including real ale sausages but the
home-made chilli and pickled eggs can be
enjoyed anytime. The landlord is the third

generation of the family to run the pub.
The Viper was voted local CAMRA *Pub of the
Year* 1997, 1998 and 1999.
▲Q✿◖✇♣●P

MOLE HILL GREEN

Three Horseshoes

Off Takeley-Elsenham road, 1 mile from Stansted Airport)
☼ 11-11; 12-10.30 Sun
☎ (01279) 870313

Draught Bass; Greene King IPA Ⓗ
If you want thatch, low beams and an
inglenook or just good beer and food you
will find them all at this 500-year-old,
original drovers' pub. The old barn hosts
impromptu music jam sessions summer
weekends. It is a good starting point for
local walks and scenic tour, taking in
Hatfield Forest and five *Guide* pubs. Large
collection of historic aircraft plates reflects
its proximity to Stansted Airport. Varied
and imaginative menu always with
vegetarian options. Booking essential for
Sun lunch. Families welcome if dining or in
outdoor seated garden area.
✿◖▲P

NORTH SHOEBURY

Angel Inn

Parsons Corner
☼ 11-3, 5.30-11; 12-3, 7-10.30 Sun
☎ (01702) 589600

Greene King IPA, Abbot; guest beers Ⓗ
First opened in 1996, this is a genuine free
house with frequent changes of guest beers
(usually four per week). No sparklers are
used. The building is a listed timber
structure dating from c1650, it has been
completely restored by the current
proprietor. The exterior has a part-thatched
roof and the interior features a carved bar
depicting angels, unpainted oak timbers

INN BRIEF

SAFFRON WALDEN
Temeraire
55 High Street
11-11; 12-10.30 Sun
**Courage Directors; Greene King IPA;
Shepherd Neame Spitfire; Theakston Best
Bitter; guest beers** Ⓗ
A pub for the younger generation
in eve but at lunchtime frequented
by every age group. Standard
Wetherspoon's fare. Large garden.

SOUTH OCKENDON
Moon under Water
Broxburn Drive
11-11; 12-10.30 Sun
**Courage Directors; Shepherd Neame
Spitfire; Theakston Best Bitter; guest
beers** Ⓗ
Restored Wetherspoon's with a
brightly coloured interior,
displaying modern art. Possibly the
cheapest pub in Essex for food and
drink. *Cask Marque* accredited.

STANSTED MOUNTFITCHET
Queen's Head
3 Lower Street
11-3, 5.30-11; 11-3, 7-11 Sat;
12-3, 7-10.30 Sun
**Draught Bass; Flowers IPA; Tolly Cobbold
Original; guest beer** Ⓗ
Comfortable, village-centre pub.
Eclectic collection of brass and old
agricultural implements adorn the
walls. No food Sun.

STEEPLE
Star Inn
The Street
12-2.30, 6-11;
12-3, 7-10.30 Sun
Nethergate IPA; guest beers Ⓗ
Quiet, friendly, comfortable, family
pub, with good, nourishing food.
Facilities for caravans/camping
available in rear field.

STISTED
Dolphin
Coggeshall Road
11-3, 6-11;
12-3, 7-10.30 Sun
Ridleys IPA, ESX Ⓖ
Picturesque, quiet, two-bar 15th-
century country pub with exposed
beams and mansard roof. No meals
Tue or Sun eves.

WARLEY
Brave Nelson
138 Woodman Road
12-3, 5.30-11; 12-11 Sat; 12-3.30,
7-10.30 Sun
**Greene King IPA; Nethergate Suffolk
County; guest beers** Ⓗ
Friendly and comfortable pub with
a nautical theme. Rare local outlet
for Nethergate. Two regularly
changing guest beers stocked.

WRITTLE
Wheatsheaf
70 The Green
11-3, 5.30-11; 11-11 Sat;
12-10.30 Sun
**Greene King IPA, Abbot;
Mighty Oak Burntwood; guest beer**
(occasional) Ⓗ
Welcoming, small local converted
from a pair of cottages comprising
a public bar and a cosy lounge. No
food served.

Check it out

**Pubs in the Good Beer
Guide may change
ownership and the
facilities listed could
alter. If a visit to a pub
in the guide involves a
lengthy journey, it is
advisable to check
before leaving that full
meals, family facilities,
accommodation or
camping sites are still
available.**

and genuine flagstones. Wheelchair access is via the rear french doors from the car park into the no-smoking area and bar (note that there are steps down from the bar to the other drinking area). The no-smoking area is reserved for diners at Sun lunch. Q☺◑&P✓

ORSETT

Foxhound
18 High Road
☺ 11-3.30, 6-11; 11-11 Sat; 12-3.30, 7-10.30 Sun
☎ (01375) 891295
Courage Best Bitter; Crouch Vale IPA; Webster's Yorkshire Bitter; guest beers Ⓗ

A pub that has retained its traditions and individuality over the years. The saloon bar has a village atmosphere with many hunting artefacts including a striking carpet featuring foxhound heads. The basic public bar is comfortable and has character. There is a separate eating place called the Fox's Den. Meals are served there every lunchtime, including Sun for traditional roast dinners and Sat eve. Other times are by arrangement only. Once a month there is a lively quiz and two or three times a year an even livelier auction. All funds raised go to the Guide Dogs for the Blind.
ⅢQ☺◑&♣P

PAGLESHAM

Punchbowl
Church End (off A127, follow signs to Rochford, Ashingdon, Canewdon, Paglesham then Church End)
☺ 11.30-3, 6.30-11; 12-3, 7-10.30 Sun
☎ (01702) 258376
Adnams Bitter; guest beers Ⓗ

Three-storey, white, weatherboarded 16th-century pub situated in a quiet, one-street village. It was originally a sailmaker's. The single bar has a low-beamed ceiling, decorative brassware and early pictures. There are two regular bitters – one, is usually a Ridleys' beer – plus two changing guest beers. The small restaurant has a regular, competitively-priced menu plus a changing blackboard. An OAP menu is offered. Plenty of outdoor drinking space with tables at the front of the pub, a pleasant suntrap and an attractive garden at the rear with a children's play area and more tables. Ample car parking at side and rear of pub. ☺◑P

PEBMARSH

King's Head
The Street (1½ miles E of A131)
☺ 12-3, 6-11 (closed Mon); 12-3, 7-10.30 Sun
☎ (01787) 269306
Greene King IPA; guest beers Ⓗ

This Grade II listed building dates back to 1450. It is situated in the picturesque village of Pebmarsh. Despite its rural location (which makes it difficult to find) the pub serves the local community and CAMRA members far and wide; confirmed by the fact that 500 guest beers have been served in 20 months. The interior is divided into three areas – traditional bar, games area and restaurant. Fireworks and festivities are organised in July and a beer festival in October.
ⅢQ☺◑♣P

PURLEIGH

Bell
The Street (off B1010, next to church on top of hill)
☺ 11 3, 6-11; 12-3, 7-10.30 Sun
☎ (01621) 828348
Adnams Bitter; Benskins Bitter; Greene King IPA; guest beer Ⓗ

Attractive old pub extensively refurbished in the 16th century. Set in a small conservation area with the church and original village buildings, on top of a hill overlooking the Blackwater estuary. Good beer and food can be quietly enjoyed in the bar (no children or music) or in warm weather the garden is ideal with its fine views. A popular watering-hole with walkers as it is situated on St Peter's Way and other circular walks. Well-behaved dogs and their owners are always welcome in this friendly, traditional pub. ⅢQ☺◑♣P

RADWINTER

Plough
Sampford Road (B1053/B1054 jct)
☺ 11.30-4.30, 6.30-11; 12-4, 7-10.30 Sun
☎ (01799) 599222
Greene King IPA; guest beers Ⓗ

Atmospheric Grade II listed building on country crossroads near the edge of the village. An attractive, large garden area at the rear boasts a vine-covered patio. The pub serves a large selection of wholesome food lunchtime and eve. Quiet, relaxing atmosphere. ⅢQ☺≈◑P

RAMSDEN BELLHOUSE

Fox & Hounds
Church Road
☺ 11.30-11, 12-10.30 Sun
☎ (01268) 710286
Greene King IPA, Ruddles County; guest beers Ⓗ

Well-supported village pub with a good range of two to four changing guest beers. There is a large garden which includes a pets corner and children's play area. The pub hosts a popular beer festival in July that welcomes those with families and provides a bouncy castle for the children. There is a separate dining area and meals are served from 12–2.30 and 6.30–9.30 and include a Sun carvery. There are occasional theme nights in the restaurant. Catering available for both indoor and outdoor functions. Weather permitting, barbecues are held in summer. ☺◑P

RAMSDEN HEATH

Nag's Head
50 Heath Road
☺ 11.30-11, 12-10.30 Sun
☎ (01268) 711875
Ridleys IPA, ESX, Rumpus, Old Bob, seasonal beers Ⓖ

Popular village pub with a comfortable, traditional interior. Beers are served on gravity from a temperature-controlled room with a viewing area and include all Ridleys' regulars plus seasonal and event beers; up to seven can be available at one time. For those who want something stronger, there is a selection of over 100 whiskies. The food is all home-made on the premises. Live jazz bands play every other Thu and Mon is quiz night. The pub has won brewery awards for being the *Best-Dressed Pub*, as well as the 'Throne Room' challenge. Dogs welcome. ❀◖▶♣P

RICKLING GREEN

Cricketers Arms
1/2 mile W of B1383 OS511298
🕓 11-11; 12-10.30 Sun
☎ (01799) 543210
website: www.cricketers.demon.co.uk
Flowers IPA; Fuller's ESB; Wadworth 6X Ⓖ
Cricket dominates this village inn as it is right next to the green. Celebrity cricket is played here regularly and in 1882 the highest score achieved in a single innings on a single day (920 runs) was witnessed. It is close to Stansted Airport and a convenient overnight stop for holiday travellers (seven en-suite guest rooms available). Dispense from a cellar behind the bar is gravity through fake barrel ends. A large selection of bottled beers is on show here too.
🏛Q⛵❀⇔◖▶P

ROCHFORD

Golden Lion
35 North Street
(N of Market Sq)
🕓 11-11; 12-10.30 Sun
☎ (01702) 545487
Fuller's London Pride; Greene King Abbot; guest beers Ⓗ
Popular local in historic village conservation area; a well-known, committed real ale free house. A former Taylor Walker, Grade II listed, 300-year-old pub, this traditional Essex weatherboarded building with lead-light windows and partitions was once called the Red Lion. A 1940s etching shows the present owner, not the licensee, now in her nineties, serving behind a largely unspoilt bar, with many artefacts still on display. Up to four guest ales always feature a mild, porter or dark beer. There is adequate free street parking outside this former local CAMRA *Pub of the Year*. Children are welcome in the family room until 8pm.
⛵❀⇔♣●

ROWHEDGE

Walnut Tree
Fingringhoe Road
(1 mile E of B1025) OS021216
🕓 8.30 (8 Thu, 7.30 Fri)-11; 12-3, 7-11 Sat; closed Mon & Wed; 12-3, 7.30-10.30 Sun
☎ (01206) 728149
Beer range varies Ⓗ
No keg-dispensing equipment whatsoever in this pub, making it unique in Essex. Five handpumps sit centre stage, serving ales from all micros, especially Mighty Oak and Humpty Dumpty. These fuel the lively and friendly atmosphere. The pub is situated on the outskirts of Colchester and is a short bus ride from the train stations. Enjoy the large beer garden with Nutty, the one-horned goat, and the chickens whose eggs can be sampled in various meals on the menu. Eve meals served daily and lunchtime food at weekends. Dogs and their well-behaved owners are always made welcome.
🏛◖▶👍♣P

SAFFRON WALDEN ❖

Old English Gentleman
11 Gold Street (near B184 and B1052)
🕓 11 (10 Tue & Sat)-11; 12-10.30 Sun
☎ (01799) 523595 website: www.gourmet-guide.com
Adnams Bitter; Greene King IPA; guest beers Ⓗ
18th-century, town-centre pub with log fires and a welcoming atmosphere. There is a selection of regularly changing guest beers. A new dining area has been added and an extensive menu is prepared by a trained chef. The special menu changes daily. Market days are Tue and Sat. Pleasant patio area for outdoor drinking. 🏛❀♣♣

SOUTHEND-ON-SEA

Cork & Cheese Ale House
10 Talza Way, Victoria Plaza (below Victoria Plaza shopping centre, opp. Wilkinsons)
🕓 11-11; closed Sun & bank holiday Mons
☎ (01702) 616914
Nethergate IPA; guest beers Ⓗ
This free house is a veritable oasis nestling in the basement of the concrete monstrosity that is Victoria Plaza shopping centre. Renowned for the ever-changing range of guest ales from independent and craft brewers, 'new brews' are a speciality. A total of over 1800 different cask ales have been stocked since 1992. Good value all round, but especially for the only permanent real ale and cask cider. The bar is bedecked with the trophies of the many beers that have been enjoyed there, while posters and pictures cover every inch of wall. Local CAMRA *Pub of the Year* four times since 1995. Note the large, unique Crouch Vale Brewery sign which erroneously gives the address as Southend. The restaurant upstairs is available for weekday lunches only.
❀◖⇌(Victoria/Central) ♣●P

SOUTHMINSTER

Station Arms
39 Station Road (near B1020/B1021 jct)
🕓 11-2.30, 6 (5.30 Thu & Fri)-11; 12-11 Sat; 12-4, 7-10.30 Sun
☎ (01621) 772225
Adnams Bitter; Crouch Vale Brewers Gold; guest beers Ⓗ
Unpretentious, friendly, weatherboarded pub that is well-known for the quality of its ever-changing range of beers that feature micro-breweries heavily. Annual beer festivals are held on the May and August bank holidays and in July, to coincide with the local flower show. Being so close to the railway station makes this former CAMRA East Anglian *Pub of the Year*, and current local *Pub of the Year* 2001 a 'must' for any serious beer lovers. Blues nights held on the third Sat of each month. Eve meals are served Thu–Sat. There is a patio area and covered barn. Weston's Old Rosie cider is stocked. 🏛Q❀◖⇌♣●

STANSTED MOUNTFITCHET ❖

Rose & Crown
31 Bentfield Green (1/2 mile W of B1383)
🕓 11-3.30, 6-11; 12-3.30, 7-10.30 Sun
☎ (01279) 812107
Adnams Bitter; Fuller's London Pride Ⓗ
Typical Victorian rural pub near the

duckpond on the edge of a small hamlet, now expanded and part of Stansted Mountfitchet village. The pub is an efficiently run free house, pristinely maintained by the landlady owner. It has been modernised to provide one large bar but still has the atmosphere of a village local. The landlady, who seems to know every customer's name and idiosyncrasies, makes everyone welcome, and the pub is well-used by the local community. Food is simple, but reliably excellent and very good value (not served Sun eve). ✿◖▶♣P

STAPLEFORD TAWNEY

Moletrap

Tawney Common (from Epping, down Stonards Hill, left at Fiddlers Hamlet, first left to Ongar and Toot Hill, second right Tawney Common, pub ½ mile on right) OSTL501014

✿ 12 (11.30 summer)-3; 6.30 (6 summer)-11; 12-4, 6-10.30 Sun

☎ (01992) 522394

Beer range varies Ⓗ

The Moletrap lies in a 'bermuda triangle' between Ongar, Epping and Stapleford Abbotts. It is difficult to find but well worth the effort for the welcome provided. It owes its unusual name to Joseph Treader who, in the early 1900s, designed a very successful moletrap. He invested his wealth in the pub and named it after his invention. A popular venue, especially at weekends, for walkers and cyclists (located on the Three Forests Way). Despite its popularity the Moletrap, a former CAMRA *Pub of the Year*, retains its traditional pub values and provides quality beer in convivial surroundings. No food served Sun eve. ♨Q✿◖▶P

STEBBING

White Hart

High Street (2 miles N of A120 Dunmow to Braintree road)

✿ 11-3, 5-11; 11-11 Sat; 12-10.30 Sun

☎ (01371) 856383

Greene King IPA; guest beer Ⓗ

15th-century beamed pub with a large open fire. A friendly village local which caters for all, including groups from indoor bowling, badminton and cricket clubs. Admire the various collections of china, chamber pots, cigarette cards and other knick-knacks. There is an old red post box in the interior bar wall. Good value, no frills food available daily (only huffers, sandwiches and toasties served on Mon). Live music Sun afternoons and occasional Sat eves. Internet PC available for use. Pleasant patio area.

♨Q✿◖▶♣P

STOCK

Hoop

21 High Street (B1007)

✿ 11-11; 12-10.30 Sun

☎ (01277) 841137

Adnams Bitter, Broadside; guest beers Ⓗ/Ⓖ

Traditional, attractive 14th-century weatherboarded pub in pretty village. The interior is comfortable with beams and coal-effect fires in each bar. There are up to eight beers, some on gravity dispense, including local beers as well as some rarities. A

changing cider is available. A beer festival is organised at the end of May. There is a pleasant garden with a heated seating area and bar. Barbecues are held during the summer. The food is all home made on the premises, even the ice cream. Darts are played in the public bar and the local village football team is supported.

Q✿◖▶♣✿

STOW MARIES

Prince of Wales

Woodham Road (2 miles from S Woodham Ferrers, off B1012) OS830003

✿ 11-11; 12-10.30 Sun

☎ (01621) 828971

Beer range varies Ⓗ

Popular village pub, in an attractive 17th century building, it has some unusual and interesting decoration. A good all-year-round pub with cosy fires in the winter and a pleasant beer garden in the summer (which is used for barbecues). The beer choice is excellent and includes a wide selection of Belgian beers. The ales change weekly and are served by friendly, knowledgeable staff. Food is varied and good value, authentic Victorian ovens are used on theme nights in winter (Thu is speciality pizza night). Live music and beer festivals take place during the year.

♨Q☎✿Ⓔ▶P

TENDRING

Cherry Tree Inn

Crow Lane (B1035)

✿ 11-3, 6-11; 12-7 Sun

☎ (01255) 830340

Adnams Bitter; Greene King IPA, Abbot; guest beers Ⓗ

For the last couple of centuries the Cherry Tree has stood at the crossroads facing the church in Tendring. Today the village church is floodlit. Although the pub cannot stage live music on Mon nights, the regulars are entertained by the church bells. After practice the campanologists retire to the pub for refreshment. The quality of the food served here is renowned throughout Tendring. The menu is changed frequently and is based on fresh ingredients. The abbot would approve! ♨✿◖▶P

THAXTED

Star

Mill End (B184)

✿ 11-11; 12-10.30 Sun

☎ (01371) 830368 e-mail: lol@starpub.freeserve.uk

Adnams Bitter; Broadside; Fuller's London Pride; Marston's Pedigree Ⓗ

Popular with locals and visitors alike, originally separate rooms but now open plan. Exposed beams and a vast open fire have been retained. Good value food is served lunchtime and eve. The pub is one of the hosts for the annual Thaxted Ring, a countryside gathering of morris men on the first weekend in June. Dancing and processions take place in the closed street and surrounding villages. See also the magnificent parish church of cathedral proportions, which is the venue for the annual June and July Thaxted festival of choral and orchestral concerts. The medieval Guildhall and the windmill are also noteworthy. This pub is a gem, not to be missed. ♨ ❀ ◑ ▲ ♣ P

TILLINGHAM

Cap & Feathers
8 South Street
🕓 12-3, 5.30-11; 11-11 Sat; 12-10.30 Sun
☎ (01621) 779212
Crouch Vale IPA, Best Bitter, Brewers Gold; guest beers 🅗

Unspoilt, welcoming 15th-century pub in a picturesque village. The timber-framed building is typical of this quiet corner of Essex. It is one of two pubs owned by Crouch Vale. The single bar has three separate areas, each with its own character. Guest beers selected from small regional and craft brewers complement the Crouch Vale range. The menu has a good range of home-cooked food (try the Tillingham Pie!) and there is a monthly fish night. Pub games include darts and bar billiards and there are regular quizzes. A separate children's room is equipped with toys and games. Comfortable accommodation usually requires early booking. Small patio with barbecue.
♨ Q ❧ ❀ ➩ ◑ ♣ ● P

WALTHAM ABBEY

White Lion
11 Sun Street (near B194)
🕓 11-11; 12-10.30 Sun
☎ (01922) 718673 e-mail: whitelion@btinternet.com
McMullen AK 🅗

This is a very small one-bar house with wood-panelled walls and a small half-moon-shaped serving area. Fortunately it is run by a tenant so he is not forced to use a cask breather. The darts teams play on both Mon and Tue nights so the pub is busier these eves.
♨ ❀ ◑ ♣

WEELEY

White Hart
Clacton Road/Weeley Heath (B1441)
🕓 11-2.30, 4.30-11 Mon-Thu; 11-11 Fri & Sat; 12-10.30 Sun
☎ (01255) 830384 e-mail: mark@whwh.fsnet.co.uk
Beer range varies 🅖

This wayside pub appeared to be doomed five years ago when a new bypass was built. It was purchased by an enterprising young landlord who chose a novel way to revive its fortunes. Food was abandoned and it became an old-fashioned, bare-boarded pub. However the landlord then chose to raise the profile of real ale. Some four years later there is a gravity bar from which up to four real ales can be served. Today it has a thriving real ale club; darts and pool also feature in the L-shaped bar area.
❀ ♣ P 🖰

WESTCLIFF-ON-SEA

Cricketers Inn
228 London Road (corner of A13/Milton Road)
🕓 11-11; 12-10.30 Sun
☎ (01702) 343168
Greene King IPA, Abbot; guest beers 🅗

Large Tudor-style pub with two bars – the smaller being a family room until 9pm. Cricket pictures adorn the walls. A Gray's pub chain outpost featuring a growing number of pump clips from their guest beer range. A large selection of glasses and Toby jugs decorate the back of the bar. Meetings every Tue of the Motorcycle Action Group and the second Tue of the month hosts pagan meetings. An extensive range of food is available – Death by Yorkshire Pudding is just one of the options. For drivers as well as the usual soft drinks, coffee is available all day. Attached to the Cricketers is the renowned music venue, Club Riga, which features live bands. If not sure of a beer on offer, ask for a sample.
❧ ◑ ➩ ⇌ (Westcliff/Central) ♣ ● P

Hamlet Court
54 Hamlet Court Road (off A13)
🕓 11-11; 12-10.30 Sun
☎ (01702) 391752
Courage Directors; Fuller's London Pride; Greene King Abbot; John Smith's Bitter; guest beers 🅗

A former bank put to better use as a pub, offering a good selection of real ales featuring two from independent brewers. It also hosts regular beer festivals. This one-bar pub offers table service. Old pictures of the local area are displayed on the walls. The Hamlet Court serves an extensive menu for lunchtime and eve with daily specials. It opens at 10am for breakfasts. During the warmer months the french doors open on to a patio area with heated lamps for cooler evenings. Quiz nights and party eves are held on a regular basis.
❀ ◑ ➩ ⇌

WHITE RODING

Black Horse
Chelmsford Road (A1060)
🕓 11-11; 12-10.30 Sun
☎ (01279) 876322 website: www.theblackhorse.org.uk
Ridleys IPA, 🅗 **ESX, Old Bob** 🅖

Village local dating from the 16th century, with oak beams and real wood log fires. The restaurant has a no-smoking area. Most of the handpumps are for show, gravity dispense straight from the cellar is preferred (other than for the IPA). The pub has facilities for darts, pool and dominoes and has a very active quiz team. The landlord has previously been awarded a *Best Cellar* award by Ridleys Brewery.
♨ ❀ ◑ ➩ ⊟ ⅙ ♣ P ⅟

WIDDINGTON

Fleur de Lys
High Street (near Mole Hall Wildlife Park – follow signs)
🕓 12-3.30, 6-11; 12-3.30, 7-10.30 Sun
☎ (01799) 540659
Adnams Bitter, Broadside; Greene King IPA; guest beers (summer) 🅗

Welcoming village local which attracts walkers. This 400-year-old pub is reputed to be haunted. Close to the source of the River Cam and Priors Hall Barn which is an English Heritage site. Bridge and quiz nights are held weekly and the local morris dancers also meet here. A pool table and electronic games are provided. The menu includes vegetarian and fish dishes and a large selection of sandwiches (no food Mon eve). Live music is a regular Fri night event. Close to Mole Hall Wildlife Park, which is well worth a visit. This pub was saved from closure by CAMRA NW Essex branch several years ago and continues to be well-used by locals and visitors alike.

🏚Q🍴🕙🕭◗♿♣P✝

WIVENHOE

Horse & Groom
55 The Cross (B1028)
🕙 10.30-3, 5.30 (6 Sat)-11; 12-3.30, 7-10.30 Sun
☎ (01206) 824928

Adnams Bitter, seasonal beers; guest beers Ⓗ
This pub, popular with locals, is situated opposite a roundabout – so caution is required when entering the car park. The pub consists of two L-shaped bars, one containing a series of local photographs and a dartboard – home to four different darts teams. The saloon bar is noted for its red flock wallpaper and fishtank occupied by busy small fry. The landlord and his bar staff are unfailingly friendly. In spite of difficulties, a mild is served regularly. The pub makes an ideal starting point to explore historic Wivenhoe.

🕭◗⌐P●

WOODHAM WALTER

Bell
The Street (off A414 near Danbury)
🕙 12-3, 7-11; 12-3, 7-10.30 (closed eve winter) Sun
☎ (01245) 223437

Adnams Broadside; Greene King IPA; guest beer Ⓗ
Picturesque 16th-century coaching house, timber-framed with exposed beams, central to the village. This traditional pub is music- and machine-free and is very popular with rambling groups as it is close to the Chelmer navigation and many areas of common land. Three cask ales are always available, with one regularly changing. Enjoy the friendly and relaxing

environment. The pub offers home-produced food, the speciality being eight varieties of ploughmans, with daily specials and extensive range of grills. Fish and vegetarian options always provided. No eve meals served on Sun or Mon. Families and private parties catered for in a separate room.

🏚Q🍴🕙🕭◗♣P✝

Cats
Blue Mill Lane (B1010) OS815076
🕙 12-3 (not Mon-Wed), 6-11; 12-3, 7-10.30 Sun
Greene King IPA, Abbot; guest beers Ⓗ
Little rural haven where time seems to stand still. Warm, cosy bar in winter and tranquil views over the Chelmer valley in summer. Three low-beamed drinking areas are set around a central fireplace. Interesting cat memorabilia pervades the pub: look for onc on the roof! You might even see the landlord's traction engine, or steam organ performing. Difficult to find as the pub masquerades as a cottage in a back lane but well worth the effort. Basic ploughmans available at lunchtime. 🏚Q♣♣

WRITTLE ❖

Inn on the Green
57 The Green
🕙 11-3, 6-11; 11-11 Wed-Sat; 12-10.30 Sun
☎ (01245) 420266
website: www.pickapub.co.uk/innonthegreen.htm
Brakspear Bitter; Mighty Oak IPA, Mighty Oak; Nethergate IPA, Suffolk County; Ⓗ **guest beers** Ⓗ/Ⓖ
This open-plan pub has one bar but distinct drinking areas at each end, with a dining area on a raised platform. Two guest beers are featured, one on handpump and one on gravity, and usually from interesting independent breweries. Good home-cooked food is served with a wide range of daily specials. Popular with ramblers, it is featured in a book of Essex walks. A beer festival with more than 30 beers is held in a marquee at Easter.

🏚🕭◗♣●P

Two Gallons a Day

Anne Boleyn as a Maid of Honour had an allowance of two gallons of ale a day – perhaps to be shared with others? – but to make such ale interesting it was served in possets and caudles, the warmed sweet liquor mixed with honey, spices, roasted crabs or anything else which took the fancy.

The weaker ales were relatively baby food. Elizabeth, when queen, issued repeated regulations in defence of weak ale and against strong beer; yet for herself, although she was abstemious, when she wished for a nip drank beer 'so strong there was no man durst touch it'.

Frank Morley, *The Great North Road,* 1961

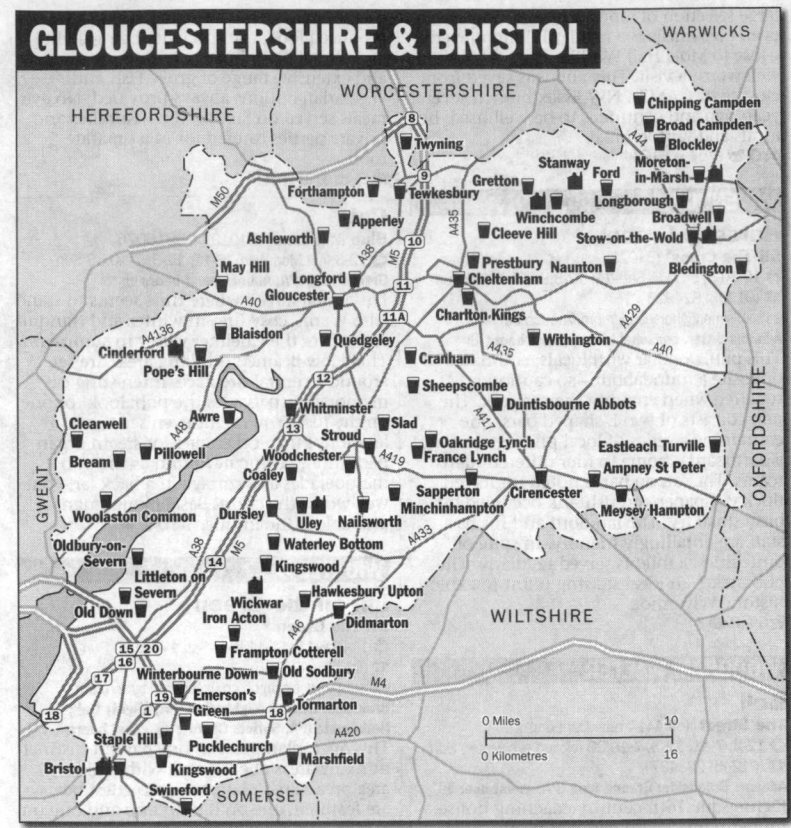

GLOUCESTERSHIRE & BRISTOL

AMPNEY ST PETER

Red Lion ☆

On A417

✪ 6-10 (11 Thu & Fri); 12-2.30, 6-11 Sat; 12-2.30, 7-10.30 Sun

☎ (01285) 851596

Hook Norton Best Bitter, seasonal beers or Flowers IPA Ⓗ

Superb, 400-year-old pub caught in a time warp where friendly conversation prevails. The two tiny flagstoned rooms are well-preserved and little seems to have changed since the jovial veteran landlord was a babe in arms. There is no bar counter, service is from the corner of one of the rooms, an open fire in each room completes the welcoming appearance of this gem. Two pub signs grace the outside, one in the distinctive oval shape of the long-defunct Stroud Brewery. ▲Q❀⊟P

APPERLEY

Coal House Inn

Gabb Lane (off B4213)

✪ 12-2.30, 6 (7 winter)-11; 12-3, 7-10.30 Sun

☎ (01452) 780211

Draught Bass; Wickwar BOB; guest beers Ⓗ

This riverside pub has been a licensed house since at least mid-18th century, when it doubled as a coal wharf with passing barges taking coal upstream. The interior is one bar, the length of the premises, with exposed beams and a tiled floor. Good-quality, home-cooked meals are served up to 1.45pm lunchtime and 9pm eves. Stone steaks a speciality. A lovely location; a patio overlooks the Severn (moorings available). The approach road is liable to flooding in winter. ▲☎❀⊲P

ASHLEWORTH

Boat Inn

The Quay   OS819251

✪ 11-2.30 (not winter Wed), 7-11; 12-3, 7-10.30 Sun

☎ (01452) 200272

Beer range varies Ⓖ

Unique, unspoilt country pub beside the Severn. Owned by the same family for 400 years this spotless gem has a small front parlour with a huge built-in settle and a pair of antique settles adorn the cosy back room. Rush mats, houseplants and fresh flowers enhance the pub. Shove-ha'penny, dominoes and cribbage are played. The ever-changing range of guest beers, mainly from local micros, are served direct from the cask. Lunchtime rolls and ploughman's are available. The courtyard is ablaze with flower tubs and there are seats and tables under cover for cooler days. This pub is a frequent CAMRA award-winner and holds a beer festival in Sept. Q❀⊲♣P

AWRE

Red Hart

Off A48 Blakeney-Newnham road   OS709080

☻ 12-3 (not Mon), 6.30-11; 12-3, 7-10.30 Sun
☎ (01594) 510220 e-mail: jeremy.bedwell@virgin.net
Beer range varies Ⓗ

Charming, 15th-century pub set in this quiet hamlet, within walking distance of the Severn. There are three river walks of varying lengths displayed outside, which are very popular, especially in summer. The Red Hart offers a separate restaurant, a no-smoking area, and a bar area which features an original well and a wealth of beams throughout. Popular for meals for special occasions, as well as for good everyday fare (no food Sun eve). Five changing guest ales are offered in a friendly atmosphere with a good mix of locals and visitors. Popular winner of the Forest of Dean CAMRA *Pub of the Year* 2000. ✿⇔◖❶P⦚

BLEDINGTON
King's Head
The Green OS243228
☻ 11-2.30, 6.30-11; 11-2.30, 6.30-10.30 Sun
☎ (01608) 658365 website:www.smoothhound.co.uk
Hook Norton Best Bitter; Wadworth 6X; guest beers Ⓗ

Delightful, 16th-century stone-built inn overlooking the village green. In 1614 Prince Rupert of the Rhine supposedly lodged here, prior to the Battle of Stow. The pub has original old beams, an inglenook and a convivial atmosphere. This free house, with its curious logo of a duck dressed in a Henry VIII outfit, is famous for its wide range of food and reservations are recommended, especially at weekends. Bledington is about four miles from Stow-on-the-Wold and a frequent winner of the Bledisloe Cup for *Best-Kept Village* award; it is an ideal centre for visiting Stow, Cheltenham, Stratford and Oxford.
🏨Q✿⇔◖❶⌂⇌♣P

BLOCKLEY
Great Western Arms
Station Road (B4479)
☻ 11.30-2.30 (3 Sat), 6.30 (6 Sat)-11; 12-3, 7-10.30 Sun
☎ (01386) 700362
Hook Norton Best Bitter, Old Hooky; guest beers Ⓗ

Situated in a sprawling, picturesque Cotswold village, this traditional two-bar pub was once a blacksmith's, but was originally built for navvies constructing the nearby railway, from which the pub takes its name. Various artefacts connected with the railway, along with old village photographs are displayed in the lounge bar. A set menu is augmented by blackboard specials, serving imaginative, home-cooked food, including vegetarian options. The patio overlooks the south eastern side of the valley in which the village lies. Children's play area and entertainment includes quizzes, dominoes, Aunt Sally and darts.
Q✿◖⌂▲♣P

BREAM
Rising Sun
High Street (centre of village opp. war memorial)
☻ 12-2.30, 6.30-11; 12-2.30, 7-10.30 Sun
☎ (01594) 564555
Beer range varies Ⓗ

Welcoming, 200-year-old stone-built pub

with spectacular views of the forest. A large building, it houses a friendly main bar with overspill into adjoining rooms, two restaurants and a large function room with bar. It offers five exciting changing guest beers; over 100 different beers were sold in the first year. Real cider is stocked in summer. A very successful October beer festival bodes well for an annual event.
🏨✿◖&▲♣●P⦚

BRISTOL ✿
Annexe Inn
Seymour Road, Bishopston (behind Sportsman

☻ 11.30-2.30, 6-11; 11.30-11 Sat; 12-10.30 Sun
☎ (0117) 949 3931
Draught Bass; Boddingtons Bitter; Courage Best Bitter; Marston's Pedigree; Smiles Best; guest beer Ⓗ

Single-storey inn, close to the county cricket ground and the football stadium. The enclosed garden and conservatory are excellent for families. Good-value bar food or restaurant meals available (not served Sun). Sparklers are removed on request. Good collection of beer pumps above the bar. Wheelchair facilities. Quiz night is Mon and darts and pool are popular here.✿✿◖&♣⦚

Bag O'Nails
141 St George's Road, Hotwells (400 yds from cathedral on College Green)
☻ 12-2.15, 5.30-11; 12-11 Fri; 4-11 Sat; 12-10.30 Sun
☎ (0117) 940 6776
website: www.bagonails.org.uk
Draught Bass; Burton Bridge Bitter; guest beers Ⓗ

Small, award-winning genuine free house where rare beers are the rule not the exception. This 200-year-old bar is wood panelled and features original gaslighting. Glass portholes are fitted into the floor. Located opposite the historic SS *Great Britain*, the world's first iron, propeller-driven steamship and close to the modern Bristol complex. Up to four ever-changing guest beers are served. A large selection of continental and British bottled beers is available. Belgian Leffe 5% ABV is found on draught. Bristol CAMRA *Pub of the Year* 2000.

Bell
21 Alfred Place, Kingsdown (take right fork up St Michael's Hill)
☻ 12-2.30 (closed Tue Lunch), 5.30-11; 12-4.30, 6.30-11Sat; 12-3.30, 7-10.30 Sun
☎ (0117) 907 7563

INDEPENDENT BREWERIES	
Bath Ales	Bristol
Donnington	Stow-on-the-Wold
Freeminer	Cinderford
Goff's	Winchcombe
Home County	Wickwar
North Cotswold	Moreton-in-Marsh
(See Breweries section)	
Smiles	Bristol
Stanway	Stanway
Uley	Uley
Wickwar	Wickwar

161

RCH Pitchfork; Uley Old Spot Prize Ale; Wickwar
BOB ⊞

Splendid local up a steep hill, but well worth the climb. Located in the Kingsdown district, and a pub since the 1870s, it is run by a long-serving landlady and is noted for its warm welcome and friendly atmosphere. The interior features much wood panelling, and the cosy ambience is enhanced by candlelight during the eve. The beers are long-stayers, but there may be occasional changes. No food is served in this genuine free house, but it is acceptable to bring in sandwiches. Good selection of wines also available. Parking can be difficult.

Q

Brewery Tap
6-10 Colston Street
(next to Smiles Brewery)
✪ 11-11; 7-10.30 Sun
☎ (0117) 921 3668 website: www.smiles.co.uk
Smiles Original, Best, seasonal beers ⊞

Award-winning, two-roomed pub only five minutes' walk from city centre. Imaginatively decorated with wood panelling, tiled floors and featuring a horseshoe, slate bar. Very close to top tourist attractions, Christmas Steps and opposite the new children's hospital. The Tap is a popular breakfast, lunch and early eve venue for local workers. Families with children are welcome in the large no-smoking room. No eve meals on Sun. Toilets are up a steep flight of stairs.

Q ◖▮▶⍭

Bridge Inn
16 Passage Street
✪ 11.30 (12 Sat)-11; 12-10.30 Sun
☎ (0117) 949 9967
Bath SPA, Gem, Barnstormer or seasonal beer ⊞

Small corner pub on the fringe of the central Bristol Broadmead shopping area, close to the former Courage Brewery. This is a good example of a small pub surviving in a city with a plethora of mega-bars. The pub has recently been pleasantly refurbished and features photographs of movie stars. TV is only on for major sporting events. Non-intrusive quality music is played – mostly from the 70s and 80s. The clientele are mainly from the business community

lunchtimes and early eves with a good mix of customers later.

◖≢(Temple Meads)

Cornubia
142 Temple Street (near Temple Meads station)
✪ 12 (5.30 summer Sat)-11; closed Sun
☎ (0117) 925 4415 e-mail: cornubia@lineone.net
Beer range varies ⊞

A constantly changing range of real ales come from micro-breweries, normally including a dark beer (very unusual for the area). Cornubia was the Roman name for Cornwall, the pub was originally a pair of Georgian houses, built in 1773, on Long Row and the original Temple Street. The Long Row street sign remains although it no longer exists in the Bristol A–Z. Very popular at lunchtime for excellent-value, home-cooked food (not served Sat or Sun). Handy for the city centre. Mobile phone use not encouraged! Bristol CAMRA *Pub of the Year* 2001.

⌖◖≢♣P

Coronation
18 Dean Lane, Southville
✪ 12-11; 12-10.30 Sun
☎ (0117) 940 9044
Hop Back GFB, Best Bitter, Crop Circle, Summer Lightning, guest beer ⊞

Near the tidal cut of the River Avon, this Victorian street-corner local is the first Hop Back-owned outlet in Bristol. This 200-year-old bar was a hotel until the 1930s. It has been sympathetically renovated with a wood-panelled bar and an elevated snug at the rear. The surrounding Georgian house once belonged to merchant venturers who had strong links to the slave trade. A quiz night is held (Mon) and a pianist plays every fortnight. Four Hop Back bottle-conditioned ales are sold along with take-away minipins and polypins, plus brewery merchandise. It is the only regular Bristol outlet for award-winning Westcroft cider. Sandwiches, rolls and excellent pizzas.

◖▮≢♣●

Hare on the Hill
41 Thomas Street North, Kingsdown
✪ 12-2.30, 5-11; 12-11 Fri & Sat;
12-10.30 Sun

INN BRIEF

☎ (0117) 908 1982 website: www.bathales.co.uk

Bath SPA, Gem, Barnstormer, seasonal beers; guest beer Ⓗ

Bath Ales' first-ever-pub, now four years old and as popular as ever with all ages. Basic, uncluttered design with wooden floor, L-shaped bar and dartboard, normally has a guest beer from an independent brewery, although this is sometimes replaced by a seasonal beer. Good range of European bottled and draught beers including the famous Budvar from the Czech Republic and over 40 malt whiskies are stocked. Sky TV for live sporting events. An array of prints and pictures are for sale and are ~~changed every few months. Previously local~~ CAMRA *Pub of the Year* 1998. Good food served (no meals Sun eve).
◑♣

Highbury Vaults
164 St Michael's Hill, Kingsdown
✿ 12-11; 12-10.30 Sun
☎ (0117) 973 3203 e-mail: highburyvaults@smiles.uk

Brains SA; Smiles Best; Young's Bitter, Triple A, Special Ⓗ

Very busy pub close to university and infirmary, so popular with students and nurses. It is named after the original owner who came from Highbury, London. There is a tiny front snug, larger rear bar and walled patio area with plenty of seating and gas heaters. Young's have recently bought the lease from Smiles. The toilets are at the bottom of a very steep flight of stairs. Good-value meals (not weekends).
Q✿◑♣

Hope & Anchor
38 Jacobs Wells Road, Hotwells
✿ 12-11; 12-10.30 Sun
☎ (0117) 929 2987 e-mail: luciferbrewing@aol.com

Beer range varies Ⓗ

Once the Lucifer Brewery brewpub and now a genuine free house with up to five regularly changing beers. Pleasantly decorated with a wide selection of old cartoons including an amusing warning from the management 'Don't Spill Beer'. The terraced and secluded rear garden can get busy in summer. A wide range of food is served all day.
✿◑

Horts
49 Broad Street
✿ 11.30-11 (11.30 Thu); 11-1am Fri & Sat; 12-midnight Sun
☎ (0117) 925 2520

Abbey Ales Bellringer; Ⓖ **Draught Bass;** Ⓟ **Wickwar BOB; guest beers** Ⓖ

Large popular pub with long single-bar that avoids the cavernous feel of some city-centre venues. Raised area at the rear has a projection screen TV and doubles as the restaurant. Entertainment includes DJs and live music on Fri and Sat eves, jazz on Sun afternoons and a quiz on Mon eve. ~~Monthly beer festivals are hosted and there~~ are regular promotions for local independent breweries. Acquired by Young's in 2001, so beer range may vary. Thatcher's and Weston's cider stocked.
🏭✿◑♿♣🐶🍴

Kellaway Arms
140 Kellaway Avenue, Golden Hill
✿ 11.30-2.30 (3 Fri), 6-11; 11-3, 5-11 Sat; 12-3, 7-10.30 Sun
☎ (0117) 949 7458

Archers Village; Courage Best Bitter; Wells Bombardier; guest beers Ⓗ

Traditional, welcoming, two-bar local near Horfield Common, comprising a large public bar and a quiet, comfortable lounge. The sizeable garden is reached through the public bar. The pub is on the site of a 19th-century off-licence, it is named after Postmaster General John Kellaway. This allows the pub to feature a version of the City of Bristol coat of arms on the pub sign. Popular match day venue for rugby and football fans as it is only 15 minutes' walk from Memorial Stadium. No food served on Sun. 11 years in this *Guide*. Q✿◑⌑♣

King's Head ☆
60 Victoria Street (near Temple Meads station)
✿ 11-3 (not Sat), 5 (7.30 Sat)-11; 11-11 Wed-Fri; 12-3, 7-10.30 Sun
☎ (0117) 927 7860

Draught Bass; Courage Best Bitter; Smiles Original Ⓗ

This friendly local dates from 1660 and is situated in a revitalised area of central Bristol. The pub, which features in CAMRA's national inventory, has a superb

---

CHIPPING CAMPDEN
Volunteer
Lower High Street
11.30-3, 5-11;
12-3, 7-10.30 Sun

Hook Norton Best Bitter; North Cotswold Genesis; Stanway Stanney Bitter; guest beers Ⓗ

Family-run stone inn at north end of Cotswold Way. The pub is 300 years old. Strong local bias. Guest beers tend to be local. Varied home-cooked menu.

COALEY
Fox & Hounds
12-3 (not Mon), 7-11;
12-3, 7-10.30 Sun

Black Sheep Best Bitter; Uley Bitter; guest beers Ⓗ

This 300-year-old Cotswold stone building became a Stroud Brewery pub 100 years ago. The pub is popular for acoustic music on Sat eve. Skittles alley.

CRANHAM
Black Horse Inn
11.45-3, 6.30-11;
12-3, 7 (8 winter)-10.30 Sun

Boddingtons Bitter; Flowers Original; Hook Norton Best Bitter; Marston's Pedigree; Wickwar BOB Ⓗ

17th-century country pub tucked away up narrow side street. Bumper portions of home-cooked food. No fod Sun eve. Quoits available.

EASTLEACH TURVILLE
Victoria
12-3, 7-11 (12-11 Sat summer);
12-3, 7-10.30 Sun

Arkells 3B Ⓗ

16th-century pub sensitively restored with public bar, lounge and dining area. Freshly prepared food – but this does not dominate the pub.

EMERSONS GREEN
Langley Arms
Guest Avenue
11-11; 12-10.30 Sun

Draught Bass; Butcombe Bitter; Courage Best Bitter; Wickwar BOB (summer) **or Olde Merryford** (winter) Ⓗ

Former farmhouse converted to a pub on a new housing estate. Good-value food. Family room and sunspot garden, worth finding. Resident ghost.

KINGSWOOD (GLOUCS)
Dinneywicks Inn
The Chippings
11.30-3, 6 (5 Fri & Sat)-11 (11.30-11 Sat);
12-3, 7-10.30 Sun

Draught Bass; Wadworth IPA, 6X; guest beer Ⓗ

Imposing three-storey, single bar whitewashed pub, named after a nearby hill that was a Civil War horses' burial ground in the. *Cask Marque* accredited.

interior. The bar area is also the corridor which leads to the rear of this small pub, furnished rather like a tramcar. Also note the splendid bar-back which, it is believed, dates from the early Victorian era. The walls are adorned with pictures of old Bristol. There is mostly a business clientele lunchtimes with locals in the eve. Good food served Mon–Fri lunchtimes. ◁⋑ (Temple Meads)

Merchants Arms
5 Merchants Road, Hotwells
✪ 12-2.30, 5-11; 12-11 Fri & Sat; 12-10.30 Sun
☎ (0117) 904 0037 e-mail: hare@bathales.com
Bath SPA, Gem, Barnstormer; guest beer Ⓗ
Bath Ales' third pub is situated close to the Cumberland basin/floating harbour area. Small and simply furnished, the lower rear area is set aside for non-smokers. There is always one guest beer from an independent brewery on sale and sometimes a second at busy times. Four-pint jugs of ale served at a small discount. Bottle-conditioned beer, carry-outs and special commemorative gift packs are available. No meals served, but filled rolls and toasted sandwiches subject to availability. Every other Mon is quiz night. Limited car parking. A great pub for conversation. Not to be missed. ⠀✄

Old Fox
Fox Road, Eastville (off Stapleton Road via Warwick Road)
✪ 7.30-11; closed lunchtimes; closed August & Xmas to New Year; 7.30-10.30 Sun
☎ (0117) 952 2674
RCH Pitchfork, Old Slug Porter; Taylor Landlord; guest beers Ⓗ
Characterful back-street free house dating back 300 years. It was restored in the 1970s when owned by CAMRA Investments; the panelled interior displays 40 old photographs of the area and its mines. Local hero WG Grace used to drink here. Games include shove-ha'penny, Shut the Box, chess and backgammon, and magazines are available. No facilities for dogs or children. Six beers usually available, including a house beer and two changing guests from micros such as Daleside. Independents' bottled beers for sale, plus around 20 single malt whiskies.
Q⋑ (Stapleton Rd) ♣✄

Prince of Wales
Stoke Lane, Westbury-on-Trym
✪ 11-3, 5.30-11; 11-3, 5-11 Fri; 11-11 Sat; 12-4, 7-10.30 Sun
☎ (0117) 962 3715
Bath SPA; Black Sheep Best Bitter; Courage Best Bitter; Fuller's London Pride; guest beers Ⓗ
This was an Inntrepreneur tied house until Feb 2001, when it was bought by the landlord. Now a popular, friendly free house with a pleasant garden. Barbecues take place in summer. An imaginative menu with daily specials at a competitive price with a good selection of wines. Popular on rugby days with large foldaway TV screen. No nitro-keg beer, a no-smoking area is available at lunchtime. ✿◁✄

Robert Fitzharding
24 Cannon Street, Bedminster
✪ 10.30-11; 12-10.30 Sun
☎ (0117) 966 2757
Draught Bass; Ⓟ **Butcombe Bitter; Courage Directors; Shepherd Neame Spitfire; Theakston Best Bitter; guest beers** Ⓗ
A Wetherspoon's conversion, this thriving local has a spacious bar with comfortable seating. The bar features much wood panelling, stained glass and plenty of books. There is no-smoking at the bar and another no-smoking section in the dining area. Very lively and busy on Fri and Sat, quieter on Sun. The usual Wetherspoon's menu is served including vegetarian dishes. The wheelchair access is on Cannon Street. Addlestone's cider is stocked. No music is played in the pub.
Q◁&⚫✄●

St George's Hall
203 Church Road, Redfield (on A420)
✪ 11-11; 12-10.30 Sun
☎ (0117) 955 1488
Draught Bass; Butcombe Bitter, Gold; Courage Directors; Shepherd Neame Spitfire; Theakston Best Bitter; guest beers Ⓗ
Popular and much improved Wetherspoon's outlet in suburban high street on A420 between the city centre and Kingswood. Originally the Granada Cinema, dating back to the days of silent movies, it later became the Granada Bingo Hall. A large central glass skylight creates an airy feel. Pictures and stories of local historical figures fill the walls. A small patio is provided and two no-smoking areas. Standard menu served all day with the curry club extended Mon–Thu. Prices tend to be a bit lower than other Wetherspoon's pubs. A special ramp is fitted for wheelchair access.
✿◁&(Lawrence Hill)✄●

Sugar Loaf
51 St Mark's Road, Easton
✪ 11-11; 12-10.30 Sun
☎ (0117) 939 4498
Greene King Abbot; Marston's Pedigree; Tetley Bitter Ⓗ
This popular and busy local has two bars and also boasts a separate room with two pool tables. There is a well-used juke box with a broad selection of compact discs and normally a live band on Thu in the larger bar (free admission). The house beer, Easton Bitter, is brewed by Moles. The pub is very much at the heart of the local community and is close to some of the finest spice shops in the city. Pleasant garden.
✿◁⋑(Stapleton Road)♣

Victoria
20 Chock Lane, Westbury-on-Trym
✪ 12-2.30, 5.30-11; 12-3, 5.30-10.30 Sun
☎ (0117) 950 0441 e-mail: thevictoria@virgin.net
Adnams Broadside; Draught Bass; Wadworth IPA, 6X, seasonal beers; guest beers Ⓗ
Hidden down a quiet lane this comfortably furnished pub, built in the 1700s, has been a courthouse and a cider house. The sloped garden has patio heaters and is perfect on summer eves. Deservedly popular pub, it has a large designated no-smoking area for drinkers and serves good food between 12–2 and 5.30–8. The dartboard has an electronic scoreboard which is unusual for the area and there is a

Sun football team. Dominoes and crib are also played. Q✿❀◑♣✦

BROAD CAMPDEN

Bakers Arms

Off B4081, at NW end of village

☼ 11.30-2.30, 4.45-11; 11.30-11 Sat & summer; 12-10.30 Sun

☎ (01386) 840515

Donnington SBA; Hook Norton Best Bitter; Stanway Stanney Bitter; guest beers Ⓗ

Fine old village local, first licensed as a public house in 1724. A photograph of the building (1905) shows it as the village bakery and grain store. It boasts Cotswold stone walls, exposed beams and a fine inglenook. Monthly (3rd Tue) is folk music night – now in its 24th year. Also displayed – and dated 1969 – is a carpet depicting the pub and the following description: pictorial rug represents 1,000 hours' work by the late Neville Hallam of Wythall, in appreciation of the happy times spent in the Bakers Arms. Excellent food is available and a children's play area. ♨Q✿◑♣✦P

CHARLTON KINGS

Merryfellow

2 School Road (near the baptist church)

☼ 11-11; 12-10.30 Sun

☎ (01242) 525883 website: www.merryfellowinn.co.uk

Gale's HSB; Greene King IPA; Taylor Landlord; Wadworth 6X; guest beer Ⓗ

Modernised local in a busy village centre. The pub retains its original Stroud Brewery windows. The excellent large outdoor drinking area has its own aviary and is safe for children. Reasonably priced meals are served throughout the day until 9pm. Facilities include a skittle alley, function room, Sky TV and a pool table. The pub has its own Jack Russell print signed by the England and Australia cricket teams – can you identify them all? ✿◑P

CHELTENHAM ✿

Adam & Eve

8 Townsend Street (near Tesco superstore)

☼ 10.30-3, 5-11; 10.30-11 Sat; 12-3, 7-10.30 Sun

☎ (01242) 690030

Arkells 2B, 3B, seasonal beers Ⓗ

Unpretentious, no-frills, friendly, terraced local, 15 minutes' walk from the town centre. The public bar and small, comfortable lounge provide a strong community focus. The skittle alley is home to many teams and the pub regularly fields two quiz teams in local leagues. Almost unnoticed are the spill of flowers on each table and the polished copper pipework in the toilets. The friendly landlady has run the pub for the past 23 years. Just off the main Tewkesbury road, it is readily accessible by public transport. Very limited on-street parking. Q⊟

Hewlett Arms

Harp Hill

☼ 11-2.30 (3 Thu & Fri; 5 Sat), 6-11; 12-5, 7-10.30 Sun

☎ (01242) 228600

website: englishlatin4666@aol.com

Black Sheep Best Bitter; Stanway Stanney Bitter; Tetley Bitter; guest beer Ⓗ

Comfortable, relaxed pub, located on the outskirts of town, it is close to the football ground and convenient for the racecourse. It can be very busy, so booking is recommended for meals (especially at popular times). Attracts a wide range of people from all walks of life. Fronted by a large garden with patio, which is very pleasant on warm days. The small car park is located alongside the garden. A collection of mugs and jugs, and the naval paraphernalia are attractive features. ✿◑P✦

Kemble Brewery Inn

27 Fairview Street (off ???)

☼ 11.30-2.30 (3 Fri), 5.30-11; 11.30-11 Sat; 12-4, 7-10.30 Sun

☎ (01242) 243446

Archers Village, Best Bitter, Golden; guest beer Ⓗ

Small, but deservedly popular back-street local; hard to find, but worth the effort. The only Archers tied house in the area, it offers good value, home-made food (not served Sun eve). The single bar can get smoky, but there is an attractive walled garden. Cheltenham CAMRA *Pub of the Year* 2001, it was originally built as a butcher's shop in 1845 and became a pub in 1847. The first owner came from Kemble and made cider from apples picked in the rear orchard. Popular with racegoers and home football supporters. Q✿◑

National Hunt

Benhall Ave

☼ 11-11; 12-10.30 Sun

☎ (01242) 527461

e-mail: nationalhunt.cheltenham@whitbread.com

Boddingtons Bitter; Goff's Jouster; Wadworth 6X; guest beers Ⓗ

1960s estate pub in the real ale desert of western Cheltenham. The single bar regularly offers up to seven real ales. A room is set aside for the pool table and another area houses the satellite TV for sporting events. Good-value meals are available throughout the week, with OAP lunch specials (12–2 Mon–Thu). Readily accessible by public transport (Stagecoach Service J stops right outside). Children are welcome until 9pm under strict parental control. Runs autumn beer festival. ✿◑⅙P

CIRENCESTER

Corinium Hotel

12 Gloucester Street (off A435 at N end of town)

☼ 11-11; 12-10.30

☎ (01285) 659711 website: www.coriniumhotel.co.uk

Beer range varies Ⓗ

The understated frontage leads, via an attractive courtyard, to a small flagstoned bar and smart lounge with a large open fire. This thriving hotel has recently been refurbished, but was originally an Elizabethan wool merchant's house, modernised in Georgian times. The restaurant, converted from the old stables, is bright and strewn with hops, as are the bar and lounge. The three guest beers are mainly from unusual micro-breweries for this area. Both bar and restaurant serve the same varied and imaginative menu. Splendid walled garden. ♨✿✦◑⅙⚓P

Twelve Bells
12 Lewis Lane
☼ 11-11; 12-10.30 Sun
☎ (01285) 644549
Beer range varies Ⓗ
Beer drinkers' haven, lovingly resurrected by the owner/landlord – a colourful local character. The front bar can be quite lively, but the panelled rooms at the rear are quieter. All rooms have open fires. There are always five guest beers (320 a year), including session beers. The food is easily as excellent as the beer, ranging from bubble 'n' squeak to king scallop and sea bream thermidor with ratatouille and parmesan tartlets. All the food is prepared from fresh produce. Gloucestershire CAMRA *Pub of the Year* 2001.
ᛗᏜ❀◑ᆭ♣P

CLEARWELL

Lamb
The Cross, Newland Road
☼ 12-3 (not Mon-Thu), 6-11; 12-3, 7-10.30
☎ (01594) 835441
Freeminer Bitter, guest beers Ⓖ
Welcoming, comfortable country pub. It has two rooms, one a delightful snug with old settles, roaring log fire and flagstone floor, the other larger room is divided into cosy seating areas and used for pub games. No food is served. Various bottled beers are available including the Freeminer Speculation. The bitter is usually on draught with at least one other guest beer, served directly from the barrels in the cellar. Clearwell is situated en route to the Wye Valley and Clearwell Caves are nearby.
ᛗᏜ❀ᆭᏜ♣P

CLEEVE HILL

High Roost
On B4632, at top of Cleeve Hill
☼ 11.30-2.30 (3 Sat), 7-11; 12-4, (closed eve) Sun
☎ (01242) 672010
Goff's Jouster; Hook Norton Best Bitter Ⓗ
Imposing Victorian stone villa, built originally as a private house, reached by a flight of steps. Now a family-run free house, perched on the highest point of the Cotswolds with spectacular views over the Severn basin. On a clear day it is possible to see Tewkesbury Abbey, the Malvern Hills and as far as the Black Mountains in Wales. The pub has an open-plan layout and a dartboard and TV are discreetly tucked away. Other facilities include a terrace for outdoor drinking, bar skittles and two car parks. Good-value food includes Welsh sirloin steaks and large Viennese baps.
❀◑♣P

DIDMARTON

King's Arms
The Street (A433) OS818875
☼ 12-2.30, 6-11; 12-2.30, 7-10.30 Sun
☎ (01454) 238245
Smiles Best; Uley Bitter; guest beer Ⓗ
The low-key frontage belies the warm and welcoming interior of this well-refurbished, 17th-century coaching inn. The style and comfort gradually increase as you progress around the central counter from the hop-strewn games/public bar to the excellent restaurant. There is a separate menu for the bar, but both are equally imaginative, using local produce. Stabling and barns have been converted to holiday cottages. A splendid ex-courtroom is available for private parties. The well-maintained walled garden includes a pétanque pitch. The pub was leased from the Beaufort family in 1760 for 1,000 years at 6 pence a year!
ᛗᏜ❀⇆◑ᆭ♣P

DUNTISBOURNE ABBOTS

Five Mile House ☆
Old Gloucester Road On old A417, follow sign at Centurion Services
☼ 12-3, 6-11; 12-3, 6-10.30 Sun
☎ (01285) 821432
Archers Village; Taylor Landlord; guest beer Ⓗ
Refurbishments of unspoilt pubs with Grade II listed interiors are rarely as successful as this. The tiny bar is virtually unchanged and strictly no food, but leads to a smart no-smoking dining room. The menu is deservedly popular and the portions generous. A small tap room is created by two venerable curving settles around a wood-burning stove, and steps down lead to a snug and then to the old cellar. The main road has been moved a few yards, leaving the old Ermin Street empty if not exactly quiet. ᛗᏜ❀◑P

DURSLEY

Old Spot Inn
Hill Road (next to bus station)
☼ 11-3, 5-11; 11-11 Fri & Sat; 12-10.30 Sun
☎ (01453) 542870 e-mail: rsainty@oldspot.fsnet.co.uk
Badger IPA; Uley Old Ric; guest beers Ⓗ
Independent free house named after the Gloucester Old Spot pig. Sympathetically restored by the owner, it was built in 1776 and has been a pub for over 100 years. Pig Face Row opposite is now a free car park. The pub has an intimate atmosphere with low ceilings, bar billiard table, log fire and has masses of brewery memorabilia in the four drinking areas (one is no-smoking). A convivial local on the Cotswold Way. Enjoy the secluded garden with a boules piste. At least three guest ales at all times (over 10 different beers per year). CAMRA Gloucestershire *Pub of the Year* 2000. A gem.
ᛗ❀◑♣✔

FORD

Plough Inn
On B4077, 4 miles W of Stow-on-the-Wold
☼ 11-11, 12-10.30 Sun
☎ (01386) 584215 e-mail: ford.glos@ukonline.co.uk
Donnington BB, SBA Ⓗ
16th-century former courthouse, the cellars were once dungeons holding prisoners and the remains of the indoor stocks can be found under the rear lounge windows. The front of this traditional Cotswold stone building overlooks the gallops of famous horse-racing stables of Jackdaw's Castle. Four interconnecting rooms are served by a central bar dispensing the highly regarded local Donnington ales. With low-beamed ceilings, flagstone floors, inglenooks with real fires, wooden shuttered windows and settles it is full of character. Although noted

for its fine home-cooked food, table reservations are not accepted, so arrive early (no food winter Sun eve). ✿⇤◑◆P

FORTHAMPTON

Lower Lode Inn
OS878317

✪ 11-3 (not winter Tue), 6-11; closed Mon; 11-3, 6-10.30 Sun

☎ (01684) 293224

Donnington BB; Goff's Jouster; Marston's Pedigree; Oakhill Bitter; Wickwar BOB Ⓗ

15th-century brick pub standing in three acres of lawned river frontage, looking across the River Severn to Tewkesbury Abbey. This family public house which has been licensed since 1590 is a popular stop-over for boats using the recently upgraded public mooring. Approach roads are liable to flooding in winter; private slipway on to the River Severn. Camping and Caravan Club hideaway site and day fishing is available. ᴁQ⌘✿⇤◑&▲◆P⊁

FRAMPTON COTTERELL

Rising Sun
43 Ryecroft Road

✪ 11.30-3, 7 (5 Thu & Fri)-11; 11.30-11 Sat; 12-3, 7-10.30 Sun

☎ (01454) 772330

Draught Bass; Butcombe Bitter; Wadworth 6X; Wickwar Coopers' WPA, BOB; guest beer Ⓗ

Superb, family-run free house, a former local CAMRA *Pub of the Year*, and a *Guide* regular for many years. Local brewers are well-supported. Deservedly popular, it has a skittle alley (which doubles as a function room) and an upper level dining area. A large conservatory has recently been added at the front of the pub, and is a no-smoking area (diners also welcome here). Food available 12–2 (book for Sun lunch). Plenty of CAMRA memorabilia here. ✿◑◆P⊁

FRANCE LYNCH

King's Head
OS903035

✪ 12-2.30 (4 Sat), 6-11; 12-4, 7-10.30 Sun

☎ (01453) 882225

Archers Best Bitter; Hook Norton Best Bitter; guest beers Ⓗ

Friendly, single-bar pub tucked away in the heart of a compact village of winding streets. The village name denotes its Huguenot connections. French and Flemish weavers came to this wool-rich area in search of employment when their own native industry foundered. The superb reclaimed garden has a children's play area. A crèche is provided Fri eve (7–9). The pub has quiz, crib and cricket teams. Live jazz, blues or folk music performed on Mon eve. No food Sun eve. ᴁQ⌘✿◑▲◆P

GLOUCESTER

Black Swan Inn
68-70 Southgate Street (200 yds S of The Cross)

✪ 11-11; 12-3, 7-10.30 Sun

☎ (01452) 523642

Beer range varies Ⓗ

Behind the austere stone frontage of this mid-19th century listed building is a warm and welcoming bar that is a great favourite with city ale-drinkers. The bar itself, slightly obscured from the entrance, sits directly above a fine medieval cellar, and its six constantly-changing ales are from craft brewers around the British Isles. Cider (or perry) is mostly from Westons. Bistro-style seating dominates, but there are easy chairs in small corners. Home-cooked bar food is available Mon–Fri. Fine B&B accommodation offered. Popular blues on Thu eve. ✿⇤◑&◆P

England's Glory
66-68 London Road

✪ 11.30-2.30, 5-11; 10.44-?; 12-10.30 Sun

☎ (01452) 302948

Wadworth IPA, 6X, JCB, seasonal beers Ⓗ

Although rebuilt internally in 1992, the lounge bar of this popular community pub has an older feel thanks to a glorious log fire, surrounded by high-backed chairs, and to its pews, old tables and old photographs. There is a partially separated area for non-smokers. A display of frogs (all gifts) leave no doubt about the landlord's nationality. The public bar has a large screen TV for sporting events, and there is a double skittle alley. A wide selection of home-cooked food is offered at reasonable prices. There are regular quizzes and a folk club meets here monthly. ᴁQ⌘◑&⌁≈◆P⊁●

Linden Tree
73-75 Bristol Road (A430 S of docks)

✪ 11.30-2.30, 6-11; 11.30-11 Sat; 12-4, 7-10.30 Sun

☎ (01452) 527869

Red Shoot Tom's Tipple; Wadworth IPA, 6X, JCB, seasonal beers; Ⓗ **guest beers** Ⓖ

Set back from a busy thoroughfare, this end property of a Grade II listed Georgian terrace has recently been refurbished throughout without destroying the 'country' feel of the bar. This popular drinking spot has beamed ceilings, exposed stone walls (of questionable origin), an open log fire with unusual canopy, carriage lamps – even a carriage wheel as a seating area boundary. A skittle alley opens up to create extra space. Eight ales are usually stocked with the guests ever-changing. ᴁQ✿⇤◑◆P●

New Inn
16 Northgate Street

✪ 11-11; 12-10.30 Sun

☎ (01452) 522177

Beer range varies Ⓗ

Built in 1455 to accommodate pilgrims to the tomb of Edward II (in the nearby Cathedral) this Grade I listed building is the finest example of a medieval galleried inn in the country. Having languished for 20 years under indifferent ownership, this fine inn is now being sensitively restored. Although there are three bars, a restaurant and coffee shop around the cobbled courtyard, cask beer is served only in the ale bar. Six are usually available, mainly from craft brewers and for one week each month a small brewer is invited to supply all pumps. Fine function room and accommodation. ✿⇤◑≈◆◍

GRETTON

Royal Oak

On Winchcombe road, 1½ miles from Winchcombe
✪ 12-3, 6-11; 7-10.30 Sun
☎ (01242) 602477

Goff's Jouster; guest beers ⊞

This 18th-century pub was bought by a
syndicate of villagers (June 2000) to
preserve it as a country inn and protect it
from ownership by a large national brewery
or pub company. The L-shaped bar serves a
long room and the modern no-smoking
conservatory offers magnificent views. The
local prize-winning Goff's beers are very
popular. Steam trains on the preserved
Gloucestershire and Warwickshire railway
between Toddington and Gotherington run
past the bottom of the garden. Regular Sun
quiz and traditional music session on Wed.
A beer and music festival is held in June.
You can work up a thirst by booking the
pub's tennis court. ♨♿◑♣♠♣P

HAWKESBURY UPTON

Beaufort Arms

High Street (near A433 turn off A46)
✪ 12-3, 5.30-11; 12-11 Fri & Sat; 12-10.30 Sun
☎ (01454) 238217

Wickwar BOB; guest beers ⊞

Traditional Cotswold stone pub in a historic
village. Popular with locals and passing
trade, it has two comfortable bars with low-
beamed ceilings with an interesting
collection of pub, brewery and local
memorabilia. The stables dining area offers
good-value food. Westons traditional cider
is offered. Added attractions include a
pleasant garden, skittle alley and popular
pub games such as crib and darts.
♨Q♿◑♣♿♠♣P

IRON ACTON

Rose & Crown

High Street (off B4058)
✪ 5 (6 Sat)-11; 12-3, 7-10.30 Sun
☎ (01454) 228423

**Draught Bass; Flowers IPA; Marston's Pedigree;
Uley Old Spot Prize Ale, Pig's Ear Strong Beer** ⊞

Excellent community local dating from the
17th century. In this *Guide* for the last eight
years and in the same hands for much
longer. There are two distinct bars, both
with log fires. The owners have always
preferred to concentrate on drink so no
food is sold. A full-sized football pitch to the
rear is owned by the pub. The pub is a
strong supporter of local brewers and rare
local outlet for Uley beers. A warm welcome
awaits. ♨Q♿♣♿♣

KINGSWOOD (BRISTOL) ✤

Kingswood Colliers

94-96 Regent Street
✪ 11-11; 11-10.30 Sun
☎ (0117) 967 2247

**Draught Bass; Butcombe Gold; Courage Directors;
Shepherd Neame Spitfire; Theakston Best Bitter;
guest beers** ⊞

New purpose-built Wetherspoon's outlet,
opened March 2000 on the site of the
former Kingswood market. The large L-
shaped bar features six regular ales and two
guest beers and is often, and deservedly,

very busy. The garden at the rear is planted
with a wide variety of trees and shrubs and
has patio heaters. Inside is a spacious no-
smoking area. The walls are adorned with
mining memorabilia and historic
information from its coal-mining heyday.
Wheelchair WC, but poorly located and
difficult to access when busy.
Q♿◑♥♿●

Highwayman

Hill Street (A420, ½ mile from centre)
✪ 11.30-2.30 (3 Sat), 6.30-11; 12-4, 7-10.30 Sun
☎ (0117) 967 1613

Draught Bass; Ind Coope Burton Ale; Tetley Bitter; ⊞

Warm and friendly, single-bar roadside
local where beams, a stone fireplace and
window seats enhance its coachhouse style.
Popular pub for games; skittles, crib and
darts are played and regular quiz nights
held. Lunchtime meals are good-value and
recommended. The no-smoking area is
available lunchtimes only. It has a well-
appointed family room at the rear and a
large, enclosed, safe garden.
♿♿◑♣P

LITTLETON ON SEVERN

White Hart

Signed from B4461
✪ 11-2.30, 6-11; 12-11 Sat; 12-10.30 Sun
☎ (01454) 412275

**Smiles Best; Young's Bitter, Special, seasonal
beer** ⊞

Recently acquired by London brewer
Young's, but beautifully refurbished by
previous owner, Smiles of Bristol, for
which it won an accolade in CAMRA's
national design competition during
the early 1990s. This large country inn
with its flagstone floors and traditional
decor oozes character. Try a room
crawl through the various drinking
areas off the main bar. The family room,
with its table football game, doubles as the
no-smoking room. A large garden at the
front is complemented by a sunny, small
courtyard.
♨Q♿♿◑♣P♥

LONGFORD

Queen's Head

84 Tewkesbury Road (A38, close to jct with A40)
✪ 11-3, 5.30-11; 12-3, 7-10.30 Sun
☎ (01452) 301882 website: www.cotswoldpubs.co.uk

**Draught Bass; Boddingtons Bitter; Eccleshall Slaters
Bitter; Fuller's London Pride; Greene King Old
Speckled Hen; Marston's Pedigree** ⊞

Dating from the 1730s this partly timber-
framed building was converted from a
blacksmith's to a pub a century ago. Now
this smart, warm and welcoming
establishment acts as a popular
community pub and noted eating house.
The stone-flagged public bar area, with its
real fire, remains the heart and soul of the
pub. In the lounge area an elevated side-
extension and a recently incorporated rear
room provide seating for the diners
attracted by award-winning food at sensible
prices (booking always advisable).
Externally the pub is transformed in
summer by a mass of colourful flower
baskets.
♨♿◑♿P

MARSHFIELD ✳

Catherine Wheel
High Street
☼ 11-3 (not Mon), 6-11, 12-3, 7-10.30 Sun
☎ (01225) 892220
Archers Village; Courage Best Bitter; Wadworth 6X Ⓗ
Beautifully restored Georgian pub on the village high street. The extensive main bar leads down from the original wood-panelled area via stone-walled rooms to the cosy patio garden at the rear. There is a very pretty dining room. In winter there is usually a superb open fire to warm your feet. The food in the bar/garden is imaginative and well-presented. Meals not served on Mon lunchtime or Sun eve.
⚌❀🏠🌗P

MAY HILL

Glasshouse Inn
Off A40 W of Huntley OS710213
☼ 11.30-3, 6.30-11; 12-3, 7-10.30 Sun
☎ (01452) 830529
Draught Bass; Butcombe Bitter; guest beer Ⓖ
Charming old building, recently extended using reclaimed old timbers to maintain the character of the old beams and flagstone floors. Divided into three rooms, one with a black leaded old range, another with a roaring open fire. The addition of a new kitchen means good food is now available six days a week. Three real ales are always on offer, one a changing guest. A fenced garden with seating provides a relaxing area for families. The car park features an ancient yew hedge with seating concealed in its depths.
⚌❀🌗♣P

MEYSEY HAMPTON

Masons Arms
28 High Street
☼ 11.30-2.45, 6-11, 12-4, 7-10.30 (not winter eve) Sun
☎ (01285) 850164m
Draught Bass; Hook Norton Best Bitter; guest beers Ⓗ
Grade II listed, 17th-century inn enjoying a picturesque setting on the village green. The pub has been thoughtfully refurbished, retaining a rustic feel. The original two bars have been knocked through with exposed stone walls, parquet floors, hops and farm implements, a large inglenook and a wood-burning stove. The two constantly changing guest beers are usually from micro-breweries. This is a community pub that also appeals to visitors for its accommodation and restaurant serving a good range of freshly prepared food at reasonable prices (not Sun eve). Wheelchair access, except restaurant.
⚌❀🏠🌗

MINCHINHAMPTON

Ragged Cot
Cirencester Road, Hyde OS887012
☼ 11-3, 5.30-11; 11-3, 6.30-10.30 Sun
☎ (01453) 884643
Draught Bass; Taylor Landlord; Uley Old Spot Prize Ale; guest beers Ⓗ
Busy, comfortable free house in open countryside near Minchinhampton

Common and Gatcombe Park. The restaurant has been extended and the whole building is now pleasantly refurbished. Over 60 malt whiskies are stocked. Usually the two guests are from local micro-breweries. It became a hostelry in 1620. The first landlord became a part-time footpad to bolster takings. His wife objected to his nefarious activities and, after a row, alledgedly fell down the stairs and died. Her ghost reputedly inhabits the pub.
⚌Q❀🏠🌗♣P

MORETON-IN-MARSH

Inn-on-the-Marsh
Stow Road (A429, at W end of village)
☼ 11-3, 6-11; 12-3, 7-10.30 Sun
☎ (01608) 650709 e-mail: bongaard@netscape.co.uk
Banks's Original; Marston's Bitter, Pedigree; guest beer (summer) Ⓗ
This was once a bakery, but became licensed premises in 1870. There is a small, comfortable bar and a large, attractive conservatory (dining and no-smoking area). The decor and atmosphere are reminiscent of an Amsterdam 'brown' cafe. There is a standard menu complemented by an ever-changing and popular list specialising in oriental food. All meals are very reasonably priced, with vegetarian options (no food Mon eve). Within the garden area, competition for nesting sites is at a premium between the resident ducks who live on the pond next door – this place is not called Inn-on-the-Marsh for nothing.
Q❀🌗♿♣P

NAILSWORTH

George Inn
Newmarket (½ mile up hill from bus station)
☼ 11-3, 6-11; 12-3, 7-10.30 Sun
☎ (01453) 833228
Archers Village; Draught Bass; Taylor Landlord; Uley Old Spot Prize Ale Ⓗ
Traditional village local with a friendly atmosphere, looking southwards over the valley above Nailsworth. Three separate chimneys indicate that the building was originally three cottages. It became a pub in 1820 and was renamed in 1910 to honour the incoming George V. Small patio at the front and limited car parking. The award-winning chef uses only fresh ingredients and even the rolls are homemade. The imaginative food is keenly priced with chicken piri-piri a superb house speciality. Food is served in the bar or in a small separate restaurant (booking essential).
Q❀🌗P

OAKRIDGE LYNCH

Butchers Arms
North edge of village, follow brown tourist signs to pub OS915038
☼ 11-3, 6-11; 12-4, 7-10.30 Sun
☎ (01285) 760371
Archers Best Bitter; Greene King Abbot; Tetley Bitter; Wickwar Coopers' WPA, BOB Ⓗ
Popular, stone two-bar local whose restaurant opens Wed–Sat, and Sun lunch. Food is available in the bars at all times except Sun eve. Excellent beer garden and large car park. There is a skittle alley and the pub runs a team in the local leauge. It also

fields its own cricket team which plays friendlies against neighbouring pubs. Noted for its consistently good beer and excellent food. Popular with walkers.
🏃Q🌂🕯🍴◖◗🍺♿♣P

OLDBURY ON SEVERN

Anchor Inn
Church Road
☼ 11.30-2.30, 6.30-11; 11.30-11 Sat; 12-10.30 Sun
☎ (01454) 413331
Draught Bass; Black Sheep Bitter (occasional); **Butcombe Bitter; Theakston Best Bitter, Old Peculier** Ⓗ

Built on the site of an old mill house, the Anchor became a public house during Oldbury's sea trading days when barges pulled up alongside. Now a traditional, two-bar country pub with a no-smoking dining room, delightful garden with benched seating and boules pitch. The pub has an unrivalled reputation for its food, serving meals made from local village produce, not forgetting Severn salmon and mullet in season. Beautiful walking area, well signposted. The nearby church commands a wonderful view of the Severn. Wheelchair access via side door. Inch's Iron Oak cider served.
🏃Q🌂◖◗🍺♿♣●P

OLD SODBURY

Dog Inn
Badminton Road (between Chipping Sodbury and A46)
☼ 11-11; 12-3, 7-10.30 Sun
☎ (01454) 312006
Fuller's London Pride; Marston's Pedigree; Wadworth 6X; Wickwar BOB Ⓗ

Popular 16th-century roadside pub with three regular ales and one guest. The interior is well-furnished and has two roaring real fires. Wooden beams abound in this historic pub which was frequented by

William Davis, a local highwayman. The Cotswold Way footpath passes close by and the pub attracts hikers among its mixed clientele. The accent is on food and a huge menu offers many vegetarian options. Children are welcomed; there is a family room and a play area forms part of the extensive garden.
🏃Q🌂🛏◖◗P✂

PILLOWELL

Swan
Off B4234 from Lydney OS625065
☼ 12-2 (3 Sat; not Mon & Tue lunch), 7-11; 12-3, 7-11 Sun
☎ (01594) 562477
Wickwar Coopers' WPA, BOB; guest beers Ⓗ

Small, comfortable, friendly pub in the heart of the Forest of Dean. It has been converted back to its original three-roomed format – now used as public bar, lounge and restaurant – using wood panelling and stained glass. There is no TV, juke box, pool table or fruit machine – so it's ideal for a quiet relaxing drink. There are also 100 bottle-conditioned beers in stock. The food is artisan, speciality cheeses from the West Country – more than 50 to choose from, either as cheeseboard meals or as ploughman's. No children.
🏃Q◖◗♣●P

POPE'S HILL

Greyhound
Off A48 at Elton Corner OS686141
☼ 11.30-3, 5.30 (6.30 Sat)-11; 12-3, 7-10.30 Sun
☎ (01452) 760344 e-mail: greyhoundi@nextcall.net
Fuller's London Pride; Taylor Landlord; guest beers Ⓗ

Tracing its origins back beyond 1836, this friendly, country pub offers good beer and food, an L-shaped bar with a welcoming open fire and good atmosphere. A well-refurbished extension on the front of the

INN BRIEF

LONGBOROUGH
Coach & Horses
Off A424
11-3, 7-11; 12-3, 7-10.30 Sun
Donnington XXX, BB Ⓗ
Friendly, one-bar pub in centre of quiet village with morris dancing tradition. It is the only pub to sell XXX all year. Walkers may bring in sandwiches.

MARSHFIELD
Lord Nelson
High Street
12-2.30, 6-11;
12-3, 7-10.30 Sun
Draught Bass; Courage Best; Flowers Original; Fuller's London Pride; Greene King Abbot; Worthington Bitter Ⓗ
Big, comfortable Cotswold stone pub set at the end of a pretty village High Street.

NAUNTON
Black Horse Inn
Off B4068 11-3, 6-11;
12-3, 7-10.30 Sun
Donnington BB, SBA Ⓗ
Traditional stone pub, one of the small but magnificent estate of Donnington Brewery. Very popular with walkers.

OLD DOWN
Fox Inn
The Inner Down
12-3, 6-11; 12-11 Sat;
12-10.30 Sun
Draught Bass; Flowers IPA; Mole's Best Bitter Ⓗ
Pleasant garden with play area, though children not allowed inside pub. Live entertainment Sat eve. Food available lunch/eve.

PUCKLECHURCH
Rose & Crown
68 Parkfield Road
11.30-3, 6-11; 12-4, 7-10.30 Sun
Draught Bass; Wadworth IPA, 6X, seasonal beer Ⓗ
Superior Wadworth pub strong on food and ale. No food Sun & Mon eves. OAP specials available. Pub games offered. Children welcome outside and in restaurant.

STOW-ON-THE-WOLD
Queen's Head
The Square
11-2.30 (3 Sat), 6-11; 12-2.30, 7-10.30 Sun
Donnington BB, SBA Ⓗ
Fine Cotswold pub in town square. Popular with both locals and visitors. No food Sun.

TEWKESBURY
White Bear
Bredon Road
11-11; 12-10.30 Sun
Wye Valley Bitter; guest beers Ⓗ
Friendly two-bar pub wih the best value pint in town. Guests are from local breweries. Home of Tewkesbury winter ale festival.

TORMARTON
Portcullis Inn
High Street
12-3, 6-11; 12-3, 7-10.30 Sun
Draught Bass; Butcombe Bitter; Otter Bitter; Wadworth 6X; guest beers Ⓗ
Imposing pub exterior constructed of Cotswold stone covered with virginia creeper set in a quiet, sleepy village.

WINTERBOURNE DOWN
Cross Hands
Down Road
12 (11 Sat)-11; 12-10.30 Sun
Draught Bass; Courage Best Bitter; Mole's Tap Bitter; Wickwar BOB; guest beers Ⓗ
Unspoilt local with two rooms and a large garden. Children welcome. No food. Live music Fri eve. Also in *Good Cider Guide*. Its sewing machine collection is notable. *Cask Marque* accredited.

premises provides a combined children's/games room, and no-smoking area. Large, pleasant garden with meandering stream and shady willow tree. Children's play area – note the dinosaur. Awarded Forest of Dean CAMRA *Pub of the Year* 1999 and 2001.

🏚Q🛏🕏🕪 🛆P⊭

PRESTBURY

Royal Oak
The Burgage
✪ 11.30-2.30, 5.30-11; 12-3.30, 7-10.30 Sun
☎ (01242) 522344 e-mail: s.daws@virgin.net
Archers Best Bitter; guest beers Ⓗ
Small, cosy, popular local in Britain's most haunted village. There is a public bar featuring low ceilings and exposed beams, and a restaurant area (until 9pm). A large garden at the rear leads to a skittle alley/function room. Popular with racegoers, especially during Gold Cup week, there is free off-road parking nearby. Opening hours may be extended during the summer months. The food is primarily home made (notably the desserts) and includes cheeses from a local producer.
Q🕏🕪

PUCKLECHURCH ✣

Star Inn
37 Castle Road (next to playing fields)
✪ 11-11; 12-10.30 Sun
☎ (0117) 937 2391
Draught Bass; Ⓖ **Marston's Pedigree or Wadworth 6X** Ⓗ
This village pub is a focus for the local community. Regular charity events, include the 'Revels', which features a beer festival and fireworks. Big on real cider, with three always available, the ale is also splendid, with Bass being brought up from the cellar in a jug. One corner of this L-shaped pub is given over to the locally sourced, no-nonsense, good-value food (not served Sun eve). No-smoking dining area. Games are popular, with a golf society, fishing clubs, crib and darts teams. The pub is a stop on the 689 bus service to Bristol city centre. Live music occasionally.
🕏🕪♣🕪P⊭

QUEDGELEY

Little Thatch Hotel
141 Bristol Road
(B4008)
✪ 12-2.30 (closed Sat), 6.30-11; 12-3, 7-10.30 Sun
☎ (01452) 720687 e-mail: jamcdou@aol.com
Otter Bitter; guest beers Ⓗ
The thatch may have gone, but the core of this fine hotel remains the wonderfully preserved building of 1351. According to legend Anne Boleyn stayed here when Henry VIII visited Gloucester in 1535, and prior to licensing in the 1950s, it was known as Queen Anne's Farm. There is excellent modern accommodation attached while the original building has two bar areas with low beams, pews, settles and horse brasses, and a dining room. Three craft brewery beers are always available, and the food is of a very high standard. Monthly jazz (first Sun).
🕏🖾🕪P

SAPPERTON

Daneway Inn
West of village OS935034
✪ 11-2.30 (3 Sat, 5 summer Sat), 6.30-11; 12-3 (5 summer), 7-10.30 Sun
☎ (01285) 760297
Wadworth IPA, 6X, seasonal beers Ⓗ
Old pub full of character, built in 1784 as three cottages for canal workers, near one end of the now disused Sapperton Tunnel. It was later used as lodging for bargees and tunnel leggers until licensed premises gradually took over all the cottages. The comfortable lounge is dominated by a magnificent carved fireplace. It is friendly and popular with walkers. There is a large garden and car park on the route of the old canal. No-smoking room for families.
🏚Q🛏🕏🕪🖴🛆♣P🗒

SHEEPSCOMBE

Butchers Arms
Signed from A46 and B4070
OS892104
✪ 11.30-3, 6.30 (6 Fri & Sat)-11; 12-3.30, 7-10.30 Sun
☎ (01452) 812113
Hook Norton Best Bitter; guest beers Ⓗ
Cosy, 17th-century village pub with a restaurant area, furnished in traditional, country style. Part of Blenheim Inns, a privately-owned company with five outlets which successfully breathes life into tired pubs. The pub has fish nights on Wed, and runs quiz and darts teams. Quoits is played. Note the interesting carved pub sign: it is thought butchering went on here when Henry VIII hunted deer in the valley. Staggering views from the tables on the steep grass behind the pub. Worth a walk to the bizarre sloping village cricket ground. The batsman cannot see the bowler running in until he is almost at the wicket because of the steep slope.
🏚Q🕏🕪♣P⊭🗒

SLAD

Woolpack
On B4070
✪ 11 (11.30 winter)-3.30, 6-11; 11-11 Sat; 12-10.30 Sun
☎ (01452) 813429 e-mail: woolpack.slad@virgin.net
Uley Bitter, Old Ric, Old Spot Prize Ale, Pig's Ear; guest beer Ⓗ
Popular 16th-century inn clinging to the side of Slad valley with superb views. Popular with walkers. Achieved fame through the late *Cider with Rosie* author, Laurie Lee, who was a regular. It has been thoughtfully restored including the addition of wooden settles in the end bar. Well-behaved children are welcome in the end room while the three bars serve the award-winning Uley beers (Old Ric is only available on Sun to cater for a specific demand). Three ciders and perries are sold: Bulmers Medium, Weston's Old Rosie and Herefordshire County Perry. No food available Sun or Mon eves. Sun lunches served from 1pm. 'Spingo' weekends are held quarterly when beer is brought from the Blue Anchor in Helston and cornish pasties are a feature. Beer festival at Easter.
🏚Q🛏🕏🕪🖴♣🕪P⊭

171

STAPLE HILL

Humper's Off-Licence
26 Soundwell Road
✪ 12-2, 5-10.30 (12-10.30 summer Sat); 12-2, 5-10.30 (12-10.30 summer) Sun
☎ (0117) 956 5525
Draught Bass; Butcombe Bitter; Smiles Best; ⊞ Wickwar BOB; Ⓟ guest beers Ⓖ
Small, friendly off-licence selling up to six real ales, including two ever-changing guests, and four real ciders, plus a large choice of bottle-conditioned beers. A wide selection of polypins is stocked in Dec at very reasonable prices. A local institution, 10 years in this *Guide*, it has also featured in CAMRA's *Good Cider Guide*. ✿

STROUD

Golden Fleece
Nelson Street
✪ 12-3, 5-11; 11.30-11 Sat; 12-10.30 Sun
☎ (01453) 764850
Draught Bass; Boddingtons Bitter; Greene King Abbot; Wadworth 6X ⊞
Stroud's jazz and blues pub; jazz plays quietly in the background and live music is performed Thu eve. The music is inclined to be louder at weekends. It has two alcoves leading off where musical instruments and jazz memorabilia decorate the walls. Two coal fires add to the homely atmosphere. Light lunches during the week and Sun lunches also served. A nearby public car park is free after 6pm and all day Sun.
▲◑≈♣

SWINEFORD

Swan
Bath Road (A431, 1 mile SE of Bitton)
✪ 11-3, 5-11; 12-3, 7-10.30 Sun
☎ (0117) 932 3101
website: www.downourlocal.com/theswan-swineford
Draught Bass; Ⓖ Butcombe Bitter; ⊞ Courage Best Bitter; Ⓖ guest beer ⊞
Converted from three cottages in a row of six, in a tiny hamlet between Bristol and Bath, opposite an old flax mill on the north bank of the Avon. The pub is famed for its Bass on gravity and the guest beer is usually a session bitter. The main bar has a log fire, a curving wood and leather bar and is popular with locals. There is also a no-smoking bar and a restaurant area; each has a distinct atmosphere. Good, home-prepared food is served daily, and booking for Sun lunch is advisable. Boules court available. Children are welcome. A free house with a wide range of good walks in the area. ▲❀◑♣Ⓟ✁

TEWKESBURY ❖

Olde Black Bear
68 High Street
✪ 11-11; 12-10.30 Sun
☎ (01684) 292202
Courage Directors; Greenalls Bitter; Wadworth 6X; Wells Bombardier; guest beer ⊞
The oldest inn in Gloucestershire, dating from 1308. It was refurbished in 1999 and features many separate rambling bar areas and leatherwork on one of the ceilings dates to the 17th century. The no-smoking area was originally the stables and the inn's front door is reputedly the second oldest in the area. Note the intriguing old photographs of Tewkesbury. Reports suggest a resident ghost. A pleasant terraced patio overlooks the garden and the river Avon (moorings available). Food served daily 12–9 (7 Sun).
▲❀◑♿▲♣✁

TWYNING

Village Inn
The Green
✪ Summer: 12-3, 5.30-11 Tue-Sat; winter: 12-3, 6-11 Thu-Sat; 12-3, 7-10.30 Sun
☎ (01684) 293500
Adnams Broadside; Greene King IPA; Tetley Bitter; guest beer ⊞
Busy village inn popular with the locals. There is a garden to the rear and the front patio overlooks the village green (car parking on the green). Pleasant walks to river where ferry runs daily to Tewkesbury and Bredon. Rambling bar area and the ceiling is decorated with an assortment of rugby ties, international tickets and other rugby memorabilia. Used by local skittle and dart teams and as a meeting place for many local societies and clubs. Watch out for low entrance doorway. The pub was built in 1457 and has low ceilings. The attractive gardens enhance the beautiful village setting.
▲❀◑▲♣

ULEY

Old Crown
The Green
✪ 11.30-2.30 (3 Sat), 7-11; 12-3, 7-10.30 Sun
☎ (01453) 860502
e-mail: sandra@oldcrownuley.freeserve.co.uk
Uley Bitter, Pig's Ear; guest beers ⊞
Welcoming, attractive whitewashed 17th-century free house set in the picturesque Uley Valley. It has a pleasant walled garden which is safe for children. The cosy main bar has a low-timbered ceiling. Close to Uley Brewery and the Cotswold Way, it is popular with walkers. The pub has a resident bluegrass band which play every Tue. A selection of bands play regularly on Fri eve. The pub was voted Dursley and district CAMRA *Pub of the Year* 2001. En-suite accommodation is available and there is good-value, home-cooked food. The enthusiastic landlady serves over 150 different guest ales each year, mainly from micro-breweries.
▲Q☎❀⇌◑♣Ⓟ

WATERLEY BOTTOM

New Inn
Signed from North Nibley OS758964
✪ 12-2.30, 7-11; 12-11 Sat; 12-10.30 Sun
☎ (01453) 543695
Bath Gem; Cotleigh Tawny; Greene King Abbot; guest beer ⊞
Lovely free house situated in the hamlet of Waterley Bottom, it is surrounded by steep hills. During the 19th century it was a cider house and was frequented by workers travelling on the adjacent path from

Wotton-under-Edge to the wool mills in Cam and Dursley. In the first week of June a ball-throwing event takes place from the New Inn over the hill in Dursley to the New Inn, Waterley Bottom. The pub has two bars and an attractive garden and is popular with walkers. An Ordnance Survey map is recommended for first-time visitors. No food served on Mon.
⌂ Q ❀ ⊄ ⊟ ♣ ● P

WHITMINSTER

Old Forge Inn
On A38, close to jct 13 of M5
☼ 11.30-3 (not Mon), 5-11; 11.30-11 Sat;
▉▉▉▉ ▋▉ ▉▉▉ ▉▋▉
☎ (01452) 741306

Black Sheep Best Bitter; Exmoor Ale; Wickwar Cotswold Way; guest beer Ⓗ

This pleasant rural pub struggles to be seen beside an adjacent hotel and shop. Inside its beamed ceiling, carpeting and fashionable curtains contribute to a homely atmosphere that is enhanced by the landlady's cheerful personality. The regulars who crowd its small bar are knowledgeable on its previous history as forge, petrol station and restaurant. Records found go back to 1535, but some of its roof trusses are thought to be Saxon. Home-cooked food is available from a blackboard selection except on Sun eve or Mon. The cider is from Thatcher's. Occasional live entertainment.
Q ❀ ⊄ ♣ ● P ⅟

WINCHCOMBE

Bell Inn
Gretton Road
☼ 11-3, 7-11; 11-11 Sat; 12-10.30 Sun
☎ (01242) 602205

Donnington BB, SBA; Greene King Abbot; Hook Norton Best Bitter; guest beers Ⓗ

This free house is immediately recognisable by its distinctive Donnington pub sign – a throwback to the days when it was owned by Donnington Brewery. The present building is the third Bell Inn, converted from a group of labourers' cottages just before the turn of the century. The original in nearby Dent's Terrace was demolished at the time of the Crimean War, while the second Bell was an ale house down the road. This popular community pub runs dart and crib teams and has satellite TV for major sporting events. Light bar snacks at lunchtime.
⌂ ❀ ⊄ P

WITHINGTON

King's Head
Yanworth Road OS036153
☼ 11-2.30, 6-11; 12-3, 7-10.30 Sun
☎ (01242) 890216

Hook Norton Best Bitter; Wickwar BOB Ⓖ

Unspoilt village local, hidden away down a side road – can be hard to find but worth the effort. The pub has been in the same family for over 80 years and is a true free house having been sold by Courage in 1956. Separate comfortable lounge and public bar where table skittles, shove-ha'penny and pool are played. No food other than crisps and pies. The landlady is a gem. Q ❀ ⊟ ♣ P

WOODCHESTER

Ram Inn
Station Road (signed from A46)
☼ 11-11; 12-10.30 Sun
☎ (01453) 873329

Archers Best Bitter; John Smith's Bitter; guest beers Ⓗ

The proposed conservatory overlooking the valley will provide a much-needed extension to this popular pub. It celebrated its 400th birthday in 2001. It offers three ever-changing ales. A beer festival is held during May bank holiday weekend and an Irish beer festival coincides with the National Hunt Festival at Cheltenham in March. Situated in superb walking country close to Selsley Common and Woodchester Mansion and park.
⌂ Q ❀ ⊄ ⊅ ⅃ ▲ ♣ ● P

Royal Oak
Church Road, North Woodchester (signed from A46)
☼ 11-3, 5.30-11; 11-11 Sat; 12-10.30 Sun
☎ (01453) 872735

Archers Best Bitter; Uley Bitter, Old Spot Prize Ale; guest beer Ⓗ

Pretty, whitewashed, recently refurbished 17th-century cottage inn with two elegant bars. This lively, friendly local attracts people from miles around to sample its ales and imaginative, freshly cooked meals. The reasonably-priced menu can contain game terrine with onion marmalade and salmon and dill fishcakes with caper mayonnaise (no food Sun eve). The dining area has a magnificent open fireplace with a log fire. Patio garden and stunning views over a typical Cotswold valley. Entertainment includes quiz night (Mon), music night (Tue) featuring folk, jazz or blues and regular race nights for charity.
⌂ Q ❀ ⊄ ⊟ ♣ P

WOOLASTON COMMON

Rising Sun
Off A48, 1 mile to Woolaston Common OS590009
☼ 12-2.30 (not Wed), 6.30-11; 12-2.30, 7-10.30 Sun
☎ (01594) 529282

Freeminer Bitter; Fuller's London Pride; Hook Norton Best Bitter Ⓗ

Lovely 350-year-old stone-built country pub with spectacular views over the Forest of Dean. The landlord has been at the pub for 23 years, and has made many sympathetic improvements during that time. The facilities comprise a large bar with open fire and a small snug. Featured in the circular pub walks of the Forest of Dean, the pub is popular with walkers. A friendly atmosphere, good varied menu of home-cooked food and three real ales on offer.
⌂ Q ❀ ⊄ ▲ ♣ P

HAMPSHIRE

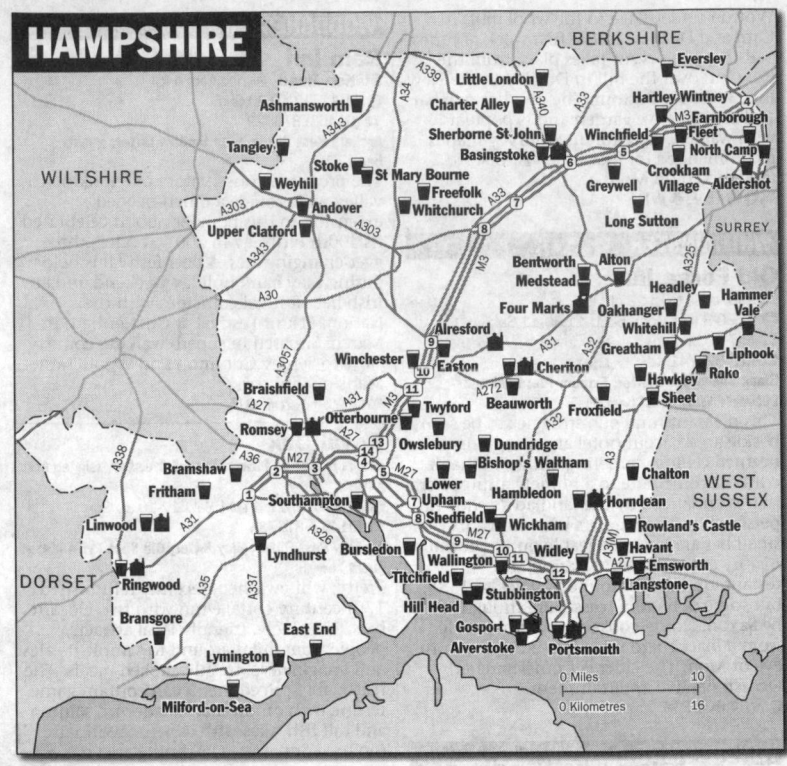

ALDERSHOT

Garden Gate
4 Church Lane East
🕓 11.30-3, 5.30-11; 11-11 Sat; 12-4, 6.30-10.30 Sun
☎ (01252) 321051
Greene King IPA, Abbot Ⓗ
Originally built for German soldiers during Victoria's reign, this pub boasts etched windows, traditional sash windows and an upstairs dining area. Popular with residents from local guest houses. The two distinct drinking areas allow the pub games fixtures to continue undisturbed. The separate back bar is open unless reserved. Lunchtime snacks are available and eve meals on request. Barbecues take place on the patio. Entertainment includes crib night (Mon), darts and quiz night (Tue). Free range eggs delivered (Wed). 🏵🛏◖◗⇌P

Red Lion
Ash Road (A323, near Manor Park)
🕓 12-2, 5-11 Thu-Sat; 12-4, 7-10.30 Sun
☎ (01252) 403503
Beer range varies Ⓗ
An air of quiet professionalism prevails in this large 1930s roadhouse, situated on the site of the original Red Lion, whose cellars were used as overnight cells for prisoners from London courts bound for transportation from Portsmouth. Local CAMRA *Pub of the Year* between 1997–99 and Wessex regional finalist in 1999. Three log fires and a secluded garden for warmer days make it justifiably popular with all age groups. The landlord is a champion of small independent breweries and is keen on

running live music nights. Lunches are served Tue–Fri. Do try the landlady's ultimate sausage sandwich. Oversized, lined glasses available on demand.
🏰Q🏵◖◗⇌♣P🗒

Royal Staff
37a Mount Pleasant Road (off A323 at jct with Waterloo Rd)
🕓 12-3, 5-11; 12-11 Sat; 12-10.30 Sun
☎ (01252) 408012
Fuller's Chiswick, London Pride, seasonal beers; guest beers Ⓗ
Back-street local at the top of a fairly steep hill, Waterloo Road, which is lined with early-Victorian villas. The pub has been beautifully refurbished in the style that the early residents of these streets would recognise. It has a comfortable, lively single bar and a strong community atmosphere. It also features a safe, fully enclosed children's garden. Handy for Aldershot Town FC. The experienced landlord keeps excellent Fuller's beers and their guests with no sign of a sparkler. One of the first pubs in the area to achieve *Cask Marque* accreditation. Lunches served Mon–Fri. 🏵◖⇌♣●

ALTON

Eight Bells
Church Street (off High St)
🕓 11-11; 12-10.30 Sun
☎ (01420) 82417
Ballard's Best Bitter; Hogs Back TEA; guest beers Ⓗ
Excellent free house, just outside the town centre, on the old Alton–Odiham turnpike. The building dates from 1640 and is steeped in history. Sweet Fanny

Adams is buried in the churchyard opposite; her murderer was tried and found guilty in the pub. One small, oak-beamed, atmospheric bar with a spacious area to the rear. One end is dominated by a magnificent fireplace in front of which the ageing, but friendly, pub dog can be found. Increasingly gaining a reputation for quality and choice and especially for local beers at very competitive prices.
♨Q❀⇔◑◐⬤🕭≈♣⬤P⮾⊟

French Horn
The Butts (close to A31 jct)
🕙 11-2.30, 5.30-11; 12-3, 7-10.30 Sun
☎ (01420) 83269
Draught Bass; Courage Best Bitter, Directors; Gale's HSB; Ushers Best Bitter, Bishop's Tipple Ⓗ

Consistently popular historic pub, renowned for its value-for-money food. It overlooks the medieval archery butts, now a public open space. Warming, roaring fire in winter lights up a tankard collection on the beams; unusual fish tank, outside aviary and several grassed drinking areas. Skittle alley adjacent and annual old-fashioned cricket tournament hosted each Father's Day. Good view of steam trains on Watercress Line. Regulars' corner near the fire is a welcoming and eccentric spot. No children under 14 are allowed in the main building.
♨Q❀⇔◑◐P

ALVERSTOKE

Alverbank
Stokes Bay Road
🕙 11-11; 12-10.30 Sun
☎ (023) 9251 0005
website: www.alverbank@clara.co.uk
Beer range varies Ⓗ

Victorian country house hotel bar in an attractive setting overlooking Stokes Bay and once frequented by Lillie Langtry. The River Alver used to flow between the hotel and Stokes Bay but has long since been diverted. There are up to five real ales from independents and micro-breweries, including a house ale (Ringwood Best Bitter rebadged). Beers from Cornwall and Kent appear regularly. A separate restaurant is open daily, except Sun eve, and there are outdoor barbecues on Sun lunchtimes in the summer. Normally a quiet, relaxing atmosphere, but beware of summer Sat weddings and pre-Christmas parties with discos.
♨❀⇔◑◐▲P

ANDOVER

Blacksmith's Arms
134 New Street
🕙 12-2 (not Tue), 5-11; 11.30-11 Sat; 12-10.30 Sun
☎ (01264) 352881
Brains Bitter; Fuller's London Pride; Taylor Landlord; guest beer Ⓗ

Red-brick, 100-year-old ex-Marston's free house on the edge of the town centre. The building accommodates a basic public bar with dartboard and a small, comfortable lounge. The latter is well-used for televised sport and the consumption of good beer in a food-free environment. The sporting theme is much in evidence in this room with some interesting memorabilia. The

guest beer usually changes weekly and mainly features ales from small independents and micro-breweries. Despite external appearances the pub is genuinely free of tie and is a rare outlet for Taylor Landlord in the area. Local CAMRA *Pub of the Year* 2000. ❀⊟♣P

Lamb Inn
21 Winchester Street (near police station)
🕙 11-3, 6 (5 Fri; 7 Sat)-11; 7-10.30 Sun
☎ (01264) 323961
Wadworth IPA, 6X, seasonal beers Ⓗ

One of Andover's most traditional-style pubs, and one of a dwindling number with a public bar. It had a long history under the now defunct Heath & Crowley breweries, before becoming Wadworth's first Andover pub in 1954. The licensee is Wadworth's longest-serving landlady and recently a special beer was brewed for her. A quiet spot can usually be found in one of the three separate bars. The small, homely lounge has a special cottage cosiness where it is not unusual to find board games being played. Live music is often featured in the larger public bar. The 'lamb' refers to Knights Templar heraldry. ♨Q⇔◑◐♣

Wyke Down Country Pub & Restaurant
Picket Piece (follow tourist signs for Wyke Down from A303)
🕙 11-2.30, 6-11 (may vary); 12-3, 6-10.30 Sun
☎ (01264) 352048 website: www.wykedown.co.uk
Ringwood Best Bitter, True Glory; guest beers Ⓗ

Wyke Down blends old and new in an early 19th-century barn with a large conservatory overlooking the surrounding countryside. In 1997 it was totally refurbished and a restaurant was added, where you can enjoy an à la carte menu or pub food with local beers and a good selection of wines. Rooms are available for private functions and there is a children's play area and indoor recreation room. Camping facilities include hardstanding bays for caravans and a swimming pool. There is also a golf driving range. Watch the web page for news of events such as car boot sales.
♨Q⛺❀◑◐▲♣P⬤

ASHMANSWORTH

Plough
1 mile off A343, S of Highclere village
🕙 12-2.30 (not Mon or Tue), 6-11 (not Mon); 12-3, 7.30-10.30 Sun
☎ (01635) 253047
Archers Village, Best Bitter, Golden; guest beer Ⓖ

Very welcoming village local set in the North Hampshire Downs, close to Berkshire

INDEPENDENT BREWERIES

Beckett's Basingstoke
Cheriton Cheriton
Gale's Horndean
Hampshire Romsey
Itchen Valley Alresford
Oakleaf Gosport
Pack Horse Portsmouth
Red Shoot Linwood
Ringwood Ringwood
Triple fff Four Marks

and Wiltshire borders. This is excellent walking country with the Wayfarers Walk running across the north of the village. The pub itself originated in 1778 as a beer house serving the local community. It has a cosy atmosphere and large open fire. Note the village photographs alongside the main bar counter as well as the collection of old agricultural implements. A selection of bar snacks is available. ♨Q♣♠

BASINGSTOKE

Basingstoke & North Hants Cricket Club

Fairfield Road (county cricket ground, S of centre)
✪ 12-2.30, 6-11; 2 (5.30 summer)-10.30 Sat;
12-10.30 Sun
☎ (01256) 473646 website: www.bnhcc.freewire.co.uk
Beckett's Old Town Bitter; Fuller's London Pride, seasonal beers; Ringwood Best Bitter; guest beers Ⓗ
Founded by Col John May, owner of May's Brewery, which ceased brewing in the late 1940s. Although a members-only club, CAMRA members are welcome on production of a valid membership card. The enthusiastic steward runs real ale festivals during the year. House beers are from Fuller's but ales from Hampshire are always represented, in particular Beckett's and Ringwood. Other beers from outside the area are sometimes available. The club has cricket, football, squash, snooker and darts teams. The atmosphere is often described as more 'pub' than 'club' and the club has won numerous regional and local CAMRA awards. ❀ঔ♣P⽊▯●

Bounty Inn

81 Bounty Road (S end of town, follow signs to Fairfields)
✪ 11-2.30, 5.30-11; 11-11 Sat & summer Fri;
12-10.30 Sun
☎ (01256) 320071
Courage Best Bitter; Greene King Abbot; Marston's Pedigree; Ushers Founders Ale, seasonal beers Ⓗ
Formerly the Cattle Market, the pub's name was changed in the 1950s to reflect its location next to May's Bounty cricket ground. The building dates from the mid-18th century and is Basingstoke's oldest pub. Like many pubs with a history, this one reputedly has its own ghost. The deep chalk cellar used to have a tunnel, one of a warren of secret passages said to be under old Basingstoke. A rare, but not too popular feature (especially during cold winters!) is the outside gents' toilet. No-smoking family/function room and limited parking. No food served Mon eve. ♨❀ঔ♣P⽊

Queen's Arms

Bunnian Place (by station)
✪ 11-3, 5-11; 11-11 Fri & Sat and last Thu in month;
12-10.30 Sun
☎ (01256) 465488
Courage Best Bitter, Directors; Theakston XB; Wadworth 6X; guest beers Ⓗ
Situated conveniently close to Basingstoke rail station, the Queen's is a survivor of the decimation of Old Basingstoke in the 1960s. Overshadowed by modern office blocks, it nestles defiantly offering a reassuring oasis of permanence in a changing town centre. Popular with a wide spectrum of drinkers, the Queen's Arms boasts the longest-serving publican in the town. The bar staff can

notch up a respectable number of years' service too! Alongside the house beers there is always an interesting guest, often from a locally-based micro such as Beckett's or Triple fff. ❀ঔ≋♣

Royal Oak

Worting Road
✪ 11 (12 Sat)-11; 12-10.30 Sun
☎ (01256) 412596 website: www.royaloakpub.com
Courage Best Bitter; Hogs Back Hair of the Hog, TEA; guest beers Ⓗ
Bright paintwork makes this pub hard to miss. It is situated a short drive from the Museum of Living History in Basingstoke. Inside there are a few interesting photographs of the old Blue Peter retread factory, which is behind the pub. A variety of live music is performed on Fri night in the public bar. There is a good choice of home-cooked food. Beckett's, the local brewery, is featured regularly and Brakspear Bitter is one of the guest ales. Covered patio available for outdoor drinking and juke box in rear bar.
Q❀ঔ◗▣♣P

Soldiers Return

80 Upper Sherborne Road (opp. Soldiers Return playing field, Oakridge Rd)
✪ 11-2.30, 5.30-11; 11-11 Fri & Sat; 12-10.30 Sun
☎ (01256) 322449
Beckett's Stoke Ale; Courage Best Bitter, Directors; guest beers Ⓗ
Pre-1850s Grade II listed building on edge of Oakridge Estate, north of town centre. Very much part of the local community, the pub is owned by a partner in Beckett's Brewery and usually stocks one of their beers but could alternatively sell a guest not normally found in the area. It has its own football team, sponsored by Beckett's, and is a firm supporter of other local sports clubs. The lounge bar has prints depicting 19th- and 20th-century military uniforms. The local motorcycle action group meets here Thu eve. The public bar is very lively and there is a no-smoking family room. Pleasant garden area at the front overlooks a playing field.
Q☎❀ঔ◗▣♣P

BEAUWORTH

Milbury's

S of A272, 1 mile beyond Beauworth Hamlet
OS570246
✪ 11-11; 12-10.30 Sun
☎ (01962) 771248
Cheriton Best Bitter, Diggers Gold; Hampshire King Alfred's, Pride of Romsey; guest beer Ⓗ
Genuine free house. A remote, 18th-century inn on a hilltop crossroads with extensive views. Inside there is a wealth of oak beams, flagstone and quarry-tile floors and bare brick walls. Furnishings include ancient settles and gnarled, uneven tables. One of the interconnected rooms has a 300ft well with a gigantic treadmill to raise the bucket. A wide-ranging menu has many home-made dishes including real pizzas; portions are generous. The house beer is a hoppy, 3.8% ABV from Triple fff Brewery; the cider is Addlestone's. Two B&B rooms provide the opportunity to sample rural tranquillity. Skittle alley available.
♨Q☎❀⍽◗Å♣♠P⽊

BENTWORTH

Sun Inn
Off A339 OS671403
🕐 12-3, 6-11; 12-10.30 Sun
☎ (01420) 562338
Badger Champion Ale; Cheriton Pots Ale; Courage Best Bitter; Ringwood Best Bitter; Stonehenge Pigswill; guest beers Ⓗ
17th-century inn with three connected rooms, each with a log fire. The central bar has a low ceiling with old oak beams and an inglenook. Families with children can use the side room, also used by diners. No music or fruit machines. Scrubbed wooden tables and walls decorated with horse brass and farm implements complete the rural picture. Beers from local micro-breweries are always available and the house beer is from Hampshire Brewery. The inn is well-known for its quality, home-made food, but it remains a pub, rather than a restaurant. Advance booking is recommended, especially at weekends.
🏚Q🕙🏛🌙P

BISHOP'S WALTHAM

Bunch of Grapes
St Peter's Street (off High St)
🕐 10-2, 6-11; 12-2, 7-10.30 Sun
☎ (01489) 892935
Courage Best Bitter; Ⓖ **Ushers Founders Ale, seasonal beers** Ⓗ
Situated in a narrow medieval street leading to the parish church, this small village pub has been run by the same family since 1913. The unspoilt interior comprises a cosy, welcoming bar which is the base for the darts teams and golfing society that is now 10 years old, with over 120 members. For a quiet drink, use the small room off the bar or the garden in summer. There is no kitchen so it is purely a drinkers' pub. Q🏛🌿

BRAISHFIELD

Newport Inn
Newport Lane (take the lane opp. village telephone box) OS372249
🕐 11-3, 6-11; 12-2.30, 7-10.30 Sun
☎ (01794) 368225
Gale's Butser, Winter Brew, HSB, Festival Mild (summer) Ⓗ
For those who remember pubs of the 1960s, this is your scene; a magical timewarp envelops this pub. No food symbols feature, since all that is on offer are ploughmans and ham or cheese sandwiches (with added tomato as an option, introduced in the 1980s) but the hungry will find their quality admirable. Sat and Sun eves, be prepared to join in the singsong around the piano, played by the landlady. Occasional folk singers call in. The clientele is extraordinarily mixed, coming from all over the county to this 'pub in aspic'. Large, somewhat unrestrained, garden.
🏚Q🏛🌿🌙P

BRAMSHAW

Bramble Hill Hotel
½ mile W of B3079 OS261158
🕐 11-3, 7-11 (not Mon-Thu eve); 11-11 Sat & Easter-

Nov; 12-10.30 (6 winter) Sun
☎ (023) 8081 3165
Ringwood XXXX Porter, Fortyniner; guest beer (summer) Ⓗ
Peaceful hotel in the depths of the New Forest. The rambling building is Victorian mock-Tudor, about 1850, with a pleasant mix of gables, chimneys, brick and timber. Surrounding the hotel are lawns and glades (best in May) and around the grounds the forest itself. The comfortable bar is lofty and wood-panelled with splendid views through the garden bar. Note that Ringwood Fortyniner is sold as Old Bramble. On winter weekdays full meals are by arrangement only. Warning for walkers: a map or wellies, and compass advised; the forest hereabouts is both wet and vague.
🏚Q🕙🏛🌙P✂

BRANSGORE

Three Tuns
Ringwood Road (1½ miles N of A35 at Hinton)
🕐 11.30-2.30 (11-3 summer), 6-11; 12-3.30, 7-10.30 Sun
☎ (01425) 672232 website: www.3tuns.com
Hampshire Strong's Best Bitter; Ringwood Fortyniner; Young's Special; guest beer Ⓗ
Picturesque, thatched 17th-century inn, close to the New Forest and the Dorset border. The recently-altered interior still retains a traditional public bar with exposed oak beams and friendly atmosphere. The lounge bar has an open fireplace with a drinking area and adjoining open-plan restaurant where high quality meals and daily specials are served (snacks not available). Outside, an enclosed patio, a beer garden and a pétanque terrain overlook open fields.
🏚Q🌙🍴🏛🅿●

BURSLEDON

Jolly Sailor
Lands End Road (park at station, follow signed path)
🕐 11-11; 12-10.30 Sun
☎ (023) 8040 5557 e-mail: jolly.sailor@ukonline.co.uk
Badger K&B Sussex, IPA, Best, Tanglefoot; guest beers Ⓗ
Cosy, multi-roomed riverside pub, parts of which date back to the 1700s. Low-beamed ceilings and flagstone and wooden floors add to the traditional atmosphere. Good quality, home-cooked food is available 12–9.30 every day; the menu is comprehensive and includes fresh fish. Access from the road is down a very steep path and even the beer arrives via its own cliff railway. Roadside parking is limited. The pub has its own moorings on the River Hamble with covered jetty and waterside terrace. Well worth seeking out. Children allowed in no-smoking area only.
🏚Q🌙🍴🌊✂●

Linden Tree
School Road (off A27/A3025)
🕐 11-2.30, 6-11; 11-11 Fri & Sat; 12-4, 7-10.30 Sun
☎ (023) 8040 2356
Draught Bass; Wadworth IPA, 6X, JCB Ⓗ
Friendly and relaxed haven from the stresses of modern life with a strong, traditional emphasis. The single, L-shaped bar has a public bar area with a dartboard

and a large lounge with real log fire. Excellent, home-cooked lunches are served Mon–Sat in the lounge, which is no-smoking at lunchtime. There are no electronic machines and be ready to pay a fine if your mobile phone rings! The terrace at the front sports a pergola with vines and there is a garden at the rear. Entertainment includes quiz night (Tue), darts (Mon and Wed in winter) and a meat draw (Sun).
♨Q❀◐P●

CHALTON

Red Lion

☼ 11-3, 6-11; 12-3, 7-10.30 Sun
☎ (023) 9259 2246 e-mail: redlionchalton@aol.com
Gale's Bulser, GB, HSB, seasonal beers; guest beers H

Probably the oldest pub in Hampshire, this thatched building nestles cosily in the South Downs. It was built in 1147, starting life as a workshop for the construction of the village church. It became a pub in 1503 and was a welcome stop on the long journey between London and Portsmouth. The pub still has both public and lounge bars, the former boasting a large inglenook and newspaper cuttings of the winter of 1962, when the pub was virtually cut off from the rest of the country. Nowadays, it successfully combines the roles of traditional village local and a place to visit and escape from the hectic urban lifestyle. The dining room doubles as a family room, no food served on Sun eve. ♨⚲❀◐ ⊟P●

CHARTER ALLEY

White Hart

White Hart Lane (1 mile W of A340)
☼ 12-2.30 (3 Sat), 7-11; 12-3, 7-10.30 Sun
☎ (01256) 850048
Morrells Varsity; Ringwood Fortyniner; guest beers H

This is the oldest building in the village. Built on the site of two houses next to the forge in 1819, this was the meeting point for folks to stop and natter; hence 'chatter alley' (later becoming 'charter alley'). There is a delightful rural ambience, with wooden beams, a skittle alley and fires in winter. In summer there is cider. From 1989 to 2001 there were 400 guest beers. Menu offerings include vegetarian meals, children's portions, a variety of steaks and their speciality – home-made pies (of course, with real ale). No meals on Mon eve.
♨Q❀◐ ⊟♣♠P⊁☐

CHERITON

Flower Pots

SW of centre, off B3046
☼ 12-2.30, 6-11; 12-3, 7-10.30 Sun
☎ (01962) 771318
Cheriton Pots Ale, Village Elder, Best Bitter, Diggers Gold, seasonal beers G

Typical village local, set in beautiful countryside on the edge of the community, famous for its own home-brewed ales produced in the newly-built, but superbly authentic, brewhouse. Beer awards festoon the traditionally-furnished rooms. Roaring fires, dried hops and a 19th-century well add that genuine rustic atmosphere. Excellent home-made food is available all sessions except Sun eve, with Wed eve

featuring Punjabi cuisine prepared by a local family. Dogs are welcome. Excellent B&B accommodation in a converted stable-block and campers may (with permission) use the adjoining field. A shaded green provides additional drinking space. Beerfest held August bank holiday weekend.
♨Q❀◣◐ Å♣P

CROOKHAM VILLAGE

Black Horse

The Street
☼ 11-2.30 (3 Fri & Sat), 5.30-11; 12-3, 7-10.30 Sun
☎ (01252) 616434
Draught Bass; Courage Best Bitter; Hogs Back TEA or seasonal beer; Wadworth 6X H

A regular *Guide* entry, this excellent, beamed village pub is well-frequented by locals and by others fortunate enough to have made the discovery. As well as the four cask ales the popular range of pub fare ensures a busy lunchtime trade (Mon–Sat); try the renowned 'dustbin omelette'! Close to the Basingstoke Canal, and in rural Hampshire, this pub provides a welcome refreshment opportunity for hikers, bikers and boaters alike. Relatively close to some built-up areas and well worth the escape.
Q❀◣P

DUNDRIDGE

Hampshire Bowman

Dundridge Lane
(1½ miles off B3035, N of Bishop's Waltham) OS578184
☼ 12-2.30 (3 Sat), 6-11; 7-10.30 Sun
☎ (01489) 892940
Archers Village, Golden; Ringwood Fortyniner; guest beer (summer) G

Remote, no-frills pub down a long country lane, with yellowed decor and a worn brick floor. The last substantial change was, apparently, when running water was installed in the 1960s. There is a small serving counter, with casks stillaged behind the bar. The menu includes pub favourites plus daily specials such as paella for two. No food Sun eve or Mon. The pub has long been known as the headquarters of the Portuguese Racing Sardine Club but nobody quite knows why. The archery club meets here and it's quiz night on Mon. Thatcher's scrumpy is served.
♨Q❀◐ Å♣❀P

EAST END (LYMINGTON)

East End Arms

Lymington Road
(3 miles E of IOW ferry) OS362968
☼ 11.30-3, 6-11 (not Mon); 12-9 Sun
☎ (01590) 626223 e-mail: jenny@eastendarms.co.uk
Ringwood Best Bitter, H **Fortyniner; guest beers** (summer) G

Unpretentious, unspoilt rural pub in a quiet backwater. The traditional public bar is preferred by the friendly locals, while the lighter, more modern and homely dining/lounge bar serves good-quality food (not on Sun eve or Mon). It stands near the Solent Way long distance footpath. It holds a children's certificate until 8pm. Thatcher's cider is stocked. It is worth making a detour to visit this pub, which caters for everyone.
♨❀◐ ⊟♣❀P●

EASTON

Cricketers

½ mile S of B3047 on Easton's main street

✪ 12-3, 6-11; 12-11 Sat; 12-10.30 Sun

☎ (01962) 779353 website: www.thecricketersinn.com

Draught Bass; Otter Ale; Ringwood Best Bitter; guest beers Ⓗ

At first glance this pub seems typical of village inns given over to food trade; it has a separate no-smoking dining room as well as allowing food service in the main bar area. In fact there's much more to it – it's a true village pub, supporting the local cricket team and offering varied entertainment and events including quiz nights. It also offers B&B (three rooms). The meals are excellent and menu interesting – phone ahead or check website to view serving times. A new guest beer is available each week – as long as it lasts. Giant jenga played. 🅼🛏️◑ 🅰️♣P

EMSWORTH ✤

Coal Exchange

21 South Street

✪ 10.30-3, 5.30-11; 10.30-11 Sat; 12-10.30 Sun

☎ (01243) 375866

Gale's Butser, GB, HSB, seasonal beers; guest beers Ⓗ

Built in the late 1600s, the building was originally a pork butchery and ale house. As the name suggests, it was also used as a place to exchange local produce with coal delivered by sea to the local harbour. Externally, the pub has an unusual (for a Gale's pub) green-tiled front and inside a single, L-shaped bar is decorated with local photographs. The pub provides lunchtime meals and also a curry night on Tue and international theme eve on Thu that are definitely worth trying. 🅼🐾◑⇌♣●

FARNBOROUGH

Prince of Wales

184 Rectory Road

✪ 11.30-2.30, 5.30-11; 12-3.30, 7-10.30 Sun

☎ (01252) 545578

Badger Best, Tanglefoot; Fuller's London Pride; Hogs Back TEA; Ringwood Fortyniner; guest beers Ⓗ

An otherwise unassuming-looking pub in the old part of Farnborough, this real ale institution celebrates 21 years as a free house in 2002. The traditional layout has a central bar with a snug (watch the cellar being filled/emptied from the window) and a larger seated area. The textbook beer operation has five regular ales plus four which change at least weekly and a lower-priced session beer which changes monthly. There is an outstanding range of mild ales in May. The attentive and (generally) knowledgeable bar staff plus affable, if opinionated, regulars will help you make your selection. Lunchtime food served Mon–Sat. Very popular on weekday lunchtimes with the discerning business drinker. Some travel a long way to visit this pub, others just move into the area! Q🐾◑⇌(North) P●

FLEET

Prince Arthur

238 Fleet Road (50 yds E of Reading Rd crossroads)

✪ 10.30-11; 12-10.30 Sun

☎ (01252) 622660

Courage Directors; Hogs Back TEA; Ringwood Fortyniner; Theakston Best Bitter; Wadworth 6X; guest beers Ⓗ

Spacious, flexible Wetherspoon's house, pleasantly converted and extended in their typical style. Five constant real ales and up to five guests, often at prices that are extremely low for the area. Varied clientele, from weekday workers to the younger set on weekend eves. Five-star toilet facilities with wheelchair WC. Standard Wetherspoon's menu with curry nights each Thu. Food served 11–10 Mon–Sat and 12–9 Sun. Budget-priced hot/cold drinks. Good range of local history pictures and popular outdoor drinking area.Q🐾◑♿✎●

FREEFOLK

Watership Down

Freefolk Priors (off B3400)

✪ 11.30-3, 6-11; 12-3, 7-10.30 Sun

☎ (01256) 892254

Archers Best Bitter; Brakspear Bitter; guest beers Ⓗ

Welcoming free house set back from the main road, named after the famous book by Richard Adams (he lives nearby). The story of the rabbits is set in the fine downland countryside to the north of the pub. The five handpumps serve a changing range of small brewers' beers, always including a real mild – rare in this area. There are two 'traditional' rooms with displays of old pictures and pump clips. An impressive collection of penny arcade machines features strongly. One area is adorned by CAMRA awards. A small conservatory has been added without detracting from the fine atmosphere. Buses stop close by and the pub is popular with walkers and cyclists. 🅼🐾◑♣P✎🍴

FRITHAM

Royal Oak

1 mile S of B3078 OS232141

✪ 11-3, 6-11; 11-11 Sat ; 12-10.30 Sun

☎ (023) 8081 2606

Ringwood Best Bitter, True Glory, Fortyniner; guest beer Ⓖ

Small, thatched pub at the end of a New Forest track, voted *Pub of the Year* several times by the local CAMRA branch. Comprising a main bar and several other rooms with hatchway service, decor is impeccably traditional: black beams, wooden floors, and wainscotted walls. Guest beers are from local, small brewers. Lunchtime home-made soup, ploughmans and home-cooked meats are offered; Mon night is 'bangers and mash' style food and Tue there is a supper club (advance booking). The very large garden, with marquee, hosts Summer events – hog roasts, and barbecues. There is a pétanque terrain. The Royal Oak is the centre for all forest and country activities and is the perfect starting/finishing point for New Forest walks. Dogs very welcome – almost mandatory! 🅼Q🐾🅰️♣●

FROXFIELD

Trooper

Alton Road (3 miles from Petersfield) OS727273

✪ 12-3, 6-11; 12-3, 7-10.30 Sun
☎ (01730) 827923
Ringwood Best Bitter; guest beers Ⓗ
Remote but friendly free house which has recently been extended for more restaurant space. The atmosphere is enhanced by candlelit tables. Very extensive food menu which varies on a monthly basis. Pleasant surroundings and varied mix of clientele. Live entertainment is staged once a month, ranging from solo artists to jazz. Worth seeking out for the food alone, popular with the country set. ⚄Q☎❀◐P

GOSPORT ✣

Clarence Tavern
1 Clarence Road
✪ 11-11; 12-10.30 Sun
☎ (023) 9252 9726
Oakleaf Bitter, Holehearted, Blake's Gosport Bitter; guest beers Ⓗ
Formerly a club, which reopened as a pub in March 1999. Unusually an 18th-century chapel was brought over from the Isle of Wight and rebuilt on to the back of the pub. A small brew plant, the Old Chapel Brewery, was installed at one end of the building. Brewing has now moved 100 yards down the road and been renamed Oakleaf. Apart from the beers listed, there are at least three other Oakleaf ales stocked. Famous for its food, the pub hosts medieval banquet nights. There are two beer festivals, one at Easter and one on August bank holiday.
⚄Q☎◐ ❸ፊ⇌ (Portsmouth Harbour) ❉P⚲

Five Alls
75 Forton Road
✪ 10-11; 12-10.30 Sun
☎ (023) 9252 9773
Draught Bass; Courage Directors Ⓗ
L-shaped locals' pub with separate bars, each with their own character. The name of the pub comes from the 'five alls' of the King, soldier, priest, judge and toff – I rule, I fight, I pray, I plea and I pay. Surprisingly, the pub is known for its toilets! They are very old and elaborate and reputedly come from the old Gosport railway station – now a ruin – just up the road. The pub can get busy and noisy on Karaoke and darts league nights and there is a quiz on Sun eve.
☎❀◐ ❸❖❤

Queen's Hotel
143 Queens Road
✪ 11.30-2.30, 7-11; 11.30-11 Sat; 12-3, 7-10.30 Sun
☎ (023) 9258 2645
website: www.downourlocal.com/queens-hotel
Archers Village; Badger Tanglefoot; Black Sheep Special; guest beers Ⓗ
Popular back-street locals' pub used by many present and retired licensees, with regular visitors from all parts of the country. Winner of many local CAMRA awards including Wessex regional *Pub of the Year* 1999. The licensee of 17 years has notched up 16 entries in this *Guide*. There are three drinking areas, the focal point is an old open fire with an elegant, carved wood surround. There are normally two regularly changing guest beers, plus a porter in winter (Archers in 2000/2001) and real cider in summer. An upstairs function room is available. ⚄❖

GREATHAM

Silver Birch
Petersfield Road (off new A3)
✪ 11.30-11; 12-10.30 Sun
☎ (01420) 538262 e-mail: www.thesilverbirchinn.co
Beer range varies Ⓗ
Built in 1908 and originally called the Woolmer Forest Inn with some interesting stories; it is linked to the film of *The Great St Trinian's Train Robbery*. You should also ask about the adjoining entrance doors to the hotel that were apparently built large enough to allow cavalry horses to enter! The entrance bar is simple and relaxing with a real fire and tiles above the bar. You would be forgiven for missing the large rear games area, this time with thatch above the bar. The original management have now returned and the pub is rapidly becoming revitalised.
⚄Q❀❄◐ ❸ፊ⇌❖❤P⚲☐

GREYWELL

Fox & Goose
The Street
✪ 11-11; 12-10.30 Sun
☎ (01256) 702062
Courage Best Bitter; Gale's HSB; guest beers Ⓗ
16th-century inn set in a picturesque

INN BRIEF

EMSWORTH
Lord Raglan
35 Queen Street
11-3, 6-11; 11-11 summer Sat; 12-10.30 Sun
Gale's Butser, GB, HSB, seasonal beers; guest beers Ⓗ
Friendly, flint-built pub with large riverside garden, at the east end of town by the Sussex border.

EVERSLEY
White Hart
The Street
11-11; 12-10.30 Sun
Courage Best Bitter, Directors; Fuller's London Pride Ⓗ
Lovely 17th-century rural inn with long-standing landlord of 33 years. Features low-beamed ceilings, log fires and games bar extension.

GOSPORT
Queen's Head
87 Brockhurst Road
11-11; 12-10.30 Sun
Often busy L-shaped, one-bar locals' pub. Has a beer fest once a year and a quiz once a month.

LIPHOOK
Green Dragon
2 London Road
11-11; 12-10.30 Sun
Courage Best Bitter; Greene King Abbot Ⓗ
Welcoming town-centre pub with two contrasting bars; bustling public bar and more sedate lounge.

PORTSMOUTH
Artillery Arms
46 Hester Road, Milton, Southsea
11-3, 6-11; 11-11 Sat; 12-10.30 Sun
Cheriton Pots Ale, Gale's GB, HSB; Ind Coope Burton Ale; Ringwood Old Thumper; guest beers Ⓗ
Ever-popular, back-street local with a lively public bar and a more relaxed lounge with live music fortnightly. *Cask Marque* accredited.

John Jacques
72-82 Fratton Road
11-11; 12-10.30 Sun
Courage Directors; Theakston Best Bitter; Wadworth 6X; guest beers Ⓗ
Typical Wetherspoon's pub situated five minutes' walk from Fratton Station. Quiet and cheap, it serves good beer and food. *Cask Marque* accredited.

village, a short distance from Basingstoke Canal, an ideal stop on local walks. A large field behind the pub is used for various events. Children are allowed in if dining. Customers with well-behaved dogs are also welcome in the garden and pub. Oversized, lined glasses are used and traditional pub games played.

♨Q✿①Å♣P☐

HAMBLEDON

Bat & Ball

Hyden Farm Lane, Clanfield (2¹/₂ miles from village on Clanfield road)) OS677167

✪ 11.30-3, 6-11; 12-11 Sat; 12-10.30 Sun

☎ (020) 8AA 2192

Gale's Butser, GB, HSB, seasonal beers Ⓗ

Set high on Broadhalfpenny Down, this pub is opposite one of the most famous cricket grounds around. In the late 1700s, this was the centre of English cricket. The landlord at that time, Richard Nyren, was said to be the best all-round player of his day. It was here that the third stump was introduced and the width of the bat was defined. Probably the most famous event occurred when Hambledon defeated All-England by an innings and 168 runs, one of 29 victories. Note the wealth of cricketing memorabilia; it is something of a museum to the game. The other item of interest is the boundary between Hambledon and Clanfield, marked on the pub floor. Before the pub was refurbished, this actually divided the bar, an important marker when each side had different licensing hours. The pub is closed weekend afternoons in winter. Shut the Box and bar skittles are played.

♨✿①Å♣P●

HAMMER VALE

Prince of Wales

Hammer Lane 1 mile S of A3 OS868326

✪ 12-3, 6-11; 12-11 Sat; 12-10.30 Sun

☎ (01428) 652600

Gale's Butser, GB, HSB, seasonal beer; guest beer Ⓖ

Nestling in a scenic wooded valley, the present building was designed by a daughter of the Gale family in 1927. Stained glass windows in the locals' public bar advertise the Old Amey's Brewery of Petersfield. The bar runs the length of the pub serving three areas; a public bar with a wood-burning stove, a small saloon, and a no-smoking restaurant area with a real fire. Superb food from an imaginative menu includes new and traditional dishes (no food Sun or Mon eves). Thu is curry night in winter and barbecues are held in summer. Outside is a large children's play area and patio seating. Ramblers are welcome. Cribbage, dominoes and shove-ha'penny are popular.

♨Q✿①⊟ఉÅ♣P

HARTLEY WINTNEY

Waggon & Horses

High Street (A30)

✪ 11-11; 12-10.30 Sun

☎ (01252) 842119

Courage Best Bitter; Gale's HSB; guest beers Ⓗ

Welcoming village-centre pub. There are some interesting photographs just inside the entrance. The lively public bar contrasts well with the quieter lounge. The winner of many local CAMRA awards. The landlady serves good food at lunchtimes. There is also a very pleasant courtyard garden at the rear. It makes a peaceful refuge after visiting the many antique shops which crowd the High Street.

♨Q✿①⊟♣

HAVANT

Old House at Home

2 South Street

✪ 11-11; 12-10.30 Sun

☎ (023) 9248 3464

Gale's Butser, GB, HSB, seasonal beers; guest beers Ⓗ

One of the oldest buildings in town, although the 1339 date inscribed on the front wall is several hundred years too early. It is one of the few buildings to have survived the 1760 fire. The building was originally five cottages, then a bakery before becoming a pub. Some of the wooden beams were recovered from the Spanish Armada. There are some interesting antiques in the public bar along with a not so old price list (compare that with current prices). It is also reputed to have shown the last dancing bear in England. Live music Sat eves.

♨✿①⊟⇌♣●

RAKE

Flying Bull
London Road
12-3, 6 (5 Fri)-11; 12-11 Sat; 12-10.30 Sun
Greene King Ruddles Best; Marston's Pedigree; Thomas Hardy Hardy Country; guest beer Ⓗ
Main road pub just inside the county border. Home-cooked food served includes fresh fish. Caravans welcome in summer.

SOUTHAMPTON

Grove Tavern
68-70 Swift Road, Woolston
12-2.30, 7-11; 12-11 Fri & Sat;
12-10.30 Sun
Fuller's London Pride; guest beer Ⓗ
Imposing former Brickwood's pub near Woolston's shipyards. Remains mainly unaltered with three bars including a snug.

Varsity
67-75 London Road
11-11; 12-10.30 Sun
Banks's Bitter; Marston's Pedigree Ⓗ
Large, modern, open-plan city pub on two levels with constant piped music; catering for students. Good value food available all day.

Wellington Arms
56 Park Road, Freemantle
11.30-2.30 (3 Fri),
5.30 (5 Fri, 6.30 Sat)-11;
12-3.30, 6.30-10.30 Sun
Fuller's London Pride, ESB; Gale's HSB; Ringwood Best Bitter, Old Thumper; guest beers Ⓗ
Two-bar free house offers bar food and a separate restaurant. No meals Sun eve. Draught Belgian beers and a good wine selection stocked.

WICKHAM

King's Head
The Square
10-11; 12-10.30 Sun
Gale's Butser, GB, HSB, seasonal or guest beer Ⓗ
Comfortable town-centre pub in the middle of market square. No food Sun eve. Skittle alley and children's certificate.

> ✳ symbol next to a main entry place name indicates there are Inn Brief entries as well.

HAWKLEY

Hawkley Inn
Pococks Lane (up steep hill and first turning on left)
OS747291
☼ 12-2.30 (3 Sat), 6-11; 12-3, 7-10.30 Sun
☎ (01730) 827205
Beer range varies H

Tucked along a little lane close to the village green and church, it's popular with walkers and surprisingly busy considering its rural location. There is a long wooden canopy at the front of the building, to which a horse or two may be tethered during summer. A single bar serves two small but distinct areas, one of which is for non-smokers. Two real fires warm the winter traveller and one has a moose's head above it, complete with hat and cigarette! There are six regularly rotating beers (all from small breweries), plus the landlord's own cider (Swamp Donkey), when in season. Live music most Sat eves in winter, plus a beer festival the first weekend in June. Patio and garden available. No meals Sun eve. Family room provided on busy days. ♨Q♿❀◑●✄

HEADLEY

Hollybush
High Street
☼ 11-3, 5-11; 11-11 Sat; 12-4, 7-10.30 Sun
☎ (01428) 712211
Draught Bass; Courage Best Bitter; Gale's Butser; Greene King IPA; guest beer H

This superb, rural inn is off the beaten track but worth seeking out through the country lanes. A warm welcome assured, particularly from the pub dog! One central bar is surrounded by four contrasting areas, designed to suit all tastes. The long lounge is decorated with sporting trophies, water jugs above the bar and Victorian pictures on the walls. A small, discrete dining area to the rear leads into the games bar. Good value food, (eve meals served Tue-Sat) with summer barbecues in the spacious garden. All a good village pub should be. ♨Q♿❀◑●❀♣●P✄▯

HILL HEAD

Osborne View
67 Hill Head Road (from Stubbington via Bells Lane and Crofton Lane)
☼ 11-11; 12-10.30 Sun
☎ (01329) 664623
Badger K&B Sussex, IPA, Best, Tanglefoot; Gribble Fursty Ferret, seasonal beers H

Imposing location on a cliff overlooking the Solent and the Isle of Wight. This old village hotel has a large conservatory added to the rear with its own bar which is open during the busy summer period. Steps lead down to the garden and directly on to the beach. Although the emphasis is on food, there is plenty of room for drinkers. Up to eight real ales are available including beers from Badger and Gribble Inn, incorporating former King & Barnes ales. ♨Q♿❀◑ ▲P✄●

HORNDEAN

Brewers Arms
1 Five Heads Road

☼ 12-2 (4 Sat; not Mon); 5 (6 Sat)-11; 12-3, 7-10.30 Sun
☎ (023) 9259 1325
Courage Directors; Fuller's London Pride; Ringwood Best Bitter; Wells Bombardier; guest beers H

Pre-war, half-brick tiled pub set back off the main Portsmouth road. Referred to by those who use it as 'a proper pub'. A genuine local where people come to drink and talk. See plans in the lounge of the original 1929 layout prior to internal alterations carried out by the previous owners, Gale's, in the early 1970s. Four regular beers are stocked, plus two guest ales which go on each Fri night, generally from small breweries. Crib, dominoes and shove-ha'penny are played. Q♿❀❑♣P

LANGSTONE

Ship
Langstone Road
☼ 11-11; 12-10.30 Sun
☎ (023) 9247 1719
Gale's Butser, GB, HSB, seasonal beers; guest beers H

Large one-bar pub situated on the shore of Langstone harbour, a popular sailing area. Hayling Island, with its campsites, is a short drive or walk across the nearby bridge. The old Hayling Island branch line ran nearby and the remains of the swing bridge across the harbour can still be seen, but there is little remaining of the berth of the long-defunct Isle of Wight train ferry. There are a number of interesting local walks along the shore and inland, including the track bed of the old railway, now the Hayling Billy Trail. ♨❀◑♿ ▲P●

LINWOOD

Red Shoot
Toms Lane (3 miles E of A338, Ellingham Cross)
OS187094
☼ 11-3, 6-11; 11-11 Sat; 12-10.30 Sun
☎ (01425) 475792 website: www.redshootinn.co.uk
Red Shoot Forest Gold, Tom's Tipple; Wadworth IPA, 6X, seasonal beers H

This rambling inn has actually only been a pub since 1963, previous lives included a private club and even a petrol station! Many original rooms have been knocked into one big L-shaped, multi-level area. Comfortably furnished with an eclectic mixture of furniture, some antique. A long bar meanders through the area. Events include a music quiz (Thu) and live music (Sun); there are beer festivals in April and October. In 1998 a $2^{1}/_{2}$ barrel brewery was added, it is viewable from the bar. ♨Q♿❀◑ ▲P●

LITTLE LONDON

Plough Inn
Silchester Road (1 mile off A340, S of Tadley)
☼ 12-2.30, 6-11; 12-3, 7-10.30 Sun
☎ (01256) 850628
Ringwood Best Bitter, True Glory, H **guest beers** G

In 1857 Daniel Holloway became the owner of the Plough and local brickworks and it has remained a traditional village pub ever since. You will find no loud music or mod cons; just an informal, relaxing atmosphere in this sympathetically restored cottage. In winter there are fires and porter is served. Baguettes are served every lunch and eve (except Sun eve), and jacket potatoes on every third Mon of the month – quiz night. There is folk music on the last Mon of every month. Ideally located for ramblers visiting nearby Roman ruins at Silchester or Pamber Woods behind the pub. 🏛Q🍴🏵⚘♣P

LONG SUTTON

Four Horseshoes
The Street
🕒 12-2.30, 6-30-11; 12-3, 7-10.30 Sun
☎ (01256) 862488 website: www.fourhorseshoes.com
Fuller's London Pride; Gale's Butser, HSB; guest beers Ⓗ

Wonderful rural retreat, just east of the attractive village centre, next to Lord Wandsworth College and looking out across open downland. It stands on an ancient trackway (Harroway); the landlord found bronze age remains when laying the pétanque terrain. The bar is open plan and retains all the traditional elements that you might expect from a good country pub; a friendly atmosphere, cosy warmth of an open fire in winter and rustic beams and brasses. The landlord's cooking has a good reputation. Usually two guest beers served including a mild (the landlord's favourite tipple). Camping at the pub by arrangement or en-suite accommodation available. Children welcome in the conservatory. 🏛Q🍴🏵🚪◑▲♣P

LOWER UPHAM

Woodman Inn
Winchester Road (B2177) OS525195
🕒 12-2.30 (5.30 Sat), 7-11; 12-5.30, 7-10.30 Sun
☎ (01489) 860270
Greene King XX Mild, IPA; guest beers Ⓗ

Parts of this roadside inn date back to 1692, the pub having been known then as the Travellers' Rest until the early 19th century. The two guest beers are from the Greene King range and up to 160 malt whiskies are stocked. During the summer, window boxes, hanging baskets and tubs are filled with plants, decorating the front of the pub in a blaze of colour. The garden has a trampoline, climbing frame and swing for the younger members of the family. The car park is reached from the lane beside the pub. Sandwiches and ploughmans are available lunchtime and early eve. 🏛🏵🚪♣P

LYMINGTON (PENNINGTON)

Musketeer
26 North Street (off A337 at White Hart roundabout)
🕒 11.30-3, 5.30-11; 12-3, 7-10.30 Sun
☎ (01590) 676527
Ringwood Best Bitter, Fortyniner; guest beers Ⓗ

Traditional, comfortable, one-bar local in the village centre. At lunchtime it offers excellent home-cooked food at affordable prices (not served Sun). An entry in this *Guide* for 23 years and run by the same family throughout that time, now well into the second generation. Pub sign aficionados are unlikely to have seen one like this

before! A self-catering, converted Edwardian coach house is available on a weekly let. Four real ales always on offer and log fires guarantee a warm welcome in winter. Pleasant patio for outdoor drinking. Worth seeking out. 🏛🍴🏵◑♣P

LYNDHURST (BANK)

Oak Inn
Pinkney Lane (off A35, 1¼ miles SW of Lyndhurst)
OS286072
🕒 11.30-2.30 (3 Sat), 6-11; 12-3, 7-10.30 Sun
☎ (023) 8028 2350
Hall & Woodhouse Tanglefoot, Badger Best Bitter, Ringwood Best Bitter; guest beers Ⓟ

18th-century building in a New Forest hamlet popular with walkers and cyclists. This characterful free house has a single, L-shaped bar decorated with hop vines, wooden floors and bar stools made from milk churns. The walls and ceilings are adorned with unusual ornaments including fishing rods and spears. The menu is varied and should cater for most tastes. Table bookings taken except for Sun lunchtime. The beer garden is large and has a mixture of covered and open seating. Well-behaved children and dogs are welcome in the bar. 🏛Q🏵◑▶P

MEDSTEAD

Castle of Comfort
Castle Street (2 miles N of Four Marks on A31)
OS655373
🕒 11-2.30 (3 Sat), 6-11; 12-3, 7-10.30 Sun
☎ (01420) 562112
Draught Bass; Courage Best Bitter; Gale's Butser; Ushers Best Bitter Ⓗ

17th-century village local tucked behind the church. There is a public bar and the small lounge is more like an old family living room; the large fireplace contains a wood-burning stove. It is music-free. A fish tank now occupies what was the serving hatch until the bar was 'updated' in the early 1960s. The pub is well-known for its splendid floral displays from spring onwards; the verandah running the length of the pub is well-decorated with hanging baskets and the front of the pub is bedecked with flower tubs. The beer is from the Innspired range. 🏛Q🏵◑🚪♣P

MILFORD-ON-SEA

Red Lion
32 High Street
🕒 11.30-2.30, 6-11; 12-3, 7-10.30 Sun
☎ (01590) 642236 website: www.redlionmilford.co.uk
Flowers Original; Ringwood True Glory; guest beers Ⓗ

Listed building in the village centre, dating from 1790, with many alterations and additions since then. The first-floor sash windows are original. The spacious interior is smart, carpeted throughout and with dark wood furniture. At one end of the main bar is a games room converted from an old stable block, at the other end is a large no-smoking area. The friendly landlord provides excellent beer in an area not known for good ale. Two guests are chosen from Brakspear Bitter, Tetley Bitter and Wells Bombardier. A wide variety of good food is available at all sessions (but not winter Sun), and the pub has en-suite accommodation. ⚒Q☀⊯◖D◖♿♣▲P⚥

NORTH CAMP

Old Ford
Lynchford Road (next to North Camp Station)
☉ 11-11; 12-10.30 Sun
☎ (01252) 544840
Brakspear Bitter; Courage Best Bitter; Fuller's London Pride; Greene King Abbot; Hogs Back TEA Ⓗ
Imposing pub next to, and in the same architectural style as, North Camp railway station, possibly named after a former crossing of the adjacent River Blackwater. Although bypassed by the new road developments, it has a strong local following and attracts rail travellers and walkers along the Blackwater Valley path. Enter through double doors straight into the single bar, which has a games room (formerly a station buffet), seating area and a dining room-cum-skittle alley to the back. The large, safe garden with children's play equipment and a pets' corner is popular for traditional Sun lunch in summer. No food Sun eve. ☞Q☀◖D⇌♣P

OAKHANGER

Red Lion
The Street
☉ 11-3, 6-11; 12-3, 7-10.30 (summer) Sun
☎ (01420) 472232
Courage Best Bitter, Directors; guest beers Ⓗ
Friendly village pub where the traditional public bar is dominated by a massive framed pike. The lounge bar/restaurant and public bar are decorated with luxuriant hop vines, both bars are warmed in winter by real fires. A superb garden, with established fruit trees and shrubbery, leads to a children's play area. Cards, darts, dominoes and shove-ha'penny are played. A proper local giving the visitor good food, washed down with quality beer. A visit involves a trip through the Hampshire lanes with the local area bristling with military hardware. If you get lost, look out for the giant white golf balls! ⚒Q☀◖D⊟◖♣P

OTTERBOURNE

Otter
Boyatt Lane (600 yds from M3 jct 12, off Otterbourne Hill) OS454223
☉ 10.30-11; 12-10.30 Sun
☎ (023) 8025 2685
Draught Bass; Boddingtons Bitter; Flowers Original; Marston's Pedigree; Wadworth 6X Ⓗ
Old coaching inn by a village green on the Winchester–Southampton 47 bus route. A thriving community local, it has a single dark-beamed, L-shaped bar with cluttered decor, including a local artist's pictures for sale, and a conifer-hedged back patio and garden. A good range of excellent food comes in generous portions. Mon quiz nights, a Sun lunchtime meat draw, summer spit-roast, ceilidhs and Hallowe'en events hosted. The Otterbourne Mummers play, described by novelist, Charlotte Yonge, is enacted nearby on the Sun before Christmas. The Otter lies on the 18-mile Keble Way which encircles Ampfield Countryside Heritage Area, and which leads

north-east by a path across Otterbourne Hill and down to the Itchen Navigation and the Itchen Way National Trail, a mile distant. ⚒☀◖P

OWSLEBURY

Ship Inn
Off B2177, 1½ miles N of Marwell zoo; follow tourist signs
☉ 11-3 (not Mon Sept-April), 6-11 (11-11 summer Sat); 12-10.30 Sun
☎ (01962) 777358 e-mail: theshipinn@freeuk.com
Cheriton Pots Ale; Greene King IPA; guest beers Ⓗ
300-year-old busy, welcoming, two-bar country inn displaying sporting memorabilia in the drinkers' Crow's Nest bar; while the Mess-Deck bar reflects the local village history and acts as the main dining area. The extensive garden has a patio, pond, play area, animals, a horse park and collections of old local pub signs and enamel advertising signs. The pub has a crib league and pétanque teams. Excellent food served, combining pub favourites and a bistro-style menu. There is a lunchtime children's menu, vegetarian main meals, daily specials and snacks. No food on winter Mon.
⚒Q☀◖D⊟♣P●

PORTSMOUTH ❖

Connaught Arms
119 Guildford Road, Fratton
☉ 11.30-2.30, 6-11; 11.30-11 Fri & Sat; 12-4, 7-10.30 Sun
☎ (023) 9264 6455 website: www.connaughtarms.com
Caledonian Deuchars IPA; Cheriton Pots Ale; Hop Back Summer Lightning Ⓗ
Imposing, Victorian 'Brewer's Tudor' pub on a corner site. A haven for those visiting for the first time and a must for those who have already discovered it. This large pub has a roughly L-shaped bar, raised seating area and walled patio. It is deservedly famed for its food. Ales are an excellent accompaniment for the delicious home-made pasties with countless different fillings. Children are welcomed and the pub has a children's certificate. It can be very busy if Pompey are playing at home, with both home and away supporters making a beeline for pre-match drinks.
☀◖♿⇌ (Fratton) ◖●

Fifth Hampshire Volunteer Arms
74 Albert Road, Southsea (200 yd E of King's Theatre)
☉ 12-11; 12-10.30 Sun
☎ (023) 9282 7161
Gale's GB, HSB, guest beers Ⓗ
Popular pub situated in a part of Southsea with several pubs and a variety of restaurants. There are two contrasting bars. The public features darts, a rock music juke box, TV, a rare collection of hard hats and an overcooked pizza. The lounge has a collection of military and naval memorabilia, hanging jugs and an array of awards from the local CAMRA branch which was founded here in February 1974. Sun eve is quiz night. The pub supports darts and a cricket team. The pub's two dogs are called Cassius and Lennox, from which you can guess their breed. Apart from the

regular beers, Gale's Festival Mild is occasionally stocked. Q♿♣●

Florist
324 Fratton Road, Fratton (Lake Rd jct)
☼ 11-2, 5-11; 11-11 Sat; 12-10.30 Sun
☎ (023) 9282 0289
Wadworth IPA, 6X, seasonal beer Ⓗ
This is a traditional 19th-century corner local, with an attractive glazed brick exterior and a witch's hat tower. The lounge, situated at the rear, is quiet and comfortable, while the lively public bar has darts, pool, juke box, TV and fruit machine. Around the walls are old photographs of the pub and a number of certificates celebrating the pub's active fundraising role in the renovation of the local church, St Mary's. Overall, an excellent pub with quality beer and a welcoming atmosphere.
Q♿≋(Fratton)♣

Isambard Kingdom Brunel
2 Guildhall Walk (opp. Guildhall and civic offices)
☼ 10-11; 12-10.30 Sun
☎ (023) 9229 5912
Courage Directors; Hop Back Summer Lightning; Shepherd Neame Spitfire; Theakston Best Bitter; Wadworth 6X; guest beers Ⓗ
Very few pubs have a war memorial attached, this, however, has two – one for each world war – to the memory of the fallen of the Portsmouth and Gosport Gas Company whose offices were on this site. It became a Wetherspoon's in April 1996 and has deservedly featured each year in this *Guide*. It was renamed and refurbished in Spring 2000 in fresh white, blue and green. There is a raised, no-smoking area with a balustrade, a lively bar and wheelchair WC and lift. The pub can be busy during the university term but the staff are always cheerful and efficient.
Q◐♿≋(Portsmouth & Southsea)♣✔●

Old Oyster House
291 Locksway Road, Milton, Southsea (off A288, near University's Langstone site)
☼ 4 (12 Fri & Sat)-11; 12-10.30 Sun
☎ (023) 9282 7456
Beer range varies Ⓗ
Spacious, traditional drinkers' pub, where five real ales, a scrumpy (Thatcher's) and a mild (usually Brains Dark) are always available. Every effort is made to obtain particularly interesting beers from small and national breweries. The pub is named after the oyster beds in Langstone harbour and stands by the only remaining section of the Portsea Canal. This Oyster House was rebuilt in the 1930s next to the original site and the decor has a nautical theme. The bar-cum-games room offers pool and table football. ❀♣●

Red White & Blue
150 Fawcett Road, Southsea
☼ 11-11; 12-10.30 Sun
☎ (023) 9278 0013
website: www.rwb.insouthsea.co.uk
Gale's Butser, GB, HSB Ⓗ
Compact street-corner local that welcomes football fans regardless of their choice of team. Food only served Sat lunchtimes, but pickled eggs and onions are always on offer. The single bar, which can get crowded on darts and dominoes eves, features

banknotes, naval badges, horses and a spare set of handpumps. The gnomes have disappeared. A wide variety of board games, including Uckers, can be played and there is a charity lending library. Canada Day (1 July) is celebrated on the nearest Sat with Canadian breakfast washed down with moose milk. Live jazz staged Wed eves.
≋(Fratton)♣

Rose in June
102 Milton Road (300 yds N of Kingston prison)
☼ 12-3, 6.30-11; 12-11 Fri & Sat; 12-10.30 Sun
☎ (023) 9282 4191
Fuller's London Pride; Gale's HSB; Wells Bombardier; guest beers Ⓗ
Welcoming, traditional back-street pub with two adjoining bars. Darts, pool and dominoes are popular here. The pub hosts occasional live music, quizzes and two beer festivals a year. The public bar is usually lively. For a more relaxed atmosphere, the lounge, with more table space and comfortable seating, is the better option. Three regular cask ales are available plus up to three guest beers. ❀♿♣

Rutland Arms
205 Francis Avenue, Southsea (400 yds S of Goldsmith Ave)
☼ 11-11; 12-10.30 Sun
Fuller's London Pride; Hampshire Strong's Best Bitter, Pride of Romsey; Taylor Landlord Ⓗ
Fairly large corner local. The main bar has a polished wooden floor and above the bar are old photographs of Portsmouth past. There is a quieter drinking area to the rear which can be curtained off for meetings. The pub can get quite noisy with the juke box. Apparently there are still bullet holes in the outside wall from a German air attack in WWII. Patio available for outdoor drinking. ❀≋(Fratton)

Sir Loin of Beef
152 Highland Road, Eastney, Southsea (opp. Southsea police station)
☼ 11-11; 12-10.30 Sun
☎ (023) 9282 0115
Hop Back Summer Lightning; Ringwood Old Thumper; guest beers Ⓗ
Friendly, true free house, close to the Royal Marines Museum and Eastney pumping station. There are up to six guest beers mainly from southern independent breweries. Prices are displayed on large easy-to-read blackboards. The pub is decorated with submarine paraphernalia including the most hated thing in the area – the klaxon that announces 'time'. The pub boasts two clocks: one is a converted depth gauge that shows the approximate time, but the second is radio-linked to an atomic clock and shows the real time. The latter determines when the klaxon is sounded. Although the 'SLOB' has a single bar it is divided into three distinct areas. There is live music once or twice a month and a quiz night on the first Sun. ◐⚓♣●

Sir Robert Peel
Astley Street, Southsea (near law courts)
☼ 11.45-3.30 (4.30 Sat), 7-11; 12-4.30, 7-10.30 Sun
☎ (023) 9234 5708
Ringwood Best Bitter; guest beers Ⓗ
1960s estate pub hidden among the tower blocks but well worth seeking out. The

lounge has recently been refurbished to a high standard, the remainder is due for renovation. The pub attracts a wide range of customers from tower block regulars to out-of-town visitors. The landlord has recently served his 400th different real ale, emphasising the appeal of this free house. Frequent speciality nights for charity are hosted and it is well-supported by ladies' and gents' darts teams. Share a golfing yarn with the golf-mad landlord or just enjoy a good pint in the very pleasant surroundings.

⊛◖⊆⊯⇌(Portsmouth & Southsea) ♣ ☀P

Still & West Country House
Bath Square, Old Portsmouth
✪ 11-11; 12-10.30 Sun
☎ (023) 9282 1567
Gale's Butser, GB, HSB, guest beers Ⓗ
Large, busy pub situated at the tip of Old Portsmouth offering an excellent view of the harbour and shipping. Inside, the walls and ceilings show pictures of the naval history of the area. On the first floor is a 160-seat restaurant, with separate function area, serving an excellent menu. Wheelchair access is not available to the restaurant but meals from the menu can be ordered from the bar (which also has its own menu). Eve meals offered in summer only. One of the best Gale's pubs in Portsmouth.
Q⊛◖◗&⇌(Harbour) ✂●

Wine Vaults
43-47 Albert Road, Southsea
✪ 12-11; 12-10.30 Sun
☎ (023) 9286 4712
Draught Bass; Courage Best Bitter; Hop Back GFB, Summer Lightning; guest beers Ⓗ
Former home of Spikes Brewery, which can still be viewed behind a glass panel in the wall. Large pub with predominantly wooden interior. Ample seating with more upstairs, plus a separate area for dining (The Vines), which offers a substantial menu with chef's specials daily, 12–9.30. Around the walls are various old advertisements and even an old push-bike. The pub can get very busy in the eve as the place is popular with students and those visiting the King's Theatre, opposite. The house beer, Offyatrolli, is Courage Directors. ◖◗

RINGWOOD

Inn on the Furlong
12 Meeting House Lane (opp. New Forest Information Centre)
✪ 11-11; 12-10.30 Sun
☎ (01425) 475139
Ringwood Best Bitter, True Glory, Fortyniner, Old Thumper, seasonal beers Ⓗ
A former private residence, rescued from 'redevelopment' in the mid-1980s and reopened as a public house – becoming Ringwood Brewery's first tied house. It is now a lively, town-centre ale house. This Victorian-built inn has a central bar serving several areas. The main flagstoned bar has a roaring fire in winter with long tables and daily newspapers. Two small snugs: one doubles as a family room, the other has a TV for sporting events. At the rear of the pub a conservatory is mainly used for dining and there is a patio for summer days.

Large car park and bus terminal opposite. Live music on Tue eve.
⸜⊛⊛◖●

ROMSEY

Three Tuns
Middlebridge Street (A3090, opp. entrance to Broadlands)
✪ 11-3, 5-11; 11-11 Fri & Sat; 12-10.30 Sun
☎ (01794) 512639
Flowers Original; Hampshire Strong's Best Bitter; Ringwood Best Bitter; Wadworth 6X Ⓗ
17th-century inn, a conversion of two cottages; still retaining a public 'cottage' bar and a characteristic bay window in the lounge bar. Situated on a former old road (Ely Walk) into Romsey, but nowadays road access is from the town bypass. A former landlord was the retired head gamekeeper of the adjacent Broadlands estate; the current landlady was awarded Fuller's *Cellarman of the Year*. 'Strongs of Romsey' cask ends in the bar confirm the pub's previous owners. Emphasis is on food with bookings taken for meals, not served Sun eve when a keenly followed quiz takes place. Enjoy a relaxed atmosphere among a more mature clientele.
Q⊛◖◗P

Tudor Rose
3 Cornmarket
✪ 10-11; 12-4, 7-10.30 Sun
☎ (01794) 512126
Courage Best Bitter, Directors Ⓗ
Small, single-bar, no-frills pub in the town centre. The original structure dates from 1450. The massive oak beams in the bar are original; the handsome fireplace was added a century or two later. In its time the building has been a workhouse, a brothel and probably served as a Guildhall. The name dates from 1928 when restoration work revealed the true age of the building. In summer the flower-filled courtyard is a pleasant place to drink. Reasonably priced food is available Mon–Sat. There is live folk music on alternate Sun eves.
⸜⊛◖◗⇌♣✂

ROWLAND'S CASTLE

Castle Inn
1 Finchdean Road
✪ 11-3, 6 (5 Fri)-11; 11-11 Sat; 12-10.30 Sun
☎ (023) 9241 2494
Gale's Butser, GB, HSB Ⓗ
Typical village pub tucked behind the railway bridge by the entrance to Stansted House. It has two bars, the public has a busy early eve trade. The second bar is split into two, separated by a central open fireplace. There are two fires in each room, characterful flagstones and bare boards. Pleasant restaurant area serves daily lunches and eve meals Tue-Sat. The fenced garden is safe for small children. Wheelchair access via rear entrance.
⸜Q⊛⊯◖◗&⇌♣P●

ST MARY BOURNE

Coronation Arms
On B3048
✪ 11-3, 6.30-11; 12-3, 7.30-10.30 Sun
☎ (01264) 738432

e-mail: davidpeartpeat32@supernet.com

Draught Bass; Ringwood Best Bitter, Fortyniner; guest beer Ⓗ

Popular local in the beautiful North Hampshire countryside. The pub was rebuilt in 1901 after a fire totally destroyed the original building. Its completion coincided with the coronation of Edward VII, hence the name. Pictures of the village, and black and white photographs of the villagers, decorate the walls. The main bar is spacious but gets busy Fri eve and Sun lunchtime. There are two eating areas and food is served daily except Sun eve. A table football machine is popular with younger customers but doesn't disturb those looking for a quiet

SHEDFIELD

Wheatsheaf Inn
Botley Road (A334)
🕐 12-11; 12-10.30 Sun
☎ (01329) 833024

Cheriton Pots Ale; Hop Back Summer Lightning; Ringwood Best Bitter; guest beers Ⓖ

Friendly, family-run pub with comfortable public bar and small lounge. A genuine free house, with usually six beers on gravity, many of them local brews, on an impressive two-tier stillage behind the bar. An interesting varied menu provides good value food at lunchtime. The pub has a well-kept garden complete with an ornamental rockery and a pair of lop-eared rabbits. Children permitted in the lounge, dogs allowed in the public bar, both in garden. The pub is situated on the main Botley to Wickham Road; take care entering and leaving the car parks. Q ❀ ◑ 🏠 ♣ ♣ P

SHEET

Queen's Head
Sheet Green
🕐 11-2.30, 5.30-11; 12-2.30, 6-11 Sat; 12-3, 7-10.30 Sun
☎ (01730) 264204

Brakspear Bitter, Special; Fuller's London Pride; Hampshire Strong's Best Bitter Ⓗ

Typical local, next to the small village green and nearby church. The public bar is 400 years old with a stone floor, wooden beams and a log fire. The lounge was added later but has a history of its own. The front part was the village butcher's and then shop until the early 1970s. It also has a log fire. Bar snacks are available and the restaurant to the rear has an Italian chef who serves up traditional (Italian) dishes. The restaurant is not open Sun eve or Mon. The pub has been run by the same family since 1959. Addlestone's cider is stocked
🏚 Q ❀ ◑ 🏠 ♣ ♣ P

SHERBORNE ST JOHN

Swan
Kiln Road (centre of village, N of Basingstoke town)
🕐 11-11; 12-10.30 Sun
☎ (01256) 850165

Flowers IPA, Original; guest beers Ⓗ

This village pub has been extended by Whitbread to add a conservatory. There are two bar rooms, one spacious, one small and real ale is served in both. The large room is used for sit-down meals from a Wayside

Inns menu but the pub has a chef, so check the blackboard for the specials. Snacks are also available in both bars. There is a large car park and a good-sized garden with children's play area. The pub attracts local people and visitors from Basingstoke, which is about two miles away. The Vyne, a National Trust house, is close by and well signposted. 🏚 ❀ ❀ ◑ 🏠 ♣ P

SOUTHAMPTON ✣

Bevois Castle
63 Onslow Road, Bevois Valley
🕐 11-11; 12-10.30 Sun
☎ (023) 8033 0350
e-mail: bevoiscastle@onslowroad.fsnet.co.uk

Thomas Hardy Pope's Traditional; guest beers Ⓗ

Situated in a fork off the main Bevois Valley road, which features a listed horse-trough monument, this imposing pub lends itself to a classic horseshoe-bar layout. Wood panelled throughout with comfortable, cosy seating. One side takes on a classic neo-Victorian snug ambience, complete with roaring fire. The other side opens out into a games area, with old Southampton FC memorabilia, pool, darts, Sky Sports TV and a juke box. To the rear of the pub is an attractive enclosed patio-garden where summer barbecues are held. Guest beers from local micro-breweries are always available, food is served until 9.30pm, with a near-legendary Sat breakfast. When Southampton FC play at home, the pub is busy but friendly. 🏚 ❀ ◑ ▶ P ☗

Bitter Virtue Off-licence
70 Cambridge Road (off The Avenue)
🕐 10.30-8.30 (closed Mon & Tue); 10.30-2 Sun
☎ (023) 8055 4881 website: www.bittervirtue.cwc.net

Brakspear seasonal beers; Cheriton Pots Ale, seasonal beers; Hop Back seasonal beers; Ⓖ **guest beers** Ⓗ

Truly a beer shop, selling only beer and cider. The wooden shelves which line the walls contain upwards of 400 different bottled beers. From the UK there are at least 100 bottle-conditioned ales. The stunning Belgian range includes all Trappist brews, many micro-brewery products and an excellent selection of traditional Lambics. There is a wide selection of classic German beers plus special ales from other countries and a range of organic beers. Two or three draught ales are available at any one time at bargain prices and polypins may be ordered. Badged glasses, T-shirts and other souvenirs are sold; mail-order and/or delivery by arrangement.

Crown Inn
9 Highcrown Street, Highfield (car park is in Hawthorn Rd)
🕐 11-11; 12-10.30 Sun
☎ (023) 8031 5033
website: www.lineone.net/~thecrown/

Archers Best Bitter; Flowers Original; Fuller's London Pride; Hampshire Strong's Best Bitter; Wadworth 6X Ⓗ

Large, single-roomed pub, handy for the University and Southampton Common. Once a tiny, two-bar hostelry, the 1980s and '90s have seen it transformed into something quite different but none the worse for that. The covered patio has heating, enabling year-round use as a necessary overflow area (children are permitted here but not in the main bar). A varied menu offering tasty food such as chicken fajitas, ribs and vegetarian options proves very popular (tables can be booked). It remains, however, a drinkers' pub, attracting a wide range of customers. ⊛◖P

Park Inn

37 Carlisle Road, Shirley (off Shirley High St)
✪ 11.30-3, 5-11; 11.30-11 Fri & Sat; 12-10.30 Sun
☎ (023) 8078 7835
Badger Tanglefoot; Wadworth IPA, 6X; guest beers Ⓗ
Compact local, dating from the 1860s when it was known as the Park Tavern. A former Whitbread house, it became one of Wadworth's first pubs in Hampshire in the 1980s. Guest beers include Wadworth's seasonal brews and beers from the pub breweries owned by the company. The single bar serves distinct public and lounge areas. A wide spectrum of customers includes trade from local businesses and shoppers at lunchtimes. The menu includes curries, ploughmans, belly-busting baguettes and chilli pickled eggs. The strong local trade supports darts, crib and football teams. Lunchtime meat draw and eve quiz on Sun. ⊛◖♣●

Platform Tavern

Town Quay Road (opp. ferry terminals)
✪ 12-11; may close 3-5 weekdays; 12-10.30 Sun
☎ (023) 8033 7232 website: www.platformtavern.com
Fuller's London Pride; Itchen Valley Godfathers; guest beer Ⓗ
The exterior belies a captivating interior. The flagstoned bar area, chesterfield suite and open (gas) fire is complemented by a carpeted area more conducive to eating. An African theme prevails, including stained glass panels designed in-house. The building incorporates a section of the original 14th-century city wall. The pub name predates the railways and refers to the former gun platform that used to defend Southampton. Live music is performed Sun and Thu (drink prices raised to cover costs). May close Sat eve for private parties. Imaginative and well-presented food. A superb pub, often difficult to leave. ◖♣

Richmond Inn

108 Portswood Road, Portswood
✪ 11-11; 12-10.30 Sun
☎ (023) 8055 4523
Greene King XX Mild, IPA; guest beers Ⓗ
Two-bar traditional town pub: a busy, boisterous public bar featuring darts, a juke box and TV, and a quieter, more comfortable lounge, though both occasionally get a little smoky. The walls are cream above dark green, and carry many pictures of ocean liners associated with Southampton, and other maritime illustrations. Note the shared bar's wonderful antique brass till. To the rear a pleasant secluded garden contains a separate function room. The long-established staff cheerfully remove sparklers on request, and the landlady is a finalist in Greene King's 2001 *Beer in Glass* award for beer quality. ⊛⋐幸(St Denys) ♣

Waterloo Arms

101 Waterloo Road, Freemantle
✪ 12-11; 12-10.30 Sun
☎ (023) 8022 0022
Hop Back GFB, Best Bitter, Crop Circle, Entire Stout, Thunderstorm, Summer Lightning, seasonal or guest beer Ⓗ
Former Strong's pub, and the first to join Salisbury's Wyndham Arms in Hop Back Brewery's small estate, this 1930s mock-Tudor building is only five furlongs from Southampton Central Station, though Millbrook is closer. The single, L-shaped bar has light wood panelling and hosts a quiz night every Tue, plus occasional live music. Although gas, the coal-effect fires are very

Wobble Sold Here

In the industrial north of the county it was not unusual in the 19th century to see a primitive sign over a cottage door bearing the inspiring words: 'Wobble Sold Here'. Wobble was obtained from the Black Country small brewer and was the last 'shut' of the brew. The first shut was ale, the second shut was beer and the third shut was wobble. It was sold to the retailer at one shilling and a halfpence a bucket, or two pence a pail, with enough barm [yeast] to 'work it' at the cottage. There was no licence needed for the sale of wobble and it was sold mainly to colliers, ironworkers, nailers and others in hot dusty work. In the centre of a foundry it was the practice to have a barrel of water with barley in it, for the loss of body moisture through perspiration was great. But the men despised the water and sent out for a pail of wobble.

Bill Gwilliam, *Worcestershire's Hidden Past*, 1991.

convincing. Spring and autumn each see a beer festival in the enclosed patio garden to the rear. ⚫◗➡(Millbrook) ♣

STOKE

White Hart
Off B3048, NE in village
🕐 12-2, 6-11; 12-2, 7-10.30 Sun
☎ (01264) 738830
Beckett's Stoke Ale; Cheriton Pots Ale; Fuller's London Pride; Ringwood Best Bitter Ⓗ

Large, sympathetically refurbished country pub set in the picturesque Bourne Valley. The pub had been closed for two years and was on the verge of being converted into houses when it was saved by Basingstoke and Deane Borough Council. It has a spacious, L-shaped bar and separate dining area; the large skittle area doubles as a function room. The Test Way runs through the valley to the south of the pub, making it a good stop-off point. All the food is home-made; large parties may be advised to phone to ensure a table. The beer range includes ales from at least two local breweries. ⚫Q⚫◗⚫♣P

STUBBINGTON

Golden Bowler
122 Stubbington Lane
🕐 11-11; 12-10.30 Sun
☎ (01329) 662845
Draught Bass; guest beers Ⓗ

Modern free house, a large Victorian country property originally attached to a nursery, which only became a licensed premises in the 1960s. The previous owner retired from the RAF, which explains why the pub got its name. The present owners have been here since 1980. The pub consists of a single large bar with a separate restaurant and a small TV room, which doubles as a function room. Three guest beers are normally available from all over the country, and previous pump clips adorn the bar area. Children are welcome in certain areas before 8pm. ⚫◗P⚫

TANGLEY

Cricketers Arms
Signed at crossroads in Tangley OS322528
🕐 11-3 (not Mon-Fri), 6-11; 12-3, 7-10.30 Sun
☎ (01264) 730283
Draught Bass; Cheriton Pots Ale Ⓖ

Remote, 16th-century drovers' inn. A large dining room at the rear has an extensive menu (including takeaway pizzas). Advisable to book a table at weekends. There are two bar areas, one a snug and the other the main bar. The thick wooden beams, large open fire and low ceiling create a cosy atmosphere. The old bookcase and cricketing pictures add interest to the main bar. Look out for the old rack that holds the barrels. This is excellent walking country and the pub is well worth seeking out. ⚫Q⚫◗P

TITCHFIELD

Wheatsheaf
East Street
🕐 12-3, 6-11; 12-11 Fri; 12-3, 7-10.30 Sun
☎ (01329) 842965

Fuller's London Pride; Woodforde's Wherry; guest beers Ⓗ

Unspoilt village local situated close to Titchfield community centre. A true free house which regularly stocks a range of guest ales from a wide range of breweries. A small snug has board games and dominoes. Another room is used for eating and drinking. It is a good pub for a quiet pint, music is occasionally played in the eve. The pub has its own small car park and a patio for outdoor drinking. ⚫Q⚫⚫◗⚫♣P

TWYFORD

Phoenix
High Street (B3335, 1 mile S of M3 jct 11)
🕐 11.30-2.30 (3 Fri & Sat), 6-11; 12-3, 7-10.30 Sun
☎ (01962) 713322 website: www.thephoenixinn.co.uk
Greene King IPA; guest beers Ⓗ

Popular pub, the centre of village life, recently repainted a slightly alarming orange! Inside, the one-time multiple bars have been converted into one long, comfortably furnished room. The no-smoking eating area has an imposing log fireplace. The main bar has plenty of counter space and stools for informal drinkers. Guest beers are from Greene King's list. A good range of competitively priced home-made food is available daily. Accommodation is available in nearby cottages, the pub can arrange introductions. A skittle alley with its own bar can be hired for functions. Large rear garden. ⚫Q⚫⚫◗♣P⚫⚫

UPPER CLATFORD

Crook & Shears
Off A343, S of Andover
🕐 12-3 (closed Tue lunch), 6-11; 12-3, 7-10.30 Sun
☎ (01264) 361543
Flowers Original; Fuller's London Pride; Ringwood Fortyniner; Taylor Landlord; guest beer (occasional) Ⓗ

This attractive, 17th-century village pub has a spacious main bar which is popular with locals and a second bar with a large fireplace and comfortable seating for a relaxing pint. A small dining area is set away from the bar. In warm weather nothing beats sitting in the huge courtyard at the back of the pub, use the serving hatch for ease. The courtyard opens on to the garden where summer barbecues are occasionally held. Superb food served. The skittle alley can be booked for functions. ⚫Q⚫◗♣

WALLINGTON

White Horse
44 North Wallington, Fareham (1/2 mile from Delme roundabout)
🕐 11-3 (4 Fri & Sat), 5.30-11; 12-4, 7-10.30 Sun
☎ (01329) 235197
Draught Bass; Oakleaf Bitter, Nuptuale, Squirrel's Delight Ⓗ

Small, cosy inn tucked down a narrow lane. It stands alongside the former Saunders Brewery now converted for residential use. The two small bars offer bar meals at candlelit tables or you can opt for the separate restaurant. Superb choice for outdoor drinking: a French-style patio at the rear with colourful hanging baskets or sit at the front, close to the Wallington River which is across the lane. 🏚Q❄◑🕮♣

WEYHILL

Weyhill Fair
On A342, 3 miles W of Andover
☼ 11.15-3, 6 (5 Fri)-11; 7-10.30 Sun
☎ (01264) 773631 website: www.weyhillfair.co.uk
Fuller's Chiswick, London Pride, seasonal beers; guest beers Ⓗ
Popular roadside free house, renowned for its changing range of beers and good home-cooked food. Once a private house, it was extended to provide sustenance and accommodation for the cattle and sheep drovers attending the now-defunct Weyhill Fair, from which the pub takes its name. A mural depicts scenes in the upstairs function room. Around 200 different beers are served each year with a well-established beer and music festival held in July. A good field at the rear provides camping facilities and the pub is also HQ of the local cycling club, which holds an annual event here. Food ranges from chunky black pudding sandwiches to jambalaya, meals not served Sun eve. The pub is on a good bus route with stops right outside. Families and children are welcome in the no-smoking area.
Q❄◑▲♣P⊬🗓●

WHITCHURCH

Prince Regent
London Road
☼ 11-11; 12-10.30 Sun
☎ (01256) 892179
Archers Best Bitter; Hop Back GFB; guest beers Ⓗ
Unspoilt, traditional town pub with a warm welcome. This basic local overlooks England's smallest town and is well worth the walk from the square. The friendly landlord is always willing to chat and takes great pride in the quality of the beers. The single bar has a cosy atmosphere and is well-used by regular customers. The pub has strong pool and quiz teams. Buses stop outside, serving the nearby towns of Basingstoke, Andover and Winchester. Limited parking.
◑⇌♣🍴P

Red House Inn
21 London Street
☼ 11.30-3, 6-11; 12-3, 7-10.30 Sun
☎ (01256) 895558
Cheriton Pots Ale; Itchen Valley Pure Gold; guest beers Ⓗ
This 16th-century coaching inn has been transformed over recent years. With two very separate bars it is a fine example of a pub that can cater for everyone. The traditional log-fired public bar with flagstone floor contrasts with the pleasant lounge. Beers are always from local brewers and the pub has a reputation for quality food at reasonable prices. Massive baguettes or dishes such as roast queen fish or pan fried tilapia are served. The atmosphere is unpretentious and friendly. The large garden has an area set aside for children. If visiting Whitchurch with its silk mill, trout and fine walks (not to mention seven other pubs!), the Red House should not be missed.
🏚Q❄◑🔁⇌P⊬

190

Cask Marque

The Cask Marque symbol with a pub entry indicates that the licensee has successfully passed a number of tests concerning beer quality, and can display a plaque to this effect. However, the choice of all pubs in the guide is made by CAMRA independently of Cask Marque. The Cask Marque symbol is added during the editing process, and Cask Marque has no say in the selection of pubs.

WHITEHILL

Royal Oak
Liphook Road (A325 to Whitehall roundabout, S of village turn E, follow signs for Liphook)
☼ 12 (4 Mon)-11; 12.10.30 Sun
☎ (01428) 751493
Fuller's London Pride; Greene King Abbot; Marston's Pedigree; guest beer (occasional) Ⓗ
Built in 1890 by Farnham and United Breweries to service the new army camp at Bordon, but is now 'out of bounds' to junior ranks. It has been converted into one large wood-panelled bar with polished wooden floor and separate games and TV areas. The landlord is happy to refer to the pub as 'a good old-fashioned watering-hole', but warns that his friendly dog will scrounge food. Live music (mainly Rock/R&B/Pop) on Fri and Sat nights. Unusual for the semi-rural location, there is an adjoining curry house. ❄◑♿P

WIDLEY

Churchillian
Widley Walk, Portsdown Hill Road
☼ 11-11; 12-10.30 Sun
☎ (023) 9237 1803
website: www.thechurchillian.main-page.net
Draught Bass; Gale's HSB; guest beer Ⓗ
Splendid position on top of Portsdown Hill, which is 400ft high. This pub looks over the city of Portsmouth and offers superb views of the Solent and Isle of Wight. Alongside is the Victorian fort, Widley and to the rear the rolling Hampshire downs stretch into the distance. The single bar is a comfortable open-plan room with memorabilia of the great man himself, after whom the pub is named. Nearby is Southwick House where the allied leaders planned the D-Day landings. The pub has a garden and a roof terrace is an unusual feature. Q❄◑♿P

WINCHESTER

Bell Inn
83 St Cross Road (extreme S edge of city, on B3335)
☼ 11-3, 5-11; 11-11 Fri & Sat; 12-4, 7-10.30 Sun
☎ (01962) 865284

Greene King IPA, Ruddles County; guest beer Ⓗ

Two widely contrasting bars give a choice of drinking style in this comfortable, traditional pub. A quiet, carpeted, conversational lounge complements the busy, cosmopolitan, flagstoned public bar. Outside is a large, safe garden with extensive children's play equipment. The Bell adjoins the Hospital of St Cross, founded in 1132, England's oldest almshouse. Impressively robed brothers often call in for a relaxing drink. The pub is a mile from the city centre by a tranquil walk through the Itchen water meadows – inspiration for Keats's *To Autumn*. No eve meals Wed or Sun. Food is usual pub grub with traditional Sun roasts. It is, however, 'a pub first'.

🏚Q🏶🍴🏵♣P

Black Boy

1 Wharf Hill (off Chesil St, B3330)

◷ 11-3, 6-11; 12-3, 7-10.30 Sun

☎ (01962) 861754

Cheriton Pots Ale; Hampshire Pride of Romsey; Ringwood Best Bitter; guest beer Ⓗ

This friendly and popular pub stands on a raised terrace across the Itchen from Wolvesey Palace and Castle, and is flanked by a raised patio garden. A genuine free house with a policy of serving beers from Hampshire breweries. It has a large, convoluted main bar almost divided in two by one of its two real fires, and a separate, homely family room which may be converted into a second, wine-orientated bar. The endlessly engrossing decor includes many old artefacts and unusual items displayed on walls, window sills, doors, beams and ceilings. No food served Mon or Fri–Sun eves.

🏚🍴🏶🍴♣

Green Man

53 Southgate Street

(370 yds S of High St on B3335)

◷ 11.30-11; 12-10.30 Sun

☎ (01962) 865429

Greene King IPA, Abbot; guest beers Ⓗ

Victorian-style corner pub on the edge of the city centre, now opened up to leave a single, high-backed island bar surrounded by irregular booths. Diversions include regular live music, tending to modern folk, on Sun and Tue, and a separate skittle alley, while Winchester's newish cinema is right across the road. Since the pub's transfer from Marston's to Greene King, the food, always of good quality, has become less expensive and more diverse, and is available during all sessions except Sun eve. Popular with students.

🍴🍴♣

Hyde Tavern

57 Hyde Street

(400 yds N of City Rd on B3047)

◷ 12-2.30, 5-11; 12-3, 6-11 Sun

☎ (01962) 862592

Greene King IPA, seasonal or guest beer Ⓗ

Very small, 15th-century timber-framed building dominated by twin dormer windows, next door but one to Hyde Parish Hall in a street where ale has been sold for over 700 years. The unspoilt interior features two bars, uneven floors and walls, and low beams – beware! Gentlemen will note the unusual corner urinal. Hyde Tavern supports a cricket club and golf society, and the conversation (expect to be drawn in) is convivial and highbrow. The ruins of Hyde Abbey and King Alfred's final resting place lie close by, but the Tavern's ghost is female: her footsteps are sometimes heard in the bar after closing time. The garden opened in spring, 2001.

🏶🍴🏵♣●

St James Tavern

3 Romsey Road (on D3040)

◷ 11.30-2.30, 5.30 (5 Fri)-11; 11.30-11 Sun; 12-3, 7-10.30 Sun

☎ (01962) 861228 e-mail: timh@easynet.co.uk

Butcombe Bitter; Wadworth IPA, 6X, JCB, Summersault (summer)**, seasonal beers** Ⓗ

Standing above pavement level on an acute terrace corner, this pub has wooden floors, tan walls with light wood panelling, and high cream ceilings. The new raised no-smoking extension contains a coal-effect gas fire, while at the far end of the single, bracket-shaped bar is Winchester's last pub bar billiards table. Mon is quiz night, and a range of good value food is available every session except Sun eve. Enjoy a drink on the patio in summer. King Alfred's College and the Royal Hampshire County Hospital are a little further up the hill, while a complex of six military museums lies just over the railway bridge downhill.

🏶🍴🍴🏵♣✄●

Wykeham Arms

75 Kingsgate Street

◷ 11-11; 12-10.30 Sun

☎ (01962) 853834

Draught Bass; Gale's Butser, GB, HSB Ⓗ

Rambling, many-roomed Georgian pub just yards from the gates of the Cathedral Close and Winchester School. The bric-à-brac and antiquities could furnish every other pub in Winchester – 2,000 tankards adorn the walls, canes cover a ceiling, Nelsoniana abounds, old school desks make compact tables. The menu has won a coveted *Michelin* award. The extensive wine list has 20 varieties by the glass, including champagne. Trollope stayed here, describing it as 'a third rate hostelry'. Now the rooms are quite certainly first rate! Can be busy, but remains civilised. Dogs are welcomed.

🏚Q🏶🛏🍴P●

Barley Mow

The Hurst

◷ 12-3 (4 Sat), 6-11; 12-4, 6-10.30 Sun

☎ (01252) 617490

Beer range varies Ⓗ

Cosy 1920s pub surrounded by Hampshire farmlands. The popular food options range from normal pub fare to more comprehensive meals available in the adjoining no-smoking restaurant, no food served on Sun eve. Unusually, the pub has its own cricket pitch available for hire! It is also located very close to a terminal point for narrow boat trips along the Basingstoke Canal. Ample car park, however, can normally cope with the resulting increased trade on fine eves and weekends.

🏚Q🏶🍴🍴♣P

HEREFORDSHIRE

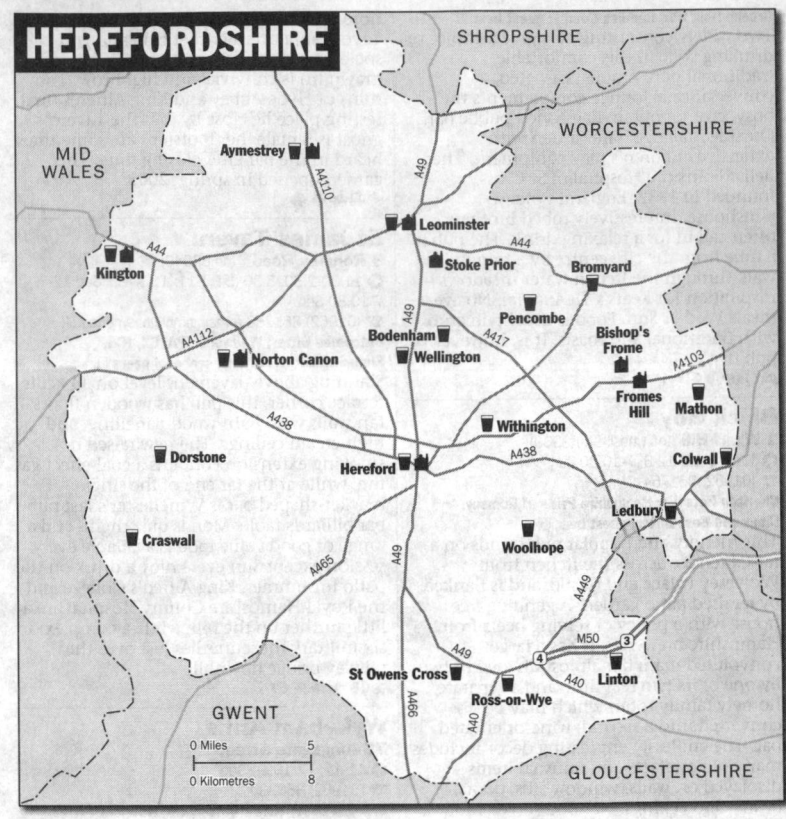

AYMESTREY

Riverside Inn
On A4110
🕐 11-11; 11-10.30 Sun
☎ (01568) 708440
Woodhampton Red Kite, Jack Snipe, Kingfisher Ale, Wagtai Ⓗ
Situated in a delightful location on the River Lugg, this comfortable pub is considered to be the tap for nearby Woodhampton Brewery. The French chef buys meat locally and offers an extensive, quite exceptional, menu of well-presented dishes. Close to the Mortimer Trail footpath, and with a mile of fishing rights, this is an excellent base for exploring the north of the county. Accommodation is in the pub and nearby annexe. Camping is also available on site – the pub occupies three acres of land. ♨Q✿🍴◑▲♣P

BROMYARD

Bay Horse
21 High Street
🕐 11-3, 5.30-11; 12-3.30, 7-10.30 Sun
☎ (01885) 482600
Hobsons Best Bitter; Marston's Pedigree; guest beers Ⓗ
Attractive black and white hotel in the town centre. It has now recovered very well from a ruthless refurbishment in the 1980s; the remaining wood panelling, seating and cushioned benches, arranged along the walls and in the bay windows, give this single lounge bar a relaxed and homely feel. Very much a pub for quiet conversation over a good pint. On-street parking is possible. ✿◑♣P

Rose & Lion
5 New Road
🕐 11-3, 6-11; 11-11 Fri & Sat; 12-10.30 Sun
☎ (01885) 482381
Wye Valley Bitter, Butty Bach, seasonal beers Ⓗ
The most unspoilt pub in Bromyard; following a very successful takeover by Wye Valley, the old place has really flourished. Run by a popular landlady, this pub sets the standard for Bromyard – if not the county. Redecoration has brought out the architectural merits of this multi-roomed traditional pub. It exudes charm and draws a strong local following, while welcoming visitors. Join the regulars in a game of dominoes or enjoy the garden for which the landlady pays a rent to Wye Valley (paid in turnips grown in the garden!). Q✿🍴♣P

COLWALL ✤

Chase Inn
Chase Road
🕐 12-2.30 (not Tue), 6-11; 12-2.30, 7-10.30 Sun
☎ (01684) 540276 e-mail: baileychase@bushnet.com
Donnington BB, SBA; Hobsons Best Bitter; Wye Valley seasonal beer Ⓗ
Two-roomed pub, in an attractive wooded setting, comprising an L-shaped public bar with a pool table and a quiet lounge. The

garden affords a superb view across Herefordshire, with the Welsh mountains in the distance. A rare outlet for Donnington beers, it is well worth the 25-minute uphill walk from Colwall Station. It offers a limited but very wholesome lunch menu – the ham is always home-cooked; no food Sun. An ideal stop when walking the Malvern Hills (drop off at the Wyche cutting); dogs welcome. Q✿◖P

CRASWALL

Bull's Head
On Milchaelchurch to Hay-on-Wye road OS278360
✿ 11-11; 12-4 (closed eve) Sun
☎ (04004) 540010

Wye Valley Butty Bach; guest beers (summer) G
Superlative example of a surviving drovers' inn; isolated on the Welsh border, high in the foothills of the Black Mountains, this pub is ideal for visitors exploring the nearby attractions including Hay Bluff and the Offa's Dyke path. Unaltered for over 125 years before being rescued from an untimely demise in 1998, the current owners have developed a good food trade: a rare mix of quality and quantity, using local ingredients – its baltis are legendary and the 'huffers' (large sandwiches) are a complete meal. But food has not spoilt the inn's character. The main bar remains untouched – with hearth, sink, settles and hatch servery. A real view into the past.
▲Q♻✿⌂◖⊖Y♠

DORSTONE

Pandy Inn
By the village green
✿ 12-2.30 (not Mon), 6-11; 12-11 Sat; 12-3, 6.30-10.30 Sun
☎ (01981) 550273

Wye Valley Bitter, Butty Bach H
Typical black and white Herefordshire village pub where new licensees are realising its true potential. Knocked through, but with discrete areas, one is a restaurant, the other two invite drinkers. At the heart of this small rural community, it benefits from passing trade with good food featuring strongly, including a varied selection of vegetarian dishes. Possibly the oldest pub in Herefordshire, it was allegedly built by Richard de Brito in 1185, while building the village church (a task he had to perform for his involvement in the murder of Thomas à Becket). ▲✿♣♠P✄

HEREFORD �

Barrels
69 St Owen Street
✿ 11-11; 12-10.30 Sun
☎ (01432) 274968

Wye Valley Bitter, HPA, Butty Bach, Supreme, Brew 69, seasonal beers; guest beer H
Home of the award-winning Wye Valley Brewery since 1986, the Barrels has developed a cult following among locals and visitors alike. One of the last multi-roomed hostelries in the city, this four-roomed pub is Hereford's cathedral to beer. Its crowning glory is a beer-cum-music festival, held for charity each August bank holiday, that always sells out in advance. Herefordshire CAMRA *Pub of the Year* on a record number

of occasions, it does what all pubs should do well – have something for everyone: games, quiet corners and boisterous areas, and it is a mecca for sports' fans. ✿⊞≈♣♠

Goodbody's
45 West Street
✿ 11-11; 12-3 Sun
☎ (01432) 265894

Wye Valley HPA, Dorothy Goodbody's Wholesome Stout, seasonal beers H
This pub caters primarily for those who wish to enjoy excellent food; it has a dining area upstairs and a cosy bar downstairs. Set in a narrow side street in the historic centre of Hereford, Goodbody's offers good restaurant fare without compromising on beer quality. This Wye Valley project has successfully converted a rather run-of-the-mill steak house into something a little more enticing. ▲Q◖♠&

Lichfield Vaults
11 Church Street (alley between cathedral and rear of M&S)
✿ 11-11; 12-10.30 Sun
☎ (01432) 267994

Marston's Pedigree; Tetley Bitter; guest beers H
Tucked away in a delightful cobbled alley housing specialist shops, this one-bar pub offers a tremendous range of guest beers with gusto. A Festival Ale House, its single large drinking area splits neatly into a busy front part and a more relaxed rear section. Sympathetically refurbished, much character has been retained with wood featuring strongly. Popular with shoppers and workers at lunchtime, it draws a more lively city crowd eves. Parking can be problematic. ✿◖♣♠

Three Elms
1 Canon Pyon Road
✿ 11-11; 12-10.30 Sun
☎ (01432) 273338

Flowers Original; Marston's Pedigree; Tetley Bitter; guest beers H
Large open-plan pub on a housing estate near the racecourse. A wide range of guest beers is stocked, usually including one from Wye Valley. Families are especially welcome – not only does the pub have a family room with an indoor play area, but in good weather there is plenty of scope for youngsters to let off steam outside. Sporting events, especially football, shown on a big screen in a corner of the bar, are popular with locals. Meals served all day Sat and Sun. Wheelchair WC. ♻✿◖&P

Victory
88 St Owen Street
✿ 11-11; 12-10.30 Sun

INDEPENDENT BREWERIES

Dunn Plowman Kington
Fromes Hill Fromes Hill
Frome Valley Bishop's Frome
Marches Leominster
Shoes Norton Canon
SP Sporting Ales Stoke Prior
Spinning Dog Hereford
Woodhampton Aymestrey
Wye Valley Hereford

☎ (01432) 274998

Spinning Dog Chase Your Tail, Muttley's Bark Mild, Top Dog; guest beers Ⓗ

Rescued from mediocrity by the Wye Valley Brewery a few years ago, this pub now houses Herefordshire's latest brewery, Spinning Dog, offering the full range of its beers and a diverse selection of guest beers. There is always something happening in this lively edge-of-city-centre pub that bears a galleon theme, through its front open area to a more discrete area towards the back. Herefordshire CAMRA *Pub of the Year* 2000, it is a venue for local bands, and 2001 saw their first (successful) beer festival. If you meet the pub dog you will appreciate the name of the brewery.

🏚Q☀️⌂◑⊕&⇌♣♠P✗⊟●

KINGTON

Olde Tavern ☆
22 Victoria Road

❂ 11.30-2.30 (not Mon-Fri), 7.30-11; 12-2.30, 7.30-10.30 Sun

☎ (01544) 231384

Ansells Bitter Ⓗ

On CAMRA's inventory of historic interiors, this one-bar pub contains many curios and a lovely beer engine. Opposite the bar is another room with a wooden settle. Highly recommended to devotees of unspoilt town pubs, a good local following and long-standing landlady make this pub a must on any visit to Kington. It has won numerous CAMRA *Pub of the Year* awards. It offers no food, but great character and charm instead. On-street parking is possible. Q♣

Queen's Head
Bridge Street

❂ 11-11; 12-10.30 Sun

☎ (01544) 231106

Dunn Plowman Brewhouse Bitter, Early Riser; guest beer Ⓗ

Home of the rekindled Dunn Plowman Brewery whose brewhouse is located to the rear of this town pub. Refurbishment over recent times has enhanced this pub – particularly highlighting many traditional features. The rounded window and wood floor in the public bar are of particular merit. The lounge offers a quieter environment in a pub that attracts a loyal following. Food is basic, but filling (not served Mon).

🏚☀️⌂◑♣P

LEDBURY

Talbot Hotel
New Street

❂ 11.30-3, 5-11; 11-11 Sat; 12-4, 7-10.30 Sun

☎ (01531) 632963 website: www.talbotledbury.co.uk

Wadworth IPA, 6X, JCB; guest beer Ⓗ

An inn since 1596, this attractive black and white Tudor hotel cannot fail to impress – the plush bar boasts an impressive fireplace and an extra drinking area, to the rear of the bar, houses a dartboard. An ideal place to spend a short break, meals are served in an oak-panelled dining room. It is convenient for town-centre shops.

🏚⌂◑⇌♣P

LEOMINSTER

Black Horse
74 South Street

❂ 11-2.30, 6-11; 11-11 Sat; 12-3, 7-10.30 Sun

☎ (01568) 611946 e-mail: peter@bhorse.fsnet.co.uk

Dunn Plowman BHB; Hobsons Town Crier; guest beers Ⓗ

This old coaching inn, on the south side of Leominster does not offer frills or a swanky interior. Years of wear and tear show at the edges, but it is comfortable, friendly and offers the best range of beers in town. Marches Brewery started in a tiny bottle store at the back of the pub in the early 1990s, and the pub still sells Marches' products. Food is typical pub fare (not served Sun); a long dining area is at the rear of this two-bar pub. Pool and darts are played in the public bar, pétanque and quoits outside.

☀️◑⊕⇌♣P

Grape Vaults
4 Broad Street

❂ 11-3, 5-11; 11-4, 6-11 Sat; 12-4, 6.30-10.30 Sun

☎ (01568) 611404

Banks's Original, Bitter; Marston's Pedigree; guest beers Ⓗ

An unpretentious exterior fails to prepare the visitor for the delightful wood-panelled interior of this wonderfully unspoilt pub. Once a 'hard-core' cider house, this central pub has much to commend it. The discrete nooks offer drinkers a cosy retreat; the snug bar is a marvel. The beer range has expanded to meet the deserved increase in trade, and often includes Marches' ales. The food is excellent. A pub to be enjoyed at one's leisure; note the stained glass. 🏚Q◑

INN BRIEF

BODENHAM

England's Gate Inn
On A417
11-11; 12-10.30 Sun
Marston's Pedigree; Wye Valley Dorothy Goodbody Traditional Bitter; guest beers Ⓗ
Recently reclaimed from neglect, its bustling bar is split into several nooks and crannies on different levels. Large garden.

COLWALL

Colwall Park Hotel
11-3, 6-11; 12-10.30 Sun
Draught Bass; guest beer Ⓗ
Pleasant, village-centre hotel by the station.

HEREFORD

Treacle Mine
83-85 St Martins Street
12-3, 6-11; 11-11 Sat; 12-10.30 Sun
Banks's Bitter; Greene King Abbot; guest beers Ⓗ
One-roomed pub, popular with sports' fans and locals.

WITHINGTON

Cross Keys Inn
7 (12 Sat)-11; 12-4.30, 7-10.30 Sun
Greene King Abbot; Hobsons Best Bitter; Wye Valley Butty Bach; guest beers Ⓗ
No-frills, roadside pub, now owned by its licensee. Stone-flagged floors feature.

Guide site

Keep your copy of the Good Beer Guide up-to-date by contacting the CAMRA website where you will find information about changes to pubs and breweries

www.camra.org.uk/gbg

LINTON

Alma Inn

1 mile from M50, jct 3 OS659255
✪ 12-2.30, 6.30 (6 Fri & Sat)-11; 12-2.30,
7-10.30 Sun
☎ (01989) 720355
**Butcombe Bitter; RCH Pitchfork; Smiles Best; guest
beer** (occasional) Ⓗ
Run by a keen publican who has
reintroduced real ale to this village pub, it
explodes the myth that rural pubs are
doomed. A three-roomed hostelry, near the
church in a hilltop village, its eclectic mix
of furniture is arranged to encourage
customers to engage in conversation. With
a warm welcome and superb fire, little
encouragement is needed. A meals service is
due to start autumn 2001 (no food Sun eve
or Mon).
𝔐Q❀⏻Ⓐ♣P

MATHON

Cliffe Arms

OS737458
✪ 12-2.30 (not Mon), 6.30-11; 12-2.30, 7-10.30 Sun
☎ (01886) 880782
**Adnams Bitter; Fuller's London Pride; Hobsons Best
Bitter** Ⓗ
Attractive, multi-roomed pub, parts of
which date back to about 1400. The public
bar houses a pool table and electronic
games while the lounge bar consists of
several distinct areas. The restaurant at the
rear is in a converted barn. A rare outlet for
Adnams, this community pub is located in a
delightful village in the shadow of the
Malvern Hills. 𝔐❀⏻Ⓐ♣P

NORTON CANON

Three Horseshoes

On A480, approx. 8 miles from Hereford
✪ 11-3, 6-11; 12-3, 7-10.30 Sun
☎ (01544) 318375
Shoes Norton Ale, Canon Bitter Ⓗ
This unpretentious roadside inn, home of
the Shoes Brewery, was local CAMRA *Pub of
the Year* 1999. It comprises two contrasting
bars; to the left as you enter is a small
lounge, furnished with comfy old sofas and
a piano in one corner. A community-
focused public bar, to the right leads to a
pool room.
𝔐Q❀⛃Ⓐ♣P

PENCOMBE

Wheelwrights Arms

Turn off A417, between Bodenham and Burley Gate
OS598528
✪ 12-3, 6-11; 12-2, 6-10.30 Sun
☎ (01885) 400358
**Butcombe Bitter; Greene King Abbot; Taylor Landlord;
Theakston Black Bull; Wood Wonderful** Ⓗ
Traditional country pub traceable to the
16th century. In 1871 Charles Lawrence
used the premises as a wheelwright, and
incidentally sold ale. Nowadays you are sure
of a pint of good beer, but bespoke wheels
are no longer available. As befits its aim to
be a village pub there is always a main meal
priced at £3. It is only four miles from
Bromyard, which hosts a gala and a folk
festival.
𝔐Q❀⛃⏻Ⓐ♣P

ROSS-ON-WYE

Crown & Sceptre

Market Place
✪ 10-11; 12-10.30 Sun
☎ (01989) 562765
**Archers Best Bitter; Fuller's London Pride; Greene
King Abbot; guest beer** Ⓗ
Beware the one-way system that blights
Ross – but once negotiated this pub stands
proudly on the old market place. Recently
refurbished to a very high standard, it
remains acceptable to traditionalists. Tables
and sofas up front give way to a long bar
with refectory feel, plus a pool and games
area at the rear. Bare boards and pleasant
furnishings make this pub popular with all,
but the younger set dominates weekend
eves when it can get very busy. A beer
festival is held Easter weekend. Parking is
tricky – try the town car parks.
𝔐❀⏻Ⓐ♣⛾

ST OWENS CROSS

New Inn

At A4173/B4521 jct
✪ 12-2.30 (3 Sat), 6-11; 12-3, 7-10 Sun
☎ (01989) 730274
**Draught Bass; Tetley Bitter; Wadworth 6X; guest
beers** Ⓗ
Two-bar, 16th-century black and white
roadside pub where hanging baskets are a
summer feature. One bar acts as a restaurant
serving good food, the other is favoured by
locals. The accommodation includes four-
poster beds. The owner takes a pride in the
quality of his beer and is knowledgeable
about the subject. 𝔐Q❀⇔⏻♣P

WELLINGTON

Wellington Inn

1 mile W of A49
✪ 11-2.30 (3 Sat), 6-11; 12-3, 7-10.30 Sun
☎ (01432) 830367
**Draught Bass; Hancock's HB; Hobsons Best Bitter;
guest beers** Ⓗ
This traditional country pub and restaurant
always has five real ales available, plus a
cider in summer. Food is a real speciality
with daily specials, and the Dangerous
Dinner Club on the first Thu of each month
should be checked out. No TV or juke box;
the locals prefer darts or cricket. A handy
detour for travellers on the A49 trunk road.
𝔐Q❀⏻Ⓐ♣P

WOOLHOPE

Crown Inn

✪ 12-2.30, 6.30-11; 12-3, 6.30-10.30 Sun
☎ (01432) 860465
Smiles Best; Wye Valley Bitter; guest beer
(summer) Ⓗ
Village pub next to St Mary's church, it is
deservedly popular with foodies from
nearby Hereford, but not at the total
exclusion of drinkers – the locals can prove
that. One large bar has a central serving area
and a small drinking zone. It stocks an
excellent range of bottled beers, but the
food is its greatest asset. An extensive,
appetising menu includes hazelnut bubble
and squeak and popular Sun roasts. It even
sells food gift vouchers. Booking for
weekend meals is advised. ⏻♣

CAMRA's National Inventory
of Pubs Interiors of Outstanding Historic Interest

West Midlands

Birmingham

Aston: Bartons Arms, 152 High Street. 1900-1: the richest interior in Birmingham with magnificent fittings.

Aston: Britannia, 287 Lichfield Road.1899-1900: good tiles and unusual glazed screen.

Digbeth: Anchor, 308 Bradford Street. 1901: four rooms: rare low partition.

Digbeth: Market Tavern, 210-212 Moseley Street. 1899-1900: original plan, fine tiles, impressive smoke room.

Digbeth: White Swan, 276 Bradford Street. 1899-1900 with tiled walls from floor to ceiling, particularly spectacular corridor.

Digbeth: Woodman, Albert St.1896-7: tiled walls, impressive rear smoke room.

Hall Green: Three Magpies, Shirley Road . 1930s 'Moderne' style suburban pub.

Handsworth: Red Lion, 270 Soho Road. Magnificent 1901-2 pub in a run-down area: tiled walls, and magnificent bar-back.

Hockley: Rose Villa Tavern, 172 Warstone Lane. 1919-20 continuing the Victorian tradition with extensive tilework and impressive windows.

Nechells: Villa Tavern, 307 Nechells Park Road . Rebuilt 1924-5 (despite what it says outside), again continuing the Victorian tradition.

Small Heath: Samson & Lion, Yardley Green Road. 1913-15: three rooms, screen dividing the public bar, flags of the Allies in lounge glass.

Stirchley: British Oak, 1364 Pershore Road. Stylish pub of 1923-4 with original multi-roomed layout and furnishings.

Winson Green: Bellefield, Winson Street. Stunning interior, particularly the all-over tiled smoke room of c.1910.

Bloxwich: Turf Tavern, 13 Wolverhampton Road. Terraced working-men's pub c.1875 with simple fittings.

Dudley: Shakespeare, Stafford Street. Wonderful, basic working-men's pub of c.1870. Tiny front bar.

Oldbury: Waggon & Horses, Church Street. Good Edwardian tiling and glass; bar with copper ceiling, lounge and drinking passage.

Sedgley: Beacon, 129 Bilston Street. Victorian brew-pub: multi-room interior. Kiosk-style servery.

Rushall: Manor Arms, Park Road, Daw End. Several rooms: no bar counter.

Smethwick: Waterloo Hotel, Shireland. Lavish Edwardian Baroque pub-cum-hotel of 1907: visit the spectacular grill room downstairs.

Wiltshire

Easton Royal: Bruce Arms. Basic roadside pub with drinking lobby and three small rooms.

Salisbury: Haunch of Venison, Minster Street. Largely unaltered 'chop house' with tiny snug; spirit cocks.

Worcestershire

Bretforton: Fleece. Lovely 17th-century building: three rooms and old furnishings.

Clent: Bell & Cross. Late 18th-century building: five small rooms: Victorian woodwork.

Defford: Cider House (on A4104). Unique cider house in thatched cottage with outside servery: sit in the bakehouse or garden. Closed Mon and lunch Tue-Thu.

Hanley Castle: Three Kings. Original core of two small rooms: lounge added c.1981 in adjoining old building.

Worcester: Paul Pry, The Butts. 1901: good tiling and woodwork.

Yorkshire (East)

Beverley: White Horse ('Nellie's'), Hengate. Justly famous for its long history, and warren of gas-lit rooms with stone-flagged floors.

Hull: Olde Black Boy, 150 High Street. Little altered since 1926, and retaining much of its old layout as a Victorian wine merchant's.

Hull: Olde White Hart, 25 Silver Street. Part late 17th-century: unaltered plan and 'Olde Englande' effects from a restoration of 1881.

Skerne: Eagle Inn. Small and unspoilt : two simple rooms : 'cash register' handpumps.

Yorkshire (North)

Beck Hole: Birch Hall Inn. Unique time-warp, lovingly preserved : two simple pub rooms either side of a tiny village shop.

Boroughbridge: Three Horse Shoes, Bridge Street. One of the best-preserved examples of a smaller 'brewers' Tudor' roadhouse.

Harrogate: Gardeners Arms, Bilton Lane. Delightful little 18th-century building: stone-flagged rooms off a central corridor.

York: Blue Bell, Fossgate. Intimate two-room interior: preserves all the fittings and panelling from a 1903 refurbishment.

York: Golden Ball, Cromwell Road, Bishophill. Victorian street corner local, replanned in 1929: unusual layout of four rooms: tiled bar front.

York: Swan, 16 Bishopgate Street, Clementhorpe. Intact 1930s redesign of an old corner pub: central standing-up lobby: two smallish rooms.

Yorkshire (South)

Sheffield: Bath Hotel, Victoria Street. Largely unaltered since a 1931 remodelling: two small rooms.

Yorkshire (West)

Bradford: Cock & Bottle, 93 Barkerend Road. Elaborately refurbished c.1900: extensive glasswork : two mahogany bar-backs: five rooms

Bradford: New Beehive, 171 Westgate. Built 1901: drinking hallway and three original rooms: tiled and terrazzo corridor.

Heath: King's Arms. Historic core of front bar and snug, first converted from cottages in the mid-19th-century: much extended.

Leeds: Adelphi, 3-5 Hunslet Road. Built 1901 as a pub-cum-hotel: multi-room interior.

Leeds: Cardigan Arms, 364 Kirkstall Road, Burley. 1895: the most complex of Leeds' surviving drinking palaces: six well-preserved rooms and lobby.

Leeds: Garden Gate, 37 Waterloo Road, Hunslet. Built 1903 and a treasure-house of Edwardian decoration: lavish ceramic work.

Leeds: Rising Sun, 290 Kirkstall Road, Burley. A more modest form of drinking palace, built 1899: four rooms: lobby with glazed screen.

Leeds: Whitelocks, Turks Head Yard, off Briggate. Character of a late Victorian luncheon bar: dark oak, mirrors, brass and copper : narrow plan.

Wakefield: Redoubt, 28 Horbury Road. Authentic Victorian character in rooms off a central corridor.

Continued on page 229

HERTFORDSHIRE

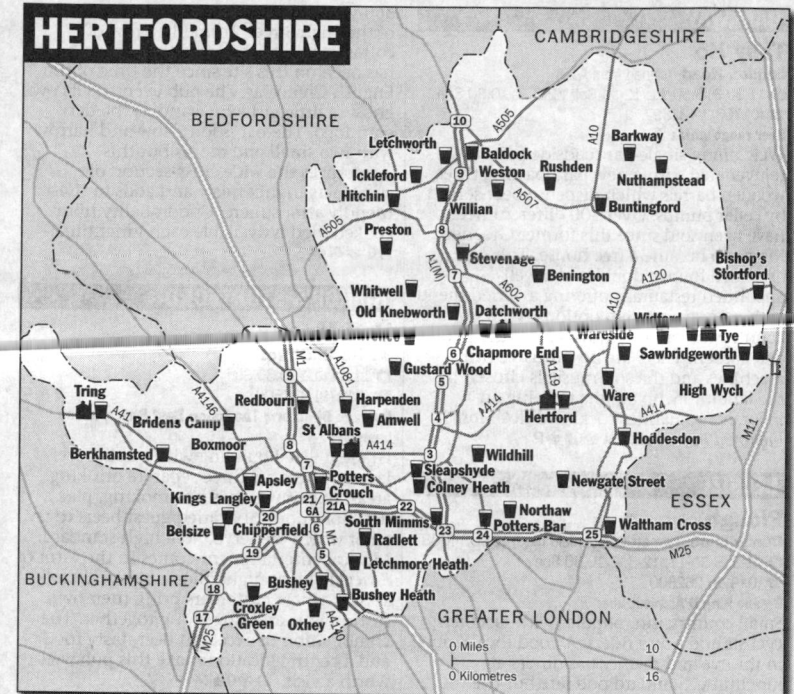

AMWELL

Elephant & Castle
Amwell Lane (left fork at top of Brewhouse Hill, Wheathampstead) OS167133
⊕ 12-3 (2.30 Oct-Easter), 5.30-11; 12-11 Sat; 12-10.30 Sun
☎ (01582) 832175
Greene King IPA, Abbot; seasonal beers or guest beers Ⓗ

Friendly, deservedly popular 18th-century pub. Formerly three cottages, the inn is in a peaceful setting, out of the way and beautifully situated. See the 200-foot well in the bar and open wood-burning fires; the floors are laid with attractive terracotta tiles. With the added asset of two large gardens, this highly successful country pub has gone from strength to strength, one of the few rural inns to sell real ale in 36-gallon casks (IPA). Local CAMRA *Pub of the Year* finalist 1999. Eve meals Tue-Sat, no lunches Mon. Pub games include spot the lager drinkers; they are difficult to find! ♨❀◖♣P●

APSLEY

White Lion
44 London Road
⊕ 11-11; 12-10.30 Sun
☎ (01442) 268948
Fuller's London Pride, ESB, seasonal beers Ⓗ

Apsley is one of those places that was once more important than it is now. John Dickinson's paper-mill employed thousands and provided the nation with 'Lion' brand stationery. Today, Apsley is by-passed and Dickinson's and many of the local pubs have disappeared or been converted into retail and business parks. This pub may appear unusual in this area of Hertfordshire in that it is a rock-solid, old-fashioned street-corner local selling quality Fuller's ales. Newspapers and TV are always available and many local charities are supported in the sort of pub every neighbourhood should have, but few do. ❀◖≈P

BALDOCK

Cock
43 High Street
⊕ 11.30-2 (not Mon, Tue or Thu), 5-11, 11.30-11 Sat; 12-4, 7-10.30 Sun
☎ (01462) 892366
e-mail: john-lone-howard@talk21.com
Greene King XX Mild, IPA, Abbot; guest beers Ⓗ

17th-century inn with an authentic beamed interior and open log fire. The drinking area is on split levels which enhances its character. Enclosed patio outside is available in suitable weather. The ancient market town of Baldock sits on the old Great North Road coaching route. A popular local with *Cask Marque* status, vinyl juke box, no games machines and TV only used for special events. Wheelchair access via patio. Market day is Wed and visitors should note that the pub does not open on Mon, Tue or Thu lunchtimes except for pre-arranged parties. ♨❀◖&≈♣●

INDEPENDENT BREWERIES

Dark Horse Hertford
Green Tye Much Hadham
McMullen Hertford
Sawbridgeworth Sawbridgeworth
Tring Tring
Verulam St Albans

BARKWAY

Tally Ho
London Road (signed from A10)
✪ 11.30-3, 5.30-11; 12-11 Sat; 12-3, 7-10.30 Sun
☎ (01763) 848389
Beer range varies Ⓖ
Welcoming single-bar roadside pub now rejuvenated with a new bar boasting three wooden barrels which dispense beer served by cellar pumps. Over 500 different beers have been sold since this former Greene King pub became a free house. The extended lounge doubles as a well-appointed restaurant offering a varied menu with many vegetarian options. Views of the countryside can be enjoyed from the patio and garden. There are no intrusive fruit machines and the soft music is chosen by the landlord who admits to being an incurable romantic. Local CAMRA *Most Improved Pub* 2000. � ❁◖▮ ♣P

BELSIZE

Plough
Dunny Lane (Sarratt-Chipperfield road) OS034008
✪ 11-3, 5.30-11; 12-3, 7-10.30 Sun
☎ (01923) 262800
Greene King IPA; guest beer Ⓗ
Small country inn, popular with ramblers, cyclists and horse riders. A good locals' pub in the eve and mainly has diners at lunchtime. Standard pub fare but the specials blackboard is more inventive and always has a vegetarian option (no meals Sun eve). If required there is a comfortable separate dining area. Enjoy the pub's own game, devised by a local, which is fun to watch or play, but you will need help to understand the rules. A piano is played during some Fri lunchtimes. The pleasant, fenced garden is busy on warm, summer days. � ❁◖▮ ♣P

BENINGTON

Lordship Arms
42 Whempstead Road (3 miles E of Stevenage via B1037) OS308227
✪ 12-3, 6-11; 12-3, 7-10.30 Sun
☎ (01438) 869665
Fuller's London Pride, ESB; Young's Special; guest beers Ⓗ
Originally named the Cricketers this excellent one-bar pub was saved from possible closure by the present landlord and landlady. One of the best free houses in the Herts area it was voted local CAMRA *Pub of the Year* 1997 and '99. Its regular range of ales is more than complemented by an ever-changing selection of beers from small breweries far and wide, together with draught cider and various fruit wines. Telephone memorabilia adorns the pub, handpumps are modelled on different styles of phone. Curry nights are a regular Wed eve feature. � ❁◖♣▮P▯

BERKHAMSTED

Lamb
277 High Street
✪ 11-3, 6-11; 11-11 Fri & Sat; 12-10.30 Sun
☎ (01442) 862615
Adnams Bitter; Fuller's London Pride; Tetley Bitter; Tring Ridgeway Bitter Ⓗ

360-year-old listed building at the Tring end of the High Street. Formerly a row of cottages, but it is believed that an ale house has been on this site since the time of the English Civil War. The pub even has its own ghost (a little girl who wanders the dark corridors). The bar is long, low and narrow with two small end rooms but this encourages the wide cross-section of customers to mix freely and adds to the friendly atmosphere. Good quality home-cooked food is available each lunchtime. ❁◖⇌♣▮

BISHOP'S STORTFORD

Half Moon
31 North Street
✪ 11-11; 12-10.30 Sun
☎ (01279) 834500
Courage Directors; Theakston Best Bitter; guest beers Ⓗ
Grade II listed building with a split-level layout. There are three separate drinking areas, one of which is no-smoking, plus a function room. Six varied guest beers to try, all of which are served to a high standard. Musical entertainment comes in the form of a weekly blues night, plus a bi-weekly folk session where customers bring their own instruments and sing along together. The combination of excellent beer, tasty food and a central location make this pub well worth a visit. Q❁◖♣▮⌁

BRIDENS CAMP

Crown & Sceptre
Red Lion Lane (off A4146)
✪ 12-3, 5.30 (6 Sat)-11, (12-11 summer Sat); 12-3, 7-10.30 (12-10.30 summer) Sun
☎ (01442) 242427
Greene King IPA, Abbot; seasonal beers Ⓗ
A pub where town meets country. It is surrounded by farmland in a quiet hamlet just off the A4146, Hemel to Leighton Buzzard road. Inside, there are low beams, settles and large fires and an oak-panelled back room which is 'Dickensian' in ambience. The 'town' atmosphere is created by the current landlords who hail from Walthamstow and offer a genuine East End welcome. Cream teas, B&B in the adjoining cottages and beer festivals in the outbuildings are other assets of this thriving lively pub. � ❁◖▮ ♣P

BUNTINGFORD

Crown
17 High Street
✪ 12-3, 5.30-11; 12-11 Sat; 12-3.30, 7-10.30 Sun
☎ (01763) 271422
Courage Best Bitter; guest beers Ⓗ
Popular, town-centre pub with a large front bar and cosy back bar. This is a real locals' local. The long-standing landlord is justly proud of running a pub which serves food and not a restaurant which serves beer. Children are welcome in the covered patio and lovely secluded garden. Theme nights, offering speciality food, are held regularly. A large function room is available for meetings and social events. A *Guide* entry for 12 consecutive years; local CAMRA *Best Community Pub* 2000. ⇌❁◖

BUSHEY

Swan

25 Park Road (off A411)
🕔 11-11; 12-10.30 Sun
☎ (020) 895 02256
Ansells Mild; Benskins Bitter; Young's Bitter, Special H

This one-bar, back-street local first appeared in this *Guide* in 1974 and was described as 'a real pub with character and atmosphere', a description that remains true today. The land on which the pub was built in 1866, cost £27. The Swan resisted change over the next century and was the last Bushey beer house to apply for and be granted a full licence in 1964. It is currently the local *CAMRA Pub of the Year* and is well worth a visit. Close to the Bushey Museum. ♨ ❀ ♣

BUSHEY HEATH

Black Boy

19 Windmill Street (off High Road, A4140)
🕔 11.30-3 (4 Sat), 5.30-11; 11.30-11 Fri; 12-4, 7-10.30 Sun
☎ (020) 895 02230
Adnams Bitter; Benskins Bitter; Greene King Abbot; guest beers H

Tucked away in the back streets, this smallish pub is worth seeking out. You are assured of a warm welcome and a good range of beers and food. The daily specials have ensured a mention in CAMRA's *Good Pub Food* and account for the large number of regular customers that visit at lunchtimes. Three times a winner of the local CAMRA *Pub of the Year* award, note the certificates on the walls. The garden is being revamped and barbecues are planned. ❀ ◑ P

CHAPMORE END

Woodman

30 Chapmore End (off B158, 1/4m SW of A602) OS328164
🕔 12-3, 6-11; 12-4, 7-10.30 Sun
☎ (01920) 463143 e-mail: woodmanpub@aol.com
Greene King IPA, Abbot; guest beers (occasional) G

Gem of a country pub in a delightful village setting complete with duck pond. Gravity dispense from cooled casks in cellar a step down from the bar. A local favourite is a pint of 'mix'. This traditional inn, quite recently renovated, retains all its character with two bars and open fires. The large gardens have a children's play area and a mini zoo. Lunches (Mon-Sat) range from sandwiches to balti. Darts and pétanque teams are based here and special events such as fireworks and musical eves are organised. ♨ Q ❀ ◑ ⊟ ♣ P ●

CHIPPERFIELD ❖

Royal Oak

1 The Street (on crossroads at Bovingdon end of village)
🕔 12-3, 6-11; 12-3, 7-10.30 Sun
☎ (01923) 266537
Adnams Broadside; Draught Bass; Young's Bitter; guest beers H /G

Fine Home Counties village with some very dark woods surrounding a pretty cricket pitch, church and common. The best beer will almost certainly be found in this pub

which has only missed one edition of this *Guide*. A former undertaker's cottage, the only link now is the abundance of polished wood and brass in the immaculate horseshoe-shaped bar. Note the unusual collection of 3D pictures and local photographs. Food is cooked to order at lunchtimes (no microwaves). A meeting room at the rear is used by many local car and sports clubs. ♨ Q ❀ ◑ ♣ P

CROXLEY GREEN

Sportsman

2 Scots Hill (A412)
🕔 12-11; 12-10.30 Sun
☎ (01923) 443360
e-mail: sportsmancroxley@barbox.net
Draught Bass; Tring Side Pocket; guest beers H

One-bar pub, decorated with sporting equipment with many games available behind the bar. Licensees are canal fans and morris dancers. Live blues bands every other Sat eve and either folk, jazz or blues jams on Sun afternoons. Genuine homemade pies included in lunchtime menu. Recently released from company tie and now able to offer a more interesting beer range with two changing guests. Pleasant patio at rear and decking area at front for outdoor drinking. ❀ ◑ ♣ P

DATCHWORTH

Tilbury

1 Watton Road (1 mile E of B197 at Woolmer Green) OS270183
🕔 11-3, 5-11; 11-11 Thu-Sat; 12-10.30 Sun
☎ (01438) 812496
Draught Bass; Museum Five Hides; guest beers H

Believed to be the only pub with this name in Britain, the friendly, two-bar pub is just off the village green. House beers from the Museum Brewing Co are brewed by the landlord himself, with Hop Pit bitter using a new and different hop in each brew. The public bar, or Tony's Ale Bar, is named after the landlord's late father and displays a collection of keg beer memorabilia. An extensive menu of good, home-cooked food is available every day (except Sun eve). Q ❀ ◑ ⊟ ▲ ♣ P

GREEN TYE

Prince of Wales

🕔 12-2.45, 5.30-11; 12-11 Sat; 12-10.30 Sun
☎ (01279) 842517
website: www.gtbrewery.co.uk
Green Tye IPA; McMullen AK; guest beers H

Small village community pub popular with walkers and cyclists. The Green Tye Brewery (adjacent to the pub) normally provides one or two regular beers, plus the IPA. Other guests are from micros. Open all day on bank holidays. Occasional live music at weekends – check the pub notice board. Darts on Wed, can be very busy for home fixtures. For special events a marquee is set up in the garden. Regular annual highlight is the May Day weekend beer festival, an old English event with live music and traditional games (try flog flumping after a few beers!). ♨ ❀ ◑ ♣ P

HARPENDEN

Carpenters Arms
14 Cravells Road (off A1081)
⏰ 11-3, 5.30-11; 12-3, 7-10.30 Sun
☎ (01582) 460311
Brakspear Bitter; Courage Best Bitter; Flowers Original; guest beers Ⓗ
Exquisite pub, run with unfailing friendliness by Harpenden's longest-serving landlord. An excellent example of a genuine local, it commands fervent and well-deserved support from its regulars. The landlord is a keen patron of small local breweries as shown by his enterprising range of guest ales which often includes one or two milds. The pub regularly wins awards for its floral displays. It is cosy, welcoming and quiet with interesting motoring memorabilia. Simple lunchtime food is terrific value, served Mon-Sat. Jap bikers beware, landlord is a Harley fanatic. Dogs, however, are most welcome! ♨Q⊛◖♣P

Cross Keys
39 High Street
⏰ 11-11; 12-10.30 Sun
☎ (01582) 763989
Boddingtons Bitter; Brakspear Bitter; Fuller's London Pride; Taylor Landlord Ⓗ
Harpenden's oldest pub, resplendent with a pewter bar top, flagstoned floor and pewter tankards (from past and present customers) hanging from the genuine oak-beamed ceiling. There has been a recent dispute over a planning application to extend at the back, which would have ruined the character of the main bar. Real fire in snug and sewing-machine tables. Food served Mon-Sat. It can be very busy at weekends, but is nonetheless worth a visit since it has managed to preserve its charm. Well-behaved dogs welcome. There is a secluded rear garden. Limited parking. ♨Q⊛◖≠

HERTFORD

Old Cross Tavern
8 St Andrew Street
⏰ 11.30-11; 12-10.30 Sun
☎ (01992) 583133 e-mail:
old@crosstavern.freeserve.co.uk
Fuller's London Pride; Ⓗ **Oakham JHB; guest beers** Ⓗ/Ⓖ
Local CAMRA *Pub of the Year* 1999 and joint winner in 2000. Superb recreation of town

free house of yesteryear in a genuinely old building of great character extended very sympathetically, with a small rear patio garden. The welcoming single bar has a 'public' and a 'saloon' end with comfortable booths. House beer, Laugh & Titter, is brewed by Mighty Oak. Guests from craft brewers near and far are all meticulously prepared. A real cider and reasonably priced quality house wines always served. Lunches Mon-Sat with specials. Occasional special eve meals. Anniversary beer festival over Whitsun weekend.
Q⊛◖≠ (North/East) ♠

White Horse
33 Castle Street
⏰ 12-2.30, 5.30-11; 12-3, 5-11 Fri; 12-11 Sat; 12-10.30 Sun
☎ (01992) 501950
Adnams Bitter; Fuller's Chiswick, London Pride, ESB, seasonal beers; guest beers Ⓗ
Old timber-framed building by Hertford Castle with two downstairs bars and upstairs no-smoking rooms open to children. A log fire downstairs in winter. Now a Fuller's 'freestyle' pub, retaining all its character, it offers a good range of guests from craft brewers alongside Fuller's. Beer festivals with 50 beers are staged over May Day weekend and in late autumn. Lunches served daily from a wide selection ranging from sandwiches and baguettes to a choice of special dishes, all reasonably priced. A favourite watering-hole for all ages.
♨Q◖Ⓖ≠ (North/East)

HIGH WYCH

Rising Sun
(1 mile W of A1184)
⏰ 12-2.30, 5.30 (5 Fri)-11; 12-3, 5-11 Sat; 12-10.30 Sun
☎ (01279) 724099
Courage Best Bitter; guest beers Ⓖ
Quintessential English pub where conviviality, conversation and wonderful beer are cherished. No piped music or electronic wizardry, sit and read, chat to friends or gossip with the locals. Strict policy regarding mobile phones. Run by the same family for many decades, locally referred to as 'Sid's'. Local CAMRA *Pub of the New Millennium*. The one or two guest beers are increasingly taking centre stage. Three-roomed pub: small central locals' room,

INN BRIEF

AYOT ST LAWRENCE
Brocket Arms
11-11; 12-10.30 Sun
Fuller's London Pride; Greene King IPA, Abbot; guest beers Ⓗ/Ⓖ
15th-century pub in village famous for being the residence of George Bernard Shaw, a noted teetotaller.

BOXMOOR
Boxmoor Vintners Off-Licence
25-27 St John's Road
9.30-1, 4.30-9.30;
12-2; 7-9 Sun
Beer range varies Ⓗ
Always at least three draught real ales available (and many interesting bottles) in this friendly, independent, street-corner 'offie'.

CHIPPERFIELD
Boot
Bovingdon Road, Tower Hill
11-11; 12-10.30 Sun
Adnams Bitter; Benskins Bitter; Fuller's London Pride; guest beers Ⓗ
Excellent pub, converted from a row of cottages. Large car park, garden and two distinct bars. *Cask Marque* accredited.

COLNEY HEATH
Crooked Billet
88 High Street
11-2.30, 5.30-11; 11-11 Sat;
12-10.30 Sun
Greene King IPA; guest beers Ⓗ
Village pub dating back over 200 years. Recently extended and offering good-value food. Large garden with play equipment.

GUSTARD WOOD
Cross Keys
Ballslough Hill (B651)
11-3, 6 (5.30 Fri & Sat)-11;
12-4.30, 7-10.30 Sun
Fuller's London Pride; Greene King IPA; guest beers Ⓗ
Friendly 17th-century country pub serving reasonably priced food. One spacious bar plus side rooms for children and non-smokers.

HITCHIN
Hitchin Rugby Football Club
King George V Playing Fields, Old Hale Way
7-11 Tue; 11-11 Sat; 12-5 Sun
Bateman XB; Brains Bitter; guest beers Ⓗ
Former East Anglian *Club of the Year*. Families welcome. Occasional beer festivals. Note limited opening hours.

spacious lounge with serving hatch (useful when the locals are in full cry at bar), separate room for pub games. Dog walkers welcomed with a smile by landlord.
🏚Q🌲🐕♣P

HITCHIN ❄

Victoria
1 Ickleford Road
⏰ 12-3, 5-11; 12-11 Sat; 12-4, 7-10.30 Sun
☎ (01462) 432682
Greene King IPA, Abbot, seasonal beer or guest beer Ⓗ
Welcoming pub on main road from station to town centre, close enough to catch passing trade but not too close to be on the centre circuit weekend crawl. Much-altered, wedge-shaped pub, the split-level bar has plenty of seating. Look out for the witch on a broomstick hanging up by the dartboard and the old pictures of Hitchin. Locals' pub, catering for all ages, which has a loyal following for pub teams and regularly does well in the Greene King quiz league.
🏚🍴⇌♣P●

KINGS LANGLEY

Saracen's Head
47 High Street (A4251 just off M25 jct 20)
⏰ 11-2.30, 5-11; 12-3, 7-10.30 Sun
☎ (01923) 400144
Fuller's London Pride, ESB; Tring Ridgeway Bitter; guest beers Ⓗ
Completely independent free house in the centre of this large village. Kings Langley is renowned as the home of England's only pope, Nicholas Brakspear, and also of the Ovaltine factory. The pub has an unusual long single-bar with old beams that give it a nautical feel. The collections of old telephones, jugs, bottles, saracens' heads and photographs give the place a traditional but very relaxed atmosphere. Lunchtime meals served Mon-Sat. 🏚🍴P

LETCHWORTH

Hogshead Ale House
The Colonnade, Station Place
⏰ 11-11; 12-10.30 Sun
☎ (01462) 486807
Boddingtons Bitter; Greene King Old Speckled Hen; Marston's Pedigree; Wadworth 6X; guest beers Ⓗ
Converted from a former electricity

board showroom this single-bar, multi-level pub was the first new pub to open in Letchworth for many years, other pub chains have followed. Recently renovated it is now light, bright and more female-friendly. Beer festivals are held in April and October. Local brewery City of Cambridge beers usually feature as guests. A traditional cider is normally available on gravity. The patio outside is now heated and inside there is a raised no-smoking area.
🏚🍴⇌♿🚭

NEWGATE STREET

Coach & Horses
61 Newgate Street Village
⏰ 11-11; 12-10.30 Sun
☎ (01707) 873236
Adnams Bitter; Fuller's London Pride; Greene King IPA Ⓗ
Genuinely old, ivy-covered pub well situated next to the attractive village church. Popular with horse riding clubs, classic car societies and classic motorcycle clubs, this Punch Taverns' pub, is well-run by two landlords both of whom are friendly and welcoming. It is set on an ancient road which ran along the ridge and through the village. If visiting Ponsbourne House, which is nearby, stop here first for some good ale.
🏚Q🐕P

NORTHAW

Two Brewers
1 Northaw Road
⏰ 11-11; 12-10.30 Sun
☎ (01707) 652420
Adnams Bitter, Broadside; Draught Bass; Greene King IPA; Ind Coope Burton Ale; Vale Black Beauty Porter Ⓗ
One-bar village pub next to a picturesque 19th-century church. Formerly owned by Allied Domecq and now a Punch house. It is divided into several drinking areas which helps maintain an intimate atmosphere. The exterior is particularly attractive in summer when the window boxes are a blaze of colour. Good selection of beers includes Tetley Bitter and Marston's Pedigree. Pub games such as Shut the Box, shove-ha'penny, crib and darts are popular. Live jazz is played Sun eve.
🏚🐕🍴♣P

HODDESDON
White Swan
95 High Street
11-11; 12-10.30 Sun
Tetley Bitter; guest beers Ⓗ
Large wooden-framed pub, food served all day, up to 10 beers on at weekends, flagstone floor in bar.

ICKLEFORD
Plume of Feathers
Upper Green
11-3, 6-11;
12-4, 7-10.30 Sun
Adnams Bitter; Boddingtons Bitter; Brains Bitter; Fuller's London Pride; Wadworth 6X; guest beers Ⓗ
Lively, friendly pub offering good quality, value-for-money food.

LETCHMORE HEATH
Three Horseshoes
The Green
11-3, 5.30-11; 11-11 Fri & Sat; 12-10.30 Sun
Benskins Bitter; Fuller's London Pride; Ind Coope Burton Ale; guest beer Ⓗ
Two-bar pub on village green by the pond, featured in numerous films and TV shows.

ST ALBANS
Farriers Arms
35 Lower Dagnall Street
12-2.30 (3 Sat), 5.30 (7 Sat)-11; 12-3, 7-10.30 Sun
McMullen AK, Country, Gladstone, seasonal beers Ⓗ
Unspoilt back-street pub. First branch meeting of CAMRA held here.

WARE
Worppel
35 Watton Road
12-2.30, 5-11; 11-11 Fri & Sat; 12-10.30 Sun
Greene King IPA, Abbot; guest beer/seasonal beer Ⓗ
One-bar pub hosted by Ware's longest-serving landlord who recently scored 100% in all *Cask Marque* categories.

WESTON
Cricketers
Damask Green Road
12-2.30 (3 Sat), 5.30-11; 12-3, 7-10.30 Sun
Fuller's London Pride; McMullen AK; guest beer Ⓗ
Cheery and welcoming, sporting a cricketing theme. Local CAMRA *Most Improved Pub* 2001.

NUTHAMPSTEAD

Woodman Inn

Signed off A10 OS413346

✪ 11-3.30, 5.30-11; 11-11 Sat; 12-4, 7-10.30 Sun

☎ (01763) 848328

Adnams Bitter; Greene King IPA; guest beers Ⓗ

17th-century free house features an L-shaped bar and wonderful open fires. The restaurant offers *à la carte* meals as well as house specials and snacks (no food Sun eve). Accommodation is available making this an excellent base for visiting local attractions such as Duxford Imperial War Museum. During WWII the USAF 398th bomber group was based locally. The B-17 flying fortresses flew many missions over Europe and the pub displays original photographs and memorabilia. A memorial is located outside. The pub was recently awarded local CAMRA *Pub of the Season.*
🏚Q✿⇘◑🅿🖪

OLD KNEBWORTH

Lytton Arms

Park Lane OS229202

✪ 11-3, 5-11; 11-11 Fri & Sat; 12-10.30 Sun

☎ (01438) 812312 website: www.the-lytton-arms.co.uk

Draught Bass; Fuller's London Pride; Woodforde's Wherry; guest beers Ⓗ

Popular inn adjoining the Knebworth estate. Fascinating photos of Knebworth House, the Lytton family and the famous pop festivals are displayed together with railway memorabilia and breweriana. It has featured in many editions of this *Guide*. At least 2,800 different real ales have been served over the past decade. Good selection of Belgian bottled beers, two draught beers and 50 malt whiskies available. Beer festivals are hosted in spring and autumn. Local CAMRA *Pub of the Year* 1992 and *Pub of the Season* summer 2000.
🏚Q✿◑❤♣🖤🅿✗

OXHEY

Victoria

39 Chalk Hill

✪ 11-3, 5.30-11; 11-11 Thu-Sat; 12-10.30 Sun

☎ (01923) 227993

Benskins Bitter; guest beer Ⓗ

Comfortable local, situated at the bottom of Chalk Hill at the junction with Aldenham Road. It has two bars and a rather strange shape. The public bar entrance is off the main road, while access to the other bar is via the small car park. Bar meals available at lunchtime. Beers are on the expensive side. The walls have a variety of knick-knacks including brasses. A Cannon Brewery mirror adorns the lounge bar, evidence of the previous owners, Taylor Walker.
✿◑🚄⇌ (Bushey) ♣🅿

POTTERS BAR

Admiral Byng

186-194 Darkes Lane (close to railway station)

✪ 11-11; 12-10.30 Sun

☎ (01707) 645484

Courage Directors; Greene King Abbot; Shepherd Neame Spitfire; Theakston Best Bitter; guest beers Ⓗ

Typical large Wetherspoon's pub much needed in an area of poor beer choice and quality. The building was converted from a former supermarket premises. Four main drinking areas are available plus, unusually for Wetherspoon's, an outdoor area, in this case a small patio to the front. Three or four guests are offered at usual Wetherspoon's prices. Q✿◑♿⇌✗✦●

POTTERS CROUCH

Holly Bush

Off A414 at St Stephen's OS116053

✪ 11.30 (12 Sat)-2.30, 6 (7 Sat)-11; 12-2.30, 7-10.30 Sun

☎ (01727) 851792

Fuller's Chiswick, London Pride, ESB; seasonal beers (occasional) Ⓗ

Attractive, early 18th-century oak-beamed pub in rural surroundings. Spotlessly clean and well-furnished throughout with large oak tables and period chairs from the Isle of Man. The landlord is a top Fuller's *Master Cellarman* and a winner of many brewery awards. The huge array of certificates displayed in the bar confirm that this is one of the best quality Fuller's outlets for miles around. Good lunchtime snacks served Mon-Sat. Pleasant large garden, ideal in summer. 🏚Q✿🅿●

PRESTON

Red Lion

The Green

✪ 12-3, 5.30-11; 12-3, 7-10.30 Sun

☎ (01462) 459585 website: timbohunter@hotmail.com

Greene King IPA; guest beers Ⓗ

Attractive Georgian-style free house on the village green. This pub became Britain's first community-owned pub in the mid 1980s. The current landlord and landlady arrived after 20 years' service at another well-known local establishment. The guest beers usually feature offerings from local breweries. Specialising in freshly prepared, home-cooked food, the pub attracts custom from far and wide. (No food Tue or Sun eves). Boasting two cricket teams and a darts team the pub is well supported locally. Voted local CAMRA *Pub of the Year* 2000 and 2001, and Hertfordshire CAMRA *Pub of the Year* 2000.
🏚Q✿◑♣🅿

RADLETT

Cat & Fiddle

14 Cobden Hill, Watling Street (A5183)

✪ 11-11; 12-10.30 Sun

☎ (01923) 469523

Greene King IPA; Shepherd Neame Spitfire; Young's Bitter Ⓗ

This 18th-century pub has three oak-panelled bars on different levels (some parts of the building are even older). Games and quizzes are popular in the public bar and the pub has a football team. There is a cosy snug and comfortable lounge with carved furniture. Fantastic collection of mainly china cats and also two fiddles. Historic photos are on display. An attractive patio and large car park to the rear. Just half a mile from Radlett railway station.
Q✿◑⇌♣🅿

Red Lion

Watling Street (A5183)

✪ 11-11; 12-10.30 Sun

☎ (01923) 855341
Young's Bitter, Triple A, Special, seasonal beers Ⓗ
This Victorian hotel was originally
Temperance. Things have now changed and
Young's bought the freehold in 2000. The
bar area is being extended to twice the size
and the restaurant reduced to 60 seats. The
14 guest rooms will be refurbished and the
function room will remain. Meals are served
12-3pm and 6-10pm. There is a small patio
overlooking the street. ⛟🏠🅾👤🚾P

REDBOURN

Holly Bush
Church End (cul-de-sac by St Mary's church, off the
common)
🍺 11.30-2.30, 5.30-11; 11.30-3, 7-11 Sat; 12-3,
7-10.30 Sun
☎ (01582) 782423
Adnams Bitter; Tetley Bitter; guest beers Ⓗ
Traditional, genuine free house in a
picturesque setting. The pub is part of a
Grade II listed conservation area, which
incorporates the almshouses opposite. The
building is 16th century with four timber-
framed bays and floor beams. Traditional
pub games are played in the public bar
while the saloon is cosy with a real fire.
Three ever-changing guests are served from
a variety of small brewers, such as Vale and
Tring. Home-cooked meals served Mon-Sat
lunchtimes. 🏃Q⛟🅾🚾P

RUSHDEN

Moon & Stars
Mill End (off A507 between Baldock & Buntingford)
OS302317
🕐 12-2.30 (not Mon & Tue), 6-11; 12-3, 6.30-11 Sat;
12-3, 7-10.30 Sun
☎ (01763) 288330
website: www.moonstars.fsnet.co.uk
Greene King IPA, Old Speckled Hen, seasonal beers Ⓗ
Lovely two-bar pub overlooking the rolling
countryside. Originally built as two separate
dwellings in the 1600s. It has been a public
house since 1802. The public bar has an
open fire which in the past was reputedly
fuelled by the customers' own firewood
when they came to sup locally brewed ales.
The lounge doubles as a restaurant and seats
up to 24. The only pub for a few miles, it is
popular with walkers and cyclists. This
community-oriented pub fields a darts and
football team. Pétanque is played.
🏃⛟🅾♣P▯

ST ALBANS ❖

Farmer's Boy
134 London Road
🕐 11-11; 12-10.30 Sun
☎ (01727) 766702
Verulam Special, IPA, seasonal beers Ⓗ
Cosy, cottage-style pub, dating from 1831.
Now the home of Verulam Brewery, which
moved here from Harpenden in 1996. Local
CAMRA *Pub of the Year* 1998. All the beers
are brewed on site, including seasonal beers
of the month. Assortment of German and
Belgian bottled beers are also available. All
the food is home made and served all day,
every day with roasts on Sun and barbecues
on the patio in summer. Satellite TV. Look
out for the unusual ashtrays on the bar.
🏃⛟🅾🚾(City)

Lower Red Lion
34-36 Fishpool Street
🕐 12-2.30, 5.30-11; 12-11 Sat; 12-3, 7-10.30 Sun
☎ (01727) 855669 website: www.thelowerredlion.co.uk
Fuller's London Pride; Oakham JHB; guest beers Ⓗ
17th-century two-bar pub near the
Cathedral and Roman Verulamium.
Genuine free house with five changing
guest beers from micro-breweries as well as
the award-winning Oakham JHB. Beer
festivals, held in the recently renovated
garden during May Day and August bank
holiday weekends, feature up to 50 unusual
beers. Good B&B, with TV and tea/coffee-
making facilities and two en-suite rooms.
Quiz nights on Wed and occasional food
nights. 🏃Q⛟🏠🅾♣P

Mermaid
98 Hatfield Road
🕐 11.30-11; 12-10.30 Sun
☎ (01727) 854487
e-mail: mermaidstalbans@btinternet.com
Adnams Bitter; Everards Beacon, Tiger; guest beers Ⓗ
Former Everards pub still features beers
from the Leicestershire brewery as well as
products from smaller breweries such as
Nethergate and B&T. It has a wooden
and stone-flagged floor, and an open
fireplace partially dividing the L-shaped bar
in two. Dating back to the 1830s, the
pub was a beer house until 1950.
Lunchtime meals are served weekdays.
Customers include students from the
college, office workers and locals.
Occasional music at weekends attracts a
lively crowd. Cashpoint machine on hand.
⛟🅾🚾(City)♣P

White Hart Tap
4 Keyfield Terrace
🕐 12.30 (12 Sat)-11; 12-10.30 Sun
☎ (01727) 860974 website: www.whitehharttap.co.uk
**Adnams Broadside; Fuller's London Pride; Greene King
IPA; guest beer** Ⓗ
This is a much improved one-bar
back-street local. It has recently been
refurbished giving it a cleaner, lighter look
while retaining the all-important
atmosphere and tradition of the English
pub. Since the tenants changed two years
ago the beer quality has improved greatly
and four beers are offered. Regular
barbecues are held in the spacious garden
during the summer. Once a month themed
food nights are held accompanied with live
trad jazz. Live music on Sat nights too is
very popular. The pub has recently twinned
with the 'Bar No Limit' in Belgrade.
🏃⛟🅾♣

White Lion
91 Sopwell Lane (off Holywell Hill, 500 yds from
Cathedral)
🕐 12-3, 5.30-11; 12-11 Sat; 12-3, 7-10.30; (12-
10.30 summer) Sun
☎ (01727) 850540 website: www.whitelionpub.co.uk
**Adnams Bitter; Greene King Old Speckled Hen; guest
beers** Ⓗ
Traditional, family-run relaxing
pub with ever-changing guest beers.
Eclectic, tasty home-cooked food for
carnivores and vegetarians alike, made by
the friendly landlord using a good
proportion of organic produce (eve meals
Tue-Fri). Imaginative sandwich selection.

Delightful beer garden with children's play area. Summer barbecues held including occasional hog roasts. Live music, particularly blues, every Sat eve. Acoustic live music on some Thu eves. Trad jazz once a month on Sun. Pétanque played in summer.
Q ⊛ ◑ ◗ ⊞ ➡ (City/Abbey) ♣ ⚲

SAWBRIDGEWORTH

Gate

81 London Road (A1184)
☼ 11.30-3, 5.30-11; 11-11 Fri & Sat; 12-10.30 Sun
☎ (01279) 722313
Adnams Btter; Fuller's London Pride; Wells Bombardier; guest beers ⊞
Thriving central village pub, popular with all ages. Home of the Sawbridgeworth Brewery brewing since July 2000.
Regular darts, quiz nights, football teams, all based in the top bar with traditional non-sporting lower bar. Interesting beer range includes at least two from the adjacent brewery. Over 2,000 guests from small independent breweries served over the past seven years. Huge collection of pump clips on display in lower bar.
⊛ ◑ ⊞ ₺ ▲ ➡ P

SLEAPSHYDE

Plough

Off A414 via Sleapshyde Lane
☼ 11.30-2.30, 5.30-11; 11-3, 6-11 Sat; 12-3, 7-10.30 Sun
☎ (01727) 823720
Fuller's London Pride; Greene King Abbot; Tetley Bitter ⊞
Old village pub featuring exposed beams and an inglenook. It hosts popular games nights and has a darts team. Good-value lunchtime meals are served. Children are welcome in the side room. ⋈ ⛵ ⊛ ◑ ♣ P

SOUTH MIMMS

Black Horse

65 Blackhorse Lane (off B556 near A1/M25 jct)
☼ 11-3, 5.30-11; 11-11 Fri & Sat; 12-10.30 Sun
☎ (01707) 642174
Greene King IPA, Abbot; guest beer (seasonal) ⊞
It may not seem possible that the narrow, winding Blackhorse Lane was once the main road linking the north-west of England to London. This is, of course, why there is a pub on the site. This busy two-bar local also caters for passing trade. The lively public bar has a thriving darts team, lino floor and bar stools. The cosy lounge has a horsy theme, an open fire, interesting furniture and bric-à-brac. Reputation for excellent food.
⋈ ⊛ ◑ ⊞ ♣ P

STEVENAGE

Marquis of Lorne

132 High Street, Old Town
☼ 11-11; 12-10.30 Sun
☎ (01438) 729154
Greene King XX Mild, IPA, Abbot; guest beers ⊞
John Douglas of Southerland (1845-1914) was the Marquis of Lorne, which is on the Isle of Mull. He became Governor General of Canada in 1880 and pictures of his travels are displayed. Voted local

CAMRA *Pub of the Season* spring 2000, the landlord and landlady also won several Greene King awards that year, including *Cellar of the Year* and one for training young managers. Popular quiz night on Mon, meat raffle on Sun. Relaxed saloon bar and TV for sport in public bar. One of very few local outlets regularly serving mild. No food Sun eve. ⊛ ◑ ◗ ⊞ ₺ ➡ ♣ P ●

Standing Order

33 High Street, Old Town
☼ 11-11; 12-10.30 Sun
☎ (01438) 316972
Courage Directors; Shepherd Neame Spitfire; Theakston Best Bitter ⊞
Friendly Wetherspoon's pub, much-extended conversion of a former bank. Excellent guest beers. Voted local CAMRA *Best New Pub* 2001. Pictures of Stevenage, old and new, and abstract paintings are displayed. The premises was once a butcher's shop, then taken over by a family who had the first car in Stevenage. The town is steeped in history. An annual fair is held which dates back to a 12th-century royal charter. The pub has two patios for outdoor drinking.
Q ⊛ ◑ ₺ ➡ P ⚲ ●

TRING

King's Arms

King Street (in 'Tring Triangle' at Aylesbury end of town)
☼ 12 -2.30 (3 Fri; 11-3 Sat), 7-11; 12-4, 7-10.30 Sun
☎ (01442) 823318 e-mail: theka@lineone.net
Wadworth 6X; guest beers ⊞
The KA, as it is known locally, is a startlingly attractive building in the back streets of this small market town. Built 160 years ago, this pub suffered near-terminal neglect until the current owners took it on 20 years ago. Now, it is fuchsia pink on the outside; green and pine-clad inside with an excellent reputation for top-quality beer and home-cooking. A genuine free house, the KA actively champions the cause of independent brewers and five or six constantly changing ales are available daily. Beer can also be taken home. A beer festival is held on August bank holiday.
⋈ Q ◑ ♣ ❀ ⚲

Robin Hood Inn

11 Brook Street (on roundabout at Hemel end of town)
☼ 11-2.30 (3 Sat), 5.30 (6.30 Sat)-11; 12-3, 7-10.30 Sun
☎ (01442) 824912
Fuller's Chiswick, London Pride, ESB, seasonal beers ⊞
This is one of those pubs that accurately reflects its landlord's passion for life. Once a small cottage dating back to 1345 near the cattle market, its walls were originally filled with dung. Now, however, the wood gleams and the walls are covered with awards for charity work and food and drink presentation. Tring is a town that could be calculated as being furthest from the sea so, of course, this pub specialises in serving fish dishes. Up to 30 may be available and all food is fresh daily. Bronze standard disabled facilities. Courtyard for outdoor drinking.
⋈ Q ⊛ ◑ ₺ ♣ ●

WALTHAM CROSS

Vault
160 High Street (opp. McDonalds in shopping centre)
🕓 11-11; 12-10.30 Sun
☎ (01992) 631600
Beer range varies Ⓗ
Friendly, family-run free house in converted bank premises. Split-level single bar has recently been refurbished. The pub has a lively atmosphere and welcomes children until 7pm. OAP special price lunches are served on Thu. The varied menu of home-cooked meals and snacks caters for vegetarians and children. Sun lunches are particularly good value. Excellent selection of up to six constantly changing beers from independents and micros. Community charity projects are well supported. Entertainment includes live bands, discos, quizzes and Karaoke. ❀◖⇌

WARE ❀

Crooked Billet
140 Musley Hill
🕓 12-2.30 (not Mon, Wed & Thu), 5.30-11; 12-11 Sat; 12-10.30 Sun
☎ (01920) 462516
Greene King XX Mild, IPA, Abbot, seasonal beer Ⓗ
Popular pub, well worth finding from the town centre (20 minutes from railway station). Two distinct bars connected by a walk-through, one has a pool table and is lively, the other is cosier and generally quieter. Carlisle United supporters are given the red-carpet treatment. Bar snacks are served and Sky Sports shown; the only outlet for mild in the area. A gem of a local. ♨❀♣♠

WARESIDE

Chequers Inn
On B1004, in centre of village by village hall
OS396156
🕓 12-3, 6-11; 12-11 Sat; 12-10.30 Sun
☎ (01920) 467010
Adnams Bitter, Broadside; Dark Horse Ale; guest beer Ⓗ
Very old pub with interesting interior, full of character with low beams and an uneven floor. Two-bar pub with a lounge, whose house beer is brewed by Dark Horse. The restaurant features local seasonal game on the extensive menu, bar meals also served. Live trad jazz performed Sun eve. The pub has a pétanque team and darts and crib are played. Popular lunchtime stop for walkers in this excellent hiking country. ♨Q❀◖❀♣♠P

WHITWELL

Maiden's Head
67 High Street (signed from B656)
🕓 11.30-3, 5 -11; 11.30-4, 6-11 Sat; 12-3, 7-10.30 Sun
☎ (01438) 871392
Draught Bass; McMullen AK, Country, seasonal beers; guest beers Ⓗ
Outstanding two-bar village local has a welcoming, homely appeal. As well as producing excellent home-cooked food, the landlord has been chosen McMullen *Master Cellarman* consecutive years since

1992. A perennial *Guide* entry, it is the flagship of McMullen beers in north Herts. Recently awarded the local CAMRA Arnold Memorial award for *Best Community Pub*, its service to local and national charities is well recognised. The public bar displays photos of the war years and the landlord has a fine collection of Dinky toys. A previous CAMRA East Anglian *Pub of the Year*. ♨❀◖❀❀P

WIDFORD

Green Man
High Street
🕓 12-3, 5.30-11; 12-11 Sat & summer Fri; 12-10.30 Sun
☎ (01279) 842846
Adnams Bitter; Green Tye Wheelbarrow, seasonal beers; McMullens AK; guest beer Ⓗ
Former McMullen's tied pub, now a genuine free house. Friendly village inn with darts, crib, dominoes and pool teams. Spacious bar with plenty of seating including comfortable chairs around the real fire. Walkers and cyclists welcomed; the pub is well situated for country hikes and cycle tours. A large and pleasant garden to the rear. The bar keeps an interesting selection of unusual malt whiskies with tasting notes. Availability of eve meals uncertain at time of publication, although food served at lunchtimes. ♨❀◖♣P

WILDHILL

Woodman
45 Wild Hill Road (between A1000 and B158)
OS265068
🕓 11.30-2.30, 5.30-11; 12-2.30, 7-10.30 Sun
☎ (01707) 642618
Greene King IPA, Abbot; McMullen AK; guest beers Ⓗ
An absolute gem. Small, friendly, village pub which specialises in beers from small micro-breweries. Often a queue to get in on Sun. Popular with office workers at lunchtime; worth missing the works canteen for! No food on Sun. This pub sponsors a Saracens rugby player and is a popular watering-hole for supporters. The landlord also supports Barnet Football Club. Features a display of woodsaws, mainly from the estate of the late Dame Barbara Cartland. Q❀◖♣P

WILLIAN

Three Horseshoes
Baldock Lane (tiny lane opp. the church, 1 mile from A1(M) jct 9)
🕓 11-11; 12-10.30 Sun
☎ (01462) 685713
Greene King IPA, Abbot, seasonal beers; guest beers Ⓗ
This pub was originally two 18th-century cottages. The 'Shoes' remained a two-roomed tavern for over two centuries until 1975 when it was converted into the cosy single bar of today. Popular with locals, it is very much a community pub, with darts, cribbage and quiz teams. Weekly raffles raise funds for local senior citizens' Christmas lunches. A function room is available for meetings and a marquee provides a venue for up to 20 people. Regular winner of *Pubs in Bloom* awards. ♨❀◖♣P

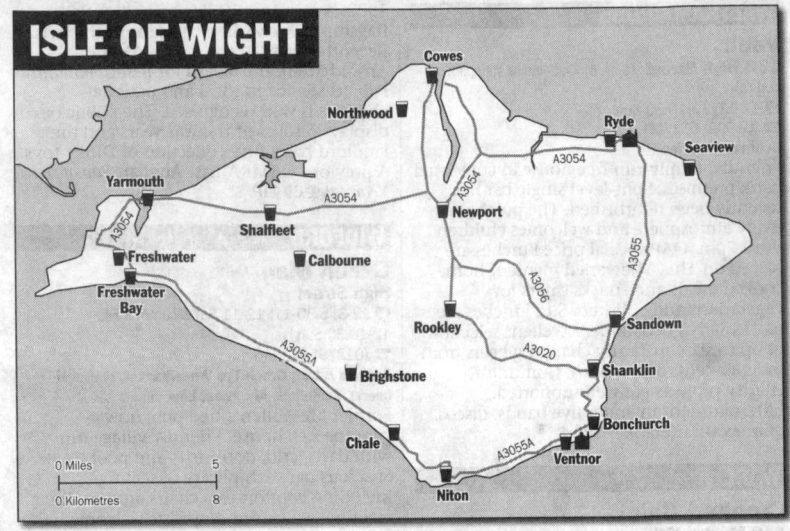

ISLE OF WIGHT

Cowes
Northwood
Ryde
Seaview
A3054
Yarmouth
A3054
Newport
Shalfleet
A3055
A3054
Freshwater
Calbourne
Freshwater Bay
A3056
Rookley
Sandown
A3055A
A3020
Brighstone
Shanklin
Chale
Bonchurch
A3055A
Ventnor
Niton

0 Miles 5
0 Kilometres 8

BONCHURCH

Bonchurch Inn
The Chute (off Sandown Road)
☼ 11-3, 6.30-11; 12-3, 7-10.30 Sun
☎ (01983) 852611 website: www.bonchurch-inn.co.uk
Courage Best Bitter, Directors Ⓖ
Superbly preserved stone pub, tucked away in a Dickensian courtyard and formerly the stables of the adjacent manor house. This is one of the most unspoilt pubs on the island, little has changed since it gained its licence in the 1840s. The floors are from a ship's deck and the chairs from a liner. Rings and bar billiards are played yet, curiously, the landlord of this very English pub is Italian. The pub featured in an episode of *The Detectives* and has numerous mementos from stars who have visited. Italian restaurant across the courtyard.
Q ☎ ⑳ ⌂ ◑ ♿ ♣ P ⌿

BRIGHSTONE

Countryman
Limerstone Road
☼ 11-3, 7-11 (11-11 summer); 12-3, 7-10.30 Sun
☎ (01983) 740616
Badger IPA, Best, K&B Old Ale, Tanglefoot Ⓗ
Spacious, friendly, country roadhouse with a large lounge bar and enthusiastic landlord. This fine family pub enjoys a reputation for good food, excellent beer and is a regular finalist in the local CAMRA *Pub of the Year* competition. The large function room is popular for wedding receptions and eve gatherings. Pleasant outdoor drinking area has superb views across the fields to the sea. The village of Brighstone gained ecclesiastical fame when three successive incumbents progressed to become bishops.
⚑ Q ☎ ⑳ ◑ ♣ P ⌿

CHALE

Wight Mouse
Church Place, Newport Road
☼ 11-midnight; 12-10.30 Sun
☎ (01983) 730431 website: www.wightmouse.co.uk

Boddingtons Bitter; Fuller's London Pride; Gale's HSB; Marston's Pedigree; Wadworth 6X; guest beer Ⓗ
Winner of several national awards, this pub has family rooms, car parks, beer gardens and swings, slides, climbing frames, small zoo, ball pond, bouncy castle, sandpit, Shetland pony rides, 366 whiskies and six real ales, not to mention the various collections including antique musical instruments adorning the walls and ceilings. The oak beams were rescued from the sailing ship, *Clarendon,* after which the adjacent hotel is named and the panelling on the bar is from another wreck, the *Varvassi.* The reasonably priced menu and location close to picturesque beaches and tourist attractions help make this pub enormously popular. Well worth a visit.
⚑ Q ☎ ⑳ ⌂ ◑ ♿ ♣ P ⌿

COWES

Anchor Inn
1 High Street
☼ 11-11; 12-10.30 Sun
☎ (01983) 292823 website: www.anchorcowes.co.uk
Badger Tanglefoot; Flowers Original; Fuller's London Pride; Goddards Fuggle-Dee-Dum; Wadworth 6X; guest beers Ⓗ
This town pub, next to the marina, tempts visiting yachtsmen for their first pint ashore. Originally named The Trumpeters, it dates from 1704. Today it is extremely popular in summer. A recent conversion has integrated the stables and created a pleasant beer garden with instant cover in case of showers. Fine beers and a good selection of fresh food offered. Live entertainment is provided on winter weekends and summer eves. The recent addition of B&B accommodation has been well received in this bustling pub. ⚑ ☎ ⑳ ⌂ ◑ ♿ ●

Kingston Arms
176 Newport Road
☼ 11-3, 6-11; 11-11 Fri & Sat; 12-4, 7-10.30 Sun
☎ (01983) 293393 e-mail: jackieadrian@hotmail.com
Gale's HSB; guest beers Ⓗ
On the main road out of Cowes towards Newport, you cannot miss the Kingston

Arms. Friendly, family and locals' pub near the yachting centre and offering good value B&B accommodation. The lively public bar has darts, pool, pétanque and any other variety of game that takes your fancy. Beer always in good order with an interesting selection of guest ales. 🛏🏵🍴🌙🍺♣🐾P

Union Inn
Watch House Lane (close to the High St)
✪ 10.30-11 (10.30-3, 6-11 winter); 12-10.30 Sun
☎ (01983) 293163 e-mail: dvcook@freeserve.com
Gale's GB, HSB; guest beer (summer) Ⓗ
Well-decorated town pub, just off the Parade and yards from the sea. One three-sided bar services the lounge, a snug, a dining area and the airy conservatory. The limited beer range is always in tiptop condition with a guest ale from the Gale's portfolio during the summer. A roaring fire in winter adds to the cosy atmosphere. The long-established landlord has acquired a reputation for good value accommodation. Maritime pictures complement the seafaring image.
🛏Q🏵🍴🌙🍺♿⚮

FRESHWATER
Prince of Wales
Princes Road
✪ 11-11; 12-10.30 Sun
☎ (01983) 753535
Bateman Mild; Boddingtons Bitter; Brakspear Special; Ringwood Fortyniner Ⓗ
Once part of the Whitbread estate and now in the free trade, this fine, unspoilt town pub is run by possibly the longest-serving landlord on the island. There is a strong games section that adds to the lively atmosphere. Situated just off the main Freshwater shopping centre, there is a large garden to relax in during the hot summer days and a pleasant snug bar to sample the well-kept ales during the winter. Should you have one too many there is no need to phone for a taxi – the landlord has one!
🏵🌙 🍺♿Å♣P🍴

FRESHWATER BAY
Fat Cat Bar
Sandpipers, Coastguard Lane (through main bay car park, clearly visible)
✪ 11-3, 6-11; 12-3, 6-10.30 Sun
☎ (01983) 758500 website: www.fatcattrading.co.uk
Beer range varies Ⓗ
A real gem of a bar tucked away within the Sandpipers Hotel situated between Freshwater Bay and the Afton Nature Reserve. There is an ever-changing range of well-kept ales served in convivial surroundings, well frequented by local drinkers, if you choose to stay and book ahead, you may well be able to choose your favourite tipple for that home-from-home feeling. Comfortable chairs, relaxing atmosphere and the friendly welcome is a joy. The adjoining hotel offers a full range of accommodation and comprehensive menu. 🛏Q🏵🍴🌙🍺♿P⚮

NEWPORT ❄
Bargemans Rest
Little London Quay (follow signs from dual carriageway)

✪ 10.30-11; 12-10.30 Sun
☎ (01983) 525828 website: www.bargemansrest.co.uk
Badger IPA, Best, Tanglefoot; guest beers Ⓗ
This locally-owned, massive pub development, is located in what has been an animal feed store, a sail loft and a rigging loft for servicing the commercial barge fleet. A recent conversion, the well-designed, huge bar provides intimate drinking areas and the nautical memorabilia, decor and ambience you would expect from a traditional, well-seasoned pub. The outdoor drinking area is only a few feet from the bustling River Medina. Beer and food are consistently good and the range varied. Entertainment offered most of the week and beer festivals are held. Q🏵🏵🌙P⚮

NITON
Buddle Inn
St Catherine's Road (follow signs to St Catherine's lighthouse)
✪ 11-11; 12-10.30 Sun
☎ (01983) 730243 e-mail: buddleinn@aol.com
Adnams Bitter; Flowers Original; Greene King Abbot; guest beers Ⓗ
16th-century inn built as a farmhouse and reputedly a smugglers' inn during the 18th century. Extensively refurbished in recent years, it still retains its ancient flagstones and beams, inglenook and many interesting photographs. The adjoining smugglers' barn was a cattle shed until 1934 when it was transformed into a dance hall. Very popular with the seasonal trade, with ample space outside to take advantage of the south-facing vista. Excellent reputation for good quality food and at least six ales, each chosen to suit the taste of the landlord.
🛏🏵🌙♣🐾P⚮

ROOKLEY
Chequers Inn
Niton Road (off A3020)
✪ 11-11; 12-10.30 Sun
☎ (01983) 840314
website: www.chequers-inn.demon.co.uk
Courage Best Bitter, Directors; Gale's HSB; Greene Kig Old Speckled Hen; John Smith's Bitter Ⓗ
Country pub at the heart of the island with beautiful views of the surrounding countryside. Considering its present popularity after an extensive rebuild, it is astonishing that Whitbread closed the pub and sold it. Dating back to the mid-1800s, it was once a customs and excise house. These days it is heavily food- and family-orientated but surprisingly still retains a flagstoned public bar and a fine pint of beer. There are some very good children's facilities including a large outdoor play area and changing room. Recent achievements have seen it voted *Family Pub of the Year*. A braille menu is available.
🛏🏵🌙🍺♿Å♣P⚮

RYDE ❄
Hole in the Wall
68 St John's Road (by St John's station)

✪ 11-11; 12-3, 7-10.30 Sun
☎ (01983) 615405
e-mail: garret@janet23.freeserve.co.uk
Draught Bass; Greene King Abbot; Oakleaf Squirrel's Delight, Holehearted Ⓗ
Sympathetically refurbished, this pub has a good local following. Once a very ordinary town pub, it had some lean years but is now flourishing under the guidance of the latest tenants. For those interested in horticulture, note the Gingko biloba tree in the garden, a species whose ancestry can be traced back over 200 million years.
🏨🛏️🅿️🍴◗≈

Lake Huron
51 Upton Road
✪ 12-11; 12-10.30 Sun
☎ (01983) 563512
Badger Best, Tanglefoot Ⓗ
Unusually well-preserved coaching inn. With its many rooms it remains a back-street local with a friendly, lively atmosphere. A small range of well-kept beers are stocked. It is the only surviving pub from the Lake family's small Ryde pub empire. Formerly a wine and spirits shop called the Eclipse, it was taken over by the Lake family in 1878 and became a staging post for the Newport–Ryde coach.
🍴⛔

Simeon Arms
21 Simeon Street (opp. the swimming pool and canoe lake)
✪ 11-3, 6-11; 11-11 Fri & Sat; 12-10.30 Sun
☎ (01983) 614954
Courage Directors; guest beers Ⓗ
A thriving, yet unlikely, gem tucked away in the oblivion of Ryde's back streets, with a Tardis-like interior and separate annexed function hall, the first impression is one of wonder. The pub is immensely popular with the local community, participating in all the winter and summer indoor leagues like darts, crib, pool, etc. and pétanque on the enormous floodlit rink during the summer. With so many male and female teams participating, nearly all divisions can expect to see themselves up against a team from the Simeon. Such a demand, as you would expect, means the beer is always in

pristine condition. Eve meals in summer only. 🛏️🅿️◗≈ (Esplanade) ♣

Caulkheads
42 Avenue Road (Sandown-Ryde Road, 200 yds from library)
✪ 11-11; 12-10.30 Sun
☎ (01983) 403878
Boddingtons Bitter; Greene King Abbot; Tetley Bitter; guest beers Ⓗ
Whitbread *Pub of the Year* 1999. Very large family orientated town pub with a good array of real ales from the Whitbread portfolio. Facilities include a 180-seat restaurant with an indoor activity centre for younger customers. Renowned for its food, its varied menu and interesting daily offers are enough to tempt all tastes and the early riser breakfasts are the talk of the town. Outside is a large garden with children's play equipment and Wendy house. There is a baby-changing room and WC with wheelchair access. 🛏️🅿️◗ ♿ ⚿ ≈🅿️⛔

Seaview Hotel
High Street
✪ 11-2.30, 6-11; 12-3, 7-10.30 Sun
☎ (01983) 612711 website: www.seaviewhotel.co.uk
Greene King Abbot; guest beer (summer) Ⓗ
It may not seem right to rave about a hotel when it's the beer that we are tasting, but to this hostelry the two are intertwined. From the moment you walk in, you will be drawn in by the history of the sea that is all around you. It captures the imagination. The public bar is quite small, but during the summer months when the pub really buzzes, there is still plenty of room to move around. The hotel, well, that's another story you will have to find out for yourself.
🏨🅿️🛏️◗ 🅿️♣🅿️

New Inn
Main Road (village centre)
✪ 12-3, 6-11; (12-11 summer); 12-3, 6-10.30 Sun
☎ (01983) 531314

CALBOURNE
Blacksmith's Arms
Park Cross, Calbourne Road
(B3401 Carisbrooke road)
11-3, 6-11 (11-11 summer); 12-10.30 Sun
Beer range varies Ⓗ
Joint CAMRA *Pub of the Year* 2001 and consistent multiple award-winner. Specialises in diverse range of real ales, including the occasional German cask-conditioned beer. *Cask Marque* accredited.

NEWPORT
Hogshead
20 High Street
11-11; 12-10.30 Sun
Boddingtons Bitter; Flowers IPA; Fuller's London Pride; Wadworth 6X; Ⓗ **guest beers** Ⓗ Ⓖ
Trendy High Street pub at the lower end of town with an unusual interior, once a bookshop. An interesting range of guest beers and a strong local following.

NORTHWOOD
Travellers Joy
85 Pallance Road
(A3020 Yarmouth road out of Cowes)
11-2.30, 5-11; 11-11 Fri & Sat; 12-3, 7-10.30 Sun
Goddards Special Bitter; guest beers Ⓗ **guest beers** Ⓗ Ⓖ
Joint CAMRA *Pub of the Year* 2001 and consistent multiple award-winner. The original island beer exhibition house with at least eight beers on offer.

RYDE
JJ Fowlers
41-43 Union Street
11-11; 12-10.30 Sun
Boddingtons Bitter; Courage Directors; Theakston Best Bitter; Ventnor Golden; Wadworth 6X; guest beers Ⓗ
Fine example of the Wetherspoon's chain. Well-placed at the head of Union Street with an ever-changing beer range. *Cask Marque* accredited.

Check it out

Pubs in the Good Beer Guide may change ownership and the facilities listed could alter. If a visit to a pub in the guide involves a lengthy journey, it is advisable to check before leaving that full meals, family facilities, accommodation or camping sites are still available.

Kitchen of an Inn

In the evening we reached a village where I had determined to pass the night. As we drove into the great gateway of the inn, I saw on one side the light of a rousing kitchen fire beaming through a window. I entered, and admired for the hundredth time that picture of convenience, neatness, and broad honest enjoyment, the kitchen of an English inn. It was of spacious dimensions; hung around by copper and tin vessels, highly polished, and decorated here and there with a Christmas green. Hams, tongues, and flitches of bacon were suspended from the ceiling; a smoke-jack made its ceaseless clanking beside the fire-place, and a clock ticked in one corner. A well-scoured deal table extended along one side of the kitchen, with a cold round of beef, and other hearty viands upon it, over which two foaming tankards of ale seemed mounting guard. Travellers of inferior order were preparing to attack this stout repast, while others sat smoking or gossiping over their ale, on two high-backed oaken settles beside the fire.

Washington Irving, *Travelling at Christmas*, 1884.

Badger Best; Draught Bass; Ventnor Golden; guest beers Ⓗ

Unmissable as you travel through Shalfleet on the Newport to Yarmouth road, the New Inn has stood at the entrance to Mill Road for 300 years. An ancient and largely unspoilt country local with a flagstone floor. The good beer and food, especially fish and seafood, for which the pub is noted, continue to entice locals from inland and seafarers up the lane from Shalfleet creek. The roaring log fire is a delight in winter and in summer, the rustic chairs and tables outside and the ample garden are ideal for families. ♨☕⚮◐Å♣P✂

SHANKLIN

Steamer Inn
Esplanade
☀ 10.30-11; 12-10.30 Sun
☎ (01983) 862641 website: www.bargemansrest.co.uk
Badger Best, Tanglefoot; Poole Bosun; Ventnor Golden; Wychwood Hobgoblin Ⓗ

A newcomer to the island's pub scene and oasis to the former beer desert of Shanklin. The Steamer, previously the Lincoln Hotel, is one of the chain which includes the Bargemans at Newport and Spyglass, Ventnor. Already earning a high reputation for its hospitality, real ale and food, it attracts locals and visitors looking for choice and quality. An ever-changing and interesting range of beers with the occasional beer festival run in conjunction with the other group pubs. Frequent live music to entertain, from some of the island's most popular groups. Q☕⚮◙◐Å⇌✂

Volunteer
30 Victoria Street
☀ 11-11; 12-10.30 Sun
☎ (01983) 852537
website: www.thevolunteer.demon.co.uk
Badger Best, Tanglefoot; Ringwood Best Bitter; Ventnor Golden; guest beers Ⓗ

Built in 1866, the Ventnor is probably the smallest pub on the island. It operated as a beer house between 1869 and 1871 and still retains many original features of the traditional drinkers' pub. Well-known for the quality of its beer and cellarmanship, which have been recognised by the many awards gained in the local *Pub of the Year* competition. No chips, no children, no fruit machines, no video games, just a pure adult drinking house and one of the few places where you can still play Rings. A gem. ♨Q♣

YARMOUTH

Wheatsheaf Inn
Bridge Road
(Wheatsheaf Lane opp. George Hotel)
☀ 11-11; 12-10.30 Sun
☎ (01983) 760456 e-mail: suzikeen@hotmail.com
Brakspear Special; Goddards Fuggle-Dee-Dum; Greene King Old Speckled Hen; Wadworth 6X Ⓗ

Old coaching house, now with additional rooms. It is spacious and comfortable with a large conservatory to the rear, ideal for families and on pleasant summer eves. The large public bar has its fair share of visiting yachtsmen tracing the few yards from the harbour. Beer complements the interesting and good value food. Yarmouth Square parking close by. Q☕⚮◐▣⇌ (Wightlink Ferry) ♣

KENT

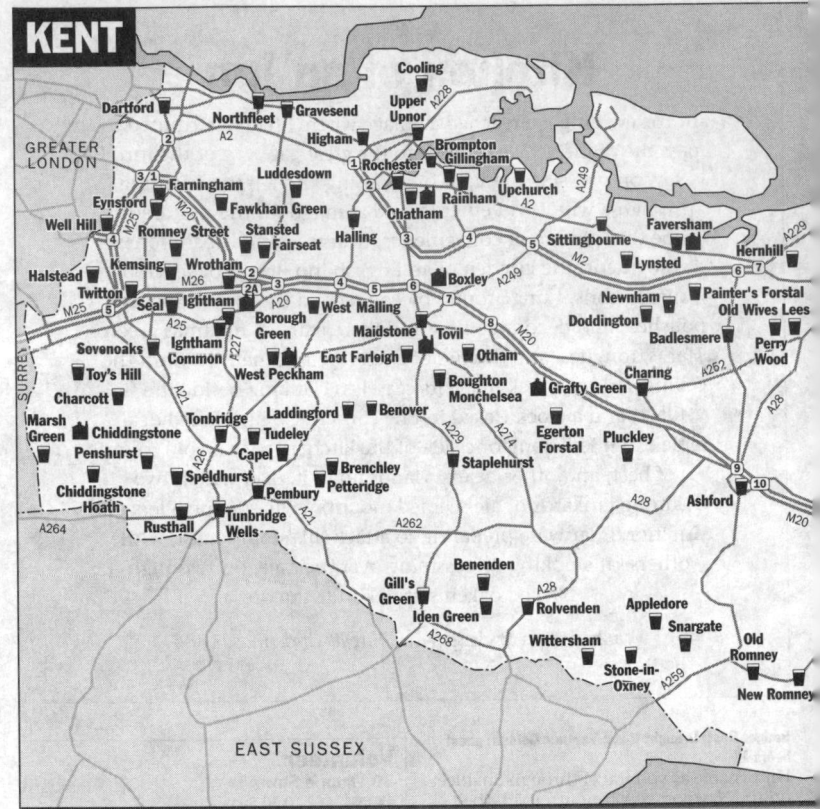

Black Lion
15 The Street
⏰ 11.30-11; 12-10.30 Sun
☎ (01233) 758206 website: www.blacklion-pub.com
Draught Bass; Hancock's HB; Black Sheep Best Bitter; guest beer Ⓗ

Formerly the Red Lion, this delightful village local stands close to the historic Royal Military Canal. The good-sized bar, with plenty of room to get served, boasts collections of pump clips, brass blowlamps, and local black and white pictures. Over 200 unusual jugs are also displayed. Three attractive menu blackboards display a huge range of over 40 dishes. Food is available 11.30–10. A popular pig roast is held bank holiday Mon.
🏠🐾❀♣♦P

Pilgrims Rest
Canterbury Road, Kennington
⏰ 11-11; 12-10.30 Sun
☎ (01233) 636863
Fuller's London Pride, ESB, seasonal beers Ⓗ

Recently refurbished Fuller's house with an old-fashioned appearance; a warm, friendly and quiet place to relax. Excellent food is served at this pub that is easy to locate on the main A28 north of Ashford.
🏠🐾❀♣◑&♣P🍴

Red Lion
Ashford Road (A251)
⏰ 12-3, 6-11; 12-11 Fri & Sat; 12-10.30 Sun
☎ (01233) 740320
Fuller's London Pride; Goacher's Mild; Greene King Abbot; Shepherd Neame Master Brew Bitter; guest beers Ⓗ

16th-century free house, originally two farm cottages, it served for a while as the local morgue, the naturally cool cellar assisting in this function just as it does today with casks of ale. Normally two guest beers are offered a week, and beer festivals are held over the Easter and Aug bank holidays; the latter is a 'folkale' event with music. Live music is also staged Fri eve. Meals are based on local products (no food Sun eve). Johnson's Farmhouse cider is normally available. Happy hour is Thu 7.30-8.30.
🏠❀◑▲♣♦P

Black Pig
Barnsole Road OS278564
⏰ 12-3, 6-11; 12-11 Sat; 12-4, 7-10.30 Sun
☎ (01304) 813000
Greene King IPA, Old Speckled Hen; Hop Back Summer Lightning Ⓗ

Centuries-old rural free house set among productive farmland for which the area is still well known, although more on an industrial scale these days. The bar houses a pool table, while the main food and drink

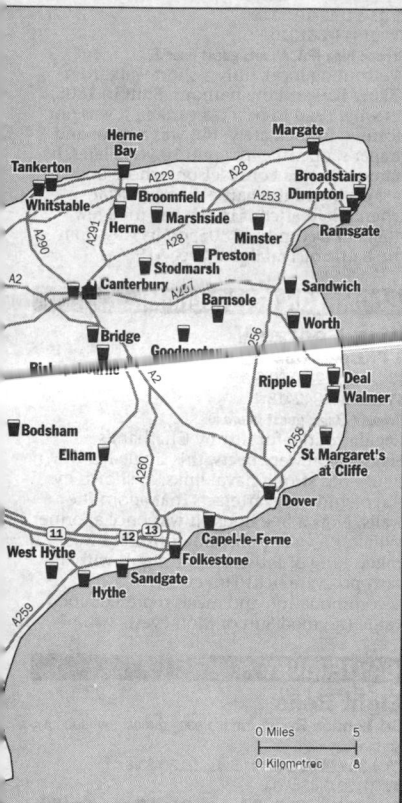

Hop pockets and antique tools adorn the walls of this popular 15th-century, beamed country inn, that serves excellent food in a friendly, relaxed atmosphere. It is now more a restaurant than a pub, but still attracts serious beer drinkers. A regular entry in past *Guides*, the beers other than Master Brew are served under blanket pressure. ♨❀◐ P

BISHOPSBOURNE

Mermaid Inn
Off A2 at Bridge, then Frog Lane or Rose Lane
✪ 12-3 (2.30 Wed), 6.10-11; 12-3, 7-10.30 Sun
☎ (01227) 830581
Shepherd Neame Master Brew Bitter, seasonal beers Ⓗ

Lovely, unpretentious village pub, a *Guide* regular for 20 years. There are three cosy bar areas, two with log fires. The walls are hung with old local photos, posters and paintings. The Elham Valley Way passes through the village and the North Downs Way is only a mile away. A bus service from Canterbury stops at the end of the lane, near the attractive church and the former home of author Joseph Conrad. A very worthwhile detour from the nearby A2.
♨Q❀◐⊟♣

BODSHAM

Timber Batts Restaurant and Ale House
School Lane OS111458
✪ 11.30-3, 7-11; 11-11 Sat; 12-10.30 Sun
☎ (0133) 7502373
e-mail: timberbatts@colourful.madasafish.com
Beer range varies Ⓗ

The Timber Batts, built during the reign of Henry VII, has seen many changes, but its historic character remains unchanged. Set atop a hill, in beautiful countryside overlooking the valley, this typical old pub boasts original oak beams, inglenooks, a large garden and good traditional fare. It is not easy to find, but worth the effort. A wide range of beers suits all pockets, and normally three beers are stocked, often including a mild. A yearly beer festival is staged. ♨❀◐⊟ÅP

BOUGHTON MONCHELSEA

Red House
Hermitage Lane, Wierton (S off B2163, down Wierton Lane and East Hall Hill) OS783488
✪ 12-3 (not Tue), 7-11; 12-11 Sat; 12-10.30 Sun
☎ (01622) 743986 website: www.the-redhouse.co.uk
Everards Tiger; Hampshire Strong's Best Bitter; guest beers Ⓗ

Traditional Kentish free house in the picturesque Weald of Kent, where six real ales usually include both a dark and a

area retains a rustic charm – no doubt due to its early release from the brewery tied house system. A far-flung permanent outlet for Hop Back, the other strong ale may vary, while the wine list showcases local vineyards, including Barnsole's very own (visitors welcome in summer). Q❀◐⊟P

BENENDEN

King William IV
The Street
✪ 11-3, 6-11; 11-11 Sat; 12-10.30 Sun
☎ (01580) 240636
Shepherd Neame Master Brew Bitter, Spitfire or seasonal beer Ⓗ

In the centre of Benenden, an unspoilt village in the Kentish Weald, this 16th-century pub was one of a number of local hostelries frequented by the notorious Hawkhurst gang of smugglers around the 1750s. The pub has two very different bars: a large inglenook is the centrepiece of the saloon bar, where good food is available (not served Sun eve), but there is no problem if you just want to sit and have a beer. The large garden has plentiful seating.
♨Q❀◐♣P

BENOVER

Woolpack
Benover Road
✪ 12-3, 6-11; 12-3, 7-10.30 Sun
☎ (01892) 730356
Shepherd Neame Master Brew Bitter Ⓗ

INDEPENDENT BREWERIES

Ales of Kent Boxley
Flagship Chatham
Goacher's Tovil
Hopdaemon Canterbury
Larkins Chiddingstone
Old Kent Borough Green
Shepherd Neame Faversham
Swale Grafty Green
Swan West Peckham

strong beer. An interesting range of bottle beers, continental beers and old English wines are also stocked, alongside a good selection of teas and coffee and soft drinks for children or drivers. It is worth finding this welcoming pub, which is next to a campsite. Chiddingstone's and Weston's cider sold. ♨☙♨◐● ♣♠♣♦P♿

BRENCHLEY

Bull of Brenchley
High Street OS679417
✪ 11.30-3, 5-11; 11-4, 6-11 Sat; 12-4, 7-10.30 Sun
☎ (01892) 722701
Greene King IPA; Harveys BB; Shepherd Neame Spitfire; guest beer ⊞
The centre of an attractive Wealden village, this is a lofty Victorian replacement for an earlier building which burnt down. The bar has three distinct sections and there is a conservatory restaurant. The decor is in muted colours and the furnishings are in Victorian style; the cast-iron and tiled fireplace is genuine. Children are admitted if dining (special menu) and a play area forms part of the garden. The seven en-suite bedrooms are furnished in appropriate period style; three are in a rear annexe.
♨❀➾◐●P

BRIDGE

Plough & Harrow
86 High Street
✪ 11-3, 5-11; 11-11 Sat; 12-3, 7-10.30 Sun
☎ (01227) 830455
e-mail: ploughandharrow@btinternet.com
Shepherd Neame Master Brew Bitter ⊞
Now in its tenth year in this *Guide*, this pub continues to be an attractive, no-frills centre for village life where the emphasis is on conversation and games. This 300-year-old former brewery is hung with hops indoors and floral baskets outside. The landlord runs cellarmanship courses for other tenants of the brewery; see him on the cover of the nude calendar which the pub produced for 2000.
♨Q♣P

BROADSTAIRS

Lord Nelson
11 Nelson Place

✪ 11-11; 12-10.30 Sun
☎ (01843) 861210
Greene King IPA, Abbot; guest beer ⊞
Welcoming local, only a short walk from Viking Bay and the harbour. Built in 1805, on what used to be a tea garden, it was not licensed immediately, but was a tailor and draper's, opening as a pub 10 years later. Its name honours Lord Nelson, whose body was on board the battle-scarred *Victory* when it laid anchor in the bay for a few hours in December 1805, on its way from the Battle of Trafalgar. ☙❀♣P

BROMPTON (GILLINGHAM)

King George V
1 Prospect Row
✪ 11-11; 12-10.30 Sun
☎ (01634) 842418
Draught Bass; guest beers ⊞
Regular outlet for nearby Chatham's Flagship Brewery beers, this single-bar town house has strong naval links, as shown by the pictures and artefacts that adorn the walls. Now a free house it was once a former Winch Brewery pub, and until 1914 was called King of Prussia. Quiz nights with a cash prize are held Thu eve. The accommodation and meals represent good value (no food Sun or Mon eves). ➾◐●♣

CANTERBURY ❖

Eight Bells
34 London Road (off the easternmost roundabout on the ring road)
✪ 4.30 (12 Fri & Sat)-11; 12-10.30 Sun
☎ (01227) 454794
Draught Bass; Fuller's London Pride; Greene King IPA; Young's Special ⊞
This cosy, red-ceilinged pub is convenient for many of Canterbury's guest houses. The layout of the pub encourages chatting with locals or the ex-legionnaire landlord and his wife. The walls are hung with Foreign Legion memorabilia and pictures of Staffordshire bull terriers. There is a piano and on Fri Country & Western or Rock 'n' Roll music is staged; a lively Irish band performs once a month. The small, but very attractive patio garden is a pleasant place to sit in summer. Sandwiches are usually available; the cider is from Addlestone's.
❀⇌(West) ♣●

INN BRIEF

BROOMFIELD
Huntsman & Horn
Margate Road
11.30-11;
12-10.30 Sun
Benskins Bitter; Tolly Cobbold Original ⊞
Cosy, listed building in a pleasant suburb of Herne Bay, comprising two drinking areas and a restaurant (no meals winter Sun eve).

CANTERBURY
Hobgoblin
40 St Peter's Street
12-11; 12-10.30 Sun
Flowers Original; Fuller's London Pride; Wychwood Hobgoblin, seasonal beers; guest beers ⊞
Late Victorian pub, formerly the Black Griffin, near the medieval Westgate Towers. This student-orientated pub offers discounts.

New Inn
19 Havelock Street
12-2, 5-11;
12-10.30 Sun
Brakspear Bitter; Greene King IPA, Abbot; Harveys BB; guest beers ⊞
Back-street free house, popular with students, academics and archaeologists, serving good value home-cooked food.

Olde Beverlie
St Stephen's Green
12-3, 6-11; 11-11 Fri & Sat;
12-10.30 Sun
Shepherd Neame Master Brew Bitter, Spitfire, seasonal beers ⊞
Lovely, beamed stone-floored pub. The game of Bat and Trap was invented in the beautiful garden. No meals Sun eve.

CHARCOTT
Greyhound
OS522472
12-3, 6-11; 12-3, 7-10.30 Sun
Adnams Bitter; Badger K&B Sussex; Flowers Original; Greene King Old Speckled Hen ⊞
Single-bar pub in a hamlet, a centre for local events including the Boxing Day conkers contest. Excellent food (not Tue or Sun eve).

DEAL
Saracen's Head
1 Alfred Square
11-11; 12-10.30 Sun
Shepherd Neame Master Brew Bitter, Spitfire, Bishops Finger, seasonal beers ⊞
Cheerful street-corner pub overlooking the square, home to darts and pool teams. Rare local outlet for Bishops Finger.

Sir Thomas Ingoldsby

5-9 Burgate (near bus station)
☼ 10-11; 12-10.30 Sun
☎ (01227) 463339
Courage Directors; Shepherd Neame Spitfire; Theakston Best Bitter; guest beers Ⓗ

Previously a furniture shop, this large, open-plan JD Wetherspoon's outlet is decorated with prints relating to the history of the area. The pub name celebrates the Kentish author of the *Ingoldsby Legends*. Close to the medieval cathedral, Canterbury's jewel, it stands just within the city wall in Burgate, opposite the 19th-century Roman Catholic church of St Thomas. The pub can get very crowded on Fri and Sat nights. Food is served all day. Outside drinking is on the pavement. Public parking is available nearby. Q ◑ ⑁ 𝄞 ⇌ (East) ⅙ ●

CAPEL

Dovecote

Alders Road (1/2 mile W of A228)
☼ 12-3 (4 Sat); 6-11; 12-4, 7-10.30 Sun
☎ (01892) 835966
Badger K&B Sussex; Harveys BB; Larkins Chiddingstone; guest beers Ⓖ

200-year-old, white-painted building; the bar has exposed brickwork and dark colours. The most notable feature is the cooled room behind the bar, fronted by false cask ends that mask the real ones from which the beers are drawn. The menu offers meals and snacks while a blackboard lists home-made specials with an oriental bias. 'Two for the price of one' meal deals are available Tue and Thu eves. Outside is a patio, a children's playground and, of course, a dovecote. Chiddingstone's cider sold.
🏠Q❀◑𝄞❀P●

CAPEL-LE-FERNE

Royal Oak

New Dover Road (B2011, E of village) OS263387
☼ 11.30-3 (4 Sat), 6-11; 12-4, 8-10.30 Sun
☎ (01303) 244787
Shepherd Neame Master Brew Bitter; guest beers Ⓗ

Split-level building, originally a farmhouse and long barn. Note the elevation at right angles to the clifftop with a blank wall facing out to sea. The view from the cliff edge takes in Cap Gris Nez (France) and across Folkestone Harbour towards Dungeness nuclear power stations. The barn is mainly a games area, with several tables. Conversation rules in the snug, along with cribbage and raffles and food cooked to order (no eve meals Wed or Sun). Two guest ales come from regional and micro-breweries, changing weekly. The coastal path is a designated cycle track; the descent to the beach can be dangerous. 🏠◑ 🕮𝄞♣P

CHARING

Bowl Inn

Egg Hill Road OS950514
☼ 5-11; 12-11 Fri & Sat; 12-10.30 Sun
☎ (01233) 712256 website: www.bowl-inn.co.uk
Fuller's London Pride; guest beers Ⓗ

On top of the North Kent Downs, this remote, 16th-century pub is well worth finding. It has been a regular CAMRA award-winner since 1994, including Kent *Pub of the Year*. The large garden has facilities for camping. An annual beer festival is held in July and offers 20-plus real ales. Inside the pub is a magnificent open fire in winter and also an unusual revolving pool table. The pub always stocks three guest beers and often stages beer promotions. Bar snacks are available until 9.45. 🏠❀🕮𝄞♣P⅙

CHATHAM

Little Crown

346 High Street
☼ 11-11; 12-10.30 Sun
☎ (01634) 844144
Adnams Bitter; Fuller's London Pride; guest beers (occasional) Ⓗ

Friendly pub near the main shopping area, but very much a local. Good value home-cooked food (not served Sat or Mon) makes it popular at lunchtime. The walls are covered with photographs of old Chatham, that have recently been joined by a growing gallery of film and recording stars from the 1940s, 50s and 60s. The garden has been recently refurbished to provide a pleasant oasis in a busy town centre. Theme nights are held monthly, and a weekly pool competition (Sun). 🏠❀◑ ⇌♣

Ropemakers Arms

70 New Road (A2)
☼ 12-3 (not Sat), 7-11; 12-3, 7-10.30 Sun

EYNSFORD

Five Bells

High Street
11-3, 5.30-11; 11-11 Sat;
12-10.30 Sun
Courage Best Bitter; Harveys BB; Taylor Landlord Ⓗ

Excellent, traditional two-bar local in a pleasant riverside village near a 12th-century castle and Roman villa. Lunchtime food.

FOLKESTONE

Clifton Hotel

Clifton Gardens, The Leas
11-3, 5.45-11;
11.30-3, 6.30-10.30 Sun
Draught Bass Ⓗ

Large Victorian hotel with olde-worlde charm, a children's room, food served lunchtime and eve, and accommodation.

GILLINGHAM

Barge

63 Layfield Road
12-3, 7-11; 12-11 Fri & Sat; 12-10.30 Sun
Flagship Joshua Ale; Wadworth 6X; guest beers Ⓗ

Single-bar pub, its walls depict life below decks, candlelit eve. Free folk night Mon. Spectacular Medway views.

Falcon

95 Marlborough Road
12-3, 5.30-11; 12-11 Sat;
12-5, 7-10.30 Sun
Greene King Ruddles Best; Wells Bombardier; guest beers Ⓗ

Busy, but compact, single-bar town house. Summer barbecues and Bat and Trap pitch in the garden. Good value food. Live entertainment Tue.

GRAVESEND

Prince Albert

26 Wrotham Road
11-11; 12-10.30 Sun
Shepherd Neame Master Brew Bitter, Spitfire Ⓗ

Two-bar, friendly town pub where quizzes, music and party nights are a regular feature.

HYTHE

Globe

6-8 High Street
10-11;
12-4, 7-10.30 Sun
Shepherd Neame Master Brew Bitter, Spitfire, Ⓗ **Bishop's Finger,** Ⓖ **seasonal beers** Ⓗ

Friendly, two-bar pub, off the town centre, within walking distance of the beach, and near Hythe Light Railway Station. Lunches served.

☎ (01634) 402121

Goacher's Light; Greene King Abbot; guest beers Ⓗ
Situated on the main A2, this roadside pub
is decorated with a mural of a Chatham
Dockyard shed, by a local artist. Regular
quiz nights are held on the first Wed of
every month. This pub has both pool and
bar billiards but is closed Sat lunchtime. No
food is served Sun. Car parking is available
adjacent to, and behind the pub. ◖⇌♣

CHIDDINGSTONE HOATH

Rock Inn
Hoath Corner (1½ miles S of Chiddingstone via Wellers
Town) OS497431
☼ 11.30-3, 6-11 (closed Mon); 12-3, 7-10.30 Sun
☎ (01892) 870296

Larkins Traditional Best Bitter, Porter Ⓗ
Old, timber-framed traditional two-bar
country pub owned by the local
Chiddingstone brewery, Larkins. The small
original interior has a quiet, cosy feel with a
brick floor, irregular beams and a large
inglenook housing a wood-burning stove.
Hops hang from the ceiling above the bar,
which features unusual wooden
handpumps. There is a garden to the rear,
with additional seating outside the front in
summer. Games include Ring the Bull. No
meals Sun eve. ﬦQ❀◖⊟♣P

COOLING

Horseshoe & Castle
Main Road
☼ 11.30-3, 7-11; 12-4, 7-10.30 Sun
☎ (01634) 221691 e-mail: horseshoe.castle@virgin.net
Adnams Bitter; Draught Bass; guest beers Ⓗ
In the middle of a peaceful village on the
edge of the North Kent marshes, this early
20th-century pub replaced an old weatherboarded inn that had been destroyed by
fire. A ruined castle, on the outskirts of the
village, was once owned by Sir John
Oldcastle, the inspiration for Shakespeare's
Falstaff, while in the local churchyard are
the tombstones of the children reputed to
have given Charles Dickens the idea for
Great Expectations. The pub specialises in
seafood on an interesting menu (no meals
Mon eve); comfortable accommodation.
Addlestone's cider is sold.
ﬦ❀⇐◖♣♠P

DARTFORD

Malt Shovel
3 Darenth Road (follow A226, turn right on East
Hill, 50 yds)
☼ 10.30-2.30, 5-11; 10.30-11 Fri & Sat; 12-3,
7-10.30 Sun
☎ (01322) 224381
Young's Bitter, Special, seasonal beers Ⓗ
Small pub with the feel of a country local,
circa 1673, looking every year of its three
centuries. Inside an aura of history clings to
the low ceilings and time-worn woodwork.
Bric-à-brac hanging from the ceiling,
includes a collection of cameras; note the
Dartford Breweries mirror. The conservatory
blends in well, while the public bar has a
character of its own. A welcome return to
this *Guide* after many years' absence. Good
value food includes a regular specials board
and theme nights.
ﬦQ⛌❀◖⊟⚓⇌P

Paper Moon
55 High Street
☼ 11-11; 12-10.30 Sun
☎ (01322) 281127
**Courage Directors; Shepherd Neame Spitfire;
Theakston Best Bitter; guest beers** Ⓗ
Converted from a former bank, attractively
situated on a corner site, the interior is in
typical Wetherspoon's style. Of interest are
the cameo descriptions of the history of
Dartford. The pub's name reflects the area's
early connections with paper-making. It
serves a wide range of guest beers, with
regular reduced price beer promotions.
Good value food is available all day, making
it popular with young and old alike.
Q◖⅊⇌⅄●

Tiger
28 St Albans Road
☼ 11-11; 12-10.30 Sun
☎ (01322) 293688
Courage Best Bitter; guest beers Ⓗ
Small, side-street corner pub frequented by
the local community. Dated 1869, the pub's
age is evident inside where cosiness is
emphasised by low ceilings and beams. The
rear of the pub is open to reveal curved
wooden braces. The windows are etched
with dramatic tigers. Sports are popular,
fielding darts, pool and football teams. The
guest beers are often from local micro-
breweries. Good value food is served at
lunchtime. ◖⅊♣

DEAL ❄

Admiral Penn
79 Beach Street
☼ 6-11; closed Sun
☎ (01304) 374279 website: www.admiralpenn.com
**Draught Bass; Fuller's London Pride; Wells
Bombardier** Ⓗ
Smart bar in a prime seafront location,
offering extensive views of passing
shipping. The nautical theme, combined
with a Dutch flavour, works well, a range of
continental spirits and liqueurs are on offer;
specialities are Dutch Kopstoot and
Jagermeister cold from the fridge. In spite,
or maybe because, of limited opening
hours, the pub is invariably well patronised
and lively. ﬦ⇌

Alma
126 West Street (parallel to High St)
☼ 10-3, 6-11; 12-3, 7-10.30 Sun
☎ (01304) 360244
Shepherd Neame Master Brew Bitter; guest beers Ⓗ
Handy for the station, this well-run, good
value house was local CAMRA *Pub of the
Year* 1999. A free house in the true sense of
the word, three guest beers are usually on
offer – the regularly changing range puts to
shame the somewhat dreary selection
sometimes on offer in other so-called free
houses. On the edge of Deal's conservation
area, this is very much a no-nonsense local
and fields darts, pool and bar billiards
teams. ❀⇌

Ship
141 Middle Street (parallel to sea front)
☼ 11-11; 12-10.30 Sun
☎ (01304) 372222
Adnams Broadside; Draught Bass; Shepherd Neame

Master Brew Bitter; Swale Kentish Pride ⌂
Cosy, traditional pub of two drinking areas (one a secluded back room). This historic tavern in the heart of Deal's conservation area, is surely light years away from the haunt of blackguards and ruffians who must have frequented these mean streets in days gone by. But don't be so sure! Enjoy startling your friends, if you get caught up in a historical re-enactment – these can occur without warning.
♨❀≠

DODDINGTON

Chequers
The Street OS935573
⌂ 11-3, 7-11 Mon-Fri; 11-11 Sat, 12-3, 7-10.30 Sun
website: www.website.fsnet.co.uk\pub
Shepherd Neame Master Brew Bitter, Spitfire or seasonal beer ⌂
This 14th-century pub was once a coaching inn and smugglers' haunt on the ancient road from Whitstable to Maidstone. At the hub of village life, where conversation and a good pint are the order of the day, the cosy saloon bar is focused around an inglenook; two spacious drinking areas boast mullioned windows, a secret room and several ghosts. The simple menu is based around home-cooked ham, with local cheeses and sausages, but food is never allowed to dominate. A previous CAMRA regional *Pub of the Year*.
♨Q❀❁◖❦♣P

DOVER

Boar's Head
46 Eaton Road (off B2011 at Elms Vale jct)
☀ 11-3, 6-11; 11-11 Sat; 12-10.30 Sun
☎ (01304) 204490
Greene King IPA; guest beer ⌂
Turn-of-the-century, suburban local on the border of Elms Vale and Tower Hamlets areas. It is owned by former Whitbread tenants who run it as a traditional community pub, with the accent on conversation and games, including quizzes and skittles. Beers tend to come from Greene King or Interbrew, but guest ales frequently showcase regionals or well-known micro-breweries, such as Bateman's or Burton Bridge. It serves as an occasional venue for musical soloists or duets, at weekends and holiday times.
❀◖≠(Priory)♣

Eight Bells
19 Cannon Street (pedestrian zone)
☀ 10-11 Mon-Sat; 12-10.30 Sun
☎ (01304) 205030
Courage Directors; Flowers IPA; Shepherd Neame Spitfire; Theakston Best Bitter; guest beers ⌂
Large, popular town-centre pub, decorated in typical Wetherspoon's style, it features a spacious no-smoking area. Pictures on the wall include eight 'Belles' and snapshots of Dover's history. It can be very crowded with young people on Fri and Sat nights. The guest beers are taken from the Wetherspoon's list and are varied by an enthusiastic management who take part in regular festivals; seasonal beers feature prominently. The food is well prepared and good value.
Q❀◖♿≠(Priory)✂●

Flagship
115 Snargate Street (A20)
☀ 12-3, 5-11; 12-11 Fri & Sat; 12-3, 6-10.30, 12-10.30 Sun
☎ (01304) 203868
Beer range varies ⌂
The first pub in Dover on the road from Folkestone, near the busy yacht marina and the Hoverspeed fast ferry terminal. Until very recently, it was known as the York House, and dates back to at least 1800. The Grand Shaft, a triple staircase in the cliff leading to former military barracks, is close by; in those days soldiers would join sailors from the docks and enjoy the many pubs and other delights in Snargate Street (Jericho to the locals). The Flagship is one of the few surviving hostelries.
◖≠(Priory)

Flotilla & Firkin
1 Bench Street (off A20, York St roundabout)
☀ 11-11; 12-10.30 Sun
☎ (01304) 204488
Draught Bass; Marston's Pedigree; Tetley Bitter ⌂
Real ale oasis amid a selection of fizz pubs and bars. Ideally located near the seafront and town centre, it is popular with locals and tourists alike; children are welcome until 6pm. Formerly the Dover Tavern, it was refurbished four years ago, displaying prints and pictures with a nautical theme, including some views of lighthouses. The food is well prepared and reasonably priced. The juke box plays constantly but is kept low. ❀◖≠(Priory)

Golden Lion
11 Priory Street (A256/B2011 jct)
☀ 10-11; 12-10.30 Sun
☎ (01304) 202919
Greene King IPA; guest beers ⌂
Just off the High Street, the Golden Lion is a one-bar, street-corner local, enjoying a large regular following, as well as making visitors very welcome. The pub is always busy yet does not become overcrowded. Pictures of the local members of the Winkle Club adorn the wall, alongside nautical artefacts and old photos of the pub. Filled rolls are available from the bar, very reasonably priced. The beer range includes a varying brew from Brains in Cardiff.
≠(Priory)

Mogul
5 Chapel Place (near A256/A20 jct at York St roundabout))
☀ 11-11; 12-10.30 Sun
☎ (01304) 205072
Beer range varies Ⓖ
Family-run genuine free house that has won several recent awards, including Kent CAMRA *Pub of the Year*. Three beers are usually available, often including a mild; customers can influence the choice of beers, or comment on those they've sampled in the Imbiber's Bible. The pub garden affords views of the castle and harbour. A log fire burns between two bars. Pictures of old Dover and Imperial India feature alongside brewery posters and chalk representations of regular customers. Easier to find on foot than in a car, but well worth seeking out. Thatcher's cider sold.
♨Q❀❀≠(Priory)♣●✂

DUMPTON

Brown Jug
204 Ramsgate Road
🕔 12-3, 6-11; 12-11 Sat; 12-10.30 Sun
☎ (01843) 862788
Greene King IPA; guest beers 🅷
This delightful pub smacks of olde-worlde charm, with its shuttered, leaded windows, flint façade, outside toilets and separate public and saloon bars. It has been extended twice, around 1810 and 1948, and is reputed to have been used as an officers' billet during the Napoleonic Wars. Note the large brown jug over the public bar entrance. The pub supports flourishing pétanque and quiz teams. Thanet CAMRA *Pub of the Year* 2001.
🏚Q🌳🏠≹ (Dumpton Pk) **P**

EAST FARLEIGH

Bull Inn
Lower Road (B2010/Station Hill jct)
🕔 11-11; 12-10.30 Sun
☎ (01622) 726282 website: www.farleigh-bull.co.uk
Adnams Bitter; Flowers Original; Fuller's London Pride; Goacher's Gold Star Ale; Shepherd Neame Master Brew Bitter; guest beer 🅷
Vibrant family-friendly pub, incorporating a shop and Post Office. The spacious L-shaped bar area and function room are adorned with historical items and pictures, including a complete set of 13 1790s' prints by Francis Wheatley of the *Cries of London*. An extensive menu includes daily specials, vegetarian and children's dishes: a traditional Sun lunch is served 12–4.30; food is limited Sun eve when live music is staged. A children's play area on the patio includes a mini-zoo, with a pot-bellied pig. Local CAMRA *Pub of the Year* 2000.
🏚Q🌳🏠👶♿≹♣✂

Victory
Farleigh Lane
🕔 11-11; 12-10.30 Sun
☎ (01622) 726591
Goacher's Best Dark; Shepherd Neame Master Brew Bitter; Tetley Bitter 🅷
Single-bar pub lying next to the River Medway and the ancient East Farleigh bridge, which affords good views of the river. A dining area is used for lunchtime and eve meals and good value Sun lunches. The garden has a play area and hosts morris dancers during the summer. Parking is available in the adjacent station car park. Entertainment comes in the form of a TV, live music and games.
🌳🏠👶≹♣

EGERTON FORSTAL

Queen's Arms
Forstal Lane OS893464
🕔 12-11; 12-10.30 Sun
☎ (01233) 756386
Goacher's Mild; Shepherd Neame Master Brew Bitter; guest beers 🅷
Hard to find, this rural local is everything a country pub should be and is well worth making an effort to seek out. Apart from the beers listed, it also stocks a house ale from Rother Valley and up to five guests, mostly from Kentish and Sussex brewers.

Biddenden cider is also available in summer. Games played here include euchre.
🏚🌳🏠👶♿♣**P**

ELHAM

Rose & Crown
High Street
🕔 11-3, 6-11; 12-3, 7-10.30 Sun
☎ (01303) 840226 website: www.roseandcrown.co.uk
Rother Valley Level Best; guest beers 🅷
This 16th-century coaching inn was extended and refronted in 1740 and once served as the courthouse for the Elham Petty Sessions. Legend has it that the man on whom Baroness Orczy's *Scarlet Pimpernel* was modelled used to stop here *en route* to France. In the beautiful village of Elham, this free house offers three cask ales, good food and accommodation in a converted stable block. It is within easy reach of Canterbury, Eurotunnel and Dover's ferry terminals.
🏚Q🌳🏠🛏♿**P**

FAIRSEAT

Vigo
On A227, 1 mile N of A20
🕔 12-2.30 (3.30 Sat; not winter Mon-Fri), 6-11; 12-3.30, 7-10.30 Sun
☎ (01732) 822547 e-mail: pjashers@aol.com
Harveys XX Mild, BB; Young's Bitter, Special; guest beers 🅷
Unspoilt ancient country inn, at the top of a steep hill on the North Downs. The pub has given its name to the new village built nearby. Run by the same family since 1930, it became a free house after they purchased it in 1965. For many years a rare outlet for Young's beers outside London, this no-frills pub is generally quiet except on Sun eve when the Daddlums Table (a rare form of table skittles) is used by the regulars.
🏚Q♣**P**✂🗎

FARNINGHAM

Chequers
87 High Street (250 yds from A20)
🕔 11 (12 Sat)-11; 12-10.30 Sun
☎ (01322) 865222 website: kent.community.com
Fuller's ESB; Oakham JHB; Taylor Landlord; guest beers 🅷
Excellent, one-bar corner pub in a picturesque village, complete with a family butcher, grocer, bank and a curry house. On the route of the Darenth footpath, it is a regular rendezvous for CAMRA members, and is frequented by a wide range of clientele. It offers the best range of high quality beer for several miles around. Note the unusual tiled roof over the bar; in spring and summer admire the exceptional floral display of the cottages opposite. 🌳🏠♣●

FAVERSHAM

Anchor
52 Abbey Street
🕔 11-3.30, 6-11; 11-11 Sat; 12-10.30 Sun
☎ (01795) 536471 website: www.upanchor.co.uk
Shepherd Neame Master Brew Bitter, Best Bitter, Spitfire, seasonal beers 🅷
17th-century two-bar pub, with 18th-century additions – the windows remain

from this latter era. Lying across the end of Abbey Street, it is just a few yards from Standard Quay housing many preserved sailing barges. One of Shepherd Neame's three original pubs where old ships' beams support the ceiling and pictures of barges adorn the walls. It offers an innovative menu, specialising in fish dishes, although there is no food Mon (all day) or Sun eve when live music is staged. Large garden.

🏚 ❀ ◖◗ ⬤

Bear Inn
3 Market Place
🕐 10.30-3, 5.30-11; 10.30-11 Sat; 12-3.30, 7-10.30 Sun
☎ (01795) 532088

Shepherd Neame Master Brew Bitter, Spitfire, seasonal beers Ⓗ

This classic pub retains its early 19th-century layout of three bars off a side corridor. Opposite the ancient Guildhall, it oozes olde-worlde charm. The pub was originally next door at No. 2 in the market place but moved in the late 1700s, and was completely rebuilt by 1800. Notable features in the back bar are a carved wooden bear and a clock on which the figures are replaced by the letters of the pub name. The food often features old English recipes.

Q ❀ ◖◗ ⬤ ≠

Crown & Anchor
41 The Mall (towards station)
🕐 10.30-3, 5.30-11; 10.30-4, 6.30-11 Sat; 12-3, 7-10.30 Sun
☎ (01795) 532812

Shepherd Neame Master Brew Bitter Ⓗ

The bitter at this friendly local is the yardstick by which to judge others. Dating from the mid-19th century, the pub is soon absorbed into the Shepherd Neame fold. Once a multi-roomed house, there is now just one, with a hop-strewn alcove leading to an area for pool and darts. Weekday lunches are served – the goulash is recommended as the landlord is Hungarian; he is also the town's longest-serving host. Don't trip over Fred, the friendly pub dog.

◖◗ ≠ ♣

Elephant
31 The Mall (towards A2 from station)
🕐 12-11; 12-10.30 Sun
☎ (01795) 590157

Bateman XB; guest beers Ⓗ

Called the Brewers' Inn when two brothers owned it and brewed on the premises, bought by Fremlins in the 1950s and renamed the Elephant, it is now a friendly community free house where three guest beers normally include a mild. An extensive menu, all home-made, separate no-smoking restaurant for pre-booked meals and Sun lunches. A friendly spook reputedly haunts the cellar – things kept disappearing, then reappearing somewhere else. Occasional brewery and race trips are organised for regulars. No food Mon-Thu eves.

🏚 ❀ ◖◗ ≠ ♣

Shipwright's Arms
Hollowshore, Ham Road (from Davington turn right into Ham Rd, left at bottom, then first right)
OS 017636
🕐 12-3, 7-11; 11-11 Sat & summer; 12-3, 6-10.30 (12-10.30 summer) Sun

☎ (01795) 590088

Goacher's Dark; Hopdaemon Skrimshander IPA; Shepherd Neame Master Brew Bitter; guest beers Ⓖ

Remote, historic 300-year-old pub on the marshes at the confluence of Faversham and Oare creeks. It generates its own electricity and possesses a very special atmosphere. Only stocking beers from Kentish breweries, there are normally five on offer. There is a strong nautical flavour, with a working boatyard next door. It often stages beer festivals at bank holidays. No food Sun eve. Children (and dogs) are welcome. Real fires, real food and real character are the hallmarks at this local CAMRA *Pub of the Year 2001*.

🏚 Q ⬤ ❀ ◖◗ ♣ P ⌿

Sun Inn
10 West Street
🕐 11-11; 12-10.30 Sun
☎ (01795) 535098

Shepherd Neame Master Brew Bitter, Spitfire, seasonal beer Ⓗ

Established during the last year of the Crusades, 1396, this ancient pub stands out, even in Faversham's historic West Street. Particularly of note are the ceiling beams, recycled from old sailing ships, and the superb wooden panelling. Nowadays the social heart of the town, just 50 yards from the market place and Guildhall, it is overseen by manager Richard, who was, and still is, a member of the well-loved band, Caravan. He'll probably try to flog you a video! The food is popular. 🏚 ❀ ◖◗ ≠ ♣ ⌿

Rising Sun
Valley Road
🕐 12-3, 6-11; 12-11 Fri & Sat; 12-10.30 Sun
☎ (01474) 872291

Courage Best Bitter, Directors; guest beers Ⓗ

Enterprising rural pub, pleasantly located on Fawkham village green, about one mile north of Brands Hatch racing circuit, and within earshot of the M20. Three changing beers come from independent suppliers, including local breweries. It has won a good reputation for food in the adjoining restaurant and B&B accommodation is recommended; four-poster beds are available. Well worth seeking out.

🏚 ❀ ☎ ◖◗ ⬤ ♣ P

Guildhall
42 The Bayle
🕐 11.30-11; 12-10.30 Sun
☎ (01303) 251393

Draught Bass; Greene King IPA; guest beer Ⓗ

This very old, traditional pub is situated in the centre of the historic Bayle in Folkestone, a short walk from the town centre. Eve meals, served until 8pm, include a curry night Wed. A second guest beer is added in summer. Local car parking is available in winter. It makes a convenient stopping-off point before crossing the channel via the tunnel.

❀ ◖◗ ⬤ △ ≠ (Central) ♣

Harvey's Wine Bar
Langhorne Hotel, 10-12 Langhorne Gardens
(main road out of centre, towards Sandgate)

✪ 11.30-11; 12-10.30 Sun
☎ (01303) 257233 e-mail: res@langhorne.co.uk
Draught Bass; Everards Tiger; guest beers Ⓗ

This justly popular basement bar on the outskirts of Folkestone attracts a mostly younger clientele and can get noisy. Sky TV is an added attraction for some. In something of a real ale desert, it offers a wide-ranging choice of guest beers and a good selection of food at reasonable prices. Like many places in Folkestone, the bar is named after William Harvey who discovered the mechanism of blood circulation. 🚗✿🔔◑≈(Central) ♣

Lifeboat
42 North Street
✪ 11 (12 Sat)-11; 12 10.30 Sun
☎ (01303) 243958
Draught Bass; Fuller's London Pride; guest beers Ⓗ

Welcoming back-street local near the harbour. As its name suggests the pub features photos of lifeboats and lifeboat crews. Food often features curries and is served Wed–Sun lunchtimes and Tue–Sat eves. Although not as popular as in its Edwardian heyday, Folkestone is still a very pleasant seaside town. The attractive seafront, the Leas, plays host in Sept to a spectacular annual air display. ✿◑▷♣

GILLINGHAM ✤

Dog & Bone
21 Jeffrey Street (off High St)
✪ 11-11; 12-10.30 Sun
☎ (01634) 576829
Beer range varies Ⓗ

Vibrant and busy, this town-centre single-bar pub has opened a 48-seater restaurant in its former public bar. The food is recommended and represents superb value for money. Four handpumps dispense many varied and unusual ales. A charity beer festival is held in July each year. The flagstone floor and conservatory are recent additions. Away football supporters are welcome. 🚗✿◑▷≈

Frog & Toad
38 Burnt Oak Terrace
✪ 11-11; 12-10.30 Sun
☎ (01634) 852231 e-mail: frogandtoad@co.uk
Fuller's London Pride; guest beers Ⓗ

Busy, town-centre pub, a single bar with a friendly welcome. Of the three handpumps, one normally offers a beer from Chatham brewer, Flagship. It has no juke box or fruit machines, but hosts live entertainment Sun lunchtime. Beer festivals are held in the garden in May and Aug. It stocks a fine selection of foreign bottled beers. Perks include free midweek lunchtime snacks and a free meat raffle (Sun lunchtime). It hosts piano eves weekly and regular gourmet nights. ✿≈♣

Upper Gillingham Conservative Club
541 Canterbury Street
✪ 11-2.30, 6.45-11; 11-3, 6.30-11 Sat; 12-2.30, 7-10.30 Sun
☎ (01634) 851403
Shepherd Neame Master Brew Bitter; guest beers Ⓗ

A warm welcome is assured in this friendly club. The building, a former military store, has been a club since 1922. Divided into two distinct drinking areas, one is a comfortable lounge, the other a spacious bar area that doubles as a function room. A snooker room houses two full-sized tables. Two of the three handpumps are used for constantly changing guest ales at very reasonable prices. Kent CAMRA *Club of the Year* 2001; show this *Guide* or CAMRA membership card to be signed in. ♣P

Will Adams
73 Saxton Street (off lower end of Canterbury St)
✪ 12-4 (not Mon-Fri), 7-11; 12-4, 7-10.30 Sun
☎ (01634) 575902
website: myfavouritepub.com/thewilladams
Fuller's London Pride; guest beers Ⓗ

Lunchtime opening varies according to the home fixtures of Gillingham FC (check with the pub). Meals are served Sat lunchtime, plus eves when the Gills play at home. This single-bar town house boasts a mural painted by local artist, Jamie Montgomery, depicting the life and times of adventurer, Will Adams, after whom the pub is named. Note the pub name in Japanese on the front wall. Five handpumps dispense beers, mainly from micros. A rare Medway outlet for real cider, which varies. ✿≈♣◐

GILL'S GREEN (HAWKHURST)

Wellington Arms
(off A229, N of Hawkhurst)
✪ 12-11; 12-10.30 Sun
☎ (01580) 753119
Harveys BB; guest beers Ⓗ

Slightly hidden away from the main road, this busy weatherboarded free house is popular with ramblers for its traditional home cooking (including a children's menu) which is available all day. The building is Elizabethan, and has been licensed since 1615. Four distinct areas include a restaurant, two bars and a pool table downstairs. It currently stocks three guest ales, mostly from micro-breweries, one a cheaper Beer of the Month promotion. Morning coffee, cream teas and Biddenden cider are available. 🚗✿◑♣◐P

GOODNESTONE

Fitzwalter Arms
The Street OS255546
✪ 12-3.30, 7-11; 12-3.30, 7-10.30 Sun
☎ (01304) 840303
Shepherd Neame Master Brew Bitter Ⓗ

Rural local in a picturesque village, named after the lord of the manor. Originally built as the bailiff's lodge to the Fitzwalter estate, it has been licensed since 1703 and retains an unspoilt Jacobean exterior. The interior has largely survived intact, with three distinct bars giving a cosy and intimate character. The garden is accessible via the saloon bar, where meals are served (booking advisable Sun lunch). The nearby Goodnestone Estate Gardens, once frequented by Jane Austen, are open to the public. 🚗✿◑▷⊞♣

GRAVESEND ✤

Jolly Drayman
1 Love Lane, Wellington Street
✪ 11.30-3, 6-11; 12-4, 7-11 Sat; 12-4, 7-11 Sun

☎ (01474) 352355 website: www.realaleguide.co.uk
Everards Tiger; guest beers H
Old, friendly and cosy town pub bearing original low beams and wood panelling. Once part of the old Wellington Brewery, the coke oven that powered the plant was sited where the present car park is – hence the locals call the pub the Coke Oven. The first meeting of the local CAMRA group was held here. Barbecues are held Fri, Sat and Sun eves in summer. ❀◖⇌♣P

HALLING

Homeward Bound
72 High Street
✪ 12-3, 7-11; 12-3, 7-10.30 Sun
☎ (01634) 240743
Shepherd Neame Master Brew Bitter H
This friendly Victorian terraced local in a quiet village was previously a masons' pub. Thanks to the recent bypass drinkers can now hear themselves talk. It is run by a local village family. The Medway Triumph motorcycle club meets here Tue eve. Darts is played on a traditional Kent board (with no trebles). ⋈⇌♣P

HALSTEAD

Rose & Crown
Otford Lane (1 mile W of A224) OS489611
✪ 11.30-11; 12-10.30 Sun
☎ (01959) 533120
Courage Best Bitter; Harveys seasonal beers; Larkins Traditional; guest beers H
This Grade II listed, 200-year-old flint-faced, two-bar pub offers three ever-changing guest beers. It is a focus for the local community, but visitors are always made welcome. A beautiful garden at the rear provides a peaceful setting in summer and a safe location for children, who are also welcome in the games room. A collection of stone hot-water bottles is displayed behind the bar, which is guarded by a friendly ghost, Humphrey. Weekday lunches served. ⋈Q☞❀◖⊟♣P

HERNE

Smugglers Inn
1 School Lane
✪ 11-3.30, 6-11; 11-11 Fri & Sat; 12-10.30 Sun
☎ (01227) 741395
Shepherd Neame Master Brew Bitter, Spitfire, seasonal beers H
Local, over 200 years old, where the attic was used as a look-out post by smugglers. The pub used to be linked to the village church by a tunnel. The saloon bar features hops, wooden beams, brass and other memorabilia. Two small areas separate diners from drinkers; one area resembles a snug. The public bar bears a nautical theme – the bar is fitted with the prow of a whaler. Traditional pub games include Bat and Trap. No food Sun. On the main Herne Bay to Canterbury bus route, it enjoys a frequent service. ❀◖⊟♣

HERNE BAY

Four Fathoms
2 High Street
✪ 11.30-11; 12-10.30 Sun
☎ (01227) 374987

Shepherd Neame Master Brew Bitter H
Friendly, corner pub in the busy High Street. The bar is open plan, with comfortable plush seating and carpeted throughout. The windows are in an unusual gothic style, but the decor is otherwise functional. There are two dartboards in the main bar and a separate area houses two pool tables; pool and darts teams compete in local leagues. The pub has a juke box, TV and gaming machines, catering for the music- and sport-loving locals. ♣♣

HERN HILL

Three Horseshoes
46 Staple Street (1 mile N of Boughton Street)
OS080601
✪ 12-3, 5-11; 12-11 Fri & Sat; 12-3, 5-10.30 Sun
☎ (01227) 750842 e-mail: horseshoes@supanet.com
Shepherd Neame Master Brew Bitter, Spitfire, seasonal beers G
Traditional country pub in a hamlet set among the fruit orchards at the centre of the Garden of England. The pub has existed since 1690 and its beers are served direct from the cask – very rare for a Shep's outlet. A friendly village local, with hops around the bar, its home-cooked meals are not served Sun, and sandwiches only are available Mon lunchtime. Local Crippledick cider is sold to take away (but not to drink in). Dogs are welcome, but mobile phones are not. ⋈Q❀◖▲♣P

HIGHAM

Stonehorse Inn
Dillywood Lane (off B2000)
✪ 11-3, 6-11; 11-11 Fri & Sat; 12-3, 7-10.30 Sun
☎ (01634) 722046
Courage Best Bitter; Shepherd Neame Master Brew Bitter; guest beers H
Classic country pub, surrounded by fields but very close to the edge of the Medway Towns. The unspoilt wood-panelled public bar boasts a log range, bar billiards and extensive brassware on the ceiling. Weekly quiz nights are held (Sun) in the quiet saloon bar. There is a large garden to the rear. Food is served lunchtime Mon–Fri and Wed–Sat eves (7–9). It is a regular outlet for local Flagship beers. ⋈Q❀◖⊟♣P

IDEN GREEN (BENENDEN)

Woodcock
Woodcock Lane (midway between Sandhurst and Benenden) OS807313
✪ 11-11; 12-10.30 Sun
☎ (01580) 240009
Greene King IPA, Ruddles County; Harveys BB; Rother Valley Level Best H
Deservedly popular pub at the heart of the Kent countryside, but difficult to find. The compact low-ceilinged bar, with old timbers and bare brickwork, is dominated by an inglenook, with comfortable sofas. A good-sized garden is popular with ramblers and families alike; food and refreshments can be ordered through the back window to the bar. A full menu caters for all tastes, with up to 10 special dishes on offer each week. All food is home-prepared, with ethnic, vegetarian and children's options; well-behaved children are welcome. ⋈Q❀◖♣P

IGHTHAM COMMON

Old House ☆
Redwell Lane (1/2 mile SW of Ightham Village, between A25 and A227) OS590559
✪ 12-3 (not Mon-Fri), 7 (9 Tue)-11; 12-3, 7-10.30 Sun
☎ (01732) 882383
Daleside Shrimpers; Ⓖ **Flowers IPA; Otter Bitter;** Ⓗ **guest beers** Ⓖ

The building appears from the outside to be a small row of red brick and tile cottages – the pub sign disappeared years ago. Open the only obvious external door into a lobby; the main public bar, where the loyal regulars drink, boasts a large open fireplace and exposed beams (part of the building is 16th century); beers on gravity are brought from the back of the bar. The parlour houses an old cash register and older furnishings. ♨Q⊕ΔP

KEMSING

Rising Sun
Cotmans Ash Lane, Woodlands OS563599
✪ 11-3, 6-11; 12-3, 7-10.30 Sun
☎ (01959) 522683
Beer range varies Ⓗ

Isolated hilltop pub in scenic countryside near the North Downs Way and local footpaths. The main bar area is a converted hunting lodge with a large open fireplace, guarded by an African Grey parrot. Unusual agricultural implements are displayed. Five handpumps provide a continually changing range of guest beers from independent micro-breweries from all over Britain, including local Flagship and Pilgrim beers. Real cider is available in summer when the pub attracts families and ramblers to the garden. Top quality home-cooked food comes in generous portions.
♨Q⛟⊛◑Δ♣♠P⊟

LADDINGFORD

Chequers
✪ 12-3, 5-11; 12-11 Sat; 12-10.30 Sun
☎ (01622) 871266
Adnams Bitter; Badger K&B Sussex; Fuller's London Pride; guest beer Ⓗ

15th-century weatherboarded former farmhouse, fronted by award-winning floral displays. The right-hand area has its own bar but is mainly for eating (excellent food; snacks only Mon lunch). The central bar area displays the many awards made to the licensee and his staff; a raised area features photos of numerous community events, and leads out to a spacious patio. The large garden has a children's play area and an enclosure with goats. A beer festival, with steam vehicles, is held at the end of April.
♨⊛⚓♣P●

LUDDESDOWN

Cock Inn
Henley Street OS664672
✪ 12-11; 12-10.30 Sun
☎ (01474) 814208 e-mail: cockinn@amserve.net
Adnams Bitter; Goacher's Mild; guest beers Ⓗ

Excellent free house offering a minimum of six real beers plus three ciders and an occasional perry. Its splendid rural location makes it popular with hikers from the Weald Way and it can be reached by public footpath from Sole Street Station. A variety of dartboards includes Kent, Quad and London Fives; shove-ha'penny is also played. A free quiz (Tue eve) is hosted by the devious quizmaster-landlord. The saloon bar features WWII memorabilia, while classic car buffs will find the public bar to their liking. ♨Q⊛◑⊕Δ♣P●

MAIDSTONE

Pilot
24 Upper Stone Street (A229)
✪ 11-3, 6 (7 Sat)-11; 12-3, 7-10.30 Sun
☎ (01622) 691162
Harveys XX Mild, BB, Armada, seasonal beers Ⓗ

Make the effort to visit Harveys' only tied house in the town, this deservedly popular no-frills local is a *Guide* regular. The Grade II listed building stands on a busy road out of town. Of the three distinct bar areas one is quiet, with a log fire. Live music is staged Sun lunchtime (when no food is served). Note the jug collection and novel headgear pinned to the beams. A secondhand bookshelf raises money for local causes. Local CAMRA *Pub of the Year* 1998 and 2001; home-made pizzas are a speciality.
♨Q⊛◑⇌ (East) ♣●

Rifle Volunteers
28 Wyatt Street
✪ 11-3, 6 (7 Sat)-11; 12-3, 7-10.30 Sun

IGHTHAM
Chequers
The Street
11-3, 6-11; 12-3, 7-10.30 Sun
Greene King IPA, Abbot, seasonal beers; guest beer Ⓗ
Traditional one-bar village local with an open fireplace. Restaurant meals are available lunchtime and eve.

LYNSTED
Black Lion
The Street
11-3, 6-11;
12-3.30, 7-10.30 Sun
Goacher's Mild, Light; guest beers Ⓗ
400-year-old village pub committed to Kentish beer, including mild, and local Pawley Farm cider. Home-cooked food lunchtime and eve.

MARGATE
Barnacles
1 King Street
11-11;
12-10.30 Sun
Draught Bass; M&B Brew XI Ⓗ
Cosy hostelry near the station, overlooking the harbour, decked out in a nautical theme. A rare outlet for Brew XI. Pub games.

Victoria
104 Ramsgate Road
11-11;
12-10.30 Sun
Beer range varies Ⓗ
Friendly local, built by Thompson Brewery of Walmer in 1885. Three bar areas, include a public and saloon.

NEWNHAM
Tapster
Parsonage Farm, Seed Road
12-11; 12-10.30 Sun
Normally six beers from regional and micro-breweries. The food is described as 'reworking English classics'. Home of Syndale Valley wines.

NEW ROMNEY
Prince of Wales
Fairfield Road
12-3, 6 (5 Thu)-11; 12-11 Fri & Sat;
12-10.30 Sun
Draught Bass; Ind Coope Burton Ale; Shepherd Neame Master Brew Bitter; guest beer (occasional) Ⓗ
Two-bar back-street local with low ceilings, hosting occasional quiz nights and social events. Short walk from the RHDR light railway.

☎ (01622) 758891
Goacher's Mild, Light, Crown Imperial Stout Ⓗ
Back-street pub, unspoilt by progress where you will find good beer at low prices and no alcopops. Excellent value food; takeaways and eve meals can be arranged. No electronic machines, only traditional games of crib and shove-ha'penny are played here; miniature soldiers have a novel use – a rare Goacher's pub that is well worth looking for, it has been run by the Marlows for over 20 years.
Q ⊛ ◑ ⇌ (East) ♣

Swan Inn
2 County Road (near East station)
✪ 11-11; 12-10.30 Sun
☎ (01622) 751264
e-mail: swan-inn@btconnect.com
Shepherd Neame Master Brew Bitter, Bishops Finger, seasonal beers Ⓗ
Popular local, a regular in the *Guide* in recent years, whose landlord has won numerous cellar awards. The split-level interior reflects the acquistion of an adjoining property many years ago, with the lower part being a quiet seating area. Pétanque is played in the garden where regular barbecues are held in summer. In addition to a range of steak meals, the pub now also offers a selection of authentic Indian meals.
⊛ ◑ ⇌ (East) ♣ ☐

MARGATE ✣

Orb
243 Ramsgate Road
(A254, just past QEQM Hospital)
✪ 11-11; 12-10.30 Sun
☎ (01843) 220663
Shepherd Neame Master Brew Bitter Ⓗ
Excellent pub, on the edge of town, close to the area's main hospital. It started out as a small farm cottage and stable on the Chappel Hill Estate, but it was in a superb position on the Margate–Ramsgate road to make a stop-off point for horse-drawn traffic. Until the start of the 20th century, it was known as the Crown & Sceptre; today, with its extensions to incorporate a dining area and games room, it is a lively local. A second Shepherd Neame beer changes regularly.
⊛ ◑ ♣ P

MARSH GREEN

Wheatsheaf
On B2028, Edenbridge-Lingfield road
✪ 11-11; 12-10.30 Sun
☎ (01732) 864091
e-mail: wheatsheafinn@netscapeonline.co.uk
Harveys BB; guest beers Ⓗ
Friendly, traditional tile-hung country pub, the focal point for the whole village community. At least six or seven real ales are always on tap and change regularly. An annual beer festival is held in July to coincide with the village fête, offering over 30 ales on gravity to complement the hog roast. The pub has two rooms, including a conservatory to the rear, where an extensive range of good home-cooked food is served. There is a large garden. Biddenden cider is stocked. ⚞ Q ⚘ ⊛ ◑ ⊟ ♣ P

MARSHSIDE

Gate Inn
Boyden Gate (take Chislet turning off A28 in Upstreet)
✪ 11-2.30 (3 Sat), 6-11; 12-4, 7-10.30 Sun
☎ (01227) 860498
Shepherd Neame Master Brew Bitter, Spitfire, seasonal beers Ⓖ
In the *Guide* for 26 years, this gem is set in idyllic surroundings near farmland and salt marshes. This unspoilt pub has two connected rooms, tiled floors, hops hung from the ceiling and old photographs of village people. An attractive garden features a duckpond and stream, apple trees and benches. Various indoor and outdoor games are played. The name refers to the old gateway to the Archbishop of Canterbury's manor house, which once stood in a nearby hamlet. An excellent, reasonably priced basic menu uses local produce.
⚞ Q ⚘ ⊛ ◑ A ♣ P ⚲

MINSTER (THANET)

New Inn
2 Tothill Street
✪ 11.30-3, 5-11; 11.30-11 Fri & Sat; 12-10.30 Sun
☎ (01843) 821294
Greene King IPA, Abbot; guest beers Ⓗ
Delightful village local oozing warmth and atmosphere; note the stained glass Cobbs windows. Built in 1837, it was a

---

PEMBURY
Black Horse
12 High Street
11-11;
12-3, 7-10.30 Sun
Badger K&B Sussex; Greene King Old Speckled Hen; Young's Special Ⓗ
Attractive, tile-hung pub, with old pews and a log fire. A real community local. No meals Sun eve.

PRESTON
Half Moon & Seven Stars
The Street
11-11;
12-10.30 Sun
Shepherd Neame Master Brew Bitter, seasonal beers; guest beers Ⓗ
Village local, circa 1627, providing lunch and eve meals (book Sun lunch) in a dining area. Garden.

ROMNEY STREET
Fox & Hounds
Romney Street, Otford Hills OS550614
12-3 (not Mon), 6 (7 Fri & Sat winter)-11;
12-10.30 Sun
Fuller's London Pride; Wells Bombardier; guest beers Ⓗ
Isolated hilltop pub near Romney Street caravan park, attracting a good local trade and ramblers. Large garden. Good food.

SANDWICH
George & Dragon
24 Fisher Street
11-3, 6-11; 12-3, 7-10.30 Sun
Harveys BB; Hook Norton Old Hooky; Shepherd Neame Spitfire, Bishops Finger Ⓗ
Smartly renovated old inn, near the station. Emphasis on food, but drinkers have their place near the bar. Patio.

SITTINGBOURNE
Fountain
Station Street
11-3, 5.30-11; 11-11 Fri & Sat;
12-10.30 Sun
Shepherd Neame Master Brew Bitter Ⓗ
Outside the main station, also near Sittingbourne and Kemsley Light Railway. Weekday lunches. Wide-screen TV for sport.

STODMARSH
Red Lion
Stodmarsh Road
11-11;
11-10.30 Sun
Greene King IPA, Abbot; guest beers (occasional) Ⓖ
Lively old inn in isolated village with interesting church. Interior is small with intimate sections. Excellent food; accommodation.

replacement for the hostelry in William Buddell's Pleasure Gardens complex. When William's son, Edward, extended the gardens, a new inn was required. Today the pub's garden is all that remains of the ample pleasure gardens, and houses an aviary and children's climbing frame. A recent extension has provided a dining area and a venue for live music. No food Mon or Sun eve. 🏚️⊛◑≠♣🐾P

NORTHFLEET

Rose
Rose Street (next to station)
❂ 11-11; 12-3, 7-10.30 Sun
☎ (01474) 365791
Shepherd Neame Master Brew Bitter Ⅲ
Small, friendly, Victorian pub, serving the small modern estate that sits alongside it. Although now one bar, its L-shaped layout still gives the impression of two, and thus much original character is retained. One local that you cannot help but notice is the colourful caged parrot, screeching an occasional obligatory 'ello'. There is a small but pleasant garden for summer drinking and, for the footballing fraternity, Gravesend and Northfleet football ground is within walking distance. ⊛&≠♣

OLD ROMNEY

Rose & Crown
Swamp Road (off A259)
❂ 11.30-11; 12-10.30 Sun
☎ (01797) 367500
Greene King IPA; Fuller's London Pride; guest beers Ⅲ
Attractive, family-run village inn, affording a good view across the marsh. Its large garden is safe for families. Excellent guest beers often include a mild, quite a rarity in these parts. The cider varies. The food is recommended, making this overall a pub that is well worth going out of the way to visit. 🏚️⊛🛏️◑⊟Å♣🐾P✂

OLD WIVES LEES

Star Inn
Selling Road
❂ 5 (12 Sat)-11; 12-10.30 Sun
☎ (01227) 730213
Shepherd Neame Master Brew Bitter; guest beers Ⅲ
Small country free house situated on the Pilgrim's Way long distance footpath. Although extensive works have been carried out, it retains its olde-worlde charm and still has a separate public bar (with pool table) and saloon bar. Quiz nights are held alternate Mon eves, and visitors are always welcome to join in. Dominoes and shove-ha'penny are also played here. ⊛⊟♣P

OTHAM

White Horse
White Horse Lane (3 miles SE of Maidstone)
OS795528
❂ 12-3, 5.30-11; 12-11 Sat; 12-4, 7-10.30 Sun
☎ (01622) 861304
Courage Best Bitter; Goacher's Light, Dark; guest beers Ⅲ
Known locally as the 'wonderful' White Horse, this pub sports a large bar with a new dining area one end, a dartboard at the other, and plenty of drinking space in

between. Since taking over, the landlord has increased the range of beers which now includes up to four guest ales, mostly from Kent breweries, and sometimes a house beer provided by Flagship Brewery. The pub hosts a spring gathering for morris dancers and increases its beer range and quantity to cope. Arriva Bus 13 stops outside. ⊛◑♣P

PAINTER'S FORSTAL

Alma
OS992589
❂ 10.30-3, 6.30-11; 12-3, 7-10.30 Sun
☎ (01795) 533835
Shepherd Neame Master Brew Bitter, Spitfire, seasonal beers Ⅲ
Weatherboarded, village-centre pub; at the heart of hop-growing country, it was nicknamed the Candle House as candles in the windows lit the way for hop-pickers to locate the pub and rid themselves of their hard-earned wages. The small, traditional public bar is popular with locals, while the larger saloon bar is used mainly by diners. The food is all home made including vegetarian options (not Sun or Mon eves). Pawley Farm cider is made 200 yards away. ⊛◑⊟Å♣P

PENSHURST

Leicester Arms
❂ 11-11; 12-3, 7-10.30 Sun
☎ (01892) 870551
e-mail: chris@leicester-arms.freeserve.co.uk
Adnams Bitter; Larkins Best Bitter; Marston's Pedigree; guest beer Ⅲ
This pub is a genuine, old timber-framed inn in a picturesque village setting, opposite the old parish church and near the entrance to Penshurst Place (open to the public). The main bar is at the front with a restaurant at the rear overlooking the river. The patio also has river views. The interior is entirely timber-framed, with a long bar in the main area and a smaller room off with an open fire. The bar boasts plenty of seating and a live parrot. 🏚️Q⊛🛏️◑P

PERRY WOOD

Rose & Crown
1 mile S of Selling OS042552
❂ 11-3, 6.30-11; 12-3, 7-10.30 Sun
☎ (01227) 752214
Adnams Bitter; Goacher's Mild; Harveys BB; guest beers Ⅲ
Beautiful and comfortable pub, noted for its excellent food, standing in 150 acres of natural woodland; it was voted local CAMRA joint *Pub of the Year* 2000. The guest beers come from independent breweries, both local and from further afield. This 16th-century free house has a magnificent award-winning garden, including a Bat and Trap pitch (available for hire) and a children's play area. There is even a hitching rail for horses and, because of its location, it is popular with walkers. No food Sun or Mon eves. 🏚️Q🛏️⊛◑♣P

PETTERIDGE

Hopbine
Petteridge Lane (1 mile SW of Brenchley)
OS668413

✪ 12 (11 Sat)-2.30, 6-11; 12-3, 7-10.30 Sun
☎ (01892) 722561
Badger K&B Mild, Sussex, Old Ale Ⓗ

On a hilly corner, this part-weatherboarded and tile-hung building has a single L-shaped bar with a central open fireplace. Originally a beer-only off-licence, it became a pub after WWII and was later acquired by King & Barnes. A good range of home-cooked meals and snacks is offered, with daily blackboard specials (no meals Wed). Well-behaved children are admitted if dining. In summer, plays are occasionally performed by local thespians in the garden. A regular entry in this *Guide*, it was local CAMRA *Pub of the Year 2000*.
🏚🏡◑♣P

PLUCKLEY

Dering Arms
Station Road (near station)
✪ 11.30-3, 6-11; 12-3, 7-10.30 Sun
☎ (01233) 840371
Goacher's Dark Ⓗ

Ideal village local, in what is reputed to be the most haunted village in England, built as a hunting lodge for the Dering estate in the 17th century. During the Civil War a member of the Dering family escaped through a window of the lodge, pursued by Roundheads. Since then, the window's unusual design was used as a pattern for all the windows on the estate. The stone-flagged bars stock a second ale and a house beer, both supplied by local brewery, Goacher's. The cider is Biddenden's. No food Sun eve or Mon.
🏚Q🛏🏡◑≈♣♠P

RAINHAM

Mackland Arms
213 Station Road
✪ 10-11; 12-10.30 Sun
☎ (01634) 232178
Shepherd Neame Master Brew Bitter, Best Bitter, Spitfire, seasonal beers Ⓗ

This small terraced pub is among a handful of real locals in the town, where a mixed clientele, from builders to bankers, ensures a varied conversation. The nickname for this house is the Office; the beers kept cover the full Shep's range. The current landlord has been here for some 15 years. Just 500 yards from the station, it provides a welcome relief for commuters from the overcrowded London trains. ≈♣

RAMSGATE

Artillery Arms
36 West Cliff Road
✪ 12-11; 12-10.30 Sun
☎ (01843) 853282
Beer range varies Ⓗ

Superb, unpretentious, little pub with attractive leaded bow windows depicting soldiers and guns from the Napoleonic Wars. Allegedly built in 1812, it was used as an officers' billet and then a brothel. A beer house for several years, it became fully licensed in 1869. It was refurbished and the interior rebuilt in 1992, after a short closure. Since then, although there have been several landlords, they have all ensured the emphasis is on real ale, with an ever-

changing roster of five beers. It sells Biddenden's Bushells cider. ▲≈♣♠

Australian Arms
45 Ashburnham Road (100 yds from High St)
✪ 11-11; 12-10.30 Sun
☎ (01843) 591489
Fuller's London Pride; Gale's HSB; guest beers Ⓗ

Although the flint building is much older, records show that a beer house existed on the site in 1849, although a full licence was not issued until the 1960s. The name is unique, and may have come from the fact that convict ships berthed in Ramsgate's Royal Harbour *en route* to the Antipodes. Alterations over the years have seen the Aussie develop into a more spacious single-bar establishment with a family conservatory and a quiet, walled garden. Children's certificate held. 🛏❀▲≈♣

Churchill Tavern
18-20 The Paragon
✪ 11.30-11; 12-10.30 Sun
☎ (01843) 587862
Courage Best Bitter, Directors; Fuller's London Pride; Greene King Old Speckled Hen; Ringwood Old Thumper; guest beers Ⓖ

This large pub, with views across the Channel, evolved out of the bars and lounges of the Paragon Hotel when it lost its hotel function. It was rebuilt in the late 1980s to resemble a country pub, using old beams and church pews, and renamed. It is popular with locals, visitors and students from nearby language schools. Although there are handpumps, all the real ale is served direct from the casks. Events and live music are regularly staged, including an annual beer festival. Good value food is served in the bar and restaurant. 🏚◑▲≈♣

Montefiore Arms
1 Trinity Place (100 yds from A255/B2054 jct)
✪ 12-2.30, 5-11; closed Wed; 12-3, 7-10.30 Sun
☎ (01843) 593265
Tolly Cobbold Original; guest beer Ⓗ

This busy, friendly back-street local, serving the Hereson Road district of town, started life as two cottages. Its name is unique, honouring the legendary Jewish centenarian and philanthropist, Sir Moses Montefiore, a campaigner for Jewish rights in the Middle East, who is principally remembered locally as a benefactor to the town's poor. He lived in Ramsgate for much of his life and when he died in 1884 he was buried in a mausoleum near the pub. Regular theme nights are held throughout the year. Q🛏≈(Dumpton Pk)♣

St Lawrence Tavern
High Street, St Lawrence
✪ 11-11; 12-10.30 Sun
☎ (01843) 592337
Beer range varies Ⓗ

Formerly the White Horse, this lively pub and restaurant is now part of the successful Thorley Tavern's chain. The original Cobb's brewery pub was built in the 18th century, some 300 yards away. Demolished in 1851, it reappeared a little later on the present car park site and finally settled on its current site in 1969. A reference in 1817 reports the death of an insane landlord who 'precipitated himself down a 160-foot well'.
🛏❀◑▲≈P

Southwood Tavern

119 Southwood Road
❂ 11-11; 12-10.30 Sun
☎ (01843) 595272
Shepherd Neame Spitfire; guest beers Ⓗ
The nearest pub to Ramsgate FC's Southwood ground. This 19th-century back-street local has previously been tied to both Tomson & Wotton and Whitbread. Some of the seating is in booths, creating a cosy feel in what is now a busy free house. The premises were probably originally occupied by a bootmaker, J Andrews, and it was his son, the unimaginatively named J Andrews Jnr, who pulled the first pint, some time around 1880. ᐟᏯᐟ❂Ⴑᗐ≋♣P

RIPPLE

Plough Inn

Church Lane
❂ 11-4, 6-11; 11-11 Sat; 12-10.30 Sun
☎ (01304) 360209
Fuller's ESB; Shepherd Neame Master Brew Bitter, Spitfire; Taylor Landlord; guest beers Ⓗ
Popular, single-bar village local enjoying a good food trade – particularly noted for its curries. The heavily-beamed interior is decorated with old farm implements, horse brasses, pump clips and a complete wagon wheel. The bar has a TV and a comprehensive selection of games. Note the fine example of a two-pump beer engine (not used) standing by the entrance. It stocks a wide selection of country wines. A small area is available for children. Senior citizens can have a reduced price meal Thu lunch; no meals Sun eve. ❂ᐯᏯ◑P

ROCHESTER

Golden Lion

147-149 High Street
❂ 10-11; 12-10.30 Sun
☎ (01634) 880521
Courage Directors; Shepherd Neame Spitfire; Theakston Best Bitter; guest beers Ⓗ
Converted from an old TSB building in Nov 1999, this Wetherspoon's pub has quickly become popular with locals for its low prices and *Cask Marque* quality beer. Its proximity to the castle and cathedral means it is popular with tourists, too, and it is usually busy. Pictures relate to local history and inevitably the relationship between Rochester and Charles Dickens. A large no-smoking section at the rear backs on to the newly discovered patio. Wheelchair WC.
Q❂◑Ⴑ≋⊀●

Man of Kent

6-8 John Street (near police station)
❂ 12-11; 12-10.30 Sun
☎ (01634) 818771
Goacher's Light, Gold Star Ale; Larkins Traditional; guest beers Ⓗ
Specialising in beers from Kentish micro-breweries, normally seven handpulls are in operation. When new micro-breweries open in Kent their products quickly appear here. There are also two handpulls for cider (Kentish of course – as is the wine on offer). Draught and bottled German beers are also available. This is a small back-street pub with a single L-shaped room. The rare, original tiled exterior is badged Style &

Winch (a Maidstone brewery, taken over and closed by Courage). ᐟᏯ≋●

ROLVENDEN

Star

30 High Street
❂ 11-11; 12-10.30 Sun
☎ (01580) 241369
Greene King XX Mild, Ruddles Best, County; guest beers Ⓗ
Very old village pub with considerable charm, extending a warm, friendly welcome to families. It serves excellent food and also offers summer barbecues. It stages regular entertainment nights, and is very close to the Kent & East Sussex Steam Railway. Well worth a visit, it is a rare outlet for mild.
ᐟᏯ◑♣

RUSTHALL

White Hart

16 Lower Green Road (2 miles W of Tunbridge Wells, on edge of common)
❂ 12-3, 6-11; 11-11 Sat; 12-3, 7-10.30 Sun
☎ (01892) 523076
Adnams Bitter; Harveys BB; Tetley Bitter Ⓗ
Small but pleasant local, facing the green. Hops decorate the main bar. It has two rooms and one of the bars has a TV used for sporting events. It houses a large collection of old photographs, and unusual artefacts include old tools and an aeroplane propellor. It retains all its original etched glass windows – note the white hart on both external doors. The main fireplace has a notable wooden carved panel above the mantelpiece. ᐟQᏯ♣P

ST MARGARET'S AT CLIFFE

Smugglers

High Street (1 mile SE of A258)
❂ 12-3, 5-11; 12-11 Sat; 12-4, 7-10.30 Sun
☎ (01304) 853404
Greene King IPA; Theakston Best Bitter; guest beers Ⓗ
Visiting St Margarets at Cliffe you might think you had stepped back 50 years – four pubs within 200 yards of each other. The smallest, the Smugglers, is a terraced property where a single long bar boasts an unusual semi-circular servery. Low-ceilinged, with much dark wood and subdued lighting, it successfully combines a popular local and a good restaurant where Mexican dishes are a speciality; the bar offers a selection of Tapas. A bus service connects with Dover and Deal until early eve. In winter guest beers only appear at weekends. Ꮿ◑

SANDGATE

Clarendon

Brewers Hill (near seafront)
❂ 11-3, 6.30-11; 12-5 Sun
☎ (01303) 248684
Shepherd Neame Master Brew Bitter, Spitfire, Bishops Finger, seasonal beers Ⓗ
To reach this historic pub you must climb 80 yards from Sandgate Esplanade (A259). Its setting, on a wide path (the original road to Shorncliff Camp), allows views across the Channel to France on a clear day. The tenants strive to make it the sort of pub

they would like to go to. It is well worth finding this two-bar pub and restaurant where all food is home made and features dishes cooked with wine and beer, and authentic curries. 🚶Q🅰🌀◑ ◒🍴

SANDWICH ✥

Crispin
2 High Street (by the Barbican)
🕐 11-11; 12-10.30 Sun
☎ (01304) 617365
Draught Bass; Everards Tiger; guest beer Ⓗ

Ancient, low-beamed house alongside the medieval Barbican which was the toll gate guarding the River Stour crossing, tolls being charged almost until the town was bypassed. Modern ideas have been incorporated into the pub with minimal visual intrusion (apart from the TV). Light meals and snacks are served weekdays (eves 5–7). Beers reflect its former Charrington days; Tiger may alternate with, say, London Pride. There is much to visit within five minutes' walk in this original Cinque Port. Across the river is a very different landscape: a giant pharmaceutical plant. ◑ ◒♣♠

SEAL

Five Bells
25 Church Street (100 yds N of A25)
🕐 11.30-11; 12-10.30 Sun
☎ (01732) 761503
Greene King XX Mild, IPA; Harveys BB; Young's Bitter; guest beer Ⓗ

Small, back-street pub formerly two cottages with one, low-ceilinged bar, decorated with old photographs of village life. The present 18th-century building is believed to stand on the site of a 15th-century original. In the 1950s it was kept by one Ratty Webb who advertised his services as a rat-catcher. The first balloon ascent in England took place in Seal in 1825 and the military had to attend to prevent the locals destroying the contraption. A mild is usually available. Weekday lunches served. 🌀◑♣

SEVENOAKS

Anchor
32 London Road
🕐 11-3 (10.30-4 Fri), 6-11; 10.30-4.30, 7-11 Sat; 12-3, 7-10.30 Sun
☎ (01732) 454898
Greene King IPA, guest beers Ⓗ

Rebuilt in 1923 to its present two-storey brick and tile-hung structure, note the unusual curved wooden doors. The original Anchor Inn is thought to have been built in the 18th century. The welcoming licensee is the longest-serving in Sevenoaks, and chairman of the local darts league and pub football team. The interior of the pub reflects his sense of humour. It hosts regular live jazz (first Wed of the month). Guest beers are usually sourced from smaller breweries. ◑♣

Chequers
71 High Street
🕐 11-11; 12-10.30 Sun
☎ (01732) 454377
Marston's Pedigree; Tetley Bitter; guest beers Ⓗ

Old, timber-framed corner building, where local sessions and manor courts were held;

executions were carried out on the gallows beside the inn. According to legend a lady who, from an upstairs window, saw her son hanged, expired on the spot. It is said that sometimes her ghost haunts the upstairs rooms, and that the window was later bricked up. A one-roomed pub, but part has the character of a public bar. Meals are served 11-5 (Mon), 11-3, 6-9 (Tue-Fri), 11-9 (Sat) and 12–5 Sun. 🌀◑♣🍴

SITTINGBOURNE ✥

Old Oak
68 East Street
🕐 10.00-4.00, 7-11; 12-4.00, 7-10.00 Sun
☎ (01795) 472685
Flowers IPA; guest beer Ⓗ

The Old Oak sits in East Street among the numerous takeaways, quietly going about its business as it has done for over 150 years. Actually the building is much older, once two shops, as can clearly be seen from the outside. The guest beer is constantly changing and has featured some very unusual ales in the past, normally special brews from regional or micro-breweries. The food is extremely reasonably priced. Joint winner of local CAMRA *Pub of the Year* 1998. 🌀◑♣♠🍴

Red Lion
58 High Street
🕐 11-3, 6-11; 11-11 Fri; 12-3, 7-10.30 Sun
☎ (01795) 472706
Fuller's London Pride; guest beers Ⓗ

This former coaching inn stands sentinel on Sittingbourne's High Street, once Watling Street, forming part of the Roman road from Chester to Dover. It is a comfortable pub, noted for both the quality of its ale and its food. There are six beers available, mostly supplied by regional brewers from around the country. In summer the courtyard offers outside drinking away from the hustle and bustle of the town centre. 🚶🌀◑♣♠P🍴

SNARGATE

Red Lion ☆
On B2080, 1 mile from Appledore Station
🕐 12-3, 7-11; 12-3, 7-10.30 Sun
☎ (01797) 344648
Goacher's Light; Rother Valley Level Best; guest beers Ⓖ

Locally known as Doris's, this traditional pub, dating from 1540, has been in the same family since 1911 and is run with love and devotion. A regular entry in this *Guide* and CAMRA Southeast region *Pub of the Year* 1999, it retains many original features. The walls are covered with memorabilia from its local history over the last century. A gem for those seeking an unspoilt pub of character which serves excellent beer by gravity dispense in a warm and friendly atmosphere. 🚶Q🌀♣●P

SPELDHURST

George & Dragon
Speldhurst Hill (3 miles W of Tunbridge Wells)
🕐 11-11; 12-10.30 Sun
☎ (01892) 863125
website: george-and-dragon-speldhurst.co.uk
Harveys Pale Ale, BB; Larkins Traditional; guest beers Ⓗ

The inn comprises two bars and two restaurants: the lounge bar is warmed by an open fire; the Village Bar captures perfectly the ambience of an ancient inn with its dark panelling and splendid fireplace. Adjoining this is the Buttery for informal dining with daily selections on the blackboard. Upstairs, the Oak Room restaurant, with its magnificent beam spanning the entire room, provides a sumptuous setting in which to appreciate fine food and wines. The garden has picnic tables for summer lunches. No meals Sun eve. ♨️🏠🕸️⌖●◑⬛⬛♣P

STANSTED

Black Horse
Tumblefield Road (1 mile N of A20) OS606621
🕿 11-11; 12-10.30 Sun
☎ (01732) 822355
Larkins Best Bitter; guest beers Ⓗ
Tucked-away downland village near the top of Wrotham Hill whose war memorial, of a most distinctive design, has often been stolen. The pub is the focus of community life and a popular port of call for ramblers. Good food is served until 10pm, with Thai cuisine a speciality (Tue–Fri) and traditional roasts on Sun. B&B accommodation is popular, so book early. It supports Kentish ales (two or three guests), ciders and wines. The large garden hosts a beerfest in summer. ♨️Q🏠🕸️🚏◑⬛♣●P

STAPLEHURST

Lord Raglan
Chart Hill Road, Chart Sutton (1 mile N off A229 at Cross at Hand garage) OS786472
🕿 12-3, 6-11; 12-4 (closed eve) Sun
☎ (01622) 843747
Goacher's Light; Harveys BB; guest beers Ⓗ
Popular, unspoilt hop-strewn pub, warmed by an open fire. It offers no distractions, other than good conversation and excellent food. Meals can be taken in the dining area or in the bar which has comfortable seating. The hosts welcome well-behaved children. The guest beer changes regularly, covering a wide variety, including the products of smaller breweries. ♨️Q🕸️◑P

TANKERTON

Marine
Marine Parade
🕿 11-11; 12-10.30 Sun
☎ (01227) 272672
website: www./shepherdneame.co.uk/marine
Shepherd Neame Master Brew Bitter, Spitfire, seasonal beers Ⓗ
The hotel affords extensive views across the Thames estuary to the Isle of Sheppey and the Essex coast. The bar is warm and friendly, with a no-smoking area, excellent wheelchair access to the rear and good facilities inside. Food, ranging from sandwiches to Chinese dishes, is available at all times. The grassy Tankerton Slopes between the hotel and the sea are a good place to allow the kids to let off steam or to have a leisurely stroll. Q🏠🕸️🚏◑⬛⬛P✶

TONBRIDGE

New Drum
54 Lavender Hill (off A26, Pembury Road)

🕿 11-11; 12-10.30 Sun
☎ (01732) 365044 website: www.thenewdrum.co.uk
Courage Best Bitter; Harveys BB; guest beers Ⓗ
Tucked away down a quiet side-street, the New Drum is a family-run local that attracts a loyal band of regulars. It dates back to 1856, having started life as two terraced cottages, knocked into one. Real ale has been a prominent feature during the past 20 years, through several changes of ownership and of name. The current owners have enlarged the pub, which now consists of a comfortably furnished L-shaped drinking area. Two TVs are evidence of the regulars' interest in sport. 🕸️🚏♣

Stag's Head
9 Stafford Road (behind castle)
🕿 11-3, 6-11; 11-11 Fri & Sat; 12-3, 7-10.30 Sun
☎ (01732) 352017
Oakham JHB; Robinson's Best Bitter; Taylor Best Bitter Ⓗ
In a conservation area behind the castle, this Grade II listed building is a real community local. Although not immediately obvious, the pub dates back to 1756 and once had its own brewhouse. The landlord is a horologist and displays a constantly changing collection of clocks. Normally a quiet atmosphere prevails, although there is a large-screen TV for live football matches and rugby internationals. It offers an unusual choice of beers for the area. 🕸️🚏♣P

TUDELEY

George & Dragon
Five Oak Green Road (B2017, Tonbridge-Paddock Wood road)
🕿 12-11; 12-10.30 Sun
☎ (01892) 832521
Greene King IPA, Triumph, Abbot Ⓗ
Attractive, part weatherboarded pub which dates back to the 16th century, with two contrasting bars. The saloon is cosy with low ceilings, plenty of old beams and a wood-burning stove housed in an inglenook. The public bar is more spacious and has a games area. A restaurant, reached via the saloon, serves an extensive range of good, home-cooked food using local ingredients (no meals Sun eve).♨️🕸️◑⬛♣P

TUNBRIDGE WELLS ✻

Crystal Palace
69 Camden Road (crossroads near centre)
🕿 11-3, 5-11; 11-11 Thu-Sat; 12-10.30 Sun
☎ (01892) 548412
Harveys XX Mild, BB, Pale Ale, seasonal beers Ⓗ
Pub situated in the older part of town, close to the attractive main shopping area, serving a good range of Harveys' beers. There are two bars, but the sliding door connecting them is permanently left open. An open fire warms the lounge bar, while darts are played in the public bar. On the outside wall note the large picture of the Crystal Palace, a smaller version is displayed in the lounge bar. ♨️🏠◑⬛♣●

Rose & Crown
47 Grosvenor Road (near Tesco's)
🕿 10.30-2.30, 5-11; 10.30-11 Fri & Sat; 12-3, 7-10 Sun
☎ (01892) 522427

Boddingtons Bitter; Brains Dark; Greene King IPA; Wadworth 6X; guest beer Ⓗ

Victorian town-centre pub, divided by a partition into public and lounge bars in the eve. At lunchtime the partition is pulled back to make one large bar, which is popular with office workers for its good range of food. It draws a mainly local crowd eves, who raise money for local charities with weekly raffles and a monthly quiz. The public bar has darts and bar billiards, and displays a fine array of trophies. The lounge boasts a large collection of unusual clocks. 🏚️Q◖🍴◗🍺🔧♣

TWITTON

Rising Sun
Twitton Lane (1 mile W of Otford along Pilgrims Way)
☼ 4 (12 Fri & Sat)-11; 12-10.30 Sun
☎ (01959) 525489
Greene King IPA, Triumph; guest beers Ⓗ

Small, friendly L-shaped bar, adorned with water jugs and china cups. It stands near a historic battleground named Dane's Hollow. Pub games include darts and Shut the Box; and Bat and Trap is played in summer. Lunches are available at weekends (Sun roast by arrangement) and special steak nights (Fri) are sometimes held. The beer garden at the back of the pub offers magnificent views of the Darent Valley and is popular with ramblers and cyclists. 🏚️🌳♣🔧

UPCHURCH

Brown Jug
76 Horsham Lane OS843674
☼ 11-2.30 (3 Sat), 6-11; 12-3, 7-10.30 Sun
☎ (01634) 235287
Shepherd Neame Master Brew Bitter Ⓗ

Unpretentious local on the edge of Upchurch village, worth seeking out for the exceptional condition of its single ale. Built in 1838 as a farm dwelling on the Horsham Farm estate, it became an alehouse in 1856. The present landlord has been incumbent since 1965. The pub consists of a simply-furnished public bar and a tiny snug. In keeping with the name, an extensive collection of jugs is displayed. Numerous darts trophies are held and the pub still runs two teams. There is a vintage vinyl juke box in the public bar. The very pleasant garden contains an aviary. 🏚️Q🌳🍴🍺♣P

UPPER UPNOR ❉

Tudor Rose
29 High Street
☼ 11-4, 7-11; 12-4, 7-10.30 Sun
☎ (01634) 715305
Young's Bitter, Special; guest beers Ⓗ

Formerly the King's Head, in 1972 the then landlord changed the name to avoid confusion with the pub up the road (see Inn Briefs). This friendly multi-roomed pub, next to Upnor Castle, overlooks the River Medway and former Chatham Dockyard (now a visitor attraction). Local CAMRA *Pub of the Year* 2000, it offers three or four guest ales and hosts an annual beer festival (May Day Bank Hol). The enclosed child-friendly garden boasts a 17th-century wall. No food served Sun or Mon eve. 🏚️🌳❉◖🍴♣

WALMER

Green Berry
23 Canada Road
☼ 10.30-2.30 (not Tue), 6-11; 12-10.30 Sun
☎ (01304) 362411
Greene King IPA, Ruddles County Ⓗ

Pleasant pub, well worth the short detour from the nearby seafront. Formerly known as the Green Beret, the pub used to be the watering-hole for the marine barracks opposite, which closed in 1996 (now being converted into luxury apartments). The pub nonetheless survived as a thriving concern and these days it acts as a focus for the local community, fielding no less than nine pool, darts and quiz teams. The downstairs bar/meeting room acts as a children's room Sun lunchtime. ❉♣P

WELL HILL

Kent Hounds
Pump Lane (off A224 through village) OS497643
☼ 10.30-2.30, 5.30 (6 Sat)-11; 12-3, 7-10.30 Sun
☎ (01959) 534288
Courage Best Bitter, Directors; Harveys BB; Marston's Pedigree Ⓗ

In a delightful rural location, well screened from the access lane (Well Hill) but with a prominent pub sign, this building is 400 years old and has been a village local for 250 years. The original access was from Pump Lane, now an unmade bridleway. Note the collection of over 3,000 key fobs

INN BRIEF

STONE-IN-OXNEY
Crown
12-3, 7-11 (not May eve);
12-5 (closed eve) Sun
Shepherd Neame Master Brew Bitter; guest beer Ⓗ
Friendly village local on the edge of Romney Marsh: beams, open fires and an inglenook; varied food menu.

TOY'S HILL
Fox & Hounds
11.30 (12 winter)-2.30, 6-11; 12-10.30 Sun
Greene King IPA, Abbot Ⓗ
Unmodernised, but attractive pub in isolated location surrounded by NT woodland. Furnished like a homely lounge with real fires and a piano.

TUNBRIDGE WELLS
Beau Nash
Mount Ephraim
12-11; 12-10.30 Sun
Greene King Old Speckled Hen; Harveys BB; Wadworth 6X; Wells Bombardier Ⓗ
Pleasant old pub, with leaded windows, in a secluded courtyard off the common. Excellent range of lunchtime food.

UPPER UPNOR
King's Arms
2 High Street
11-11; 12-10.30 Sun
Courage Best Bitter; Fuller's London Pride; Shepherd Neame Master Brew Bitter; guest beers Ⓗ
Village local, regularly serving Flagship beers. The saloon bar displays guns and armour. Log fire. Eve meals Tue-Sat; lunches daily.

WEST HYTHE
Boltolph's Bridge Inn
Boltolph's Bridge Road
11.30-2.30, 6-11; 11.30-3, 7-11 Sat; 12-4, 7-10.30 Sun
Greene King IPA; guest beers Ⓖ
Warm, friendly olde-worlde, isolated pub serving four guest beers and excellent food all sessions. Well worth a visit.

WORTH
Blue Pigeons
The Street
12-2.30 (not winter Mon-Wed), 5.30-11; 12-11 Sat; 12-10.30 Sun
Draught Bass; Benskins Bitter; guest beers Ⓗ
Traditional village local: main front bar, with dining and pool areas at rear. No food Sun eve. Accommodation; garden at the rear.

hanging from the ceiling and a doodlebug shell in a showcase. The large garden houses an aviary. Popular with walkers; groups should book in advance if the good snacks or lunches are sought. A little gem. 🏕️❀◖&♣P

WEST MALLING

Lobster Pot
47 Swan Street
✪ 12-3; 5 (6 Mon & Sat)-11; 12-4, 7-10.30 Sun
☎ (01732) 843265
Adnams Bitter; guest beers Ⓗ
Once known as the Kent Arms, the name now reflects its popular restaurant's specialisation in seafood (no meals Sun eve). All six handpumps are normally in use, stocking a wide range of lesser-known beers, usually with a Kent and Sussex bias. A regularly updated blackboard lists the beers planned for the coming weeks. A past local CAMRA *Pub of the Year*, it is now a regular in this *Guide*. An indoor skittle alley upstairs is available for hire. ❀◖♣♠

WEST PECKHAM

Swan on the Green
The Green OS644524
✪ 11-3 (4 Sat), 6-11 (9 Mon); 12-4, 7-9 Sun
☎ (01622) 812271
e-mail: goodbeer@swan-on-the-green.co.uk
Swan Whooper Pale, Old Fashioned Mild, Ginger Swan, Trumpeter Best, Stout, Parliament Ale Ⓗ
With parts of the building dating from the 16th century, and licensed since 1685, the Swan has recently established itself as a brew-pub, with its own lager and stout on tap, as well as a selection of cask ales, all brewed on site. Recently refurbished, there is now one main bar, with a restaurant area (no food Mon eve). At the end of a quiet cul-de-sac, the pub overlooks the village green. Bus No. 123 from West Malling Station stops nearby weekdays. 🏕️❀◖P

WHITSTABLE

New Inn
30 Woodlawn Street
✪ 11-11; 12-4, 7-10.30 Sun
☎ (01227) 264746
Shepherd Neame Master Brew Bitter Ⓗ
Small, friendly, back-street local built in the 19th century to serve local oyster dredgers, mariners and shipyard craftsmen. Still very much a community pub, it supports active darts and quiz teams and charity events. Etched glass in the doors denotes the original four rooms into which the long, narrow pub was divided. A sympathetic extension provides a games area. It is worth finding for a serious beer session, and for those wishing to discover the real Whitstable. ☞♣♠

Noah's Ark
83 Canterbury Road
✪ 11-11; 12-10.30 Sun
☎ (01227) 272332
Shepherd Neame Master Brew Bitter, Spitfire, seasonal beers Ⓗ
You will be welcomed by friendly licensees and staff to a community pub with a characterful atmosphere. The pub boasts four darts teams and two quiz teams. It

hosts occasional music and charity events. The licensee learnt the pub trade from her parents, who also ran a Whitstable pub listed in this *Guide*. This pleasant harbour town has recently seen a resurgence in popularity and attracts many weekenders escaping from London. ❀◖☐♣P

Prince Albert
Sea Street
✪ 11.30-11; 12-10.30 Sun
☎ (01227) 273400
e-mail: simon@whitecroft80.freeserve.co.uk
Draught Bass; Greene King IPA; guest beer Ⓗ
Locals were pleased when Albert's reverted to its original name recently. The pub is near the beach, and you can ask for a plastic glass to drink outside, perhaps with fish and chips from the traditional chip shop in Harbour Street. The guest beer changes weekly. Historical features include the Tomson & Wotton Brewery windows and the flood mark from 1953. It serves very good value home-cooked food. ❀◖♣♠

Ship Centurion
111 High Street
✪ 11-11; 12-10.30 Sun
☎ (01227) 264740
Adnams Bitter; Elgood's Black Dog Mild; guest beers Ⓗ
This town-centre pub can get very busy at weekends. The main bar displays fascinating photographs of old Whitstable, and the conservatory has Sky TV. The only pub in the area to always serve mild, the guest beers vary, but one is usually from Kent's Swale Brewery. Some bar meals feature authentic German produce. A free seafood selection appears on the bar Sun, followed by live music in the afternoon (live music also Thu eve). ☞◖♣♠●

WITTERSHAM

Swan Inn
1 Swan Street
✪ 11-11; 12-10.30 Sun
☎ (01797) 270913
Goacher's Mild, Light; Ⓗ **guest beers** Ⓖ
Comfortable local at the village centre, originally a drovers' pub mentioned first in 1684. The guest beers, often featuring Kent micros, are served in the back bar. Unusually for today, the pub has been restored from open plan into two bars. It hosts a beer festival in August. Other events feature live music and annual conker championships. Wittersham is on the No. 12 bus route. Eve meals served Wed–Sun. 🏕️❀◖☐♣P

WROTHAM

Rose & Crown
High Street (off A227/A20 jct)
✪ 12-3, 5.30 (6 Sat)-11; 12-4, 7-10.30 Sun
☎ (01732) 882409
Shepherd Neame Master Brew Bitter, Bishops Finger, seasonal beers Ⓗ
Ancient village pub, in the centre of picturesque Wrotham below the North Downs. The Rose & Crown comprises two buildings, the older part is the main pub which has been sympathetically altered to create a pleasant dining area (eve meals are served Tue–Sat). 🏕️❀◖♣P

CAMRA's National Inventory
of Pubs Interiors of Outstanding Historic Interest

WALES

Gwent

Grosmont: Cupid's Hill Inn. Single basic room.

Mid Wales

Hay-on-Wye: Three Tuns, Broad Street. Basic, single room with simple Victorian furnishings.

Llanfihangel-yng-Ngwynfa: Goat. Rural beerhouse with two basic bars.

Rhayader: Royal Oak, East Street. Former 1880s hotel: original bar fittings: pewter bar top.

Welshpool: Grapes, Salop Road. Four-room terrace pub built in 1835.

West Wales

Llandovery: Red Lion, Market Square. No-frills small urban pub.

Pontfaen: Dyffryn Arms (off B4313). Simple village pub refitted in the 1920s.

SCOTLAND

The Borders

Ancrum: Cross Keys. 1906 refronting: excellent small front bar and corridor.

Fife

Kirkcaldy: Feuars Arms, Commercial Street, Pathead. Fine tiled interior of 1904: impressive gents.

Grampian

Aberdeen: Grill, 213 Union Street. 1926 interior: good ceiling.

The Lothians

Edinburgh: Abbotsford, 3-5 Rose Street. 1902 with massive island bar and decorated ceiling.

Edinburgh: Bennets Bar, 8 Leven Street, Tollcross. 1891 with ornate interior featuring a spirit cask gantry.

Edinburgh: Cafe Royal, West Register Street. Finest Victorian interior in Scotland (1898-1901), also Bistro Bar upstairs has ornate features

Edinburgh: Kenilworth, 152-4 Rose Street. Tiled walls and impressive central gantry.

Edinburgh: Leslie's Bar, 45 Ratcliffe Terrace. 1896. Good woodwork: ticket booth-style openings in servery.

Edinburgh: Oxford Bar, 8 Young Street. Simple two-room pub.

Strathclyde

Glasgow: Horseshoe Bar, Drury Street. 1885-7 interior with impressive mirrors and, at 104 feet, what is claimed as the longest continuous bar counter in the UK.

Glasgow: Old Toll Bar, 1/3 Paisley Road West. 1892-3: gantry with whisky barrels: four large advertising mirrors

Glasgow: Steps Bar, 62 Glassford Street. 'Moderne' interior of 1938: stained glass showing the newly-built Queen Mary.

Paisley: Bull, 7 New Street. 1901. Wonderful interior with three snugs at rear, Art Nouveau glass, gantry with spirit and 24 spirit cocks.

Renton: Central Bar. c.1893 basic bar, snugs,

semi-circular bar and gantry with spirit barrels.

Lochgilphead: Commercial ('The Comm'). Untouched 1940s interior with three panelled rooms.

Shettleston: Portland Arms, 1169 Shettleston Road. Intact 1930s pub with four small snugs.

Uddingston: Rowan Tree, 60 Old Mill Road. Single-storey three-room pub.

Tayside

Dundee: Clep, 92-8 Clepington Road. 1941 with marvellously intact furnishings of the time: ladies' snug.

Dundee: Speedwell, 165-7 Perth Road. 1903: bar split by a screen: two sitting rooms on left.

NORTHERN IRELAND

County Antrim

Ahoghill: Gillistown House. Small single bar: bottled beer only.

Ballycastle: House of McDonnell. Former spirit grocers, hence the partition: two other small rooms: splendid mirrors.

Ballyeaston: Carmichael's. Basic two-room pub: bottled beer only: ancient toilets.

Bushmills: Bush House (Charles H. Callaghan). Small basic bar, later lounge: former kitchen is a third room: bell pushes still work.

County Armagh

Portadown: Mandeville Arms (McConville's), West Street. Superb Victorian pub: 10 snugs, stained glass and Titchborne Claimant cigar-lighter on the counter.

Belfast

City Centre: Crown, 46 Great Victoria Street. Britain's most spectacular Victorian pub: numerous snugs, colourful tiled bar, etched mirrors, splendid bar back and marble counter.

West Belfast: Fort Bar (Gilmartin's), 25 Springfield Road. Late 19th-century: extraordinary rich bar back and six snugs.

County Fermanagh

Enniskillen: Blake's Bar, 6 Church Street. Four snugs and marble counter.

Irvinestown: Central Bar. High bar-back featuring spirit barrels: superb snug and three other rooms.

Tempo: J. McCormick's. Basic pub with 'Moderne' style counter: bottled beer only.

Compiled by Geoff Brandwood, Dave Gamston and Michael Slaughter

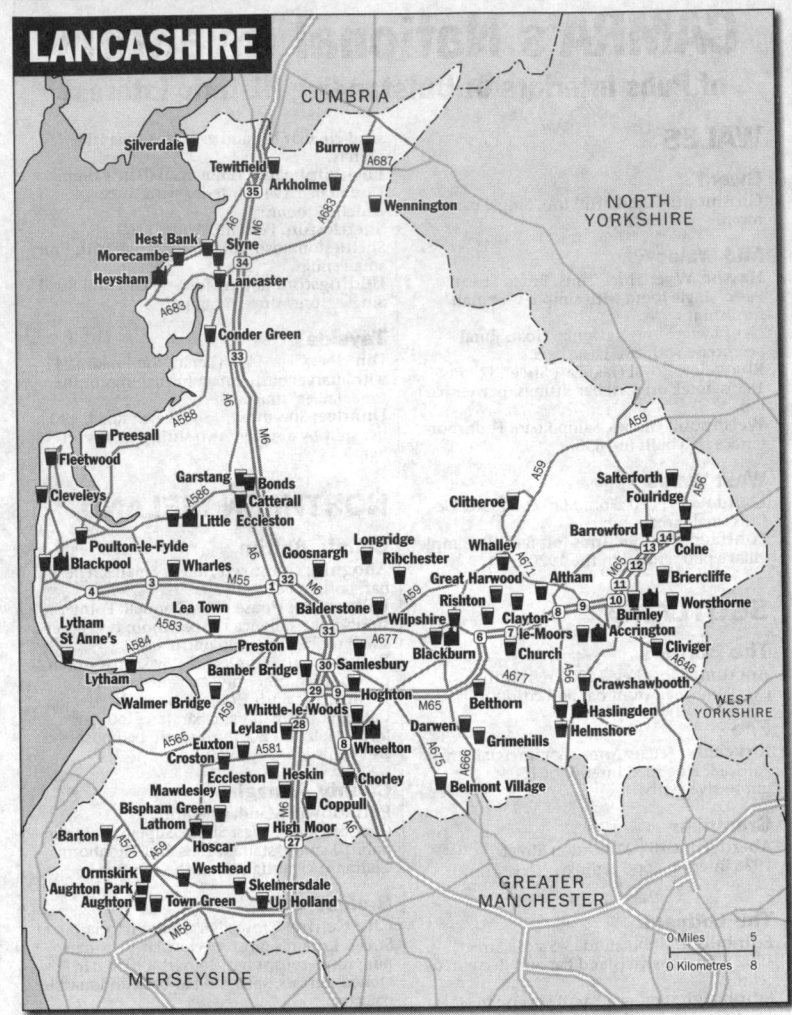

LANCASHIRE

Abbey Hotel
46 Bank Street (just off A680 Manchester Rd)
☼ 12-4, 7-11; 12-4, 7-10.30 Sun
☎ (01254) 235727
John Smith's Bitter; guest beers Ⓗ
Two-roomed local set in an area of
specialised shops just outside the town
centre. Major refurbishment is planned but
it won't affect the character of the pub. This
is definitely not a circuit pub and tends to
attract a mature clientele. There is always a
dominoes game in progress and the locals
are keen on competitions and quizzes. A
regular quiz is held each Tue eve. Up to two
guest beers are available in this small,
friendly pub. ⌖ ≋ ♣

Arden Inn
85 Abbey Street (A680)
☼ 12-11; 12-10.30 Sun
☎ (01254) 385971
website: www.accrington.fsbusiness.co.uk
Boddingtons Bitter; Lees Bitter; guest beers Ⓗ
Welcoming, family-run pub on the edge of

the town centre. It is mostly open plan,
with one good-sized room, useful for darts
matches and meetings. Has a good selection
of old photos of Accrington. Popular for
pub games with teams in many leagues. A
good range of guest beers are sold. Usually
two are available mainly from small
independent breweries. These beers are
changed regularly. Former CAMRA *Pub of
the Year* 2000. The pub has a strong regular
clientele. ≋ ♣

Red Lion Hotel
6 Moorgate, Green Haworth (1½ miles off
Blackburn Road, up Willows Lane)
☼ 12-3, 7-11; 12-11 Fri & Sat; 12-10.30 Sun
☎ (01254) 233194
**Picks Moorgate Mild, Bedlam Bitter, Porter, Lions
Pride** Ⓗ
Long-established pub, for the past four years
it has been the brewery tap of Picks micro-
brewery. The brewery relocated from the
tiny pub cellar to larger premises on a
nearby industrial estate in August 2000. The
pub is at the top of Willows Lane, served by
buses from Accrington centre every two

hours during the day. Lunchtime pub food is available to accompany the beers on offer. At the weekend a fifth Picks beer (Lions Main or Pale Ale) is sold. Well worth a visit. ❀◗♣P⊟

ALTHAM

Walton Arms
Burnley Road (A678)
🕐 11.30-3; 5.30-11; 12-10.30 Sun
☎ (01282) 774444
Jennings Bitter, Cumberland Ale, seasonal beers H
Popular village local next to a picturesque church. A former coaching inn originally called the Black Bull, it was renamed the Walton Arms in 1820 as a compliment to the lord of the manor (R. T. Wroe Walton). The pub was taken over by Jennings some time ago and refurbished. The emphasis is on food and there are a number of alcoves for more private drinks and meals. An extension menu and specially-themed dishes are served to cater for all tastes.
❀◗P●

ARKHOLME

Bay Horse
On B6254
🕐 11-3 (not winter Mon), 6-11; 12-3, 6-10.30 Sun
☎ (015242) 21425
Boddingtons Bitter; guest beers H
Old village inn which retains a homely, rustic feel. A three-roomed pub with a bowling green and an outdoor drinking area with seats to the front. One guest beer is offered in winter and two in summer. Most of the pub's customers now arrive in cars for meals. Q❀◗P

Red Well
Kirkby Lonsdale Road (B6254, between Arkholme and Over Kellet)
🕐 12-11.30; 12-10.30 Sun
☎ (015242) 21240 website: www.redwellinn.co.uk
Coniston Bluebird; Dent Bitter; guest beer H
Although the postal address is Arkholme, this pub is closer to Gressingham and Over Kellet. It has a single, large bar, a function room and a pool room. Serving good food, Mon is steak night and fish night is Fri. 'Happy Hour' is from 4.30–6.30. The beers on offer, Coniston Bluebird and Dent Bitter, alternate. This pub has a garden and patio and attracts a varied clientele from a wide area. ⚲❀◗&♣P

AUGHTON

Derby Arms
Prescot Road (B5197)
🕐 11.30-11; 12-10.30 Sun
☎ (01695) 422237 e-mail: janthelandlady@aol.com
Beer range varies H
Traditional country pub that is full of nooks and crannies, complete with no-smoking room. The roaring real fires, warm welcome for all and the organised clutter of interesting artefacts that adorn all possible wall spaces, combine to create a relaxing atmosphere. Locals request their favourite ales and every effort is made to satisfy the demand; local micro-breweries are supported. Quiz night is Tue and many special events are arranged. CCTV protects the car park. Three ever-changing guest

beers are stocked.
⚲❀◗≢(Town Green)♣P⊬

AUGHTON PARK

Dog & Gun
233 Long Lane (off B5197)
🕐 5-11; 12-3, 6-11 Sat; 12-2, 7-10.30 Sun
☎ (01695) 423303
Burtonwood Bitter, Top Hat H
This is a prime example of a traditional, unspoilt village local. The current licensee has been in charge for the past 31 years and she comments that not much has changed in that time. The major incident was when Burtonwood removed cask mild. The pub is a simple three-roomed layout, the middle room features the bar and a small seating area. Both the lounge and snug have real fires, with darts and dominoes played in the bar. The other attraction is the bowling green. ⚲Q❀母≢P

BALDERSTONE

Myerscough
Whalley Road (A59)
🕐 12-3, 5-11; 12-11 Sat; 12-10.30 Sun
☎ (01254) 812222
Robinson's Hartleys XB, Best Bitter, Frederics, H
Old Tom (winter), G **seasonal beer** H
This country inn, close to Samlesbury Aerodrome, is resplendent in summer with hanging baskets and flowers. Choose the small no-smoking room, the bar, or sit in the bay windows or on the wooden-backed benches in the wood-panelled lounge with its authentic beams. The inn is said to be haunted and some interesting artefacts are on display. There is a large garden to the rear and three double en-suite rooms have recently been added. Quality meals at lunch and eve finish at 9.30 but are served all day on Sun. Look out for the psychopathic Great Dane called Winston.
Q☎❀母◗P⊬

BAMBER BRIDGE

Olde Original Withy Trees
157 Station Road (B6258)
🕐 11-11; 12-10.30 Sun
☎ (01772) 330396
Burtonwood Bitter; guest beer H
Lively, former 17th-century farmhouse, reputedly the oldest building in the village. The pub hosts a large number of teams for pub games, including Welsh Don. A fine children's play area is to the rear. The pub is handy for the Bamber Bridge FC ground and is popular with supporters on match days. The guest beer changes about once a month

INDEPENDENT BREWERIES

Blackpool Blackpool
Brysons Heysham
Hart Little Eccleston
Moorhouses Burnley
Old Wheelton Wheelton
Picks Accrington
Porter Haslingden
Three B's Blackburn
Thwaites Blackburn

and is from Burtonwood. This is the nearest Burtonwood pub to Preston to serve real ale.

❀⇌♣P

BARTON

Blue Bell
1 Southport Road (A5147)
✪ 12-11; 12-10.30 Sun
☎ (01704) 841406
Tetley Bitter; guest beers Ⓗ
Cheerful, welcoming pub featuring three ever-changing guest beers. The menu offers outstanding value for money, meals are very filling. The pub is dominated by a central bar and real log fire. This year the Bell won a CAMRA merit award from the Southport and District branch. The local bike club meet on Mon eve and enjoy the hospitality. Behind the pub is a large beer garden with a children's play area. You can join the old Cheshire lines railway cycle path nearby.
♨⊱❀◑♣P

BELMONT VILLAGE

Black Dog Inn
2 Church Street (A675)
✪ 12-4 (3 Tue & Wed), 7-11; 12-4, 6.30-10.30 Sun
☎ (01204) 811218
Holt Mild, Bitter Ⓗ
Homely, traditional multi-roomed village pub, decorated with antiques and pictures. Originally an 18th-century farmhouse where the local village court was held. Seats for the judge and jury can be seen around one alcove. The bar has hanging glasses and tankards and serves Holt beers to the sound of classical music. The landlord's whistling is an added bonus. No mobile phones allowed. The pub has won many awards for being the cheapest Lancashire premises serving meals and drinks, ranging from a sandwich to a full meal. ♨Q⊱❀⊜◑♣P

BELTHORN

Dog Inn
Belthorn Road (off B6232, M65 jct 5)
✪ 12-3, 5-11; 12-11 Sat; 12-10.30 Sun
☎ (01254) 690794
Boddingtons Bitter; Flowers Original; Marston's Pedigree; guest beer Ⓗ
The Dog is the only pub in the village itself. The only other pub is on the main road which bypasses Belthorn. A single-roomed, rather small but friendly, local with a restaurant that is open eves. This cosy pub has stone-flagged floors, traditional beamed ceiling and a large open fire. There are extensive views from the rear looking towards Darwen Tower on the opposite side of the valley and also Pickup Bank. The guest beer is supplied through Interbrew at present. ♨❀◑P

BISPHAM GREEN

Eagle & Child
Malt Kiln Lane (off B5246)
✪ 12-3, 5.30-11; 12-10.30 Sun
☎ (01257) 462297
Moorhouses Black Cat; Thwaites Bitter; guest beers Ⓗ
Outstanding, 16th-century village local with antique furniture and stone-flagged floors. Renowned for its food, it also hosts a beer festival at Whitsun in a marquee to the rear of the pub. Tables around the bowling green afford superb views of the surrounding countryside. The front of the pub overlooks the village green.
♨Q⊱❀◑♣P⼂

BLACKBURN ❁

Fox & Grapes Hotel
3 Limefield, Preston New Road
(300 yds E of A677/B6447 jct)
✪ 12-3.30, 5.30-11; 12-11 Fri & Sat; 12-4, 7-10.30 Sun
☎ (01254) 53902
Thwaites Mild, Bitter Ⓗ

INN BRIEF

ACCRINGTON

Grey Horse
263 Whalley Road
12-2, 4.30-11; 12-11 Fri & Sat; 12-10.30 Sun
Thwaites Mild, Bitter Ⓗ
Good example of a Thwaites local. Horse-racing and cricket memorabilia festoon the walls. Separate areas encourage quiet conversation.

Victoria Hotel
161 Manchester Road
3 (1 Fri & Sat)-11; 1-10.30 Sun
Thwaites Mild, Bitter Ⓗ
Large, open-plan roadside pub, one spacious U-shaped room with a pool table.

BARROWFORD

White Bear
Gisburn Road
11.30- (11 Sat)-11; 12-10.30 Sun
Draught Bass; Worthington Bitter; guest beer Ⓗ
The building is circa 1607, and the imposing fireplace is original. It is well-refurbished with a separate no-smoking dining room.

BLACKBURN

Adelphi Beer Emporium
133 Railway Road
11-11; 12-10.30 Sun
Boddingtons Bitter; guest beers Ⓗ
Large town-centre pub at bus and rail station. Food at lunchtimes (not Sun). Special drinks offers 12-6 Mon-Fri.

BLACKPOOL

Auctioneer
235-237 Lytham Road
11-11; 12-10.30 Sun
Boddingtons Bitter; Courage Directors; Shepherd Neame Spitfire; Theakston Best Bitter; Thwaites Mild; guest beers Ⓗ
Wetherspoon's pub, opened in Dec. 1999. It has modern surroundings and a good mix of locals and tourists. *Cask Marque* accredited.

BONDS

Church
33 Bonds Lane, Garstang
11-3, 6-11; 11-11 Sat; 12-3, 7-10.30 Sun
Theakston Best Bitter; guest beer Ⓗ
Within easy reach of Garstang centre but retaining a rural atmosphere. A single bar with separate games and dining areas.

BURNLEY

Garden Bar
131-133 St James Street
11-11; 12-10.30 Sun
Lees Bitter Ⓗ
A friendly welcome attracts diverse clientele: shoppers at lunchtime, dancers on Fri and Sat and gay scene eve and Sun.

CHORLEY

Albion
29 Bolton Street
12-11; 12-10.30 Sun
Tetley Dark Mild, Bitter Ⓗ
Unspoilt gem of a local with a traditional tap room and cosy lounge. Near to Chorley's 'big lamp' landmark.

CHURCH

Bridge Inn
135 Henry Street
11-11; 12-10.30 Sun
Camerons Strongarm; Tetley Dark Mild; guest beer Ⓗ
A L-shaped pub with a large raised seating area with big-screen TV. Guest beer from Tapsters range. See the 1920s' urinals.

Welcoming, sympathetically refurbished lounge with comfortable seating, plenty of bar space and large dining room to rear. Outside chance of a Thwaites seasonal beer. Food ranges from traditional British to Chinese provincial and Thai dishes. Baguettes are popular. Requests for special dietary dishes are considered. Meals are served 12–3 and 6–9 (not Sun eve). Unchanged snug behind the bar can be used as a family room. B&B is offered all year round. Music, TV and pool table provided. Two pool teams play each Mon. Three original bar stools have been retained.
⚲✓/⚑🅿

Malt & Hops
11 Barton Street (near college and Waves Leisure Centre)
✪ 11-11 (midnight Wed; 1am Fri & Sat); 12-10.30 Sun
☎ (01254) 699453
Boddingtons Bitter; Flowers Original; Greene King Abbot; Moorhouses Black Cat; guest beer Ⓗ
Good town-centre pub attracting students on weekdays. Open plan with dark-stained wood, a long snakelike bar has stools and large alcoves with wooden-backed pew seating. Barrels are used as tables and there are plenty of old photographs and pictures on display. At night there is a dance area with a juke box providing the music. There are two large-screen TVs for sports fans. The pub offers wholesome meals (including breakfast) and snacks. Outside area with picnic tables is a pleasant suntrap.
✸◑⇌♣

Navigation Inn
Canal Street, Mill Hill (off A6062)
✪ 10.30-11; 12-10.30 Sun
☎ (01254) 53230
Thwaites Mild, Bitter Ⓗ
Unpretentious, welcoming local run by one of the town's longest-serving landladies. Sympathetic refurbishment has retained much of the pub's original character. Thriving darts, dominoes and pool teams

for both sexes. The vault has Sky TV and is a good place for conversation. The pub is next to bridge No. 96A on the Leeds–Liverpool Canal, so handy for the towpath. There are canal moorings on the same side as the pub and a cobbled parking area and a couple of benches outside. Snacks such as barm cakes are usually available. Blackburn Rovers' Ewood Park ground is within walking distance.
🏠⇌(Mill Hill) ♣

Bispham Hotel
Red Bank Road (near promenade)
✪ 11-11, 12-10.30 Sun
☎ (01253) 351752
Samuel Smith OBB Ⓗ
Short walk from the seafront and Bispham tram station, this pub was built in the 1930s and revamped in 1985. The interior still retains its smart period decor with an impressive plasterwork ceiling and stepped floor levels. One area is used for occasional entertainment and a popular Thu quiz. One of the few pubs hereabouts to retain a separate vault where pool and darts are played. This two-bar pub attracts locals and holidaymakers. Food is served until 7.30 daily (no meals Sun). Renowned for serving one of the best, lowest priced pints of cask ale in town.
Q◑🏠&⊖(Bispham Tram Station)

Number 4 & Freemasons
Newton Drive (B5266 at Layton Rd jct)
✪ 12-11;12-10.30 Sun
☎ (01253) 302877
Thwaites Bitter Ⓗ
Smart, comfortable pub in residential area, a short distance from the town centre. Both the lounge and games room have split-level drinking areas, with both snooker and pool in the games room. Sports TV is prominent and the pub has an active sports and social club. Regular happy hours, with the introduction of guest beers and eve meals

---

CLEVELEYS
Victoria
183 Victoria Road West
11-11;
12-10.30 Sun
Samuel Smith OBB Ⓗ
Imposing spacious 1930s local with restaurant and games room. Close to seafront. Usually best-value pint in Cleveleys.

ECCLESTON
Original Farmers Arms
Towngate
11.30-11; 12-10.30 Sun
Boddingtons Bitter; Taylor Landlord; Tetley Bitter; guest beers Ⓗ
Whitewashed village pub noted for its food. En-suite accommodation available.

EUXTON
Travellers Rest
Dawbers Lane
12-3, 6-11; 12-11 Sat; 12-10.30 Sun
Draught Bass; Greenalls Bitter; Marston's Pedigree Ⓗ
Country pub offering traditional games in snug. Lounge, restaurant and garden with children's play area.

FLEETWOOD
Queens
Poulton Road
12-11; 12-10.30 Sun
Thwaites Bitter Ⓗ
Busy corner pub with games room and Sky TV.

FOULRIDGE
Hare & Hounds Hotel
Skipton Old Road
12-3, 7-11;
12-10.30 Sun
Tetley Bitter; guest beer Ⓗ
In 1993 named 'scruffiest pub in the country' by News of the World. Now modernised! Popular for food. B&B accommodation. Moorhouses house beer stocked.

LANCASTER
George & Dragon
24 St George's Quay
11-11;
12-10.30 Sun
Brains SA; Greene King IPA; Tetley Bitter Ⓗ
Small, narrow, terraced pub. Design is unfussy but comfortable. Outside seating and pétanque pitch to rear. Near the Maritime Museum.

LEA TOWN
Smith's Arms (Slip Inn)
Lea Lane
12-2, 4-11; 12-11 Sat;
12-10.30 Sun
Thwaites Bitter, seasonal beers Ⓗ
Splendid country pub next to the BNFL factory, with hunting decor. Good value food at lunchtimes. Note the lack of pump clips.

LYTHAM ST ANNE'S
Hole in One
Forest Drive, South Park
12-3, 5.30-11;
12-11 Fri & Sat;
12-10.30 Sun
Thwaites Bitter Ⓗ
Popular, large, modern local. Full of golfing memorabilia. Home-cooked food served lunchtime and early eve.

MORECAMBE
Imperial
29 Regent Road
11-11;
12-10.30 Sun
Holt Bitter; guest beer Ⓗ
1940s pub with single, large bar which acts as a local. Low prices.

planned. The car park is shared with the adjacent fitness centre. There is a small pavement forecourt for outdoor drinking. ❀◑⊟♣P

Saddle Inn

286 Whitegate Drive (2½ miles from end of M55 on corner of Preston Old Rd)
☺ 11.30-11; 12-11 Sun
☎ (01253) 798900
Draught Bass; Worthington Bitter; guest beers Ⓗ
Blackpool's oldest pub (established 1770) has cosy wood-panelled rooms showing pictures of sporting heroes. The garden has a play area for children. The reasonably priced menu includes daily specials (see the chalkboard). The pub hosts a beer festival every Easter. The small bar gets very busy especially at weekends. One room is used as a no-smoking dining room at lunchtimes. The pub is well-served by buses; South Pier to North Station, No. 26 and the Blackpool to Preston bus route is nearby. ⛰❀◑▶♿P⚟

Shovels

260 Common Edge Road, Marton (B5261, ½ mile from A5230 jct)
☺ 11.30-11; 12-10.30 Sun
☎ (01253) 762702
Beer range varies Ⓗ
Large, award-winning pub with four ever-changing beers usually from small micro-breweries and brew-pubs. It hosts an annual week-long beer festival usually in October. The pub is home to many sports teams and has a thriving darts and dominoes team. Thu is quiz night. There is a separate games area and big-screen TV. Extensive menu available from the steak and ale range, it also offers many specials. Local CAMRA *Pub of the Year* 2001, the landlord writes a regular column for the local branch newsletter. ⛰❀◑▶♿⛺♣P⚟

Stanley Beer Engine

139 Church Street (near Winter Gardens)
☺ 11-11; 12-10.30 Sun
☎ (01253) 626582
Boddingtons Bitter; guest beers Ⓗ
Busy, sometimes noisy, town-centre pub with a range of ages from students to the elderly. Friendly welcome assured from the landlord and bar staff. The pub is a 10-minute walk from the railway station and the promenade. An ever-changing range of guest beers from larger breweries to micros is stocked. Pub games are popular here, try your hand at Connect 4, Giant Jenga, pool or darts. ◑⇌(North) ♣

Wheatsheaf

194-196 Talbot Road (100 yds from train and bus station)
☺ 10.30-11; 12-10.30 Sun
☎ (01253) 625062
Theakston Mild, Best Bitter, Old Peculier; guest beers Ⓗ
Lively, basic, down-to-earth drinking house with a touch of sophistication (a chandelier in the lounge). If the lounge is too smart there is an uncarpeted area with a pool table and chess and darts are played. This jewel in the crown has collections of mannequins, giant fish, flags, wartime posters and other intriguing memorabilia. A full menu is offered daily from 10.30–8. Small outdoor drinking area available. ⛰❀◑⇌(North) ♣

BRIERCLIFFE

Roggerham Gate Inn

Todmorden Road
☺ 11-11 (11-3, 7-11 Mon); 12-10.30 Sun
☎ (01282) 422039
McEwan 80/-; guest beers Ⓗ
Excellent, two-roomed pub on the minor road between Worsthorne and Briercliffe. At least one guest beer is stocked at the weekend. The slightly elevated position offers superb views from the large windows, while the spacious lounge has comfortable seating and plenty of room for standing and talking. The small back room has a TV, but this is the only distraction to conversation, unless you count the food, which is very good, reasonably priced and definitely worth trying. Day tickets for trout fishing are available from the bar. ⛰Q☋❀◑▶⛺♣P

BURNLEY ❄

Coal Clough

41 Coal Clough Lane (200 yds E of M65 jct 10)
☺ 11-11; 12-10.30 Sun
☎ (01282) 423226 website: www.coalcloughpub.co.uk
Worthington Bitter; guest beers Ⓗ
This end-of-terrace community local is always busy and friendly. There is a separate games room with a popular afternoon TV racing channel. A folk club meets on Tue, other events include quiz night on Wed and entertainment on Thu. The Massey's bitter is specially brewed by Bass Museum to an old local brewery recipe. Guest beers are available, often from Bass Museum. The pub holds regular beer festivals (check their website) and has won Bass and CAMRA awards. ⊟⇌(Barracks) ♣

Sparrow Hawk Hotel

Church Street (A682)
☺ 11-3, 7-11 (1am Fri & Sat); 12-10.30 Sun
☎ (01282) 421551
Moorhouses Premier, Pendle Witches Brew; Wells Bombardier; guest beers Ⓗ
Large hotel with excellent accommodation and restaurant facilities. There is a large popular bar, separate games room, a café bar and upstairs restaurant. Usually five ever-changing guest beers are offered from micro-breweries plus a good selection of foreign bottled beers. Quiz night is on Thu while entertainment and late-night opening at weekends attracts people of all ages and creates a lively atmosphere. Regular beer festivals are held at Easter, in October and February. A regular CAMRA award-winner. ⛟◑▶♿⇌(Central) ♣P⊡

BURROW

Whoop Hall

Kirkby Lonsdale, Carnforth (A65, 1 mile from Kirkby Lonsdale)
☺ 11-3, 5.30-11; 12-10.30 Sun
☎ (015242) 71284 website: www.whoophall.co.uk
Black Sheep Best Bitter; Flying Firkin Aviator; guest beers Ⓗ
Really was a hall once but its name is a mystery; 'Whoop' is pronounced 'Hoop'. Greatly extended, it is now a smart hotel with the usual facilities and a growing reputation for food (the same menu is served in the bar and the restaurant). The open-plan bar is in the old hall, note the

original black-and-white façade at first-floor level. A downstairs annexe houses the pool table. Too remote from settlements to have many regular locals, it's inevitably a 'destination' pub. ⚑⚑◐♿▲♣P

CATTERALL

Pickerings
Garstang Road (B6430)
🕐 11-11; 12-10.30 Sun
☎ (01995) 600999
Theakston Best Bitter; guest beers Ⓗ
A 16th-century residence in its own extensive grounds, much extended and altered to give a hotel with all the amenities you would expect including a small bay-windowed bar. There is a surprising selection of beer (four guests), due to an enthusiastic new (2000) owner. Q✿⚑◐P

CHORLEY ✣

Malt & Hops
50-52 Friday Street (close to station exit on platform 2)
🕐 12-11; 12-10.30 Sun
☎ (01257) 260967
Boddingtons Bitter; Coach House Gunpowder Strong Mild; Taylor Landlord; Theakston Cool Cask; guest beers Ⓗ
Resembling a long-standing, street-corner watering-hole, this has in fact only been a pub for about 12 years, having been converted from a corner shop. The Victorian-style decor reflects the ale house atmosphere and emphasises that this is a pub for drinkers. No food is served, except for special theme nights, such as New Year's Eve and St Patrick's Day, when a free buffet is laid on. There is a quiz every Wed eve. Usually four or five guest beers from all over the country are on tap. ⚑

Plough
139 Pall Mall (B5251)
🕐 11-4, 7-11; 12-4, 7-10.30 Sun
☎ (01257) 271958
Banks's Original, Bitter Ⓗ
Situated on Pall Mall on the edge of the town centre, the pub is a recently acquired Banks's house serving its handpumped beers in full measured glasses. It has been refurbished from a large one-roomed pub into a more traditional house, complete with a games room and a comfortable spacious lounge, both connected by a central bar. The Plough is a good illustration that a pub refurbishment need not be a complete disaster for the customer, as it is vastly improved from its previous incarnation. Live entertainment on Fri night. ⊟♣P⊟

Potters Arms
42 Brooke Street (off ring road, A6)
🕐 12 (Wed 7)-11; 12-3.30, 7-11 Sat; 12-5, 7-10.30 Sun
☎ (01257) 267954
Moorhouses Premier; Tetley Bitter; guest beer Ⓗ
Small, family-run free house named after its owners, situated at the bottom of Brooke Street, alongside the railway. The central bar serves the games areas and the two comfortable lounges are popular with the locals. The Potters also contains a fine

collection of photographs from the world of entertainment. There is a display of beer bottles from long-closed breweries. The guest beers come from independent breweries, such as Greene King and Jennings. ⚑♣P

Prince of Wales
9-11 Cowling Brow (off B6228)
🕐 11-11; 12-10.30 Sun
☎ (01257) 413239
Jennings Dark Mild, Bitter, Cumberland Ale, seasonal beers; guest beer Ⓗ
Stone-built terraced pub in the south-eastern part of town near the Leeds–Liverpool Canal. It has a uniquely unspoilt interior which has a traditional tap room, games room, large lounge and a comfortable snug complete with a real fire. The pub is noted for its love of jazz music and has live music for all tastes at weekends. Note the interesting collection of brewing artefacts. Guest ales are from a range of regional brewers. This was the first pub in Chorley to be awarded *Cask Marque* accreditation. ⚑✿⊟⚑♣●

CHURCH ✣

Stag Inn
1 Bank Street (B6231, corner of Henry St/Bank St)
🕐 12-11; 12-10.30 Sun
☎ (01254) 399906
Holt Bitter; Moorhouses Black Cat; guest beer Ⓗ
What a turn around here. It has always been a good pub but real ale hasn't been popular until the arrival of the current licensees. Now it sells very well. The area has several old people's homes and the pub organises many events to involve them. This is the perfect example of a successful community pub. Q⊟⚑ (Church & Oswaldtwistle) ♣P

CLAYTON-LE-MOORS

Albion
243 Whalley Road (A680)
🕐 12 (5 Mon & Tue)-11; 12-10.30 Sun
☎ (01254) 238585
e-mail: stereospaceboy@hotmail.com
Porter Dark Mild, Bitter, Rossendale Ale, Porter, Sunshine, seasonal beers Ⓗ
Large, open-plan pub close to the midpoint of the Leeds–Liverpool Canal. Bud-free and nitro-free zone. Events here include two cider festivals (Easter and Autumn) and a summer beer festival making good use of the canalside bar and patio area. Normally more than 20 gravity-dispensed beers are on tap as well as Dave Porter's excellent beers upstairs at festivals. Six Porter's beers are on sale throughout the year. ✿♣●P

CLITHEROE

New Inn
Parsons Lane (B6243)
🕐 11-11; 12-10.30 Sun
☎ (01200) 423312
Coach House Coachman's Best Bitter; Moorhouses Black Cat; guest beers Ⓗ
Opposite the imposing ruin of Clitheroe Castle, this is a perfect pub. Three rooms, small bar area and dining room, with friendly locals, two roaring fires and great beers. The landlord only serves what the clientele want, not what the big brewers try

to supply and he is rewarded with a very busy pub. At weekends, in addition to the two standard beers, up to nine guest beers are on offer. Every Fri eve is live folk night and this is the only music you will hear, other than the music of conversation.
ⓂQ❀◑Å⇌P

CLIVIGER

Queen
412 Burnley Road (A646)
✪ 1-11; 12-10.30 Sun
☎ (01282) 436712
John Smith's Bitter; Webster's Green Label; guest beer Ⓗ
Small, friendly two-roomed village local where the emphasis is on good beer and conversation. Both rooms are cosy and convivial and are worth a visit for the interesting collection of local historical photos which clutter the walls. Three guest beers are usually available from micro-breweries. The pub is situated amid the spectacular scenery of the Cliviger Gorge Valley (an old glacial overflow channel). It makes an excellent starting (and finishing) point for many worthwhile local walks.
ⓂQ⌑♣

COLNE

Admiral Lord Rodney
Waterside Road, Mill Green (close to Leeds-Liverpool Canal)
✪ 12-2.30 (not Mon), 5 (7 Mon)-11; 12-11 Sat; 12-10.30 Sun
☎ (01282) 866565
Old Bear Bitter; guest beers Ⓗ
Excellent local in the Waterside area of town, saved from closure two years ago by the Old Bear Brewery. Named after a naval hero of the late 18th century, the present pub dates from early last century and still has some of the original ornate tiling. The pub boasts two teams in the local quiz league and hosts a quiz night. Occasionally live bands perform at weekends. Meals served daily except Sun eve and Mon. Thatchers real cider stocked. Ⓜ◑♣♠

CONDER GREEN

Stork
On A588 near Glasson
✪ 11-11; 12-10.30 Sun
☎ (01524) 751234
Boddingtons Bitter; guest beers Ⓗ
Long, wood-panelled building with several small rooms and, down a level, the main bar and restaurant. There is a play area in the garden. The best road to this pub is to walk or cycle along the Lune Estuary Path, leave at the Conder Green picnic site. The house beer is supplied by Interbrew and there are two ever-changing ales, mostly from small breweries. Ⓜ❀◑Å♣P

COPPULL

Red Herring
Mill Lane (off B5251)
✪ 12-11; 12-10.30 Sun
☎ (01257) 470130
Beer range varies Ⓗ
This classic red-brick pub is a cask oasis in a village that is predominantly a keg desert.

The building itself was the former offices of the imposing mill that stands next door. It was converted into a pub some time ago. The bar serves a large single room and there is an upstairs function room for hire. TV sports addicts are catered for and the fishing fraternity will enjoy the mill pond to the front of the pub. The landlord of this CAMRA award-winning pub is known to keep a soda syphon handy for unruly customers. Ⓜ❀◑&Å♣P

CRAWSHAWBOOTH

White Bull
612 Burnley Road (A682)
✪ 5 (12 Sat)-11; 12-10.30 Sun
☎ (01706) 260394
Beartown Bear Ass, Bearskinful, Polar Eclipse, Wheat Bear, Bruins Ruin Ⓗ
This 200-year-old pub is Beartown's second acquisition, and the first in Lancashire. Reputedly haunted by a teetotal female ghost who turns taps off on barrels and kegs and knocks bottles off shelves! Beartown's Spindledicks Ale is named after a local ale taster who enjoyed his job a bit too much and was regularly arrested for being drunk and disorderly. In his day the pub was used as a waiting room for the horse bus between Burnley and Rawtenstall. Occasional guest beers are available and once you've drunk your fill try the Indian restaurant upstairs.
❀⇌ (Rawtenstall/East Lancs rlwy) ♣P

CROSTON

Black Horse
Westhead Road (A581)
✪ 11.30 (11 Sat)-11; 12-10.30 Sun
☎ (01772) 600338
website: www.blackhorsecroston.co.uk
Black Sheep Best Bitter; Moorhouses Premier; Theakston Mild; Worthington Bitter; guest beers Ⓗ
Large, solidly-built pub with separate no-smoking dining room, snugs, bar area and games room with rustic interior. A cobbled area to the front has benches and there is a patio and children's play area to the rear overlooking the popular Crown Green bowling green and boules pitch. Five bowling and two boules teams play in international matches with twinned French town to this prize-winning Lancashire village. All the food is home-cooked with specials for pensioners and children. Regular beer festivals are held in April and October.
Ⓜ❀◑⌑&Å⇌♣P

Crown Hotel
Station Road (B5247)
✪ 11.30-11; 12-10.30 Sun
☎ (01772) 601989
Thwaites Mild, Bitter Ⓗ
Brick-built village pub with a cobbled roadside area. The lounge bar is divided into several comfortably furnished areas. The public bar and games room are separated by a bar screen, and the front room has an attractive bay window. Good value, home-cooked meals are served at lunchtimes. Enjoy the pleasant garden and try the boules pitch, accessible via a small bridge from the large rear car park. The Crown is a member of the local boules league.
❀◑Å⇌♣P

DARWEN

Black Horse
72 Redearth Road (200 yds from Sainsbury's)
☼ 12-11; 12-10.30 Sun
☎ (01254) 873040 website: www.rarebeerfest.ic24.net
Beer range varies Ⓗ
This friendly and welcoming community local has seen four handpumps installed over the past two years in a move towards promoting cask ale and cider. Micros and more interesting ales often feature as guests with a real cider (Thatchers or Westons) served on handpull from the cellar. Blue Orbit is brewed by Moorhouses. With a large enclosed patio and cosy atmosphere this is a fine, traditional pub. The Rare Beers Festival is set to become a town standard during the May bank holiday. Visiting football fans should ring for bookings or meals. ♿≠♣♠P

Crown
24 Redearth Road (100 yds S of town centre)
☼ 12-11; 12-10.30 Sun
☎ (01254) 703192
Camerons Strongarm; Courage Directors; Tetley Dark Mild, Bitter Ⓗ
Prominent, popular Pubmaster pub. This lively bar is the music venue of Darwen; nightly Karaoke and live groups every Wed and Sun perform on stage in the lounge. Recently refurbished, the new bar has brass work and there is a large brass ornamental lion over the entrance. The pub has a games room (with a polished wood floor) where the pool team play in league matches. Outside there is a raised courtyard with tables and chairs. ♿≠♣

Greenfield
Lower Barn Street (A666)
☼ 12-3.30 (not Tue), 5.30-11; 12-11 Fri & Sat; 12-10.30 Sun
☎ (01254) 703945 website: pubs2go2.co.uk
Greene King Abbot; Taylor Landlord; Tetley Bitter; guest beers Ⓗ
Large, open-plan pub next to the Sough Tunnel. Long wooden bar with stained glass top panels and hooks for coats underneath. There is a brick fireplace with brasses, blow lamps, teapots and other ornaments. No juke box or games, but live music every Sun and quiz night every Mon (free meal for the winner). There are regular theme nights. The resident chef serves good value home-cooked food until 8pm daily (no food on Tue). Fine selection of wines available with three regular and four guest cask beers. Q◑

Pub
210 Duckworth Street (100 yds N of town centre)
☼ 11-11; 12-10.30 Sun
☎ (01254) 708404
Moorhouses Black Cat; Thwaites Bitter; guest beers Ⓗ
Succinctly-named free house on the main A666 road. Original tiled entrance with red lions. The central bar is very lively on Fri and Sat eves. It has a large-screen TV and raised seating area with a juke box, two pinball machines, pool and table football. Five handpumps serve two regular beers and three ever-changing guests. Enjoy the beer garden on summer days.
♿≠♣P

FLEETWOOD ❖

North Euston Hotel
The Esplanade (opp. tram terminus)
☼ 11-11; 12 4, 7-10.30 Sun
☎ (01253) 876525
Courage Directors; Theakston Mild, Cool Cask; Webster's Yorkshire Bitter; guest beers Ⓗ
Large hotel lounge bar providing a commanding view of the River Wyre and Morecambe Bay. The family room and no-smoking areas are both close at 7.30pm. Lunchtime food is served and there is a garden for outdoor drinking. Good selection of beers. ♿❀⛺♿&⊖(Tram/Ferry)

Wyre Lounge Bar
Marine Hall, The Esplanade (past pier)
☼ 1 (12 Fri & Sat)-4, 7-11; 12-4, 7-10.30 Sun
☎ (01253) 771141
Courage Directors; Moorhouses Pendle Witches Brew; John Smith's Magnet; guest beers Ⓗ
Quiet lounge bar overlooking the Wyre Estuary. It is part of the Marine Hall entertainment complex. Fleetwood's beer festival is held here. The guest beers usually include at least one beer from Phoenix Brewery. ♿&⊖(Tram/Ferry)

GARSTANG

Royal Oak
Market Place (B6430)
☼ 11-3 (4 Thu), 6-11; 11-11 Fri & Sat; 12-10.30 Sun
☎ (01995) 603318
Robinson's Hatters Mild, Hartleys XB, Best Bitter, seasonal beers Ⓗ
17th-century coaching inn which has been sympathetically renovated. It retains three small rooms (one a games room) alongside the main bar and restaurant. This pub has been run by the same family since 1959. There are tables for drinkers on the cobbled market square – markets now take place elsewhere. ♿Q♿❀⛺◑♣♠P

GOOSNARGH

Grapes
Church Lane (off B5269)
☼ 11.30-3, 5.30 (7 Mon)-11; 11-11 Thu-Sat; 12-10.30 Sun
☎ (01772) 865234 e-mail: harryatgrapes@aol.com
Boddingtons Bitter; Tetley Mild, Bitter; Theakston Best Bitter; guest beers Ⓗ
Charming, low-beamed community pub with a wonderful, large open fire in the centre of the main drinking area, splendid in winter. Specialities on the menu are often made with local produce, such as Lancashire cheese or Goosnargh duck (no food Mon eve). The guest beers often come from micros in the region. A bowling green and function room are available. A selection of pump clips, reflecting past guest beers, hang in the bar area. Close to the village green and near Chingle Hall, which is reputedly the most haunted house in the country. Handy for the nearby Beacon Fell.
♿Q♿❀◑⊕♣P

GREAT HARWOOD

Duke of Wellington
Towngate (off B6535)
☼ 11-11; 12-10.30 Sun
☎ (01254) 885979

Theakston Cool Cask, Old Peculier; guest beer ⊞
Originally part of the Massey Burnley
Brewery portfolio, subsequently subsumed
into the Bass empire, it is now owned by
MGM Leisure. This fine old building, which
has been very successfully renovated, has
much exposed stonework in the
atmospheric lounge. It is comfortable with
booth seating. Live music is performed on a
monthly basis, Thu eve and Sun lunch
(phone for details). Lunches served Sat and
Sun. ◐ё▲♣

Royal Hotel
Station Road (off A680, jct Queen St Park Rd)
✪ 12-1.30 Thu; 12-2 Fri; 12.2.30 Sat; 7-11 Mon-Sat;
12-3, 7-10.30 Sun
☎ (01254) 883541
website: www.s-h-systems.co.uk/hotels/royalhotel
Beer range varies ⊞
A *Guide* entry for 10 years, this pub has won
several CAMRA awards. It sells up to five
constantly changing beers mainly from
small independent breweries plus a good
range of foreign bottled beers. Try the
excellent home-cooked food. The pub has
an open-plan layout with no music or pool
table; it is a haven of tranquility. The
railway came to Great Harwood in 1877,
Daniel Thwaites was granted a licence for
the hotel to be built near the station. The
railway went long ago but the Royal is still
going strong as a true free house.
Q❀◐▲P▽

GRIMEHILLS (DARWEN)

Crown & Thistle
Roman Road (on old road Darwen to Edgworth)
✪ 12-2 (not Mon), 6-11; 12-11 Fri & Sat; 12-10.30
Sun
☎ (01254) 702624
**Boddingtons Bitter; Greene King Old Speckled Hen;
Shepherd Neame Bishops Finger; Taylor Landlord;
guest beer** ⊞
Traditional country roadside pub with
wooden beams decorated with horse
brasses. There is a welcoming homely
atmosphere, a piano, real fire, wooden pew
seating, and interesting whisky jars, Russian
dolls and display cases with breweriana in
the separate dining room. The local paper's
award-winning restaurant serves an
international menu with daily and monthly
specials, vegetarian options and an
excellent wine list. Good value, tasty food
complemented by good beers, the Greene
King Old Speckled Hen rotates with the
other listed cask ales. ▲❀◐P

HASLINGDEN

Griffin Inn
86 Hud Rake (off A680)
✪ 12-11; 12-10.30 Sun
☎ (01706) 214021
**Porter Dark Mild, Bitter, Rossendale Ale, Porter,
Sunshine, seasonal beer** ⊞
Conversation is the name of the game here
– what better way to put the world to rights
than over a pint (or more) of Dave Porter's
excellent ales. Bud-free and nitro-free zone
and also home of Porter's Rossendale
Brewery. The bar area retains some
character while good views can be enjoyed
from the lounge.
▲♣

HELMSHORE

Robin Hood
280 Holcombe Road (B6214)
✪ 4 (1 Sat)-11; 1-10.30 Sun
☎ (01706) 213180
Tetley Bitter; guest beer ⊞
Small, characterful, community pub. The
front windows are etched with the name of
the Glen Top Brewery of Waterfoot.
Displays of cigarette card collections and a
superb log fire are found in the front room.
The landlord is fanatical about ornamental
ducks. Over 300, of every conceivable type,
adorn the pub. Enjoy the terraced beer
garden overlooking the old mill lodges and
spot the ducks here too. The area was
famous for cotton and weaving mills and
these lodges belong to what is now the
Helmshore Textile Museum. Guest beer
supplied by Phoenix. ▲❀♣

HESKIN

Farmers Arms
Wood Lane (B5250)
✪ 12-11; 12-10.30 Sun
☎ (01257) 451276 website: www.farmersarms.co.uk
**Boddingtons Bitter; Castle Eden Ale; Flowers IPA;
Taylor Landlord** ⊞
18th-century coaching inn, originally called
the Pleasant Retreat, only acquiring its
present name in 1902. Family-run pub
which has a local reputation for its food, a
family member is the head chef. Unlike
many country pubs of this sort the Farmers
has retained a public bar for drinkers.
Upstairs there are five en-suite guest rooms,
one of which has a four-poster bed. The
Farmers is about a mile from the Park Hall
conference centre and the Camelot
amusement park and is close to Jct 27/M6.
❀⇌◐⊟♣P

HEST BANK

Hest Bank
2 Hest Bank Lane (off A5105)
✪ 11.30-11; 12-10.30 Sun
☎ (01524) 824339
**Boddingtons Bitter; Robinson's Best Bitter; guest
beers** ⊞
Read about the history of this pub inside
over a pint. It was once the last stop for
travellers beginning the perilous crossing of
the sands. Transportation developments
and suburban sprawl have cut it off from
the sea but left it with a pleasant canalside
garden. The licensed area was greatly
extended for the benefit of car-borne diners
but two older rooms – a locals' bar and a
games room (the latter being on the first
pub's level) – were retained unaltered. It is
popular as a local and as an eating house
and has an attractive no-smoking
conservatory. ▲Q❀ё▲♣P

HIGH MOOR (WRIGHTINGTON)

Rigbye Arms
2 Whittle Lane (off B5246)
✪ 12-3, 5.30-11; 12-11 Sat, 12-10.30 Sun
☎ (01257) 462354
**Greene King Old Speckled Hen; Ind Coope Burton Ale;
Marston's Pedigree; Tetley Dark Mild, Bitter** ⊞
This pub nestles in the heart of rural
Lancashire although it is only three miles

from Jct 27/M6. Always a hostelry, it was built in the 1600s and named after Sir John Rigbye, it still retains the character and distinct flavour of those bygone days. It is a Lancashire Life award-winner for its food. A log-burning stove in the public bar is popular with ramblers. The comfortable bar is warmed by open coal fires and includes a snug area where children are welcome. It has a well-kept bowling green.

🏛Q❀◑🍴P

HOGHTON

Royal Oak

Blackburn Old Road, Riley Green

(A675/A674 jct)

✪ 11.30-3, 5.30-11; 12-10.30 Sun

☎ (01254) 201445

Thwaites Mild, Bitter, seasonal beers Ⓗ

Traditional, stone-built pub on the old road between Preston and Blackburn. Close to the Riley Green Basin on the Leeds–Liverpool Canal, the Royal Oak is rightly popular with diners. Rooms and alcoves generate from the central bar and there is a separate dining room. The pub has low-beamed ceilings and various brasses adorning the walls. This Thwaites tied house is a regular outlet for the brewery's seasonal beers.

🏛Q❀🛏◑P🍴

HOSCAR

Railway Tavern

Hoscar Moss Road (by station) OS468116

✪ 12-3 (not Mon), 5-11; 12-11 Wed-Sat; 12-10.30 Sun

☎ (01704) 892369

Jennings Bitter; Tetley Dark Mild, Bitter; guest beers Ⓗ

Superb, unspoilt rural local, popular with cyclists. There is a real locals' tap room where the world is put to rights. Two roaring coal fires warm your visit and create a cosy atmosphere. The walls display famous railway engine prints and pictures of military aircraft. Children are welcome in one room that opens out on to the patio and pleasant garden, perfect to relax in on summer days. An added bonus is watching the trains pass. However, if it is chilly try one of the 30 malt whiskies and you will soon warm to the occasion.

🏛Q🍃❀◑🛏&🅰🚉(Hoscar Moss)♣P

LANCASTER ❄

Bobbin

36 Cable Street (opp. bus station)

✪ 11-11; 12-10.30 Sun

☎ (01524) 32606

Beer range varies Ⓗ

Substantial, late 19th-century street-corner pub. Its single, large bar was last renovated in 1997 with a varnished floor and conspicuous curtains, but also with a 'Lancashire cotton industry' theme. (Lancaster's steam-age industry was oilcloth and linoleum, but never mind.) A number of strange objects are fastened to the walls. Attracts a mainly, but not entirely, youthful clientele. Big-screen TV is on most eves. The Bobbin hosts live music Thu. The beers are often from Everards.

&♣♣

Boot & Shoe

171 Scotforth Road (A6)

✪ 11-3, 6-11; 11-11 Sat; 12-10.30 Sun

☎ (01524) 63011

Boddingtons Bitter; Flowers Original; Worthington Bitter; guest beer Ⓗ

A village inn until Lancaster grew around it, though it still has a fairly rural aspect. Most of the old rooms have been converted into one large lounge. A chunk of this is set aside for diners while food is available. Meals are served daily and until 6pm on Sun. However, there is still a public bar and two tiny snugs, one has a TV and the other is a no-smoking room. There is a bowling green. Cars can be parked behind Booth's supermarket.

❀◑🛏♣P🍴

John O'Gaunt

53 Market Street (off A6)

✪ 11-3 (5 Sat), 6 (7 Sat)-11; 11-11 Thu & Fri; 12-4, 7-10.30 Sun

☎ (01524) 65356

Boddingtons Bitter; Ind Coope Burton Ale; Jennings Bitter; Tetley Bitter; guest beers Ⓗ

The handsome, original frontage hides a narrow, busy pub. The walls are crammed with a variety of objects: beer mats, jazz posters and photos of musicians (reflecting one of the licensee's enthusiasms) and a growing collection of awards from a number of organisations. At lunchtime customers are mainly from nearby banks and offices, in the eve mainly regulars. Live music in a variety of styles is performed Mon–Thu eves, 'Jazz, Dogs and Sausages' Sun lunchtimes. Guest beers usually include ones from Blackpool, Greene King or Taylor. Small, but perfectly formed, beer 'garden'. ❀◑🚉♣

LATHOM

Briars Hall Hotel

Briars Lane (off A5209 E of Burscough)

✪ 11.30-11; 12-10.30 Sun

☎ (01704) 892368 website: www.briarshallhotel.co.uk

Tetley Dark Mid, Bitter; Thwaites Bitter; guest beers Ⓗ

The Briars Hall Hotel is a handsome, imposing building set in its own landscaped grounds. The hotel was built in the 19th century as a private residence for a wealthy local corn-milling family. Some original features have been retained and the stable block is particularly impressive. The style of the Briars Hall is that of a residential hotel and restaurant. Nevertheless, the areas set aside for beer drinkers are comfortable and well-appointed. One is a spacious, well-decorated bar, the other is a small, relaxing lounge next to the restaurant.

Q❀🛏◑🛏&🅰🚉(Burscough Jct)♣P🍴

Ship Inn

4 Wheat Lane (off A5209, over canal swing bridge)

OS451115

✪ 11.30-3, 5-11; 11.30-11 Fri & Sat; 12-10.30 Sun

☎ (01704) 893117

Moorhouses Black Cat, Pendle Witches Brew; Taylor Landlord; Theakston Best Bitter, Old Peculier; guest beers Ⓗ

Situated in a conservation area at the junction of the Rufford Branch and the Leeds–Liverpool Canal, the pub is at the

heart of the canal community with early boatmans' cottages, locks and a dry dock nearby. Locally known as the 'Blood Tub', the name dates from the time canal boats delivered the ingredients for the famous Lancashire black pudding. This excellent free house offers traditional home-cooked food in pleasant surroundings. The beer range includes five guests and a house beer. Local CAMRA *Pub of the Year* 2000.
Q ⌚ ◑ ➤ (Burscough Jct) P

LEYLAND

Dunkirk Hall
Dunkirk Lane (B5253)
⊙ 12-3, 5-11; 12-11 Fri & Sat; 12-10.30 Sun
☎ (01772) 422162 e-mail: dunkirkhall@aol.com
Courage Directors; John Smith's Bitter; Webster's Green Label; guest beer Ⓗ
The date carved in stone of the pub's entrance is 1628. You might think drinking had been going on here for over 370 years. However, this former 17th-century manor house only became a pub 15 years ago. For most of the 20th century the offices of a local engineering firm were based here. It was fortuitous, therefore, that just as the area was being developed, the building became available, thus saving the locals from having some soulless estate pub inflicted upon them. It is a lively pub with a pleasant beer garden and quiz every Wed.
⋈ ⌚ ◑ P

Eagle & Child
Church Road (B5248)
⊙ 11.45-11; 12-10.30 Sun
☎ (01772) 433531
Burtonwood Bitter, seasonal beers; guest beers Ⓗ
Ancient inn nestling snugly behind the 1,000-year-old parish church and the old Grammar School, now serving as South Ribble's museum. Inside, the low-ceilinged interior has been opened up from the original separate rooms but the result has not been too traumatic. The pub caters for all ages but there is a local custom that on entering the pub those under, say, 30 years of age, turn to the right-hand side of the bar to drink, while those over 30 turn to the left. It has its own bowling green (Crown Green, of course!) and team. ⌚ ◑ ♣ P

LITTLE ECCLESTON

Cartford Hotel
Cartford Lane (by the toll bridge, 1/2 mile from A586)
⊙ 12 (11.30 Sat)-3, 7 (6.30 Fri)-11; 12-10.30 Sun
☎ (01995) 670166
Fuller's London Pride; Wadworth 6X; guest beers Ⓗ
The Cartford Hotel is a converted 17th-century farmhouse on the banks of the River Wyre. A genuine free house, with a range of ever-changing guests and usually two beers from the Hart Brewery, it is popular with walkers, cyclists and caravanners in summer. Four times winner of West Pennine's *Pub of the Year*. A comprehensive menu features curries, vegetarian options and children's meals. Play area for small children too. A number of guest rooms with en-suite facilities are available for those wishing to stay overnight. Watch out for George, the friendly ghost. ⋈ Q ⌚ ◑ ♿ ♣ ⬥ ⯅ P

LONGRIDGE

Old Oak
111 Preston Road (B6243/B6244 jct)
⊙ 12-11; 12-10.30 Sun
☎ (01772) 783648
Theakston Mild, Best Bitter; Wells Bombardier; guest beers Ⓗ
Welcoming, community local with wood settles and a real fire in the comfortable lounge. Large games room has big-screen TV. A pet rabbit often wanders around the pub. Lunchtime meals served plus a tandoori menu at night (except Mon) 7.30–10, with takeaways till 11pm. There is a no-smoking area at lunchtimes. The two guest beers change daily. The pub has its own beer appreciation society and runs competitions such as big onion, pie-making and alcoholic jelly contests. A large collection of pump clips and various stuffed cartoon characters are found around the pub. ⋈ ⌚ ◑

White Bull Hotel
1A Higher Road (at jct with road to Blackburn/Clitheroe)
⊙ 12-2 (not winter), 5.30-11; 12-11 Fri & Sat; 12-10.30 Sun
☎ (01772) 783198
e-mail: fred-whitebull@ukonline.co.uk
Worthington Bitter; guest beers Ⓗ
Lively local usually with a disco on weekend nights. Quieter at other times, this 18th-century, stone-built inn offers an old-fashioned vault with darts and the local nine-spot dominoes. A snug has a cosy open fire in the winter and two other comfortable rooms for more boisterous activities. A mezzanine room boasts a bevy of pool tables. The pub pool team has represented Lancashire in a national competition. Small patio available. Worthington Bitter is the stock cask ale. Guest ale policy is to provide two ales each week, always good session beers. On bus route, so easily accessible from Preston. ⋈ ⌚ ◑ ➡ ♣ P

LYTHAM ST ANNE'S ❖

Station Tavern
Station Square
⊙ 11-11; 12-10.30 Sun
☎ (01253) 734252
Theakston Cool Cask; guest beers Ⓗ
Large pub next to the railway station, it used to be the waiting room and booking office. The front of the building is original and is listed. The Castle Eden Squires and Moorhouses Dr Beeching beers are house beers. There is a no-smoking area. Currently food only served at lunchtimes but eve meals are planned. Patio available for outdoor drinking. Thu is jazz night with a live group performing. Note the collection of goods sold in an old-fashioned corner shop. ⋈ ⌚ ◑ ♿ ⬥ ♣ ⬥ ⊁

Taps
12 Henry Street (behind Clifton Arms Hotel)
⊙ 11-11; 12-10.30 Sun
☎ (01253) 736226
Beer range varies Ⓗ
Very busy Hogshead pub. The building was converted from ostlers' cottages over 100 years old. This basic but cosy ale house offers an ever-changing range of beers and

always includes a mild in its nine beers. The house beer is brewed by Titanic and a real cider is stocked. The landlord is the only person to win the local CAMRA *Pub of the Year* with two different pubs. Note the collection of bottled beers and the bust of the landlord's father who was landlord of the infamous 'Tommy Ducks' in Manchester. Food served 12–2 daily, except Sun. ⚅Q⚭◐&≈♠

MAWDESLEY

Black Bull
Hall Lane (off B5246) OS499151
🕐 12-11; 12-10.30 Sun
☎ (01704) 822202
Greenalls Bitter; Robinson's Best Bitter; Taylor Landlord; guest beers Ⓗ
This stone-built inn dates from 1580 and, according to records, has been a pub since 1610. The structure of the low-ceilinged building follows Elizabethan lines with magnificent oak beams from which hop bines are hung. The older residents of the village know the pub as 'Ell 'Ob', which is a corruption of 'Helen's Hob' – a reference to a coal-fired cooking range. Above the bar there are many certificates listing the pub's success in the Lancashire *Best-Kept Village* competition. There is such a marvellous array of hanging baskets in summer, the Black Bull almost vanishes behind them. ⚅⚭◐&♣P⁄

Robin Hood Inn
Bluestone Lane (off B5250) OS506163
🕐 11.30-3, 5-11; 11-11 Sat; 12-10.30 Sun
☎ (01704) 822275
e-mail: robin.hood-mawdesley@talk21.com
Boddingtons Bitter; Taylor Landlord; Tetley Bitter; guest beers Ⓗ
Charming, white-painted inn at crossroads between the three old villages of Mawdesley, Croston and Eccleston. The 15th-century building was substantially altered during the 19th century. The connection with Robin Hood is a tenuous one, but he was much admired by the yeomen of the Middle Ages, who often named their properties in his honour. The pub has been run by the same family for over 30 years, it has a reputation for good food but still finds room for the drinker. Six ales are always on tap. ⚅⚑⚭◐P⁄

MORECAMBE ✣

Smugglers' Den
56 Poulton Road (near police station)
🕐 11-3, 7-11; 12-10.30 Sun
☎ (01524) 421684
Boddingtons Bitter; Tetley Bitter; guest beers Ⓗ
At the heart of the old fishing village of Poulton, which was swallowed by Morecambe 150 years ago. The current name and decor – dark, low-beamed, stone-flagged floors, tables shaped like casks – date from 1960. Since then there has been a single change of licensee, from father to son. The pair have accumulated a large collection of mostly nautical artefacts. Impressive stained glass windows and a small garden with caged birds are unusual features. ⚅⚭♣P

ORMSKIRK

Hayfield
22 County Road (A59)
🕐 12-11; 12-10.30 Sun
☎ (01695) 571157
Beer range varies Ⓗ
Large, modern pub on outskirts of town centre with large car park, fronting the Liverpool to Preston road (A59). The spacious lounge areas are attractively decorated and comfortably furnished and served by a long, L shaped bar. Principally open plan, though a platform area, rails and screens lend an impression of different rooms. A constantly changing range of up to 10 real ales is served in oversized glasses. An extensive menu offers great-value food. Picnic tables and a low retaining wall offer outdoor seating areas during summer. ⚭◐&≈P♿

Queen's Head
30 Moor Street
🕐 12-11; 12-10.30 Sun
☎ (01695) 574380
Beer range varies Ⓗ
This Victorian corner pub is located in the principal shopping street of the town. Formerly multi-roomed, it has been opened out as part of the Festival Ale House concept, with all areas being served by a long bar. Simply, but comfortably decorated, it is a pub popular with students, regulars and shoppers. Up to four real ales are available at any one time, which usually includes two regularly changing guests. Good value food is served at lunchtimes, except Sun. Q⚭◐≈

POULTON-LE-FYLDE

Thatched House
12 Ball Street (next to parish church)
🕐 11-11; 12-10.30 Sun
Boddingtons Bitter; Theakston Cool Cask; guest beers Ⓗ
Half-timbered building in St Chad's churchyard, a picturesque exterior matched by a spotless, welcoming interior. Although this building is only 10 years old, the pub is the oldest continuously licensed premises on the Fylde. The first winner of the local CAMRA *Pub of the Season* award. Extremely busy most eves, especially weekends. Weekday lunchtimes it is a haven of peace and good conversation without the distraction of piped music, noisy cutlery, crockery or children. The landlord takes a great pride in the condition of his beers and refuses to sell alcopops or 'cream-flow' beers. ⚅Q&≈

PREESALL

Black Bull
192 Park Lane (B5377, village centre)
🕐 12-3 (not Mon), 6-11; 12-3, 7-10.30 Sun
☎ (01253) 810294
Jennings Bitter; Tetley Mild, Bitter; guest beers Ⓗ
Originally three separate thatched single-storey dwellings with walls of pebbles and rocks from nearby beaches, the upper floors were added to create the 17th-century coaching inn. Inside this multi-roomed village local the cosy public areas include a small dining room and a couple of alcoves. A list of licensees since 1776 hangs near the

bar. An upstairs function room accommodates 60 people. There is an outside drinking area with tables. Look out for the resident ghost. Q ☼ ◑ ♣ P ⚱

PRESTON ❖

Ashton Institute

10-12 Wellington Road, Ashton (near Sacred Heart church)

☺ 7 (4 Fri & Sat)-11; 4-10.30 Sun

☎ (01772) 726582

website: www.drink.to/ashtoninstitute

Boddingtons Bitter; Worthington Bitter; guest beers Ⓗ

Lively, enterprising club, recently freed of tie for cask beers, so guest beers are often from small breweries. It is the oldest club in Preston to remain on its original premises, dating from 4/4/44. It hosts an annual beer festival (October). The recently refurbished function room is for hire and the main room features snooker, pool tables, facilities for various card games and a table-soccer machine. Various press cuttings from beer events can be read on the walls. A local CAMRA award-winner, show this *Guide* or CAMRA members card to be signed in. ♣

Black Horse ☆

166 Friargate (near market)

☺ 10.30-11; 7-10.30 (closed lunch) Sun

☎ (01772) 204855

Robinson's Best Bitter, Frederics, Old Tom, seasonal beers Ⓗ

Classic, Grade II listed pub in the main shopping area and close to the historic open market. It is deservedly on CAMRA's national inventory. With its exquisite tiled bar and walls and superb mosaic floor, it is an English Heritage/CAMRA award-winner. There are two separate front rooms with photos of old Preston and the famed 'Hall of Mirrors' seating area to the rear. An interesting collection of memorabilia (from a previous landlord) is set in a glass partition. The modern upstairs bar is usually open at weekends. ⚞

Limekiln

288 Aqueduct Street (off A583)

☺ 11-11; 12-10.30 Sun

☎ (01772) 493247

Banks's Original, Bitter Ⓗ

Locals' pub, north-west of the centre, just off (and visible from) Fylde road. Customers are mainly regulars but visitors are made welcome in one of a group of pubs acquired by Banks's well away from their main trading area. A central bar serves four drinking areas including pool and darts rooms. Unusually for Preston the Original (mild) sells as well as the bitter. The aqueduct referred to no longer exists but the Lancaster Canal terminus is only 200 yards from the pub. ☼ ♣ P

Market Tavern

33 Market Street (overlooking market)

☺ 10.30-11; closed Sun

☎ (01772) 254425

Beer range varies Ⓗ

Slightly hidden away from the town-centre drinking circuit, this pub faces on to Preston's impressive Victorian outdoor, covered market. A blue plaque, nearby, identifies where John Wesley once preached. It was awarded the local CAMRA *Pub of the Season* winter 2001 for 'most improved pub'. The Market Tavern was totally refurbished in 2000 with a new interior layout. Most importantly, the landlord (an ex-S&N line manager) opted for a greater emphasis on real ale by selling three changing handpumped beers. At least one is from Pictish Brewery. ⚞

New Britannia

6 Heatley Street (off Friargate)

☺ 11-3, 6-11; 11-11 Sat; 7-10.30 (closed lunch) Sun

☎ (01772) 253424

Boddingtons Bitter; Castle Eden Ale; Goose Eye Brontë; Marston's Pedigree; guest beers Ⓗ

Small, friendly, single-bar pub which attracts an amazing number of real ale drinkers to sample its consistently excellent

INN BRIEF

PRESTON

Avenham Park

Avenham Lane

11-11; 12-10.30 Sun

Greene King IPA; Marston's Pedigree; guest beer Ⓗ

Close to town centre. A basic street-corner local that has been rescued from keg obscurity by a keen landlady.

Fylde Tavern

300 Fylde Road

11-11; 12-10.30 Sun

Boddingtons Bitter; Moorhouses Black Cat; guest beer Ⓗ

Modern locals' pub at a busy junction. Separate lounge and public bar. The house bitter, Steamer, is from Ushers.

Mitre Tavern

90-91 Moor Lane

12-3, 7-11; 12-10.30 Sun

Boddingtons Bitter; Tetley Bitter; guest beers Ⓗ

Two-bar local at A6 junction. Guest beers are changed weekly (usually two on). Quiz night Thu and occasional live music eve.

Moorbrook Inn

370 North Road

4-11; 12-3, 7-10.30 Sun

Thwaites Bitter; seasonal beers Ⓗ

Homely local with two small rooms and bar area. Folk music is performed Fri eve. It boasts a pewter tankard collection and a large range of malt whiskies.

Toby Carvery

849 Blackpool Road, Lea

11-11; 12-10.30 Sun

Draught Bass; guest beer Ⓗ

Bass branded house, formerly the Pig & Whistle, situated in the upmarket extreme west of Preston.

SALTERFORTH

Anchor Inn

Salterforth Lane

12-11; 12-10.30 Sun

Courage Directors; Greene King Ruddles Best; John Smith's Bitter; Theakston Best Bitter Ⓗ

Adjacent to Leeds-Liverpool Canal, this building dates back to 1655. Large garden, children's play area and car park provided. Moorings are nearby.

SKELMERSDALE

Tawd Vale Inn

11 Berry Street

2 (12 Fri & Sat)-11; 12-10.30 Sun

John Smith's Bitter; guest beer Ⓗ

Takes its name from a former colliery. Has two lounge rooms, a games room and bar area with an open-plan feel. Quiz on Thu eve.

Guide site

Keep your copy of the Good Beer Guide up-to-date by contacting the CAMRA website where you will find information about changes to pubs and breweries

www.camra.org.uk/gbg

beers and unusual guests. Real cider is also served. The recent refurbishment has not spoilt the character of the pub. The etched Britannia windows are an interesting feature. Lunches are served 11–2 Mon–Fri and 12–4 on Sat. Singers perform on Wed eve. The landlady of this town-centre pub is continuing to develop the fine traditions set by her parents. ⚜🌓🎵🌸

Old Black Bull

35 Friargate (Ringway jct)
🕓 10.30-11; 12-10.30 Sun
☎ (01772) 823397
Boddingtons Bitter; Cains Bitter; guest beers Ⓗ

T... ...tre ...b with much Tudor frontage, tilework and its name spelt out in large ceramic letters. A small front vault, main bar with distinctive black-and-white tiles, two comfortable lounge areas and pool table make it a popular venue, along with the rear courtyard. Big-screen TV and live music most Sat nights are on offer. There are usually eight beers on tap, often from micros. ⚜🌓🍴🌓🌸♣

Old Blue Bell

114 Church Street (near bus station)
🕓 11-3 (3.30 Mon; 4 Fri), 6-11; 11-4, 7-11 Sat; 12-3, 7-10.30 Sun
☎ (01772) 251280
Samuel Smith OBB Ⓗ

Small, white-fronted pub, not far away from main shopping areas. The wood-lined bar counter has an overhead gantry for glasses. There is a small lounge off the main room and a snug at the rear. Note the extensive array of prints. This pub offers the cheapest beer in a brewery-owned pub in town. It is a listed building (dating from 1722) with the remains of an old passageway to the parish church in the cellar. Good value lunches served 11.30–2 and a popular quiz on Tue eve. A good pub for conversation and relaxation. ♨Q🌓

Olde Dog & Partridge

44 Friargate (off Ringway)
🕓 11-2 (3 Sat), 6 (7 bank hols)-11; 12-3, 7-10.30 Sun
☎ (01772) 252217 website: www.drink.to/dandp
Fuller's London Pride; Highgate Dark; Marston's Pedigree; guest beers Ⓗ

Well-known (internationally) as a bikers' pub. An impressive array of motorcycles are parked outside in summer. Music from the DJ and juke box is predominantly rock. The landlord has been at the pub for over 20 years. It is decorated with military memorabilia and memorial plaques to former regulars. A noticeboard advertises bikes. Successful Punch Taverns pub with guests from their list. It is a rare town-centre outlet in the area for both mild and real cider. Tends to be busy and loud weekend eves. Basic lunchtime food available (not Sun). 🌓🌓♣🌸

Real Ale Shop

47 Lovat Road (off A6, Garstang Rd)
🕓 11-2, 5-10; 12-2, 6-10 Sun
☎ (01772) 201591
Beer range varies Ⓗ

Well-established real ale off-licence tucked away in the back streets of North Preston. One draught real ale on tap during the week, two at

weekends and sometimes midweek, plus upwards of 50 British bottle-conditioned beers and up to 300 Belgian and German bottled beers. Draught ale is available in four-pint containers, polypins and party barrels (with loan of handpump). Upstairs is a thriving fancy-dress hire business (different hours, phone for details). To beat the local one-way system, take St George's Road off Garstang Road (A6) and turn left into Arkwright Road. 🌸

Cross Keys Hotel

Fleet Street Lane (B6245)
🕓 12-2, 5-11; 12-10.30 Sun
☎ (01254) 878353
e-mail: marc@crosskeys-hotel.fsnet.co.uk
Moorhouses Black Cat, Premier; Three B's Bobbin's Bitter; guest beers Ⓗ

Traditional coaching inn on a sharp bend on the Longridge Road. Small north-west breweries make up the vast majority of the guest ales stocked. A collection of bottled ales is on display above the bar and plenty of leaflets for local attractions, including the Roman museum. The pub has a traditional restaurant with modern touches, which enjoys a good reputation for generous portions. Occasional events include quizzes and folk nights. Enjoy the beer garden and splendid views of the Ribble Valley. ♨🍷🌓🗡♣P

Rishton Arms

Station Road (off A678)
🕓 7 (12 Sat)-11; 12-10.30 Sun
☎ (01254) 886396
Thwaites Mild, Bitter, seasonal beers Ⓗ

Large, comfortable local next to the railway station. There are two rooms, the regular drinking room-cum-lounge and a tap room with pool table and dartboard. As well as the mild and bitter there is always a Thwaites seasonal beer on. This is one of the best Thwaites outlets that can be found and is why the pub is in the *Guide* for the ninth consecutive year. The landlord and regulars are very welcoming. 🌓♣P

New Hall Tavern

Cuerdale Lane (opp. Samlesbury Brewery)
🕓 11.30-11; 12-10.30 Sun
☎ (01772) 877217
website: www.btinternet.com/~newhall
Beer range varies Ⓗ

Welcoming country pub at a rural crossroads. It was originally called the Cobblers' Arms as it was near a tannery. The pub is beamed with wood-backed seating and decorative hops. The games section is directly off the wood-lined bar, Sky Sports is popular on match days. Traditional home-cooked food is served at reasonable prices (all day Sun until 9pm) and children are allowed at any time. There is a supper licence. The four guest beers change at least three times a week. Varied live music is performed every second Thu. Campsite and fishery nearby.

🏚️⊛◑ Å♣P✗

SILVERDALE

Woodlands

Woodlands Drive (off Cove Rd)
⊛ 12-3 (not Mon-Fri), 7-11; 12-3, 7-10.30 Sun
☎ (01524) 701655
Beer range varies Ⓗ

Large country house, circa 1878, on the edge of the village with its back to Eaves Wood, hence the name. The current owner is slowly restoring it to its former glory. Easily overlooked by the casual visitor to Silverdale, so most of the trade is provided by locals. Even when you find it, it doesn't look much like a pub. Through the stunning entrance hall and a lounge lies a cosy bar with splendid views across the bay. Pool room also on offer. 🏚️Q🌣⊛Å♣P🖥

SLYNE

Slyne Lodge

Main Road (A6)
⊛ 11-11; 12-10.30 Sun
☎ (01524) 825055
Jennings Dark Mild, Bitter, Cumberland Ale Ⓗ

Elegant Georgian house with terraced garden. It was a country club until 1981 but once it gained a full licence it slowly changed, through a succession of owners, into an eating house. However, its latest change of owner (2000) has made it more of a pub again. Most of the trade still arrives by car. Large central servery, dark wood panelling, soft lights and (in season) a log fire. There is a separate, rustic galleried restaurant on one side and a modern conservatory on the other. Quiz night is Thu. 🏚️🌣⊛◁◑Å♣P●

TEWITFIELD

Longlands

(A6070)
⊛ 11-11 (midnight Mon & Thu; 1am Fri & Sat); 12-10.30 Sun
☎ (01524) 781256
e-mail: info@thelonglandshotel.co.uk
Theakston Best Bitter; guest beers Ⓗ

In a hamlet at the present northern limit of navigation on the Lancaster Canal, although the giant car park attests to the main means of transport for its customers. Single, large bar with a half-timbered look divided up into several separate 'rooms' including a dining room and pool room. Attracts both regulars and diners, the latter especially for its 'happy hour' on food (5.30–6.30 Mon–Fri, 5–6 Sat & Sun). Entertainment includes bands on Mon and a disco on Thu and Sat. Forthcoming alterations seem unlikely to alter its character significantly.
⊛◑Å♣P

TOWN GREEN

Stanley Arms

St Michaels Road, Aughton (off A59 from Liverpool-Ormskirk)
⊛ 11.30-3, 5-11; 12-10.30 Sun
☎ (01695) 423241

e-mail: stanleyarmspub@dial.pipex.com
Marston's Pedigree; Taylor Landlord Ⓗ

Homely, traditional 'country cottage' pub with a warm, friendly atmosphere, catering for regulars and passing trade from the A59. Main features are the wooden bar and beamed ceilings. The front room is on a lower level, as is 'the well' area, the rest of the pub is L-shaped. Home-cooked food is freshly prepared daily. Live music on Fri eve, quiz night on Tue and impromptu choir singing sessions on Mon. Other amenities are the bowling green and outdoor children's play area. Finally, don't forget Ollie, the friendly Cromwellian ghost.
⊛◑≈ (Aughton) P

UP HOLLAND

Old Dog

6 Alma Hill (off A577)
⊛ 7-11; 12-10.30 Sun
☎ (01695) 623487
Draught Bass; Boddingtons Bitter; Weetwood Old Dog Bitter; guest beer Ⓗ

Small village pub at the bottom of the steep Alma Hill. The building dates back to 1743 and is made of local Up Holland sandstone. The pub has a main bar, two small lounges and a small games room with a TV. It is on a number of levels due to its hillside location. A function room is for hire upstairs
🍺♣

White Lion

10 Church Street (just off A577 by church)
⊛ 5 (12 Sat)-11; 12-10.30 Sun
☎ (01695) 622727
Thwaites Bitter, seasonal beers (occasional) Ⓗ

Welcoming watering-hole in a village locally famous for Georgian lady of letters, Helen Weeton, and highwayman, George Lyon. This multi-roomed local stands in the shadow of St Thomas's church. There is a chequered porch, a games room (the TV is tucked away in here) and an unobtrusive juke box. Note the old edition of the *Wigan Observer* and ornamental surround with inlaid mirror over the cast-iron fireplace in the lounge. The bar and two back rooms have decorative swags and William Morris wallpaper. Quiz night is Wed.
🏚️Q⊛🍺♣P

WALMER BRIDGE

Longton Arms

2 Liverpool Old Road (off A59)
⊛ 12.30 (2.30 Mon & Tue)-11; 12-10.30 Sun
☎ (01772) 612335
Greenalls Mild, Bitter Ⓗ

White-painted, brick-built end-of-terrace village pub. A fine community local with a warm welcome. There are benches outside the pub with colourful window boxes and hanging baskets. Splendid small front snug and rear lounge with serving hatch and big-screen TV. Note the duck frieze over the bar. The pub is a haunt of wildfowlers from nearby Longton Marsh and home to a golf society and football team. Longton Picnic Club organise splendid days out for members and raise money for charity. A board listing all the presidents since 1980 is on display in the front lounge.

WENNINGTON

Bridge

Tatham (on B6480 S of station)

☼ 12-3, 6-11; 11-11 Fri & Sat; 12-10.30 Sun

☎ (01542) 21326

Boddingtons Bitter; Taylor Landlord; Tetley Bitter Ⓗ

The old tiny rooms have been opened out to form a single bar which is still small enough for there to be only one conversation. There is a restaurant, also small and intimate. This is a pretty isolated spot, but a surprisingly large proportion of the customers are locals. The pub features in a Turner painting. Camping facilities (including caravans) are available nearby.

🏚️🕮🖵🕀🕭🛆🏕️🍴P

WESTHEAD

Prince Albert

109 Wigan Road (A577) OS438078

☼ 12-11; 12-10.30 Sun

☎ (01695) 573656

Tetley Dark Mild, Bitter; guest beers Ⓗ

The Prince Albert is situated on the A577 between Ormskirk and Skelmersdale and is therefore popular with both communities. It is home to two darts and two dominoes teams, and is particularly popular with visiting teams. The pub is renowned for good meals, which are home-made and excellent value, with a weightwatchers' menu also available. The bar has an interesting collection of old beer bottles, and there are two real coal fires, a welcome sight in winter. The room at the front of the pub was once used as a funeral parlour.

🏚️🕮🖵🕀🛆🍴P

WHALLEY

Dog Inn

55 King Street (B6246)

☼ 11-11; 11-10.30 Sun

☎ (01254) 823009

Theakston Best Bitter; guest beers Ⓗ

Originally a village stable, in 1877 the Dog was first licensed as a one-roomed ale house. It has since expanded into a multi-area pub with a pleasantly 'organic' feel. The rear of the pub is considerably lower than the front, necessitating a step in the L-shaped bar. Very lively on Fri and Sat eves, this is a true local. When the local church was being refurbished the original ale house room was consecrated and used for Thu morning services. The pub

newspaper (*Boring Old Farts Herald & Chronicle*) keeps patrons abreast of the many pub activities. 🕮🕀♨♣

WHARLES

Eagle & Child

1 Church Road (3 miles NE of Kirkham) OS448356

☼ 12-3 (not Mon-Fri), 7-11; 12-4, 7-10.30 Sun

☎ (01772) 690312

website: www.yell.co.uk/sites/eagle-child

Beer range varies Ⓗ

Pleasant, relaxing atmosphere in this thatched 17th-century ex-farmhouse which stands clear of the few houses that make up Wharles. Unspoilt, country free house in the same ownership for many years. The long, beamed lounge has an open fire and cast-iron stove, magnificent wooden settles, farm implements and brewery mirrors. Normally music-free, children-free, and not serving meals, it is a pub for conversation and quietly to enjoy the well-kept beers. The pump clip collection indicates the range of guest beers over the years.

🏚️Q🕮♣P

WHEELTON

Dressers Arms

Briers Brow (near A674)

☼ 11-11; 12-10.30 Sun

☎ (01254) 830041

e-mail: dressers.turner250@virgin.net

Boddingtons Bitter; Taylor Landlord; Tetley Bitter; guest beers Ⓗ

This pub has been converted in recent years from a number of terraced cottages into a large multi-roomed establishment. A comfortable bar is complemented by a lounge, a games room and snug. There is a cosy no-smoking lounge behind the bar area. Good food is served downstairs and there is the added attraction of an authentic Chinese restaurant upstairs. Up to four changing guest beers are on sale including occasional beers from its new on-site microbrewery. Winner of the *Real Fire Pub of the Year*. Meals served all day Sun until 9pm.

🏚️🛏🕮🕀🛆♣P✂

Top Lock

Copthurst Lane, Heapey (alongside canal at Johnsons Hillock)

☼ 11-11; 12-10.30 Sun

☎ (01257) 263376

Black Sheep Best Bitter; Coniston Bluebird; guest beers Ⓗ

A recent convert to real ale after many years as a keg-only pub. The Top Lock sits beside the Leeds–Liverpool Canal at the series of locks known as Johnsons Hillock. A fine example of a country pub with a single bar downstairs and an upstairs dining area which serves as an authentic Indian restaurant on Fri and Sat nights. Popular with walkers and narrow boat owners due to its close proximity to the canal. At least three beers are usually on sale, all from regional or micro-breweries. 🛏🕮🕀🍴✂

WHITTLE-LE-WOODS

Royal Oak

216 Chorley Old Road (off A6)

☼ 2.30-11; 12-10.30 Sun

☎ (01257) 276485
e-mail: patrogoakbushinternet.com
Boddingtons Bitter; Hanby Premium; Wells Bombardier Ⓗ

Small, single-bar, terraced village local, built in 1820 to serve the adjacent branch of the Leeds-Liverpool Canal, the tramway to Preston and the Lancaster Canal. In 1969 the canal was filled in for the M61 construction but the bridge is still visible. *Guide* entry for 25 years consecutively, the present landlord has been here for 16 years. Long, narrow pub with a small bar and separate games room, very much a community pub full of local characters. Haunt of mature motorcycle enthusiasts. Note the fine Nuttalls windows and try the malt whiskies and pickled eggs.
🏮♿♣

WILPSHIRE

Bull's Head Hotel
779 Whalley New Road
(A666, ½ mile N of jct with A6119)
✪ 11-11; 12-10.30 Sun
☎ (01254) 248274 Ⓗ
Beer range varies Ⓗ

Spacious, well-furnished pub offering three cask beers from independent brewers plus an extensive menu. Sport, particularly Sky Channel, is very popular as the four TV screens and thriving football team testify. Wood panelling and brass footrails add character and the mix of age groups makes it an attractive venue. Occasional barbecues are held; there are picnic tables in the garden. Wheelchair access is via the front door, not side entrance. There are active charity fundraisers, by the landlord running marathons and holding raffles and firewalking events. Close to train station and bus routes, or there are redeem pay & display parking vouchers in the pub.
🏮◖♿≉ (Wilpshire/Ramsgreave) ♣P✠

Rising Sun
Whalley New Road (A666, ½ mile N of jct with A6119)
✪ 11.30 (12 Sat)-11; 12-10.30 Sun
☎ (01254) 247379
Theakston Best Bitter; guest beer Ⓗ

Small, two-roomed, characterful pub. Note the photographs of Blackburn, trams, ships and Blackburn Rovers' FC and the interesting Trueman's mirror. the cosy vault or 'parlour' is an excellent place for conversation. The pub has a TV, three air filters and a piano. Legendary Blackburn musician Bert Grainger tickles the ivories on Sat night. The handpump in the compact, refurbished lounge serves the guest beer. Note the 'Nuttall & Co Lion Ales Double Stout' window. The only food is pickled eggs and crisps. Owned by Royal Bank of Scotland and run by Scotco.
🏮Q◖♿≉ (Wilpshire/Ramsgreave)

WORSTHORNE

Crooked Billet Inn
Smith Street
✪ 5 (2 Thu & Fri; 12 Sat)-11; 12-10.30 Sun
☎ (01282) 429040
Marston's Pedigree; Taylor Landlord; Tetley Bitter; guest beer Ⓗ

Close to the village centre, this gem is a riot of colour in the summer; planters, window boxes and hanging baskets abound and the pub has won awards for *Best Pub in Bloom*. Inside, you are surrounded by beautifully-kept oak panelling setting off a tiled and glass-panelled bar. The small snug is always popular and the lounge has comfortable seating – but get there early! The three standard beers are always available, the guest, which comes from Vantage Inns, is always on at weekends. Meals served on Sun 12–6pm. There is a small patio and limited parking. 🏮Q🏮◖P

Ale As Clear As Amber

Boniface: Sir, I have now in my cellar ten tun of the best ale in Staffordshire; 'tis smooth as oil, sweet as milk, clear as amber, and strong as brandy; and will be just 14 year old the fifth day of next March, old style.

Aimwell: You're very exact, I find, in the age of your ale.

Boniface: As punctual, sir, as I am in the age of my children. I'll show you such ale: I have lived in Lichfield, man and boy, about eight-and-fifty years, and, I believe, have not consumed eight-and-fifty ounces of meat.

Aimwell: At a meal, you mean, if one may guess your sense by your bulk.

Boniface: Not in my life, sir, I have fed purely upon ale; I have eat my ale, drank my ale, and I always sleep upon ale.

George Farquhar, *the Beaux-Stratagem,* 1707.

CAMRA's Beers of the Year

The beers listed below are CAMRA's Beers of the Year. They were short-listed for the Champion Beer of Britain competition in August 2001, and the Champion Winter Beer of Britain competition in January 2001. The August competition judged Dark and Light Milds, Bitters, Best Bitters, Strong Bitters, Speciality Beers, and Bottle-conditioned Beers, while the winter competition judged Old Ales and Strong Milds, Porters and Stouts, and Barley Wines. Each beer was found by panels of trained CAMRA judges to be consistently outstanding in its category and they all receive a 'full tankard' ❦ symbol in the Breweries section.

DARK AND LIGHT MILDS

Bateman's Dark Mild
Boat Man in the Boat
Brains Dark
Brakspear Mild
Cains Mild
Elgood's Black Dog
Moorhouses Black Cat

BITTER

Adnams Bitter
Barge and Barrel Bargee
Black Sheep Best
Brakspear Bitter
Bullmastiff Gold
Butts Jester
Caledonian Deuchars IPA
Harviestoun Bitter and Twisted
Goose Eye Barmpot
Hop Back GFB
Oakham JHB
Triple fff Afterglow
Wickwar Coopers WPA
Woodforde's Wherry

BEST BITTERS

Abbey Bellringer
Crouch Vale Brewers Gold
Eccleshall Slaters Original
Goddards Special
Harveys Sussex Best (BB)
Hogs Back TEA
Inveralmond Ossian
Otter Ale
Plassey Welsh Fusilier
RCH Pitchfork
Taylor Landlord
Triple fff Moondance
Wylam Turbinia
Woodforde Nelson's Revenge

STRONG BITTERS

Butcombe Gold
Eccleshall Slaters Supreme
Goacher's Gold Star
Hexhamshire Whapweasel
Hop Back Summer Lightning
Plassey Cwrw Tudno
Ridleys Old Bob

OLD ALES AND STRONG MILDS

Buffy's Hollybeery
Gale's Festival Mild
Harveys Sussex Old Ale
Hogs Back Advent Ale
Sarah Hughes Dark Ruby Mild
Orkney Dark Island
Young's Winter Warmer

PORTERS AND STOUTS

B&T Edwin Taylor's Extra Stout
Bateman's Salem Porter
Big Lamp Summerhill Stout
Hop Back Entire Stout
Nethergate Old Growler
O'Hanlon's Port Stout
RCH Old Slug Porter

BARLEY WINES

Adnams Tally Ho
Bass Museum No 1
Exmoor Beast
Lees Moonraker
Orkney Skullsplitter
Robinson's Old Tom
Woodforde Headcracker

SPECIALITY BEERS

Cheriton Village Elder
Durham NeueSchloss
Harviestoun Schiehallion
Heather Fraoch
Nethergate Umbel Ale
Oakham White Dwarf
Rebellion Blonde Bombshell

BOTTLE-CONDITIONED BEERS

Burton Bridge Empire Pale Ale
Freeminer Trafalgar IPA
Fuller's 1845
Hop Back Summer Lightning
RCH Ale Mary
RCH Pitchfork
Young's Special London Ale

CHAMPION WINTER BEER OF BRITAIN

Orkney Skullsplitter

CHAMPION BEER OF BRITAIN

Oakham JHB

LEICESTERSHIRE & RUTLAND

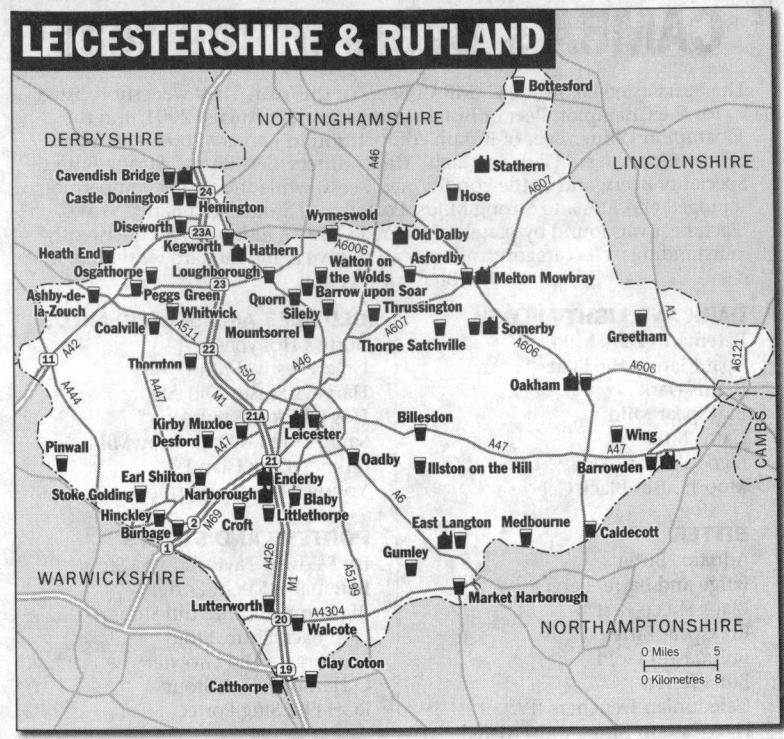

ASFORDBY

Crown Inn
106 Main Street
⊘ 6.30-11; 12-11 Fri & Sat; 12-10.30 Sun
☎ (01664) 812175
Beer range varies Ⓗ

18th-century friendly local with a low
ceiling and doorways, nooks to sit in, and
exposed beams. Local stone has been used
in the construction of the bar, but beware of
its sloping top. This pub was renovated five
years ago which has actually added to its
character; it was nearly converted into a
house, but locals persuaded the landlord to
reopen. A true free house, the range of beer
is constantly changing; Belvoir, Brewster's
and other local micro-brewery products
often feature. Popular for Sunday lunches, it
is on bus routes to Loughborough, Melton
Mowbray and Leicester.
🏚Q🕭🕭🍺🕼🍀P

ASHBY-DE-LA-ZOUCH

Plough Inn
The Green
⊘ 11-11; 12-10.30 Sun
☎ (01530) 412817
website: www.the-plough-ashby.co.uk
Draught Bass; Marston's Pedigree; guest beers Ⓗ

Parts of this pub date back to the 1580s,
although it has been modernised into a
single bar, split into various cosy areas. A
friendly local, it fields darts, dominoes
and cribbage teams; major rugby
matches are screened here. This pub
has a rural feel, despite being in the centre
of a small town. The guest beers are
constantly changing (see website); a

cider is sometimes sold. The food is home
cooked and of excellent quality and value.
Daytime buses run from Leicester, via
Coalville. 🏚Q🕭🕭🕼🍀🍀

BARROW UPON SOAR

Navigation
Mill Lane
⊘ 11-3, 5.30-11; 11-11 Sat; 12-3, 7-10.30 Sun
☎ (01509) 412842 website:
www.countryfocus.co.uk/barrowuponsoar/navigation
**Banks's Bitter; Belvoir Star Bitter; Marston's
Pedigree; Old Laxey Bosun Bitter; guest beer** Ⓗ

Built at the same time as the Grand
Union Canal in the 1760s, this
waterside pub is popular with the
locals and passing summer boat trade
(moorings available nearby). The main
lounge area boasts an old penny bar counter
and much brass bric-à-brac; the cosy snug
now has its own bar. The pub has recently
been refurbished without losing its
character. It stands on a regular bus route
and the railway station is only a short walk
away. Q🕭🕭🕼🍀

BILLESDON

New Greyhound
2 Market Place (old A47)
⊘ 12-2, 5-11; 12-11 Sat; 12-3.30, 7-10.30 Sun
☎ (0116) 259 6226
website: www.newgreyhound.co.uk
newgreyhound@hotmail.com
Banks's Original; Marston's Bitter, Pedigree Ⓗ

This 17th-century building has been a
village pub for over 100 years. A welcoming
watering-hole for many ramblers and
walkers, a friendly farmer nearby may allow
camping. Recently extended at the rear to

accommodate functions, the pub hosts many local and Leicester club meetings. The three-roomed pub has a bandit- and music-free lounge bar and a public bar with pool table. The landlord is a supporter of Marston's Bitter, recently saved from extinction. Filled cobs are available. Q ☕ ⌘ ⌀ ♣ P

original etched glass windows. The pub name indicates a close relationship existed with the medieval church that overlooks it from the hill on which the town was built. A pub of great character, with home-cooked food served weekdays and a cosy atmosphere; it lies on a regular bus route. ⌂ Q ⌀ ♣ P

BLABY

Black Horse
Sycamore Street
🕐 12-11; 11-4, 6-11 Sat; 12-4, 7-10.30 Sun
☎ (0116) 277 1209
Greenalls Mild, Bitter; Marston's Bitter, Pedigree; Tetley Bitter ⍩
This three-roomed pub consists of a bar, lounge and vault in the village centre. The latter has a TV for sporting occasions, otherwise the sound is muted. Children are welcome, so are dogs. Regular quiz nights are held in the lounge. ⌀ ⌀ ♣

BOTTESFORD

Rutland Arms
2 High Street
🕐 12-4.30, 5.30-11; 11-11 Fri & Sat; 12-10.30 Sun
☎ (01949) 843031
Draught Bass; Courage Directors; Greenalls Mild, Original Ⓗ
Pub in the centre of a large village: two rooms plus a restaurant. A comfortable carpeted lounge has a disused brick fireplace, containing a menu board; a fish tank aids relaxation, while upholstered benches and stools complement wooden chairs and tables. The beamed bar, with a horseshoe-shaped bar houses a pool table and three games machines; darts and dominoes are played. The restaurant serves good value English fare with curry nights (Tue). ⌂ ☕ ⌀ ⌀ ⌀ ⌀ ⌀ ⌀ ♣ P ⌀ 🍴

BURBAGE

Sycamores Inn
60 Windsor Street
🕐 11-11; 12-10.30 Sun
☎ (01455) 239268 e-mail: thesycamoreinn@aol.com
Marston's Bitter, Pedigree Ⓗ
Named after the two trees which stood on this site until the pub was built in 1925, it consists of two rooms, one of which is a basic tile-floored bar, and a lounge where children may go. The garden also includes a play area. The landlord here started the successful campaign to save Marston's Bitter in 1998 when extinction was on the cards; the beer is very popular around here. Note: the Banks's Original is nitro-keg. Q ☕ ⌀ ♣ P

CASTLE DONINGTON ✳

Cross Keys
90 Bondgate
🕐 12-2.30, 5-11; 12-11 Sat; 12-10.30 Sun
☎ (01332) 812214 website: www.midlandspubs.co.uk/leicestershire/crosskeys
Draught Bass; Marston's Pedigree; Theakston Best Bitter; guest beers Ⓗ
Spacious local where the single bar is divided into three areas. This pub sponsors the local rugby and cricket teams and hosts an annual spring beer festival. Note the carved Cross Keys sign in the bar, and the

CATTHORPE

Cherry Tree
Main Street (near church)
🕐 5 (12 Sat)-11; 12-10.30 Sun
☎ (01788) 860430
Ansells Mild, Bitter; Draught Bass; Hook Norton Best Bitter; guest beers ⍩
This small, friendly two-roomed free house attracts locals and drinkers from a wider area. The most southerly pub in Leicestershire, it boasts unusual cast diamond windows brightened by flower boxes and hanging baskets in summer; the old painted Phipp's Brewery sign can just be made out. Inside, the bar is comfortable and often very busy. The landlord likes to change the guest beer regularly, often buying from local micro-brewers. The skittle room, which was once stables, is also the venue for occasional live music. Outside summer drinking is in the car park. ⌂ Q ⌀ ♣ P

CAVENDISH BRIDGE

Old Crown Inn
400 yds off A6 at Trent Bridge
🕐 11-3, 5-11; 12-4.30, 7-10.30 Sun
☎ (01332) 792392
Draught Bass; Marston's Pedigree; guest beers Ⓗ
Friendly, 17th-century coaching inn, now a cosy atmospheric village pub on the south side of the River Trent. Several hundred water jugs hang from the lounge ceiling while the walls are crammed full of brewery and railway memorabilia; the display even extends into the lavatories. Up to six guest beers are on tap, often featuring beers from the Shardlow Brewery, just across the river; a guest cider is available in summer. Lunches are home cooked. Daytime buses run from Derby and Loughborough, but service is limited. ⌂ Q ⌀ ⌀ ⌀ ♣ P

CLAY COTON

Fox
On road between Yelvertoft and Stanford Hall
🕐 12-2, 6-11; 12-11 Sat; closed Mon; 12-10.30 Sun

INDEPENDENT BREWERIES

Belvoir Old Dalby
Blencowe Barrowden
Brewster's Stathern
Everards Narborough
Featherstone Enderby
Grainstore Oakham
Hoskins & Oldfield Leicester
John O'Gaunt Melton Mowbray
Langton East Langton
Parish Somerby
Shardlow Cavendish Bridge
Wicked Hathern Hathern

☎ (01788) 860363 e-mail: thefox@boozer.co.uk

Hook Norton Best Bitter; Wells Bombardier; guest beers Ⓗ

The Fox is a family-run pub set in lovely countryside. This 19th-century building is full of personal and musical memorabilia. With open fires in winter, the Fox has a wonderful atmosphere. It hosts a folk club (Tue eve), quiz night (Wed), acoustic rock (Thu) and bands (Sat). String quartets and Shakespeare in the lovely garden make this a great venue for entertainment. An appetising bar menu is complemented by a good range of beers, including one always from the Shepherd Neame stable. Children are welcome.
Ⓜ❀ⓄⒹ Å ♣ ♠ P

COALVILLE

Bull's Head

Warren Hills Road (B587, between Copt Oak and Whitwick) OS464142
✪ 11-2.30, 7-11; 12-3, 7-10.30 Sun
☎ (01530) 810511
Draught Bass; Ind Coope Burton Ale; Marston's Pedigree; Tetley Bitter Ⓗ
This is Leicestershire's highest pub, at 787 feet above sea level, and dates from the 18th century. Its single bar is very cosy; note the bar built from local granite and odd Whitwick red brick. Original paintings are displayed, and the beams are hung with brass blow lamps and horse brasses. The large garden has a children's play area at the rear, overlooking Charnwood Forest. High quality home-cooked lunches are served at this friendly local. Ⓜ Q ❀ Ⓒ Å P

Stamford & Warrington

72 High Street
✪ 10.30-3, 7-11; 12-3, 7-10.30 Sun
☎ (01530) 833278
Marston's Pedigree Ⓗ
Formerly a coaching inn, next to the level crossing, this two-roomed pub with a bar and smoke room is the kind of basic local where darts and dominoes are played. Although the choice of beer is limited, what is on offer is as good as it can get. This pub used to be frequented by the Earls of Stamford and Warrington. There are regular Arriva bus services from Leicester and Loughborough. Q ❀ ⒺⒹ ♣

CROFT

Heathcote Arms

Hill Street
✪ 11.30-11; 12-10.30 Sun
☎ (01455) 282439
Everards Beacon, Tiger, Original Ⓗ
Whitewashed pub in a prominent position overlooking the village war memorial, its heart is the cosy public bar, where locals drink with workers from the nearby quarry. The beamed ceiling and leather upholstered settles give the room a timeless feel, accentuated by old photos of Croft. The simply decorated lounge features bench seating along the walls. Outside is a split-level garden and an outbuilding where long alley skittles may be played by prior arrangement. The pub is close to Croft Hill, SSSI. Ⓜ Q ❀ Ⓒ Ⓓ ♣ P

DESFORD

Roebuck Inn

100 Newbold Road
✪ 12-1.30 (3 Sat), 7-11; 12-3, 7-10.30 Sun
☎ (01455) 822541
Everards Beacon, Tiger Ⓗ
Quiet, comfortable village pub, popular with both locals and passing trade, it is a regular finalist in Everards' Spencer Memorial Garden Competition for floral displays, taking first prize in 1997. The pub has two rooms, one of which has a piano and hosts regular singalongs (Wed, Fri and Sat eves) that are very popular. The smaller room has a low ceiling, and pictures of the floral displays adorn the walls. Q ❀ ⒸⒹ P

DISEWORTH ✤

Bull & Swan

Grimes Gate
✪ 11.30-2.30, 6 (7 Sat)-11; 11.30-3, 5-11 Fri; 12-3, 7-10.30 Sun
☎ (01332) 853960
Draught Bass; Marston's Pedigree; guest beers Ⓗ
Originally two pubs, the Bull's Head and the Swan, it is multi-roomed on different levels, with lots of cosy corners, but watch your head on the low beams and doorways. There is an upstairs function/dining room and a pool room; copper and brass bric-à-brac decorate most rooms. The outdoor seating area overlooks the village church. Although close to East Midlands Airport,

INN BRIEF

Leicestershire

CASTLE DONINGTON

Jolly Potter
36 Hillside
11-11;
12-10.30 Sun
Draught Bass; Marston's Pedigree Ⓗ
Built at the turn of the 20th century, this characterful pub has two rooms, the front one split into two distinct areas. Open fires make this a cosy local.

Lamb Inn
22 Station Road
11-11;
12-10.30 Sun
Mansfield Cask Ale; Marston's Pedigree Ⓗ
Small, two-roomed traditional local with a skittle alley. It fields skittles and darts teams.

DISEWORTH

Plough
33 Hallgate
11.30-3, 5 (6 Sat)-11;
12-10.30 Sun
Draught Bass; Marston's Pedigree; guest beer Ⓗ
17th-century pub with low ceilings and doorways; multi-roomed with real fires. Food is served lunchtime and eve. Popular with airport staff.

KEGWORTH

Anchor
139 Station Road
12-11;
12-10.30 Sun
Draught Bass; guest beer Ⓗ
Three-roomed, traditional village pub, which supports darts, dominoes, crib and fishing teams. Real fires warm the two rooms.

Cap & Stocking
20 Borough Street
11.30-2.30, 6.30-11;
12-3, 7-10.30 Sun
Draught Bass; Ⓖ **Hancock's HB; guest beer** Ⓗ
Three-roomed pub in the old part of the village, handy for the M1, East Midlands Airport and Donington Park. Lovely garden.

LOUGHBOROUGH

Beacon
Beacon Road
12-3, 6-11; 12-11 Sat; 12-10.30 Sun
Home Mild, Bitter; Marston's Pedigree; Theakston XB; guest beer Ⓗ
1960s local, off Epinal Way; it has a large lounge, a bar with pool table and TVs, a skittle alley and a pétanque pitch.

and popular with its staff, you are more likely to hear noise from the race track at Castle Donington. Regular daytime bus services run from Loughborough and Long Eaton. ▲Q⇆✿◑🌣⊟♣👝P⅄

EARL SHILTON

Dog & Gun
72 Keats Lane (600 yds off A47)
✪ 12-2 (2.30 Fri; not Mon-Wed); 5.30-11; 11.30-3.30, 5.30-11 Sat; 12-3, 7-10.30 Sun
☎ (01455) 842338
Banks's Original; Marston's Bitter, Pedigree Ⓗ
Just a short way down Keats Lane off the main A47 through the village, the pub is set back from the rest of the buildings on the street, as it was built behind the original pub after it was demolished in 1932. It has three rooms including a snug; the bar has a tiled floor and a large log fire. With a number of walking routes in the area, the pub runs its own rambling club and takes part in many local charity events.
▲Q✿◑⊟♣P

EAST LANGTON

Bell Inn
Main Street
✪ 11.30-2.30, 7 (6 Fri & Sat)-11; 12-4, 7-10.30 Sun
☎ (01858) 545278 website: www.thebellinn.co.uk
Greene King IPA, Abbot; Langton Caudle Bitter, Bowler; seasonal beers; Ⓗ **guest beers** Ⓖ
This 17th-century listed building is at the heart of Leicestershire's hunting country. A pretty walled garden, very low beams and an open log fire all add to its appeal. Quality food, produced from local ingredients, is freshly prepared each session, offering anything from a light bite to a banquet. Should you wish to extend your stay, B&B accommodation is provided in en-suite bedrooms. Langton Brewery, which started up in Nov 1999, is situated in buildings behind the inn. ▲Q✿🛏◑P

GUMLEY

Bell Inn
2 Main Street
✪ 11-3, 5.30-11; 12-3, 7-10.30 Sun
☎ (0116) 279 2476
Boddingtons Bitter; Everards Tiger; Greene King IPA; guest beers Ⓗ

Early 19th-century free house, popular with local rural and commuting urban clientele, where cricket memorabilia adorns the entrance hall. Pride of place is given to a cabinet containing miniature cricket bats, each inscribed with a county name, along with the signatures of the players. The beamed interior comprises an L-shaped bar and a no-smoking restaurant serving an extensive menu (no food Sun eve); senior citizen's lunch is offered at £3.50 Mon-Sat. The extensive patio garden to the rear is suitable for children or dogs.
▲Q✿◑♣P

HEATH END

Saracen's Head
Heath End Lane (minor road, linking B587 and B5006) OS368214
✪ 11-2.30, 7-11; 12-2.30, 7-10.30 Sun
☎ (01332) 862323
Draught Bass Ⓖ
Traditional, Victorian two-roomed pub, run by the same family since 1937. The brightly-lit bar has a quarry-tiled floor and scrubbed tables, while the lounge is comfortably furnished with more atmospheric lighting. Near Calke Abbey and Staunton Harold Church, it makes an ideal stop for walkers. This is one of the few places in the county where gravity Bass is served from a jug. Note, this place is not marked on most maps, and there is no public transport available.
▲Q✿⊟♣P

HEMINGTON

Jolly Sailor
21 Main Street
✪ 11-2.30, 4-11; 11-11 Sat; 12-10.30 Sun
☎ (01332) 810448 website:
www.midlandspubs.co.uk/leicestershire/jollysailor
Draught Bass; Greene King Abbot; M&B Mild; Mansfield Cask Ale; Marston's Pedigree; guest beers Ⓗ
Small, friendly village pub that started life as a farmhouse before being converted sometime around the mid-19th century. Both of the heavily-timbered rooms are warmed by real fires in winter, and decorated with collections of blow lamps and water jugs. As well as two changing

---

MELTON MOWBRAY
Boat Inn
57 Burton Street
12-2 (not winter Mon-Thu), 5-11; 12-3, 7-10.30 Sun
Burtonwood Bitter, Top Hat; guest beer Ⓗ
One-roomed traditional pub warmed by open fires.

Harboro Hotel
Burton Street
11-11;
12-10.30 Sun
Draught Bass; Bateman XB; guest beer Ⓗ
This former coaching inn retains its 18th-century character; note the old stone flags in the bar area. Food includes a Sunday carvery; 27 guest rooms.

MOUNTSORREL
Swan Inn
10 Loughborough Road
12-2.30, 5.30-11; 12-11 Sat; 12-3, 7-10.30 Sun
Greene King Ruddles County; Theakston Best Bitter, XB, Old Peculier; guest beer Ⓗ
Traditional village pub, where open fires enhance a cosy atmosphere. High quality food is served lunchtime and eve (booking advisable).

QUORN
Blacksmith's Arms
29 Meeting Street
12-2 (11-2.30 Sat), 5.30-11; 12-3, 7-10.30 Sun
Marston's Bitter, Pedigree Ⓗ
Busy village local with a low-beamed bar and a cosy snug and open fires. Usual pub games played.

Rutland
WING
King's Arms
Top Street
12-2.30 (not Mon), 6-11 (12-11 Fri & Sat summer); 12-3, 7-10.30 (12-10.30 summer) Sun
Beer range varies Ⓗ
Much extended inn, dating from 1649; King's Bar is the oldest part. Emphasis is on food; beer range always includes a Grainstore brew.

> ❋ symbol next to a main entry place name indicates there are Inn Brief entries as well.

guest beers and a real cider in summer, it stocks a range of more than 40 malt whiskies. Eve meals are served Fri and Sat, 6–8.30. ⚌Q✿①❶♣♣P

HINCKLEY

Railway Hotel
Station Road
✪ 11-11; 11-3.30, 7-11 Sat; 12-3.30, 7-10.30 Sun
☎ (01455) 615285
Banks's Original; Marston's Bitter, Pedigree Ⓗ
Spacious local where the basic bar, adorned with railway pictures, has recently been refurbished without losing any of its character. The lounge is comfortable and occasionally stages live music. The conservatory houses a pool table. Lunches are served Mon–Sat. Q✿✿❶♪❶◀♣P

HOSE

Black Horse
21 Bolton Lane OSSK734294
✪ 12-2.30 (not Tue), 7-11; 12-4, 7-10.30 Sun
☎ (01949) 860336
Brains Mild; Castle Eden Bitter; Home Bitter; guest beers Ⓗ
Traditional pub, with a beamed, carpeted lounge, upholstered wooden furniture and a brick fireplace where blackboards displaying food and drink menus hang by the corner bar. The unspoilt public bar has a tiled floor and simple wooden furniture, again the bar has a blackboard displaying the ales available. A wood-panelled restaurant serves a menu based on local produce; an embellished brick fireplace provides a focal point.
⚌Q✿❶⊟♣♣P

Rose & Crown
43 Bolton Lane
✪ 12-2.30 (may close winter Mon-Wed), 7 (5 Fri)-11; 12-3.30, 7.30-10.30 Sun
☎ (01949) 860424
Greene King Abbot, IPA; guest beers Ⓗ
A stone bar divides the public bar area from the lounge. The bar boasts copper-topped tables made from old barrels and a stone fireplace. Darts and pool are played and the juke box is kept turned down low. The lounge, converted from three rooms is, like the bar, beamed and carpeted, decorated with rural artefacts and furnished with comfortable benches, tables and chairs. The patio and safe garden are popular in summer. It always has a mild and one or two other guest beers.
⚌✿❶♣♣P

ILLSTON ON THE HILL

Fox & Goose
Main Street (off B6047, near Billesdon)
✪ 12-2.30 (not Mon-Tue or Wed-Thu winter), 5.30 (7-Mon)-11; 12-2.30, 7-10.30 Sun
☎ (0116) 259 6340
Everards Beacon, Tiger, Original; guest beer Ⓗ
A gem: a cosy, unchanged village pub with a timeless feel, displaying a fascinating collection of local mementos and hunting memorabilia. Tucked away, but it is well worth seeking out. Note the restricted lunchtime opening, especially in winter.
⚌Q✿⊟♣

KEGWORTH ✳

Red Lion
24 High Street
✪ 11-11; 12-10.30 Sun
☎ (01509) 672466 website: www.kegworthvillage.com
Adnams Bitter; Banks's Original; Courage Directors; guest beers Ⓗ
Partly dating from the 15th century, this central pub has three bars and a no-smoking room/children's room. A special feature is a range of Polish and Ukrainian vodkas, together with a good selection of malt whiskies and four guest beers. Pétanque is a popular game here, played on five courts; it also boasts a skittle alley and two darts rooms. The large garden with a children's play area makes a good vantage point for viewing aircraft in their final approach to East Midlands Airport. Eve meals served weekdays 5.30–8; no food Sun.
⚌Q✿✿❶⊟♣♣P

KIRBY MUXLOE

Royal Oak
35 Main Street
✪ 11-2.30 (3 Sat), 6-11; 12-3, 7-10.30 Sun
☎ (0116) 239 3166
Adnams Bitter; Everards Beacon, Tiger; guest beer Ⓗ
Built in the 1970s to replace the original Royal Oak, this pub opened as the Spanish Blade, but soon reverted to its original name. Despite its modern external appearance, the interior comprises a comfortable, traditionally-styled lounge bar, a restaurant and function room. The restaurant offers excellent home-made food with a good value 'early birds' menu at teatime. The bar offers traditional meals and snacks, including a wide range of filled baguettes. Popular with both locals and business folk, the pub hosts an angling club.
✿❶P

LEICESTER

Aberdale
111 Shackerdale Road, West Knighton
(A563, southern outer ring, W of Welford Rd)
✪ 11-11; 12-10.30 Sun
☎ (0116) 288 2231
Everards Beacon, Tiger, Original or seasonal beer Ⓗ
This lively 1960s pub is a true local, attracting customers from all walks of life from the surrounding area. There are two bars: one a large room with distinct areas, including a comfortably upholstered section and a no-smoking conservatory; the second, the 'snug' is the games room, off which another comfortable seating area serves as a family room until 8.30pm. It is pleasantly decorated and airy and has received the MBLR *Fresh Air* award. A varied menu always includes vegetarian options.
✿✿❶⊟♣P✗

Ale Wagon
27 Rutland Street
✪ 11-11; 12-10.30 Sun
☎ (0116) 262 3330
Hoskins & Oldfield Mild, Bitter, Ⓗ **Tom Kelly's Stout, EXS Bitter** Ⓟ **guest beers** (occasional) Ⓗ
Formerly the Queen's until 1999 when the Hoskins family acquired it as their only tied house and renamed it. A real local atmosphere pervades the 1930s

interior which boasts the original oak staircase, parquet and tiled floors. Two rooms and a central bar are supplemented by two function rooms upstairs. It always has six Hoskins & Oldfield beers on tap and is popular with rugby fans and drinkers visiting Leicester. ♨ 🍴 ♣

Black Horse
1 Foxon Street (on Braunstone Gate)
🕐 12-3 (not Tue-Thu), 5-11; 12-11 Fri & Sat; 12-10.30 Sun
☎ (0116) 254 0030
Everards Beacon, Tiger; guest beers Ⓗ
Small, traditional corner pub with two rooms and a central bar, untouched by refurbishment. Its unique boast is that it is the only known pub in Leicester with two swingboards outside. Guest beers are sourced from Everards Old English Ale Club. Darts and dominoes are played and it hosts a general knowledge quiz Sun eve. Q ♣

Hat & Beaver
60 Highcross Street
🕐 12-11; 12-6 Sun
☎ (0116) 262 2157
Hardys & Hansons Best Mild, Best Bitter, Classic Ⓗ
Basic, two-roomed pub with a relaxed atmosphere, one of Leicester's few remaining traditional locals. Well-filled, good value cobs are available lunchtime and early eve. It is handy for the Shires shopping centre. It has a TV in the bar and fields darts and cribbage teams. The pub closes on Sun when the last customer goes, but not before 6pm. ♣

Swan & Rushes
19 Infirmary Square (by Royal Infirmary)
🕐 12 (11 Sat)-11; 12-10.30 Sun
☎ (0116) 233 9167 e-mail: swanandrushes@bieressansfrontieres.org.uk
Hardys & Hansons Best Bitter, seasonal beers; Oakham JHB; guest beers Ⓗ
Triangular, two-bar 1930s boozer, recently refurbished to a high standard and now a shrine to great beer from Britain and beyond, stocking five real ales, four imported draught beers and around 90 top-rated bottled beers, mainly from Belgium and Germany. It boasts probably the best range of traditional Belgian Lambics of any UK pub, and stages occasional beer tastings and festivals. A cider is sometimes served. Food is always available, from good bread and cheese to full meals. It is close to the rugby and football grounds, so expect crowds before major games. ❀◗♠≠♣◆

Talbot
4 Thurcaston Road (road access from Loughborough Rd only)
🕐 11-2.30, 6-11; 11.30-4, 6.30-11 Sat; 12-4, 7-10.30 Sun
☎ (0116) 266 2280
Ansells Mild, Bitter; Marston's Pedigree; guest beers Ⓗ
A pub has stood on this site since the 15th century, but the cellars date back to the 12th century (owned by the church until the 19th century). This friendly local, in the heart of Old Belgrave, consists of two lounge areas, with a restaurant soon to be added (no food Sun). Handy for historic

Belgrave Hall, Abbey Pumping Station and Space Centre, it is only five minutes from the Great Central Steam Railway (Leicester North Station) which connects to nearby Rothley and Loughborough. ❀◗♣P

Vaults
1 Wellington Street (near Fenwicks' store)
🕐 5 (12 Fri & Sat)-11; 12-3, 7-11 Sun
☎ (0116) 255 5506 website: www.the-vaults.co.uk
Steamin' Billy Bitter; Old Laxey Bosun Bitter; guest beers Ⓗ
Small cellar bar with a friendly atmosphere selling beers only from micro-brewers, including one from the Isle of Man. Customers from far and near appreciate the ever-changing variety from seven handpumps; sales exceed 15 different cask beers weekly. Live music is performed Sat and Sun, when no charge is normally made. The Vaults can get very busy Sat afternoons. It is a rare outlet for traditional ciders, usually supplied by Weston's or Saxon. ≠(Midland) ◆⚋

Plough Inn
7 Station Road
🕐 11-2.30 (3 Sat), 6-11; 12-3, 7-10.30 Sun
☎ (0116) 286 2383
Everards Beacon, Tiger, seasonal beers; guest beers Ⓗ
This thatched village local attracts a wide range of customers. The oldest part dates from the 16th century, and the pub consists of a bar with beamed ceiling, a small cosy lounge and a dining area decorated with tapestries produced by the landlady. Outside a patio area has picnic tables and award-winning floral displays in summer. Long alley skittles may be played by arrangement, and the pub runs a chess club. No eve meals Sun. ❀◗◗⚋≠(Narborough) ♣P

Albion
Canal Bank
🕐 11-3 (4 Sat), 6-11; 12-3, 7-10.30 Sun
☎ (01509) 213952 e-mail: albioninn@hotmail.com
Mansfield Dark Mild, Cask Ale; Samuel Smith OBB; guest beer Ⓗ
Tranquil, canalside pub with a bar, darts room and a quiet lounge serving good value beer and home-cooked food. Outside drinking is on the canal bank or patio, which houses an aviary. The beer range frequently includes one from the Shepherd Neame brewery. The lounge is designated a no-smoking area until 8pm. ♨Q❀◗◗⚋≠♣P⚋

Greyhound Inn
69 Nottingham Road
🕐 5.30 (3.30 Fri; 11 Sat)-11; 12-10.30 Sun
☎ (01509) 216080
Marston's Pedigree Ⓗ
One of the oldest pubs in Loughborough, formerly a coaching inn, it used to have a football ground at the back where Loughborough Town Football Club beat Arsenal 13–0, but that was in December 1896. The famous cricketer, WG Grace, also once played a game of cricket here. The

interior has been knocked around a bit and is really only a bar with a lounge area at the back. This down-to-earth local fields a darts and several pool teams.
爱&≭♣P

Swan in the Rushes
21 The Rushes
✪ 11-11; 12-10.30 Sun
☎ (01509) 217014
Archers Golden; Marston's Pedigree; Tetley Bitter; guest beers Ⓗ
This traditional pub, part of the Tynemill Group, has three rooms (one no-smoking) and is popular with the locals for its constantly changing guest beers, which always include a mild. It also has a function room where you can be entertained by musicians most weeks. Two beer festivals are staged each year, during the spring and autumn when 30-plus beers are available. Continental beers are stocked, both draught and bottled, plus a good selection of malt whiskies. All food is freshly cooked; eve meals are served Mon–Fri.
🏠Q爱🖤✪(🛏🍴&≭♣🍴P

Tap & Mallet
36 Nottingham Road
✪ 12-2.30, 5-11; 11.30-11 Sat; 12-10.30 Sun
☎ (01509) 210028
Courage Best Bitter; Marston's Pedigree; Theakston Mild; guest beers Ⓗ
Genuine free house between the town centre and the station, usually stocking up to five guest beers, most of them from micro-breweries, often local. Theakston's Mild is sometimes replaced by a micro's mild and Hoegaarden is available on draught. There is only one bar/lounge, however the lounge can be sectioned off for private functions. The pub supports several darts teams. At the rear, a pleasant garden has a children's play area and pets corner.
🏠Q爱≭♣🍴

LUTTERWORTH

Fox Inn
34 Rugby Road (near M1 jct 20)
✪ 12-4, 5 (6.30 Sat)-11;
12-4, 7-10.30 Sun
☎ (01455) 552677
Flowers Original; Marston's Pedigree; guest beers Ⓗ
Single-roomed, 18th-century pub benefiting from both passing and local trade, this former Flowers house offers a good range of real ales and food in generous portions. The pub, which takes its name from Leicestershire's famous hunting tradition, features a large enclosed garden, a 50-seater function room and original stabling – for ther horse, Annie. Two rotating guest beers include a session ale of less than 4% ABV and a stronger ale. The pub may stay open in the afternoon, if there is customer demand.
🏠爱🖤(🛏P

MKT HARBOROUGH (Little Bowden)

Cherry Tree
Church Walk, Kettering Road
✪ 12-2.30 (not Mon or Wed), 5-11; 12-11 Fri & Sat; 12-10.30 Sun
☎ (01858) 463525
Everards Beacon, Tiger, Original Ⓗ

This spacious pub is characterised by low beams and a thatched roof. Drinkers and diners can choose from many small alcoves and seating areas. The pub is actually in Little Bowden, but is very much part of the adjoining Market Harborough community. Eve meals are served Mon–Sat, 6–9.
(🛏≭♣P🍴

MEDBOURNE

Nevill Arms
12 Waterfall Way
✪ 12-2.30, 6-11; 12-3, 7-10.30 Sun
☎ (01858) 565288
Adnams Bitter; Fuller's London Pride; Greene King Abbot; guest beers Ⓗ
The original building on this site was destroyed by fire in 1856. It is thought that a spark caused the fire after the village blacksmith wagered he could support an anvil on his chest while a horseshoe was forged upon it. The initials MGN over the door are those of Captain Nevill, who was heir to the nearby Holt estate when this former coaching inn was rebuilt in Tudor style, using local ironstone, during 1863. Outside, the banks of the Medbourne brooke abound with ducks; inside, a warm welcome awaits in the heavily beamed bar with its large inglenook.
🏠爱🖤(🛏♣P

MELTON MOWBRAY ☀

Crown
10 Burton Street
✪ 11-3, 7-11; 11-11 Sat; 12-4, 7-10.30 Sun
☎ (01664) 564682
Everards Beacon, Tiger; guest beers Ⓗ
Friendly, two-roomed town pub, run by a long-serving landlord. When this pub was refurbished recently the bar and lounge areas were exchanged, but kept as separate rooms. The lounge is designated no-smoking while lunchtime meals are being served, when it is popular with office workers and shoppers. It attracts all ages eves. Note old photographs of Melton Mowbray. Regular bus services run from Leicester, Loughborough and Nottingham.
🏠Q🍴爱🖤(🛏≭♣

Mash Tub
58 Nottingham Street
✪ 11-11; 12-10.30 Sun
☎ (01664) 410051
Banks's Original, Bitter; guest beer Ⓗ
This pub was recently refurbished, but retains the same single-roomed, split-level bar, with several well-defined seating areas. It has also maintained its local pub image during the week, but now attracts younger folk at weekends. It fields two well-established darts teams. The guest beer changes monthly.
(🛏≭♣

MOUNTSORREL ☀

Lindens Hotel
22 Halstead Road
✪ 12-4, 6-11; 12-11 Fri & Sat; 12-10.30 Sun
☎ (0116) 230 2163
website: www.country-focus.co.uk/mountsorrel/linden
Everards Beacon, Tiger, Original; guest beer Ⓗ

Built in 1901 as a family home, it was converted into a pub in 1951, comprising a large lounge and a bar, plus a pool room. The pub supports darts, pool and pétanque teams and holds a quiz every Sun eve. Both the lounge and bar are comfortably furnished and display contemporary illustrations. Note too, old photos of the building when it was a private residence. The gardens at the side house the pétanque court and children's play area. Occasional barbecues are organised at weekends. A regular bus service runs from Leicester and Loughborough. ▲Q⛄⚓♪◗♣P

Waterside Inn
Sileby Road
✪ 11-3, 6-11; 12-10.30 Sun
☎ (0116) 230 2758
Everards Beacon, Tiger, Original; guest beer Ⓗ
Built at the same time as the Loughborough–Leicester Canal (part of the Grand Union), in 1791, it is situated in front of Mountsorrel Lock. In summer you can sit outside and watch narrow boats pass through the lock. For thirsty boaters moorings are available nearby. The pub has a split-level lounge, part of which used to be the stables, and a cosy snug. Note the collection of canal and shipping memorabilia. It carries an extensive range of malt whiskies and English country wines.
▲Q⛄◗♣&P

OADBY

Cow & Plough
Stoughton Farm Park, Gartree Road (close to BUPA Hospital)
✪ 12-2.30, 5-9; 12-9 Sat (hours extend summer); 12-4, 7-9 Sun
☎ (0116) 272 0852 website: www.steamin-billy.co.uk
Steamin Billy Bitter; Hoskins & Oldfield Bitter; guest beers Ⓗ
Housed in a converted barn, this pub is replete with breweriana, mirrors and signs from bygone breweries and pubs, while photos of many of Leicester's historic pubs hang on the walls. The pub consists of vaults, a snug and a no-smoking room. Twice CAMRA East Midlands *Pub of the Year*, it is the home of Steamin' Billy beers, named after the owner's Jack Russell, who features on all pump clips in differing cartoon guises. Steamin' Billy beers are brewed under licence by Grainstore. Guest beers from local and micro-breweries are always available.
Q⛄⚓&♣●P⤬

OSGATHORPE

Storey Arms
41 Main Street
✪ 12-3, 7.30-11; 12-3, 7.30-10.30 Sun
☎ (01530) 224166
Banks's Original; Draught Bass; Mansfield Cask Ale; Marston's Pedigree; guest beer (occasional) Ⓗ
Traditional country pub with a 1960s-style bar and lounge. It fields both a men's and ladies' darts team and holds regular quiz nights. It hosts barbecues in the summer and an autumn beer festival. Occasionally on Sat eve, live music is staged for the entertainment of regulars. There is a very limited bus service here, operated by Arriva.
▲Q⛄⚓&♣P

PEGGS GREEN

New Inn
Clay Lane (B587, 200 yds from A512 at Griffydam roundabout)
✪ 12-2.30, 5.30-11; 12-3, 6.30-11 Sat; 12-3, 7-10.30 Sun
☎ (01530) 222293 e-mail: martina@aol.com
Draught Bass; Marston's Pedigree Ⓗ
Traditional 19th-century village pub with a cheeky Irish welcome, now run by the second generation of the same family. What makes it special, apart from quality beer, is the amazing collection of bric-à-brac and old photos that adorn every room. The three rooms are full to the brim with interesting artefacts, some have a local connection, but a lot of the items have been collected from all over the country, often donated by happy customers. A daytime bus service runs from Leicester, Coalville and Ashby-de-la-Zouch; alight at the Griffydam roundabout. ▲Q⚓◗&♣P

PINWALL

Red Lion
Main Road (B4116, 1 mile from A5)
✪ 11-11; 12-10.30 Sun
☎ (01827) 712223
Draught Bass; Marston's Pedigree; Taylor Landlord; guest beers Ⓗ
Very rural, cosy local on the B4116, it is just one of five or six buildings that make up the hamlet of Pinwall, not shown on most maps. Although encompassing a restaurant and hotel, these do not spoil the character of the pub itself. It usually has two guest beers on tap; no meals are served Sun eve. The hotel has nine guest rooms; prices may be negotiated for weekend stays.
▲Q⛄⚓◗P

QUORN ⛄

White Hart
32 High Street
✪ 11.30-11; 12-10.30 Sun
☎ (01509) 412704
Greene King IPA; Ind Coope Burton Ale; Marston's Pedigree; guest beers Ⓗ
This pub dates from 1690 and is now the oldest in Quorn, however, it has been modernised, and little evidence remains to show its true age. There are three distinct areas, all with open wood-burning fires; one section doubles as a dining area. Apart from the usual pub food, an extensive vegetarian menu is available and all food is freshly prepared on the premises. Pétanque is played in the grounds of the pub. A very frequent bus service (reduced eves) runs to Loughborough and Leicester.
▲Q⚓◗&♣P

SILEBY

Free Trade Inn
27 Cossington Road
✪ 11.30-2 (3 Fri), 5.30-11; 11-3, 6.30-11 Sat; 12-3, 7-10.30 Sun
☎ (01509) 814494
Everards Beacon, Tiger, Original Ⓗ
Thatched, timber-framed, 14th-century building, where the oldest part is at the front, and a thatched extension has been added at the rear. Grade I listed, it has been

modernised from a three-roomed pub into a single bar with three distinct areas. Note the photographs of old Sileby on the wall. Sun lunch is very popular, so it is advisable to book. A large garden at the back houses a pétanque court. Regular bus and train services run to this village. ⚟Q✿⊄⊨♣P

SOMERBY

Old Brewery Inn
39 High Street
✪ 12-2.30, 6.30-11; 12-10.30 Sun
☎ (01664) 454777
Draught Bass; Fuller's London Pride; Parish Special, Poachers', Baz's Bonce Blower Ⓗ
Formerly the Three Crowns, this 15th-century pub was given by Sir Richard Sutton to Brasenose College, Oxford in 1508. At that time the pub was thatched, with stabling for hunting horses, a coach house and adjoining walled garden. The pub has changed much, but remains a cosy place. The outbuildings are used by the Parish Brewery, who have brewed the strongest beer in the world (23% ABV). The strongest draught beer on the bar is Baz's Bonce Blower at 10% ABV. Note the glass-topped well next to the bar. Live music is performed every Sat. No food Sun eve. ⚟Q✿⊄⊔♣P

STOKE GOLDING

White Swan
High Street
✪ 12-2 (3.30 Sat), 6-11; 12-4, 7-10.30 Sun
☎ (01455) 212313
Adnams Bitter; Everards Tiger; guest beer Ⓗ
Despite a Warwickshire postal address, this 200-year-old pub is firmly in Leicestershire. Built for the navvies employed on the construction of the nearby Ashby Canal, the Swan is a typical, unspoilt two-roomed village local with two lounges to be precise. Food is good value, home made where possible, but does not intrude unduly on the drinking. Children's meals are exceptional value. Social events organised range from weekend breaks to a midsummer ball. ⚟Q✿⊄⊔♣P

THORNTON

Bricklayer's Arms
213 Main Street
✪ 12-3, 6-11; 11-11 Sat; 12-10.30 Sun
☎ (01530) 230808
Everards Tiger; guest beer Ⓗ
Traditional village local, dating partly from the 16th century, the pub consists of a cosy bar with a beamed ceiling and real fire, a lounge with a feature brick fireplace and a small dining room (no meals Sun eve or Mon). Views over nearby Thornton Reservoir can be enjoyed from the end of the large garden that houses a play area for children. There is also the possibility of a close encounter with one of the ducks or rabbits kept at the pub. ⚟Q✿⊄⊔♣P

THORPE SATCHVILLE

Fox
13 Main Street
✪ 12-3 (not Mon), 6.30-11; 12-4, 6.30-10.30 Sun
☎ (01664) 840257

John O'Gaunt Robin A Tiptoe, Coat O' Red; Mansfield Cask Ale Ⓗ
At this, the brewery tap for the John O' Gaunt Brewery, it is quite likely that you will meet the brewer behind the bar. The pub is surprisingly modern, given its rural location. Built in 1930s, it has a lounge, bar and dining room and supports cribbage, darts, pétanque, pool and skittles teams. A friendly local for all ages, it is popular with walkers. A limited daytime bus service runs to the village. ⚟Q✿✿⊄⊔♣P

THRUSSINGTON

Blue Lion
5 Rearsby Road
✪ 12-3 (4 Sat), 6-11; 12-4, 7-10.30 Sun
☎ (01664) 424266
Marston's Bitter, Pedigree, seasonal beers; Mansfield Dark Mild Ⓗ
Traditional village local, with a lounge and bar, built in 1785, but extended in later years. Note the collection of teapots in the lounge which overflows into the bar to compete for space with a display of bottled beers from around the world. The pub stocks an extensive range of malt whiskies. A children's play area and pétanque pitch are features of the attractive garden which is home to various poultry. A limited bus service from Leicester and Melton Mowbray is operated by Arriva.
Q✿⊄⊔♣P

WALCOTE

Black Horse
Lutterworth Road (A4304, 1 mile E of MI jct 20)
✪ 12-2 (not Mon-Thu or Sat), 7 (5.30 Fri; 6.30 Sat)-11; 12-3, 6.30-10.30 Sun
☎ (01455) 552684
Greene King Abbot; Hoskins & Oldfield Bitter; Oakham JHB; Taylor Landlord; guest beers Ⓗ
Single bar free house, well worth the one mile detour from the M1 motorway (junction 20), but note it is closed most lunchtimes. As well as four regular beers, two guest beers are normally on tap, usually sourced from independent breweries. Home-cooked Thai food is a speciality here; lunches are served Fri and Sun.
⚟✿⊄P

WALTON ON THE WOLDS

Anchor
2 Loughborough Road
OS591198
✪ 12-3, 7-11; 12-3, 7-10.30 Sun
☎ (01509) 880018 e-mail: blossom@jivenet.co.uk
Adnams Bitter; Taylor Landlord Ⓗ
Two 18th-century cottages were joined together to make this cosy rural pub in a village unspoilt by modern developments. There is a bar billiards table in the bar area, and a notable collection of pewter mugs on the beams in the lounge area. Locals say that the Anchor was so-named in honour of a locally-born admiral of the Turkish navy. This pub is popular with walkers and cyclists throughout the year, but public transport is poor. Eve meals are served Tue–Sat. Pétanque is played in the grounds.
Q✿⊄⚹♣P

WHITWICK

Lady Jane
Hall Lane OS443149
🕓 12-3, 6-11; 12-3, 6-10.30 Sun
☎ (01530) 836889
Mansfield Dark Mild; Marston's Pedigree; guest beer Ⓗ
Estate pub built in the 1960s, with a cellar designed for keg beer only, but the landlord has installed self-tilting stillages to enable sales of real ale. The bar has a pool table and dartboard, and supports pub football, cribbage and pool teams. There is a comfortable lounge in which live entertainment is staged. Buses from Leicester and Coalville stop nearby. ♿🍴🏠⚘🕯🛏♣️🅿️●

Three Horseshoes
11 Leicester Road
🕓 11-3, 6.30-11; 12-2, 7-10.30 Sun
☎ (01530) 837311
Draught Bass; M&B Mild Ⓗ
Unspoilt, traditional ale house, known locally as Polly's. It has a basic bar, popular with the locals and a tiny smoke room furnished with pews and decorated with commemorative plates of the area's coal mines. Regular bus services from Coalville, Leicester and Loughborough pass nearby. ♿Q🕯♣️

WYMESWOLD

Three Crowns
45 Far Street
🕓 12-2.30, 5.30 (6 Sat)-11; 12-3, 7-10.30 Sun
☎ (01509) 880153 website: www.country-focus.co.uk/wymeswold/threecrowns.htm
Adnams Bitter; Marston's Pedigree; guest beers Ⓗ
Late 18th-century pub, standing opposite the church, this friendly village local features beamed ceilings in the bar and a split-level snug/lounge. Locals are always on the piste (pétanque) or doing the *Telegraph* crossword. Two guest beers are stocked, one is always from a micro, often the local Belvoir Brewery. This pub holds a small beer festival each autumn in aid of local charities. A regular daytime bus service is operated by Kinch Bus. ♿Q🍴🕯🛏♣️🅿️

Rutland

BARROWDEN

Exeter Arms
28 Main Street
🕓 12-2, 6-11; 12-3, 7-10.30 Sun
☎ (01572) 747247
Blencowe Beach Boys, Naughty Boys, seasonal beers; guest beers Ⓗ
In a wonderful setting overlooking the village duck pond, this is the home of Blencowe Brewery. Good food is served (not Sun eve or Mon) but the pub manages a good balance between visitors and locals who play pub games, including pétanque. A fine stone exterior under Collyweston roof tiles, opens into one long room. Live music is performed regularly. ♿🕯🛏🍴♣️🅿️🅿️

CALDECOTT

Castle Inn
Main Street (outside village on B6003 to Rockingham) OS867934

🕓 12-3, 6-11; 12-3, 7-10.30 Sun
☎ (01536) 770641
Grainstore Triple B; Marston's Pedigree; Taylor Landlord; Theakston Best Bitter; Ⓗ
Just outside this Welland Valley village, by a disused railway line, this free house takes its name from Rockingham Castle, a mile up the road, across the river. The present owners reopened it in June 1998 after 18 months' closure for rebuilding and refurbishment works. A patio is used for outside drinking. No meals Sun eve. ♿Q🕯🛏🍴♣️🅿️♿

GREETHAM

Plough
23 Main Street
🕓 11-3, 5-11; 11-11 Fri & Sat; 12-10.30 Sun
☎ (01572) 813613
website: ploughgreetham@netscapeonline.co.uk
Grainstore Mild, Cooking, Triple B, Ten Fifty, seasonal beers Ⓗ
Welcoming village local, effectively tied to Grainstore Brewery in Oakham; the guest beers tend to be the brewery's seasonal offerings. Although meals are not served in the pub, filled baguettes are sold by the inch or foot, with local cheese a speciality. The building has been a public house since the late 18th century. Quoits played. Q🕯🛏🍴♣️🅿️

OAKHAM

Grainstore Brewery Tap
Station Approach
🕓 11-2.30, 5-11; 11-11 Fri & Sat; 12-10.30 Sun
☎ (01572) 770065 e-mail: grainstorebry@aol.com
Grainstore Mild, Cooking, Triple B, Steamin' Billy Bitter, Ten Fifty, seasonal beers Ⓗ
This refurbished grainstore is home to the brewery of the same name. The brewery is above the bar. Third-pint sampling glasses are available if you want to try all the wares in smaller quantities. Two sets of handpumps are in use, one with sparklers, one without. It is very handy for the station. Filled baguettes are usually available. Q🕯♿🚆♣️🅿️🖥

WING ❄

Cuckoo
3 Top Street
🕓 11.30-2.30 (not Tue), 6.30-11; 12-4, 7-10.30 12-10.30 (summer) Sun
☎ (01572) 737340
Fuller's London Pride; Marston's Pedigree; guest beers Ⓗ
A warm welcome and excellent beer awaits in this unspoilt 17th-century village free house. The large garden with play area is popular in summer, and the game of boules is played occasionally. Nearby the 'Wing Maze' is a curiosity dating from medieval times. No meals are served Tue. ♿Q🕯🛏🍴A♣️🅿️

Beer site
Keep in touch with CAMRA:
www.camra.org.uk

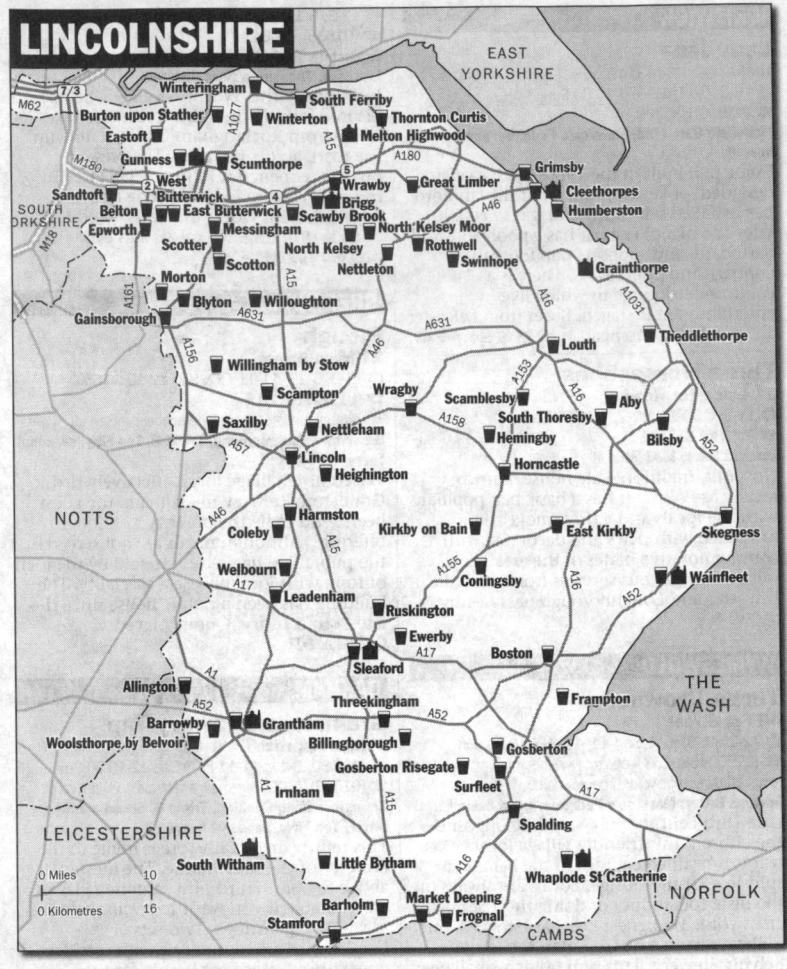

LINCOLNSHIRE

ABY

Railway Tavern
Main Road (off A16 via South Thoresby)
⚫ 12-3, 7-midnight (supper licence); (closed Tue winter); 12-3, 7-10.30 Sun
☎ (01507) 480676
Everards Tiger; guest beer Ⓗ
Friendly village pub serving splendid home-cooked food (home of Desperate Dan pie). It offers a warm welcome in its open bar with small seated area, real fire and dining section. There is an adjoining games room. Twice regional finalist for the Homefire *Pub of the Year*. Note the display of railway and agricultural memorabilia. The pub has a pleasant garden. ⚌Q✿⏍♣P⅄

ALLINGTON

Welby Arms
The Green (3 miles from A1)
⚫ 12-3, 6-11; 12-3, 7-10.30 Sun
☎ (01400) 281361
Draught Bass; John Smith's Bitter; Taylor Landlord; guest beers Ⓗ
This excellent inn has been local CAMRA *Pub of the Year* on several occasions recently.

It has a large bar area, offering a friendly welcome, plus good home-cooked food in the separate, no-smoking restaurant. Opening hours are 12–2 and 6.30–9.30 daily. A comprehensive menu is served including vegetarian options. The pub can provide accommodation, three double rooms are available. Good selection of beers and oversized, lined glasses are used.
⚌Q✿⏍⏍♣⅄✿♣P⏍

BARHOLM

Five Horseshoes
At end of lane, off sharp bend on main street
⚫ 5 (12.30 Sat)-11; 12-10.30 Sun
☎ (01778) 560238 e-mail: barholm22@aol.com
Adnams Bitter; Oakham JHB; Theakston Cool Cask; guest beers Ⓗ
Constructed of locally-quarried stone from Barnack, this 18th-century building can be difficult to find. Once located, the creeper-covered patio and large, well-appointed garden will be enjoyed by families in the summer months. The real fires will ward away winter chills. Pétanque is played here. The occasional house beer is brewed by Rooster's. ⚌Q⏍✿♣P

BARROWBY

White Swan
High Street (2 miles from Grantham)
☼ 11.30-11; 12-10.30 Sun
☎ (01476) 562375

Adnams Broadside; Draught Bass; Boddingtons Bitter; Marston's Pedigree Ⓗ

Close to the village green, the pub retains two bars; the small lounge is quiet and comfortable, while the larger public bar has pool, darts, cribbage and dominoes. Well-supported by village teams, it is busy when Barrowby village gala is held. The garden is very popular in summer. This is an unspoilt local with traditional values. **Q✿◑⊟♣P**

BELTON

Crown Inn
Stocks Hill, Churchtown (behind church)
☼ 4 (12 Sat)·11; 12-10.30 Sun
☎ (01427) 872834 website:
www.pub-explorer.com/olpg/crowninn/belton/index
John Smith's Bitter; Theakston Best Bitter; guest beer Ⓗ

Set midway between Doncaster and Scunthorpe in the fertile farmland of the Isle of Axholme, Belton is popular with commuters from both towns. Hidden behind the church and difficult to find, the Crown Inn dates back to an age when agriculture was the main employment. It is worth the effort to track down this friendly locals' pub, which is popular with young and old alike. There is an open-plan bar/lounge and a separate pool room. Although the pub does not provide meals, if you ask the landlord he may let you eat your own food at lunchtime, as long as you sup a few pints as well! **🚶✿♣P🍴**

BILLINGBOROUGH

Fortescue Arms
27 High Street
☼ 12-2.30, 6-11; 12-3, 7-10.30 Sun
☎ (01529) 240228
Greene King IPA; Ind Coope Burton Ale; guest beers Ⓗ

Fine country inn with an olde-worlde charm, set in a village on the edge of the fens, with the Roman Carr Dyke close by. There is a friendly, comfortable feel and two restaurants serve excellent home-made food (booking advisable). Nearby is the priory of St Mary, set up by Gilbert, later St Gilbert of Sempringham, the eldest son of a wealthy Norman knight. He founded the Gilbertine monastic order here in 1135, the only one originating in England. At the dissolution, all the buildings were pulled down but the stone has been reused locally. This pub has some of it in its thick walls. **✿◑⊟♣P**

BLYTON

White Hart Inn
66 High Street (A159, between Scunthorpe and Gainsborough)
☼ 12-3 (not Mon), 7-11; 11-11 Sat; 12-10.30 Sun
☎ (01427) 628683
Beer range varies Ⓗ

Three-roomed village pub. The bar is small with armchairs and a cosy fire, creating a homely atmosphere. The lounge is spacious and the games room has pool and large-screen TV. The pub hosts dominoes and

ladies' darts. Beers from Highwood Brewery are often featured. Meals are served Sun lunchtime only. There is a pleasant patio available for outdoor drinking.
🚶🚲✿◑♣P

BOSTON

Ball House
Wainfleet Road (A52, 1 mile from centre)
☼ 11.30-3, 6.30-11; 12-3, 7-10.30 Sun
☎ (01205) 364478 website: www.the ballhouse.co.uk
Draught Bass; Bateman XB, XXXB; guest beer Ⓗ

Mock-Tudor pub that is very welcoming and friendly. This is its ninth entry in this *Guide*. Sited on a former cannonball store – hence its unusual name. It boasts award-winning floral displays in summer, in fact with tubs, planters and hanging baskets, the pub is draped in a blanket of flowers. Certificates adorn the walls, awarded annually by the brewery recognising superb horticultural skills. Freshly cooked meals are served eves and Sun lunch using local produce. During fine weather in the summer, barbecues are held.
🚶✿◑P

Britannia
4 Church Street (near Assembly Rooms)
☼ 11-11; 12-10.30 Sun
☎ (01205) 365178
e-mail: manager@britanniainn.fsnet.co.uk
Draught Bass; Bateman XB Ⓗ

Recently refurbished, busy town-centre pub, it is one of the oldest in the area. The exterior is one of the most photographed pubs in the county, due to its proximity to the Boston Stump (St Botolph's parish church). Many of the internal features and breweriana associated with this pub have disappeared since the redecoration but there is a pleasing, refreshing atmosphere. The small beer garden overlooks the River Haven, the saltside of the River Witham. No food served on Sun. **✿◑**

Coach & Horses
86 Main Ridge (100 yds E, John Adams Way)
☼ 5 (6 Fri)-11; 11-3, 7-11 Sat; 12-3, 7-10.30 Sun
☎ (01205) 362301
Bateman XB, XXXB Ⓗ

This is a one-roomed pub in the traditional style. Visitors are always assured a friendly welcome from the landlord, and the regulars are keen to chat. Handy for the local football ground which is nearby, the pub does get busy on match days. Dominoes, darts and pool teams play here. Cosy real fire during winter months. **🚶♣**

INDEPENDENT BREWERIES

Bateman Wainfleet
Blue Bell Whaplode St. Catherine
Blue Cow South Witham
DarkTribe Gunness
Donoghue Grainthorpe
Happy Hooker Sleaford
Highwood Melton Highwood
Newby Wyke Grantham
Oldershaw Grantham
Orchard Brigg
Willy's Cleethorpes

Cowbridge

Horncastle Road (B1183, N of town)
✪ 11-3, 6-11; 12-4, 7-10.30 Sun
☎ (01205) 362597
Home Bitter; Theakston Mild; guest beers Ⓗ
Just out of town, this pub is popular with drinkers and diners. The pub is separated into three main areas, a traditional, no-nonsense public bar, a smaller lounge and a modern restaurant. The public bar offers a friendly drinking environment with darts, pool and other pub games plus a large display of football scarves. The lounge doubles as a reception area for the restaurant, which serves excellent, well-priced food. The lounge has a large open fire and an enormous collection of baseball caps from around the world. The pub is handy for Boston Golf Club. ♨☸◑⌂♿♣P

Eagle

144 West Street (near station)
✪ 11-3, 5-11; 11-11 Fri & Sat; 12-10.30 Sun
☎ (01205) 361116
Adnams Broadside; Banks's Bitter; Taylor Landlord; guest beers Ⓗ
Back in the early 1980s, this was the first pub in Boston to have a good selection of beers. This Tynemill-owned pub is a delight. The small, comfortable lounge has an open fire in winter. The L-shaped bar area has a pool table and dartboard and a large projector screen TV now shows major sporting events. An upstairs room is used by a number of societies including the Boston folk club. As well as stocking the regular guest ales, the pub runs themed beer festivals. Occasional live music is performed in the bar. There is always a cheap bitter available. ♨☸◑≒♣●

Goodbarns Yard

8 Wormgate
✪ 11.30-11, 12-10.30 Sun
☎ (01205) 355717 website: www.goodbarns.com
Courage Directors; Greene King Old Speckled Hen; Theakston XB; guest beer Ⓗ
Primarily a restaurant but it has a public bar serving real ale. The food is excellent quality and value for money. Booking advisable but not always necessary and catering for large parties is possible. A free meal is offered on your birthday (providing proof is given). Ring for details. Goodbarns Yard has won the local *Good Food Guide* award for the past five years. In the summer your meal or drink can be enjoyed in the garden or patio area overlooking the River Witham. Inside the pub beer and brewery memorabilia decorate the walls; plaques, pictures and pump fronts. The pub is set in the most historic part of Boston. ♨☸◑

Ship Tavern

Custom Lane (off South Sq)
✪ 11-11; 12-10.30 Sun
☎ (01205) 358156
Bateman Mild, XB; Greene King IPA; guest beer Ⓗ
This one-roomed pub is actually very spacious with distinct areas for pool and darts, etc. A mixture of wooden pews, cushioned seating, a farmhouse table and benches creates a traditional feel. Breweriana adorns the walls in this popular town pub. A limited daily choice of rolls and sandwiches are for sale but no meals are served. The small patio area is ideal in summer. ☸≒♣♣

CLEETHORPES

Crow's Nest Hotel

Balmoral Road
✪ 11-3, 6-11; 12-4, 7-10.30 Sun
☎ (01472) 698867 e-mail: cnesthotel@aol.com
Samuel Smith OBB Ⓗ
Welcoming estate pub with a strong community focus. The smart, quiet lounge (with no-smoking area) contrasts with a sometimes boisterous public bar. The pub interior has remained virtually unchanged since it was built. It is the only local pub to have received two merit awards from the local CAMRA branch. Well worth the visit despite being 20 minutes' walk from the seafront. (It is on the No. 4 bus route from the pier.) It offers the cheapest pint in Cleethorpes and is the only Sam Smith's outlet for miles. A classic example of 1950s pub architecture. Q☸✍◑⌂♣♿

Smugglers

Highcliff Road
✪ 11-11; 12-10.30 Sun
☎ (01472) 200866
Banks's Original, Bitter; Camerons Strongarm; Marston's Pedigree; guest beer Ⓗ

INN BRIEF

BILSBY
Three Tuns
Thurlby Road
11.30-2.30 (not Sat), 7-11;
7-10.30 Sun
Bateman XB; guest beers (summer) Ⓗ
Typical village pub built around 1900. Decorated with a huge collection of teapots. Meals served all sessions.

BRIGG
Black Bull
Wrawby Street
11-3 (4 Thu), 7-11; 11-11 Sat;
12-3, 7-10 Sun
John Smith's Bitter; guest beers Ⓗ
Homely town-centre pub popular on market days. Beer garden and good food available.

BURTON UPON STATHER
Ferry House Inn
Stather Road
12-4.30 (not Mon-Fri), 7-11 (extended hours Sat in summer); 12-10.30 Sun
Beer range varies Ⓗ
Popular pub alongside River Trent. The large garden is perfect for watching ships go by. Live music Sat eves in summer.

GAINSBOROUGH
Peacock
Corringham Road
11-11 (may vary); 12-10.30 Sun
Camerons Bitter; Marston's Pedigree; guest beer Ⓗ
Good facilities at this pub: family room, children's play area, musical entertainment performed monthly and excellent food. Even has its own ghost.

GRANTHAM
Lord Harrowby
65 Dudley Road
4 (12 Sat)-11;
12-10.30 Sun
Draught Bass; Worthington Bitter; guest beer Ⓗ
Traditional two-roomed pub on the outskirts of town. Piano played Sat eve in lounge.

HARMSTON
Thorold Arms
High Street
12-2, 6-11 (11-11 summer);
12-4, 7-10.30 Sun
John Smith's Bitter; guest beers Ⓗ
250-year-old stone-built village pub. One of the guest beers is usually from a smaller local brewery.

Semi-subterranean bar; the cellars of a former hotel, the building is now private flats. The layout gives the feel of a multi-roomed pub, albeit served by one bar. Wholesome food is served at reasonable prices and special offers are often available. Regular 'happy hours' are advertised. The pub has only recently undergone a full refurbishment and provides a comfortable retreat during a day at the seaside!
❀◑⇌♠P⚲

Willy's Pub and Brewery
17 Highcliff Road
❂ 11-11; 12-10.30 Sun
☎ (01472) 602145
Bateman XB, Willy's Original Bitter, guest beers H

A popular seafront bar, Willy's has been in this *Guide* since it opened in 1985. A policy of serving beers from micros as well as regional breweries has proved successful. The pub has its own brewery attached which commenced operations in 1989 and produced its millionth pint in late 2000. Providing excellent food at a reasonable price has long been a hallmark of this pub. Attracting customers of all ages during the day, the bar is predominantly aimed at the younger generation in the eve, but don't let this put you off! The brewery can be viewed from the bar. A seaside gem.
◑⇌

COLEBY

Tempest Arms
Hill Rise (off A607, 7 miles S of Lincoln)
❂ 11.30-2.30, 6.30-11; 12-3, 7-10.30 Sun
☎ (01522) 810287
Bateman XB; guest beers H

At the heart of a quiet village, standing on the Viking Way, this pub offers fabulous views over the Trent Valley. Well-furnished and traditional, it stocks one regular real ale plus changing guest beers. Excellent bar meals are served and a small restaurant is also available. Popular with locals, it also provides a warm welcome to visitors, particularly from the friendly pub dog. The village is well served by the Lincoln to Grantham bus service which has a late bus on Fri and Sat eves. This is the pub's tenth consecutive entry in this *Guide*.
❀◑&♣P

CONINGSBY

Leagate Inn
Leagate Road (B1192, E of village, off A153)
❂ 11-3, 7-10.30; 6-11 Fri & Sat; 12-10.30 Sun
☎ (01526) 342370
Marston's Pedigree; Theakston XB H

Historic pub, dating back to the 16th century, when it was a guide house in the fens, with a blazing torch held high on the gable. The iron holder for the beacon remains today, as a reminder of times gone by. The pub has retained its original internal layout, with beamed ceilings, open fireplaces and high oak settles. Today's travellers can dine in what used to be the stables, now an unusual long, low restaurant, boasting a good range of home-cooked meals. ❀Q❍❀♠◑⊟♣P

EAST BUTTERWICK

Dog & Gun
High Street (signed from A18)
❂ 7 (5 Thu & Fri; 12 Sat)-11; 12-10.30 Sun
☎ (01724) 783419
DarkTribe Dixie's Mild, Galleon; John Smith's Bitter H

Basic but welcoming local alongside the River Trent. Three rooms are served by a central bar. This village pub is renowned for its real fires. It is now also well-known as one of two regular outlets for local micro, DarkTribe. Other DarkTribe beers are rotated with Galleon as available. The mild is a regular feature. The pub has a strong local following and attracts many visitors enjoying its pleasant location. The Hewitts Brewery sign on the wall shows its former pedigree. ❀❀♣P

EAST KIRKBY

Red Lion
Main Road
❂ 12-2.30, 7-11; 12-3, 7-10.30 Sun
☎ (01790) 763406
Draught Bass; Broadstone Best Bitter; guest beers H

Typical village pub used extensively by locals and visitors alike. This three-roomed inn is full of antiques, clocks, old tools and breweriana. The pub is close to a WWII air museum, once a fully operational airfield. The Red Lion offers a warm welcome and good, home-cooked meals.
❀❍❀◑▲♠P

HORNCASTLE
Admiral Rodney Hotel
North Street
11-3, 5.30-11; 11-11 Sat;
11-10.30 Sun
Courage Directors; John Smith's Bitter; guest beers H
Lively town-centre pub adjoining a hotel. The bar bears a maritime theme.

KIRKBY ON BAIN
Ebrington Arms
Main Street
12-3, 7-11;
12-3.30, 7-10.30 Sun
Bateman XB; guest beers H
16th-century village-centre pub with a constantly changing choice of guest beers. The restaurant is noted for good food.

LEADENHAM
Willoughby Arms
5 High Street
12-3 (not Mon-Wed), 5 (6 Sat)-11;
12-3, 7-10.30 Sun
Adnams Bitter; Draught Bass; Marston's Bitter; guest beers H
Recently refurbished and reopened village inn with emphasis on food. Wood-panelled bar with comfortable armchairs.

LINCOLN
Tap & Spile
21 Hungate
11.30-11;
12-10.30 Sun
Beer range varies H
Known as the White Horse until 1993. Home to the world circular chess society plus two quizzes. Popular with a wide clientele.

NORTH KELSEY
Royal Oak
High Street
12-2 (4 Sat), 7-11;
12-2, 7-10.30 Sun
Barnsley Bitter; Marston's Pedigree; guest beers H
Extensively refurbished pub in quiet village. Real fire and wood-burning stove in lounge. Reasonably priced food served Tue-Sun.

SCAWBY BROOK
King William IV
177 Scawby Road
12-2, 6-11; 12-3, 7-10.30 Sun
Theakston Best Bitter; Worthington Bitter; guest beers H
Small, friendly local with much royal memorabilia. Meals served Sun lunchtime only.

EASTOFT

River Don
Sampson Street (On A161, Gainsborough-Goole road)
☼ 12-2 (not Tue), 6 (7 Tue)-11; 12-11 Sat; 12-10.30 Sun
☎ (01724) 798040
Barnsley Bitter; John Smith's Bitter; guest beers H
Remote village pub transformed by its new owner. The introduction of well-kept real ales and delicious 'hot skillet' meals have attracted customers from far and wide. No food served on Tue. A separate restaurant is also available. Stock beers are supplemented by Yorkshire independents such as Daleside, Hambleton, Rooster's and Taylor, plus others such as Dent and Moorhouses. It hosts regular party themes nights and ferret races in season (Oct–Mar), on alternate Tue eves enjoy bingo or a quiz. ♨❀◑♣P

EPWORTH

Red Lion Hotel
Market Place
☼ 11-11; 12-10.30 Sun
☎ (01427) 872208
Ind Coope Burton Ale; Tetley Bitter; guest beer H
Located in historic Epworth (home of the Wesleys and unofficial capital of the Isle of Axholme), this residential, old coaching inn is in sight of the ancient market cross from which John Wesley used to preach. Although now open plan, the pub is divided into several distinct drinking areas including a pleasant conservatory and a no-smoking area, which is much appreciated but most unusual for these parts. The restaurant is popular with both residents and visitors, it has an extensive menu with sizzling steaks a particular speciality. ♨❀✑◑P✁

EWERBY

Finch Hatton Arms
Main Street
☼ 12-3, -11; 12-3, 6-10.30 Sun
☎ (01529) 460363
Blue Bell Olde Honesty; Everards Tiger; guest beer H
Built in the early 1870s as the Angel Inn, it was bought by Lord Winchelsea in 1875 and given his family name. Until the mid-1960s it was a traditional brewery-owned village pub, it then started the transition into the free house it is today. A later transformation turned it into a small fully-equipped hotel offering excellent value for money. The attractive Tudor-style bar and restaurant provide a homely, but lively atmosphere. ♨Q❀✑◑ ⊟P⊟

FRAMPTON

Moores Arms
Church End (take A16 1 mile E, from Kirton roundabout to Marsh)
☼ 11.30-3, 6-11, 11.30-11 Sat; 12-10.30 Sun
☎ (01205) 722408
Draught Bass; Bateman XB; guest beer H
Very attractive, friendly village pub dating back to 1690. Situated near the marshes and world-famous RSPB nature reserve, it is popular with walkers and birdwatchers. An extensive, home-cooked menu is available in the bar and restaurant. Very family-

friendly. The guest beer is usually Fuller's London Pride or Black Sheep Best Bitter. ♨Q❀✑◑⊟♿✑♣❀P✁⊟

FROGNALL

Goat
155 Spalding Road (B1525, Deeping-Spalding road)
☼ 11.30-2.30, 6-11; 12-3, 6.30-10.30 Sun
☎ (01778) 347629
Beer range varies H
Set well back from the main road, this pub dates from around 1640 and consists of a bar and smaller drinking area by the entrance. Families are welcome in the large dining room which serves wholesome meals. The spacious garden has a splendid play area for under-fives and many toys. The beer range is always interesting with many smaller breweries featured among the hundreds of beers sold to date. ♨❀◑♿▲P⊟

GAINSBOROUGH ❖

Eight Jolly Brewers
Ship Court, Silver Street (off market place)
☼ 11-11; 12-10.30 Sun
☎ (01427) 677128
Caledonian Deuchars IPA; Highwood Tom Wood Best Bitter; Taylor Landlord; guest beers H
Real ale oasis and freqent CAMRA award-winner. A small but very lively town-centre pub with folk club on alternate Fri eves. Bustling bar with TV downstairs and quiet lounge above. Three regular beers are offered plus five ever-changing guests mainly from small breweries. Stocks a wide selection of European bottle-conditioned beers. Good food is served daily (not Sun). Note the enormous collection of pump clips covering the walls and ceiling. A real cider is available. Q❀✑♣❀P✁⊟

GOSBERTON

Bell Inn
High Street
☼ 11.30-3, 5.30-11; 11.30-11 Sat; 12-3, 7-10.30 Sun
☎ (01775) 840186
Draught Bass; guest beer H
This family-run pub offers two bars and is located in the centre of the village. The restaurant has been recently refurbished and bar snacks are also available. There is a no-smoking area upstairs. The pub is very popular with locals and has darts and quiz teams. ♨❀◑P✁

GOSBERTON RISEGATE

Duke of York
106 Risegate Road
☼ 12-11; 12-4, 7-10.30 Sun
☎ (01775) 840193
Bateman XB; John Smith's Magnet; guest beers H
Friendly, bustling village local with a widespread and growing reputation for its reasonably-priced beer and food. At the centre of local community life, the pub hosts a variety of charity fundraising events. The multi-roomed interior includes a no-smoking dining room (no food Mon lunchtime) and a separate games area. The ever-changing range of excellent guest beers

ensures every palate is catered for, making the pub well worth a visit. The large garden has a children's play area and goats and other animals are an added attraction.
🏠Q❀◖●Å♣P

GRANTHAM ❄

Blue Pig
9 Vine Street
☀ 11 (10.30 Sat)-11; 12-10.30 Sun
☎ (01476) 563704
Castle Eden Ale; Flower's Original; York Yorkshire Terrier; guest beers Ⓗ
Lovely olde-worlde inn which has been part of Grantham's pub scene since 1820. A true popular meeting place catering for customers of all ages. The delicious home-cooked meals are good value for money which means it is often busy. The real fire adds to the country atmosphere although the Blue Pig is located in the town centre. 🏠◖●🍴

Hogshead
8 Market Place
☀ 11-11; 12-10.30 Sun
☎ (01476) 571660
Boddingtons Bitter; Marston's Pedigree; Wadworth 6X; guest beers Ⓗ
Modern, open-plan pub attracting a wide range of customers. Pictures of Grantham's local history decorate the walls. Regular beer, wine and cider festivals are held. Along with the regular ales stocked, there is a good range of continental beers served. Reasonably priced meals are offered lunchtime and eve. ◖●&♣🍴

Nobody Inn
North Street
☀ 12-11; 12-10.30 Sun
☎ (01476) 565288 website: www.nobodyinn.com
Beer range varies Ⓗ
Unpretentious, traditional corner pub, with an accent on an ever-changing range of interesting beers. The choice includes ales from Barnsley, Kelham Island, Newby Wyke, Oakham, Oldershaw and Sam Smith. This busy pub attracts a good mix of drinkers. Pool, darts and bar billiards feature. Be wary of the disguised loo doors! &≈♣

GREAT LIMBER

New Inn
High Street (A18)
☀ 11-3, 6.30-11; 11-11 Fri & Sat; 12-10.30 Sun
☎ (01469) 560257
Boddingtons Bitter; Samuel Smith OBB; guest beers Ⓗ
Imposing building on the main road, the pub sits on a bend in this attractive village. It has a thoroughly well-deserved reputation for food which is served mainly in the lounge. The public bar has a traditional feel about it and proves a popular haunt for villagers and visitors alike. The beer garden is a pleasant spot to enjoy a beer or two on a hot summer's eve, perhaps more if you are staying overnight at the pub!
🏠Q❀🛏◖●🍴♣P

GRIMSBY

Rutland Arms
26-30 Rutland Street (off A1098 Cleethorpe road behind Ramsdens store)

☀ 11-11; 7-10.30 Sun
☎ (01472) 268732
Old Mill Mild, Bitter, Bullion Ⓗ
Splendid conversion from a run-down social club, to a truly locals' local. One of Old Mill's earlier purchases, the interior features stained wood and exposed brickwork. The games area is separated from the comfortable main lounge. There is an occasional Karaoke session, and on Sun lunchtime a free snack meal is available to all customers. The outdoor drinking area is on the street.
❀≈ (New Clee) ♣

Swigs
21 Osborne Street
☀ 11-11; 7-10.30 Sun
☎ (01472) 354773
Bateman XB; Willy's Original Bitter; guest beers Ⓗ
Second outlet for Willy's Brewery of Cleethorpes. It has a continental café atmosphere and offers excellent home-made food at lunchtime when it is busy with shoppers and local office workers. Sometimes boisterous in the eve when it is popular with students. A worthy recipient of an award by the local CAMRA branch to celebrate 10 consecutive years in this *Guide*.
◖≈ (Town)

Tap & Spile
Garth Lane (Behind Freshney Place shopping centre)
☀ 12-11; 12-10.30 Sun
☎ (01472) 357493
Beer range varies Ⓗ
Excellent conversion of the ground floor of an old Victorian flour mill. Eight ever-changing guest ales and also one of the few pubs in the locality to serve real cider. Quizzes are held weekly on Mon and Thu eves. Music featured on a Fri and Sat night covers all tastes from acoustic blues, jazz, rock and contemporary music. Lunchtimes and Fri and Sat eve, excellent home-made meals are available. There is a balcony for outside drinking in summer. Worthy 2001 winner of the local CAMRA *Pub of the Year* – an absolute gem in a desert of mediocrity.
❀◖≈ (Town) ●

Yarborough Hotel
29 Bethlehem Street (next to station)
☀ 11-11; 12-10.30 Sun
☎ (01472) 268283
Bateman Mild; Courage Directors; Shepherd Neame Spitfire; Theakston Best Bitter; Wadworth 6X; guest beers Ⓗ
Local CAMRA *Pub of the Year* 1998-99, the spacious ground floor of a grand Victorian hotel which has been beautifully restored by Wetherspoon's. There are two large bar areas, with no music or TV. The bigger bar is mainly used by regulars while the rear one is usually popular with customers enjoying a quiet meal. There is no obligation to dine, you may simply prefer a smoke-free, quiet, relaxed atmosphere. The pub is well-patronised and attracts all age groups – it tends to have a lively crowd at weekends. Food is served all day.
Q❀◖&≈ (Town) ●●

GUNNESS

Jolly Sailor
Station Road
✪ 12-11; 12-10.30 Sun
☎ (01724) 782423
DarkTribe Honey Mild; John Smith's Bitter; guest beer Ⓗ
Roadside village local situated on main A18. Single bar serves cosy, quiet lounge and separate public bar. Improvements are planned following the purchase of the pub. A function room is available for meetings and special occasions and a beer garden has recently opened. Friendly, welcoming atmosphere. It is a regular outlet for local DarkTribe beers, such as the Jolly Jack Tar which is a house beer brewed for the pub. The guest beer is from DarkTribe or occasionally from another independent brewery.
🏚Q❀✿🚄 (Althorpe) ♣P

HEIGHINGTON

Butcher & Beast
High Street
✪ 11-4, 7-11; 11-11 Sat & summer; 12-10.30 Sun
☎ (01522) 790386
Draught Bass; Bateman XB, XXXB; guest beers Ⓗ
18th-century pub in the centre of a much enlarged village just south of Lincoln. Its picturesque setting includes award-winning floral displays. The several drinking areas are usually well populated. Dominoes, darts and crib are popular. Home-cooked food is served at lunchtime and excellent eve meals are offered in the restaurant. Try the pies, the pub speciality. Look out for the original 1920s beer engine behind the bar; still in daily use. Children are welcome in the garden, restaurant and games area.
🏚Q❀✿♣P🍺

HEMINGBY

Coach & Horses
Church Lane (between A158/A153, next to village church)
✪ 12-2 (not Mon or Tue), 7 (6 Wed-Fri)-11; 12-3, 7-10.30 Sun
☎ (01507) 578280
Bateman Mild, XB; guest beer Ⓗ
Regular entry in this *Guide*, this friendly, popular village local is well worth seeking out. The pleasant, cosy interior is enhanced by a low-beamed ceiling and a roaring log fire ensures a warm welcome on the coldest of winter days. An increasingly rare outlet for Bateman Mild. The guest beer is usually from an interesting micro. The well-cooked, nicely-presented food complements the fare making this an excellent all-round pub. No food Mon or Tue, lunchtime meals Wed–Sun, evening meals Wed–Sat. 🏚Q❀✿ Å♣P

HUMBERSTON

Trading Post
Grimsby Road
✪ 11-11; 12-10.30 Sun
☎ (01472) 601092
website: www.grimsbyandistrict.com
Mansfield Cask Ale; Marston's Pedigree Ⓗ
With an American log cabin theme, this recently-built pub is an unusual addition to the area. A wealth of memorabilia adorns the walls and ceilings. Large portions of reasonably priced food complement the excellent beers on offer. The pub is a paradise for children with 'Fort Apache' guaranteed to keep them happy. The beer garden features a climbing frame that appeals to a wide age range, making the pub a firm family favourite. It can get busy, so you may have to wait a short while for a table if you wish to eat. ❀❀✿P

IRNHAM

Griffin Inn
Bulby Road (2 miles from Corby Glen)
✪ Winter: 12-3; closed Mon-Thu winter; 12-3, 7 10.30 Sun
☎ (01476) 550201
Theakston Old Peculier Ⓗ
This inn, built of local stone, has been serving the Irnham estate since 1895. Note the stone griffin over the portico. This quiet and friendly rural retreat has mainly unmodernised rooms with wood-burning open fires in the bar and lounge, and a restaurant serving good, home-cooked food. (Steak special on Fri night.) The pub also has its own darts, dominoes and pool teams. For the last nine years it has held a 30-barrel beer festival with music (July).
🏚Q❀✿✿ Å♣P

LINCOLN ❀

Cornhill Vaults
Exchange Arcade, Cornhill (next to central market)
✪ 11-11; 8-10.30 Sun
☎ (01522) 535113
Samuel Smith OBB Ⓗ
19th-century, historic corn store with classic, vaulted brick ceiling, converted to a pub in 1976. Although it is in the city centre its atmophere has much in common with that of village pubs around the city, perhaps due to its strong regular trade. There is an interesting, frequently changed, menu of home-cooked food that caters for most tastes (includes vegetarian and vegan options). A juke box with an excellent range of material is switched on after 3pm. Pool, darts and table football are played. A family room is available at lunchtime only.
❀✿🚄 (Central) ♣

Golden Eagle
21 High Street (1 mile from centre)
✪ 11-3, 5-11; 11-11 Fri & Sat; 12-10.30 Sun
☎ (01522) 521058
Bateman XB; Everards Beacon; guest beers Ⓗ
A real city local with a boisterous, sports orientated public bar where local games teams play. The second bar is traditionally decorated with wainscotted walls, comfortable bench seating and pictures of old Lincoln. Spot the golden eagle pub signs on the stairs to the upstairs meeting room. The reasonably priced range of beers always includes a mild. Pétanque can be played in the garden. This pub, which is part of the Tynemill group, has appeared in this *Guide* for 10 consecutive years. Q❀✿♣❀P

Jolly Brewer
27 Broadgate
✪ 11-11; 12-10.30 Sun
☎ (01522) 528583

Draught Bass; Theakston XB; guest beers Ⓗ
Popular city-centre local which was known as the Unity until reopening under its current name in 1982. It has been a regular *Guide* entry ever since. The pub is decorated in an *art deco* style and is the home to a highly varied clientele. There is always a wide range of enterprising guest beers, including one at a special price, and the early eve 'happy hour' offers further generous discounts. The home-made food is much appreciated by local workers at lunchtime. The unobtrusive table football is popular as is the dartboard. Tue quizzes add to the lively atmosphere. This pub has been run by three generations of the same family and was the winner of the local CAMRA *Pub of Merit* award in 2001. ♨️❀◐♿️⇌⬤P♣

Morning Star

11 Greetwell Gate (200 yds from cathedral)
🕒 11-11; 12-10.30 Sun
☎ (01522) 527079

Draught Bass; Greene King Ruddles Best, Abbot; Tetley Bitter; Wells Bombardier Ⓗ
Friendly, unspoilt pub that stands in the shadow of Lincoln Cathedral. It is a haven for drinkers with at least five real ales on at any one time. A local pianist plays on Sat eve and there are jazz nights and barbecues held in the beer garden throughout the summer months. ♨️Q❀◐P

Peacock Inn

23 Wragby Road
🕒 11.30-11; 12-10.30 Sun
☎ (01522) 524703

Hardys & Hansons Best Mild, Best Bitter, Classic, seasonal beers Ⓗ
Street-corner coaching inn, in the uphill area of the city, between the hospital and the cathedral. A large brick fireplace divides the TV and games area from the dining room. This busy, friendly pub tries to suit everyone and even has its own golf society. Excellent value main course dishes are offered including English cuts of sirloin and fresh fish. Patio available for outdoor drinking. ♨️❀◐♣P

Queen in the West

12 Moor Street
🕒 12-3, 5.30-11; 11.30-11 Fri; 12-5, 7-11 Sat; 12-5, 7-10.30 Sun
☎ (01522) 880123

Greene King Old Speckled Hen; Shepherd Neame Spitfire; John Smith's Bitter; Theakston XB; Wells Bombardier; guest beers Ⓗ
This two-roomed back-street pub is in the west end of the city. It is an oasis for drinkers and is a long-standing *Guide* entry, reflecting its commitment to real ale with seven beers usually available. Busy eves and quieter lunchtimes when good food is served. The pub has a cosy, comfortable lounge with a slightly rural feel. The bar is friendly, welcoming and full of character. Q◐🪑♣

Sippers Free House

26 Melville Street (near bus and rail stations)
🕒 11-2, 5 (4 Fri; 7 Sat)-11; 7-10.30 (closed lunch) Sun
☎ (01522) 527612

Courage Directors; Greene King Old Speckled Hen; Marston's Pedigree; John Smith's Bitter; Theakston Cool Cask; guest beers Ⓗ
Comfortable two-roomed corner pub with

an interesting display of nautical items and paintings. It offers two guest beers from independent brewers, plus good-value food (not served Sun or Sat eve). The speciality home-cooked ham is worth a try. Busy weekday lunchtimes. Deservedly, a regular *Guide* entry. ◐⇌

Strugglers

83 Westgate (NW of castle)
🕒 11.30-11; 12-10.30 Sun
☎ (01522) 535023

Draught Bass; Fuller's London Pride; guest beers Ⓗ
This pub appears to have been a terraced property, but is now in splendid isolation, with a coach park one side and a car park the other. It was first registered as an ale house in 1836 and called Struggler in the Globe. The present sign depicts a hanging – the public gallows was once nearby. The bustling bar contrasts with the cosy lounge and has numerous photographs of old Lincoln. The pleasant patio is very popular with families in the summer.
♨️Q❀🪑♣

Victoria

6 Union Road
🕒 11-11; 12-10.30 Sun
☎ (01522) 536048
website: www.tynemill.co.uk/lincoln/victoria

Bateman XB; Everard's Original; Taylor Landlord; guest beers Ⓗ
A *Guide* regular, this two-roomed city local is a gem. Now part of the Tynemill chain, it stands next to the west gate of the castle. A constantly changing range of guest beers, including a mild, is available and features beers from regional brewers and many micro-breweries. Biddendens dry cider is stocked. Home-cooked, hot food is served at lunchtime. Brewery feature nights occur throughout the year, together with two or three, week-long beer festivals. Live music is occasionally performed by a local band and a Sun afternoon folk session once a month is popular. Enjoy a pint on the recently installed patio.
Q❀◐🪑⬤

Willoughby Arms

Station Road
🕒 12-2, 5-11; 12-11 Sat; 12-10.30 Sun
☎ (01787) 410276 website: www.willoughbyarms.co.uk

Bateman XB; guest beers Ⓗ
Traditional country pub specialising in real ales from micro-breweries. Six beers are generally on sale. Each year there are two regular beer festivals in May and on August bank holiday, plus mini beerfests take place. A games area and roaring log fires maintain a traditional feel. Generous portions of food make this pub a popular place to eat. A cellar bar is the venue for live music at weekends. A new purpose-built brewery is in progress. The house beers will be supplied by Newby Wyke from the new brewery.
♨️Q❀🛏️◐🪑♣P🚲⬤

Mason's Arms

Cornmarket
🕒 11 (9.30 for coffee)-11; 11-3, 7-10.30 Sun
☎ (01507) 609525 website: www.themasons.co.uk

Bateman Mild, XB, XXXB; Marston's Pedigree; John Smith's Bitter; Taylor Landlord; guest beers Ⓗ

Early 18th-century coaching inn on the market square. Quiet, comfortable hotel bar where good food is offered lunchtime and eve from 6–9 (children are welcome while food is served). A separate market bar stocks up to seven real ales. The upstairs restaurant is open Fri and Sat eve and Sun lunch. Winner of Lincolnshire Life *Best Pub Food* award 2001.

Q ⊨ ◑ ▮

Wheatsheaf Inn
62 Westgate
✪ 11-3, 5-11; 11-11 Sat; 12-4, 7-10.30 (12-10.30 summer) Sun
☎ (01507) 603159

Boddingtons Bitter; Flowers Original; Taylor Landlord; guest beers Ⓗ

Elegant location in a Georgian terrace close to St James church, which boasts the tallest spire in England. The Wheatsheaf is an attractive, traditional inn which dates back to 1625 and retains some original features. There are three bars, each with a real coal fire during the winter months. Local photographs and rural memorabilia adorn the walls. An annual 'beer and bangers' festival is held during the last week in May and the first week in June. Children are allowed in at lunchtime and early eve and dogs are welcome in the beer garden. The house beer, Tipsy Toad, is not brewed on Jersey. Lunchtime food served Mon–Sat.

🏠 Q ❀ ◑ ●

White Horse
24 Kenwick Road (A157, 1 mile from centre)
✪ 12-3, 6-11; 5.30 (6 Sat)-12; 12-3, 6-11 Sun
☎ (01507) 603331

Draught Bass; Highwood Tom Wood Best Bitter; Ind Coope Burton Ale; guest beer Ⓗ

Substantially extended in the 1990s, this established two-roomed inn has a modern feel. The pub has a strong local following and offers a cosy, friendly atmosphere. Entertainment includes regular live music and a popular Fri eve quiz. Darts is played in the main bar along with shove-ha'penny and there is a pool table annexe. The huge grassed area is ideal in summer. With a deserved reputation for good food, the pub has a separate dining room (no food Mon lunchtime Nov–April).

❀ ◑ ♣ P

Woodman
134 Eastgate
✪ 11-3.30, 7-11; 11-11 Fri & Sat; 12-4, 7-10.30 Sun
☎ (01507) 602100
website: www.woodman.hypermart.com

Greene King Abbot; John Smith's Bitter; guest beers Ⓗ

19th-century town-centre pub attracting a good mix of customers. The original multi-roomed design creates many separate drinking areas in the single bar. A strong film theme dominates to the front with cinema posters covering walls and ceiling. A games area to the rear features pool and table football. Two rotating guest beers are always available. There is an upstairs bar (with two real ales) which opens to host monthly rock/blues bands from the European circuit. Lunchtime food is served (not Sun). ❀ ◑ ♣ P

Woolpack
Riverhead
✪ 11-3 (not Mon), 5 (7 Mon)-11; 12-4, 7-10.30 Sun
☎ (01507) 606568

Bateman Mild, XB, XXXB, seasonal beers; Greene King Triumph; guest beers Ⓗ

Friendly edge-of-town pub, this 18th-century hostelry stands at the head of Louth Canal. Recommended locally for its delicious home-cooked food (served Wed –Sat eves and Tue–Sun lunchtimes). Long-standing entry in this *Guide*. Local musicians have a session here most Wed eves. It is the current location for Louth Beer Festival each July and home to numerous games teams in local pub leagues. Louth CAMRA *Pub of the Year* 1997, '98, 2000 and 2001. 🏠 Q ❀ ◑ ◨ 㕙 ♣ P

MARKET DEEPING

Bull
19 Market Place (main town square)
✪ 11-11; 12-10.30 Sun
☎ (01778) 343320

Everards Tiger, Original; guest beers Ⓗ

16th-century coaching house of some character, named after a Papal Bull relating to Crowland Abbey across the Fen. The Dug Out snug bar with bench seats should not be missed. Lunchtime meals are served and there is an upstairs function room. Outside drinking is possible in the rear yard. Superb location on the market place of this attractive village, now thankfully bypassed by heavy traffic. 㔼 ❀ ♣

MESSINGHAM

Horn Inn
High Street
✪ 11-11; 12-10.30 Sun
☎ (01724) 762426

John Smith's Bitter; guest beers Ⓗ

Welcoming, roadside local in the heart of the village. It has been sympathetically refurbished in a country inn style. A central bar serves a large single room, divided into distinct drinking and eating areas. The low-beamed ceiling, wooden fixtures, plaster walls and rural artefacts enhance the rustic atmosphere. Lunchtime and eve meals are very popular and all food is home-cooked. The rear of the pub has been extended to form an attractive dining area. There is a small garden which has its own snack menu during the summer months. Two guest beers are always available, usually from independent brewers. Wheelchair access is at the rear of the pub. 🏠 Q ❀ ◑ 㕙 ♣ P

MORTON

Crooked Billet
1 Crooked Billet Street
✪ 12-11; 12-10.30 Sun
☎ (01427) 612584

Worthington Bitter; guest beers Ⓗ

Large Victorian pub with a lively local clientele, many of whom are pictured in sketches in one of the three bars. The landlord is keen to promote real ale and provides a wide variety of guest beers which change constantly. The food is excellent and cheap, and the pub often features live entertainment. In WWI part of the pub served as the local mortuary, so watch out for ghosts as you quaff your ale! ⚰Q◐⌂❒

NETTLEHAM

Black Horse
Chapel Lane
✪ 11.30-3 (4.30 Sat), 6-11; 12-5.30, 7-10.30 Sun
☎ (01522) 750702
Bateman XB; Brains Dark; Highwood Tom Wood Best Bitter; Tetley Bitter; Theakston Best Bitter; guest beers H
Attractive stone, mid-18th century pub, with later alterations, it stands off the village green. A large stone fireplace features in the lounge where meals can be taken. Eve meals finish at 8pm. The bar is the place for pub games including pool. Music nights occur about twice a month, well-known folk or blues players often perform. Pictures of previous artists can be seen decorating the pub walls. The range of real ales usually includes two constantly changing guest beers. ⚰Q◐⌂♿&♣

Plough
1 The Green
✪ 3.30-11; 12-3, 7-10.30 Sun
☎ (01522) 750275
Bateman XB, seasonal beers; guest beer H
Small stone-built local overlooking the village green. The single bar area has recently been extended and an upstairs restaurant is planned. The current limited opening hours are to be increased. Traditional pub games are played and there is a pleasant garden. ☼♣

NETTLETON

Salutation Inn
Church Street
✪ 12-3, 6-11; 12-3, 7-10.30 Sun
☎ (01472) 851228
Highwood Tom Wood Best Bitter; Taylor Landlord; Wadworth 6X; guest beers H
A homely, relaxed atmosphere exists in this friendly pub. There is a separate dining room and excellent meals are served. A Mon night special of Grimsby haddock and chips is well worth a try. Sun eve is quiz time, always a popular event. Children are welcome here and will like the pets corner in the beer garden. Wheelchair access. Camping facilities for caravans nearby. ⚰☼◐&▲P

NORTH KELSEY ✿

Butcher's Arms
Middle Street
✪ 4 (12 Sat)-11; 12-10.30 Sun
☎ (01652) 678002
Highwood Tom Wood Best Bitter, Tom Wood Harvest Bitter; guest beers (summer) H
Owned by Highwood Brewery, this small, refurbished traditional pub is tucked away in a village side street so customers are usually locals. In essence one room; a lounge bar decorated in farmhouse style, noted for its real fire, plus a snug which contains the dartboard. Two large bay windows overlook the car park and the outdoor drinking area, which has rustic furniture under mature trees. A *trompe-l'oeil* on the corridor wall suggests a view of the Highwood Brewery through a window.

⚰Q❀♣P

NORTH KELSEY MOOR

Queen's Head
Station Road (near disused North Kelsey station)
OS070018
✪ 12-2 (4 Sat; not Mon, Wed or Thu); 7-11; 12-4, 7-10.30 Sun
☎ (01652) 678055
Theakston Best Bitter; guest beer H
Well-appointed old free house with a sympathetic modern extension. In a rural setting, the pub is enhanced by a well-kept beer garden. A cosy public bar with coal fire is decorated with a collection of beer bottles and beer mats. The comfortable lounge with solid fuel stove has two seating areas, and there is a smart dining room. There is a quiz Thu eve. Pensioners are offered special lunches on Tue and Fri. No food Sun eve. ⚰Q❀◐⌂♣P

ROTHWELL

Blacksmith's Arms
Hillrise
✪ 11-11; 12-10.30 Sun
☎ (01472) 371300
Courage Directors; Theakston XB; guest beers H
Beautiful, traditional pub that dominates an equally attractive village nestling in the Lincolnshire wolds. First called the Blacksmith's Arms, the pub was then known as the Nickerson Arms for 20 years or so. Reverting to the original name is a refreshing change in this era of silly names! The landlord is keen to maintain a policy of reasonable prices for beers, as well as quality. A large function room allows live music nights to take place without destroying the peace and quiet of the pub itself. Good quality food proves popular with customers. The surrounding area is ideal for walkers and the pub provides a good base for a day's hike. ⚰Q❀◐P

RUSKINGTON

Black Bull
10 Rectory Road
✪ 11.30-2.30, 6-11; 12-3, 7-10.30 Sun
☎ (01526) 832270
Draught Bass; Bateman XB; guest beers H
Warm, comfortable, friendly and popular pub in a rapidly expanding village. It retains its local atmosphere but also attracts visitors, especially for Sun lunches (booking advised) and Wed quiz nights. An attractive building and one of the village's oldest, though not Tudor as the exterior suggests. The leaded windows are unusual in the district. The two sculptures above the front entrance were made by a local craftsman some years ago and are worth a second glance. ◄◐⌂⇌♣P

SANDTOFT

Reindeer Inn
Station Road
✪ 12-4 (not Mon-Thu), 6 (7 Fri & Sat)-11; 12-4, 7-10.30 Sun
☎ (01724) 710774
John Smith's Bitter; Worthington Bitter H
Welcoming free house set in the Dutch-style landscape of the Isle of Axholme where many an unwary motorist has come

to grief in the deep roadside dykes. The Reindeer is the focal point of the village. It consists of a large, L-shaped lounge with adjoining restaurant. Eve meals are served daily and lunchtime food Fri–Sun. This pub is popular with locals, visitors and volunteers from the nearby Sandtoft Transport Museum which houses the largest collection of trolley buses in the country. Evidence of one of the pub's former owners – the original Barnsley Brewery – can still be seen with the faded 'Oakwell Ales sold here' painted on the tiled roof.

🏠🛏️❄️🕙🍴♣️P🗝️

SAXILBY

Anglers
65 High Street
🕐 11.30-2.30, 6 (5 Fri, 7 Sat)-11; 12-3, 7-10.30 Sun
☎ (01522) 702200
Home Bitter; Theakston Best Bitter; guest beer Ⓗ
Thriving and friendly village pub, run by a local man. Pub games are an essential element; there are teams for darts, pool, cribbage and dominoes, and match eves can be lively. Lunchtimes are usually quieter and table skittles is sometimes played. The lounge bar has a small, but interesting, collection of old photographs of the village, and is the monthly meeting place of the local history group. The pub name refers to the hordes of anglers who once flocked to the banks of the nearby Foss Dyke, which is the country's oldest canal. 🍴🚂♣️P

SCAMBLESBY

Green Man
Old Main Road (off A153)
🕐 12-11; 12-10.30 Sun
☎ (01507) 343282
e-mail: thegreenman@onetel.net.uk
Black Sheep Best Bitter; guest beers Ⓗ
200-year-old coaching inn, situated in the Wolds, just over a mile away from Cadwell Park international racing circuit. It is next to the Viking Way footpath. Apart from the bar and games area, there is a separate lounge with children's certificate. Two rooms are available for B&B. General pub fare offered, ranging from pickled eggs to Sun roast. Large car park and motorcycle friendly. 🏠❄️🛏️🕙🍴♣️P

SCAMPTON

Dambusters Inn
High Street
🕐 12-2.30 (3 Sat), 5-11; 12-3, 7-10.30 Sun
☎ (01522) 731333
Greene King IPA, Abbot; guest beer (summer) Ⓗ
Modern, stone-built village pub, converted from the landlord's house! An open island fire warms both sides of the room. Drinks are served from a bijou bar bedecked with hops. The walls are covered with memorabilia and artefacts from 617 Squadron, the Dambusters, which used Scampton airfield, close by. The pub has won awards for its excellent food (not served Mon lunch). Tables are laid out at the front of the building. The Post Office is attached, showing a way for a pub to suvive in a small village. 🏠❄️🕙P

SCAWBY BROOK ❄️

Horse & Cart
185 Scawby Road (on B1206, 1 mile W of Brigg)
🕐 12-2.30, 5-11; 12-11 Sat; 12-10.30 Sun
☎ (01652) 652150
Highwood Tom Wood Shepherd's Delight; John Smith's Bitter; Theakston Cool Cask; guest beers Ⓗ
Free house built on the site as previous pubs of the same name. Ample parking and large garden. Several changes of landlord in the recent past have resulted in a falling-off of local trade but the incumbent is making a considerable effort to market real ale. A different guest beer features almost every week. Food is also a selling point, the chef having won 'highly commended' in the national finals of the Meat and Livestock Commission's *Steak Pie of the Year* competition 2001, for his special steak and mushroom pie with sherry gravy. No food Sun eve.
❄️🕙🍴🛏️🅰️♣️P

SCOTTER

White Swan
9 The Green
🕐 11.30-3, 6.30-11; 11.30-11 Fri & Sat; 12-10.30 Sun
☎ (01724) 762342
John Smith's Bitter; Webster's Yorkshire Bitter; guest beers Ⓗ
This is a large pub on the attractive village green, and is full of character despite having been extensively modernised. There is a busy trade in food, but drinkers have not been forgotten with two excellent guest beers. Ales from Highwood Brewery often feature, and are deservedly popular. This is a great place to visit if you like eating out, but still want to enjoy a decent pint.
🕙P🗝️

SCOTTON

Three Horseshoes
Westgate
🕐 12-3 (not Mon-Fri), 7-11; 12-3, 7-10.30 Sun
☎ (01724) 763129
Greene King IPA; John Smith's Bitter Ⓗ
Unspoilt village local at the heart of the community. The small bar is cosy and has a welcoming atmosphere. The comfortable lounge features an interesting collection of character jugs. Real ales available can vary, but each tends to stay for a good few months. Note that this pub does not serve food – nevertheless, it is highly recommended. Q❄️🛏️P🗝️

SCUNTHORPE ❄️

Blue Bell
Oswald Road (500 yds from station)
🕐 11-11; 12-10.30 Sun
☎ (01724) 863291
Courage Directors; John Smith's Bitter; Theakston Best Bitter; guest beers Ⓗ
A Wetherspoon's house, the Blue Bell is named after a long-closed town-centre hostelry. Converted from three former terraced shop units into a large ground-floor pub with a single bar, the Blue Bell is a popular stop-off point for those on the weekend town-centre pub circuit. It is a little more civilised during the week but still

likely to be the busiest pub in the area. In common with other Wetherspoon's outlets it holds annual beer festivals. Three guest beers are usually available. Outside drinking possible on the patio. Q❀❂◐≠⅄●

Honest Lawyer

70 Oswald Road (300 yds from station)
❂ 11-11; 7-10.30 Sun
☎ (01724) 849906
Beer range varies Ⓗ
Small ground-floor bar with an upstairs drinking area. It has a range of five rotating guest beers. It sports an ale house look and feel, with lots of dark wood and legal artefacts and draws a varied clientele, with the accent on youth at weekends. Big-screen TV upstairs. Regular outlet for local Highwood Tom Wood beers. ≈

Malt Shovel

219 Ashby High Street, Ashby
❂ 11-11; 12-10.30 Sun
☎ (01724) 843318
Barnsley Bitter; Courage Directors; John Smith's Bitter; Theakston Old Peculier; guest beers Ⓗ
Town pub furnished in olde-worlde style with an abundance of wood and floral furnishings. It has a quiet, convivial atmosphere. Very popular at lunchtime and early eve for the range of good value hot meals. Two guest beers are generally stocked from independent brewers, plus a real cider in summer. The adjoining licensed snooker club also serves real ale; full and social membership available and guests can be signed in. Q❀◐♣

Queen Bess

Derwent Road, Ashby (near A18/Grange Lane S jct)
❂ 11.30-3.30 (4 Sat), 6-11; 12-3, 7-10.30 Sun
☎ (01724) 840827
Samuel Smith OBB Ⓗ
1960s estate pub with well-appointed, cosy lounge with real fire, plus separate public bar. A function room is available for hire, it

is used by many local groups and societies. Very much a locals' pub, but always welcoming and serves the best Sam Smith's in town. Recent *Pub of the Season* award-winner, the licensee has also received a *Real ale Excellence* award from the local CAMRA branch in recognition of 20 years' service at the pub. Families welcome, the pub has a children's certificate. Trestle tables are set out in summer. ♨❀◐ ⊟♣P

Vine Hotel

Vine Road, Seacroft (1 mile S of centre, off Drummond Rd)
❂ 10-3, 6-11; 11-3, 6-10.30 Sun
☎ (01754) 763018
Bateman Mild, XB, XXXB, seasonal beers Ⓗ
Delightful hotel set in its own peaceful and secluded grounds away from the bustle of the resort. A severe contrast to the Skegness razzmatazz, it is one of the town's oldest buildings with an interesting history and tales of smuggling connections and ghostly revenue men. Tennyson knew this part of the Lincolnshire coast and may have visited. Still worth a visit at any time of the year, but when that bracing Skegness summer air changes into a biting winter wind the roaring open fires provide the perfect antidote. ♨⛴❀☜◐⊟♣P

Marquis of Granby

Westgate
❂ 12-11; 12-10.30 Sun
☎ (01529) 303223
Flowers Original; Tetley Bitter; guest beer Ⓗ
No-frills pub in rural setting just outside the town centre. Located on one of the four compass point roads of this market town, this former home-brew house was licensed under the Beer House Act of 1830 which allowed a householder or ratepayer on the payment of two guineas to turn a private

INN BRIEF

SCUNTHORPE

Queensway
Ashby Road
11-11; 12-10.30 Sun
Black Sheep Best Bitter; Boddingtons Bitter Ⓗ
Large pub in its own grounds by the Queensway roundabout on A18. Very popular for meals.

SOUTH FERRIBY

Hope & Anchor
Sluice Road
11.30-11; 12-10.30 Sun
Adnams Bitter; Mansfield Riding Bitter Ⓗ
Village pub overlooking River Humber with strong nautical theme. Separate restaurant. Very popular with day trippers in summer.

SPALDING

Olde White Horse
Churchgate
11.30-2.30, 5-11; 11-4, 7-11 Sat;
12-4, 7-10.30 Sun
Samuel Smith OBB Ⓗ
Imposing 14th-century thatched building by the town bridge. Refurbished with stone-flagged floors and comfortable lounge.

STAMFORD

Daniel Lambert
20 St Leonard's Street
11.30-3, 6 (5 Fri)-11; 11-11 Sat;
12-3, 7-10.30 Sun
Adnams Bitter; Banks's Bitter; Courage Directors; Taylor Landlord; guest beer Ⓗ
200-year-old stone-built pub with no-smoking cellar bar. Food available except Sun and Mon eves. *Cask Marque* accredited.

THEDDLETHORPE

King's Head
Mill Road
12-3 (not Mon & Wed in winter), 7-11;
12-10.30 Sun
Greene King IPA, Abbot; guest beer Ⓗ
Attractive 16th-century, thatched, oak-beamed pub. Now modernised it has two comfortable rooms and a garden with children's play area.

WAINFLEET

Jolly Sailor
19 St John Street
12-2, 4.30-11; 12-11 Fri & Sat;
12-10.30 Sun
Bateman Mild, XB Ⓗ
Traditional no-frills pub. No music or food, just a good, old-fashioned drinking house. Bateman's bottled beers always available.

WEST BUTTERWICK

Three Horseshoes
1 North Street
12-3 (not Mon-Fri), 7 (4.30 Fri)-11;
12-3, 7-10.30 Sun
John Smith's Bitter; Tetley Mild, Bitter; guest beer Ⓗ
Cosy 17th-century rural pub with exposed beams and real fires. Meals on Fri eve and Sat lunchtime. Small garden.

WHAPLODE ST CATHERINE

Blue Bell
Cranesgate South
12-4 (not Mon-Fri), 7-11;
12-4, 7-10.30 Sun
Blue Bell Olde Honesty Ⓗ
Extended 17th-century local and micro-brewery. Lively with a warm welcome and excellent food. Real fires and no music.

❄ **symbol next to a main entry place name indicates there are Inn Brief entries as well.**

house into a public house. It is now a single bar, back-street local with teams entering all the traditional pub games. The pub has a cosy atmosphere and extends a warm welcome to visitors. 🏠🚭♣🍴

SOUTH THORESBY

Vine Inn

1 mile from A16
☼ 12 (7 Mon)-11; 12-3, 7-10.30 Sun
☎ (01507) 480273
Bateman XB; guest beer Ⓗ

Pleasant two-roomed pub with additional restaurant. Ideal base for exploring the Lincolnshire Wolds area as it is halfway between Louth and Alford. The large garden attracts families during the summer. The small stone-flagged entrance bar is an ideal place to sit and chat to the locals. Dogs are welcome if kept under control but beware of the cat and look out for the parrot. 🏠Q🏠🍴◀🈁▲P

SPALDING ✤

Birds

108 Halmer Gate (follow A151 off A16 bypass, heading into town)
☼ 11-11; 12-10.30 Sun
☎ (01775) 723329
Greene King IPA; guest beer Ⓗ

Large, modern, estate-style pub. It has recently been refurbished as part of the Hungry Horse chain. Popular with locals for its all-day food as well as the excellent beer. The large outdoor area is ideal for children. Karaoke and other entertainments are staged regularly. The pub is only a short distance from the Spalding bypass. 🏠◀♿P

Lincoln Arms

4 Bridge Street
☼ 11-3 (3.30 Sat), 7-11; 12-3, 7-10.30 Sun
☎ (01775) 722691
Banks's Original; Mansfield Dark Mild, Riding Bitter, Cask Ale, seasonal beers Ⓗ

Traditional, 18th-century riverside local situated close to the town bridge. It is very popular with the locals and is the meeting place for a number of clubs including the Fenland branch of CAMRA who choose this pub to hold their committee meetings. There is a folk club gig fortnightly on Wed eve. Do not cause any trouble here, as the landlord is an ex-boxer. 🈁🚭♣

Red Lion Hotel

Market Place
☼ 11-11; 12-10.30 Sun
☎ (01775) 722869
website: www.redlionhotel-spalding.co.uk
Draught Bass; Blue Bell Olde Honesty; Fuller's London Pride; Greene King Abbot; Marston's Pedigree Ⓗ

Historic market town hotel bar, richly refurbished yet retaining a lively atmosphere. Popular with the locals and visitors to the Fenland area, though can get a little smoky at times. It is also home to the Spalding Blues Club which puts on live bands on Sun eve every two weeks. Recent gigs have included the likes of the Mick Pini Band and former Groundhogs lead guitarist, Tony (TS) McPhee. The market place is closed to cars

until 4pm Mon–Fri. Tables are set up outside the pub. No food on Sun eve. 🏠Q🏠🈁◀🍴🚭

STAMFORD ✤

Green Man

29 Scotgate (B1081 northbound at edge of town centre)
☼ 11-11; 12-10.30 Sun
☎ (01780) 753598
Theakston Best Bitter, Cool Cask; Ⓗ
guest beers Ⓗ/Ⓖ

A short walk from the centre of 'England's finest Georgian town', this pub is definitely worth finding. Voted Peterborough CAMRA *Pub of the Year* 2000, the Green Man is a showcase for small micro-brewer's wares. It has one L-shaped, split-level bar with an array of handpumps in constant use. Cask cider is always available. The beer garden is home to a very successful beer festival twice a year. Notice the stone-carved 'upping block' which was once used to assist corpulent customers on to their waiting steeds. No food Sun. 🏠🏠🈁🚭♣♠🍴

Periwig

7 All Saints Place (just off B1081 near Brewery Museum)
☼ 11-11; 12-10.30 Sun
☎ (01780) 762169
Adnams Bitter; Hop Back Summer Lightning; Marston's Pedigree; Oakham JHB; guest beers Ⓗ

Formerly called the Marsh Harrier, this is a refurbished, open-plan pub. It features a large split-level bar; the upstairs balcony and room are popular with students. On the whole the pub attracts a younger clientele. Unusually for local pubs it is fully air-conditioned for those rare hot summer months. Lunchtime food is available Mon–Sat and the pub has an excellent selection of beers. The town-centre location means it is handy for both bus and train stations. ◀🚭

SURFLEET

Mermaid

2 Gosberton Road (B1356 near bridge)
☼ 11-3, 6.30-11; 12-3, 7-10.30 Sun
☎ (01775) 680275
Adnams Broadside; John Smith's Bitter; guest beers Ⓗ

In a former brewery on the River Glen this pub offers a warm atmosphere and great value meals in the bars and restaurant. Some visitors find the food too dominant eves and weekends. The large garden is ideal for children in summer. A ship's riding light in the bar is a memento of a previous landlord. He was a seaman at Boston Docks before he retired. 🏠Q🏠🈁◀P

SWINHOPE

Click 'Em Inn

☼ 12-3, 7 (11 Sat)-11; closed Mon;
12-3, 7-10.30 Sun
☎ (01472) 398253
Theakston XB; guest beers Ⓗ

This unusually-named pub is situated in the Lincolnshire Wolds close to the old RAF camp at Binbrook. Offering a homely atmosphere, it has a few small rooms connected to the main bar. Low-beamed ceilings and old photographs of the area are featured. The conservatory is reserved for diners only and is a no-smoking zone. A popular quiz is hosted on Mon eve and 'happy hour' is held between 7–8pm Mon–Fri. The house beer is Click 'Em Inn Bitter.

⊛❀♣P

THORNTON CURTIS

Thornton Hunt Inn
Main Street (A1077, between Wooton and Barton)
✪ 12-3, 6.30-11; 12-3, 6.30-10.30 Sun
☎ (01469) 531252 website: www.thornton-inn.co.uk
Taylor Landlord; Tetley Bitter; guest beer Ⓗ
This well appointed village local has a comfortable, attractively furnished interior. The single, L-shaped bar has wood panelling and beams decorated with Toby jugs and tankards which add to the olde-worlde atmosphere. The excellent and extensive range of home-cooked food draws diners from far and wide. In addition to the pub meals there is a separate bistro. The local brewery, Highwood, launched its beers here and they are still available as guest ales today. Families are welcome and there is a children's fun trail and garden play area. Delightful rural setting close to the ruins of Thornton Abbey.

Q⊛≈◖Ь♣P

THREEKINGHAM

Three Kings Inn
Salters Way (100 yds S of A52)
✪ 11-3, 7-11; 12-3, 7-10.30 Sun
☎ (01529) 240249
Draught Bass; Shepherd Neame Bishops Finger; Worthington Bitter Ⓗ
Welcoming, cosy pub offering good beers and food in convivial surroundings. The panelled lounge contains framed notes on the pub's history and a word-play on Lincolnshire place names. The village supposedly takes its name from the 9th-century battle of nearby Stow Green, when the Danes were routed and three chieftains or kings were killed. Look for the effigies above the pub's entrance. Stow Green was also famous for one of England's oldest chartered fairs, developing into a horse and pleasure fair which lasted for several weeks. It was not always popular with villagers because of the bad behaviour of some visitors.

▲⊛◖Һ♣P

WELBOURN

Joiners Inn
21 High Street (off A607)
✪ 12-3 (not Mon & Tue), 6-11; 12-3, 7-10.30 Sun
☎ (01400) 272430
e-mail: freeman@joinersinn.fsnet.co.uk
Everards Tiger, Original; Ⓗ **guest beers** Ⓗ/Ⓖ
Sympathetic refurbishment of the former Joiners Arms has created a friendly welcoming inn. The pub offers an interesting range of traditional ales. At least one guest is usually from a small local brewery. A feature of the pub is that one of the guest beers is served on gravity. The food is excellent but never dominates in what is still the village local. A small, intimate dining area is available if required.

No food served Sun or Mon eves. Limited B&B accommodation can be arranged via the landlord in the nearby village of Brant Broughton. There is also a small camping site at Mill Hill. Occasional impromptu music and mini beer festivals hosted.

▲⊛≈◖♣P

WILLINGHAM BY STOW

Half Moon
23 High Street (just off B1241 Gainsborough-Saxilby road)
✪ 12-2 (not Mon-Wed; 3 Sat), 7-11; 12-3, 7-10.30 Sun
☎ (01427) 788340
Castle Eden Ale; guest beers Ⓗ
Traditional, family-run, two-roomed village free house which dates back to 1835. The pub was converted from an agricultural labourer's cottage under the provisions of the Duke of Wellington's Beer House Act. Two regularly rotating guest beers are available. A beer festival featuring around 12 beers is normally held in August. The pub is well-known for its good value home-cooked food and in particular for the fish and chip night held on the second and last Fri of each month (booking advised). Real fires feature in both rooms and the pub is home to darts, dominoes and football teams. Bar skittles and shove-ha'penny are also played and a prize quiz night is held every Thu. The landlord offers a low-cost taxi service to local towns and villages.

▲Q⊛◖Һ♣

WILLOUGHTON

Stirrup Inn
1 Templefield Road (off B1398)
✪ 7.30 (12 Sat)-11; 12-3, 7.30-10.30 Sun
☎ (01427) 668270
John Smith's Bitter; guest beer Ⓗ
Fine old stone pub awarded Gainsborough CAMRA *Pub of the Season* winter 2001. Family-run for the past 11 years, this traditional village free house draws a strong local following. It is the centre for local football teams and pub games such as darts and dominoes are played in a designated area. It is the only pub in the village able to attract visitors for the quality of beers rather than the food being the main focus. The guest beer changes weekly and includes Black Sheep and Everards ales.

▲Q⊛Һ♣P

WINTERINGHAM

Bay Horse
2-6 West End
✪ 12-11; 12-10.30 Sun
☎ (01724) 732865
Tetley Bitter; guest beers Ⓗ
Traditional decor with wooden beams, brasses and rural pictures feature in this welcoming village local. A function room is available for meetings and celebrating special occasions. Home-cooked food from an extensive menu is offered Fri–Sun lunchtime and Tue–Sun eve. Two guest beers are usually stocked, concentrating on regional and micro-breweries. Four en-suite guest rooms offered. Wheelchair WC.

▲⊛≈◖Ь♣P

WINTERTON

Lion's Head
55 Park Street (on village outskirts)
🕐 5 (11.30 Fri & Sat)-11; 12-10.30 Sun
☎ (01724) 733343
Worthington Bitter; guest beers Ⓗ

Friendly village local built in 1906. The L-shaped lounge bar has an adjoining section for darts, which along with dominoes, is very popular here. There is a comfortable snug. Regular weekend entertainment is organised and a quiz night is held each Wed. The pub runs football, cricket and ladies' hockey teams. The vintage motorcycle club holds its meetings at the pub. Pleasant garden and patio available.
🏠🏵♣P

WOOLSTHORPE BY BELVOIR

Rutland Arms
Woolsthorpe Wharf, Sedgebrook Road (1 mile E of Belvoir Castle)
🕐 12-3, 6-11; 12-11 Sat; 12-10.30 Sun
☎ (01476) 870111
Draught Bass; John Smith's Bitter; Tetley Bitter (occasional) Ⓗ

Two-roomed country pub in the shadow of Belvoir Castle. It has a wonderful position next to the Grantham–Nottingham Canal. Very popular with anglers and walkers – it gets very busy in summer. Large children's play area and facilities for campers and caravanners available. Enjoy the excellent ales and fresh home-cooked meals. Dominoes, darts and pool are played. This is an ideal retreat from today's busy world.
🏠Q🏵◗🍴🛏👜▲♣P

WRAGBY

Turnor Arms
Market Place (A158)
🕐 5 (12 Sat)-11; 12-2.30, 7-10.30 Sun
☎ (01673) 858205
Highwood Tom Wood Best Bitter, seasonal beers; John Smith's Bitter; guest beer Ⓗ

Formerly a hotel on the main A158 east coast road. A friendly welcome awaits, and if you are into quiz nights Sun (music) and Wed (general knowledge) are for you. Also a Karaoke eve once a month may appeal. The lounge is of a good size with a stone fireplace and plenty of wood panelling. Children are allowed in the games room. The bar is quite lively and caters for the younger generation. There is a change of Tom Wood seasonal beers every two months. Wheelchair access is via the car park entrance. Lunchtime food has recently been introduced.
🏠🛏🏵◗🍴🛏♣P

WRAWBY

Jolly Miller
Brigg Road (A18)
🕐 12-2, 5-11; 12-11 Sat; 12-10.30 Sun
☎ (01652) 655658
website: www.jollymiller.co.uk
Highwood Tom Wood Harvest Bitter; guest beers Ⓗ

Pleasant village pub fitted-out in comfortable country inn style. A collection of local photographs and paintings adorns the walls reflecting life in the village. A warm welcome is assured. The pub hosts entertainment most Sat eves. There is an active darts and dominoes team. Accommodation is offered in en-suite rooms, or choose the popular caravan site to the rear with full facilities. A camping area is also available. It is only four miles from Humberside airport and one mile from the bustling market town of Brigg. Wrawby village boasts the last surviving post mill in the area and the Humber Bridge is close by. The pub is on the 909 bus route between Doncaster/Sheffield and Hull/Grimsby.
🏠🏵🛏◗▲♣P

The Crown's Landlady

It was called the Crown. They said it had once been the Crown and Cushion, but the cushion was so hard to paint, and no one knew which a crown should be cushioned or a cushion crowned, and it was such a big name for the shanty, that it was diminished to the Crown. But it had those four windows with crimson blinds, and the landlady was said to be a Gypsy and was followed wherever she went by a white-footed black cat that looked as though it was really a lady from a far country enchanted into a cat. The Gypsy was a most Christian body. She used to treat with unmistakable kindness, whenever he called at the inn, a gentleman who was notoriously an atheist and a teetotaller. When asked upbraidingly why, she said: 'He seems a nice gentleman, and as he is going to a place where there won't be many comforts, I think we ought to do our best to make this world as happy as possible for him'.

Edward Thomas, *The Happy-go-lucky Morgans*, 1913.

Beer Festival Calendar 2002

CAMRA stages a large number of beer festivals every year. They are magnificent shop windows for cask ale and give drinkers the opportunity to sample beers from independent brewers rare to individual localities. Beer festivals are enormous fun: many offer good food and live enterainment and, where possible, facilities for families. Some seasonal festivals specialise in spring, autumn and winter ales. Festivals range in size from small local events, to large regional ones. The Campaign holds two national festivals, for winter beers in January, and the Great British in August; the latter features around 500 beers. The list below offers a sample of the festivals planned for 2002. For up-to-date information, contact the CAMRA website: **www.camra.org.uk**. By joining CAMRA – there is a form at the back of the Guide – you will receive 12 editions of What's Brewing, which lists every festival on a month-by-month basis.

JANUARY
Great British Winter Beer Festival, Manchester
Cambridge winter festival
Hitchin winter festival
St Neots winter festival

FEBRUARY
Ashfield
Bishops Auckland
Bradford
Bristol
Chesterfield
Dover
Rotherham

MARCH
Darlington spring festival
Hitchin
Leeds
Leicester
London Drinker

APRIL
Bury St Edmunds
Dunstable
Mansfield
Newcastle
Paisley

MAY
Alloa
Cambridge
Colchester
Doncaster
Glenrothes
Newark
Ongar

JUNE
Devizes
Northampton
Thurrock

JULY
Boston
Canterbury
Chelmsford
Cotswolds
Derby
Louth

AUGUST
Great British Beer Festival, London
Barnsley
Clacton
Larling (Norfolk)
Peterborough

SEPTEMBER
Chappel (Essex)
Darlington
Hull
Ipswich
Keighley
Lincoln
Maidstone
St Albans
Sheffield
Troon

OCTOBER
Alloa
Bedford
Gravesend
Huddersfield
Middlesbrough
Norwich
Nottingham
Wakefield

NOVEMBER
Aberdeen
Barnsley winter festival
Rochford

DECEMBER
Pig's Ear (London)
Ipswich winter festival

GREATER LONDON

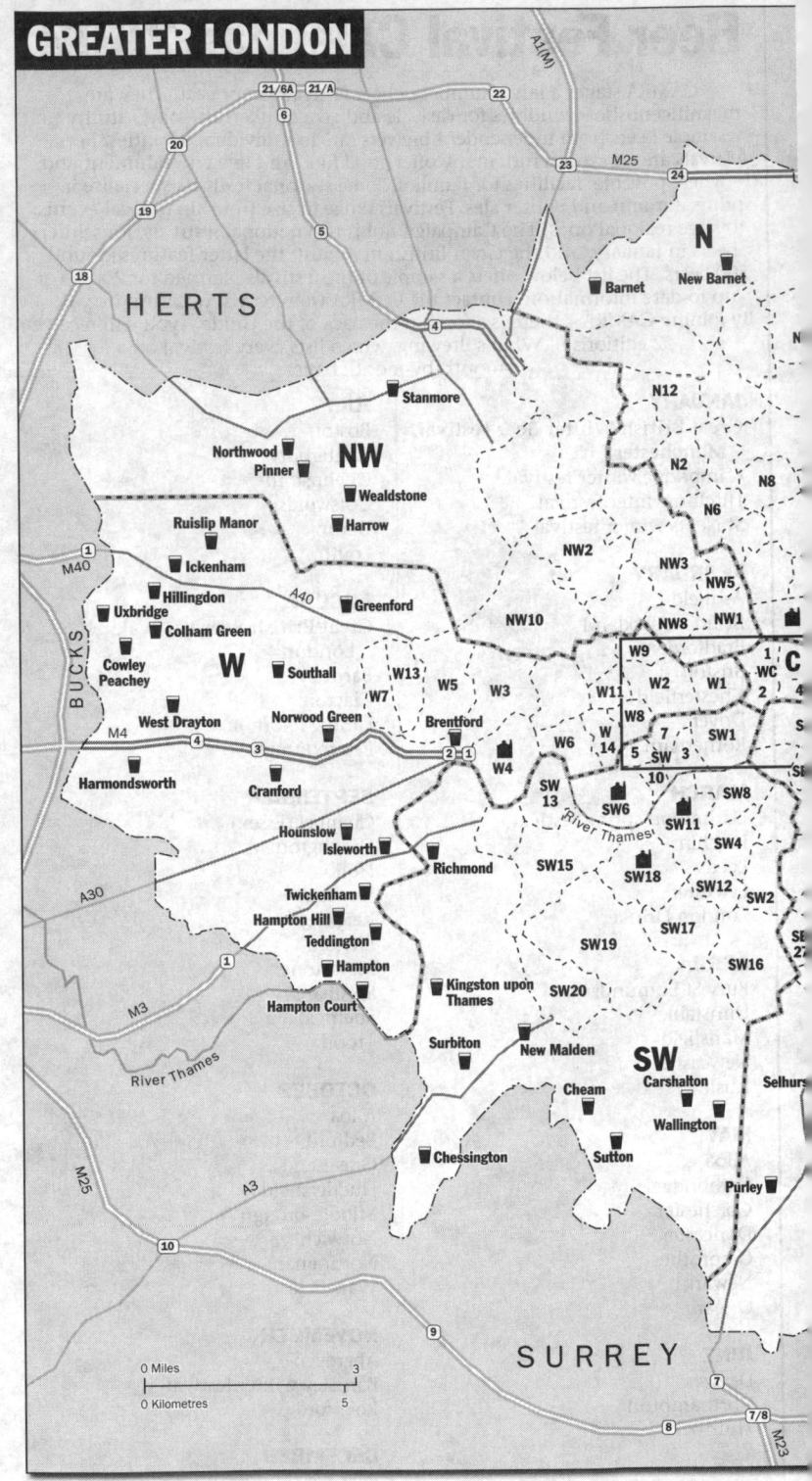

ESSEX

Enfield Town

N9
E4
Woodford Green
E17
E11
Ilford
Chadwell Heath
E
Hornchurch
N16
E5
E10
E7
E15
Barking
E2
E3
E1
E16
SE16
Belvedere
SE8
SE7
SE18
Bexleyheath
SE3
SE4
SE13
SE9
Bexley
SE22
SE6
Sidcup
North Cray
SE26
Footscray
SE20
Bromley
Chislehurst
SE25
Beckenham
Petts Wood
Croydon
SE
Bromley Common
Orpington
Addiscombe
South Croydon
Shirley
Chelsfield
Selsdon
Leaves Green
Cudham
Downe

KENT

River Thames

Districts with recommended pubs

Inner London inset map

London 'sector' boundaries

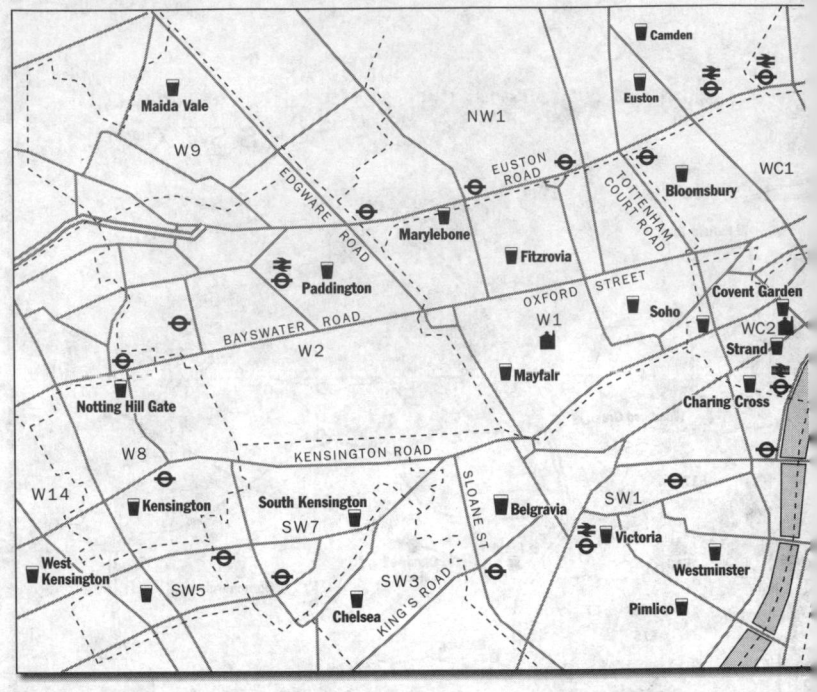

Greater London is divided into seven areas: Central, East, North, North-West, South-East, South-West and West, reflecting the London postal boundaries. Central London includes EC1 to EC4 and WC1 and WC2. The other six areas have their pubs listed in numerical order (E1, E4, etc) followed in alphabetical order by the outlying areas which do not have postal numbers (Barking, Hornchurch, and so on). The Inner London map, above, shows the area roughly covered by the Circle Line. Note that some regions straddle more than one postal district.

Central London

EC1: CLERKENWELL

Jerusalem Tavern
55 Britton Street
🕐 11-11; closed Sat & Sun
☎ (020) 7450 4281
Beer range varies Ⓐ

This tiny, cosy pub is named after the Priory of St John of Jerusalem and has occupied several sites in the area since the 14th century; the current building dates from 1720. St Peter's Brewery has a policy of continuous innovation, this is reflected in the six beers available on a rotating basis. These are complemented by the full bottled range (16 at present). Candlelit tables ensure a warm welcome and although it often becomes crowded, a good-natured atmosphere pervades.
🏚Q✿◖≉ (Farringdon) ❺

Sekforde Arms
34 Sekforde Street
🕐 11-11; 12-4 (closed eve) Sun
☎ (020) 7253 3251
Young's Bitter, Special; guest beer Ⓗ

Lively local on the fringes of the City. This wedge-shaped pub is friendly and comfortable and serves all tastes. Good, reasonably priced food complements the beers. The decor features panelling, yellow-painted walls and pictures, including the Sekforde Arms, from which the pub takes its

name. The upstairs restaurant is available for hire as a function room eves.
◖≉ (Farringdon) ♣♠

EC1: HATTON GARDEN

Melton Mowbray
18 Holborn
🕐 11-11; closed Sat & Sun
☎ (020) 7405 7077
e-mail: melton.mowbray@fullers.co.uk
Fuller's Chiswick, London Pride, ESB, seasonal beers Ⓗ

Former shop premises converted into a typical, but attractive Fuller's Ale & Pie House, comprising a large single bar on the ground floor with a mezzanine and small patio. Another bar in the basement opens at busier times and can be booked for functions. The clientele is predominantly office workers from Gray's Inn and Smithfield. The decor features lots of dark wood panelling and many old photographs of the local area. Newspapers are provided for those with time to enjoy a more leisurely drink.
✿◖≉ (City Thameslink) ❺ (Chancery Lane) ●

EC1: SMITHFIELD

Butchers Hook & Cleaver
61 West Smithfield
🕐 11-11; closed Sat & Sun
☎ (020) 7600 9181
e-mail: butchers.hook@fullers.co.uk

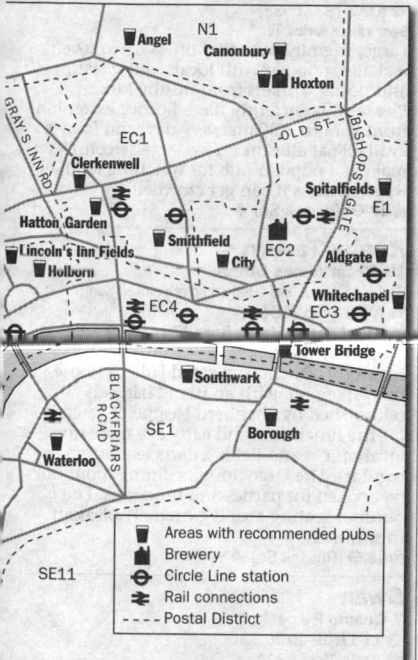

Situated in the heart of the market, where real fishmongers, butchers and dealers in game still ply their trade, this fine old pub has been run by the same family for over 50 years. Set out on four levels, the bar area was increased by the addition of a mezzanine floor in the mid-1980s. It was the first pub in the City to have a no-smoking bar. Such is the character of the place that it has been used by film crews. No full meals are served, but the hot beef French bread sandwiches are very popular. Q ⇌ (Liverpool St) ⊖ (Monument) ♣ ⅟

EC4: CITY

Bell
29 Bush Lane
✿ 11-10; closed Sat & Sun
☎ (020) 7626 7560
Courage Best Bitter; Directors; Shepherd Neame Spitfire Ⓗ

One of the smallest pubs in London, parts of which are relieved to have survived the Great Fire in 1666; it is Grade II listed. It has had the same landlady as a tenant for over 40 years. There is no TV, music, games, hot food or cigarette machine, but sandwiches are available at any reasonable time. A most interesting collection of pictures and artefacts adorn the walls, including some from the licensee's family's previous pubs. Furnishing is basic, this is mainly a stand-up to drink pub. Mind the step when entering and leaving. Q ⇌ (Cannon St) ⊖

Elephant
119 Fenchurch Street
✿ 11-9; closed Sat & Sun
☎ (020) 7623 8970
Young's Bitter, Triple A, Special Ⓗ

Walking down Fenchurch Street, look for the unusual pub sign outside the modern office building that houses this old pub. The ground-floor bar is a small room with bare boards; the cellar bar is more spacious and comfortable with plenty of seating. A good quality menu is served. ◖🄴⇌ (Fenchurch St) ⊖ (Aldgate/Tower Hill DLR) ♣

Harrow
22 Whitefriars Street
✿ 11-11; closed Sat & Sun
☎ (020) 7427 0911
Draught Bass; Fuller's London Pride Ⓗ

Situated a few yards south of Fleet Street, this pub is popular with lawyers from nearby Temple. The split-level bar has plenty of seating. Taped music plays in the background, and quiet games machines allow easy conversation. A recent

Fuller's Chiswick, London Pride, ESB, seasonal beers Ⓗ

Fuller's Ale & Pie House, formed from two ex-commercial premises. From the spacious ground-floor bar a wrought-iron spiral staircase leads to a mezzanine seating area. The decor comprises pale green walls, dark wood, old photographs of the Smithfield area, attractive murals and images of livestock. A striking feature is a large brass chandelier, while the outside is brightened by hanging baskets and window boxes. No eve meals Fri. The licensee has won Fuller's *Master Cellarmanship* award.
◖▷⇌ (Farringdon) ⊖●

EC2: CITY

Dirty Dick's
202 Bishopsgate
✿ 11-10.30 (may close earlier if quiet); closed Sat & Sun
☎ (020) 7283 5888
Young's Bitter or Triple A, Special; guest beer Ⓗ

1870s pub opposite Liverpool St Station. The ground-floor bar gets especially busy towards the end of the week. The basement is quieter for lunchtime food (closes 3pm) while upstairs a more formal lunchtime menu is served. The pub's name commemorates an 18th-century gentleman who lived at the site. His wife-to-be died on the eve of their wedding, leaving him distraught, and he descended into a life of squalor. ◖⇌ (Liverpool St) ⊖⅟

EC3: CITY

Lamb Tavern
10-12 Leadenhall Market
✿ 11-9.30 (may vary); closed Sat & Sun
☎ (020) 7626 2454
Young's Bitter, Triple A, Special, Winter Warmer Ⓗ

refurbishment has created a bright, but comfortable pub. Pavement tables allow for outside drinking in good weather.
❀◖⇌(Cannon St/Blackfriars) ⊖ (Temple)

WC1: BLOOMSBURY

Calthorpe Arms
252 Gray's Inn Road
✪ 11-11; 12-10.30 Sun
☎ (020) 7278 4732
Young's Bitter, Triple A, Special, seasonal beers; guest beer (occasional) Ⓗ

This friendly, single-bar, corner pub is popular with locals and office workers alike. Expect the occasional offering of a Smiles beer as a guest. The upstairs dining room is open at lunchtime (eve meals may be available on request); this room can also be booked for functions. No music is played, except on New Year's Eve. Local CAMRA *Pub of the Year* 2001.
❀◖⇌ (King's Cross) ⊖ (Russell Sq)

King's Arms
11a Northington Street
✪ 11-11; closed Sat & Sun
☎ (020) 7405 9107
Draught Bass; Greene King IPA; Old Speckled Hen Ⓗ

Quiet, friendly corner pub where the single bar retains a number of the better features from its days as a Charrington's house. It provides a welcome retreat from the bustle of nearby Gray's Inn Road. There are two meeting rooms upstairs, the larger holds up to 50, while the smaller one is no-smoking. The beer range may vary. A pavement patio area comes into use in fine weather.
Q❀⊖ (Russell Sq) ♣

Lamb
94 Lamb's Conduit Street
✪ 11-11; 12-3.30, 7-10.30 Sun
☎ (020) 7405 0713
Young's Bitter, Triple A, Special, seasonal beers Ⓗ

Very friendly, cosmopolitan pub, housed in an attractive Grade II listed building. Furnished with green upholstery, it features original Victorian snob screens, a snug to suit non-smokers and a pavement patio. The pub also boasts a working music hall 'polyphon' which can be played in aid of charity. The upstairs dining room serves excellent food. ❀◖⊖ (Russell Sq) ♣✂

Old Monk
39-41 Gray's Inn Road
✪ 11-11; closed Sat & Sun
☎ (020) 7831 0714
Adnams Bitter; Brakspear Bitter; Fuller's London Pride; Theakston Best Bitter; Young's Bitter Ⓗ

Converted retail premises, part of a growing pub chain. Since refurbishment, the bar now faces the road (clearly visible through the large picture windows). The style is modern, dominated by wood panelling. The front bar has high stools and tables around the edge of a central standing area. The back room is comfortably arranged into small booths to create more private drinking areas. Beer range can be reduced due to the weekend closing. Meals served all day. ❀◖ ⊖ (Chancery Lane)

Pakenham Arms
1 Pakenham Street
✪ 9am-1.30am

☎ (020) 7837 6933
Beer range varies Ⓗ

Large, friendly pub, that offers up to seven real ales, popular with locals, office staff, and postal workers from nearby Mount Pleasant. It currently has a licence extension from 9am to 1.30am every day, and food is available at all times. Two large-screen TVs make it a popular pub for watching football, which means it can get crowded.
❀◖⊖ (Russell Sq) ♣

Rugby Tavern
19 Great James Street
✪ 11-11 (12-3, 6-11 Sat summer); closed Sun
☎ (020) 7405 1384
Shepherd Neame Master Brew Bitter, Spitfire, Bishops Finger, seasonal beers Ⓗ

Formerly a Nicholson's and Fuller's house, this large pub, with an island bar, was refurbished by Shepherd Neame. It caters for the lunchtime and early eve trade from local offices and fields a darts team from its regulars. The large upstairs dining room can be booked for parties and functions. The outdoor seating area is extremely pleasant in summer.
❀◖▶ ⊖ (Russell Sq) ♣

Swan
7 Cosmo Place
✪ 11-11; 12-10.30 Sun
☎ (020) 7837 6223
Courage Directors; Greene King Abbot; Theakston Best Bitter, Old Peculier; guest beers Ⓗ

Single-bar, wood-panelled pub in an area that has a busy hotel and restaurant trade. Part of the T&J Barnard's Ale House chain, it attracts a predominantly young clientele. One or two guest beers are available and food is served at all times.
◖▶ ⊖ (Russell Sq)

WC1: HOLBORN ❖

Cittie of Yorke
22 High Holborn
✪ 11-11; closed Sun
☎ (020) 7242 7670
Samuel Smith OBB Ⓗ

This outstanding pub stands next to the gatehouse to Gray's Inn. The panelled, intimate front bar lies above an extensive bar that was the old cellar of an earlier 17th-century coffee house. The real splendour comes in the rear bar that resembles a large baronial hall, with its vaulted ceiling, long bar, handsome screenwork, compartments for virtually private drinking and massive mounted vats. In winter this bar is warmed by a triangular coal stove, dated the year of Waterloo; the smoke escapes through a chimney under the floor.
▲Q❀◖⊖ (Chancery Lane)

Overdraught's
6 Dane Street
✪ 11.30-11; closed Sat & Sun
☎ (020) 7405 6087
Badger Best; Greene King IPA; Thwaites Best Bitter Ⓗ

Just south of Red Lion Square, unprepossessing from the outside, this is a well-run little pub with a loyal following. The main bar is at street level, where the TV quietly buzzes with sport. Downstairs is another bar – for functions, where there is more seating, a dartboard and a pool room.

Ask at the bar for backgammon, crib, dominoes or Shut the Box. There are plenty of restaurants nearby for eve meals. ◖⊖♣

Penderel's Oak
283-288 High Holborn
✪ 11-11; 12-10.30 Sun
☎ (020) 7242 5669
Courage Directors; Fuller's London Pride; Hop Back Summer Lightning; Shepherd Neame Spitfire; Theakston Best Bitter; guest beers Ⓗ

Legend has it that Richard Penderel, who was associated with this area, and his oak tree gave shelter to King Charles I in his flight from the Parliamentary forces. This huge converted premises now gives warm shelter to the beer drinker. The cellar bar features large-screen TVs for sport and music, so it can be noisy; the upstairs bar is quieter, but expect it to be busy early eve. It is well designed, providing clearly defined and some semi-private drinking areas. Children's certificate at weekends. The wheelchair WC is an award winner.
Q ⊛◖♦ ♿⊖✗ ●

Three Cups
21-22 Sandland Street
✪ 11-11; closed Sat & Sun
☎ (020) 7831 4302
Smiles Best; Young's Bitter, Triple A, Special, seasonal beers Ⓗ

Comfortable, convivial, one-bar pub close to Gray's Inn. Like many pubs in the area it can be very busy early eve, thinning out as city workers head for home. A large mirror in the far corner creates light and space while prints of old London catch the eye. Nearby eateries include one of London's best chippies, the Fryer's Delight on Theobald's Road. ⊛◖⊖

WC2: CHARING CROSS

Hogshead
5 Lisle Street
✪ 11-11; 12-10.30 Sun
☎ (020) 7437 3335
Beer range varies Ⓗ/Ⓖ

Opened in 1998, in a former hospital with an impressive Dutch-style frontage in red sandstone, the interior is fairly modern bearing much polished wood, stone-flagged flooring, plain brickwork and exposed ventilation pipes. A more comfortable, no-smoking section is at the rear. Two staircases and a lift connect with the upper bar that affords a limited view of Leicester Square. Wall prints reflect its former use as a library for Pathé News. Very busy and noisy at times, it employs doormen. Prices are reasonable for the area.
◖◗ ♿≢⊖ (Leicester Sq) ✗

Marquis of Granby
51 Chandos Place
✪ 11-11; 12-10.30 Sun
☎ (020) 7836 7657
Adnams Bitter; Fuller's London Pride; Taylor Landlord; guest beers Ⓗ

Having undergone quite a few changes of ownership over the past few years, the pub now features some chapel-style partitions and unusual ceiling heaters. It offers a good malt whisky range and an excellent menu, including vegetarian daily specials, and traditional Sun roasts. A local highwayman,

Claude Duval, was arrested in a tavern on this site (the Hole in the Wall) while sleeping off a hangover. The upstairs room, which has a bar, is available for hire – it is comfortable and well furnished.
Q ◖◗ ≢⊖

Ship & Shovell
1-3 Craven Passage
✪ 11 (12 Sat)-11; closed Sun
☎ (020) 7839 1311
Badger K&B Sussex, IPA, Best, Tanglefoot Ⓗ

A pub of two halves, it stands on two sides of Craven Passage. This once-popular free house, that was closed for many years, has undergone an attractive refurbishment. The pub is named after Sir Cloudesley Shovell, whose fleet was wrecked off the Scilly Isles in the 18th century, owing to a tragic miscalculation in navigation.
◖≢⊖ (Embankment) ●

WC2: COVENT GARDEN ❖

Hogshead
23 Wellington Street
✪ 12-11; 12-8 Sun
☎ (020) 7836 6930
Beer range varies Ⓗ

Formerly the Old Bell then the Gilbert & Sullivan, this long, narrow, split-level pub, with an upstairs bar, serves an ever-changing range of guest beers, including many that are rarely found in the London area. Almost next door to the Lyceum Theatre, it is handy for the Theatre Museum, the London Transport Museum, the Strand and all the attractions of Covent Garden.
◖◗ ⊖ (Charing Cross)

Porterhouse
21-22 Maiden Lane
✪ 11-11; 12-10.30 Sun
☎ (020) 7836 9931 website: theporterhouse.com
Beer range varies Ⓗ

Stunning new building opened in 2000, comprising three floors and two mezzanines. This rambling pub is built to a high standard with a wide use of copper, wood and leather. A variety of drinking areas, all interconnected, give a surprisingly cosy feel. The main ground-floor area features a beautiful ceramic bar surround, and a mechanical clock. The upper floor, reached by iron staircases, forms a galleried area. The basement bar is used mainly eves. Glass cabinets exhibit a huge bottle collection; around 100 bottled beers are for sale. The single regular ale (TSB) is brewed specially in the Porterhouse Dublin brewery.
⊛◖◗ ♿⊖

Sun
21 Drury Lane
✪ 11-11; closed Sun
☎ (020) 7240 2489
Boddingtons Bitter; guest beers Ⓗ

Now reverted to its original name, after a period as a Hogshead, this small, friendly corner pub is a welcoming oasis to the north of Covent Garden. There is no hot food but a range of baguettes is available at lunchtime. It stands almost opposite the New London Theatre.
Q⊖

WC2: LINCOLN'S INN FIELDS

Knights Templar
95 Chancery Lane
🕐 11-11 (7.30 Sat);
12-7.30 Sun
☎ (020) 7831 2660
Boddingtons Bitter; Fuller's London Pride; Hop Back Summer Lightning; Shepherd Neame Spitfire; guest beers Ⓗ
Enormous, elaborately decorated Wetherspoon's free house in former bank premises, belonging to the Union Bank of London. It is situated at the heart of London's legal quarter – the Royal Courts of Justice are just down the road. Unusually for pubs in this area, it is open at weekends. The wheelchair entrance is round the corner in Carey Street.
Q ◑ & ⊖ (Temple) ✄ ●

WC2: SOHO

Moon Under Water
105-107 Charing Cross Road
🕐 11-11; 12-10.30 Sun
☎ (020) 7287 6039
Draught Bass; Courage Directors; Fuller's London Pride; Shepherd Neame Spitfire; guest beers Ⓗ
Said to be London's largest free house, this enormous Wetherspoon's pub was once the Marquee music venue. Spread over three levels, with lift access for disabled customers, it is brightly decorated with an Art Nouveau theme. The pub is divided into small drinking spaces; a high balcony serves as a no-smoking area. It appeals to a very wide range of customers.
Q ◑ & ⊖ (Leicester Sq/Tottenham Crt Rd) ✄ ●

WC2: STRAND

Edgar Wallace
40 Essex Street
🕐 11-11; closed Sat & Sun
☎ (020) 7353 3120
Adnams Broadside; Boddingtons Bitter; Brakspear Bitter; Fuller's London Pride; guest beers Ⓗ
Small, corner pub, just off the Strand near the Temple Inns of Court. It is named after Edgar Wallace, the journalist and writer of thrillers who had a long association with nearby Fleet Street. It is traditionally decorated and can get very busy at times.
◑ ⊖ (Temple)

East London

E1: ALDGATE

Castle
44 Commercial Road
🕐 11-11; closed Sat & Sun
☎ (020) 7481 2361
Courage Best Bitter, Directors; guest beer (occasional) Ⓗ
Bright green triangular pub, just off the Aldgate one-way system, heading east on the Commercial Road; pedestrians use exit 26 of the subway system. Downstairs, two distinct areas are served from a central bar; upstairs, which has two pool tables, is available for private functions (no real ale). The clientele varies according to the time of day – predominantly office workers at lunchtime and early eve, but more mixed at other times. Parking is difficult until 7.30 or so. ◑ ⊖ (East) ♣

E1: SPITALFIELDS

Pride of Spitalfields
3 Heneage Street
🕐 11-11; 12-10.30 Sun
☎ (020) 7247 8933
Crouch Vale IPA; Fuller's London Pride, ESB; guest beers Ⓗ
Small, back-street pub, off Brick Lane, a popular stop on the 'curry circuit'. The walls are adorned with photos and prints of local residents and buildings of the area from the first 40 years of the 20th century. Check out the pump clips above the bar – many of the beers are no longer brewed, and some are from defunct breweries.
◑⇌ (Liverpool St) ⊖ (Aldgate East)

E1: WHITECHAPEL

Black Bull
199 Whitechapel Road
🕐 11-11; 12-10.30 Sun
☎ (020) 7247 6707
Nethergate Suffolk County, Old Growler Ⓗ

INN BRIEF

Central London

WC2: COVENT GARDEN
Cross Keys
31 Endell Street
11-11; 12-10.30 Sun
Courage Best Bitter, Directors; Marston's Pedigree; guest beer Ⓗ
Intimate, dimly-lit pub bedecked with greenery outside. Note the Isleworth Brewery sign by the grandfather clock.

North-West London

WEALDSTONE
Sarsen Stone
32 High Street
11-11; 12-10.30 Sun
Courage Directors; Shepherd Neame Spitfire; Theakston Best Bitter; guest beer Ⓗ
Long, narrow, Wetherspoon's pub whose walls feature prints of old Wealdstone. *Cask Marque* accredited.

South-East London

SE1: BOROUGH
Lord Clyde
27 Clennam Street
11-11; 12-4, 8-11 Sat;
12-4, 8-10.30 Sun
Courage Best Bitter; Greene King IPA; Shepherd Neame Spitfire; Young's Special Ⓗ
Traditional, back-street boozer, with an outstanding tiled exterior. Food is available 12-3 and 5.30-11 Mon-Fri; 8-11 Sat.

Shipwrights Arms
88 Tooley Street
11-11;
12-10.30 Sun
Beer range varies Ⓗ
Large, former Courage pub with beers supplied by the Unique Pub Co., whose range is very unimaginative.

SE1: TOWER BRIDGE
Anchor Tap
28 Horselydown Lane
11-11;
12-10.30 Sun
Samuel Smith OBB Ⓗ
Multi-roomed house near Tower Bridge, formerly Courage's Anchor Brewery tap, now a rare real ale outlet for Samuel Smith's in London.

SE25: SOUTH NORWOOD
Alliance
91 High Street
11-11;
12-10.30 Sun
Courage Best Bitter; Shepherd Neame Spitfire; guest beers Ⓗ
Street-corner local by the clock tower, handy for Selhurst Park football ground.

The Black Bull has a large, single bar, frequented by friendly regulars who live and work in the area; actors from the nearby theatre are frequent visitors. Within walking distance of both Brick Lane and Petticoat Lane markets, this pub can get crowded at weekends. The landlord is of the old school, rating good beer and customer satisfaction high on his list of priorities.
◁⊖

E2: BETHNAL GREEN

Camdens Head
456 Bethnal Green Road
✪ 11-11; 12-10.30 Sun
☎ (020) 7613 4283

Courage Directors; Greene King Abbot; Theakston Best Bitter; guest beers Ⓗ
Small for a Wetherspoon's pub, this is a local, which is a good example to the rest of the chain. Comfortable and modest, it is run by friendly staff. The small backyard is a quiet haven, shaded and cool in summer, and ideal for families. The pub is conveniently located a short walk from both Underground and rail stations, and attracts a good mix of locals and office workers.
Q❀◁⇌⊖⚥●

E3: BOW

Coborn Arms
8 Coborn Road
✪ 11-11; 12-10.30 Sun
☎ (020) 8980 3793

Young's Bitter, Triple A, Special, seasonal beer; guest beer Ⓗ
Pleasant, mid-terraced one-bar local in a residential side street off the busy Mile End Road. The spacious, attractive bar has level access from the street. The large horseshoe-shaped counter – dark wood with polished brass rails – divides it into two distinct areas, with the food servery to the rear. A large side room, up some shallow steps, provides more seating and one of the two dartboards. The pub sign depicts Charles Coborn, a local music hall celebrity who was born locally and took his stage name from the road. Meals served 1-9 weekends.
❀◁&⊖ (Mile End/Bow Rd) ♣

E4: CHINGFORD

Kings Ford
250 Chingford Mount Road
✪ 11-11; 12 10.30 Sun
☎ (020) 8523 9365

Boddingtons Bitter; Courage Directors; Greene King Abbot; Wadworth 6X; guest beer Ⓗ
Typical Wetherspoon's conversion, on this occasion from a furniture showroom. Unusually, part of the upstairs is occupied by a long-established dental practice. As is usual in this company's pubs there are lots of local history panels. This was assisted by Waltham Forest having two museums – one dedicated to a past resident, designer William Morris. The long bar has just one set of six handpumps, but they are usually well-supplied. The wheelchair WC has a RADAR key.
Q◁&⚥●

E5: CLAPTON

Anchor & Hope
15 High Hill Ferry
✪ 11-3, 5.30-11; 11-11 Sat; 12-10.30 Sun
☎ (020) 8806 1730

Fuller's London Pride, ESB Ⓗ
Community pub where all mix together to set the world to rights over a glass or two of beer. A recent local CAMRA *Pub of the Year*, it stands on the bank of the River Lea with a marina, canoe hire/training and campsite close by. Popular with walkers and cyclists, outside drinking is on the river path. The landlord of 48 years runs this traditional establishment with admirable care and skill.
❀▲♣

Princess of Wales
146 Lea Bridge Road
✪ 11-11; 12-10.30 Sun
☎ (020) 8533 3463

Young's Bitter, Special Ⓗ
Spacious canalside pub, popular with locals and boaters. The tables next to the canal are often full. The pub was the Prince of Wales until the death of Diana. The panelled lounge bar looks out at one end over the canal, and is lined with bookcases at the other. The public bar houses a dartboard.
ੋ❀◁◁⇌P

BELVEDERE
Great Harry
99 Parsonage Manorway
11-11; 12-10.30 Sun
Courage Best Bitter; Greene King Abbot Ⓗ
Large, modern one-bar pub with a garden and conservatory that doubles as a family area.

CHELSFIELD
Five Bells
Church Road
11-3, 6-11; 12-4, 7-10.30 Sun
Courage Best Bitter; guest beer (occasional) Ⓗ
Village pub, run by the same family for over 65 years.

> ✳ symbol next to
> a main entry place name
> indicates there are Inn
> Brief entries as well.

CHISLEHURST
Sydney Arms
Old Perry Street
11-3, 5.30-11;
11-11 Fri & Sat;
12-10.30 Sun
Courage Best Bitter, Directors; Wells Bombardier; guest beers Ⓗ
Spacious, two-bar pub off the A222, benefiting from a large garden. The conservatory doubles as a family room.

SELHURST
Two Brewers
221 Gloucester Road
11-11;
12-10.30 Sun
Shepherd Neame Master Brew Bitter, Best Bitter, Spitfire, Bishops Finger Ⓗ
Cosy, low-ceilinged community pub that feels like a country inn; a rare outlet in the area for Shepherd Neame.

SHIRLEY
Orchard
116 Orchard Way
12-11;
12-10.30 Sun
Greene King IPA; Harveys BB; guest beers Ⓗ
Roomy, comfortable, 1970s pub, deep in a residential area affording a traditional atmosphere in a modern setting.

South-West London

WESTMINSTER
Sanctuary House
33 Tothill Street
11-11;
12-10.30 Sun
Fuller's Chiswick, London Pride, ESB, seasonal beers Ⓗ
Ale & Pie house with 34 guest rooms. It was used by MI5 during WWII and stands on the site of a monastery. *Cask Marque* accredited.

E7: FOREST GATE

Spotted Dog
212 Upton Lane
🕐 12-11; 12-10.30 Sun
☎ (020) 8472 1794
Courage Directors; Greene King Old Speckled Hen; Marston's Pedigree; Wadworth 6X; Wells Bombardier; guest beers Ⓗ

The Spotted Dog is a pub steeped in history, with connections to Henry VIII and the Boleyn estates. The original building's Dog Bar is complemented by the more modern and comfortable back bar. The restaurant upstairs is renowned for quality and caters for vegans. Meals are served 12-6 then 7-9.15. Dogs are welcome in the Dog Bar – children in the conservatory.
🏚🐾🏵️◑🍴⇌P

E10: LEYTON

Drum
557-559 Lea Bridge Road
🕐 11-11; 12-10.30 Sun
☎ (020) 8539 6577
Courage Directors; Greene King Abbot; Shepherd Neame Spitfire; Theakston Best Bitter, Old Peculier; guest beers Ⓗ

This small, street-corner Wetherspoon's is easily accessible by bus from both Central London and Walthamstow. The yard at the back is away from the main road and there is competition for space in the summer. In winter the armchairs around the fireplace are favoured as the 'hot spots'. The split-level bar is well frequented by locals who often have the choice of up to five guest ales.
🏚Q🏵️◑⇌(Midland Rd)⊁●

William IV
816 High Road
🕐 11-11; 12-10.30 Sun
☎ (020) 8556 2460
Fuller's London Pride, ESB; Sweet William East London Mild, Just William, William the Conqueror; guest beers Ⓗ

Full of plants, pictures, statuettes and pots, little of this pub is left undecorated. Split into two bars, the back room is usually without service but the unusual vaulted ceiling is worth a look. Now serving beers from its own brewery situated behind the pub, new and experimental beers are often available. Do not be put off by the wine bar signs outside – this is a real ale pub through and through. TV football is shown on the big screen, and the pub boasts close connections with the local team – Leyton Orient.
🏚🏵️◑♣

E11: LEYTONSTONE

Birkbeck Tavern
45 Langthorne Road
🕐 11-11; 12-10.30 Sun
☎ (020) 8539 2584
Courage Best Bitter; guest beer Ⓗ

Traditional two-bar Victorian corner pub that has remained largely unchanged through two changes of ownership in recent years. The public bar is smaller and gets more crowded than the high-ceilinged lounge. The guest beer is usually from a (frequently local) micro-brewery,

and the house beer Rita's Special – named after a former landlady – has been a favourite for many years. Although in a quiet back street, the pub is reached by one of the many buses that run along Leyton High Road.
🏵️🍴⊖(Leyton)♣◐

E11: WANSTEAD

Duke of Edinburgh
79 Nightingale Lane
🕐 11-11; 12-10.30 Sun
☎ (020) 8989 0014
Adnams Bitter; Tetley Bitter; Young's Bitter; guest beers Ⓗ

Warm, friendly local with wood-panelled walls; it was voted by the East London Premier Darts League as supplier of the best food in the league. Beware when approaching this house, as Nightingale Lane has a strange kink in it and it would be very easy to miss the pub. The TV only tends to be used when big football games are on, so it is usually quiet; almost a country pub within London.
◑⊖(Snaresbrook)♣

George
159 High Street
🕐 11-11; 12-10.30 Sun
☎ (020) 8989 2921
Courage Bitter; Greene King Abbot; Shepherd Neame Spitfire; Theakston Best Bitter; guest beers Ⓗ

Ex-Grand Met/Truman pub, now under the Wetherspoon's banner. This house displays a collection of photographs all around the bar area; each depicting a famous actor, singer, sportsman or political figure bearing the name George. The drinking area is comfortably furnished with an area for non-smokers. This establishment does not have the Wetherspoon's identikit look or feel about it.
Q🏵️◑&⊖P⊁●

E14: LIMEHOUSE

Barley Mow
44 Narrow Street
🕐 12-11; 12-10.30 Sun
☎ (020) 7265 8931
Greene King IPA; Ind Coope Burton Ale; guest beer Ⓗ

Situated on the Thames, next to the entrance to Limehouse Basin, it was formerly the dockmaster's house. It now benefits from a large riverside patio set with tables. The large bustling bar, decorated with nautical memorabilia, is divided with small screens that make the room cosy. Food is served Mon to Fri, plus weekends in summer.
🏵️◑⇌⊖(DLR)♣

Grapes
76 Narrow Street
🕐 12-3, 5.30 (7 Sat)-11; 12-3, 7-10.30 Sun
☎ (020) 7987 4396
Adnams Bitter; Ind Coope Burton Ale; Marston's Pedigree Ⓗ

Behind the ornate etched glass frontage of this cosy riverside pub, a warm welcome is guaranteed. From the bare boards and wood panelling of the bar, to the award-winning seafood restaurant upstairs, this is truly a pub not to be missed. On hot summer days an early arrival is necessary to secure a place on the small, but popular, deck area with its scenic views of the Thames. Look out for the oil painting of the pub on the wall of the bar – it has been exhibited at the Royal Academy. ♨Q✿◑➿⊖(Westferry DLR) ♣

E15: STRATFORD

Golden Grove
146-148 The Grove
☼ 11-11; 12-10.30 Sun
☎ (020) 8519 0750
Shepherd Neame Spitfire; Theakston Best Bitter; guest beers ⊞
This very popular pub in the town centre is a Wetherspoon's house, decorated with photos of the nearby Theatre Royal and local industry. Both of the outside drinking areas (one is to the side of the pub) are very popular in summer. There is limited parking behind the pub but it is easier to use the ample public transport that serves this area.
Q✿◑占➿⊖P✗●

E16: CANNING TOWN

Ordnance Arms
110 Barking Road
☼ 11-9; 12-9 Sun
☎ (020) 7476 2216 website: www.greeneking.co
Greene King IPA, Abbot, seasonal beers ⊞
The pub suffered bomb damage in WWII and its U-shaped bar displays artefacts dating from before the rebuilding in 1952. Also on show are artworks and prints of horse-racing, cricket and other sports. It is easily accessible from Canning Town Station and buses from the City. Meals are served all day until 8pm. Games include pool and chess. ◑➿⊖♣

E17: WALTHAMSTOW

Flowerpot
128 Wood Street
☼ 12 (11 Sat)-11; 12-10.30 Sun
☎ (020) 8223 9941
Draught Bass ⊞
Single-roomed pub with an island bar, the Flowerpot is renowned for the quality of its Bass, the only real ale available, and the pub has been a regular *Guide* entry since 1980. Part of the Bass East London Pub Company chain, the decor features notable old brewery mirrors. Occasional barbecues are hosted in the back yard in summer.
✿➿(Wood St)

BARKING

Britannia
1 Church Road (near A123)
☼ 11-3, 5-11; 12-11 Sat; 12-10.30 Sun
☎ (020) 8594 1305 website: www.youngs.co.uk
Young's Bitter, Triple A, Special, Winter Warmer, seasonal beers; guest beer ⊞
Young's East London outpost has a spacious saloon with a piano, and a more basic public bar. Note the caryatids on the outside of the pub – a now rare example in East London. This local CAMRA *Pub of the Year* 2000 is an excellent traditional local. The guest beers come from Smiles; note a 'tight' sparkler is used on the Triple A. Meals include a traditional Sun roast; no lunches served Sat; eve meals available Mon-Thu.
✿◑⌺➿⊖♣P

CHADWELL HEATH

Eva Hart
1152 High Road (A118)
☼ 11-11; 12-10.30 Sun
☎ (020) 8597 1069
Courage Directors; Greene King Abbot; Shepherd Neame Spitfire; Theakston Best Bitter; guest beers ⊞
Large, comfortable, fairly typical Wetherspoon's conversion of what was once the local police station, on the site of the original village stocks. The pub is named after a local lady who was the oldest survivor from the *Titanic* disaster in 1912 and there are various items of memorabilia in the pub. It operates a vigorous guest beer policy and there are normally three or four guest ales available. The extensive no-smoking area includes a gallery. Good value food is available throughout the day.
✿◑占➿P✗●

HORNCHURCH

Chequers
North Street (near A124)
☼ 11-11; 12-10.30 Sun
☎ (01708) 442094
Ansells Bitter; Friary Meux Bitter; Greene King Abbot; Young's Bitter ⊞
Small, traditional, unspoilt boozer on a traffic island. It sells good value beers and is definitely a drinkers' pub. A very busy local, especially early eve, it enjoys a keen darts following and fields several teams. There is an unobtrusive TV in one corner for sports fans, but secluded seating elsewhere. A well-deserved local CAMRA *Pub of the Year* in 1997-99 and again in 2001. Lunchtime meals are served Wed-Fri.
◑占➿(Emerson Pk) P

ILFORD

Prince of Wales
63 Green Lane (A1083)
☼ 11-midnight; 12-10.30 Sun
☎ (020) 8478 1326
Ind Coope Burton Ale; Tetley Bitter; guest beers ⊞
Pleasant local on a busy road, just east of Ilford town centre. A recent refurbishment has smartened up the public bar and lost the snug, but the character of the pub remains intact. A pleasant split-level garden provides one of Ilford's best places to sit out when weather permits. The beer range has increased in recent years, with usually four guests, tending to be from regionals, such as Adnams and Fuller's; Adnams Bitter is usually available. It is one of the few London pubs that still sells Burton Ale.
✿⌺♠P

WOODFORD GREEN

Cricketers
299-301 High Road (A11)
☼ 11-11; 12-10.30 Sun
☎ (020) 8504 2734
McMullen AK, Country Bitter, Gladstone, seasonal beers ⊞
Friendly, suburban pub with a cosy, comfortable saloon bar and a more basic public bar. There is a good community focus, as the pub has its own golf society and stages monthly quizzes (last Tue). It has also been a long-time supporter of the

Guide Dogs for the Blind Association, as attested by the many certificates and photographs displayed in the bar. There is a small patio for outdoor drinking. ⊛◖❧♿P

Travellers Friend
496-498 High Road (A104)
✪ 11-11; 12-10.30 Sun
☎ (020) 8504 2435
Courage Best Bitter; Fuller's London Pride; Greene King Abbot; Ridleys IPA; guest beer Ⓗ

Small, but very busy, pub lying back from the High Road, which, according to all and sundry, has never ever sold any keg bitter. In the dark days of the 1960s, Draught Bass was the mainstay here. The pub, which has a very warm, friendly atmosphere, is wood-panelled throughout and retains the original snob screens at one side of the bar. Although pretty much a local, visitors from further afield are always made to feel welcome. The car park is tiny. ⊛◖P

North London

N1: ANGEL

Prince of Wales
1A Sudeley Street
✪ 11-11; 12-10.30 Sun
☎ (020) 7837 6173
Young's Special Ⓗ

A stone's throw from the bustling crowds of lively Upper Street, the Prince is a reminder of how suburban London pubs were before the 'brewery improvement squads' moved in. With its 1930s wood panelling largely intact and comfortable seating, a restful visit, surrounded by early 20th-century local photos, is assured. The larger of the two bars is a canalside lounge. The building dates from the 1860s and is an ideal stop on a stroll along the Regent's Canal towpath. Home-made lunches are served weekdays. ◖❧

N1: CANONBURY

Compton Arms
4 Compton Avenue
✪ 12-11; 12-10.30 Sun
☎ (020) 7359 6883
Greene King IPA, Triumph, Abbot Ⓗ

With its compact dimensions and simple brick and wood decor, you get something of a country pub atmosphere here in the heart of trendy Islington. The Compton has a narrow wood-floored 'public' where the rugby crowd gathers on match days. A smaller dining room-cum-saloon features old local prints; a lower lounge area opens on to the patio. Eve meals finish at 8.30; not served Tue. ⊛◖▶≠(Highbury & Islington) ❧

Marquess Tavern
32 Canonbury Street
✪ 11-11; 12-10.30 Sun
☎ (020) 7354 2975
Young's Bitter, Triple A, Special, seasonal beers Ⓗ

Large, friendly pub with one main bar, and a room to the rear. The pub, built circa 1852-56, is listed; Young's acquired and restored it in 1979. The back room was formerly the Paris Hall, and may have been used as a mortuary during the last war. The pub boasts a good collection of darts trophies, but the team has now given way to an enthusiastic cricket team. A monthly quiz takes place on the first Mon. The pub boasts of a visit from the team with their trophy when Arsenal last won the FA Cup. This local CAMRA *Pub of the Year* 1998, serves food all day (11-9), except Sun (12-3). A Smiles beer is occasionally stocked. ⋈⊛◖≠(Essex Rd) ❧(Highbury & Islington) ♣

N1: HOXTON

Beer Shop
14 Pitfield Street
✪ 11-7; 10-4 Sat; closed Sun
☎ (020) 7739 3701
website: www.pitfieldbeershop.co.uk
Beer range varies

North London's premier specialist beer off-licence is the best place to find the extensive range of bottle-conditioned organic beers produced by the neighbouring Pitfield Brewery. Many rarities are to be found among the more than 500 different bottled beers from Britain and the rest of the world, with a particularly good range of Belgian specialities. Polypins and firkins can be ordered; also stocked are bottled cider and organic wines, beer books, and supplies for home-brewing and winemaking. ≠(Old St) ❧

Wenlock Arms
26 Wenlock Road
✪ 12-11; 12-10.30 Sun
☎ (020) 7608 3406 website: www.wenlock-arms.co.uk
Adnams Bitter; guest beers Ⓗ

Situated just two minutes from the Regent's Canal, this lively street-corner pub, with a large island bar and alcove seating, provides a friendly welcome to locals and visitors. A wide, and frequently changing, range of beers, includes a mild; a regular cider or perry is also available on tap. Occasional music nights feature, in addition to a regular Sun lunchtime jazz session. Bar food includes its famous salt beef 'sandwedges'. North London CAMRA *Pub of the Year* 2000. ⋈≠(Old St) ❧♣●

N2: EAST FINCHLEY

Madden's
130 High Road
✪ 11-11; 12-10.30 Sun
☎ (020) 8444 7444
Fuller's London Pride; Greene King Abbot; guest beers Ⓗ

Converted shop, refurbished and revitalised by the current owners. Up to four guest beers supplement the regular range. Unusually, the pub food is supplied by an adjacent Chinese restaurant. It is handy for the Phoenix Cinema, one of London's last independently-owned cinemas. Pub posters indicate a strong interest in horse-racing and Arsenal FC; a large-screen TV is used for sport. A notable floral display brightens the pub exterior. No food Mon lunchtime. ⊛◖❧

N6: HIGHGATE

Flask in Highgate ☆
77 Highgate West Hill
✪ 11-11; 11-10.30 Sun
☎ (020) 8348 7346

Adnams Bitter; Harveys BB; Highgate Dark; Ind Coope Burton Ale; Taylor Landlord Ⓗ
At the heart of Highgate Village, this pub boasts spacious low-ceilinged rooms, wood panelling, exposed beams, open fires and many more original features. Built in 1663, the original listed bar dates from 1716, with sash windows opening for service. Right by Highgate cemetery, it is handy for Hampstead Heath and Kenwood House. The Flask serves traditional British food, a range of foreign bottled beers, and a selection of freshly-produced fruit and vegetable juices. Benefiting from a convivial garden, why not follow in the footsteps of Hogarth and Betjeman? ♨ Q ❄ ◑ ➊ ♣ ❤ ⤤ ●

Gatehouse
1 North Road
🕐 11-11; 12-10.30 Sun
☎ (020) 8340 8054
Courage Directors; Greene King Abbot; Shepherd Neame Spitfire; Theakston Best Bitter; guest beers Ⓗ
Imposing Tudor-style building at the top of the village and probably Highgate's oldest pub – a licensed building has stood on the site since 1337, next to a toll gate. Previously used as a courtroom, a rope dividing the borough boundary between London and Middlesex ran through the building. Byron, Cruikshank and Dickens were all regular visitors. Upstairs the theatre stages regular performances. There are reputedly two active ghosts here. A pleasant walled garden and good food contribute to make this Highgate's busiest pub.
❄ ◑ ⅙ ⊖ (Archway) ⤤ ●

N8: CROUCH END

Harringay Arms
153 Crouch Hill
🕐 12-11; 12-10.30 Sun
☎ (020) 8340 4243
Courage Best Bitter, Directors Ⓗ
Delightful, unobtrusive town-centre local; the interior of this small, single-bar pub is a mix of dark wood-lined walls and red plush upholstery. Near the entrance is a display to delight local historians, including a list of licensees since 1851, copies of OS maps of the area dating back to 1815, many old photos of Crouch End, including two of this pub, and copies of documents relating to this former beer house. Sandwiches and ploughmans are served at lunchtime. Outdoor seating is in a walled courtyard.
Q ❄ ⇌ (Crouch Hill)

N8: HORNSEY

Toll Gate
26-30 Turnpike Lane
🕐 11-11; 12-10.30 Sun
☎ (020) 8889 9085
Courage Directors; Greene King Abbot; Shepherd Neame Spitfire; Theakston Best Bitter; guest beers Ⓗ
Handy for Wood Green shopping centre, this large, traditionally decorated Wetherspoon's pub, converted from several shops, was refurbished in 1998 in the then house style of dark wood and brightly-coloured carpet and upholstery. The rear of the pub is brightened by two extensive skylights. Food is available all day until half an hour before closing. Children are only allowed in the street-side patio area. It can be uncomfortably noisy at weekends.
Q ❄ ◑ ⇌ ⊖ (Turnpike Lane) ⤤ ●

N9: LOWER EDMONTON

Beehive
24 Little Bury Street
🕐 11-11; 12-10.30 Sun
☎ (020) 8360 4358
Adnams Bitter; Ansells Bitter; Marston's Pedigree; Tetley Bitter Ⓗ
Friendly local in a back-street residential area: one large, U-shaped comfortable bar with a TV on one side, pool table and darts on the other. A tropical fish tank graces the centre section. Live jazz, and barbecues are planned for the summer. The beers may vary. No eve meals Sun.
❄ ◑ ♣ P

N12: NORTH FINCHLEY

Tally Ho
749 High Road
🕐 11-11; 12-10.30 Sun
☎ (020) 8445 4390
Courage Directors; Shepherd Neame Spitfire; Theakston Best Bitter; guest beers Ⓗ
Spacious Wetherspoon's real ale oasis in a busy town centre, swamped by fake Irish pubs. The garden area, a secluded island in the middle of the High Road, is a perfect spot for a summer drink. Nostalgic photographs of Old Finchley, well-priced beers from regional and micro-breweries, and the ever-popular 'two meals for a fiver' menu are added attractions. Note the chair backs carved to resemble an elephant. The restaurant is upstairs.
Q ❄ ◑ ♣ ⤤ ●

N16: STOKE NEWINGTON

Rochester Castle
145 Stoke Newington High Street
🕐 11-11; 12-10.30 Sun
☎ (020) 7249 6016
Fuller's London Pride; Greene King Abbot; Hop Back Summer Lightning; Shepherd Neame Spitfire; Theakston Best Bitter; guest beers Ⓗ
Giant, single-bar Wetherspoon's house, divided into three distinct areas. Note the original tiled mosaic doorstep and the decorative tiled entrance walls of the bar, both listed. Up to six micro-brewery beers are stocked. The front area is often busy, with animated conversation; the central area, more popular with Sunday 'broadsheet browsers', is generally quieter. The natural light from the vaulted skylight makes for a comfortable read or convivial chat in the flanking alcoves. The conservatory area is frequented by chess players, and leads to a tree-shaded patio, which closes at 8pm. Baby-changing facilities are provided. Meals are served all day.
❄ ◑ ⇌ ⤤ ●

N21: WINCHMORE HILL

Dog & Duck
74 Hoppers Road
🕐 11-11; 12-10.30 Sun
☎ (020) 8886 1987
Greene King IPA; Wadworth 6X; Young's Special Ⓗ
Small, friendly, cottage-style local frequented by a loyal band of regulars. A

recent refurbishment was carried out with no loss of character. The attractive etched glass in the front door suggests that the pub previously had two bars. It is close to the shops and transport links of Green Lanes (parking is difficult). Expect unobtrusive background music, Sky TV for sport and a monthly quiz. The small, secluded garden at the rear is popular.
🏨🌣≉♣

Orange Tree
18 Highfield Road
✪ 11-11; 12-10.30 Sun
☎ (020) 8360 4853
Greene King IPA; guest beers Ⓗ
Popular local hideaway, just off Green Lanes, signed on the main road. The large garden offers barbecue, chairs, tables with umbrellas and a children's play area with swings and a climbing frame. The single large bar is warmed by two coal fires; a TV for sporting events, horse brasses, sporting trophies; a dartboard and pool table complete the picture. Booking is advised for the good value meals. Local CAMRA *Pub of the Year* 1999 and 2000.
🌣◖≉♣P

BARNET

Albion
74 Union Street
✪ 11-11; 12-10.30 Sun
☎ (020) 8441 2841
Greene King IPA, Abbot; Ind Coope Burton Ale Ⓗ
Traditional local two-bar boozer where various board games are set into tables in the public bar. It is probably the only remaining pub in Barnet with an outside gents' toilet – and is proud of the fact. In the saloon bar, a display of WWI memorabilia pays tribute to the casualties that were admitted to a hospital that once stood opposite. Humphrey Lyttleton frequented the pub when there was a jazz club next door. 🌣⊟⊖ (High Barnet) ♣🐾P

King William IV
18 Hadley Highstone (A1000)
✪ 11-3, 5.30-11; 11-11 Fri, Sat & summer; 12-10.30 Sun
☎ (020) 8449 6728
Adnams Bitter; Greene King IPA; Ind Coope Burton Ale; guest beer Ⓗ
17th-century roadside inn, near picturesque Hadley Common, site of the Battle of Barnet in 1471, and opposite a golf club. Quiet and characterful, with warm, intimate drinking areas, the 'Willy' has remained largely unchanged for many years. Its two real fires earned the pub a recent award from Homefire. A full menu is served eves and weekends in the restaurant area to the rear. A house ale, Hadley Bitter, is an Ushers beer from the Thomas Hardy Brewery. 🏨Q🌣◖P

Olde Mitre
58 High Street
✪ 11-11; 12-10.30 Sun
☎ (020) 8449 6582
Adnams Bitter; Tetley Bitter; Wadworth 6X; guest beers Ⓗ
A regular entry in this *Guide*, this 17th-century former coaching inn, a Grade II listed building, is now an ale house. Wood panelling and subdued lighting help create a cosy atmosphere; maps and pictures of Old Barnet adorn the walls: one bar serves three split-level drinking areas: the middle section is for non-smokers, with a raised bar; the area at the back shows TV sport. A 50p fine is imposed for mobile phone use – proceeds go to charity.
◖⊖ (High Barnet) ♣P✏

Olde Monken Holt
193 High Street
✪ 11-11 (midnight Fri & Sat); 12-10.30 Sun
☎ (020) 8449 4280
Courage Best Bitter, Directors; Greene King IPA; guest beer Ⓗ
This intimate pub is an 18th-century former dwelling house, close to Hadley Common. It may be named after General Monk who camped in Barnet on his way to support Charles II. This former coaching inn features extensive wood panelling. At the rear, a dumb waiter is used for meals service – food is good value, with an extensive menu. A popular local, it has a small walled garden. It hosts live music Fri and Sat (no entry after 10.30pm). 🌣◖

ENFIELD TOWN

King's Head
Market Place
✪ 11-11; 12-10.30 Sun
☎ (020) 8366 9381
Adnams Bitter; Greene King IPA; Tetley Bitter Ⓗ
This fine 1899 pub, by well-known Victorian architects Shoebridge and Rising, stands at the back of Enfield's small, colourful market (market days Thu-Sat). A pub has stood on this site since the market was granted its charter by James I. The accommodation includes a split-level bar with some old etched windows, a small 'snug' (often reserved) with comfortable armchairs and a TV for sports events, and an upstairs games room with three pool tables and two dartboards. Food is served 11.30-7. 🌣◖≉♣

Old Wheatsheaf
3 Windmill Hill
✪ 11-11; 12-10.30 Sun
☎ (020) 8363 0516
Adnams Bitter; Benskins Bitter; Tetley Bitter; guest beers Ⓗ
Traditional, two-bar pub, near the station, noted for its floral displays. This comfortable, but rather expensive hostelry is popular with locals. The saloon bar is decorated with pictures of Old Enfield, and offers a TV and fruit machine by way of amusement. There is a body-building gym, with weights, at the rear of the pub. Bar meals are served weekday lunchtimes. It hosts regular quiz nights and a folk club. ◖⊟≉(Enfield Chase) ♣

NEW BARNET

Hadley Hotel
113 Hadley Road
✪ 11-11; 12-10.30 Sun
☎ (020) 8449 0161
Fuller's London Pride; Greene King Old Speckled Hen; Marston's Pedigree Ⓗ
Tucked away in leafy suburbia, ideally located for a stroll through Hadley Woods,

it is the only pub in the area to provide accommodation. The bar is split into three areas: the right-hand bar boasts a mural of the 1471 Battle of Barnet; the other two areas are traditionally decorated and display paintings by a local artist that are for sale. Watch out for the pub cat. Eve meals are served Thu-Sat; no food Sun. 🏠🛏️◐

Railway Bell
13 East Barnet Road
🕐 11-11; 12-10.30 Sun
☎ (020) 8449 1369
Courage Directors; Shepherd Neame Spitfire; Theakston Best Bitter; guest beers Ⓗ
Recent refurbishment and the addition of a dining room area, with fresh flowers on every table, gives this Wetherspoon's pub a cosy feel. Popular with an older set at lunchtime, quietly contemplating their crosswords, it can be noisy eves with the younger generation (but sadly, fewer real ale drinkers). It has a garden at the rear.
Q🏠◐🚃♣P✗●

North-West London

NW1: CAMDEN

Spread Eagle
141 Albert Street
🕐 11-11; 12-10.30 Sun
☎ (020) 7267 1410
Young's Bitter, Triple A, Special, seasonal beers; guest beer Ⓗ
Elegantly decorated pub, divided into two rooms: the elongated bar is carpeted and furnished with benches and stools; the other room is large and bright, filled with tables and chairs, benefiting from a panoramic window. Old framed prints and attractive dark wood panelling add character. The guest beer is usually Smiles Bitter or a Smiles seasonal brew. Food is served 12-7.30 (5 Sun). Benches and tables along the quieter side road of Albert Street provide an outdoor drinking area.
Q🏠◐🚃 (Camden Rd) ↔ (Camden Town)

NW1: EUSTON

Head of Steam
1 Eversholt Street
🕐 11-11; 12-10.30 Sun
☎ (020) 7388 3359
website: www.theheadofsteam.com
Banks's Hanson's Mild; Black Sheep Best Bitter; Hop Back Summer Lightning; guest beers Ⓗ
Formerly called Rails, it adopted its new name in 1995. The single bar has a raised no-smoking area. It boasts nine handpumps and stages regular beer festivals – at least once a month. The pub is full of railway memorabilia and transport models (many are for sale), paintings and prints. This local CAMRA *Pub of the Year* 1999 offers bar billiards, Sky TV for sport, and Internet access. Ask at the bar for the code to use the toilets. Eve meals are served weekdays 5-8. An occasional perry complements Weston's vintage cider.
◐🚃↔♣✗●

Square Tavern
26 Tolmers Square
🕐 11-11; closed weekends
☎ (020) 7388 6010

Young's Bitter, Triple A, Special, seasonal beers Ⓗ
Modern, purpose-built pub, erected in 1981 when this run-down square was completely rebuilt. The square formerly housed the cheapest cinema in the country, which moved to Victoria. This is a lock-up pub, and although called the Square Tavern, its one bar counter is semi-circular. Although formerly a free house, it has always stocked Young's beers, but a Smiles brew has made an occasional appearance. Loud music is played at times. There is an adjoining wine bar. 🏠◐🚃↔↔

NW2: CRICKLEWOOD

Beaten Docket
50-56 Cricklewood Broadway
🕐 11-11; 12-10.30 Sun
☎ (020) 8450 2972
Courage Directors; Greene King Abbot; Shepherd Neame Spitfire; Theakston Best Bitter; guest beers Ⓗ
It is not so much that this pub revitalised the real ale scene in Cricklewood, rather this pub *is* that scene. Now well established, attracting a wide range of drinkers, a series of well-defined drinking areas disguise the vastness of the place. The pub's name refers to a losing betting slip; plenty of prints and paraphernalia reinforce the theme. Like many Wetherspoon's pubs, it also features prints of the local area (immortalised by Alan Coren). There is a good choice of excellent, good value restaurants nearby (try the Khana). Q🏠◐🚃✗●

NW3: BELSIZE PARK

Washington
50 Englands Lane
🕐 10-11; 12-10.30 Sun
Adnams Bitter; Draught Bass; Fuller's London Pride; Greene King IPA; Ind Coope Burton Ale; Tetley Bitter Ⓗ
Magnificent corner house built in 1865 by a relative to the current licensee, and named after his birthplace, Washington in Sussex. Grade II listed, it was carefully restored after being bombed during WWII. A Victorian-style large main bar of carved wood, surrounded by a wealth of etched glass, mirrors and original tiling are the main features. Home to many local clubs, a small downstairs bar is also used as a comedy venue. Full English breakfast is served Mon-Fri 10-2.30; main meals 2.30-10.
◐↔♣

NW3: HAMPSTEAD

Duke of Hamilton
New End
🕐 11-11; 12-10.30 Sun
☎ (020) 7794 0258
Fuller's London Pride, ESB, seasonal beers; guest beer Ⓗ
Friendly one-bar pub, often full of locals. Around 200 years old, it was named after a well-known Royalist from the Civil War. The walls are hung with old prints, photos and sporting memorabilia. Inquests were held here during the 19th century. A cellar bar is available for hire and the pub also stocks 15 different malt whiskies. Local CAMRA *Pub of the Year* in 1997, and still just as good. Lunchtime snacks are served.
🏠↔●●

Flask

14 Flask Walk
☼ 11-11; 12-10.30 Sun
☎ (020) 7435 4580
Young's Bitter, Special, seasonal beers Ⓗ

Classic, famous Hampstead Village pub, is a glorious Victorian building, retaining many traditional features. Four separate, distinctive drinking areas include, rarely for the south-east, a genuine public bar. The establishment attracts a very cosmopolitan clientele, who enjoy its wood-panelled, cut glass and mirrored environment. Former local CAMRA *Pub of the Season,* it can be very busy with tourists on summer days – there is some pavement seating. Meals are served 12-9.30 (3 Sun). ▲Q❁◑❺⊖

Holly Bush ☆

22 Holly Mount
☼ 5 (12 summer)-11; 12-10.30 Sun
☎ (020) 7435 2892
Adnams Bitter, Broadside; Benskins Bitter; Fuller's London Pride Ⓗ

Back in the *Guide* after a gap of several years, having survived the threat of a drastic refit by previous owners, Allied. Converted from stables in 1896, it consists of a front bar and three other rooms, newly refurbished by the landlord, using wood and items acquired from other pubs. Unfortunately the old gas lighting has been condemned by the council. Parts of the building have been altered, but sympathetically. A rare local outlet for Benskins, it boasts a superb brewery mirror. Even dogs are allowed in this excellent pub. ▲Q❦◑♣♠

NW5: KENTISH TOWN

Pineapple

51 Leverton Street
☼ 12 (11 Sat)-11; 12-10.30 Sun
☎ (020) 7485 6422
Boddingtons Bitter; Fuller's London Pride; Marston's Pedigree Ⓗ

Family-run, cosy, back-street Victorian local, enjoying a loyal following. It has a pleasant atmosphere, and it is worth a visit simply to admire the old Bass mirrors. The beer range may vary occasionally. A small patio area on the pavement caters for outside drinkers in good weather. ❁≢⊖♠

NW8: ST JOHNS WOOD

Clifton

96 Clifton Hill
☼ 11-11; 12-10.30 Sun
☎ (020) 7372 3427 e-mail: johnsheila@virgin.com
Adnams Bitter; Draught Bass; Fuller's London Pride; Taylor Landlord; Tetley Bitter Ⓗ

Built as a merchant's villa in 1837, the Clifton became a pub in 1894. Originally with four rooms, it now has two, served by a central bar. Acquired by Nicholson's in 1994, it has been restored in a very ornate style, using carved wood panelling, Persian rugs and a wonderful Temperance Society mirror. It is rumoured that Edward VII conducted his liaisons with Lillie Langtry here, although not in the smaller room, which now shows Sky Sports when required. Sun meals are served 12-6. ◑♠

NW10: HARLESDEN

Grand Junction Arms

Acton Lane
☼ 11-11; (1am Fri; midnight Sat); 12-10.30 Sun
☎ (020) 8965 5670
Young's Bitter, Triple A, Special, seasonal beers Ⓗ

In warm weather, take advantage of the huge outside drinking area, combining garden, children's amusements and patio alongside the Grand Union Canal (moorings available). This imposing pub offers three contrasting bars: the front public bar, newly carpeted, has two pool tables and a large sports TV screen; the smaller, middle bar also has a TV, while the beamed back bar with canalside view has a children's certificate and offers a special menu for them at weekends until 7pm. Fri and Sat nights see live music or disco in the back bar (no admission after 10.30). ❁◑♣≢⊖♠P

STANMORE

Malthouse

7 Stanmore Hill
☼ 4-11 (midnight Wed & Thu; 1am Fri & Sat); 12-10.30 Sun
☎ (020) 8420 7265
Beer range varies Ⓗ

This community pub is split into two rooms on different levels. A true free house, it makes a welcome change from the large Pub Co establishments that dominate the local scene. Two guest beers, mainly from micros change regularly – over 700 have featured since it opened in 1994. Quiet during the week, it gets busier weekend eves, when a late licence applies. The decking at the front was built by a regular and makes a very pleasant, flower-filled setting for summer barbecues. ❁⊖

Vine

Stanmore Hill
☼ 12-11; 12-10.30 Sun
Adnams Bitter; Benskins Bitter; guest beers Ⓗ

This old coaching inn comes as a welcome relief if you've had to climb Stanmore Hill to reach it. In summer, the attractive frontage is enhanced by a flower-bordered drinking area, with a small garden to the rear. Inside, one bar serves all parts but there is a distinct difference between the front and rear of the pub. ❁♠P

WEALDSTONE ❁

Royal Oak

60 Peel Road
☼ 12-11; 12-10.30 Sun
Adnams Bitter; Draught Bass; Ind Coope Burton Ale; Tetley Bitter Ⓗ

Large 1930s pub in a quiet back street, a welcome relief from the bustle of the High Street. The public bar was lost in a recent refurbishment, however this pleasant, airy pub retains the atmosphere of a multi-roomed house as there are several distinct drinking areas, plus a conservatory. Probably the only traditional pub left in town following the opening of many fake 'Oirish' bars nearby, it is handy for Harrow Leisure Centre, but parking is limited. ❁≢ (Harrow & Wealdstone) ⊖P

South-East London

SE1: BOROUGH ❋

George Inn ☆
77 Borough High Street
✪ 11-11; 12-10.30 Sun
☎ (020) 7407 2056
Boddingtons Bitter; Fuller's London Pride; Greene King Abbot, Old Speckled Hen; guest beers Ⓗ
Impressive, galleried 17th-century coaching inn consisting of five small rooms with two bars. A serving hatch is open in summer to supply the large outdoor seating area. It is known that the George Inn existed in the 16th century, although the present building dates from 1677; both Shakespeare and Dickens partook of its hospitality. The inn is now owned by the National Trust and leased to Whitbread (now Laurel Pub Co). Its popularity with tourists makes it an expensive pub, best enjoyed mid-week when less crowded. Bishops Beer is brewed by Crouch Vale. No food Sun eve.
Q ❀❀◖◗≢(London Bridge) ⊖

Market Porter
9 Stoney Street
✪ 11-11; 12-10.30 Sun
☎ (020) 7407 2495
Harveys BB; guest beers Ⓗ
Up to eight ales at a time can be found in this popular pub, overlooking Borough market. A strong supporter of small breweries, it has featured well over 1,000 beers since the present landlord took over a few years ago. A refurbishment during 2000 has opened up the pub and brightened the interior, without damaging the atmosphere or altering the basic layout. It opens 6-8.30am to serve the market workers.
◖◗≢(London Bridge) ⊖

SE1: SOUTHWARK

Royal Oak
44 Tabard Street
✪ 11-11; closed Sat & Sun
☎ (020) 7357 7173
Harveys XX Mild, Pale Ale, BB, seasonal beers Ⓗ
Chaucer's pilgrims, who started their journey from the Tabard (now long-gone), would have felt at home in the quiet, convivial atmosphere of this sympathetically restored hostelry. On what was once the main road to Dover, this Harvey's outpost now lies off the beaten track, yet only 100 yards from the tube station. It is well worth seeking out to sample the fine range of ales. Urban elegance and country tradition are combined in this spacious two-bar pub.
Q ◖◗◖≢(London Bridge) ⊖ (Borough) ●

SE1: TOWER BRIDGE ❋

Pommelers Rest
196-198 Tower Bridge Road
✪ 11-11; 12-10.30 Sun
☎ (020) 7378 1399
Courage Directors; Shepherd Neame Spitfire; Theakston Best Bitter; guest beers Ⓗ
Handy for some of London's best-known tourist spots, such as Tower Bridge and the Tower of London, it is part of the Wetherspoon's chain. Unusually,
it is divided into two distinct areas – a split-level drinking area overlooking the street corner, is separated from a designated family area that shuts at 9pm. At least two guests are normally on tap. The Bermondsey area is historically known for breweries and the leather trade; the pub's name alludes to saddle-makers.
Q ❀◖◗≢(London Bridge) ⊖ ●

SE1: WATERLOO

Film Café
National Film Theatre, South Bank Centre, Belvedere Road
✪ 11-11; 12-10.30 Sun
☎ (020) 7928 5362 website: www.bfi.org.uk
Young's Bitter, Special Ⓟ
The Film Café is situated on the ground floor of the National Film Theatre, overlooking the River Thames. It is convenient for all the attractions of the South Bank, including the BFI, London Imax Cinema (boasting Britain's largest screen), National Theatre, Royal Festival Hall and London Eye. The café is open to the general public from 10am, the food counter is open daily until 9pm (8.30 Sun).
❀◖◗♿⊖✦

SE3: BLACKHEATH

Hare & Billet
Hare & Billet Road
✪ 11-11; 12-10.30 Sun
☎ (020) 8852 2352
Adnams Bitter; Flowers Original; Fuller's London Pride; Greene King IPA, Abbot; Tetley Bitter; guest beers Ⓗ
Dating from 1560, this Hogshead pub has a resident ghost called George, obviously attracted by the friendly atmosphere and conversation. Situated opposite the site of the original Blackheath Golf Club, it commands extensive views over the heath. Across the road, summer drinkers tend to congregate around the pond. A wide selection of wines includes a 'wine of the month'. Bottled Belgian beers, plus annual real cider and Belgian beer festivals add variety to the extensive range of real ales.
Q ◖◗≢

SE4: BROCKLEY

Brockley Barge
184 Brockley Road
✪ 11-11; 12-10.30 Sun
☎ (020) 8694 7690
Courage Directors; Shepherd Neame Spitfire; Theakston Best Bitter; guest beers Ⓗ
The former Breakspeare Arms was closed for several years until JD Wetherspoon bought it. Following a major refurbishment the Brockley Barge was opened in October 2000, and offers the usual Wetherspoon's range of good value food and drink. The pub name is due to its proximity to the old Croydon Canal, that ran from West Croydon to New Cross Gate in the early 19th century, following the existing railway route. The pub is a welcome addition to an area where good real ale is scarce.
Q ◖◗♿≢✦●

SE4: CROFTON PARK

Brockley Jack
410 Brockley Road
✪ 12-11; 12-10.30 Sun
☎ (020) 8699 3966
Greene King IPA, Triumph, Abbot, Old Speckled Hen Ⓗ
Built in 1898 on the site of the old Brockley Castle, a rambling wooden hostelry, that was allegedly frequented by highwaymen, the pub's name is taken from Jack Camp, a notorious landlord of the Castle who supplemented his income by highway robbery. Brockley Jack in highwayman's gear is depicted on the sign. In the mid-1990s it was converted into a single-bar, open-plan format, with a small theatre. Following another refurbishment in 2000, the guest beer was withdrawn and more emphasis placed on food. ✿◖ ঙ ≈P

SE6: CATFORD

Catford Ram
9 Winslade Way
✪ 11-11; 12-10.30 Sun
☎ (020) 8690 6206
Young's Bitter, Triple A, Winter Warmer Ⓗ
The Ram stands at the Broadway entrance of Catford shopping centre. Recently refurbished in the style of a hotel lounge, it is air-conditioned with a large, raised seating area. A large-screen TV is used for sporting events. It has appeared in many previous editions of this *Guide*, and is handy for the Catford beer festival held in June each year. ◖ ঙ ≈

London & Rye
109 Rushey Green
✪ 11-11; 12-10.30 Sun
☎ (020) 8697 5028
Theakston Best Bitter; guest beers Ⓗ
Wetherspoon's conversion of a funeral parlour with a modern café-style interior. Local history is depicted in wall displays. Regular dark beers are featured. The name originates from the London-Rye road, now known as the A21, that actually goes to Hastings. Meals are served all day until 10pm. Q✿◖ ঙ ≈⅄●

SE8: DEPTFORD

Dog & Bell
116 Prince Street
✪ 12-11; 12-10.30 Sun
☎ (020) 8692 5664
Fuller's London Pride, ESB; guest beers Ⓗ
Genuine free house in a back street, on the route of the Thames Path national trail. Twice local CAMRA *Pub of the Year*, it stocks a varying range of micro-breweries' beers and 15-plus whiskies. It hosts a 'Pickles' contest every winter, with prizes for the best pickles, jams, paintings and photos. Food is served weekdays in a side room (no children under 14). Games include chess, shove-ha'penny and bar billiards. There is a secluded walled garden at the rear.
⌂Q✿◖ ♣♠●

SE9: ELTHAM

Howerd Club
**St Barnabas Church Hall,
447 Rochester Way**

✪ 12-3 (not Mon-Fri), 7.30-11; 12-2.30, 7.30-10.30 Sun
☎ (020) 8856 7212
Fuller's London Pride; Shepherd Neame Master Brew Bitter; guest beer Ⓗ
Small, but friendly, bar situated behind the St Barnabas Church Hall, a regular *Guide* entry since 1997 and CAMRA *Club of the Year* 1996. The club was named after the comedian Frankie Howerd who was born locally. Regular quiz nights are held in the main hall attached to the bar area. The walls are decorated with posters of Frankie Howerd, and brewery advertisements. The bar has a patio. Q✿≈

SE10: GREENWICH

Admiral Hardy
7 College Approach
✪ 11-11; 12-10.30 Sun
☎ (020) 8858 6452
Courage Best Bitter; Shepherd Neame Spitfire, guest beers Ⓗ
Admiral Hardy (captain of Nelson's *Victory*) was governor of the nearby Royal Naval Hospital, now the Royal Naval College, when the pub first opened in 1830. Although recently refurbished, the plain solid wooden seating and tables help maintain a traditional atmosphere. The menu has a fish and seafood emphasis (eve meals Mon-Thu). It backs on to Greenwich market where there is a covered outdoor drinking area and the pub has its own shop selling fish, cheeses and *charcuterie*. It is central for the tourist attractions including the Cutty Sark tea clipper.
✿◖ ≈⊖(Cutty Sark DLR) ♣

Ashburnham Arms
25 Ashburnham Grove
✪ 12-3, 6-11; 12-3, 7-10.30 Sun
☎ (020) 8692 2007
Shepherd Neame Master Brew Bitter, Best Bitter, Spitfire, seasonal beers Ⓗ
Popular, mid-19th century community pub, acquired by Shepherd Neame in 1975, with a small conservatory added in 1995. It has a small bar area, adorned with Greenwich scenes by local artists, and bar billiards at the rear. Food, including pizzas and jacket potatoes is available lunchtime (not Mon) and on Tue and Fri eves. A patio at the front and small, secluded garden at the rear, are added attractions at this previous London and local CAMRA *Pub of the Year*.
✿◖ ≈⊖(DLR) ♣

Morden Arms
1 Brand Street
✪ 11-11; 12-10.30 Sun
☎ (020) 8858 2189
Shepherd Neame Master Brew Bitter, Best Bitter, Spitfire Ⓗ
This is a very well hidden, back-street corner local; Circus Street, across the junction of the two main roads opposite Greenwich Station, will lead you straight to it. Solidly built in 1824, it became a licensed premises in 1832, under the provisions of the 1830 Beer Act. A free-standing solid fuel burner warms the single bar. Live music by a duo with acoustic guitar is staged Fri and Sat eves and Sun afternoons when there is a popular blues session.
⌂✿≈⊖(DLR)

Plume of Feathers
19 Park Vista
✪ 11-11; 12-10.30 Sun
☎ (020) 8858 0533

Adnams Bitter; Fuller's London Pride; Greene King Old Speckled Hen; Webster's Yorkshire Bitter Ⓗ

A deceptively large pub; its small green-tiled exterior belies the spacious interior. Dating from 1691, it stands opposite Greenwich Park, a few yards from the National Maritime Museum. As it is just feet away from the Meridian, you can work out pub opening times in the rest of the world as you drink. At the back of this single room, there's a garden for summer eating and drinking. A quiz is held Wed eve.
☞✿◑▶≠ (Maze Hill)

Richard I (Tolly's)
52-54 Royal Hill
✪ 11-11; 12-10.30 Sun
☎ (020) 8692 2996

Smiles Best; Young's Bitter, Special Ⓗ

Traditional, no-frills local with no gaming machines, music or TV to distract the serious drinker. Bare floorboards run throughout the two bars. The nickname, still used by some older regulars, dates back to when the pub was owned by Tollemache's Breweries Ltd. A varied menu is available daily until 10pm (9.30 Sun), meals are all freshly cooked to order. A large outdoor paved drinking area admits children and hosts weekend barbecues. The Sat and Sun antiques market takes place nearby. Q✿◑▶◁▷⊖(DLR)

Trafalgar Tavern
Park Row
✪ 11.30-11; 12-10.30 Sun
☎ (020) 8858 2437

Courage Best Bitter, Directors; Flagship Trafalgar Bitter; Greene King Old Speckled Hen; guest beer Ⓗ

Imposing riverside tavern dating from 1837, frequented by Dickens and immortalised in his novel *Our Mutual Friend*. Now a free house, its four inter-connected rooms are decorated with naval mementos and offer splendid river views. The guest beer is normally from Flagship Brewery; a good range of whiskies is also on offer. The end room serves as a restaurant (not Sun or Mon eves). Don't miss the rogues gallery or celebrity visitors. The elegant Regency banqueting hall upstairs hosts functions, including the annual charitable 'Ministerial Whitebait Dinner'. Live bands play Fri and Sat eves.
▲☞◑▶᳐≠(Maze Hill) ⊖(Cutty Sark DLR)

SE13: LEWISHAM

Dacre Arms
11 Kingswood Place (off A20)
✪ 11-11; 12-10.30 Sun
☎ (020) 8244 2404

Courage Best Bitter; Greene King IPA; Shepherd Neame Spitfire; guest beers Ⓗ

Little gem, hidden in the back streets; essentially a quiet pub, although there is some background music and the TV screens show major international matches. Rowdiness is not tolerated. Comfortably decorated, plates, china tankards and photographs of the area lend a country feel to the interior. Copies of complimentary newspaper articles are displayed on the wood-panelled walls. A neat but attractive garden is a suntrap. The Astronomer Royal, Edmund Halley, of comet fame is said to be buried in the nearby churchyard.
✿≠(Blackheath)

Hogshead
354 Lewisham High Street
✪ 11-11; 12-10.30 Sun
☎ (020) 8690 2054

Boddingtons Bitter; Marston's Pedigree Ⓗ **; guest beers** Ⓗ/Ⓖ

A constantly changing range of good beers on handpump and from two barrels behind the bar is available in this cosy, quiet and friendly pub. The welcoming atmosphere more than compensates for the fake decor, with bare boards, barrels and beams recreating a nostalgic sense of rustic charm. Although the management value the priceless quality of peace and quiet, it is a lively and convivial place to eat and drink. Food is scheduled for every session but is not always available.
✿◑▶≠(Ladywell)

Watch House
198 Lewisham High Street (at south end of pedestrian/bus zone)
✪ 11-11; 12-10.30 Sun
☎ (020) 8318 3136

Courage Best Bitter, Directors; Shepherd Neame Spitfire; Theakston Best Bitter; Wadworth 6X; guest beers Ⓗ

Wetherspoon's pub, named after the old village green, known as Watch House Green, long since covered by shops and offices. An archetypal Wetherspoon's, with bookcases full of engagingly dated, rarely-read hardbacks, sturdily-framed prints, stained glass screened alcoves, and rose festooned carpets, it is a spacious, comfortable town pub, with ample seating and a largely local clientele. Often busy, but it maintains an efficient, friendly service with the good value associated with this chain.
Q◑▶᳐≠⊖(DLR) ●✠●

SE16: ROTHERHITHE

Mayflower
117 Rotherhithe Street
✪ 12-11; 12-10.30 Sun
☎ (020) 7237 4088

Greene King IPA, Abbot; guest beer Ⓗ

Famous old riverside pub dating back to the 17th century. The Pilgrim Fathers are reported to have set sail from this pub for their journey to the New World. Flagstoned floors and exposed beams give this pub a cosy atmosphere. A large deck extending over the Thames provides an outside area to drink and enjoy the river views. Bar snacks are served lunchtime; the upstairs restaurant is open eves (no food Sun or Mon).
✿◑▶⊖

SE16: SURREY DOCKS

Ship & Whale
2 Gulliver Street
✪ 12-3, 6-11; 11-11 Sat & summer; 12-10.30 Sun
☎ (020) 7237 7072

Shepherd Neame Master Brew Bitter, Spitfire,

seasonal beers Ⓗ
Old docks pub, now refurbished to a high and comfortable standard, serving a good range of Shepherd Neame beers including bottles. A distinctive menu offers varied sausage and mash specialities. Sofas, chairs and pews, and friendly bar staff help create a relaxed atmosphere. Occasional live music is performed. Simple courtyard at the back provides a good outdoor drinking area.
✿ⓓ♣

SE17: WALWORTH

Beehive
60 Carter Street
✿ 11-11; 12-10.30 Sun
☎ (020) 7703 4992
Courage Best Bitter, Directors; Fuller's London Pride; Wadworth 6X Ⓗ
Handy for East Street market, this excellent, largely unspoilt, back-street local is surprisingly upmarket for the area, and serves a first-class menu. An area is set aside for diners with children. A traditional oasis in a desert of theme bars, it is close to the former Labour Party HQ in Walworth Road, but a 'non-partisan' balance is maintained in the display of political memorabilia. An extensive wine list and over 40 malt whiskies complement the beers (which should be bought by the pint as there is a significant mark-up on halves).
✿ⓓ⊖ (Kennington) ♣

SE18: WOOLWICH

Prince Albert (Rose's)
49 Hare Street
✿ 11-11; 12-3 (closed eve) Sun
☎ (020) 8854 1538
Beer range varies Ⓗ
Do not request directions to the Prince Albert – you could be sent to a pub on Plumstead Common! Anybody who knows their Woolwich pubs knows this cracking, unspoilt boozer as Rose's – until 1985 this genuine free house was owned by EJ Rose & Co. A constantly changing selection of at least three beers is supplemented by cider at weekends. Generously filled rolls and hot snacks are available at most times. Besides the conventional board there is a Kent dartboard. Two single and two twin rooms offer reasonably priced B&B.
⊨≠≈ (Arsenal) ♣●ⓓ

SE19: GIPSY HILL

Railway Bell
14 Cawnpore Street
✿ 12-11; 12-10.30 Sun
☎ (020) 8670 2844
Young's Bitter, Special Ⓗ
Small Young's pub, not far from Crystal Palace Park. Its walls are decorated with railway memorabilia, while numerous miniature bottles and ornamental teapots are on display around the bar. A quiz is held Tue eve. Lunch is served 12-3 (1-5 Sun); bar snacks are available eves. Special late party licences apply in the summer. 1970s music is featured every Fri eve. Children are welcome until 7pm.
✿ⓓᴀ≈♣♣

SE20: PENGE

Moon & Stars
164-166 High Street
✿ 11-11; 12-10.30 Sun
☎ (020) 8776 5680
Courage Directors; Greene King Abbot; Shepherd Neame Spitfire; Theakston Best Bitter, Old Peculier; Wadworth 6X; guest beers Ⓗ
Wetherspoon's pub with an unusual story: it had been intended to convert the cinema on the site, but this proved impossible, and the cinema had to be demolished. As a result, this is undoubtedly one of the best designed brownfield site pubs in the estate. Built in 1994, it is very spacious, but with a number of partitioned alcoves, thus avoiding the usual featureless open-plan Wetherspoon's layout; note the superb woodwork throughout.
Q✿ⓓ⅋≈ (Penge E/Kent House)
⊖ (Beckenham Rd Tramlink) ●P⅄●

SE22: EAST DULWICH

Clockhouse
196a Peckham Rye
✿ 11-11; 12-10.30 Sun
☎ (020) 8693 2901
Young's Bitter, Special Ⓗ
Previously an off-licence, this pub was converted in 1971 and extended in 1999. This lively pub hosts a quiz night Tue and live music Wed. It has won numerous awards for floral displays – a magnificent effort for a pub without a garden. The decor features clocks of unusual design and a large collection of jugs. Note that a cask breather may be used on Triple A and seasonal beer when the turnover is low. Q✿ⓓ⅋

SE25: SOUTH NORWOOD ❄

Portmanor
Portland Road (A215)
✿ 11-11; 12-10.30 Sun
☎ (020) 8655 1308
Courage Best Bitter; Fuller's London Pride; Greene King Abbot; guest beers Ⓗ
Large, one-bar free house serving a wide range of guest beers, mostly from micro-breweries. The small outside patio area is popular in summer. The pub hosts regular beer festivals with reasonable prices. It gets busy on Selhurst Park match days. The Manor Restaurant opens eve, and all day Fri, Sat and Sun, serving a wide range of food, including some well-priced specials; bar food is also good. Sky TV is shown on screens behind the bar, without sound.
✿ⓓ≈ (Norwood Jct) ⊖ (Harrington Rd Tramlink)

SE26: UPPER SYDENHAM

Dulwich Wood House
39 Sydenham Hill
✿ 11-11; 12-10.30 Sun
☎ (020) 8693 5666
Smiles Bitter; Young's Bitter, Special, seasonal beers Ⓗ
This deservedly popular pub was designed as a private residence in 1857 by Sir Joseph Paxton, the architect of the Crystal Palace for the Great Exhibition in 1851. In summer, the garden hosts barbecues and an

outside bar serves real ales by electric pump. Near Dulwich and Sydenham Hill golf course, the pub has its own golf society. The boules piste has been revamped as a drinking patio.

ᴍᴀQ❀◖Å⇌ (Sydenham Hill) ♣P

SE27: WEST NORWOOD

Hope Tavern
49 Norwood High Street
✪ 11-11; 12-10.30 Sun
☎ (020) 8670 2035
Young's Bitter, Special, seasonal beers Ⓗ
Small, mid-Victorian, one-bar pub with a friendly atmosphere, decorated with bric-a-brac, including local prints, books, numerous stuffed fish, and a German WWII helmet. It stages occasional discos and quizzes. It is handy for South London Theatre and West Norwood cemetery. Games facilities include shove-ha'penny and backgammon. Q❀◖⇌♣

ADDISCOMBE

Claret Free House
5a Bingham Corner, Lower Addiscombe Road (A222)
✪ 11.30-11; 12-10.30 Sun
☎ (020) 8656 7452
Palmers IPA; Shepherd Neame Spitfire; guest beers Ⓗ
Former shop premises converted to provide an attractive single bar, with a distinctly pub feel. Old brewery posters and mirrors adorn the walls, together with historic photographs of the Croydon area. The guest beers are usually sourced from small independent breweries and the pub is a rare outlet for Palmers. A must for visitors using the new tram system – Addiscombe tram stop is just round the corner. ⊖(Tramlink)

BECKENHAM

Jolly Woodman
9 Chancery Lane (between A222 and B230)
✪ 11.30-2.30, 4.30-11; 11.30-11 Fri & Sat; 12-10.30 Sun
☎ (020) 8663 1030
Draught Bass; Fuller's London Pride; Harveys BB Ⓗ
This popular, back-street, former beer house only gained a spirits licence about 15 years ago. Although there is only one bar, the divide between the two formerly separate rooms means that the TV in one does not intrude much into the other. There is a pleasant courtyard at the back and a couple of picnic benches in front. The house bitter is M&B Brew XI rebadged. Real ales are discounted Tue. Several buses and the Croydon Tramlink are within 10 minutes' walk. ❀⇌(Jct)♣

BEXLEY

Cork & Cask (off-licence)
3 Bourne Parade, Bourne Road
✪ 12-2, 4-10; 10-10 Sat; 12-3, 7-10 Sun
☎ (01322) 528884
Beer range varies Ⓖ
Oasis of take-home real ale in an area diminished of such outlets in recent times. Nearly 800 different real ales, mostly from independent breweries, have been offered in the six years since opening. Draught ciders are also regularly stocked, alongside an excellent selection of bottled beers and ciders from independent producers, imported bottled beers, (particularly Belgian) and a good range of wines and spirits. Carry-out containers are sold, and polypins can be ordered. ⇌◉

King's Head
65 Bexley High Street
✪ 11-11; 11-4, 6-11 Sat; 12-4, 7-10.30 Sun
☎ (01322) 526112
Courage Best Bitter; Greene King IPA, Abbot Ⓗ
Popular pub, particularly busy early eves with commuters. Dating from the 16th century, this is one of the oldest buildings in historic Bexley village. A pub for almost 300 years, the picturesque weatherboarded exterior makes it a local landmark. The interior boasts many original oak beams, and a few not so genuine ones following Victorian alterations. The function room doubles as a restaurant for Sun lunch and hosts live jazz Mon eve. Picnic tables on the forecourt allow for outdoor drinking. ❀◖P

BEXLEYHEATH

Robin Hood & Little John
78 Lion Road
✪ 11-3, 5.30 (7 Sat)-11; 12-4, 7-10.30 Sun
☎ (020) 8303 1128
Brakspear Bitter; Courage Best Bitter; Flagship Futtock, seasonal beers; Harveys BB; Shepherd Neame Spitfire; guest beers Ⓗ
Circa 1854, this friendly, back-street local has a drinking area in front and a small garden. Note the tables made from old Singer sewing machines. This family-run pub has an extensive lunchtime menu (not Sun). Supplemented by daily themed home-made specials (vegetarian, fish, Italian, hot and spicy, grills) and offers an excellent daily Italian pasta dish. CAMRA regional *Pub of the Year* 2000, and local winner 2000 and 2001, it was voted *Best Pub* by a local newspaper. Over 21s only admitted. ❀◖

Royal Oak (Polly Cleanstairs)
Mount Road
✪ 11-3, 6-11; 11-11 Sat; 12-3, 7-10.30 Sun
☎ (020) 8303 4454
Courage Best Bitter; Shepherd Neame Spitfire; guest beers Ⓗ
This attractive, weatherboarded pub looks out of place, surrounded as it is by 1930s housing estates. Inside, the country feel is maintained, for this is a very quiet, comfortable, relaxing pub with lots of different seating areas. The ceiling is hung with pewter tankards and jugs, while plates and horse brasses line the walls. The pub's nickname refers to a house-proud Victorian landlady who washed the steps every day. Rolls and sandwiches are available lunchtime (not Sun). Children are allowed in the garden. Q❀P

BROMLEY

Bitter End (off-licence)
139 Masons Hill
✪ 12-3 (not Mon), 5-10 (9 Mon); 11-10 Sat; 12-2, 7-9 Sun
☎ (020) 8466 6083
Beer range varies Ⓖ
A beer festival in a shop is the aim of this

gem of an off-licence, serving an ever-changing range of cask ales. Containers of varying sizes can be purchased and, with advance notice, particular beers can be obtained. A small number of bottled foreign beers are stocked as well as English bottled beers (some bottled-conditioned). The draught cider varies. ≈ (South) ●

Bricklayers Arms
141-143 Masons Hill
✪ 11-3.30, 5.30-11; 11-3, 7-11 Sat; 12-3, 7-10.30 Sun
☎ (020) 8460 4552
Shepherd Neame Master Brew Bitter, Spitfire, Bishops Finger, seasonal brews Ⓗ
Although set on the busy A21 out of Bromley, this spacious traditional pub has a country feel, enhanced by attractive chandeliers and oak tables and chairs. The bar is divided into three areas connected by arches or doorways. Pictures throughout the pub include framed cartoons. Quiet, 'easy listening' background music is played. A small patio provides some outside seating. ❀Ⓓ曲≈ (South)

Bromley Labour Club
HG Wells Centre, St Marks Road
✪ 11-11, 12-10.30 Sun
☎ (020) 8460 7409
Shepherd Neame Master Brew Bitter; guest beer Ⓗ
Friendly, local club comprising a main bar area with a mahogany-effect bar and a pool area, brightly lit by three large windows. Cosy, alcove seating and a number of upholstered chairs at wooden tables make it a comfortable place to sit; amusements include two slot machines, a juke box and Sky TV. Display boards provide details of the club and committee. CAMRA members are requested to show membership cards. ❀≈ (South) ♣P½

Red Lion
10 North Road
✪ 11-11, 12-10.30 Sun
☎ (020) 8460 2691
Beards Best Bitter; Greene King Abbot; Harveys BB; Shepherd Neame Spitfire; guest beers Ⓗ
Local pub in a residential road with a fairly spacious L-shaped bar, complete with a juke box, slot machine and darts area. Notable features are some original tiling, part slate floors and pictures showing images of brewing and barrel-making. It also boasts a large collection of pump clips and some ornate drinking vessels. It always has two guest beers on tap.
🏚❀Ⓓ≈ (North)

BROMLEY COMMON

Bird in Hand
62 Gravel Road, Keston (near Bromley bus garage)
✪ 11-11; 12-10.30 Sun
☎ (020) 8462 1083
Courage Best Bitter; guest beers Ⓗ
Dating from 1830 as part of an estate built by a local firm (Smith's), it has a lively but friendly feel. In contrast to the old building there is a brick-built extension at the back; an excellent example of how old and new can work together. Barbecues are held in the garden in summer. Note: there is no access to Gravel Road from the A21, cars should

approach via Oakley Road and Cross Road; number 320 and 61 buses stop close by. ❀Ⓓ

Two Doves
37 Oakley Road, Keston (A233, 1/4 mile from A21 jct)
✪ 12-3, 5.30 (5 Mon & Fri; 6 Sat)-11; 12-3, 7-10.30 Sun
☎ (020) 8462 1627
Courage Best Bitter; Young's Bitter, Triple A; guest beers Ⓗ
Genuine 150-year-old free house, sympathetically refurbished to retain such details as the leaded windows at the front, setting it apart from less successful efforts elsewhere in the 1990s. The garden is very popular, and the atmosphere inside is relaxed, helped by the absence of fruit machines or TV. This local CAMRA *Pub of the Year* 2000 offers 300-400 different guest beers during the course of a year. The Triple A was being trialled at the time of survey. Rolls and toasties are usually available. The 320 bus stops outside. Q ❀❀♣½

CHISLEHURST ❀

Bull's Head
Royal Parade
✪ 11-11; 12-10.30 Sun
☎ (020) 8467 1727
Young's Bitter, Special, seasonal beers Ⓗ
Large, multi-roomed hotel with five double bedrooms. Refurbishment is due to be completed by summer 2001, when it will be able to welcome children. This is a previous Kent CAMRA *Town Pub of the Year* winner. Hot food is not served in lounge bar; no food available Sun eve.
Q❀🛏ⒹP½

CROYDON

Dog & Bull
24 Surrey Street
✪ 11-11; 12-10.30 Sun
☎ (020) 8667 9718
Young's Bitter, Special, seasonal beers Ⓗ
Located on Croydon's street market, a pub has stood on this site since 1431. The large rear garden, which is unusual for a pub so near the town centre, used to serve as the village pound for stray animals. This unspoilt market pub, a Grade II listed building, has been sympathetically extended into the adjoining property in the last few years. It was in this former CAMRA London *Pub of the Year* that the photo of Prince Charles pulling a pint (reproduced in many Young's houses) was taken. A classic town pub. No food Sun.
Q❀Ⓓ≈ (East/West)
➍ (Church St/George St Tramlink) ♣

Fisherman's Arms
78 Windmill Road (A213)
✪ 12-11; 11-11 Sat; 12-10.30 Sun
☎ (020) 8689 7887
Fuller's London Pride, ESB Ⓗ
Popular Fuller's pub, first opened in 1847, it was at one time owned by Charringtons. The comfortably furnished bar is on a split level: the lower part was the original bar, the upper level being added later. A river once flowed at the bottom of the garden where locals used to fish. Good home-

cooked lunches are served daily; Sun roasts are popular, as are the summer barbecues. ✿◗◣♣

Princess Royal

22 Longley Road (off A213/A235)
✪ 12-3, 5.30 (8 Sat)-11; 12-11 Fri; 12-3, 8-10.30 Sun
☎ (020) 8240 0046
Greene King XX Mild, IPA, Ruddles County, Abbot, Old Speckled Hen, seasonal beers Ⓗ

Small, one-bar pub where the warm welcome is enhanced by a log fire. Visitors can join the locals in conversation or spend time investigating the huge quantity of bric-à-brac, including limited edition plates. The reverse of the pub sign shows its other name the Glue Pot which refers to a local factory. An attractive garden with a pond provides a pleasant option in summer. It is probably the only pub in the area which always serves mild. No food Sun eve. ✿Q✿◗◨⇌(West)♣

Royal Standard

1 Sheldon Street (off High St)
✪ 11.30-11; 12-10.30 Sun
☎ (020) 8688 9749
Fuller's Chiswick, London Pride, ESB, seasonal beers Ⓗ

Small back-street corner pub opened in 1869, now owned by Fuller's, it is very popular with the local community. The tiled exterior features some fine etched glass windows. A central bar serves three interconnected areas: the public side has plain wooden flooring and a darts area; the saloon is carpeted, with table seating; the snug has stone-flagged floors and a serving hatch to the bar. The garden is across the road. CAMRA London *Pub of the Year* 1996. Q✿◗◗⇌(East/West) ⊖(Church St/George St Tramlink)♣●

Ship of Fools

9-11 London Road (opp. station)
✪ 11-11; 12-10.30 Sun
☎ (020) 8681 2835
Courage Directors; Greene King Abbot; Theakston Best Bitter; Wells Bombardier; guest beers Ⓗ

Converted from shop premises this Wetherspoon's outlet is handy for public transport. A deep, narrow bar widens out at the rear to provide a no-smoking area. The walls are adorned with Croydon memorabilia; the premises housed a very early Sainsbury's shop around 1900. To discover the reason for the pub's name look over the mantelpiece. The award-winning ladies toilet features a fountain. A heavy emphasis is placed on guest beers (up to five). Meals are served all day. Q◗◗◣⇌(West) ⊖(West Croydon Tramlink)♣⊁●

Blacksmith's Arms

Cudham Lane South OS445601
✪ 11-11; 12-10.30 Sun
☎ (01959) 572678
Courage Best Bitter, Directors; Greene King IPA; Shepherd Neame Spitfire Ⓗ

Historic pub in buildings dating back to 1628, first licensed in 1730. It is worth visiting for the excellent restaurant (booking advised) which offers a Tue eve fish menu (no food Mon eve). A no-

smoking area is available for diners. It was the birthplace of the music hall star Little Tich in 1865. Friendly locals help create a pleasant atmosphere. ✿Q✿◗◗♣P

George & Dragon

26 High Street
✪ 12-11; 12-10.30 Sun
☎ (01689) 889031
Draught Bass; Fuller's London Pride; guest beer Ⓗ

This low-beamed country pub is situated close to historic Downe House, now a museum dedicated to the life of Charles Darwin. The guest ale is always cheaper than the regular beers. This is a food orientated pub that welcomes children, despite only having one bar. A play area is provided for them outside. A regular *Guide* entry over the past decade. It hosts a weekly quiz (Sun) and fields a darts team. ✿✿◗◨♣

Seven Stars

Footscray High Street
✪ 11.30-11; 12-6 (closed eve) Sun
☎ (020) 8300 2057
Adnams Bitter; Draught Bass; Greene King IPA Ⓗ

16th-century local in what was once a quaint village, now rather over-developed. Three main drinking areas include a space for lunchtime meals. A mix of old and new, many original features contrast with fruit and pinball machines. See if you can spot the carving above one of the fireplaces. The pool table has recently been removed to allow more seating. Live music is staged Fri and Sat eves. ✿◗P

King's Arms

Leaves Green Road (A233, N of Biggin Hill)
✪ 11-11; 12-10.30 Sun
☎ (01959) 572514
Courage Best Bitter; Greene King Old Speckled Hen; Harveys BB Ⓗ

Parts of this pub date back to the 15th century, and it is reputedly haunted. There is an outside play area for children. Live music is performed Fri eve. Bus route 320 from Bromley stops outside. Meals are served in the restaurant area, but no provision is made for non-smokers (no eve meals Mon or Tue). Background music is played in all bars, but usually at low volume. ✿✿◗◗P

White Cross

146 North Cray Road
✪ 11-11; 12-10.30 Sun
☎ (020) 8300 2590
Courage Best Bitter, Directors; guest beer Ⓗ

One of the few old buildings to survive when the dual-carriageway was cut through the historic village in the 1960s, the pub was known as the Red Cross from 1730 until 1935, when the War Office decreed the name contravened the Geneva Convention. Its comfortably-appointed interior boasts copper and brass utensils hanging in the front bar. Very popular for meals, particularly lunchtime, food is served all day Sat and Sun. Vehicle access is from the northbound carriageway of road; it is on the 492 bus route.

&⊕◖P

ORPINGTON

Cricketers
93 Chislehurst Road
⊕ 12-3, 5-11; 12-10.30 Sun
☎ (01689) 812648
Greene King Ruddles Best; Wadworth 6X; guest beers ⊞

Small, single-bar pub, with a spacious area set aside for children who can also enjoy the garden behind the pub. There is a large TV screen in the main bar. ⊞⊕❀≠♣P⅊

Harvest Moon
141-143 High Street
⊕ 11-11; 12-10.30 Sun
☎ (01689) 876931
Courage Best Bitter, Directors; Theakston Best Bitter; Wadworth 6X; guest beers ⊞

Large Wetherspoon's pub in the middle of the High Street. The friendly staff and beer served at a good temperature make this pub stand out. The fact that there is no music allows easy conversation, without having to resort to raised voices. Q◖▷占≠⅊●

PETTS WOOD

Sovereign of the Seas
109-111 Queensway
⊕ 11-11; 12-10.30 Sun
☎ (01689) 891606
Courage Directors; Greene King Abbot; Shepherd Neame Spitfire; Theakston Best Bitter; Wadworth 6X; guest beers ⊞

Typical Wetherspoon's pub; the rear area is a designated no-smoking area. An occasional beer festival adds to the already large range of ales always available. The usual range of good value Wetherspoon's food is served. Wheelchair WC. ◖▷占≠⅊

PURLEY

Foxley Hatch
8-9 Russell Hill Parade, Russell Hill Road
(A23, one-way system)
⊕ 11-11; 12-10.30 Sun
☎ (020) 8763 9307
Courage Directors; Shepherd Neame Spitfire; Theakston Best Bitter; Wadworth 6X; guest beers ⊞

Small, popular Wetherspoon's pub opened in 1993, named following the suggestion of a local CAMRA member (old Purley was once named Foxley). The L-shaped bar is carpeted throughout, and has comfortable seating. Contemporary art adorns most of the walls, but scenes of old Purley can be found on the staircase and landing. It regularly features guest beers from micro-breweries, price promotions and beer festivals. Choose from a standard Wetherspoon's menu or daily specials board (meals served until one hour before closing).
Q◖▷占≠●⅊●

SELSDON

Sir Julian Huxley
152-154 Addington Road (on A2022)

⊕ 11-11; 12-10.30 Sun
☎ (020) 8657 9457
Courage Directors; Greene King Abbot; Shepherd Neame Spitfire; Theakston Best Bitter; guest beers ⊞

A welcome Wetherspoon's addition to this suburban shopping street. Laid out in a colourful, modern, café-bar style on two levels, entry is on the lower level where the bar is situated. Steps lead up to two more drinking areas, one of which is no-smoking. To the rear of the lower level, a conservatory leads out to the garden. Food is served all day.
Q⊕◖▷占⅊●

SHIRLEY ❖

Sandrock
152 Upper Shirley Road (off A232)
⊕ 12-11; 12-10.30 Sun
☎ (020) 8662 1931
Draught Bass; Fuller's London Pride ⊞

Serving beer at keen prices, this friendly pub shows Sky Sports. A collection of books is available for customers' perusal. Close to Shirley Windmill, a notable local landmark, the pub's interior has hardly been altered; note the carved wood above the bar and the snob screen. The rear section doubles as restaurant and no-smoking area. It is a pleasant 10-minute stroll from the tramlink through the wood, but not recommended after dusk.
⊕◖▷⊖(Coombe Lane Tramlink) ♣P⅊

SIDCUP

Alma
10 Alma Road
⊕ 11-2.30, 5.30-11 Mon-Thu; 11-11 Fri; 11-3, 6-11 Sat; 12-3, 7-10.30 Sun
☎ (020) 8300 3208
Courage Best Bitter; Fuller's London Pride; Shepherd Neame Master Brew Bitter, Spitfire ⊞

Very popular back-street local, where early eves are busy with commuters recovering from travelling from London on crowded trains. The building dates from 1868 when it was known as the Railway Tavern; it was extended in 1897 by the addition of a large billiard room (now a function room). The pub was extended again in 1934, but still retained a sizeable garden, popular in summer. Some of its Victorian character remains despite recent redecoration in pale colours. Weekday meals served. The car park is tiny.
Q⊕◖▷≠♣P

SOUTH CROYDON

Rail View
188 Selsdon Road (off A235)
⊕ 11-11; 12-10.30 Sun
☎ (020) 8688 2315
Adnams Bitter; Fuller's London Pride; Hancock's HB; Young's Special ⊞

Friendly local, on a fairly prominent corner site, near a very low railway bridge. Although named Rail View, the sound of the nearby London-Brighton line is more noticeable. Numerous pictures from the railway steam age are displayed in the comfortable lounge, where the main pastime is conversation. In the public bar very civilised games of cribbage and dominoes are nearly always in play; non-regulars will get a game without any difficulty. A good selection of food is served. ✿◖⊟≢♣P

South-West London

SW1: BELGRAVIA

Star Tavern
6 Belgrave Mews West
✿ 11.30-11; 11.30-3, 6.30-11 Sat; 12-3, 7-10.30 Sun
☎ (020) 7235 3019
Fuller's Chiswick, London Pride, ESB Ⓗ
Well-hidden mews pub near the German Embassy. This pub has been in every edition of this *Guide* and was West London CAMRA *Pub of the Year* 2001. Customers come from all sections of society, including tourists, and all who enjoy a good pint in convivial surroundings. A Grade II listed building, it has a small front bar and an attached kitchen which serves excellent food, carpeted saloon with real fire, and an upstairs lounge with its own bar that can be hired for private functions. It is not the easiest pub to find, but worth the effort.
🚲Q◖▷⊖ (Knightsbridge/Hyde Pk Cnr) ●

SW1: PIMLICO

Morpeth Arms
58 Millbank
✿ 11-11; 12-10.30 Sun
☎ (020) 7834 6442
Smiles Best; Young's Bitter, Triple A, Special, seasonal beers Ⓗ
Imposing corner pub overlooking the MI6 building on the other side of the Thames at Vauxhall, and situated close to the Tate Britain art gallery. This Young's pub caters for locals and tourists alike. The saloon is carpeted and the walls are decorated with dark brown wallpaper. There is a rear snug where the owner's dog is always resting. As in most Young's pubs a picture of the Queen Mother pulling a pint is proudly displayed on the wall. Smiles Best may be replaced by a seasonal brew.
Q✿◖▷≢ (Vauxhall) ⊖

Pimlico Tram
6 Charlwood Street
✿ 11-11; 12-10.30 Sun
☎ (020) 7828 0448
Greene King IPA, Abbot; guest beer Ⓗ
This recent convert back to real ale has been refurbished by Greene King. The main bar area has a pool table and a juke box. It shows a vast improvement from its keg days under Bass Charrington and is popular with locals. 'Happy hour' (5-7 Sun-Thu) applies to a selected real ale. The guest beer is always from the Greene King portfolio.
◖▷≢ (Victoria) ⊖

SW1: VICTORIA

Wetherspoon's
Victoria Island, Victoria Station
✿ 11-11; 12-10.30 Sun
☎ (020) 7931 0445
Courage Directors; Fuller's London Pride; Theakston Best Bitter; guest beers Ⓗ
New Wetherspoon's pub above WH Smith's bookstore between platforms 7 and 9, it is a good place to wait for your train to be listed on the departure indicators. There are two bars, the left-hand bar is the no-smoking area and generally quiet; the right-hand bar overlooks the platform indicators and can be smoky. The pub makes a good meeting point. Regular beer festivals are held and, as with most Central London Wetherspoon pubs, they start at the beginning of the week and end on a Fri. Q✿◖▷≢&≢⊖¼⊘

SW1: WESTMINSTER ✤

Buckingham Arms
62 Petty France
✿ 11-11; 12-5.30 Sun
☎ (020) 7222 3386
Smiles Best; Young's Bitter, Triple A, Special, seasonal beers Ⓗ
Popular pub, next to the Passport Office. A 'silver selection' pub, it has appeared in every edition of this *Guide* and deservedly so. It boasts a side corridor drinking area, original leaded windows and is Grade II listed by English Heritage. Excellent bar meals are available and Sky TV is tuned into sport, political programmes and news. Smiles Best may be replaced by a seasonal beer. ◖▷≢(Victoria) ⊖ (St James's Pk/Westminster)

Cask & Glass
39 Palace Street
✿ 11-11; 11-3, 6-11 Sat; 12-3 (closed eve) Sun
☎ (020) 7834 7630
Shepherd Neame Master Brew Bitter, Best Bitter, Spitfire Ⓗ
This pub is a Shepherd Neame tied house and until recently used to serve beer only in half pints. The smallest pub in Westminster, the exterior boasts an attractive floral display, and it is a haven from the bustle of nearby Victoria Street. The bar area is wood panelled featuring old prints showing the pub in its original Watney days and portraits of MPs and lords; models of aircraft abound around the bar. Snacks are available at lunchtime.
≢(Victoria) ⊖ (St James's Pk)

Jugged Hare
172 Vauxhall Bridge Road
✿ 11-11, 12-10.30 Sun
☎ (020) 7828 1543
Fuller's Chiswick, London Pride, ESB, seasonal beers; guest beer Ⓗ
Typical Fuller's Ale & Pie House converted from a former NatWest bank on the busy Vauxhall Bridge Road near Tachbrook Street market. A contrast to other pubs in the area, during the week the clientele is mainly business people; weekends can be quiet but it occasionally picks up with regulars. The decor is identikit Ale & Pie House-style with chandeliers. An upstairs balcony doubles as a function room. The rear room that used to be the bank manager's office is a no-smoking area. The toilets are in the former bank vaults. Q◖▷≢ (Victoria) ⊖ (Pimlico) ¼ ●

Lord Moon of the Mall
16-18 Whitehall
✿ 11-11; 12-10.30 Sun
☎ (020) 7809 7701
Courage Directors; Fuller's London Pride; Shepherd Neame Spitfire; Theakston Best Bitter; guest beers Ⓗ
Fine Wetherspoon's conversion where a

cash dispenser serves as a reminder of its previous life as a bank. The large, single bar includes a no-smoking area; the walls carry prints of local sights and monuments, with informative captions. It is near the National Gallery, but pay special attention to the pub's oil painting of an 18th-century grandee, he may look vaguely familiar – no prizes for guessing why. It can get very crowded. Q ◑ ⊅ ≠ (Charing Cross) ⊖ ✁ ●

Royal Oak
2 Regent Street
◐ 11-11; 12-4 Sun
☎ (020) 7834 7046
Young's Bitter, Triple A, Special, seasonal beers Ⓗ
Quiet corner house, first licensed in 1831, and situated just off Horseferry Road, the pub has been saved from destruction by a local campaign. A former Watney's pub, now owned by Young's, it has been heavily refurbished into open plan with bare floorboards and clear windows where people walking past can watch you drink. This local is an ideal watering-hole after visiting the Horticultural Halls.
◑ ≠ (Victoria) ⊖ (Pimlico/St James's Pk)

Westminster Arms
9 Storeys Gate
◐ 11-11 (8 Sat); 12-6 Sun
☎ (020) 7222 8520
Adnams Bitter; Draught Bass; Brakspear Bitter; Greene King Old Speckled Hen; guest beer Ⓗ
Situated next to the Queen Elizabeth Centre and just off Parliament Square, the pub is popular with tourists and MPs (the pub has its own division bell). There is an attached restaurant and wine bar where lunchtime and eve meals are served. It was originally called the Red Lion until 1969 when it gained its present name. Like other Regents Inn pubs it participates in an annual beer festival every spring. ≠ ●

SW2: BRIXTON

Crown & Sceptre
2 Streatham Hill
◐ 11-11; 12-10.30 Sun
☎ (020) 8671 0843
Courage Directors; Greene King Abbot; Hop Back Summer Lightning; Shepherd Neame Spitfire; Theakston Best Bitter; guest beers Ⓗ
Transformed from a music/drug pub in 1990, this is the earliest and the finest Wetherspoon's in south-west London. First named JJ Moon's, the change back to the original was requested by the Streatham Society, and the fascia was cleaned to reveal its old identity and that of Truman's its former owners. Different levels give it great character and allow for easy conversations. The high turnover of cask beer ensures rock-bottom prices; Summer Lightning is particularly popular.
Q ❀ ◑ ≠ (Streatham Hill) P ✁ ●

SW3: CHELSEA

Cooper's Arms
87 Flood Street
◐ 11-11; 12-10.30 Sun
☎ (020) 7376 3120 website: www.thecoopers.co.uk
Young's Bitter, Triple A, Special, seasonal beers Ⓗ
Close to the King's Road and attracting a young, lively and affluent crowd, it offers

modern decor and amenities in a traditional pub atmosphere. The large, open-plan bar, hewn out of this late-Victorian pub, is light and airy with pale woodwork, heavy wooden furniture with some upholstered seats. Stuffed animals, including a large bear, are prominently displayed. Quality newspapers and magazines are available. Food is excellent, served in the bar or upstairs restaurant. ♨ Q ◑ ⊖ (Sloane Sq)

Crown
153 Dovehouse Street
◐ 11-11; 12-10.30 Sun
☎ (020) 7352 9505
Adnams Bitter; Fuller's London Pride Ⓗ
Small, narrow, corner local off the Fulham Road, close to the Royal Marsden Hospital; the latest refurbishment has smartened up both the tiny bar and rear dining area. Food is a major factor at this village-like pub, where a varied menu appeals to a cosmopolitan clientele. Dating from 1867, it has had a varied history, with real ale surviving through the 1960s and 70s but facing a decline in the 80s; it is now revitalised under new management.
❀ ◑ ⊖ (S Kensington)

Surprise
6 Christchurch Terrace
◐ 12-11; 12-10.30 Sun
☎ (020) 7349 1821
Draught Bass; Fuller's London Pride Ⓗ
Chelsea's Surprise is well named – hard to find and unexpected, it is a hidden gem. In fact, the name refers to the ship that took Napoleon's body back to France in 1820. Built in 1853 in a quiet, smart, residential area, the pub reflects its affluent surroundings. The mature clientele enjoy quiet conversation, with board games and a TV at low volume, for distraction. The main bar boasts a high, ornate ceiling, and an attractive bar counter with painted frieze. The beer range is supplemented by Hoegaarden on tap and Belgian bottled beers. Q ♣ ♣

SW4: CLAPHAM ✷

Rose & Crown
2 The Polygon
◐ 11.30-11; 12-10.30 Sun
☎ (020) 7720 8265
Greene King IPA, Old Speckled Hen; guest beers Ⓗ
Near the Polygon's six other pubs, this is easily the best. The 'Noted Simonds Ales and Stouts' fascia reminds older drinkers of that wonderful ale range. It is still a traditional ale house. A compact L-shaped bar area is divided by pillars and wood partitions; low ceilings create an intimate atmosphere. It enjoys a regular local trade, most of whom come for the unusual range of beers (from the Beer Seller list). Eve meals served Mon-Thu. Over 21s only admitted.
❀ ◑ ⊕ ⊖ (Common)

SW5: EARL'S COURT

Blackbird
209 Earl's Court Road
◐ 11-11; 12-10.30 Sun
☎ (020) 7835 1855
Fuller's Chiswick, London Pride, ESB, seasonal beers Ⓗ

This typical, if rather small Fuller's Ale & Pie House in a former bank, converted in 1993, has improved the drinking options in the area. The horseshoe-shaped bar dominates the single room, and is likely to be surrounded by locals. Tourists drift in later to fill up the main bar and the rear drinking area, which may be quieter at other times. At weekends the atmosphere can be boisterous, rather loud and smoky, but it always remains friendly. ◑ ✪ ●

SW6: FULHAM

Imperial
577 King's Road

✪ 11-11; 12-10.30 Sun

☎ (020) 7736 9179

Haggards Imperial Best Bitter; guest beer Ⓗ

A recent addition to London's micro-breweries, Haggards set up in Battersea in 1998 to serve this, its only pub, plus other outlets by request. The guest beer is often from another micro-brewery. The pub is light and airy, appealing to the younger crowd, with the feel of a contemporary bar; colourful murals feature a nautical theme and furnishings consist of mismatched tables and chairs. A rear area is used mainly by diners, and leads to an enclosed garden. It is very popular and noisy in the eve, but surprisingly quiet at other times. Built in 1860, the Imperial is named after the Gas, Light & Coke Company, whose prominent gasometers stand nearby. ✪◑

SW6: PARSONS GREEN

Duke of Cumberland
235 New King's Road

✪ 11-11; 12-10.30 Sun

☎ (020) 7736 2777

Smiles Bitter, seasonal beers; Young's Bitter, Triple A, Special, seasonal beers Ⓗ

This quintessential late Victorian pub epitomises the grand building ideas of those days. Internally there is much that remains, including glazed tiles (once part of a side corridor), but changes have been made, including the public bar added in the 1980s and later knocked through. This rear section has exposed brickwork and a more subdued feel than the main room – but both have a real fire. A large horseshoe-shaped bar dominates the spacious and decorative lounge which is comfortably furnished. An often overlooked gem. ⚶Q◑▯ᴑ♣♣

White Horse
1-3 Parsons Green

✪ 11-11; 12-10.30 Sun

☎ (020) 7736 2115 website: www.whitehorsesw6.com

Draught Bass; Harveys BB; Highgate Dark; Rooster's Ranger, Yankee; guest beers Ⓗ

Well-known, and deservedly popular, upmarket pub facing the Green. Originally licensed in 1688, the most recent building (circa 1882) was expanded into the adjacent property in 1894 to create a large but harmonious pub, visually appealing both inside and out. Large leather sofas and long pew-like benches ensure comfortable drinking while a large terrace adds space in summer. Food is excellent and includes breakfasts; there is a new dining room. Service is fast and efficient. Renowned for

the range of both draught and bottled beers, it hosts regular beer festivals, including an old ale fest (Nov). ⚶Q✪◑ ⊖●

SW7: SOUTH KENSINGTON

Anglesea Arms
15 Selwood Terrace

✪ 11-11; 12-10.30 Sun

☎ (020) 7373 7960

Adnams Bitter, Broadside; Brakspear Bitter, Special; guest beers Ⓗ

Regular *Guide* entry with exceptional credentials, this free house offers traditional facilities in a cosy atmosphere. Although upmarket, the pub welcomes all and may be quite a crush most eves, but weekends are quieter. Built in 1827 it boasts literary connections including Dickens. The decor is basic, but rather smart with a plain wooden floor, leather covered seats, wooden stools and oil paintings. The rear bar is now an elegant dining room, but more drinking space is available on the raised patio out front. Both British and Belgian bottled beers are stocked. Q✪◑ ⊖

SW8: SOUTH LAMBETH ✣

Priory Arms
83 Lansdowne Way, Stockwell

✪ 11-11; 12-10.30 Sun

☎ (020) 7622 1884

Adnams Bitter, Broadside; Harveys BB; guest beers Ⓗ

True free house, run by the owners; the fact that it was voted SW London CAMRA *Pub of the Year* for the maximum five times in the 1990s testifies to its commitment to real ale. This Grade II listed building, with a single bright, comfortable bar offers a good selection of continental bottled beers, plus a German beer festival in Oct. Three guest beers usually come from small independent breweries. Good food includes a popular traditional Sun lunch. ✪◑⊖(Stockwell) ▯●

Surprise
16 Southville

✪ 11-11; 12-10.30 Sun

☎ (020) 7622 4623

Young's Bitter, Special, seasonal beers Ⓗ

In a quiet cul-de-sac next to Larkhall Park, this was a beer-only house until the 1950s and retains many ale house traditions, with beer still accounting for the highest sales. The quiet back room now has a pin table, and is adorned with skilful caricatures of regulars, past and present. A succession of devoted licensees has ensured the beer quality, so that it has appeared in all but one edition of the *Guide*. It boasts an all-weather boules pitch. ⚶✪◑⊖(Stockwell)

SW9: BRIXTON

Trinity Arms
45 Trinity Gardens

✪ 11-11; 12-10.30 Sun

☎ (020) 7274 4544

Young's Bitter, Special, seasonal or guest beers Ⓗ

Quiet retreat, but just a few hundred yards from Brixton's busy town centre; locals in the know are treated to fine beers here. Built in 1850, the pub stands in Trinity Gardens, named after the Trinity Asylum that stood in nearby Acre Lane. Q✪◑≠⊖

SW10: WEST BROMPTON

Chelsea Ram
32 Burnaby Street
✪ 11-11; 12-10.30 Sun
☎ (020) 7351 4008
Young's Bitter, Triple A, Special, seasonal or guest beers Ⓗ
Almost a sister pub to the Cooper's Arms in Chelsea (qv), the Ram lies in the revitalised area around Lots Road and Chelsea Harbour. The new prosperity and popularity of the district is reflected in a contemporary pub style with an emphasis on food and wine. The spacious L-shaped bar is attractively decorated with quality furniture and art objects. It still manages to be a real pub drawing a lively 20-30-something crowd. Q ◖◗ �&

SW11: BATTERSEA

Castle
115 Battersea High Street
✪ 12-11; 12-10.30 Sun
☎ (020) 7228 8181
Smiles seasonal beers; Young's Bitter, Special, seasonal beers Ⓗ
Bright, cheerful estate pub, built in 1965, although a pub is believed to have been sited here since 1600. It has been refurbished in a café-bar style. Although food and wine are taken seriously, it retains a pub atmosphere; the bar contains a large (unused) fireplace that displays an old spit-roasting mechanism. Pot plants are a feature of the bar and conservatory. The furnishings come in all shapes and sizes, and include two leather sofas. Children are welcome in the bar until 7.30, but drinkers in work clothes/boots are not admitted. Eve meals are available Sun. Q ❀ ◖◗ P

SW12: BALHAM

Grove
39 Oldridge Road
✪ 11-11; 12-10.30 Sun
☎ (020) 8673 6531
Smiles Best; Young's Bitter, Triple A, Special Ⓗ
Huge gin palace-type Young's house, very underused, which is a pity. A very good South London local, and easily the best Young's pub in Balham; gin palace green and gold decor. It is undergoing a refurbishment that is expected to be sympathetic although likely to lead to the loss of the public bar. It stocks the full Young's range of bottled beers.
◖◗ ≠ ⊖ (Clapham South) ♣

SW13: BARNES

Coach & Horses
27 Barnes High Street
✪ 11-11; 12-10.30 Sun
☎ (020) 8876 2695 e-mail: messitt@dircon.co.uk
Young's Bitter, Special, Winter Warmer Ⓗ
Former coaching inn, first leased by Young's in 1831. This single-bar pub is fronted by some fine etched windows. Barnes is often described as one of London's villages and a good 'villagey' atmosphere exists. At the rear is a function room and a sizeable garden (large enough for a boules pitch), which is popular with families, especially for summer weekend barbecues. Run by an

enterprising couple, it was local CAMRA *Pub of the Year* 1998. ᴁ Q ❀ ◖◗ ≠ (Bridge)

Rose of Denmark
28 Cross Street
✪ 11-11; 12-10.30 Sun
☎ (020) 8392 1761
Brakspear Bitter; Taylor Landlord; Woodforde's Wherry Ⓗ
Street-corner local, tucked away but well worth finding. It is comfortable, friendly and surprisingly roomy. The landlord listened to customers' requests, hence the regular availability of the Wherry and Landlord. Now open all permitted hours, it offers snacks and basket meals at any time, even for take-aways. Keep turning left from the station, or negotiate the back alleys to reach this pub named after Queen Alexandra, wife of Edward VII.
❀ ◖◗ ≠ (Bridge)

SW15: PUTNEY ❅

Jolly Gardeners
61-63 Lacy Road
✪ 11-11; 12-10.30 Sun
☎ (020) 8780 8921
Adnams Bitter; Fuller's London Pride Ⓗ
Following a recent gutting and full refurbishment, the Jolly Gardeners has recovered its good reputation to the full. The new one-room layout with a smaller, less obtrusive central bar, provides a pleasant, convivial atmosphere. One side is taken up principally by the pool table and large screen for Sky Sports, but this does not intrude on the rest of the drinking area, which hums with conversation. The rare (for this area) availability of Adnams makes this worth the detour. No food Sun eve.
❀ ◖◗ ≠

SW16: STREATHAM COMMON

Pied Bull
498 Streatham High Road
✪ 11-11; 12-10.30 Sun
☎ (020) 8764 4003
Smiles Best; Young's Bitter, Triple A, Special, seasonal beers Ⓗ
Large, recently renovated three-roomed pub, with an island bar, opposite the common. There are comfortable sofas and padded chairs; pictures and prints adorn every wall. Low-level background music is played in the largest room where there are a few (quiet) games machines and a dartboard. A varied selection of meals and snacks are available (not Sun eve), plus an extensive range of wines. A large-screen TV is used for major sports events. A jazz band plays alternate Suns and Karaoke sessions are held Fri eve. ᴁ Q ❀ ◖◗ ⊟ ≠ ♣ P

SW16: STREATHAM HILL

Hogshead
68-70 Streatham High Road
✪ 11-11; 12-10.30 Sun
☎ (020) 8696 7587
Boddingtons Bitter; Brakspear Bitter; Fuller's London Pride; Ⓗ **guest beers** Ⓗ/Ⓖ
Formerly Il Caretto Italian restaurant, this Hogshead unusually is on split levels, enhancing the varied drinking areas. The excellent management team always try to

make it different from others in the same chain and one good quality beer is always sold at a bargain price for the area. Good quality food is unobtrusively served at all times. The best bet in this cinema area, which gets very busy at weekends.
♛◑♿≠●⚡

SW17: SUMMERSTOWN

Prince of Wales

646 Garratt Lane
⊙ 11-11; 12-4, 7-10.30 Sun
☎ (020) 8946 2628
Young's Bitter, Special, seasonal beers Ⓗ
Reassuringly consistent, down-to-earth, three-roomed local, on a corner of busy Garratt Lane, handy for Wimbledon Greyhound Stadium and Sunday market. Note the handsome tiled exterior, and the false 'mirror' inside. The family room is used for darts some eves; Mon and Tue are ladies' nights. The beer is cheaper in the public bar. Weekday lunches are served.
♛♉❀◑⊟♣P

SW17: TOOTING

Gorringe Park

29 London Road
⊙ 11-11; 12-10.30 Sun
☎ (020) 8648 4478
Young's Bitter, Triple A, Special, seasonal beers Ⓗ
Charming little two-bar pub, a former hotel, a few doors along from Tooting Station, and attracting a delightfully diverse clientele. The popular public bar is at the front, while the cosy, wood-panelled lounge is entered from the side street. Fans of cryptic crosswords will appreciate the pub sign.
♛❀◑⊟≠♣

SW18: WANDSWORTH ❄

Grapes

39 Fairfield Street
⊙ 11-11; 12-10.30 Sun
☎ (020) 8877 0756
Young's Bitter, Special Ⓗ
Small, traditional, one-bar local, with notable wood panelling and mirrors along one wall. A conservatory is planned which will enable the pub to admit children. The pub dates from at least 1833. It has a dartboard and fields a darts team. Enjoy the award-winning garden in fine weather. Lunchtime food served weekdays mostly takes the form of burgers, omelettes and toasties. ❀◑≠(Town) ♣

Old Sergeant

104 Garratt Lane
⊙ 11-11; 12-10.30 Sun
☎ (020) 8874 4099
Young's Bitter, Special; guest beer (occasional) Ⓗ
Two-bar Young's pub, run by a long-standing and respected landlord. The pub dates from the 18th century – note the coach house doors. The public bar has Sky TV and a dartboard and fields teams in the local leagues. The lounge bar is comfortably furnished; the fireplace is bedecked with brass ornaments. About five minutes' walk from the town centre, buses 44 and 270 serve the pub. Good value food is served weekdays. The guest beer is from the Smiles range. ❀◑⊟♣

SW19: MERTON

Princess of Wales

98 Morden Road
⊙ 11-3, 5-11; 11-11 Fri & Sat; 12-10.30 Sun
☎ (020) 8542 0573
Young's Bitter, Triple A, Special, Winter Warmer, seasonal beers; guest beer (occasional) Ⓗ
The single main bar leads to an area that is usually quiet; to one side the former public bar has darts and TV. Originally the Prince of Wales, the pub dates from around the mid-19th century. It is twinned with the Horse Brass Pub, Portland, Oregon, whose regulars commissioned the portrait of the Princess by American artist James Mackie. The pub is home to two friendly Boxer dogs. It offers good value home-cooked food (eve meals weekdays). The guest beer is from the Smiles range.
♛❀◑⊖ (Morden Rd Tramlink/S Wimbledon) P

SW19: SOUTH WIMBLEDON

Sultan

78 Norman Road, Colliers Wood
⊙ 12-11; 12-10.30 Sun
☎ (020) 8542 4532
website: www.battersea-beer-festival.org.uk/thesultan
Hop Back GFB, Thunderstorm, Summer Lightning, seasonal beers Ⓗ
Hop Back's London house is situated on a residential road and was built in the 1950s to replace a bombed pub, named after a 19th-century racehorse. Hop Back took it over in 1994. Special events here include an annual beer festival, summer barbecues, Hallowe'en and New Year's Eve parties. The Sultan hosts a ladies' darts Mon eve, a quiz Tue eve and a beer club Wed, with all real ales at £1.50 per pint from 6pm to 9pm. This two-bar pub, with a tiny car park, was local CAMRA *Pub of the Year* 1999.
❀♿⊖♣P

SW19: WIMBLEDON ❄

Brewery Tap

68 High Street
⊙ 11-11; 12-10.30 Sun
☎ (020) 8947 9331
Adnams Bitter; Fuller's London Pride; Tetley Bitter; guest beers Ⓗ
Small, friendly pub with large windows looking out on to Wimbledon Village, serving a mixed clientele of all ages. Recently refurbished, it is larger than it first appears. A wide range of guest beers is stocked, mainly from smaller and more remote breweries. It offers excellent bar food and snacks – the marinated olives and anchovies are superb. ◑≠⊖

Hand in Hand

7 Crooked Billet
⊙ 11-11; 12-10.30 Sun
☎ (020) 8946 5720
Young's Bitter, Special, seasonal beers Ⓗ
The pub is on the site of the house of Daniel Watney whose great-grandson founded the brewery. The present building started in 1865 as a bakehouse and grocer's. It started selling beer two years later but did not receive a full licence until 1974. The single bar is divided into several distinct areas. Over 21s only in summer, when the small green outside serves as a garden

extension. It has won both the local CAMRA and *Evening Standard Pub of the Year* awards. 🏰Q🕳️🍽️🅿️◐⊡♣✂

Rose & Crown
55 High Street
🕐 11-11; 12-10.30 Sun
☎ (020) 8947 4713
Young's Bitter, Triple A, Special, Winter Warmer; guest beer Ⓗ

Excellent, single-bar pub with a number of distinct drinking areas, on the edge of the common, in marked contrast to the trendy branded bars and bistros that now make up Wimbledon Village. The emphasis here is on real ale (the guest is from Smiles), but food is becoming more important. This former coaching inn was the first stage from London, and until the 19th century passengers had to take 'Dutch courage' before facing hazards of highwaymen on the common. 🏰🐾🍽️◐🅿️⊡✂

CARSHALTON

Greyhound Hotel
2 High Street (A232)
🕐 11-11; 12-10.30 Sun
☎ (020) 8647 1511 e-mail: greyhound@youngs.co.uk
Young's Bitter, Special, Ⓗ **seasonal beers;** Ⓗ/Ⓖ **guest beer** Ⓗ

Grade II listed building, opposite Carshalton ponds and close to the ancient parish church and the Sutton Heritage Centre. The original building dates from about 1706 while the brick and stone western end was added later. An extension to create a 21-roomed hotel was completed in 2000. Of the two contrasting bars, the Swan Bar is olde-worlde with a real fire, grandfather clock and antique artefacts. Two ghosts apparently haunt the pub. Guest beers are from Smiles. Meals are highly recommended; Sun food service is 12-7. 🏰Q🍽️◐⊡≈♣🅿️

Windsor Castle
378 Carshalton Road (A232/B271 jct)
🕐 11-11; 12-10.30 Sun
☎ (020) 8669 1191
Fuller's London Pride; Hancock's HB; guest beer Ⓗ

This CAMRA-award winning pub is a haven for real ale connoisseurs especially for beers from small micro-brewers. Every one of the beers depicted in its impressive pump clip

display has been sold in the pub at some time. Usually about six guest beers are on sale, and for added value a four-pint jug of any beer is sold for the price of three pints; a board in the bar indicates additional beers available from the cellar in four-pint jugs. Beer festivals are held at least once a year, when the beer range easily rivals many smaller CAMRA festivals. No food Sun eve. 🍽️◐≈(Beeches)♣🅿️

KINGSTON UPON THAMES

Canbury Arms
49 Canbury Park Road
🕐 11-11; 12-10.30 Sun
☎ (020) 8288 1882 e-mail: padams@tinyworld.co.uk
Courage Best Bitter; Greene King Abbot; Wychwood Hobgoblin; guest beers Ⓗ

Victorian pub with a rural, mock-Tudor interior. Children can use the smallish back room and garden. Two or three different guest beers change weekly and every Easter there is a cider festival. Baldrick and Lucy, the pub dogs, provide endless amusement; customers bringing their own dogs must phone first. Live music is performed Fri and Sat; the Sun quiz makes use of a large library to resolve disputes. This local CAMRA *Pub of the Year* 2000 can be dominated by TV sport. 🍽️≈♣🅿️⊡

Kelly Arms
2 Glenthorne Road
🕐 11-11; 12-10.30 Sun
☎ (020) 8296 9815
Courage Best Bitter; guest beers Ⓗ

Back-street local that is hard to find but well worth the effort. It serves food all day until 10pm (9pm Sun); telephone orders can be taken for food. There is a pool table, darts, table football, pin table, trivia machine and a TV which shows most live sports events. A Sunday barbecue is held in the garden, weather permitting. Parking can be difficult, but there are no street restrictions eves or Sun. A mild is quite often available. 🍽️◐♣🅿️

Park Tavern
19 New Road
🕐 11-11; 12-10.30 Sun
Brakspear Special; Young's Bitter; guest beers Ⓗ

INN BRIEF

South-West London

SW4: CLAPHAM

Bread & Roses
68 Clapham Manor Street
11-11; 12-10.30 Sun
Adnams Bitter; guest beer Ⓗ
An unusual modern pub, (which used to be an old 'fizz house'), serving house beer from Smiles.

SW8: SOUTH LAMBETH

Mawbey Arms
7 Mawbey Street
11-11; 12-10.30 Sun
Shepherd Neame Master Brew Bitter, Spitfire Ⓗ
Beautiful building housing a J-shaped bar, partitioned into three distinct areas. Fine quality food is served.

SW15: PUTNEY

Green Man
Putney Heath
11-11; 12-10.30 Sun
Smiles Best; Young's Bitter, Special, seasonal beers Ⓗ
Putney's best-known ale house – a traditional local opposite the Putney Heath bus terminus.

SW18: WANDSWORTH

Cats Back
86 Point Pleasant
12-3, 5.30-11; 11-11 Fri & Sat; 12-10.30 Sun
Eccleshall Slaters Bitter; O'Hanlon's Blakeley's Best, Port Stout Ⓗ
Small, one-bar genuine free house displaying work by local artists. Another O'Hanlon's beer replaces the Port Stout at times. Imaginative menu.

SW19: WIMBLEDON

Alexandra
53 Wimbledon Hill Road
11-11; 12-10.30 Sun
Young's Bitter, Triple A, Special, Winter Warmer Ⓗ
Busy, town pub near Wimbledon Station, a single bar with separate areas, licensed until 1am Fri and Sat. A Smiles' beer is usually stocked.

Crooked Billet
15 Crooked Billet
11-11; 12-10.30 Sun
Young's Bitter, Special, seasonal beers Ⓗ
Large, comfortable inn, dating from 1509, on the fringes of the common. The restaurant serves excellent meals and wines.

Single-bar local, the nearest pub to the Kingston gate of Richmond Park. A roaring fire is a bonus in winter. It has a strong rugby following and most live sports events are shown on the large-screen TV. The outside drinking area consists of a couple of tables out front; the rear garden is usually only open for the annual fireworks and pig roast, on Nov 5th. Parking in the road is restricted. The three guest beers are usually below 5% ABV. ▲ Q ❀

Willoughby Arms
47 Willoughby Road
◑ 10.30-11; 12-10.30 Sun
☎ (020) 8546 4236

e-mail: rick@thewilloughby.freeserve.co.uk

Flowers Original; Fuller's London Pride; Marston's Pedigree; Taylor Landlord ℍ

Large, two-bar pub hidden in the back streets of North Kingston. The sports bar offers pool, darts and a large-screen TV for televised events. The saloon bar features wood settles, pictures of old Kingston pubs and unusual handpump handle lampstands. It fields several darts teams and holds two annual beer festivals (St George's Day and Hallowe'en). The upstairs function room was used for rehearsal by the Yardbirds in the 1960s. ❀❷◑♣●

Wych Elm
93 Elm Road
◑ 11-3, 5-11; 11-11 Sat; 12-10.30 Sun
☎ (020) 8547 0321

Fuller's Chiswick, London Pride, ESB, seasonal beer ℍ

Two-bar, back-street pub with a good local following. The traditional, plain public bar is complemented by a comfortable lounge bar where the green papered walls are covered with prints and a large Fuller's mirror. The impressive floral displays outside have won the pub several awards and extend to the pleasant garden. Home-cooked food is available Mon-Sat. Look for the picture of the locally-made Spanish Navy Matador aircraft in the public bar. ❀◑❷♣●

NEW MALDEN

Woodies
Thetford Road
◑ 11-11; 12-10.30 Sun

☎ (020) 8949 5824

Adnams Broadside; Flowers Original; Fuller's London Pride; Young's Bitter, Special; guest beers ℍ

Originally Fyffes (of banana fame) sports and social club, this popular free house is believed to be the only public house in Britain sited in a wooden pavilion. Famed for its sporting, film, TV and theatrical memorabilia covering the walls and ceilings, the landlord welcomes further additions. The pub runs its own cricket, football and ladies' darts teams, plus a popular quiz Tue eve – arrive early to get a seat. Two guest beers are usually available. Its smoke extraction system is efficient. ▲ Q ❀◑♿♣P

RICHMOND ✳

Red Cow
59 Sheen Road
◑ 11-11; 12-10.30 Sun
☎ (020) 8940 2511 e-mail: tom@redcowpub.com

Young's Bitter, Special, seasonal beers ℍ

Popular local, a short walk from Richmond's shops and station. Like many pubs of its era, partitions between separate bar areas have been removed in recent years, but there are still three distinct drinking areas. The first floor has recently been converted to provide four en-suite bedrooms. Good lunches are served daily, and eve meals until 8.30 on weekdays. Tue is quiz night. ▲🛏◑≠⊖♣

Triple Crown
15 Kew Foot Road
◑ 11-11; 12-10.30 Sun
☎ (020) 8940 3805

Beer range varies ℍ

True free house serving four regularly changed ales, by Richmond Athletic Ground, and close to Old Deer Park and Kew Gardens. Convenient for Richmond Station, the pub is small and narrow but still has room for darts at the far end, and it is popular for the Tue eve quiz and Sun afternoon jazz. There are a couple of tables on the front pavement, and an upstairs function room has its own bar (with handpumps) and a small balcony. No lunches Sun. ❀◑≠⊖

Cavern
100 Coombe Lane
11-11; 12-10.30 Sun
Fuller's London Pride ℍ
Busy, lively, one-bar pub with raised seating areas, featuring rock'n'roll nostalgia and a popular juke box.

CHEAM
Prince of Wales
28 Malden Road
11 (12 Sat)-11;
12-10.30 Sun
Adnams Bitter; Fuller's London Pride; Greene King Old Speckled Hen; Tetley Bitter ℍ
Spacious, comfortable pub where a regularly changed menu of home-cooked dishes caters for all tastes.

CHESSINGTON
North Star
271 Hook Road
12 (11 Sat)-11; 12-10.30 Sun
Adnams Bitter; Draught Bass; Fuller's London Pride ℍ
Large community pub, open plan but with distinct areas. Food is served lunchtime and early eve (not Sun eve). Wheelchair WC.

RICHMOND
Old Ship
3 King Street
11-11; 12-10.30 Sun
Young's Bitter, Triple A, Special, seasonal beers ℍ
Nautically-themed pub in a principal shopping street. This former mail-coach stop, a Young's house since 1869, is popular for lunches.

SURBITON
Cap in Hand
174 Hook Rise North
11-11; 12-10.30 Sun
Courage Directors; Fuller's London Pride; Shepherd Neame Spitfire; Theakston Best Bitter; Wadworth 6X; guest beers ℍ
1930s roadhouse, now owned by Wetherspoon's but retaining the atmosphere of a local. Families are welcome in the conservatory. *Cask Marque* accredited.

> ✳ symbol next to a main entry place name indicates there are Inn Brief entries as well.

Watermans Arms
12 Water Lane
✪ 11-3, 5.30-11; 11-11 Sat; 12-10.30 Sun
☎ (020) 8940 2893
Young's Bitter, Special, Winter Warmer Ⓗ
Historic pub, one of the oldest in Richmond (rebuilt in 1895), retaining its Victorian two-bar layout, in a lane leading to the White Cross and the river. Generations of watermen have drunk here, and some, along with others in riparian occupations, still do. With lots of character, the pub has a true local feel; games include shove-ha'penny, Horsey-horsey and Shut the Box.
Q ◖ ≉ ⊖ ♣

White Cross
Riverside, Water Lane
✪ 11-11; 12-10.30 Sun
☎ (020) 8940 6844
Young's Bitter, Triple A, Special, seasonal beers Ⓗ
This well-known, popular pub is a prominent feature of Richmond's waterfront. A stained glass panel reminds drinkers that it is on the site of a former convent of the Observant Friars, whose insignia was a white cross. The present building, dating from 1835, is reached by steps, for good reason – the river floods at this point, as unwary motorists have found when returning to parked cars. Inside is an island bar and two side rooms (one at mezzanine level). An unusual feature is a fireplace underneath a window. A ground-level patio bar also opens at busy times; the patio boasts a rare Green Whitebeam tree.
ᗑ ❀ ◖ ≉ ⊖

SURBITON ✣

Lamb Inn
73 Brighton Road (A243)
✪ 11-11; 12-10.30 Sun
☎ (020) 8390 9229 e-mail: thelamb@globalnet.co.uk
Greene King IPA; Marston's Pedigree; Young's Special; guest beer Ⓗ
Small, one-bar local offering a range of beers to suit most tastes, and a regularly changing guest beer. Buzzing eves, with a mixed clientele and a retro juke box, darts and board games are played, and there is a large-screen TV for football matches and rugby internationals. A pleasant patio and garden hosts occasional barbecues. Tue night is quiz night and there is a monthly Karaoke (first Sat). Home-cooked lunches are served Mon-Sat. ❀ ◖ ♣ ♣

Waggon & Horses
1 Surbiton Hill Road (A240)
✪ 11-11; 12-10.30 Sun
☎ (020) 8399 0211
Young's Bitter, Triple A, Special, Winter Warmer, seasonal beers Ⓗ
Pub built in 1888 on the site of a coaching inn, where an extra horse was supplied to heavy wagons for the climb up Surbiton Hill. Unfortunately, recent changes have led to the loss of the public bar, but the Green Room and upper level drinking area have been retained. The pub is noted for charity collections, for which the landlord has been honoured by the Queen. It hosts a weekly quiz and a carol concert at Christmas. Thai food is served by a Thai family most days; English food is available Tue-Fri lunch (no

food Sat lunch, Sun eve or Mon).
Q ❀ ◖ ◗ ≉ P ⚊

SUTTON

Little Windsor
13 Greyhound Road (off A232)
✪ 11.30-11; 12-10.30 Sun
☎ (020) 8643 2574 e-mail: windyalan@aol.com
Fuller's Chiswick, London Pride, ESB, seasonal beers; guest beer Ⓗ
Originally named the Windsor Castle, the pub has formally adopted its Little Windsor nickname that was used to distinguish it from a pub of the same name in nearby Carshalton. A tiny, single-bar street-corner local in Sutton's old town area, it was acquired by Fuller's in the 1980s and refitted. It has now been extended, but still befits the 'small is beautiful' description. Crib and chess are available. ❀ ◖ ≉ ♣ ●

New Town
7 Lind Road (off A232)
✪ 12-3, 5-11; 12-11 Fri & Sat; 12-10.30 Sun
☎ (020) 8770 2072
Smiles Best; Young's Bitter, Triple A, Special, seasonal beers Ⓗ
Attractive street-corner local in Sutton's 'New Town' district, an area well-endowed with good pubs. The saloon bar is unusual as it is on three levels, with quiet areas; the lower level is used by non-smokers. The public bar frequently shows major sporting events on TV, and at other times games are played; a few pence price differential applies. A secluded private garden behind the pub is popular with families. A good menu is served (not Sun eve) with all dishes home-cooked to order; daily specials include vegetarian options. Q ❀ ◖ ◗ ⊟ ≉ ♣ ⚊

WALLINGTON

Duke's Head
6 Manor Road (A237/A232 jct)
✪ 11-11; 12-10.30 Sun
☎ (020) 8401 7410
Young's Bitter, Special, seasonal beer Ⓗ
Set back from Manor Road behind Wallington Green, it is now a comfortable local, but started life as a mid-19th-century rural inn. One wall still bears a sign saying Duke's Head Livery and Bait Stables (bait was a word for providing food for horses). The Manor Road entrance leads to the public bar; access to the saloon is from Wright's Row. Part of the saloon has low ceilings and wood panelling, and leads on through to the hotel extension at the rear.
Q ❀ ⇌ ◖ ◗ ⊟ ⚿ ≉ ♣ P

West London

W1: FITZROVIA ✣

Duke of York
47 Rathbone Street
✪ 11-11 (5 Sat); closed Sun
☎ (020) 7636 7065
Greene King IPA, Abbot Ⓗ
Sympathetically refurbished, Victorian street-corner local, in pedestrianised Charlotte Place. The pub is always popular with the locals and tourists from the Rathbone Hotel opposite and also boasts a central bar, upholstered benches and a

dartboard in one corner. It is often crowded, but benefits from a pleasant pavement terrace. Lunches may be available by the time of publication.
✿✤⊖(Goodge St/Tottenham Ct Rd)

Hogshead
72 Grafton Way
✪ 11 (12 Sat)-11; closed Sun
☎ (020) 7387 7923
Boddingtons Bitter; Brakspear Bitter; Ⓗ guest beers Ⓗ/Ⓖ
Popular with local university students and office workers, can get very busy at times. This Hogshead, formerly the Grafton Arms, has retained its beers on gravity (up to four) and offers the best choice of ales in Fitzrovia. The long, narrow bar is light and bright but with a rather cramped feel; try the upstairs bar or even the roof garden in fine weather. ✿◖▶⇌(Euston) ⊖(Warren St)

W1: MARYLEBONE ✤

Golden Eagle
59 Marylebone Lane
✪ 11-11; 12-10.30 Sun
☎ (020) 7935 3228
Adnams Bitter; Brakspear Bitter; Fuller's London Pride; guest beer Ⓗ
Just a few minutes' walk from Oxford St, this small, single-bar free house is frequented by local residents, artisans and office staff. It has undergone some recent refurbishment, but retains its character with fine bar mirrors. Brakspear's beers are favoured here; their seasonal and one-off beers are usually stocked. Lunchtime snacks (weekdays) are baguettes and Biggles sausages (their shop is in the lane). A pianist plays from 8.30pm Thu and Fri to complete the traditional atmosphere.
⊖(Bond St)

Turners Arms
26 Crawford Street
✪ 11-11; 12-10.30 Sun
☎ (020) 7724 4504
Young's Bitter, Special; guest beers Ⓗ
This pub has seen many significant changes in the past 10 years or so but now, as a free house, is a real asset to the area. It could be easily overlooked, with its narrow frontage; internally it is small and basic but quite smart with bare wooden floors, stools at the bar and more comfortable seating to the rear. Generally a quiet pub, but a juke box is available. The cider is Addlestone's (in both draught and keg form). Guest beers are sometimes from micros. ◖⇌⊖♣♠🖫

Wargrave Arms
40 Brendon Street
✪ 11-11; 12-10.30 Sun
☎ (020) 7723 4504
Young's Bitter, Triple A, Special, seasonal beers Ⓗ
One of the most consistently good pubs in W1, this L-shaped ex-Finch's house, built in 1866, is a most pleasing sight both inside and out. Some modern touches have been added, but it remains a pub of character. Comfortable chairs line one side of the 'L' while the other side, with tables and chairs, is popular with diners. The service is friendly and the atmosphere conducive to good conversation. Q◖▶⇌(Paddington) ⊖(Edgware Rd/Paddington)

W1: MAYFAIR

Guinea
30 Bruton Place
✪ 11 (6.30 Sat)-11; closed Sun
☎ (020) 7409 1728
Young's Bitter, Triple A, Special, seasonal beers Ⓗ
Just off Berkeley Square, this small mews pub clearly reflects its location. Once called the 'One Pound One' it is the oldest pub in Mayfair, dating from 1675. The clientele is mainly local office staff, plus a few tourists (often American) who enjoy the simplicity of this establishment. Divided into two sections, it may be crowded at times, making outside drinking quite popular (no seating). It boasts a top-class restaurant, famous for steak and kidney pies, which often attracts celebrities from stage and screen. Q◖▶⊖(Bond St/Green Pk)

Hogshead
11-13 Dering Street
✪ 11 (12 Sat)-11; closed Sun
☎ (020) 7629 0531 e-mail:
w1.deringstreet@whitebread.com
Adnams Bitter; Boddingtons Bitter; Fuller's London Pride; Marston's Pedigree; Wadworth 6X; Ⓗ guest beers Ⓗ/Ⓖ
Considerably extended from a tiny former Wethered's pub (the Bunch of Grapes) this Hogshead is now the primary ale outlet in the area. It maintains the original 'ale house' concept serving up to 10 ales at any time, plus a cider (usually from Inch's), and a small selection of Belgian bottled beers. A comprehensive menu is available until 9pm (8pm Fri and Sat). Fri eve is busy and noisy, but by day the pub is a haven from the bustle of Oxford Street.
◖▶&⊖(Bond St) ♠✂

W1: SOHO

Ain't Nothin' But...
20 Kingly Street
✪ 5.30-12.45am; 6-2.45am Fri & Sat; 5-11.45 Sun
☎ (020) 7287 0514 website: www.aintnothinbut.co.uk
Adnams Bitter; guest beers Ⓗ
This well-established blues club offers three ales from regional brewers. Entry is free, except Fri & Sat eve (£3 after 9pm, £5 after 11pm). Beer prices are around 20% higher than Soho pubs, but there is live blues every night and a late licence. The club is small and intimate, with a New Orleans feeling, in a colourful area of Carnaby Street. It attracts 30-something night owls, and may be crowded and smoky. Tables and chairs near the tiny stage fill up quickly.
▶⊖(Oxford Circus) ●

Clachan
34 Kingly Street
✪ 11-11; 12-5 Sun
☎ (020) 7494 0834
Fuller's London Pride; Greene King IPA; Taylor Landlord; guest beers Ⓗ
The Clachan, Gaelic for stone, was recently acquired by Bass. It has retained its ornate Victorian mahogany bar and is wood-panelled throughout, displaying brewery mirrors, old photographs and prints of the locality. The upstairs function room houses a dartboard. A full, varied *table d'hôte* menu is served, with vegetarian options available. Children are welcome until 7pm.

☃ ◖ ⊖ (Oxford Circus) ♣

Coach & Horses
29 Greek Street
✪ 11-11; 12-10.30 Sun
☎ (020) 7437 5920
Fuller's London Pride; Ind Coope Burton Ale; Marston's Pedigree ⊞

Nostalgic Soho institution, also known as Norman's in honour of the long-serving landlord Norman Balon. Caught in a 1960s timewarp, partitions provide three drinking areas; note the Heath cartoons and a portrait of the landlord. Old-fashioned, simple furniture offers basic comfort to a wide variety of drinkers in this bustling part of the West End. 'Happy hour' is 11-4 weekdays and all day Sun (which is usually quiet). It is a popular meeting place eves but service does not suffer. **Q** ⊖ (Leicester Sq) ✗

King's Arms
23 Poland Street
✪ 11-11; 12-10.30 Sun
☎ (020) 7734 5907
Courage Best Bitter, Directors ⊞

The landlord is now an honorary member of the Ancient Order of the Druids which was revived in a tavern here on 28th November 1781, but the pub's history dates back further to 1728. The King's Arms is a well-known gay pub that has an upstairs room with a bar, where several clubs meet. A good range of meals suits all palates, vegetarians included; a speciality of the house is a filled giant Yorkshire pudding. An extensive range of pop music, going back to the 60s, is mixed with more modern pieces. **Q** ◖ ⊖ (Oxford Circus)

Ship
116 Wardour Street
✪ 11-11; closed Sun
☎ (020) 7437 8446 website: www.fullers.co.uk
Fuller's London Pride, ESB, seasonal beers ⊞

Rare Fuller's outlet in the West End, the Ship boasts an extensive collection of pop CDs from the 60s through to the 80s, with some more modern additions. The music can be loud, especially Fri and Sat eves, but on weekdays it is generally 'quiet'. In the 1950s this Victorian building suffered a gas explosion, destroying many original fittings, but following restoration it features dark wood panelling with attractive etched glass behind a long bar sporting two banks of handpumps. The lunch menu changes regularly and offers vegetarian options. ◖ ᕔ ⊖ (Piccadilly Circus)

Star & Garter
62 Poland Street
✪ 11-11; closed Sun
☎ (020) 7439 0218
Courage Best Bitter; Fuller's London Pride; Shepherd Neame Spitfire ⊞

Small old-fashioned pub circa 1825, little changed under the long-serving landlord. The interior is all wood panelling and shades of brown, with comfortable benches and stools on a bare wood floor. Brass, copper and ceramic breweriana is complemented by old photos and drawings. Note too, the painted mirror depicting the Star & Garter. The background music is usually blues – the landlord's choice, and the TV is on sports, but mercifully muted. It

attracts office workers, who happily spill on to the street in good weather.
◖ ⊖ (Oxford Circus)

Three Greyhounds
25 Greek Street
✪ 11-11; 4-10.30 Sun
☎ (020) 7287 0754
Adnams Bitter; Draught Bass; Fuller's London Pride; Taylor Landlord; Tetley Bitter ⊞

At the heart of a very well-pubbed area, this is one of the best. The tall, striking 'brewer's Tudor' exterior hides a small, single intimate room that can often be a quiet haven from the lively and colourful Old Compton Street. It can be extremely busy eves, especially when theatre-goers spill out from the Prince Edward opposite. The interior has a 'medieval' look with dark heavy furniture, beams and leaded windows. Despite the inevitable tourists, it attracts a loyal crowd of locals. The beer range may change; the cider is Addlestone's. ◖ ⊖ (Leicester Sq/Tottenham Ct Rd)

W2: PADDINGTON ❄

Archery Tavern
4 Bathurst Street
✪ 11-11; 12-10.30 sun
☎ (020) 7402 4916
Badger K&B Mild, Sussex, Best, Tanglefoot ⊞

Popular pub near Paddington Station. Decorated with dried hops, plates and various prints, there is a TV for sporting events and a dartboard in an uncarpeted room to the rear of the pub. A selection of board games is available, if you ask at the bar. It serves tasty hot and cold food and a good choice of beers. Mild is available as a seasonal beer.
❀ ◖ ⇌ ⊖ (Lancaster Gate) ♣ ●

Mad Bishop & Bear
First Floor, The Lawn, Paddington Station
✪ 11-11; 12-10.30 Sun
☎ (020) 7402 2441
Fuller's Chiswick, London Pride, ESB, seasonal beers; guest beers ⊞

Newly-built and popular Fuller's pub overlooking Paddington Station. The long bar is spacious and pleasantly decorated, with a no-smoking area and piped music. The guest beers change regularly. There is seating both inside and outside, with a view of the station concourse. Hot and cold food is available throughout the week, and breakfast is served from 7.30am (Sun from 8.30). ◖ ᕔ ⇌ ⊖ ✗ ●

W4: CHISWICK

Bell & Crown
11-13 Thames Road, Strand on the Green
✪ 11-11; 12-10.30 Sun
☎ (020) 8994 4164
Fuller's Chiswick, London Pride, ESB, seasonal beers ⊞

Fuller's riverside pub, within five minutes' walk of Kew Bridge. The inside of this popular pub is well-decorated and warmed by a log fire. The conservatory towards the rear of the pub and the patio area afford some pleasant and spectacular views of the Thames. A range of hot and cold food is served. ⚓ ❀ ◖ ⇌ (Kew Bridge) ✗

George & Devonshire
8 Burlington Lane
☺ 11-11; 12-10.30 Sun
☎ (020) 8994 1859
Fuller's Chiswick, London Pride, ESB, seasonal beers Ⓗ

A few minutes' walk away from Fuller's Griffin Brewery, this pub benefits from its own parking and an outside area for drinking. The pub has a lounge bar and a public bar; the latter, which is uncarpeted, has a pool table and a TV, and displays its *Cask Marque* award. ❀◑▤♣P●

Old Pack Horse
434 Chiswick High Road
☺ 11-11; 12-10.30 Sun
☎ (020) 8994 2872
Fuller's Chiswick, London Pride, ESB Ⓗ

Large corner pub within a few minutes' walk of Chiswick Park station. It boasts some impressive ornate woodwork inside, and the front area of the pub is partly uncarpeted. A TV is used for sporting events. Thai food is available lunchtime and eve Mon-Sat and lunch Sun. The pub gets busy eves.
❀◑≉(Gunnersbury) ⊖(Chiswick Park) ●

W5: EALING ✣

Castle
36 St Mary's Road
☺ 11-11; 12-10.30 Sun
☎ (020) 8567 3285
Fuller's Chiswick, London Pride, ESB Ⓗ

A friendly atmosphere can be enjoyed in this traditional local, opposite Thames Valley University. The exterior is worth a close look; the interior has received a sympathetic refurbishment, becoming slightly more open plan, but it has retained an interesting snug to the right of the entrance, separated only by a wooden partition. A genuine stone-flagged floor completes the picture. ❀◑å⊖(South)

Duffy's
124 Pitshanger Lane
☺ 11-11; 12-10.30 Sun
☎ (020) 8998 6810
Draught Bass; Fuller's London Pride; Greene King Abbot; Hancock's HB; Young's Bitter Ⓗ

Welcome oasis in the severely under-pubbed Pitshanger area, north of Ealing town centre. Duffy's started life in 1910 as a shop (which it still resembles) belonging to United Dairies, it was then a wine bar before becoming a pub in 1985. A single bar serves two distinct areas: the front is the more basic and houses the TV; a more comfortable section further back leads to a downstairs restaurant area. It hosts occasional live music and more occasional beer festivals. ◑◗

Red Lion
13 St Mary's Road
☺ 11-11; 12-10.30 Sun
☎ (020) 8567 2541
Fuller's Chiswick, London Pride, ESB, seasonal beers Ⓗ

Single-bar institution, opposite Ealing Film Studios, hence its alternative name, Stage Six. The walls of this traditional pub are lined with pictures from the many films and BBC programmes which originated over the road. There is an attractive courtyard garden at the rear. Dating from at least the early 18th century, the Red Lion later benefited from the coach route between Kew and Uxbridge. One of the very few local pubs to successfully resist the keg tide of the 1960s and early 70s, it became a regular fixture in this *Guide*.
Q❀◑≉(Broadway) ⊖(South) ●

W6: HAMMERSMITH ✣

Andover Arms
57 Aldensley Road
☺ 11-11; 12-3.30, 7-10.30 Sun
☎ (020) 8741 9794
Fuller's Chiswick, London Pride, ESB, seasonal beers Ⓗ

Well hidden in Brackenbury village lies a gem of a pub; it is just off Glenthorne Road, but you may need a map. This back-street local offers a cosy and comfortable atmosphere in which to enjoy good food. Thai cuisine is the speciality, but traditional lunches are also available. The two bars fill up quickly, so that in the evening, the rear restaurant is very welcome. Once discovered it's likely to be a firm favourite.
◑◗⊖(Ravenscourt Pk) ●

Brook Green Hotel
170 Shepherd's Bush Road
☺ 11-11; 12-10.30 Sun
☎ (020) 7603 2516 e-mail: brookgreen@youngs.co.uk
Young's Bitter, Triple A, Special, seasonal beers Ⓗ

Imposing Victorian building, facing the green, recently reinstated as a hotel with 14 rooms. This major refurbishment has also modernised the spacious main bar, while retaining its period feel, by preserving main features such as the fireplace and back bar. The colourful, contemporary furnishings and decor complement the whole design. Brook's Wine Bar in the basement is somewhat bolder, but may be closed at quiet times. The small enclosed patio garden is an added attraction, as is the excellent, good value food.
🛏❀⇋◑å⊖

Dove ☆
19 Upper Mall
☺ 11-11; 12-10.30 Sun
☎ (020) 8748 5405
Fuller's London Pride, ESB Ⓗ

Famous riverside pub reached by the river path from Hammersmith Bridge. This charming tavern has historical connections; Charles II and Nell Gwyn drank here and Thomas Arne wrote *Rule, Britannia* in an upstairs room. Very popular, especially in fine weather, with excellent views from the terrace over to Fuller's brewery in Chiswick. The main bar is small and cosy, but the public bar is the smallest anywhere (according to the *Guinness Book of Records*). The raised bar at the rear offers more seating (mainly for diners).
Q❀◑⊖(Ravenscourt Pk)

Salutation
154 King Street
☺ 11-11; 12-10.30 Sun
☎ (020) 8748 3668
Fuller's Chiswick, London Pride, ESB, seasonal

beers Ⓗ
Edwardian pub where a striking purple tiled exterior bears the brewer's full name and the date of construction. Tiles also line the small passageway towards the one large bar, divided into separate drinking areas. The central section features a skylight and a fine fireplace; beyond lies a modern conservatory leading to an attractive garden, unusual for the area. Patrons enjoy the more relaxed atmosphere and better service than other local pubs provide. Handy for the cinema; quiz night is Tue.
⊛❶↔ (Ravenscourt Pk) ●

W7: HANWELL

Dolphin

13 Lower Boston Road
✪ 12-11; 12-10.30 Sun
☎ (020) 8840 0850
Brakspear Bitter; Fuller's London Pride; Greene King Old Speckled Hen; Marston's Pedigree; Wadworth 6X Ⓗ
Almost a brewery museum, festooned with numerous posters and panels advertising defunct breweries' products. The pub has developed a loyal customer base since its refurbishment nearly five years ago by Gibbs Mew (now also defunct). Belonging to the stripped wood school of pub interiors, nevertheless, the atmosphere is an oasis of tranquillity, rare for modern revamping, enlivened by the buzz of conversation. No food Mon. Q❶❶⇌♣⚲

Fox

Green Lane
✪ 11-11; 12-10.30 Sun
☎ (020) 8567 4021
Brakspear Bitter; Fuller's London Pride; Taylor Landlord; guest beers Ⓗ
Set back from the canal at the foot of the Hanwell flight of locks, the pub dates back to 1807, but has seen many alterations since; fortunately, the threat of closure was removed with its recent change to a proper free house. Occasional guest beers tend to coincide with bank holidays. The large garden hosts barbecues summer weekends. The home-cooked food features fresh vegetables from allotments across the road. Accompanied children (and dogs) are always welcome. ⚶⊛❶⇌♣P

W8: KENSINGTON ❈

Churchill Arms

119 Kensington Church Street
✪ 11-11; 12-10.30 Sun
☎ (020) 7727 4242
Fuller's Chiswick, London Pride, ESB, seasonal beers Ⓗ
This popular Fuller's pub displays a collection of Churchillian memorabilia and a plethora of photos, bric-à-brac and awards, including *Evening Standard Pub of the Year*. There are two TV sets which are used for sporting events. If you are hungry, try either the well-known Thai restaurant in the conservatory at the rear of the bar, or the pub grub from the food counter.
Q❶↔ (Notting Hill Gate) ●

W8: NOTTING HILL GATE

Uxbridge Arms

13 Uxbridge Street
✪ 11-11; 12-10.30 Sun
☎ (020) 7727 7326
e-mail: uxbridgearm.w8@whitbread.com
Brakspear Special; Fuller's London Pride; guest beers Ⓗ
This friendly, back-street local, is a little hard to find but worth it. Just off the main shopping area, it offers a changing guest beer. There is a TV which is switched on occasionally for special sporting events. Benches on the pavement allow for outside drinking. Q⊛↔

W9: MAIDA VALE

Warrington Hotel ☆

93 Warrington Crescent
✪ 11-11; 12-10.30 Sun
☎ (020) 7286 2929
Brakspear Special; Fuller's London Pride, ESB; Young's Special; guest beer Ⓗ
Pass through the ancient portals of this superb pub and be transported: the stained glass windows, the classic marble columns supporting intricately carved wooden arches, the flowered tiling and pipe-playing fauns, transform a corner of Maida Vale into a Temple of Dionysus. For the more down-to-earth drinker, there is a staid public bar where darts can be played. It draws a mainly young clientele. A Thai

INN BRIEF

West London

W1: FITZROVIA

Hope
15 Tottenham Street
11-11; 12-10.30 Sun
Brakspear Bitter; Flowers Original; Fuller's London Pride; Ⓗ **guest beers** Ⓗ/Ⓖ
Good selection of beer, with usually two on gravity, is served in this tiny, busy corner pub; sausages are the speciality on the menu.

W1: MARYLEBONE

Beehive
7 Homer Street
11-3, 5.30-11; 11-11 Fri & Sat; 12-10.30 Sun
Fuller's London Pride; Young's Bitter Ⓗ
Small, side-street pub featured in many editions of this *Guide*, with a loyal clientele. No food eves.

W2: PADDINGTON

Victoria
10A Strathearn Place
11 (12 Sat)-11;
12-10.30 Sun
Fuller's Chiswick, London Pride, ESB, seasonal beers Ⓗ
Ornate Fuller's pub, boasting a set of magnificent etched and coloured mirrors and serving a good range of hot and cold food.

W5: EALING

Ealing Lawn Tennis Club
Daniel Road
(off Creefield Rd)
6-11;
2.30-10.30 Sun
Fuller's London Pride; guest beer Ⓗ
Single bar in a Tudor-style clubhouse where one or two guest beers are usually available.

W6: HAMMERSMITH

Thatched House
115 Dalling Road
11-11;
12-10.30 Sun
Young's Bitter, Triple A, Special, seasonal beers Ⓗ
Popular pub with loyal customers; one large modernised bar, it is comfortably furnished with a rear section mainly for diners.

W8: KENSINGTON

Britannia
1 Allen Street
11-11;
12-10.30 Sun
Smiles Best; Young's Bitter, Triple A, Special, seasonal beers Ⓗ
In every edition of this *Guide*: a pleasant back-street pub, off Kensington High St. Recent refurbishment lost the public bar.

restaurant upstairs opens eves; lunches are served in the pub itself.
🕮🕮 🕮🕮 (Warwick Ave) ♣

W11: BAYSWATER

Cock & Bottle
17 Needham Road
🕐 12-11; 12-10.30 Sun
☎ (020) 7229 1550
Brakspear Bitter Ⓗ

Originally the Swan, built in 1851, it is now a very friendly, traditional back-street pub with a loyal following. The main bar, with a high ceiling and ornate carved wood back bar, has comfortable seating and a TV tuned to sport. An additional lounge bar, reached through swinging (saloon) doors, is well-used at lunchtime for good value meals, and on Tue eve for the popular quiz. It is worth seeking out this unchanged local in an increasingly trendy area.
🕮🕮 (Notting Hill Gate)

W13: WEST EALING

Drayton Court
2 The Avenue
🕐 11-11; 12-10.30 Sun
☎ (020) 8997 1019
Fuller's Chiswick, London Pride, ESB, seasonal beers; guest beer (occasional) Ⓗ

Large, popular local where facilities include separate bars, a function room, a big garden, a theatre downstairs and conference facilities upstairs. Set behind a splendid neo-gothic exterior, it is a frequent winner of local CAMRA *Pub of the Year*. A splendid establishment, not to be missed. 🕮🕮🕮🕮🕮🕮

BRENTFORD

Brewery Tap
47 Catherine Wheel Road
🕐 11-11; 12-10.30 Sun
☎ (020) 8560 5200
Fuller's Chiswick, London Pride, ESB, seasonal beers Ⓗ

Originally the tap of the William Gomm Brewery, purchased by Fuller's in 1908 but subsequently closed. Of Victorian origin, the pub is reached by steps from road level as the river used to flood here. Recently saved from demolition under area

development plans, following vigorous campaigning by the landlord and locals, new plans include a garden and decking down to the nearby canal. In recent years the pub has become well known for its Tue and Thu eve jazz, plus other live music at weekends. Lunches are popular (book Sun).
Q🕮🕮≈🕮♣

Globe
104 Windmill Road (off A4, almost under the M4 flyover)
🕐 11-11; 12-10.30 Sun
☎ (020) 8580 0086 website: www.theglobe.freeuk.com
Fuller's London Pride, ESB, seasonal beers Ⓗ

Chameleon of a pub, drawing a different clientele lunchtimes, eves and to its live music nights (Thu, Sat and Sun) when it can get crowded and smoky, although the area near the pool table can still be comparatively quiet. At lunchtime it caters for those who work nearby, and can be busy, particularly for food. Enjoy a good pint and a friendly atmosphere, but beware, you may find yourself singing along with the band. 🕮🕮≈🕮 (Northfields/Boston Manor)

Magpie & Crown
128 High Street
🕐 11-11; 12-10.30 Sun
☎ (020) 8560 5658
Brakspear Bitter; guest beers Ⓗ

Mock-Tudor pub opposite the Magistrates' Court, set back from the road, so providing an outside drinking area. Three constantly changing guest beers, mainly from regional and micro-breweries, have made it a magnet for ale lovers. A varying cider (or occasionally perry) is available, plus draught Budvar and Hoegaarden, and a selection of continental bottled beers. Weekday lunches are served. Fri is Karaoke night; major sports events are shown on TV. Photos of bygone Brentford adorn the walls of this local CAMRA *Pub of the Year* 1999 and 2000. 🕮🕮≈♣🕮🕮

COLHAM GREEN ✜

Hut
2 Old Orchard Close, Hillingdon
🕐 11-11; 12-10.30 Sun
☎ (01895) 437935
Beer range varies Ⓗ

W11: NOTTING HILL
Ladbroke Arms
54 Ladbroke Road
11-3, 5.30-11; 11-11 Sat; 12-10.30 Sun
Courage Best Bitter, Directors; Everards Tiger; Greene King Abbot, Old Speckled Hen; guest beer Ⓗ
Smart, comfortable free house, refurbished to a high standard in 1999; food is popular. Raised front patio for summer drinking.

W14: WEST KENSINGTON
Britannia Tap
150 Warwick Road
11-11; 12-10.30 Sun
Young's Bitter, Triple A, Special, seasonal beers Ⓗ
Once possibly the smallest pub in London, with extra space on the front patio or rear garden. Nice pub, serving Thai food, near Olympia.

Seven Stars
253 North End Road
11-11;
12-10.30 Sun
Fuller's London Pride, ESB Ⓗ
Imposing 1930s Art Deco pub, hosting frequent Karaoke and serving good value lunches. Enclosed rear patio for barbecues in summer.

COLHAM GREEN
Crown
Colham Green Road
11-11;
12-10.30 Sun
Fuller's London Pride, ESB Ⓗ
Still a compact, two-bar local that lost most of its trade when a line of terraced cottages was demolished to make way for its car park!

TWICKENHAM
Hogshead
33-35 York Street
11-11; 12-10.30 Sun
Boddingtons Bitter; Brakspear Bitter; Fuller's London Pride; Greene King Abbot; Wadworth 6X; Ⓗ **guest beers** Ⓗ/Ⓖ
Relatively new, but now established on the Twickenham pub scene, serving constantly changing guest beers and food until 8pm (6 Fri and Sat).

UXBRIDGE
Pipemakers Arms
57 St John's Road
11-11; 12-10.30 Sun
Adnams Bitter, Fuller's London Pride; Marston's Pedigree; Theakston Best Bitter Ⓗ **guest beers** Ⓗ/Ⓖ
Pleasantly located on the River Colne, this pub serves excellent Thai food.

Near Hillingdon Hospital, this is a miraculous survivor; having escaped redevelopment just a couple of years ago, it has been revived by keen licensees. It now offers a regularly changing duo of real ales, thereby despatching its previous reputation as a confirmed keg emporium when it was part of the old Taylor Walker estate. Still effectively two bars, the public features an increasingly rare (for the area) bar billiards table, although the distinction between that bar and the lounge is somewhat academic. ❀♣P

COWLEY PEACHEY

Paddington Packet Boat
High Road
✪ 12-11; 12-10.30 Sun
☎ (01895) 442392 e-mail: calster@tinyworld.co.uk
Fuller's Chiswick, London Pride, ESB Ⓗ

A *Master Cellarman* runs this large, friendly pub which celebrated its second centenary in 2001. Although it enjoys a good passing trade, most of the customers are local, and include workers on the almost adjacent Grand Union Canal. Despite having been completely modernised, it retains some old fittings and mirrors, and displays memorabilia relating to the old packet-boat service to Paddington. The pub fields its own rugby team. Live music is performed Fri and Sat eves. Sun lunch is served until 4pm (no meals Sun eve). Dogs are welcome. ㎖❀✿◑&♣P

CRANFORD

Jolly Gardeners
144 High Street
✪ 11-11; 12-10.30 Sun
☎ (020) 8897 6996
Tetley Bitter; guest beer Ⓗ

Cosy, two-bar local; each bar has its own real fire for winter warmth, while in summer a large garden with swings and slides will keep children happy. The landlord's selection of guest beers tends to be unusual for the area; see his illustrations of them on a large chalkboard by the bar. The basic home-cooked lunches (roasts on

Sun) are exceptionally good value, and come in gargantuan portions. B&B is available weekdays. ㎖❀✿◑♣P

GREENFORD

Bridge Hotel
Western Avenue (A40/A4127 jct)
✪ 11-11; 12-10.30 Sun
☎ (020) 8566 6246
Young's Bitter, Special, seasonal beers Ⓗ

Opened in 1937, it was one of two licensed premises built in the area by the same developer, one to be called the Bridge and the other the Greenford. The names were accidentally transposed on the licence application forms, which is why the Bridge Hotel is nowhere near a bridge (although a flyover on the A40 now runs close by). It was redeveloped in 1989 and 68 bedrooms added, the original pub being retained alongside, with the bars restored in traditional style. No food weekends. ❀✿◑&⇌⊖♣P

HAMPTON

Jolly Coopers
16 High Street
✪ 11-3, 5-11; 11-11 Sat; 12-10.30 Sun
☎ (020) 8979 3384
Brakspear Bitter; Courage Best Bitter; Greene King Ruddles County; Marston's Pedigree; Theakston Best Bitter Ⓗ

Popular, homely pub, whose landlord was the youngest licensee in England when he first took it over. Interesting paraphernalia has accumulated over the years, much of it drinks-related. A recent refurbishment has created a restaurant area and a small patio at the rear, from which there is wheelchair access. The restaurant has an *à la carte* menu and opens 7-9.30 Tue-Sat eves. Food at the bar is offered weekday lunchtimes. ❀◑&⇌

White Hart
70 High Street
✪ 11.30-3, 5.30-11; 11.30-11 Sat; 12-10.30 Sun
☎ (020) 8979 5352
Greene King Abbot; Tetley Bitter; guest beers Ⓗ

For several years now, the White Hart has stocked the widest range of ales in the area, with up to eight regularly available. A historic pub, it was rebuilt in 1898, but before that it was once owned by the famous actor David Garrick, and is mentioned by Dickens in *Oliver Twist*. The large bar area has a good atmosphere and lunches are served on weekdays; the first-floor restaurant is open eves (not Mon) and all day Sat and Sun. ㎖❀◑

HAMPTON COURT

King's Arms
Lion Gate, Hampton Court Road
✪ 11-11; 12-10.30 Sun
☎ (020) 8977 1729
Badger K&B Sussex, IPA, Tanglefoot, seasonal beers Ⓗ

Imposing, historic hostelry, by the Lion Gate entrance to Hampton Court, backing on to the famous maze. Of the three bar areas, one boasts a 300-year-old mosaic floor, in which the pub's name is depicted.

Cask Marque

The Cask Marque symbol with a pub entry indicates that the licensee has successfully passed a number of tests concerning beer quality, and can display a plaque to this effect. However, the choice of all pubs in the guide is made by CAMRA independently of Cask Marque. The Cask Marque symbol is added during the editing process, and Cask Marque has no say in the selection of pubs.

Another, called the Wives' Bar, has pictures of Henry VIII's six wives eyeing you from below the bar. In front is a hedged seating area. The pub opens at 9am for breakfast, after which good quality meals are available until 9.30pm daily.

❀◑≠♣●

HAMPTON HILL

Roebuck
72 Hampton Road
☼ 11-11; 12-10.30 Sun
☎ (020) 8255 8133
Badger Best; guest beer Ⓗ
This used to be one of the area's most wonderful pubs, but not any more. The current owners have created a welcoming, comfortable establishment, displaying an ever-increasing collection of bric-à-brac, mainly nautical but including traffic lights and a local bus stop sign. The pub is technically in Teddington, but is much closer to Hampton Hill's main street. Bus routes 285 and R68 pass by. Lunches are served Mon-Fri, and two bedrooms are available for B&B. The guest beer changes monthly. ♨❀⋈◑≠ (Fulwell) ♣

HARMONDSWORTH

Five Bells
High Street
☼ 11-11; 12-10.30 Sun
☎ (020) 8759 4713
Adnams Bitter, Broadside; guest beer Ⓗ
Situated at the far end of this cul-de-sac village, the small, public bar frontage of this free house disguises the much larger saloon where the real ales are to be found. Of the half a dozen offered at any one time, up to three are usually from the Adnams range. Within the adjacent 12th-century churchyard rest the remains of one Mr Cox of Orange Pippin fame. Q❀◑⊟♣

HARROW

Village Inn
402-408 Rayners Lane
☼ 11-11; 12-10.30 Sun
☎ (020) 8868 8557
Courage Directors; Theakston Best Bitter, XB; guest beers Ⓗ
Conventional Wetherspoon's shop conversion, on the one-way system. The interior is L-shaped, traditionally styled on two levels: the bar in the upper part with wheelchair WC adjacent, down six steps are booths and a no-smoking area. Invariably three guest beers are available, often one is dark. Meal prices are reasonable. An abundance of 'Metroland' and local interest panels are worth a look.
Q❀◑♿⊖(Rayners Lane) P⌇●

HILLINGDON

Oak Tree
132 Ryefield Avenue
☼ 11-11; 12-10.30 Sun
☎ (01895) 238085
Fuller's London Pride, ESB Ⓗ
Built in 1956, to serve a new estate, the Oak Tree is tucked well away. A well-used, traditional back-street local, it has an unusually small private bar, accessed

through the central door of the pub. Children are welcome in the lounge bar (when it's open).
♨Q❀P

HOUNSLOW

Cross Lances
236 Hanworth Road (A314)
☼ 11-11; 12-10.30 Sun
☎ (020) 8570 4174
Fuller's London Pride, ESB, seasonal beers Ⓗ
Dark red-tiled Victorian local, the Cross Lances, now with a *Master Cellarman* landlord, was extended in 2001 to give more bar space and better access to the garden, which took second prize in Fuller's *Pub Garden* competition 2000. The new extension provides wheelchair access. There is frequently something going on here: crib on Mon, quiz Thu, darts and pool matches and weekly meat raffles. A band (usually jazz) performs bank holiday Sun afternoons. Huge lunches are served daily, with senior citizens' discount Tue.
❀◑⊟♿≠(Hounslow) ♣P

ICKENHAM

Tichenham Inn
11 Swakeleys Road
☼ 11-11; 12-10.30 Sun
☎ (01895) 678916
Courage Directors; Fuller's London Pride; Theakston Best Bitter; Shepherd Neame Spitfire; guest beers Ⓗ
Newly-built Wetherspoon's free house on an old garage site, where the old forecourt provides outdoor drinking space. Tichenham derives from the 1086 Domesday survey. Young male staff feature on a raunchy calendar for testicular cancer research. Not large by current Wetherspoon standards, it stands opposite pretty St Giles' church; parking is difficult at most times, folding doors open up on hot summer days. Wall panels provide plenty of local interest, in this usually busy pub that features very 'brown' decor (but not too dark for reading). Q❀◑♿⊖⌇●

ISLEWORTH

Coach & Horses
183 London Road (A315)
☼ 11-11 (midnight on live music eves); 12-10.30 Sun
☎ (020) 8560 1447
Young's Bitter, Triple A, Special, seasonal beers Ⓗ
First leased by Young's in 1831, this is one of the few remaining coaching houses that were once abundant on this road. There have been a few changes since it was mentioned by Dickens in *Oliver Twist*, including the removal of bar partitions, but it is still a pub of great character. Music eves are now a feature – usually jazz Mon, folk or blues Tue, and various bands Fri and Sat. Meals (except Sun eve) are served either in the bar or from the Thai-based restaurant. There is a family-orientated garden at the rear.
♨❀◑♿≠(Syon Lane) ♣P

Red Lion
92-94 Linkfield Road
☼ 11-11; 12-10.30 Sun
☎ (020) 8560 1457
Brakspear Bitter, Special; guest beers Ⓗ
Spacious, two-bar free house with a very

strong community focus – there is always something going on. It might be a pantomime, or a summer production in the garden, by their own theatre group, the Hiss and Boo Co, who have appeared on Granada TV, or live music (Sat and Sun eves), or the Thu quiz, or the monthly 'retro nights' (last Fri). Regular theme nights, darts and pool competitions, and summer barbecues complete the picture. Weekday lunches served. ✿◖⊞≠♣⊟

NORTHWOOD

Olde Northwood
142 Pinner Road
✪ 11-11; 12-10.30 Sun
☎ (01923) 840862
Beer range varies Ⓗ
Grade II listed, corner local with a somewhat uninspiring and jaded frontage, this pub has had a chequered history, previously as the Clifton and originally the Iron Bridge. However a warm welcome awaits within this locals' local. Beware the Karaoke (Fri eve) and the 'exotic' dancers (2-6 Mon-Fri). The guest beer is always from the Nethergate Brewery, very unusual for the area. Meals are not generally available, but a Sun roast is served and a curry on Mon eve. Q♣P

Sylvan Moon
27 Green Lane
✪ 11-11; 12-10.30 Sun
☎ (01923) 820760
Courage Directors; Fuller's London Pride; Shepherd Neame Spitfire; Theakston Best Bitter; guest beers Ⓗ
Rather unusual, outrageous pastel green livery adorns the frontage of this typical corner Wetherspoon's house, complete with hanging baskets during the warmer months. A good mix of all ages frequents this busy local, especially Thu and Fri eves when the nearby college comes to the end of another week. At least two guest beers are on tap at any one time. Beware the perfect punctuality at closing time! Q◖▶♿⊖⌧●

NORWOOD GREEN ✣

Plough
Tentelow Lane (A4127)
✪ 11-11; 12-10.30 Sun
☎ (020) 8574 1945
Fuller's Chiswick, London Pride, ESB Ⓗ
Having now all but abandoned its once six-strong Southall estate and even its two nearby motel outlets, Fuller's has retained its increasingly isolated and oldest pub. Dating from the 14th century – although the current building is a mere 400 years old – it continues to offer the full regular range of Chiswick-brewed ales in convivial surroundings. Good value Sun lunches are a new feature to tempt more visitors across the fields from nearby Osterley House, park and farm. No food Sun eve. ✿◖▶♣P

PINNER

Oddfellows
2 Waxwell Lane
✪ 11-3, 5.30-11; 12-3, 7-10.30 Sun
☎ (020) 8866 7372
Fuller's London Pride; Greene King IPA, Young's Special Ⓗ

Grade II listed building, first licensed in 1854. A local, well-respected gentleman, Mr Ellement, belonged to the local Oddfellows Society; he borrowed money from them to build the pub in 1853 and named it in recognition of the subsidy. A very comfortable 'village' local at the end of the High Street, get there early for the comfy sofas. Much extended over the years, it displays a collection of hats and post-war memorabilia. The large garden is an asset in summer. Q✿◖

Queen's Head
31 High Street
✪ 11-3.30, 5-11; 12-3.30, 7-10.30 Sun
☎ (020) 8868 9844
Adnams Bitter; Benskins Bitter; Fuller's London Pride; Greene King Abbot, Tetley Bitter; Young's Special Ⓗ
Grade II listed building, the oldest pub in Pinner, partly dating back to 1540, although an ale house is believed to have been on this site since the first Pinner Fair in 1336. Exposed beams, attractive decor and an open fire make this well worth a visit, but beware minimal seating is available on quiz night (usually Mon). A no-smoking area is available at lunchtime. ♨Q✿◖▶P⌧

RUISLIP MANOR

JJ Moon's
12 Victoria Road
✪ 11-11; 12-10.30 Sun
☎ (01895) 622373
Courage Directors; Fuller's London Pride; Shepherd Neame Spitfire; Theakston Best Bitter; Wadworth 6X; guest beers Ⓗ
Usually busy, this regular *Guide* entry is overseen by one of Wetherspoon's longest-serving managers. He has reintroduced the famous marquee for the two annual beer festivals, when often 20 or more varieties are available on gravity. Moon's consistently sells most of the local CAMRA branch quota of *London Drinker* magazine. Steps at the rear lead to an area that is mostly no-smoking and usually preferred by diners. Q✿◖▶♿⊖♣⌧●

SOUTHALL

Beaconsfield Arms
63-67 West End Road (off A4020)
✪ 11-11; 12-10.30 Sun
☎ (020) 8574 8135
Draught Bass; Greene King Abbot; Scanlon's Spike; guest beers Ⓗ
Intriguingly situated, halfway down a residential street, this campaigning local survives when so many other Southall pubs have closed. Never an architectural gem, the frontage has at least been improved by the recent removal of ugly iron window screens.

Star pubs
Pubs with a star symbol next to their names are listed in CAMRA's National Inventory of pubs with interiors of outstanding interest. The full list is printed in the guide.

Once inside there are still a few traces of its former glory. Its real claim to fame though is that it always has cask mild available, making it a firm favourite with not just locals but also drinkers from further afield, hence the achievement award from Reading CAMRA displayed behind the bar.
❀⇌♣P⌂

Southall Conservative Club
Fairlawn, High Street (behind fire station)
✪ 11.30-2.30, 6-11; 12-2, 7-10.30 Sun
☎ (020) 8574 0261
Courage Best Bitter; guest beer H
Community-orientated club complete with its own bowling green and snooker hall attached (four tables). Monday is quiz night, which perhaps brings in a larger cross-section of patrons than other days, but any card-carrying CAMRA members or those with a copy of this edition of the *Guide* are welcome at any time. Try the inexpensive lunches served weekdays accompanied maybe, by a pint of the guest brew, often from the Rebellion stable. Ocasional live bands.
Q❀◖⇇♣P

TEDDINGTON

Lion
27 Wick Road
✪ 12-11; 12-10.30 Sun
☎ (020) 8977 6631 e-mail: ask@thelionpub.co.uk
Fuller's London Pride; Greene King Abbot; Young's Bitter; guest beer H
About three years ago this pub probably sold more ice creams to local families than it did pints of ale. However, CAMRA award-winning tenants have totally refurbished and transformed the pub that now attracts custom from further afield. In a side street, just a short walk from Hampton Wick Station, it is establishing a reputation for excellent food (not served Sun eve) and an imaginative modern menu. Features include a dining/function room and an attractive garden. A bit pricey, but it is well worth finding.
🚄❀◖⇌ (Hampton Wick) ♣

Queen Dowager
49 North Lane
✪ 11-11; 12-10.30 Sun
☎ (020) 8977 2583
Young's Bitter, Special, seasonal beers H
New licensees, in 2000, have ensured the continuation of the excellent reputation of this pub, gained over many years by the previous long-serving landlord. They are, however, planning some alterations and the separate public bar may disappear by the time this *Guide* goes to print. In a side turning off Teddington's main street, this friendly local, has many regular, loyal customers. Dating from 1906, although there has been a pub on the site since at least 1747, it had a beer-only licence until 1950. It has a surprisingly large garden.
❀◖⊞⇌♣

TWICKENHAM ❂

Eel Pie
9-11 Church Street
✪ 11-11; 12-10.30 Sun
☎ (020) 8891 1717

Badger K&B Sussex, IPA, Best, Tanglefoot; guest beer H
Perhaps surprisingly, the Eel Pie has only been a pub for less than 20 years – it was previously a wine bar. It has all the trappings of a traditional pub with different drinking areas and various paraphernalia – much of it rugby-orientated. The Badger beers are usually complemented by a guest from the Gribble Inn at Oving, Sussex, and Inch's Stonehouse cider is regularly stocked. All the food is home-made, with lunches daily and eve snacks until 10pm (except Sun). A bar billiards table is available.
◖⇇♣♠●

Prince Blucher
124 The Green
✪ 11-11; 12-10.30 Sun
☎ (020) 8894 1824
Fuller's Chiswick, London Pride, ESB, seasonal beers H
Probably the only pub in the country with this name – a plaque inside tells the story. It is a large family-orientated pub with a single bar, but several distinct drinking areas, and a large child-friendly garden. It is extremely popular, never more so than for major televised football and rugby matches when you have to arrive early to get a seat in a viewing position. Nowadays eve meals are available (except Sun) as well as the popular lunches. 🚄❀◖⇌ (Strawberry Hill) P●

UXBRIDGE ❂

Load of Hay
Villier Street
✪ 11-3, 5.30 (7 Sat)-11; 12-3, 7-10.30 Sun
☎ (01895) 234676
website: www.loadofhay-uxbridge.co.uk
Brains Buckley's Best Bitter, Bitter; guest beers H
Originally the officers' mess of the Elthorne Light Militia before becoming a pub in the late 1870s. It used to be linked to the pub opposite, alas long since closed, but a tunnel still links the cellars. The larger part of the current pub is a conversion of an old stable block, however the smaller front bar is a gem. The range of guest beers features mainly brews from micros and the quality is such that it frequently picks up the local CAMRA *Pub of the Year* award. No food Sun eve. Q⏚❀◖♣P↯

WEST DRAYTON

De Burgh Arms
Station Approach
✪ 11-11; 12-10.30 Sun
☎ (01895) 432823
Adnams Broadside; Ansells Bitter; Fuller's London Pride; Marston's Pedigree; Tetley Bitter; guest beer H
Large 17th-century, Grade II listed building by the station that featured in the famous *Genevieve* film. Although it has been knocked through, local photographs and an unusual assortment of memorabilia, give the place something of an olde-worlde atmosphere. All handpumps have sparklers, but the staff willingly remove them on request. There is no music, other than snatches played during the Wed music quiz, and no TV. A general knowledge quiz is held Sun. Food, from snacks to a three-course meal, is served from noon until 9.45 (6.45 Sun). ❀◖♿⇌♠P

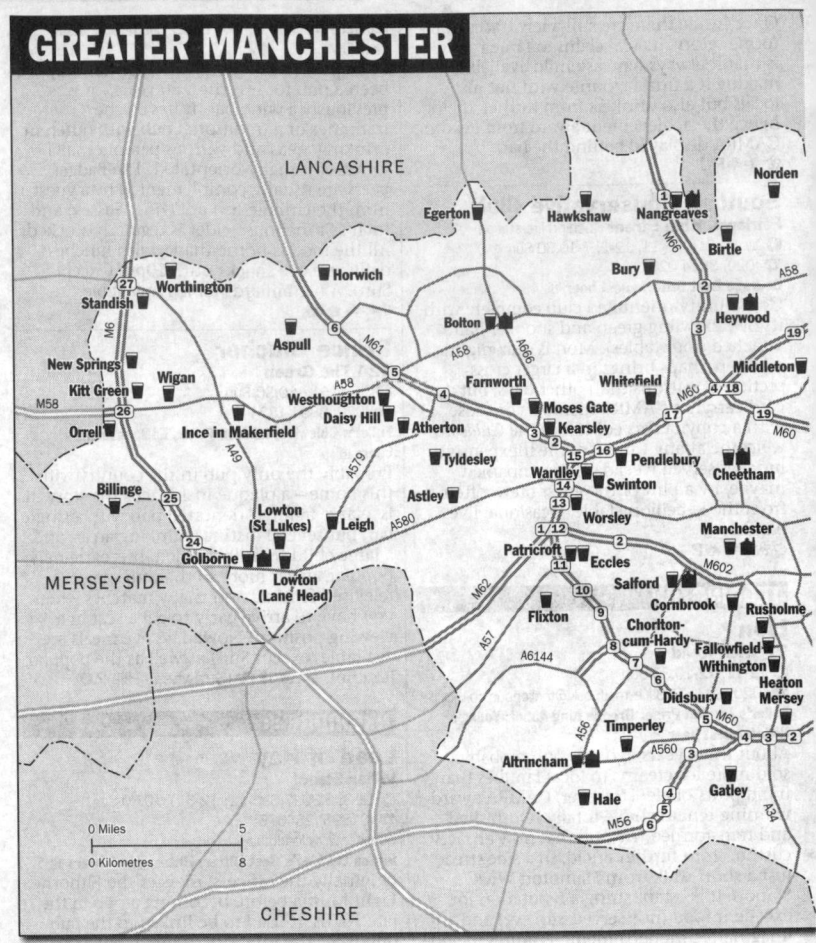

GREATER MANCHESTER

LANCASHIRE

MERSEYSIDE

CHESHIRE

0 Miles 5
0 Kilometres 8

ALTRINCHAM

Old Market Tavern
Old Market Place
🕐 12-3, 5-11; 12-11 Fri; 12-10.30 Sun
☎ (0161) 927 7062
Beer range varies H

1740s coaching inn, it was extended in the 1860s and acted as Altrincham Town Hall into the 1890s. An early landlord had Altrincham's first gasworks built behind the pub and installed gas lighting inside and in the old market place. An ever-changing range of up to 11 beers and four ciders are complemented by a choice of Belgian ales and good food. The pub is home to Cheshire Cat Ales from the Altrincham Brewing Company and stocks their products as available. 🏚🚭🕏🍴≠😊●✦

ASHTON-UNDER-LYNE ☼

Caledonia Hotel
13 Warrington Street
🕐 11-11; 12-4, 7-10.30 Sun
☎ (0161) 339 7177
Robinson's Hatters Mild, Best Bitter, Frederics, seasonal beers H

Three-storey, town-centre pub, that has been recently well refurbished to create three distinct drinking areas and a raised dining area. Dark-stained wood and fabrics lend a warm feel to a friendly, sociable atmosphere. The pub serves good value meals and has accommodation. Parties are catered for and theme nights are occasionally held. 🚭🛏🍴◑≠P

Dog & Pheasant
528 Oldham Road, Waterloo (A627)
🕐 12-11; 12-10.30 Sun
☎ (0161) 330 4894
Banks's Original; Marston's Bitter, Pedigree, HBC H

Known as the Top Dog, this popular, friendly local is near the Medlock Valley Country Park. A large bar serves three distinct areas, plus another room at the front. Good value food is available (not served Tue or Sun eve), and the extensive menu includes vegetarian options. On Tue and Thu eves, a disc jockey provides music (mainly 1950s, 60s, and 70s rock, soul and blues) and a quiz, usually well attended. Also, monthly entertainment is staged Sun teatime. 🏚🚭◑▶P

Junction Inn
Mossley Road, Hazlehurst
🕐 12-11; 12-10.30 Sun
☎ (0161) 343 1611

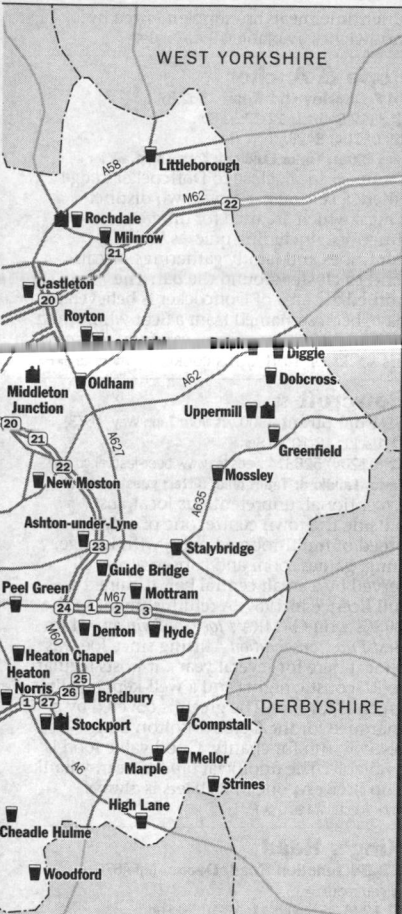

the walled patio with its pool of Koi carp hosts informal (free) barbecues.
Q🌳♿⇌♣✔

ASTLEY ☼

Manchester Road Inn
Manchester Road
☀ 12-3 (not Mon), 5.30-11; 12-11 Sat; 12-10.30 Sun
☎ (01942) 883019
Hydes Bitter; Taylor Landlord; guest beers Ⓗ
Situated opposite Astley golf range, the inn's main bar is separated into several small comfortable seating areas; one set aside for TV and games. At the side of the bar are steps up to the larger back bar and lounge. It stages occasional beer festivals, making good use of the garden, and food theme nights. The pub boasts its own cricket team which plays in a local pub league. Eve meals served 6–7.45 (not Mon); Sun meals 12–6.45. 🌳◑♣P

ATHERTON ☼

Pendle Witch
2-4 Warburton Place
☀ 2 (12 Fri & Sat)-11; 12-10.30 Sun
☎ (01942) 884537
Moorhouses Black Cat, Premier, Pendle Witches Brew, seasonal beers; guest beers Ⓗ
Hidden from the main Market Street shopping area, access is also available down an alley from the public car park. The Pendle, once two town houses, is now a popular Moorhouses' pub. Its single-roomed bar has several seating areas, one raised (toilets are upstairs). The lounge offers pool and darts. The suntrap paved garden is surrounded by shops and housing. Occasional beer festivals are held. 🌳

BILLINGE

Holt's Arms (Foot)
Crank Road (opp. hospital)
☀ 12-11; 12-10.30 Sun
☎ (01695) 622705
Burtonwood Bitter; guest beers Ⓗ
A *Guide* regular, this listed building (circa 1721) of low ceilings and old beams, once housed the hospital mortuary. Locals say that the bracket on the beam was used to lift up coffins. The pub is known locally as the Foot, or Foot o' Causeway, due to its proximity to the base of Billinge Hill. Regular events include quizzes, barbecues and a summer beer festival. A bowling green is an added attraction.
🛏Q🌳◑🏕♣P✔

Robinson's Hatters Mild, Best Bitter, Frederics Ⓗ
Small stone pub of great character, which remains little altered, close to open country and Ashton golf course. Like so many of the borough's pubs, it was built in the first half of the 19th century and was intended to last. The small cosy rooms make it very welcoming and the unpretentious tap room is traditional in every aspect. If you are hungry, try the home-made rag puddings – well worth it.
Q🌳◑🍴♣P

Oddfellows Arms
1-7 Alderley Street, Hurst (off King's Rd)
☀ 11-11; 12-10.30 Sun
☎ (0161) 330 3656 website: www.theoddies.com
Robinson's Hatters Mild, Best Bitter, Old Tom, seasonal beers Ⓗ
Street-corner terraced local, run by the same family since 1914, and an established *Guide* entry. A small hatch and screen lead to the fine polished wood of the bar with its stained glass; on the left are two small rooms, the tap and the 'Vestry'. The standing area in front of the bar has nooks and crannies. Adjoining the comfortable lounge is Tom's Room (no-smoking), named after the late licensee, displaying large prints of military aircraft. In summer

INDEPENDENT BREWERIES

Altrincham Altrincham
Bank Top Bolton
Holt Cheetham
Hydes Manchester
Lees Middleton Junction
Leyden Nangreaves
Marble Manchester
McGuinness Rochdale
Pictish Rochdale
Phoenix Heywood
Robinson's Stockport
Saddleworth Uppermill

BIRTLE

Pack Horse Inn
Elbut Lane
(N of B6222 at Jericho, opp. Bury Hospital) OS836125
☼ 11.30-11; 12-10.30 sun
☎ (0161) 764 3620
Lees GB Mild, Bitter, seasonal beers Ⓗ

Cosy, rural, stone pub dating from the 18th century; its olde-worlde interior is replete with horse brasses, grandfather clocks and copper kettles. The impressive iron firegrate was made at the Yewtree Ironworks, in Hollinwood. A derelict barn has been converted into a restaurant decorated with a large agricultural tableau, featuring a farm cart, milk churns and hop sacks. Meals served 12–9.30. A more modern conservatory allows drinkers and diners to enjoy views over adjoining fields. Two small snugs provide quieter areas for conversation. ♨️☀️◖&P

BOLTON

Bob's Smithy
1448 Chorley Old Road
(B6226 ½ mile from A58 ring road)
☼ 12-3 (not Mon), 4.30-11; 12-11 Sat; 12-10.30 Sun
☎ (01204) 842622
Draught Bass; Boddingtons Bitter; Taylor Best Bitter; Tetley Dark Mild, Bitter; guest beers Ⓗ

Cosy stone-built hostelry, on the edge of the moors, handy for walkers and visitors to Reebok Stadium. A genuine free house, run by friendly enterprising owners, the pub has been in existence for around 200 years, and is named after a regular, Bob the blacksmith, who used to work across the road. Guest beers are usually sourced from small independent breweries. ♨️☀️◖P

Hen & Chickens
143 Deansgate
(near bus station, off A676)
☼ 11.30-11; 7.30-10.30 Sun
☎ (01204) 389836
Greenalls Mild, Bitter; guest beers Ⓗ

Busy, friendly, town-centre local with a central bar, standing opposite the Post Office. It was originally known as the Higher Hen & Chickens as, until 1888, there was another pub of the same name lower down the street. Local CAMRA *Pub of the Year* 2000, it regularly stocks three changing guest beers; enter by the door to the right to see the guest beer pumps. Good value

lunchtime meals are supplemented by sandwiches available all day. ◖🍴

Hope & Anchor
747 Chorley Old Road (B6226)
☼ 3 (12 Sat)-11; 12-10.30 Sun
☎ (01204) 842650
Lees Bitter; Taylor Landlord; Tetley Mild, Bitter Ⓗ

Compact local, close to Doffcocker Lodge where a central bar serves two distinct snugs, which are used for different functions, including quizzes, darts, dominoes and family gatherings. Locals tend to cluster around the bar. The immediate area of Doffcocker is believed to have been so named from a Scot who, when crossing a nearby stream, carefully removed his socks or 'doffed his cockers'. ♨️☀️♣️P

Howcroft ☆
36 Pool Street (300 yds from Topp Way, A673)
☼ 12-11; 12-10.30 Sun
☎ (01204) 526814 website: www.beer-festival.co.uk
Taylor Landlord; Tetley Mild, Bitter; guest beers Ⓗ

Exceptional, unpretentious local, just outside the town centre; one of a dying breed of multi-roomed pubs, with lounge, snug, games room and conservatory, all served by a small central bar. It gained a full licence in 1957. A refurbishment in the 1980s won CAMRA's *Joe Goodwin* award for *Best Pub Conservation* – fitting since Joe was a local here for several years. It hosts regular folk/acoustic nights and a well-kept bowling green is for hire. The green is covered by a marquee for the October Bolton beer festival, run for charity. Good value food is available. The unofficial tap for nearby Bank Top Brewery, one of its beers is always stocked. ♨️☀️♣️P

King's Head
52-54 Junction Road, Deane (off A676, Wigan road)
☼ 12 (3.30 winter)-11; 12-10.30 Sun
☎ (01204) 62609
Moorhouses Pride of Pendle; Taylor Landlord; Tetley Mild, Bitter; guest beers Ⓗ

300-year-old, Grade II listed pub, adjacent to the Deane Clough Nature Trail; the area (Dene) was mentioned in the *Domesday Book*. The pub was refurbished in 1991 to provide three distinct drinking areas, the largest of which has York stone flooring and an authentic-looking range. All three areas are served by one long bar. A well-used Crown bowling green at the rear is available

INN BRIEF

ASHTON-UNDER-LYNE

Witchwood
152 Old Street
12-11; 12-10.30 Sun
John Smith's Bitter; Theakston XB; Wadworth 6X; guest beers Ⓗ
Lively, down-to-earth, no-nonsense bar with a good reputation as a live music venue.

ASPULL

New Inn
55-57 Ratcliffe Road
7-11; 12-10.30 Sun
Burtonwood Bitter; guest beer Ⓗ
Open-plan local, with two drinking areas and a real fire in the lounge. The upstairs function room lays on buffets on request.

ASTLEY

Cart & Horses
221 Manchester Road
12-11; 12-10.30 Sun
Holt Mild, Bitter Ⓗ
Impressive pub frontage, garden and a cobbled outside drinking area; a comfortable lounge and tap room. Food: 12-2, 4-6 daily.

ATHERTON

Atherton Arms
6 Tyldesley Road
12-11; 12-10.30 Sun
Holt Mild, Bitter Ⓗ
Spacious, town-centre pub: a lounge, tap room with snooker and pool tables and a function room. Occasional Karaoke is staged.

BREDBURY

Traveller's Call
402 Stockport Road West
11-11; 12-10.30 Sun
Lees Bitter Ⓗ
Lively, community pub, attracting all ages. Stockport's only Lees tied house brings variety to the local beer scene.

BURY

Arthur Inn
97 Bolton Road
11-11; 12-10.30 Sun
Porter Dark Mild, Bitter, Rossendale Ale, Sunshine Ⓗ
Welcoming local on the outskirts of town with cheap beer and a front room for non-smokers.

for hire, and supports five teams. No juke box, but piped music and TV underlie the buzz of conversation. A Bank Top beer is usually available. ✿◑▶♣P

Lord Clyde
109 Folds Road (A676)
✪ 11-11; 12-10.30 Sun
☎ (01204) 521705
Hydes Light, Dark Ⓟ
Friendly local within minutes' walk of the town centre. It consists of a small, L-shaped vault and a second vault behind the bar. The larger lounge houses a pool table and stages regular Karaoke and disco nights as part of an active social life. Children are welcome until 7pm. Weekly meetings of 'the Knights of the Golden Horn' are held at the pub – note the beautifully crafted certificates on the walls. ➳✿🏠♣P🍴

Olde Man & Scythe
6-8 Churchgate
✪ 11-11; 12-10.30 Sun
☎ (01204) 527267
website: www.manandscythe.co.uk
Boddingtons Bitter; Flowers Original; Greene King Old Speckled Hen; Holt Bitter; Wadworth 6X; guest beers Ⓗ
Reputedly the fourth oldest pub in Britain, whose barrel-vaulted cellar was probably built before 1200. The first record of the pub's existence was 1251; the present building dates from 1636. In 1651 the seventh Earl of Derby spent the night here before his execution in the market place outside for his part in the 1644 Bolton Massacre. A long bar area, with stone-flagged floor, is flanked by two side rooms. Known locally as the Cider House, for many years it was the only outlet for traditional cider in the town. It hosts a variety of events and entertainment. ⛺✿◑≈♣●

Spinning Mule
Unit 2, Nelson Square (off Bradshawgate)
✪ 11-11; 12-10.30 Sun
☎ (01204) 533339
Boddingtons Bitter; Courage Directors; Thwaites Mild; guest beers Ⓗ
Town-centre pub, newly built in 1998, in a very busy area with many pubs. This open-plan, split-level building in a modern Wetherspoon's style has a comfortable dining area. It hosts popular beer festivals (especially at Hallowe'en), with cheap beers. The former pub sign showed a mule (the animal) spinning around as though it had had a few drinks, rather than the Crompton's Mule (a revolutionary invention in cotton spinning which made Bolton famous throughout the world). The original artefact may be seen in the town's museum. The pub is always busy; it has a long bar and food is served all day. Q◑≈◑≠●

Varsity
37-41 Churchgate
✪ 11-11; 12-10.30 Sun
☎ (01204) 363987
Banks's Bitter; Marston's Pedigree Ⓗ
Spacious, modern pub opened by Banks's in 1999, on the site of the former Boar's Head, it is themed as a student pub with discounts often available in mid-week. Food is served all day, every day until 10pm. The split-level interior includes a no-smoking area. Being one of the few town-centre pubs with a garden makes it a very popular choice in summer. ✿◑占≈≠🍴

Dusty Miller
87 Crostons Road (B621/B6214 jct)
✪ 2 (12 Fri & Sat)-11; 12-10.30 Sun
☎ (0161) 764 1124
Moorhouses Black Cat, Premier, Pendle Witches Brew; guest beers Ⓗ
This is a proudly traditional local that caters for a mixed clientele. Its position at a busy main road junction makes parking difficult but it is well worth making the journey out of Bury to visit. One of the few Moorhouses tied pubs, it is divided into two rooms served by a central bar. It also boasts a covered courtyard and outdoor seating in summer. 🍺☻

Old Blue Bell
2 Bell Lane (B621/B622 jct)
✪ 12-11; 12-10.30 Sun
☎ (0161) 761 3674
Holt Mild, Bitter Ⓗ
Prominent, solidly-built pub on a busy road junction. Its traditional exterior is matched by the interior where, with several rooms, there is space to be found even when the pub is busy. Comfortable and welcoming, it hosts live music Sat afternoon, Thu and Sun eves. Well-behaved children are welcome until 6pm. Q🍺☻♣

Blue Bell
840 Manchester Road
11.30-11; 12-10.30 Sun
Holt Mild, Bitter Ⓗ
Imposing, traditional local whose three rooms include a vault and a comfortable lounge.

CHEADLE HULME
Church
90 Ravenoak Road
11-11; 12-10.30 Sun
Robinson's Hatters Mild, Old Stockport, Best Bitter Ⓗ
Attractive, cottage-style pub where both lounges feature real fires. It also boasts a small, traditional vault. No food Sun eve.

DIDSBURY
Fletcher Moss
1 William Street
12-11; 12-10.30 Sun
Hydes Mild, Bitter, Jekyll's Gold Ⓗ
One of the few pubs in Didsbury that retains a local feel and avoids being a food-driven operation.

GATLEY
Horse & Farrier
144 Gatley Road
11.30-11; 12-10.30 Sun
Hydes Light, Bitter, Jekyll's Gold Ⓗ
Multi-roomed, high-ceilinged coaching inn with ornate glass screens between some of the rooms, plus a lunchtime restaurant.

HYDE
White Hart
47 Old Road, Newton
11.30-11; 12-10.30 Sun
Robinson's Hatters Mild, Best Bitter Ⓗ
Warm, friendly local, almost unchanged, with a multi-room layout around a central bar. Deservedly popular.

KITT GREEN
Latham House Inn
Latham Lane
2 (1 Sat)-11; 12-10.30 Sun
Lees Bitter; Tetley Dark Mild Ⓗ
Photos of old Wigan decorate this popular local where original architraves surround the doors. Children are welcome. Garden.

Rose & Crown
36 Manchester Old Road
⊛ 12-3, 5-11; 12-11 Thu-Sat; 12-10.30 Sun
☎ (0161) 764 6461
Beer range varies Ⓗ
Attractive, traditional end-of-terrace pub, offering up to eight real ales. One large room is divided into distinct drinking areas where no juke box will distract you from the pleasures of imbibing; The TV only comes on for sport. Very much a community pub, it supports a number of charities as well as Bury FC. Good value lunches are available weekdays. It stocks an ever-increasing range of malt whiskies, wine and continental bottled beer. ◑⊖

CASTLETON

Blue Pits Inn
842 Manchester Road (A664)
⊛ 12-4 (5 Fri & Sat), 7.30-11; 12-5, 7-10.30 Sun
☎ (01706) 632151
Lees GB Mild, Bitter Ⓗ
Blue Pits was a tiny hamlet incorporated into Castleton in the mid-19th century. Early records are unclear, but the building certainly pre-dates the railway to which it later belonged. As well as being the social centre of Blue Pits, the cellar served as the morgue (inquests were held upstairs). With such a history, ghost stories are not surprising. There are three distinct drinking areas: a very busy tap room fielding strong darts and quiz teams, a comfortable back lounge and a bar area, free from juke box and pool tables. Note the wonderful Lees Brewery tile set outside. 🏠⇌♣P

CHEETHAM

Queen's Arms
6 Honey Street (E of A665, S of A6010 jct)
⊛ 12-4; 12-10.30 Sun
☎ (0161) 834 4239
Phoenix Bantam; Taylor Landlord; guest beers Ⓗ
Popular free house on the northern fringe of Manchester's Northern Quarter. Original Empress Brewery tiles cover the left façade; the right is a modern extension, which added a second room. The many real ales (five or six guests) are augmented by Belgian bottled and draught beers and an imaginative menu. Families are welcome, with a play area in the large garden which also features a barbecue and a panoramic view of Manchester across the Irk Valley. Pinball wizards are attracted by the regular turnover of machines.
🏠🐕⊛◑⇌(Victoria) ⊖♣

CHORLTON-CUM-HARDY

Beech Inn
72 Beech Road
⊛ 11-11; 12-10.30 Sun
☎ (0161) 881 1180
Boddingtons Bitter; Flowers Original; Taylor Best Bitter, Landlord; Tetley Dark Mild; Whitbread Trophy Ⓗ
Thriving, three-roomed pub, with a simple bar, just off the village green. Free from food, music or other gimmicks, it is something of an oasis, as the rest of Beech Road continues the trend toward the café-bar ethic. Those that embrace both styles

can drink at the Beech and eat down the road. Q⊛⊟♣

Marble Beer House
57 Manchester Road
⊛ 12-11; 12-10.30 Sun
☎ (0161) 881 9206
Marble Chorlton Bitter, N/4 Bitter, Cloudy Marble, Uncut Amber, Old Lag; guest beers Ⓗ
Southern cousin of the Marble Arch in Manchester's Northern Quarter, but very different in style, this former shop has been converted into a continental-style café-bar with pavement seating. Always serving the current range of Marble organic beers (which are not fined and are thus suitable for vegetarians), a wide range of Belgian and German bottled beers are also stocked. It offers no food, other than nibbly snacks, but there are plenty of restaurants nearby.
Q♣⊛

COMPSTALL

Andrew Arms
George Street
⊛ 11.30-11; 12-10.30 Sun
☎ (0161) 427 2281
Robinson's Hatters Mild, Best Bitter Ⓗ
Detached stone pub in a quiet village, off the main road, close to the Etherow Nature Reserve with wildlife and river valley woodland walks. The pub has been a deserved continuous entry in this *Guide* since the mid-1970s. it has a comfortable lounge and a small traditional games room, a true local, it caters for all tastes. 🏠⊛◑♣P

CORNBROOK

Hope Inn
297 Chester Road
⊛ 11-5, 8-11; 12-5, 7-10.30 Sun
☎ (0161) 848 0038
Hydes' Light, Bitter, seasonal beers Ⓗ
Still surviving despite nearby road developments and the encroachment of new flats extending out of the city centre. The Hope is a rarity – one of the few remaining examples of a Manchester 'stand up'. A local that has a TV but lots of conversation, it is a 15-minute walk from both Old Trafford cricket and football grounds – and arguably the best pint close to either. Well worth the 20-minute walk from the Castlefield end of the city centre.
⇌(Deansgate) ⊖(G.Mex) ♣⊟

DAISY HILL

Rose Hill Tavern
321 Leigh Road, Westhoughton (B5235)
⊛ 12-11; 12-10.30 Sun
☎ (01942) 815776 e-mail: keubugpub@aol.com
Holt Mild, Bitter Ⓗ
Large, welcoming pub, now opened out, but retaining the outline of the old room plan, with two rooms taken up by games of all sorts. Often referred to by the locals as the Bug, since an orphanage (the Bug House) was demolished to make way for the pub. It was built in 1889, a year after the railway came to the village. It was originally owned by the Oldfield Brewery of Poolstock, Wigan, whose crest can be seen over the door.
⊛⇌P

DELPH

Royal Oak (Th'heights)
Broad Lane, Heights (1 mile above Denshaw Road) OS982090
☼ 7-11; 12-4, 7-10.30 Sun
☎ (01457) 874460
e-mail: michael.royaloak@zoom.co.uk
Boddingtons Bitter; Coach House Gunpowder Strong Mild; guest beers H

Isolated, 250-year-old stone pub on a packhorse route, overlooking the Tame Valley; set in a popular walking area, it offers outstanding views of the local countryside. The pub, which once had its own brewhouse, now comprises a cosy bay and three rooms, each with an open fire. The refurbished side room features a hand-carved stone fireplace while the comfortable snug has exposed beams and old photos of the pub. Good home-cooked food (Fri–Sun eve) often features home-bred pork and beef. The house beer is brewed by Moorhouses. ♨Q❄🌓P

DENTON

Lowes Arms
301 Hyde Road
☼ 12-3, 5-11; 12-10.30 Sun
☎ (0161) 336 3069
Boddingtons Bitter; guest beers H

The Lowes, on the main Hyde-Denton road, is an imposing former home-brew pub from the turn of the 19th century. Due to careful management, it is now a thriving hospitable local where up to four guest beers always come from independent breweries. The lounge is comfortable, with a pleasant dining area for the good value meals that are served. The games room is spacious and traditional. Occasional live music is performed. Well worth a visit.
❄🌓 ⚲⇌ (Hyde Central) ♣P

DIGGLE

Diggle Hotel
Station Houses (1/2 mile off A670) OS011081
☼ 12-3, 5-11; 12-11 Sat; 12-3, 5-10.30 Sun
☎ (01457) 872741
e-mail: dawn@digglehotel.freeserve.co.uk
Boddingtons Bitter; Taylor Golden Best, Landlord; Wadworth 6X H

Family-run stone pub in a pleasant hamlet close to the recently reopened Standedge canal tunnel under the Pennines. Originally built as a merchant's house in 1789, it became an ale house and general store on the construction of the nearby railway tunnel in 1834. Set in a picturesque area, with fine views of the surrounding Saddleworth countryside, this makes a convenient base in a popular walking area. The pub comprises a bar area and two rooms, with the accent on home-cooked food (served all day Sat). ❄⇌🌓P

DOBCROSS

Navigation
Wool Road (A670)
☼ 11.30-3, 5-11; 11.30-11 Sat; 12-10.30 Sun
☎ (01457) 872418
Tetley Bitter; Theakston Mild; guest beers H

Next to the Huddersfield Narrow Canal, this stone pub was built in 1806 to slake the thirsts of the navvies cutting the Standedge tunnel under the Pennines. The tunnel was recently reopened and boat trips through it are available. The open-plan bar area is a shrine to brass band music – live concerts are staged Sun afternoons in summer, and it is a popular venue for the Whit Friday brass band contest. A comprehensive menu of home-cooked food includes the 'navigation trencher' mixed grill. Stoelschijven (a Danish board game) is played Mon eve.
❄🌓▲♣P

Swan Inn (Top House)
The Square
☼ 12-3, 5-11; 12-3, 7-10.30 Sun
☎ (01457) 873451
Moorhouses Pendle Witches Brew; Phoenix Best Bitter, Thirsty Moon, Wobbly Bob, seasonal beers; Theakston Mild, Best Bitter H

This village local, circa 1765, was built for the Wrigley family of chewing gum fame, but part of the building was later used as a police court and cells. Overlooking the attractive village square, the pub has been well renovated, with flagged floors and three distinct drinking areas, plus a characterful function room upstairs which caters for 80 people. It gets busy during local events such as the Whit Friday brass band contest and the August Rushcart Festival. Good value home-cooked food includes Indian dishes (no food Sun eve).
♨Q❄🌓⌖

ECCLES

Lamb Hotel ☆
33 Regent Street (A57, by Metrolink terminus)
☼ 11-11; 12-4, 7-10.30 Sun
☎ (0161) 789 3882
Holt Mild, Bitter H

Built 1906, this is probably the best and least altered example of Holt's high Edwardian style (Grade II listed). From its imposing exterior, to the sumptuous interior of full-height mahogany bar, tiled lobby and staircase, and the adjoining snug, vault and lounge, it exudes an air of quality and grandeur. The jewel in the crown lies to the rear – a full-sized billiard table in its own purpose-built room, a highly revered and well-used facility. Eccles pubs have seen much competition lately, with the arrival of the tram and Wetherspoon's. The Lamb just seems to rise above it all.
Q⚲⇌☉♣P

White Lion
133 Liverpool Road
☼ 11-11; 12-10.30 Sun
☎ (0161) 707 5184
Holt Mild, Bitter H

This is still one of the quieter pubs in Eccles (and without the historical notoriety of some) – except perhaps during the popular Fri eve singalongs. A street-corner local, first licensed in 1864 as a beer house, having previously been a shop at the end of a row of cottages; it was leased by Edward Holt in 1893 and bought outright in 1898. Both the front lounge and the side vault have perimeter seating, and there is a quieter, easily overlooked snug at the back.
Q⚲⇌ (Eccles/Patricroft) ♣

EGERTON

Cross Guns
Blackburn Road (A666, northern outskirts of Bolton)
✪ 12-11; 12-10.30 Sun
☎ (01204) 303341
Bank Top Brydge Bitter; Boddingtons Bitter; guest beers Ⓗ
A recent refurbishment has enhanced this warm, cosy and comfortable late Georgian pub on the edge of a moorland village. Comprising a small pool room, a TV corner and a larger dining area, serving good quality home-cooked meals, it is popular with locals and visitors. A pavement area allows for outside drinking in summer.
🏨✿◑P⅊

FALLOWFIELD

Friendship Inn
353 Wilmslow Road
✪ 11.30-11; 12-10.30 Sun
☎ (0161) 224 5758
Hydes Light, Bitter, Jekyll's Gold, seasonal beers Ⓗ
Popular main road pub, a traditional local at the heart of a buzzing student area of café bars and fast food joints. A recent successful refurbishment has left a horseshoe-shaped bar which serves one large open-plan area, attracting a mixed clientele of locals and students. The patio is popular in summer and affords an excellent view of what is allegedly the busiest bus route in Europe. The large-screen TVs can be intrusive on football nights. A reliable outlet for Hydes' high quality range of seasonal beers; food serving times vary.
✿◑♣P

FARNWORTH

Britannia
34 King Street (opp. bus station and market, off A6053)
✪ 11-11; 12-10.30 Sun
☎ (01204) 571629
Moorhouses Premier; Whitbread Trophy Ⓗ
Typical, lively, town-centre pub which has a small, recently refurbished lounge area (note the brass ornaments) and a larger, basic vault; the central bar serves both areas. The pub hosts two popular mini beer festivals (May and Aug bank holiday weekends) with around six beers each session, in a specially-built (covered) outside bar. The lunches are good and well priced – worth trying. ✿◑⊟≉♣

FLIXTON

Church Inn
34 Church Road (B5123, near station)
✪ 11-11; 12-10.30 Sun
☎ (0161) 748 2158
Cains Bitter; Greenalls Mild, Bitter; Taylor Landlord Ⓗ
Situated in the old part of Flixton, and a handy five-minute walk from the railway station, this is a former schoolhouse and courtroom. What perhaps appears to be an unpromising pub externally, is soon dispelled on entering. The pub has various seating areas and is comfortably furnished. Well run by the long-standing landlord, it is a rare outlet for traditional mild – worth a visit in itself. ✿◑▶≉P

GATLEY ✦

Gothic Bar
61 Church Road
✪ 12-11; 12-10.30 Sun
☎ (0161) 491 1966
Cains Mild, Bitter, FA, seasonal beers; guest beers Ⓗ
Gothic Bar dates back to 1841, when it was built as a Methodist chapel following a visit to the village by Thomas Butler, a famous missionary. It remained a chapel for the next 130 years, prior to becoming Greater Manchester's first Cains' tied pub. The ecclesiastical exterior hides a cosy single bar, with an upstairs gallery. A raised seating area is used for weekday meals; food is home-cooked with daily specials and a vegetarian option always available. Entertainment includes a monthly theme night. The pub is situated close to the pretty village green. ◑≉♣●

GOLBORNE

Railway
131 High Street
✪ 12 (11 Sat)-11; 12-10.30 Sun
☎ (01942) 728202
Greene King IPA; Sarah's Hophouse Mild, Bitter, Black Mamba Mild, Chocolate Stout; Theakston Mild Ⓗ
Popular pub, on the edge of the town centre, which provides its own beers from the brewery in the car park. A long, comfortable lounge hosts live music Fri eve. Beer festivals are staged and brewery trips are always available. Amber and Hop To It alternate on the bar due to congested space. This biker-friendly pub is a stop on regular Sunday bike runs. The brewery dray is a VW trike. It is a good place to stay when touring the north-west. A room at the side of the bar houses pool and darts. ⊨✿♣P▯

GREENFIELD

King William IV
134 Chew Valley Road (A669/Ladhill Lane jct)
✪ 11.30-11; 12-10.30 Sun
☎ (01457) 873933
Draught Bass; Highgate Dark; Tetley Bitter; Worthington Bitter; guest beers Ⓗ
Detached, cosy local in the village centre, comprising a central bar area and two small rooms. A cobbled forecourt provides an outdoor area with wooden benches. At the crossroads of old packhorse routes, it is now the centre of village life, participating in the annual beer walk, Rushcart Festival (Aug) and hosting the Whit Friday brass band contest, so important in Saddleworth. Traditional food is served all day until 7.30pm. Handy for walks over the Saddleworth hills. ✿◑▶≉♣P

Railway
11 Shaw Hall Bank Road (opp. station)
✪ 5 (12 Fri & Sat)-11; 12-10.30 Sun
☎ (01457) 872307
John Smith's Bitter; Taylor Landlord; guest beers Ⓗ
Friendly, no-frills village local, in a stone terrace, with a central bar and games area. The public bar displays an interesting collection of old Saddleworth photos. Located in a picturesque area, close to the recently reopened Huddersfield Narrow Canal, it provides a good base for walking, rock climbing and other outdoor pursuits.

Live music, including Cajun, R&B and jazz is performed Thu and Fri eves and Sun afternoons. Accommodation is in four reasonably priced, well-furbished bedrooms, two affording good views over Chew Valley. ﾑﾑﾑﾑﾑﾑﾑﾑﾑﾑ

GUIDE BRIDGE

Boundary
2 Audenshaw Road
☼ 11-11; 12-10.30 Sun
☎ (0161) 330 1677
Phoenix Best Bitter; guest beers H
Very busy, friendly pub on a main road junction, handily placed for Guide Bridge railway station across the road and next to the Ashton Canal. Good value meals are a feature at the pub, which usually hosts an annual beer festival in June. All in all, an enterprising pub doing an extremely good job. ◑ᎯᎯᎯᎯᎯ P

HALE

Railway
128-130 Ashley Road (opp. station)
☼ 11-11; 12-10.30 Sun
☎ (0161) 941 5367
Robinson's Hatters Mild; Hartleys XB, Best Bitter, seasonal beers H
Reputedly haunted, but friendly and unspoilt, this 1930s multi-roomed local has a relaxed atmosphere. The side rooms are often quiet, with good conversaton. The original wood panelling has been retained. The pub forms a traditional focal point for this small commuter village, now merged into Altrincham. No food Sun.
Q❀◑ᎯᎯᎯ (Altrincham) ⊖♣

HAWKSHAW

Red Lion
81 Ramsbottom Road (A676) OS753150
☼ 12-3, 6-11; 12-10.30 Sun
☎ (01204) 856600
Jennings Bitter, Cumberland Ale; guest beer H
Attractive, stone pub, nestling in a picturesque village where you will find a single large room, friendly locals and an excellent menu. Very popular with diners, you can choose to eat either in the pub or the adjacent restaurant, which offers an extensive range of freshly-prepared delights. Meals are served all day Sun. The pub is on the very outskirts of Bury, but its popularity with locals and those from further afield proves that it is well worth seeking out. ﾑ◑●

HEATON CHAPEL

Hind's Head
Manchester Road (A626)
☼ 11.30-11; 12-10.30 Sun
☎ (0161) 431 9301
Fuller's London Pride; Marston's Pedigree; John Smith's Bitter; Taylor Landlord; Thwaites Bitter; guest beer H
Recently built from reclaimed materials, this pub looks far older than it is. Set back from the main road, with a large garden and patio, inside a comfortable multi-level single room is served from a long bar. A conservatory on the pub's south side is used as a dining area, but most of the pub is

dedicated to drinking, and sales of its six cask ales have grown continuously, with guest beers changing fortnightly. Featured in CAMRA's *Good Pub Food*, inexpensive food includes an eclectic range of daily specials, equalled by its wine list. Q❀◑ᎯᎯ P

HEATON MERSEY

Griffin
552 Didsbury Road (A5145)
☼ 12-11; 12-10.30 Sun
☎ (0161) 443 4077
Holt Mild, Bitter H
Always busy, and deservedly so, this main road establishment is dominated by the exquisite Victorian mahogany and etched glass bar which, years ago, was saved from destruction by a petition to the brewery from the regulars. It was then faithfully replicated in the spacious lounge extension. The multi-roomed layout is an integral part of the pub's character, with areas to suit all tastes, including a large, well-used, no-smoking room. A varied choice of reasonably priced lunches is a big attraction, especially the pensioners' specials. A true Holt's gem. ❀◑Ꭿ (E Didsbury) P⅟

HEATON NORRIS

Moss Rose
63 Didsbury Road
☼ 11.30-11; 12-10.30 Sun
☎ (0161) 432 5168
Hydes Light, Bitter P
The phrase 'don't judge a book by its cover' could have been coined for the Moss Rose. Outwardly, an unpromising example of modern pub design, once inside you will find a comfortable, welcoming and down-to-earth local. There is a large vault, displaying an impressive array of sports trophies, and an extensive lounge. Popular with all ages, local dedication to cask beer is shown by the fact that the pub boasts separate cellars for mild and bitter. Food is confined to weekday lunchtime snacks. ᎯᎯ P☐

Nursery ☆
Green Lane (off Wellington Road North, A6)
☼ 11.30-3, 5.30-11; 11.30-11 Sat; 12-10.30 Sun
☎ (0161) 432 2044
Hydes Mild, Bitter, P **Jekyll's Gold, seasonal beers** H
Hidden away down a cobbled street, in a pleasant conservation area, this 1930s house was local CAMRA *Pub of the Year* 2001. The lounge, with its superb light oak panelling, serves as a dining room at lunchtime. There is also a spacious lobby, a smoke room to the rear of the bar, a busy vault (reached by a separate side entrance), and upstairs is another large room. At the rear of the pub, an immaculate bowling green plays host to a number of teams. The pub serves excellent food and children are welcome if dining. ❀◑ᎯᎯ P☐

HEYWOOD

Wishing Well
89 York Street (A58)
☼ 12-11; 12-10.30 Sun
☎ (01706) 620923
Moorhouses Premier, Pendle Witches Brew; Tetley Bitter; guest beers H

Very popular free house in the centre of Heywood, that is an oasis for local real ale drinkers. There are several comfortable drinking areas to choose from, as you ponder the extensive beer list. Local brewers, Phoenix, are a particular favourite, as is Moorhouses of Burnley. The landlord has been the recipient of many *Best-Kept Cellar* awards, as is evident in the quality of his beer. The pub is easily accessible by public transport, with the frequent Bury–Rochdale buses stopping right outside.
⊄P

HIGH LANE

Royal Oak
Buxton Road (A6)
✪ 12-3, 5.30-11; 12-11 Sat & summer; 12-10.30 Sun
☎ (01663) 762380
Burtonwood Bitter; guest beer Ⓗ
The Royal Oak is a well-appointed pub standing on a busy main road. It has a pleasing exterior with a good garden and children's play area. Although open plan, the pub has three distinct drinking areas, one of which is used for games. There is usually live entertainment on Fri eve. Burtonwood beer makes a welcome addition to the usual range offered in the area. Eve meals finish early.
🏠⊄♣P

HORWICH

Crown Hotel
1 Chorley New Road (A673/B6226 jct)
✪ 11-11; 12-10.30 Sun
☎ (01204) 690926
Holt Mild, Bitter Ⓗ
Imposing pub on the edge of town – convenient for the Reebok Stadium. A spacious, well-furnished drinking area surrounds the central bar, and to the rear is a vault housing a pool table. All ages are catered for and it is particularly popular with locals who provide their own, very popular, Sun eve singalongs. The lunches represent good value. A superb backcloth is provided by local beauty spot, Rivington Pike, where a beacon was lit to announce the arrival of the Armada in 1588.
🏠🏌️🏠⊄🏠♣P

HYDE ❋

Sportsman Inn
57 Mottram Road
✪ 11-11; 12-10.30 Sun
☎ (0161) 368 5000
Plassey Bitter; Taylor Landlord; Whim Magic Mushroom Mild, Hartington Bitter; guest beer Ⓗ
Brilliant, spacious local that has risen from the ashes to become a thriving hub of the community. Gradually renovated and decorated, with the floors stripped back to bare boards and the original tiling restored, it is a pleasure to sit on the original bench seating and enjoy good beer. The pub has three pleasant rooms, plus an upstairs room. Games feature strongly, including snooker and log-end darts. The Sportsman was a recent regional CAMRA *Pub of the Year*.
🏠Q🏠⊄🏠➡(Newton/Central) ♣🏠P🏠

White Lion
7 Market Place
✪ 11-11; 11-5, 7-11 Sat; 12-4, 8-10.30 Sun
☎ (0161) 368 2948
Robinson's Hatters Mild, Best Bitter, Old Tom Ⓗ
This pub is a genuine market place local, with no pretensions to be anything else, and it is all the better for that. All types and ages rub shoulders here, particularly on market days when it is usually very busy. It is a spacious two-roomed pub that boasts a noteworthy long bar in the tap room. Another feature is the impromptu singalongs that often take place.
⊄🏠(Central) ♣

INCE IN MAKERFIELD

Black Diamond
243 Warrington Road, Lower Ince
✪ 12-2 (not Mon), 5-11 (12-11 summer); 12-10.30 Sun
☎ (01942) 237846
John Smith's Bitter; Theakston Mild, Cool Cask; guest beer Ⓗ
Previously known as the Ince Hall Hotel, but has now inherited its nickname; this is a surprisingly large pub with lots of nooks and crannies and a pool room on a mezzanine floor. The open fire dominates the atmosphere and the bare brick decor is very effective. The well-appointed dining-room is a recent addition. The large-screen TV is reserved for major sporting events. A function room is upstairs.
🏠⊄🏠➡♣

KEARSLEY

Clock Face
63 Old Hall Street
(off A5082/A6053 jct)
✪ 5 (3 Fri; 12 Sat)-11; 12-4.30, 7-10.30 Sun
☎ (01204) 400292
Holt Mild, Bitter Ⓗ
In a quiet area off a busy road junction, this is a real gem. Formerly serving the mining community, it takes its name from a clock, originally on the front of an adjacent cottage, but now gracing the pub's façade. The interior reflects the pub's humble origins: the large vault is furnished with basic wooden bench seating while the front snug is a small room with a bookcase full of novels. The larger back room is the quietest, where the only sound is conversation. The clientele is mainly mature, local drinkers.
🏠Q🏠♣

LEIGH

Musketeer
15 Lord Street
✪ 11-11; 12-3, 7-10.30 Sun
☎ (01942) 701143
Boddingtons Bitter; Greenalls Mild; guest beers Ⓗ
One of the few town-centre locals left, a large open-plan lounge divided into three drinking areas. The lounge houses a vast collection of commemorative pit plates from the Lancashire coalfield; the tap room has its own street entrance and local Rugby League teams' pictures decorate the walls. Handy for town-centre shops, no food is served Sun.
⊄🏠♣

Nevison

96b Plank Lane (A578, 1 mile W of centre)
✪ 12-11; 12-10.30 Sun
☎ (01942) 671394

Bateman XB; Robinson's Hatters Mild, Best Bitter; Tetley Bitter; guest beers ⓗ

Named after the highwayman, William Nevison (1639–84), the pub is situated close to the Plank Lane swingbridge on the Leigh branch of the Leeds–Liverpool Canal. Once surrounded by the Bikershaw Colliery it now stands in open land. The interior is very mixed: the large vault, with pool table, is quite new compared to the front parlour, where wood and ornaments abound. The lounge bar leads to the garden. Children are allowed in until 9pm. Mon night is for darts and dominoes. Meals served 12–7.30 (no food Mon).
♨ ⑂ ❀ ◑ ◗ ♣ P

LITTLEBOROUGH

Red Lion Hotel

6 Halifax Road (A58, just under railway arch)
✪ 12 (3 Mon-Thu)-11; 12-10.30 Sun
☎ (01706) 378195

Boddingtons Bitter; Lees Bitter; Taylor Landlord; guest beers ⓗ

This stone free house stands between railway and canal. Originally a farmhouse, it was first licensed in 1760. Traditionally run, by a licensee of 20 years standing, it provides very good value in the five rooms. The regular beers are supplemented by a house beer from Phoenix and four guests, including a mild. Real cider, plus a range of Belgian and foreign beers (bottled and draught) help to satisfy the wide cross-section of clientele the pub attracts. Traditional music is performed Sun eve.
♨ Q ◑ ◻ ❦ ♣ ⬧ ◑ P ⑂

LONGSIGHT

Sir Edwin Chadwick

587 Stockport Road (A6, near A6010 jct)
✪ 11-11; 12-10.30 Sun
☎ (0161) 256 2806

Boddingtons Bitter; Shepherd Neame Spitfire; Theakston Best Bitter; guest beers ⓗ

Successful Wetherspoon's conversion of a former shop into a thriving community pub. A beacon of quality in this inner city area, the pub is popular with all ages. It boasts a patio to the front and a rear garden. The licensee endeavours to keep two guest beers available, and participates in all Wetherspoon's beer festivals. Named after a local who rose to prominence by introducing some of Britain's earliest public health legislation, it breaks the mould by having no circuit drinkers, no dress code and no door staff. Q ❀ ◑ ◗ ⚤ ⑂ ●

LOWTON (LANE HEAD)

Red Lion

324 Newton Road
✪ 12-11; 12-10.30 Sun
☎ (01942) 671429

Greenalls Mild, Bitter; Marston's Pedigree; guest beers ⓗ

Large, popular local, catering for all ages, including varied sports enthusiasts. Its

situation, just off the A580, between Manchester and Liverpool, makes it a good base for touring the area; local attractions include Haydock Park and Penington Country Park. The pub is divided into three lounge areas: the main bar has a raised seating area, with a lounge/dining room at the side. A smaller lounge leads to the garden and bowling green. It hosts occasional 'retro' discos and a friendly quiz.
❀ ⑂ ◑ ◗ ◻ ♣ P

LOWTON (ST LUKES)

Hare & Hounds

1 Golborne Road
✪ 11-11; 12-10.30 Sun
☎ (01942) 728387

Tetley Mild, Bitter; guest beers ⓗ

Large, popular local, which has undergone several renovations in its long history, the most recent addition being a children's play room with ball pit, and a no-smoking area. The rest of the pub is served from a horseshoe bar; choose from a low-beamed tap room, the lounge, or a second lounge on a lower level, which is also used as a dining area. During excavation of this lounge the original pub well was discovered. Meals, from a fixed menu and a specials board, are served 11–9.30. ☞ ❀ ◑ ◗ ♣ P ⑂

MANCHESTER CITY CENTRE ❉

Bar Fringe

8 Swan Street (N of A665/A62 jct)
✪ 12-11; 12-10.30 Sun
☎ (0161) 835 3815

Beer range varies ⓗ

Styled as a 'unique Belgian Brown Bar' it is, for many, the hub of the Northern Quarter cluster of pubs. Animated by an energetic licensee, it specialises in wheat, fruit and other beers, draught and bottled, from the Low Countries. But the Fringe also has a trio of handpumps dispensing British real ales, one of which is always a guest from Bank Top. Hot and cold food is available from 12–7. Not a pub for the faint-hearted or reclusive, but a firm favourite with its regulars. ❀ ◑ ◗ ⇌ (Victoria) ⊖ (Market St)

Beer House

6 Angel Street
✪ 11.30-11; 12-10.30 Sun
☎ (0161) 839 7019

John Smith's Bitter; Taylor Landlord; guest beers ⓗ

Extremely popular ale house, close to the Northern Quarter of the city. The single entrance brings you into the basic, open aspect pub, where the bar boasts up to 15 handpumps. A huge blackboard lists all the ales and foreign, draught beers available, including a guest mild. The upstairs function room has exposed brickwork and is the venue for the pub's numerous beerfests. The menu features a wide range of good value lunches, with eve meals just on Thu (5–8). Q ❀ ◑ ◻ ⇌ (Victoria) ⊖ ♣ ⬧

Castle

66 Oldham Street (near A62/A665 jct)
✪ 12-11; 12-10.30 Sun
☎ (0161) 236 2945 e-mail: thecastlepub@aol.com

Robinson's Hatters Mild, Old Stockport, Hartleys XB, Best Bitter, Frederics, Old Tom, seasonal beer ⓗ

A superb tiled exterior greets the visitor;

inside, the front bar is also clad in period sculpted tiling. This bustling front room feeds a small, far quieter snug, while further back a concert/games room houses darts, table football, pool and pinball machine. The back room occasionally hosts live bands for gigs and warm-ups. Following the Euro '96 football championships, the pub has established a rapport with the Czech Republic in running tours to that country. This 18th-century Grade II listed building is unique within the Robinson's estate, in having all seven ales on sale all year round.
Q ⊞≈ (Piccadilly/Victoria) ⊖ (Piccadilly Gdns) ♣

City Arms
48 Kennedy Street
✪ 11.30-11, 11.30-3, 7-11 Sat; closed Sun
Tetley Bitter; guest beers Ⓗ
Former Festival Ale House, surviving (at the time of writing) unchanged under Punch Taverns' ownership but soon to have a new Wetherspoon's as a neighbour. With a listed exterior (and partly listed interior), situated in the heart of Manchester's financial centre, the City is at its busiest weekday lunchtimes when the suits come in for food – all simple stuff but done well and served quickly. The beer range changes regularly and quickly (usually six guests) and the bar staff are happy to make recommendations.
◖≈ (Oxford Rd) ⊖ (St Peters Sq)

Grey Horse
80 Portland Street
✪ 11-11; 12-10.30 Sun
☎ (0161) 236 1874
Hydes Mild, Bitter, Jekyll's Gold Ⓗ
One of three classic city-centre pubs occupying an early Victorian terrace (the others being the Circus Tavern and the Old Monkey, both worth a visit), this much-loved haunt is now back to its best. Just one compact room, the pub is ideal for a drink and a chat, and makes a welcome refuge from the bustle of Portland Street. It is an ideal port of call for visitors to Chinatown which occupies the blocks to the rear.
≈ (Piccadilly) ⊖ (Piccadilly Gdns)

Jolly Angler
47 Ducie Street (behind Piccadilly Station)
✪ 12-3, 5.30-11; 11-11 Sat; 12-4, 8-10.30 Sun
☎ (0161) 236 5307
Hydes Mild, Bitter, seasonal beers Ⓗ
Acquired by Hydes in 1885, this is the second oldest house in their tied estate. In a

somewhat remote location, the Angler maintains a loyal following from far and wide. It has two rooms; one heated by a coal fire, the other is a touch more spartan, complete with a disused juke box. A recent redecoration has removed much of the pub's former Irish character, but occasional Irish music sessions are a feature. The bar is the life and soul of the place with often lively conversation.
🏠≈ (Piccadilly) ⊖ ♣ ●

Lass o'Gowrie
36 Charles Street
✪ 11-11; 12-10.30 Sun
☎ (0161) 273 6932
Boddingtons Bitter; Lass o'Gowrie 42; Marston's Pedigree; guest beers Ⓗ
Famous Whitbread brew-pub, boasting a justifiably-praised authentic tiled exterior. The bare-boarded interior is in ale house style, though no longer branded as a Hogshead; it retains an attractive snug and the malt extract brewery can be viewed through glass panels. Beloved of generations of students, due to its proximity to Manchester Metropolitan University, it also draws custom from the nearby BBC. Good value food is served until 6pm. An interesting selection of guest ales complements the reformulated house beers. A range of Belgian bottled beers is also stocked.
◖&≈ (Oxford Rd) ● ⤫

Marble Arch
73 Rochdale Road (300 yards from A664/A665 jct)
✪ 11.30 (12 Sat)-11; closed Sun
☎ (0161) 832 5914
Marble N/4 Bitter, Cloudy Marble, Uncut Amber, The Old Lag, Chocolate Heavy; guest beers Ⓗ
Built in 1888 as one of the first tied houses of McKenna's Harpurhey Brewery (1868–1903), it is the best preserved of several of their premises in Manchester's Northern Quarter. Notable features include a polished granite exterior, green and brown tiling within, with a notorious sloping mosaic following the gradient of Gould Street. A well-established free house, the Marble first reinvented itself as a brew-pub, then embraced organic (and now fully vegan) brewing. View the brewery from the rear tap room. Meals are served 11.30–10 (8 Fri) and 12–4 Sat.
◖▶≈ (Victoria) ⊖

MANCHESTER CITY CENTRE
Britons Protection ☆
50 Great Bridgwater Street
11-11; 12-10.30 Sun
Jennings Bitter; Robinson's Best Bitter; Tetley Bitter; guest beer Ⓗ
Historic pub; many original features remain in the rear rooms. Good lunchtime food, and a large selection of whiskies, bourbons and wine are on offer.

Hare & Hounds ☆
46 Shudehill
11-11; 12-10.30 Sun
Holt Bitter; Tetley Bitter Ⓗ
Classic tiled Grade II listed pub, drawing a mature, lively clientele who enjoy piano singalongs.

Paddy's Goose
29 Bloom Street
11-11; 12-10.30 Sun
Lees Bitter; Robinson's Best Bitter; Taylor Landlord; Theakston Best Bitter Ⓗ
Situated in Manchester's 'gay village' this single-roomed pub serves a mixed clientele.

Ox
71 Liverpool Road
11-11; 12-10.30 Sun
Boddingtons Bitter; Taylor Landlord; guest beers Ⓗ
For decades called the Oxnoble, named after a potato, it is handy for museums, and places a heavy emphasis on food.

NEW MOSTON
New Moston
52-54 Belgrave Road
12-11; 12-10.30 Sun
Camerons Bitter; Marston's Bitter Ⓗ
Busy local, tucked away behind Failsworth Station. It hosts a sea fishing club and quizzes.

NORDEN
Bridge Hotel
741 Edenfield Road
12-11; 12-10.30 Sun
Jennings Bitter, Cumberland Ale Ⓗ
Comfortable, friendly local, a rare outlet for Jennings in this area.

Peveril of the Peak ☆
127 Great Bridgewater Street
✪ 11.30-3 (not Sat), 5-11; (closed lunch) 7-10.30 Sun
☎ (0161) 236 6364
Boddingtons Bitter; Marston's Pedigree; Wells Bombardier; guest beer Ⓗ

One of the city centre's oldest pubs, which thankfully survived attempts in the early 1980s to demolish it in a road scheme. Named after a historic coach service, the pub has been run by the Swannick family for well over 30 years. The unusual wedge-shaped pub is still largely clad in the original tiles; note, in particular, the original pub signage, revealed when the Wilson Brewery lights were removed. In addition much of the internal stained glass and woodwork remain. The 'Pev' opens Sat lunchtimes when Manchester United play at home.
🏨 ✪ ◖❶ ≢ (Oxford Rd) ❺ (St Peters Sq) ♣

Rain Bar
80 Great Bridgewater Street
✪ 11-11 (midnight Fri & Sat); 12-10.30 Sun
☎ (0161) 235 6500
Lees GB Mild, Bitter, Moonraker, seasonal beers Ⓗ

The pub name comes from the building's previous use as an umbrella factory – rather than from Manchester's rainy reputation. On three floors, the pub was converted by local brewers, JW Lees in 1999, employing the three contrasting styles. Downstairs is more 'pubby' with lots of wood, a stone floor and a slate-topped bar. Upstairs is in a café-bar style, the top floor being a private room for hire. The rear terrace overlooks the Rochdale Canal and the ever-growing development of trendy flats.
✪ ◖❶ ♿ ≢ (Oxford Rd) ❺ (St Peters Sq)

Smithfield Hotel & Bar
37 Swan Street (A665, S of A664 jct)
✪ 12-11; 12-10.30 Sun
☎ (0161) 839 4424
Greene King XX Mild; Ⓗ **guest beers** Ⓗ/Ⓖ

If you are looking for affordable city-centre accommodation, as well as good and rare beers, this is the pub for you. If you enjoy beer festivals that concentrate on new micros, some of them very distant, some short-lived, then you will make a bee-line for the Smithfield, with its seven handpumps and jugs of ale straight from the cellar. The house bitter is brewed by Phoenix. Inexpensive food is served all day. A pool table dominates the entrance area,

while the back of the pub is redolent of a domestic parlour.
🏨 ◖❶ ≢ (Victoria) ❺ (Market St) ♣

White House
122 Great Ancoats Street
✪ 12-4 (5 Fri; 4.30 Sat), 8-11; 12-4, 8-10.30 Sun
☎ (0161) 228 3231
Holt Bitter; guest beer Ⓗ

Opened around 1811 as the Prince Regent's Arms, it hosted the first meeting of the Manchester Radicals in 1812, which was raided by the constable and armed soldiers. The last licensee of any note was 'Dolly' May in the 1960s, who was renowned for doll-making. The pub then fell into decline and eventual closure, reopening under the present management in 1985 as a free house, attracting local workers and residents at lunchtimes, and regulars eves, who often travel from a wide catchment. The surrounding area is being developed for housing, entertainment and light industrial purposes. ✪ ◖❶ ≢ ❺ (Piccadilly) ♣

White Lion
43 Liverpool Road
✪ 11.30-11; 12-10.30 Sun
☎ (0161) 832 7373
Taylor Landlord; Tetley Bitter; guest beers Ⓗ

Popular, constantly busy pub, despite the spread of trendy bars in the nearby Castlefield basin. It stands opposite the Air and Space Museum and the outside drinking area is almost among the Roman remains. The L-shaped bar not only serves beers as listed (which always includes guests from Phoenix and Coachman), but stocks a massive selection of whiskies and cognacs, plus an excellent wine list. Food is served from 12–9 (6 Fri–Sun). Very much a Manchester United stronghold, on match days it runs a barge trip to Old Trafford.
✪ ◖❶ ♿ ≢ (Deansgate) ❺ (G.Mex)

Railway
223 Stockport Road, Rose Hill
✪ 11.45-11; 12-10.30 Sun
☎ (0161) 427 2146
Robinson's Hatters Mild, Best Bitter Ⓗ

This impressive, spacious pub opened in 1878 alongside Rose Hill Station whose Manchester commuters it still serves. It replaced a former beer house known as the

---

OLDHAM

Gardeners Arms
Dunham Street, Lees
11.30-11; 12-10.30 Sun
Robinson's Hatters Mild, Best Bitter Ⓗ
Attractively furnished, three-roomed pub; brewery postcards are framed on the lounge wall. Food is served 12-2 Mon-Fri.

ROCHDALE

Albion
600 Whitworth Road
5 (12 Sat)-11; 12-10.30 Sun
Taylor Dark Mild, Best Bitter; Tetley Bitter; guest beers Ⓗ
Community local, offering an excellent choice of beers, situated just north of the town centre.

Britannia Inn
4 Lomax Street
12-11;
12-10.30 Sun
Lees Bitter, seasonal beers Ⓗ
The wooden fireplace surround in the best room is dated 1881. Food is served 12-2, 5-7 Mon-Fri.

Flying Horse
37 Town Hall Square
11-11;
12-10.30 Sun
Lees Bitter; Taylor Golden Best, Landlord; Theakston Best Bitter Ⓗ
Conveniently situated, opposite the town hall, it serves lunchtime food 12-2.30 Mon-Sat.

ROYTON

Railway Hotel
1 Oldham Road
12-11;
12-10.30 Sun
Lees GB Mild, Bitter Ⓗ
Busy, town-centre pub: a large central lounge, a games area and a smaller side lounge.

SALFORD

Welcome
Robert Hall Street
12-4, 7.30-11;
12-3, 7-10.30 Sun
Lees GB Mild, Bitter, seasonal beers Ⓟ
Smart 1970s pub serving the local community with a games room, alcoved lounge and function room.

Gun Inn. The pub was first opened by Bells Brewery from Hempshaw Brook in Stockport, and is little changed externally. Handy for walkers or cyclists on the nearby Middlewood Way (the former trackbed of the railway to Macclesfield), it has an open-plan layout with two large comfortable rooms. This excellent local caters for all tastes; children welcome until 3pm. ❀◖♿� (Rose Hill) P

MELLOR

Oddfellows Arms
73 Moor End Road (2 miles from Marple Bridge on back New Mills road)
✪ 11-3, 5.30-11 (closed Mon); 12-3, 7-10.30 Sun
☎ (0161) 449 7826
Adnams Bitter; Flowers IPA; Marston's Pedigree; guest beers Ⓗ
The Oddfellows is an elegant three-storey building totally in keeping with its surrounding picture postcard setting. Sympathetically restored internally, a good sociable atmosphere prevails in its comfortable bar and lounge. The upstairs restaurant enjoys an excellent reputation, with a strong accent on quality food.
🏚Q❀◖♿P🗋●

MIDDLETON

Old Boar's Head ☆
Long Street
✪ 11-11; 12-10.30 Sun
☎ (0161) 643 3520
Lees GB Mild, Bitter, seasonal beers Ⓗ
This excellent pub combines good beer with an atmosphere that befits such a truly historic building. Rightfully included in CAMRA's National Inventory of pubs with outstanding interiors, this is Middleton's oldest hostelry. Originally separate dwelling houses, it is believed the building dates from 1632, as this is cut into a stone lintel in the cellar. It has been an inn since at least 1737, although local brewers JW Lees did not acquire it until 1986. They refurbished it in 1989 and made it the comfortable watering-hole it is today. ❀◖♿P

Tandle Hill Tavern
Thornham Fold, Thornham Lane (1 mile off A671 or A664, along unmetalled road) OS898091
✪ 7 (5 summer; 12 Sat)-11; 12-10.30 Sun
☎ (01706) 345297
Lees GB Mild, Bitter, Moonraker (winter) Ⓗ
This charming inn is off the beaten track, but is well worth seeking out. Small and cosy, it offers the traveller two rooms to relax in, and a guaranteed friendly welcome. It opened its doors as a beer house in around 1850. JW Lees of Middleton have had an interest in the property since the turn of the last century, but only purchased it in 1932. The pub hosts the annual Tandle Hill Fun Run, when the normally quiet pub becomes busy as participants quench their thirst. 🏚Q❧❀

MILNROW

Crown & Shuttle
170 Rochdale Road (A640)
✪ 12-11; 12-10.30 Sun
☎ (01706) 648259
Lees GB Mild, Bitter Ⓗ

Traditional pub, popular with locals and homeward-bound workers. Usually busy, with a friendly atmosphere, the three rooms provide a homely feel. The upstairs function room houses the landlord's military museum; his collection started with the acquisition of a WWI memorial board. The pub has charity collections for a local ex-servicemen's home and has even been visited by Chelsea Pensioners. An unusual 'hoop' game is played in the tap room and the pub supports cricket, netball and rounders teams. 🏚❀♣P

MOSES GATE (FARNWORTH)

Railway Hotel
Egerton Street (off B6053)
✪ 12 (11.30 Sat)-11; 12-10.30 Sun
☎ (01204) 571858
Holt Mild, Bitter Ⓗ
Lively, unpretentious local, next to the station. A central bar serves both the vault and a large main drinking area. A pool table is housed in the room at the rear. Regular Karaoke and discos feature, with occasionally live acts performing Sun eve. The name of the area refers not to the biblical prophet, but to a gate which leads to the nearby Kearsley Mosses, now part of a roundabout over the A666. ➳♣

MOSSLEY

Church Inn
82 Stockport Road
✪ 11-11; 12-10.30 sun
☎ (01457) 832021
John Smith's Bitter; Theakston Cool Cask; guest beers Ⓗ
The exterior of the inn is typical of so many northern town pubs: stone built in a terraced row, giving an impression of permanence and of always doing the job it was intended to. This is a traditional local in every sense, with a layout of lounge, snug and tap room. On the top road to Uppermill it benefits from good views out across the valley. If you want your beer in an oversized lined glass, ask. ❀◖➳♣P🗋

Rising Sun
235 Stockport Road (1 mile N of Top Mossley on A670)
✪ 6-11; 12-10.30 Sun
☎ (01457) 834436
Black Sheep Best Bitter; Coach House Coachman's Best Bitter; Taylor Landlord; Tetley Bitter; guest beers Ⓗ
The Rising Sun is stone built and weatherbeaten; standing on the edge of town in an area known as Haddens, it commands good views out over the valley to Greenfield and the moors beyond. The interior is deceptively larger than the exterior would suggest. A Wilson's house from late Victorian times, it reverted to the free trade in 1988. Comfortable, with a good atmosphere, the pub is a watering-hole for locals and travellers alike, maintaining an inventive guest beer policy. Q❀♣P

MOTTRAM

White Hart
91 Market Street
✪ 11-11; 12-10.30 Sun

☎ (01457) 766953

Phoenix Bantam; Plassey Bitter; Taylor Landlord; Whim Hartington Magic Mushroom Mild; guest beers Ⓗ

Village centre, terraced local in a conservation area, sister pub of the CAMRA award-winning Sportsman, two miles away in Hyde. It has a comfortable lounge, tap room and a bare-boarded open area around the bar. Formerly all keg, the pub was purchased in May 2000 and is going from strength to strength; a draught, ever-changing real cider and a wheat beer accompany the regular beers. Bar snacks served 12–6 include a wide vegetarian choice. ⚏Q❄&♣♠

NANGREAVES

Lord Raglan
Mount Pleasant
✪ 12-3, 7-11; 12-10.30 Sun
☎ (0161) 764 6680
e-mail: leydenbrewery@tinyworld.co
Leyden Nanny Flyer, Light Brigade, Raglan Sleeve, Crowning Glory, seasonal or guest beers Ⓗ

The Leyden family have run this charming country inn for almost 50 years. Decorated with many items of interest, including antique glassware, pottery and old pictures, much of furniture is also noteworthy. The home of the Leyden Brewery, there are usually six cask ales on handpump. Several Belgian beers are also stocked, plus a wide choice of wines. A beer festival is held each summer (late June). The pub is renowned for its good food; the chef is also the head brewer. Meals are served all day Sun. ❄◖●P

NEW SPRINGS

Colliers Arms
192 Wigan Road (B5238, between Wigan and Aspull))
✪ 1.30-5.30, 7.30-11 (not Wed & Thu eves); 12-5, 7.30-10.30 Sun
☎ (01942) 831171
Burtonwood Bitter Ⓗ

Known locally as the Stone, this popular two-roomed inn is making its 18th consecutive appearance in this *Guide* (a feat unrivalled by any other pub in the local area). A striking mock-Tudor building, dating from 1700, it displays much memorabilia from local collieries, including a pit helmet in the lounge. Bottles are ranged around the bar, as well as books on walking and rambling. With an outside bench, next to the smallest car park in Wigan, it is handy for nearby attractions such as Haigh Hall and the Leeds–Liverpool Canal. ⚏Q❄P

OLDHAM ❖

Ashton Arms
28-30 Clegg Street (by Town Square shopping centre)
✪ 12-11; (closed lunch) 7-10.30 Sun
☎ (0161) 284 2070
Porter Dark Mild, Bitter, Rossendale Ale, Porter, Sunshine; guest beer Ⓗ

Opposite the old town hall, this split-level building is in old Oldham, part of the town-centre conservation area. A former free house, revitalised by Porter's Brewery into a popular venue, it keeps six ales, including

Sunshine, prizewinner at the local CAMRA beer festival. A traditional cider and a variety of continental bottled beers are also stocked to accompany the good value food. A seat at the 200-year-old stone fireplace makes a change from the trendy outlets on nearby Yorkshire Street. ⚏Q◖≢(Mumps)♣♠

Royal Oak
176 Manchester Road, Werneth
✪ 12-11; 12-5, 8-11 Sat; 12-10.30 Sun
☎ (0161) 624 5795
Robinson's Hatters Mild, Best Bitter Ⓗ

Traditional Robinson's house, where four distinct drinking areas are served from a central bar. Recently comfortably refurbished to a high standard, it retains the character of a community local, with much of the wood panelling and old-fashioned cast-iron radiators remaining. Unusual features include a very old Gledhill sterling cash register and a rare Old Tom mirror in the games room. The mainly mature clientele are keen games players and enjoy the regular Sat eve entertainment and monthly prize quizzes.
❄≢(Werneth)♣

ORRELL

Robin Hood
117 Sandy Lane (400 yds from station)
✪ 12-11; 12-10.30 Sun
☎ (01695) 627479
Beer range varies Ⓗ

Small, unspoilt, sandstone, two-roomed, family-run pub, themed on the well-known freedom fighter from Sherwood. Pictures of Robin Hood abound, and the fairer sex can freshen up in the 'Damsels'. It looks like the sort of place that ought to sell real ale and now does, after many years in the keg wilderness. Home-cooked food and a quiz (Wed eve) complete the picture.
Q◖⋐≢♣P

PATRICROFT

Stanley Arms
295 Liverpool Road (250 yds from Patricroft canal bridge, A57/B5211 jct)
✪ 12-11; 12-10.30 Sun
☎ (0161) 788 8801
Holt Mild, Bitter Ⓗ

Of the 130 Holt's tied pubs, only seven are tenanted, this delightful pub is one. Basic and unpretentious, with a vault and two 'best' rooms for convivial drinking, this local serves a loyal following as well as visitors who call in from all parts of Britain. At the rear of the pub is an old-fashioned iron range circa 1900, awaiting restoration. The corridor from the bar to the best room is steeped in nostalgia, displaying old pictures of Eccles (one showing trams of the 1940s). The small best room is well decorated with a multitude of framed prints. ⋐≢♣

PEEL GREEN

Grapes Hotel
439 Liverpool Road (A57, near M60 jct 11)
✪ 11-11; 12-10.30 Sun
☎ (0161) 789 6971
Holt Mild, Bitter Ⓗ

Imposing, listed Edwardian pub, where a

327

mosaic-floored lobby is surrounded by massive mahogany and etched glass features, green tiling, a bar and four rooms. Across the bar, an airy vault has more original glass and timber. The double doors of the 'billiards room' reveal a long bay window, a mahogany fireplace and a pool table. The front parlour has an ornate tiled fireplace, while the smoke room has been extended, doubling its size, but keeping two distinct areas. A new enclosed garden is at the back. Mon is quiz night and live artistes appear Sat. A family room is open Sun until 6pm.
Q❀⊟♣P

PENDLEBURY

Lord Nelson
653 Bolton Road (A666, near B5321 jct)
☼ 11-11; 12-10.30 Sun
☎ (0161) 794 6348
Holt Mild, Bitter Ⓗ
The enormous lounge of this 1969 pub has the feeling of a club room, with a recessed, raised stage complete with piano. Here artistes entertain (Sun) and a 1960s disco is held (Fri); Thu is quiz night. Windows from the old pub have been cleverly incorporated into the back of the bar. Near the entrance is a snug area, but it is not fully separated from the lounge. The other room, with its own bar, is a somewhat spartan vault with a few Nelson-related decorations and a projection TV.
Q⊟♣P

ROCHDALE ❖

Cask & Feather
1 Oldham Road (top of Drake St Hill)
☼ 11-11; 11-10.30 Sun
☎ (01706) 711476
McGuinness Feather Plucker Mild, Best Bitter, Junction Bitter, Tommy Todd's Porter Ⓗ
Large, traditional, one-roomed pub, famous locally for brewing the McGuinness range of beers which it sells at knock-down prices. Conveniently placed close to the town centre, it is handy for both bus and rail stations. A wide mix of customers are attracted, not only by the beers on offer, but also the good food. There is a public car park opposite. ◖≠

Healey Hotel
172 Shawclough Road (B6377)
☼ 12 (3 Tue & Wed)-11; 12-10.30 Sun
☎ (01706) 645453
Robinson's Best Bitter, Old Tom, seasonal beers Ⓗ
This 18th-century stone pub at the entrance to Healey Dell Nature Reserve is a gem in a sea of urbanity. Many original and interesting features remain: a splendid bar, original oak doors and tilework from a 1930s refurbishment. A traditional layout consists of a quiet, no-smoking front parlour decorated with local scenes, a rear 'gentleman's' room with a sporting theme and a bar/lounge displaying film star portraits. The extensive beer gardens boast an international standard pétanque piste (and a thriving team). It stocks a selection of malt whiskies, vodkas and rums.
♨Q❀▲♣⊬

Merry Monk
234 College Road (near A6060/B6222 jct)
☼ 12-11; 12-5, 7-10.30 Sun
☎ (01706) 646919
Banks's Bitter; Marston's Pedigree; guest beers Ⓗ
Victorian brick detached pub, first licensed in 1850; part of its history can still be seen in the fine pair of Phoenix tile sets in the entrance. Ownership passed to Cornbrook (and subsequently Bass) in 1937 until it was bought as a free house in 1984. As a popular, unpretentious local hostelry, it serves one or two guest beers. The open-plan layout is home to strong darts and quiz teams while in the garden a pétanque piste provides entertainment. ❀♣P

ROYTON ❖

Dog & Partridge
148 Middleton Road
☼ 12-11; 12-10.30 Sun
☎ (0161) 628 4198
Lees GB Mild, Bitter Ⓗ
A short walk from the town centre, this friendly local was built in the early 1800s. It has been fortunate enough not to have undergone any major rebuilding work, and retains some of the original floor plan, with separate drinking areas. It boasts a thriving sports following, fielding three darts teams, a football team and quiz team. It stocks a good selection of malt whiskies. The pub does not have a garden as such, but an area at the rear is often used in summer for outdoor drinking. ❀♿

RUSHOLME

Osborne House
32 Victory Street (off Wilmslow Rd via Platt Lane or Claremont Rd)
☼ 11.30-11; 12-10.30 Sun
☎ (0161) 224 9534
Hydes Mild, Bitter, seasonal beers Ⓗ
Welcoming, no-nonsense, back-street local, refurbished in ale house style a few years ago, where one central bar serves several drinking areas. The walls are festooned with old photos, old advertising signs and Manchester City memorabilia. Several games teams are based here and, as the pub is not far from Main Road, it can get busy on match days. It is also close to Rusholme's famous 'curry mile'. A new mosque under construction next door emphasises the ethnic diversity of the area. ♣P

SALFORD ❖

Albert Vaults
169 Chapel Street (A6, by central station)
☼ 11-11; 12-10.30 Sun
☎ (0161) 819 1368
Phoenix Arizona; guest beer Ⓗ
Large pub in a prominent position, opposite the former Threlfall's Brewery, which made Chester's ales and the short-lived Bridgewater Brewery, whose ales were sold at the pub. A long lounge leads to the small, oddly-shaped basic back vault with a pool table, and minimal seating. The second front room has a small stage and is more cosy. Live acts appear from time to time. Take a look at the 'rogues' gallery of the pub's regulars. Q❧⊟≠ (Central) ♣

Crescent
18-20 Crescent (A6, between University and Cathedral)
✪ 11.30-11; 12-10.30 Sun
☎ (0161) 736 5600
Hydes Bitter, Jekyll's Gold; Phoenix Thirsty Moon; Rooster's Special; guest beers Ⓗ
A crescent moon hangs outside this free house; inside, three eccentric rooms surround an island bar. The Festival Vault hosts functions, games (including table football) and six annual beer festivals. Foreign bottled and draught beers are well represented. Seven guest beers include a mild, and the food is equally eclectic with curry night (Wed) and Sunday breakfasts and lunches; vegetarian options are available. At the back is a neat, enclosed garden. Close by are the Irwell Valley Walk and Art Gallery, with the Lowry Centre and Castlefield quite near.
♨❀◐ ≹(Central) ♣🍎P🥤

Eagle Inn
17 Collier Street, Greengate (250 yds from A6041/A6042 jct)
✪ 11-11; 12-10.30 Sun
☎ (0161) 832 4919
Holt Mild, Bitter Ⓗ
The Eagle was totally hidden among industrial property until, with the opening of Trinity Way (A6042), it is now possible to see the pub; for the first-time visitor it can still be a little tricky to find. This is a small, traditional local, with strong support for its darts teams who play in the back room. There is a wonderful atmosphere, in quiet, comfortable surroundings. The best room displays Pre-Raphaelite prints and in the passageway by the bar, is a framed LS Lowry print. During the 1930s a shop next door sold paraffin, and the Eagle is still affectionately known as the Lamp Oil.
⊟≹(Central) ♣

King's Arms
11 Bloom Street (off A6, opp. A34 jct)
✪ 12-11; 12-7 Sun
☎ (0161) 832 0167
Moorhouses Black Cat; Phoenix Navvy; Pictish Brewer's Gold; guest beers Ⓗ
The King's is in an area that is witnessing massive change; formerly surrounded by decaying properties, these have now been demolished to create luxury apartments. In an unusually-shaped building a corridor leads from the entrance to a lounge with pinball machine, then to the main room with curved walls and bar area. It is home to the Salford Arts Collective, who display works here, and hosts regular events – jazz (Wed), quiz (Thu), and fortnightly bands (Sat). The food includes oddities such as Lancashire Tapas. Cider is normally from Pitching Green or Saxon from Yorkshire.
◐ ⊟≹(Central) 🍎

Olde Nelson
285 Chapel Street (A6, near Cathedral)
✪ 12 (11.30 Sat)-11; 12-10.30 Sun
☎ (0161) 281 9607
Boddingtons Bitter; Flowers IPA; Lees Bitter Ⓗ
This lofty Victorian hotel bears an ornate ceramic exterior, while high ceilings give an airy and spacious feeling inside. A big front vault has a projection TV screen for important matches. Around the entrance to the bar is a lobby area, with limited seating, and at the back is a large, plush lounge. Ladies darts matches take place Mon, quiz teams meet Wed and dominoes and crib are played Thu. An artiste is featured monthly and trips are run to the 'dogs' and Chester races.
Q⛾⊟≹(Central) ♣P

Union Tavern
105 Liverpool Street (parallel to A6 and A57)
✪ 11-11; 12-10.30 Sun
☎ (0161) 736 2885
Holt Mild, Bitter Ⓗ
Surprisingly, this Holt's pub has changed very little, in an area that has seen dramatic changes. Basically a drinkers' pub offering dedicated support to its five darts teams; trophies are displayed behind the bar. It caters mainly for locals but attracts visitors who like its genuine basic style. In an area of commercial buildings and industrial property, this outlet is a survivor when other pubs have had to make way for a ski-slope and recreation facility.
⊟♿≹(Crescent) ♣P

STALYBRIDGE

Station Buffet Bar ☆
Platform 1, Stalybridge Station, Rassbottom Street
✪ 11-11; 12-10.30 Sun
☎ (0161) 303 0007
Boddingtons Bitter; Flowers IPA; Wadworth 6X; guest beers Ⓗ
This well-known, privately-owned buffet bar is worth missing a train for. This premier free house is decorated in a restrained manner throughout its four rooms and includes much railway memorabilia and photographs. The real fire gives the bar a cosy atmosphere with the rumble of passing trains and station announcements outside. It offers six guest beers from independent breweries, plus an occasional cider and hosts frequent beer festivals.
♨Q❀◐ ≹🍎P

STANDISH ❄

Globe
94 High Street (A49)
✪ 11.30-11; 12-10.30 Sun
☎ (01257) 400759
website: www.theglobestandish.co.uk
Theakston Cool Cask; guest beer Ⓗ
Large, roadside, family-run pub situated in the middle of Standish, next to the main bus stop. Good value home-cooked food is served in the open-plan lounge area. The games room houses a large-screen TV for major sporting events. The function room upstairs can cater for 60. The pub has a children's certificate. Q⛾◐♿♣P⚟

Horseshoe
1 Wigan Road (A49)
✪ 12-11; 12-10.30 Sun
☎ (01257) 400716
Burtonwood Bitter; guest beer Ⓗ
Recently renovated and now open-plan, but the Horseshoe has benefited from this face-lift. Snob screens abound, with darts and pool available at either end of the pub,

which has more than one TV set. It serves good value, home-cooked food and is popular with diners, so it can get very busy at weekends. The car park is small. ◑♣P

STOCKPORT

Arden Arms ☆
23 Millgate (behind Asda in town centre)
✪ 12-11; 12-10.30 Sun
☎ (0161) 480 2185 website: www.ardenarms.com
Robinson's Hatters Mild, Best Bitter, Frederics, seasonal beers Ⓗ
This Grade II listed building has remained largely unchanged over the last 150 years, but has recently undergone a thorough redecoration to return to the condition of its heyday and the period fireplaces have been reinstalled. The large cobbled courtyard reveals the pub's former guise as a coaching inn. The present licensees ran a successful restaurant. Now the pub is a gastronomic oasis serving a range of home-cooked quality specials. A narrow drinking lobby leads to a comfortable lounge and the Millgate Room. The small snug is a gem; with just three tables, this delightful, cosy little room makes a perfect intimate venue. ⋈Q❀◑⬥≠

Armoury
Shaw Heath
✪ 11-11; 12-10.30 Sun
☎ (0161) 480 5055
Robinson's Hatters Mild, Best Bitter, Ⓗ **Old Tom** Ⓖ
Rebuilt in the 1920s, this superb, traditional local retains its original layout and many original features, not least evidence of the pub's former ownership by Bell & Co in the interior glasswork. The numerous rooms comprise a bright lounge (where weekend singalongs sometimes take place), an excellent vault (one of the best in town), a drinking lobby and a rear snug, given over to darts. A mature clientele ensures a large turnover in beer sales and the Thu eve folk sessions add to the traditional feel. Accommodation is basic, but good value. ⌂⊨⬥≠♣

Blossoms
2 Buxton Road, Heaviley
✪ 12-3, 5-11; 12-11 Sat; 12-10.30 Sun
☎ (0161) 477 2397
Robinson's Hatters Mild, Best Bitter, Ⓗ **Old Tom** Ⓖ
Multi-roomed Victorian gem, retaining its

original layout of drinking lobby and three rooms off (one given over to pool). The star is the rear smoke room, complete with carved fireplace and coloured window panels. An upstairs function room completes the picture. The emphasis here is on tradition – epitomised by the welcome sight of a cask of Old Tom on the bar in winter. Lunchtime food may include pork pies made by the landlord's son – a real treat. This friendly pub was local CAMRA *Pub of the Year* 1998. ◑⬥≠♣P

Crown Inn
154 Heaton Lane
✪ 12-3, 6-11; 12.30-11 Sat; 12.30-2.30, 7.30-10.30 Sun
☎ (0161) 429 0549
Boddingtons Bitter; guest beers Ⓗ
Stockport's top pub for choice and variety, with 10 handpumps dispensing an ever-changing range of beers. One pump is reserved for a Bank Top beer and another always features a mild. This early Victorian pub retains many original features in its numerous rooms: a games room, gas-lit vault and three lounges (one no-smoking). It can get very busy eves, particularly for the increasingly popular music sessions, but is quieter at lunchtime, which is surprising, given the very good value food that is available. ❀◑⬥≠♣♠✶

Olde Vic
1 Chatham Street
✪ 5 (7 Sat)-11; 7-10.30 Sun
☎ (0161) 480 2410
Jennings Bitter; guest beers Ⓗ
The Olde Vic has a place in the hearts of many local drinkers as the first pub in Stockport to offer a constantly changing range of guest beers. After a fallow couple of years, the pub is now triumphantly back on form, following the arrival of a new licensee, who stocks four guest beers, usually from micros, plus a traditional cider on handpump. Despite its easy-going atmosphere, this is a tightly-run ship – swear and you're out. At the back is an excellent outdoor drinking area, which is a real suntrap. ⋈❀≠♠

Olde Woolpack
70 Brinksway
✪ 11.30-3, 5.30-11; 11.30-11 Fri; 11.30-4, 7.30-11 Sat; 12-10.30 Sun

INN BRIEF

STANDISH
Dog & Partridge
33 School Lane
11-11; 12-10.30 Sun
Boddingtons Bitter; Tetley Mild, Bitter; guest beers Ⓗ
Bustling, well-appointed local boasting attractive leaded windows and snob screens throughout. Sport is regularly featured on TV.

SWINTON
Farmer's Arms
160 Manchester Road
11-11; 12-10.30 Sun
Boddingtons Bitter; Cains Bitter; Greenalls Mild; guest beer (occasional) Ⓗ
Displaying a Grade II listed Swales Brewery frontage, the pub is much altered inside but remains comfortable and popular.

White Swan
186 Worsley Road
12-11; 12-10.30 Sun
Holt Mild, Bitter Ⓗ
Large four-roomed, 1920s pub with wood panelling, a function room and busy vault. Children are welcome Sun lunchtime.

TYLDESLEY
Half Moon
115-117 Elliott Street
11-11; 12-10.30 Sun
Boddingtons Bitter; Holt Bitter; guest beers Ⓗ
Good town-centre pub with a comfortable lounge bar and lounge, plus a paved garden at the rear.

WIGAN
Moon under Water
5-7a Market Place
11-11; 12-10.30 Sun
Cains Mild; Courage Directors; Shepherd Neame Spitfire; guest beer Ⓗ
Usual Wetherspoon's layout, right in the centre of town; very popular at weekends. *Cask Marque* accredited.

WITHINGTON
Victoria Hotel
438 Wilmslow Road
11.30-11; 12-10.30 Sun
Hydes Mild, Bitter, Jekyll's Gold, seasonal beers Ⓗ
Deceptively large, open-plan pub with a multi-roomed feel. A varied clientele enjoy many activities, including music around the piano.

☎ (0161) 429 6621

Theakston Best Bitter, Cool Cask; Wells Bombardier; guest beers Ⓗ

First a Greenalls pub, then a failed free house, the Woolpack was rescued from dereliction 12 years ago. Now the emphasis is always on quality, from the two ever-changing guest beers to the tasty food; the latter is particularly popular with workers from the Co-operative Bank's giant blue pyramid office block which dwarfs the pub. Semi open-plan, the pub retains several distinct rooms, including a popular vault where cards are very much to the fore. Local CAMRA *Pub of the Year* 1999. Q❀◑♣

Railway

1 Avenue Street (off A560, opp. Peel Centre)
🕓 12-11; 12-10.30 Sun
☎ (0161) 429 6062

Porter Dark Mild, Floral Dance, Bitter, Rossendale Ale, Porter Ⓗ

An impressive row of eight handpumps greets the visitor to this single-roomed pub where you will find no pool table, TV or obtrusive games machines, just a warm welcome and good conversation. Occasional brews and an increasing range of bottled beers offer something for all tastes. The cider (or perry) is cooled on the bar by a refrigerated jacket to ensure top condition. Low beer prices and home-cooked food make this pub a must visit (no food Sun). Q❀◑♣♠

Red Bull

14 Middle Hillgate
🕓 11-11, 12-3, 7-10.30 Sun
☎ (0161) 480 2087

Robinson's Hatters Mild, Best Bitter Ⓗ

Although situated in the centre of Stockport, the pub exudes a warm country feel, particularly in the stone-flagged period snug with pew seating off the main bar. Dark wood, traditional pub colours, and bric-à-brac decorate the four rooms. The fairly complex, two-bar multi-level layout also boasts another small snug at the back, that accommodates just eight drinkers. The pub can be busy weekday lunchtimes, with a vibrant food trade. The car park is tiny. Q◑⇌P

Spread Eagle

31 Lower Hillgate
🕓 11-11, (closed lunch), 7.30-10.30 Sun
☎ (0161) 480 5055

Robinson's Hatters Mild, Best Bitter, Old Tom Ⓟ

Built into the front of Robinson's brewery, this tap was sadly neglected for many years, but the current enterprising licensees have seen its fortunes transformed. The pub layout has been altered into a main U-shaped area, running the full length of the pub, with an almost separate pool room. Over the past few years the pub has (proudly) boasted an enviable quality of beer; the Old Tom is also available in 'nip' sized glasses. Three excellent home-made curries is the only hot food available. Thrice-weekly 'happy afternoons' see cask beer prices reduced. ❀◑♣♠🍴

Swan with Two Necks ☆

36 Princes Street (behind Woolworth's, rear of precinct)
🕓 11-11; closed Sun

☎ (0161) 480 2341 e-mail: paulstanye@aol.com

Robinson's Hatters Mild, Best Bitter, Frederics, Old Tom, seasonal beers Ⓗ

Small, town-centre pub, the perfect escape from the surrounding busy shopping area. Superb oak panelling predominates in the multi-roomed layout, which was last refurbished in the 1920s. Each room has its own character; the previously unused room at the rear has now been sympathetically refurbished to give extra drinking space, and at midday it is mainly used by diners. Lunches are served six days a week; the house speciality is Bev's lasagne made with Old Tom. Other Robinson's beers are occasionally stocked. Well worth a visit. ◑🍴♣♠

Tiviot

8 Tiviot Dale (near A560/B6167 jct)
🕓 11-11, 12-3.30, 7.30-10.30 Sun
☎ (0161) 480 4109

Robinson's Hatters Mild, Best Bitter, Ⓟ **Old Tom** Ⓖ

Classic town pub with a comfortable old-fashioned atmosphere providing a welcome refuge from the bustle of the nearby Merseyway precinct. The four rooms include a dining room, games room with table football and a classic vault. Quieter eves, the pub is busy at lunchtimes with a mix of shoppers and long-time regulars, attracted by the straightforward, good value food (not served Sun). Long-serving licensees and bar staff have ensured a continuity rarely found today. ◑🏠♣🍴

STRINES

Royal Oak

121 Strines Road (1½ miles from Marple on New Mills Road)
🕓 12-3, 5-11; 12-11 Sat; 12-10.30 Sun
☎ (0161) 427 2430

Robinson's Hatters Mild, Best Bitter, Ⓗ **Old Tom,** Ⓖ **seasonal beer** Ⓗ

This village pub was probably opened as an ale house about 1865. It stands by the Peak Forest Canal that accounted for much of its trade years ago. Now the canal is used for leisure only, the pub's customers come from the village community and passing trade. The Royal Oak comprises a vault that has been recently extended and refurbished, a warm cosy bar/lounge, with an open fire and a small dining room where the landlord's wife serves simple tasty food (lunches Wed-Sun).
🏚Q🐾❀◑♣🏠🅰⇌P🍴

SWINTON ❋

White Lion

242 Manchester Road (A6/A572 jct)
🕓 11-11; 12-10.30 Sun
☎ (0161) 288 0434

Robinson's Hatters Mild, Best Bitter, seasonal beers Ⓗ

Licensed in 1790, and the first spiritual home of Swinton Football Club whose nickname 'the Lions' derives from the pub, where the rear lounge is now designated the official Swinton RLFC hall of fame. The main lounge is on two levels, with a low step; a large vault houses a pool table, while a new extension created a small room which connects them. Standard bar food includes a roast lunch on

Sun (eve meals served 5–7). It hosts a folk club (Mon eve) and an annual folk festival in October. ⛟❀◗🖰⬱♣P

TIMPERLEY

Quarry Bank Inn
Bloomsbury Lane
❍ 11.30-11; 12-10.30 Sun
☎ (0161) 980 4345
Hydes Mild, Bitter, seasonal beers Ⓗ
Thriving suburban local on the edge of the old village centre, with a popular vault and a quieter lounge/restaurant. One of the only pubs locally to retain a crown green for the bowling team. At one time a basic local, the pub has received a sympathetic refurbishment and now attracts a wider clientele from surrounding commuterland. The restaurant is popular with all ages for its good value meals (no food Sun eve).
Q⛟❀◗🖰⬱♣P

UPPERMILL

Cross Keys
Off Running Hill Gate
❍ 11-11; 12-10.30 Sun
☎ (01457) 874626
Lees GB Mild, Bitter, Moonraker, seasonal beers Ⓗ
This attractive 18th-century stone building with exposed beams throughout, overlooks Saddleworth church. The pub bar boasts a stone-flagged floor and a Yorkshire range. The centre for many activities, including a mountain rescue team, clay pigeon club, Saddleworth Runners and the Garland Girls, it is busy during annual events such as the charity beer walk (June) and the Saddleworth Rushcart Festival (Aug). It hosts folk nights (Wed and Sun) in the barn. The patio and garden are popular. Good value home-cooked food is served until 7pm (all day Sat and Sun). Children's certificate. ᴹQ⛟❀◗🖰⬱♣P

WARDLEY

Morning Star
520 Manchester Road (A6, between Swinton and Walkden)
❍ 12-11; 12-10.30 Sun
☎ (0161) 794 4927
Holt Mild, Bitter Ⓗ
Consisting of a small front lounge which leads through to a large square main lounge, and a long, narrow, traditional vault around a central bar, this is a friendly community pub. It fields men's and ladies' darts teams and a dominoes team. The excellent value home-made lunches are served weekdays, and the pub has been given a silver award from the local area health authority for its kitchen excellence and hygiene. Entertainment at weekends is provided by a singer (alternate Sat) and a disco every Sun eve.
❀◗🖰≢(Moorside) ♣P

WESTHOUGHTON

White Lion
2 Market Street (B5235, next to town hall)
❍ 11-11; 12-10.30 Sun
☎ (01942) 811191
Holt Mild, Bitter Ⓗ
An inn has been on this site for about 250

years; it was acquired by Holts in 1925. Today it is a totally unspoilt and unpretentious pub. Its most attractive feature is the curved, shuttered island bar serving the five distinct drinking areas: a vault (with its own entrance), a cosy bar/parlour, smoke room (now used for darts), a lounge and a lobby area. Most of the furniture and fittings have been restored in keeping with this old-fashioned inn. ❀P

WHITEFIELD

Coach & Horses
71 Bury Old Road (A665)
❍ 12-11; 12-10.30 Sun
☎ (0161) 798 8897
Holt Mild, Bitter Ⓗ
Traditional, multi-roomed local that still bears many of its original characteristics. Built in 1830, it derives its name from its use as a stopping-place on the Burnley–Manchester mail run. It also served as a stop for the daily omnibus service between Manchester and Bury. Local people still argue as to whether it belongs to Whitefield or Prestwich, as it stands on the boundary. There is a tap room, snug and lounge. Q❀⊖(Besses o' th' Barn) ♣P

Eagle & Child
Higher Lane (A665/A56 jct)
❍ 12-11; 12-10.30 Sun
☎ (0161) 766 3024
Holt Mild, Bitter Ⓗ
Large, black and white pub, set back from the road; it has a large L-shaped main bar and a cosy side room. The well-kept bowling green at the rear is very popular in summer. The building only dates from 1936, replacing the original Eagle & Child which was the first hostelry on Higher Lane (built 1802). The current pub is the last; in between, five other pubs have come and gone. Originally a Whitefield Brewery pub, it has belonged to Holt's of Manchester since 1907. ❀◗⊖(Besses o' th' Barn) ♣P

WIGAN ❄

Anvil
Dorning Street (off Hallgate, next to bus station)
❍ 11-11; 12-10.30 Sun
☎ (01942) 239444
Hydes Dark, Bitter, Jekyll's Gold, seasonal beers; guest beers Ⓗ
There is a very modern feel to this town-centre Hydes' outlet in a former Karaoke bar. With a bus station on one side, railway station on the other and in the shadow of Wigan parish church, it is well situated. Regular guest beers join the impressive Hydes' range. A wide-screen TV caters for sports fans in a separate room and there is also a designated no-smoking area. A friendly haven away from the clubs and wine bars, it is well worth a visit.
❀◗≢(North Western/Wallgate) ♣⚹

Bold Hotel
161 Poolstock Lane, Worsley Mesnes
❍ 2-4.30, 7-11; 12-3, 7-10.30 Sun
☎ (01942) 241095
Burtonwood Bitter; guest beer Ⓗ
Local CAMRA *Pub of the Year* 2000, this small, friendly local stands on the B5238, between Wigan and the M6. The tap room

boasts a fine display of Rugby League memorabilia, while the lounge is favoured by locals keen on conversation. An excellent example of an unspoilt roadside pub, it is far enough from the town centre to avoid the developers' gaze. Q⊟♣

Bowling Green

106-108 Wigan Lane

⊙ 4-11 (5 Fri; 12 Sat); 12-10.30 Sun

☎ (01942) 516004

Caledonian Deuchars IPA; Lees Bitter; Tetley Dark Mild, Bitter; guest beers Ⓗ

Very impressive, ex-Walker's house, complete with etched windows. A vibrant vault leads into the only waitress-serviced lounge in the area. Lots of original woodwork is festooned with the usual pub memorabilia. Several times winner of the local CAMRA *Pub of the Year* award, it is famed throughout the area for its impromptu folk/jam sessions. It is warmed by several log-burning fires during the winter months.

⛫❀⊟▯

Douglas Bank Tavern

215 Woodhouse Lane

⊙ 12-11; 12-10.30 Sun

☎ (01942) 829005

e-mail: chrisquasi@netscapeonline.co.uk

Holt Mild, Bitter Ⓗ

Friendly, two-roomed local on the edge of town, within easy reach of the JJB Stadium. Having undergone many changes over recent years, it is now established as a traditional Holt's house. A central bar serves a large games room and a comfortable lounge, with Holt's Mild, which is rare even in this area, and good value pub food. Live entertainment is staged Sun eve, plus a friendly quiz (Thu) and games nights during the week. ◐◑♿♣P

Millstone

67 Wigan Lane

⊙ 3.30 (12 Fri & Sat)-11; 12-10.30 Sun

☎ (01942) 245999

Thwaites Bitter Ⓗ

A locals' pub in the best sense of the word. Note the *Art Nouveau* lamps in the courtyard. This warm, friendly watering-hole is popular with dominoes players. It is one of the few Thwaites' outlets in the area. ❀◐♣

Orwell

Wigan Pier, Wallgate (500 yds from town centre)

⊙ 11-11; 12-10.30 Sun; (hours vary winter)

☎ (01942) 323034 website: www.wiganpier.co.uk

Beer range varies Ⓗ

Converted Victorian cotton warehouse on the Leeds–Liverpool Canal, approximately 10 minutes' walk from the JJB Stadium (home of Wigan Athletic and the Wigan Warriors). The lunch menu includes a large selection of home-made soups and hot and cold sandwiches. This free house, run by long-term CAMRA members, has sponsored Wigan beer festival since 1998 and was local *Pub of the Year* that year. It offers the widest range of beers from micro-breweries anywhere in the area, with seasonal ales from the likes of Bank Top, Blackpool, Phoenix and Pictish.

❀◐♿⇌ (North Western/Wallgate) ♣P⊬

Swan & Railway

80 Wallgate

⊙ 12 (11 Sat)-11 12-10.30 Sun

☎ (01942) 495032

Banks's Original, Bitter; Camerons Strongarm; Mansfield Dark Mild; guest beer Ⓗ

Classic, largely unspoilt boozer, saved from unsympathetic treatment by the local CAMRA branch a few years ago. The mosaic porch in the doorway and tiled bar are the highlights, but there are attractive stained glass inserts in the vault, commemorating local locomotives and Victorian still life prints. It is handy for both railway stations. Sport is shown on TV for those who enjoy it. ⇆◐⇌ (North Western/Wallgate) ♣

WOODFORD

Davenport Arms (Thief's Neck)

550 Chester Road

⊙ 11-3.30, 5.15-11; 11-11 Sat; 12-3, 7-10.30 Sun

☎ (0161) 439 2435

Robinson's Hatters Mild, Best Bitter, Fredericks (occasional), **Old Tom, seasonal beers** Ⓗ

This superb, unspoilt multi-roomed farmhouse pub, on the edge of suburbia, has been run by the Hallworth family for over 70 years. The two front rooms comprise a traditional vault and a no-smoking snug with a real fire. The larger back room houses the bar, and can get very busy at times. Food is served every day (12–2 Sun–Fri; 12–7 Sat) and is all home cooked on the premises. Children are welcome at lunchtime in the snug and the large attractive garden at the rear.

⛫Q☕❀◐⊟♣P⊬

WORSLEY

John Gilbert

Worsley Brow (A572, in shadow of M60 jct 13)

⊙ 11.30-11; 12-10.30 Sun

☎ (0161) 703 7733

Boddingtons Bitter; Hardys & Hansons Best Bitter, Classic Ⓗ

Opened in the late 1990s as one of Yates' Watling Street Inns dining pubs, this house, like most of that estate was sold to Hardys & Hansons in 2000. A fine building, formerly the lodge to Worsley Hall, it was renovated and extended to form a very pleasant venue. The name celebrates a canal engineer. With the emphasis on comfort and dining, the pub attracts a fairly affluent crowd and is well suited to Worsley. Meals are served 12–8 (7 Sun). ❀◐◑P⊬

WORTHINGTON

Crown Hotel

19-20 Platt Lane, Standish (off A5016)

⊙ 11-11; 12-10.30 Sun

☎ (01257) 421354

Boddingtons Bitter; Tetley Bitter; guest beers Ⓗ

A large mahogany-panelled bar and antique furniture feature in this warm, welcoming, rural hostelry. Located just outside Standish village, it benefits from views of the surrounding countryside. There is always a mild available on tap. The recent addition of accommodation has not damaged the feel of the pub; TV is unobtrusive and there is a games room to the rear. Meals can be taken in the restaurant. ⛫❀⇆◐◑♣PÁ

Transport to Pubs

BUSES

Bus Traveline

Most – and soon all – local authorities will use the national Traveline for bus timetable information:

This is: 0870 608 2608   Textphone: 0870 241 2216

Websites
Some cover other public transport information

www.pti.org.uk/index.cfm   www.traveline.org.uk   www.ukbus.co.uk

If these are not available it is advisable to contact your County or Unitary Council or Passenger Transport Executive to ascertain the right contact details. Details of these appear in full in the National Rail Timetable (from main stations and W H Smith outlets), or others in the www.ukbus.co.uk website.

National Express   **Scottish City Link**

For longer distance coach services contact National Express – their line number is:-

National Express: 08705 808080   Website: www.gobycoach.com

Scottish Citylink: 08705 505050   Website: www.citylink.co.uk/index.html

Other Websites
Other important bus websites often give information – the main ones are:

www.ukbus.co.uk Station Master Bus & Train Information & Journey Planners with telephone numbers.
www.arriva.com Arriva Buses & Trains
www.firstgroup.com First Group Buses & Trains
www.stagecoachplc.com Stagecoach Buses & Trains

Many local authorities are setting up their own websites – information available by local contact.

TRAINS

National Train Information Line
The national hotline for all train information is:- 08457 484950
Minicom: 0845 60 50 600

Websites
Enquiries: www.nationaltrainenquiries.co.uk   www.railtrack.co.uk
Planning: www.travelinfosystems.com
Current state of rail services: www.natioanlrail.co.uk
Booking services: www.thetraainline.com   www.railplanner.co.uk
London: www.londontransport.co.uk
Europe: www.raileurope.co.uk   www.railchoice.co.uk

NATIONAL INFORMATION

The Government has split up the DETR (Departments for Transport and for Environment) and their new websites will be useful for those interested in following transport policies. Their details are as follows:-

Department of Transport, Local Government & the Regions (DTLR): www.dltr.gov.uk
Department of Environment, Food & Rural Affairs (DEFRA): www.defra.gov.uk

For other information about contacts, but not timetable enquiries, please contact the CAMRA Public Transport Task Group by e-mail: MikePCAMRA@aol.com or by post via CAMRA Headquarters, 230 Hatfield Road, St Albans, AL1 4LW.

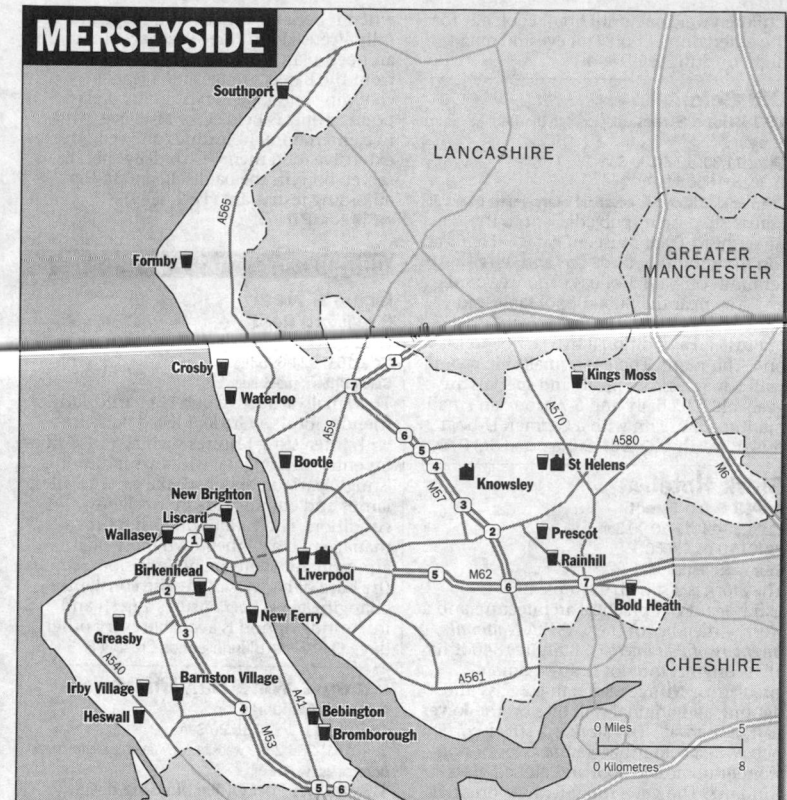

MERSEYSIDE

Southport
Formby
Crosby
Waterloo
Bootle
New Brighton
Liscard
Wallasey
Birkenhead
Greasby
Irby Village
Heswall
Barnston Village
New Ferry
Liverpool
Knowsley
Prescot
Rainhill
Bold Heath
Bebington
Bromborough
Kings Moss
St Helens

LANCASHIRE

GREATER MANCHESTER

CHESHIRE

0 Miles 5
0 Kilometres 8

BEBINGTON

Rose & Crown
57 The Village (opp. Town Hall)
☼ 11.30-11; 12-10.30 Sun
☎ (0151) 643 1312
Thwaites Best Bitter Ⓗ
Bustling, friendly, multi-roomed local, built (in 1732) on the site of a much older pub. It is popular with office workers and shoppers at lunchtime, local residents at night. Adjacent to the pub lie Mayer Park and Pennant House. This was the home of local benefactor Joseph Mayer and is now municipal offices. In recent years the pub has seen major refurbishment including an extension to the lounge with provision of a bar counter. The public bar and games room have changed little over the years. The base of the bar counter is said to be original. Weekday lunches are served. There is limited parking. Q ◖ ⌷ ⇌ ♣ P

Travellers Rest
169 Mount Road
☼ 12-11; 12-10.30 Sun
☎ (0151) 608 2988
Boddingtons Bitter; Cains Bitter; Flowers IPA; Greene King Abbot; Taylor Landlord; guest beers Ⓗ
Wirral CAMRA *Pub of the Year* 1998-99, this is a deservedly popular and comfortable pub. Reputedly over 300 years old, it features a beamed ceiling adorned with numerous brasses. Ales are dispensed from a central bar area which feeds two other rooms, one no-smoking. The five regular ales are supplemented with two guests, usually from small breweries. Popular every night, but especially Mon eve for the quiz. The pub has also received a *Parliamentary Food Club* award for quality food (served lunchtime only, not Sun). Q ◖ ⌷ & ♣ ✕

BIRKENHEAD

Crown Ale House
128 Conway Street (by Europa Centre)
☼ 11-11; 12-10.30 Sun
☎ (0151) 647 0589
Cains Bitter; Greenalls Mild, Bitter; Taylor Landlord; guest beers Ⓗ
Large, listed building on the fringe of the main shopping area. Local CAMRA award-winning pub which, over the last decade, has become the town's best-known real ale outlet. After a degree of neglect in recent times, the present licensees have revitalised the pub and made the most of its fine, original fixtures and fittings. A bar, side lounge and rear room are all served by a central area. There is an extensive menu with food served daily from noon to 6pm. Generally four guest ales are available.

INDEPENDENT BREWERIES

Beecham's St. Helens
Cains Liverpool
Cambrinus Knowsley
Liverpool Liverpool
Passageway Liverpool

Children welcome until 8pm. Look out for the entertainment on Thu eve and quiz night on Sun. ⚮⏻⊑≝♣

Old Colonial
167 Bridge Street (adjacent to the Tram Museum garage)
⊛ 12-11.30; 12-10.30 Sun
☎ (0151) 650 1110
Cains Mild, Bitter, FA, seasonal beers; guest beers Ⓗ
Refurbished Cains pub adjacent to the Birkenhead Tram Museum garage. Trams run from the Woodside bus and ferry terminus on bank holidays and weekends and stop near the pub. A pool table and dartboard are provided. There is no juke box but instead a traditional live jazz band play on a Thu night. There is a small side room with bar access. Set meals and specials are available 12-3 daily and 5-7 Mon-Sat, small maritime museum with a German U-boat hulk is nearby. Q⚮⏻⊖(Hamilton Sq) P●

Stork Hotel ☆
41-43 Price Street
⊛ 11.30-11; 12-10.30 Sun
☎ (0151) 647 7506
Beer range varies Ⓗ
The Stork is a superb example of extravagant but practical architecture and a worthy member of the CAMRA *National Inventory of Pub Interiors*. Built in 1840 it has all its original interior fittings; ornate circular bar with leaded stained glass and lighting and original wall tiles on the lower half of the wall. The Stork is a street-corner pub with a colourful ceramic exterior and wonderful mosaic floor and etched glass windows. The news room with its original bell pushes, etched windows and door is a no-smoking area. This pub is a must for traditional pub lovers. Food served daily 12-2 and 4.30-6.30.
☎⚮⏻≝(Hamilton Sq/Conway Pk) ♣✂

BOLD HEATH

Griffin
184 Warrington Road (Clock Face Road/Warrington Road, A57 jct)
⊛ 12-11; 12-10.30 Sun
☎ (0151) 424 5143
Beer range varies Ⓗ
Large, attractive pub with part-beamed ceilings. The pub was formerly a 19th-century coaching inn. Beer range comprises two cask beers on handpump plus a single rotating guest beer. Food is served all day, seven days a week, and families are well catered for with both a family eating area, and a children's play area in the spacious garden. The new conservatory offers pleasant views of the countryside. There is ample car parking. ⚮⏻&P✂

BROMBOROUGH

Dibbinsdale Inn
Dibbinsdale Road
⊛ 11 (11.30 Sat)-11; 12-10.30 Sun
☎ (0151) 334 5171
Banks's Bitter; Camerons Strongarm; Marston's Pedigree; guest beers Ⓗ
Dating from 1835, this charming, small country hotel is situated a short distance from the open Wirral countryside. The building was a private house until 1966,

when it became a restaurant, reopening as a fully-licensed inn three years ago. Featuring an open-plan bar area, it serves three ales from the Banks's range and a regularly-changing guest ale, served in lined glasses. A popular quiz is held every Mon eve, while live entertainment features on Wed. An extensive food menu, with daily specials, is served both in the bar itself, and in the adjoining restaurant (12-9 daily).
⇔⏻&≝P⊟

CROSBY ☀

Crow's Nest
63 Victoria Road
⊛ 11.30-11; 12-10.30 Sun
☎ (0151) 924 6953
Cains Bitter; guest beer Ⓗ
This small, attractive pub is a particularly friendly local. A Grade II listed building with interesting features such as a tiled floor on entry and original windows indicating 'snug', 'parlour' and 'bar', the external tiles, lamps and entrance are in excellent condition. The various divided rooms all manage to create their own individual atmosphere. There are no intrusions; simply the buzz of conversation. The constantly changing guest beer ensures a fresh and interesting option is available every other day. Q⚮⊑≝(Blundellsands/Crosby) P

Stamps Wine Bar/Bistro
4 Crown Buildings
⊛ 10.30-11; 10.30-10.30 Sun
☎ (0151) 286 2662 website: www.stampsbistro.co.uk
Beer range varies Ⓗ
This former Post Office building has a typical bistro atmosphere. The lower floor, with bare bricks and wooden floorboards, provides a comfortable and inviting ambience. The varied background music is aimed at the 25+ age group. There are live acoustic sessions on Thu eve, a resident band on Sat eve and live performances on Sun afternoon. The upper floor has a bright, colourful, continental feel and is a pleasant place to spend time. Food is available every day from 10.30am until 5pm, Tapas available after 5pm. Constantly busy, this cosy, warm bar attracts a younger clientele.
≝(Blundellsands/Crosby)

FORMBY

Freshfield Hotel
1 Massams Lane, Freshfield
(½ mile from B5424)
⊛ 12-11; 12-10.30 Sun
☎ (01704) 874871 website: www.blemon.demon.co.uk
Boddingtons Bitter; Castle Eden Ale; Flowers IPA; Fuller's London Pride; Moorhouses Black Cat; guest beers Ⓗ
Popular local with 12 real ales always available, many from small independent brewers. Former Hogshead with many fascinating photographs of old Formby, antique tools on the walls add character. A bar is attached to the lounge on the lower level with a function room at the rear. Occasional themed nights and a local guitar club holds meetings. Red squirrels may be spotted in a National Trust area close by, this nature reserve leads to the beach at Formby Point.
⇔⚮⏻≝(Freshfield) P

GREASBY

Irby Mill
Mill Lane
✪ 12-11; 12-10.30 Sun
☎ (0151) 604 0194
Cains Bitter; Jennings Bitter, Sneck Lifter; Taylor Landlord; Theakston Best Bitter; guest beers Ⓗ
Traditional country pub built in 1980 on an ancient mill site, a local favourite haunt of bikers and hikers during the 1920s. Two rooms are linked by a narrow bar full of characters and friendly banter. The pub is a haven with 13 handpumps and has been the recipient of many CAMRA awards. Year 2000 Birkenhead *Pub of the Festival* it was rewarded in 2001 by receiving the industry's *Cask Pub of the Year* award. Popular with country walkers, close to Royden Park, this superb pub, with no slot machines or music, promises a warm welcome. Q✿◑ⅅℙ●

HESWALL

Dee View Inn
Dee View Road
✪ 12-11; 12-10.30 Sun
☎ (0151) 342 2320
Boddingtons Bitter; Cains Bitter; Taylor Landlord; Tetley Bitter; guest beers Ⓗ
This pub was built around 1860-80 by Joseph Ellis and sold by the family to Birkenhead Brewery in 1918. It passed to Whitbread in 1971. Slate-roofed and white-walled, this popular locals' pub dominates Dee View corner. A large mirror stands opposite to help travellers negotiate the hairpin bend and junction. Beyond this is a small park with breathtaking views of the Dee Estuary and Welsh hills. A popular pub quiz is held on Tue and fun nights have raised money for the local children's hospice. Advisable to book for large Sun lunches (no food Mon). Mobile-phone free or £1 to charity box! ◑♣ℙ

Johnny Pye
Pye Road (opp. bus station)
✪ 11-11; 12-10.30 Sun
☎ (0151) 342 8215
Banks's Original, Bitter Ⓗ
Named after a local 1920s entrepreneur John Pye, who operated a local omnibus company. A lively, modern Banks's pub with a bright, open-plan interior and polished wood floor. It features a selection of pictures of historic Heswall. The raised lounge seating area is L-shaped with a similar separate area set aside for non-smokers. It also provides large-screen TV for sports and can be lively during the more popular football matches. Pub quiz held on Thu eve. Beer is served in oversized lined glasses. No food served on Sun.
✿◑ᙘ♣ℙ⊬🖫

KINGS MOSS

Colliers' Arms
37 Pimbo Road
(off B5205, Rainford Road, near Billinge)
✪ 12-11; 12-10.30 Sun
☎ (01744) 892894 e-mail: jfbolton@lineone.net
Beer range varies Ⓗ
Traditional-style pub with a warm, friendly atmosphere. Good home-cooked food is served at lunchtimes and eves, and all day Sun. Beer range includes up to three guest beers. This pub is located in the tiny hamlet of Kings Moss, near Billinge. It was built in 1850 and has a stonc-flagged floor and an attractive garden to the rear. A row of former miners' cottages is situated opposite, and during spells of bad winter weather the miners collected their wages from the pub; hence the name 'Colliers' Arms'.
🏚Q✿◑ ⅅᙘ♣ℙ⊬

LISCARD

Stanley's
83 Seaview Road (just outside main shopping area)
✪ 11-11; 12-10.30 Sun
☎ (0151) 639 9736
McEwan 80/-; Theakston Cool Cask; guest beers Ⓗ
Since its opening in 1997 Stanley's has become one of Wallasey's best real ale outlets, with a good range of guest beers from micro-breweries all over Britain and three beers on at any one time, alongside various Scottish Courage products. To complement the beers, the eclectic food menu is an eye-opener. The pub itself is newly-built, the interior walls are bare brick and seating is church pews, but comfortable nonetheless. The real cider on offer is Addlestone's Cloudy. ✿◑ᙘ♣ℙ

LIVERPOOL: *CENTRE*

Baltic Fleet
33a Wapping
✪ 11.30-11; 12-10.30 Sun
☎ (0151) 709 3116
Passageway Wapping, Extra, seasonal beers; guest beers Ⓗ
This Grade II listed building offers a welcome oasis of real ale away from the keg establishments dominating the nearby Albert Dock tourist honeypot. The nautical theme is apparent on approaching the pub; the 'flat-iron' shape closely resembles a ship. Somewhat neglected in recent years, the pub has now been returned to its former glory. The quality of the food on offer is every bit as good as the beer, with the Sunday speciality of Welsh Black beef unlikely to disappoint. Local CAMRA *Pub of the Year* 2000. 🏚Q✿◑ⅅ⊖(James St.) ♣ℙ⊬

Belvedere
8 Sugnall Street (off Falkner Street near the Philharmonic Hall)
✪ 11-11.30; 5-10.30 Sun
☎ (0151) 709 7525
Beer range varies Ⓗ
Recently refurbished two-roomed pub on the edge of the inner city, the Belvedere offers no gimmicks and no frills, merely two regularly changing guest beers in a friendly atmosphere. Given the unfortunate disappearance of other real ale outlets in this area, the renaissance of what was a relatively uninspiring back-street local is most welcome. The bar area is quite small but service is available from the corridor between the two rooms. A local delicatessen supplies sandwiches and the kitchen provides simple but tasty food. ✿◑

Brewery
21-23 Berry Street (300 yds from the Chinatown entrance arch)

☼ 12-2am; closed Sun
☎ (0151) 709 5055
Liverpool Blondie, Celebration, seasonal beers Ⓗ
Anyone who thinks that young people
don't drink real ale should take a look in
here late at night. The Brewery takes full
advantage of its 2am licence, which places it
firmly on the city-centre student drinking
circuit. A wide range of beers on offer, all
are brewed on the premises. Large windows
afford a clear view of the brewing plant
both from the street and from inside. Live
bands often play at night. That, and the
wide variety of events to be found in the
upstairs 'Lemon Lounge', ensures a vibrant
and cosmopolitan clientele. ⊖(Central)

Cambridge
51 Mulberry Street (near Catholic cathedral)
☼ 11.30-11; 12-11 Sat; 12-10.30 Sun
Burtonwood Bitter, Top Hat; guest beers Ⓗ
Cosy, bustling pub set in the Liverpool
University campus and therefore very busy
with students during term-time but with
the atmosphere of a popular, traditional
corner local all year round. At one time
knocked through to the adjoining house
which now forms the snug, both rooms
have bare wooden floors and an intimate
style. One of the few Burtonwood-managed
houses, which not only has real ale but a
guest beer changing every couple of days. A
juke box and Sky Sports are available plus
quiz night Sun with free food. Speciality
Sun breakfasts 12-2pm must be tried. There
is no food on Sat. ⛺◖⊖(Central) ♣

Carnarvon Castle
5 Tarleton Street
☼ 11-11 (8 Mon & Tue); 12-6 Sun
☎ (0151) 708 0516
Cains Mild, Bitter; guest beer Ⓗ
This little gem of a pub is right in the centre
of the main shopping area. A narrow front
bar area with a real fire and a small rear
lounge are the extent of the pub, and
consequently it can sometimes be crowded.
A mixed clientele of regulars, passers-by and
shoppers taking a break are treated to as
good a pint of Cains Mild and Bitter as is
available in Liverpool, together with the
recently introduced rotating guest beer.
Quiz night is Tue.
♨Q➤(Lime St) ⊖ (Central)

Cracke
13 Rice Street (off Hope St, near Philharmonic Hall)
☼ 11.30-11; 12-10.30 Sun
☎ (0151) 709 4171
**Cains Bitter; Marston's Pedigree; Phoenix Old Oak,
Wobbly Bob; guest beers** Ⓗ
Unique, multi-roomed pub hidden in a
back street. The Rice Street entrance leads
straight into the public bar; the second
entrance, up a short alley, opens into the
pub's central corridor. The 'war office' is a
quiet snug while darts, cards and chess are
played in the games room. The main bar
area opens out at the end of the corridor
and has stained glass windows and screens.
The final room has sketches of the local
area.
Q◖➤(Lime St) ⊖ (Central)♣ ●

Dispensary
87 Renshaw Street
☼ 11.30-11; 12-10.30 Sun

☎ (0151) 709 2160 www.cainsbeers.com
Cains Mild, Bitter, FA, seasonal beers; guest beers Ⓗ
This is an award-winning, classical Victorian
corner ale house. Both CAMRA and English
Heritage have bestowed honours, just taste
the ale and look around to see why. Four
ever-changing guest beers, pub festivals and
Cains' own product range, also imported
bottles, ensure that every thirst is catered
for. As for history, the 100-year-old Irish bar
is the overwhelming feature, but also notice
the etched windows, the Cains mirror, the
beer bellows and the classic chandeliers.
The reference to the Grapes is a historical
throwback, and indeed the original pub was
a Cains' house.
◖&➤(Lime St) ⊖ (Central) ● ●

Doctor Duncan's
St John's House, St John's Lane
☼ 11.30-11; 12-10.30 Sun
☎ (0151) 709 5100 website: www.cainsbeers.com
**Cains Mild, Dr Duncans IPA, Bitter, FA, seasonal
beers; guest beers** Ⓗ
Regular award-winner, Doctor Duncan's was
the regional CAMRA *Pub of the Year* for
2000, also local *Pub of Excellence* 2000. One
bar serves several rooms, including the
classic Victorian tiled room. Four ever-
changing guests and a house beer
complement the Cains' range. An annual
beer festival in April is a highlight as is the
newly introduced special Belgian and
German week promotions. Some of these
beers have now been incorporated into the
permanent range. Top-quality food is served
until 7pm. The family room is designated as
the no-smoking area.
Q➤⛺◖➤(Lime St) ⊖ (Central) ● ✗ ●

Everyman
5-9 Hope Street (opp. Catholic Cathedral)
☼ 12-midnight (1am Thu; 2am Fri & Sat); closed Sun
☎ (0151) 708 9545 website: www.everyman.co.uk
Beer range varies Ⓗ
Subterranean, Bavarian-style bistro bar
beneath the Everyman Theatre. Busy before
and after performances, lunchtimes and for
its late licence, with a cosmopolitan
clientele. Usually carries three or four beers
such as Cains, Landlord and Pedigree and a
guest from Hanby or Derwent, plus a wide
range of wines and Belgian beers. The
Everyman is famed for its food and is listed
in CAMRA's *Good Pub Food* and other food
guides for its wide range of vegetarian
dishes, puddings, starters and cheeses, with
emphasis on organic produce. Frequent
functions include a 60s disco on Thu eve,
poetry readings and acoustic sets.
◖➤(Lime St) ⊖ (Central) ●

Globe
17 Cases Street (opp. Central station)
☼ 11-11; 12-10.30 Sun
☎ (0151) 709 5060
Cains Mild, Bitter Ⓗ
The Globe's quaintness stands in sharp
contrast to the bland modernity of the
adjacent Clayton Square shopping centre.
The present building dates from 1888. A
lively atmosphere exists in the pub, no
matter what the time of day. If visiting this
pub as part of a crawl, take care to moderate
your earlier consumption, as the sloping
floor tends to magnify the effect of
inebriation on the drinker's sense of

balance. Background music is mainly drawn from the 1960s, and the volume can at times make conversation difficult. ⚑ (Lime St) ⊖ (Central)

Head of Steam
7 Lime Street (inside Lime St Station)
☼ 11-2am (but may vary with demand); 12-10.30 Sun
☎ (0151) 707 9559 website: www.headofsteam.co.uk
Holt Bitter; Hydes Mild, Bitter Ⓗ
Large pub on the ground floor of the old North Western Hotel, Lime Street Station. Three of the five bars serve good real ale. Studio 58 is a modern café bar-style area with four real ales and large comfy leather sofas. The display bar is designed as a traditional railway bar, with up to six ales available. The decor of the grand hall, the connoisseurs bar, reflects the original splendour of the building. There are up to 14 real ales on offer. The pub has become very popular in the short time that it's been open. Q ◗ ⊞⅃⚳⚱ ⚑ (Lime St) ⚱⚔

Lion Tavern ☆
67 Moorfields (close to station)
☼ 11-11; 12-10.30 Sun
☎ (0151) 236 1734
Cains Bitter; Lees Bitter Ⓗ
Victorian splendour lives on in this traditional street-corner pub, albeit the public bar has more recently acquired an Irish feel. An extravaganza of wood and tiles, the central bar serves the no-frills public bar as well as the two more comfortable rear lounges. Much of the original glazing survives and the amazing glass cupola in the rear lounge should not be missed. This is the smallest of Liverpool's Victorian gems. Food is served daily from 11-2. A rare outlet in Liverpool for the excellent Lees bitter. ◗⊞⊖ (Moorfields)

Ma Boyles
Tower Buildings, Tower Gardens,
off Water Street
☼ 11-11; closed Sun
☎ (0151) 236 1717
Hydes Bitter; guest beer Ⓗ
Since 1870 Ma Boyle's Oyster Bar has been a Liverpool institution. A lunchtime refuge for the business community, where many a deal has been concluded over a pint and a plate of oysters. Tucked away at the end of a lane off Water Street by St Nicholas church gardens this superb pub is well worth seeking out not just for the beer but the excellent food served Mon to Fri 11.30-9. If you tire of the beer why not try a pint of prawns or the house speciality, an Eccles cake with Stilton. A friendly welcome is guaranteed in either the upstairs or quieter downstairs bars. Jazz on Wed eve.
Q ◗ ⊖ (Moorfields/James St)

Peter Kavanagh's
2-6 Egerton Street
☼ 12-11; 12-10.30 Sun
☎ (0151) 709 8443
Cains Bitter; Greene King Abbot; guest beers Ⓗ
Unusual back-street local on the outskirts of Liverpool city centre. Lively and very much at the heart of the local community, this Victorian pub has expanded into the two adjoining properties. The exterior is tiled and the windows contain stained glass. The small bar area is cluttered with assorted bric-à-brac. There are two small, quiet snug rooms either side of the bar, these have large murals by artist Eric Robertson. A book has recently been published about the 150-year history of the pub.
Q ◗⚑ (Lime St) ⊖ (Central) ⚱⚔

Poste House
23 Cumberland Street
☼ 11-11; 12-10.30 Sun
☎ (0151) 236 4130
Cains Mild, Bitter Ⓗ
Lively conversation abounds in a friendly atmosphere. The gloomy surroundings belie the warm welcome which awaits. Inside, the pub exudes cosiness in its two small rooms on two floors. Attractive stained glass screens surround the ground-floor seating booths. The Poste House can boast a notable clientele in the distant and not so distant past. Liverpool cotton merchant John Maybrick, thought by many to have been Jack the Ripper, was a regular. More recent times have seen up-and-coming rock stars dropping in to whet their whistles before playing the Lomax Club, which stood over the road until recently.
◗⚑ (Lime St) ⊖ (Moorfields)

Railway Hotel
18 Tithe Barn Street
☼ 11-11; 12-10.30 Sun
☎ (0151) 236 7210
Cains Mild, Bitter; Marston's Pedigree Ⓗ
Large, friendly Victorian pub close to Moorfields Station (next to the Lion Tavern, which is run by the landlord's father). The pub is clad in Cains' livery but is owned by Inn Partnership. The original stained glass screens are still in the window. A multi-roomed pub with a large single bar, the ceiling has been sympathetically restored. There are two quiet snugs at the rear of the pub. It is popular with the locals and the surrounding business community.
Q ◗⚑ (Lime St) ⊖ (Moorfields) ⚱

Roscoe Head
24 Roscoe Street
☼ 11-11; 12-10.30 Sun
☎ (0151) 709 4365
Jennings Bitter Ⓗ
Present in this *Guide* since 1974, this delightful, back-street, unspoilt pub has a front snug, tiny front bar, rear lounge snug and small main bar. The Roscoe has been run by the same family for 17 years and is a pub where everybody knows everybody's name. There is even a charity CD 'Rocking at the Roscoe' with staff and regulars singing. Once there were over 300 pubs named 'The Roscoe' after William Roscoe the philanthropist and anti-slavery campaigner who lived in Roscoe Street. Entertainment includes quiz night on Tue and cribbage on Wed. Traditional home-cooked lunches. ⚐◗⚑ (Lime St) ⊖ (Central)

Ship & Mitre
133 Dale Street
☼ 11.30 (12.30 Sat)-11; 2.30-10.30 Sun
☎ (0151) 236 0859 www.shipandmitre.co.uk
Beer range varies Ⓗ
Friendly city-centre pub, the current building was completed in the early part of the last century. The main island bar serves two areas with gas lighting enhancing a

nautical flavour. A constantly changing selection of real ales is provided together with numerous foreign beers; ranging from draught beers to bottled beers from around the world and two real ciders. Low cost, high quality food is served lunchtime and early eve. Popular quarterly beer festivals are held with beers on stillage in the upstairs Art Deco-styled function room as well as served from the bar.
Q ◁≉ (Lime St) ⊖ (Moorfields) ● ☐ ●

Vernon Arms
69 Dale Street
☼ 11.30 (12 Sat)-11; closed Sun
☎ (0151) 236 4525
Coach House Gunpowder Strong Mild; guest beers Ⓗ
This welcoming pub, located near the business district, offers six guest beers alongside a permanent mild. The owners, the Liverpool Brewing Company, supply one guest beer. A range of bottled Belgian beers is also available. There are three main areas: a small snug to the front, a long main room, and a back room. The sloping floor may catch out the unwary. Excellent food – the day's specials are displayed on a blackboard. Many meals include delicious thick, home-made chips. Winner of a local CAMRA *Pub of Excellence* award 2000. ◁●≉ (Lime St) ⊖ (Moorfields)

White Star
4 Rainford Gardens
☼ 11.30-11; 12-10.30 Sun
☎ (0151) 231 6861
Beer range varies Ⓗ
In the heart of the famous Cavern Quarter this pub is an oasis for real ale. A traditional Liverpool boozer with plenty of ale, banter and a warm welcome. The front room features a traditional wooden bar and has pictures of local boxing legends coupled with nautical liners from the legendary White Star Line. The comfortable back lounge has a Beatles corner and an extremely large Bass mirror. Sporting events are covered by multi-screen Sky presentations. The friendliness is typified by the twinning of the pub with those in both Norway and the Czech Republic. Three ever-changing guest beers on offer.
◁●≉ (Lime St) ⊖ (Moorfields/Central)

LIVERPOOL: EAST

Wetherspoon's
690 Queens Drive, Stoneycroft
☼ 11-11; 12-10.30 Sun
☎ (0151) 220 2713
Shepherd Neame Spitfire; Cains Mild; guest beers Ⓗ
Very comfortable pub with a combination of drinking areas in what is essentially a single room. Down by the marble-topped bar is an open-plan area with a spacious feel. There is a designated no-smoking area on the higher level with tables and soft furnishings. This area is characterised by quiet alcoves. In this friendly pub there is great emphasis on service and value. This outlet fully participates in all Wetherspoon's promotions and beer festivals; during the latter, real cider is usually on offer. Q ❀◁● ⊬●

Willowbank
329 Smithdown Road, Wavertree
☼ 12-11; 12-10.30 Sun
☎ (0151) 733 5782
Beer range varies Ⓗ
This pub has been popular with locals and students for many years. An ever-changing range of up to 11 good quality real ales is enhanced by occasional beer festivals. Bar food is available including several vegetarian options and a choice of very affordable specials on weekday eves until 8pm. There is a separate public bar and some interesting photographs of old Liverpool are displayed throughout the premises. The present interior with mock beams (part of the Festival Ale House refurbishment) compares unfavourably with the earlier furnishings, but is well compensated for by the warm atmosphere and friendly staff. Enjoyable quiz on Wed eve. ❀◁● ⊖♿♣P

LIVERPOOL: NORTH

Bull
2 Dublin Street (close to Stanley Dock market)
☼ 11-11; 12-10.30 Sun
☎ (0151) 207 2802
Beer range varies Ⓗ
In the heart of the northern dock area, with so many pub closures locally, the Bull has thrived recently. On Sun it is the drinking home of the local Stanley Dock market, and throughout the week the emphasis is on the

INN BRIEF

BARNSTON VILLAGE
Fox & Hounds
107 Barnston Road
11-11; 12-10.30 Sun
Theakston Best Bitter, Cool Cask, Old Peculier; Webster's Yorkshire Bitter; guest beers Ⓗ
Built in 1911 on the site of an 18th-century pub. Lounge, tiled bar and snug offering real home-cooked pub grub. On CAMRA's 13 pubs walk.

BOOTLE
Cat & Fiddle
St Martins House, Stanley Road
11.30-11; 12-10.30 Sun
Cains Bitter; guest beer Ⓗ
Lively pub with entertainment nightly. Dancing area, widescreen TV. Regular guest beer. Aimed at over 25s. No food Sun.

CROSBY
Crosby
75 Liverpool Road (A565)
11-11; 12-10.30 Sun
Guest beers Ⓗ
Lively, large one-roomed pub with music and large-screen TV. Two constantly-changing guest beers.

IRBY VILLAGE
Shippons Inn
8a Thingwall Road
11-11;
12-10.30 Sun
Banks's Original, Bitter; Camerons Strongarm; Marston's Pedigree; guest beers Ⓗ
Traditional village pub converted from 18th-century farm building. Retaining its inglenook. Folk music and imaginative theme nights.

LIVERPOOL: CENTRE
Post Office
2 Great Newton Street
12 (7.30 Sat)-11;
7.30-10.30 Sun
Cains Bitter; guest beers Ⓗ
Two-roomed Victorian pub near the hospital and university campus. Popular with students. Food served weekday lunchtimes.

Wetherspoon's
1-2 Charlotte Row
11-11;
12-10.30 Sun
Cains Mild; guest beers Ⓗ
Generic Wetherspoon's, can be very busy. Food every day. Beer festivals.

local workers and community. There is always a warm welcome – especially when you 'ask for cask', as the pub does serve nitro. The single handpull usually has Fuller's London Pride or Young's Special at a great value price. The same can be said of the hot lunches and often free plates of sandwiches and pies are circulated.
Q ◁ ≉ (Sandhills)

LIVERPOOL: *SOUTH*

Allerton Hall (Pub in the Park)
Springwood Avenue, Clarke Gardens
✪ 11-11; 12-10.30 Sun
☎ (0151) 494 2664
Cains Bitter; Marston's Pedigree; guest beers Ⓗ
Large pub in a public park (Clarke Gardens), next to Springwood Crematorium. After two fires on the premises the pub was almost totally rebuilt by Greenalls Brewery. The interior decoration is in keeping with the elegance of the building. There is a large bar stocking six ales with up to four guests. Food is served all day. An area is set aside specifically for families with small children, complete with outside play area.
Q ⛺ 🐾 ◁

Brewery Tap
35 Grafton Street
✪ 11-11; 12-10.30 Sun
☎ (0151) 709 2129
www.cainsbeers.com/pubs/brewerytap
Cains Mild, Dr Duncans IPA, Bitter, FA, seasonal beers; guest beers Ⓗ
An original fixture of the Victorian Robert Cain Brewery, the Tap was Cains' first tied pub. Magnificently restored, the former Grapes reopened in 1994 and won the CAMRA/English Heritage *Refurbishment Award* 1995. It has a fine moulded brick and terracotta façade and engraved windows. The bar counter with its scrolled supports was rescued from a nearby pub, while the gantry came from a dogs' home. An interesting collection of breweriana includes beer labels from Merseyside's former breweries. The Tap serves the full range of Cains beers and three guests from micro-breweries. Popular with brewery and other workers and as host to brewery tours, it is 15 minutes' walk from the city centre, near the Anglican cathedral. Weekday lunches 🐾 🍎 ♦

NEW BRIGHTON ✻

Albion Hotel
104 Albion Street
✪ 11-11; 11-10.30 Sun
☎ (0151) 639 1832
e-mail: albionhotel-newbrighton@ukf.net
Barnsley IPA; Lees Bitter; Wells Bombardier; guest beers Ⓗ
Built in 1832, this large community pub has a warm, welcoming atmosphere. With three distinctly different rooms: public bar, function/family room and upstairs restaurant (open eve only), this pub has something for everyone. Recently awarded local CAMRA Pub of the Year, it boasts five cask handpumps, featuring three regular ales, an ever-changing guest and rotating Cains' beers handpump. A dedicated real cider handpump and continental bottled beers are available. Home-cooked food is served all week. A traditional-style inn with a large room for any functions, including New Brighton's pubs' summer real ale festival. ⛺🐾≉◁◁⊖🐾Å🚫♣♦P🚭

NEW FERRY

Cleveland Arms
31 Bebington Road
✪ 11-11; 11-10.30 Sun
☎ (0151) 645 2847
Thwaites Mild, Bitter Ⓗ
Popular and friendly local in a pedestrianised area. The bar is a traditionally-styled wood and brass design with handpull dispense of their cask beers. Drinks' prices are very reasonable. The pub has two TVs, turned on as and when requested, a juke box and pool and darts are played. There is live light entertainment every Sun afternoon. The pub is open plan with two seated areas and a third pool table area. ≉ (Bebington) ♣P

PRESCOT

Clock Face
54 Derby Street (A57)
✪ 11-11 (winter 11-3, 7-11); Sat 12-3, 7-10.30, (12-10.30 summer) Sun
☎ (0151) 292 4121
Thwaites Bitter Ⓗ
Imposing former Georgian mansion, previously owned by Lord Derby, on main Liverpool to Prescot road. Attractively decorated and comfortably furnished, this

---

Childwall Abbey
Childwall Abbey Road
12-11; 12-10.30 Sun
Burtonwood Top Hat; Cains Bitter; guest beer Ⓗ
Comfortable, suburban multi-roomed pub in quiet location close to Childwall parish church. Good-value food.

Kelly's Dispensary
154-158 Smithdown Road
11.30-11;
12-10.30 Sun
Cains Mild, Bitter, FA, seasonal beers; guest beers Ⓗ
Suburban pub on main thoroughfare popular with locals and students. Tastefully refurbished by Cains in 1998.

LIVERPOOL: *NORTH*
Raven
72 Walton Vale
11-11;
12-10.30 Sun
Cains Mild, Bitter; Shepherd Neame Spitfire; guest beers Ⓗ
This large, one-roomed Wetherspoon's pub is bustling and friendly. *Cask Marque* accredited.

LIVERPOOL: *SOUTH*
Storresdale
43-47 Storresdale Road
3 (11.30 Sat)-11;
12-10.30 Sun
Taylor Landlord Ⓗ
Small, cosy back-street local off Mather Avenue. Separate bar at rear.

NEW BRIGHTON
Clarence Hotel
89 Albion Street
11-11; 12-10.30 Sun
Draught Bass; Boddingtons Bitter; Brakspear Special; Cains Bitter; guest beers Ⓗ
Recently refurbished and extended traditional pub now with disabled facilities. Good home-cooked food.

> ✻ symbol next to a main entry place name indicates there are Inn Brief entries as well.

multi-roomed pub is served by one long bar. A warm welcome and friendly service ensure that you will stay for more than one pint in this rare outlet for Thwaites in the Liverpool area. The pub benefits from a large car park to the front and an open aspect which makes sitting at the benches and tables outside enjoyable in the summer months. Watch out for the two ghosts! ❀◖≉♣P

Sun Inn
11 Derby Street (A57)
✪ 12-11; 12-10.30 Sun
Beer range varies Ⓗ
A stone-façaded, double-fronted building located on main Liverpool to Prescot road. A basic public bar and three lounge areas make up this traditional-style pub. The front lounge is quiet and has a real fire. All areas are served from the central bar. The lounge areas are comfortably furnished and the rear lounge is decorated with an assortment of Victorian photographs. One rotating guest beer is offered and forthcoming beers are advertised on blackboards. The original, attractive, etched glazing survives in the front windows and entrance door. Q◱≉♣

RAINHILL

Commercial
12 Station Road (off A57)
✪ 11-11; 12-10.30 Sun
☎ (0151) 430 8473
Cains Bitter Ⓗ
Overlooking Rainhill Station which is well depicted pictorially within the pub's four separate drinking areas where many other prints and photographs, mainly scenes of old Rainhill and Prescot, are displayed. Always busy, the racing channel dominates in the afternoon before the serious drinking takes over. Once owned by Joseph Jones, a brewery acquired and closed by Higsons in the 1920s. Sadly the evidence of this has almost disappeared and all but two of the 'Joseph Jones Knotty Ash Ales' windows have now been replaced. ◱≉♣P

ST. HELENS

Beecham's Bar & Brewery
Water Street (A58, near clock tower)
✪ 12-11; closed Sun
☎ (01744) 623420
Beer range varies Ⓗ
This bar and brewery are situated in the ex-Beecham's Powders offices, now part of St Helens College. The students learn about brewing and bar management which includes organising Karaoke and quiz nights. The beer range includes two in-house brewed beers, Thwaites Bitter or one of Thwaites seasonal beers, plus a range of up to three guest beers. The adjacent brewhouse can be viewed through a glass screen from the bar, which attracts students, locals and visitors. The college rugby and football teams hold meetings in the bar. ♿≉✂️🗄

Sutton Oak
73 Bold Road (B5204)
✪ 12-11; 12-10.30 Sun
☎ (01744) 813442 website: thesuttonoak.co.uk

Black Sheep Best Bitter; guest beers Ⓗ
Small, friendly community pub built in 1870, offering traditional pub games including dominoes, darts, pool and cribbage. Close to a nature trail through a wildlife conservation area, the pub has its own angling club which meets regularly, and also holds Karaoke and quiz nights. Customers have access to a computer linked to the internet, which is situated in the lounge bar. It was previously known as the Boundary Vaults owing to its close proximity to the borough boundary, and was renamed the Sutton Oak only two years ago. Real cider is served during the summer. ❀◖≉♣P

SOUTHPORT

Barons Bar, Scarisbrick Hotel
239 Lord Street (opp. tourist information office)
✪ 11-11; 12-10.30 Sun
☎ (01704) 543000 website: www.scarisbrickhotel.com
Taylor Landlord; Tetley Bitter; guest beer Ⓗ
The Barons Bar is located within the historic Scarisbrick Hotel which has an imposing position in the centre of Lord Street. The bar is furnished, as its name suggests, in the style of a medieval baronial hall with weaponry and hatchments decorating the walls, a vaulted and arched bar and furnished with comfortable leather armchairs. The house beer is Flag and Turret, a session bitter. The Barons Bar can be reached from the hotel reception area or from an entrance off the pedestrianised thoroughfare next to the hotel. A beer festival is held every year during the first week in May commencing at 6am on May Day morning. ◱≉●

Berkeley Arms
(formerly Blakes Hotel)
19 Queens Road (opp. Trinity church)
✪ 4-11; 12-11 Sun
☎ (01704) 500811 www.berkeley-hotel.co.uk
Adnams Bitter; Banks's Bitter; Camerons Strongarm; Fuller's London Pride; Marston's Pedigree; Moorhouses Black Cat Ⓗ
Popular with local residents, this pub is housed within an imposing Victorian semi-detached residence which once served as a seaside hotel. Bed & breakfast accommodation is available and excellent home-made pizzas are a speciality. The drinking area is divided into a small, cosy bar with a golfing theme and a larger drinking area (part of which is no-smoking). There is a comfortable family room to the rear. Eight real ales are always available with beers from Moorhouses of Burnley predominating. Some beers are always at discounted prices during the pub's 'happy hour' 4-7 weekdays. ♿❀◖≉♣P✂️

Falstaff Inn
68 King Street
✪ 11-11; 12-10.30 Sun
☎ (01704) 530123
Theakston Mild, Best Bitter; Wells Bombardier; guest beers Ⓗ
Superb advert for real ale, and deservedly voted local CAMRA *Pub of the Year* 2001. With an array of handpumps to slake the keenest thirst, the Falstaff has been transformed from an empty pub selling keg-only beer into one of the busiest in town.

The pub has a reputation for excellent food with competitive prices. A short walk from the railway station and town's famous Lord Street and its shops and arcades, the Falstaff is now the place to go in Southport for the keen beer drinker. Q ✪ ◁▷ ⇥ ♣ ✄

London
14 Windsor Road
☼ 12-11; 12-10.30 Sun
☎ (01704) 542885
Oakwell Barnsley Bitter, Old Tom Ⓗ

This pub is the only outlet in Southport for beers brewed at the Oakwell Brewery in Barnsley, South Yorkshire. The London is a large and relaxing pub which has recently been tastefully refurbished to a high standard. The main drinking area is spacious and divided into comfortably furnished areas. The pub boasts a tap room as well as a separate family room. The London offers facilities for playing darts, dominoes and pool and outside there is a bowling green and a beer garden. The pub is approximately 10 minutes' walk from Southport Station. Q ⏚ ✪ ◁▷ ⇥ ♣ P

Up Steps
20 Upper Aughton Road, Birkdale
☼ 11.30-11; 12-10.30 Sun
☎ (01704) 569245
Coach House Coachman's Best Bitter, Gunpowder Strong Mild; Theakston Mild, Best Bitter; guest beers Ⓗ

Traditional, street-corner local, one of a dying breed. The landlord and landlady celebrated 10 years in charge of the pub in 2001, and still refuse to sell nitro-keg beers. The only outlet in Southport for Coach House beers, which customers come from miles around to try. The Up Steps was once three-times Grand National winner Red Rum's local, as his stables were down the road from the pub. Darts, dominoes and quiz teams play at home here, and it is always a popular venue with away teams. Easily the best pub in Birkdale.
Q ✪ ⇥ (Birkdale) ♣ P

WALLASEY

Farmer's Arms
225 Wallasey Village
☼ 11.30-11; 12-10.30 Sun
☎ (0151) 638 2110
Cains Mild, Bitter; Tetley Bitter; Theakston Best Bitter; guest beer Ⓗ

Prior to 1924 the Farmer's Arms was a single-room bar between two stone cottages. It now has three distinct drinking areas to suit most tastes; busy front bar with TV, a side snug and a juke box-free back lounge. The licensee is one of Wirral's longest serving. Throughout various ownerships he has ensured quality of service and ales. Weekday lunches include Chinese stir-fries. Quiz night on Tue and the pub runs a golf society. Several awards have been presented by the local CAMRA branch. The guest beer pump can be found in the bar.
◁▷ ⇥ (Grove Rd)

WATERLOO

La Barbacoa
49-51 Mersey View
☼ 12-3 (closed Mon), 7-12; 12-midnight Sat; 12-11 Sun
☎ (0151) 924 0445
Beer range varies Ⓗ

This large, modern, comfortably furnished pub draws an all-age clientele. It is spacious, has a long central bar and attractive conservatory adding space and light to the rear. During the summer months the beer garden opens, with barbecue facilities at weekends. The pub attracts capacity crowds on Tue eve when excellent bands play. A resident duo perform Sat eve. The upstairs restaurant provides a full, interesting menu comparable to most specialist restaurants. The usual pub food is also available down in the bar at lunchtimes and eves (not Mon). Four constantly changing guest beers are on offer. ◁▷ ⇥

Volunteer Canteen
45 East Street
☼ 12-11; 12-10.30 Sun
☎ (0151) 928 6594
Cains Bitter Ⓗ

Traditional Edwardian back-street pub with a friendly atmosphere. Table service in the lounge. A community local with original early 1900s façade and interior, and a distinctive screened counter to the lounge. Dartboard and TV are provided in the bar with a large collection of trophies displayed. Beautifully maintained and furnished, this classic pub is a firm favourite with many. Small beer garden to the rear with charity barbecues held May-Sept. A consistent entry in this *Guide*. Small, but well worth the visit.
🏛 Q ✪ ◁▷ ⇥ ♣

Johnnie Dowie's Tavern

Johnnie Dowie was the sleekest and kindest of landlords. Nothing could equal the benignity of his smile when he bought in a bottle of ale to a company of well-known and friendly customers. It was a perfect treat to see his formality in drawing the cork, his precision in filling the glasses, his regularity in drinking the healths of all present in the first glass (which he always did, and at every successive bottle), and then his douce civility in withdrawing. Johnnie lived till within the last few years and with laudable attachment to the old costume, always wore a cocked hat, and buckles at knee and shoes, as well as a cane with a cross top, somewhat like an implement called by Scottish gardeners 'a dibble'.
William Home, *The Year Book*, 1839. Dowie died in 1817. His Edinburgh tavern was frequented by Robert Burns and Adam Smith.

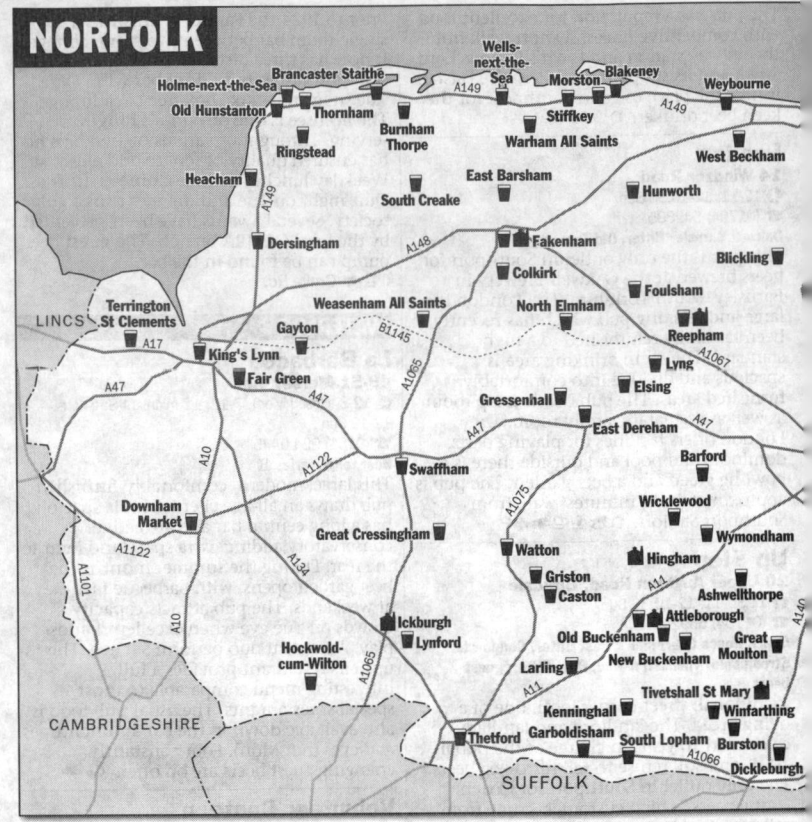

NORFOLK

Holme-next-the-Sea
Brancaster Staithe
Wells-next-the-Sea
Morston
Blakeney
Weybourne
A149
Old Hunstanton
Thornham
Stiffkey
Burnham Thorpe
Warham All Saints
West Beckham
Ringstead
A149
Heacham
East Barsham
Hunworth
South Creake
A149
Dersingham
A148
Fakenham
Blickling
Colkirk
Terrington St Clements
Weasenham All Saints
North Elmham
Foulsham
LINCS
Gayton
B1145
Reepham
A17
King's Lynn
A1065
Lyng
A1067
Fair Green
A47
Elsing
A47
A47
Gressenhall
East Dereham
A47
A10
A1122
Swaffham
Barford
A1075
Wicklewood
Downham Market
Great Cressingham
Wymondham
A1122
A134
Watton
Hingham
Ashwellthorpe
A11
A1101
A10
Griston
Caston
Attleborough
A140
Ickburgh
Lynford
Old Buckenham
Great Moulton
Hockwold-cum-Wilton
A1065
Larling
New Buckenham
A11
Tivetshall St Mary
CAMBRIDGESHIRE
Kenninghall
Winfarthing
Thetford
Garboldisham
South Lopham
Burston
Dickleburgh
A1066
SUFFOLK

ASHWELLTHORPE

White Horse
49-55 The Street
🕐 12-2.30 (not Mon & Tues), 5.30-11; 12-3.30, 7-10.30 Sun
☎ (01508) 489721
e-mail: white@freehouse.freeserve.co.uk
Fuller's London Pride; guest beers Ⓗ
Village-centre free house with original beams and collection of beer posters. Small, reduced inglenook with an armorial fireback and woodburner in separate dining area. Lunch hours are occasionally extended (check in advance). The pub holds midsummer balls, charity and theme eves. Attractive large garden at the rear and tables at the front. Note the Webster's mirror in the gents. The woman trying to enter the pub through a bricked-up door is the resident ghost.
🏚️❀🆗♣P

ATTLEBOROUGH

Cock
1 High Street
🕐 11-3, 6-11 Mon-Thu; 11-11 Fri & Sat; 12-10.30 Sun
☎ (01953) 452570
Adnams Bitter; Wells Bombardier; guest beer Ⓗ
Friendly, two-bar pub with pool table in an annexe to the main bar. The landlord of 12 years standing is a mine of information on this 18th-century former coaching inn.

Photos of old Attleborough pubs are displayed in the smaller bar – see if you can identify the one you are standing in. There are active crib and pool teams and among the more unusual games played is Ring the Bull. With its red furnishings and ornamental horse brasses, the pub has a 1970s feel. Wall-mounted juke box in the main bar doesn't disturb the relaxed atmosphere.
Q❀🆗Å⇌♣P

Griffin Hotel
Church Street
🕐 11-3, 5.30-11 Mon-Thu; 11-11 Fri & Sat; 11-4, 7-10.30 Sun
☎ (01953) 452149
Greene King Abbot; Wolf Bitter, Coyote Bitter; guest beer Ⓗ
Charming 16th-century former coaching inn featuring original beams and mellow brick, with a separate dining room, a function room and a snug. This hotel is at the centre of the community and has a varied clientele. The Griffin has a strong relationship with the local Wolf Brewery, their ales always feature in the pub's range, including one of their rarer beers. Excellent menu of home-cooked food using local suppliers wherever possible. Eight guest rooms are available and brewery tours can be arranged for guests.
🏚️Q❀🛏️🆗🍴🏧Å⇌P

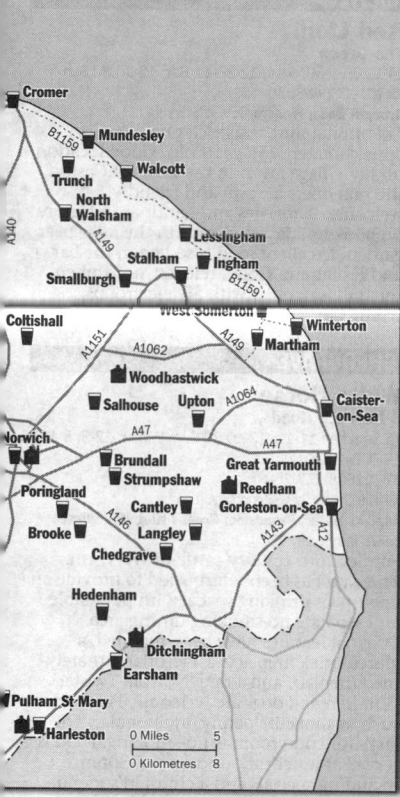

popular with tourists with its narrow streets and attractive buildings. The quay is particularly pleasant and nearby Blakeney Point is a favourite with birdwatchers and for boat trips. This pub has had only two licensees in the over 40 years. There is a large beer garden. Seven en-suite guest rooms are available, each with TV.
Q ⛄ ❀ ⇔ ◖◗ ⊟ ▲ ♣ P ⊁ 🗍

BLICKLING

Buckinghamshire Arms
On B1354, just outside Aylsham
🕓 11.30-3, 6.30-11; 12-3, 7-10.30 Sun
☎ (01263) 732133
Greene King IPA, Abbot; guest beer (summer) Ⓗ
At the gates of Blickling Hall (NT), this unspoilt free house is one of Norfolk's finest examples of a traditional coaching inn. Built in 1693 for guests and servants of Blickling Hall, it has a delightful, intimate snug with unusual wooden handpump handles. The lounge bar has wainscotting and a woodburner. Food is served here or in the separate dining room with its huge fireplace and longcase clock. No food winter Sun eve. The house beer, Blickling Ale, is brewed by Woodforde's. B&B accommodation is available with four-poster beds. Occasionally open all day Sun. ⇔ Q ❀ ⇔ ◖◗ ⊟ ♣ P

BRANCASTER STAITHE ❄

Jolly Sailors
Main Road (A149)
🕓 11-11; 12-10.30 Sun
☎ (01485) 210314 website: www.the-jolly-sailors.co.uk
Greene King IPA; Iceni Fine Soft Day; Woodforde's Wherry; guest beers Ⓗ
Busy, authentic village local with a varied clientele. Food is available all day, including breakfast from 10am. The restaurant specialises in local seafood including Brancaster mussels. There is a large, sheltered garden with a well-equipped children's play area. Can get very busy at weekends. ⇔ Q ❀ ◖◗ ⅟ ♣ P

BROOKE

White Lion
49 The Street OS289992
🕓 12-3 (not Mon), 5.30-11; 12-11 Sat; 12-10.30 Sun
☎ (01508) 550443
Adnams Bitter; Greene King IPA; guest beers Ⓗ
Attractive thatched pub with part clay-tiled floor and a very low ceiling in the long narrow bar. This friendly local has a peaceful rural setting opposite the mere (pond). ⇔ ❀ ◖◗ ♣ P

BARFORD

Cock Inn
Watton Road (B1108)
🕓 12-3 (not Mon), 6-11; 12-4, 7-10.30
(may extend summer) Sun
☎ (01603) 757646
Blue Moon Easy Life, Sea of Tranquility, Hingham High; guest beers Ⓗ
Former coaching inn, still has rings where the drovers' cattle were tethered. Two bars; one with a wooden floor and real fire, the other is carpeted, with a restaurant beyond. An old plough stands in the car park. The landlord has recently bucked the trend by reopening the village shop and the pub is soon to have its own brewery. Up to six real ales should be available. Fines are imposed for using mobile phones (proceeds to the lifeboats). Bowling green scheduled to reopen. No food Mon. ⇔ ❀ ◖◗ ▲ ♣ ♣ P

BLAKENEY

King's Arms
Westgate Street
🕓 11-11, 12-10.30 Sun ☎ (01263) 740341
Adnams Bitter; Ⓖ Greene King Old Speckled Hen; Marston's Pedigree; Webster's Yorkshire Bitter; Ⓗ Woodforde's Wherry Ⓖ
Large, white-painted flint inn. Two inter-connecting bars have clay-tiled floors. An additional bar beyond the public bar features a flint-panelled wall. Food is available all day, every day. The village is

INDEPENDENT BREWERIES

Ale Wife Harleston
Blanchfield Fakenham
Blue Moon Hingham
Buffy's Tivetshall St. Mary
Chalk Hill Norwich
Humpty Dumpty Reedham
Iceni Ickburgh
Reepham Reepham
Tindall Ditchingham
Wolf Attleborough
Woodforde's Woodbastwick

BURSTON

Crown Inn
Crown Green
☼ 12-2 (2.30 Sat), 6-11; 12-3, 7-10.30 Sun
☎ (01379) 741257
Adnams Bitter; guest beers Ⓖ

This village is famous for the Burston school strike (the longest strike in history). The school is now a museum. The Crown Inn built c1850 has a no-smoking lounge with a railway station featured. There are chalk/charcoal characters on the log-ends in the fireplace and collages in the entrance porch and displayed in the loos. The public bar has a pool table and juke box. Usually at least one local beer is on offer, normally from the Old Chimneys Brewery. Fresh food is served in the separate, no-smoking dining room. ⚌Q❀❍►ⓆⒷ♣Å♣P✂

CAISTER-ON-SEA

Ship
2 Victoria Street
☼ 11-11; 12-10.30 Sun
☎ (01493) 728008
Greene King IPA, Old Speckled Hen; guest beers Ⓗ

Close to the beach, this pub enjoys a good local trade. A single bar is divided into several drinking areas and there is a pleasant patio courtyard. Food is served in a separate dining area. Comfortable and full of character, the Ship is worth seeking out. Limited parking. ⚌☍❀❍ⒶP

CANTLEY

Cock
Manor Road
☼ 11-3.30, 6-11; 12-5, 7-10.30 Sun
☎ (01493) 700895
Adnams Bitter; guest beers Ⓗ

Located just outside the village, about one mile from Cantley Station. The origins of this pub can be traced back to the late 1800s, note the fascinating old photos around the pub. There is one bar serving several drinking areas with lots of beams and exposed brickwork. The beer range is always interesting with many beers coming from smaller brewers. There is a separate non-smoking restaurant. Addlestones cider is available.
⚌☍❀❍►♣⬤P

CASTON

Red Lion
The Green
☼ 11.30-2.30, 5-11; 11.30-11 Sat; 12-10.30 Sun
☎ (01953) 488236
Draught Bass; Woodforde's Wherry Ⓗ

Traditional flint and brick pub approximately 150 years old. Good location on the village green in the heart of Caston, the pub offers a warm and friendly welcome. Barbecues and bands are a feature on bank holiday weekends in the large beer garden. Excellent food is served in the bar and restaurant. Good, relaxed atmosphere, the pub is popular with all age groups.
Q❀❍►ⒷP

CHEDGRAVE

White Horse
5 Norwich Road
☼ Summer: 11-11; 12-10.30 Sun; Winter: 12-3, 5-11; 12-3, 5-10.30 Sun
☎ (01508) 520250
website: www.thewhitehorsepub.co.uk
Adnams Bitter, Broadside; Greene King IPA; guest beers (summer) Ⓗ

Former 16th-century cattle drovers' inn. This pub has been refurbished to provide an open-plan drinking space, with pool table and separate no-smoking dining area. Original features have been retained, a glazed-brick fireplace, a Victorian ornately-tiled fireplace and a rare 'Norfolk Twister'. Children and dogs are welcome. Pub games, such as shove-ha'penny, are popular. The large function room is no-smoking. Food is served at lunchtime and from 5.30pm, including specials and a children's menu. The huge garden has patio and bowling green. Car parking is available opposite the pub. ⚌❀❍►Å♣✂⬤

COLTISHALL

Red Lion
77 Church Street
☼ 11-11; 11-3, 5-11 summer, 11-11; 12-10.30 Sun
☎ (01603) 737402
website: lamby-redlion@supanet.com
Adnams Bitter; Greene King Abbot Ⓗ

Comfortable 17th-century pub, the Red Lion name may date back to a 13th-century inn on the site. The warm, cosy interior is

INN BRIEF

BRANCASTER STAITHE
White Horse
Main Road
11-11; 12-10.30 Sun
Adnams Bitter; Greene King IPA, Abbot; guest beer Ⓗ
Locals' pub with conservatory restaurant, outdoor drinking area with views of marshes and Scolt Head island.

BRUNDALL
Yare
Station Road
10.30-2.30, 5-11; 10.30-11 Sat; 12-10.30 Sun
Woodforde's Wherry; John Smith's Bitter; guest beers Ⓗ
Large rambling riverside pub, a genuine free house. Families welcome. A few yards from the Broads and the railway station.

BURNHAM THORPE
Lord Nelson
Walsingham Road
11-3 (2.30 winter), 6-11; 12-3, 7-10.30 Sun
Greene King IPA, Abbot; Woodforde's Wherry, Nelson's Revenge Ⓖ
Gem of a pub with settles and flagstone floors. Beer straight from the tap room. Try the Nelson's Blood!

COLKIRK
Crown
Crown Road
11-2.30, 6-11; 12-3, 7-10.30 Sun
Greene King XX Mild, IPA, Abbot; guest beer Ⓖ
Attractive pub in rural setting. Red-tiled floor in single bar that has been divided into two drinking areas.

DOWNHAM MARKET
Cock Tavern
43 Lynn Road
11-2.30, 7-11;
12-2, 7-10.30 Sun
Adnams Bitter; Brakspear Bitter; guest beer Ⓗ
This local has a children's certificate and healthy eating award. Beer festival held each spring bank holiday. Internet facilities available.

FAKENHAM
Bull
Bridge Street
11-3, 7-11; 11-11 Thu-Sat; 12-3, 7-10.30 Sun
Blanchfield Black Bull Mild, Bull Best Bitter, Raging Bull Bitter Ⓗ
Home to Blanchfield Brewery, produces all the house beers.

divided into three distinct areas. The large balcony restaurant separates into different rooms and is decorated with traditional farming tools. Wooden beams in the main bar are hung with tankards and jugs. The smaller balcony bar has a dartboard and displays more tankards and also brass plates. Q❀◑&♣P✗⊟

CROMER

Anglia Court Hotel
5 Runton Road (on A149 coast road to Sheringham)
☼ 11-11; 12-10.30 sun
☎ (01263) 512443
website: smoothhound.co.uk/hotels/anglico.html
Woodforde's Wherry, Great Eastern; Ⓖ guest beers (summer) Ⓗ

Large clifftop hotel with 30 rooms and fine sea views. The Smugglers Bar is on the ground floor with a patio drinking area. The bar is named after Cromer's sea shanty singers who perform at the pub regularly. Fishing nets hang from the ceiling. Lunches are served in summer and evening meals all year round. Received RAC *Dining Award* 1999 and 2000. ❀⌂◑&▲≈P✗

DERSINGHAM

Feathers Hotel
Manor Road
☼ 11-2.30, 4.30-11; 12-3, 7-10.30 Sun
☎ (01485) 540207
Adnams Bitter; Draught Bass; guest beer Ⓗ

Comfortable, three-bar hotel on the Sandringham estate. Two of the bars are wood-panelled and are in the main building with the restaurant. There is a separate Stable bar for the younger clientele, this is bustling and often features live music. A good-value menu includes daily specials. Old portraits of the Royal Family are displayed. The extensive gardens include a well-eqipped children's play area. ⌂Q❀⌂◑▲P

DICKLEBURGH

Crown
The Street
☼ 12-3, 7 (5 Fri)-11; 11-11 Sat; 12-10.30 Sun
☎ (01379) 741475
website: www.dickleburghcrown.co.uk

Buffy's Bitter; Greene King IPA; guest beer Ⓗ
400-year-old hostelry on the former Norwich-Ipswich turnpike. The lower level is split into two by an ancient back-to-back fireplace and chimney-breast. The smaller of these two areas contains the large Sky TV screen. This keen footballing pub fields three teams. The heavily-beamed upper level houses a juke box and two pool tables. Don't challenge anyone to a match though as there are four resident pool teams. All three real ales are sold at the same low price irrespective of gravity. Occasional live music. No meals served Sun eve or Wed. ⌂◑▲♣P

DOWNHAM MARKET ❊

Live & Let Live
22 London Road
☼ 12-2 (not winter Mon-Thu), 7-11; 12-10.30 Sun
☎ (01366) 383933
Beer range varies Ⓗ

Busy town pub serving three ever-changing beers from independent breweries. The split-level bar has a quieter area above where dominoes and cribbage are played. The lower bar has large-screen TV, pool table and dartboard. Football is the main topic of conversation, the 'Livey' has its own Sunday league team. Live music most weekends in the lower bar. Parking is available in the Tesco car park, access through back gate. ❀⌂≈♣

EARSHAM

Queen's Head
Station Road
☼ 12-3, 6-11; 12-3, 7-10.30 Sun
☎ (01986) 892623
Beer range varies Ⓗ

Dating from 1684 (with subsequent additions) this is Earsham's only remaining pub. The main drinking area has a clay-tiled floor, a real fire and timber posts and beams. The side bar houses the pool table and there is a separate restaurant. There are up to three ever-changing ales from micros, often from the Midlands due to the licensee's contacts. The pub also doubles up as the village Post

---

GRISTON
Waggon & Horses
Church Road
11-3, 6.30-11 (sometimes closed later in afternoon);
11-3, 6.30-11 Sun
Greene King IPA, Abbot, Old Speckled Hen; guest beer Ⓗ
Cosy 17th-century pub, serving good range of real ales with an ever-changing guest beer. Extensive menu served.

KING'S LYNN
Fenman
Blackfriars Road
11-11; 12-3, 7-10.30 Sun
Greene King IPA, Abbot; guest beer Ⓗ
Spacious one-roomed modern bar opposite the railway station.

White Horse
9 Wootton Road
11-3, 5.30-11; 11-11 Fri & Sat;
12-3, 6.30-10.30 Sun
Adnams Bitter; Greene King IPA; guest beer Ⓗ
Traditional two-bar pub near the Gaywood clock.

LESSINGHAM
Star
School Road
12-3, 7-11 (11-11 summer);
12-4, 7-10.30 Sun
Greene King IPA, Abbot; Shepherd Neame Best Bitter Ⓗ
Built around 1740, one low-beamed bar with wood-burning stove. Home to the village Post Office and shop. Touring caravan site at rear.

LYNDFORD (MUNDFORD)
Lynford Hall
Lynford Estate
11-11; 12-10.30 Sun
Iceni Fine Soft Day; Woodforde's Wherry Ⓗ
Don't be overawed by the impressive building; the bar is as welcoming as any local. Bar food and restaurant. Extensive grounds open to visitors.

MUNDESLEY
Ship Inn
Beach Road
11.30-2.30, 6.30-11; 12-2.30, 6.30-10.30 Sun
Adnams Bitter; Flowers IPA; Greene King Abbot; guest beer Ⓗ
Impressive flint building on the seafront. Popular with locals and holidaymakers.

Office. There are plans to open a micro-brewery (subject to planning approval). No food Sun eve.

EAST BARSHAM

White Horse Inn
Fakenham Road (near manor house)
✪ 11-3, 6.30-11; 12-3, 7-10.30 Sun
☎ (01328) 820645
Adnams Bitter; Greene King IPA, Abbot; guest beers Ⓗ

17th-century inn, a true free house, it retains many original features, not least the log-burning inglenook. There is an extensive bar meal and restaurant menu with home-cooked food. The traditional Sun lunches are very popular. Good-value accommodation in this popular tourist area. Glimpse the magnificent Tudor brick manor house from the pub car park (manor not open to public). Henry VIII stayed here and walked barefoot to the shrine of Our Lady of Walsingham. Charming pub not to be missed. ▦Q✿🖙❶Ⓓ P

EAST DEREHAM

George Hotel
Swaffham Road
✪ 11-11, 12-10.30 Sun
☎ (01362) 696801
website: www.george-hotel.get-the-web.com
Adnams Bitter; Draught Bass; Greene King Abbot; Woodforde's Wherry, Nelson's Revenge Ⓗ

17th-century, Grade II listed building. This attractive hotel has a large wood-panelled bar with numerous alcoves. Bar meals are available and there is a separate restaurant. Alternative drinking area just inside hotel entrance, away from bustle of main bar. Alongside the real ale selection there are some interesting malt whiskies. Eight comfortable en-suite guest bedrooms.
Q✿🖙❶Ⓓ 🚆 (Mid Norfolk Railway) P 🚻

ELSING

Mermaid Inn
Church Street (opp. church)
✪ 12-3, 6 (7 Jan-Mar)-11; 12-3, 6 (7 Jan-Mar)-10.30 Sun
☎ (01362) 637640 e-mail: tomj@faxvia.net
Adnams Bitter; Woodforde's Wherry; guest beers Ⓗ

17th-century free house. The beamed bar area is split into a drinking area with open fire and a games area. The house beer, Mermaid Ale, is rebadged Morrells IPA. 80% of the guest ales are local, lined glasses on request; look for the mermaids on the handpumps. Wide menu of traditional pub fare and specials (using local produce), is served in the bar or in the separate restaurant. Occasionally open all day at weekends (check in advance). B&B available next door. Visit the church which has the widest single-spanned Norman nave in England and houses the Hastings Brass. ▦✿🖙❶Ⓓ♣P🚻

FAIR GREEN

Gate Inn
North off A47
✪ 12-2.30, 7 (5.30 Fri)-11; 12-3, 7-10.30 Sun

☎ (01553) 840518
Greene King IPA; guest beers Ⓗ

Regular *Guide* entry. Friendly village local, near Middleton just east of King's Lynn. The three small rooms include a back room with a pool table, a small dining area and a comfortable bar. Two guest beers are usually available. The excellent, tasty food is good value. No meals Mon eve. Enjoy the pleasant garden during the summer with its award-winning hanging baskets. ▦Q✿❶♣P

FOULSHAM

Queen's Head
2 High Street
✪ 11-3, 7-11; 12-3, 7-10.30 Sun
☎ (01362) 683339
e-mail: colinrowe@queenshead.fsnet.co.uk
Adnams Bitter; Woodforde's Wherry; guest beers (summer) Ⓗ

Relaxing, homely atmosphere in this friendly 17th-century free house in a central village location. The low-beamed main bar area has a wooden fronted bar and a fireplace at each end. The small snug has a woodburner and there is a no-smoking dining area. Varied menu using local produce. Walkers and cyclists welcome – the pub is on route 1 of the National Cycle Network – camping possible in the large garden (no facilities), also a bowling green. Afternoon hours may extend. Watch out for the cat by the fire, and the watercolour in the gents. ▦✿❶Ⓓ ▲♣P✁

GARBOLDISHAM

Fox Inn
The Street (at A1066/B1111 jct)
✪ 11.30-2.30, 5-11; 11.30-11 Sat; 12-10.30 Sun
☎ (01953) 688151
Adnams Bitter; Greene King IPA; Shepherd Neame Spitfire; guest beer Ⓗ

Cosy, old inn built in 1640, of traditional clay lump construction, retaining many original features. Friendly welcome and a good ambience in which to enjoy a pint or two. Well-behaved children and dogs welcome. Food from sandwiches to full meals, all freshly prepared to order, using local produce where possible. The pub is renowned for its sausage specialities. Beer range is augmented by guests, often from local micro-breweries. The village name is one of many in Norfolk where the spelling doesn't help; Garboldisham = Garble+shum. ▦Q✿❶♣P

GAYTON

Crown
Lynn Road
✪ 11.30-2.30, 6 (5.30 Fri)-11; 11-3, 6-11 Sat; 12-7-10.30 Sun
☎ (01553) 636252 e-mail: crownatlzwf@supanet.com
Greene King XX Mild, IPA, Ruddles County, Abbot, Old Speckled Hen Ⓗ

A long-standing entry in the *Guide*, this pub is at the hub of village life and has a strong local trade. It features a garden, a children's room, two bars and a separate restaurant. It can be very busy, especially in summer, but is also an excellent place to visit on a cold winter's evening to be warmed by the roaring fire. It enjoys a good reputation for food. There are regular events such as quizzes and live music. ♨️🏠🏮🌙🍴♣️P●

GORLESTON-ON-SEA

Dock Tavern
Dock Tavern Lane
✪ 12-11; 12-10.30 Sun
☎ (01493) 442255
Adnams Broadside; Elgood's Black Dog Mild; Fuller's London Pride; Greene King IPA; guest beers Ⓗ
L-shaped drinking area featuring an upside-down rowing boat cut in half over the bar. Pub was originally one of three built by the owner of a large fishing fleet to satisfy the recreational needs of his employees and must be one of the few to have a road named after it (rather than the other way round). Nautical memorabilia and brasses abound and markers show the various flood levels over the years – so if the nearby river has burst its banks, bring your wellies! Live music on Sat eve. Up to six guest beers and Norfolk cider on offer. ⚽●

GREAT CRESSINGHAM

Windmill Inn
Water End (off A1065 4 miles S of Swaffham)
✪ 11-2.30, 6-11; 12-3, 6.30-10.30 Sun
☎ (01760) 756232 e-mail: halls232@aol.com
Adnams Bitter, Broadside; Greene King IPA; guest beers Ⓗ
Quality free house under same family ownership for last 46 years. 10 separate drinking, eating and socialising areas include a conservatory. Beer range includes two regular guest ales plus a house beer, Windy Miller. The main pub dates from the 17th century, but many areas have been sympathetically extended over the years. There is live music Tue and Thu eves (this does not permeate through the whole pub). There is a large, child-friendly garden with sandpit, and a campsite a stone's throw away. Aunt Sally is played here.
♨️Q🏠⚽🌙🍴♿A♣️P

GREAT MOULTON

Fox & Hounds
Frith Way
✪ 11-2.30 (not Tue), 7-11; closed Mon; 12-2.30, 7-10.30 Sun
☎ (01379) 677506
Adnams Bitter; Black Sheep Best Bitter; guest beer Ⓗ
This quaint village free house has been called the Fox & Hounds since 1789. The cosy low-beamed bar has comfy settees and chairs by a large inglenook, painted wall panelling and an eclectic mix of old pictures and plates. The curtains depict hunting scenes. Note the stuffed owl by the fireplace. The pub is popular for food and there is a separate restaurant area with a varied menu. Wed is curry night. The garden (dogs not allowed) has a large pond and a children's play area.
♨️⚽🌙P🍴

GREAT YARMOUTH

Gallon Pot
Market Place
✪ 10-11; 12-10.30 Sun

☎ (01493) 842230
Beer range varies Ⓗ
Large and rambling corner pub on the north-west of the market place. Opposite is the largest parish church in England. The market is always busy on Wed and Sat. The pub offers affordable, tasty food and is very popular, particularly at lunchtimes. Note the old Lacon's tankard and moulding around the architrave. No-smoking area for drinkers 12-3, sometimes early eves.
🌙🍴A♿🚭●

Red Herring
24 Havelock Road (near town wall)
✪ 12-2.30 (3 Sat), 6-11; 12-3, 7-10.30 Sun
☎ (01493) 383334
Adnams Bitter; guest beers Ⓗ
Victorian, street-corner pub away from the main tourist areas. Worth seeking out for an outstanding diversity of ales, plus cider in summer, in pleasant surroundings. Read a book from the 'library', play pool or buy 'farm fresh' eggs. A great place to relax, and not an amusement arcade in sight. A good rock collection but not the sort Yarmouth is famous for. ♣️●

St John's Head
58 North Quay
✪ 11-11; 12-10.30 Sun
☎ (01493) 843443
Beer range varies Ⓗ
Single bar, a modern-style drinking pub between the town centre and the river. Nearby see the ships moored on the quay. Trace the 'rows' or alleys which were unique to Yarmouth.
⚽🍴A🚉(Vauxhall) ♣️

Troll Cart
729 Regent Road
✪ 11-11; 12-10.30 Sun
☎ (01493) 332932
Courage Directors; Greene King Abbot; Theakston Best Bitter; Woodforde's Wherry; guest beers Ⓗ
Large, single-bar pub in resort's main tourist street. Usually extensive Wetherspoon's beer range and food. Can be crowded in season but worth seeking out, in an area dominated by keg fizz outlets and extortionate prices, in the holiday season.
🍴♿🚉(Vauxhall) ●●

GRESSENHALL

Swan
The Green OS964165
✪ 12-2.30 (not Mon; 12-3 Sat), 6-11; 12-3, 7-10.30 Sun
☎ (01362) 860340
e-mail: joan@classic-car.demon.co.uk
Greene King IPA, Abbot, Marston's Pedigree; guest beer (summer) Ⓗ
In an idyllic village green setting, this attractive white-painted brick-built pub is the only one in the village; once Gressenhall boasted three. The guest beer is from the Pubmaster range and currently only available during the summer. Single, L-shaped bar with an archway and centrally located real fire and separate dining area (eve meals Tue-Sat). The Swan has pool, darts and cribbage teams. It is convenient for the Norfolk Rural Life Museum.
♨️⚽🌙♣️P

HARLESTON

Duke William
28 Redenhall Road
⊕ 11-11; 12-10.30 Sun
☎ (01379) 853183
Adnams Bitter; Courage Directors; Woodforde's Wherry; guest beers Ⓗ
Popular town local, it has two heavily-beamed bars and an easy-going, no-frills atmosphere. The 16th-century Grade II listed building is built of clay lump faced with red brick. The frontage has a heraldic sign with the motto, *'insolens negare est'*. There is also an old Lacons wall plaque. The landlady concentrates on providing good quality real ale, so no food other than filled rolls. Note the collection of keg founts and jugs in the public bar. Pleasant large garden at the rear. ❀♧♣

HEACHAM

Fox & Hounds
22 Station Road (turn left into Heacham at Norfolk Lavender – 1/2 mile)
⊕ 12-3, 6-11; 11-11 Fri & Sat; 12-10.30 Sun
☎ (01485) 570345
Draught Bass; Iceni Boadicea, Chariot Ale, seasonal beers; Ⓗ **Lidstones Rawalpindi IPA** Ⓗ /Ⓖ
Revitalised local pub it has developed as a real ale haven for the many tourists who come to Heacham each year. The pub has been transformed and now boasts six handpumps serving local ale from the Iceni Brewery as well as guest ales from all over the country, with Sheffield beers featured regularly. The back room is fast becoming a venue for a wide range of music – from jazz to Country and Western – and is given over twice a year to beer festivals featuring local breweries. In winter no food Mon and Tue, or Sun eve. ❀♢AP

HEDENHAM

Mermaid
Norwich Road
⊕ 12-3, 7 (5 Fri)-11; 12-4, 7-10.30 Sun
☎ (01508) 482480
Greene King IPA; Tindall Best Bitter; guest beer Ⓗ
300-year-old former coaching inn, it is a large timber-framed building in a remote location serving a small rural village. Oak beams together with brick floors and real fires add to its charm. There is a separate restaurant to ease congestion as the food is very popular. The once bright yellow external paint has toned down to give a pleasing appearance in keeping with the locality. Children are welcome in the pub and there is a play area. There is now a half-hourly bus service from Norwich and Bungay during the day. ♨❀♢AP

HOCKWOLD-CUM-WILTON

Red Lion
114 Main Street
⊕ 12-2.30, 6-11; 11-11 Sat; 12-10.30 Sun
☎ (01842) 828875
Adnams Bitter; Greene King IPA; guest beer Ⓗ
Thriving village local which has been extended over the years, the oldest part is over 300 years old. Located opposite a small green and a war memorial. Very busy due to a well-deserved reputation for excellent food. There is an extremely popular carvery on Wed (get in early!), and also a curry night on Mon, advisable to book at other times. Comfortable lounge to relax in. Come and win a great prize at the pop quiz on Sun eve. ❀♢P

HOLME-NEXT-THE-SEA

White Horse
40 Kirkgate Street
⊕ 11.30-3, 6.30-11 (opens 15 minutes later lunch and eve, winter); 12-3, 7-10.30 Sun
☎ (01485) 525512
Adnams Bitter; Flowers Original; Marston's Pedigree; guest beer (summer) Ⓗ
Run by the same family since 1943 this pub manages to preserve its traditional atmosphere while offering an extensive range of seafood and other local produce in its large restaurant. The pub is ideally situated for walkers as it is at the junction of the Peddars Way and the Norfolk Coastal Path. A golf course, bird reserve and extensive beaches are within easy walking distance and you may even find another Seahenge at low tide. As well as an excellent range of beers, the bar sports a collection of police memorabilia. Q❀♢♣♨

HUNWORTH

Bluebell Inn
The Green
⊕ 11-3, 5.30-11; 12-4, 6.30-10.30 Sun
☎ (01268) 712300
Adnams Bitter; Greene King IPA, Abbot; Ⓗ **Woodforde's Wherry;** Ⓖ **guest beer** Ⓗ
Also known as the 'Hunny Bell', this free house, in a picturesque setting by the green, is popular with tourists and locals. The bar is relaxed and features beams, a large woodburner and some rather impressive log tables (non-mathematical). The home-cooked food has an excellent reputation, and is mostly made with local produce. An adjoining flint-walled barn has been converted to provide a spacious, airy drinking and dining area. Cider is stocked in summer. Families catered for and there is a large garden with a play area. Plenty of accommodation available locally.
♨Q❀♢♨P⚲⊟

INGHAM

Swan Inn
Town Road (B1151)
⊕ 11-3, 7-11; 12-3, 7-10.30 Sun
☎ (01692) 581099
Woodforde's Mardler's Mild, Wherry, Great Eastern, Norfolk Nog Ⓗ
Large, flint building, typical in Norfolk, it dominates Ingham corner. Full of character, old beams, photos and farming memorabilia. Split-level pub; lower level drinking area and restaurant with large food board, the bar is on the upper level at the rear. ♨Q⛌❀♢P

KENNINGHALL

Red Lion
East Church Street
⊕ 12-3, 6.30-11; 12-11 Fri & Sat; 12-10.30 Sun
☎ (01953) 887849
e-mail: brucemandyberry@ukonline.co.uk

Greene King XX Mild, IPA, ⊞ Abbot; ⑤ guest beer ⊞
400-year-old pub, sympathetically refurbished, to include wood panelling and a quarry-tiled floor. There is one bar serving several drinking areas including a cosy snug and a dining room. Unusual daily specials are offered. Voted local CAMRA *Pub of the Year* 2000 it stocks a house beer, Billy's Best, brewed by Wolf. Both the ladies' and gents' toilets have a jokes' panel which is very popular with all visitors and updated on a regular basis. The pub overlooks the village church and offers B&B accommodation. It is an ideal base to explore the surrounding area. ▲Q❀⌂⇦◑◗♣P

KING'S LYNN

Live & Let Live
18 Windsor Road
✪ 12.15-11; 12.15-10.30 sun
☎ (01553) 764990
Beer range varies ⊞
Busy locals' pub with a small, cosy lounge bar and a larger public bar, just off London Road opposite the Catholic church. The beer range varies, generally including a mild and a beer from the Wolf Brewery among its range. It has been licensed since 1846 and has an interesting array of old pictures displayed. ⊟⇌♣⏃

London Porterhouse
78 London Road
✪ 11-11; 12-10.30 Sun
☎ (01553) 766842
Greene King IPA, Abbot; ⑤ **guest beer** ⊞
Small, lively one-roomed locals' bar standing on its own near the town's historic southgates, recently sympathetically refurbished. It has been a pub since 1864 and serves its IPA and Abbot from barrels behind the bar using cooling jackets to keep the beer at a constant temperature during all weathers. The guest beer is served from newly-installed handpumps. Q❀♣

Ouse Amateur Sailing Club
Ferry Lane (off King St)
✪ 12-4, 7-11; 12-11 Fri; 12.30-4, 8.30-10.30 Sun
☎ (01553) 772239
Bateman XB, XXB; guest beers ⑤
Very popular, cosy club at the end of Ferry Lane, next to the West Lynn Ferry, with a wooden verandah overlooking the river. Originally a pub, the building was taken over by the sailing club in the 1930s and they have recently extended the premises by building a function room. The club won CAMRA National *Club of the Year* 1998. Lunch is served daily except Sun. Show CAMRA membership card or this *Guide* for entry. ▲❀◑♣♦

Stuart House Hotel
35 Goodwins Road
✪ 6.30 (7 Fri & sat)-11; 12-3, 7-10.30 Sun
☎ (01553) 772169
website: www.stuart-house-hotel.co.uk
Beer range varies ⊞
Welcoming bar in a privately-owned hotel, close to the local attractions. Comfortable surroundings with real fire in winter and access to pleasant gardens in summer. Varying range of three ales offered. Regular special events include live music in the bar and murder mystery eves in the restaurant.

A beer festival is held in summer. These events are helping to attract local trade and adding to the large number of satisfied hotel guests. Note the bar is closed lunchtimes (except Sun) unless there is a special event. ▲❀⇦◗P

LANGLEY

Beauchamp Arms
Buckenham Ferry (between Claxton and Langley village) OS350043
✪ 12-3, 7-11; 11-11 Sat & summer; 12-10.30 Sun
☎ (01508) 480247
e-mail: beauchamp@buckenhamferry-fsb
Greene King IPA; Woodforde's Wherry, guest beer (summer) ⊞
Large, multi-roomed free house in a remote tranquil location on the south bank of the River Yare. Extensive recent refurbishment has enhanced the cosy atmosphere. Boat moorings are free for customers. Situated by site of old Buckenham ferry, which crossed the Yare at this point and gave access to Buckenham Station on opposite side of river. Good home-cooked food available in bar or separate restaurant with vegetarian options served. Children welcome, and outdoor play area includes bouncy castle in summer. Opening hours could vary in winter. ▲➦❀⇦◑◗♿⏃♣P

LARLING

Angel
Norwich Road (A11, ½ mile S of Snetterton market/racetrack)
✪ 10.30-11; 12-10.30 Sun
☎ (01953) 717963
Adnams Bitter; guest beers ⊞
This family-run free house goes from strength to strength. Four guest beers continually change, coming from all over the country, most are medium strength. One pump is for mild only: a recent decision. Good food, bookings are advised at busy times. Features in CAMRA's *Room at the Inn* publication; en-suite accommodation available. The public bar is particularly popular with the farming community and always has a lively buzz. Brewery trips organised and the local West Norfolk CAMRA festival is held in the third week in August. ▲❀⇦◑◗⊟♿⇌ (Harling Rd – limited stops) ♣P⏃

LYNG

Fox & Hounds
The Street
✪ 12-3, 5-11; 11-11 Sat; 12-4, 7-10.30 Sun
☎ (01603) 872316
website: www.foxandhoundslyng.co.uk
Adnams Broadside; ⊞ **Buffy's Mild;** ⑤ **Greene King IPA, Abbot; Woodforde's Wherry; guest beers** ⊞
18th-century free house with comfy heavily-beamed bar and large fireplace. Old photos of the pub adorn the dartboard recess. Reading material and games are provided. Jazz/folk sessions, quizzes and food 'theme' nights are held. Mobile phones are discouraged. Varied menu with a separate no-smoking restaurant. Games room suitable for under 14s. There are tables on the grass at the front of the pub. Lined glasses on request. Situated in the Wensum Valley, an area popular for fishing.

The resident ghost likes changing keys in the locks. 🏠Q⚫🍴🅿️🚭

MARTHAM

King's Arms
15 The Green (10 miles NW of Yarmouth off A149, opp. village green)
☺ 11 (12 winter)-11; 12-10.30 Sun
☎ (01493) 740204
Adnams Bitter, Broadside; guest beers Ⓗ

Large 17th-century pub, previously a church. Characterful interior with public bar, lounge and restaurant completely separate. Idyllic situation opposite the village pond. The pub is popular with locals and holidaymakers. Good food utilising local produce with steaks a speciality – both full restaurant and bar meals served. At the rear is one of the oldest pub bowling greens still in use in the county. Beer festival held every February. Live music is performed, mainly folk. There are quiz and darts teams and a pool table in the public bar.
🏠Q⚫🍴🔷♣P

MORSTON

Anchor
The Street
☺ 11-3, 7-11 11-11 Sat & summer; 12-10.30 Sun
☎ (01263) 740791
Woodforde's Wherry; guest beer (summer) Ⓗ

18th-century flint free house, in a pretty fishing village. Run by the same family for over 100 years. Locals' pub with informal folk sessions in the friendly, intimate bar area, rich in local paintings, photos and sketches. A house beer is available in summer. A dining area is a recent extension and extremely popular with tourists – children welcome. Full-size snooker table provided with antique scoreboard, and boat trip booking office. Meals served all day in summer, when the wider menu specialises in locally-caught seafood, otherwise lunchtime bar snacks only; eve meals Fri-Sun winter only. 🏠Q⚫🍴♣P

NEW BUCKENHAM

King's Head
Market Place
☺ 12-2.30 (3.30 Sat), 7-11; 12-4, 7-10.30 Sun
☎ (01953) 860487
Adnams Bitter; guest beer Ⓗ

Traditional village local overlooking the green at the centre of this former medieval market town. The plush, carpeted front lounge bar with its brass and copper ornaments leads through to a flagstoned public bar with low ceilings and match-boarded walls. Quiz nights held every Thu and themed meals once a month. A good menu, which claims to contain no genetically modified ingredients, includes a vegetarian option (no food Mon). Small collection of bottled beers (display only) behind the bar includes some rare examples. One beer from the Iceni Brewery is usually among the real ale selection.
🏠Q⚫🍴♣

NORTH ELMHAM

Railway
40 Station Road (off B1145) OS995202

☺ 11-11; 12-10.30 Sun
☎ (01362) 668300
e-mail: julie@therailway96.freeserve.co.uk
Beer range varies Ⓗ

Former railway hotel, now one bar divided to give country seating around an open log fire. There is a beer garden and camping is allowed in the pub grounds. Small, intimate dining room serves good home-made food – traditional English to Thai dishes. The pub has been run by the same family for over 40 years. Four ever-changing guest beers are available with Elgood's, Tolly and Wolf ales often featured. Real cider is occasionally served. Nearby are the remains of a Saxon cathedral.
🏠⚫🍴♣P🚭

NORTH WALSHAM

Orchard Gardens
Mundesley Road
☺ 12-11 (can vary in winter); 12-10.30 Sun
☎ (01692) 405152
Courage Directors; guest beers Ⓗ

Lively local pub not far from town centre which places a keen emphasis on real ale. Up to four guest beers at any one time, with a good mix of local beers and some from further afield. Beer festival held over spring bank holiday weekend each year. Run by a musical family, there is live music every weekend, with a wide range of social activities throughout the year. Children are allowed in the conservatory and there is a large beer garden on site of former bowling green.
⚫♣P

NORWICH ✣

Alexandra
16 Stafford Street
☺ 10.30-11; 12-10.30 Sun
☎ (01603) 627772 website:
www.norwich2nite.co.uk/pubs/alexandra/alexandra
Chalk Hill Tap, CHB; guest beers Ⓗ

Deservedly popular Victorian corner local, unusual in that it hasn't been knocked through into one bar. The public bar is bare-boarded and adjacent to the pool table and juke box, while the carpeted lounge provides a quieter, more relaxed drinking environment. There is a mix of artefacts including stained glass and blackboards from the former Reindeer brewpub and naval memorabilia. *Al fresco* drinking possible in front of the pub. Guest beers come from the Chalk Hill Brewery as well as established family/regional brewers.
🏠Q⚫♣

Beehive
30 Leopold Road (off A11)
☺ 11-3, 5.30-11; 11-11 Sat; 12-3, 7-10.30 Sun
☎ (01603) 451628
Courage Best Bitter, Directors; Wolf In Sheeps Clothing, Wolf Bitter; guest beers Ⓗ

Quiet street-corner local. The unspoilt three-bar layout includes a tiny snug that houses a cigarette machine and about a dozen people at a push! The public bar features a pool table and dartboard while the comfortably furnished lounge bar has a tropical fish-tank. Food (weekday lunch only) is limited to hot daily specials, sandwiches and filled rolls. Limited parking outside the pub and in the streets nearby. An upstairs function room can be hired and charity barbecues are hosted in summer.

Q ✿ ☽ ◖ ◓ ♣ ♠

Champion
101 Chapelfield Road
✪ 10.30-11; 12-10.30 Sun
☎ (01603) 765611
Buffy's Bitter, IPA; Elgood's Black Dog Mild; Greene King IPA, Abbot Ⓗ

Former Whitbread pub, now a free house serving a house beer (brewer varies). Has been transformed into a thriving community pub, former winner of the Eastern Evening News *Pub of the Year* competition. Splendid collection of Toby jugs: a couple of hundred hang from the ceiling. Function room now available; lunchtime snacks.

Coach & Horses
82 Thorpe Road (400 yds from station)
✪ 11-11; 12-10.30 Sun
☎ (01603) 477077
Chalk Hill Tap, CHB, Dreadnought, Flinknapper's Mild; Taylor Landlord; guest beers Ⓗ

Home of Chalk Hill Brewery which is visible at the rear of the building. One large bar is divided into several drinking areas, with an interesting herringbone wooden floor. Sells CHB that won *Beer of the Festival* at Norwich 2000. Serves excellent food but you must be hungry, portions are very large. Food served all day. It gets very busy on matchdays.

⚒ ✿ ☽ ◖ ≈ ♣ ♠ P

Eaton Cottage
75 Mount Pleasant
✪ 11-11; 12-10.30 Sun
☎ (01603) 453048
Adnams Bitter; Fuller's London Pride; Marston's Pedigree; guest beers Ⓗ

Corner pub built around 1867 as a grocery store with off-licence section. Started trading solely as a public house in 1887. In 1889 it became a tied house of the Steward, Patteson & Finch Brewery and their emblem can be seen over the two corner windows. An alcove in the lounge was the wicket from which off-sales were obtained and they are still available from the snug. The public and lounge bars are connected by a long, winding corridor. Live music played Thu eve. Old Eatonian, brewed by Wolf Brewery, is the house beer. ✿ ◓ ♣

Fat Cat
49 West End Street
✪ 12 (11 Sat)-11; 12-10.30 Sun
☎ (01603) 624364 website: www.fatcatpub.co.uk
Adnams Bitter; Fuller's ESB; Greene King Abbot; Hopback Summer Lightning; Taylor Landlord; guest beers Ⓗ/Ⓖ

Late Victorian red-brick corner pub, extended to include a back room with TV for sport. Timber alcoves and wood panelling feature throughout the pub which is decorated with old pub signs and breweriana. After refurbishment trade has escalated to reach today's mini-beer festival level of more than 20 ales, 12 on handpump, the rest on gravity. Four Belgian draught beers plus 12 in bottles along with a range of fruit wines. The Banham Cider is complemented by a dry cider in summer. This is a beer drinkers' paradise.

Q ✿ ♣ ● ◗ ●

Ketts Tavern
Ketts Hill (50 yds from Gurney Rd/Barrack St roundabout on inner ring rd)
✪ 11-11; 12-10.30 Sun
☎ (07931) 794354
Buffy's Bitter; Taylor Landlord; Woodforde's Ketts Rebellion; guest beers Ⓗ

This free house stands on the lower slopes of Mousehold Heath with both the road name and pub name commemorating the 1549 rebellion by William Kett of Wymondham and his 30,000 followers against the landed classes' enclosure of the common land. The tavern however is a more peaceful refuge offering a selection of small brewery products and an extensive menu, in an open-plan bar with a large and comfortable conservatory to the rear.

☕ ✿ ◖ ◐ ≈ ♣ ✁

King's Arms
22 Hall Road (300 yds from city centre)
✪ 11-11; 12-10.30 Sun
☎ (01603) 766361
Adnams Bitter, Broadside; Greene King Abbot; Wolf Coyote; guest beers Ⓗ

Sympathetically restored former Greene King hostelry, stocking an ever-changing array of up to 10 regional beers. Themed beer festivals held every three months. Pub has a policy of allowing customers to bring in their own food. Choose from a number of local take-away restaurants. Plates,

INN BRIEF

NORWICH
Angel Gardens
96 Angel Road
11-3, 5.30-11; 11-11 Fri & Sat; 12-10.30 Sun
Flowers IPA; Greene King IPA; Wells Bombardier; guest beers Ⓗ
A comfortable locals' pub. Holds a children's certificate. Separate restaurant doubles as a function room.

Dyers Arms
2-4 Lawson Road
10.30-2.30, 6.30-11; 10.30-4, 7-11 Fri & Sat; 12-3, 7.30-10.30 Sun
Adnams Bitter; Draught Bass; guest beer Ⓗ
Cosy, corner local. One bar serves several drinking areas. *Cask Marque* accredited.

Whalebone
144 Magdalen Road
11-11, 12-10.30 Sun
Adnams Bitter; Shepherd Neame Spitfire; Woodforde's Wherry; guest beers Ⓗ
An attractive corner pub. Lots of wood-panelling and a timber floor. Two bars, the rear bar has a split-level seating area. Beer festival held in May.

OLD BUCKENHAM
Ox & Plough
The Green
12-3, 6.30-11; 12-11 Sat; 12-10.30 Sun
Adnams Bitter; Greene King IPA; guest beer Ⓗ
Friendly village pub. Good value food served. Holiday cottages are available.

REEPHAM
King's Arms
Market Place
11.30-3, 5.30-11; 11-11 Sat; 12-3, 7-10.30 Sun
Adnams Bitter; Draught Bass; Greene King Abbot; Woodforde's Wherry; guest beers Ⓗ
Attractive listed pub in centre of village. Lots of exposed brickwork and beams. Three real fires ensure a warm welcome.

SALHOUSE
Bell
3 Lower Street
11-3, 7-11; 12-4, 7-10.30 Sun
Courage Best Bitter; Elgood's Greyhound Strong; guest beer Ⓗ
17th-century coaching inn with its own bowling green. Handy for Salhouse Broad.

cutlery and assorted condiments are provided. Rear garden/patio area is popular and barbecues are held regularly. Lined glasses are always used. Many visiting football supporters use the pub as it is close to the football ground. CAMRA regional *Pub of the Year* 1999. ❀✿⊡

Rosary Tavern
95 Rosary Road
✪ 11.30-11; 12-10.30 Sun
☎ (01603) 666287
Adnams Bitter; Ⓗ Draught Bass; Ⓖ Black Sheep Best Bitter; guest beers Ⓗ
Single-roomed local with high-backed seating dividing the rom into two. Conservatory and rear garden area suitable for meetings and barbecues. Runner-up in the Eastern Evening News *Pub of the Year* competition 2000. Regular supply of newspapers, very much a community local with football, crib, darts and quiz teams. Shove-ha'penny and bar billiards played. French folk dancing and pipe club of Norfolk also meet here. Sun lunch served. ❀◖≈♣♠

Steampacket
39 Crown Road
✪ 11-11; 7-10.30 Sun
☎ (01603) 441545
Adnams Bitter, Broadside, seasonal beers; guest beers Ⓗ
Traditional pub located behind Anglia Television. Serves award-winning pork pies (organic) from the Handmade Food Company as featured on Radio Norfolk. Small back room available for meetings. Quiz night every Wed eve. Wooden floors and interesting portfolio of photographs of 'landlad' on wall. Formerly known as the Market Tavern it was nearest pub to the old cattle market (now the Castle Mall shopping centre). Close to the 'Waterfront' Norwich's alternative music venue run by UEA students union. Occasional pole dancing!
❀≈ (Thorpe)

Trafford Arms
61 Grove Road
✪ 11-11; 12-10.30 Sun
☎ (01603) 767863 website: www.traffordarms.co.uk
Adnams Bitter; Tetley Bitter; Woodforde's Mardler's Mild, seasonal beers; guest beers Ⓗ
Popular, open-plan pub serving a wide range of ales, normally including two milds and one permanent. Regular beer festival held in a marquee during Valentine's week, usually themed. Near the city centre, it attracts a wide ranging clientele from office workers to students. Elegant interior with bare bricks and memorabilia displayed. Traditional food available at lunchtimes (no-smoking area available) with full roasts on Sun. Original pub on this site was bombed in WWII and totally rebuilt in the 1950s. The Terry Storer Memorial Cycle Rack here is a fitting tribute to a popular CAMRA member.
❀◖♠

Vine Tavern
7 Dove Street (50 yds from market place)
✪ 10.30-11; 12-10.30 Sun
☎ (01603) 629258 e-mail: thevine@dialstart.net
Adnams Bitter, Fisherman, Broadside; guest beers Ⓗ

The smallest pub in the city, a stone's throw from Norwich centre. Single-bar pub with interesting layout. A friendly atmosphere pervades this former Courage house. Taken over by Adnams, it is often busy with local trade from the nearby market. A welcome stopping place for shoppers. An outside seating area is provided, if you don't mind the many 'colourful' characters that call this part of the city home. Occasionally hosts acoustic 'blues' eves. ❀

Wig & Pen
6 St Martins at Palace Plain (close to Cathedral and Law Courts)
✪ 11.30-11; 12-5 Sun
☎ (01603) 629715
Buffy's Bitter; guest beers Ⓗ
Superb local with an ever-changing range of guest ales. Mystery beer competition held. This pub has an outstanding frontage, with beamed interior (16th century). Formerly the White Lion, the coat of arms on the front belongs to the Blomfield family who were local historians. Reputedly the oldest ale house in Norwich. Food is served from a wide ranging menu. Regular pick-up point for Norwich and Norfolk CAMRA's county branch mystery trips. Patio area and seating outside front of pub. ♨❀◖▶

OLD HUNSTANTON

Ancient Mariner
Golf Course Road
✪ 11-3, 6-11 (11-11 summer); 12-10.30 Sun
☎ (01485) 534411 website: www.abacushotels.co.uk
Adnams Bitter, Broadside; Draught Bass; guest beer Ⓗ
Large, busy pub attached to the Le Strange Arms Hotel. Converted from an old barn 20 years ago, the pub, with its nautical theme, has numerous rooms for drinking or eating. Children are welcome in the two family rooms and there is a large play area in the garden. Enjoy your pint beneath a boat hanging from the ceiling or take it out into the garden which runs down to the beach.
♨⚓❀✿◖▶♣P✂

PORINGLAND

Royal Oak
44 The Street
✪ 12-2.30, 6 (5 Sat)-11; 12-3 (may extend), 7-10.30 Sun
☎ (01508) 493734
Adnams Bitter; guest beers Ⓗ
Rare example of an ale house in rural Norfolk. Built in 1898, this locals' pub has been much extended. Up to six guest ales, such as Mauldons Moletrap, are available. The pub stands on the main road in the village and four buses an hour pass daily from Norwich, plus eve and Sun buses. Theme nights (such as Chinese, Indian) are held on Thu eve. A mini beer festival is hosted annually. ⚓❀♣♠P

PULHAM ST. MARY

King's Head
The Street
✪ 11.30-3, 5.30-11; 11.30-11 Sat & summer; 12-10.30 Sun
☎ (01379) 676318
Adnams Bitter; Buffy's Bitter; guest beers Ⓗ

Late 17th-century timber-framed pub with a friendly welcome. The cosy main bar has a large woodburner. A propeller from an early 20th-century airship is displayed over the fireplace. These were built on the local airfield and known as 'Pulham Pigs'! Good value food (including specials and children's choices), meals are served in the bar or in the no-smoking dining area. Food is available all day Sun. This family pub has something for all ages: a large garden with children's play area, a bowling green and an adult games room in a converted stable. Champagne quiz nights held fortnightly.
▲♨✍①♣P

RINGSTEAD

Gin Trap Inn
High Street
✪ 11.30-2.30, 6.30 (7 winter)-11; 12-2.30, 6.30 (7 winter)-10.30 Sun
☎ (01485) 525264 website: www.gintrap.co.uk
Adnams Bitter; Greene King Abbot; Woodforde's Nelson's Revenge; Norfolk Nog Ⓗ
Classic village local; sometimes struggles to contain all the visitors. Excellent food is served in a split-level bar with a separate dining area. There is a large garden. It has changed little over the years; there is an unchanging selection of Norfolk beers, the house beer comes from Woodforde's. Fearsome display of animal traps festoon the ceiling. A converted barn at the rear of the pub is available for short lets.
▲Q♨✍①P

SMALLBURGH

Crown
North Walsham Road (A149)
✪ 12-3, 5.30 (7 Sat)-11; 12-3 (closed eve) Sun
☎ (01692) 536314
Adnams Broadside; Greene King IPA, Abbot; Tetley Bitter; guest beer Ⓗ
Comfortable, two-bar village pub with a friendly atmosphere, situated on the main A149 road from North Walsham to Stalham. Close to the Norfolk Broads and coast. Cosy, welcoming log fire in bar, where the tables and chairs are made from old beer barrels and firkins. Built in the 15th century as a coaching inn, some of the original timbers can still be seen, note the interesting collection of old sepia photos. There is an attractive beer garden at rear. Good selection of home-cooked food available in bar or separate dining room.
▲Q♨✍①⊟Å♣P

SOUTH CREAKE

Ostrich Inn
1 Fakenham Road (B1355 Fakenham-Burnham Market road)
✪ 12-3 (not Tue), 7-11; 12-3, 7-10.30 Sun
☎ (01328) 823320 website: www.ostrichinn.co.uk
Adnams Broadside; Greene King IPA, Abbot, seasonal beer; guest beers Ⓗ
Centrally-located in long, straggling village, this 17th-century inn provides a warm welcome. A true free house. The long, single bar is divided into various different areas. Cosy armchairs round a woodburner for cooler evenings (but look out for the bear); formal restaurant and comfortable bar area.

Wheelchair WC and babychanging facilities available. Superb, comprehensive menu includes vegetarian selection and ostrich dishes. The accommodation includes one unit to disability standards. Handy for visitors to the north Norfolk coast, and its many attractions. The Ostrich is the crest of the Coke family of the huge Holkham estate. ▲Q♨✍①⊟Å♣P

SOUTH LOPHAM

White Horse
The Street (A1066)
✪ 11-3, 6-11; 12-3, 6.30-10.30 Sun
☎ (01379) 687252
~~Adnams Bitter; Broadside; Greene King IPA~~ Ⓗ
Fine old inn on the main road. Usual history of conversion into a single bar. Variety of drinking areas and pleasant welcome for all. Good mix of locals and visitors. Child-friendly; play area is provided at rear. Food is based on traditional home cooking. Large car park. Close to popular garden centres, including Blooms of Bressingham.
▲♨①⊟♣P

STALHAM

Swan
High Street
✪ 11-11, 12-10.30 Sun
☎ (01692) 581482
Adnams Bitter, Broadside Ⓗ
Situated at the heart of the Norfolk Broads in a small but busy town. This comfortable two-bar pub is popular with locals and tourists. ▲Q♨①⊟Å♣P

STIFFKEY

Red Lion
44 Wells Road (A149)
✪ 12-3, 6-11; 12-3, 6-11 Sun
☎ (01328) 830552 e-mail: matthewredlion@aol.com
Greene King IPA, Abbot; Ⓗ **Woodforde's Wherry;** Ⓗ/Ⓖ **guest beers** Ⓗ
White-painted flint and brick building on the north Norfolk coast road. Comprises a number of inter-connecting rooms with a restaurant at the rear. The floors are a mixture of pannets (clay tiles) and floorboards and there are four real log fires. There are wooden pews and bookcases throughout. The pub closed down in 1969 but reopened in 1990 having been refurbished. Has a deserved good reputation for food. The village is famous for one of its former clergymen (see board in pub for more details). Children are welcome.
▲Q♨①⊟♣P✂

STRUMPSHAW

Shoulder of Mutton
Norwich Road
✪ 11-11; 12-10.30 Sun
☎ (01603) 712274
Adnams Bitter, Broadside; Greene King IPA; guest beers Ⓗ
Set back from the road, the pub has recently been extended with a new lounge bar and games room. The large garden and pétanque courts are an unusual bonus. The bar boasts several sporting trophies.
▲⏃♨①♣P

SWAFFHAM

George Hotel
Station Street (A1065)
☼ 11-2.30, 6.30-11; 11-2, 7-10.30 Sun
☎ (01760) 721238
e-mail: georgehotel@bestwestern.co.uk
Greene King IPA, Abbot Ⓗ
Split-level public bar in an 18th-century town-centre hotel. Excellent views of the market place and attractive church. Although part of a large hotel chain, the George is very much part of the local community with a busy lunchtime crowd. Swaffham is home to Europe's largest wind turbine, this is two minutes from the George by car. From the 14th-century church to the 18th-century pub, a pint and then 21st-century ecotechnology, the best type of time travel. Q ⇔ ◖◗ ♣ P

TERRINGTON ST CLEMENTS

County Arms
Marshland Street
☼ 7-11; 12-3, 7-11 Sat; 12-3, 7-10.30 Sun
☎ (01553) 828511
Greene King IPA, Abbot Ⓗ
Three-bar local; a true drinkers' pub. Comfortable, well-decorated and full of character. This is an unusual pub for Norfolk in that it does not serve food. Patio for outdoor drinking. Note that the pub is closed weekday lunchtimes. ❀ ⊟ P

THETFORD

Albion
93-95 Castle Street (opp. Castle Park on main road from town centre)
☼ 11-2.30 (3 Fri & Sat), 6-11; 6 (5 Fri)-11; 12-3, 7-10.30 Sun
☎ (01842) 752796
Greene King IPA, Abbot; guest beers Ⓗ
Former flint cottages in the old part of town. Pub knocked through for sports room, toilets and bar on one level. Low ceilings match the low prices. Popular with tourists visiting the famous castle park opposite. Used by local dramatic society who run Sunday quiz nights (monthly). Darts, pool, cribbage and dominoes are played. Pub landlords can be traced back to 1895, run by the current family for 30 years. ⋈ Q ❀ ◖ ଐ ♣ P ●

Dolphin Inn
Old Market Street (backs on to Castle Park)
☼ 11-3, 6-11; 12-3, 7-10.30 Sun
☎ (01842) 752271
Greene King IPA; guest beers Ⓗ
Situated in the oldest part of the town, it bears the date '1694' on frontage. This flint pub is as recognisable today as it was a century ago. Not far away is the old jail used in the 18th century and the former Bidwells Brewery. ⋈ Q ❀ ◖ ଐ P

King's Head
27 White Hart Street (next to Ancient House museum)
☼ 11-11; 12-10.30 Sun
☎ (01842) 753050
Greene King XX Mild, IPA, Abbot; guest beers Ⓗ
Dating from 1789, it is a former coaching inn. The archway leads not to stables but a safe, enclosed garden. One main beamed

room has spacious, airy feel, while a smaller, quieter area can be used by families. Straightforward basic drinkers' pub with no food. Lively but friendly setting, can get noisy during busy periods, not a pub for a quiet pint. Occasional live music and rock style juke box maintains pub's reputation as an unpretentious venue. Guest beers are interesting additions to regular ales, coupled with a popular beer festival in June. ⊃ ❀ ⇔ ≈ ♣ P

THORNHAM

Lifeboat
Ship Lane
☼ 11-11; 12-10.30 Sun
☎ (01485) 512236 website: www.lifeboatinn.co.uk
Adnams Bitter; Draught Bass; Greene King IPA, Abbot; Woodforde's Wherry; guest beers Ⓗ
In recent years this 16th-century smugglers ale house has been transformed into a busy inn with good food and accommodation. The original character remains in the 'smugglers bar' with its roaring fires, warm glow of paraffin lamps and chance to play 'pennies'. The game was outlawed by George III but is still played regularly here. The pub is on the edge of the saltmarsh, close to nature reserves and wide sandy beaches. A large conservatory at the rear leads to a sunny patio with extensive outdoor eating facilities. ⋈ Q ⊃ ❀ ⇔ ◖ ଐ ♣ P

TRUNCH

Crown Inn
Front Street (next to church)
☼ 12-3, 5.30-11; 11-11 (summer); 12-10.30 Sun
☎ (01263) 722341 website: thecrowninntrunch.co.uk
Greene King IPA; Adnams Bitter; guest beers Ⓗ
Originally part of former Trunch Brewery estate this is an attractive, family-run free house. With its single bar, small cosy restaurant and log fire it offers a warm welcome to locals and visitors. It has a selection of four real ales with more in the summer months. It hosts a beer festival in August. ⋈ Q ❀ ◖ & Å ♣ P ●

UPTON

White Horse
17 Chapel Road
☼ 11-11; 12-10.30 Sun
☎ (01493) 750696
Adnams Bitter; St. Peter's Best Bitter; guest beers Ⓗ
Traditional village local handy for the Broads. Separate restaurant area offers good quality home-made food at reasonable prices. A new conservatory is underway to provide another drinking area for 2002. Take-away fish and chips on Fri are a local legend. ❀ ◖ Å ♣ P

WALCOTT

Lighthouse
Coast Road
☼ 11-11; 12-10.30 Sun
website: diningout.com/norfolk/norwich/lighthouseinn
Adnams Bitter; Tetley Bitter; guest beers Ⓗ
Very popular pub with locals and holidaymakers. You can always be assured of a warm welcome. Standing almost alone except for the church, it's a welcome sight

on the coast road. A function room with a new marquee adds an extra dimension. It has a dining room with a no-smoking area (food all day). Has its own pool and darts teams and is very much the hub of the village life. Among special events organised are a fireworks' display, carol service at Christmas and regular barbecues in summer with a children's disco.

♨⍩❀❄◑▲♣Ⓟ●

WARHAM ALL SAINTS

Three Horseshoes ☆
The Street
☼ 11.30-2.30, 6-11; 12-2.30, 6-10.30 Sun
☎ (01328) 710547

Greene King IPA; Ⓗ **Woodforde's Wherry;** Ⓖ **guest beer** Ⓗ

Characterful flint and pantiled village free house, has been a pub since at least 1725. Revamped in the 1920s, the original bar area retains its hole-in-the-wall bar, gaslight fittings, open fire, 'Norfolk Twister' game and stone floors. Sympathetically extended to provide comfortable seating areas with subdued lighting and an eclectic mix of paintings, china and memorabilia. Popular for its home-cooked food, the pub has a wide menu and extensive daily specials board – it doesn't have any chips, keg or nitro-keg. Accommodation is available at 'The Old Post Office' next door (dogs welcome – no children under 14).

♨Q❀❄◑▲Ⓟ✄

WATTON

Breckland Wines (off licence)
80 High Street (opp. police station)
☼ 9-9; 9-9 Sun
☎ (01953) 881592
Beer range varies

Vast selection of bottle-conditioned beers – all the local micros that bottle have an outlet here. Plans are well under way to stock draught beer and ciders. Now with an organic selection for ales and ciders, any drinker wanting to see the diversity of brewing in East Anglia should visit. The owner is a real ale enthusiast and is more than happy to walk visitors through the selection on offer, pointing out his personal favourites. ♣

WEASENHAM ALL SAINTS

Ostrich Inn
Cross Roads (A1065)
☼ 11.30-2.30 (3 Fri & Sat), 7-11 (not Mon); 12-3, 7-10.30 Sun
☎ (01328) 838221

Adnams Bitter; guest beer (occasional) Ⓗ

Behind the unpretentious exterior of this rural free house lurks a wonderfully idiosyncratic local. Set back from the road, it has been a pub since 1830. The current landlord and landlady have run the pub for over 20 years, and offer a friendly welcome and respite from the modern world, no fruit machines, TV or music. The loos are outside – the ladies' is in a former forge. An eclectic mix of items adorn the walls of the cosy, dimly-lit bar. An impressive fireplace stands at one end. Bar snacks often available, also fruit and veg from the stall outside.

♨Q❀♣Ⓟ

WELLS-NEXT-THE-SEA

Crown Hotel
The Buttlands
☼ 11-2.30, 6-11; 12-2.30, 7-10.30 Sun
☎ (01328) 710209

Adnams Bitter; Draught Bass; guest beer Ⓗ

Coaching inn by the green known as Buttlands, surrounded by fine buildings and close to the town centre. The comfortable bars are complemented by a superb restaurant. The extensive menu is renowned, and the five chefs use local produce. The hotel is ideal for a relaxing break in an area of outstanding natural beauty, famous for beaches, birdwatching, and many visitor attractions, including Holkham Hall in the next village. In the day Wells is a bustling, old-fashioned town, and in the evening a pleasant, safe place to stroll.

♨Q❀❄◑◱▲≉ (Wells/Walsingham light railway) Ⓟ✄

Edinburgh
Station Road
☼ 11-2.30, 7 (6.30 Sat)-11; 12-3, 7-10.30 Sun
☎ (01328) 710120

Draught Bass; Hancock's HB; guest beers Ⓗ

Large, Victorian pub on the main shopping street. Cosmopolitan mix of customers with many family groups. Friendly and welcoming this is a busy pub, popular with shoppers; in the summer holidaymakers add to the bustle. This pub has maintained the tradition of serving Bass, a legacy from the days when many Midlanders came to north Norfolk by rail for their holidays. Wells has one of the finest beaches in Britain, the area also has many other tourist attractions, but the historic buildings of Wells should not be missed, and shopping as it used to be.

♨Q❀❄◑▲≉ (Wells/Walsingham light railway) ♣☗

WEST BECKHAM

Wheatsheaf Inn
Church Road
☼ 12 (11.30 summer); 12-3, 7-10.30 Sun
☎ (01263) 822110 website: wheatsheaf.org.uk

Woodforde's Wherry, Ⓗ **Neson's Revenge, Norfolk Nog;** Ⓖ **guest beers** Ⓗ

Formerly a farmhouse in a quiet North Norfolk village, the Wheatsheaf has only been a pub since 1984. There is a single, irregularly shaped bar, with real fire and a separate no-smoking dining area. Pool and traditional pub games, including shove ha'penny and dominoes, are available in the separate games room. The food menu includes daily specials and an extensive dessert menu. Occasional live music in summer – jazz or the Sheringham Shantymen. In addition to the beer garden there is a covered pergola. Accommodation is self-catering. No food Sun eve.

♨⍩❀❄◑♣●Ⓟ

WEST SOMERTON

Lion
On jct B1152/B1159
☼ 11-4 (3 winter), 6-11; 11-11 Sat; 12-5, 7-10.30 Sun
☎ (01493) 393289

Greene King IPA, Abbot; guest beers Ⓗ

Traditional two-bar country local, close to Norfolk Broads and coast, and serving a good selection of real ales and food. Originally an old Lacons Brewery pub, it was closed by the brewery in 1955, thus rendering the village 'dry' until being reopened as a free house almost 20 years later. Over 200 years old, the pub was originally thatched, and parts of the original beams are still visible. In an ideal area for ramblers and hikers, it is just a short walk from West Somerton Staithe and Horsey windpump. Guest beers invariably come from Mauldons and Elgood's in summer. 🍴🛏️❄️◐🍺♣️🍺P

WEYBOURNE

Ship
The Street
✪ summer: 11 (12 Mon)-3, 6-11; 11-11 Sat; 12-4, 6-10.30 Sun
winter: 12 (not Mon)-3, 7-11; 12-11 Sat; 12-4, 7-10.30 Sun
☎ (01263) 588721 e-mail: shipweybourne@aol.com
Greene King IPA, Abbot; Ⓗ guest beers Ⓗ/Ⓖ
19th-century brick and flint building features Steward & Patteson windows. The entrance has its own period verandah. Comfortable lounge, bar, dining-room and games area, with cosy real fires and attractive restored parquet flooring. Pub hosts occasional theme nights and live music on Sat eve. Popular with locals, birdwatchers and visitors to the North Norfolk Railway (3/4 mile away) and to the Muckleburgh collection (military museum). No eve meals winter Mon; no-smoking area available in summer. 🍴❄️◐🍺🚹♣️P✄

WICKLEWOOD

Cherry Tree
116 High Street (on Wymondham edge of village)
✪ 12-2 (3 summer), 6-11, 12-11 Sat; 12-10.30 Sun
☎ (01953) 606962
Buffy's Bitter, Mild, seasonal beers; Ⓖ guest beers Ⓗ
Friendly village local recently leased by Buffy's so with real commitment to real ale. White-painted, brick building partly dates back to 17th century. Very low ceilings, it is due to be sympathetically refurbished. Pleasant beer garden; well-behaved children are welcome in the pub. Guest beers are from the Buffy's stable. Ales on gravity are brought from the cellar. Thatchers cider is stocked. ❄️◐🚹♣️🍺P

WINFARTHING

Fighting Cocks
The Street (B1077)
✪ 11-3, 5.30-11; 11-11 Sat; 12-10.30 Sun
☎ (01379) 643283
Adnams Bitter; Ⓖ Buffy's Bitter; guest beers Ⓗ
Welcoming inn dating from 1620. Though opened up, the bar retains many original features, including a log fire in an inglenook which never goes out. There is a separate games room for darts and pool. Families are welcome. All food is home-cooked with a good English traditional menu with options to suit all tastes. Central to village life, the pub even has its own football pitch, and monthly live music sessions. Tents and caravans can use pub field free of charge and rallies and groups are welcome.

Children's certificates

When pubs are described as having 'children's certificates', this indicates that local licensing authorities are satisfied that the pubs in question have environments suitable for children under 14, and that meals and non-alcoholic drinks are available. Some authorities demand more wide-ranging facilities – such as non-smoking areas, an absence of gaming machines, nappy-changing provision, junior WCs and basins, and furniture suitable for small children — before granting certificates, which must be prominently displayed.

Breakfasts can be served. Convenient for visitors to Banham Zoo. 🍴🛏️❄️◐🚹♣️P

WINTERTON

Fisherman's Return
The Lane (off B1159)
✪ 11-2.30, 6.30-11; 11-11 Sat; 12-10.30 Sun
☎ (01493) 393305
website: www.fishermans-return.co.uk
Adnams Fisherman; Woodforde's Wherry, Norfolk Nog; guest beers Ⓗ
300-year-old flint and brick building, with wood panelling and inviting open fire. Run by long-standing landlord and lady, who pioneered the introduction of guest ale in their formerly tied pub. Meals include local fish and game. A wide range of guest beers in summer, including Mauldons, a mild and sometimes cider. Interesting collection of old photos, including former village pubs. Pub sign depicts wives waiting for their fisherman husbands to return from the sea. The village actually stands on the site of the former Bulmer village, Winterton Ness having long-since disappeared under the sea. 🍴Q🛏️❄️🚃◐🚹♣️P✄

WYMONDHAM

Feathers
13 Town Green (400 yds W of town centre)
✪ 11-3, 7-11; 12-3, 7-10.30 Sun
☎ (01953) 605675
Adnams Bitter; Greene King Abbot; Marston's Pedigree; guest beers Ⓗ
A short walk from the market cross and the historic abbey, the Feathers carries the best selection of real ales in Wymondham. This popular single-bar pub, with upstairs function room, is sub-divided along one side by wooden rails into a series of nooks and booths. Embellished with agricultural bygones adorning the walls. A rear door beside the ARP warden's bike, leads into a quiet courtyard, ideal for idling away a summer's lunchtime. Suffolk brewer Mauldon's brews the house beer. No food Sun eve. ❄️◐♣️P

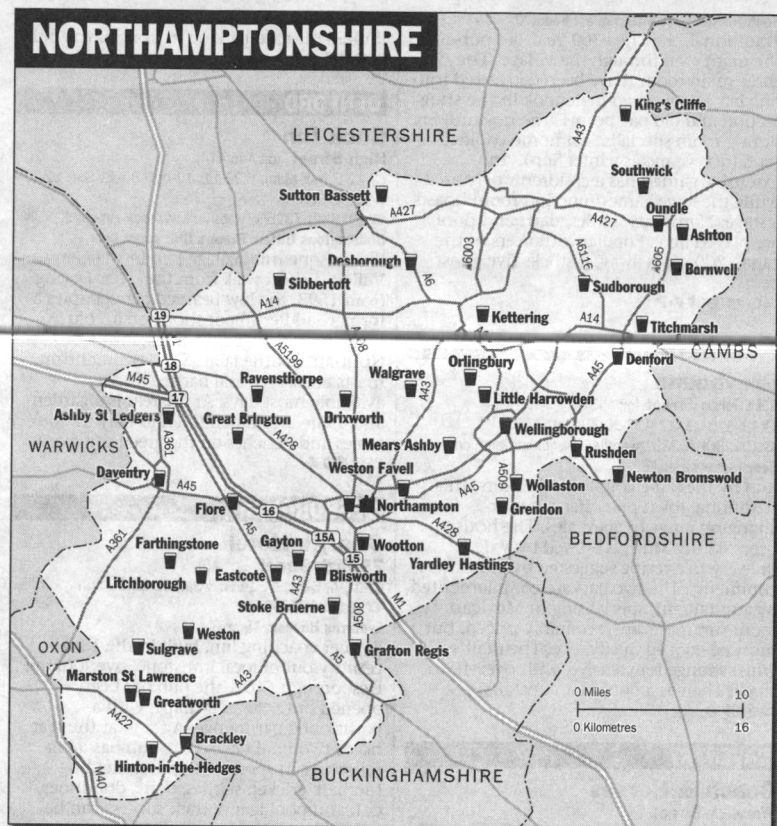

NORTHAMPTONSHIRE

ASHBY ST LEDGERS

Olde Coach House Inn
On main street, off A361
☼ 12-2.30, 6-11; 12-11 Sat; 12-10.30 Sun
☎ (01788) 890349
website: www.theoldecoachhouse.co.uk
Everards Old Original; Flowers Original; guest beers Ⓗ
This former 19th-century farmhouse is a popular village inn and a regular *Guide* entry. Built from local golden ironstone, like the rest of the picturesque village, the interior consists of a bar with TV, a no-smoking family room and a series of interconnected rooms leading to the award-winning restaurant. Beams, wood panelling and high-backed benches complement the log fire. A free house, the guest ales come from local brewers such as Frankton Bagby and other small independents. Beer festivals spring and autumn, and barbecues are sometimes held in the large mature garden.
♨Q☎❀✑◑ ⊞&P⚲⊟

ASHTON

Chequered Skipper
The Green (1 mile from A605, Oundle jct)
☼ 11.30-3, 6-11; 11.30-11 Sat; 12-10.30 Sun
☎ (01832) 273494
e-mail: theskipper@ashtonongreen.freeserve.co.uk
Oakham JHB; guest beers Ⓗ
The traditional thatched exterior belies the modern interior, which is a result of a disastrous fire some years ago. The outside drinking area is actually the village green, the scene of the annual National Conker Championships in October. The pub, along with the whole village, was rebuilt as a model village in the early 20th century by the owner, Mr Rothschild. The name is taken from a rare butterfly; the Dragonfly Museum is nearby. Q❀◑&Å●P⚲

BARNWELL

Montagu Arms
¼ mile off A605
☼ 12-3, 6-11; 12-11 Sat; 12-10.30 Sun
☎ (01832) 273726
Adnams Bitter, Broadside; Flowers IPA, Original; guest beer Ⓗ
Situated in a quiet village, beside a stream, the Montagu is an ideal stopping-off point when in the area. The front bar has low ceilings with exposed beams and a flagstone floor. Outside is probably the largest pub garden in these parts, complete with children's play area and crazy golf. Accommodation is available, should you be unable to drag yourself away from this atmospheric 16th-century pub.
♨Q❀✑◑ÅP●

BLISWORTH

Royal Oak
1 Chapel Lane (A4300)
☼ 12-11; 12-10.30 Sun
☎ (01604) 858372

Hook Norton Best Bitter; guest beers Ⓗ

Traditional, thatched 300-year-old pub on the main road through the village. The three main rooms have been converted into one bar area with an inglenook in the snug section and old oak beams. The no-smoking dining room specialises in home-cooked food (no eve meals winter Sun). An extensive garden has a children's play area while the large games/function room boasts a stage; Northants skittles, darts and pool are played here. Popular with users of the canal, 200 yards away, it stocks five guest beers.

ﾑQ🍴🐕◑♣P

BRACKLEY

Greyhound

131 High Street (off A43)

✪ 11-3, 5-11; 12-4, 7-10.30 Sun

☎ (01280) 703331 website: www.pubssearch.com

Beer range varies

Run by the same couple for 24 years, this traditional town pub offers an ever-changing range of guest ales. The house beer, Skinny Mutt, is brewed by Vale Brewery to a recipe suggested by customers' comments. The two bars are complemented by a restaurant, specialising in Mexican food; Sun roasts are favourably priced, but must be booked in advance. The malt whisky range is extensive, with over 40 in stock. There is a pool room upstairs.

ﾑ🌸◑♣

DAVENTRY

Coach & Horses

Warwick Street

✪ 11.30-2.30, 5-11; 12-3, 7-11 Sat; 12-3, 7-10.30 Sun

☎ (01327) 876692

Greene King IPA, Abbot; Ind Coope Burton Ale; Tetley Bitter; guest beer Ⓗ

Traditional pub, on the edge of the town centre, it features open fires and a flagstoned floor. The beer range includes a regularly changing guest ale, which is often from a small regional brewery. The stables across the coaching yard host a jazz band (alternate Thu eves); entry is free of charge. The stables can also be used for small private functions. A popular general

knowledge quiz is held Sun eve. There is limited off-road parking in front of the pub.

ﾑQ🌸◑

DENFORD

Cock Inn

High Street (off A45/A14)

✪ 12-3 (not Mon), 5.30-11; 12-4, 6.30-11 Sat; 12-3, 7-10.30 Sun

☎ (01832) 732565 website: www.cock-inn.co.uk

Boddingtons Bitter; Flowers IPA; guest beer Ⓗ

Picturesque rural village pub in the Nene Valley, a short walk from the river. Dating from 1593, the low-beamed bar occupies a former saddler's/boot shop and an old blacksmith's forge now houses the Northants skittle table. Sunday lunchtime roasts are served and bar snacks are available most days. At the rear is a garden and a safe area for children to play in, plus tables and benches on the green out front.

ﾑQ🌸◑♣

DESBOROUGH

George Hotel

79 High Street (off A6)

✪ 11-4, 6-11; 11-11 Fri & Sat; 12-10.30 Sun

☎ (01536) 760271

Everards Beacon, Tiger Ⓗ

Former coaching inn, built in the 18th century out of local ironstone, overlooking Desborough Cross, the pub has been opened out into an L-shape, with a partitioned bar/lounge. A room at the rear holds two pool tables. The pub has a big following in sports and games, fielding football, cricket, skittles, darts, dominoes, crib and pool teams; their success can be judged by all the cups and shields on display. A motorcycle club and local pigeon club meet in the pub's yard. ﾑ🌸�♣P

EASTCOTE

Eastcote Arms

6 Gayton Road (off A5, 2 miles N of Towcester)

✪ 12-2.30 (not Mon; 12-3 Sat), 6-11; 12-4, 7-10.30 Sun

☎ (01327) 830731

Adnams Bitter; Draught Bass; Greene King IPA; Young's Bitter Ⓗ

Unspoilt, popular village pub, offering a

INN BRIEF

BRIXWORTH

Coach & Horses

Harborough Road

11.30-2.30, 5.30-11;

12-3, 5-10.30 Sun

Adnams Bitter; Frankton Bagby Old Chestnut; Marston's Pedigree Ⓗ

17th-century, oak-beamed inn with two lounge bars and a restaurant, where special theme nights take place.

FLORE

Royal Oak

28 High Street

12-11;

12-10.30 Sun

Beer range varies Ⓗ

Former farmhouse, with four inter-connected rooms around a central bar. One beer is always from the Featherstone Brewery.

GRAFTON REGIS

White Hart

Northampton Road

12-2.30, 6-11; (closed Mon);

12-2.30, 7-10.30 Sun

Greene King IPA; Abbot Ⓗ

Roadside inn enjoying a good reputation for quality food on an extensive menu, with fish a speciality.

GREAT BRINGTON

Althorp Coaching Inn/ Fox & Hounds

High Street

12-3, 5-11; 12-11 Sat; 12-10.30 Sun

Fuller's London Pride; Greene King IPA, Abbot; Old Speckled Hen; Marston's Pedigree; guest beers Ⓗ

Stone pub with low beams, booths and an enormous fireplace, close to the Spencer estate. Live bands perform Tue; up to six guests on tap.

KETTERING

Park House

Holdenby

11-11;

12-10.30 Sun

Banks's Original, Bitter Ⓗ

Large, modern pub near the cinema and Tesco's. The ground-floor bar is divided into smaller areas; the restaurant is upstairs.

KING'S CLIFFE

Cross Keys

2 West Street

11-3, 6-11;

12-3, 7-10.30 Sun

Ind Coope Burton Ale; Tetley Bitter; guest beer Ⓗ

Stone-built, street-corner local offering pub games, including Northants skittles. Meals are served.

FARTHINGSTONE

King's Arms
Main Street (off A5)
🕐 12-3 (not Mon-Fri), 7-11 (not Mon or Wed); 12-3, 7-11 Sun
☎ (01327) 361604
e-mail: paul@kingsarms.fsbusiness.co.uk
Hook Norton Best Bitter; guest beers Ⓗ
This fine 18th-century listed popular village pub always serves a changing range of up to three guest ales and delicious home-cooked weekend lunches (booking advised). The garden (where herbs are grown for the kitchen) is a delightful place to sit and enjoy your favourite tipple. The bar is extra cosy when the fire is lit, and has a homely atmosphere, particularly in the area with the sofa and comfy chairs (always in demand). The bar offers speciality British cheeses for sale, ask for a menu. ⚞Q⚛◑♣P

GAYTON

Eykyn Arms
20 High Street
🕐 11.30-2 (3 Sat), 7-11; 12-3, 7-10.30 Sun
☎ (01604) 858361
Fuller's London Pride; Greene King IPA; Wells Eagle; guest beer Ⓗ
A *Guide* regular, it has been run by the same landlord for over 10 years, but was only converted to a free house in 1994. Named after a Captain Eykyn, this is a welcoming local with a lounge at the front and a bar at the rear. The large conservatory at the side is a no-smoking restaurant, serving good value food (booking advisable). It is a mobile phone-free zone. Northants skittles is played in the bar. The car park is located 75 yards from the pub.
⚞Q⚞⚛⚞◑Ⓗ⚞♣♦⚞P⚞⊟

GREATWORTH

Inn
Chapel Road
🕐 12-2.30 (not Mon), 6.30-11; 12-3.30, 6.30-10.30 Sun
☎ (01295) 710976
Hook Norton Mild, Best Bitter, Old Hooky, guest beers Ⓗ
The name is short, but the welcome is large in this 16th-century local where families with children are made welcome. It has a large bar with an inglenook, and a no-smoking dining room. The menu offers excellent quality food, specialising in fish dishes. Twice-monthly supper nights (first and third Tue) feature good value fish and chips. Aunt Sally is played in the garden and customers are invited to see if the dormant resident in the aquarium ever moves. This classic country pub is well worth a visit. ⚞Q⚛◑♣P

GRENDON

Crown Inn
34 Manor Road (off A509)
🕐 12-2.30, 6 (6.30 Sat)-11; 12-10.30 Sun
☎ (01933) 663995
Adnams Bitter; Marston's Bitter, Pedigree; Thwaites Bitter; guest beer Ⓗ
This old local is listed and dates back to 1734. There are two bars and a restaurant (open Tue–Sat eves). The frontage proclaims 'Praeds Noted Ales and Stout' – a reminder of a long-gone Wellingborough Brewery. Situated in the village centre, it is close to Grendon Lakes, which has a caravan site.
⚞⚞⚞⊟♣P

HINTON-IN-THE-HEDGES

Crewe Arms
Off A43/A422
🕐 12-2.30, 6-11; closed Mon; 12-3, 7-10.30 Sun
☎ (01280) 703314
Hook Norton Best Bitter; guest beers Ⓗ
Tucked away in this small hamlet, this country pub is a must to visit. Choose from several rooms to drink in, or dine in the Italian restaurant, Lucia's, in the former function room. Another dining area within the pub is a no-smoking zone and serves good quality food. The bar has a welcoming open fire, and the former games room is ideal for meetings. Folk sessions are held (alternate Sun eves) when everyone is welcome to perform. It is hard to imagine how this pub could be bettered.
⚞Q⚛◑♣P

KETTERING ❉

Piper
Windmill Avenue (off old A6, by Wicksteed Park)
🕐 11-3 (4 Sat), 6-11; 12-10.30 Sun
☎ (01536) 513870
Theakston Mild, Best Bitter, XB, Old Peculier; guest beers Ⓗ
Popular, two-roomed 1950s pub, opposite the Tresham College annexe, and close to Wicksteed Park, an excellent venue for a day out with the children. The games room is regularly populated by younger drinkers, while the lounge bar is more sedate, and buzzes with conversation. Across the road in front of the pub are tables that are ideal for summer drinking. Note the pub sign features two different pipers. Two guest beers are always on tap.
⚛◑⚞♣P

LITCHBOROUGH

Old Red Lion
4 Banbury Road (off A5)
🕐 11-3, 6.30-11; 12-3, 6.30-10.30 Sun
☎ (01327) 830250
Banks's Bitter; Marston's Pedigree; Morrells Varsity Ⓗ
This picturesque, almost quaint pub, in an unspoilt village is a must. The bar features oak beams and a flagstoned floor; a cosy inglenook invites you to sit and read while

---

INDEPENDENT BREWERY
Frog Island Northampton

warming by the open log fire. A games room houses Northants skittles and pool. Meals are unfortunately no longer served but bar snacks are available. Popular with locals, walkers and cyclists, the pub welcomes bikers and well-behaved children. Fruit wines are stocked.

♨ Q ❀ ♣ P 🖰

MARSTON ST LAWRENCE

Marston Inn
Off A422
✪ 12-3 (not Mon), 7 (6 Sat)-11; 12-4, 7-10.30 Sun
☎ (01295) 711906
Hook Norton Mild, Best Bitter, Old Hooky, Double Stout, seasonal beers Ⓗ

Village local where lively conversation is the norm and the landlord reflects everything that is right with a true country pub. He is a motorcycle enthusiast and displays many photos of former world champions on the bar walls. The no-smoking dining area offers a varied menu. This is an adult-only pub without music or TV. A perry is served in the summer; drink it in the large garden at the front.

♨ Q ❀ ◑ 🍴 ▲ ♣ P ⚹

MEARS ASHBY

Griffins Head
28 Wilby Road
✪ 11.30-2.30, 5.30-11; 12-3, 6-11 Sat; 12-10.30 Sun
☎ (01604) 812945 website: www.mearsashby.com
Adnams Bitter; Everards Beacon, Tiger; Marston's Pedigree; Wells Eagle; guest beer Ⓗ

This bustling village local has two large rooms and a small restaurant offering an interesting and varied menu. No meals are served Sun or Mon eves. Darts and Northants skittles are played in the bar, while the cosy lounge features an inglenook. ♨ Q ◑ 🍴 P

NORTHAMPTON ❖

Duke of Edinburgh
3 Adelaide Street
✪ 12-2.30 (not Mon; 12-3 Fri), 5-11; 11-11 Sat; 12-3, 7-10.30 Sun
☎ (01604) 637903
Wells Eagle, Bombardier; guest beer Ⓗ

Single-roomed local with an L-shaped bar

and a village atmosphere, yet close to the town centre. A good old-fashioned, back-street boozer, it serves the local community and staff from the nearby Post Office sorting office. Skittles, darts and pool are played and live entertainment and discos staged at weekends. A regularly changed guest ale is always at a reasonable price. It is close to Racecourse Park, the venue for the Northampton Balloon Festival (Aug). Good use is made of the patio garden for barbecues. The landlord has been a runner-up in the Guinness *Bar Person of the Year* competition. ❀ ♣ ●

Malt Shovel Tavern
121 Bridge Street (facing Carlsberg brewery)
✪ 11.30-3, 5-11; 12-4, 7-10.30 Sun
Banks's Bitter; Frog Island Natterjack; Fuller's London Pride; Tetley Bitter; guest beers Ⓗ

Local CAMRA *Pub of the Year* 1997-2000, its warm interior is full of breweriana, including items from Phipp's and NBC Breweries, which both brewed opposite (demolished in 1974 when the site was sold to Carlsberg). Up to nine guest beers are supplemented by regular beer festivals. A good choice of Belgian bottled and draught beers, plus Belgian fruit gins, English country wines and 50 single malt whiskies make this a discerning drinkers' paradise, free from games machines. Tasty home-cooked food is served (eve meals finish early; no food Sun). It hosts live blues Wed eve. Q ❀ ◑ ⅄ ≈ ♣ ●

Racehorse
15 Abington Square
✪ 11-11; 12-10.30 Sun
☎ (01604) 631997
Banks's Original; Camerons Strongarm; Marston's Bitter, Pedigree; guest beer Ⓗ

Large pub with two areas and back room for bands and other functions. It serves fresh home-cooked food (not Wed) and hosts barbecues in the vast garden. A quiz night is held on Mon; noticeboards are useful for advertisements of other local events. The pub's decor features a range of beer bottles. The rotating guest beer, due to its tie, is from the W&D range. Strictly no children in the pub, although they may use the garden if supervised. The pub fields a cricket team. ❀ ◑ ♣ P

INN BRIEF

LITTLE HARROWDEN
Lamb Inn
24 Orlingbury Road
12-11;
12-10.30 Sun
Marston's Pedigree; Wells Eagle, Bombardier; guest beers Ⓗ
Extended village local, with a cosy small bar, games room, and small dining area. Northants skittles feature.

NEWTON BROMSWOLD
Swan
6 Church Lane
11-2.30 (not Mon), 5-11;
12-3, 7-10.30 Sun
Greene King IPA, Ⓗ **Abbot** Ⓖ
Idyllic country pub where two rooms and a conservatory provide a focal point for village life, and good value food.

NORTHAMPTON
Crown & Cushion
276 Wellingborough Road
11-11;
12-10.30 Sun
Banks's Bitter Ⓗ
Red-brick Victorian pub with a U-shaped bar, popular with families in summer.

Fish
11 Fish Street
11-11;
12-10.30 Sun
Courage Directors; Marston's Pedigree; Theakston Best Bitter, Old Peculier; guest beers Ⓗ
Victorian town pub with a three-sided bar, plenty of wood panelling, and wooden seats. Accommodation available.

King Billy
2 Commercial Street
12-11; 12-10.30 Sun
Adnams Bitter; Draught Bass; Greene King Abbot, Old Speckled Hen; Ind Coope Burton Ale; guest beers Ⓗ
Former Firkin on the 'Bridge Street run', catering for a mixed clientele with live music, quiz and curry nights and up to five guest ales.

OUNDLE
Rose & Crown
11 Market Street
11-11 (opens 9am Thu, market day);
12-10.30 Sun
Banks's Bitter; Mansfield Cask Ale; Marston's Pedigree Ⓗ
Two-roomed, town-centre pub where the lounge bar is split level with a dining area. No food Sun eve. *Cask Marque* accredited.

ORLINGBURY

Queen's Arms
11 Isham Road (off A509/A43)
☼ 12-2.30, 6-11; 12-11 Sat; 12-10.30 Sun
☎ (01933) 678258
Courage Directors; Tetley Bitter; guest beers Ⓗ
Cheery, welcoming, true village pub where the large lounge is divided into three drinking areas around the bar. A separate room is used as a restaurant and the extensive garden has a children's play area. The pub dates back to about 1750 and was originally called the King's Arms but changed its name in 1840 for the coronation of Queen Victoria. The new landlord is carrying on the fine tradition of serving a range of frequently changing beers, including seasonal and topical ales and hosting an annual beer festival.
Q❀◑⅃P

OUNDLE ✤

Ship Inn
18 West Street (near market place)
☼ 11-11; 12-10.30 Sun
☎ (01832) 273918 e-mail:
shipinn@funkmaster.demon.co.uk
Draught Bass; Black Sheep Best Bitter; Hop Back Summer Lightning; guest beer Ⓗ
Grade II listed building in the main street, 100 yards from the town centre, this stone-built, Collyweston slated pub is reputedly haunted by a previous landlord who flung himself from an upstairs window. A more regal pub ghost can be found at the Talbot Hotel just around the corner. The pub is divided into several bars which makes for a homely and cosy atmosphere. Nearby, Oundle School is one of the largest independent schools in the country, founded in 1556. No eve meals Wed.
ﲟQ❀⇐◑P⅄Ұ

RAVENSTHORPE

Chequers
Church Lane (off High St, 1½ miles off A428)
☼ 12-3, 6-11; 12-11 Sat; 12-3, 7-10.30 Sun
☎ (01604) 770379 e-mail: gordonwalker@byte-it.net
Fuller's London Pride; Greene King IPA, Abbot; Jennings Bitter; Thwaites Bitter Ⓗ
Friendly village free house with an L-shaped bar and a restaurant in a small area, partitioned off by an old stable wall. The food is excellent. With beams and bric-à-brac, this local is popular with cyclists and walkers who frequent this part of the country. A games room housing Northants skittles and pool is across the courtyard.
Q❀◑♣P

RUSHDEN

Rushden Historical Transport Society
The Station, Station Approach (off A6 one-way system)
☼ 12-3 (not Mon-Fri), 7.30-11; 12-2.30, 7.30-10.30 Sun
☎ (01933) 318988 website: www.rhts.co.uk.
Fuller's London Pride; guest beers Ⓗ
Joint winners of CAMRA *Club of Britain* 2000, the Society was founded in 1976. The gaslit station bar is located in the split-level ladies waiting rooms where the walls are adorned with loco name plates and pictures, and old advertising boards. The bar stocks five guest beers (over 200 in the last year). The waiting room is a transport museum displaying railway and road memorabilia. The Society has two working locos which are run by an steaming weekends six times a year. It also owns two vintage buses, two fire engines and other vehicles.
ﲟQ❀P⅄

SIBBERTOFT

Red Lion
43 Welland Rise (off B4036)
☼ 12-3 (not Mon or Tue), 6.30-11; 12-3, 7-10.30 Sun
☎ (01858) 880011
Draught Bass; Everards Tiger; guest beer Ⓗ
Rural whitewashed, 200-year-old village pub, with a low-beamed ceiling, consisting of two rooms, a bar and a restaurant serving *à la carte* meals. There is a patio garden in the yard where the old stables have been converted into two studio suites for overnight guests. Sibbertoft overlooks the Welland Valley and lies two miles from the site of the Battle of Naseby.
Q❀⇐◑P●

SOUTHWICK

Shuckburgh Arms
Main Street (near Southwick Hall)
☼ 12-2 (not Mon or Tue), 6-11; 12-3, 7-10.30 Sun
☎ (01832) 274007
Fuller's London Pride; guest beers Ⓗ
Cosy, village pub dating from the 16th century and situated virtually on the village cricket pitch. A large, enclosed garden to the rear offers a variety of play equipment and wooden benches. Bar billiards is played. Eve meals are served Wed–Sat. There is another Shuckburgh Arms not far away in Stoke Doyle, so ask for directions carefully.
ﲟQ❀◑Ⴑ♣P

STOKE BRUERNE

Boat Inn
Off A508
☼ 9-3, 6-11; 9-11 Fri, Sat & summer; 12-10.30 Sun
☎ (01604) 862428 website: www.boatinn.co.uk
Banks's Bitter; Frog Island Best Bitter; Marston's Bitter, Pedigree; guest beer Ⓗ
Run by the fourth generation of Woodward's this popular canalside free house dates back to 1877. The cosy thatched bars retain their original stone floors and open fires. The restaurant is in a later extension, with a view overlooking the canal lock. The lounge leads through to an area that was used for stabling the canal horses, and is now devoted to breakfasts, meals and snacks. Opposite is the famous Canal Museum and a short walk takes you to the awesome Blisworth Tunnel.
ﲟⴄ❀◑⇐Ⴑ♣P

SUDBOROUGH

Vane Arms
High Street (off A6116)
☼ 12-3 (not Mon-Wed), 5.30 (6 Sat)-11; 12-3, 7-11 Sun
☎ (01832) 733223 website: www./thevanearms.com
Beer range varies Ⓗ

This long, stone, thatched building, is set in an equally attractive village. The public bar houses pool, darts and Northants skittles; the larger lounge bar is divided into a number of alcoves by stone walls, maintaining a cosy atmosphere. It stocks nine continually-changing guest beers (samples available); country fruit wines, Hoegaarden on tap and an occasional real cider add variety. An upstairs restaurant serves Mexican and English meals, with bar snacks at lunchtime and traditional Sun lunches. Three en-suite rooms are in a separate converted building.

🏚️🌸⛄🍴⬜♣⬜P

SULGRAVE

Star Inn
Manor Road
⊘ 11-2.30, (12-3 summer), 6-11; 12-5, 7-10.30 (not winter eve) Sun
☎ (01295) 760389 website: www.starinnsulgrave.co.uk
Hook Norton Best Bitter, Generation, Old Hooky Ⓗ

In an idyllic village location on the Oxfordshire border, the 300-year-old Star Inn offers home-cooked food and four well-appointed en-suite bedrooms. It is an 'adult sanctuary', close to Sulgrave Manor, the ancestral home of George Washington's family. A stone-flagged floor, beams and an inglenook are attractive features, while George, the resident skeleton sits beside the fire and adds character. The restaurant offers an extensive menu. Skittle eves can be arranged for parties of 10 or more. A thoroughly civilised place.

🏚️Q🌸🏚️⛄⬜P

SUTTON BASSETT

Queen's Head
Main Street (off A427)
⊘ 12-2.30, 6.30-11; 12-2.30, 6.30-10.30 Sun
☎ (01858) 463530
Adnams Bitter; Taylor Landlord; guest beers Ⓗ

19th-century rural village pub of whitewashed walls in a pleasant part of the county, overlooking the Welland Valley. A corridor connects the two rooms, with low-beamed ceilings and a variety of pictures; upholstered settles and candles in bottles on the tables give it a taverna feel. The cosy back room houses a piano that anyone who can play is welcome to use. The pub serves good value food with Italian cuisine a speciality; Sun roasts are served 12–2.

🏚️Q🌸⛄♣P

TITCHMARSH

Dog & Partridge
6 High Street (½ mile off A605)
⊘ 12-2 (4 Sat), 6 (6.30 Sat)-11; 12-3.30, 7-11 Sun
☎ (01832) 732546
Wells Eagle, Bombardier, seasonal beers; guest beer Ⓗ

Centrally situated in the village, this local CAMRA *Gold Award* pub offers a warm, friendly welcome from the long-serving landlord. Outside there is a pleasant patio area, and indoors, skittles and table football are played at this regular *Guide* entry.

🏚️Q🌸♣P⬜

WALGRAVE

Royal Oak
Zion Hill (off A43)
⊘ 12-3, 6-11; 12-3, 6-10.30 Sun
☎ (01604) 781248
Adnams Bitter; guest beers Ⓗ

This old ironstone building has been used as a village pub since 1840. The large front bar is used for meals in addition to the restaurant at the back, reached via a comfortble lounge area, that has a small back bar. No meals served Sun eve. The pub is popular with diners as well as those who come to sample the choice of guest beers. It is frequented by walkers at the weekends. The MX5 Club and Vintage Sports Car Club both hold their monthly meetings here.

🏚️Q🌸⛄♣P

WELLINGBOROUGH

Vivian Arms
153 Knox Road (near station)
⊘ 12.30 (12 Sat)-11; 12-10.30 Sun
☎ (01933) 223660
Wells Eagle; guest beer Ⓗ

The last remaining three-bar pub in Wellingborough has a quiet front lounge and wood-panelled public bars, with a large games room to the rear. A collection of key rings adorn the glass shelf over the bars while rows of head plaques look down in the public bar. The large garden is an added attraction. The Vivian has featured in most editions of this *Guide*.

🏚️Q🌸🏚️🍴♣P

Wellingborough Old Grammarians Association
46 Oxford Street
⊘ 12-2.30, 7-11; 12-11 Fri & Sat; 12-10.30 Sun
☎ (01933) 226188
Hook Norton Best Bitter, Old Hooky; Wells Eagle; guest beers Ⓗ

This sports and social club caters for most outdoor games and table tennis. The rugby team regularly reaches the later stages of the Tetley Bitter trophy. This friendly town-centre club has a small TV lounge, a long bar and a games/function room. Access is from the rear car park (stair lift for wheelchairs); press the voicecom button. Open to all, regular visitors will be asked to join. This fine club is a former East Midlands CAMRA *Club of the Year*. There are always three guest beers, mainly from micro-breweries, plus Weston's cider.

🍺⛄♣P

WESTON

Crown
2 Helmdon Road
⊘ 12-2.30 (not Mon), 6-11; 12-2.30, 7-10.30 (closed winter eve) Sun
☎ (01295) 760310
Greene King IPA; Wadworth 6X; guest beers Ⓗ

Family-run local with a no-smoking family dining room, it places an emphasis on good quality food and ale. A well is a feature of the games room that offers pool and darts. The beamed function room hosts live music. According to a newspaper report, the pub was visited by Lord

Lucan on his way to a local airfield. Locals talk of a friendly ghost that has a warm presence; this all adds to the character of the pub, which is well worth a visit.

🅰🆀☕🏠🌙◑♣P♿

WESTON FAVELL

Bold Dragoon
48 High Street
🕐 11-3, 5.30-11; 11-11 Sat; 12-3, 7-10.30 Sun
☎ (01604) 401221

Banks's Bitter; Boddingtons Bitter; Fuller's London Pride; Greene King IPA; guest beers Ⓗ

Busy pub on the edge of Northampton, just off the A4500. Deservedly voted Northamptonshire CAMRA *Pub of the Year* 2000 runner-up, it serves two constantly-changing guest ales. The pub has been much extended and pleasantly refurbished to include a conservatory restaurant, where above-average meals are served. There is also a comfortable lounge and a bustling traditional public bar with music and games. A large patio area, with benches and tables, makes summer eves very pleasurable.
Q🌙◑⌕♣P

WOLLASTON

Boot
35 High Street
🕐 12-2 (not Mon-Wed), 6-11; 12-11 Fri & Sat; 12-10.30 Sun
☎ (01933) 664270

Greene King IPA, Abbot; Tetley Bitter; Wadworth 6X; guest beer (occasional) Ⓗ

Three cottages, built some 400 years ago, were amalgamated to form the Boot 250 years later. The name celebrates the local boot and shoe industry which now produces 'Doc Martens' (although the local factories may close). The rear public/sports room features Northants skittles, and a set of old pictures on the wall. Sports and games equipment over the bar includes a mystery board for a game nobody can name (including the donor). A shove-ha'penny board and dominoes are available. In summer pig roasts and barbecues are held in the garden. 🅰🌙⌕♣

Crispin Arms
14 Hinwick Road
🕐 12-11; 12-10.30 Sun
☎ (01933) 664303

Caledonian Deuchars IPA; Fuller's London Pride; Shepherd Neame Spitfire; Theakston Best Bitter; guest beers Ⓗ

This small, two-roomed local has a welcoming atmosphere, and the open fire gives a particularly cosy feel in winter. The range of regular and guest beers is exceptional for an Enterprise Inn. Take time to peruse the large collection of Guinness material on the walls, together with other Irish posters. A small display of lasts in the windows reflects the local shoe industry. Outside drinking is on a paved area. 🅰🌙P

WOOTTON

Wootton Workingmen's Club
23 High Street (near M1 jct 15)
🕐 12-2 (not Thu), 7-11; 12-11 Sat; 12-3, 7-10.30 Sun
☎ (01604) 761863

Greene King IPA; guest beers Ⓗ

This club has an excellent reputation for its ever-changing range of five guest ales, normally sourced from micro-breweries. Formerly the Red Lion, this club still has a pub atmosphere in the main bar area. A games room and a quiet lounge are recent additions and complete the facilities which include a concert room with a large TV screen. CIU regulations apply. It was regional CAMRA *Club of the Year* in 1997 and '98. ♣P

YARDLEY HASTINGS

Rose & Crown
4 Northampton Road
🕐 12-3, 6-11; 12-3, 7-10.30 Sun
☎ (01604) 696276

Adnams Bitter; Greene King Abbot; Wadworth 6X Ⓗ

Some parts of this stone-built building are believed to date back to the 15th century, however, this one-time brewhouse is reported to have been a pub only since the early 18th century. It was considerably changed and modernised in the 1980s but has retained stone-flagged floors and beamed ceilings throughout. The single room has a large dining area where good value meals are served all day. The new landlord's future plans include serving local beer and developing the garden to create a quiet drinking area and space for children to play. ◑P🕱

Cask breather

Where an entry states that some beers in a pub are served with the aid of cask breathers, this means that demand valves are connected to both casks and cylinders of gas; as beer is drawn off, it is replaced by applied gas (either carbon dioxide, nitrogen or both) to prevent oxidation. The method is not acceptable to CAMRA as it does not allow beer to condition and mature naturally. The Campaign believes brewers and publicans should use the size of casks best suited to the turnover of beer in order to avoid oxidation. If a pub in the Good Beer Guide uses cask breathers, we list only those beers that are free of the device.

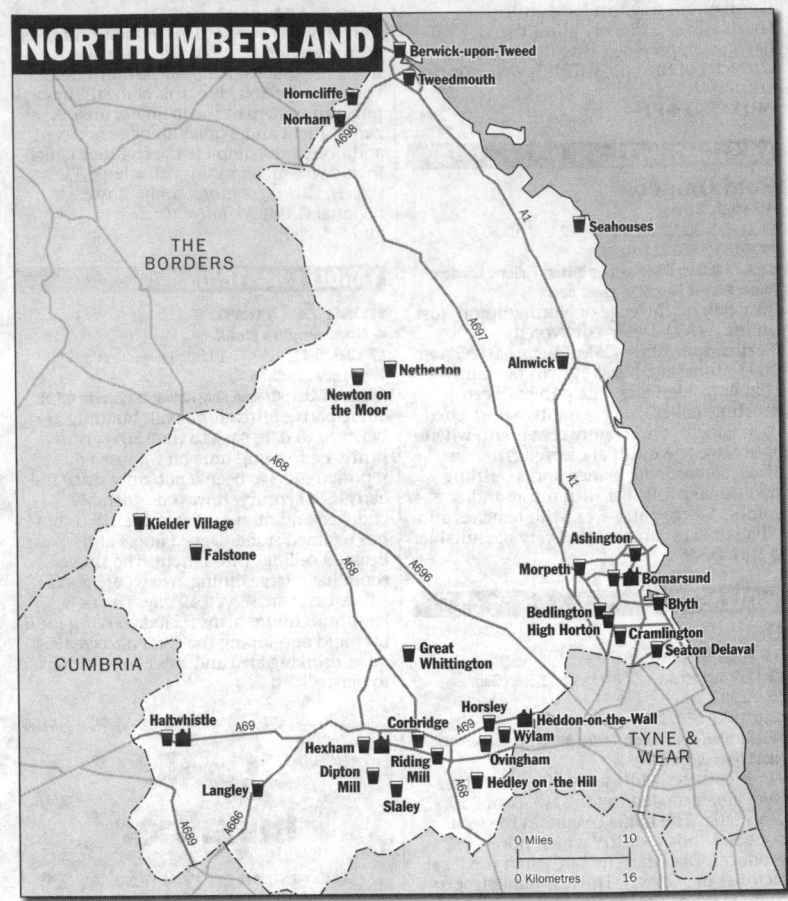

NORTHUMBERLAND

ALNWICK

John Bull Inn
12 Howick Street
🕒 12-3 (not Wed; 11-2 Sat), 7-11; 12-3, 7-10.30 Sun
☎ (01665) 602055
Tetley Bitter; guest beers Ⓗ
Small, cosy local in a row of terraced houses. This one-roomed pub is popular with regulars who enjoy the changing guest beers. On entering the front door you could be forgiven for thinking that you had walked into someone's house, but just carry on through the hallway to find the bar, which offers one of the largest selections of malt whiskies in Northumberland. Triominoes (three-sided dominoes) is played here. Q♣♠

ASHINGTON ❖

Bubbles Wine Bar
58A Station Road
🕒 11-11; 12-10.30 Sun
☎ (01670) 850800 website: www.bubblesbar.co.uk
Beer range varies Ⓗ
Just off the main paved shopping street of what was once the largest mining village in the world, lies an excellent pub with an unlikely name. The local Northumberland brewery is always supported and their beers enjoy good sales here. There is always something going on in the evenings, with a music quiz (Wed), live bands or disco (Thu and Sat) and weekend Karaoke. ❖◗

Elephant
Newbiggin Road
🕒 11-11; 12-10.30 Sun
Bateman XB Ⓗ
Three-storey, imposing, late-Victorian building, with a large bar and comfortable lounge. Popular with the locals, it also offers B&B accommodation, but no food. In what was once a real ale desert, Ashington does now offers a fair selection of beers, but there are still more clubs than pubs here. ♨🛏

Rohan Kanhai
1-4 Woodhorn Road
🕒 11-11; 12-10.30 Sun
☎ (01670) 857692
Boddingtons Bitter; Castle Eden Nimmo's XXXX; Courage Directors; Theakston Best Bitter; guest beers Ⓗ
Named after a famous cricketer who once played for the town as the club professional, this friendly, purpose-built Wetherspoon's is all on one level, allowing good wheelchair access. As one would expect with this pub group, there is an excellent range of guest beers, and meals are served all day. There is a patio for outside drinking. Q❖◗&✕●

BEDLINGTON

Northumberland Arms
112 Front Street East
✪ 11-3 (not Mon or Tue), 7-11; 11-11 Thu-Sat; 12-10.30 Sun
☎ (01670) 822754
Beer range varies Ⓗ
This is very much a local where all are made to feel welcome. The pub specialises in quality beer and food. A comfortable atmosphere prevails in the bar/lounge, with a pool room and a function room upstairs. Guest beers are always available; some of the regulars include southerners Fuller's London Pride and Charles Wells Bombardier. Mon is quiz night. ♣

Wharton Arms
Burdon Terrace
✪ 12-11; 12-10.30 Sun
☎ (01670) 822214
Greene King Abbot; Tetley Bitter Ⓗ
Terraced building in the centre of town, with wood panelling and bare wood floors. Good quality beers are found in this local with a bar and lounge. Pool and darts are played in the bar. ♣🍴

BERWICK UPON TWEED ❄

Barrels
Bridge Street
✪ 11-11; 12-10.30 Sun
☎ (01289) 308013
Boddingtons Bitter; Hadrian & Border Farne Island Pale; guest beers Ⓗ
At the end of the historic Elizabethan bridge over the Tweed, this pub is a splendid mix of traditional and modern, and has, in the last decade, built up a tremendous reputation for its quality and range of beers and excellent food. It is always innovative and universally popular. The pub has two rooms and a basement (used for regular live events). The front bar is divided into two areas, a raised level with dining tables and a lower level with one large table and ample standing room. A second room contains many strange items including ancient space invader tables and gothic-style chairs. ♣≈

Foxtons
Hide Hill
✪ 11-11; closed Sun
☎ (01289) 303939
Caledonian Deuchars IPA; guest beers Ⓗ
In a part of town littered with pubs, but seemingly bereft of decent beer, Foxtons is easily overlooked. Behind its disguise as an upmarket coffee bar/restaurant lies a superb atmosphere where excellent food and beer can be enjoyed. A long central bar serves three bright, lively areas: the lower area looks out on the busy street; the other two areas concentrate on food but still create a fine environment for drinkers. The decor is modern wood, brass and steel, blackboards detail food and drink. ♣≈

BLYTH

Oliver's Bar
60 Bridge Street
✪ 11 (1 Sat)-11; 12-10.30 Sun
☎ (01670) 540356
Marston's Pedigree; Wells Bombardier; guest beers Ⓗ

Comfortable town free house that was originally a newsagent's shop. The pub is small – only one room – but it is well decorated, cosy and friendly. A guest ale is usually available at weekends. This is very much a people's pub where conversation comes first. Food consists of well-presented, tasty sandwiches. Q

Ridley Park Hotel
10-14 Wensleydale Terrace
✪ 11-11; 12-10.30 Sun
☎ (01670) 352927
Northumberland Castles; guest beers Ⓗ
Privately-owned hotel, offering good quality accommodation and great pool also with usually a guest beer at weekends. Displays of paintings by a local artist are available to buy. It hosts a quiz night and regular entertainment, including a folk group. Good home-cooked food is available and children are welcome. It makes a good base for exploring the lovely Northumberland coastline and countryside. ⚘🛏🍴

BOMARSUND

Cat & Sawdust
Earth Balance, West Sleekburn Farm (3/4 mile N of A189/A1147 intersection) OS273843
✪ 11-2 Mon-Fri; 7-11 Wed; 12-5 Sat (may vary summer); 12-5 summer Sun
☎ (01670) 822112
website: www.made-in-northumberland.co.uk
Beer range varies Ⓗ
The Northumberland Brewery tap opened in 1998 after the brewery moved from Ashington to the environmentally-sustainable Earth Balance community site. The bar is built out of old pallets and rough wood; the room is furnished by items donated by customers or picked up from car boot sales – two skulls guard either end of the bar. Two beers are always available on handpump. Come and meet the resident cat and enjoy the sawdust on the floor. Ring to check opening hours as they can vary, especially in winter.
Q♣P

CORBRIDGE ❄

Dyvels
Station Road
✪ 4 (12 Sat)-11; 12-4, 7-10.30 Sun
☎ (01434) 633633
Draught Bass; Black Sheep Best Bitter; guest beers Ⓗ
Small public bar of an independently-owned, old-style country hotel. Over the bridge, it is just out of the town centre, but very handy for the station. Popular in summer as a base for exploring Hadrian's Wall and other Roman sites, it also has pleasant riverside walks nearby. The friendly landlord is keen on outdoor pursuits and owns working dogs; he makes all dogs and their owners particularly welcome.
🏚⚘🛏≈♣P🍴

INDEPENDENT BREWERIES

Black Bull Haltwhistle
Hexhamshire Hexham
Northumberland Bomarsund
Wylam Heddon-on-the-Wall

CRAMLINGTON

Plough
Middle Farm Buildings
☺ 11-11; 12-10.30 Sun
☎ (01670) 737633
Theakston XB; guest beers Ⓗ
Popular pub, created from farm buildings at the heart of an old village. Rough stone walls inside and lots of old beams feature; see the display of photos on the stairs depicting the buildings before conversion. The lounge and unusual gingan provide plentiful, comfortable seating space. The three guest beers change regularly and are often from local micro-breweries. The pub is a busy meeting place eves; children welcome at lunchtime. ♿◑⊟&⇌P

DIPTON MILL

Dipton Mill Inn ←
Dipton Mill Road (2 miles from Hexham)
☺ 12-2.30, 6-11; 12-4, 7-10.30 Sun
☎ (01434) 606577
Hexhamshire Devil's Elbow, Shire Bitter, Devil's Water, Whapweasel Ⓗ
The tap for Hexhamshire Brewery, a small low-ceilinged pub. The landlord brews excellent beers which are always available to accompany the great home-cooked meals. The pub has won several CAMRA awards in recent years. It is well worth seeking out. The large garden has a stream running through it, and there is plenty of countryside to explore. ♿Q❀◑⊟

GREAT WHITTINGTON

Queen's Head Inn
☺ 12-2.30 (not Mon), 6-11; 12-3, 7-10.30 Sun
☎ (01434) 672267
Black Sheep Best Bitter; Hambleton Bitter; guest beers Ⓗ
This inn, dating from the 15th century, is reputedly the oldest in the county. Four handpumps serve a variety of guest ales. The house beer, Queen's Head bitter, is brewed by Hambleton. Set in the heart of Hadrian's Wall country, the pub makes an ideal watering-hole. The food is excellent – all made using local produce whenever possible, the menu is extensive with dishes to suit all tastes. There is a small friendly bar with a roaring fire and a restaurant. ♿Q◑P

HALTWHISTLE

Black Bull ←
Market Square
☺ 12-3 (not Mon-Wed), 7-11; 12-4, 7-11 Sat; 12-3, 7-10.30 Sun
☎ (01434) 320463
Jennings Cumberland; guest beers Ⓗ
Superb pub boasting an open fire, beams, horsebrasses and a welcoming landlord. The small, low-ceilinged bar is already a showcase for many of the finest independent breweries, with guest ales from local micros; the owners are now producing their own beers and aim to have three different brews on handpump. ♿Q⇌

HEDLEY ON THE HILL

Feathers
☺ 12-3 (not Mon-Thu), 6-11; 12-3, 7-10.30 Sun
☎ (01661) 843607
Boddingtons Bitter; guest beers Ⓗ
Splendid country pub in a lofty hilltop location. Real fires in both the bar and the lounge give a warm friendly welcome. Quality food is offered eves and weekend lunchtimes, to accompany the range of three guest beers. The pub hosts a mini beer festival every Easter when there is also a barrel race among local drinkers – the contestants have to roll a barrrel uphill to the pub! The winners are well rewarded (with beer obviously). ♿Q❀◑P

HEXHAM

Forum
Market Place
☺ 11-11; 12-10.30 Sun
☎ (01434) 609190
Courage Directors; Theakston Best Bitter; guest beers Ⓗ
Typical Wetherspoon's split-level conversion of a cinema, latterly used as a bingo hall. The original Art Deco-style decor has been retained to complement film memorabilia. The screen has been replaced by a massive window affording expansive views across the town. Unusually, after such a conversion, a cinema still operates above the pub. At the heart of this historic town, the pub is close to both the ancient abbey and Moot Hall. Q◑&⇌✠●

INN BRIEF

ASHINGTON
Black Diamond Inn
29 Douth View
11-11; 12-10.30 Sun
Beer range varies Ⓗ
Converted in 1996 from a Co-op dairy; a bar and lounge/diner. The house beer is produced by Northumberland Brewery. Read about local mining history around the pub.

BERWICK UPON TWEED
Pilot
31 Low Greens
12-11; 12-3, 7-10.30 Sun
Federation Buchanan's Original; Hadrian & Border Farne Island Pale Ⓗ
Friendly two-room pub behind Berwick Infirmary, full of nautical memorabilia. Regular folk eves.

CORBRIDGE
Black Bull
Middle Street
11-11; 12-10.30 Sun
Boddingtons Bitter; Castle Eden Ale; Flowers Original; guest beers Ⓗ
Friendly pub with flagstoned floor. There is always one guest beer available, lunches and eve meals.

FALSTONE
Black Cock Inn
12-2.30 (not Mon-Fri), 7-11 (12-3, 6.30-11 summer); 12-3, 7 (6.30 summer)-10.30 Sun
John Smith's Magnet; Theakston Cool Cask; guest beer Ⓗ
Village local near Kielder Dam. Dining room (for lunches) pool and accommodation. Black Cock Ale is John Smith's Bitter rebadged

HORNCLIFFE
Fishers Arms
Main Street
12-3, 6-11; 12-11 Sat; 12-10.30 Sun
Castle Eden Bitter, Ale Ⓗ
An angling theme runs throughout the bar and dining areas (meals all sessions and takeaways available). Children welcome in dining area. Pool and darts room.

KIELDER VILLAGE
Anglers Arms
12-3, 7-11; 12-11 Sat;. hours vary winter; 12-10.30 Sun
Beer range varies Ⓗ
The social centre of the village, built in 1982 as a club. Located below the castle; handy for Kielder Water.

Tap & Spile
Battle Hill
✪ 11-11; 12-3, 7-10.30 Sun
☎ (01434) 602039
Black Sheep Bitter; Theakston Best Bitter; guest beers Ⓗ
Despite transfer of ownership between pub companies and changes in guest beer policy, with the largest number of real ales for miles, this is still a flagship of the chain. Its ale house style bar area, with bare boards and a service hatch, plus a comfortable lounge is popular with many customers, including tourists, shoppers and live music fans. Regular music nights, from rock and blues to folk, are hosted by well-known Northumbrian musician Mike Tickell.
Q◖≢

HIGH HORTON

Three Horse Shoes
Hatherley Lane OS276794
✪ 11-11; 12-10.30 Sun
☎ (01670) 822410
Greene King Old Speckled Hen; Ind Coope Burton Ale; Marston's Pedigree; Tetley Bitter; guest beers Ⓗ
Well-established free house enjoying a good reputation for food and offfering a good selection of real ales including two, often local, guests. Its mini beer festivals feature beers not usually found in this area. The pub which overlooks the main road, has remained largely unchanged, however a glass conservatory, running the length of the building has been added. Inside, beams and panels enhance a very homely atmosphere. Children are welcome; there is an outdoor play area. ❀◖▶P

HORSLEY

Lion & Lamb
✪ 12-3, 6-11; 12-11 Fri & Sat; 12-10.30 Sun
☎ (01661) 852952
Boddingtons Bitter; Castle Eden Ale; guest beers Ⓗ
Spacious pub with several drinking areas where good food complements the excellent beer range. There are always guest beers from local micro-brewers, including Durham and Mordue. The restaurant can get very busy. The stone-built pub boasts beams, real fires and plenty of pictures and eye-catching items. It stands just off the Military Road and the main east-west routes. Hadrian's Wall is close by and the pub makes an excellent watering-hole for those exploring the area. ♨◖▶P

LANGLEY

Carts Bog Inn
3 miles off A69 on A686 to Alston
✪ 12-3, 7-11; 12-3, 7-10.30 Sun
☎ (01434) 684338
Marston's Pedigree; Theakston Best Bitter; guest beers Ⓗ
Unspoilt country pub, owned and run by the same family for several generations. It dates from 1730 and it's built on the site of an ancient brewery (circa 1521). An unusual open fire divides the two rooms and heats both. The separate games room does not disturb the rest of the pub. The name is derived from a steeply banked corner on the old road, where, on wet days, the horse-drawn carts were invariably bogged down. Excellent home-cooked food is available, making this a popular venue for Sunday lunch. ♨Q❧❀◖⬥P

MORPETH

Joiners Arms
3 Wansbeck Street
✪ 12 (11 Wed, Fri & Sat)-11; 12-10.30 Sun
☎ (01670) 513540
Draught Bass; Tetley Bitter; guest beers Ⓗ
Old-style, traditional, two roomed pub, consisting of a basic but comfortable bar, that houses an unusual collection of stuffed birds and animals in glass cases. The small cosy lounge offers a pleasant view of the River Wansbeck. A Fitzgerald's house, it has a good reputation for its beer and local micro-breweries' products are often guests. A pub with no frills, just a friendly place to enjoy a decent pint. Q◔

Tap & Spile
23 Manchester Street
✪ 11-11; 12-3, 7-10.30 Sun
☎ (01670) 513894
Beer range varies Ⓗ
Popular pub, with a proper bar and comfortable lounge. The latter is sometimes used by the local Northumbrian Pipe Society on Sun eve. It has an excellent reputation for its range of real ales; eight handpumps ensure an excellent choice. The pub is frequent local CAMRA *Pub of the Year* winner. Children are welcome in the lounge. In spite of the change of ownership, this pub has remained true to the original Tap & Spile concept, largely due to the excellent management and staff. Q◖♣

NETHERTON

Star Inn ☆
Off B634 from Rothbury
✪ 12-1.30, 7-10.30 (11 Fri & Sat); winter hours may vary; 12-1.30, 7-10.30 Sun
☎ (01669) 630238
Castle Eden Ale Ⓖ
Unspoilt gem, unchanged for the last 80 years, it was planned as an hotel for the new railway line. The line never reached the pub but fortunately the customers did. It is privately-owned, and as you enter you almost feel as if you are in someone's living room. The single beer is served direct from the cellar at a serving hatch in the panelled entrance hall. The bar area is basic, with benches round the wall. The only pub in Northumberland to appear in every edition of this *Guide*. Q❀P

NEWTON ON THE MOOR

Cook & Barker
✪ 12-11; 12-10.30 Sun
☎ (01665) 575234
Boddingtons Bitter; Marston's Pedigree; guest beers Ⓗ
Large pub just off the A1, south of Alnwick. Food is very much the main business here and it can be washed down with some excellent real ales. The beautiful Northumberland coastline is nearby and the town of Alnwick, with its castle, is worth a visit. Guest beers are available.
♨◖▶P✂

NORHAM

Masons Arms
16 West Street
✪ 12-3, 7-11; 12-3, 7-10.30 Sun
☎ (01289) 382326
Castle Eden Bitter, Ale, Nimmo's XXXX; guest beers Ⓗ

Former coaching house, circa 1700, in a border village. Locals and visitors from both sides of the River Tweed are greeted with a warm welcome. There is a real fire in this one-roomed pub where a wooden gantry above the bar holds an extensive water jug collection and the walls display photographs of old Norham and the River Tweed in flood. Interior leaded glass is featured on walls and the ceiling. Nearby, Norham Castle is floodlit by night.
♨Q🛏◖▣ᴴ

OVINGHAM

Bridge End Inn
West Road
✪ 12-11; 12-10.30 Sun
☎ (01661) 832219
Stones Bitter; Taylor Landlord; Tetley Bitter; guest beer Ⓗ

Comfortable, old-style pub with a bar and lounge which doubles occasionally as a music room. A friendly welcome is assured. Handy for walks in picturesque Whittle Dene. ♨Q🛏♣P▯

RIDING MILL

Wellington
On A695
✪ 11-11; 12-10.30 Sun
☎ (01434) 682531
Courage Directors; Theakston Best Bitter, Cool Cask; guest beer Ⓗ

Originally a private residence for the local postmaster, this large roadside inn dates back in part to 1660. Following a well-publicised 'witch finder' trial a few years later it became notorious as the meeting place for a witches' coven. Licensed for over 175 years and named after the hero of Waterloo, it is now part of S&N's food-oriented Chef & Brewer chain. However its distinct drinkers' bar area, much frequented by locals, has the ambience of a good village pub. ♨❀◖▣≉P

SEAHOUSES

Olde Ship Hotel
7-9 Main Street
✪ 11-4, 6-11; 11-11 Fri & Sat & summer Mon-Thu; 12-10.30 Sun
☎ (01665) 720200 website: www.seahouses.co.uk
Beer range varies Ⓗ

The Olde Ship, owned by the same family since 1910, was built as a farmhouse about 1745 and first licensed in 1812. This nautically-themed hotel boasts a main bar of tremendous character, lit by stained glass windows and warmed by a glowing open fire. It contains a treasure trove of maritime memorabilia. A smaller low-beamed snug has three handpumps. Recently renovated, the saloon retains the original panelling. Eight handpumps serve a good selection of real ales, with guests offered in summer.
♨Q🛏◖AP

SEATON DELAVAL

Keel Row
Foremans Row
✪ 11-11; 12-10.30 Sun
☎ (0191) 237 0060
Draught Bass; Courage Directors; Theakston Best Bitter Ⓗ

Fully-refurbished, large pub with a restaurant area, serving good food. The building was originally a row of terraced houses. Note the wooden keel boat at the car park entrance, a memento of the keel boats that were used on the local rivers to ship coal downstream to the ships waiting at the harbour. Inside beams and wood panelling help create a warm atmosphere. ◖▣♿P

SLALEY

Travellers Rest
On B6306, 1 mile N of village
✪ 11-11; 12-10.30 Sun
☎ (01661) 673231
Boddingtons Bitter; guest beers Ⓗ

Licensed for over 100 years, this welcoming inn started life in the 16th century as a farmhouse. Living up to its name, it offers the traveller an excellent choice of guest beers. The main area has several distinct cosy areas and a large open fire. Stone walls, flag floors and comfortable furniture add to its appeal. There is a restaurant, but meals are also served in the bar; the menu is creative and extensive, using local produce. Children are welcome and there is a safe play area. ♨❀🛏◖P

TWEEDMOUTH

Angel
Brewery Bank
✪ 11-11; 12-10.30 Sun
☎ (01289) 303030
Hadrian & Border Cowie, Rampart; guest beers Ⓗ

Bought and refurbished as the brewery tap for the Border Brewery, this pub is now in private ownership, and the brewery has moved (as Hadrian & Border) to Newcastle. The pub retains its links with the brewery: the old Border sign hangs outside and the bar usually carries at least two of the beers. The defunct brewery building is at the foot of the bank, beside Crawford's joinery who supplied many of the wooden bar fittings. The pub has two rooms, TV and a pool table. ▣≉P

WYLAM

Boathouse
Station Road
✪ 12-11; 12-10.30 Sun
☎ (01661) 853431
Beer range varies Ⓗ

This pub, just next to the station, is the tap for the Wylam Brewery. The brewery is outside the village at Heddon-on-the-Wall, but the beers are loved by all who visit. The Boathouse has eight handpumps offering a variety of beers, some from local micros; there are always at least two Wylam brews on sale – sometimes up to four. The house beer, Landlord's Choice, is also brewed by Wylam. Local CAMRA *Pub of the Year* 2001.
♨Q⚲❀◖≉

Brewery Museums and Visitor Centres

Bass Museum of Brewing, Horninglow Street, Burton-on-Trent. Open every day except Christmas Day, Boxing Day and New Year's Day, 10-4. Includes an Edwardian bar, vintage vehicles, shire horse stables, harness room, and shop. The site also houses the Museum Brewing Company, which recreates old Bass beers. Phone 01283 511000.

Bateman's Brewery Experience & Visitor Centre, Salem Bridge Brewery, Wainfleet, Lincolnshire. Visitor Centre and shop open daily, 11-4. Brewery tours Mon-Thu at 2pm. Phone 01754 880317

Black Sheep Brewery Visitor Centre, Wellgarth, Masham, North Yorkshire. Includes a bistro, shop, video show, and brewery tours. Shop 10-5 Wed-Sun Jan/Feb; Tue-Sun and Bank Holidays from March; every day July/Aug. Tours by arrangement on shop opening days. Phone 01765 680100

Elgood's Brewery and Gardens, North Brink, Wisbech, Cambridgeshire. Open May-Sept. Shop and gardens open Wed-Fri, Sunday and Bank Holidays 1-5. Brewery tours Wed-Fri, 2pm. Phone 01945 583160.

Gale's Brewery Tours, Horndean, Hampshire. Walk-in tours offered from the brewery shop Tuesdays, 10.30am, May-Oct; Tuesdays and Thursdays 10.30 am, June-Aug. Phone 02392 571212.

Greene King Brewery Museum and Shop, Westgate, Bury St Edmunds, Suffolk. Brewery tours Mon-Fri, 10am, 2pm and 7pm; Saturdays 10am & 2pm. Book in advance on 01284 714382. Museum includes displays of coopering and the vats where old 6X matures for two years before being blended with a younger beer to make Strong Suffolk Ale. Museum and shop open Mon to Friday 1-4; Saturday 11-4, Sunday (peak seasons) 11- 4.

Hook Norton Brewery and Visitor Centre, Brewery Lane, Hook Norton, Oxon, has a small museum and shop open Mon-Fri, 10- 4.30. Brewery tours must be booked in advance. Phone 01608 737210.

Jennings Bros Brewery Tours, Castle Brewery, Cockermouth, Cumbria. Tours every day Feb-Oct, 11am and 2pm. Additional tour 12.30pm mid-July-Aug. Book in advance, phone 01900 821011. Shop open 9-5 Mon-Sun summer.

St. Austell Brewery Visitor Centre, Trevarthian Road, St. Austell, Cornwall. Guided tours of the brewery twice daily at 11am and 2.30pm. Visitor Centre and shop open Mon-Fri, 9.30-4.30. Phone 01726 66022.

Theakston Brewery Visitor Centre, Wellgarth, Masham, North Yorkshire. Audio-visual presentation of the brewery and cooperage, Wed-Sat,10.30- 4, Easter-Oct; Wed, Sat & Sun Nov-mid-Dec. Shop open daily, Apr-Oct; limited opening Nov-Dec. Brewery tours, phone 01765 684333.

Tolly Cobbold Brewery Tours, Cliff Road, Ipswich, Suffolk. Victorian tower brewery with a steam engine. Tours at 2.30pm on Mondays and Fridays, July/Aug. Tours for parties of 10 or more are available throughout the year, including evenings: must be booked in advance. Cliff House at the brewery has a bar, restaurant and shop. Phone 01473 231723.

Tuckers Maltings, Teign Road, Osborne Park, Newton Abbot, Devon. Guided tours of England's only traditional working malthouse open to the public; includes Teignworthy Brewery and a free sample of Reel Ale. Easter-Oct from 10.30 am. Last tour 3pm; Bank Holidays and July-Sept, 3.45 pm. Phone 01626 334734.

York Brewery Tours, 12 Toft Green, Micklegate, York. Tours Mon-Sat 12.30, 2, 3.30 and 5. Visitor Centre and Tap Room. Phone 01904 621162

Young's Brewery Tours and Brewery Tap Visitor Centre, 68 High Street, Wandsworth, London, SW18. Tours run Tues, Wed, Thu and Sat at 12pm and 2pm. Also family tours of the stables. Book on 020 8875 7005.

NB Melbourn Bros All Saints Brewery (formerly Stamford Brewery Museum), All Saints Street, Stamford, Lincolnshire, is undergoing redevelopment work. Further infomation. phone 01780 752186.

Brewers Quay and the Timewalk, Hope Square, Weymouth, Dorset. The former Devenish Brewery has been converted into a tourist attraction of speciality shops and the Timewalk, a museum with animated scenes of Weymouth life and history. The old Devenish brewing vessels are still in situ, and the Quay micro-brewery can also be seen. Free sample of a Dorset brewer's beer at end of tour. Open daily, 10-9 summer; 9-5 winter. Phone 01305 777622

See the Breweries section for e-mail addresses and websites. See also the Breweries section for details of breweries that offer tours.

Compiled by Michael Slaughter

NOTTINGHAMSHIRE

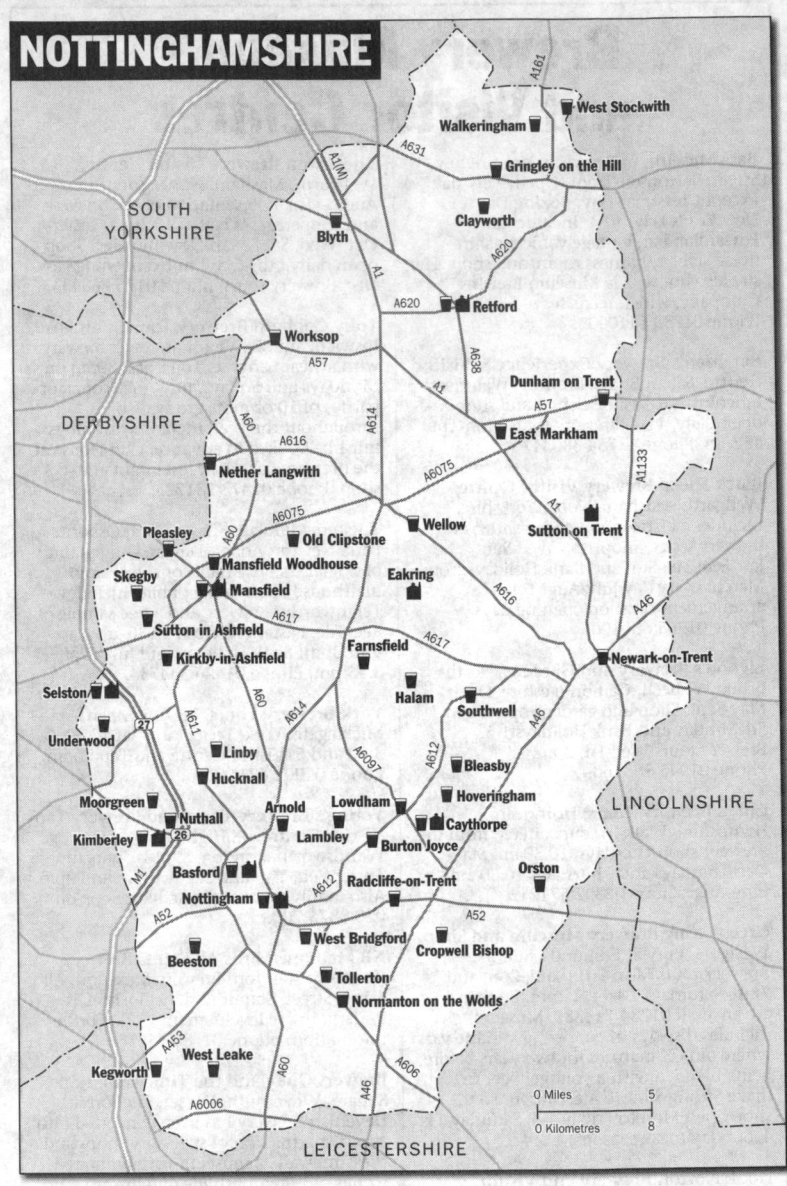

West Stockwith
Walkeringham
Gringley on the Hill
SOUTH YORKSHIRE
Clayworth
Blyth
Retford
Worksop
Dunham on Trent
DERBYSHIRE
East Markham
Nether Langwith
Wellow
Sutton on Trent
Pleasley
Old Clipstone
Mansfield Woodhouse
Eakring
Skegby
Mansfield
Sutton in Ashfield
Farnsfield
Newark-on-Trent
Kirkby-in-Ashfield
Halam
Selston
Southwell
Underwood
Bleasby
Linby
Hoveringham
Hucknall
LINCOLNSHIRE
Moorgreen
Lowdham
Caythorpe
Nuthall
Arnold
Kimberley
Lambley
Burton Joyce
Basford
Orston
Nottingham
Radcliffe-on-Trent
West Bridgford
Beeston
Cropwell Bishop
Tollerton
Normanton on the Wolds
West Leake
Kegworth
LEICESTERSHIRE

0 Miles 5
0 Kilometres 8

ARNOLD

Ernehale
149-151 Nottingham Road
🕐 11-11; 12-10.30 Sun
☎ (0115) 967 4945
Courage Directors; Marston's Pedigree; Shepherd Neame Spitfire; Theakston Best Bitter; Wadworth 6X; guest beer Ⓗ

The unusual name of this pub originates from the old Saxon term for the town, a Nottingham suburb. A typical Wetherspoon's conversion of a former shop, dating from 1904, the interior features one large split-level drinking area. A small outside patio is popular in summer. The walls display interesting information and pictures featuring local landmarks and people. The usual Wetherspoon's menu is available all day. It is popular at weekends, when door staff admit entry. Q ✿ ⌾ ⅅ & ⅊ ●

BASFORD ✳

Fox & Crown
33 Church Street
🕐 12-11; 12-10.30 Sun
☎ (0115) 942 2002
e-mail: dallen@alcazar.freeserve.co.uk
Alcazar Ale, Brush Bitter, New Dawn, Vixen's Vice, seasonal beers; guest beers Ⓗ

The tap for the Alcazar Brewery (established 1999), brewing various regular, seasonal and one-off brews. The owners have returned the pub to its previous popular peak; its central circular bar boasts 12 handpumps showcasing the brewery's products and a selection of regularly changing guest ales. It also stocks a range of bottled beers. On the food front, pizzas are a house speciality (available weekday eves and weekends). The pub is the oldest in the area, although now much changed, and a ghost is said to inhabit the cellar. ♨❀◑◐♿P

Horse & Groom

462 Radford Road (near ring road)
✪ 11-11; 12-10.30 Sun
☎ (0115) 970 3777
Draught Bass; Belvoir Star Bitter; Courage Directors; Wells Bombardier; guest beers Ⓗ
This pleasant local was once the Shipstone's tap, and displays much memorabilia from the former brewery. Very friendly and constantly busy, it always has a range of eight real ales on offer. Live music is staged in the old back stables at weekends. Good value food is served at lunchtime. ◑●

BEESTON

Victoria Hotel

Dovecote Lane (by station)
✪ 11-11; 12-10.30 Sun
☎ (0115) 925 4049 website: www.tynemill.co.uk
Bateman XB; Caledonian Deuchars IPA; Castle Rock Hemlock; Everards Tiger; guest beers Ⓗ
Busy, carefully restored, Victorian architectural gem, buzzing with lively conversation. A traditional layout features three rooms with bare boards, and scrubbed tables, plus a no-smoking restaurant. Regular events include brewery eves, free live music, wine tastings, and a summer beer festival. An excellent varied menu is complemented by carefully selected wines. Around 120 malts, foreign beers, a varying cider or two and free newspapers add to its appeal. The Stan Peterson cellar is dedicated to a well-known local CAMRA member. Note the impressive stained glass window upstairs. ♨Q❀◑◐♿≹●P

BLEASBY

Waggon & Horses

Gypsy Lane (1 mile S of station)
✪ 12-2.30 (not Mon), 6-11; 12-3, 7-10.30 Sun
☎ (01636) 830283
Banks's Bitter; Mansfield Dark Mild; Marston's Pedigree Ⓗ
Once a simple farmhouse, this unassuming whitewashed pub is now the local, serving a very quiet village. It enjoys a rural setting, overlooking the church, with a campsite opposite that also admits caravans. There is a nice lounge and a cosy bar with a pool table. Children are welcome in one area and the garden hosts barbecues in summer. Bar snacks are normally available. ♨❀◻▲P

BLYTH

Angel Inn

Bawtry Road (off A1)
✪ 11.30-2.30, 6-11; 12-3, 6.30-10.30 Sun
☎ (01909) 591213
Hardys & Hansons Best Mild, Best Bitter, Classic, seasonal beers Ⓗ
Coaching inn, that has been in the *Guide* for over 20 years, this is one of the Kimberley Brewery's most northerly outposts. Situated opposite the church, which is all that remains of an 11th-century priory, the Angel was once on the Great North Road, but is now bypassed by the A1. About ten years ago the pub was extensively altered by opening out the lounge and incorporating the tap room. It is now very popular for food, which is served at both sessions. Q❀❀⇌◑◐♿♣P⚞

CAYTHORPE

Black Horse

29 Main Street (take A612 from Lowdham island)
✪ 11.45-2.30 (not Mon), 5.30-11; 7 (8 winter)-10.30 Sun
☎ (0115) 966 3520
Caythorpe Dover Beck Bitter; guest beers Ⓗ
All that a village inn should be, dating back over 30 years and reputedly once a haunt of Dick Turpin. Accomplished home cooking makes good use of fresh seasonal ingredients, particularly fish, and can be savoured with a pint of Caythorpe beer brewed on the premises. The guest beers often include a second Caythorpe brew. Booking for eve meals (not served Sun) is essential. The pub maintains a friendship with a darts team from Bavaria. ♨Q❀◑◐◻♣P

CLAYWORTH

Blacksmith's Arms

Town Street
✪ 11.30-3, 6-11; 12-3, 7-10.30 Sun
☎ (0177) 818171
Stones Bitter; Worthington Bitter; guest beers Ⓗ
Smart, two-roomed village local, very popular with early evening diners taking advantage of the excellent bar food. One of the rooms is always heated by a welcoming open fire in cold weather. Attached is a two-storey restaurant, where the first floor can be booked for private functions. The restaurant food is based on continental cuisine, which may be accompanied by wine from a good range. ♨Q❀◑◐♿P⚞▯

CROPWELL BISHOP

Wheatsheaf

11 Nottingham Road OSSK684354
✪ 11-11; 12-10.30 Sun
☎ (0115) 989 2247
Mansfield Dark Mild, Riding Bitter, Cask Ale; Marston's Pedigree Ⓗ
A beamed, former coaching inn, thought to be at least 400 years old, that apparently gave shelter to Dick Turpin. The carpeted and beamed lounge is split by a staircase; pictures and horse brasses decorate the walls. The public bar is tiled and beamed; at the rear, a raised area contains a pool table

INDEPENDENT BREWERIES

Alcazar Basford
Broadstone Retford
Castle Rock Nottingham
Caythorpe Caythorpe
Hardys & Hansons Kimberley
Holland Kimberley
Leadmill Selston
Mallard Nottingham
Mansfield Mansfield
Maypole Eakring
Springhead Sutton on Trent

and TV. Upholstered benches, chairs and stools surround wooden tables throughout. Superb authentic Chinese banquets can be booked for parties of 10 or more in an upstairs room (no other food is served). ✿⌂♣P

DUNHAM ON TRENT

Bridge Inn
Main Street
✿ 12-3, 5-11; 12-11 Sat; 12-10.30 Sun
☎ (01777) 228385
Beer range varies Ⓗ
On the busy A57, close to the Dunham toll bridge, it attracts much passing trade as well as being a popular village local. The decor features agricultural artefacts on the walls and ceilings. When it is cold there is always a roaring open fire. An excellent range of food includes a daily specials board and early diners (5–7) can have a choice from a special low-priced menu. At least one of the beers is usually competitively priced; the range includes a local Broadstone brew. ⋈Q✿❊⌂◑Ⓗ♣P✕

EAST MARKHAM

Crown Inn
High Street
✿ 12-3 (not Mon), 5-11; 12-11 Sat; 12-10.30 Sun
☎ (01777) 870870
Tetley Bitter; guest beers Ⓗ
Comfortable, modern, one-roomed pub, with a restaurant area at one end. A focal point for the village, the pub enjoys a cosy atmosphere, a real welcoming environment for the casual visitor and regulars alike. The landlord is justifiably proud of the quality and variety of his predominantly home-cooked menu, ranging from bar snacks to full restaurant meals, complemented by a varied wine list. A regular feature is the Fri night quiz. ✿◑ⒽP

FARNSFIELD

Red Lion
Main Street
✿ 11-3, 6.30-11; 12-3, 7-10.30 Sun
☎ (01623) 882304 e-mail: m44j42red@aol.com
Banks's Bitter; Mansfield Riding Bitter, Cask Ale; Marston's Pedigree; Morrells Varsity Ⓗ
Friendly, family-run village pub on the main road through the village in rural

Nottinghamshire at the heart of Robin Hood country. Good food can be enjoyed in the extended restaurant area. A Mansfield tied house with the same tenants for over 10 years, the recent sale to Wolverhampton & Dudley has seen the introduction of beers from Marston's and Morrells. Farnsfield is a picturesque village with a dynamic community as is clear from the Red Lion's trade. ⋈Q✿◑Ⓗ♣P⊟●

GRINGLEY ON THE HILL

Blue Bell
High Street
✿ 6 (12 Sat)-11; 12-10.30 Sun
☎ (01777) 817406 website: www.seattlestyle.com
Marston's Pedigree; John Smith's Bitter; guest beers Ⓗ
Village local, warmed by open fires in winter, where an unusual feature is the basement pool room. Bar meals are served daily, except Mon but note that chips are not sold here and vinegar is out of the question in case it affects the quality of the beer. Attached is a very good restaurant called Seattle Style, run by an American chef, although the food is mainly French, except on Sun when an American brunch is served. ⋈✿◑Ⓗ♣P⊟

HALAM

Waggon & Horses
The Turnpike
✿ 11-3, 5.30-11; 11-11 Sat; 12-10.30 Sun
☎ (01636) 813109
Fuller's London Pride; Wells Bombardier; guest beers Ⓗ
Popular pub set in a village location at the heart of rural Nottinghamshire. In addition to the constantly changing range of ales, the food is of a high standard and the restaurant is always popular (Sun eve meals finish at 6pm). The pub takes part in local darts and dominoes leagues and many a winter's eve is brightened up by these pursuits. Halam is a village community in the traditional style. Well worth a visit. Q✿◑Ⓗ♣P

INN BRIEF

BASFORD
Lion
44 Mosley Street
11-11; 12-10.30 Sun
Draught Bass; guest beers Ⓗ
Back-street pub offering up to 10 beers, including a house ale from Bass Museum. Live music, lunchtime food and real fires are features.

BURTON JOYCE
Famous Lord Nelson
Chestnut Grove
12-11; 12-10.30 Sun
Greenalls Bitter; Mansfield Cask Ale; guest beer Ⓗ
Village pub with a nautical theme in its bar and restaurant serving an extensive menu every day.

HOVERINGHAM
Reindeer
Main Street
12-2.30 (not Mon), 5-11; 12-10.30 Sun
Brewster's Marquis; Wells Bombardier; guest beers Ⓗ
Cottage-style village pub with a serving hatch on to the cricket pitch. Excellent food is served in the restaurant, open 5-10, Tue-Sun.

KIMBERLEY
White Lion
74 Swingate
12-11; 12-10.30 Sun
Draught Bass; guest beer Ⓗ
Traditional local with a room for children/pool/long alley skittles. The garden has a play area.

MANSFIELD
Nell Gwynne
117 Sutton Road
12-4, 7-11; 12-3, 7-10.30 Sun
Draught Bass; guest beers Ⓗ
Originally a private club (Bleak House) offering a warm, homely atmosphere, it is now a free house open to all.

NOTTINGHAM
Peacock Hotel
11 Mansfield Road
11.30-11; 12-10.30 Sun
Mansfield Cask Ale; Marston's Pedigree; Theakston XB; Wells Bombardier Ⓗ
Attractive, two-bar pub with an authentic period interior. The lounge is served by table bell as there is no bar that side.

HUCKNALL

Pilgrim Oak
44-46 High Street
✪ 10.30-11; 12-10.30 Sun
☎ (0115) 963 2539
Courage Directors; Theakston Best Bitter; guest beers Ⓗ

Wetherspoon's pub, splendidly converted from a derelict supermarket. Pew-style seating along the central area is flanked by cubicles. Pictures of old Hucknall and local personalities, including Lord Byron and Eric Coates, famous for composing the *Dambuster's March*, are displayed. A no-smoking area is situated to the rear of the pub. The name, Pilgrim Oak, is taken from a tree in the grounds of nearby Newstead Abbey, ancestral home of the Byron family. Q ⑪ & ≉ ✕ ●

KEGWORTH

Station Hotel
Station Road (1½ miles from the Leicestershire village)
✪ 12-2.30 (3 Sat), 6-11; 12-3, 7-10.30 Sun
☎ (01509) 672252
Courage Directors; Marston's Pedigree; guest beer Ⓗ

Although the station has long since closed, this Victorian hotel still offers accommodation. The pub has three public rooms, one of which features railway memorabilia, including engine nameplates, displayed to advantage upon bare brick walls. An extensive and varied menu, including vegetarian options, is served, while an upstairs *à la carte* restaurant is open at weekends. Customers admiring the views from the garden can still hear the sound of the London trains. ⛺ ❀ ⊷ ⑪ ⊟P

KIMBERLEY ✿

Nelson & Railway
12 Station Road (opp. brewery)
✪ 10.30-3, 5-11; 10.30-11 Thu-Sat; 12-10.30 Sun
☎ (0115) 938 2177
Hardys & Hansons Best Bitter, Ⓗ **Classic, seasonal beers** Ⓗ

Pleasant, friendly pub situated less than 100 yards from the brewery. The wood-panelled bar is complemented by the beamed lounge, with an adjoining dining area. It is renowned for good value food and B&B. The front garden is a real treat in summer.

The landlord has now been at the pub for over 30 years. ❀ ⊷ ⑪ ⊟ ♣ P ●

Stag Inn
67 Nottingham Road
✪ 5 (2 Sat)-11; 12-10.30 Sun
☎ (0115) 938 3151
Boddingtons Bitter; Greenalls Mild, Bitter; Marston's Pedigree; guest beer Ⓗ

This superb village inn dates back to 1537. Its two characterful rooms feature low beams and settles. The large rear garden has a play area for children. Table skittles are played here. The Stag stocks an ever-changing range of guest beers, but no food is served in this popular local. Q ❀ ⊟ ♣ P

KIRKBY-IN-ASHFIELD

Countryman
Park Lane (B6018/B6019 jct)
✪ 11-11; 12-10.30 Sun
☎ (01623) 752314
website: www.alibo.free-online.co.uk
Fuller's London Pride; Theakston Best Bitter, Cool Cask; XB; guest beers Ⓗ

Family-run, 18th-century roadside inn, comprising two rooms. Live entertainment is staged Fri eve in the function room, which is also available for private parties. Local micro-breweries feature regularly as guests and the walls of the bar and ceiling beams display pump clips of past beers. The cider varies. Good value, home-cooked food (not served Mon or Sun eves) includes daily specials and traditional Sun lunches. A friendly welcome is offered to all, including children, bikers, hikers and even dogs. A summer beer festival is held and regular barbecues. ⛺ ⌂ ❀ ⑪ & ▲ ♣ ● P

LAMBLEY

Robin Hood & Little John
82 Main Street
✪ 11-3 (12-5 Sat), 6-11; 12-5, 7-10.30 Sun
☎ (0115) 931 2531
Banks's Bitter; Mansfield Dark Mild, Cask Ale; Marston's Pedigree Ⓗ

Originally a WH Hutchinsons and Sons house, this popular drinkers' pub is thought to be the oldest in the village. It has a bar and lounge, with a function room at the back where the local darts team play. Lunchtime food is served Tue–Sat. Robin

---

Plough Inn
17 St Peter's Street, Radford
11-11;
12-10.30 Sun
Beer range varies Ⓗ
Two-roomed, genuine local hosting music Sun afternoons. Three Castle Rock beers, plus guests are stocked. Pleasant garden.

Portland Arms
24 Portland Road
11-3, 5-11; 11-11 Mon, Fri & Sat;
12-10.30 Sun
Hardys & Hansons Best Bitter, Classic, seasonal beers Ⓗ
Friendly, open-plan local off Canning Circus, staging regular live music. Good value Sun lunch is served until 4pm.

Turf Tavern
64 Upper Parliament Street
11-11; 12-10.30 Sun
Tetley Bitter; Young's Special Ⓗ
Pleasant city-centre corner pub, where a single bar shows Sky Sports. Food includes Caribbean specialities. A house beer is stocked.

OLD CLIPSTONE

Dog & Duck
Main Road
11-3, 6 (5.30 Fri & Sat)-11; 12-4,
7-10.30 Sun
Barnsley Bitter; Courage Directors; Greene King Old Speckled Hen; Marston's Pedigree; Theakston Old Peculier; guest beers Ⓗ
Traditional country pub on the cycle route within Sherwood Forest. An extensive menu is freshly cooked (no food Sun eve).

RADCLIFFE-ON-TRENT

Black Lion
Main Road
12 (11 Sat)-11;
12-10.30 Sun
Courage Directors; Home Bitter; guest beers Ⓗ
Large, comfortable village pub, serving three guest beers, with a smart lounge and lively public bar. Food is served daily 12-9.

RETFORD

Albert Hotel
Albert Road
11.30-11; 12-10.30 Sun
Hardys & Hansons Best Bitter; guest beers Ⓗ
Busy terraced pub, south of the town centre, serving very good, home-cooked food at lunchtime. *Cask Marque* accredited.

Hood is a popular pub name in Nottinghamshire, for obvious reasons. The reference to Little John may come from an old rhyme, 'You gentlemen and yeomen good / come in and drink with Robin Hood. / If Robin Hood be not at home / come in and drink with Little John'.

ᗰQᗰᗺ♣P

LINBY

Horse & Groom
Main Street
🕓 12-11; 12-10.30 Sun
☎ (0115) 963 2219
Home Mild, Bitter; guest beers Ⓗ
Multi-roomed gem of a village pub, north of Nottingham. The public bar, snug and 'Green' room have real fires, the one in the public bar, being an inglenook. Four cask ales are sold and the guest beers are often from surrounding small East Midlands breweries. The village is very picturesque, voted the *Prettiest in Britain* in 1997. The pub has acquired a deserved reputation for good quality meals, served in all areas including the restaurant. Regular music nights, courtesy of a pianist, are staged Tue and quiz nights Thu.

ᗰQᗝ❀ᗰᗺᗺ♣P

LOWDHAM

World's End Inn
Plough Lane
🕓 12-3, 5.30-11; 12-4, 7-10.30 Sun
☎ (0115) 966 3857
Banks's Bitter; Marston's Bitter, Pedigree; Mansfield Cask Ale Ⓗ
Circa 1744, this traditional village pub has been separated from the main village by the bypass. It boasts vibrant floral displays against a white exterior with the inside displaying brassware, exposed beams, plates and jugs. The flagpole, easily seen from the main road, was brought from its old site at Nottingham Forest FC, many years ago. The pole apparently contains an ancient time capsule of old coins – recently added to with more coinage and business cards by the current landlord. The menu is extensive, with optional outside (covered) dining in summer.

ᗰQ❀ᗰ≈P

MANSFIELD ❄

Bold Forester
Botany Avenue (1/2 mile from bus station along A38)
🕓 11-11; 12-10.30 Sun
☎ (01623) 623970
Boddingtons Bitter; Castle Eden Bitter; Flowers Original; Greene King Abbot; Marston's Pedigree; guest beers Ⓗ
Large pub on the outskirts of the town centre. Although newly-built, it has the feel of a traditional local, due to the friendly welcome. A constantly-changing range of six guest beers from regional and micro-brewers is complemented by various ciders. It hosts quiz nights (Mon, Tue and Thu) and live bands – usually blues/rock – every Sun eve. Good value meals are served lunchtime and early eve in a no-smoking restaurant area, but food does not dominate

here. A popular beer festival (32 beers) is held every year, around St George's Day.
❀ᗰᗺ≈❀P✕

Railway Inn
9 Station Street
🕓 11-11; 12-10.30 Sun
☎ (01623) 623086
Bateman XB Ⓗ
Rare Bateman's outlet in the Mansfield area, although serving only one real ale, it is one of the cheapest around. Reasonably priced home-cooked lunches are available, with bar snacks eves. Children are welcome if dining. Across the car park from Mansfield Station (Robin Hood line), it is close to the town's main shopping area. Unusually it serves a good choice of cocktails. The pub has featured on TV quite often – once for somebody being buried underground in the garden and once for one of its customers getting married – to the pub!
Qᗝ❀ᗺᗺ♣

MANSFIELD WOODHOUSE

Greyhound Inn
82 High Street
🕓 12-11; 12-3, 7-10.30 Sun
☎ (01623) 464403
Courage Directors; Home Mild, Bitter; Mansfield Cask Ale; guest beer Ⓗ
Friendly local, consisting of two rooms: the comfortable, quiet lounge (which only gets noisy due to good conversation), and the lively tap room that houses a dartboard and pool table. On the main road through the village, it is about half a mile from Mansfield Woodhouse Station on the Robin Hood line. A regular venue for CAMRA meetings, when everybody is made welcome, with a tray of sausages, but otherwise food is not usually available.
Q❀ᗺ≈♣P

MOORGREEN

Horse & Groom
Church Road (B600)
🕓 11-11; 12-10.30 Sun
☎ (01773) 713417
Hardys & Hansons Best Bitter, Classic, seasonal beers Ⓗ
Attractive, 17th-century country pub with one large L-shaped room. At the rear is an extensive garden, with a children's play area and a covered outdoor drinking area. Located a few hundred yards from a popular garden centre, the pub is also handy for Beauvale Abbey and the Robin Hood's Well. The small town of Eastwood, and the DH Lawrence Museum can also be visited (less than two miles away). Meals are served all day (12–9); an upstairs restaurant can be booked for parties/weddings. ᗰ❀ᗺP●

NETHER LANGWITH

Jug & Glass
Queens Walk (A623)
🕓 11.3-11 (11.30-4, 6-11 Oct-April); 12-4, 7-10.30 Sun
☎ (01623) 742283
website: www.jugandglass@btinternet.co.uk
Hardys & Hansons Best Bitter, Classic, seasonal beers Ⓗ
Contemporary with Welbeck Abbey, the

pub (circa 1179), probably housed monks who farmed the surrounding land. The first record of a licensee was in 1787 who rented the building from the sixth Duke of Portland. A social meeting place for locals and mine workers; until 1863 mineworkers' wages were paid here. The pub has only had 16 licensees; the present landlord has undertaken a major refurbishment but retained its charm and comfortable atmosphere. Popular for summer outdoor drinking, sitting on the River Poulter, it serves an excellent range of home-cooked food and has an *à la carte* restaurant. B&B is in three superbly restored oak-beamed rooms. ▨◸❀✍◖◗♿⬥P✂🛈

NEWARK ON TRENT

Castle & Falcon
10 London Road
✪ 12 (10.30 Fri)-3 (not Tue or Thu), 7-11 ; 12-4, 7-11 Sat; 12-4, 7-10.30 Sun
☎ (01636) 703513
John Smith's Bitter; guest beers Ⓗ
Dating back to the early 1800s, this building was formerly a coachhouse on the main London–York run. Located in the shadow of the now derelict James Hole's Castle Brewery, this town-centre pub caters mainly for regulars, but is both lively and welcoming. Split into three distinct drinking areas: bar, lounge and children's area, a function room is also available. The guest beers change on a regular basis and tasters are offered to help you decide. With several darts, dominoes and pool teams, there is something happening most nights in this excellent, no-nonsense boozer.
◸❀◖◗≈(Castle) ♣P

Fox & Crown
4-6 Appletongate (near market square)
✪ 11-11; 12-10.30 Sun
☎ (01636) 605820 website: www.tynemill.co.uk
Bateman XB; Castle Rock Hemlock; Everards Tiger; Hook Norton Best Bitter; Marston's Pedigree; guest beers Ⓗ
Tynemill pub opened in 1997, following closure by Courage in 1974. A popular town pub, it has an open aspect, but with several distinct drinking areas. An excellent range of beer is complemented by bottled beers from Belgium and across Europe, plus a choice of over 60 malt whiskies. Good value food is freshly prepared using local produce with daily specials. Hot drinks include freshly ground coffee from the local roasting house. It hosts monthly brewery nights and occasional live music.
Q◖◗♿≈(Castle/Northgate) ♣✂

Mailcoach
13 London Road
✪ 11.30-3, 5.30-11; 11-11 Sat; 12-3, 7-10.30 Sun
☎ (01636) 605164
Boddingtons Bitter; Flowers IPA, Original; guest beers Ⓗ
Former coaching inn, dating back to 1778, previously known as the Cross Keys. The traditional Georgian architecture has been rendered and the ground floor opened up to provide a comfortable, sweeping room, but with four distinct, comfy drinking areas. Regular music eves (usually Thu) cater for a wide variety of tastes. The Mailcoach has been in this *Guide* for the last decade. A

patio provides outdoor drinking space.
❀◸◖◗≈(Castle/Northgate) P

Old Malt Shovel
25 Northgate (by traffic lights, Sleaford Rd jct)
✪ 11.30-3, 5.30-11; 12-10.30 sun
☎ (01636) 702036
Adnams Broadsde; Everards Tiger; Taylor Landlord; guest beers Ⓗ
Comfortable single-roomed pub that boasts a covered long alley skittles pitch. It runs its own Real Ale Tasting Society (RATS) and a golf society. On the site of a 16th-century bakery, the pub serves meals in its garden room restaurant. No food is available Mon and those wishing to dine on Tue must book. ▨Q◖◗♿≈(Castle/Northgate) ♣

Wing Tavern
Market Place
✪ 11-3 (2.30 Tue & Thu), 7-11; 12-3, 7-10.30 Sun
☎ (01636) 702689
Theakston Best Bitter, XB, Old Peculier Ⓗ
One of Newark's hidden gems, tucked away in the corner of the market place, this multi-roomed pub is renowned locally for its beers and no-nonsense atmosphere. Basic in nature, it comprises a bar, pool room and small family room. Outside, the small paved area and long alley skittles pitch have the magnificent parish church of St Mary Magdalene as a backdrop. One of the oldest pubs in the town, it stands above a vast expanse of cellar workings (unfortunately not open to the general public) and has played its part in Newark's history. A pub full of character, it is well worth seeking out. ◸❀◖◗≈(Castle/Northgate)♣

Woolpack
46 Stodman Street (off Castlegate)
✪ 11-4, 7-11; 12-4, 7-10.30 Sun
☎ (01636) 704326 website: www.castlegate-com
John Smith's Bitter; guest beers Ⓗ
Reputedly the oldest pub trading in Newark, built in 1465, it is a rare example of a Wealden timber-framed building in this area of the country. The low-ceilinged pub, largely unaltered, certainly in recent times, consists of three small rooms: a bar, lounge and smoke room. To the rear is a patio garden and a long alley skittles pitch. You can be sure of a warm welcome from the landlady, who provides excellent, good value, home-made food on huge plates; breakfast is also available from 9am.
▨◸◖◗≈(Castle) ♣

NORMANTON ON THE WOLDS

Plough
Old Melton Road (off A606)
✪ 11-3, 5.30-11; 11-11 Fri & Sat; 12-4, 7.30-10.30 Sun
☎ (0115) 937 2401
Draught Bass; John Smith's Magnet; Theakston Best Bitter Ⓗ
Old country pub, just a short drive from Nottingham, with two small bars and a no-smoking dining area. Children over the age of eight are welcome in the dining area, where traditional fare with tasty variations is served (eve meals Tue–Sat, finish at 8.45). The large garden has a four lane boules pitch; barbecues can be arranged; families are accommodated under large gazebos in summer. ▨Q◖◗◖♿P

NOTTINGHAM ✤

Bell

18 Angel Row

✪ 10.30-11; 12-3, 7-10.30 Sun

☎ (0115) 947 5241

Draught Bass; Black Sheep Special; Brains SA; Greene King Abbot; Jennings Mild, Bitter; Mansfield Cask Ale; guest beers Ⓗ

Described as having a Tardis-like quality where small rooms at the front lead to a large main bar, which features live music Sun–Wed eve. This historic wood-panelled pub dates back to 1437 and offers a range of home-cooked food in the pub and restaurant area; 'lunchtime' extends to 7pm Thu–Sat. A function room is also available with private bar. There is space for outdoor summer drinking in front of the pub.
Q✿◑●

Fellows Morton & Clayton

54 Canal Street

✪ 11-11; 12-10.30 Sun

☎ (0115) 950 6795 website: www.galleyrestaurant.com

Boddingtons Bitter; Castle Eden Ale; Fellows Bitter; Post Haste; guest beers Ⓗ

Whitbread home-brew pub, close to the town centre; the brewhouse can be seen to the rear of the pub, in the former offices of Fellows Morton & Clayton Narrowboat Company. It offers a choice of nine beers, of which two are brewed on the premises (using malt extract). A restaurant to the rear of the pub serves good value British and continental cuisine until 10pm. This pub has won awards for its external floral displays, a big attraction for visitors to Nottingham. A large-screen TV shows sport.
◑❑&≢P

Golden Fleece

105 Mansfield Road (opp. Victoria bus station)

✪ 11-11; 12-10.30 Sun

☎ (0115) 947 2843

Adnams Bitter; Cains Mild; Flowers Original, Marston's Pedigree; guest beers Ⓗ

Two-bar pub on three levels, serving a constantly changing range of guest beers. It hosts 'open mike' sessions Mon and Tue; live music most Fri and Sat eves and folk music every other Sun. Home-made food, including a wide range of vegetarian dishes, is served 12–8 (4 Sun). The roof garden is an unusual feature, very popular in summer – it is great for barbecues. ✿◑♣

Langtry's

4 South Sherwood Street

✪ 11-11; 12-10.30 Sun

☎ (0115) 947 2124

e-mail: langtrys/pubandbars/whitbread

Beer range varies Ⓗ/Ⓖ

Small, friendly, split-level pub by the new Corner House (Trinity Square) development. It stands across the road from the Theatre Royal and Royal Concert Hall, so expect to see the occasional celebrity. Ten beers are normally available: eight on handpull and two on gravity, with various offers, such as four pints for the price of three and 20p discount off a pint for card-carrying CAMRA members. It also stocks a small selection of Belgian bottled beers and Hoegaarden on draught; the cider is Weston's Old Rosie. Meals are served 12–9 (8 Fri and Sat). Q◑&♣✄

Lincolnshire Poacher

161 Mansfield Road (5 mins' walk uphill from Victoria Centre)

✪ 11-11; 12-10.30 Sun

☎ (0115) 941 1584 e-mail: tynemill@tynemill.co.uk

Archers Golden; Bateman, XB, XXXB; Caledonian Deuchars IPA; Fuller's London Pride; guest beers Ⓗ

Two-roomed pub (the smaller one no-smoking) with a conservatory and garden at the rear. Popular with real ale drinkers doing the Mansfield Road Crawl, this was probably the first pub in Nottingham to sell an ever-changing range of real ales from micro-breweries on a regular basis. It always offers numerous guest beers and a range of continental beers on draught or in bottle. It boasts the largest selection of whiskies in Nottingham, and an extensive food menu (including vegetarian dishes) Tue–Thu; eve meals 5–8. Occasional live music is performed. Q✿◑◑♣✄

Olde Trip to Jerusalem ☆

1 Brewhouse Yard (underneath Nottingham Castle)

✪ 11-11; 12-10.30 Sun

☎ (0115) 947 3171 website: www.triptojerusalem.com

Hardys & Hansons Best Mild, Best Bitter, Classic; Marston's Pedigree; seasonal beers Ⓗ

Reputedly Nottingham's oldest pub, it is a must for the first-time visitor to the city. Many of the rooms are dug out of the sandstone rock below the castle, which is a maze of caves and passages. Its attractions include a haunted gallery, the *History of Nottingham* tapestry and Baiting the Bull game. The date 1189 on the outside has led to stories that Crusaders gathered here *en route* for Jerusalem (hence the name), but this has been disputed. The building most likely originated as a brewhouse to the castle, only becoming a pub in the 18th century. Meals are served 11 (12 Sun)–6; the house beer is from Hardys & Hansons.
🏚Q✿◑◑≢♣✄

Red Lion

21 Alfreton Road (off Canning Circus)

✪ 11.30-11; 11-11 Sat; 12-10.30 Sun

☎ (0115) 952 0309

Boddingtons Bitter; Marston's Pedigree; Thwaites Bitter; guest beers Ⓗ

Up to eight different beers are available in this one-roomed, split-level pub. Sporting events can be viewed on an unobtrusive TV at the back of the bar. An unusual outside drinking terrace is accessed up a flight of steps at the rear of the pub. Basic, good value food is available lunchtimes, with a limited selection Sat, while on Sun a popular brunch (including a vegetarian choice) is served 11–2. ✿◑

Salutation Inn

Maid Marian Way

✪ 11-11; 12-10.30 Sun

☎ (0115) 988 1948

Boddingtons Bitter; Marston's Pedigree; Wadworth 6X; guest beers Ⓗ

Historic pub with stone flags and bare boards. A staircase from the open-plan bar leads to another large room. There are two snugs downstairs, and below ground, an assortment of reputedly haunted caves and a deep well. Ask behind the bar when it is not busy for a tour of the caves. Meals are served all day until 8pm. The pub hosts beer festivals and wine festivals; the cider is Weston's Old Rosie. Ghost walks start from this pub every Sat eve between Jan and Nov. ◑≠♣

Vat & Fiddle
12-14 Queens Bridge Road (100 yds from station)
☼ 11-11; 12-10.30 Sun
☎ (0115) 985 0611
Caledonian Deuchars IPA; Castle Rock Hemlock, seasonal beers; guest beers Ⓗ
Consistently good beer comes from a choice of 10 handpulls including a mild. This ex-Hoskin's pub is now run by Tynemill and is situated next door to the Castle Rock Brewery, from where you will find at least two of their beers always on tap. Also on offer are 70-plus malt whiskies. This single roomed pub is only a minute's walk from the railway station. On the walls are photos of pubs from the Old Meadows area which have long been demolished. Beer festivals are held here occasionally, and some weekends live bands perform. Parking is limited. Q ⊛◑&≠♣P

NUTHALL

Three Ponds
Nottingham Road (just off M1, jct 26)
☼ 11-11; 12-10.30 Sun
☎ (0115) 938 3170
Hardys & Hansons Best Bitter, Classic, seasonal beers Ⓗ
Refurbished and extended in Sept 2000, the pub has developed into one of the brewery's pubs specialising in good food. The front has been retained as a comfortable drinking area while the rear is aimed at diners, who are treated to a range of traditional and imaginative pub fare, served all day until 9pm. At the back of the pub is a patio area and a good-sized garden, complete with children's play equipment. Quizzes take place Sun eve, with a special music quiz Tue eve. ⊛◑&P●

ORSTON

Durham Ox
Church Street
☼ 12 (11.30 Sat)-3, 6-11; 12-10.30 Sun
☎ (01949) 850059 e-mail: orston.pub@virgin.net
Home Bitter; Marston's Pedigree; Theakston Cool

Cask; guest beers Ⓗ
Delightful village pub, popular with locals and visitors alike, it has a garden and pavement tables in summer and a roaring fire in winter. Hitching rails are provided for horses. The divided room displays a collection of whisky bottles on a top shelf in the comfortable lounge side, while the bar section features airforce pictures and memorabilia. There is no hot food but filled rolls are made to order. Darts, dominoes and long alley skittles are played. ♨Q♞⋇⊛♣P⊬🍴

PLEASLEY

Olde Plough
Chesterfield Road North (3 miles NW of Mansfield on A617)
☼ 11.30-3, 5.30-11; 11-11 Sat; 12-3, 7-10.30 Sun
☎ (01623) 810386
Marston's Bitter, Pedigree, seasonal beers Ⓗ
On the main Mansfield–Chesterfield road, this busy and deservedly popular, open-plan pub has undergone extensive refurbishment and is now cosy and comfortable. The extensive menu of home-cooked food includes daily specials and a 'light bites'; section; food is available all week except Sun eve. Quiz nights are a regular feature, with music (Tue) and noughts and crosses Sun eve; live acoustic music is performed monthly (first Thu). ⊛◑🍴♣P

RETFORD ⋇

Clinton Arms
24 Albert Road (near canal basin)
☼ 11-11; 12-10.30 Sun
☎ (01777) 702703 website: www.bluesmusic.co.uk
Black Sheep Best Bitter; John Smith's Bitter; Wells Bombardier; guest beers Ⓗ
19th-century end-of-terrace pub, named after the seventh Earl of Lincoln, it has now been refurbished, but retains old features such as the tiled façade from the 1960s. There are three rooms – a quiet, comfortable lounge, a busy public bar and a games/children's room. Outside is a small fenced garden and play area. The Clinton is a renowned live music venue (rock and blues), usually staged Thu and Sat eves. It has a big-screen TV for live sports. Several local groups and organisations meet here.

INN BRIEF

White Houses
London Road
11-3.30, 5-11; 11.30-11 Sat;
12-10.30 Sun
Boddingtons Bitter; Castle Eden Ale; guest beers Ⓗ
Busy pub with a games area, restaurant and outdoor play area. Popular for its beers and food.

SUTTON IN ASHFIELD
King & Miller
Kings Mill Road East
11-11; 12-10.30 Sun
Hardys & Hansons Best Bitter, Classic, seasonal beers Ⓗ
Purpose-built, open-plan pub geared to family dining. The public bar has a no-smoking section. Supervised children's play area. *Cask Marque* accredited.

WELLOW
Durham Ox
12-11;
12-10.30 Sun
Banks's Original; Marston's Pedigree; John Smith's Bitter Ⓗ
Large, popular village pub on different levels, often very busy. Choose from an extensive menu.

WEST BRIDGFORD
Southbank Bar
1 Bridgford House
11.30 (11 Sat)-11;
12-10.30 Sun
Fuller's London Pride; Mallard Duck & Dive Ⓗ
Sports-orientated young person's wine bar-style pub. It opens 9am Sat and Sun for breakfast.

WEST STOCKWITH
Waterfront
Canal Lane
11-11;
12-10.30 Sun
John Smith's Bitter; guest beers Ⓗ
Busy pub with a restaurant, near the canal basin marina, popular with holidaymakers and villagers alike.

WORKSOP
Shireoaks Inn
81-83 Westgate
11-3, 6-11;
12-4, 7.30-11 Sun
Bransley Bitter; guest beers Ⓗ
Cosy pub of many interconnecting rooms, fielding active pool and darts teams. No meals Sun eve.

Guest beers usually come from small brewers. Q ⑤ ❀ ◗ 딕 읁 ≋ ♣ ◉ P 旦

Market Hotel
West Carr Road
🕐 11-3, 6-11; 11-11 Sat; 12-4.30, 7-10.30 Sun
☎ (01777) 703278
Adnams Bitter; Mansfield Dark Mild; Marston's Bitter, Pedigree; Morrells Varsity; guest beers Ⓗ
Run by the same family for 40 years, this comfortable, deservedly popular, one-roomed pub serves up to 10 real ales – five of them as guests. Situated on the outskirts of town, in the suburb of Ordsall, it is just a few minutes' walk from the station (East Coast main line and Sheffield–Cleethorpes line). It is well known locally for its food, particularly the variety of fish and the Sun carvery, complemented by a small but varied wine list. The restaurant seats 80. Children are welcome early eve.
Q ❀ ◗ ᠔ 읁 ≋ P

SELSTON

Horse & Jockey
Church Lane (¹/₂ mile off B6018) OS464539
🕐 12-2.30, 5-11; 12-3, 7-10.30 Sun
☎ (01773) 781012
Draught Bass; Ⓗ **Greene King Abbot; Taylor Landlord;** Ⓖ **guest beers** Ⓗ/Ⓖ
Family-run village local, dating back to 1664; allegedly, there are only 12 pubs in England older than this one. Low-beamed ceilings and flagstoned floors feature in all its rooms: a main bar with open real fire, snug, a lounge with cast-iron range and a games room (pool and darts). Wed is folk night when all are welcome – bring your instrument. On Sun eve a quiz is held. Food is served weekdays and although basic fare, the quality is high; freshly carved roast meats feature most days. The pub is believed to be haunted by a friendly ghost.
⚌ ⑤ ❀ ◗ ᠔ ♣ ◉ P

SKEGBY

Fox & Crown
116 Dalestorth Road (A6075/B6014 jct)
🕐 11-11; 12-10.30 Sun
☎ (01623) 552436
Mansfield Cask Ale; Theakston Mild, XB; guest beer Ⓗ
Deservedly popular, spacious open-plan 'Steak and Ale' pub with a no-smoking room and a restaurant. A regular lunch stop for local workers, it is also used as a traditional local. Dark wood panelling is used extensively on the bar and walls which are hung with old pictures of the surrounding area. A large-screen TV features prominently with sports programmes listed on a board. Food is served 11–9.30 (12–8 Sun), with regular speciality nights. The pub's outdoor children's play area gets quite popular in summer. ❀ ◗ ♣ P ⊁

SOUTHWELL

Old Coach House
69 Easthorpe (A612, sharp bend by racecourse entrance)
🕐 5 (4 Fri; 12 Sat)-11; 12-10.30 Sun
☎ (01636) 813289
Draught Bass; guest beers Ⓗ
Everyone's ideal local, a friendly corner free house dating back to the 17th century,

divided into various sections and boasting three real fires. Six beers are always on offer, including a mild, and shot glasses are used for sampling prior to decision-making. Twenty different beers, on average, are available weekly, mostly from local independents. There is a large selection of board games including cribbage, which is a rarity in this area. It is close to the racecourse, the Minster and a restored workhouse and lies on a Newark–Nottingham bus route. ⚌ ❀ ♣ ◉

SUTTON IN ASHFIELD ❖

Picture House
Fox Street (near bus station)
🕐 11-11; 12-10.30 Sun
☎ (01623) 554627
Courage Directors; Theakston Best Bitter; guest beers Ⓗ
Large, open-plan Wetherspoon's pub, a refurbishment of the old cinema, hence the name. Very popular during lunchtime and eve, it always has at least one relatively cheap beer and quite reasonably priced food, served 11–10 (12–9.30 Sun). Wood panelling predominates and the very high ceiling can create an echoing effect which can be rather noisy when the pub is full. Pictures of old Sutton decorate the walls, as well as little write-ups of famous people associated with the area. An annual beer festival is held in April. ◗ ᠔ ⊁ ◉

TOLLERTON

Air Hostess
Stanstead Avenue
🕐 11.30-3 (not Mon), 5.30-11; 12-3, 7-10.30 Sun
☎ (0115) 937 2485
website: www.midlandspub.co.uk
Belvoir Mild Ale, Star Bitter; Mansfield Cask Ale; guest beers Ⓗ
Two-roomed pub in the form of a cross, in a quiet village on the outskirts of Nottingham. Friendly atmosphere where pleasant staff serve a lounge and a public bar with a pool table. Memorabilia include numerous aeronautical photos and maps and a large pub sign depicting an air hostess. The pub is home to a thriving pétanque team, which plays in the garden. Three guest beers vary regularly.
Q ❀ ◗ 딕 ᠔ ♣ P

UNDERWOOD

Red Lion
134 Church Lane (off B600, near church)
🕐 12-3, 5.30-11; 12-11 Sat; 12-10.30 Sun
☎ (01773) 810482
Boddingtons Bitter; Marston's Pedigree; guest beers Ⓗ
300-year-old, beamed village pub with a friendly landlord and staff. The bar area has a quarry-tiled floor, with a step up to raised carpeted dining area (children are welcome in the latter). A good variety of excellent meals and snacks are served and barbecues are held in summer. The large garden has a paved patio and lawned area and a children's area with play equipment. On Mon eve a general knowledge quiz is held and a raffle for a cash jackpot.
Over the years the pub has won a number of local CAMRA awards. ❀ ◗ P ⊁

WALKERINGHAM

Three Horseshoes
High Street
🕑 11.30-3, 7-11; 12-4, 7-10.30 Sun
☎ (01427) 890959
Draught Bass; Stones Bitter; Worthington Bitter; guest beer Ⓗ

This village pub has a large lounge-style bar plus a restaurant. The local village trade is boosted by visitors attracted by the pub's reputation for good quality home-cooked food – choose from the blackboard and eat in the pub or restaurant (no food Sun eve or Mon). Always one ever-changing guest beer is stocked. During the summer the pub is noted for its award-winning flower displays, and a new Japanese garden is planned.
Q ◑ & Å ♣ P 🏠

WELLOW ❖

Olde Red Lion
Eakring Road (2 miles from Ollerton, off A616)
🕑 11.30-3.30, 6-11; 12-10.30 Sun
e-mail: redlion@freeneasy.com
Black Sheep Best Bitter; Castle Eden Ale; Maypole Lion's Pride; Wells Bombardier Ⓗ

400-year-old traditional pub with exposed beams, it stands opposite the maypole in a quiet north Nottinghamshire village. Close to Clumber Park and Rufford Park, Centre Parc's holiday village is also within two miles. It sells four traditional cask ales, including local Maypole beers. Facilities here include a 20-seat restaurant, a bar for smokers and one for non-smokers, a snug and a garden. Q ❀ ◑ 🍴 ♣ P ⌀

WEST BRIDGFORD ❖

Meadow Covert
Alford Road, Edwalton (near Edwalton Golf Club)
🕑 11-11; 12-10.30 Sun
Hardys & Hansons Best Bitter, Classic Ⓗ

Situated on the edge of Edwalton, this fairly modern pub offers something for everyone. The public bar houses two pool tables, while darts and TV are also on offer. The comfortable L-shaped lounge is designed to relax both the drinker and diner; eve meals are served weekdays 5.30-7.30. A garden, complete with children's play area, comes into its own in summer. ❀ ◑ 🍴 ♣ P ●

Stratford Haven
2 Stratford Road
🕑 10.30-11; 12-10.30 Sun
☎ (0115) 982 5981
Adnams Bitter; Bateman XB; Caledonian Deuchars IPA; Castle Rock Hemlock; Hook Norton Old Hooky; guest beers Ⓗ

Formerly a pet shop, it is now a fine pub, handy for cricket lovers as it stands close to the Trent Bridge cricket ground. Part of the Tynemill Group, it is very popular with all ages, in particular appealing to the discerning drinker, with a good range of real ales. It can get very busy at weekends.
❀ ◑ & ⌀

WEST LEAKE

Star Inn
Melton Lane
🕑 11-2.30, 6-11; 12-3.30, 7-10.30 Sun
☎ (01509) 852233

Draught Bass; guest beers Ⓗ

On the southerly outskirts of the small village of West Leake near the Leicestershire border, you will find a friendly welcome at this white-fronted, 200-year-old pub. Outside, a large garden, with a pleasant patio area, provides views over the surrounding countryside. Inside, three rooms include a family room. Food, which is available every lunchtime and Tue–Sat eves (6.30–8.30), is served in the wood-panelled lounge. The two guest beers change frequently. ♨ Q ❀ ❀ ◑ 🍴 & ♣ P

WORKSOP ❖

Greendale Oak
41 Norfolk Street (500 yds from market place)
🕑 12-11; 12-4, 7-10.30 Sun
☎ (01909) 489680
website: www.downourlocal.com/greendale-oak-worksop
Stones Bitter; guest beers Ⓗ

This terraced pub was built in 1790 to house textile workers. Standing over one of the mill wells, it was noted by the Hodson brothers of the Park Brewery in Sheffield, to have a cellar of good beer-keeping quality and its first licence is believed to have been granted under the Beerhouse Act of 1832, which encouraged the conversion of houses to pubs. It takes its name from a famous oak tree which stood in Welbeck Park. This very small pub still has gas lighting and an intimate atmosphere in which to enjoy a superb range of home-made food. An ever-changing range of guest beers always includes a mild. ❀ ❀ ◑ Å ⇌ ♣ P ⌀ ●

Newcastle Arms
88 Carlton Road
🕑 11-2.30, 5.30-11; 11-11 Fri & Sat; 12-4, 7-10.30 Sun
☎ (01909) 485384
Home Bitter; Ruddles Best Bitter; guest beers Ⓗ

Worksop is the gateway to the 'Dukeries' and the Newcastle Arms takes its name from the Duke. This small pub dates from 1910 but became a pool and snooker hall during the 1980s. It reopened in the mid-1980s and continues to offer a warm, friendly environment in which to sample excellent home-cooked food and a regularly-changing guest beer range. The interior is cottage-style, with lots of tables which encourages good conversation in a pub generally free from loud music. Framed local press cuttings from the last 100 years provide interesting reading. Beer is discounted between 9 and 11pm. ❀ ❀ ◑ & Å ⇌ ♣

OXFORDSHIRE

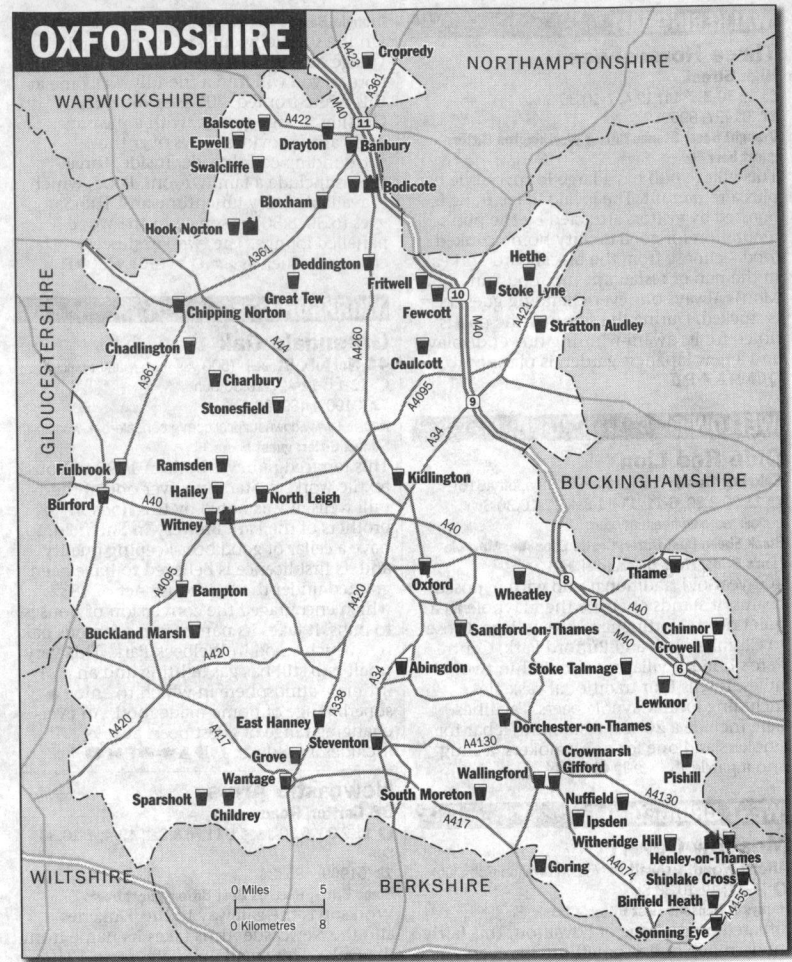

ABINGDON

Punch Bowl
Market Place
⊕ 10.30-3, 7-11; 10.30-11 Mon, Fri & Sat; 12-3, 7-10.30 Sun
☎ (01235) 520230
Greene King IPA, Morland Original ⊞
A drinking house since 1587, the public bar is a traditional serious drinkers' lively venue; in total contrast, the lounge bar is a wood-panelled room with an individual atmosphere. The drinker can relax and unwind with a sense of bygone days when life moved at a much slower pace. At the centre of this historic market town, the Punch Bowl is overshadowed by the County Hall, built in 1682 by Christopher Kempster of Burford, the most trusted builder of Sir Christopher Wren.
Q ⇄ ◑ ⊈ ৬ ♣ ♠

BAMPTON

Elephant & Castle
Bridge Street
⊕ 12-3 (not Mon), 5-11; 11-11 Sat; 12-5, 7-10.30 Sun
☎ (01993) 850316

Adnams Bitter; Archers Village; Arkells 3B; guest beer ⊞
Friendly village local, this picturesque Cotswold pub was reputedly built using stone from the local castle. It concentrates on the beer drinker, offering an excellent and ever-changing range of real ales. The interior is spacious with attractive stonework, beams and log fires. Accommodation is in the old dairy behind the main pub building. A large garden and bar food add to its appeal. ⛺ ❀ ⇄ ◑ ⊈ ♣ P

Morris Clown
High Street
⊕ 5 (11-Sat)-11); 12-10.30 Sun
☎ (01993) 850217
Archers Village; Courage Best Bitter; guest beer ⊞
Village local with an L-shaped single bar, warmed by a large open fire in winter, and complemented by a pleasant garden at the rear for summer drinking. Always busy, with a friendly crowd, it is active in the local darts, bar billiards and Aunt Sally leagues. The village lays claim to being the cradle of morris dancing and supports three teams; the pub hosts a major annual competition on spring bank holiday Mon.
⛺ ❀ ♣ ♠ P

BANBURY

Bell

12 Middleton Road, Grimsbury (near station)
🕓 12.30-3, 7-11; 12-11 Sat; 12-4, 8-10.30 Sun
☎ (01295) 253169
Hancock's HB; Highgate Dark; Worthington Bitter; guest beers Ⓗ

Welcoming, friendly, two-roomed town pub. Dominoes and pool are played in the bar, darts played in the lounge that is warmed by an open fire. Near to the canal, it is also handy for the bus and rail stations. Bar snacks are available Mon-Fri.
🏚🕸🍴🛏➤♣P

Olde Reindeer

47 Parsons Street
🕓 11-11 (10 Mon); closed Sun
☎ (01295) 264031
Hook Norton Mild, Best Bitter, Generation, Old Hooky; guest beer Ⓗ

Superb 15th-century former coaching inn with a famous Jacobean wood-panelled room known as the Globe Room. The pub runs a no-under 21s policy that helps to make it a relaxed venue for town; tidy dress is required. The lunches are home cooked. Regular quiz nights are popular with locals. A rare outlet for Hooky Mild, it also sells mulled wines in winter; search out the different fruit wines sold from jars. This lovely old pub is worth seeking out.
🏚🕸🍴➤P

BINFIELD HEATH

Bottle & Glass

Harpsden Road (off A4155, ½ mile NE of village centre)
🕓 11-3.30, 6-11; 12-3.30, 7-10.30 Sun
☎ (01491) 575755 website:thebottleandglass.co.uk
Brakspear 2.5, Bitter, Old, Special Ⓗ

Picturesque, thatched, beamed, country pub with a flagstoned floor in its main bar. Parts of the building date from the 14th century. The reasonably priced, home-cooked food includes vegetarian options, traditional English roasts and salads are served Sun 12-1.30 (no meals Sun eve). The right-hand bar is no-smoking. The large, well tended garden features a well and a pond with a small waterfall.
Q🕸🍴P✗

BODICOTE

Plough Inn

9 High Street (off A4260, 1 mile S of Banbury)
🕓 11-2.30, 6-11; 12-3.30, 7-10.30 Sun
☎ (01295) 262327
website: www.banbury-cross.co.uk/bodicotebrewery
Bodicote Bitter, No. 9, Triple X, Porter, seasonal beers Ⓗ

Doreen and Jim Blencowe took over this beamed, pleasant and friendly village pub, in 1957. Their son Jimmy learnt to brew with Peter Austin, a retired head brewer, in Ringwood, after which Bodicote Brewery began to produce their own beer in 1982. No. 9 is named after the pub's High Street address and Triple X for Doreen and Jim's 30th wedding anniversary. There are well attended beer festivals twice a year. Doreen cooks the meals to order, with help at busy times.
🏚Q🍴🛏

BUCKLAND MARSH

Trout at Tadpole Bridge

Off A420 to Bampton OS335004
🕓 11-3, 6-11; 12-2, 7-10 Sun
☎ (01367) 870382 website: www.trout-inn.co.uk
Archers Village; Fuller's London Pride; guest beer Ⓗ

This Grade II listed local stone building dates from the 17th century and has been a pub for over 100 years. In a picturesque setting on the Thames, its garden runs right down to the river's edge. The pub boasts a stone floor, original beams and high-backed benches. Highly recommended for its award-winning meals, newly-built accommodation has been sympathetically matched to the existing building. A genuine free house with a frequently changing guest beer, it is ideal as a starting point for a Thames path walk. 🏚Q🕸🛏🍴🛏🛗Å♣P

BURFORD

Lamb

Sheep Street
🕓 11-2.30, 6-11; 12-2.30, 7-10.30 Sun
☎ (01993) 823155
Badger Best; Hook Norton Best Bitter; Wadworth 6X Ⓗ

Immensely characterful, stylish and cosy bar in a comfortable 15th-century hotel, with friendly service, traditional Cotswold stone-flagged floors and four real fires. The superb lounge facilities are available to drinkers as well as hotel guests. The Lamb exudes good taste and quality, even down to the brass fittings in the toilets. The award-winning walled garden sometimes plays host to visiting morris dancers in summer. 🏚Q🕸🛏🍴🛗

CAULCOTT

Horse & Groom

Lower Heyford Road
🕓 11-3, 6-11; 12-3, 7-10.30 Sun
☎ (01869) 343257
Hook Norton Best Bitter; guest beers Ⓗ

From the outside this small, stone and thatched pub, with a roadside garden, is the picture of a rural gem. Step inside and a cosy bar, a friendly welcome and, like as not, Harvey, the characterful Westie, will greet you. The pump clips beside the open fire record the 200-plus different beers offered annually; with three constantly changing ales, there is always something different to try. À la carte meals, daily specials and an impressive selection of speciality sausages are served in the bar or adjoining restaurant. Local CAMRA *Pub of the Year* 2000 winner. 🏚Q🕸🍴

CHADLINGTON

Tite Inn

Mill End
🕓 12-2.30, 6.30-11; closed Mon; 12-3, 7-10.30 Sun
☎ (01608) 676475 website: www.titeinn.com

INDEPENDENT BREWERIES

Brakspear Henley-on-Thames
Hook Norton Hook Norton
Plough Inn Bodicote
Wychwood Witney

Archers Village; Fuller's London Pride; Young's Special; guest beers Ⓗ

Family-run Cotswold stone free house at the edge of the village, affording fine views over surrounding countryside and a lovely garden. Two comfortably furnished connecting bars and the restaurant are supplemented by the garden room in summer which boasts a well-established vine across the ceiling. Well-behaved children are welcome. Enjoy excellent, freshly-prepared food and a well-chosen wine list. It is a focus for village activities, including an annual pantomime, cricket team, Easter egg rolling and an investors' club. ⚌Q✿◖&A♣P

CHARLBURY

Rose & Crown
Market Street
✪ 12 (11 Sat)-11; 12-10.30 Sun
☎ (01608) 810103 website: www.topbeerpub.co.uk
Archers Village; guest beers Ⓗ

Popular, traditional, town-centre free house where an excellent rotation of guest beers features many from micro-breweries. Traditional ciders plus a good selection of Belgian bottled beers are also stocked. It has a simply furnished split-level bar, a pool room and patio courtyard. On the Oxfordshire Way long distance path, walkers may eat their own food in the bar. A Guide entry for 16 years, it is a pub for the discerning drinker who enjoys a good pint without the intrusion of cooking smells. ⚌✿A≈

CHILDREY

Hatchet
High Street
✪ 12-2.30 (3 Sat), 7-11; 12-4, 7-10.30 Sun
☎ (01235) 751213
Greene King Morland Original; guest beers Ⓗ

Friendly local in a picturesque downland village setting. The white-painted building has changed little in over 100 years, with its original beams adorned with horse brasses, beer taps and brass hatchets. The bar, serving four changing guest beers, has an open-plan area with pub games and a quiet dining area. There is easy access for walkers to the Ridgeway Path; the landlord is sympathetic to passing campers. The name probably originates from local 'bodgers' or chair makers visiting Childrey to have axes sharpened. The garden has tables and children's play equipment. ✿◖♣P

CHIPPING NORTON

Chequers
Goddards Lane (next to theatre)
✪ 11-11, 12-10.30 Sun
☎ (01608) 644717 website: www.chequers-pub.co.uk
Fuller's Chiswick, London Pride, ESB, seasonal beers Ⓗ

Outstanding, award-winning pub, comprising three interconnecting bars furnished in traditional style, with gentle lighting. The courtyard restaurant is light and airy with a bare wood floor, simple furniture and an interesting menu. No fruit machines, pool or TV, this is a pub for conversation; the long-serving publicans are actively involved, and always happy for a chat. Local CAMRA Pub of the Year 1999 and twice Fuller's Pub of the Year. ⚌Q◖♣●

CROPREDY

Red Lion Inn
8 Red Lion Street (near Cropredy Lock)
✪ 12-3, 6 (5.30 summer)-11; 12-4, 7-10.30 Sun
☎ (01293) 750224
Hook Norton Best Bitter; Greene King Ruddles County; Tetley Bitter; guest beers Ⓗ

This North Oxfordshire classic is well established – the road is named after it. Built in 1545 of local honey-coloured ironstone, under a thatched roof, it is surprisingly large for what appears to be a couple of cottages, comprising a locals' bar, family games room and a large, well-appointed restaurant with an emphasis on traditional home-cooked food. No meals Sun or Mon eves in winter. Cropredy hosts the annual Fairport Convention concerts (Aug). Hard to find, but it is worth seeking out. ⚌☎✿◖⊟♣P

CROWELL

Shepherd's Crook
The Green (off B4009 between Chinnor and M40 jct 6) OS744997
✪ 11.30-3, 5-11; 11-11 Sat; 12-5, 7-10.30 (12-10.30 summer) Sun
☎ (01844) 351431 e-mail: scrook@supernet.com
Batham Best Bitter; Donnington BB; Hook Norton Best Bitter; Taylor Landlord; guest beers Ⓗ

In the foothills of the Chilterns you will find this comfortable inn (known as the Catherine Wheel until 1991). The current landlord, who took over in 1996, is a real ale fanatic, and this is one of the few pub's to sell Batham's locally, and the only one selling Donnington's outside the Cotswolds. A former fish merchant, the landlord obtains supplies delivered directly from the West Country and shellfish from the Norfolk coast, while excellent steak and kidney pies and steaks come from a local butcher. ⚌Q✿◖♣P

CROWMARSH GIFFORD

Queen's Head
72 The Street (500 yds W of A4130/A4074 roundabout)
✪ 12-3, 5-11; 12-3, 7-10.30 Sun
☎ (01491) 839857 e-mail: booqueens@aol.com
Fuller's Chiswick, London Pride, ESB, seasonal beers or guest beer Ⓗ

The Queen's Head is frequented by local office workers, boaters from the River Thames (5 min walk), and walkers from the Ridgeway long distance footpath under a mile away. The restaurant area has parts dating back to 1341, and a mock minstrel gallery. The food includes vegetarian choices. It is advisable to book for eve meals (served Tue-Sat) including monthly theme nights. There are occasional barbecues in the large, cultivated garden, which is safe for children. ⚌Q✿◖&AP

DEDDINGTON

Crown & Tuns
New Street (B4260)
✪ 11-3 (may vary afternoons), 6-11; 12-3, 7-10.30 Sun

☎ (01869) 337371

Hook Norton Mild, Best Bitter, Old Hooky, seasonal beers; guest beer (occasional) Ⓗ

Two-bar traditional pub that has appeared in every edition of this *Guide*. The building dates from the 16th century when it served as a coaching inn, on the main road through Deddington village. Good value bar snacks are served at lunchtime – try the home-cooked gammon, egg and chips. B&B is offered in a homely atmosphere; the full English breakfast is also offered to non-residents at weekends. The garden is home to an Aunt Sally pitch.

❀❀⊷◑⊖▲♣

Brakspear Bitter; Fuller's London Pride; Hook Norton Best Bitter; guest beer Ⓗ

Genuine free house with a pleasant garden on the main street of an attractive Vale village. The spacious, comfortable and well-restored bar has a quietly relaxed atmosphere. The German landlord, a proud advocate of the traditional English pub, removed the pool table and juke box on the very day that he took over. Meet, converse and imbibe in a civil environment. There is a large no-smoking dining area at one end, serving a varied menu. There are always some bottles of German beers available.

Q❀◑◐▲P

DORCHESTER ON THAMES

Chequers

20 Bridge End (off High St)
✪ 12-2 (not Mon or Wed; 12-3 Sat), 7-11; 12-3, 7-10.30 Sun
☎ (01865) 340015

Courage Best Bitter; Hook Norton Best Bitter; Wadworth IPA; guest beers (summer) Ⓖ

300-year-old local that eschews electronic games and music, where the real ale is fetched from the cellar. The no-smoking family room houses a bar billiards table (the pub team is one of the best in the country). Aunt Sally, the local Oxfordshire game is played alternate Fri eve in summer (not one of the best teams in the country!). Euchre and other games are also regularly played. The pub is in an attractive, village which was a Roman City, and boasts an abbey and many fine, old buildings. Handy for walkers and the rivers Thames and Thame. Sandwiches are available. ❀Q❀❀⊷♣P✗

EAST HANNEY

Black Horse

Main Street (200 yds from Hanney crossroads, off A338)
✪ 12-2.30, 6-11; closed Mon; 12-3, 6-10.30 Sun
☎ (01235) 868212
website: www.blackhorse.homepage.com

EPWELL

Chandlers Arms

Sibford Road (off B4039 Banbury-Shipston road)
OS353403
✪ 12-2.30, 5.30-11; 12-11 Sat; 12-10.30 Sun
☎ (01295) 780394

Hook Norton Mild, Best Bitter, seasonal beers; guest beers Ⓗ

On the Warwickshire border, in a popular walking area, this tied house is run by ex-brewer Ian Merivale (from Edgecote and Warden breweries). Families are welcome, and a small but variable menu is served in the family dining room; locally sourced organic sausages and fish fresh from Billingsgate are specialities. The garden is suitable for children and houses an Aunt Sally. Dominoes, crib and darts keep the locals engaged in the single bar.
❀Q❀❀◑◐⊖♣♣P

FEWCOTT

White Lion

Fritwell Road (off A43 at Ardley, near M40 jct 10)
✪ 7-11; 11-11 Sat; 12-4, 7-10.30 Sun
☎ (01869) 346639

Beer range varies Ⓗ

This lively, 18th-century stone village pub, with a large open bar offers a constantly changing range of four guest ales. These

INN BRIEF

BALSCOTE

Butcher's Arms
Shutford Road
12-2 (not Mon-Tue; 12-3.30 Sat), 6.30-11; 12-3.30, 7-10.30 Sun
Hook Norton Mild, Best Bitter, seasonal beers; guest beers Ⓗ
Traditional village local, unspoilt by progress. No food served.

BLOXHAM

Elephant & Castle
Humber Street (off A361)
11-3, 5-11; 11-11 Sat; 12-10.30 Sun
Hook Norton Best Bitter; guest beers Ⓗ
Community-focused, 16th-century coaching inn run by the same landlord for 27 years. No food Sun.

CHINNOR

Red Lion
High Street
11.30 (11 Sat)-11; 12-10.30 Sun
Brakspear Bitter; Fuller's London Pride, Greene King IPA; guest beers Ⓗ
Friendly village local, about 300 years old, originally three cottages. Food available lunchtime and eves, except Sun.

DRAYTON

Olde Roebuck Inn
Stratford Road
11-3, 6-11; 12-3, 7-10.30 Sun
Hook Norton Best Bitter; Fuller's London Pride; Taylor Landlord; guest beers Ⓗ
Popular free house with 3 inter-connecting bars and a large, comfortable restaurant.

FULBROOK

Masons Arms
Shipton Road (A361 Burford road)
12-2 (not Mon-Thu), 6.30-11 (not Mon); 12-3, 7-10.30 Sun
Hook Norton Best Bitter; Wadworth 6X; guest beer (occasional) Ⓗ
200-year-old pub offering a traditional atmosphere with real fire. Good, home-cooked food.

> ✻ symbol next to a main entry place name indicates there are Inn Brief entries as well.

HAILEY

Lamb & Flag
Middletown (B4022, 2 miles from Witney)
12-3, 7-11; 12-3, 7-10.30 Sun
Greene King IPA, Abbot; guest beers (summer) Ⓗ
Low-beamed, one-room bar with a welcoming open fire. The restaurant offers excellent food.

HENLEY-ON-THAMES

Saracen's Head
129 Greys Road
12-2.30, 5.30-11; 12-11 Sat; 12-10.30 Sun
Brakspear Mild, Bitter, seasonal beers Ⓗ
Popular and busy local with an emphasis on pub games. The large garden is safe for children. No food.

OXFORD

Original Swan
188 Oxford Road, Cowley
12-3, 6-11; 12-11 Fri & Sat; 12-10.30 Sun
Arkell's 2B, 3B, seasonal beers Ⓗ
Large pub near Oxford business park, acquired by Arkell's in 1997 and totally refurbished. Reputedly haunted by ghost of former landlord.

typically come from outside the region and include rarely seen micros, so there is usually something new and interesting to try. There is a strong emphasis on games and sport – pool and darts are played in a side room and Aunt Sally in the large garden. The pub is also the base for the local football team. 🏠⛱️♣P

FRITWELL

King's Head
92 East Street
(2 miles from M40 jct 10)
🕐 12-3, 7-11; 12-4, 7-10.30 Sun
☎ (01869) 346738 website: www.thekingsheadfritwell
Hook Norton Best Bitter; Fuller's London Pride; guest beer 🅗
This 17th-century Cotswold stone pub, with a well in its small front garden, has recently undergone refurbishment. It now pleasantly combines a village pub atmosphere within a rural 'bistro' setting and attracts a wide range of clientele, ranging from diners to the local dominoes and card schools. Interesting food includes bar meals and an *à la carte* menu served in the restaurant.
🏠⛱️◗♣

GORING

Catherine Wheel
Station Road
🕐 11.30 (12 Sat)-3, 6-11; 12-3, 7-10.30 Sun
☎ (01491) 872379
Brakspear Mild, Bitter, Old, Special, seasonal beers 🅗
The oldest pub in this lovely riverside village features oak beams and an award-winning inglenook. An L-shaped bar on different levels extends into the often busy Forge Bar dining area where children are welcome. This used to be the blacksmith's shop (complete with anvil) – try to find the gents loo hidden behind a secret panel. Popular with hikers and cyclists from the nearby Ridgeway and Thames long distance footpaths, it serves good value, home-cooked meals (including vegetarian) with daily specials (no food Sun eve). Accommodation is in a nearby cottage.
🏠Q⛱️◗⧖♣

GREAT TEW

Falkland Arms
Off A361 and B4022
🕐 11.30-2.30 (3 Sat), 6-11 (11.30-11 summer Sat); 12-3, 7-10.30 (12-10.30 summer) Sun
☎ (01608) 683653
website: www.banbury-cross.co.uk/falklandarms
Wadworth IPA, 6X; guest beers 🅗
In an idyllic thatched village, this award-winning, attractive pub has become increasingly popular with drinkers who enjoy an unspoilt, relaxed atmosphere without the intrusions of modern life, like mobile phones. Simple wooden furniture, oak settles, flagstoned and bare boarded floors, an inglenook and gentle lighting create a wonderful ambience. Alongside five guest beers, it stocks a large range of malt whiskies and country wines and a real cider. The landlady is very proud of her *Cask Marque* award. The large garden is a bonus.
🏠Q⧖⛱️◗♣⧫●

GROVE

Volunteer
Station Road (A338, 2 miles N of Wantage)
🕐 11-11; 12-10.30 Sun
☎ (01235) 769557
Hook Norton Best Bitter, Generation, Old Hooky, seasonal beers 🅗
Ex-railway inn, by the main Paddington/Bristol line, it provides lunchtime food for passing trade and the local Formula One racing car industry. One of Hook Norton's most southerly pubs, it stocks a good range of this popular brewery's beers. Beer bottles adorn the walls of the U-shaped bar, with pub games to one side and small tables on the other. A drinkers' pub serving local villages, it offers a Sun roast and live entertainment most Sat eves. A paved patio and children's play area are at the end of a large car park.
⛱️⧖◗♣P

HENLEY-ON-THAMES ✤

Bird in Hand
61 Greys Road (200 yds off A4155)
🕐 11.30-2.30, 5-11; 11.30-11 Sat; 12-10.30 Sun
☎ (01491) 575775
e-mail: celia@birdinhand.fsnet.co.uk
Brakspear Mild, Bitter; Fuller's London Pride; guest beers 🅗
Friendly, one-bar, town local, Henley's only independent free house, it attracts locals and visitors. It holds fortnightly fun quizzes (Wed eve). The surprisingly large garden, with aviary, pond and pets, is safe for children. The two guest beers are often from micros. Reasonably priced weekday lunches are served. Henley is famed for the Royal Regatta (July), its Festival (Sept) and the River and Rowing Museum. Q⧖◗🅰️⮕♣

HETHE

Whitmore Arms
🕐 7 (6 summer)-11; 12-2.30, 7 (6 summer)-11 Sun
☎ (01869) 277654
Brakspear Bitter; Hook Norton Best Bitter, 🅗 **seasonal beers** 🅖
This 18th-century, stone pub in a quiet hamlet, was originally attached to its own malthouse and called the Maltster's Arms. It apparently gained its present name in 1810 when the landlord left it in his will to his friend, Thomas Whitmore. Old implements and memorabilia adorn the walls and a large inglenook sits at one end of the open bar. Good value bar meals are available in a quiet, relaxed atmosphere; eve meals are served daily, plus weekend lunches.
🏠Q⧖⛱️◗🅰️♣P

HOOK NORTON

Pear Tree Inn
Scotland End (near brewery)
🕐 11.30-2.30, 6-11; 11.30-11 Sat; 12-4, 7-10 Sun
☎ (01608) 737482
website: www.peartree.freeserve.co.uk
Hook Norton Mild, Best Bitter, Generation, Old Hooky, Double Stout, seasonal beer 🅗
Now that Hook Norton Brewery's visitor centre is fully open, this will be your first port of call after your brewery visit, as it is effectively the brewery tap. This small, 18th-century one-roomed brick pub features

exposed beams. Six Hook Norton beers are available all year round. The large garden has a dedicated area for children. The home-cooked bar food (not served Sun eve) features a changing blackboard menu at reasonable prices. A rural gem.

🚾Q❀✍◖①▲♣P

IPSDEN

King William IV
Hailey OS643858
✪ 11.30-2.30, 6-11; 12-3, 7-10.30 Sun
☎ (01491) 681845
Brakspear 2.5, Mild, Bitter, Old, Special, seasonal beers Ⓖ

Lovely, country pub in an outstanding location, affording fine open views over rolling hills and the nearby Well Place Zoo. Although tricky to find, off the narrow lanes, you will be rewarded by local Brakspear ales served directly from the cooled casks. A good variety of food is on offer (with vegetarian options), made from fresh produce; a 'beehive oven' is used as an alternative to barbecues. Popular with hikers from the Ridgeway long distance footpath $1^1/_2$ miles away. Families are welcome, with play equipment in the garden. 🚾Q❀◖P

KIDLINGTON

King's Arms
4 The Moors (off end of High St)
✪ 11-2.30, 6-11; 11-11 Sat; 12-10.30 Sun
☎ (01865) 373004
Greene King IPA; Ind Coope Burton Ale; guest beer Ⓗ
Popular, attractive village pub with two small bars and a covered outdoor drinking area. Aunt Sally is played in this area, and it is also used to host beer festivals in spring and autumn. Very reasonably priced food is served Mon-Sat lunchtimes. The guest beer changes regularly. ✍❀◖♣P

LEWKNOR

Olde Leatherne Bottel
1 High Street (off B4009, near M40 jct 6)
✪ 11-2.30 (3 Sat), 6-11; 12-3, 7-10.30 Sun
☎ (01844) 351482
Brakspear Bitter, Old, Special, seasonal beers Ⓗ
Traditional, 400-year-old, unspoilt, English country inn, at the heart of a Chilterns village. It has two main bar areas and a central servery, complete with low beams and three fireplaces – one an attractive inglenook. Very popular with locals and travellers alike (only a minute from the M40), it has a large, well-kept garden, with a children's play area. High quality, good value food from an extensive menu includes vegetarian options (eve meals Fri & Sat). The no-smoking, family room is a comfortable extension to one of the bar areas, in this almost constant *Guide* entry.
🚾Q✍❀◖&♣P✦

NORTH LEIGH

Woodman Inn
New Yatt Road (off A4095, Witney-Woodstock road)
✪ 12-2.30, 6-11; 12-10.30 Sun
☎ (01993) 881790
Hook Norton Best Bitter; Wadworth 6X; guest beers Ⓗ

A focus for community activities, this friendly one-bar local is noted for its good food. A spacious bar, with simple wooden furniture, offers plenty of space for drinkers and diners. Fresh flowers on the tables and a wood-burning fire add to its appeal. The long-serving landlord and landlady pride themselves on personal service and high standards. The attractive terrace and garden host very successful beer festivals (now in their 13th year).
🚾❀✍◖♣P●

NUFFIELD

Crown
Gangsdown Hill (A4130, 4½ miles E of Wallingford)
✪ 11-2.30 (3 Sat), 6-11; 12-3 (closed eve) Sun
☎ (01491) 641335
Brakspear Bitter, Special, seasonal beers Ⓗ
Right on the Ridgeway long-distance footpath, it welcomes walkers who remove muddy boots before entering. The front of the pub is a 12th-century A-frame building with no first floor, extended to the back in the 15th century. The front bar is usually laid out for diners, but you can also eat in the back bar (book for lunch Fri-Sun). A wide range of English food, plus continental dishes are freshly prepared. Children are welcome in the small family room and the garden play area. It backs on to a golf course and is near Nuffield Place, former home of Lord Nuffield (of Morris Cars) – open in summer.
🚾Q🥾❀◖P

OXFORD ❖

Angel & Greyhound
30 St Clements Street
(across Magdalen Bridge from High St)
✪ 11-11; 12-10.30 Sun
☎ (01865) 242660
Young's Bitter, Triple A, Special, seasonal beers Ⓗ
One-room pub, with patios to front and rear, and an adjacent public car park. The best Young's pub in the city, it has a bright, airy interior, with raised seating areas and a single bar. Smiles Best is sometimes sold. Once called the Oranges and Lemons, the current name comes from nearby meadows, which were used for grazing horses, stabled at two coaching inns, the Angel (demolished in 1875) and the Greyhound, now part of Magdalen College. No food Sun eve.
🚾Q❀◖♣

Bear Inn
6 Alfred Street
(behind Town Hall)
✪ 12-11; 12-10.30 Sun
☎ (01865) 728164
Bateman XXXB; Hook Norton Old Hooky; guest beers Ⓗ
Ancient pub dating from 1242, and reputedly the smallest in Oxford, renowned for its collection of ties, one of which helped Inspector Morse solve one of Oxford's many fictional murders. The pub comprises two small, low-beamed rooms. Its pewter-topped bar is a rare feature that was retained after a recent sympathetic renovation. Five beers are usually available, including interesting guests. Lunch is served 12-4. 🚾Q❀◖≈

Butcher's Arms
5 Wilberforce Street, Headington
☼ 12-2.30, 5-11; 12-11 Fri & Sat; 12-10.30 Sun
☎ (01865) 761252 e-mail: g.young2000@aol.com
Fuller's Chiswick, London Pride, ESB, seasonal beers; guest beer Ⓗ

For ten years the Youngs have successfully run the only tenanted pub in Headington – and earned a Fuller's *Master Cellarman* certificate. Its friendly atmosphere welcomes families and there is good wheelchair access to this back-street Victorian pub that has recently been extended. Quiz night Sun, and major sporting events are shown on TV – there is a strong football theme, as Manor Ground, the old home of Oxford United, is nearby. Oxford CAMRA *Pub of the Year* 1999. No food Sat.
ⓜＱ❄◖♣

Harcourt Arms
1-2 Cranham Terrace
☼ 12-2.30 (3 Fri & Sat), 5.30-11; 12-3, 7-10.30 Sun
☎ (01865) 310630
e-mail: johnjackman@harcourt-arms.fsnet.co.uk
Fuller's Chiswick, London Pride, ESB Ⓗ

A pub has stood on this site since 1871, when the terrace was built, but the current house was built by Ind Coope in the 1930s. Now owned by Fuller's, it is cosy and atmospheric – enhanced by two log fires and subdued lighting. The walls are decorated with modern prints and, behind the bar, an impressive collection of international bank notes. A wide variety of board and card games are available. Bar snacks are served eves until 10pm. ⓜ❄◖♣

Hobgoblin
108 St Aldates (opp. Town Hall)
☼ 11-11; 12-10.30 Sun
☎ (01865) 250201
Wychwood Shires; guest beers Ⓗ

Formerly the Bulldog, this pub was refurbished and reopened by Wychwood in 1998. It comprises a large, high-ceilinged front bar, and a lower area at the rear. Four guest beers are available at a time (over 500 since the pub opened). The M4 Mild is exclusive to this pub and its sister in Reading – mild is a rarity in Oxford since the demise of Morrells. Promotions and student deals are offered during term time. Oxford CAMRA *Pub of the Year* 2000. Meals are served 12-6 (4 Sun).
◖≠

Lamb & Flag
12 St Giles
☼ 11-11; 12-10.30 Sun
☎ (01865) 515787
Brakspear Bitter; Fuller's London Pride; Theakston Old Peculier; guest beers Ⓗ

This 15th-century coaching inn comprises four rooms and two bars, and is accessed off a narrow passage, linking St Giles with the university science area. It is surrounded by the historic buildings of St John's College which reacquired and sympathetically refurbished the pub in 1998. Another hostelry with Morse connections, it is famous as a meeting place for literary figures such as Tolkein and CS Lewis, who also frequented the Eagle & Child opposite. Skinners beers often feature as guests. Ｑ◖≠

Marlborough House
60 Western Road
☼ 11.30-2.30, 6-11; 11-11 Sat; 12-10.30 Sun
☎ (01865) 243617
Benskins Bitter; Greene King IPA Ⓗ

Named after a three-masted man-of-war sailing ship. In a reversal of the modern trend the Marlborough was built in 1888 as a private dwelling but converted into a pub in 1897. It is a small, friendly, back-street pub, popular with students and locals alike. It features three intimate downstairs rooms and a larger pool room upstairs. Darts is also played and a live music eve is staged Wed.
◖♣

Old Bookbinder's Ale House
17-18 Victor Street, Jericho
☼ 12-11; 12-10.30 Sun
☎ (01865) 553549
Fuller's London Pride; Morrells Oxford Blue, Varsity; Ⓗ **guest beers** Ⓗ/Ⓖ

The first, and by far the most successful, of the Morrell's Ale House chain, converted from a failing corner pub in 1999. The exterior is almost original, as featured in Inspector Morse; inside bric-à-brac and bare boards abound in true ale house style. Six beers are offered on handpump, and several more are available from the stillage behind

---

INN BRIEF

PISHILL
Crown
On B480, 5 miles N of Henley
11.30-2.30, 6-11; 12-3, 7-10.30 Sun
Brakspear Bitter; Fuller's London Pride; guest beer (occasional) Ⓗ
Attractive, 15th-century former coaching inn with ghost. Noted for its food (children welcome in the restaurant). Accommodation in cottage in grounds.

SHIPLAKE CROSS
Plowden Arms
Reading Road
(A4155, 2½ miles S of Henley)
11.30-2.30, 6 (6.30 winter)-11; 12-3, 7-10.30 Sun
Brakspear Bitter, Special Ⓗ
Pleasant roadside pub with a no-smoking lounge bar, family room and a large garden. Lunches and eve meals (Tue-Sat). Shiplake Cross appears as Shiplake on most maps.

WALLINGFORD
King's Head
2 St Martin's Street
11-11;
12-10.30 Sun
Brakspear Bitter Ⓗ
Busy town local, popular with all ages, although weekend eves tend to attract younger clientele.

WANTAGE
King's Arms
39 Wallingford Street
11-11;
12-10.30 Sun
Greene King IPA, Morland Original; guest beers (occasional) Ⓗ
Grade II listed building with a mock-Tudor exterior, this local prides itself on the price and quality of its beers.

WHEATLEY
Railway
Station Road
12 (4 Mon)-11;
12-10.30 Sun
Fuller's London Pride, ESB Ⓗ
Victorian pub displaying railway memorabilia, although the railway is no longer there. The function room hosts live music.

WITNEY
Three Horseshoes
78 Corn Street
12-3, 6.30-11 (not Mon eve);
12-3, 7-10.30 Sun
Greene King Morland Original, Abbot; guest beer Ⓗ
17th-century, cosy pub converted from cottages. Good food, with no-smoking areas for diners. Three real fires.

Cask Marque

The Cask Marque symbol with a pub entry indicates that the licensee has successfully passed a number of tests concerning beer quality, and can display a plaque to this effect. However, the choice of all pubs in the guide is made by CAMRA independently of Cask Marque. The Cask Marque symbol is added during the editing process, and Cask Marque has no say in the selection of pubs.

the bar, with a wide range of guests, plus Bulmers cider in summer. Meals are served 12-9 in this lively local. ≜◑☾♣♠

Rose & Crown
14 North Parade Avenue
✪ 11-3, 5 (6 Sat)-11; 12-4, 7-10.30 Sun
☎ (01865) 510551
Adnams Bitter; Ind Coope Burton Ale Ⓗ
Excellent Victorian north Oxford local: two small rooms and a corridor drinking area with a serving hatch. The large garden is covered and heated in winter. A pub for conversation, free from music and intrusive machines, which attracts a mix of locals and academics; a chess night is held weekly. Souvenirs donated by regulars who pursue more active sports (Formula One motor racing and ice hockey) adorn the back room. Observe the mobile phone ban, or face a charity fine. ≜Q☸◑☾

Wharf House
14 Butterwyke Place, St Ebbes
✪ 11-3, 5.30 (6 winter)-11; 11-11 Sat; 12-4, 7-10.30 Sun
☎ (01865) 246752
Hook Norton Best Bitter; RCH Pitchfork; Ⓗ **guest beers** Ⓗ/Ⓖ
Built when coal and goods were transported by River Thames and canal, this historic building stands aloof from the busy roads that now flank it. Entering is like going into someone's front room. It stocks a range of rare foreign beers unobtainable elsewhere and in season there are some fine draught ciders and perries from small English and continental producers. This friendly local attracts an interesting mix of customers. Q☸☾⇌♣♠P

RAMSDEN

Royal Oak
High Street (B4022, Witney-Charlbury road)
OS356153
✪ 11.30-3, 6.30-11; 12-3, 7-10.30 Sun
☎ (01993) 868213
Archers Golden; Hook Norton Best Bitter, Old Hooky, West Berkshire Good Old Boy Ⓗ
This 17th-century coaching inn has recently undergone some refurbishment to increase the bar area and dining room, without losing any of the building's charm. A varied and imaginative menu is served in the restaurant and bar, using best quality local products. It offers regular guest beers, usually from local breweries. Bedrooms in the former coach house and stable block have en-suite facilities. Popular with walkers, it is convenient for several circular routes. ≜Q☸☾◑☾♣P冒

SANDFORD-ON-THAMES

Fox
25 Henley Road
✪ 12-3, 6.30-11; 12-3, 7-10.30 Sun
☎ (01865) 777803
Morrells Oxford Blue, Ⓗ/Ⓖ **Varsity** Ⓗ
This long-standing *Guide* entry has been in the same family for many years. One of few Morrells' pubs that has not been refurbished, it retains a classic, basic bar. Very much a locals' meeting place – the village has been bypassed for many years – it serves the cheapest Morrells' for miles around. Beer will be served on gravity on request. Note that no food is served – a rarity these days. Games include an Aunt Sally in the garden. ≜Q☸♨♣P

SONNING EYE

Flowing Spring
Henley Road (A4155, 2 miles E of Caversham)
✪ 11.30-11; 12-10.30 Sun
☎ (0118) 969 3207
website: www.theflowingspring.com
Fuller's Chiswick, London Pride, ESB, seasonal beers Ⓗ
Traditional country local, with a sympathetic extension and veranda, overlooking the large garden (children's swings). The bar is now effectively an island almost surrounded by drinking areas. Traditional pub food includes vegetarian options (eve meals Wed-Sat, plus Tue in summer); it hosts occasional barbecues. Walkers come from the footpaths in the surrounding countryside and the Thames long-distance footpath one mile away. Quiz night is Sun. ≜Q☸☸◑☾♣P⚹

SOUTH MORETON

Crown
High Street (S off A4130, 2 miles from Didcot)
✪ 11-3, 5.30-11; 12-3, 7-10.30 Sun
☎ (01235) 812262
Adnams Bitter; Badger Tanglefoot; Wadworth IPA, 6X; Ⓗ **guest beer** Ⓖ
Friendly, country village local, simply furnished in rustic style. A regularly changing guest beer is served from cooled casks behind the bar. Children are welcome throughout the pub, which is near Didcot's steam train centre. It is popular for good value meals (with vegetarian choices), and its quiz (Mon). The Crown doubles as the local library; bring your unwanted books to be sold for charity.
≜☸◑☾♣P

SPARSHOLT

Star
Watery Lane
✪ 12-3, 6-11; 12-11 Sat; 12-10.30 Sun
☎ (01235) 751539

Butts Barbus Barbus; Greene King Morland Original; guest beers Ⓗ
This lively, friendly, 17th-century, oak-beamed village pub is frequented by the horseracing community who watch events on TV here. The long single bar is divided into a bare-boarded public/games area, featuring a bar billiards table, and a carpeted lounge/dining area. A further dining room is available in an extension at the rear; well-behaved children are welcome. The food is very well regarded locally, in particular the enormous mixed grill (no food Sun). B&B not available Mon. ⌂⏸&Å♣⌿

STEVENTON

Cherry Tree
33 High Street
⊕ 11.30-2.30, 5-11; 11-11 Fri & Sat; 12-10.30 Sun
☎ (01235) 831222
Red Shoot Tom's Tipple; Wadworth IPA, 6X; guest beers Ⓗ
Originally two 18th-century cottages, situated at the foot of Steventon Hill, wood predominates in both the large main bars of this friendly pub. Weekly meat raffles are held in aid of village charities, Mon is quiz night, and the pub has an Aunt Sally pitch. Watch out for the occasional mini beer festival and live English folk music (third Sun in month). An excellent range of food is all home made. ⌂⏣⏸♣P⌿

STOKE LYNE

Peyton Arms ☆
1/2 mile off B4100, near M40 jct 10
⊕ 12-2.30 (not Mon or Tue), 6.30 (6 Fri & Sat)-11; 12-2.30, 7-10.30 Sun
☎ (01869) 345285
Hook Norton Mild, Best Bitter, Generation, Old Hooky, seasonal beers Ⓖ
Step into this unspoilt quiet village hideaway and you step back into a bygone era of simple, rural pubs. The Peyton Arms offers a refuge from the distractions of our modern age. The beers are dispensed in the adjoining tap room directly from wood casks reserved by Hook Norton especially for the pub. Other than this and numerous whiskies, the drink range is fairly minimal. The decor in the small bars has changed little over decades. Aunt Sally is played in the garden.
⌂Q⏣Å♣P

STOKE TALMAGE

Red Lion ☆
1¼ miles off A40 at Tetsworth OS681994
⊕ 12-2.30 (not Mon-Thu), 6-11; 12-3.30, 7-10.30 Sun
☎ (01844) 281651
Beer range varies Ⓗ
Unspoilt, basic, friendly pub, well supported by locals, and popular with walkers and cyclists, it is located in quiet countryside. In the same family for 60 years, it is part of a 20-acre farm with sheep, horses and poultry. Three beers are usually available – one generally from a local micro. One or two gravity-dispensed ciders are also stocked. An Aunt Sally pitch and other parts of the garden are floodlit; amusements are provided for children. Not many pubs like this remain and there is no intention to change it. ⌂Q⏢⏣⏸&Å♣⛟P🖵

STONESFIELD

Black Head
Church Street
⊕ 11-2.30, 5.30-11; 11-11 Fri & Sat; 12-10.30 Sun
☎ (01993) 891616 website: www.touchoxford.com
Courage Best Bitter; guest beers Ⓗ
Friendly local, in a village once famous for its slate mines. A comfortable cosy lounge bar features fresh flowers on the tables and a real fire; the more basic, large public bar houses a pool table. Live music, by well-known local duos, has proved to be very popular. Good quality food at reasonable prices includes a take-away service. Three guest beers come from micro-breweries. On the Oxfordshire Way long-distance footpath, this pub welcomes walkers, children and dogs, and is handy for touring the Cotswolds, Blenheim Palace and Oxford. ⌂⏣⏸⏸⛟♣P

STRATTON AUDLEY

Red Lion
Church Street (A421 Buckingham-Bicester road)
⊕ 12-3, 6-11; 12-11 Sat; 12-10.30 Sun
☎ (01869) 277225
e-mail: robtalbotcooper@talk21.com
Greene King Ruddles Best; Hook Norton Best Bitter; guest beers Ⓗ
Charming, 18th-century stone house where a warm, inviting, relaxing bar offers three real ales. A large patio garden is the ideal place to enjoy balmy summer eves. High quality food can be eaten in the bar or dining room. Although in a classical village setting, the Red Lion is only a short distance from the busy market town of Bicester and the Bicester Village retail shopping outlet, where designer bargains can be found. ⌂Q⏣⏸♣

SWALCLIFFE

Stag's Head
The Green (B4035, 6 miles W of Banbury)
⊕ 11.30-2.30 (3 Sat), 6.30-11; 12-3, 7-10.30 Sun
☎ (01295) 780232
website: www.stagsheadswalcliffe.co.uk
Brakspear Bitter; Hook Norton Best Bitter; guest beer Ⓗ
This attractive thatched pub stands in a picturesque village, near an impressive tithe barn. Two cosy bars: one with pews for seating; the other is more spacious. Jugs hang from the beams and an attractive alcove contains shelves of books. The furniture has been chosen with great care and adds to the relaxed, comfortable atmosphere. The landlady prides herself on cooking with high quality ingredients and offers a seasonal menu (bookings advisable). A beautiful terraced garden goes down to a stream. Opening hours may vary seasonally. ⌂Q⏢⏣⏸♣P⌿

THAME

Swan Hotel
9 Upper High Street
⊕ 11-11; 12-10.30 Sun
☎ (01844) 261211 e-mail: swanthame@hotmail.com
Brakspear Bitter; Hook Norton Best Bitter; guest beers Ⓗ
Market town hotel of 16th-century origin: a place to meet friends, do business or to

come on your own for a quiet drink. Two guest beers are sourced from near and far. The seating, fixtures and fittings present a variety of styles and objects; note the boar's head. Outside seating is provided in summer. Good food is served in the bar or upstairs restaurant where the painted ceiling dates from Tudor times. Accommodation includes some four-poster beds. 🚲🏡☕️🛏️◀️❶

WALLINGFORD ✣

Cross Keys
48 High Street
🕐 12-3, 5-11; 12-11 Fri & Sat; 12-10.30 Sun
☎ (01491) 826377 e-mail: crosskeysthepub@aol.com
Brakspear Bitter, Old, Special H

Unspoilt, 17th-century, pub near both Wallingford's parks and the Town Museum. A small lounge bar leads to the family room/dining area (book eve meals), on the other side the public bar has steps up to the darts room. Low beams and polished wood floors feature. Predominantly a local, it fields teams in crib, darts and dominoes leagues. Live music is staged monthly (third Tue). The large fenced garden, with a children's play area, stands on what are believed to be Saxon town ramparts.
🚲🐕☕️◀️🚭🍴P

WANTAGE ✣

Abingdon Arms
87 Grove Street (A38, 1/2 mile from market place) OS729018
🕐 12.30 (11.30 Fri)-2.30 (12-4.30 Sat), 7-10.30 (11 Fri & Sat); 12-4.30, 7-10.30 Sun
☎ (01235) 763957
Greene King Morland Original, Triumph; guest beer H

Welcoming, traditional pub, formerly known as the Squirrel, then owned by the now-defunct Wantage Brewery; there has been a pub on this site for the past 200 years. It has been extended on three occasions and is now Grade II listed. The local morris men meet here once a week, as do the local RNLI group. The pub hosts live folk music from time to time, and organises occasional trips to the races and dog meetings. The bus service from Oxford stops directly outside the pub. A fenced garden area is ideal for young children. Sandwiches are usually available. 🚲Q☕️🍴P

Royal Oak
Newbury Street
🕐 5.30-11; 12-2.30, 7-11 Sat; 12-2, 7-10.30 Sun
☎ (01235) 763129

Marston's Pedigree; Wadworth 6X; West Berkshire Maggs Magnificent Mild, Dr Hexter's Wedding, Dr Hexter's Healer; guest beers H/G
This beer-mad town local was justly regional CAMRA *Pub of the Year* 1999. The two bars have quite distinct personalities: the small public bar features a football table and naval memorabilia and is frequented by the younger set and ex-servicemen; the larger lounge bar is the haunt of locals and adorned with a huge array of pump clips. The landlord commissioned two beers that bear his name; West Berkshire seasonal and one-off beers feature frequently.
🍴🍺♣🖐

WITHERIDGE HILL

Rising Sun
1 1/2 miles S of Nettlebed OS697842
🕐 11-3, 6-11 (11-11 summer Sat); 12-3, 7-10.30 (12-10.30 summer) Sun
☎ (01491) 641455 website: www.therisingsuninn.com
Brakspear 2.5, Bitter, Special H
Recently sympathetically extended, this old country pub is hidden away, off a minor track through the hamlet of Witheridge Hill. There are light, airy, dining areas with bare floorboards and rugs as well as ample bar space. The original bar to the right is less formal and welcomes walkers from the many local paths in this lovely Chilterns area. A wide range of freshly-prepared food (including vegetarian) is available, including a three-course lunch special offer on weekdays. The pub is the home of the 'Rising Sun Players' who perform an open-air Shakespeare play in the summer. Wheelchair WC.
☕️◀️♿♣P

WITNEY ✣

House of Windsor
31 West End
🕐 12-3 (not Mon-Fri), 6-11; 12-4.30, 7-10.30 Sun
☎ (01993) 704277
Fuller's London Pride; Hook Norton Best Bitter; guest beers H
Popular, single bar free house on the edge of the town centre, this stone pub's homely atmosphere is enhanced by a roaring fire. The beer range is varied and well chosen. Beware the proximity of the bar when you enter through the front door. The small restaurant area at the rear is not open Sun-Tue eves. Note pub is not open weekday lunchtimes, however lunch is served Sun.
🚲Q☕️◀️♣

Store of Good Ale

Though it was but about the middle of August, and in some places the harvest hardly got in, we saw the mountains covered with snow, and felt the cold very acute and piercing, but we found, as in all these northern counties, the people had a happy way of mixing the warm and the cold together; for store of good ale which flows plentifully in the most mountainous parts of this country seem abundantly to make up for all the inclemencies of the season, or difficulties of travelling.

Daniel Defoe, *A Tour Through the Whole Island of Great Britain*, 1726.

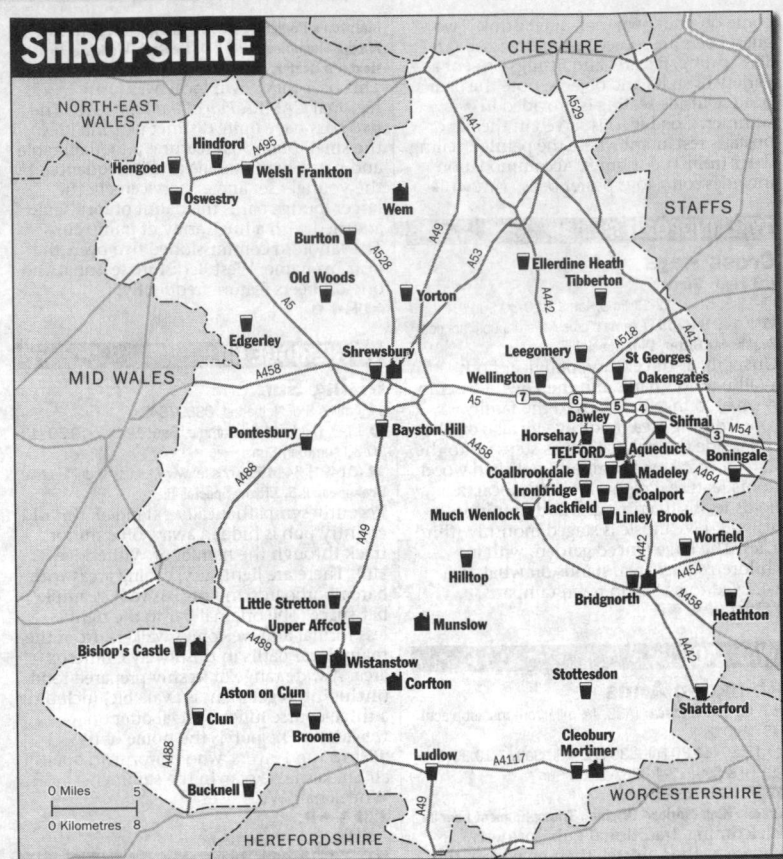

SHROPSHIRE

ASTON ON CLUN

Kangaroo

Clun Road (B4368, between Clun and Craven Arms OS503981)
☼ 12-3 (not Mon & Tue), 7-11; 12-11 Fri & Sat; 12-10.30 Sun
☎ (01588) 660263
e-mail: thekangarooinn@yahoo.com
Wells Bombardier; guest beers Ⓗ

Cosy village pub with a warm, friendly atmosphere, near the station at Broome. No Aussie theme bar – the name dates from the 19th century. It has a games room and a large garden at the rear. Regular barbecues and an annual beer festival are held in summer. Home-cooked food features occasional international themed evenings. The house beer, Roo Brew, comes from the Six Bells Brewery at Bishop's Castle. Leave your name and address for a monthly newsletter listing forthcoming events.
♨❀◑❶⊟♿▲⇌(Broome) ♣P

BAYSTON HILL

Compasses Inn

Hereford Road (A49, 2 miles S of Shrewsbury)
☼ 5 (12 Fri & Sat)-11; 12-10.30 Sun
☎ (01743) 872921
Draught Bass; Fuller's London Pride; M & B Brew XI; guest beers Ⓗ

Welcoming inn on the A49 as you approach Shrewsbury from the south. Unspoilt, and providing a traditional separate bar and snug, its internal decor is based on a maritime theme. The well-presented and extensive garden to the rear, overlooking the village green, is ideal for families. An annual beer festival is held in spring.
Q❀⊟♿♣P⚲

BISHOP'S CASTLE

Castle Hotel

Market Square
☼ 12-2.30, 6.30-11; 12-2.30, 7-10.30 Sun
☎ (01588) 638403 website: www.bishops-castle.co.uk
Draught Bass; Hobsons Best Bitter; Six Bells Big Nev's; guest beer Ⓗ

Fine period hotel lovingly cared for by its owners, comprising a public bar, lounge and a small snug bar, plus dining room. The latter two rooms and entrance hall in particular, boast much original woodwork. The furnishings and a host of local artefacts throughout help create a timeless ambience. A connoisseur collection of whiskies, and excellent home-cooked food provide the icing on the cake. The already large, pleasant garden is being developed further.
♨Q❀⇌◑❶⊟♣P

Six Bells

Church Street
☼ 12-2.30 (not Mon, or winter Tue & Wed), 5-11; 12-11 Sat; 12-10.30 Sun
☎ (01588) 630144 website: www.bishops-castle.co.uk

Six Bells Big Nev's, Marathon A/C, Cloud Nine, Brew 101, seasonal beers ⊞

This 17th-century, two-roomed coaching inn is the tap for Six Bells Brewery, situated behind the pub. Although quite small, both rooms are charming: the public bar has exposed stonework, beams and an inglenook; the lounge is carefully furnished and decorated to reflect its origins. Popular with locals it also offers generous portions of excellent, freshly-prepared food. Runner-up in national CAMRA *Pub of the Year* 2001, it is a venue for the town's annual real ale festival (July). ▲Q❀⊟ఈ♣

BONINGALE

Horns

Holyhead Road (A464 near Albrighton)

☼ 12-3, 6-11; 12-3, 7-10.30 Sun

☎ (01902) 372347

Badger Tanglefoot; Draught Bass; Enville Ale; Highgate Dark; Hook Norton Old Hooky; Worthington Bitter; guest beers ⊞

Large, rural, 18th-century pub between Shifnal and Wolverhampton, that was a regular stop for the Shropshire cattlemen. It has three linked rooms, serving food in all areas. Two restaurants serve a full *à la carte* menu and there is always a midweek special offer. Large parties can be catered for, with special menus if required. No eve meals Sun. The toilet facilities are exceptional, including a wheelchair WC. Children are made very welcome. No accommodation is available but a neighbouring farmhouse provides B&B. ▲Q❀◐ఈP

BRIDGNORTH

Railwayman's Arms

Platform One, Severn Valley Railway Station, Hollybush Road

☼ 12-3 (11-3.30 summer), 7-11; 11-11 Sat; 12-10.30 Sun

☎ (01746) 764361 website: www.svr.co.uk

Batham Mild, Best Bitter; Hobson's Best Bitter; guest beers ⊞

This characterful, charismatic drinking spot is of particular interest to steam enthusiasts, but appealing to all cask beer drinkers. You can drink in the bar, the old part of which is the original licensed refreshment room, boasting a superb Cheshire's Brewery (Smethwick) mirror, or sit out on the platform and soak up the atmosphere of the steam era, particularly pleasant eves when the trains are being put to bed. The three guest beers tend to be from smaller breweries, frequently local. Cider is stocked in summer. ▲Q❀≠(SVR)♣⇙P⇙

BURLTON

Burlton Inn

On A528, near B4397 jct

☼ 11-3, 6-11; 12-2, 7-10.30 Sun

☎ (01939) 270284

e-mail: reservations@burltoninn.co.uk

Banks's Bitter; guest beers ⊞

A free house, this attractive country pub is situated near the North Shropshire lakes between Shrewsbury and Ellesmere. It offers three constantly changing guest beers and award-winning, home-cooked food, based on local produce. Largely geared to eating, drinkers are nonetheless made welcome.

Tucked away behind the inn are new cottages offering six individually designed, en-suite bedrooms. ▲Q❀⊨◐▲♣P

CLUN

Sun Inn

☼ 12-11, 12-3; 6-11 Sat; 12-3, 7-10.30 Sun

☎ (01588) 640559

Banks's Original Bitter; Hobsons Best Bitter; guest beer ⊞

Set as, Housman once said, in one of the quietest places under the sun, this 15th-century cruck-framed building has a wealth of exposed beams. The most interesting bar must be the public – its huge stone flags and high-backed settles give the impression that little has changed for many a year. By contrast, the lounge (separate from the residents' lounge) is smart and comfortable. Note the unusual set of three 'signal lever' handpumps. To the rear, a patio is used in fine weather. Limited parking. Accommodation is in separate buildings. ▲Q❀⊨◐⊟▲♣P

EDGERLEY

Royal Hill

Between Melverley and Pentre OSSJ3517

☼ 12-2 (3 Sat, not winter), 6.30-11; 12-2, 7-10.30 Sun

☎ (01743) 741242

Salopian Ruby Mild, Shropshire Gold ⊞

This hidden away local, affording spectacular views, is set beside the River Severn. The 18th-century building comprises three cosy rooms, one with an open fire. The beers come from the local Salopian Brewery. A warm friendly welcome is extended not just to regulars but also to canoeists and fishing enthusiasts enjoying the nearby river. Camping is available at the rear of the pub. The garden faces the river. Fish and chips are available from a visiting van (7pm Thu). ▲Q⛵❀⊟▲P

ELLERDINE HEATH

Royal Oak

Midway between A442 and A53 OS603226

☼ 12 (11 Sat)-11; 12-10.30 Sun

☎ (01939) 250300

Hanby Drawwell; Hobsons Best Bitter; Salopian Shropshire Gold; Shepherd Neame Spitfire; guest beer ⊞

The Royal Oak offers a friendly atmosphere and good food at very reasonable prices (not served Tue). Based around a central bar, the pub has something for everyone, including a play area in the garden and a games room

INDEPENDENT BREWERIES

All Nations Madeley (future in doubt)

Corvedale Corfton

Dolphin Shrewsbury

Hanby Wem

Hobsons Cleobury Mortimer

Munslow Munslow

Salopian Shrewsbury

Six Bells Bishop's Castle

Three Tuns Bishop's Castle

Wood Wistantow

Worfield Bridgnorth

where children are welcome. Its local nickname, Tiddlywink, is believed to date from before the turn of the last century when the word was used to describe an unlicensed ale house or pawn shop. Good value guest beers promote local breweries. A cider festival is held in July. ▲Q✿❍❈▲♣P

HEATHTON

Old Gate Inn

Between B4176 and A458 near Halfpenny Green
OS814923

✪ 12-2.30, 6.30-11 (closed Mon); 12-3,
6.30-10.30 Sun
☎ (01746) 710431 website: www.oldgateinn.co.uk

Enville Ale; Wells Bombardier; guest beers Ⓗ

Busy pub in a rural part of the county serving food of restaurant quality (no meals Sun eve). The extensive menu is offered at reasonable prices and caters for all tastes. The two rooms, decorated with an aviation theme, feature exposed beams, real fires and a cosy atmosphere – music is played at low volume so conversation is still possible. Addlestone's cider is sold. Children are welcome and the large garden has a safe play area. Well worth a visit.
▲✿❍▲♣P

HENGOED

Last Inn

Off B4579 3 miles N of Oswestry OS680979
✪ 7-11; 12-3, 7-10.30 Sun
☎ (01691) 659747

Boddingtons Bitter; guest beers Ⓗ

1960s one-bar pub, embracing an older structure, in the Welsh border area that is popular with tourists. Hengoed is Welsh for old wood; the pub name derives from its days as a cobbler's. In this *Guide* for 20 years continuously, the five guest beers are predominantly sourced from regional and micro-breweries. A fine collection of vintage pub photographs, and many brewery trays are displayed. It has featured in all editions of CAMRA's *Good Pub Food* (no meals Tue eve). The games room has two pool tables. ▲Q➹♣P

HILLTOP

Wenlock Edge Inn

On B4371, 4 miles from Much Wenlock
✪ 11.30-2.30 (not Mon); 6.30-11; 12-2.30, 6.30-10.30 Sun
☎ (01746) 785678
website: www.wenlockedgeinn.co.uk

Hobsons Best Bitter, Town Crier Ⓗ

This delightful country inn sits on top of a 400 million-year-old coral reef. Built with local limestone in the 17th century as cottages for quarrymen, it was licensed in the 1920s. There are three small rooms and a lovely stepped patio. The room to the right, which leads to the dining room, retains original stone walls, beams and an inglenook. The left-hand room boasts a solid oak bar and little pews from a Methodist church in Blackpool. The local story-tellers club meets monthly (second Mon). The varied homemade menu enjoys a very good reputation, as does the accommodation. Q✿✍❍❈P☂

HINDFORD

Jack Mytton Inn

Off A495, Oswestry-Ellesmere road
✪ 12-3, 6-11 (12-11 summer); closed winter Mon;
12-3, 6-10.30 Sun
☎ (01691) 679861

Beer range varies Ⓗ

Attractive rural hostelry by the side of the popular Llangollen Canal. A former farmhouse, the name commemorates an infamous flamboyant 19th-century landowner, hence it is known locally as Mad Jack's. Four real ales are always available while a large canalside garden, with an outdoor bar and a well-appointed restaurant combine to make the pub a very worthwhile visit. Nearby are substantial earthworks of the Welshpool to Whitchurch railway (ex-Cambrian and Great Western) that closed in 1965. ▲Q✿❍▲P

LINLEY BROOK

Pheasant Inn

Britons Lane (off B4373, Bridgnorth-Broseley road)
OS680979

✪ 12-2 7 (6.30 summer)-11; 12-3, 7 (6.30 summer)-10.30 Sun
☎ (01746) 762260

Beer range varies Ⓗ

Picturesque pub, set in idyllic rural countryside about halfway between Bridgnorth and Broseley, with a strong commitment to real ale and traditional pub values. It supports local breweries as well as stocking beers from further afield. Although a little hard to find on the first visit, it is well worth seeking out, as you will want to come back time and again. A room with a serving hatch contains a bar billiards table. The same licensee has run this pub for the past 18 years. ▲Q✿❍❈♣P

LITTLE STRETTON

Ragleth Inn

Ludlow Road (just off A49)
✪ 12-2.30, 6-11; 12-11 Sat; 12-10.30 Sun
☎ (01694) 722711 website: www.theraglethinn.co.uk

**Brains Rev James; Hobsons Best Bitter, Old Henry;
Theakston Old Peculier; guest beers** Ⓗ

In good walking country, close to the Long Mynd, the Ragleth is named after a local hill. Dated 1650, it is a warm, quiet pub, replete with inglenook, oak beams, antiques and a brick and tiled floor. The garden is very attractive, with climbing frames and a trampoline for children and a rare tulip tree. There is always a Shropshire beer on tap and whisky-lovers can choose from a selection of over 80 malts. Traditional games played in the bar include shove-ha'penny and skittles. ▲Q✿❍❈▲♣P✦

LUDLOW

Charlton Arms Hotel

Ludford Bridge
✪ 12-3, 6.30-11; 12-11 Sat; 12-10.30 Sun
☎ (01584) 872813

Hobsons Best Bitter; guest beers Ⓗ

Overlooking the River Teme by Ludford Bridge, the Charlton Arms is a fine hotel on the outskirts of this historic town. Five guest ales are supplied by breweries from the surrounding area, including Wood's. Real cider and perry are sometimes available. An extensive menu offers good value home-cooked food (vegetarian meals on request). This former coaching inn offers accommodation, with a full Shropshire breakfast. It has a pool room; and hosts monthly live folk music (third Fri).

⚌ ⚙ ⇄ ◑ ⇌ ⚑ P 🍴

Church Inn
Buttercross

🕐 11-11; 12-10.30 Sun

☎ (01584) 872174 website: www.thechurchinn.com

Courage Best Bitter; Dunn Plowman Falstaff; Hook Norton Old Hooky; Weetwood Eastgate Ale; Wye Valley Bitter; guest beers Ⓗ

This town-centre inn is the oldest in Ludlow, and the only free house within the town walls. Two bars, which are warm and welcoming, offer a good selection of beers and food to complement them; Hook Norton beers are a firm favourite and a welcome change in South Shropshire. The landlord is a former Mayor of Ludlow, and very keen on real ale. Situated close to the market square and castle, this is a must to visit or even stay.

⚌ ⇄ ◑ Å ⇌ ⇌ 🍴

Nelson Inn
Rocks Green (A4117, Kidderminster road)

🕐 12-3 (not Tue), 7-11; 12-11 Fri & Sat; 12-10.30 Sun

☎ (01584) 872908

e-mail: alan@thenelson.fsbusiness.co.uk

Banks's Original; Flowers Original; guest beers Ⓗ

Wonderful, 300-year-old pub, on the outskirts of Ludlow, comprising two rooms. The lounge bar is decked out with musical instruments on the walls and a collection of mugs; the public bar houses a pool table and four-ring quoits. Next door is a guest house, convenient for longer stays. The pub reputedly has a dominoes-playing ghost. Regular beer festivals, plus music nights are staged. Three guest beers are joined by a real cider in summer.

⚌ ◑ Å ⇌ ♣ ⚑ P 🍴

MUCH WENLOCK

George & Dragon
2 High Street

🕐 12-2.30 (not Wed), 6-11; 12-2.30, 7-10.30 Sun

☎ (01952) 727312

Hook Norton Best Bitter; guest beers Ⓗ

Popular, intimate local that can trace its ownership to 1714, providing a friendly welcome to visitors and locals alike. The bar, where the beams are hung with water jugs and walls bedecked in breweriana, serves an extensive selection of changing guest beers from local breweries such as Hobsons and Salopian, and from further afield. Close to the picturesque Guildhall, museum and historic priory, it is an ideal venue for a pint, snack or a meal in the excellent no-smoking restaurant, while visiting this peaceful market town. Q ◑ ♣

OLD WOODS

Romping Cat
🕐 1-3 (not Wed or Fri; 12.30-3.30 Sat), 7-11; 12-2.30, 7-10.30 Sun

☎ (01939) 290273

Boddingtons Bitter; Fuller's London Pride; Greene King Abbot; guest beers Ⓗ

Nestling in the Shropshire countryside, this pub is a haven of peace and quiet, popular with discerning drinkers. In summer, the seating outside provides a pleasant diversion, away from the hustle and bustle of nearby Shrewsbury; security for cycles is thoughtfully provided. Originally the Railway, a Southam's (Shrewsbury) pub, it has always been known by locals as the Cat, for reasons lost in the mists of time. It underwent a name change in the 1980s.

⚌ Q ⚙ P 🍴

OSWESTRY

Black Gate
7 Salop Road

🕐 12-3 (not Thu), 6.30-11; 12-3, 7-10.30 Sun

INN BRIEF

BROOME
Engine & Tender
12-3, 7-11;
12-3, 7-11 Sun
Draught Bass; Greene King Old Speckled Hen; Wood Parish Ⓗ
Friendly local, popular for food: a dining room, lounge and games room. Camping available. No food Mon. Station 200 yards.

BUCKNELL
Baron of Beef
Bridgend Lane
12-3, 6.30-11;
12-3, 7-11 Sun
Greene King IPA; Wye Valley Bitter; guest beers Ⓗ
Converted house in a quiet village with a railway station, close to the Welsh border. Food available.

CLEOBURY MORTIMER
Old Lion Inn
Lower Street
4 (12 Sat)-11;
12-10.30 Sun
Hobsons Best Bitter, Town Crier, Old Henry Ⓗ
Basic, no-nonsense pub; the split-level bar features beams and bare boards. No food. No car park.

SHREWSBURY
Shrewsbury Hotel
Bridge Place
11-11; 12-10.30 Sun
Boddingtons Bitter; Courage Directors; Salopian Shropshire Gold; Theakston Bitter; guest beers Ⓗ
Cask Marque-accredited large bar divided into distinct areas for some privacy. Convenient for the town centre and Quarky Park, it offers accommodation.

TELFORD: AQUEDUCT
Britannia
Aqueduct Road
12-3, 6-11; 11.30-11 Sat; 12-3.30, 7-10.30 Sun
Banks's Original, Bitter; Marston's Pedigree Ⓗ
Built in 1860, this two-roomed pub hosts meetings for the local historical society and regular charity events. Banks's and Marston's Special brews stocked.

> ✻ symbol next to a main entry place name indicates there are Inn Brief entries as well.

DAWLEY
Three Crowns
Hinkshay Road
11.30-3, 7-11; 12-4, 7-10.30 Sun
Banks's Original, Bitter; Marston's Pedigree; guest beer Ⓗ
Pleasant summer pub, cosy in winter. Comfortable and friendly, if offers pool, darts and dominoes. Children welcome until 9pm.

WELSH FRANKTON
Narrowboat Inn
Ellesmere Road (A495, Oswestry road)
11-3, 6-11; 12-3, 6-10.30 Sun
Beer range varies Ⓗ
One of only three Narrowboat pubs by the Shropshire Union (Llangollen) Canal, formerly the office of a canal-carrying company. Boats for hire from adjacent boat yard. Food all sessions.

WISTANTOW
Plough Inn
11.30-2.30, 6.30-11 (may vary winter);
12-2.30, 7-10.30 Sun
Wood Parish, Special, Shropshire Lad, seasonal beers Ⓗ
Food-oriented tap for the adjacent Wood Brewery in a quiet village. Addlestone's cider available in summer.

☎ (01691) 653168 e-mail: ronatblack-gate.fsnet.co.uk
Thwaites Bitter, seasonal beers; guest beers Ⓗ
Named after the gateway in the south part of the 13th-century town wall, demolished in 1771, this Grade II listed, timber-framed free house has been a pub only since 1995. A rare outlet in the area for Thwaites' beers, guest ales usually come from small breweries. A bare-boarded bar and cosy lounge display wall panels revealing the original wattle and daub structure. The HQ for the local quiz league, it is also near the Cambrian Railways' Society Museum which displays locomotives and rolling stock.
Q ⚘ ♣

PONTESBURY

Horseshoes Inn
Minsterley Road OSSJ3906
🕐 12-3, 6-11; 12-4, 7-10.30 Sun
☎ (01743) 790278
Castle Eden Ale; Flowers Original; guest beers Ⓗ
Busy, friendly local in a large village, conveniently placed for walking in the South Shropshire hills. Very active in local games leagues, including pool, darts and dominoes, it hosts a quiz (Thu) and supports a cricket team in summer. Two regular guest beers from Wye Valley Cottage or Hanby Brewery may be joined by a third. Two rooms are available for bed and breakfast; Sunday lunches are very popular. ⚘ 🛏 ◖ ♣ P

SHATTERFORD

Red Lion Inn
Bridgnorth Road (A442)
🕐 11.30-2.30, 6.30-11; 12-3, 7-10.30 Sun
☎ (01299) 861221
website: www.redlionshatterford.co.uk
Banks's Original, Bitter; Ⓟ **Batham Best Bitter; guest beers** Ⓗ
Built in 1834 after the Duke of Wellington's beer house reform, the pub lies right on the Worcestershire border, a mile outside the village. The owners have more than doubled the size of the pub, adding a restaurant at the rear. There is also a small lounge/bar with a hunting theme, and a small no-smoking lounge. Ramps and extra-wide doors have

been fitted as well as a wheelchair WC and dedicated parking. Local seasonal produce is used (vegetables, game and meat) and the pub enjoys a good reputation for its fish dishes.
🛏 Q ⚘ ◖ & P ⚡ 🍴

SHIFNAL

White Hart
4 High Street
🕐 12-3, 5.30-11; 12-11 Fri & Sat; 12-10.30 Sun
☎ (01952) 461161
Enville Ale; Fuller's London Pride; Holden's Mild, Bitter; Ind Coope Burton Ale; guest beers Ⓗ
Fine old black and white timbered building, dating from 1595, comprising two similar lounge-style bars, both full of character and with numerous exposed beams. Guest beers are always available, sourced from local breweries and further afield. The pub has won several CAMRA awards and has been a bastion of cask ale for many years. Lunches include locally famous home-made burgers. It attracts a friendly, mature crowd, with children welcome until 7.30pm. A fine pub with a great atmosphere.
⚘ ◖ ♣ P ●

SHREWSBURY ❋

Armoury
Victoria Quay, Victoria Avenue
🕐 12-11; 12-10.30 Sun
☎ (01743) 340525
Boddingtons Bitter; Wadworth 6X; Wood Shropshire Lad; guest beers Ⓗ
Three regular, and five constantly-changing guest beers aim to suit a wide range of tastes. Tasting notes are provided on blackboards above the bar. Some 70 malt whiskies and 20 bourbons are also kept. An excellent range of food on an original menu is served in the bar or dining area. Children are welcome until 9pm. Once an armoury, it was renovated and appropriately renamed in 1995. A spacious room, furnished with large tables and chairs, displays local memorabilia. Quiet during the day, it turns into a busy eve pub.
Q ◖ & ≈ ♣

Boat House
New Street, Port Hill
🕐 11-11; 12-10.30 Sun
☎ (01743) 362965
Boddingtons Bitter; Marston's Pedigree; guest beers Ⓗ
Approached by foot through Quarry Park over the Port Hill Bridge, this half-timbered Hogshead house occupies an imposing position on the River Severn. It is accessible by car via the Welsh Bridge and Bishop's Castle road. Up to five guest beers are available, together with a selection of Belgian bottled beers, and a comprehensive wine list. Three rooms, with bare boards, oak pillars and dark panelling display advertising posters from long-gone Shrewsbury businesses. Food is always available; children are welcome in the restaurant areas, which overlook the river and terraced gardens. The cellars hide a grisly secret, having been used as a charnel house, storing the corpses of Shrewsbury's plague victims.
🛏 Q ⚘ ◖ 🍴 ≈ ♣ ⚲ P

Cask Marque

The Cask Marque symbol with a pub entry indicates that the licensee has successfully passed a number of tests concerning beer quality, and can display a plaque to this effect. However, the choice of all pubs in the guide is made by CAMRA independently of Cask Marque. The Cask Marque symbol is added during the editing process, and Cask Marque has no say in the selection of pubs.

Star pubs

Pubs with a star symbol next to their names are listed in CAMRA's National Inventory of pubs with interiors of outstanding interest. The full list is printed in the guide.

Coach & Horses
Swan Hill (behind Music Hall)
☉ 11-11; 12-10.30 Sun
☎ (01743) 365661
Draught Bass; guest beers Ⓗ
Busy, thriving town-centre pub near the central square. Victorian in style, it has a wood-panelled bar and a larger restaurant area to the rear. Excellent food, at reasonable prices, is available most of the time. Three guest beers are usually available, one often being Goodalls Gold (brewed by the local Salopian Brewery).
Q◑⊟

Dolphin
48 St Michaels Street
☉ 5 (3 Fri & Sat)-11; 5-10.30 Sun
☎ (01743) 350419
Beer range varies Ⓗ
Popular ale house, within easy walking distance of Shrewsbury railway station. It is gaslit, and symmetrical in style, with one side being the bar, the other the lounge. The Dolphin Brewery has recently started up at the rear of the pub, and house beers are usually on tap here. Up to five real ales are available altogether, plus an occasional cider (Weston's). Q⊟≠●

Loggerheads ☆
1 Church Street
☉ 11-11; 12-3, 7-10.30 Sun
☎ (01743) 355457
Banks's Original, Bitter; Draught Bass; Marston's Pedigree; guest beers Ⓗ
One of the few remaining pubs that Banks's has not spoiled 'by progress'. Situated in the heart of town, this classic boozer is separated into four distinct, cosy bars. Two bars are served by a hatchway in a stone-flagged corridor, one bar was a gentlemen-only bar until the early 1980s, with traditional settles and scrubbed-top tables. The other smaller bar is wood-panelled. Guest beers are changed regularly and the landlord pursues a policy of no music.
Q◑⊟≠♣⊓

Three Fishes
4 Fish Street
☉ 11.30-3, 5-11; 11.30-11 Fri & Sat; 12-3, 7-10.30 Sun
☎ (01743) 344793 website: www.threefishes.co.uk
Adnams Bitter; Fuller's London Pride; Taylor Landlord; guest beers Ⓗ
Thoroughly-deserved first entry in this *Guide* for current licensees, now a family-run pub, the no-smoking policy has been retained, along with up to five beers, usually including a local brew. The 15th-century building stands in the shadow of two churches, within the maze of cobbled streets and passageways of the medieval town centre. Once a four-roomed pub, it was knocked through in the 1970s, but retains a wealth of original timbers and stone flags. Food is freshly prepared (not served Sun eve).
Q◑≠⊬●

STOTTESDON

Fighting Cocks
1 High Street
☉ 12-3 (not Mon), 7-11; 11-11 Sat; 11-10.30 Sun
☎ (01746) 718270
Hobsons Best Bitter, Town Crier; guest beers Ⓗ
Rural Shropshire at its best (OS *Landranger* 138 is useful); the black and white split level, unspoilt building comprises a comfortable bar, a no-smoking dining room and a family dining room. A pub since 1830 when the village blacksmith became the first landlord, and once a slaughterhouse – a giant pulley used for a carcass hoist is still intact, it was also, as the name suggests, a centre for cockfighting. The menu of home-cooked food places a strong emphasis on traditional country meals, including Sunday roasts, using produce from local farms (eve meals Tue–Sat).
♔Q♉❀◑⊟♣P

TELFORD: *COALBROOKDALE* ❄

Coalbrookdale Inn
12 Wellington Road (near Ironbridge Gorge Museum)
☉ 12-3, 6-11; 12-3, 7-10.30 Sun
☎ (01952) 433953
website: www.coalbrookdale.inn.com
Adnams Broadside; Fuller's London Pride Ⓗ
Friendly village local where the bar is full of beer and brewing artefacts, plus other amusing items. The pub is a RNLI lifeboat station and the crew regularly drink in the bar. A former national CAMRA *Pub of the Year,* it has appeared in the last 10 editions of this *Guide*. 'St Beard's Day' is celebrated in the New Year. Home of the world's worst choir, it hosts live piano music monthly (first Tue). Leave all previous pub experiences behind when you enter Coalbrookdale Inn, which offers five rotating guest beers, and meals (Mon–Sat).
♔Q❀◑♣●

COALPORT

Shakespeare Inn
High Street (follow signs for China Museum)
☉ 6 (12 Sat)-11 (closed Mon); 12-10.30 Sun
☎ (01952) 580675
Beer range varies Ⓗ
Ideally situated on the River Severn, this free house recently reopened after a total refurbishment with a style more akin to a wine bar than a pub. Of the three defined areas in this open-plan bar, two are for dining (but not exclusively). The food is of superior quality (and quantity), with a decidedly Mexican flavour (no eve meals Sun). Old photographs of Coalport adorn the walls, while the world-renowned China Museum is a short walk away. A terraced garden (steep access) contains a children's play area.
❀◑P⊓

HORSEHAY

Station Inn
Station Road, Dawley
(off B4373, near Horsehay Steam Trust)
✪ 12-2 (3 Sat), 7-11; 12-3, 7-11 Sun
☎ (01952) 503006
Flowers Original; Marston's Pedigree; guest beer H
Traditionally-decorated pub boasting huge personality and excellent ales. One minute from Horsehay Steam Trust with its historic trains, it is one of Telford's best places for meals, having won three *Happy Heartbeat* awards for healthy food. It offers almost every kind of fish and meat dish, vegetarian and children's specialities, daily roast dinners and a great range of desserts. Breakfasts are also available. The large beer garden has a play area for children.
🏠🌲🛏🍴◗ ♿ ♣ P 🍽

IRONBRIDGE

Robin Hood
33 Waterloo Street
(B4373 by Jackfield Free Bridge)
✪ 11-11; 11.45-10.30 Sun
☎ (01952) 433100
Salopian Golden Thread; guest beers H
Overlooking the River Severn, this lovely 17th-century free house is situated within a World Heritage site. The warm, friendly interior of this two-bar inn makes you want to stay inside, but the two patios and children's adventure area are popular in summer. The five guest beers always feature local brews, although Greene King's Abbot appears every Fri. The real cider is Weston's Old Rosie. The food is superb and very reasonably priced – the Sunday carvery is excellent value.
🌲🛏◗ ♣ P 🍴

JACKFIELD

Boat Inn
209 Ferry Road
✪ 5.30 (12 Sat & summer); 12-10.30 Sun
☎ (01952) 882178 website: www.theboatinn.net
Banks's Original, Bitter; Marston's Pedigree; guest beers (summer) H
Excellent, olde-worlde riverside pub renowned for regular flooding (see the wall marks). This traditional, reputedly haunted pub eschews modern trappings (no jukebox, pool table, or gambling machines). All food is prepared on the premises (no meals Sun eve). Jackfield village festival is held next to the pub (Sept) and it is handy for the Tile and China Museums and Maws Craft Centre. Home of Jackfield British Legion, it stands by the only bridge that is a war memorial in Britain. Impromptu folk nights occur Thu eve. 🏠🌲◗ ♣ 🍽

LEEGOMERY

Malt Shovel
Hadley Park Road (off A442, through 'old' Leegomery village)
✪ 12-2.30 (3 Sat), 5-11; 12-3, 7-10.30 Sun
☎ (01952) 242963
Banks's Original; Ind Coope Burton Ale; Marston's Pedigree; guest beer H
Once a main road pub, now in a cul-de-sac on the edge of a housing estate, in the past 25 years very little has changed other than the decor. By day the Malt Shovel is frequented by white collar workers from the nearby industrial estate, sinking pints of Pedigree accompanied by BLT sandwiches with chips. At night it reverts to a local where the only sounds are the clink of glasses, the rattle of dominoes and conversation. A must for dedicated Marston's drinkers. 🏠Q🌲◗ ♣ P 🍽

MADELEY

Foresters Arms
41 High Street (off A442, follow signs for Open Air Museum)
✪ 12-2.30, 6-11; 12-11 Fri & Sat; 12-10.30 Sun
☎ (01952) 581767
Draught Bass; Worthington Bitter; guest beers H
Recently refurbished pub where two drinking areas are served from a central bar: downstairs is a traditional drinkers' bar with a pool table, dartboard and satellite TV; upstairs is more sedate with a distinctive lounge feel. Good food is served at lunchtime (eve meals can be booked). Assorted bric-à-brac and photographs of old Madeley decorate throughout. To the rear is a seated patio, while a half mile walk down Silkin Way footpath brings you to the Blists Hill Open Air Museum. 🏠🌲◗ ♣ P

OAKENGATES

Pear Tree Bridge Inn
Holyhead Road
✪ 6 (12 Fri & Sat)-11; 12-10.30 Sun
☎ (01952) 272458
Marston's Pedigree; Wells Bombardier; Worthington Bitter; guest beers H
Once a busy pub on a main route, it is now a friendly local, due to road diversions. The pleasant L-shaped room has an area for games (including bar skittles) and a carpeted area for chatting and drinking. Named after a local canal bridge, sadly both bridge and canal have gone. Sat eve sees regular live amplified music catering for all ages; Thu eve is given over to more sedate acoustic music, when anyone is welcome to join in.
🌲♿ ≈ ♣ P

ST GEORGES

St Georges Sports & Social Club
Church Road
✪ 7 (11 Sat)-11; 12-3.30, 7-10.30 Sun
☎ (01952) 612911
Banks's Original, Bitter; P **guest beers** H
Lively club whose steward presents an ever-changing range of guest beers, mainly from local Shropshire and Black Country breweries. Used by a large number of local sports teams as their social base; trophies won by the teams are displayed here. A previous winner of CAMRA West Midlands *Club of the Year*, it was also the local *Club of the Year* for 2000. The club overlooks the cricket ground used for some of Shropshire county's first team matches. 🚲🌲♿ ♣ P

WELLINGTON

Cock Hotel
Holyhead Road
✪ 4 (12 Thu-Sat)-11; 12-4, 7-10.30 Sun
☎ (01952) 244954

e-mail: cockhotel@telfordpages.co.uk

Hobsons Best Bitter; Holden's Mild; Wye Valley Dorothy Godbody Wholesome Stout; guest beers Ⓗ
With the licensee's commitment to real ale, it is not surprising that this classic independent ale house is enjoying its fourth consecutive year as local CAMRA *Pub of the Year*. Up to seven real ales, including a stout and a mild, plus a traditional cider, are available in the Old Wrekin tap bar, which links, via a wood-panelled reception area, to a quieter no-smoking lounge. An outside drinking area in the stable courtyard is a reminder of its 18th-century roots as a coaching inn.
ℳQ✿✿⟨🅙⟩⟶♣♠P¼🅷

TIBBERTON

Sutherland Arms
High Street (off B5062)
✪ 12-2.30, 6 (5 Fri)-11; 12-11 Sat; 12-10.30 Sun
☎ (01952) 550533 e-mail: suthy@btinternet.com
Banks's Original; Marston's Bitter, Pedigree Ⓗ
Typical rural pub, set in a picturesque village approximately four miles from Newport. There is a bar with pool table, a lounge and dining room. The large garden is partly shaded by an awning attached to the building. A cosmopolitan place, it is frequented by the farming community, business people and students from Harper Adams Agricultural University College. It boasts over 100 whiskies in stock. Very good value food is served in the restaurant daily except Mon.
ℳQ✿⟨🅙⟩🅖&♣P

UPPER AFFCOT (CHURCH STRETTON)

Travellers Rest Inn
On A49
✪ 11-11; 12-10.30 Sun
☎ (01694) 781275
website: www.travellersrestinn.co.uk
Ansells Mild; Draught Bass; Boddingtons Bitter; Hobsons Best Bitter; Wood Shropshire Lad; guest beers Ⓗ
Spacious, roadside pub, a welcome addition to the *Guide* for travellers as food is served all day. Some overnight accommodation is adapted for the needs of disabled guests; there is also camping in the pub grounds. It nevertheless attracts locals, and is the base

for the Welsh League Pentre tug-of-war team (one time Welsh champions). While the drinking area is one large extended room, there are many different sections, including a quieter one and space for games, plus a new no-smoking conservatory. Cider is stocked in summer. Children's certificate.
Q✿✿⟨🅙⟩&♠♣♠P¼

WORFIELD

Dog
Main Street (off A454, 3 miles W of Bridgnorth)
✪ 12-2.30, 7 (6 Sat)-11; 12-3, 7-10.30 Sun
☎ (01746) 716020 e-mail: dogworfield@aol.com
Courage Directors; Highgate Session Bitter; Wells Bombardier; guest beer Ⓗ
Previously the Greyhound and the Davenport Arms, but always known as the Dog, this traditional local is tucked away in a delightful village whose charm is enhanced as there is no through vehicular access. Recently refurbished, this two-bar pub, first licensed in 1790, is well supported by locals and welcomes visitors attracted by the excellent food. The pub and entire village is a floral delight during the annual three-day flower festival (June). Children's certificate.
ℳQ✿⟨🅙⟩🅖&♣P

YORTON

Railway Inn
✪ closed Mon-Thu; 12-3.30, 6.30-11; 12-3, 7-10.30 Sun
☎ (01939) 220240
Greene King Old Speckled Hen; Salopian Golden Thread; Wadworth 6X; Wood Special, Shropshire Lad; seasonal beers Ⓗ
Near the picturesque village of Clive, this small, friendly country pub has been run by the same family for over 60 years. The simple bar with settles, quarry-tiled floor, dartboard and dominoes table is favoured by locals. The well-appointed lounge area, popular in summer, displays a fine collection of trophies, including a large carp, caught at a local pool many years ago. This room is a regular venue for social events and meetings. The pub is a regional CAMRA *Pub of the Year* winner.
ℳQ⇌♣P

Small Beer for Lunch

The servants had unlimited access to beer, which was specially brewed for them; and were fed for breakfast on bacon, bread and skim milk. Lunch, or 'noonchine' (nuncheon or luncheon) on bread and cheese and small beer carried in kegs to the field. Dinner between three and four o'clock consisted of pickled pork or bacon with potatoes, cabbages, turnips or greens and broths of wheat flour and green stuff; supper of bread and cheese, a pint of ale and remains of dinner if any.

Charles Vancouver,
General View of the Agriculture of Hampshire, 1810.

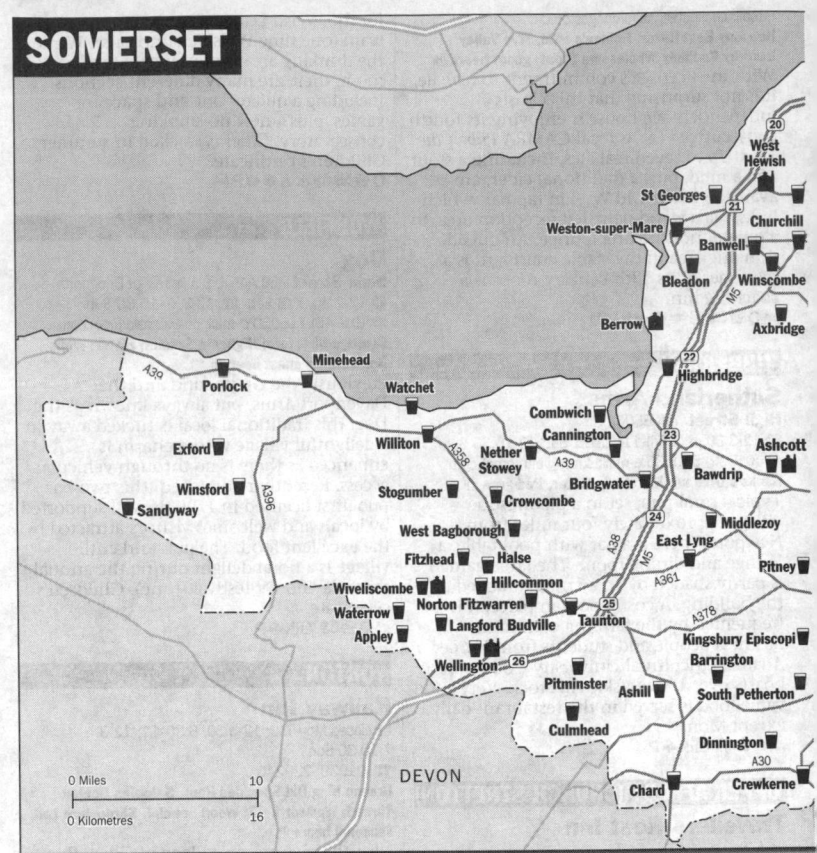

SOMERSET

APPLEY

Globe Inn ☆
2½ miles N of A38 at White Ball Hill OS071215
☀ 11-3, 6.30-11 (closed Mon); 12-3, 7-10.30 Sun
☎ (01823) 672327
Cotleigh Tawny; guest beer Ⓗ
Lovely old inn tucked away in the rolling countryside on the Devon border. A real gem with a wealth of collectables and curios. Several cosy rooms lead off the brick-floored corridor bar area (with serving hatch) including the dining room and the family area. Well-behaved children are allowed in all but one of the rooms and there is a small amount of play equipment in the attractive garden. This pub is on CAMRA's national inventory of heritage pubs. It is well known for its excellent, high quality food so it is advisable to book at weekends. Guest beers are usually from South-west micros.
🏚Q🕭🏵🕭🕀🛆♣P⅌

ASHCOTT

Ring O'Bells
High Street (off A39)
☀ 12-2.30, 7-11; 12-2.30, 7-10.30 Sun
☎ (01458) 210232 website: www.ringobells.com
Beer range varies Ⓗ
Traditional, multi-level inn situated next to the village hall and church. It has cosy bar areas, a separate restaurant, a new function room seating 80, a new skittle alley and an attractive garden. At least one beer comes from Ashcott's Moor beer company, plus two guests chosen from a wide range, often featuring West Country ales. Wilkins cider is stocked. The pub has won several awards for its home-cooked food. The same menu is available in the bars and restaurant (reasonable prices). Families are welcome. Somerset CAMRA *Pub of the Year* 1998. A totally independent free house.
🕭🏵🕭🛆♣P

ASHILL

Square & Compass
Windmill Hill (off A358) OS310166
☀ 12-2.30, 6.30-11; 12-3, 7-10.30 Sun
☎ (01823) 480467
Exmoor Ale, Gold; guest beers Ⓗ
Inviting, friendly country pub situated off the A358 towards Windmill Hill. The pub has an extensive menu offering a wide choice of home-made food, prepared by their excellent chef. Enjoy superb views over the Blackdown Hills and the pleasant garden with children's play area. Occasional summer barbecues are held (weather permitting). Exmoor Brewery beers are the beers of choice, with guest ales often available. Some good local walks nearby.
🏚Q🏵🕭🛆P

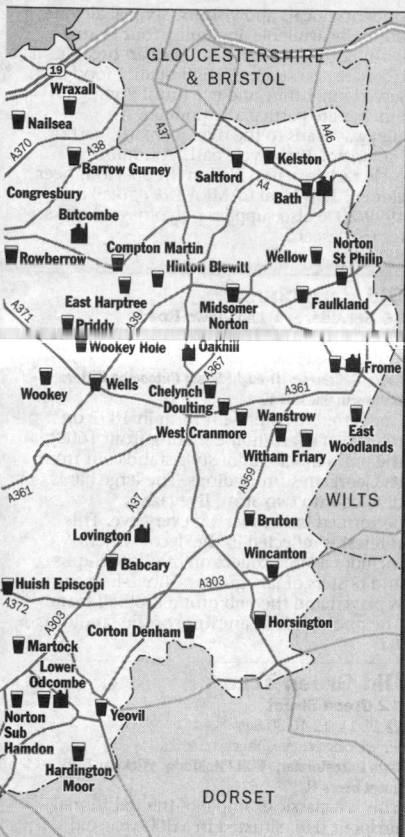

in the same spot for 100 years. There is an L-shaped front bar and beers served usually from South-west micros. Book for meals at weekends; the food is excellent and freshly prepared (no meals Sun eve or Mon). A visit is highly recommended.
Q ⌂ ❀ ◑ ⊟ ♣ P

BANWELL

Bell
1 The Square
🕐 3-11; 12-10.30 Sun
☎ (01934) 822330
Butcombe Bitter; Greene King Old Speckled Hen; guest beers Ⓗ

16th-century coaching house, now a popular village local. The public bar houses table skittles and a real fire, while the attractive lounge bar has a piano. The pub does not open at lunchtimes and does not serve any food, preferring to concentrate on the drinks trade. Entertainment includes a skittle alley, folk music performed on the first Thu of each month, and occasionally other live acts are featured. ♨ ❀ ⊟ ♣

BARRINGTON

Royal Oak
Off B3168 between Ilminster and Curry Rivel
🕐 12-3, 5.30-11; 12-11 Fri & Sat; 12-10.30 Sun
☎ (01460) 53455 website: www.mbbservices.co.uk
Fuller's London Pride; Greene King Abbot; Young's Bitter, Special Ⓗ

Popular village local at the heart of this pretty Somerset village. The small public bar area is attached to a large games room with pool table and dartboard. The lounge bar/restaurant serves excellent, good value food. It is a rare outlet in the area for Young's beers. Regular quiz nights and live music also feature. A function room is available for hire. Warm welcome guaranteed. Q ◑ ⊟ ♣ P

BARROW GURNEY

Princes Motto
Barrow Street (off A38)
🕐 10.30-11; 12-10.30 Sun
☎ (01275) 472282
Draught Bass; Butcombe Bitter; Wadworth IPA, 6X Ⓟ

Charming inn which has been a public house for over 100 years. Cosy and multi-roomed, it is the focus of local life in the village. The walls are covered with interesting photographs and sketches, and hops adorn the ceiling. The landlord drank here in his younger days before taking on

AXBRIDGE

Lamb Inn
The Square
🕐 11 (11.30 winter)-11; 12-10.30 Sun
☎ (01934) 732253
Butcombe Bitter, Gold; Wadworth 6X Ⓗ

Located in the main square of this historic and well-preserved market town, the Lamb Inn is a central focus. Dating back to the 15th century, the Lamb was a former coaching inn on the Bristol to Wells road. Many of its original features remain. There is a single bar with several beamed drinking areas, a separate dining room and a terraced garden at the rear. It is very popular with local drinkers and diners and can get busy at weekends. Parking is in the market square. Q ❀ ⇋ ◑ ♣ ⌂

BABCARY

Red Lion
Main Street (signed off A37, 2 miles from A303)
🕐 12-3, 6-11; 12-3, 7-10.30 Sun
☎ (01458) 223230
Beer range varies Ⓗ

Stone-built, thatched pub in rural surroundings, converted from two former cottages. The interior has a wealth of original features; the public bar has huge well-worn flagstones, attractive settles and benches and there is table skittles which, judging by the old photographs, has been

INDEPENDENT BREWERIES

Abbey Ales Bath
Berrow Berrow
Butcombe Butcombe
Cotleigh Wiveliscombe
Cottage Lovington
Exmoor Wiveliscombe
Juwards Wellington
Milk Street Frome
Moor Ashcott
Oakhill Oakhill
Odcombe Lower Odcombe
RCH West Hewish

his current role about 10 years ago. The pub has two dartboards and five teams. A regular quiz night is held. Home-made specials are served 12–2 (Mon–Fri); the same chef has been preparing the excellent food for 13 years. ♨❀◖♣P

BATH ❉

Bell
103 Walcot Street
✪ 11.30-11; 12-10.30 Sun
☎ (01225) 460426
Abbey Bellringer, Bath Barnstormer; Courage Best Bitter; Smiles Best; guest beer Ⓗ
Popular city-centre pub with a largely younger clientele, the Bell has live bands performing regularly in the eve on the small central stage. There is a long main bar and a collection of smaller rooms at the rear. The unexpectedly large terraced garden has plenty of seating. Much of the wall space inside is taken up with posters for local gigs and other forthcoming events in the Walcot area. Walcot Street is well known for its Bohemian atmosphere and the local shops are well worth a visit.
❀⇌♣♠

Coeur de Lion
17 Northumberland Passage
✪ 11-11; 12-8 Sun
Draught Bass; guest beers Ⓗ
Situated in a narrow passageway opposite the Guildhall in the city centre, this pub claims to be the smallest in Bath. As it contains only four tables in the single small bar, this may well be true. There is an intimate, Bohemian atmosphere, which is enhanced by the flowers and candles. In warm weather, the seating capacity is increased by the use of tables and chairs outside. The stained glass window at the front of the pub is a good example of its kind. Note the early closing hour on Sun eve and that no food is served Sun lunchtime. ◖♣

Curfew
11 Cleveland Place West
✪ 5-11; 12-11 Sat; 12-10.30 Sun
☎ (01225) 424210
Draught Bass; Badger Tanglefoot; Wadworth 6X, JCB Ⓗ
This is one of the few Wadworth pubs in the city, probably the only one to commemorate the Civil War. The sign is a cavalry trooper, such as fought at the nearby Battle of Lansdown. The main bar is a small, wood-panelled solid, honest and unfussy room. By contrast, the second room upstairs is a comfortable lounge, inviting the drinker to recline and sprawl to their heart's content. Children are welcome upstairs. A small courtyard for summer drinking is a bonus and meals are served eves and lunchtime Sat. ⇱❀◗♣

Hop Pole
Albion Buildings, Upper Bristol Road
✪ 12-3, 5-11; 12-11 Fri & Sat); 12-10.30 Sun
☎ (01225) 446327
Bath SPA, Gem, Barnstormer; Butcombe Gold; guest beer (occasional) Ⓗ
This was Bath Ales' first pub in Bath. Situated between Victoria Park and the River Avon, it attracts a mixed clientele;

students, locals and visitors. Six real ales are normally available, including four from Bath. Bottled foreign beers and an organic cider are also stocked. High quality food is served lunchtime and eve (until 9pm). Sun lunches are particularly popular. An alleyway leads to the river towpath, part of the Bristol–Bath cycle path. A number of cycle racks are provided in the spacious beer garden. This local CAMRA *Pub of the Year* 1999/2000 also supplies polypins and casks for parties, etc.
❀◖♣✂

Old Farmhouse
25 Belvedere, 1 Lansdown Road
✪ 11-11; 12-10.30 Sun
☎ (01225) 316162
Abbey Bellringer; Draught Bass; Butcombe Bitter; Wadworth 6X, JCB Ⓗ
Converted to its present form in 1892 on the site of a farmhouse (dating from 1600), the pub's mock-Tudor style stands out from its Georgian surroundings. The large bar is divided into two areas; live jazz is performed in the rear bar every eve. This interest is reflected in the decor which includes a large collection of photographs and posters of jazz groups. Shove-ha'penny is played and the pub runs a football team. The pub sign is a caricature of the landlord.
♣P

Old Green Tree ☆
12 Green Street
✪ 11-11; 12-10.30 Sun
e-mail: oldgreentree@fsnet.co.uk
Bath Barnstormer; RCH Pitchfork; Wickwar BOB; guest beers Ⓗ
This is a classic example of the traditional, unspoilt pub. Situated in a 300-year-old building in a narrow street near the centre of Bath, its atmosphere of dim cosiness pervades all three of the small oak-panelled rooms. The panelling dates from the 1920s. The comfortable lounge bar at the front is decorated with the owner's collection of pictures of WWII aircraft. During Bath's annual Fringe Festival, these are replaced by the works of selected local artists. The back bar, which is the largest of the three rooms, is a no-smoking area. There is an extensive range of single malt whiskies.
Q◖⇌(Spa) ♣♠◗♠

Pig & Fiddle
2 Saracen Street
✪ 11-11; 12-10.30 Sun
☎ (01225) 460868
Abbey Bellringer; Bath Gem, Barnstormer; Hop Back Summer Lightning; Otter Bitter Ⓗ
A large and busy town-centre pub, with a youthful clientele, occupying the end of a row of shops, one end is an old shop front, the other an outside courtyard packed with drinking benches. Inside is a long room on two levels, with an annexe on the other side of the bar. The partially glazed roof gives an airy feel to the pub in daylight that fits in with the bare boards, wood panelling and dark red ceiling. The decor is an esoteric mix of framed rugby memorabilia, such as signed shirts, mixed with beer promotions and topped off with a plastic pig stuck (upside down) to the ceiling. Meals served until 7 pm.
❀◖⇌♠

Pulteney Arms
37 Daniel Street
✪ 11-3, 5.30-11; 11-11 Sat; 12-10.30 Sun
☎ (01225) 463923
**Abbey Bellringer; Ⓖ Draught Bass; Smiles Best;
Ushers Best Bitter; Wadworth 6X** Ⓗ

Handsome corner pub with a lively
atmosphere. The building dates from 1759
and is known to have been a pub in 1812.
The three separate rooms all feature
gaslights and there are four lamps outside
the pub. Sport is highlighted in the decor,
particularly rugby, and the pub can raise
rugby and cricket teams when invited.
Extensive and popular food menu, with a
no-smoking room at lunchtime. The cat
symbol on the pub sign is (probably) a
reference to the Pulteney coat of arms.
🛏 🅓 ≢ (Spa) ♣ ✂

Rummer
5 Newmarket Row, Grand Parade
✪ 11-11; 12-10.30 Sun
☎ (01225) 339345
**Courage Best Bitter; Hop Back Crop Circle; guest
beer** Ⓗ

A fine blend of traditional and modern in a
recently refurbished pub near Bath's famous
Pulteney Bridge, it offers a welcome retreat.
The main nicotine-painted, street-level bar
is supplemented by two small first-floor
rooms, one overlooking the River Avon and
the weir. The rectangular bar has a cosy
atmosphere enhanced by gas fires and wood
panelling. It maintains the 19th-century
tradition for public houses in Newmarket
Road. The single guest beer is usually West
Country but varies widely. Next to the pub
is the old East gate of the city in a sunken
passageway that leads to the river.
🅓 ≢ ♠

Star Inn ☆
23 The Vineyards
✪ 12-2.30, 5.30-11; 12-11 Sat; 12-3, 7-10.30 Sun
☎ (01225) 425072 website: www.star-inn-bath.co.uk
Abbey Bellringer; Ⓗ **Draught Bass;** Ⓖ **guest beer** Ⓗ

This pub is one of the oldest in Bath. A
recent refurbishment has done nothing to
detract from the superb interior of this
listed building. The many small rooms
feature oak panelling and 19th-century bar
fittings. Casks of Bass are brought up using
a special lift which rises through a trap door
behind the bar. It is then served, as it has
been for many years, from jugs. The
smallest bar, used by the older regulars, has
a long wooden bench known as 'death row'.
Lunchtime meals are served on Fri and Sat.
🛏 Q 🛏 🅓 ≢ ♣

BLEADON

Queen's Arms
Celtic Way (300 yds from A370, S of Weston-S-
Mare)
✪ 11-2.30, 5.30-11; 11-11 Sat; 12-10.30 Sun
☎ (01934) 812080
**Badger Tanglefoot; Draught Bass; Butcombe Bitter;
Ⓖ Palmers BB,** Ⓗ **IPA; Ringwood Old Thumper; guest
beers** Ⓖ

After a varied recent history with
different owners, this pub is now well-
established again as a true free house
with a good reputation for its range of
ales mostly straight from the cask. The
regular beers are mainly from West
Country brewers with at least two
guest ales plus a local real cider. An
attractive and atmospheric low-beamed
country inn, it is popular with locals and
walkers. The West Mendip Way passes
nearby and the pub regularly tops the
fundraising on the annual walk for a local
charity. There is a skittle alley and regular
quiz nights.
🛏 Q 🏵 🅓 🗗 ♣ ♠ P ✂

BRIDGWATER

Annie's Bar
21-23 North Street (100 yds from broadway)
✪ 12-3 (not Mon-Wed), 5-11; 11-11 Sat; 12-3,
6-10.30 Sun
☎ (01278) 433053
Butcombe Bitter; guest beers Ⓖ

Formerly the North Pole Inn, now a free
house serving three ales mainly from West
Country micros. Although the beers
available are displayed on handpumps
at the bar, they are actually served by
gravity dispense from the cellar. This is a
cosy, split-level pub with the floors

INN BRIEF

BATH

Cross Keys
Midford Road, Combe Down
11-2.30, 6-11; 11-3, 7-11 Sat;
11.30-10.30 Sun
Courage Best Bitter; Ushers Founders Ale,
Bishops Tipple, seasonal beers; guest
beers Ⓗ
This is a classic wayside pub on the
largely residential Combe Down
side of the city. It is family-friendly
with a strong local following. The
small lounge bar leads to the cellar
restaurant.

Hatchetts
6-7 Queen Street
11-11; 12-10.30 Sun
Abbey Bellringer; guest beer Ⓗ
This pub can be found in a small,
cobbled street near Queen Square.
The decor has a strong motorbike
theme and the atmosphere is
cheerfully casual. The Hatchetts
beer is usually a rebadged local beer
generally at a competitive price.

BAWDRIP

Knowle Inn
115 Bath Road
11-3, 4.30-11; 11-11 Sat;
12-10.30 Sun
Flowers IPA; guest beers Ⓗ
16th-century inn with stone floors
and exposed beams. Regularly
changing guest beers. Excellent
choice of home-made food, fish a
speciality.

CHELYNCH

Poachers Pocket
½ mile N of A361 at Doulting
12-3, 6-11; 12-3, 7-10.30 Sun
Butcombe Bitter; Oakhill Best Bitter;
Wadworth 6X; guest beers Ⓗ
A much extended, part 14th-
century, village pub still managing
to retain a good local following
despite the addition of a large
function room and skittle alley.
Flagstone floors, scrubbed pine
tables and an open fire, make for a
comfortable atmosphere.

COMPTON MARTIN

Ring o' Bells
Bath Road
11.30-3, 6.30-11;
12-3, 7-10.30 Sun
Butcombe Bitter, Gold; Wadworth 6X;
guest beers Ⓗ
Pub for everyone – excellent family
room, lovely garden, good value
food and various traditional pub
games. Former local CAMRA *Pub of
the Year.*

EAST HARPTREE

Castle of Comfort
12-3, 6 (5 Fri)-11; 12-11 Sat;
12-10.30 Sun
Draught Bass; Butcombe Bitter;
guest beers Ⓗ
Situated in a lovely position on the
top of the Mendip Hills. Locally
brewed beer, local cider and locally
produced meals (lunch and eves).

featuring a mix of slate tiles and bare boards. The walls, which are a mix of wood panelling and exposed brickwork, are adorned with a variety of bric-à-brac and memorabilia. A large sign from the former Starkey, Knight and Ford brewery takes pride of place. At the back of the pub there is a separate dining area/function room with its own bar and, further on, a deceptively large garden. Good value meals served.

Q ֎ ◑ ♣

BRUTON

Royal Oak

21-25 Coombe Street   (B3081, Shepton Mallet road)

✪ 12-2.30, 5 (6 Sat)-11; 12-2.30, 7-10.30 Sun

☎ (01749) 812215

Butcombe Bitter; guest beer Ⓗ

This comfortable and welcoming pub is larger inside than it appears from the road. Although the pub is open-plan there are several distinct areas, none of which is confined to diners. The menu is reasonably priced and ranges from sandwiches to full meals. There is direct access to the skittle alley from the bar. The house beer (Sharpe's Brew) is Fuller's London Pride. The guest beer changes weekly. The car park is fairly small but there is adequate parking in nearby streets.

Q ⍤ ◑ ≢ ♣ P ⌿

CANNINGTON

Malt Shovel Inn

Blackmoor Lane, Bradley Green   (off A39, E of Cannington)

✪ 11.30-3, 6.30 (7 winter)-11; 12-3, 6.30-10.30 (closed winter eve) Sun

☎ (01278) 653432 website: www.cannington.org.uk

Butcombe Bitter; Exmoor Fox; guest beers Ⓗ

This 300-year-old free house was first licensed in 1866. It is situated north of the Quantock Hills close to the coast, and attracts walkers and cyclists. The bar area has an inglenook with woodburner, and there is also a snug, a dining room, a family room (high chairs provided) and a large garden. Accommodation consists of one double and one twin room; there is also a large function room. Good value, home-cooked food is served, together with a selection of single malt whiskies.

⚌ Q ⚲ ֎ ⍤ ◑ ♠ P

CHARD

Bell & Crown Inn

Coombe Street   (towards Combe St Nicholas from town centre)

✪ 12-3 (not Mon), 7-11; 12-3, 7-10.30

☎ (01460) 62470

Otter Bitter; guest beers Ⓗ

Once a set of cottages, this pub still retains gaslighting around the bar. The beer range is mainly from West Country breweries but some are sourced from other parts of the country. During the winter months (Sept to May) a monthly beer festival of local ales is held, usually on the first weekend of each month. Good value food is available at lunchtimes and Weston's cider is served.

⚌ ֎ ◑ ♣ ♠ P

CHURCHILL

Crown Inn

The Batch, Skinners Lane   (small lane S of A38/A368 jct)

✪ 12-3.30, 5.30-11; 12-11 Thu-Sat; 12-10.30 Sun

☎ (01934) 852995

Draught Bass; Palmers IPA; RCH Hewish IPA, PG Steam; guest beers Ⓖ

Unspoilt cottage-style pub of character on the edge of the Mendip Hills. With two stone-floored bars and real log fires, this was local CAMRA *Pub of the Year* 1999. A true free house and a regular in this *Guide* with local breweries strongly featured. The house beer, Batch Bitter, is Cotleigh Harrier rebadged. Two to three guests are available. Good home-made food at lunchtimes uses fresh local produce. In a popular area for walkers, just across the A38 is Dolebury Warren, well worth a visit with spectacular views from this imposing iron age hillfort.

⚌ Q ֎ ◑ ♠ P

COMBWICH

Old Ship Inn

Ship Lane

✪ 12-3, 7-11; 11-11 Fri & Sat; 12-10.30 Sun

☎ (01278) 652348

Teignworthy Reel Ale, Old Moggie; guest beers Ⓗ

Comfortable, old village pub in a lane leading down to the river. Popular with walkers, it is the last pub on the River Parrett Trail which extends from the Dorset Hills to the Bristol Channel. This free house serves four ales mainly from West Country micros. It has been sympathetically modernised, featuring a split-level, single bar/restaurant with inglenook and beams. It features a modern skittle alley where children are welcome. This doubles up as a function room available for private hire. Attractive beer garden with views of the river. Good value meals served. ⚌ ֎ ◑ ♣ ♠ P

CONGRESBURY

Plough

High Street   (off A370)

✪ 11-2.30, 5-11; 11-11 Sat; 12-4, 7-10.30 Sun

☎ (01934) 832475 website: www.plough-inn.co.uk

Draught Bass; Ⓟ **Butcombe Bitter;** Ⓗ **Wadworth 6X; Worthington Bitter; guest beers** Ⓟ

Part 17th century, the pub, despite alterations, still has several drinking areas with some flagstone flooring giving an atmosphere full of character. Table skittles and shove-ha'penny played. This is not a food pub and consequently the friendly landlord and landlady can concentrate on providing quality cask ales for discerning customers. There is a good range of single malt whiskies plus an ever-popular locally produced real cider. There are normally two beer festivals a year which are well worth a visit. Check out the pub's website for details. Regular buses run to Congresbury from Bristol and Weston-super-Mare. ⚌ ֎ ♣ ♠ P

CORTON DENHAM

Queen's Arms

3 miles from A303, E of Sparkford

✪ 12-3, 7-11; 12-3 Sun

☎ (01963) 220317

Arkells BB; Cotleigh Tawny; guest beers Ⓗ

One of the best selections of real ales in this part of Somerset. This well-maintained pub has a blackboard featuring forthcoming ales (and also the ones you have missed). Rich's cider is served. There is a good range of home-cooked meals to choose from. This pub is close to South Cadbury Castle and is situated in an area which is an excellent base for walking. B&B accommodation is available. ♔Q❀🛏◐🍏P

CREWKERNE

Crown

34 South Street (A356 towards railway station)

⏲ 6.30-11; 12-3, 7-10.30 Sun

☎ (01460) 72464

Ringwood Old Thumper; guest beers Ⓗ

Former coaching inn situated some five minutes' walk from the centre of this market town. The Crown, which dates back to the 17th century, has a small, quiet front bar that serves beers from Exmoor and Ringwood breweries. A larger rear bar is popular with darts and skittles players, both areas have been refurbished in a traditional style. The pub is reputed to have a ghost, a woman in a dark ankle-length skirt and cream blouse who performs various domestic tasks. No food available, but reasonbly priced B&B is offered. There is a pleasant courtyard for outdoor drinking with ample seating and attractive shrubs and flowers. ♔❀🛏⊟♣

CROWCOMBE

Carew Arms ☆

Signed from A358 between Taunton and Williton

⏲ 11.30-3, 6-11; 12-3, 7-10.30 (closed eve Jan & Feb) Sun

☎ (01984) 618631

Exmoor Ale; Ⓖ **guest beers** Ⓗ

Unspoilt village pub; step back in time into the public bar with its well-preserved, original features. The rear bar has comfortable seating. Well-cooked, wholesome traditional meals are offered at competitive prices. This is a good base for exploring the Quantocks. The West Somerset Railway is nearby. The Carew Arms is on CAMRA's national inventory of pub interiors of outstanding interest. ♔Q♞❀🛏◐⊟⛺♣🍏P

CULMHEAD

Holman Clavel

From Taunton, left at crossroads after Blagdon Hill village

⏲ 12-3, 5 (6 Sat)-11; 12-3, 7-11 Sun

☎ (01823) 421432

Butcombe Bitter, Gold; guest beers Ⓗ

14th-century, traditional country inn featuring genuine oak beams and real fires. Situated in excellent walking country, this pub serves fine food and specialises in fish and game. It has a warm and friendly atmosphere and the guest beers come from near and far, often from Juwards and Church End. The pub is rumoured to be haunted by a resident ghost who was once a monk, and appears in the fireplace. It is the only 'Holman Clavel' in England and the name comes from *holman* which means holly and *clavel* which is the beam above the fireplace. ♔Q❀◐⛺♣P

DINNINGTON

Rose & Crown

1 mile on left of road between Ilminster and Crewkerne

⏲ 11.30-3.30, 6-11; 12-4, 7-10.30 Sun

☎ (01460) 52397

Butcombe Bitter; Teignworthy Making Ends Meet; Wadworth 6X; guest beers Ⓗ

This 300-year-old pub is locally known as 'Dinnington Docks' and features a selection of pictures and signs of rail and maritime subjects, the origins of which can be found if you visit. A popular inn with locals and regular functions are held to support local charities. Every six weeks, haircuts are provided by a visiting hairdresser. The DT Society (Docks Transport), meet on the first Wed of each month with their collection of old cars and motorbikes. A good stop-off point for walkers. ♔Q♞❀◐♣🍏P

DOULTING

Abbey Barn Inn

On A361, about 1 mile E of Shepton Mallet

⏲ 12-2.30, 6-11; 12-2.30, 7-10.30 Sun

☎ (01749) 880321

Draught Bass; Oakhill Best Bitter; guest beers Ⓗ

Friendly, well-run pub which has just been awarded *Real Fire Pub of the Year*. Having separate public and lounge bars together with a skittle alley allows the pub to cater for a wide variety of trade. Addlestone's Cloudy cider is stocked along with regular guest beers. The pub is thought to have been rebuilt in 1725. The name and the medieval tithe barn nearby may point to a link with Glastonbury Abbey. Food can be ordered at all sessions. Individually decorated rooms are available for B&B. ♔❀🛏◐⊟♿♣🍏

EAST LYNG

Rose & Crown

On A361, 6 miles E of Taunton

⏲ 11-2.30, 6.30-11; 12-3, 7-10.30 Sun

☎ (01823) 698235

Butcombe Bitter, Gold; Eldridge Pope Royal Oak Ⓗ

This charming, 13th-century coaching inn has a timeless quality enhanced by comfortable antique furniture and a large stone fireplace complete with a log fire in winter. The skittle alley is an added bonus. As well as the excellent real ale there is a full and varied menu including several vegetarian dishes. Tasty, home-cooked food is served in the no-smoking restaurant which boasts an inglenook and old oak beams. For all its olde-worlde charm, the pub is up-to-date with the menu, current prices and directions on the website and bookings may be made by e-mail. Two double bedrooms provide accommodation for visitors. ♔Q❀🛏◐♿P⊘

EAST WOODLANDS

Horse & Groom

1 mile SE of A361/B3092 jct OS792445

⏲ 11.30-2.30 (not Mon), 6.30-11; 12-3, 7-10.30 Sun

☎ (01373) 462802

Branscombe Vale Branoc; Butcombe Bitter; Greene King IPA; Wadworth 6X Ⓖ

An attractive pub tucked away down a narrow country lane on the edge of Longleat estate. Open fire, flagstone floor

and comfortable settles add to the atmosphere of the public bar where traditional pub games are played. The same four ales (served direct from the barrel) are kept as 'our regulars like them'. The lounge bar, conservatory and restaurant cater for diners. An imaginative menu uses local ingredients where possible, with food freshly cooked to order. All bread is made on the premises. The pleasant garden is bordered by unusual pollarded trees. Listen carefully and you just might hear the lions!
♨Q❀⇰◑⊟占♣♠P

EXFORD

White Horse Inn
Opp. bridge over the Exe
✪ 11-11; 12-11 Sun
☎ (01643) 831229
Exmoor Ale, Gold; Greene King Old Speckled Hen; Marston's Pedigree; Tetley Bitter ⊞
Welcoming 16th-century, ivy-covered inn and hotel based in a busy Exmoor village. The bar has plenty of thick wooden beams, rural artefacts on the walls, a warming fire in winter and true local feel despite its popularity with visitors. The food is good and the beers are superbly kept. Four-wheel-drive safaris to see the countryside and Exmoor's red deer can be arranged through the inn as well as riding, clay pigeon shooting and fishing.
♨Q❀⇰◑Å P

FAULKLAND

Tucker's Grave ☆
On A366, 1 mile E of village
✪ 11-3, 6-11; 12-3, 7-10.30 Sun
☎ (01373) 834230
Draught Bass; Butcombe Bitter ⒢
This is a real classic. A genuine country local that has not changed in many years (apart from new, less smelly loos!). The regulars are a colourful and friendly lot. The beers are kept in casks in the bay window in the tiny middle room, from where the landlady will serve you. You can then take your drink to the comfortable parlour or to the original settle-lined snug across the hall. Out the back is a pretty garden where you can admire the amazing roofline of this ancient pub. Tucker, by the way, hanged himself nearby. ♨Q❀Å♣P

FROME

Griffin
Milk Street
✪ 5 (11 Sat)-11; 12-10.30 Sun
☎ (01373) 467766 website: milkstreetbrewery.co.uk
Milk Street Funky Monkey, Nicks, Zig Zag, Beer; guest beers ⊞
An interesting pub, situated in the older part of Frome, which has been sympathetically renovated by the present owners, Milk Street Brewery. A small brewhouse was constructed in the former function room producing a wide range of good quality ales which are on sale in the Griffin alongside regular guest ales. The single bar has retained many of its original features, open fires, etched glass wndows and wood floors, giving a basic but very popular pub. To encourage the reluctant Sunday trade lunches will soon be served. There is a small garden. ♨❀◑≈♣ 🍴

HARDINGTON MOOR

Royal Oak Inn (Sonny's)
Moor Lane (take the Hardington Mandeville road from A30)
✪ 12-2.30 (not Mon), 7 (6 Fri & Sat)-11; 12-2.30, 7-10.30 Sun
☎ (01935) 862354 website: www.sonnysroyaloak.co.uk
Butcombe Bitter; guest beers ⊞
Known to the locals as Sonny's (a long-serving previous landlord) the Royal Oak is situated some four miles west of Yeovil. A former farmhouse, it is adorned with hanging baskets. In summer it is well worth a visit. Inside the open-plan bar there is always a friendly welcome. A range of good food is served (not Mon) with a selection of West Country ales. Ask to see the Art Alley (a skittle alley with a difference). The landlord (a keen biker) welcomes motorcyclists. The annual beer festival held in May usually offers 20 beers. Parrots, Oscar and Dolly preside over this pub.
♨Q❀◑♣❀P

HIGHBRIDGE

Coopers Arms
Market Street (by railway station)
✪ 11-3.30, 5-11; 11-11 Fri & Sat; 12-4, 7.30-10.30 Sun
☎ (01278) 783562

INN BRIEF

FITZHEAD
Fitzhead Inn
Off B3187 at Milverton
12-2 (3 Sat; not Mon or Tue); 7-11; 12-3, 7-10.30 Sun
Cotleigh Tawny; guest beers ⊞
Cosy village pub with warm atmosphere. Excellent food with game and fish as specialities. Accommodation includes wheelchair facilities.

HALSE
New Inn
12-2.30, 7-11; 12-2.30, 7-10.30 Sun
Cotleigh Tawny; Juwards Bitter; guest beer ⊞
Pleasant inn serving local beers only two miles from West Somerset Railway. Accommodation is available. Beer garden in summer.

HILLCOMMON
Royal Oak Inn
On B3227 between Taunton and Milverton
11.30-2.30 (not Mon), 7.30-11; 11.30-2.30, 7-10.30 Sun
Cotleigh Tawny; Juwards Bitter; guest beers ⊞
This free house serves local beers and good-value food. It has two bars and a large garden. Popular with locals.

KINGSBURY EPISCOPI
Wyndham Arms
12-3, 6.30-11; 12-3, 7-10.30 Sun
Fuller's London Pride; Otter Bright; Teignworthy Reel Ale; Worthington Bitter ⊞
Unspoilt 17th-century inn with flagstone floors. Burrow Hill cider always available. Traditional pub food served at all sessions.

MIDSOMER NORTON
White Hart ☆
The Island
11-11; 12-10.30 Sun
Draught Bass; Butcombe Bitter ⒢
Inside a slightly tatty exterior lies a superb Victorian pub. Its multi-room layout has not changed in years.

MINEHEAD
Old Ship Aground
Quay Street
11-11; 12-11 Sun
Courage Best Bitter; Greene King Ruddles County; St Austell Somerset IPA ⊞
Situated next to Minehead harbour, this pub dates from the 19th century. St Austell seasonal beers sometimes available.

Fuller's London Pride; Greene King Abbot; RCH East
Street Cream; guest beers H

Large pub near station with car parking. The
main public bar has a pool table section and
dartboard. An unusual feature is the skittle
alley which is incorporated into the bar
area, making it popular for league skittles
and fundraising events. Blackboards listing
available beers are behind the bar. Most
guest ales are around 5% ABV as these are
the most popular with the locals. There is
an upstairs function room for hire, it is also
used for watching major sporting events on
large TV screen. This pub has a cosy
atmosphere brought about by subtle
lighting and exposed wooden beams.
Q 🏠 ♿ ♣ 🚆 🐕 P

HINTON BLEWITT

Ring o' Bells

Between A37 and A368 on hill above Bishop Sutton
OS594570

🕐 11-3.30, 5 (6 Sat)-11; 12-4, 7-10.30 Sun

☎ (01761) 452239

Butcombe Bitter; Wadworth 6X; guest beers H

Hilltop village inn on edge of the Mendips,
with views of Chew Valley, in a maze of 'C'
roads between Bishop Sutton and Temple
Cloud. This is a small, friendly local set back
from the village green that also attracts
visitors for its high quality meals. There is a
busy bar with seating alongside and a snug.
The entrance is through a yard with outside
tables. Popular in summer with ramblers
and cyclists. The pub supports several sports
teams due to the enthusiasm of the young
landlord who has run this free house for six
years. Children and dogs welcome.
♨ Q 🏠 ♿ ♣ 🐕 P

HORSINGTON

Half Moon Inn

200 yds off A357 between Wincanton and
Templecombe

🕐 12-2.30 (3 Sat), 6-11; 12-3, 7-10.30 Sun

☎ (01963) 370140 e-mail: halfmoon@horsington.co.uk

Fuller's London Pride; Wadworth 6X; guest beers H

Alcohol has been made and sold on the site
of the Half Moon Inn since the 17th
century. It was originally a barn in
which cider was made from apples grown in
local orchards, and it became a pub in the
19th century. Since taking over closed
premises in 1991 the present owners have
built up a successful and popular country
pub specialising in local food products and
real ales. The latter range from Branscombe
Vale Branoc (3.8%) to Badger's Tanglefoot
(5.1%) with up to four others in between.
Facilities include a function room where the
annual beer festival is held plus
accommodation and skittles. No meals on
Sun eve.
♨ 🛏 🏠 ♿ ♣ 🐕 P

HUISH EPISCOPI

Rose & Crown (Eli's) ☆

A372, 1 mile E of Langport

🕐 11.30-2.30, 5.30-11; 11.30-11 Fri & Sat;
12-10.30 Sun

☎ (01458) 250494

Teignworthy Reel Ale; guest beers H

Known affectionately as Eli's after the
present landlady's father, this 17th-century

thatched inn has been in the same family
for 130 years. Little has changed over the
years. The pub has no bar, drinks are served
from a flagstoned tap room where an
eclectic mix of drinkers also congregate.
Farmhouse cider is still drawn from wooden
barrels and the till consists of a wooden
drawer. All the food is homemade, steak
and ale pie being a favourite staple.
Camping is available when no cricket or
sheep racing takes place.
Q 🏠 ♿ ♿ ♣ 🐕 P

KELSTON

Old Crown

Bath Road (A431, 3 miles from Bath)

🕐 11.30-2.30, 5-11; 11.30-11 Sat; 12-10.30 Sun

☎ (01225) 423032

Draught Bass; Bath Gem; Butcombe Bitter, Gold;
Wadworth 6X H

Superb, low-ceilinged traditional 18th-
century coaching inn. The pub, owned by
Butcombe Brewery, features a flagstone
floor and church pew seats, note the old
beer engine in the main bar. A friendly
atmosphere and competitively priced
home-cooked food make for a busy, popular
pub. Eve meals are served Tue–Sat and there
is a separate restaurant. No children under
14 are admitted. There is a large, attractive
garden at the rear and a roadside drinking
area. The car park lies across a busy road.
♨ Q 🏠 ♿ ♿ P

LANGFORD BUDVILLE

Martlet Inn

1/2 mile off B3187, between Wellington and Milverton

🕐 12-2.30 (not Mon), 7-11; 12-3, 7-10.30 Sun

☎ (01823) 400262 e-mail: martlet@fsbdial.co.uk

Cotleigh Tawny; Barn Owl; Exmoor Ale; guest beer
(summer) H

Welcoming old village inn which has been
improved over the years. The flagstoned
public bar area has exposed beams and a
cosy wood-burning stove, which effectively
separates off the dining area. A couple of
steps lead up from the bar area to the
lounge bar, where there is a second wood-
burning stove. The skittle alley is well-
equipped and doubles as a room for
functions and meetings. The Martlet has an
increasing reputation for good-value, home-
cooked food which ranges from simple bar
snacks to full à la carte, with chef's specials
on the board. There is a fairly large garden
which has some children's play equipment.
♨ Q 🏠 ♿ ♿ ♣ P ✕

LOWER ODCOMBE

Masons Arms

41 Lower Odcombe (off Yeovil-Montacute road at
Greensleeves Nursery)

🕐 1-3, 7-11; 12-3, 7-10.30 Sun

☎ (01935) 862591

e-mail: charteris@odcombe41.freeserve.co.uk

Butcombe Bitter; Otter Bright; guest beer H

Home of Odcombe Ales, this 500-year-old
thatched Hamstone pub had a brand new
one-barrel brewery installed in late 2000.
The only pub left in this village, it is a true
country local. Guest beers usually come
from West Country breweries. Odcombe
Bitter is brewed on the premises. A beer and
music festival held in September makes

good use of the extensive garden. Food is limited to authentic curries on Thu eve and traditional Sun roast lunches. Not particularly easy to find but well worth the effort, especially as it is the only place to drink Odcombe ales. Use the old Yeovil to Montacute road, not the A3088. ❀▲♣♦P

MARTOCK

Nag's Head

East Street (off B3165 at market house/pinnacle)
✪ 12-2.30 (not Mon), 6-11; 12-3, 6-10.30 Sun
☎ (01935) 823432 website: www.thenagsheadinn.com
Otter Bitter; guest beers Ⓗ

Just north of the A303, this 200-year-old former cider house is located in a pretty Hamstone village. The landlord of this free house selects his two guest beers from around the country. A 6–7pm weekday 'happy hour' offers real ales at £1.20 a pint. The interesting menu is based on fresh produce cooked to order. Steaks are recommended as are the authentic curries offered on Thu eve. Entertainment includes live music played in the lounge bar every Sat eve and a skittle alley. The public bar is the 'club house' for Martock Rugby Club. There is a landscaped garden and a substantial fenced-off children's play area. Accommodation is offered in a luxurious self-contained flat. No food Mon.
❀⌂◑⊟▲♣P✕

MIDDLEZOY

George Inn

42 Main Road (1 mile from A372/A361 jct)
OS378327
✪ 12-2.30 (3 Sat; not Mon), 7-11; 12-3, 7-10.30 Sun
☎ (01823) 698215 e-mail: wilzoy@aol.com
Butcombe Bitter; guest beers Ⓗ

17th-century, traditional village pub with oak beams, stone flags and a log fire. Located in the middle of the Somerset Levels, this is a favourite with anglers, birdwatchers and walkers as well as being a popular locals' pub. A warm welcome can be guaranteed. Home-cooked food is served (not Sun or Mon eve) and there is always an excellent selection of cask ales available as well as the house bitter and regular appearances for favourite beers. At least two new cask ales offered every week. Somerset CAMRA *Pub of the Year* 2000.
⌸Q❀⌂◑♣P✕

MINEHEAD ❀

Queen's Head Inn

Holloway Street (just off the parade at the top of The Avenue)
✪ 12-3, 7-11; 12-3, 7-10.30 Sun
☎ (01643) 706000
Draught Bass; Exmoor Hart; Fuller's London Pride; Oakhill Bitter Ⓗ

Large town-centre pub with one main bar supplemented by areas for eating and pub games. Pleasantly decorated with much use of pine, this pub offers a warm welcome to people of all ages with facilities for both young and old. The friendly host is always ready to engage in conversation. A traditional brick-floored cellar ensures the beers are served at the optimum temperature. Food is available every day up to one hour before closing time with a

menu ranging from sandwiches to steaks, home-made pies are a speciality. Sun lunches served.
◑▲≠ (W Somerset Railway)♣✕

NAILSEA

Blue Flame

West End (1 mile SW of Nailsea) OS449690
✪ 12-3 (5 Sat), 6-11; 12-5, 7-10.30 Sun
☎ (01275) 856910
Draught Bass; Fuller's London Pride; Smiles Best, Heritage; guest beer (summer) Ⓖ

Wonderfully unspoilt 19th-century pub on the outskirts of town. In addition to the four regular ales and Thatcher's cider, a locally produced organic cider is available on draught and in bottles. The apples often originate from the pub's very pleasant garden. Social events include barbecues in summer and folk music on the third Tue of each month. Crib, dominoes, darts and table skittles are played. The cosy, intimate nature of the pub, coupled with its real fire make it an equally attractive venue in winter and summer. Off the beaten track but well worth seeking out. ⌸Q❀▲♣♦P

NETHER STOWEY

Rose & Crown

St Mary Street (off A39, Bridgwater-Minehead road)
✪ 12-11; 12-5, 7-10.30 Sun
☎ (01278) 732265
Beer range varies Ⓖ

Welcoming 16th-century coaching inn at the centre of this lovely village nestling at the foot of the Quantock Hills. An ideal base for walking, the pub enjoys a strong local following and this ensures a good turnover of quality real ales. The restaurant is open from Wed–Sat, serving local and home-grown produce. Coleridge Cottage, a National Trust property, can be found nearby. Up to five real ales are served. These come mainly from West Country breweries.
Q❀⌂◑⊟♣♦

NORTON ST PHILIP

Fleur de Lys

On B3110, about 1½ miles from A36 jct
✪ 11-3, 5-11; 11-11 Sat; 12-3, 7-10.30 Sun
☎ (01373) 834333
Draught Bass; Butcombe Bitter; Wadworth 6X Ⓗ

This ancient stone building has been extensively but sympathetically refurbished. The repositioned bar is on the site of the old passageway through which the pub ghost reputedly passed on his way to the gallows. This pub is situated directly opposite the recently refurbished, medieval George Inn. The Fleur de Lys serves first-class and very reasonably priced food. ⌸Q◑♣P

NORTON SUB HAMDON

Lord Nelson

Rectory Road (1½ miles S of A303)
✪ 12-2.30, 6.30-11; 12-11 Sat; 12-10.30 Sun
☎ (01935) 881473 website: www.thelordnelson.co.uk
Teignworthy Reel Ale; Worthington Bitter; guest beers Ⓗ

300-year-old converted farmhouse with slate floors that has been sympathetically refurbished. This popular village pub offers an extensive menu every session and stocks four real ales, of which two are guests, along with two farmhouse ciders – Burrow Hill and Weston's Old Rosie. The main dining area is no-smoking and a large smoke extractor in the main bar maintains a relatively smoke-free environment. Other features include a log fire in the centre of the bar, scrubbed table tops, interesting tiles and a barbed wire loo seat in the gents! The innkeeper advertises as 'specialists in the restoration of jaded palates to the citizens of the locality'. ⚨Q⚙✿⚫◀◗♣♠P⚡✦⬤

PITMINSTER

Queen's Arms
3 miles S of Taunton off B3170
☼ 11-11; 12-11 Sun
☎ (01823) 421529
Cotleigh Tawny; Exmoor Gold; Hop Back Crop Circle; guest beers Ⓗ

Cosy village pub selling locally-brewed beers. The main bar is divided by a wood-burning stove and there is a traditional underfloor cellar. This pub was mentioned in the *Domesday Book!* Small, but interesting menu of home-cooked food and excellent wine list (no meals on Mon). Spanish, Mexican, French and medieval theme nights have been hosted and there are occasional live music performances; the function room has bar facilities. This is a true locals' pub with a friendly atmosphere. Children are welcome. Skittles, an attractive garden and excellent accommodation are other bonuses. ⚨Q⚙✿⚫◀◗⚱♣P

PITNEY

Halfway House
Pitney Hill (B3153, between Langport and Somerton)
☼ 11.30-3, 5.30-11; 12-3, 7-10.30 Sun
☎ (01458) 252513
Butcombe Bitter; Hop Back Crop Circle; Otter Ale; Teignworthy Reel Ale; guest beers Ⓖ

Superb example of an old village pub. This no-frills inn serves a wide range of mainly local ales. Hecks cider is served in winter and Wilkins cider in summer. No juke box, music or machines, just the buzz of friendly conversation. Flagstone floors throughout are ideal for walkers and dog lovers. This family-orientated pub welcomes children. Basic, but excellent quality food served at lunchtime with a superb selection of delicious home-cooked curries in the eve (no food Sun). Awarded national CAMRA *Pub of the Year* 1996, Somerset *Pub of the Year* 1995, 1997 and 2001, this is a real gem not to be missed. ⚨Q⚙◀◗⚋♣♠P

PORLOCK

Ship Inn
High Street (A39, foot of Porlock Hill)
☼ 11-11; 12-11 Sun
☎ (01643) 862507
Cotleigh Barn Owl; Courage Best Bitter; guest beers Ⓗ

Picturesque, thatched inn which dates from the middle ages and is a great base from which to explore Lorna Doone country. The cosy bar boasts a Victorian beer engine while outside in the oldest part of the building there is an ancient window. Renowned visitors in the past have included

poets Robert Southey and Samuel Taylor Coleridge. Guest beers come from Cotleigh, Oakhill, Cottage, Barum and Hop Back. The last Fri of the month usually sees a spontaneous folk session. ⚨Q⚙✿◀◗⚋♣P

ROWBERROW

Swan Inn
Off A38, 1 mile S of Churchill
☼ 12-3, 6-11; 12-3, 7-10.30 Sun
☎ (01934) 852371 e-mail: swanbob@x-stream.co.uk
Draught Bass; Butcombe Bitter, Gold; guest beer Ⓗ

Located near Black Down, the highest point on the Mendip Hills, the Swan is an ideal base for hillwalking in this area of outstanding natural beauty. Originally a farmhouse, the pub now consists of two large but cosy bars with open fires in winter. A full range of food is served lunchtime and eve and the varied menu of home-cooked dishes makes the Swan a popular destination for diners. A low-gravity guest beer, usually from a small independent brewery, is always available. There is a large and well-landscaped garden opposite the pub with fine views of Dolebury Hill Fort to the north. ⚨Q⚙◀◗⚋P

ST GEORGES

Woolpack
Shepherds Way (near M5 jct 21, off A370 to Weston-s-Mare))
☼ 12-2.30, 6-11; 12-3, 7-10.30
☎ (01934) 521670 e-mail: woolpackinn@hotmail.com
Oakhill Best Bitter; guest beers Ⓗ

A warm and friendly 17th-century former coaching house and woolpacking station. There is a wide range of good quality food, specialising in fresh fish and shellfish. Despite the popularity of the food operation the landlord ensures that this is not at the expense of the cask ales with three guest beers normally on offer. A skittle alley doubles as a function room. If you ask the landlord nicely when booking this room he may be able to get a specially requested beer in for you. ⚨Q⚙◀◗⚋⚋≠(Worle Parkway)♣P

SALTFORD

Bird in Hand
58 High Street (400 yds off A4)
☼ 11-3, 6.30-11; 11-3.30, 6-11 Fri & Sat; 12-3.30, 6.30-10.30
☎ (01225) 873335
Abbey Bellringer; Draught Bass; Courage Best Bitter; guest beers Ⓗ

Smart, well-decorated village local, alongside the River Avon and Bristol–Bath cycle track. Good home-cooked food is eaten in the no-smoking conservatory-style dining area. It is very popular and advance bookings are not taken. Excellent views of the picturesque Avon Valley. There is a small family area where children are welcome. Thatcher's cider is stocked. Wheelchair WC. Darts and shove-ha'penny are played. Q⚤⚙◀◗⚋♣♠P

SANDYWAY

Sportsman's Inn
Between Withypool and N Molton OS793333
☼ 12-3, 6.30-11; 12-3, 7-11 Sun
☎ (01643) 831109 website: www.sportsmansinn.co.uk

Exmoor Ale, Fox; guest beers ⒣
Traditional rural inn situated in a small hamlet high up on Exmoor, close to the Devon border. Popular with both locals and visitors, it was originally two cottages before becoming an inn in the 1840s. Interior features include the original inglenooks to be seen at each end of the roomy bar and restaurant area. There is also a well in the bar area. Food is sourced from local producers and the beers are mainly from Exmoor Brewery, with their seasonal beers often appearing as guests. Cider comes from Hancocks. Skittles and chess are popular here. ♨Q❀⇆◑♣●P

SOUTH PETHERTON

Brewers Arms
18 St James Street (½ mile off A303)
☼ 11.30-2.30, 6-11; 12-10.30 Sun
☎ (01460) 241887
Otter Bitter, Worthington Bitter; guest beers ⒣
Easily reached from the A303, this busy, friendly one bar 17th-century former coaching inn is in the centre of a picturesque Hamstone village. The two guest beers may come from any part of the country; over 500 different ones have appeared in the past six year. An annual beer festival is held over the late May bank holiday weekend, also a festival of Somerset beers and ciders on August bank holiday weekend. An excellent range of home-cooked food is available seven days a week. The pub caters for all age groups and is heavily involved with the local community. An enclosed courtyard to the rear adds to its appeal in the summer months. 1999 Somerset CAMRA *Pub of the Year*.
♨❀◑Å♣●

STOGUMBER

White Horse
High Street (opp. church in village centre)
☼ 11.30-3, 6-11; 12-3, 7-10.30 Sun
☎ (01984) 656277
Cotleigh Tawny, Exmoor Ale; guest beers ⒣
Well-presented, village-centre pub offering a range of traditional meals at reasonable prices. The two bars have a comfortable seating layout. The pub houses a large collection of rolling pins and the remains of a 12-foot cabbage! Good area for walking and a mile from the West Somerset Steam Railway. This village is very picturesque and well worth looking at, especially in the area around the church. ♨Q⏚⇆❀◑P

TAUNTON

Eagle
46 South Street (400 yds S of East Reach)
☼ 12-2 (not Mon; 3 Fri & Sat), 6.30-11; 12-4, 7-10.30 Sun
☎ (01823) 275713
Smiles Best; guest beers ⒣
Welcoming Victorian pub with one bar divided into three areas for eating, drinking and games. The large blackboard menu offers a wide range of meals, often with an international flavour as well as more traditional meals. Sun lunches are also served. The pub boasts two skittle alleys and has numerous skittles, darts and pool teams and as such has a strong local following

with a friendly atmosphere. One of the skittle alleys is also a function room with a separate bar and is available for hire. Live music is sometimes featured, with an emphasis on jazz and blues.
♨❀◑♣P

Hankridge Arms
Hankridge Way, Riverside (in retail park, off jct 25 of M5)
☼ 11-11; 12-10.30 Sun
☎ (01823) 444405
website: www.big-gig.co.uk/hankridge
Badger Best, Tanglefoot; guest beers ⒣
Situated in the Riverside Retail and Business Park, this pub dates back to the 16th century when it was a working farmhouse. Now a Grade I listed building, it has been carefully renovated retaining original features such as inglenooks, flagstone floors, exposed timbers and a priest's hole. The single bar provides ample seating for both eating and drinking and there is also the Tapestry restaurant which is mainly no-smoking. A varied menu is offered with home-made meals using fresh ingredients. The guest beers are from either Hall & Woodhouse's matched King & Barnes range or the Gribble Brewery.
♨❀◑♿ÅP●

Harpoon Louies
75 Station Road (150 yds from station, towards town centre)
☼ 6-11 (11.30 diners) open lunchtime Dec; 7-10.30 (March-Dec) Sun
☎ (01823) 324404
Otter Ale; guest beers ⒣
This small, welcoming pub/restaurant has an excellent *à la carte* menu with separate dining areas. Seafood is the house speciality. The menu changes regularly and bar snacks are always available. Beers are mainly local, up to four handpumps are used and customers' opinions are welcomed on choice of guest beers. Music nights are held occasionally at weekends. Interesting ambience, well worth a visit.
◑⇌♣

Masons Arms
Magdelene Street (adjacent to St Mary's church, Hammet St)
☼ 10.30-3, 5-11; 10.30-11.30 Sat; 12-4, (check for eves) Sun
☎ (01823) 288916
website: www.masonsarms.freeuk.com
Exe Valley Bitter, Jurwards Bitter; guest beers ⒣
The Masons Arms has a history dating back to 1809 and Taunton's longest-serving licensee is more than happy to relate this to his customers. The small, friendly traditional pub serves mainly local ales in excellent condition. This may be in part due to the cellar being directly below the bar. Interesting menu is available during all sessions, including sizzling steaks and unusual soups. A good range of fine wines is always stocked. This is a quiet pub with interesting and varied conversation. There is a skittle alley and limited parking.
Q❀⇆◑♣P

Wyvern Club
Mountfields Road (turn off B3170 to Corfe about ¾ mile from centre)
☼ 7-11; 12-2.30, 7-10.30 Sun

☎ (01823) 284591 e-mail: wyvernclub@fsmail.net
Exmoor Ale; guest beers Ⓗ

Large, busy sports and social club serving
eve meals until 10pm (9pm Sun), also hot
and cold bar snacks available. and Sun
lunches. Guest beers are often from West
Country micro-breweries as well as more
well-known brands. Comfortable
surroundings and friendly bar staff ensure a
warm welcome. The bar is also open from
4pm when either home football or cricket
teams are playing. The club has a large
function room and skittle alley which are
both available for hire. Show this *Guide* for
entry or CAMRA membership card.
▶ ♿ ♣ P

the main shopping street and ideally
placed if you are visiting the local
cinema. The bar area is divided into
lounge and public by the chimney
breast and fire (not real). The lounge area
has comfortable seating, black beamwork
and brass knick-knacks, with many prints of
old maps and pictures. Usually fairly busy, it
is the home of darts and skittles teams and
there always seems to be someone to chat
to. One of the few permanent outlets for
Wellington's local brewery Juwards, there
are good-value basic lunches available daily
(not Sun). Small garden with decking and
limited parking.
❀ ◀ ⑪ ♿ ♣ Å ♣ P

WANSTROW

Pub at Wanstrow
Station Road
🕐 12-3 (not Mon), 6.30-11; 12-3, 7-10.30 Sun
☎ (01749) 850455
Beer range varies Ⓗ/Ⓖ

A gem. A friendly, well-kept village local. A
cosy lounge bar with open fire and
flagstone floor leads to a small dining area.
The public bar also has an open fir and has
three casks on the bar to serve beer direct.
Another two to three guest beers on
handpump are also kept along with
farmhouse cider. Beers change on a regular
basis. A skittle alley leads off the public bar.
A small but very imaginative menu is
offered. All food is home-made. Well worth
a visit.
🕮 Q ❀ ⑪ ♿ ♣ ♣ ● P

WELLOW

Fox & Badger
Railway Lane   (2 miles W of B3110 at Hinton)
🕐 11.30-3.30, 6-11; 11.30-11 Fri & Sat;
12-10.30 Sun
☎ (01225) 832293 website: www.foxandbadger.co.uk
**Draught Bass; Butcombe Bitter; Wadworth 6X; guest
beer** Ⓗ

Cosy, two-bar local in the village
centre. Unusually the public bar is carpeted
and the lounge bar has flagstones. There is a
skittle alley at the rear. Serves well-kept
Bass, Butcombe Bitter and Wadworth 6X,
plus a 'long-term' guest beer usually on for
several months. Extensive menu of
traditional and more unusual dishes, all
good quality and value. Can be difficult to
park. 🕮 ❀ ⑪ ♿ ♣ ♣ P

WELLINGTON

Cottage Inn
31 Champford Lane
🕐 11-3, 6-11; 12-4, 7-10.30 Sun
☎ (01823) 664650
Fuller's London Pride; Juwards Bitter; guest beer Ⓗ
Convenient back-street local, just off

WELLS

City Arms
69 High Street
🕐 10-11; 12-10.30 Sun
☎ (01749) 673916
website: www.wwevents.com/net/thecityarms
**Butcombe Gold; Oakhill Mendip Gold; Palmers IPA;
guest beers** Ⓗ

INN BRIEF

NORTON FITZWARREN
Crosskeys
11-11; 12-10.30 Sun
**Courage Best Bitter, Directors;
guest beers** Ⓗ
Large Chef & Brewer with two
regularly changing guest beers.
Extensive menu with fresh fish a
speciality. The pub dates back to
1860.

PRIDDY
Queen Victoria Inn
Pelting Drove
12-3, 7-11; 12-11 Sat;
12-10.30 Sun
**Butcombe Bitter, Gold or Wadworth 6X;
guest beer** (occasional) Ⓗ
This attractive 300-year-old rural
pub is a community meeting place.
Wide range of food served. Scenic
garden with children's play items.

WATCHET
Star Inn
Mill Lane
11-3 (not Mon in winter), 6.30-11;
12-3, 6.30-11 Sun
**Cotleigh Tawny; Oakhill Best Bitter; guest
beers** Ⓗ
Built in 1680 as three cottages, this
pub, close to the sea has a
welcoming atmosphere and a good
range of food. Mainly local beers.

WATERROW
Rock Inn
On B3227 between Wiveliscombe and
Bampton
11-3, 6-11; 12-3, 7-10.30 Sun
Cotleigh Tawny; Exmoor Gold Ⓗ
Traditional English inn set in a
rockface. Picturesque setting and
locally brewed beers.

WINSCOMBE
Winscombe Club
British Legion Building, Sandford Road
11-2.30 (3 Sat), 7-11; 12-3, 7-11 Sun
**Courage Directors; Wickwar BOB; guest
beer** Ⓗ
Competitively priced beer, with
card-carrying CAMRA members
admitted. Guest beer often from
micro-breweries. Good range of
pub games.

WINSFORD
Royal Oak Inn
At foot of Winsford Hill
11-2.30, 7 (6 summer)-11; 12-3,
7-10.30 Sun
Cotleigh Barn Owl; Ⓗ **Exmoor Ale;** Ⓖ
guest beers Ⓗ
Thatched inn in centre of Exmoor's
prettiest village. Two bars with log
fires in winter. Good home-cooked
food. Guest beers mainly served in
summer. Wheelchair WC.

WITHAM FRIARY
Seymour Arms
Off B3092
11-3, 6-11; 12-3, 7-10.30 Sun
Ushers Best Bitter Ⓖ
Classic old country pub with two
basic rooms and a small serving
hatch in the entrance lobby.
Mainly a cider house. The large
garden has children's play
equipment.

YEOVIL
Armoury
1 The Park
11.30-2.30, 6-11; 11-11 Thu-Sat;
12-10.30 Sun
**Butcombe Bitter; Wadworth IPA, 6X,
seasonal beers; guest beer** Ⓗ
Open-plan town pub with simple
furnishings. Serves excellent pub
food (not Thu eve). Attractive patio
overlooks a small park; a peaceful
spot close to the town centre.

> ❈ symbol next to
> a main entry place
> name indicates there
> are Inn Brief entries
> as well.

Splendid, old, city-centre pub, part of which used to be the local jail. One of the few bastions of real ale left in Wells where alcopops seem to rule! The landlord is trying hard (and succeeding) to create a traditional, old-style hostelry with the emphasis on good beer and food and a warm welcome to all. The regulars, Butcombe Gold, Palmers IPA and a dark offering in winter, are supported by a wide range of guest beers always on sale. There is a large range of British bottled beers too. The freshly-cooked food uses local ingredients where possible.
🛏🏵🕽♣🍺

WEST BAGBOROUGH

Rising Sun Inn
Off A358 OS171334
🌣 12-3, 7-11; closed Mon; 12-3, 7-10.30 Sun
☎ (01823) 337035
Butcombe Gold; Cotleigh Tawny; RCH Pitchfork Ⓗ
16th-century olde-worlde inn set in the Quantock Hills. Homely atmosphere of a real country pub, with log fire, old beams and rural decorations. This pub is much used by walkers and cyclists as well as locals, and although there is no garden, outdoor seating is provided. Good international cuisine; home-made dishes are competitively priced. Lanes cider is served.
🛏🕽🍺

WEST CRANMORE

Strode Arms
E of Shepton Mallet, S of A361
🌣 11.30-2.30, 6.30-11; 12-3, 7-10.30 Sun
☎ (01749) 880450
Oakhill Best Bitter; Wadworth IPA, 6X; guest beer (occasional) Ⓗ
This pub has an idyllic setting in a pretty village, overlooking the duck pond and adjacent to the local steam railway. Originally a 15th-century farmhouse, a roaring log fire, complete with railway line fender, greets you in winter. A guest ale is offered from Easter to Christmas. Wilkins cider, straight from the barrel, is also served. No-smoking bar and restaurant areas are available. A varied menu is offered with all food made on the premises using fresh ingredients.
🛏Q🕽⇌ (E Somerset Railway) 🍺P✠

WESTON-SUPER-MARE

Dragon
15 Meadow Street (jct with High St and Regent St)
🌣 10-11; 12-10.30 Sun
☎ (01934) 621304
Butcombe Bitter; Courage Directors; Theakston Best Bitter; guest beers Ⓗ
Town-centre pub close to the main shopping area. This is a popular Wetherspoon's outlet. Can get busy at weekends and eves, particularly when special food promotions are running, so you may need to be patient when waiting to be served. Beer quality and food consistently found to be good with prices probably the most competitive in the town centre. Various beers from Exmoor and RCH are also stocked. The main bar area can get smoky, however the far end of the pub is a designated no-smoking area and is quieter.

Many interesting facts about the town are displayed on the walls.
Q🏵🕽🧍🚻Å⇌🍺✠🍺●

Off the Rails
Station Approach, Station Road
🌣 10-11; 12-10.30 Sun
☎ (01934) 415109
Beer range varies Ⓗ
Cosy, small single-roomed pub serving two to three real ales. These are mainly from local breweries such as RCH, Oakhill, Smiles and Berrow. The pub has a strong local following. It contains two TVs, a free juke box and three fruit machines. Added local atmosphere is provided by 19th-century photographs of Weston Station. The bar is run by friendly staff who offer excellent service and are interested in other beers that customers would like to try. Adjoining the bar is the station buffet where children are welcome.
Å⇌

Regency
22-24 Lower Church Road (opp. technical college, near seafront)
🌣 11-11; 12-10.30 Sun
☎ (01934) 633406
Draught Bass; Bath Gem; Boddingtons Bitter; Wadworth 6X; Webster's Yorkshire Bitter; guest beer Ⓗ
One bar, plus a pool room in this welcoming pub which attracts a wide range of customers. Small, sheltered patio for outdoor drinking. The guest beer is often from a local/regional brewery such as Smiles, Moles or Hop Back. The management team have developed a strong bond with their customers, organising highly successful outings. The pub also hold occasional mini beer festivals and live music events. 🏵🕽♣

WILLITON

Foresters Arms
55 Long Street (on edge of village near West Somerset Railway)
🌣 11-11; 12-11 Sun
☎ (01984) 632508 website: www.forarms.fsnet.co.uk
Cotleigh Harrier, Tawny; John Smith's Bitter; guest beer Ⓗ
Modernised, 17th-century coaching inn, situated on the A39 on the edge of Williton. Ideal for exploring the Somerset coast or the surrounding Quantock and Brendon Hills. Beers are usually from local breweries although some are from further afield. Cotleigh Tawny has been sold here almost since it was first produced. This is a popular pub with locals and occasionally features live music. The West Somerset Railway is nearby and rail enthusiasts are always welcome as are touring cricket teams in the summer.
🛏Q🏵🛏🕽🍴⇌(W Somerset Railway) ♣🍺P

WINCANTON

Bear Inn
12 Market Place (opp. town hall)
🌣 11-11; 12-10.30 Sun
☎ (01963) 32581
Draught Bass; Greene King Abbot; Ringwod Best Bitter; guest beers Ⓗ

The Bear is a traditional coaching inn dating from 1720. In the heyday of horsedrawn transport it was an important staging point being halfway between London and Plymouth. Today, situated in the centre of Wincanton, the Bear still provides good value hospitality, home-cooked food, comfortable accommodation and, of course, a good range of real ales. A log fire complements food and drink in the main bar. Skittles, darts and pool are played elsewhere in the pub. The inn was mentioned in the *Diary of a Country Parson* by James Woodforde.

🏚🍴🛏🍺🌶♣P

WIVELISCOMBE

Bear Inn
10 North Street
✪ 12-3, 5-11; 11-11 Fri, Sat & summer; 12-10.30 Sun
☎ (01984) 623537
Cotleigh Tawny, Gilden Eagle; Hop Back GFB; guest beers Ⓗ

Friendly town-centre pub usually serving at least two guest beers. The 17th-century buildings contain a bar area and separate restaurant area where families are welcome. This is a pub well-used by local people and a warm welcome is assured. Home-made food is available and curries are a speciality. There is a large garden and patio at the rear. Beer lovers' weekends are organised in conjunction with the two local breweries.

🏚🍴🛏🍺🌶♣P

WOOKEY

Burcott Inn
Wookey Road (B3139, 2 miles W of Wells)
✪ 11.30-2.30, 6-11; 12-3, 7-10.30 Sun
☎ (01749) 673874
Beer range varies Ⓗ

Deservedly popular country pub with at least two different ales on offer. Throughout the year over 60 local and regional beers are served across the copper-topped, L-shaped bar. Old pine tables, settles, low beams and an open fire create a welcoming atmosphere. There is something for everyone here; a games room for darts and shove ha'penny, and cribbage competitions are held every Thu. An excellent menu includes daily specials (no food Sun or Mon winter eves). The extensive garden has the remains of a cider press and splendid views of the Mendip Hills.

🏚Q🍴🌶🍺🌶♣P

WOOKEY HOLE

Wookey Hole Inn
Wookey Road (opp. Wookey Hole caves, near Wells)
✪ 12-3, 6-11; closed Mon; (times may vary in summer); 12-4, 7-10.30 Sun
☎ (01749) 676677 website: www.wookeyholeinn.com
Taylor Landlord; guest beers Ⓗ

This successful pub conversion is a very exciting new addition to the local food and drink scene. Four ever-changing guest beers are supplemented by eight draught Belgian beers plus Old Rosie cider. The pastel-coloured decor is truly different with an assortment of subdued lighting. A somewhat bizarre collection of furniture includes three-piece suites straight from the 1960s and wicker stools. Add to this an odd

assortment of artefacts, but somehow it works. A large sculptured garden has seating for 100 and a small side area known as the Spanish Room is set aside for drinking. High quality food, priced accordingly, is served from a totally visible kitchen and is very popular at weekends. A cheaper, reduced menu is served at lunchtimes. The four bedrooms are not aimed at the budget conscious. Live jazz held on Sun afternoons. The pub hosts Somerset's only cider festival.

🏚Q🌶🛏🍺🌶♣P

WRAXALL

Old Barn
Bristol Road (in grounds of Wraxall House off B3130)
✪ 11.30-3, 5-11; 11.30-11 Fri & Sat; 12-3, 7-10.30 Sun
☎ (01275) 819011
Draught Bass; Bath Gem; Moles Best Bitter; Oakhill Best Bitter; Wickwar Olde Merryford Ⓖ

An imaginative barn conversion has produced an atmospheric and highly-regarded pub. The Old Barn only opened in July 1998 yet secured its place in this *Guide* in its first year. The five ales, served direct from the casks behind the bar, are sometimes supplemented by guest beers. The pub holds occasional real ale festivals and live jazz events. The pleasant, large grounds are regularly used for barbecues in the summer. Lunchtime food is served Wed–Fri.

🏚Q🌶🍺♣P

YEOVIL ✜

William Dampier
97 Middle Street
✪ 11-11; 12-10.30 Sun
☎ (01935) 412533
Butcombe Gold; Courage Directors; Exmoor Gold, Stag; Shepherd Neame Spitfire; Theakston Best Bitter; guest beers Ⓗ

Large, single-roomed Wetherspoon's house, decorated in their typical style with Yeovil history displayed on the walls. This modern building was formerly a furniture store although a pub stood on the site many years before. A long single bar boasts 18 handpumps. One door conveniently faces Yeovil bus station while the opposite entrance is at the lower end of Yeovil's pedestrianised main street. A number of outside tables are positioned here. The pub is named after a local explorer.

Q🌶🍺♿≠ (Pen Mill) ✚●

Epitaph

She drank good ale, good punch and wine,
And lived to the age of ninety-nine.

Epitaph to Rebecca Freeland
(1741) at Edwalton, Notts.

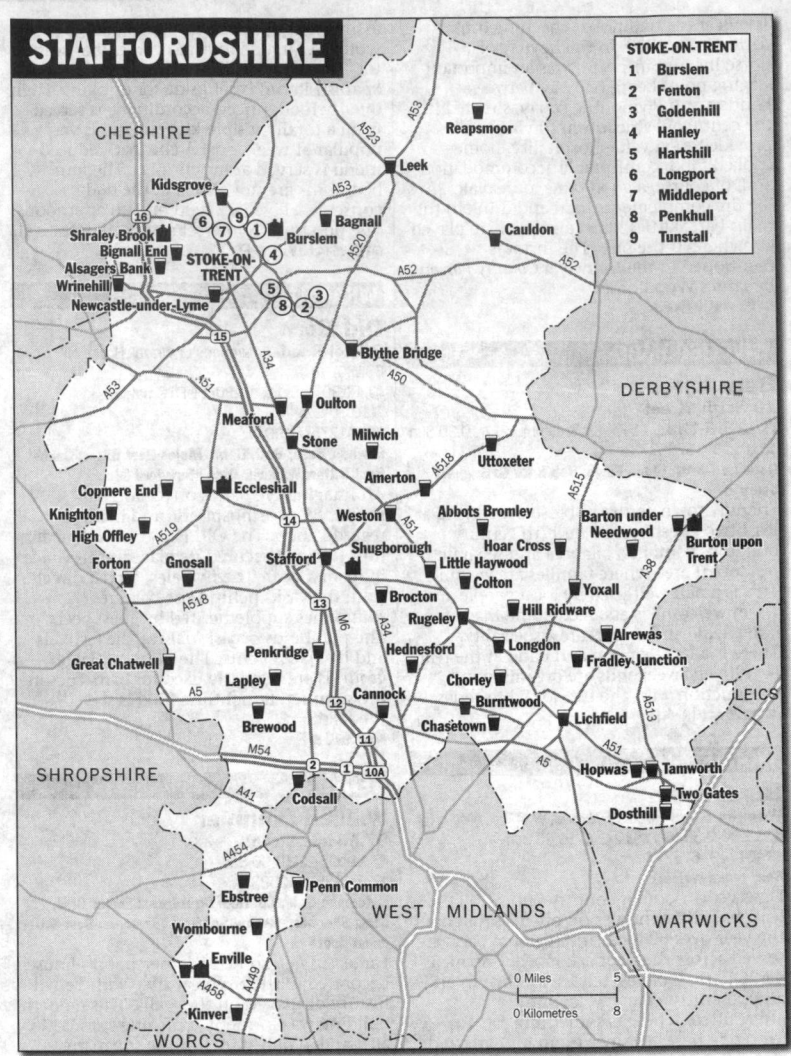

STAFFORDSHIRE

STOKE-ON-TRENT

1 Burslem
2 Fenton
3 Goldenhill
4 Hanley
5 Hartshill
6 Longport
7 Middleport
8 Penkhull
9 Tunstall

CHESHIRE

DERBYSHIRE

LEICS

SHROPSHIRE

WEST MIDLANDS

WARWICKS

WORCS

0 Miles 5
0 Kilometres 8

ALREWAS

George & Dragon
120 Main Street
☻ 11.30-2.30 (3 Sat), 5-11; 12-3, 7-10.30 Sun
☎ (01283) 791476
Banks's Bitter; Marston's Pedigree Ⓗ

Popular village-centre local. The bar has three distinct drinking areas. The separate lounge doubles up as a dining room when meals are available (not Sun). Despite some refurbishment the original beamed ceilings are still visible. The pub is well worth the short walk from bridge 48 on the Trent & Mersey Canal. A small, outdoor tarmaced drinking area, with an enclosed children's playground, is ideal in fine weather. Pub served by the Burton to Lichfield bus route.
☙❶🖢🄿●

ALSAGERS BANK

Gresley Arms
High Street (B5367)
☻ 12-3, 6-11; 12-10.30 Sun

☎ (01782) 720297
Beer range varies Ⓗ

Traditional village local with a hilltop location commanding magnificent views over three counties and Wales beyond from the beer garden and children's play area. The pub comprises a traditional bar, comfortable lounge, family/games room and dining area. The four ever-changing guest beers are mainly from smaller breweries and micros. ♨Q🍃❀❶🖢🄿

BIGNALL END

Plough Inn
2 Ravens Lane (½ mile E of Audley on B5500)
☻ 12-3, 7-11; 12-11 Fri & Sat; 12-10.30 Sun
☎ (01782) 720469
Banks's Bitter; guest beers Ⓗ

A constantly changing range of guest ales from small independent and micro-breweries as well as excellent value meals are just two of the qualities that have made this roadside hostelry popular. Catering for local and passing trade, there is a bar and a split-level lounge. Sign outside proudly proclaims this as a former CAMRA Potteries *Pub of the Year*. Consistent quality is assured by beer enthusiast owners. No food Sun eve. ✿◖▶♣P

BREWOOD

Swan Hotel
Market Square
✿ 12-2.30 (3 Fri; 4 Sat), 7-11; 12-10.30 Sun
☎ (01902) 850330
Mansfield Riding Bitter; Marston's Pedigree; Theakston XB; guest beers Ⓗ
Comfortable pub with low-beamed ceilings, where two cosy snugs are complemented by a skittle alley upstairs. Situated in the centre of five-times running Staffordshire best-kept village. Normally two guest beers available, this pub is a previous local CAMRA *Pub of the Year* (1999). A typical village local with a warm welcome guaranteed. Not far from Shropshire Union Canal and on a bus route from Wolverhampton to Stafford. Good value home-cooked food available (not Sun). ◖♣P

BROCTON

Chetwynd Arms
Cannock Road (A34)
✿ 11-11; 12-10.30 Sun
☎ (01785) 661089
Banks's Original, Bitter, Marston's Pedigree; guest beer Ⓗ
Extended by Banks's over the years, but the 'Chet' retains its original charm. The thriving public bar is a haven for conversation and traditional pub games while the comfortable lounge accommodates both drinkers and diners, with meals served all day until 9.30pm. Its regular listing in this *Guide* recognises the excellence of the beer and the manager was recently the regional winner of Banks's *Best-Kept Cellar* award. The beer garden includes a children's play area. Brocton is an ideal base for exploring Cannock Chase, an area of outstanding natural beauty.
Q✿◖⊟♣P

BURNTWOOD

White Swan
2 Cannock Road
✿ 5 (12 Sat-11; 12-3.30, 7-10.30 Sun
☎ (01543) 675937
Ansells Bitter; Greene King Abbot; Ind Coope Burton Ale; guest beers Ⓗ
Situated at the heart of the small town of Burntwood, the White Swan is a very popular, and often very busy, one-roomed pub. Dating from the late 19th-century it has always been in every sense at the hub of the local scene in the town. Very much a community pub mainly frequented by local residents. The one bar is long and narrow which adds to the feeling of a bustling, closely-knit establishment.
♣P

BURTON UPON TRENT ✤

Alfred
51 Derby Street
✿ 11-3, 6-11; 11-11 Fri & Sat; 12-3, 7-10.30 Sun
☎ (01283) 562178

Burton Bridge Bridge Bitter, Golden Delicious, Porter, Gold Medal Ales; guest beer Ⓗ
Double-fronted, terraced pub, part of the Burton Bridge Brewery group, offering two bars and a games room. A raised area in the left-hand bar is no-smoking. The pub has been refurbished in a traditional style. A central bar serves both rooms and there are leaded, stained glass topped partitions. Two beer festivals are held annually; at Easter and around bonfire night. Comfortable, congenial pub for conversation, known for its quiz nights and selection of fruit wines. Reasonably priced accommodation, handy for railway station. ✿⇔◖▶♿♣P⊬

Bass Museum (Burton Bar)
Horninglow Street
✿ 11-7 (5 Sat); 12-5 Sun
☎ (01283) 511000 (ext. 3513)
website: www.bass-museum.com
Draught Bass; Worthington E; guest beers Ⓗ
All guest beers served at the Bass Museum are brewed on site in the Museum Brewing Company's micro-brewery. Always four guest beers on handpumps offered at any one time from a range of 12-15 beers. It is now the new home to the famous Worthington White Shield. The Burton Bar is inside the museum where shire horses and steam engines are on show. Free admission for current card-carrying CAMRA members. Q➤✿◖⇔♣P●

Burton Bridge Inn
24 Bridge Street (end of Trent Bridge, A511)
✿ 11.30-2.15, 5.30-11; 12-2, 7-10.30 Sun
☎ (01283) 536596
Burton Bridge Bridge Bitter, Golden Delicious, Porter, Festival; guest beer Ⓗ
Mid 17th-century inn, formerly the Fox and Goose. Opened as the Burton Bridge in 1982 and is the site of the brewery and the brewery tap. After major and thoughtful alterations, the Bridge is now a two-roomed establishment; one room is totally non-smoking. Both rooms are served by a central bar. The smoking room has a wooden floor, (part carpeted) and half-panelled, wood-clad walls. Good range of malt whiskies and fruit wines. Function room and skittle alley are other assets. Good-value food and excellent Sun lunches. ⇔Q◖♣⊬

Cooper's Tavern
43 Cross Street (off Station St)
✿ 12-3, 5.15-11; 12-3, 7-10.30 Sun
☎ (01283) 532551
e-mail: broadhurst@broadhurst52fsnet.co.uk
Draught Bass; Ⓗ **Hardys & Hansons Best Bitter, Classic;** Ⓖ **Marston's Pedigree;** Ⓗ **seasonal beers** Ⓖ
Classic, unspoilt 19th-century working-class ale house, it was once regarded as the Bass brewery tap. Dispense is a mix of gravity

INDEPENDENT BREWERIES

Burton Bridge Burton upon Trent
Eccleshall Eccleshall
Enville Enville
Marston's Burton upon Trent
Old Cottage Burton upon Trent
Shraley Brook Shraley Brook
Shugborough Shugborough
Titanic Burslem
Tower Burton upon Trent

and handpumps. There is an efficient cask cooler system for use during hot weather. Drinks are served from a small counter adjacent to the cask stillages. Always a welcoming atmosphere in the inner tap room which has barrel tables, if possible sit on the raised bench seats. Ample seating in the main lounge and a small family room which can be used for meetings. Good value food available weekday lunchtimes. Impromptu folk music on Tue eve. Q ☎ ◖≠

Devonshire Arms

86 Station Street (300 yds from railway station)
✪ 11-2.30, 5.30-11; 11-11 Fri & Sat; 12-3, 7-10.30 Sun
☎ (01283) 562392
Burton Bridge Bridge Bitter, Stairway to Heaven, seasonal beers; guest beer Ⓗ
Local CAMRA *Pub of the Year* 2000. Possibly the oldest operating pub in Burton, originally the site was a market garden. The exterior is Grade II listed. Observe the interesting 1853 map of Burton and the unusual arched wooden ceilings. Comfortable two-bar pub with a relaxed atmosphere. Try the exotic European bottled beers and English fruit wines. Excellent home-made Sun lunches. Eve meals Mon-Thu. ❀◖ ⌑≠♣P✠

Thomas Sykes

Anglesey Road (1 mile from station, towards Branston, B5017)
✪ 11.30-2.30, 5 (7 Sat)-11; 11.30-11 Fri; 12-2.30, 7-10.30 Sun
☎ (01283) 510246
Draught Bass; Marston's Pedigree; guest beers Ⓗ
Classic ale house in the former stables and wagon sheds of the old Thomas Sykes Brewery. Listed building with cobble-stoned floors, high ceilings and breweriana offers an unspoilt, traditional atmosphere. The Sykes has a large function room, where skittles can be played, and a small, cosy lounge. Two guest beers are available on a regular changing rota. Note the unusual anvil table. Children are allowed until 8.30pm. Q ☎ ❀◖≠♣P

CAULDON

Yew Tree Inn

Off A52/A523 OS077493
✪ 11-3, 6-11; 12-3, 7-10.30 Sun
☎ (01538) 308348

Draught Bass; Burton Bridge Bridge Bitter; Titanic Mild Ⓗ
A visit to this unique pub is a must. Over 300 years old, it has been in the same family for 40 years. During that time an amazing collection of antiques and artefacts has been acquired. These include working polyphons, pianolas, grandfather clocks, musical instruments, radios, penny farthing bicycle – the list is endless. Note the Acme dog-carrier. There is an eclectic mix of seating including settles and pews. It has won many awards and has featured in the national press and on TV.
Q ☎ ❀♣P

CHASETOWN ✳

Uxbridge Arms

2 Church Street
✪ 12-3, 5.30-11; 12 Fri & Sat; 12-10.30 Sun
☎ (01543) 674853
Draught Bass; Highgate Dark; Stones Bitter; guest beers Ⓗ
Popular, comfortable local dating from the 1830s. The pub features a split-level lounge with an extensive collection of china plates. Extended public bar and a separate pool room. Two regularly changing guest beers are always stocked, often from smaller breweries. There is a large range of malt whiskies and a collection of country wines. No food Sun eve. Forecourt area for outdoor drinking.
❀◖ ⌑♣P

CHORLEY

Malt Shovel

Green Lane OSSK0611
✪ 7-11; 12-3 Sat (summer only); 12-3, 7-10.30 Sun
☎ (01543) 685277
Ansells Mild, Bitter; Tetley Bitter; guest beer Ⓗ
200-year-old traditional local in a quiet village fairly close to Cannock Chase. Pub games are played in the bar whereas the lounge is quiet, unexpectedly spacious but nevertheless cosy with two real fires. You can join in the old-fashioned singalong which takes place on the first Sat of the month. Guest ales are popular with the locals and change two or three times per week.
🏠Q ❀⌑▲♣P

INN BRIEF

ABBOTS BROMLEY
Bagot Inn
Bagot Street
12-3, 5-11; 12-11 Sat;
12-10.30 Sun
Marston's Pedigree Ⓗ
18th-century farm converted to an inn on the Uttoxeter road. Close to Blithfield Reservoir. Real fire in winter.

AMERTON
Plough
11-11;
12-10.30 Sun
Banks's Bitter; Mansfield Cask Dark Mild; Marston's Pedigree; guest beer Ⓗ
Ex-farmhouse with seating for 75 diners. Accommodation comprising six en-suite bedrooms. Extensive grounds for touring caravans. Children's play area.

BAGNALL
Stafford Arms
The Green
12-3.30, 6-11; 11-11 Sat; 12-10.30 Sun
Draught Bass; Hydes Bitter, Jekyll's Gold; guest beers Ⓗ
17th-century stone country inn just 10 minutes from city centre. Food available all times from sandwiches to full *à la carte* menu.

BARTON UNDER NEEDWOOD
Shoulder of Mutton
Main Street
11-3, 5-11; 11-11 Fri & Sat; 12-10.30 Sun
Draught Bass; Marston's Pedigree; guest beers Ⓗ
Excellent local at the centre of village life. Guest ales change almost daily. Over 265 served last year always in impeccable condition.

BLYTHE BRIDGE
Duke of Wellington
Uttoxeter Road
12-3, 6-11; 12-3.30, 5-11 Sat;
12-3, 7-10.30 Sun
Greene King Abbot; Marston's Pedigree; guest beers Ⓗ
Friendly, Victorian village local attracting broad-ranging clientele. Good food lunchtimes.

BURTON UPON TRENT
Derby Inn
17 Derby Road
11-3, 5.30-11; 11-11 Fri & Sat;
12-3, 7-10.30 Sun
Marston's Pedigree Ⓗ
Traditional two-roomed pub on edge of town. Locally grown produce available at weekends.

CODSALL

Codsall Station
Chapel Lane
✪ 11.30-2.30, 5-11; 11-11 Sat; 12-10.30 Sun
☎ (01902) 847061

Holden's Bitter, Golden Glow, Special Bitter; guest beer Ⓗ

Grade II listed railway station buildings sensitively restored by Holden's. Features three medium-sized drinking areas together with a conservatory and a patio. Good value home-cooked food – advisable to book for Sun lunch (no food Sun eve). A short train ride from Wolverhampton or Telford and a 10-minute walk from the bus terminus. Voted local CAMRA *Country Pub of the Year* 2000, just 18 months after opening. Railway Bitter is brewed by Holden's for the pub, and alternates with Holden's XB. Try the boules piste adjacent to the car park.
☸◑⇌P

COLTON

Greyhound
Bellamour Lane (B5013)
✪ 5.30-11; 12-11 Sat; 12-10.30 Sun
☎ (01889) 586769

Banks's Original; Draught Bass; Fuller's London Pride; Greene King Abbot; Marston's Pedigree Ⓗ

Classic, unspoilt village pub. Original building dates from 1830s and was refurbished by Banks's Brewery in mid 1980s. The games room upstairs was converted to living quarters, and the ground floor to bar and lounge. The splendid bar features a brick-lined real fire, stone floor and authentic wooden beams. There is an attractive garden area in front of the inn. Within easy reach of Rugeley Trent Valley Station. Blithfield reservoir is two miles to the north. No food Sun eve or Mon. ▟☸◑⊟♣P

COPMERE END

Star
1½ miles W of Eccleshall OS803294
✪ 12-3, 6-11; 12-11 Sat; 12-3, 7-10.30 Sun
☎ (01785) 850279

Draught Bass; Mansfield Cask Ale; guest beer (summer) Ⓗ

Off the beaten track, this former Joules' house is very much a locals' pub, visitors however are made very welcome in this cosy, traditional establishment. Parts of the building are thought to be around 200 years old. The pub is popular with walkers, cyclists and anglers. The Star angling club makes good use of Cop Mere, a 42-acre lake situated opposite the pub. The garden is set out with tables and has a large lawned area with trees and children's swings. Delicious home-cooked meals but no food served Sun eve. ▟Q☸◑⊟P

DOSTHILL

Fox Inn
105 High Street (off B5404)
✪ 12-3, 6-11; 12-3, 7-10.30 Sun
☎ (01827) 280841

Ansells Mild; Draught Bass; Greene King Abbot; Tetley Bitter; guest beers Ⓗ

Welcoming village pub with an ever-changing range of guest beers. Normally one of these is from the Church End Brewery; up to three guest beers are on at one time. A separate bar with a dining room adjoining the lounge with an outside drinking area; advisable to book for the restaurant. Q☸◑⊟♣P

ECCLESHALL

George
Castle Street
✪ 12-11; 12-10.30 Sun
☎ (01785) 850300

Eccleshall Slaters Bitter, Original, Top Totty, Premium, Supreme, seasonal beers Ⓗ

Famous for being the home of Slater's Brewery, it is difficult to believe that in the 1970s it was the only Eccleshall pub that did not sell real ale. Since the Slater family bought the former coaching inn over 10 years ago the bar and lounge areas have been thoughtfully redecorated. The cosy, unspoilt interior has a stone floor and log fire. Accommodation and meals are excellent and the pub has its own café bar. ▟☸⇌◑P

FORTON

Swan at Forton
Eccleshall Road (A519)
✪ 12-3, 6-11; 12-10.30 Sun
☎ (01952) 812169

Draught Bass; Boddingtons Bitter; Greene King Old Speckled Hen; Marston's Pedigree; guest beers Ⓗ

CANNOCK

Stumble Inn
264 Walsall Road, Bridetown
12-3, 6-11; 7-12 Sat;
12-10.30 Sun
Banks's Original; Marston's Pedigree; Taylor Landlord; guest beers Ⓗ
Comfortable one-roomed pub with late licence for Sat.

CHASETOWN

Junction
High Street
7 (5 Fri) 12-4, 7-11 Sat;
12-4, 7-10.30 Sun
Banks's Bitter; Draught Bass; Holden's Golden Glow; M&B Brew XI Ⓗ
Popular local dating from the 1850s, and featuring a single L-shaped room.

EBSTREE

Hollybush Inn
Ebstree Road, Trysull
11.30-3, 6-11; 12-4, 7-10.30 Sun
Greene King Abbot; Ind Coope Burton Ale; guest beer Ⓗ
Pleasant country inn. Large lounge and public bar. Garden with play area. Food now includes Sun lunches.

ENVILLE

Cat Inn
Bridgnorth Road
12-3, 7-11 (6-11 Wed-Fri, summer); closed Sun
Enville Ale; Everards Beacon; guest beers Ⓗ
The nearest outlet to Enville Brewery. This 16th-century inn has four lounges and a restaurant. Food highly recommended.

NEWCASTLE-UNDER-LYME

Hogshead
Ironmarket
11-11; 12-10.30 Sun
Boddingtons Bitter; Marston's Pedigree; Wadworth 6X; guest beers Ⓗ/Ⓖ
Former CAMRA Potteries branch *Pub of the Year* 1998. Refurbished in new Hogshead style but still offers largest range of ales in town.

RUGELEY

Plaza
Horsefair
11-11;
12-10.30 Sun
Banks's Original, Bitter; Shepherd Neame Spitfire; Theakston Best Bitter; Wadworth 6X Ⓗ
Sympathetically refurbished cinema on three levels. Food served all day. *Cask Marque* accredited.

Family-friendly,18th-century coaching inn on the Newport to Eccleshall road. Run by Mercury Management Traditional Free Houses since summer 2000, the Swan retains a distinctive atmosphere with large high-ceilinged, Georgian rooms. A conservatory accommodating an extensive restaurant is the only major refurbishment. Nine guest rooms are available in an adjacent converted barn. Popular with diners, particularly at weekends. ▲⊛✑◑ ÅP

FRADLEY JUNCTION

Swan Inn
OS140140
✪ 11-3, 6-11; 12-2.30, 7-10.30 Sun
☎ (01283) 790330
Ansells Mild, Bitter; Ind Coope Burton Ale; Marston's Pedigree Ⓗ
Originally part of the Shugborough estate of the Earls of Lichfield, the 200-year-old Swan is picturesquely situated next to the towpath of the Trent & Mersey Canal, at its junction with the Coventry Canal. This is a popular mooring point for pleasure craft and activity on the canal can be enjoyed from the outdoor drinking area beside the towpath. Internally the bar has original beams and high-backed settles. There is a separate lounge and a small cellar drinking area. ▲⊛◑P

GNOSALL

Royal Oak
Newport Road (A518)
✪ 12-3, 6-11; (12-11 summer Sat); 12-4, 7-10.30 Sun
☎ (01785) 822362
website: www.theroyal-oak.co.uk/gnosall
Greene King Abbot; Ind Coope Burton Ale; Tetley Bitter; guest beer Ⓗ
Popular village local, once a coaching inn although the exact date of the building is not clear. In the 1920s a weekly cattle market was held at the Royal Oak as a sale poster in the lounge reminds us. The upstairs function room serves as a family room and as a restaurant where customers can enjoy the carveries held on Sat eve and Sun lunchtime. The garden has a children's play area with a climbing frame. ▲⏟⊛◑ ⊟♣P

GREAT CHATWELL

Red Lion
2 miles E of A41, near Newport OS792143
✪ 6 (11 Sat)-11; 12-10.30 Sun
☎ (01952) 691366
Everards Beacon, Tiger; Flowers IPA; Worthington Bitter; guest beers Ⓗ
Welcoming, family-run country pub in a small village. The Red Lion features two separate bars, a restaurant and a large games room. Part of the building dates from the 18th century. The pub was sensitively refurbished and extended in 1991, when a children's play area and aviary were created in the garden. Popular local venue in the summer months and has a reputation for good value food, and for being family-friendly.
▲⏟⊛◑ ⊟Å♣P

HEDNESFORD

Queen's Arms
37 Hill Street (off A460)
✪ 12-3, 7-11; 12-3, 7-10.30 Sun
☎ (01543) 878437
Draught Bass; Highgate Dark; Worthington Bitter Ⓟ
Very popular pub situated on the main road between Cannock and Rugeley, south of the town centre. The first recorded landlord was in 1866. The lounge, where quizzes are held on Mon eve, used to be two rooms, one of which was the outdoor bar. Now decorated with many brasses, copper kettles, and miners' lamps over the bar. Meals are very good value. Q◑♣P

HIGH OFFLEY

Anchor ☆
Peggs Lane, Old Lea (by bridge 42 of Shropshire Union Canal) OS775256
✪ Summer: 11-3, 6-11; 12-3, 7-10.30 Sun; Winter: 11-3 Fri only, 7-11 Fri & Sat ; 12-3 Sun
☎ (01785) 284569
Marston's Pedigree (summer)**; Wadworth 6X** Ⓗ /Ⓖ
Situated on the Shropshire Union Canal this Victorian two-bar inn is a rare example of an unspoilt, traditional, country pub. Cask ales are dispensed by the jug from the cellar. Open only Fri to Sun in winter, this free house has been run by the same family since 1870, when it was called the Sebastopol. Busy in the summer with passing canalside traffic, it features a canalware gift shop at the rear. About two miles from the A519, the pub is not easily found by road, but well worth the trip. Local CAMRA *Pub of the Year* 2000.
▲Q⊛⊟Å♣P

HILL RIDWARE

Chadwick Arms
Uttoxeter Road
✪ 11.30-3 (not Mon), 5 (6 Mon)-11; 12-3, 5-10.30 Sun
☎ (01543) 490552
Banks's Bitter; Ⓟ **Marston's Pedigree; guest beer** (occasional) Ⓗ
300-year-old rural pub centrally located in this quiet village, close to the River Trent. Plenty of seating space within the three rooms which are for drinking only. Separately-run Chinese restaurant specialising in Cantonese meals accessible directly from the lounge. Ample parking and a bowling green at the rear. The pub acts as a focus for a number of local societies. Locally, visit the old church at Mavesyn Ridware and the theatre in Pipe Ridware (a former church). Q⊛◑ ⊟Å♣P

HOAR CROSS

Meynell Ingram Arms
OS SK1323
✪ 12-11; 12-10.30 Sun
☎ (01283) 575202
Marston's Pedigree; Shepherd Neame Spitfire; Taylor Landlord Ⓗ
Unspoilt village pub in a pleasant rural setting. The Meynell dates from the early 16th century when it formed part of the Earl of Shrewsbury's estate. It was named after the Meynell family who purchased nearby Hoar Cross Hall. It features original

beams, quarry-tiled floor and log fires. The bar has several different drinking areas and there is a small lounge and a restaurant/function room converted from former outbuildings. No food Sun eve. Attractive paved courtyard. ▨Q☸◑♣P

HOPWAS

Red Lion
Lichfield Road
✪ 11.30-2.30; 5-11; 11.30-11 Sat; 12-10.30 Sun
☎ (01827) 62514
Ansells Mild, Ⓟ Bitter; Marston's Pedigree; guest beer Ⓗ

Canalside village local with safe garden, easily found via Tamworth to Lichfield bus route. A large fireplace divides the bar into two areas, a large collection of miniatures is displayed. A separate restaurant area is in the lounge. Visitors should beware of the humpback bridge on leaving and also check if food is available if planning to dine on Sun or Mon eves. Guest beers are normally changed weekly. ☸◑Ⅎ♣P

KIDSGROVE

Blue Bell
25 Hardingswood (300 yds from rail bridge over A50 on canal)
✪ 1-3.30 (not Mon), 7.30 (7 Sat)-11; 12-3.30, 7.30 (7 summer)-10.30 Sun
☎ (01782) 774052
e-mail: davewashbrook@hotmail.com
Thwaites Bitter; guest beers Ⓗ

Genuine free house of four small rooms in a canalside location. The beers change rapidly here. On a busy Fri or Sat eve four of the six handpumps may change clips. Most beers are from micros and small breweries across the country, 800 in three years. Real cider or perry is always available, plus two draught lager beers and a wheat beer, and around 30 Belgian and German bottled beers. No TV, juke box, pool or bandits disturb the atmosphere. CAMRA Potteries & Staffordshire *Pub of the Year* and Potteries Pub Preservation Group *Community Pub* 2000. Q☸≈♦P⌿

KINVER

Olde White Harte Hotel
111 High Street
✪ 11.30-11; 12-10.30 Sun
☎ (01384) 872305
Banks's Original, Bitter; Ⓟ Marston's Pedigree, seasonal beers Ⓗ

This old village-centre pub has existed since at least the early 17th century. Former coaching inn on the old route between Chester and the south-west, it is a lively pub, popular with visitors and locals alike. The interior has been modernised and is generally open plan but with a separate no-smoking verandah for both diners and drinkers. There is also a pleasant enclosed patio area at the rear with a children's play area. Meals are served all day. ☸◑P⌿⊟

Plough & Harrow
82 High Street
✪ 6 (12.30 Sat)-11; 12-10.30 Sun
☎ (01384) 872659
Batham Mild, Best Bitter, XXX Ⓗ

Two-roomed pub known locally as 'The

Steps' as the rooms are on ascending levels. Popular with walkers, campers and cyclists as well as locals. A lively village-centre pub about 500 yards from Staffordshire & Worcestershire Canal. A Batham's tied house since 1952, like many pubs in the area it was previously a home-brew house. The basic bar has pub games while the plusher lounge's walls are adorned with pictures of film stars. Hosts live music most Sun and Thu eves. Food is available weekends only, and real cider served in summer. ☸◑Ⅎ♦P

Vine
1 Dunsley Road (just off High St)
✪ 12-11; 12-10.30 Sun
☎ (01384) 877291
Enville Ale; Wood Shropshire Lad; guest beers Ⓗ

One-roomed canalside pub founded in competition with the Lock Inn (which stood opposite until its demolition) on completion of the Dunsley section of the Staffordshire & Worcestershire Canal. The pub has extended into adjacent cottages over the years and most interior walls were removed during alterations in 1980. It has extensive canalside gardens with children's play area. Food is served in a dining area (all day at weekends). ☸◑P⊟

KNIGHTON

Haberdasher's Arms
Between Adbaston and Knighton OS753276
✪ 12.30-11 (may close afternoon); 12-10.30 Sun
☎ (01785) 280650 e-mail:
trevor@haberdashers.freeserve.co.uk
Banks's Original, Bitter; guest beers Ⓗ

Sadly country pub closures have been a common occurrence over the last decade. This pub is an example of a closure threat with a happy ending. Following plans to close the Haberdasher's in 1997, over 200 villagers signed a petition and fortunately saved it. Built in the 1840s, this traditional community pub has four rooms and one small bar. Large garden used for local events including an annual potato club show. Local CAMRA *Pub of the Year* 1999. ▨Q☙☸Ⅎ▲♣P⊟

LAPLEY

Vaughan Arms
Bickford Lane (1½ miles N of A5 near Penkridge) OS874130
✪ 12.30-2.30 (not Mon), 7-11; 12-3, 6.30-11 Sat; 12-3, 7-10.30 Sun
☎ (01785) 840325
Banks's Original; Marston's Bitter, Pedigree; guest beers Ⓗ

Friendly village pub named after the Vaughan family who resided at Lapley Hall. The pub was originally located 200 yards from its current site, but moved in the 1890s due to complaints by Hall residents of rowdiness at closing times. This lively pub can get busy at weekends despite its relatively isolated location. Food is a prominent feature, and the Vaughan Arms has an excellent local reputation. Regular quizzes are held and it is a convivial meeting place for local clubs, establishing it firmly as a community pub. ▨☸◑♿▲♣P

LEEK

Den Engel
23-25 St Edward Street
✪ 5-11; 12-11 Fri & Sat; 12-3, 7-10.30 Sun
☎ (01538) 373751 e-mail: denengel@netcentral.co.uk
Beer range varies Ⓗ
Outstanding, even in an exceptional drinking town. Prominent brick building, which houses a superb Belgian-style bar. Up to four ever-changing cask ales together with a selection of over 130 Belgian bottled beers, all served in the correct glass by waiter service. Also over 35 Belgian Genevers available, one of which is always being promoted. Small, but cosy Flemish restaurant on the first floor offers beer-based cuisine including Stoverj (beef in Belgian abbey beer) (lunches Fri and Sat; eve meals Wed-Sat). Bar meals also offered. Q ◖◗ ●

Swan
2 St Edward Street
✪ 11-3, 7-11; 12-3, 7-10.30 Sun
☎ (01538) 382081
e-mail: the.swan.leek@amserve.net
Draught Bass; Fuller's London Pride; Greene King IPA; Highgate Dark; Young's Special; guest beers Ⓗ
Leek's oldest pub, parts of the building date back to the 15th century. Three-roomed layout comprises public bar, lounge and snug. The lounge is given over mainly to non-smoking diners at lunchtimes. The long-serving licensees have won many awards and create, together with the staff, a friendly, welcoming atmosphere. The large Georgian-style function suite hosts many events including weddings. The Cuckoo's Nest folk club is long-established here and enjoys a loyal following. Downstairs is DJ's Sports Bar and bistro catering for the younger set.
Q ❀ ◖◗ ⊟ & ● ⚤

Wilke's Head
16 St Edward Street
✪ 11-11; 12-10.30 Sun
☎ (01538) 383616
Whim Arbor Light, Magic Mushroom Mild, Hartington Bitter, Hartington IPA, seasonal beers; guest beers Ⓗ
The town's second oldest pub, a former coaching inn dating back to about 1800. It has an unspoilt interior with three areas. The main drinking area is around the bar, where robust conversation is the norm. There is a smaller area to the rear, while the third option is the family room, which also hosts acoustic music sessions on Mon eve. Large courtyard doubles as a car park and beer garden. Outside events held here during the summer. ☙ ❀ P

LICHFIELD

Acorn Inn
12 Tamworth Street
✪ 11-11; 12-10.30 Sun
☎ (01543) 263400
Banks's Bitter; Courage Directors; Theakston Best Bitter; guest beers Ⓗ
Large Wetherspoon's establishment previously derelict shops, has neighbouring pubs on both sides, one of which was formerly the Acorn. The choice of name for this pub was the result of a local drinker writing to the group advising of the general disappointment when the next-door pub

changed its name. The pub is typical of the group with a strict no-smoking policy at the bar and a good-sized no-smoking area at the rear. An interesting feature is the purpose-built bridge over the drinking area along which casks are delivered to the stillage.
Q ◖◗ ≋ (City) ⚤ ●

Earl of Lichfield Arms
10 Conduit Street
✪ 11-11; 12-10.30 Sun
☎ (01543) 251020
Banks's Original, Bitter; Marston's Pedigree, seasonal beers Ⓗ
Popular, market-place pub known locally as 'The Drum'. The nickname is claimed to have arisen during the 1800s when army recruiting officers used to stand outside to the sound of a drum. Around 30 years ago the small single-roomed pub took over an adjacent barber's shop which became the bar. A more recent change resulted in an open-plan design with a multi-level, bare-boarded floor. Part of the original wooden framed structure is visible opposite the main servery. The enclosed beer garden is a welcome retreat in the summer. Good value lunches are served Mon-Sat.
❀ ◖◗ ≋ (City)

George & Dragon
28 Beacon Street
✪ 12-11; 12-3.30, 8-10.30 Sun
☎ (01543) 263554
Banks's Original, Bitter; Ⓟ **Marston's Pedigree** Ⓗ
Traditional, two-roomed pub close to the cathedral. Choose the public bar for pub games and TV sport while the cosy lounge is good for conversation. A former toll house is next door. The George flag is displayed outside on St George's Day and other suitable occasions. To the rear is a small paved outdoor drinking area, adjacent to the car park.
Q ❀ ⊟ ≋ (City) P

Queen's Head
Queen Street
✪ 12-11; 12-3, 7-10.30 Sun
☎ (01543) 410932
e-mail: queens@atworldonline.co.uk
Adnams Bitter; Marston's Pedigree; Taylor Landlord; guest beers Ⓗ
Bustling, single-roomed pub only five minutes' walk from the cathedral and city centre. A rare example of a Marston's Ale House, built in 1837 and named to commemorate the coronation of Queen Victoria. Frequented by many real ale loving sports fans, home to two local cricket teams and many rugby fans. A popular feature is the speciality cheese counter where up to 15 unusual cheeses can be purchased.
Q ◖◗ ≋ (City) ♣

LITTLE HAYWOOD

Red Lion
Main Road
✪ 4 (12 Fri & Sat)-11; 12-10.30 Sun
☎ (01889) 881314
Banks's Bitter; Marston's Bitter, Pedigree Ⓗ
Excellent, two-roomed village local that has changed little since being rebuilt in the 1930s. A brief history of the pub is displayed in the lounge. At the side of the pub is an immaculate garden which

together with the hanging baskets has brought success in the *Stafford-in-Bloom* and the *Best-kept village* contests. Convenient for visitors to nearby Cannock Chase and the National Trust property Shugborough Hall. A specially brewed monthly beer from Banks's, Marston's or Mansfield is stocked. ⚏✿⊞♣P

LONGDON

Swan with Two Necks
40 Brook End
🕓 12-2.30, 7-11; 12-3, 7-11 Sat; 12-3, 7-10.30 Sun
☎ (01543) 490251
Ansells Bitter; Draught Bass; Ind Coope Burton Ale; guest beer Ⓗ
This inn is the very essence of all that is good about an English village pub. Yet it is run by a Frenchman, who is famous in the locality for his giant home-grown onions and marrows. It has featured in all but one of the last 24 editions of this *Guide*. Alongside his English wife, his enthusiasm for his beer, especially his beloved guest ales, is matched only by his more predictable love of good food. A friendly atmosphere pervades the low-beamed, quarry-tiled bar. A lounge and small restaurant are more secluded areas for diners. Children under 14 and dogs are not admitted. ⚏Q✿◖P

MEAFORD

George & Dragon
On A34, N of Stone, 100 yds S of A34/A51 jct
🕓 11-11; 12-10.30 Sun
☎ (01785) 818497 e-mail: bobbyq@barclaysnet.co
Burtonwood Bitter, Top Hat; guest beer Ⓗ
The village of Meaford is mentioned in the *Domesday Book*. The inn was rebuilt in 1887 by Lady Forester of Meaford Hall. The pub sign of copper and wrought iron still swings in the wind today. The pub is spacious, wood-panelling predominates and it has a superb upstairs restaurant. Children welcome. Burtonwood has bestowed many awards upon the vastly experienced licensee from *Pub of the Year* (on more than one occasion) to *Best Pub Frontage* 2000. Ideally situated for the Potteries, two miles from the Wedgwood Visitor Centre and only a short walk from the Trent & Mersey Canal. ✿◖&♣P

MILWICH

Green Man
Sandon Lane (B5027)
🕓 12-2 (not Mon-Wed), 5-11; 12-11 Sat; 12-10.30 Sun
☎ (01889) 505310
Draught Bass; Worthington Bitter; guest beer Ⓗ
Reputedly the pub where Thomas Moss sold his wife to John Keeling in 1763 for two guineas. This superb village local dates from the late 15th century. A list of landlords since 1792 is displayed in the bar. The current host always has one guest ale on sale, the next choice on the board entices the locals into a rapid turnover, so quality is assured. Visitors are always made to feel welcome, popular with walkers and cyclists. Food available Thu-Sun. ⚏✿◖▲♣P

NEWCASTLE-UNDER-LYME ❖

Albert Inn
1 Brindley Street (off A34/A523 ring road)
🕓 11-3 (not Tue-Thu), 5-11, 12-11 Fri; 11-4, 7-11 Sat; 12-4, 7-10.30 Sun
☎ (01782) 615525
Burtonwood Bitter, Top Hat Ⓗ
Victorian, street-corner local popular with all age groups. Named after Queen Victoria's consort, licensees have been traced back as far as 1861, the year of Albert's death. The one drinking area is comfortably furnished, bench seats run down both sides, the walls are adorned with photographs of old Newcastle and a collection of clay pipes hangs over the entrance. The tiled mural on the exterior is a modern replacement. ♣

Museum Inn
29 George Street (on A52, ¼ mile E of centre)
🕓 12-11; 12-4, 7-10.30 Sun
☎ (01782) 623866
Draught Bass; Flowers Original; Worthington Bitter; guest beer Ⓗ
Very traditional, street-corner locals' pub. The public bar is an unspoilt gem and popular while the lounge is suitable for a quieter drink and available for parties and meetings. Rotating guest beer is displayed at the entrance and is usually from the Museum Brewing Company of Burton. A lunchtime special is available together with a choice of sandwiches. This is a real pub in an area dominated by the plastic equivalent. ✿◖♣♣

OULTON

Brushmaker's Arms
Kibblestone Road
(corner of Church Lane)
🕓 12-3, 6.30-11; 12-3, 6-10.30 Sun
☎ (01785) 812062
Draught Bass; Worthington Bitter; guest beers Ⓗ
A former house licensed as a pub in 1865. One of only two pubs in the country named after the former cottage industry of brushmaking. One mile north-east of Stone, this gem of a village pub has a basic unspoilt bar with Joules' memorabilia. Pictures and postcards of Oulton and Stone adorn the walls, reflecting a bygone era. The lounge is small, quaint and comfortable. Creamflow 'out' and guest ales 'in' has pleased most customers. ⚏Q✿⊞♣P

PENKRIDGE

Boat
Cannock Road (by Staffs & Worcs Canal)
🕓 11-11; 12-10.30 Sun
☎ (01785) 714178
Ansells Bitter; Marston's Pedigree; guest beer Ⓗ
Built two centuries ago alongside the newly excavated Staffordshire & Worcestershire Canal, this pub is deservedly popular with the seasonal boat trade. The building has been modernised and extended in recent years but it retains a homely atmosphere, with a pleasant outdoor drinking area alongside and overlooking the canal. Tue is quiz night. ⚏✿◖&♣P

PENN COMMON

Barley Mow

Pennwood Lane (follow signs for Penn Golf Club from A449) OS949902

☼ 12-2.30, 6-11; 12-11 Sat; 12-10.30 Sun

☎ (01902) 333510

Banks's Original; Greene King Abbot; Ind Coope Burton Ale; guest beers Ⓗ

Welcoming pub next to Penn Golf Club. The original building dates from the 1630s with a small extension added in 1999. Warning, if you are over 5'6" tall be prepared to duck as the original section has a very low ceiling. Excellent home-made food, the meat is supplied from the landlord's own butcher's shop. Popular pub with garden and play area, ideal for a drink after a round of golf. ❀◑P

REAPSMOOR

Olde Butcher's Arms

Off B5053 Thorncliff to Warslow road OS082014

☼ 7-11; 12-4, 7-10.30 Sun

☎ (01298) 84477

Beer range varies Ⓗ/Ⓖ

Genuine rural gem, stone-built in an isolated situation surrounded by open moorlands. Very difficult to find but worth the effort. Comprises several small rooms, some of which used to be cattle accommodation when it was a farm pub. Layout is partly open plan but the pub is traditionally decorated and furnished. Each room has a cosy open fire. The dining room serves good value meals. Free camping at rear for customers. Excellent walking country nearby in Peak District National Park. ⋈Q✿◑⊟▲♣●P

STAFFORD ❊

Bird in Hand

Victoria Square (opp. Crown Court)

☼ 12-11; 12-10.30 Sun

☎ (01785) 252198

Courage Best Bitter, Directors; John Smith's Bitter; Worthington Bitter Ⓗ

The crosses each side of the main door are now the only indication that the 'Bird' was once owned by Joules' Brewery of Stone. The pub's layout has changed little over the years and is unusual in having four separate rooms. The bar with TV, quieter snug, games room with pool tables and large lounge attract a broad range of customers. It is just a few yards from the Ancient High House, England's largest timber-framed house, and is on the direct pedestrian route between the railway station and town centre. ❀◑⊟≠♣

Hogshead

Unit 3, Earl Street (opp. St Mary's church)

☼ 11-11; 12-10.30 Sun

☎ (01785) 241560

Banks's Bitter; Boddingtons Bitter; Marston's Pedigree; Wadworth 6X; guest beers Ⓗ

Conversion of the former county education offices, a formidable building, has created one of the town's largest pubs. The Hogshead has lofty ceilings, many windows, 40 tables and local photographs from early last century when it was built. Prime location, sandwiched between the Crown Court and Stafford College, the pub has

many customers from both institutions. Although quiet enough at lunchtimes, the piped music volume can be noisy late eve. A 20p a pint discount for guest beers is given on production of a CAMRA membership card. ◑⬥≠●⑆

Stafford Arms

Railway Street (opp. station)

☼ 12-11; 12-4, 7-10.30 Sun

☎ (01785) 253313

Titanic Best Bitter, White Star, guest beers Ⓗ

Circuit drinkers are deterred by the five minute walk from the town centre and instead the Stafford Arms' clientele is a happy band of discerning drinkers, mostly Staffordians and rail travellers. Owned by Titanic Inns for six years, the pub was bought in 1999 by Punch, who soon learnt that success depended on a good choice of beer from both Titanic and other micros. Renowned for its beer and awarded CAMRA Stafford and Stone *Pub of the Decade* for the 1990s, it also offers superb food, having appointed the head chef from a top local hotel. No food Sun. Q✿⋈◑≠♣●P

Tap & Spile

59 Peel Terrace (off B5066, 1 mile from centre)

☼ 4.30-11; 12-11 Fri & Sat; 12-10.30 Sun

☎ (01785) 223563

e-mail: stevetideswell@hotmail.com

Beer range varies Ⓗ

Built early last century as 'the cottage by the brook', this large pub's fortunes changed on being converted to a Tap & Spile in 1994. Now a thriving community local, with several sports teams, include darts, crib, football and women's netbal. Its four drinking areas including a long bar, sizeable no-smoking room and separate lounge. There's a free bar billiards table and regular quiz nights. The eight regularly-changing handpumped beers, mostly from regional and micro-brewers, total over 600 a year and casks sometimes last for less than an hour. ⋈❀⊟♣⑆

STOKE-ON-TRENT: BURSLEM ❊

Bull's Head

St John's Square

☼ 5-11 Mon-Wed; 12-3, 7-11 Thu; 11-11 Fri & Sat; 12-10.30 Sun

☎ (01782) 834153

Titanic Best Bitter, Premium, White Star, Captain Smith's, seasonal beers; guest beers Ⓗ

Welcome return to this *Guide* for the Titanic brewery tap. Two-roomed, town-centre pub with much memorabilia relating to the ill-fated Titanic, after which the brewery is named. The captain was born in Stoke-on-Trent and the brewery has named a beer after him. A tied house that is more of a free house, guest beers are always from other micro-breweries. Regular beer festivals held during the year. Popular with old and young alike. Bar billiards and table skittles played. ⋈Q❀⊟♣

FENTON ❊

Malt 'n' Hops

295 King Street

☻ 12-3, 7-11; 12-3, 7-10.30 Sun
☎ (01782) 313406
Highgate Dark; guest beers Ⓗ
Busy, genuine free house, one of the very
few in the city. Comprising a single room
greatly extended over the years, a split-level
layout gives the impression of two rooms, a
traditional bar and a comfortable lounge.
Ever-changing independents make this a
very beer-orientated pub noted for choice
and quality. Belgian beers are also available.
≠ (Longton)

HANLEY

Golden Cup
65 Old Town Road (off B5017 town road near
A50, Potteries Way ring road)
☻ 11.30-11; 12-4, 7-10.30 Sun
☎ (01782) 212045
Draught Bass Ⓗ
Friendly Potteries local, a short walk from
city-centre shops and cultural quarter. An
ornate ceramic exterior proclaims 'Bass
only' while the traditional bar contains
splendid original fittings. First recipient of the
Potteries Pub Preservation Group's
Community Pub of the Year 1998 in
recognition of its value to the locality, the
pub runs a thriving pensioners club. ❀◑♣

Hogshead
2-6 Percy Street
☻ 11-11; 12-10.30 Sun
☎ (01782) 209585
**Boddingtons Bitter; Flowers IPA; Marston's Pedigree;
Wadworth 6X;** Ⓗ **guest beers** Ⓗ/Ⓖ
Large city-centre Hogshead with
comfortable surroundings and welcoming
staff. The split-level interior contains several
distinct areas, the focus is the long bar with
eight handpumped beers and four on
gravity. Glass panes in the roof create a
refreshing atmosphere on sunny days.
Handy for the cultural quarter venues,
Regent Theatre and Victoria Hall. Rare
outlet for local Titanic Brewery ales.

Frequent festivals offer spring, summer and
winter ales from small breweries and
micros. ◑ &

HARTSHILL

Jolly Potters
296 Hartshill Road (A52)
☻ 12-11; 12-10.30 Sun
☎ (01782) 845254
**Draught Bass; Flowers Original; Museum Joules Bitter;
Wadworth 6X; guest beer** Ⓗ
Nestling in the shadow of Hartshill church
this 160-year-old pub retains a traditional
style and character. The four separate rooms
have a central bar servery. Located within
the Hartshill Conservation Area created by
Thomas Minton, the famous potter,
founder of the world-renowned tile
company. Many of the Minton family are
buried in the churchyard. No juke boxes,
pool tables or gaming machines. Soft
background music is played, but can be
turned down by request. An ideal venue for
meeting friends and enjoying a quality pint
in a convivial atmosphere. ⚘❀Ⓗ♣

LONGPORT

Packhorse
8 Station Street (A527)
☻ 12-11; 12-10.30 Sun
☎ (01782) 577322
**Caledonian Deuchars IPA; Marston's Pedigree;
Theakston Best Bitter; guest beer** Ⓗ
Located on the main road alongside Trent &
Mersey Canal and Longport Marina, the
single bar has a section reserved for diners,
selection of real ales and good-value
traditional pub food. Other attractions
include live music on Fri and Sat eve and
twice-yearly beer festivals. These events are
held in an excellent function room in a
converted stable block to the rear. Pleasant
courtyard patio is perfect for warm summer
eves.
❀◑≠♣

INN BRIEF

STAFFORD
Lord Nelson
31 Eastgate Street
11.30-11; 12-10.30 Sun
**Theakston XB; Wells Bombardier;
guest beer** Ⓗ
Unpretentious former coaching inn
and ex-Butlers pub. Juke box in
bar, pool and darts in games room.
Often two guest beers.

Railway Inn
Castle Street, Castletown
12-2, 6-11; 12-3, 7-10.30 Sun
**Draught Bass; Greene King Abbot; Tetley
Bitter; guest beers** Ⓗ
Traditional end-of-terrace pub near
railway station and Sainsbury's
superstore. Three rooms. Children
are welcome.

STOKE ON TRENT: BURSLEM
Vine
Hamil Road
12-11; 12-10.30 Sun
**Courage Best Bitter, Directors;
guest beers** Ⓗ
1930s pub refurbished in recent
years but retaining local
atmosphere. Handy for Port Vale
FC. Solid, reliable local in centre of
Burslem.

FENTON
Potter
King Street
12-11, 11-11 Sat; 12-10.30 Sun
**Draught Bass; Everards Beacon;
Worthington Bitter; guest beers** Ⓗ
Free house consisting of bar, snug
and games room. Warm welcome
to all customers old and new in
relaxed atmosphere.

GOLDENHILL
Cushion
230 Broadfield Road
5 (3 Fri)-11; 12-5, 7-11 Sat; 12-10.30 Sun
**Greenalls Bitter; Marston's Pedigree;
guest beers** Ⓗ
Small, well-refurbished free house.
One bar but gives the impression of
two rooms. Offers a remarkably
rural outlook for a town pub.

STONE
Star
21 Stafford Street
11-11; 12-10.30 Sun
**Banks's Original, Bitter; Marston's
Pedigree; guest beer** Ⓗ
Dating from 1568, original bar
unspoilt by recent extensions to
the catering-orientated lounge area.
On Trent & Mersey Canal.

TWO GATES
Bull's Head
Watling Street
12-2.30 (3 Sat), 6.30-11; 12-2.30;
7-10.30 Sun
Banks's Original; Marston's Pedigree Ⓗ
Popular local featuring comfortable
bar and lounge. Excellent value
food available lunchtimes except
Sun. Pub has its own golf society.

Check it out

**Pubs in the Good Beer
Guide may change
ownership and the
facilities listed could
alter. If a visit to a pub
in the guide involves a
lengthy journey, it is
advisable to check
before leaving that full
meals, family facilities,
accommodation or
camping sites are still
available.**

MIDDLEPORT

White Swan
107 Newport Lane (B5051)
☼ 11-11; 11-4, 7-11 Sat; 12-3, 7-10.30 Sun
☎ (01782) 813639
Draught Bass; Boddingtons Bitter; Brakspear Special; Flowers IPA Ⓗ

A real gem; popular free house hidden in the back streets among the local 'pot banks'. A real community local, it attracts pottery workers, residents, football fans and local beer lovers for its down-to-earth friendliness and good ale. Lively conversation is the norm. Well worth seeking out. Other beers are available from time to time including real cask mild.
⇋Q⌂≠ (Longport) ♣

PENKHULL

Greyhound
Manor Court Street
☼ 11-11; 12-10.30 Sun
☎ (01782) 848978
e-mail: pam@the-greyhound.fsbusiness.co.uk
Greene King Old Speckled Hen; Marston's Pedigree; Tetley Bitter; guest beer Ⓗ

This typically English pub oozes history. The public bar was built in 1540 and extended in 1704. It boasts an oak-beamed ceiling from its days as the manor courthouse of Newcastle-under-Lyme. The separate lounge has a log fire, and an area known as the Judges robing room. Food available includes some Australian delicacies, the landlord also ensures the Aussie flag flies proudly above the building, making it hard to miss for anyone entering Penkhull village. Also sells Hoegaarden on draught. No food Sun eve.
⇋Q❀◖P

Marquis of Granby
St Thomas's Place
☼ 12-11; 12-10.30 Sun
☎ (01782) 847025
Banks's Original, Bitter; Camerons Bitter; Marston's Pedigree Ⓗ

Imposing red-brick building in the centre of Penkhull, the pub is particularly well-furnished. Fine public bar with full set of engraved windows proclaiming it as 'The Vaults' and traditional bench seating. Very comfortable lounge with separate bar and corner snug areas off main section. Food served lunchtimes (when section is no-smoking). Keenly-priced menu offers plenty of choice including vegetarian options and children's menu. Excellent covered patio and large terraced garden.
❀◖⌂♣P●

TUNSTALL

White Hart
43 Roundwell Street (¼ mile W of Haymarket roundabout on A50)
☼ 11-11; 12-10.30 Sun
☎ (01782) 835817
Marston's Bitter, Pedigree Ⓗ

A modest exterior conceals a comfortable single bar in this community local. Friendly atmosphere and Marston's ales attract punters from miles around. A beer drinkers' pub where preference is for quality rather than variety. Attractions include regular

Karaoke and occasional barbecues in summer. There's a strict ban on bad language. ❀

STONE ❀

Red Lion
25 High Street
☼ 11-11; 12-10.30 Sun
☎ (01785) 814500
Everards Tiger; guest beers Ⓗ

Reputedly Stone's third oldest pub, the earliest licence was recorded in 1793. Joules' memorabilia is displayed in the quiet lounge which overlooks the High Street. The bar is spacious having been recently extended. The current licensee has rejuvenated this house; a tenant of Punch Taverns, his guest beer rights are fully utilised, bringing superb ales from the length and breadth of Britain. One regular guest ale is Museum Joule's Bitter. Excellent jazz nights every Mon. Pool table and darts at the rear of bar.
⌂♣

Swan
18 Stafford Street (by Trent & Mersey canal)
☼ 11-11; 12-10.30 Sun
☎ (01785) 815570 website: www.into-stone.co.uk
Joule Old Knotty, Old Priory, Victory; guest beers Ⓗ

This 18th-century, Grade II listed building was converted to a pub in the mid-19th-century. Superbly renovated in 1999 into the comfortable hostelry it is today. Guest beers bring a diversity of ale to a town (via 10 handpulls) bereft of choice during the '80s and '90s. RCH and Hart often available. Beer festival every July to coincide with the Stone festival. Three nights of live entertainment, quiz nights on Tue. Basic food available Mon-Sat, the oatcake dishes are superb. Two traditional ciders, Apples and Saxon, always stocked.
⇋❀◖& ♦

TAMWORTH

Albert
32 Albert Road (near station)
☼ 5-11; 12-3, 7-11 Sat; 12-3, 7-10.30 Sun
☎ (01827) 64694
Banks's Original, Bitter; Camerons Strongarm; guest beer Ⓗ

Popular local where a warm welcome is guaranteed. Handy for the railway station. A previous local CAMRA *Pub of the Year* winner. The guest beer is from Banks's portfolio. Roadside seating available for outdoor drinking.
❀≠⌂&≠♣P❏

Jailhouse Rock Café
97a Lichfield Street
☼ 12-11; 12-10.30 Sun
☎ (01827) 61280
Marston's Pedigree; guest beer Ⓗ

Lively pub on the edge of the town centre. Recently refurbished it attracts a varied clientele including bikers. Loud rock music, played by the pub's own DJ, in the back room. Pool, table football and quiz machines available and large TV screen for sport. Guest beer changes regularly. Patio area for outdoor drinking. Topless barmaids on Sun lunchtimes.
❀◖&✂

White Lion

Aldergate (next to council offices)

✪ 11-11; 12-10.30 Sun

☎ (01827) 64630

Banks's Original, Bitter; guest beer Ⓗ

Lively, two-roomed town-centre pub. The White Lion is popular with all age groups and tends to get busy at weekends. The guest beer is often from local micro-breweries. Lunchtime meals are served and the Sunday roasts are particularly recommended. The pub has its own car park. ◑&≉P

UTTOXETER

Roebuck

Dove Bank (A518)

✪ 11-2.30, 5-11; 11-11 Fri & Sat; 12-4, 7-10.30 Sun

☎ (01889) 565563

Theakston Best Bitter, XB; guest beers Ⓗ

Serving three guest beers, this pub offers the best choice of real ales in town and is well-patronised by discerning drinkers. Dating from the 17th century, this former beer retailing premises became a pub 100 years ago. There are five distinct bar areas which support several games teams and a football team. Handy for Uttoxeter National Hunt racecourse which also hosts antique fairs. Ghostly apparitions have been witnessed inside the pub. The outside drinking area is not suitable for children.
❀◑⌂Å≉♣P

Vaults

Market Place

✪ 11-3 (4 Wed, Fri & Sat), 5.30 (5 Fri; 7 Sat)-11; 12-3, 7-10.30 Sun

☎ (01889) 562997

Draught Bass; Marston's Pedigree; Worthington Bitter Ⓗ

One of the town's oldest pubs, the Vaults is a sound ale house which has remained virtually unchanged for decades. Lined up behind the narrow, terraced frontage are three separate rooms each with the emphasis on traditional pub games. Darts is keenly played in the front and back rooms while table skittles can be enjoyed in the centre one. Traditional mummer's plays are performed at Christmas with actors from the pub visiting other hostelries in the town. Acoustic instrumental jam sessions take place on last Sun of each month. ⌂Å♣

WESTON

Woolpack

The Green

✪ 11-3 (11 Fri, Sat & summer); 5.30-11; 12-10.30 Sun

☎ (01889) 270238

Banks's Original, Bitter, Marston's Pedigree Ⓗ

Often referred to as 'the inn on the green', the Woolpack is an excellent village pub that caters well for locals and diners. Four bays inside are evidence that the building was originally a row of cottages. Over the years the inn has been thoughtfully extended creating separate areas for drinkers and diners. One end of the pub is effectively a public bar which serves as a base for numerous games and sports teams.
🏚❀◑⌂♣P

WOMBOURNE

New Inn

1 Station Road (½ mile from A459/A463 jct)

✪ 11-3, 5.30-11; 11-11 Thu-Sat; 12-10.30 Sun

☎ (01902) 892037

Banks's Original, Bitter, Ⓟ **seasonal beers** Ⓗ

Large roadhouse pub close to the village centre at the junction of Station Road and Ounsdale Road. There is no longer a railway station, but there are bus services from Wolverhampton, Stourbridge and Kinver. The basic bar is popular with locals for pub games including pool. There is a large, comfortable lounge. Outside is a grassed, well-equipped children's play area. Food is served Mon-Sat. The pies and burgers are home made. Quizzes on Tue and entertainment on Thu eve.
❀◑⌂P⬚

WRINEHILL

Crown Inn

Den Lane (signed from A531)

✪ 12-3 (not Mon-Fri), 6-11; 12-3, 7-10.30 Sun

☎ (01270) 820472

Banks's Original; Marston's Bitter, Pedigree; guest beers Ⓗ

Welcoming pub in rural setting. A former coaching inn on London-Chester road, it is the oldest pub in the neighbourhood. Previously owned by Joules' Brewery, it has been a free house for 24 years, with a strong commitment to real ale. The six handpumps usually offer three guest ales which change frequently and come from a wide range of breweries. One comfortable lounge bar with genuine exposed beams and brickwork. The no-smoking zone is much appreciated. No juke box, TV, bandits or pool. Traditional bar food served.
🏚Q❀◑P⊬

YOXALL

Golden Cup

Main Street (A515)

✪ 12-3.30, 5.30-11; 12-11 Sat; 12-10.30 Sun

☎ (01543) 472295

Marston's Pedigree; guest beers Ⓗ

300-year-old inn situated opposite St Peter's church in the pretty village of Yoxall. Smart lounge accommodates diners attracted by the extensive menu. The snooker table is popular in the large bar. Attractive garden area for drinkers leads down to the River Swanbourn.
❀🏚◑⌂&Å♣P

Star pubs

Pubs with a star symbol next to their names are listed in CAMRA's National Inventory of pubs with interiors of outstanding interest. The full list is printed in the guide.

SUFFOLK

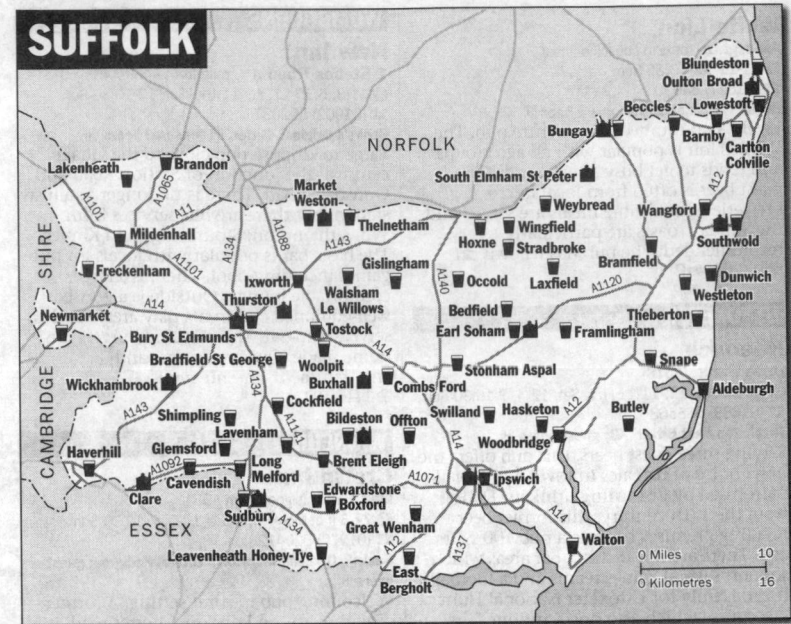

ALDEBURGH

Mill Inn
Market Cross Place
🕐 11-3, 6-11; 11-11 Fri & Sat; 12-10.30 Sun
☎ (01728) 452563
Adnams Bitter, Broadside H

Steet-corner inn opposite the ancient Moot Hall, once the centre of town but now almost on the beach due to coastal erosion. Fresh fish features on the menu, food is served in all three bar areas plus the dining room at the rear. This room doubles as a meeting room for local clubs. The local RNLI often drink here as the landlord is a crew member as well as still being a working fisherman with his own boat. You can buy fresh fish from the seafront huts opposite the pub. 🚪◑▶

White Hart
222 High Street
🕐 11.30-11; 12-10.30 Sun
☎ (01728) 453205
Adnams Bitter, Broadside H

Single-room pub which was formerly the public reading room. Always very popular with locals and holidaymakers. Conveniently next door to Aldeburgh's renowned fish and chip shop. The wood-panelled walls with nautical pictures reflect its closeness to the sea. There is a small patio area for those lazy summer days plus benches on the front pavement. Don't be offended if the landlord dashes off, he is a member of the local lifeboat crew. Occasional live music, mostly folk. The small open fire warms the whole room in winter. 🏰❄🚪♣●

BECCLES

Bear & Bells
Old Market (next to bus station)
🕐 11-3, 5.30-11; 12-3, 7-10.30 Sun
☎ (01502) 712291
Adnams Bitter; Greene King IPA; guest beers H

Comfortable Victorian pub located on a site which has supported licensed premises since at least the 16th century. Close to the town centre near the River Waveney so it is handy for visitors to the Broads. There is a spacious drinking/eating area with a central bar. A private function room is available for meetings. Sample good local regional ales, including a dark ale during winter months, the pub is also renowned for wholesome food (not served Mon). Quiz nights are very popular. Q◑▶≠

BEDFIELD

Crown
Church Lane (head N from Earl Soham)
🕐 11.30-3 (may vary), 6-11 ; 12-4, 7-10.30 Sun
☎ (01728) 628431
Greene King IPA; guest beer H

This pub is off the beaten track, but worth seeking out. It has a small cosy bar and a no-smoking area. One of the few pubs to have a bar billiards table to keep you occupied between pints. It has been a regular entry in this *Guide*. The excellent beers are complemented by good food (not served Tue). 🏰❄◑▲♣P⚲

BILDESTON

King's Head
132 High Street (B1115, Hadleigh-Stowmarket Road)
🕐 12-3, 5-11; 12-11 Sat; 12-10.30 Sun
☎ (01449) 741434
King's Head Best Bitter; guest beer H

Always an interesting range of beer on the bar here, brewed on site by the King's Head Brewing Co which was set up as the Brettvale Brewing Co in 1996 by the current brewer and long-serving landlord. His daughter and son-in-law now run the pub.

Although now opened out into a single bar, the history of this substantial village-centre inn is still very visible. Two large brick fireplaces and high-beamed ceilings add character to the main bar. Live music every weekend and annual beer festival with 30 beers in May. No food Sun eve. ☸🛏️🌓♣P

BLUNDESTON

Plough
Market Lane
🕓 12-2.30, 7-11; 12-3, 7-10.30 Sun
☎ (01502) 730261
Adnams Bitter, Broadside; Greene King IPA Ⓗ
Village inn, next to a bowling green and close to the village hall. It has an attractive garden with a large car park. Interesting literary connection, the pub is mentioned in Dickens' novel *David Copperfield* as the starting point of Barkis the carrier on his journey to Yarmouth. Not surprisingly the contemporary pub has plenty of Dickensian memorabilia. The large main bar houses the traditional game of bar skittles and has a pool room annexe. The separate lounge, for diners only, serves good quality food.
🛏️Q☸🌓🍴♣P

BOXFORD

White Hart
Broad Street
🕓 12-3, 6-11; 12-3, 7-10.30 Sun
☎ (01787) 211071 website: www.white-hart.co.uk
Adnams Broadside; Greene King IPA; guest beers Ⓗ
Timber-framed free house beside the River Box in the centre of this attractive village. Guest beers change regularly. A varied menu offers good value for money. In the 19th century the pub was home to the Boxford Brewery and during the 20th century to the legendary Tornado Smith, the wall-of-death rider whose pet lion rode in the sidecar. Ask the landlord where the lion is buried! In the 21st century the pub is home to the Hadleigh and District Classic Motorcycle Club. 🛏️☸🌓♣P

BRADFIELD ST GEORGE

Fox & Hounds
Felsham Road
🕓 11.30-3, 5.30-11; closed Mon; 12-3, 7-10.30 Sun
☎ (01284) 386379
Buffy's IPA; Nethergate Suffolk County; guest beer Ⓗ
On the village outskirts close to the historic coppiced woodland of the Suffolk Wildlife Trust, this free house and country restaurant is a beautifully restored Victorian inn. Refurbished to provide a unique combination of a real ale pub with an *à la carte* restaurant and B&B accommodation, it offers excellent service and a warm welcome. Comfortable, attractive interior with two wood-fronted bar areas, one of which has a wood block floor, pine seating and a wood-burning stove. Fast gaining a reputation for superb meals.
🛏️Q☸🛏️🌓🍴P

BRAMFIELD

Queen's Head
The Street
🕓 11-3, 6-11; 12-2.30, 7-10.30 Sun
☎ (01986) 784214 e-mail: qhbfield@aol.com

Adnams Bitter, Broadside, seasonal beers Ⓗ
Pleasant 16th-century pub next to the thatched church which has a separate round tower. The main bar has an impressive high-beamed ceiling and large brick fireplace. Old agricultural implements adorn the walls. A few steps down lead to a lower bar where children are welcome. The small no-smoking dining room is through a passage from the main bar. Note the unusual exposed section of wattle-and-daub wall in this passage. The food is renowned for its certified organic selection, mostly from local suppliers. Crones organic cider is available. 🛏️Q🌓☸🌓♣P

BRANDON

Five Bells
Market Hill
🕓 11-11, 12-10.30 Sun
☎ (01842) 813472
Greene King IPA, Abbot Ⓗ
Nicely situated at the corner of the market square (market days Thu and Sat) and ideal for a relaxing pint after the rigours of shopping! Ancient building based on a 17th-century, timber-framed structure with some later extensions, the exterior is now flint faced in local style as are many houses in the locality. Nearby is Brandon Heritage Centre with much to interest visitors with local history exhibits and information on local attractions of which the Thetford Forest with its fine walks is the most famous.
☸🌓🍴♣P

BRENT ELEIGH

Cock ☆
Lavenham Road OS941478
🕓 12-3, 6-11; 12-3, 7-10.30 Sun
☎ (01787) 247371
Adnams Bitter; Greene King IPA, Abbot, seasonal or guest beer Ⓗ
Absolute gem! Always spotless and well cared for, this pub manages to transport you back to a time most pubs have long forgotten. In the winter both tiny bars are snug and warm, in summer with the door open the bar is as one with its surroundings. Good conversation is guaranteed – sit and listen and you will be involved. Mention CAMRA and the landlord will bait you mercilessly! Close to Lavenham and the

INDEPENDENT BREWERIES

Adnams Southwold
Bartram's Thurston
Cox & Holbrook Buxhall
Earl Soham Earl Soham
Green Dragon Bungay
Green Jack Oulton Broad
Greene King Bury St Edmunds
Kings Head Bildeston
Lidstones Wickhambrook
Mauldons Sudbury
Nethergate Clare
Old Cannon Bury St Edmunds
Old Chimneys Market Weston
St Peter's South Elmham St Peter
Tolly Cobbold Ipswich

beautiful Brett Valley, the comfortable B&B is recommended. CAMROT (Campaign for Real Outside Toilets) approved. Don't miss it! ♨♿Q⊛☎🍴🍺♣♠P

BUNGAY ❉

Green Dragon
29 Broad Street
☼ 11-11; 12-10.30 Sun
☎ (01986) 892681

Adnams Bitter; Green Dragon Chaucer Ale, Bridge Street Bitter, Ⓗ Dragon, seasonal beers Ⓖ

Green Dragon beer is brewed at the rear of this spacious two-bar inn. Brewery tours by arrangement. Occasional bottled conditioned beers are brewed which complement their quality draught ales. The pub has a separate dining room/family area leading to the garden which is surrounded by hops. Food served weekday lunchtimes with curry nights on Wed eve. There are also occasional speciality eves.
♨🛏⊛☎🍺🅰♣P

BURY ST EDMUNDS

Greyhound
28 Eastgate Street
☼ 11-11; 12-10.30 Sun
☎ (01284) 752358

Greene King IPA, Abbot Ⓗ

Quiet side-street inn displaying many photos of old Bury pubs. It is close to the historic abbey gardens and well placed for local amenities such as tenpin bowling, the snooker hall and Bury Town football ground. Play traditional pub games here or enjoy a pint in the patio garden.
⊛♣P

Old Cannon
Cannon Street
☼ 11-3 (not Mon), 6-11; 12-3, 6-10.30 Sun
☎ (01284) 768769

Old Cannon Best Bitter, Gunner's Daughter, seasonal beer; guest beers Ⓗ

This is the only pub offering the popular Old Cannon Brewery beers. The full range is brewed on the premises and the brewery is sited in the bar. Formerly the St Edmunds Head this pub/brewery is on the same site as the original Cannon Brewery. Since Dec 1900 when it opened it has fast established itself as the place in town for the real ale fan. Three guest beers are offered from mainly small breweries. A high-quality

menu and accommodation are also available from this excellent new venture.
⊛🛏🍴♿≠P

Queen's Head
39 Churchgate Street
☼ 11-11; 12-10.30 Sun
☎ (01284) 761554 e-mail: queens-head.org.uk

Adnams Broadside; Ind Coope Burton Ale; Nethergate IPA; guest beer Ⓗ

This lively town-centre pub, a former 18th-century coaching inn, has survived the tests of time. It has been extended, modernised and redecorated but still retains its original charm. A true free house, it is dedicated to providing good quality beer, including a house ale, at competitive prices. The staff at this family-run pub are welcoming and there is a comprehensive menu offered all day, every day until 9pm. There is a large conservatory, games room with pool table and patio area. ⊛🍴♿♣✂●

Rising Sun
98 Risbygate Street
☼ 11-3, 6-11; 11-11 Wed, Fri & Sat; 12-4, 7-10.30 Sun
☎ (01284) 701460

Greene King XX Mild, IPA, Abbot, seasonal beers Ⓗ

Unspoilt 16th-century beamed pub in busy side street. No-smoking area for dining, no eve meals available Fri-Sun. There is a large patio and extensive garden. Entertainment includes traditional pub games and Karaoke on Tue eve and live music on Sat night.
🛏🍴♣P

Rose & Crown
48 Whiting Street (fronts on to Westgate St.)
☼ 11.30-11; 11-3, 7-11 Sat; 12-2.30, 7-10.30 Sun
☎ (01284) 755934

Greene King XX Mild, IPA, Abbot, seasonal or guest beer Ⓗ

Highly recommended and still very much a town local. This listed red-brick and tile-faced street-corner pub has been run by the same family for 26 years. Retaining two bars plus a rare off-sales counter, the interior is traditional and immaculate; both bars have a subtle pig theme. It is within sight of Greene King's Westgate Brewery and frequented by all ranks of its staff. Well-known for their mild which nearly outsells IPA. Good-value lunches (Mon-Sat). Pub games played and help with the crossword always welcome. Occasional last-minute accommodation available. 🛏🍴♣●

INN BRIEF

BARNBY
Swan Inn
Swan Lane
11-3, 7-11; 12-3, 7-10.30 Sun
Adnams Bitter; Draught Bass; Greene King IPA, Abbot, seasonal beers Ⓗ
Popular inn with restaurant specialising in fish dishes. Booking advisable.

BUNGAY
Chequers Inn
23 Bridge Street
12-11; 11-11 Sat; 12-10.30 Sun
Adnams Bitter; Fuller's London Pride; Taylor Landlord; guest beers Ⓗ
Popular 17th-century inn with a partially covered patio at the rear. Weekday lunches served. *Cask Marque* accredited.

BUTLEY
Oyster
Orford Road
11-3, 6-11; 11-11 Sat; 12-3, 7-10.30 Sun
Adnams Bitter, Broadside Ⓗ
Welcoming country pub with an enthusiastic landlord. The bar is beamed, traditionally furnished and includes a no-smoking area.

DUNWICH
Ship Inn
St James Street
11-3, 6-11 (may vary winter);
12-3, 7-10.30 Sun
Adnams Bitter, Broadside; guest beer Ⓗ
Popular with visitors, tends to be busy in summer. Good food. *Cask Marque* accredited.

EAST BERGHOLT
Royal Oak (Dickey)
East End Lane
11.30-2.30, 5.30-11; 11.30-3, 6-11 Sat; 12-3, 7-10.30 Sun
Greene King IPA, Abbot, seasonal beers Ⓗ
Excellent rural pub may be difficult to find (follow signs to Grange campsite). *Cask Marque* accredited.

GLEMSFORD
Angel
Egremont Street
12-3, 7-11;
12-3, 7-10.30 Sun
Greene King IPA; guest beer Ⓖ
Historic, traditional village-centre pub with beer still served direct from the cellar.

CARLTON COLVILLE

Bell Inn
The Street (off B1384)
✪ 11-3, 7-11; 11-11 Fri & Sat; 12-10.30 Sun
☎ (01502) 582873
Green Jack Bitter, Canary, Grasshopper, Orange Wheat, Gone Fishing, seasonal beers; guest beers Ⓗ
Well-renovated, open-plan pub owned by Green Jack Brewery. A central fireplace separates the drinking area from the restaurant which serves good quality meals (booking advisable). Food is available, however, throughout the inn. The original flagstone floor has been well maintained. The no-smoking area doubles as a family room (children's certificate). Enjoy the open fires in winter. Green Jack seasonal beers, including all dark beers, are stocked throughout the year. Some beers are served direct from the cellar by gravity dispense. ▨Q☜❀◑よ▲P⌿

CAVENDISH

Bull
High Street
✪ 11-3, 6-11; 12-3, 7-10.30 Sun
☎ (01787) 280245
Adnams Bitter, Broadside Ⓗ
This friendly pub is in one of the most picturesque villages in Suffolk. It is a rare Adnams tied house for this side of the county. The single bar is heavily-timbered and offers several dining areas. A wide selection of superb food is available (owing to its excellent reputation, booking is necessary for weekend eves and Sun lunch). Enjoy a pint on the terrace on warm, sunny days. ▨Q❀◑よP

COCKFIELD

Three Horseshoes
Stowes Hill (A1141 to Lavenham)
✪ 11-3 (not Tue), 6-11; 12-3, 7-10.30 Sun
☎ (01284) 828177
e-mail: threehorseshoes@tinyworld.co.uk
Greene King IPA; Shoes Bitter; guest beer Ⓗ
The comfortable bar is heavily timbered and offers excellent handpulled ales. A fine selection of food is served in the no-smoking lounge-cum-dining room (no meals Tue). Camping facilities for five caravans plus tents available. Traditional pub games, such as Ring the Bull, are played. ▨❀◑⊟よ▲P●

COMBS FORD

Gladstone Arms
2 Combs Ford (1 mile from Stowmarket centre on Needham Rd)
✪ 11-3, 5 (6 Sat)-11; 12-3, 7-10.30 Sun
☎ (01449) 612339
Adnams Bitter, Broadside Ⓗ
This inn is an Adnams tied house in a hamlet on the southern outskirts of the mid-Suffolk market town of Stowmarket. The pub has a large bar with distinct drinking areas. The beer garden is pleasantly located beside a stream (beyond the car park). Lunches are served 12-2pm daily and eve meals from 7-9pm (not Sun). The pub is only a mile away from the excellent Museum of East Anglian Life.
❀◑♣P

EARL SOHAM

Victoria
On A1120
✪ 11.30-2.30, 5.30-11; 12-3, 7-10.30 Sun
☎ (01728) 685758
Earl Soham Gannet Mild, Victoria, Albert Ale, seasonal beers Ⓗ
Enter this pub through its tiny porch with a small bench on either side to find a down-to-earth pub which offers a friendly atmosphere and a good choice of beer and food. Beers are from the local brewery formerly operating behind the pub but now relocated to larger premises across the road. A very traditional, no-frills pub which appeals to all. The excellent home-cooked meals are served lunchtime and eve. The pub's football team has had success in national competition, and has won at Wembley!
▨Q❀◑♣P

EAST BERGHOLT ✤

Hare & Hounds
Heath Road
✪ 12-2.30, 5-11; 12-2.30, 6-10.30 Sun
☎ (01206) 298438
Adnams Bitter, Broadside; Ⓗ **guest beers** Ⓖ
Friendly traditional village pub with a relaxed, cosy atmosphere and long-standing landlord and landlady celebrating over 25 years' service at this pub. Built in the 15th century it retains a pargetted ceiling (deep plaster relief), circa 1590, in the lounge. Guest beers come mainly from local breweries. No food is served Tue. This fine pub offers something for everyone including a family room, pleasant garden and a separate public bar.
▨Q☜❀◑⊟よ▲♣P●

EDWARDSTONE

White Horse
Mill Green OS951429
✪ 12-2 (not Mon, Tue & Thu), 6.30-11; 12-3, 7-10.30 Sun
☎ (01787) 211211
Greene King IPA; guest beers Ⓗ
Off the beaten track so an OS map is needed to find this two-bar rural free house. It boasts an interesting collection of enamel signs in both bars and a wide choice of pub games including Ring the Bull in the public bar. A wall facing the road has Olivers lettering, a brewery taken over by Greene King in 1919. Accommodation is available in two new purpose-built holiday homes in the pub grounds. On early summer evenings you can hear nightingales calling from nearby woods.
▨Q☜⬳◑⊟▲♣P

FRAMLINGHAM

Station
Station Road
✪ 12-3, 5-11; 12-3, 7-10.30 Sun
☎ (01728) 723455
Earl Soham Gannet Mild, Victoria, Albert Ale, seasonal beers Ⓗ
Homely furnished pub whose decor

reflects the railway era. A fine bank of handpumps stands proudly on the bar. Beyond the main bar is a smaller, cosier drinking area. An ideal place to stop while visiting this historic market town. Plenty of attractions here: visit the castle where Mary Tudor was proclaimed queen and the church with its fine monuments and outstanding organ. Walk around the mere and explore the streets. Can you find the tomb house of Thomas Mills?
⌂Q❀◑◐♣P

FRECKENHAM

Golden Boar

The Street (B1102, 2½ miles from A11 at Mildenhall)
✪ 11.30-11; 12-4, 7-10.30 winter Sun, 12-10.30 summer Sun
☎ (01638) 723000 e-mail: thegoldenboar@talk21.com
Adnams Bitter; Elgood's Black Dog Mild; guest beers Ⓗ

Former 16th-century coaching inn. The village is said to be the most inland port in the country in years gone by. Extensive sympathetic restoration has exposed many original features hidden for many years. The stones surrounding the fireplace came from the old church in the village after it was razed to the ground in the 15th century. Excellent home-cooked food with a specials board. Booking is advised especially for lunches (some eves food not available). Newly completed chalets with B&B now available. The pub supports local breweries and frequently stocks Nethergate beers.
❀⛟◑◐♿♣P

GISLINGHAM

Six Bells

High Street
✪ 12-3, 7 (6 Fri)-11; 12-3, 7-10.30 Sun
☎ (01379) 783349
Beer range varies Ⓗ

Spacious village centre pub which supports local micro-breweries. A fine display of pump clips decorates the walls of the bar. A large function room at the back holds craft fairs and welcomes all parties. Excellent home-made food in the bar or in the no-smoking Columbine restaurant, where an. interesting menu is served Tue-Sun. Note the well, illuminated to display the drop to the water. The columbine has connections with the local church; it is believed that the 15th-century stained glass window there is one of the earliest pictorial records of flowers in the country. Q❀◑◐♿▲♣P

HASKETON

Turk's Head

Low Road OS247506
✪ 12-2.30, 6-11; 12-3 Sat and summer; 12-4, 7-10.30 Sun
☎ (01394) 382584 e-mail: tom@turkshead.fsnet.co.uk
Tolly Cobbold Mild, Original; guest beers Ⓗ

Cosy village pub with two bars and low beams. In winter huge log fires blaze, comfortable seating is provided with high-backed wooden settles in the public bar. The pub is adorned with breweriana. The building (in part 16th century) is set in extensive grounds; admire the views. The caravan/camping facilities here are free for patrons but the close proximity to the Suffolk Heritage coast makes the site popular, booking is advised. Good home-cooked food (not Sun or Mon) plus outside catering service for social events.
⌂Q❀◑◐▲♣P

HAVERHILL

Queen's Head

Queen's Street
✪ 11-11; 12-10.30 Sun
☎ (01440) 702026
Courage Directors; Greene King Old Speckled Hen; Nethergate Suffolk County, Augustinian Ale; guest beers Ⓗ

Handsome Grade II listed building dating from 1470, quite possibly the oldest building in town. Traditional etched glass in all ground floor windows gives character to a popular pub the in main shopping area (pedestrianised daytime). Inside a cosy atmosphere is created by three bars, one largish with games, pool etc., but two other small rooms are gems and just invite settling down for a good pint! Straightforward pub food at reasonable prices available lunchtimes Mon-Sat.
◑♣P

HOXNE

Swan

Low Street
✪ 11-3, 6-11 Sat; 12-10.30 Sun
☎ (01379) 668275 e-mail: hoxneswan@supanet.com
Adnams Bitter, Broadside; Ⓖ **guest beers** Ⓗ

A splendid timber-framed building, the main bar has fine reeded beams, There is a separate bar to the rear. Large inglenook for toasting the toes. Popular pub games such as Shut the Box played. For the summer there is a large garden away from the road with cool shade from willows by the river. Newlyweds should beware the curse of St Edmund who was allegedly betrayed by such a couple and was martyred near this spot by the Danes.
⌂Q❀◑◐♣P

IPSWICH ❊

Fat Cat

288 Spring Road
✪ 12-11; 11-11 Sat; 12-10.30 Sun
☎ (01473) 726524
e-mail: ifm@fatcat-ipswich-fsnet.co.uk
Adnams Bitter; Ⓗ **Fuller's London Pride;** Ⓖ **Wells Bombardier; Woodforde's Wherry;** Ⓗ **guest beers** Ⓗ/Ⓖ

Paradise for the discerning drinker. Normally up to 20 real ales stocked, real cider and selection of Belgian bottled and draught beers, with local fruit wines. The guest ales change frequently. Traditional yet comfortable decor with wooden floors and bench seating plus an interesting display of original pub memorabilia. Peaceful atmosphere with no music, fruit machines or TV. Usually a selection of good value home-made snacks available, but customers are welcome to bring their own food in. Barbecues held on summer Sun afternoons. Voted Suffolk CAMRA *Pub of the Year* 1998. Can camp on pub lawn by prior arrangement. Q❀▲⇌(Derby Rd) ♣●●

Greyhound
9 Henley Road
✪ 11-2.30, 5-11; 11-11 Sat; 12-10.30 Sun
☎ (01473) 252105
Adnams Bitter, Fisherman, Broadside; Fuller's London Pride; guest beers Ⓗ

Busy community pub just a short walk from the town centre. A traditional-style public bar is complemented by a larger lounge and outdoor patio drinking area. The pub enjoys a good reputation for food including unusual and regularly changing home-cooked dishes. Pub games available are darts, dominoes, cards and chess. The local darts variation known as 'fives' is played. The Greyhound appeared in the very first *Guide* in 1974, and most of the subsequent editions, showing a consistency of quality all too rarely seen. Q✿◗⤵❀♣P●

Hogshead
22 Lloyds Avenue (near Tower Ramparts bus station)
✪ 11-11; 12-10.30 Sun
☎ (01473) 250036
Adnams Bitter; Banks's Bitter; Boddingtons Bitter; Fuller's London Pride; Wadworth 6X; Ⓗ **guest beers** Ⓗ/Ⓖ

Spacious, well-lit open-plan pub in former Job Centre. The sensitive rebuilding features lots of exposed brickwork, wooden beams and pillars. Hop bines decorate the bar back. Ornate partitions create a relaxed atmosphere even during busy sessions. No-smoking area to the rear. The upstairs room (open lunchtimes) can be booked for private parties (eves). 'Off-circuit', the pub attracts a mix of regulars and passing trade; tends to get busy at weekends. Local breweries' beers, some on gravity dispense, are often featured as guests. A selection of Belgian bottled beers is available. Tasty home-cooked pub fare includes vegetarian dishes. ♨◗&♣♠✂

Milestone Beerhouse
5 Woodbridge Road (opp. Odeon)
✪ 12-3, 5-11; 12-11 Fri & Sat; 12-10.30 Sun
☎ (01473) 252425
website: www.milestonebeerhouse.co.uk
Adnams Bitter; Draught Bass; Fuller's London Pride; Greene King IPA, Abbot; guest beers Ⓗ/Ⓖ

Tolly mock-Tudor pub with large patio drinking area at front. The open-plan interior with its long, L-shaped bar, low-key lighting and efficient smoke extractors make the pub popular with real ale drinkers, music fans and visitors to the nearby Regent Theatre. There are usually 12 ales on handpump, plus up to 24 on gravity dispense from the tap room. Real ciders such as Westons Old Rosie may be available, there are also around 35 whiskies to try. Home-cooked meals, including vegetarian and vegan meals, are served lunchtimes and 5-9pm (not Thu-Sun). Skittle alley at rear of pub.
♨✿◗&♣●P⌷

Woolpack
11 Tuddenham Road (next to Christchurch Park)
✪ 11-3, 5-11; 11-11 Sat; 12-10.30 Sun
☎ (01473) 253059 e-mail: porkpie@mustard71
Adnams Bitter; Broadside; Tolly Cobbold Original; guest beers Ⓗ

Imposing building, probably the oldest red-

brick pub in town (some parts 16th century). Known locally as the country pub in town. Marvellous snug bar in oldest part of building whose regulars have earned it the name of the Muppets bar. Patio areas at front and back have hanging baskets and raised flower beds. The new rear extension houses a modern kitchen which supplies good quality, value-for-money meals served during all sessions (including Sun roast). Occasional entertainment. The large lounge bar has a roaring fire in winter. ♨Q✿◗&P

Greyhound
49 High Street
✪ 11-3, 6-11; 12-3, 7-10.30 Sun
☎ (01359) 230887
Greene King XX Mild, IPA, Abbot, seasonal beers Ⓗ

Welcoming, traditional three-bar pub retaining a marvellously intimate snug. A pub has been standing on this site since Tudor times. Traditional pub games, such as dominoes, crib, darts and pool are promoted. Games eves are also hosted to raise funds for local charities. Bar meals are served daily, 11am-2pm and 6-8pm. The pub takes party bookings with a choice of catering, roast dinners or buffet menus for 8-20 people. ✿◗⤵Å♣P●

Brewer's Tap
54 High Street
✪ 12-11; 12-4.30, 7-10.30 Sun
☎ (01842) 862328
Beer range varies Ⓗ

Probably originating as a workman's cottage in the village centre, this small pub of character is a find for real ale enthusiasts being truly 'free' in an area dominated by one brewer (Greene King). Always a good atmosphere, this is the true village local without doubt. Do not be put off by the frontage size, the extension and patio at the rear make the pub larger than it appears. Good value food available at lunchtimes; eve meals must be booked
✿◗♣

Half Moon
4 High Street
✪ 12-3, 6-11; 12-10.30 Sun
☎ (01842) 861484
Greene King XX Mild, IPA, Abbot; guest beers Ⓗ

Largish pub in fine flint building dating back to early 1800s. Retains layout of two bars with servery for off-sales between – a common feature in times past but removed in many recent pub rebuilds. Recently added dining room has increased eating capacity considerably but this has not dominated the pub which still has games teams and some entertainment nights. A large garden and patio are available emphasising that this is very much a family pub. ♨✿◗⤵P●

Angel
Market Place
✪ 11-11; 12-10.30 Sun
☎ (01787) 247388

website: www.lavenham.co.uk/angel

Adnams Bitter; Greene King IPA, Abbot; Nethergate Suffolk County H

Lavenham is reputedly England's finest medieval village and this is its oldest inn, first licensed in 1420. It sits opposite the Guildhall in the market place. The choice of eating and drinking areas includes some that are no-smoking, with plenty of room in the garden or on the front terrace in summer. A busy place for food, the menu changes twice daily and all food is prepared from fresh ingredients on the premises. All the beers on handpump are brewed in Suffolk. There are eight comfortable well-equipped en-suite bedrooms with good-value midweek breaks. ♨Q❁⇔◑占♣P

LAXFIELD ❖

King's Head (Low House) ☆
Gorams Mill Lane (off B1117, below churchyard)
◷ 11-3, 6-11; 11-11 Tue; 12-4, 7-10.30 Sun
☎ (01986) 798395

Adnams Bitter, Broadside; Greene King IPA; guest beers G

A pub without a bar; in the finest tradition of the beer house, ales are dispensed by gravity from the tap room at the back. This pub is a testament to the enduring formula that is the English ale house. Multiple rooms and outdoor drinking areas provide convivial space for all, including a family room. A cosy retreat summer and winter, this East Anglian region CAMRA *Pub of the Year* 2001 should not be missed. Known locally as The Low House, the house beer, Low House Bitter, is brewed by Earl Soham. Bought by Adnams in August 2001 so beer range may change. ♨Q✌❁◑ Å♣P

LEAVENHEATH HONEY-TYE

Lion
◷ 11-3, 5.30-11; 12-10.30 Sun
☎ (01206) 263434

website: www.thelionleavenheath.co.uk

Adnams Bitter; Greene King IPA; guest beer H

Large free house on the main Sudbury to Colchester road. The single bar leads to an informal dining area, then on to a separate restaurant. The pub strikes a good balance between food and drink, keeping room for community focus, supporting the local cricket club. The food offered is varied and has a good reputation locally. Uusually two guest beers are available. Wheelchair access is via the restaurant. ♨Q❁◑占♣P

LOWESTOFT

Oak Tavern
Crown Street West (off B1074)
◷ 10.30-11; 12-10.30 Sun
☎ (01502) 537246

Greene King Abbot; guest beers H

Back-street local on the north side of town with a large open-plan bar. Stocks a large range of Belgian bottled beers in the appropriate glass for the aficionado; admire all the Belgian beer memorabilia. There is a four handpump display with Greene King Abbot as a permanent fixture. The house beer is brewed by Woodforde's. Beer varies on the other two pumps. Very popular with sports fans, it has a large screen TV for sports events, and fields its own football, pool and darts teams ❁≈♣P

Triangle Tavern
29 St. Peter's Street
◷ 11-11; 12-10.30 Sun
☎ (01502) 582711

Green Jack Bitter, Canary, Grasshopper, Orange Wheat, Gone Fishing, seasonal beers; guest beers H /G

Popular town-centre pub owned by Green Jack Brewery situated on the Triangle Market Place. Cosy front bar festooned with beer mats and a garland of hop bines to decorate the bar. Live music on Thu and Fri nights. Open-plan back bar with pool table.

INN BRIEF

GREAT WENHAM
Queen's Head
Capel St Mary Road
12-2.30, 6.30-11; 12-2.30, 7-10.30 Sun
Adnams Bitter; Greene King IPA, Abbot; guest beers H
Attractive mid 19th-century country pub. No-smoking restaurant, renowned for its food, particularly the curry.

IPSWICH
Dales
Dales Road
11-2.30, 4.30-11; 6.30-11 Sat; 12.30-3.30, 7-10.30 Sun
Adnams Bitter; Draught Bass; Tolly Cobbold Mild, Bitter; guest beers H
Modern two-bar free house with home-cooked lunches and can book themed eve meals. Patio and lawn drinking areas for summer.

LAXFIELD
Royal Oak
High Street
11-3 (not Mon), 6-11; 11-11 Fri & Sat; 12-10.30 Sun
Adnams Bitter; guest beers H
Regularly changing selection of guest beers, often from micros. Restaurant serving excellent food (not Sun eve or Mon).

LONG MELFORD
Swan
Hall Street
11-3, 5-11;
12-3, 7-10.30 Sun
Greene King IPA, Abbot H
Popular local with a keen darts team. Good-value food available in the rear dining room. *Cask Marque* accredited.

MARKET WESTON
Mill Inn
12-3, 7-11; closed Mon;
12-3, 7-10.30 Sun
Adnams Bitter; Greene King IPA; Old Chimneys Military Mild, Great Raft Bitter H
Free house serving excellent fresh food and keeping two ales from the local Old Chimneys Brewery.

SHIMPLING
Bush
The Street
11-3, 5.30-11;
12-3, 7-10.30 Sun
Greene King IPA, Abbot; guest beer H
Recently freed of Greene King tie this comfortable village local has great character and good value meals.

SNAPE
Golden Key
Priory Road
12-3, 6-11;
12-3, 7-10.30 Sun
Adnams Bitter, Broadside H
Bar has wooden settles and a real fire in winter. Good restaurant and patio area. Handy for nearby Snape Maltings.

Guide site

Keep your copy of the Good Beer Guide up-to-date by contacting the CAMRA website where you will find information about changes to pubs and breweries

www.camra.org.uk/gbg

Customers are welcome to bring their own food. Green Jack seasonal beers, including all dark beers, are available throughout the year. Some beers are served direct from the cellar by gravity dispense. Quarterly beer festivals are held and over 300 ales from micro-breweries have been enjoyed over the past year. 🏚🍺🚬🕯

MILDENHALL

Queen's Arms
Queensway (follow signs for West Row)
✪ 12-2.30, 7-11; 12-3, 7-10.30 Sun
☎ (01638) 713657
Greene King IPA, Abbot; guest beer Ⓗ
Cosy, one-roomed pub, which draws good local trade, on outskirts of town. Strongly supported by regulars though newcomers are made welcome. Good home-cooked food is available at lunchtimes, but not always eves so bookings sometimes required (phone first). Guest ale from Greene King list. Good-size beer garden sometimes used as camping ground at air fête weekends (Whitsun). Limited parking. 🏚🍺🏕♣P

NEWMARKET

New Wellington
81 Cheveley Road (turn at 'clock tower', follow signs for Clare)
✪ 11.30-2.30, 6-11; 12-3, 7-10.30 Sun
☎ (01638) 662137
Greene King XX Mild, IPA, Abbot; guest ale Ⓗ
Situated on the edge of town just off the Clare road. Reputed to be the only pub in town selling a cask mild. This pub has been a large charity fundraiser in the years that the landlord has been a tenant; just look at the large cheques surrounding the public bar. Also Anglia regional CAMRA *Community Pub of the Year* finalist. Good community support and active pub golfing trips with a large following. Good value home-cooked food available, but no Sun lunches. A warm welcome awaits. Limited parking. 🍺🚪♣P

OCCOLD

Beaconsfield Arms
Mill Road (by school and Baptist Chapel)
✪ 11-3, 6-11; 12-3, 7-10.30 Sun
☎ (01379) 678648
Adnams Bitter; Greene King IPA; guest beer Ⓗ
Village centre local with separate restaurant which places emphasis on freshly prepared food. Another survivor of the great Pubmaster sell-off which customers prove does have a future. Used by young and old, with room for everyone. The main bar area has a flagstone floor, low ceiling and cosy position by the fire to add to its appeal. 🏚🍺P

OFFTON

Limeburners
Willisham Road
✪ 12-2 (not Mon), 5-11; 11-11 Sat; 12-4, 7-10.30 Sun
☎ (01473) 658318
Adnams Bitter; Wells' Eagle; guest beer Ⓗ
This two-bar local has a large garden with barbecue facilities. The pub takes its name

from a disused lime kiln in the quarry opposite. It is, in fact, on the boundary of the parish of Offton but is actually in Willisham. Enjoy the music on Sun night when it's buskers' night. Traditional pub games are played and food served daily. 🏚🍺♣P

SOUTHWOLD

Harbour Inn
Black Shore
✪ 11-11; 12-10.30 Sun
☎ (01502) 722381
Adnams Bitter, Broadside, seasonal beers Ⓗ
Riverside pub to the south of the main town. The flood levels marked on the outside wall show how the river can rise. Inside the pub is divided into two marked levels, the lower bar with its quarry-tiled floor and Suffolk stove, ideal for those winter days with a wet, muddy dog. The upper level is a warm, cosy room with a small fish tank. A recent extension provides extra dining space and doubles as a venue for live music. The patio and garden at the rear overlook the town marshes. Children welcome until 9pm. 🏚❀🍺♣P●

Lord Nelson
East Street
✪ 10.30-11; 12-10.30 Sun
☎ (01502) 722079
Adnams Bitter, Broadside, seasonal beers Ⓗ
Much Nelson memorabilia (including a scale model of the Victory) adorns this busy town pub, which is next to the sailor's reading room museum and just a stone's throw from the sea. There are three rooms, with children welcome in the side room. The bar is flagstoned and has an open fire for the winter. Access to the covered patio at the rear is through the bar. This pub is renowned for its good value food and beer. 🏚❀🍺🏕●

STONHAM ASPAL

Ten Bells
The Street (A1120)
✪ 11.30-2, 5-11; 12-11 Sat; 12-3, 7-10.30 Sun
☎ (01449) 711601
Adnams Bitter; Greene King IPA; Tolly Cobbold Mild; guest beer Ⓗ
Late 16th-century pub with three distinct bars. A large public bar, a delightful small front snug and a lounge with dining area beyond. Interesting variety of pictures and prints in lounge area. Meals served all sessions with vegetarian options (6-9pm Mon-Sat and 7-9 Sun eve). A pub that promotes mild! 🏚Q❀🍺🚪🏕♣P

STRADBROKE

White Hart
Church Street
✪ 11.30-3, 6.30-11; 12-3.30, 7-10.30 Sun
☎ (01379) 384310
Adnams Bitter; Flowers IPA; guest beer Ⓗ
A pub that has been at the heart of its community for the last 200 years that owners, Pubmaster, tried to close. Villagers, CAMRA, and others fought back. Two years on, its presence in this *Guide* is a testimony to the value of fighting for a good cause. Normally selling three beers from the

Pubmaster stable, this inn does brisk trade and is home to a darts team, domino and cribbage leagues, and, rare for the area, its own bowls green (so attractive to the asset strippers). 🏠❀◑♣P

SUDBURY

Waggon & Horses
Acton Square
🕐 11-3, 6.30 (5 Fri)-11; 12-3, 7.30-10.30 Sun
☎ (01787) 312147
Greene King IPA; guest beer Ⓗ
This local can be difficult to find in the back streets of Sudbury but offers a warm welcome. It has several drinking areas and a small restaurant area. Booking is advised for the restaurant. Guest beer tends to be from the Greene King list. The landlord is a former mayor of Sudbury and, as can be seen from the colourful beer garden in summer, is active with the *Sudbury in Bloom* organisation.
🏠Q🍴❀◑≈♣

SWILLAND

Moon & Mushroom
High Road
🕐 11-2.30, 6-11; closed Mon; 12-2.30, 7-10.30 Sun
☎ (01473) 785320
Buffy's Hopleaf; Nethergate Umbel Ale; Wolf Bitter, Coyote Bitter; Woodforde's Wherry, Norfolk Nog Ⓖ
Extremely popular, out-of-the-way pub that attracts all types. Welcoming landlord whose wife cooks the excellent meals. Features include a cosy open fire and oak beams. Try a game of shove-ha'penny on one of the best boards in Suffolk. All real ales by gravity dispense from cooled casks. Pleasant patio for outside drinking.
🏠Q❀◑♣P⌇

THEBERTON

Lion
The Street
🕐 11-3, 5.45-11; 12-3, 6.45-10.30 Sun
☎ (01728) 830185 website: www.thelioninn.co.uk
Adnams Bitter; Woodforde's Wherry; guest beers Ⓗ
Brick-built friendly village local opposite the thatched church. Regularly changing list of guests usually from East Anglia. Photographs displayed include some of the Zeppelin shot down here in 1917, part of which can be seen in the church. Watch out if the landlord needs access to the cellar, the trap door is between the bar and the door. A regular spot for jazz-lovers the first Sun of the month. Popular quiz nights (Wed) help raise funds for local charities and the village fête. There's a meadow for camping and caravans at the rear of the pub.
🏠❀◑▲♣P

THELNETHAM

White Horse
Hopton Road
🕐 11-3, 5-11; 11-11 Sat; 12-3, 7-10.30 Sun
☎ (01379) 898298
Adnams Bitter; Greene King IPA; guest beers Ⓗ
On the Norfolk border, this lovely, remote rural free house serves a local beer range with house specials brewed by Old Chimneys in neighbouring Market Weston. Originally four rooms, the bar retains a cosy

country atmosphere with areas well separated. The games room has a pool table and motor racing memorabilia. The dining room offers an extensive menu and all meals are home-prepared with fresh vegetables. In summer enjoy a meal or drink in the enclosed rear garden or sit on the front patio and watch the world go by – very slowly! 🏠❀◑♣P●

TOSTOCK

Gardeners Arms
Church Road
🕐 11.30-2.30, 7-11; 12-3, 7-10.30 Sun
☎ (01359) 270460 e-mail: ragransome@aol.com
Greene King IPA, Abbot, seasonal beers Ⓗ
Fine old building retaining many original low, black beams. The pub is set near the peaceful village green. The lively public bar has a stone floor. Darts, pool, crib and shove-ha'penny are played here. Quiz nights are popular. The lounge bar has carver chairs and a large fireplace. There is a no-smoking dining area. Enjoy good value bar snacks and tasty home-made meals. This very popular pub has a splendid large garden, perfect in summer.
🏠❀◑⊟▲♣P●

WALSHAM LE WILLOWS

Six Bells
Sumner Road
🕐 11.30-2.30, 5.30 (6.30 Sat)-11; 12-2, 7-10.30 Sun
☎ (01359) 259726
Greene King XX Mild, IPA, Ruddles Best, Abbot Ⓗ
Former wool merchant's house in the centre of this pretty village. This substantial thatched building partly dates from the 16th century. High-quality heavily carved timbers are exposed in the main bar. The six individual rooms and two bars offer a great variety. The use of open studs allows some rooms to be light and airy, while the huge fireplaces and dark timbers create a cosy atmosphere. Traditional pub run by a local couple, who were regulars before taking it on. They concentrate on beer sales so only sandwiches and rolls served lunchtimes (no food Sun). Dog friendly.
🏠Q❀◪⊟♣P●

WALTON

Half Moon
303 Walton High Street
🕐 12-2.30, 5-11; 12-11 Sat; 12-3, 7-10.30 Sun
☎ (01394) 216009
website: www.halfmoonfelixstowe.com
Adnams Bitter, Broadside; guest beer Ⓗ
Splendid, traditional drinkers' pub with a friendly welcome, situated on the approaches to Felixstowe. No fruit machines or food to disrupt the atmosphere. Darts, dominoes and cribbage can be played in the public bar, as can a piano should you wish to entertain (or annoy!) your friends. The lounge is larger; note the stained glass screens above the bar. Both bars display old photographs of the area. Racks of secondhand books are on sale for charity. Ask the landlord about the 'word of the week'. Garden play equipment available for the younger clientele. 🏠Q❀⊟▲♣P●

WANGFORD

Plough
London Road
⊕ 11-2.30 (3 Sat), 7-11; 12-3, 7-10.30 Sun
☎ (01502) 578239
Adnams Bitter, Broadside Ⓖ
Small 18th-century former coaching inn that is cut off from the rest of the village by the busy A12. The bar is very comfortable with a wood-burning stove and beer dispensed by gravity. The handpumps on the bar are just to show what beer is available. There is a separate dining room that is very popular and a small snug at the back. Watch out for curry night on the last Fri of each month. Caravan club site (for five caravans) at the rear of the pub.
ᗰQ❀◑♣P

WESTLETON

White Horse Inn
Darsham Road
⊕ 12-3 (not Tue), 7-11; 12-4, 7-10.30 Sun
☎ (01728) 648222
Adnams Bitter, Broadside, seasonal beers Ⓗ
Lovely setting next to the village green and duck pond, this is a brick-built local with interesting Dutch gables. Inside, the main bar is split into two with a separate dining room downstairs. The long-serving landlord is a previous winner of the barrel rolling competition at the village barrel fair held in the summer. Popular pub with walkers and birdwatchers visiting the nearby Minsmere Bird Reserve. ᗰ❀◑♣P

WEYBREAD

Crown
The Street
⊕ 11-11; 12-10.30 Sun
☎ (01379) 586710
Greene King IPA, Abbot; guest beers Ⓗ
Unusually for the area this house is a Victorian building; don't race down the old Roman road and miss it. A good pub for a sit at the bar and a chinwag. A good line in home-cooked food, check out the monthly curry night. Beers are from regional and micro-breweries and, especially welcome to the thirsty traveller, they are served all day.
ᗰ❀⇦◑♣P

WINGFIELD

De La Pole Arms
Church Road (by Wingfield College and church)
OS229769
⊕ 11-3, 6-11 Tue-Sat; 12-3 Sun
☎ (01379) 384545
St Peter's Best Bitter, Wheat Beer, Strong Ale Ⓗ
Fine oak joinery is testimony to the effort spent in bringing this pub back from closure. The style is simple and entirely in keeping with this 16th-century building. For the warmer months there is a sheltered terrace to the rear which also provides wheelchair access, (gravel drive to the front). This is one of only two St Peter's houses outside London, thereby offering a rare opportunity of sampling several of their draught ales (perhaps more familiar in the pasteurised bottle form found on supermarket shelves).
ᗰ❀◑&P

Cask breather

Where an entry states that some beers in a pub are served with the aid of cask breathers, this means that demand valves are connected to both casks and cylinders of gas; as beer is drawn off, it is replaced by applied gas (either carbon dioxide, nitrogen or both) to prevent oxidation. The method is not acceptable to CAMRA as it does not allow beer to condition and mature naturally. The Campaign believes brewers and publicans should use the size of casks best suited to the turnover of beer in order to avoid oxidation. If a pub in the Good Beer Guide uses cask breathers, we list only those beers that are free of the device.

WOODBRIDGE

Anchor
16-19 Quay Street
⊕ 12-11; 12-10.30 Sun
Greene King IPA, Abbot Ⓗ
Original 17th-century building that was given a Victorian extension when the railway came to Woodbridge. The small, intimate front bar has wood panelling and complementary seating. The older part of the building is to the rear at a lower level. The low beamed ceiling is a good backdrop for the pub's nautical theme. In the winter there are open fires and a wood-burning stove. Good value bar food available and paintings by local artists on sale. Station car park opposite is free after 6pm. ᗰ❀◑⇌♣

WOOLPIT

Bull Inn
The Street
⊕ 11-3, 6-11; 12-3, 7-10.30 Sun
☎ (01359) 240393
Adnams Bitter; Young's Best Bitter, seasonal beer; guest beer Ⓗ
Welcoming family-run inn with separate restaurant. Daily home-cooked specials, Sun lunch particularly recommended, no food Sun eve. Large pleasant garden and play area ideal for families. The village houses a very attractive church and thriving community. The publican supports all local activities with outside bars and fund raising. A monthly chart is displayed in the main bar listing all matches, meetings and events planned. Even a short stay would reward the visitor with a slice of rural Suffolk life and a relaxed base. Q❀⇦◑♣P

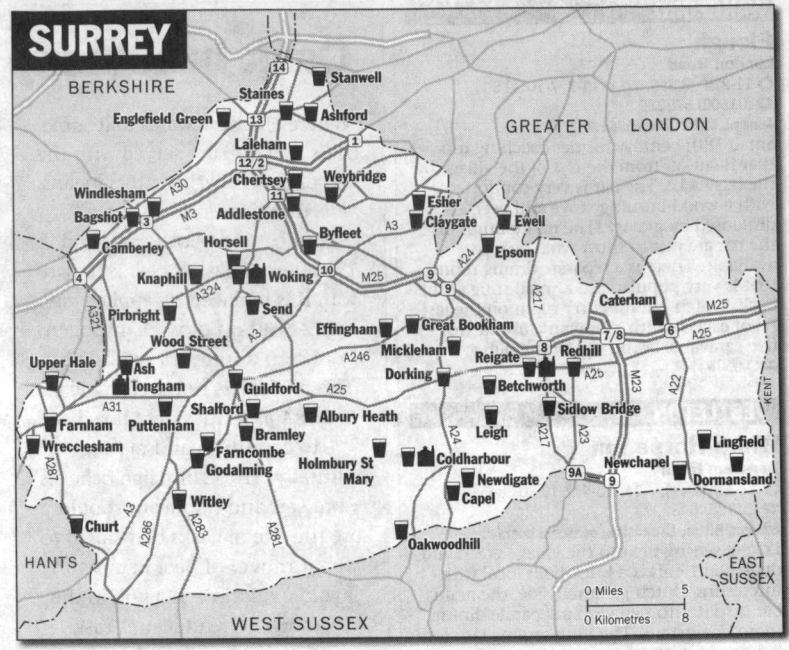

SURREY

BERKSHIRE · GREATER LONDON · KENT · EAST SUSSEX · WEST SUSSEX · HANTS

(Map locations: Stanwell, Staines, Ashford, Englefield Green, Laleham, Weybridge, Windlesham, Chertsey, Addlestone, Esher, Claygate, Ewell, Bagshot, Horsell, Byfleet, Camberley, Knaphill, Woking, Epsom, Pirbright, Send, Caterham, Wood Street, Effingham, Great Bookham, Mickleham, Reigate, Redhill, Upper Hale, Ash, Tongham, Guildford, Dorking, Betchworth, Farnham, Shalford, Albury Heath, Leigh, Sidlow Bridge, Puttenham, Bramley, Wrecclesham, Farncombe, Godalming, Holmbury St Mary, Coldharbour, Lingfield, Witley, Newdigate, Newchapel, Dormansland, Capel, Churt, Oakwoodhill)

0 Miles 5 · 0 Kilometres 8

ADDLESTONE

Queen's Arms
107 Church Road (B3121)
☼ 11-3, 5.30-11; 11-11 Sat; 12-3, 7-10.30 Sun
☎ (01932) 847845
Courage Best Bitter; Young's Special, guest beer Ⓗ
Small, former Ashby (Staines) brewery house, built in 1867; the 436 bus service will drop you off nearby. You can sit at bench tables on the front on warm days and watch the world go by. Be prepared for a 'real' Irish welcome here. There is a quiz eve on the last Thu of the month. ✿◗♣P

Waggon & Horses
43 Simplemarsh Road (off A318)
☼ 11-11; 12-10.30 Sun
☎ (01932) 828488
Ushers Best Bitter, seasonal beers Ⓗ
Family local on the western edge of town, worth seeking out. It was InnSpired Pubs *Pubs in Bloom* national winner 2000, also *Best Floral Display* and first prize winner of *Runnymede in Bloom* 2000. The U-shaped drinking area boasts two cuckoo clocks and a bar billiards table. Quiz eve is Tue at 9pm. Music nights are quite popular, fortnightly on Sat. A new dining area and rear patio are being added in 2001. Eve meals served Wed-Sat. ▲✿◗♣P

ALBURY HEATH

William IV
Little London OS066467
☼ 11-3, 5.30-11; 12-3, 7-10.30 Sun
☎ (01483) 202685
Flowers IPA; Hogs Back TEA, Hop Garden Gold; guest beers Ⓗ
Traditional, 16th-century country pub; popular with walkers. The lower part of the bar is divided into two areas and has flagstones, beams and a large inglenook. A

third, carpeted, area at the back up a few steps is mainly used by diners (eve meals Tue-Sat). The first-floor restaurant is open Fri and Sat eves serving a different menu from that in the bar. The two guest beers change regularly and are usually from independents. ▲Q✿◗♣P

ASHFORD

Ash Tree
Convent Road (B378/Feltham Hill Rd jct)
☼ 11-11; 12-10.30 Sun
☎ (01784) 252362
Fuller's Chiswick, London Pride, ESB Ⓗ
Fuller's managed two-bar pub, built in the early 1960s, in a residential area outside the town centre. The small restaurant area specialises in Thai food, with a limited choice of English meals. The excellent value food can also be eaten in the bar or as a take-away (no food Sun). Twenty minutes' walk from the rail station, it is on several bus routes.
✿◗◗♣P●

BAGSHOT

Foresters Arms
173 London Road (A30 towards Camberley)
☼ 12-2.30, 6-11; 12-3, 7-10.30 Sun
☎ (01276) 472038 e-mail: p.savage1@ntlworld.com
Courage Best Bitter; Fuller's London Pride; Greene King IPA; Hogs Back TEA; guest beers Ⓗ
Though somewhat away from the village centre, this comfortable little pub, with three connected seating areas around the bar, remains very much a local where all generations feel at home. The traditional range of good food attracts a regular lunchtime trade, while the seven cask ales are popular at all times. The adjoining skittle alley (with its own bar) can be hired for private functions (food can

be served eves if required). On the 34
Woking-Camberley bus route. ⊛◑♣P

BETCHWORTH

Dolphin Inn
The Street (off A25)
☼ 11-3, 5.30-11; 11-11 Sat; 12-10.30 Sun
☎ (01737) 842288
Young's Bitter, Triple A, Special, Winter Warmer Ⓗ
This busy local is also very popular with
visitors. Dating from the 16th century, it
features a flagstone floor and two wood-
burning inglenooks. A good selection of
food is served in the three bars, with
specials always available. In summer
drinkers take advantage of the many seats
outside and in the garden. Noted for serving
some of the best pints of Young's anywhere,
it also stocks a good range of wines. On Tue
eve you can listen to the campanologists
practising at the church opposite.
⚏Q⊛◑♣

BYFLEET

Plough
104 High Street (off A245)
☼ 11-3, 5-11; 12-3, 7-10.30 Sun
☎ (01932) 353257
Courage Best Bitter; guest beers Ⓗ
Wonderful free house with seven ever-
changing guest beers. Magnificent fires,
18th-century timbers and no-nonsense
tables and chairs create an atmosphere of
quiet reassurance. Often the only sounds to
be heard are the crackle of the fire, glasses
being placed on tables and that ever so
precious commodity – conversation. Mobile
phones are banned. Children are catered for
in the no-smoking conservatory which they
must enter from the garden, not via the bar.
One of the best pubs for miles around.
⚏Q⊛◑&♣P✂●

CAMBERLEY

Crown
469 London Road (A30 towards Blackwater)
☼ 12-3, 5-11; 12-11 Sat; 12-4, 7-10.30 Sun
☎ (01276) 709376
Courage Best Bitter; guest beers Ⓗ
Set back from the parade of shops on this
stretch of the busy A30, this unpretentious
pub can be difficult to spot, but it is worth
the search. The three beers are modestly
priced, as is the good range of pub grub,
making it particularly popular at lunchtime
(eve meals served Mon-Thu). It hosts live
music once or twice a month, including
Irish. The pub fields active darts and pool
teams in the local leagues and shove-
ha'penny is also played.
⚏⊛⇔◑⊟⇌(Blackwater)♣P

CAPEL

Crown
98 The Street (off A24)
☼ 11-2.30, 5-11; 11-11 Sat; 12-10.30 Sun
☎ (01306) 711130
Fuller's London Pride; guest beers Ⓗ
Large village inn dating from the 17th
century, comprising two bars. The front one
acts as a public bar; this is split level, with
pool, and TV for sporting events. The
lounge bar has a restaurant area at the back

serving good food. The beer names are
handwritten on pump clips. The guest beers
change frequently, but often include
Cottage Brewery beers. Live music features
once a month (Fri or Sat). ⊛◑⊟♣P✂

CATERHAM

Clifton Arms
110 Chaldon Road (B2031)
☼ 11.30-11; 12-10.30 Sun
☎ (01883) 343525
Young's Bitter, Special; guest beers Ⓗ
Old photos and other artefacts and
memorabilia feature in the main bar; the
small back bar tends to be for food and
opens into an area with a stage. Lunches are
served Sun-Fri; eve meals Tue-Sat. On Fri the
landlord plays tracks from his collection of
pre-1955 records, while Sat usually features
live music from the 60s and Sun rock and
roll with Karaoke. Live trad jazz is staged
alternate Wed; Tue is quiz night. One or
two guest beers are stocked – one often
unusual for the area. Biddenden cider is
sold. ⊛◑♠P

King & Queen
34 High Street (B2030)
☼ 11-11; 12-10.30 Sun
☎ (01883) 345438
Fuller's Chiswick, London Pride, ESB Ⓗ
Originally cottages built 400 years ago, it
became a pub in the 1840s, with three
distinct drinking area. The middle room has
a high ceiling, large inglenook and a small
space at the back reserved for diners. There
is also a front bar and a room to the side
where darts can be played. The food (not
served Sun) is freshly cooked using local
produce and includes authentic oriental
dishes. ⚏⊛◑♣P●

CHERTSEY

Coach & Horses
14 St Annes Road (B375)
☼ 12-11; 12-3, 7-10.30 Sun
☎ (01932) 563085
Fuller's Chiswick, London Pride, ESB, seasonal beers Ⓗ
Attractive tile-hung pub whose exterior is
festooned in summer with hanging baskets
of colourful flowers, floodlit eves. Sitting
outside at the bench tables you can watch
planes fly over from Heathrow. A children's
fenced-off area has a chalkboard for young
artists. Admire the excellent Fuller, Smith &
Turner mirror inside. Vegetarian dishes are
available (no meals weekends or Mon eve).
⊛⇔◑♣P●

CHURT

Crossways Inn
Churt Road (A287)
☼ 11-3.30, 5-11; 11-11 Fri & Sat; 12-4, 7-10.30 Sun
☎ (01428) 714323
Cheriton Best Bitter; Courage Best Bitter; Ⓗ
Ringwood Fortyniner; guest beers Ⓖ

INDEPENDENT BREWERIES

Boston Experience Woking
Hogs Back Tongham
Leith Hill Coldharbour
Pilgrim Reigate

437

This recent Surrey CAMRA *Pub of the Year* is a true village local with a cottage-like exterior and comfortable half-panelled saloon and public bars. Four or five guest beers are always available, now running at some 400 a year, and there are four changing real ciders on stillage. The food is wholesome and well-priced, with a variety of home-made specials. Being near good walking country, ramblers are welcome. The summer beer festival is extremely popular. Q ❀ ◖ ⊟ ▲ ♣ ♦ P ⊟

CLAYGATE

Foley Arms
Foley Road
✪ 11-11; 12-10.30 Sun
☎ (01372) 463431
Young's Bitter, Special, seasonal beers; guest beer (occasional) ⊞
Occupying a prominent position on the crown of a bend, this imposing Victorian local attracts a varied clientele. The lounge bar is popular with more mature customers at lunchtimes. Jazz is played in the club room on bank holidays, while barbecues are held in the large garden on summer weekends. A well-equipped children's play area makes it popular with families.
▨ Q ❀ ◖ ⊟ ⇌ ♣ P

Griffin
58 Common Road
✪ 11-11; 12-10.30 Sun
☎ (01372) 463799
Badger Best; Fuller's London Pride; Pilgrim Surrey Bitter; guest beer ⊞
Tucked away in residential Claygate, this pleasant, relaxing pub can be hard to find, but is only a short walk from the village centre (and on the K3 bus route). Well worth seeking out for its enterprising beer range, both saloon and lively public bars are served from the horseshoe-shaped bar. The public features a large-screen TV, and the lounge boasts fine original Mann Crossman & Paulin windows. There is a good selection of home-cooked lunches; and eve meals served Fri and Sat. ▨ Q ❀ ◖ ♣ P

Swan
2 Hare Lane
✪ 11-11; 12-10.30 Sun
☎ (01372) 462582
Draught Bass; Brakspear Bitter; Fuller's London Pride; Greene King IPA ⊞
Popular, upmarket pub overlooking a green, refurbished in ale house style. An L-shaped bar area leads through to a Thai restaurant at the rear (Sun roasts served). There is a large-screen TV for major sporting events. An annual beer festival is held in the spacious patio garden August bank holiday. ◖ ⇌ P

COLDHARBOUR

Plough Inn
Coldharbour Lane
(Leith Hill-Dorking road) OS152441
✪ 11.30-3, 6-11; 11.30-11 Sat; 12-10.30 Sun
☎ (01306) 711793
Badger Tanglefoot; Hogs Back TEA; Leith Hill Crooked Furrow, Tallywhacker; Ringwood Old Thumper; guest beers ⊞
Nestling among the Surrey hills in good

walking country, this is a gem of a rural brewpub. The cosy bar, well-used by locals, features eight handpumps (one devoted to Biddenden cider). Excellent home-made meals are served in the dining room and, in summer, in the large garden. There is a pool table in the public bar area. The Leith Hill Brewery, located at the rear, has been expanded as part of a remodelling, which has also created guest accommodation.
▨ Q ⊱ ❀ ⊠ ◖ ◗ ♦ P

DORKING ❄

Old House at Home
24 West Street (A25, one-way system)
✪ 11-3, 5.30-11; 12-3, 7-10.30 Sun
☎ (01306) 889664
Young's Bitter, Triple A, Special, Winter Warmer ⊞
One-bar pub in a street renowned for its antique shops. Conversation is the main attraction here – the TV is only turned on occasionally for football matches; in-house sport can be found in the shape of a bar billiards table. Thu is quiz night and there is a monthly folk music eve, the third Sun. A small restaurant area to the back of the pub serves traditional English food (no meals Sun eve). ▨ ❀ ◖ ⇌ (West) ♣

Queen's Head
Horsham Road (A25, one-way system)
✪ 11-11; 12-10.30 Sun
☎ (01306) 883041
Fuller's Chiswick, London Pride, ESB ⊞
Lively, family-run pub, with a distinctive mansard roof, guarding the southern corner of a one-way system which is well served with pubs. The single L-shaped bar has a pool table and two dartboards. There is also a surprisingly large garden. A monthly quiz (first Thu) and a 'happy' hour from 5-7pm (except Sun) are added attractions. Lunches served Mon-Sat. ❀ ◖ ♣ ●

DORMANSLAND

Old House at Home
63-65 West Street (S of B2028) OS402422
✪ 11-3, 6-11; 12-3, 7-10.30 Sun
☎ (01342) 832117
Shepherd Neame Master Brew Bitter, Best Bitter, Ⓖ **Spitfire, Bishops Finger, seasonal beers** ⊞
Traditional, family-run pub, dating back to the 16th century, in a side street (but signed). The main bar has beams, brass plates and half-barrels in the bar front and a sofa and armchairs in one corner. The public bar to the side has darts and, occasionally, football on TV. The restaurant area at the back serves a different menu from the bar, Wed-Sat eves (no Sun eve meals in winter). ▨ ❀ ◖ ♣ P

EFFINGHAM

Plough
Orestan Lane
✪ 11-3, 5.30-11; 12-3, 7-10.30 Sun
☎ (01372) 458121
Young's Bitter, Special ⊞
Traditional English pub serving good food in a relaxed atmosphere, free from background music and fruit machines. The menu of freshly-produced, home-made food – a mix of traditional and modern British – changes monthly, with daily specials

available. Young's head brewer lives locally and visits regularly, which is as good an endorsement as you can get. Q❀◐P⊬✕

ENGLEFIELD GREEN

Beehive
34 Middle Hill (off A30 at Egham Hill)
☺ 12-11; 12-10.30 Sun
☎ (01784) 431621
Brakspear Bitter; Fuller's London Pride; Gale's GB, HSB; Hop Back Summer Lightning; guest beer ⊞
Small, recently refurbished one-bar village pub serving the local community and nearby university. Despite redecoration, it has kept its welcoming atmosphere. Usually busy throughout the week, but there is always room for another customer. It stages well-attended beer festivals summer bank holiday weekends in the garden. There are also regular quiz nights; games include Shut the Box. The guest beer changes weekly.
🏚❀◐♣P

EPSOM

Amato Inn
18 Chalk Lane (Epsom Downs end of Worple Road)
☺ 11-3, 5-11; 11-11 Sat; 12-4, 7-10.30 Sun
☎ (01372) 721642
Adnams Bitter, Broadside; Friary Meux Bitter; Fuller's London Pride; Young's Bitter ⊞
To reach this cosy, yet spacious, one-bar pub by car you must circumnavigate a tortuous one-way system – it's easier to walk. The real fire and knick-knacks, including horse brasses and coats-of-arms, are pleasing to the eye. Amato won the Derby in 1838 and all Derby winners' horseshoes are mounted in the pub. The large garden is popular in summer. Look out for food theme nights. Eve meals served Tue-Sat. 🏚❀◐P

Barley Mow
Pikes Hill (off A2022)
☺ 11-11; 12-10.30 Sun

☎ (01372) 721044
Fuller's Chiswick, London Pride, ESB ⊞
Lone Fuller's outpost in this part of Surrey, 100 yards from the council car park on Upper High Street. Refurbished a couple of years ago, it retains a feeling of separate areas. A large garden gives a pleasant break from the hustle and bustle of Epsom's shopping centre. The pub is continuing to develop its local trade. Eve meals (not Sun) are planned for Oct 2001. 🏚Q❀◐≒♣●

Railway Guard
48 Church Road (off A2022)
☺ 12-11; 12-10.30 Sun
☎ (01372) 721143
Beer range varies ⊞
Friendly local, a short stroll from the town centre. A small triangular paved area provides outdoor seating, with a single long bar indoors. A good range of single malt whiskies complement the varying beer range that includes several old favourites. When not supping the fine ale, one can while away the time on the unusual hexagonal pool table or take part in the monthly quiz. Sporting events are shown on TV (although not to the detriment of the atmosphere). Weekday lunches served.
❀◐≒♣●

EWELL

Eight Bells
78 Kingston Road (off A240/B2200)
☺ 12-11; 12-10.30 Sun
☎ (020) 8393 9973
Greene King IPA, Abbot; guest beers ⊞
Welcoming, Edwardian pub with a large bar area, recently extended and redecorated in a more modern, but generally sympathetic style and including a no-smoking area. Up to three guest beers, although one may come from the Greene King range. Unobtrusive background music is played most of the time, with live music Sat eve. Good value food is served (eve meals end

INN BRIEF

ASH
Dover Arms
31 Guildford Road
11-3, 6-11; 12-4, 7-10.30 Sun
Beer range varies ⊞
The name is a corruption from an 18th-century cattle droving route. Two contrasting bars.

BRAMLEY
Jolly Farmer
High Street
11-3, 6-11; 12-3, 7-10.30 Sun
Badger Best; Draught Bass; Hogs Back TEA ⊞
Always an inn, with records dating from 1720. Note the copper panelling behind the bar. A Sussex barn behind serves as the restaurant.

DORKING
Cricketers
81 South Street
12-11; 12-10.30 Sun
Fuller's Chiswick, London Pride, ESB, seasonal beers ⊞
Bare brick walls are covered with pictures and a large etched mirror depicts a cricketer. Pleasantly sheltered patio garden. *Cask Marque* accredited.

King's Arms
45 West Street
11-11; 12-3, 7-10.30 Sun
Draught Bass; Fuller's London Pride; Greene King IPA; Wadworth 6X; guest beer ⊞
Old, beamed pub with a restaurant and several drinking areas, hosting music and quiz nights. The guest is usually from a small brewery.

Watermill
Reigate Road
11-3, 6-11; 11-11 Sat & summer; 12-10.30 Sun
Beer range varies ⊞
Small bar attached to a restaurant and function rooms hosting folk Wed, jazz Thu. Up to five beers listed on posters above bar.

ESHER
Albert Arms
82 High Street
11-11; 12-10.30 Sun
Draught Bass; Boddingtons Bitter; Brakspear Special; Fuller's London Pride; Hogs Back TEA; Young's Bitter ⊞
This pub has a 'café-bar' feel, dominated by the large bar counter. The restaurant is growing in popularity. A genuine free house.

Bear
71 High Street
11-11, 12-10.30 Sun
Young's Bitter, Triple A, Special, seasonal beer ⊞
Handsome, 18th-century coaching inn, where a long single bar links several drinking areas (one no-smoking). Food is served at all sessions.

FARNHAM
Lamb
43 Abbey Street
11-2.30, 5-11; 11-11 Fri & Sat; 12-10.30 Sun
Shepherd Neame Best Bitter, Spitfire, seasonal beers ⊞
Extremely popular and sometimes crowded, between the station and the Maltings. Unusual terraced garden lies to the rear.

Queen's Head
9 The Borough
11-11; 12-10.30 Sun
Gale's Butser, GB, HSB; guest beer ⊞
Gale's pub since 1888 right in the middle of the town centre, a short walk from the castle. *Cask Marque* accredited.

8pm); Sun is quiz night, when meals are not served. The large garden has a children's play area; small car park.
❀❶▸❺≋(West)♣P✄

FARNCOMBE

Cricketers
37 Nightingale Road
(turn left from main station entrance)
❀ 12-3, 5.30-11; 11-11 Sat; 12-10.30 Sun
☎ (01483) 420273
Fuller's Chiswick, London Pride, ESB, seasonal beers Ⓗ
Friendly, back-street local of a kind now rare in Surrey, it is approached from the front by steep steps. Proud to be 13 consecutive years in this *Guide*, its previous stickers are prominently displayed. As its name implies there is a strong cricketing theme, including photographs and memorabilia. Four drinking areas surround the central bar, although the far end is more likely to be used by diners. Beer and food quality have resulted in the accolade of Fuller's *Country Pub of the Year*. Q❀❶≋♣✄●

FARNHAM ❖

Duke of Cambridge
East Street
❀ 12-3, 5.15-11; 12-11 Fri & Sat; 12-10.30 Sun
☎ (01252) 716584
Beer range varies Ⓗ
A short walk from the town centre, this pub's impressive entrance stands between two substantial pillars. The single bar has spacious alcoves, wood panelling and an exposed brick fireplace. Seven handpumps dispense an ever-changing range of interesting beers; Duke's Tipple and Duke's Pride come from Itchen Valley and Triple fff respectively. Karaoke is staged Thu and Sat eves. It is served by buses running between Farnham and Aldershot. ▟❀❶≋♣●

Shepherd & Flock
22 Moor Park Lane (off A31)
❀ 11-3, 5.30-11; 11-11 Fri & Sat; 12-10.30 Sun
☎ (01252) 716675
Courage Best Bitter; Hogs Back TEA; Ringwood Old Thumper Ⓗ
On the edge of town just off the Farnham bypass, it likes to be known as the 'great little pub on Europe's largest roundabout' – access is from the Farnham end. Eight handpumps dispense five changing beers. A narrow bar frontage leads to a large dining/quiz area while the other end is more traditional, and sometimes has TV on. Choose from two outdoor areas: a lovely enclosed rear garden or a front area to watch the traffic. Q❀❶P

GODALMING

Anchor
110 Ockford Road
(A3100, signed Milford from inner ring road)
❀ 12-2.30 (3 Sat), 5.30-11 (6 Sat); 12-3, 7-10.30 Sun
☎ (01483) 417085
Badger Tanglefoot; Brakspear Bitter; Gale's HSB; Hop Back Summer Lightning; guest beers Ⓗ
Former Friary Holroyd pub on the outskirts of town, rebuilt in 1911 and now elevated above the road, making vehicle access and parking difficult. The single L-shaped bar

boasts an unusual circular rotating pool table. An excellent garden, at two levels, descends towards the stream and railway and a children's play area. Strong emphasis is put on music which can be loud – Sun is buskers' night. Outside toilets have a chalkboard for graffiti. Discount jugs of beer available. ❀❶♣♣P

Red Lion
1 Mill Lane (High St jct)
❀ 11-11; 11-3, 6.30-11 Sat; 12-3, 7-10.30 Sun
☎ (01483) 415207
Bateman XB; guest beers Ⓗ
Pub with strong historical connections in a town that was once dominated by the wool trade. The relatively small, cosy saloon served as the Assizes in the 17th century, with the prisoners being kept in the cellar. The large public bar was the Oddfellows Hall from 1802 and later Godalming Grammar School, the *Alma Mater* of Jack Phillips, the *Titanic's* radio operator. An enterprising management, now free of tie, offers three ever-changing guest beers and 76 different bottled beers from around the world. Q❀❶❺♣≋♣☐

GREAT BOOKHAM

Anchor
161 Lower Road (off A246, via Eastwick Rd)
❀ 11-3 (3.30 Sat), 5.30-11; 12-3, 7-10.30 Sun
☎ (01372) 452429
Courage Best Bitter, Directors; guest beer Ⓗ
Grade II listed pub: the single bar has wooden flooring, posts and beams – which are a bit low in places. There are also exposed brick walls and a large inglenook. Toby jugs hang from the beams and cases of medals line the walls. The cosy, friendly atmosphere makes it popular, especially early eve and for lunch (served Mon-Sat). The outside patio and award-winning garden area, with wooden seating gets busy in good weather; the pond with Koi Carp, and a set of stocks add interest. ▟Q❀❶P

GUILDFORD

Robin Hood
Sydenham Road
❀ 11-3, 5-11; 11-11 Fri & Sat; 12-4 (closed eve) Sun
☎ (01483) 888307
Draught Bass; Young's Bitter Ⓗ
One of the few genuine locals' pubs in town. Only a minute's walk from the centre and historic castle, the pub welcomes newcomers as friends in a relaxing atmosphere. The bar curves round to a raised seating area at the back. Meals come in substantial portions. On Fri live bands are very popular indeed – organised jam sessions are firmly established; quiz night Wed. ❶≋(London Rd)

Varsity Bar
Egerton Road
(off A3 at university exit, past Forte Posthouse)
❀ 12-2.30, 5-11; 12-8.30 Sat; 12-10.30 Sun
☎ (01483) 306224
Beer range varies Ⓗ
Excellent university sports bar, off-campus and open to the public, with access via the shop at the lower level. It serves five ever-changing beers per week and hosts two beer festivals: bottled beers in the spring and

cask ales in the autumn. Capable of either being very quiet or extremely boisterous on match days, when, despite its size, there is little escape. Always worth taking the short bus ride from the town centre, but hours may vary outside term and it is occasionally closed Fri eve for socials. ◁P

HOLMBURY ST MARY

King's Head
Pitland Street (50 yds off B2126)
✪ 11-3, 6-11; 11-11 Sat & summer; 12-10.30 Sun
☎ (01306) 730282
Fuller's London Pride; Triple fff Pressed Rat & Warthog; Ringwood Best Bitter; guest beers Ⓗ
Just off the main road, this pub has bare boards and basic furniture. The bar incorporates a six-pump beer engine, featuring constantly changing guest beers from micro-breweries. Two wood burning open fires help create a cosy atmosphere. Good food is served all sessions except Sun eve. Seats outside, in front of the pub and in the garden, make this a good midday halt for walkers and cyclists, at the foot of Holmbury Hill in the Hurtwood. ⚲✿◁▸♣P

HORSELL

Plough
Cheapside (off South Road) OS996599
✪ 11-3, 5-11; 11-11 Sat; 12-4, 7-10.30 Sun
☎ (01483) 714105
Draught Bass; Bateman XB; Greene King Abbot; guest beers Ⓗ
Small, friendly pub set back from the road, adjoining Horsell Common in excellent walking territory, a short stroll from the Woking suburbs. An excellent guest beer policy usually includes local independents (especially Beckett's and Itchen Valley) as well as beers from further afield. Its reputation for quality food, from the usual to the exotic such as game curries is growing, but the emphasis on beer is never compromised. ✿◁▸P

LALEHAM

Feathers
The Broadway (B377)
✪ 11-11; 12-10.30 Sun
☎ (01784) 453561
Courage Best Bitter; Fuller's London Pride; guest beers Ⓗ
Friendly, traditional village local in an area resisting the suburban sprawl, a short walk from the Thames and two miles south of Staines on the 481 bus route. A central bar serves two drinking areas. A patio garden provides shady outdoor drinking at the rear, plus benches at front of pub. Usually two or three changing guest beers come from the Beer Seller range, many from smaller breweries. It hosts occasional beer festivals. Good pub food is served from 12-9 daily. ⚲✿◁▸⚑♣P

LEIGH

Plough
Church Road OS224468
✪ 11-11; 12-10.30 Sun
☎ (01306) 611348
Badger K&B Sussex, Best, Tanglefoot, seasonal beers Ⓗ

Very attractive old pub in a small village. The two bars are contrasting and date from different centuries. The Victorian public bar has darts, plus a wide variety of board and table games. The 15th-century lounge bar has a restaurant to the rear. A good menu is served throughout the pub (all day Sat and Sun). A cricket team is based here as are very active golf and clay pigeon societies. ✿◁▸⚑♣P

MICKLEHAM

King William IV
Byttom Hill (off A24 southbound)
✪ 11-3, 6-11; 12-3, 7-10.30 Sun
☎ (01372) 372590
Adnams Bitter; Badger Best; Hogs Back TEA; guest beers Ⓗ
18th-century pub nestling on the slopes of the North Downs; it became an ale house for Lord Beaverbrook's estate staff. The small front bar affords picturesque views across the Mole Valley. A real fire adds to the cosy atmosphere of the main bar. The attractive terraced gardens are supplied from a serving hatch. The *Best Dining Pub in Surrey* 2001, the chef/proprietor offers an extensive menu. The hillside location and steps may make access difficult for the infirm. ⚲✿◁▸♣

Running Horses
Old London Road
✪ 11.30-3, 5-11; 12-3.30, 7-10.30 Sun
☎ (01372) 372279
Adnams Bitter; Fuller's London Pride; Greene King Abbot; Young's Bitter; guest beer Ⓗ
Listed, 16th-century coaching inn on the old route to London. Racehorses used to be trained on the Mickleham Downs and were stabled here. The inn is named after a run-off of the 1828 Derby after a dead heat – see the details on the inn sign. The pub is in popular walking country below Box Hill (NT) and is close to Denbies Vineyard visitor centre. Of the two traditional bar areas, the main one is dominated by a large fireplace. Children are welcome in the restaurant (no meals Sun eve). ⚲✿⚑◁▸♣P

NEWCHAPEL

Blacksmith's Head
Newchapel Road (B2028)
✪ 11-3, 5.30-11; 12-3, 6-11 Sat; 12-3 (closed eve) Sun
☎ (01342) 833697
Brakspear Bitter; Fuller's London Pride, ESB; guest beer Ⓗ
Near the imposing Mormon Temple, this pub was built on the site of a smithy. There is a single open bar with a restaurant area to the side (no meals Sun eve). The bar has a fire and a wood-burning stove. The garden offers two areas: one for families and the other with flower beds. The guest beer changes regularly and is usually from a small independent brewery. ⚲✿◁▸⚑♣P●

NEWDIGATE

Surrey Oaks
Parkgate Road, Parkgate
(between Newdigate and Leigh) OS205436
✪ 11.30-2.30, 5.30-11; 11.30-3, 6-11 Sat; 12-3, 7-10.30 Sun

441

☎ (01306) 631200 website www.surreyoaks.co.uk
Adnams Bitter; guest beers Ⓗ

Tucked away, this country local has all that is best in traditional old pubs. The guest ales change every cask and feature beers from around the country as well as local brews. In winter dark beers are popular, with wheat beers being favoured in summer. Cider is sold from the cellar. The food, served in the bar and restaurant, features good quality home-made specials (eve meals Tue-Sat). A lovely garden has doves flying around. A beer festival is held August bank holiday at this frequent local CAMRA *Pub of the Year* winner. ⚌Q✿◑🍴P

OAKWOODHILL

Punchbowl
Oakwoodhill Lane, near Ockley (off A29)
☻ 11-11; 12-10.30 Sun
☎ (01306) 627249
Badger Best, Tanglefoot; seasonal beers Ⓗ

Delightful pub opposite the village cricket green. Originally two cottages, dating from the 15th century, it became a tavern in the 1800s and remains popular with walkers, anglers and the local hunt. Its proximity to Stane Street, the London-Chichester Roman road, adds to the air of antiquity. The building is tile-hung and incorporates a large inglenook and huge local flagstones. Even the pigsty (in the car park) is a listed building. Excellent home-cooked food (not served Sun eve). ⚌Q☷✿◑🖳♣P●

PIRBRIGHT

Royal Oak
Aldershot Road (A324, W of Pirbright) OS945543
☻ 11-11; 12-10.30 Sun
☎ (01483) 232466
Flowers IPA, Original; Hogs Back TEA; guest beers Ⓗ

Superb, 400-year-old, picturesque country pub beside a stream, in a large, popular garden. It enjoys a strong food trade, but retains a pub atmosphere. An ale enthusiasts' mecca, with six guests, regular brewery weeks highlight beers from local breweries, often followed by a coach trip to the brewery itself. The enterprising landlord runs a golf society, clay pigeon club and a cask ale club. Local CAMRA *Pub of the Year* 2001. Just off the 28 Woking-Guildford bus route. ⚌Q✿◑🖳ᴧP⍓

PUTTENHAM

Good Intent
62 The Street (off B3000)
☻ 11-2.30, 6-11; 11-11 Sat; 12-10.30 Sun
☎ (01483) 810387
Courage Best Bitter; Theakston Old Peculier; Young's Bitter; guest beers Ⓗ

Highly regarded pub with a relaxing, comfortable atmosphere. In an attractive village with a 'timewarp' feel from the 1950s, it offers a pleasant retreat from the bustle of the nearby Hogs Back (A31). Seven handpumps cater for at least three drinking areas that can be given over to diners, enjoying the Pakistani chef's authentic curries (eve meals Tue-Sat). A magnificent fireplace dominates and the bar area is covered with hop vines. ⚌◑ᴧ♣P

442

REDHILL ✵

Garland
5 Brighton Road (A23, S of centre)
☻ 11-11; 12-3, 7-10.30 Sun
☎ (01737) 760377
Harveys XX Mild, Pale Ale, BB, Armada, seasonal beer Ⓗ

Excellent, town-centre local selling the entire Harveys' range. Note the collection of over 2,000 clowns throughout the pub. Darts is very popular but it does not intrude. Unusually the pub has no optics. Built in 1865 as the Anchor, it was renamed in 1992 when Harvey's bought it and it remains their only tied house in Surrey. Weekday lunches served. Limited parking. ✿◑⇌♣P●

REIGATE

Barley Mow
3 Eastnor Road, South Park
☻ 11-11; 12-10.30 Sun
☎ (01737) 242304
Ansells Mild; Greene King IPA; guest beers Ⓗ

Built as a cider house in the 1860s, and supplied by orchards at the back, this is very much a traditional local, tucked away in the back streets to the south of Reigate (limited parking). Mary, a previous landlady, reputedly haunts the pub. Folk nights are held Thu, and morris dancers visit in summer. The two guest beers are usually from the brewery's list but occasionally one comes from a local independent. ✿♣P

Nutley Hall
8 Nutley Lane
(behind council car park at west end of town)
☻ 11-11; 12-10.30 Sun
☎ (01737) 241741
Badger K&B Sussex, Best, Tanglefoot Ⓗ

Once a fairly dark street-corner local, a recent refurbishment has turned this L-shaped bar into a much brighter airy affair with clear windows, allowing in natural light, yellow walls, reclaimed floorboards and just a few tables. A smoke extractor has put the icing on the cake. The Nutley is home to a successful darts team, while a cricket and football teams also make this their base. The food (not served Sun eve or Mon) is of a high quality. ✿◑⇌♣P

SHALFORD

Queen Victoria
Station Road (off A281)
☻ 11-11; 12-10.30 Sun
☎ (01483) 561733
Greene King IPA; Wadworth 6X; guest beer Ⓗ

The mid-19th-century architecture here corresponds to the arrival of the railway. On an unmade slip road, the pub is largely unspoilt by so-called 'progress' in marked contrast to some other pubs in the area. It sponsors the local football side and fields a winning darts team, but is enormously welcoming and accommodating to visitors. Simple, straightforward, cosy and relaxed around a U-shaped bar, it is fronted by a pair of large windows. No food Sun; eve meals served Fri and Sat. ⚌Q✿◑⇌♣P

SIDLOW BRIDGE

Three Horseshoes Inn

Ironsbottom (off A217, Reigate-Horley Road)
OS252461

☼ 12-2.30 (3 Sat), 5.30-11; 12-3, 7-10.30 Sun
☎ (01293) 862315 website: www.sidlow.com
Fuller's London Pride, ESB; Harveys BB, Old; Young's Bitter; guest beer Ⓗ

A true country local that offers a warm welcome to those just passing through. While the clientele leans towards the more mature, all ages can be found drinking here. An extension has been added to the rear, without detracting from the character of the place, resulting in three distinct drinking areas served by one bar. Good quality lunches; the guest beers are not available in summer.
🏰Q🏠🛏🌙Ⓟ●

STAINES

Angel

24 High Street (off A308)

☼ 11-11; 12-10.30 Sun
☎ (01784) 452509
Adnams Broadside; Courage Best Bitter; guest beers Ⓗ

A *Guide* regular for many years now, this hotel continues to thrive despite the increasing proximity of town-centre developments; a hotel has stood on this site since 1309. The main bar has several areas rambling off it, including an attractive conservatory where good value meals can be enjoyed, but avoid the view to the rear! The guest beers tend to be sourced from the Hogs Back Brewery. Prices are very reasonable for the area; beer festivals are held at Easter and in the autumn.
🏠🛏🌙⇌

Bells

124 Church Street (off B376)

☼ 11-11; 12-10.30 Sun
☎ (01784) 454240
Young's Bitter, Triple A, Special, seasonal beers Ⓗ

Friendly, 18th-century pub in the quieter, residential end of the street, in the shadow of St Mary's church. It is a few steps from the riverside path upstream of Staines bridge. It has recently undergone some enlargement, but retains its welcoming ambience. A pleasant garden can be enjoyed for both drinking and eating, and a room is available for private parties.
Q🏠🌙♿

George

2-8 High Street (A308, opp. Town Hall)

☼ 11-11; 12-10.30 Sun
☎ (01784) 462181
Courage Directors; Shepherd Neame Spitfire; Theakston Best Bitter; guest beers Ⓗ

Ever-popular, town-centre Wetherspoon's free house, arranged on two floors, with most customers frequenting the light and airy ground level where large windows allow a view of the busy High Street. An upper level offers a quieter, more intimate area. Local history of the town is reflected in the recently refurbished interior, indeed the pub name recalls an earlier George Inn that traded until the late 18th century. Wheelchair WC.
Q🌙♿⇌🚭●

STANWELL

Rising Sun

110 Oaks Road

☼ 11.30-11; 12-10.30 Sun
☎ (01784) 244080
Ind Coope Burton Ale; Fuller's London Pride; Greene King Abbot Ⓗ

Comfortable, one-bar pub, adjacent to the cargo area of Heathrow Airport, and popular with its staff. Though a bit off the beaten track, it is well worth seeking out. Aircraft models adorn the bar, where the TV is often tuned to sports events, however, it is not intrusive and there are areas for a quiet drink. One of the best bets for a good pint in the area. 🌙Ⓓ Ⓟ

UPPER HALE

Ball & Wicket

104 Upper Hale Road (A3016)

☼ 4 (12 Sat)-11; 12-3, 7-10.30 Sun
☎ (01252) 735278
Courage Best Bitter; Fuller's London Pride; Young's Bitter; guest beers Ⓗ

Cheerful, hospitable little pub with the appearance of a country local. It overlooks Hale Cricket Club and the former Bishops of Winchester's hunting grounds, now known as Farnham Park. The lower part of the split-level interior is decorated with antique carpenters tools. The raised dais has been recently enlarged to give more seating without ruining the look of this timber-beamed gem. On the local 4/5 bus route from Aldershot and Farnham. 🏰Q🏠Ⓟ

WEYBRIDGE ❅

Jolly Farmer

41 Princes Road (off A317) OS080643

☼ 10.30-3, 5-11; 10.30-11 Sat;
12-3.30, 7-10.30 Sun
☎ (01932) 856873 e-mail: dee.jolly@virgin.net
Hop Back Best Bitter, Summer Lightning, seasonal or guest beers Ⓗ

Local near the cricket green, an ex-Watneys house as the sign depicts. The L-shaped single bar, has cream plastered walls with black beams, displaying framed photos of old Weybridge. The floor is carpeted throughout, and wooden benches against the walls are softened with cushions. There are a few tables outside the front and a good-sized garden at the rear where barbecues are held. One of the few pubs tied to the Hop Back Brewery. No food Sat.
Q🏠🌙

WINDLESHAM ❅

Half Moon

Church Road
(from A30 take School Road, then first right)

☼ 11-3; 5.30-11 (11-11 summer); 12-4, 7-10.30 Sun
☎ (01276) 473329
Brakspear Bitter; Fuller's London Pride; Hop Back Summer Lightning; Ringwood Fortyniner; Theakston Old Peculier; guest beers Ⓗ

The Sturt family has been involved with this attractive pub since 1904, and sets high standards. They hold awards for hygiene and for their floral displays. Eight ales and a cask cider are served. The large garden includes a Wendy house and slide in the children's play area. The pub has a

children's certificate. A good range of meals is served (no food Sun eve). An arboretum nearby is open to the public in summer.
🏛Q🐕🌓◑❤️P

WITLEY

Star Inn
Petworth Road (A283)
🕐 12-2.30, 4.30-11; 12-11 Fri & Sat; 12-3.30, 7.30-10.30 Sun
☎ (01428) 684656 website: www.thestaratwitley.com
Friary Meux Bitter; Fuller's London Pride; guest beers Ⓗ

Originally a 17th-century mill for the preparatory processes in woollen cloth-making that once dominated this area of Surrey, it was converted into a pub in 1851 and is now Grade II listed. Dominated by a superb, and often very busy, public bar with a low ceiling; the original oak beams are supported by 19th-century cast-iron pillars. The saloon area is smaller, more food orientated (pizzas are home-made) and looks out on to a safe, enclosed garden with a children's climbing frame.
Q🐕🌓◑🍴🅰️♣️P

WOKING

Wetherspoon's
51-59 Chertsey Road
🕐 11-11; 12-10.30 Sun
☎ (01483) 722818
Courage Directors; Hogs Back TEA; Shepherd Neame Spitfire; Theakston Best Bitter; guest beers Ⓗ

One of Wetherspoon's finest with constantly changing guest beers (up to five at weekends). Originally a Woolworth's store, but now a major player in the town centre's social scene, it attracts all ages, and is often crowded. Large tables, screens and side booths successfully give the impression of separate drinking areas. An unusual metal sculpture of a seated man and a backward clock on the ceiling, operated by push button, represent an H G Wells theme. A large, quieter and more airy no-smoking area bears pictures of old Woking.
Q🌓◑🚭❤️●

WOOD STREET

Royal Oak
89 Oak Hill OS958510

🕐 11-3 (3.30 Sat), 5-11; 12-3.30, 7-10.30 Sun
☎ (01483) 235137
Courage Best Bitter; Hogs Back TEA; guest beers Ⓗ

Legendary free house of enduring popularity, stocking four, ever-changing guests of which one will always be a mild, bringing the total up to 1,500 beers since the pub opened. Run by two Olivers: one thinks he is the boss and enjoys his ego stroked, while the real boss just prefers his fur stroked! An excellent enclosed garden for children, superb, home-cooked food (no chips) and a Hodgson's of Kingston Brewery plaque add to its appeal. 🌓◑♣️●P

WRECCLESHAM

Bat & Ball
15 Bat & Ball Lane, Boundstone (off Upper Bourne Lane) OS834444
🕐 12-3, 5.30-11; 12-11 Fri & Sat; 12-11 Sun
☎ (01252) 792108
Archers Village; Brakspear Bitter; Fuller's London Pride; guest beers Ⓗ

Excellent free house, sporting seven handpumps. Relatively isolated, despite being close to housing, pedestrian access via the Bourne stream or by steps at the rear (challenging in the dark). You have to be 'in the know' to gain road access and don't expect taxi drivers to be in that position. Popular with both drinkers and diners (no food Sun eve); children are catered for in the conservatory/extension and can exhaust themselves in a superb garden. 🐕🌓◑P

Sandrock
Sandrock Hill Road, Upper Bourne (off B3384, towards Rowledge) OS830444
🕐 11-11; 12-10.30 Sun
☎ (01252) 715865 website: www.sandrockpub.co.uk
Batham Best Bitter; Enville Ale; guest beers Ⓗ

Wonderful mecca for real ale tipplers, deep in the heart of Farnham suburbia, but retaining a rural feel. It attracts drinkers from far and wide to sample the range of ales, usually with a Black Country flavour. No frills, but always comfortable and relaxing with a proven formula for success – good beer, well-managed, a roaring fire, sturdy furniture and the buzz of conversation. Beer festivals are held under a marquee in the garden. Local CAMRA *Pub of the Year* 2000. No food Sun.
🏛Q🐕🌓◑♣️P

INN BRIEF

KNAPHILL
Hooden Takes a Knap
134 High Street
11-11; 12-10.30 Sun
Hancock's HB; guest beers Ⓗ
Cosy atmosphere, dark and woody with candles and low beams. Strong food emphasis with Mexican specialities. Strong community focus.

LINGFIELD
Old Cage
Plaistow Street
11-11; 12-10.30 Sun
Courage Best Bitter; Fuller's London Pride; Greene King Old Speckled Hen; Harveys BB Ⓗ
16th-century free house with inglenook and different areas. Food all day. Jailors is a house beer from different breweries.

REDHILL
Hatch
44 Hatchlands Road
12-3, 5.30-11; 12-3, 7-10.30 Sun
Shepherd Neame Master Brew Bitter, Spitfire, Bishops Finger, seasonal beer Ⓗ
Smart, comfortable stone-clad local, serving good food, with an Edwardian theme.

SEND
New Inn
Send Road
11-2.30, 5.30-11; 12-3.30, 7-10.30 Sun
Adnams Bitter; Fuller's London Pride; Greene King Old Speckled Hen; Marston's Pedigree; guest beers Ⓗ
Canalside pub with three drinking areas; the garden is popular. Food served lunch and eve. Guest beers are from the Carlsberg-Tetley list.

WEYBRIDGE
Prince of Wales
Anderson Road, Oatlands Village
10.30-11; 12-10.30 Sun
Adnams Bitter; Fuller's London Pride; Tetley Bitter; guest beer Ⓗ
Floral haven in a suburb of Weybridge. A central bar serves two distinct areas, plus a dining area. House beer is Fuller's Chiswick. *Cask Marque* accredited.

WINDLESHAM
Bee
School Road
11-11; 12-10.30 Sun
Brakspear Bitter; Courage Best Bitter; Hop Back Summer Lightning; Wells Bombardier Ⓗ
An inn since 1865, it has a play area. Live jazz on alternate summer Sun; barbecues held.

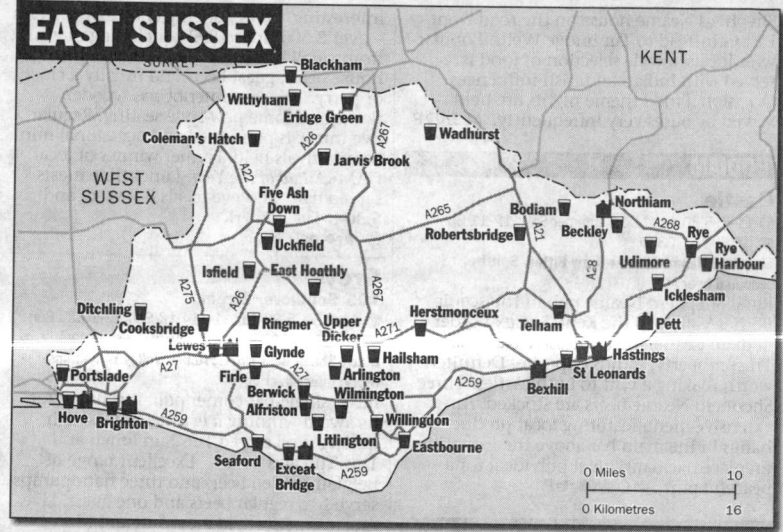

EAST SUSSEX

SURREY
KENT
WEST SUSSEX
Blackham
Withyham
Eridge Green
Coleman's Hatch
Wadhurst
Jarvis Brook
Five Ash Down
Bodiam
Northiam
Uckfield
Robertsbridge
Beckley
Rye
Isfield
East Hoathly
Udimore
Rye Harbour
Ditchling
Icklesham
Cooksbridge
Ringmer
Upper Dicker
Herstmonceux
Telham
Pett
Lewes
Glynde
Arlington
Hailsham
Hastings
Portslade
Firle
Berwick
Wilmington
St Leonards
Hove
Alfriston
Bexhill
Brighton
Willingdon
Seaford
Litlington
Eastbourne
Exceat Bridge

0 Miles 10
0 Kilometres 16

ALFRISTON ❄

Old Smugglers Inne
Waterloo Square (village centre, by market cross)
🕐 11-3, 6.30-11; 12-3, 7-10.30 Sun
☎ (01323) 870241
Harveys BB, Old; Sussex Pett Progress Ⓗ
Unusual village pub with two names – it is also known locally as the Market Cross. The building retains much character in the main bar and has a rambling set of other small rooms, featuring low-beamed ceilings and interesting curios. Hops decorate the bar. Locals believe it is haunted by two ghosts! There is a 'devil's' step leading to the no-smoking conservatory and an enclosed beer garden. A popular 'haunt' of walkers on the South Downs Way. ▲Q❀◑♣🌳⚥

ARLINGTON

Old Oak Inn
Just outside village on Hailsham-Wilmington road
OS558078
🕐 11-3, 6-11; 12-3, 7-10.30 Sun
☎ (01323) 482072
Badger Best; Harveys BB; Young's Special Ⓖ
Cosy, quiet pub close to Michelham Priory and Abbots Wood, part of Wilmington Forest which is great for walks. Built in 1773, it is full of character with low ceilings. Sit in the comfy lounge and the pub dog, a friendly Basset Hound, joins you by the fire! No music or games machines, just a pleasant, peaceful atmosphere. Always popular at lunchtimes and weekends. A good restaurant and large beer garden are assets. ▲Q❀◑P

BECKLEY

Rose & Crown
Northiam Road (B2188/B2165 jct)
🕐 11-3, 5.30-11; 11-11 Fri & Sat; 12-11 Sun
☎ (01797) 252161
Fuller's ESB; Harveys BB; Hook Norton Best Bitter guest beers Ⓗ
First-class free house serving a great range of beers at their very best, many of which are from distant breweries. This spacious family

pub offers separate areas for drinkers and diners. The long bar has wooden flooring and decorative hops. Locals and visitors are made most welcome in this country pub which has an excellent menu and fine views from the garden. ▲Q❀◑♣P

BERWICK

Cricketers Arms
Off A27, W of Drusilla's roundabout
🕐 10-3, 6-11; (11-11 summer Sat); 12-10.30 (6 winter) Sun
☎ (01323) 870469
Harveys BB, seasonal beers; guest beers Ⓖ
This unspoilt two-bar village pub was once two cottages. No trace of the theme pub generation here. The quarry-tiled floor means walkers from the South Downs are welcomed, boots and all! Lovely, quiet local in winter which becomes very busy in summer. Two beer gardens, front and rear, provide plenty of tables. Ample parking with two car parks. A local buys the old antique cricket bats which hang around the walls. Regulars and staff all help to create this pub's friendly, welcoming atmosphere. No eve meals Sun. ▲Q🛏❀◑🍴🎏⚥♣P

BLACKHAM

Sussex Oak
On A264 2 miles W of Ashurst village OS487392
🕐 11-3, 6-11 (11-11 summer); 12.10.30 (5 winter) Sun
☎ (01892) 740273
Shepherd Neame Master Brew Bitter, Best Bitter, Spitfire Ⓗ

INDEPENDENT BREWERIES

Cuckmere Haven Exceat Bridge
Dark Star Brighton
First Inn Last Out Hastings
Harveys Lewes
Kemptown Brighton
Rother Valley Northiam
Sussex Pett
White Bexhill

Shepherd Neame house on the road from East Grinstead to Tunbridge Wells. Popular with locals, a wide selection of food is served with Indian and Irish influences. Occasional food theme nights are held. Served by buses very infrequently. 🚌❀❀◑P

BODIAM

Castle

❀ 11-3, 5.30-11 (11-11 summer Sat); 12-11 Sun
☎ (01580) 830330
Shepherd Neame Master Brew Bitter, Spitfire, seasonal beer H

Rural Shepherd Neame pub in the scenic Rother Valley on the Kent–Sussex border. Bodiam Castle, the impressive National Trust property, stands opposite. Definitely worth making a visit to both castles. Three Shepherd Neame beers are stocked. An extensive menu featuring local produce hangs in the main bar above the imposing fireplace. Pleasant, quiet pub ideal for a peaceful pint. 🚌Q❀◑⬤≈P

BRIGHTON ❀

Basketmakers Arms

12 Gloucester Road (N of Prince Regent pool)
❀ 11-3, 5.30 (5 Wed & Thu)-11; 11-11 Fri & Sat; 12-10.30 Sun
☎ (01273) 689006
Gale's Butser, GB, HSB, Festival Mild, seasonal beers; guest beers H

Traditional, street-corner pub with diverse clientele. Single-bar Gale's tied house which can be very busy in the eve at weekends. Walls are decorated with antique adverts and storage tins. Tucked away in a side street but convenient for visitors to the Dome entertainment complex. The pub is featured in CAMRA's *Good Pub Food* and has a good range of malt whiskies. Food served daily at lunchtimes, eve meals only on weekdays. Deservedly popular pub worth finding. ◑≈

Battle of Trafalgar

34 Guildford Road
❀ 11-11; 12-10.30 Sun
☎ (01273) 327997
Fuller's London Pride; Harveys BB; Young's Bitter, Special H

Popular pub, a short walk up a steep hill from the railway station. The small frontage is deceptive as the interior is spacious with a separate dining area. Lunchtime meals served 12–2 Mon–Fri, 12.30–4.30 Sat and Sun. As the name would suggest, the decor features pictures of old sea battles and other nautical memorabilia. During the winter, live jazz is usually featured on Sun eve. The background music of jazz or blues is kept at a sensible level. It would be easy to miss your train in here! ❀◑≈♣

Evening Star

55-56 Surrey Street (near station)
❀ 11.30 (11 Sat)-11; 12-10.30 Sun
☎ (01273) 328931
Dark Star, Sunburst, Dark Star, seasonal beer; guest beer H

Friendly, popular town pub which is the home of the Dark Star Brewery. The busy corner bar has nine handpumps serving an interesting, ever-changing choice of real ales – over 2,500 since 1992 – including many from small breweries. The selection includes house beers, guest beers and usually a cider or perry. The cosy interior has wooden floors and some pew-style seating. Regular live music is performed and occasional mini beer festivals held. Former winner of local CAMRA *Pub of the Year*. Lunchtime meals served daily and eve meals 6-9 Wed, and 5.30-8 Tue and Fri. ❀◑≈⬤

Greys

105 Southover Street
❀ 11-3.30, 5.30-11; 11-11 Fri & Sat; 12-10.30 Sun
☎ (01273) 680734 website: www.greyspub.com
Black Sheep Best Bitter; Itchen Valley Wykehams Glory; guest beer H

Busy, single-bar corner pub. It is noted for its award-winning *à la carte* menu. High quality food served Tue–Sun lunch and Tue–Thu and Sat eve. Excellent range of Belgian bottled beers and three handpumps serve two regular beers and one guest. Live music is performed most Sun and Mon eves, and has included some well-known acts. ◑

Hand in Hand

33 Upper St James's Street
❀ 12-11; 12-10.30 Sun
☎ (01273) 699595
Badger Best, Tanglefoot; Kempton Brighton Bitter, Kemptown, Ye Old Trout Ale, SID; guest beers H

Cosy brewery tap of Kemptown Brewery, not far from the seafront. Resembles a large front room with a bar. Wallpapered with newspapers and suggestive photos can be seen on the ceiling! A collection of ties, fairy lights and old earthenware vessels add colour. Its claim to be the smallest pub in Britain with its own brewery has not been refuted and the beer prices are some of the best in Brighton. The brewer will sometimes be serving at the bar. Very much a local. Former local CAMRA *Pub of the Year* 1995. Q◑⬤

Lord Nelson

36 Trafalgar Street (close to station)
❀ 11-11; 12-10.30 Sun
☎ (01273) 695872
Harveys XX Mild, Pale Ale, BB, Armada, seasonal beers H

Deservedly popular two-bar Harveys tied house with an additional back room suitable for meetings or small functions. The bars are separated by an unusual screen. Walls are adorned with memorabilia relating to the Albion Football Club and (predictably) Nelson and Trafalgar. Pleasant patio area for use in good weather. Attracts a wide clientele including local workers and Brighton Station commuters. The pub fields its own cricket team. Serves a wide range of Harveys beers and excellent bar lunches Mon–Sat. Q❀◑⬤≈⬤⬤

Prestonville

64 Hamilton Road
❀ 5 (4 Fri; 11 Sat)-11; 12-10.30 Sun
☎ (01273) 701007
Gale's Butser, GB, HSB, seasonal beers; guest beer (occasional) H

Friendly corner pub. Hard to find but well worth the effort. The single-bar interior is decorated with breweriana and is free from electronic games and pool. There are regular pub quizzes and live music. The beer range is from Gale's and there are occasional guest ales. Good choice of single malt whiskies available with regular special offers. The menu includes good home-made food such as burgers and chilli, lunch served weekends only. ✪◖●

Ranelagh Arms
2-4 High Street
✪ 10.30-11; 12-10.30 Sun
☎ (01273) 681634
Fuller's London Pride; Wells Bombardier; Young's Special Ⓗ
Small one-bar pub that is adorned with blues ephemera and has old 78rpm records covering the ceiling. A popular venue for live music on Sun eve. The enclosed patio allows drinkers to watch passers-by in this cosmopolitan area. Food is served all day on Sun. ✪◖

Sir Charles Napier
50 Southover Street
✪ 5-11; 12-11 Fri & Sat; 12-10.30 Sun
☎ (01273) 601413
Gale's Butser, GB, HSB, seasonal beers; guest beers Ⓗ
Welcome return to the *Guide* after a year's break due to a change of landlord. Fortunately no changes other than a lick of paint. Street-corner local set on a steep hill in the Hanover area. Surprisingly roomy interior is divided into three areas. The panelled single bar is decorated with maps and pictures of old Brighton, a collection of bottles and items (including an 1851 letter) relating to Sir Charles Napier. Lunches served Fri–Sun and occasional theme nights organised. ✪◖♣♠

COLEMAN'S HATCH

Hatch Inn
In village, 400 yds S of A2110 OS452335
✪ 11.30-3, 5.30-11 (11-11 summer Sat); 12-10.30 Sun
☎ (01342) 822363 website: www.hatchinn.co.uk
Harveys BB; Larkins Traditional; guest beers Ⓗ
This single-bar pub features beams and hops. Watch out for particularly low beams on the way to the toilets! The pub is judged by the Cyclists' Touring Club as 'cyclist friendly'. This is one of very few genuine free houses in the area, where local ales such as Larkins are supported. Daily papers are provided for customers, along with a very good food menu during most sessions (not Sun and Mon eves). Buses from East Grinstead pass 400 yards away, useful as parking can be difficult. ♨Q✪◖P

COOKSBRIDGE

Pump House
Main Road
✪ 11-3, 6-11; 12-3, 7-10.30 Sun
☎ (01273) 400852
Harveys BB; guest beers Ⓗ
Popular U-shaped local in village outside Lewes. Quiet two-bar pub and restaurant with an extensive menu. Pool table and fruit machine are provided. Landlord ensures regular attraction of micro-brewed beers. Large garden is much used in summer. The decor is smart and there is an impressive set of pump clips of local micros behind the bar. ✪◖⇌P

DITCHLING

Sandrock
26 High Street (B2112, just N of crossroads)
✪ 11-11; 12-2.30 Sun
☎ (01273) 842777
Harveys BB; guest beers Ⓗ
A local, but still welcoming to visitors. The dining area is designated as a no-smoking area. The decor, which is not overdone, is on a 'wild west' theme, with rodeo posters, ten-gallon hats and the like. The food, however, is good English fare with generous portions at reasonable prices. Live folk music is performed on last Mon of each month (except bank holidays). Otherwise the background music is at a sensible level. The nearby Ditchling Village Museum is well worth a visit. Children are welcome. ♨✪◖♣P✂

White Horse
16 West Street (B2116, just W of crossroads)
✪ 11-11; 12-10.30 Sun
☎ (01273) 842006
Harveys BB; guest beers Ⓗ
Large, popular free house run by a CAMRA member. Awarded local *Pub of the Year* 1998 and runner-up for the past two years. The village church is opposite and Anne of Cleves' house is nearby. The pub stands near the foot of Ditchling Beacon, the highest point of the South Downs. Bar billiards and darts are played in the games area and there is a separate restaurant. A number of British bottled beers are stocked and the food menu is extensive with vegetarian options. The cellar reputedly has a resident ghost. ♨✪◖♣P●

EAST HOATHLY ✤

King's Head
1-3 High Street (off A22)
✪ 11-4, 6-11; 12-4, 7-10.30 Sun
☎ (01825) 840238
Fuller's London Pride; Harveys BB; guest beers Ⓗ
Spacious village-centre pub with many interesting features. Much used by locals and visitors. This pub tends to get involved in running competitions to raise money for charities throughout the year. There is a separate restaurant that serves food of the highest quality every day. The bar food includes fresh fish cooked in beer batter to eat in or take away. Tables and chairs set on the forecourt for outdoor drinking. Small car park available. ✪◖P

EASTBOURNE ✤

Alexandra Arms
433 Seaside (A259, 2 miles E of centre)
✪ 11.30-3, 5-11; 12-3, 7-11 Sun
☎ (01323) 720913
Greene King IPA, Ruddles Best, Triumph, Abbot, Old Speckled Hen, seasonal beer; Harveys BB Ⓗ
Friendly, well-run two-bar pub with eight pumps on tap. Seasonal and guest beers from the Greene King range. Features include curry nights (first Fri of each month), bar billiards, weekly quiz on Sun,

darts, crib and dominoes. The pub produces its own newspaper, the PTN, copies available for a donation to charity. Pleasant conservatory and garden. Food served all sessions except Mon eve. No drinking out of bottles permitted and fines for use of mobile phones. Ramp for wheelchair access available on request.

⚘◐▶ 🖳♣P

Buccaneer

10 Compton Street (next to theatres and Devonshire Park tennis courts)
☼ 11-11; 12-10.30 Sun
☎ (01323) 732829
Ind Coope Burton Ale; Marston's Pedigree; Tetley Bitter; guest beers Ⓗ

Busy pub at the heart of Eastbourne's theatreland, popular with theatre-goers and actors. This large one-bar pub has partitions and a raised no-smoking area. The walls are adorned with curios, from taps and spiles to autographed theatre posters. Many pictures of old Eastbourne are displayed. Three regular beers and three guest ales make this pub worth a visit. No food Sun eve.

◖♿♣♠

Hurst Arms

76 Willingdon Road
(A22, 1½ miles N of centre)
☼ 11-11; 12-10.30 Sun
☎ (01323) 721762
Harveys BB, Old, Armada Ⓗ

Very lively local on the main road into the town centre. Imposing Victorian building with an L-shaped public bar and smaller, more peaceful saloon. The public bar is busy and noisy with music, a pool table, dartboard and fruit machine. The comfortable saloon with plenty of seats overlooks the main road. Outdoor seating on roadside gets very busy. A *Guide* regular since 1978.

⚘🖳●

ERIDGE GREEN

Huntsman

Eridge Road (off A26, next to station)
☼ 12-2.30 (3 Sat), 6-11; 12-3, 6-11 Sun
☎ (01892) 864258
Badger K&B Sussex, Tanglefoot; guest beers Ⓗ

Homely two-bar ex-King & Barnes pub

lies in the hamlet of Eridge, close to Tunbridge Wells. Now run by Badger but K&B beers are available, although brewed in Dorset. Hearty menu of international cuisine is served along with more traditional pub food. Set next to the River Medway and close to the Uckfield branch line this pub is very popular with a varied clientele.

Q⚘◐▶ Å⇌♣ 🖤P

EXCEAT BRIDGE

Golden Galleon

On A259, just outside Seaford
☼ 11-11; 12-4 (Sept-Easter Sun), 12-10.30 Sun
☎ (01323) 892247
Cuckmere Haven Downland Bitter, Best Bitter, Guvnor, Golden Peace; guest beers Ⓗ

Home of the Cuckmere Haven Brewery, now moved to larger location next to main bar. Nine real ales and a good selection of ciders stocked. The brewer is a well-known author. Originally a tearoom, this pub has recently been extended to provide a meeting room with its own bar. The pub has started to grow its own hops. First-class food available with an Italian flavour. The splendid grounds are very popular in summer, the pub has fantastic views across the estuary. Ideal stopping-point if walking over the Seven Sisters on the South Downs.

🛥⚘◐▶♿ 🖤P

FIRLE

Ram Inn ☆

The Street
☼ 11.30-11; 12-10.30 Sun
☎ (01273) 858222
Harveys BB; guest beers Ⓗ

Traditional village local with three bars: main bar, family room and a no-smoking bar. The area is of historic interest, Firle is noted for being the home of the commander of the Charge of the Light Brigade. Excellent selection of high quality food. Unusual in having baby-changing facilities in male and female toilets. Local societies regularly use the bars for traditional Sussex music.

🏭Q🛥⚘🖳◐▶♣🖤⤬⊟

INN BRIEF

ALFRISTON

Wingrove
High Street;
11-3, 6-11; 11-11 Sat;
11-10.30 Sun
Harveys BB, Old; Hook Norton Old Hooky; Shepherd Neame Spitfire; guest beers Ⓗ
Family-owned country inn overlooking South Downs. Large outdoor area and live entertainment at weekends. Wide range of food available.

BRIGHTON

Constant Service
96 Islingword Road
12-11; 12-10.30 Sun
Harveys BB; Wadworth 6X Ⓗ
Pleasant corner pub attracting younger drinkers. The walls are adorned with prints of old Brighton.

Dover Castle
43 Southover Street
12-11; 12-10.30 Sun
Shepherd Neame Master Brew Bitter, Spitfire, seasonal beers Ⓗ
Traditional pub in a conservation area providing an unusual variety of vegetarian food. Disco music is played most weekday eves.

Prince Arthur
38 Dean Street
12-11; 12-10.30 Sun
Fuller's London Pride; Harveys BB; guest beers Ⓗ
Single-bar, wood-panelled pub free from games or TV. Handy for the main Brighton shopping area. Locals and visitors warmly welcomed.

Pump House
46 Market Street
11-11; 12-10.30 Sun
Draught Bass; Fuller's London Pride; Harveys BB Ⓗ
Situated in the heart of the Lanes area. Takes its name from the building that pumped seawater ashore for bathing. Cellars are medieval.

EAST HOATHLY

Foresters
6 South Street
11-11.30;
12-10.30 Sun
Harveys BB, seasonal beers Ⓗ
Welcoming atmosphere. Traditional old building with separate bar. Darts and pool played. *Cask Marque* accredited.

FIVE ASH DOWN

Fireman's Arms

400 yds off Uckfield bypass, on old A26
☼ 11-3, 6-11; 11-11 Sat; 12-3, 6.30-11 Sun
☎ (01825) 732191

Badger IPA; Harveys BB; guest beers ⊞

Busy, unspoilt pub with a steam railway theme in the public bar. Landlord hosts a vintage steam engine rally on New Year's Day. Good selection of food available (not Tue eve). Darts and pool offered in public bar, the saloon is quieter. Excellent range of real ales and cider stocked. Winner of Sussex CAMRA *Pub of the Year* 2000.
🛏Q⊕🕦♣🖐

GLYNDE

Trevor Arms
The Street
☼ 11-11; 12-10.30 Sun
☎ (01273) 858208

Harveys Pale Ale, BB, seasonal beers ⊞

Traditional, friendly local tucked away in a picturesque South Downs setting. Two bars cater for a wide range of customers. Note pictures of village life in the large main bar. Secluded snug and separate restaurant area, food can also be eaten in the public bar. Lovely large garden, popular with families in summer. The pub is handy for the railway station and is close to the world-famous Glyndebourne estate with its annual opera festival.
🕸⊕≒♣P⅌●

HAILSHAM

Grenadier
67 High Street
☼ 11-11; 12-10.30 Sun
☎ (01323) 842152

Harveys BB, seasonal beers ⊞

Harveys house just west of the town centre, this Victorian-style pub has two distinctly different bars; a saloon where children are admitted up to 9pm and a public bar with games and TV. The pub is busy but not raucous with an active charity group called the 'Milk and Ale' club. Since they started about 10 years ago they have raised over £90,000 for Guide Dogs for the Blind – note the pictures of the dogs over the bars. The dogs are named,

mostly, after regulars. The secure garden is ideal for children. Q🛏🕸⊕🕦♣P●

HASTINGS

Jenny Lind
69 High Street, Old Town

Hook Norton Best Bitter; Taylor Landlord; guest beers ⊞

Large, lively free house set in the historic old town of Hastings. Handy for the beach or shops or numerous tourist attractions. The pub tends to get busy at weekends when live music is performed. A large central bar features three to four beers, usually one local micro is offered. Excellent range of food with an Indian flavour served Wed–Sat eves. 🛏🛏🕸🕦🖐Å

HOVE

Cliftonville Inn
98-101 George Street (500 yds W of town hall)
☼ 10.30-11; 12-10.30 Sun
☎ (01273) 726969

Courage Directors; Hop Back Summer Lightning; Shepherd Neame Spitfire; Theakston Best Bitter; Wadworth 6X; guest beers ⊞

Spacious, busy Wetherspoon's pub sited in a converted shop premises in a pedestrianised street at the heart of one of the main shopping areas. The first Wetherspoon's on this part of the south coast opening some five years ago and by far the cheapest pub in the area. The Cliftonville offers up to five changing guest ales at a time and hosts regular beer festivals (April and October). Close to Hove town hall, home of the Sussex branches beer festival. The pub name originates from an area around Hove railway station. Q⊕⅋≒⅌●

Eclipse
33 Montgomery Street (S of railway, between Hove and Aldrington)
☼ 11-3, 5-11; 11-11 Sat; 12-10.30 Sun
☎ (01273) 272212

Harveys Pale Ale, BB, Armada, seasonal beers ⊞

Traditional pub in Poets' Corner, a quiet part of town. Fire gutted the premises in 1992, but after total refurbishment by Harveys it reopened in 1995. Rapidly re-established as a haunt for Brighton & Hove Albion fans who even played a role in saving the club from closure. Named after a

---

EASTBOURNE

Lamb Inn
High Street, Old Town
10.30-3, 5.30-11; 10.30-11 Fri & Sat;
12-4, 7-10.30 Sun
Harveys XX Mild, Pale Ale, BB, seasonal beers ⊞
Three rooms with two bars in an attractive beamed building. A passage used to lead to the church next door. Parts of the pub date back to 1290.

Victoria
27 Latimer Road
11-11;
12-10.30 Sun
Harveys Pale Ale, seasonal beers ⊞
Close to the seafront, old-style locals' pub. Excellent for a quiet drink. B&B is available.

Wetherspoon's Cornfield Garage
21-23 Cornfield Road
11-11; 12-10.30 Sun
Courage Directors; Hop Back Summer Lightning; Oakham JHB; Theakston Best Bitter; guest beers ⊞
Town-centre pub with 15 hand-pumps. Quiet during the day, lively in eve. No-smoking area and patio garden. *Cask Marque* accredited.

HERSTMONCEUX

Brewers Arms
Gardener Street
11-2.30, 6-11; 12-3, 7-10.30 Sun
Greene King IPA, Triumph; Harveys BB; guest beers ⊞
Lively, village local with good food, pub games and regular theme nights. Large beer garden.

LEWES

Snowdrop Inn
119 South Street
11-11;
12-10.30 Sun
Harveys BB, seasonal beers; guest beers ⊞
Popular pub on outskirts of town. Drinking areas spread over two floors. Good menu includes organic vegetarian and seafood meals.

RYE

Standard Inn
The Mint
12-11;
12-6 Sun
Sussex Forge Bitter; Young's Special ⊞
On main road, large single-bar pub. Good for food and folk music. Hops decorate the bar.

horse-racing event, the theme continues with many pictures inside. The pub sign shows Eclipse and Diamond, two horses galloping past the winning post. A highly successful Harveys venture. Food is served daily at lunchtime and 6.30–9pm Tue–Sat.
Q ◑ ⊞≈ (Aldrington/Hove) ♣ ●

ICKLESHAM

Queen's Head
Parsonage Lane (off A259)
✿ 11-11; 12-10.30 Sun
☎ (01424) 814552
Beer range varies Ⓗ
Welcoming country inn offering a great range of beers at their very best. Built in 1632 and converted into an ale house in the 19th century, this delightful part timber-framed pub has its name on the roof, clearly seen when approaching from the south. Superb views and a fine collection of farm tools add to its appeal. There is live music every Tue eve. Former local CAMRA *Pub of the Year*. Wide range of excellent food is served so can get busy at meal times. It is well worth finding.
🏠Q✿●◑♣●P⅓🗂

ISFIELD

Laughing Fish
Station Road (W of A26, 2 miles S of Uckfield)
✿ 11.30-3, 5.30-11; 11-11 Sat; 12-4, 7-10.30 (12-10.30 summer) Sun
☎ (01825) 750349
Greene King XX Dark Mild, IPA, Abbot, seasonal beers; guest beers Ⓗ
Victorian pub on the edge of a small village. Next to a level crossing on the disused Lewes to Uckfield line, which is now the Lavender Line restaurant, it is close to Bentley Wildfowl Reserve. Bars are approached up steps covered by a porch which was reputedly constructed by the Canadian army team who accidentally blew up the original during WWII. An underground stream cools the cellar and the pub has an angling theme. 🏠♋✿◑♣P⅓

JARVIS BROOK

Wheatsheaf
Mount Pleasant Road (off B2101) OS530293
✿ 12-3, 5-11; 11-11 Fri & Sat; 12-4, 7-10.30 Sun
☎ (01892) 663756
Harveys Pale Ale, BB, seasonal beers Ⓗ
Unspoilt pub in the suburb of Crowborough although retaining a rural feel. A fine range of Harveys beers is available. The pub is split into two levels, please mind the step! An attractive central wooden bar serves the three separate bars. One bar is mainly set aside for games, with darts and Toad in the Hole played. The pub offers good home-cooked food, a spacious garden and quiz nights every Tue.
🏠Q✿◑≈ (Crowborough) ♣P●

LEWES ✸

Black Horse
55 Western Road
✿ 11-2.30, 5.30 (6 Sat)-11; 12-2.30, 7-10.30 Sun
☎ (01273) 473653
Greene King IPA, Triumph; Harveys BB; guest beers Ⓗ
This former coaching inn features two

contrasting bars. The public bar has a fascinating collection of old photographs of the historic town, while the smaller lounge is a quiet oasis of calm, even though it contains a piano! The Sussex game of Toad in the Hole can be played in the public bar.
Q✿🛏◑♣

Lewes Arms
Mount Place
✿ 11-11; 12-10.30 Sun
☎ (01273) 473152
Greene King Abbot, seasonal beers; Harveys BB, Old Ale (winter) Ⓗ
This historic, curved-fronted pub is built into the castle ramparts. Features include a tiny front bar, a patio on the upper storey and a tiny stage in the upstairs function room. This room is the venue for meetings of the Lewes Folk Club. Look out for a display of Beard's Brewery dray horse tack in the back bar. Well-behaved children are welcome until 8pm in the games room that houses darts, Toad in the Hole and pictures by local artists. No mobile phones. Many community and charity events organised.
🏠Q◑≈♣♣

LITLINGTON

Plough & Harrow
Between Alfriston and Exceat OS523018
✿ 11-3, 6.30-11; 12-3, 6.30-10.30 Sun
☎ (01323) 870632
Badger IPA, Best, Tanglefoot; Harveys BB, Old; guest beer (summer) Ⓗ
Spacious county pub nestling in a quiet village on the beautiful South Downs. It is very popular with walkers and locals. The attractive interior has seating made from wooden barrels. Background music is played and various pub games are offered such as darts and chess. A wide range of meals are served daily and there is a separate dining area. This is a rare outlet for Badger beers locally. 🏠Q✿◑♣●P⅓

PORTSLADE

Stanley Arms
47 Wolseley Road (400 yds N of station)
✿ 1 (12 Fri & Sat)-11; 12-10.30 Sun
☎ (01273) 701590 e-mail: stanleyarms@altavista.com
Beer range varies Ⓗ
Built in 1882 this former Tamplins house was in a sad decline until the present owners bought it five years ago. Since then the Stanley has been transformed, stocking three ever-changing ales from independent breweries and a good selection of bottled Belgian beers. The pub won local CAMRA *Pub of the Year* 2000 and 2001. A lively, friendly local, it hosts live music, morris dancing, quizzes and has a crib team. A beer festival (Sept) is an annual event.
🏠Q✿⊞≈ (Fishersgate) ♣●🗂

RINGMER

Cock Inn
Uckfield Road (A26, between Lewes and Uckfield)
✿ 11-3, 6-11; 12-3, 7-10.30 Sun
☎ (01273) 812040
Fuller's London Pride; Harveys XX Mild, BB, Old; Rother Valley Spirit Level; guest beer (occasional) Ⓗ
Situated on the old A26 which is now a slip road west of the new A26 and dating from

the 16th century this cosy, oak-beamed pub has an attractive inglenook in the small bar area, and a stone floor. Former Evening Argus *Pub of the Year* and mentioned in various food guides, it has an extensive menu to suit all tastes and two eating areas. Approached up stone steps with adjoining gardens. ⚠🌳♿🕭🅿✦

ROBERTSBRIDGE

Ostrich
Station Road (opp. railway station)
🕓 6-11; 11-11 Sat; 12-4, 6.30-10.30 Sun
☎ (01580) 881737
Adnams Bitter; Harveys BB; guest beers Ⓗ
Former Station Hotel, now a much improved free house with a welcoming atmosphere and cheerful service. A spacious pub with a range of areas each featuring interesting items. A separate games room is well used by regulars. The gardens have been landscaped in Italian-style with many specimen tropical plants and bamboos thriving. Statuary adds to the scene and is enhanced by other planting providing colour all year round. Basic snacks are available.
🕭🕽➾🅿

RYE HARBOUR

Inkerman Arms
Harbour Road (off A259)
🕓 12-3, 7-11 (closed winter Mon); 12-3, 7-10.30 (not winter eve) Sun
☎ (01797) 222464
Rother Valley Level Best; Sussex Old Forge Bitter, Pett Progress; guest beers Ⓗ
Quiet, friendly, traditional pub that is worth finding. It offers up to four beers with the local micros being favoured as suppliers. Excellent meals, fish dishes a speciality, can be enjoyed in secluded dining areas. The large garden to the rear has a boules piste. The pub stands next to Rye Harbour Nature Reserve and has a very busy summer trade.
⚠Q🕭🕽♿✦🅿✦

ST LEONARDS

Bull
530 Bexhill Road (A259 near Bexhill)
🕓 12-3, 6-11; 12-4, 7-10.30 Sun
☎ (01424) 424984
Shepherd Neame Master Brew Bitter, Best Bitter, Spitfire, Bishops Finger or seasonal beer Ⓗ
Welcoming roadside pub noted for a range of Shepherd Neame beers served at their very best. This friendly local offers an excellent menu (book at weekends: no food Sun eve). There is a separate dining room, a bar billiards table in one corner and a large car park at the rear, which offers much more space than appears at first sight. The pub is at the western end of St Leonards so is handy for Glynde Gap shops.
⚠Q🕽♿♣🅿

Dripping Spring
34 Tower Road (off A2100, 1 mile N of Warrior Sq)
🕓 12-3, 5-11; 11-11 Fri & Sat; 12-3, 7-10.30 Sun
☎ (01424) 434055
Goacher's Light; Oakhill XXX Mature; Taylor Best Bitter; guest beers Ⓗ
Superb, family-run local situated in the

bohemian quarter of town. A constantly changing selection of guest beers means all tastes are catered for. To date 1,400 different beers have been featured and an impressive collection of pump clips adorns the walls. Winner of the local CAMRA and Sussex's *Pub of the Year* two years running and in 2000 it reached the final of the national round. The annual beer festival (Sept) held in the pigeon 'loft' holds an extra eight beers to the usual six. This lively pub, among other events, hosts a trivia quiz each Sun eve.
❀➾(Warrior Sq) ♣👤

Duke
48 Duke Road, Silverhill
🕓 11-11; 12-10.30 Sun
☎ (01424) 436241
Greene King IPA, Old Speckled Hen; guest beers Ⓗ
Traditional, busy street-corner pub with a cosy, welcoming atmosphere in its two bars. Excellent beer range, choose from five or six ales on tap. The pub hosts a beer festival on the first bank holiday in May. Held in a marquee in the rear garden, beers are served by gravity. If you like reading while you drink there are shelves of books to be found in the rear bar. Q❀🕽♣

Horse & Groom
Mercatoria Street
🕓 11-3.30, 5-11; 12-4, 7-10.30 Sun
☎ (01424) 420612
Greene King IPA; Harveys BB; Wells Bombardier; guest beer Ⓗ
First-class free house in the heart of old St Leonards. Serves a good range of beers at their very best. The 1829 listed building has an unusual horseshoe bar, which has created two separate bars, one leads to a further quiet room at the rear of the pub. The restaurant and accommodation, which were recently added, are now well-established. The pub gets busy at weekends. No food is served on Sun.
⚠Q❀🛏🕽➾(Warrior Sq)

SEAFORD

Wellington
Steyne Road (E side of old town, close to seafront)
🕓 11-11; 12-10.30 Sun
☎ (01323) 890032
Fuller's London Pride; Greene King IPA, Abbot; Harveys BB; guest beers Ⓗ
Comfortable, two-bar pub with a large lounge and a smaller public bar. This historic inn is thought to date back to the 17th century. Standing on what was once the old quayside of the Cinque Port, the pub was originally called the New Inn. In late Victorian times the name changed following a newspaper account (printed 40 years earlier!) of a mystery visitor to the inn. The pub has a darts and pool team and hosts folk music every Fri (except school holidays). Lunchtime meals offered Mon–Sat. The Martello Museum is nearby.
⚠Q🕽♿➾✦♣

TELHAM

Black Horse
Hastings Road (A2100, Battle road)
🕓 11-3, 6-11; 12-3, 7-10.30 Sun
☎ (01424) 773109

Shepherd Neame Master Brew Bitter, Spitfire, Bishops
Finger, seasonal beers Ⓗ

A fine roadside pub between Battle and
Hastings. It has been a regular entry in the
Guide for many years. There is an unusual
skittle alley in the attic and two boules
pistes outside. A four-day music festival is
held in a marquee every spring bank
holiday. Monthly jazz (and occasionally
folk) sessions are held in the bar. A wide
range of excellent food is served.
🏚⊛🛈🍺♣P

UCKFIELD

Alma
Framfield Road
(B2102, E of centre)
❂ 11-2.30, 6-11; 12-2, 7-10.30 Sun
☎ (01825) 762232
**Harveys XX Mild, Pale Ale, BB, Armada, seasonal
beers** Ⓗ

This is the only pub for miles around where
you can sample the full Harveys range –
including seasonal and occasional brews.
Run by the same family for generations, it
has a traditional public bar with games and
a truly local atmosphere. The saloon is
comfortable with an adjoining family/no-
smoking room. The pub is just a few
minutes from the town centre in a
residential area. There is a small garden and
no food served on Sun.
Q♿⊛🛈🍴&≠♣P🍺🚬●

UDIMORE

King's Head
Rye Road
(B2089, W of village)
❂ 11-4, 5.30-11; 12-4, 7-10.30 Sun
☎ (01424) 882349
Harveys BB; guest beers Ⓗ

Built in 1535 and extended in the 17th
century, this traditional village ale house
boasts beams, two open fires, wood floors,
and a very long oak bar which was installed
in the 1930s and has to be seen and leant
on to be believed. The pub serves excellent
home-cooked food and has a no-smoking
dining room. Situated in an area of
outstanding natural beauty, there are many
scenic walks nearby.
🏚Q♿⊛🛈🍴♣P

UPPER DICKER

Plough
Coldharbour Road
(between A27 and A22 on main road through Upper
Dicker)
❂ 12-3, 6-11; 12-3, 7-10.30 Sun
☎ (01323) 844859
**Shepherd Neame Best Bitter, Bishops Finger, seasonal
beer** Ⓗ/Ⓖ

Lively local offering all you would expect
from a village pub. Pub games, such as
boules and horseshoe toss are played. Tasty
food is served daily, a set menu at
lunchtime and *à la carte* in the eve. Relax on
comfy sofas in front of a real log fire with
no juke box to disturb the peace. The
excellent real ale is gravity fed. A pub of
character, part of the original 17th-century
interior is on show now having been
discovered during recent refurbishment. No
under 14s in lower bar. 🏚⊛🛈🍴&♣P

WADHURST

Greyhound
St James Square, High Street
❂ 11-11; 12-10.30 Sun
☎ (01892) 783224
Draught Bass; Harveys BB; guest beers Ⓗ

This ancient inn dates back to 1502 and was
a haunt of the notorious Hawkhurst gang,
an anarchic group of smugglers in the 18th
century. Now a smart, popular pub offering
four beers. There is a separate restaurant and
impressive inglenook enhancing this
village-centre local. 🏚🛈♣P

WILLINGDON

Red Lion Inn
99 Wish Hill (A22)
❂ 11-11; 12-3, 7-10.30 Sun
☎ (01323) 502062
**Badger K&B Sussex, Best, Gribble K&B Mild Ale,
Fursty Ferret** Ⓗ

Two storey, half-timbered building was
originally a small cottage ale house. Once
had a mangle room where the local
washerwoman would wring out clothes for
a penny a bundle. It has a famous literary
reference, George Orwell, in *Animal Farm*,
describes Mr Jones, the farmer, as sitting in
the tap room of the Red Lion at Willingdon.
Local village pub with a beer garden, family
room, and very long bar, one end of which
is the games area. ⊛🛈♣P🚫

WILMINGTON

Giant's Rest
On A27 Polegate-Lewes road
❂ 11-3, 6-11 (11-11 summer); 12-3, 6-10.30 Sun
☎ (01323) 890207 website: www.giantsrest.co.uk
**Harveys BB; Hop Back Summer Lightning; Taylor
Landlord; guest beer** Ⓗ

Lovely, quiet free house nestling on the
South Downs alongside the Long Man
landmark. Popular with walkers and locals
alike. An interesting menu is served daily. A
unique feature of the Giant's Rest is the
puzzles and games on all the tables from
Chinese wooden puzzles to 3D Connect
Four. Every so often new games creep in to
keep you occupied. Freshly squeezed fruit
juice is available along with excellent beers
and real cider. Ramps available for
wheelchair access. Camping facilities
available on neighbouring property.
🏚⊛🛈&🍺♣P🚫

WITHYHAM

Dorset Arms
On A2110 OS496357
❂ 11.30-3 (2.30 Mon), 5.30 (6 Fri & Sat)-11 (5.30-
10.30 Mon); 12-3, 7-10.30 Sun
☎ (01892) 770278 website: www.dorset-arms.co.uk
Harveys Pale Ale, BB, seasonal beers Ⓗ

Picturesque old pub, built in 1556, set in
what was once the industrial heartland of
England. Its unspoilt low-ceilinged bar has a
wooden floor of unvarnished local oak. The
restaurant is in a separate room, good food
served each lunchtime and Tue–Sat eves.
There is a large grassed area outside which is
busy on warm days. Ashdown Forest is not
far away and worth visiting. Frequent buses
from East Grinstead.
🏚⊛🛈P●

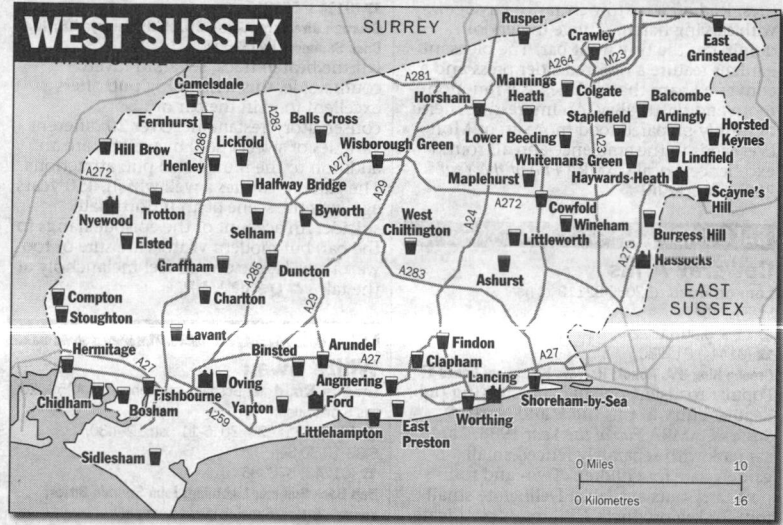

ANGMERING

Spotted Cow

High Street (off B2225, ½ mile E of village centre)
OS075043

☼ 10.30-3, 5-11; 10.30-11 Sat; 12-10.30 Sun

☎ (01903) 783919

Badger K&B Sussex; Courage Best Bitter, Directors; Greene King Old Speckled Hen; Young's Special; guest beer H

This 18th-century building was once a meeting place for smugglers. Quiet public bar, popular with locals. Features 'the wheel', an unusual ceiling-mounted game, the origins of which are unknown. Separate lounge/restaurant where children are allowed. Bar menu, *à la carte*, plus specials offered every day. Outside are grassed drinking areas, a children's play area and a boules pitch. Annual charity conkers competition and occasional hog roasts. The pub is popular with walkers. The 'Scotch' club (Spotted Cow Opportunity To Create Help) raises funds for charities.
ﾙ Q ✿ ◑ ⊟ ♣ P

Woodman Arms

Hammerpot (1 mile N of Angmering, access A27 eastbound only) OS067058

☼ 11-3, 6-11; 12-3, 7-10.30 Sun

☎ (01903) 871240

Gale's GB, HSB; guest beer H

Tall people beware in this 16th-century low-beamed Gale's house. The landlord has won Gale's *Cellar Craft* and *Safe Cellar* awards for several years; the pub has won awards in the *Loo of the Year* competition. Bar menu plus house specials on offer daily, with traditional roast plus specials lunchtime (no food Sun eve). All products are home-made and GM-free. Wide range of Gale's country wines available. Award-winning gardens. Walkers actively welcomed – leaflets detail walks from the pub. Folk music every other Sun night, and an annual 'Woodmanstock' fundraising folk event is hosted in August.
ﾙ Q ✿ ◑ ♣ P ⚹

ARUNDEL

White Hart

12 Queen Street (50 yds SE of bridge over River Arun)

☼ 11.30-3, 5.30-11; 11-11 Sat & summer; 12-10.30 Sun

☎ (01903) 882374

Harveys BB; guest beers H

Built around 1790, and originally belonging to the Constable Brewery across the road, this beamed property is a fairly recent addition to the Harveys estate, offering Harveys BB plus up to two other Harvey portfolio ales, including seasonal brews. The main bar area is divided in two by a central fireplace with the real fire accessible from both sides. Although no separate family room as such, an area to the rear of the pub is suitable for young families and children may be allowed in other areas at the landlord's discretion. ﾙ ✿ ◑ ⚹ Å ⇌ ●

ASHURST

Fountain Inn

On B2135, 3 miles N of Steyning

☼ 11.30-2.30 (4 Sat), 6-11; 12-3, 7-10.30 Sun

☎ (01403) 710219

Adnams Bitter; Fuller's London Pride; Harveys BB; Shepherd Neame Master Brew Bitter; H **guest beers** G

Delightful 16th-century hostelry of real character overlooking the village duckpond. Two bars and a dining room, with low, exposed beams, flagstone floors and open

INDEPENDENT BREWERIES

Arundel Ford
Ballard's Nyewood
Brewery on Sea Lancing
Dark Star Haywards Heath
Gribble Inn Oving
Hepworth Horsham
King Horsham
Rectory Hassocks
Spinnaker Lancing

fires, lead off a narrow entrance passageway with serving hatch. A huge inglenook dominates the tiny front bar. The pleasant gardens feature a restored cider press and a converted barn that doubles as a function room and skittle alley. An interesting menu of freshly prepared food (not Sun or Mon eves) adds to the ambience and all-round excellence. Local CAMRA *Pub of the Year* 2001. ᴬ⁴Q❀◑P

BALCOMBE

Cowdray Arms

London Road (B2036/B2110 jct near to M23 jct 10A)
☼ 11-3, 5.30-11; 12-3, 7-10.30 Sun
☎ (01444) 811280

Greene King IPA, Abbot; Harveys BB; guest beers Ⓗ
Popular roadside, one-bar Greene King pub. Regular entry in this *Guide* and North Sussex CAMRA *Pub of the Year* 1998. Large car park with separately fenced small garden, safe for children. Two- and four-pint carry-outs available. Deliberate small font for keg products. Children's certificate. Good selection of reasonably priced home-cooked meals – current CAMRA *Good Pub Food* entry. Bar and restaurant menu plus specials board. Large, airy conservatory for non-smokers. Cellar situated in room next to bar, handy for beer festivals. The pub is close to High Beeches Gardens and Worth Abbey. Q❀◑♣P

BALLS CROSS

Stag

Off A283 2 miles NE of Petworth OS987263
☼ 11-3, 6-11; 12-3, 7-10.30 Sun
☎ (01403) 820241

Badger K&B Sussex, Best, Old Ale, Tanglefoot Ⓗ
This 16th-century country pub was on an old coaching route. It has an unspoilt interior with original stone floor and inglenook. A reasonable turnout can be expected for elections as the pub serves as the local polling station. It is very much the centre of local life. ᴬ⁴Q❀◑♣P

BINSTED

Black Horse

Binsted Lane (off A27/B2132) OS980064
☼ 11-3, 6-11; 12-3, 7-10.30 Sun

☎ (01243) 551213

Courage Directors; Gale's GB, HSB; Harveys BB; Hop Back Summer Lightning Ⓗ
Off the beaten track, set amid lovely countryside, this welcoming pub offers excellent food in the bar or conservatory/restaurant. Over 20 different varieties of sweets, sold by weight, are an addition to the more usual pub attractions. The garden features a well which, 110 years ago, was the scene of an unfortunate suicide. An account of the episode hangs in the bar, but modern visitors are sure of too warm a welcome ever to feel melancholy at the tale. ᴬ⁴Q❀◑Ꮹ♣P

BOSHAM

White Swan

Station Road (at Bosham roundabout on A259, 200 yds S of station)
☼ 12-3, 5-11; 12-4.30, 6-11 Sat; 12-4.30, 6.30-10.30 Sun
☎ (01243) 576086

Hop Back Summer Lightning; John Smith's Bitter; Young's Bitter, Special; guest beers Ⓗ
An inn for 300 years, this welcoming roadside local is child-friendly. It is spacious and cosy with beams, timbers, bare bricks and a log fire. With easy access by road and rail, this is a good stopping point for visitors to the nearby site of Canute and his tidal trick. A range of good beers (and cider) is served in lined glasses. A skittle alley doubles as a function room for community activities. Excellent restaurant with local fish a speciality, no food Sun eve. Highly recommended. ᴬ⁴Q❀◑Ꮹ⚠♣●P🍺

BURGESS HILL

Watermill

1 Leylands Road, Worlds End (near Wivelsfield station)
☼ 11-11; 12-10.30 Sun
☎ (01444) 235517

Brakspear Bitter; Shepherd Neame Spitfire; Young's Special; guest beer (occasional) Ⓗ
Single-bar, community pub in Worlds End on the outskirts of Burgess Hill. The Watermill boasts a scuba-diving society in addition to more traditional pursuits like the darts, football and cricket teams. A stoolball club is also planned. Major sports events are shown on TV and occasionally

INN BRIEF

ARDINGLY

Oak Inn
Street Lane
11-3, 6-11; 11-11 Fri & Sat; 12-10.30 Sun
Harveys BB; guest beers Ⓗ
Traditional, low-ceilinged pub that was originally three labourers' cottages. Excellent restaurant and resident ghost.

CAMELSDALE

Mill Tavern
Liphook Road, Shottermill
11-3, 6-11; 5.30-11 Fri; 12-4, 7-10.30 Sun
Bateman XB; Fuller's London Pride; Wells Bombardier; guest beers Ⓗ
Once a 15th-century farmhouse with large beer garden and extensive menu. A previous landlord's ghost inhabits the cellar.

CHARLTON

Fox Goes Free
11-3, 5.30-11; (11-11 summer); 12-3, 6-10.30 (12-10.30 summer) Sun
Ballard's Best Bitter; Draught Bass; Ringwood Best Bitter Ⓗ
Wonderful old pub in downland village. Fires and stoves in winter, large garden in summer make this attractive inn a great venue.

CLAPHAM

Coach & Horses
Arundel Road
11-3, 5.15-11; 12-3, 7-10.30 Sun
Adnams Broadside; Arundel Castle; Fuller's London Pride; Young's Special; guest beers Ⓗ
Former coaching inn, just west of Worthing on A27. Still providing food and drink to travellers, established 1790. Quiz Tue 8.30pm.

COWFOLD

Hare & Hounds
Henfield Road (A281)
11.30-2.30 (3 Sat), 6-11; 12-3, 7-10.30 Sun
Greene King IPA; Harveys BB; Tetley Bitter; guest beers Ⓗ
Victorian village local refurbished in 1995 from timber fallen in the hurricane nearby. Popular with locals. *Cask Marque* accredited.

FERNHURST

Red Lion
The Green
11-3, 5-11; 12-3, 7-10.30 Sun
Badger K&B Sussex; Hogs Back TEA; guest beers Ⓗ
Excellent 17th-century pub beside the village green. Secluded garden. Small family room and boules played. Wide selection of meals.

live music is performed. Background music at a reasonable level lends itself to conversation. A regular venue on the local CAMRA trail. 🚶🛏🌓◑⇌ (Wivelsfield) ♣P

BYWORTH

Black Horse Inn
100 yds from A283 OS985212
🕓 11-2.30 (3 Sat), 6-11; 12-3, 7-10.30 Sun
☎ (01798) 342424
Fuller's London Pride; Shepherd Neame Spitfire; guest beers Ⓗ

Unspoilt, rural pub (built circa 1791). This village free house has oak beams, bare floorboards and a large fireplace. Unlike many such establishments it has kept provision of food and drink apart. The adequately proportioned bar is for drinkers, and is very welcoming with a warm, friendly atmosphere. The remainder of the pub is given over to diners, and is usually very busy. The ploughmans lunch of local bread and cheese, is a speciality. The large garden has good views of the undulating Sussex countryside. 🚶Q🌓♣P

CHIDHAM

Old House at Home
Cot Lane (1 mile S of A259 between Chichester and Emsworth) OS787040
🕓 11-3, 6-11; 12-3, 7-11 Sun
☎ (01243) 572477 website: www.oldhouse.co.uk
Ringwood Best Bitter, Old Thumper; guest beers Ⓗ

Charming 17th-century inn located in one of the remoter areas around Chichester harbour. The traditional interior and smallish one-bar layout has a cosy and friendly atmosphere. A genuine free house, the guest beers are from local independent breweries. The source of the Old House Bitter is a secret. Formerly the home of Chidham Brewery in the early 1980s, the pub is now renowned for its food, served in the bar or a small adjoining dining area. May remain open throughout the afternoon. 🚶Q🌓◑P

COLGATE

Dragon
(On road from Horsham to Pease Pottage) OS229327
🕓 11-3, 5-11; 12-3, 7-10.30 Sun
☎ (01293) 851206
Badger K&B Sussex, Best, Tanglefoot, seasonal beer Ⓗ

The village of Colgate, according to legend, is where the last sighting of a dragon in England took place. This former King & Barnes house has a small public bar and the emphasis is firmly on beer. The Dragon is largely unspoilt – to the extent of not even having an electric till! Snacks and sandwiches are available. It attracts many walkers enjoying the beautiful surrounding countryside. The pub is served by an infrequent bus service from Horsham. 🚶Q🌓⊟P

COMPTON

Coach & Horses
The Square (B2146)
🕓 10.30-2.30 (3 Sat), 6-11; 12-3, 7-10.30 Sun
☎ (023) 9263 1228
Fuller's ESB; Heritage Stonehenge; guest beers Ⓗ

16th-century pub in a charming downland village, surrounded by excellent walking country. The large front bar has two open fires and internal window shutters. There is also a smaller rear bar, and a fine beamed restaurant (closed Sun eve) that has a good reputation. A skittle alley and bar billiards machine are added attractions. The guest beers are always an interesting selection. Compton is a lively place and the pub is in the village square. 🚶🌓◑♣

CRAWLEY

Shades
85 High Street
🕓 10-11; 12-10.30 Sun
☎ (01293) 514105
Flowers IPA; Greene King Abbot; Young's Special; guest beers Ⓗ

The building dates from the 14th century and was originally Chandlers Brewery until bought by Whitbread in the 18th century. The pub recently changed its name from the Brewery Shades; the beer brewed by Chandlers was called 'Shades'. The pub has a sinister past. It used to have holding cells for the local police. A passage linked the pub with the George Hotel (opposite the town square), condemned prisoners would be led through and hanged in the main square. Not surprisingly this very lively pub is thought to be haunted! ◑&⇌✄

DUNCTON

Cricketers
On A285, 2½ miles S of Petworth
🕓 11-2.30, 6-11; 12-3, (closed eve) Sun
☎ (01798) 342473
Archers Golden; Young's Bitter Ⓗ

Charming, ex-Ind Coope free house set slightly back from the main road. What could have been 'just another roadhouse' is highly popular and has been local CAMRA *Pub of the Year* in recent years. Even following a change of ownership it remains a worthy oasis. Sadly the skittle alley has given way to a function room, but the current licensee has worked at the pub since the age of 15 and she intends to preserve its charm and commitment to good real ale and excellent food. The spacious garden has also won awards. 🚶Q🌓◑P

EAST GRINSTEAD

Ship Inn
Ship Street (off High St)
🕓 11-11; 12-10.30 Sun ☎ (01342) 312089
Smiles Best; Young's Bitter, Special Ⓗ

Recent Young's acquisition, a one-bar pub that is almost circular in shape and features two real fires. Many pictures of ships adorn the walls. The pub fields two football teams, two cricket teams and a darts team. By the *Guide* publication date, the pub will have undergone major refurbishment that will greatly enhance its appearance. Smiles Best is now stocked following Young's takeover. 🚶🌓⊟◑♣P

EAST PRESTON

Fletcher Arms
Station Road, Rustington (opp. Angmering Station)

❂ 11-11; 12-10.30 Sun

☎ (01903) 784858

Adnams Broadside; Fuller's London Pride; Greene King Abbot; Marston's Pedigree; Ringwood Best Bitter; Young's Special; guest beers Ⓗ

Lively, community pub, named after John Fletcher, the dramatist. The large family garden boasts a boules piste, a children's play area, pets corner and popular summer barbecues. There is a varied selection of bric-à-brac, old local photographs and window seats in both bars. The old barn has been converted to a function/family room. It was once part of the Post Office and used for stage-coach repairs. Older regulars talk of a young man being hanged here for a dastardly crime! There are occasional live music nights. Ramp available for wheelchair access. No food Sun eve.

🏠Q❀🍴◑ 🚲🚵≈ (Angmering) ♣P✂●

ELSTED

Three Horseshoes

Between Midhurst and Harting villages

❂ 11-2.30, 6-11; 12-3, 7-10.30 Sun

☎ (01730) 825746

Ballard's Best Bitter; Cheriton Pots Ale; guest beers Ⓖ

Traditional village pub originally built as a drovers' inn. Low beams, tiled floors and small rooms create a very cosy and friendly atmosphere. The huge garden has splendid views. The pub is one of the stops on the annual Ballard's Walk – a pub crawl for charity! The third beer is either Taylor Landlord or Fuller's London Pride with more beers and Inches cider in summer. Home-cooked food is always available with a choice of a dozen fish, game, pie or roast main dishes. Closed on Sun eve from October to Easter.

🏠Q❀◑ ♣P

FERNHURST ❄

King's Arms

Midhurst Road (A286, 3/4 mile S of village)

❂ 11.30-3, 5.30 (6.30 Sat)-11; 12-3 (closed eve) Sun

☎ (01428) 652005

Cheriton Pots Ale; Otter Bright; RCH Pitchfork; Ventnor Golden; guest beers Ⓗ

Sussex sandstone pub set amid rolling farmland. This popular free house has been a pub since the 17th century. L-shaped interior with a drinking area at one end and restaurant with inglenook at the other. Wide-ranging, monthly changing seasonal menu of home-made food, specialising in fish (no food Sun eve). There is also a small private dining room. Large enclosed rear garden and patio. Wisteria-covered Sussex barn for functions. Interesting guest beers always stocked. Camping facilities available behind pub, 24 hours' notice required.

🏠Q❀◑ ▲♣P

FINDON

Gun

The Square

❂ 11-11; 12-10.30 Sun

☎ (01903) 873206 e-mail: guncow@aol.com

Adnams Bitter; Fuller's London Pride; Gale's HSB; Harveys BB; guest beers Ⓗ

Dating back to 1450, the Gun was first licensed in 1619. In the 18th century it was a coaching inn with a brewhouse, a cockpit and a gunsmith's shop. By 1996 it was a moribund Whitbread pub scheduled for demolition. A vigorous two year 'Save the Gun' campaign succeeded and it is now a sensitively refurbished free house. Handy for the South Downs Way, the pub has one large bar and two separate rooms for dining and functions. Home-cooked food and a good range of Belgian bottled beer offered. Occasional live music.

Q🚲❀◑ �& P✂

GRAFFHAM

Forester's Arms

3 miles W of A285 OS931177

❂ 11-2.30, 5.30-11; 12-3, 7-10.30 Sun

☎ (01798) 867202

Cheriton Pots Ale; guest beers Ⓗ

Close to the South Downs Way, a fine free house with a pleasant, sizeable garden and large inglenook. The original building is circa 1609. The pub was first owned by the Chichester Brewers, Henty & Constable and called the Star and Garter. The current name arose as it was a meeting place for the free foresters. During Victorian times an extension was added. This now houses the restaurant. 🏠Q❀◑ ▲P

HALFWAY BRIDGE

Halfway Bridge Inn

On A272, between Midhurst and Petworth

❂ 11-3, 6-11; 12-3, 7-10.30 (not winter eve) Sun

☎ (01798) 861281

Cheriton Pots Ale; Fuller's London Pride; Gale's HSB; guest beer Ⓗ

Smart, 18th-century coaching inn with rural atmosphere. The many small inter-connecting rooms, each with an open fire, are regularly filled with appreciative diners enjoying the imaginative, varied menu which features locally-grown fresh produce. Drinkers are catered for in the rear bar which leads through to a patio area and offers an unusual selection of table games to play while you enjoy your pint. The guest beer is normally from local independent brewers. Recent conversion of the barn has provided eight comfortable double bedrooms.

🏠Q❀🍴◑ ♣♠P

HENLEY

Duke of Cumberland Arms

Just off A286, 2 1/2 miles N of Midhurst OS894258

❂ 11-3, 5 (6 Sat)-11; 12-3, 7-10.30 Sun

☎ (01428) 652280

Adnams Broadside; Gale's Butser, HSB; Hop Back Summer Lightning; guest beers Ⓖ

Small, welcoming free house (15th century) nestling near the top of Henley Hill with fine views north across the Sussex and Surrey Weald. With its cosy bar and dining room, quarry-tiled floor, genuine beams, pine panelling and log fires, this virtually unaltered pub is a real gem. In summer the large garden becomes busy with drinkers and diners seated among the spring-fed trout ponds. The menu features freshly-prepared English food (specialising in trout from the garden ponds). No food Sun eve.

🏠Q❀◑ ♠P

HERMITAGE

Sussex Brewery

36 Main Road (A259 1/2 mile E of Emsworth)

✪ 11-11; 12-10.30 Sun

☎ (01243) 371533

Smiles Best; Young's Bitter, Triple A, Special, Winter Warmer Ⓗ

Cosy, bare-boarded local with open fires. Now a Young's tied house with a full range of beers including Hermitage Best. A Grade II listed building, this pub has sawdust on the floor and is traditional with a capital 'T'. Set in a fishing village, not surprisingly, local fish is a speciality in the restaurant. More unusual is the extensive sausage menu available in the bar and restaurant. There is a lovely walled garden.

🏚 Q ✿ ◖ Å ≈ (Emsworth) P

HILL BROW

Jolly Drover

At jct of B2070/B3006

✪ 11-2.30, 6-11; 12-3, 7-10.30 (closed winter eve) Sun

☎ (01730) 893137 e-mail: barringtonco@aol.com

Draught Bass; Black Sheep Best Bitter; Hook Norton Old Hooky; Taylor Landlord; guest beer Ⓗ

Built in 1820 by a drover, this watering-hole lies midway between Petersfield and Liphook on the old A3, just outside Liss. Welcoming family-run country local. The atmosphere is enhanced by original beams, an extremely large log fire (with stacks of logs) and two chesterfields. Interesting and varied bric-à-brac includes a bar price-list from the 1950s. The well-proportioned bar and dining area offer over 20 home-made daily specials. The five cask ales include an interesting independent changing guest. Swamp Donkey real cider is sold.

🏚 Q ✿ ◖ ♠ P

HORSHAM

Bear

17 Market Square

✪ 11-3, 5-11; 10-11 Sat; 12-3, 7-10.30 Sun

☎ (01403) 260700

Badger K&B Sussex, Best, Tanglefoot, seasonal beers; guest beers Ⓗ

Wonderful, unspoilt town-centre pub, the building dates back to the 12th century. Offers a wide range of Badger beers including seasonal ales. The pub's decor has changed little over the years. The serving area has wood-panelled walls and a wealth of ursine ornaments. Beside the bar there is a hidden door in the wall. It is reputed to be haunted by three ghosts. Very popular with cricket fans as it is within easy walking distance of Horsham Cricket Club.

✿ ◖ ≈

Green Dragon

12 Bishopric

✪ 11-11; 12-10.30 Sun

☎ (01403) 252286

Badger K&B Sussex, Best, Tanglefoot, seasonal beers Ⓗ

Large, busy town-centre pub near the Shelley Fountain. The original building (circa 1449) was timber-framed with wattle and daub panels. It was once the centre of administation for the lord of the manor. There is a large conservatory with a central

well that at one time supplied water to the brewery. The conservatory is no-smoking while food is served (Mon–Thu 5.30–9pm). There are two main drinking areas; one has a large-screen TV, the other has plenty of seating and offers bar billiards. Pleasant patio area to the front of pub.

✿ ◖ ₲ ♿ ≈ ♠ P ✾ ●

Malt Shovel

15 Springfield Road (Albion Way jct)

✪ 11-11; 12-10.30 Sun

☎ (01403) 254543

Boddingtons Bitter; Gale's GB; guest beers Ⓗ /Ⓖ

Traditional, spacious pub with seven guest beers (four on handpump and three on gravity) and a draught cider, usually Bibbenden. Between 200–300 beers are sold each year. Helpful staff will let you try a taster before you order your beer. Belgian bottled beer is stocked. An annual beer festival held (Feb/March) at this North Sussex CAMRA *Pub of the Year* 1998/99. The pub has an attractive outside drinking area with hanging baskets that have been commended by *Horsham in Bloom*. Quiz on Sun eve. 🏚 ✿ ◖ ≈ ♣ ♠ P

Tanners Arms

78 Brighton Road

✪ 11-3 (4 Sat), 7-11; 12-4, 7-10.30 Sun

☎ (01403) 250527

Badger K&B Mild, Sussex, Best, Old Ale, Tanglefoot Ⓗ

Good, no-frills community pub, very much like one would find 25 years ago. The only food you are likely to encounter here is rolls and savoury snacks. The emphasis is on good ale and friendly service. The current licensees had a regular *Guide* entry in their previous pub. The pub has a long, narrow public bar well-used by locals and a small snug/lounge bar for that quiet moment of contemplation. Q ₲ ♣

HORSTED KEYNES

Green Man

The Green (access via B2028 or A275) OS385283

✪ 11.30-3, 5.30 (6 Sat)-11; 12-3, 7-10.30 Sun

☎ (01825) 790656 website: thegreenman.co.uk

Greene King IPA, Abbot, seasonal beer; Harveys BB Ⓗ

Popular village-centre pub close to the Bluebell Railway. A single bar with a separate no-smoking eating area; the wooden beams are decorated with hops and the impressive fireplace dates back to the 1700s. The exterior of the pub is not so old following a fire in 1920. The pub is named after a pagan symbol, prominent in great houses of religion and symbolises eternity and rebirth. There is a varied menu of home-cooked food plus special themed dishes. Pub appears in current CAMRA *Good Pub Food*. 🏚 ✿ ◖ ♣ ♠ P ✾

LAVANT

Earl of March

Lavant Road (A286, 2 miles N of Chichester)

✪ 10.30-3, 6 (5.30 summer)-11; 10.30-11 Sat; 12-3, 7-10.30 Sun

☎ (01243) 774751

Cottage Golden Arrow; Ringwood Old Thumper; guest beers Ⓗ

Friendly village pub catering for everyone. Popular with visitors and locals alike. The large wood-panelled single bar exhibits a mainly naval theme as the landlord is an ex-submariner, with an extensive display of ships' badges and other artefacts. A fine vista of the South Downs is afforded from the compact garden. Close to the historic Goodwood motor racing circuit and the annual festival of Speed Hillclimb. Good value food features local game and fish in generous home-cooked portions. The pub has a children's certificate and live music is staged every Thu eve. Dogs welcome with well-behaved owners!

❀◑♣🍺P

LINDFIELD

Linden Tree
47 High Street
❁ 11-3, 6-11; 12-3, 7-10.30 Sun
☎ (01444) 482995
Arundel Best; Harveys BB; Ringwood Old Thumper; guest beers Ⓗ
Small, friendly free house with shop-like frontage, situated in the High Street of this picturesque village. There are the remains of a long-disused brewery at the rear. A newly-opened extension provides extra room for those dining. There are usually six real ales at any one time.

🏚Q❀◑

LITTLEHAMPTON

Dewdrop
96 Wick Street
❁ 10.30-3, 5.30-11; 10.30-11 Sat; 10.30-10.30 Sun
☎ (01903) 716459
Gales's GB; guest beer Ⓗ
Built in the 1860s as part of a row of terraced houses, this unassuming and welcoming free house is one of an increasingly rare breed of unpretentious and down-to-earth local pubs, situated in the Wick area of the town. The rather snug saloon bar was originally 'the house next door', dating from a distant time when the more spacious and typically basic public bar was three bars. There is a choice of two to three real ales, always in excellent condition. It serves probably the best pint of Ringwood XXXX Porter in the area in winter.

🍺

LITTLEWORTH

Windmill
Littleworth Lane
(from A24, take B2116, Partridge Green, pub sign 2 miles on left) OS193205
❁ 11.30-3, 5.30-11; 12-3, 7-10.30 Sun
☎ (01403) 710308
Badger K&B Sussex, Best, seasonal beer Ⓗ
You can be sure of a warm welcome at this wisteria-covered country pub. It has a comfortable beamed lounge and a rustic, flagstoned public bar with a collection of old bottles and farm implements. Fri eve is take-away fish and chip night. In winter you can cook your steak over the fire. No food Sun eve. The landlord can arrange tours of the local St Hugh's Monastery (gentlemen only). Indoor boules and Jack in the Box played.

🏚Q❀◑🍺&♣P

LOWER BEEDING

Plough
Leech Pond, Hill Road (B2110, 500yds from jct A281, 4 miles S of Horsham) OS220274
❁ 11-3, 5.30-11; 11-11 Fri & Sat; 12-10.30 Sun
☎ (01403) 891277
Badger K&B Sussex, Best, Ⓗ **Tanglefoot** Ⓖ
Basic, no-frills two-bar pub offering cheap beer for the area. Stands in a vulnerable position on the outside of a sweeping bend which has caused a few lorries to 'drop in' in the past. Current licensees have been at the pub for over 18 years. Snacks and sandwiches available lunchtime. Warm welcome assured. 🏚Q🍺♣P

MANNINGS HEATH

Dun Horse
On A281, 2 miles S of Horsham OS201286
❁ 11-3, 5.30-11; 11-11 Sat; 12-10.30 Sun
☎ (01403) 891208
Draught Bass; Taylor Landlord; guest beers Ⓗ
Roadside two-bar pub on the A281 at Mannings Heath. Exterior is notable for stained glass windows promoting 'Rock Ales'. The interior has a beamed ceiling with hanging hops. A varied menu of excellent food is served at all sessions. Adjacent to the route of an hourly Horsham to Brighton bus service.

🍴◑🍺P✝

MAPLEHURST

White Horse
Park Lane (midway between A281 and A272) OS190246
❁ 12 -2.30, 6-11; 11.30-3, 6-11 Sat; 12-3, 7-10.30 Sun
☎ (01403) 891208
Harveys BB; guest beers Ⓗ
Welcoming country pub with stunning view over the Sussex Weald. Good selection of guest beers with three during the week and up to five at weekends. The bar is reputedly the largest in Sussex. Made from one piece of wood, it measures 12'6" × 3' wide. Landlord is a classic car fanatic and has a few cars for hire for special occasions. A visit on Sat morning may include informal discussion by the locals' 'gardening club'. Awarded North Sussex CAMRA *Pub of the Year* and runner-up South-East *Pub of the Year* 2000.
🏚Q🍂❀◑♣P✝

OVING

Gribble Inn
Gribble Lane
❁ 11-3, 5.30-11 (11-11 summer); 12-3, 7-10.30 (12-10.30 summer) Sun
☎ (01243) 786893
Gribble Fursty Ferret, Ale, Plucking Pheasant, Porterhouse, Reg's Tipple, Pig's Ear, seasonal beers Ⓗ
Originally two agricultural workers' cottages, this 16th-century thatched pub was previously the residence of Miss Rose Gribble – who is depicted on the pub sign. Home to Gribble Brewery's award-winning beers (the brewhouse adjoins the skittle alley, where production can be viewed). A mobile phone-free zone, drinkers happily mingle with diners in all areas, with one no-smoking bar. Traditional good quality food

is always available, but once a month (Tue) special trad jazz themed food eves (Thai, Chinese, Italian, Greek, Cajun, Curry, etc.) are staged. Delightful cottage garden.
🏛Q♿☎🍴♣♠♦P✠●

SCAYNE'S HILL

Sloop
Sloop Lane, Freshfield
✪ 12-3, 6 (5.30 Sat)-11; 12-10.30 Sun
☎ (01444) 831219 e-mail: nigel.cannon@lineone.net
Greene King XX Mild, IPA, Ruddles County, Abbot; guest beer Ⓗ

Unspoilt, two-bar rural pub with excellent snug. The emphasis is on food in the upmarket saloon bar, with an original New England flavour. The local farming clientele frequent the public bar. Newsletters keep customers informed. Interesting set of railway and angling pictures. Good selection of wine offered and plans to stock real cider. This pub is next to the Ouse Canal and boasts three perfectly-kept gardens. 🏛❀🍴◑😐♣P

SELHAM

Three Moles
1 mile S of A272, midway between Midhurst and Petworth OS935206
✪ 12-2, 5.30-11; 11.30-11 Sat; 12-10.30 Sun
☎ (01798) 861303 website: www.thethreemoles.co.uk
Badger K&B Sussex, Ballard's Midhurst Mild; Skinner's Betty Stogs Bitter; guest beers Ⓗ

Very traditional small country pub set well off the beaten track in the Rother Valley. Named after the coat of arms of the Mitford family, who own it. Opened in 1872 to serve Selham Station, the Moles has long outlived the railway line. The landlady is a former customer who saved the pub from possible closure a few years ago. She presides over a free house which is both a haven of quiet conversation and a lively local by turns. No food served, and the only music heard will be played or sung live at occasional singsongs. 🏛Q❀♣♠

SHOREHAM-BY-SEA ✤

Green Jacket
225 Upper Shoreham Road
(opp. Buckingham Park)
✪ 11.30-3, 6-11; 11.30-11 Sat; 12-10.30 Sun
☎ (01273) 452556
Draught Bass; Harveys BB; Wadworth 6X; guest beers Ⓗ

Built in 1937 for the Kemptown Brewery, now a Punch Tavern, the Green Jacket is a spacious, friendly three-bar local. The large public bar is home to the darts and pool teams and there is a comfortable snug and a lounge bar/restaurant featuring home-made specials (eve meals Wed-Sat). The inn sign depicts a soldier from Wellington's era but the pub name is thought to come from troops who were stationed at nearby Buckingham Park during WWII. The regularly changing guest ales are from independent breweries and Hoegaarden is served on draught. Pétanque played.
🏛Q❀◑😐♣♠P

Red Lion Inn
Old Shoreham Road
✪ 11-3, 5.30-11; 11.30-11 Sat; 12-10.30 Sun
☎ (01273) 423171
Courage Best Bitter, Directors; Fuller's London Pride; Harveys BB; Young's Special; guest beers Ⓗ

Popular 16th-century free house conveniently situated at the southern end of the Downs Link Way. Always busy in summer with walkers and cyclists. Pleasant garden at the rear with a large patio area in the front. The annual Adur beer festival (Easter) is held here. A smaller festival is held in Sept to coincide with the RAFA Airshow at Shoreham Airport. Good food is always available in the no-smoking restaurant. Pleasant views over the Downs and Lancing College. It stands close to the ancient toll bridge. Ever-changing range of beers mainly from micros.
🏛Q❀◑😐P

INN BRIEF

FISHBOURNE
Woolpack Inn
71 Fishbourne Road
11-11; 12-10.30 Sun
Adnams Bitter; Draught Bass; Greene King Abbot; Young's Bitter; Ⓗ guest beers Ⓖ
Imposing 1930s red-brick roadhouse with comfortable modern interior. Incorporates a Thai restaurant (eves only).

LICKFOLD
Lickfold Inn
11-3, 6-11; 12-3, 7-10.30 Sun
Ballard's Best Bitter; Hogs Back TEA; guest beer Ⓗ
15th-century free house with pleasant garden. Good restaurant with very imaginative cuisine.

RUSPER
Plough Inn
High Street
11-2.30, 6-11; 11.30-3, 7-10.30 Sat; 12-3, 7-10.30 Sun
Badger K&B Sussex; Courage Directors; Fuller's London Pride; guest beer Ⓗ
Traditional, beamed one-bar pub with an ever-changing range of seasonal and guests. Excellent food and a 30-place meeting room.

SHOREHAM-BY-SEA
Lazy Toad
88 High Street
11-11; 12-10.30 Sun
Greene King Abbot; Shepherd Neame Spitfire; guest beers Ⓗ
Former wine bar and Conservative club. There are usually at least four or five beers available, served from a behind bar stillage.

Royal Sovereign
6 Middle Street
11-11; 12-10.30 Sun
Badger K&B Sussex; Brakspear Special; Castle Eden Ale; Flowers Original; Fuller's London Pride; guest beer Ⓗ
Classic, back-street pub with original United Brewery green tiles and leaded windows. Guest ale is from an independent brewery.

WISBOROUGH GREEN
Three Crowns
11-3, 6-11; 12-3, 6-10.30 Sun
Beer range varies Ⓗ
On village green fronting the A272 a 15th century building with wood panelling and exposed beams. Two ever-changing beers – one from a large independent, the other from a small local micro.

WORTHING
Castle Tavern
1 Newland Road
11-3, 5-10.30-11; 11-11 Fri & Sat; 12-3, 7-10.30 (may extend summer) Sun
Arundel Castle; Harveys BB; Hop Back Summer Lightning; Shepherd Neame Bishops Finger; guest beers Ⓗ
Friendly, refurbished Victorian pub. Guest beers come from micro-breweries. No food Sun eve or Mon.

Golden Lion
7 The Strand, Goring-by-Sea
11-11; 12-10.30 Sun
Flowers Original; Taylor Landlord; Tetley Dark Mild Ⓗ
Large pub with separate games room, just north of Durrington railway station. Main bar is usually lively and bustling.

Richard Cobden
2 Cobden Road
11-3.30, 5.30-11; 11-11 Fri & Sat; 12-4, 7-10.30 Sun
Greene King IPA, Abbot; Young's Bitter, Special Ⓗ
Friendly town local. Uses lined glasses.

SIDLESHAM

Crab & Lobster

Mill Lane (750 yds off B2145) OS862973

✪ 11-3, 6-11; 12-3, 7-10.30 (not winter eve) Sun

☎ (01243) 641233

Cheriton Pots Ale; Itchen Valley Fagin's; guest beers Ⓗ

Pleasant, two-bar, 15th-century village inn, on the edge of Pagham harbour. Popular with walkers, cyclists and ornithologists, the pub is a tranquil haven of real character with oak beams and log fires. Excellent, varied menu of reasonably priced meals. The wide selection includes crab and lobster dishes, plus vegetarian options. The long-standing landlord and landlady make everyone welcome. ⅏Q❀◖P

STAPLEFIELD

Jolly Tanners

Handcross Road (B2114)

✪ 11-3, 5.30-11; 11-11 Sat; 12-10.30 Sun

☎ (01444) 400335 website: jollytanners.co.uk

Fuller's Chiswick, London Pride; Harveys BB; guest beer Ⓗ

Cosy, free house opposite the cricket green. The pub dates back to 1600, a former coaching inn and hotel. It comprises a main bar plus a smaller seated area that used to be a public bar, both have real fires. Photographs of the locality and a vast array of brass feature. Good selection of home-cooked food served and barbecues held during summer in the spacious rear garden. A regular *Guide* entry, this pub is handy for local attractions including Nymans Garden (NT). ⅏Q❀◖P

STOUGHTON

Hare & Hounds

Off B2146 through Walderton OS803115

✪ 11-3, 6-11; 12-3, 7-10.30 Sun

☎ (02392) 631433 website: www.yellcom.hare&hounds

Draught Bass; Gale's Winter Brew, HSB; Greene King IPA; Taylor Landlord; Young's Bitter Ⓗ

Distinctive, 350-year-old Sussex flint building, set in an area of outstanding natural beauty where the South Downs jostle for prominence on the skyline. Discover ancient burial mounds on nearby Stoughton Down, or view the working dairy farm within easy walking distance. Walkers and mountain bikers converge here to enjoy good value, home-made food including fresh local seafood and game. Fronted by a patio and a sizeable garden to the rear with scenic views of the valley. 27 years in the *Guide*. ⅏Q❀◖▣♣P

TROTTON

Keepers Arms

250 yds E of Trotton Bridge traffic lights on A272

✪ 11 (12 Sat)-2.30; 6.30-11; closed Mon; 12-2.30 (closed eve) Sun

☎ (01730) 813724

Ballard's Best Bitter, Nyewood Gold; Cheriton Pots Ale; guest beers Ⓗ

Delightful rural pub near Trotton Common. Close to an ancient church with the oldest brass rubbings in the country. Wooden floors, beams, log fire and an oak-panelled bar create a homely atmosphere. There is a private collection of intriguing ornaments and furniture. Very popular restaurant for home-cooked meals (not Sun eve or Mon). Reservations are recommended. Bar food served 12–2pm. The sunny terrace is well used in season where walkers and visitors quench their thirst with excellent real ale or cider. ⅏Q❀◖●P✠

WEST CHILTINGTON

Five Bells

Smock Alley (signed on Storrington-West Chiltington road) OS091172

✪ 12-3, 6-11; 12-3, 7-10.30 Sun

☎ (01798) 812143

K&B Sussex; guest beers Ⓗ

The genial landlord will be pleased to share his enthusiasm for good beer. The changing ales are selected from such brewers as Hop Back, Ballard's, Palmers, Ringwood, Black Sheep, Jennings, Taylor, Hook Norton and Hogs Back. One of the range of beers is always a mild. The open-plan interior is quiet and comfortable with an interesting collection of lamps and brass ornaments. The unusual fireplace is made of a bent piece of iron and has a magnificent brass canopy. There is a distinctive conservatory restaurant next to the peaceful garden. No food Sun eve.

⅏Q❀◖♣●P

WHITEMANS GREEN

Ship Inn

On jct of B2114/B2115

✪ 12-3, 5.30-11; 12-11 Sat; 12-3, 7-10.30 Sun

☎ (01444) 413219

Fuller's London Pride; Greene King Abbot; Harveys BB; guest beers Ⓖ

Friendly village local. Welcoming, experienced landlord who is meticulous about serving ales in peak condition. A single low bar has an array of handpumps which are not used. All real ales are dispensed direct from casks kept in the cooled cellar room. Extensive dining area and spacious bar with plenty of seating and a superb log fire. Local and thematic memorabilia and pictures adorn wood and exposed brick walls, and dark, cosy boarded ceilings are all in keeping with the atmosphere of the pub. Separate games area. ⅏⇔◖●P

WINEHAM

Royal Oak

Wineham Lane (off B2116 or A272) OS236206

✪ 11-2.30, 5.30 (6 Sat)-11; 12-3, 7-10.30 Sun

☎ (01444) 881252

Harveys BB; Marston's Pedigree Ⓖ

Wonderfully unspoilt, this very traditional country pub has the features one would hope to find in a top-class pub. The stone-flagged floor, low beams and inglenook help to complement the beers that are served by gravity from a side room. A gem of a pub, surprisingly missing from CAMRA's national inventory. ⅏Q❀P

WISBOROUGH GREEN ❖

Cricketers Arms

Loxwood Road (300 yds from A272)

✪ 11-2.30, 6-11; 11-11 Sat; 12-10.30 Sun

☎ (01403) 700369

Cheriton Pots Ale; Fuller's London Pride; Wadworth 6X; guest beer Ⓗ

Pleasant country pub overlooking the village green. Wood block floors and a wealth of beams set off a central fireplace with a wood-burning stove. Home of English motor-mower racing with monthly meetings. Hot air balloons occasionally take off from the village green creating a wonderful sight and there is a large event over August bank holiday. Good food served (not Sun eve).

🏚ⅅ♣P

WORTHING ✿

Charles Dickens
56 Heene Road (just N of seafront)
✪ 11-11; 12-10.30 Sun
☎ (01903) 603791
Greene King Abbot; Harveys BB; Taylor Landlord; Woodforde's Wherry; guest beers Ⓗ

Comfortable free house in traditional oak-beamed style. First floor comprises bar area, lounge, including no-smoking area, and separate restaurant. Additional seating and TV/children's area on ground floor. The Copperfield Suite in the basement is a self-contained function room. Pleasant rear garden and patio and smaller patio to the front. Restaurant offers à la carte and speciality fish menus. Occasional beer festivals during the year. Sun night is 'Golden Oldies' night, with records from the 50s, 60s and 70s; Mon is quiz night; monthly jazz eve with a house trio and guest artists.

✿ⅅ♣✄🖶

George & Dragon
1 High Street, Tarring
✪ 11-3, 5.30-11; 11-11 Fri & Sat; 12-10.30 Sun
☎ (01903) 202497
Courage Directors; Hop Back Summer Lightning; John Smith's Bitter; Wells Bombardier; Young's Bitter; guest beer Ⓗ

Thriving, 16th-century community local in a well-preserved village high street. The welcoming bar, with low exposed oak beams and dark wood panelling, has been sympathetically extended into outer rooms to retain the feel of a traditional multi-roomed pub. Darts, football, golf and horseracing are popular in the old 'public end' while the 'saloon end' has newspapers, a cosy snug and a separate eating area. Good wholesome food is served (Mon-Sat) but the emphasis is very much on the traditions of drink, good company and conversation. Pleasant tranquil garden.

Q✿ⅅ≢(West)♣P

Selden Arms
41 Lyndhurst Road
✪ 11 (12 Sat)-11; 12-10.30 Sun
☎ (01903) 234854 e-mail: selden.arms@bun.com
Ringwood Fortyniner; Wolf Bitter; guest beers Ⓗ

This small, community local is a true free house. The pub had been unoccupied for some time, when it was purchased a few years ago and has been completely refurbished. It is blessed with a very lively landlady, keen on traditional ale from independent breweries. One of the six handpumps is always reserved for a dark beer and a range of bottled Belgian beers is on offer too. The Selden attracts a loyal

clientele and was local CAMRA *Pub of the Year* 2000 and 2001. No food served on Sun.

🏚Qⅅ≢(Central)♣🖶●

Swan
79 High Street
✪ 11-2.30, 6-11; 11-11 Sat; 12-10.30 Sun
☎ (01903) 232923
Greene King Abbot; Harveys BB; Shepherd Neame Spitfire; guest beers Ⓗ

Friendly town pub where a warm welcome is assured. There is a 1930s front extension to the original 18th-century building and Kemptown Brewery leaded windows. Note the collections of bottles, glasses, antique beer taps and engines. Enjoy the large comfortable bar, separate restaurant area (where lunchtime meals are served), plus the pleasant patio. Bar billiards is played here.

🏚✿ⅆ≢(Central)♣

Vine
27-29 High Street, Tarring
✪ 12-3, 6-11; 12-11 Fri & Sat; 12-10.30 Sun
☎ (01903) 202891 e-mail: thevine@talk21.com
Badger K&B Sussex, Best, Tanglefoot; Gribble Fursty Ferret; Hop Back Summer Lightning; Ringwood True Glory Ⓗ

Historic Tarring village is surrounded by suburban Worthing, many regard the Vine as its cultural centre. It features nine handpumps and gives a good impression of a free house – it is the only Badger pub with guest ales. This was a brew-pub until the late 1930s and the old Parsons Brewery can still be seen at the back of the pub. The large garden is perfect for summer eves and home-cooked food, regular live music and beer festivals ensure that all customers are catered for.

✿ⅅ♿≢(West)P●

YAPTON

Lamb Inn
Bilsham Road (B2132, S of village)
✪ 11-3, 5.30 (5 Sat)-11; 12-4.30, 6.30-10.30 Sun
☎ (01243) 551232
Greene King Abbot; Harveys BB; guest beer Ⓗ

Friendly roadside pub on the southern edge of the village. The large garden houses play equipment, an animal enclosure and boules courts. The new restaurant is no-smoking. An excellent community pub.

🏚Q✿ⅅ🍴♣P

Maypole Inn
Maypole Lane (off B2132, ½ mile N of village)
OS978041
✪ 11-3, 5.30-11; 12-3, 7-10.30 Sun
☎ (01243) 551417
Ringwood Best Bitter; guest beers Ⓗ

Small flint-built free house, tucked away down a lane away from the village centre. First licensed in 1783 it was originally a pair of cottages alongside a well-used road, but the road was cut off by the railway line in 1846 and the pub has enjoyed its quiet isolation ever since. The cosy lounge bar features an impressive log fire and an imposing row of handpumps dispensing an ever-changing range of independent beers. The larger public bar has darts, pool and TV, plus juke box, and a skittle alley is available (book ahead). Children's certificate. 🏚Q✿ⅅ🍴♣♣P●

TYNE & WEAR

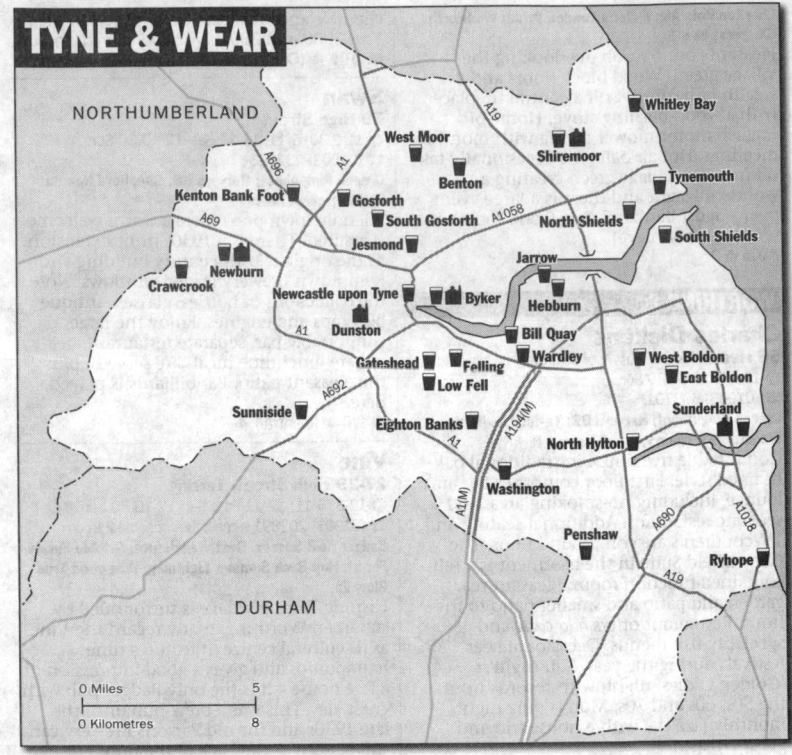

NORTHUMBERLAND

Whitley Bay
West Moor
Shiremoor
Benton
Tynemouth
Kenton Bank Foot
Gosforth
South Gosforth
North Shields
Jesmond
South Shields
Newburn
Jarrow
Crawcrook
Newcastle upon Tyne
Byker
Hebburn
Dunston
Bill Quay
Gateshead
Wardley
Felling
West Boldon
Low Fell
East Boldon
Sunniside
Sunderland
Eighton Banks
North Hylton
Washington
Penshaw
Ryhope

DURHAM

0 Miles 5
0 Kilometres 8

BENTON

Benton Ale House
Front Street
⚙ 11-11; 12-10.30 Sun
☎ (0191) 266 1512
Banks's Bitter; Camerons Bitter, Strongarm; Marston's Pedigree; guest beers Ⓗ

Large, busy pub with one central bar serving two main areas: a comfortable lounge to the right of the front door and at the rear a bar with pool and darts. Guest ales are now restricted to those supplied by owners Wolverhampton & Dudley. Bar meals and snacks are available throughout the day until mid-eve. Wheelchair access is good with dedicated parking spaces and a ramp into the pub. There is a quiz Wed eve.
◑ & ⊖ (Four Lane Ends) P 〒

BILL QUAY

Big River
Reay Street (at foot of hill on river bank)
⚙ 4 (12 Sat)-11; 12-10.30 Sun
☎ (0191) 469 2418
Black Sheep Best Bitter; Fuller's London Pride; guest beers Ⓗ

On weekdays this opened-out, pleasantly refurbished bar/lounge with a large conservatory draws a mainly local clientele. However at weekends it is far livelier with Karaoke sessions and other entertainment attracting customers from further afield. Its isolated position overlooking the riverside industries along a wide bend in the River Tyne has inspired the change of name from the Albion. The owners have a long-standing policy of competitively pricing

their real ales. The availability of two real ciders is unusual for the area.
🏚 ⊛ ⊖ (Pelaw) ◖ P

BYKER ❄

Cluny
36 Lime Street
⚙ 11-11; 12.30-3.30, 5.30-11 Mon; 12-10.30 Sun
☎ (0191) 230 4474
Banks's Bitter, Big Lamp Prince Bishop Ale; Mordue Five Bridges; Workie Ticket; guest beers Ⓗ

Formerly 19th-century mills, then warehouses (a bond for Cluny Whisky – hence the name) the pub comprises a bar/café, a performance area, and an art gallery used as a showplace by the 50 or so artists and craftsmen who work in the rest of the building. Guest beers are from local micro-brewers, and seasonal beers from Durham are also stocked. Good quality home-made food is served all day; a rotating range of continental beers and a good rum selection add interest. There is no pub sign; the main entrance is at the top of a cobbled bank leading down to the Ouseburn next to Byker City Farm. ◑

Tyne
1 Maling Street
⚙ 12-11; 12-10.30 Sun
☎ (0191) 265 2550
Black Sheep Best Bitter; Durham Magus, seasonal beers; Mordue Five Bridges, Workie Ticket, seasonal beers Ⓗ

This single-roomed pub crouches under Glasshouse Bridge, which acts as an unusual roof to the garden. It makes it hard to find at first, but once found visitors return again and again. The walls are covered in posters for music events and newspaper cuttings, creating a colourful patchwork. The pub can get very busy with a good mix of clientele. Live bands perform Sun eve and it hosts occasional poetry readings by local poets. Toilets are up a flight of stairs. ❀

CRAWCROOK

Rising Sun
Bank Top (1/2 mile S of main crossroads)
❂ 11-11; 12-10.30 Sun
☎ (0191) 413 3310
Boddingtons Bitter; Castle Eden Ale; Mordue Workie Ticket; guest beers Ⓗ
Lively, thriving local, offering something for everyone. Well situated, on most of the Tyne Valley routes between Blaydon and Hexham, the spacious interior affords numerous drinking areas and a balance between good value meals and a haven for the discerning drinker. Serving one of the best selections of real ales in the area, there are always two guest beers on tap. ❀◑P

EAST BOLDON

Black Bull
Front Street (A184)
❂ 11-11.30; 12-11 Sun
☎ (0191) 536 3969
McEwans 80/-; Wells Bombardier Ⓗ
Large, one-roomed, air-conditioned pub with a horseshoe bar, the Black Bull caters for all ages. Sedate lunchtime sessions, with specials on the menu, contrast with lively Karaoke competitions and quiz nights. Big-screen Sky Sports vie with Sun afternoon darts and dominoes – all popular with both locals and visitors, especially the 'travelling locals' who come from outlying areas on a regular basis. Cashback facilities available.
❀◑⇌≠♣P

Grey Horse
Front Street
❂ 11-11; 12-10.30 Sun
☎ (0191) 536 4186
Greene King Ruddles Best; John Smith's Magnet; Wells Bombardier Ⓗ
The Grey Horse is on the main road through the village and has a very distinctive Tudor front. Inside, the lounge has subdued lighting and is decorated in a similar Tudor-style with oak beams. The room is divided into two main areas, a raised area used chiefly for meals and a lower level consisting of several alcoves where patrons can sit and enjoy their beer in small groups. The L-shaped public bar is brighter and has a large-screen TV for important sporting events. Upstairs there is an excellent function room available for private parties.
Q❀◑⇌≠♣P

FELLING

Old Fox
Carlisle Street
❂ 12-11; 12-10.30 Sun
☎ (0191) 420 0357
Banks's Bitter; guest beers Ⓗ
Recently refurbished to a high standard, the Old Fox is a lively, friendly pub stocking an ever-changing range of beers. The bar hosts

regular darts matches and there is a pool table in the back of the pub. The real emphasis however is on the beer that attracts drinkers from around the region. A paved area at the back of the pub serves as a garden in summer. ❀⇌⊖

Wheatsheaf
26 Carlisle Street
❂ 12-11; 12-10.30 Sun
☎ (0191) 420 0659
Big Lamp Bitter, Prince Bishop Ale Ⓗ
This pub, rebuilt in 1907, features an impressive faïence exterior and a number of original cut and etched windows. The entire floor area of the original pub is now one room, retaining the original bar and impressive back fitting. An area, formerly the licensee's lounge, provides an almost separate room. Darts, dominoes and card games are played regularly and sandwiches are available. Big Lamp Brewery own the pub and their seasonal beers are usually stocked.
▥⊖♣

GOSFORTH

County
70 High Street
❂ 12 (11 Fri & Sat)-11; 12-3, 7-10.30 Sun
☎ (0191) 285 6919
Courage Directors; Greene King Old Speckled Hen; Marston's Pedigree; McEwan 80/-; Theakston Best Bitter; guest beers Ⓗ
One of the most well-known pubs in the area, the County is an impressive listed building, guarding the southern end of the High Street. Notorious for links with the criminal underworld during the 19th century, many original features betray its Victorian origins. Part of the T&J Bernard chain, the long L-shaped bar offers two ever-changing guest beers, plus Bulmer's traditional cider most of the time. Popular with locals and students, it can get very busy at weekends (no eve meals Fri or Sat). Limited parking.
▥Q◑⊖(Ilford Rd) ●

HEBBURN

Dougie's Tavern
Blackett Street (on riverside road 5 mins from Jarrow metro)
❂ 11.30-11 (12.30am Thu-Sat); 12-10.30 Sun
☎ (0191) 428 4800 website: www.dougiestavern.co.uk
Theakston Cool Cask; guest beers Ⓗ
Friendly pub near the banks of the River Tyne, serving good food, it hosts live music Thu, ocasional 'sportsman's evenings' and quizzes. There is a secure outdoor play area and garden, and the pub holds a children's certificate; popular with families, it has a traditional feel. 'Happy hours' last from 2 until 9pm Mon-Fri and 7-9 weekends; two guest beers are usually on tap.
⌛❀◑&⊖(Jarrow) P

INDEPENDENT BREWERIES	
Big Lamp	Newburn
Darwin	Sunderland
Federation	Dunston
Hadrian & Border	Byker
Mordue	Shiremoor

JARROW

Ben Lomond
Grange Road West
✪ 11-11; 12-10.30 Sun
☎ (0191) 483 3839
Courage Directors; Theakston Best Bitter; guest beers Ⓗ

Popular, busy, town-centre pub, refurbished by the Wetherspoon's chain. Open plan, the split-level first floor has partial wood panelling and banister-style partitioning, leading to the second floor. Prints depict local history. As with all Wetherspoon's, there is no music, and good food is served all day. A third beer from a regional brewer is usually on tap, plus at least two guest ales. An annual beer festival is staged.
Q◖◗♿♨✕●

JESMOND

Collingwood Arms
Brandling Village
✪ 11-11; 12-10.30 Sun
☎ (0191) 281 1271
Courage Directors; Mordue Workie Ticket; Taylor Landlord; Theakston Best Bitter; guest beers Ⓗ

T&J Bernard pub in the middle of a residential area in the affluent suburb of Jesmond. The long, narrow bar used by local residents and students can get busy. Big-screen TV for sport, and an unobtrusive juke box make for a friendly atmosphere. Photographs of old Jesmond are displayed. The bar and serving area are at the front of the pub. The main seating area to the left consists of bench seats and chairs. ♨◖◗⊖P

KENTON BANK FOOT

Twin Farms
22 Main Road
✪ 11-11; 12-10.30 Sun
☎ (0191) 286 1263 website: www.sjf.co.uk
Mordue Workie Ticket; Taylor Landlord; guest beers Ⓗ

New building, in traditional style, on the site of a farm. It has a spacious, open-plan main room but, by the clever use of alcoves, it gives the feel of several small rooms. Two real log fires and a huge black kitchen range add character. There are no-smoking areas but, as the whole place is fully air-conditioned, smoke and food smells are reduced. The beers feature two former *Champion Beers of Britain*, Workie Ticket and

Landlord. The two guest beers change weekly. ♨Q♨◖◗♿⊖(Bank Foot) P✕

LOW FELL

Aletaster
706 Durham Road
✪ 12 (11 Sat)-11; 12-10.30 Sun
☎ (0191) 487 0770
Courage Directors; Mordue Workie Ticket, Radgie Gadgie; Theakston Best Bitter, Cool Cask, Old Peculier; guest beers Ⓗ

Popular, suburban, main road pub where 11 handpumps offer a good range of beers, often including micros as guests, plus a cider. Attracting customers from far and near, its ale house style includes a public bar of bare boards, featuring nicotine-coloured walls and lots of photographs, including many spoofs of ale-tasting. Note the coloured glass leaded windows at the rear depicting George IV (the pub's original name). Its much smaller cosy, carpeted lounge is served by a small hatch. It hosts occasional beer festivals and live music.
♨⊟♣P

NEWBURN

Keelman
Grange Road
✪ 11-11; 12-10.30 Sun
☎ (0191) 267 0772
Big Lamp Bitter, Summerhill Stout, Prince Bishop Ale, Premium, seasonal beers Ⓗ

The pub opened in this Grade II listed former water pumping station in 1996 and Big Lamp Brewery – the region's oldest micro, soon followed. It offers the full range of Big Lamp beers, which have built a strong following since the brewery moved from a district of Newcastle, still known to many as the Big Lamp. Good value food is available, although a pleasant atmosphere for drinking prevails. The adjoining lodge offers quality accommodation along with an outdoor drinking area in an attractive setting by Tyne Riverside Country Park. The keelmen, boatmen who plied the Tyne shipping coal, are commemorated in old photographs. ♨⊨◖◗P

NEWCASTLE-UPON-TYNE ❖

Bodega
125 Westgate Road

INN BRIEF

BYKER

Free Trade
St Lawrence Road
11-11;
12-10.30 Sun
Marston's Pedigree; Mordue Five Bridges, Geordie Pride, Workie Ticket, seasonal beers Ⓗ
Deliciously basic pub offering wonderful views up the Tyne towards the bridges; outside seating.

EIGHTON BANKS

Lambton Arms
Rockcliffe Way
11-11; 12-10.30 Sun
Beer range varies Ⓗ
Popular roadside pub; a choice of four beers and quality restaurant. Good views of the countryside.

GATESHEAD

Borough Arms
80-82 Bensham Road
(250 yds from metro station via subway)
11-3, 7-11; 12-10.30 Sun
Draught Bass; Black Sheep Best Bitter; Wells Bombardier; guest beers Ⓗ
Only real ale outlet in town centre: up to three guest beers. Regular folk night. No children.

NEWCASTLE UPON TYNE

Hotspur
103 Percy Street
11-11; 12-10.30 Sun
Courage Directors; McEwan 80/-; Theakston Best Bitter, Cool Cask, Old Peculier; guest beers Ⓗ
Single-roomed pub, offering interesting guest beers and friendly atmosphere; busy on match days.

SOUTH SHIELDS

Beacon
100 Greens Place, Lawe Top
11-11;
12-10.30 Sun
Adnams Broadside; Marston's Pedigree; Taylor Landlord Ⓗ
Open-plan pub with a spectacular river view and nautical theme. Pleasant, quiet atmosphere.

SUNDERLAND

Harbour View
Harbour View, Roker
11-11;
12-10.30 Sun
Draught Bass; guest beers Ⓗ
Lounge with horseshoe-shaped bar, overlooking Roker Marina. Three guests, often from local micro-breweries are sold.

🕐 11-11; 12-10.30 Sun

Big Lamp Prince Bishop Ale; Durham Magus; Mordue Workie Ticket; guest beers Ⓗ

Apart from the good beer choice, the highlight of every visit to this pub is a study of the two original glass ceiling domes. The pub is very popular with football fans and, as it is next to the Tyne Theatre and Opera House, it also attracts music fans, and all mix together giving an excellent atmosphere. The single bar room offers a number of seating and standing spots, including snug cubicles. The house beer from local Mordue Brewery, Number 9, reflects footballing interests (it is the number worn by famous Magpies' centre forwards).

◖⊖(Central) ♣

Bridge Hotel
Castle Square

🕐 11-11; 12-10.30 Sun

☎ (0191) 232 6400

Black Sheep Best Bitter; Boddingtons Bitter; Mordue Workie Ticket; guest beers Ⓗ

Large pub looking towards the keep of the old 'new' castle, it rests at the side of Stephenson's massive high level bridge, immortalised in *Get Carter*. At the back of the pub is a garden encircled by the old town walls, offering excellent river views. The single room is divided into various seating areas by screens and glass panels: note the decorative metal plaques. The bar can get packed at weekends. The upstairs function room hosts what is reputed to be the oldest folk music club in the country.

🕯◖≈⊖(Central)

Crown Posada ☆
33 The Side

🕐 11 (12 Sat)-11; closed lunch; 7-10.30 Sun

☎ (0191) 232 1269

Draught Bass; Jennings Bitter; guest beers Ⓗ

Tiny, but always welcoming, this pub is possibly, architecturally, the finest in Newcastle. Beautiful stained glass windows and unusual ceilings add to the appeal. Long and narrow, known locally as the Coffin, it has comfortable seating at one end and a tiny snug at the other. The word Posada comes from Portuguese and by local legend dates back to the city's maritime heritage. It can get busy, as it is now on the circuit following the regeneration of the

quayside; however if visiting Newcastle and you have time to visit just one pub, make it this one.

Q⊼≈(Central) ⊖(Monument)

Duke of Wellington
High Bridge

🕐 11 (12 Sat)-11; 12-10.30 Sun

☎ (0191) 261 8852

Ind Coope Burton Ale; Marston's Pedigree; Tetley Bitter; guest beers Ⓗ

Single-roomed pub stocking a rapidly changing range of guest beers from all over the country. The pub history boasts that a former licensee was one of the world's largest men weighing in at about 50 stones. The pub holds regular beer festivals and can get very busy, but it is worth seeking out to sample the guest beers. ◖≈⊖(Monument)

Head of Steam
Neville Street

🕐 12-11; 12-10.30 Sun

☎ (0191) 232 4379

Black Sheep Best Bitter; Caledonian Deuchars IPA; Taylor Landlord Ⓗ

This two-roomed pub has an upstairs bar, a downstairs bar (not always open) and toilets on the ground floor between the two. The owner runs a chain of pubs but this one is very much the odd one out, drawing a young crowd and placing emphasis on music eves. It does not really attract the 'ale and rail' crowd who frequent other pubs in the chain. The building was always dark, being part of a concrete office block, but it has been brightened up by the current owner. ◖≈⊖(Central)

New Bridge
2 Argyle Street

🕐 11-11; 12-10.30 Sun

☎ (0191) 232 1020

Beer range varies Ⓗ

Recently refurbished, and very comfortable, it features some nice old photographs of the building of Tyne Bridge and good old mirrors. The Millennium Bridge, the latest to span the Tyne, can be viewed from the side door. The staff are friendly and it attracts a wide cross-section of regulars and visitors, being close to a multi-screen cinema. Two constantly changing guest beers generally come from independent micro-brewers. Good home-made food is served. ◖⊖(Manors)

Ropery
Websters Bank, Deptford
11-11;
12-10.30 Sun
Bateman XB; Boddingtons Bitter; Flowers IPA; Wadworth 6X Ⓗ
Multi-roomed pub in an 18th-century building on the banks of the River Wear, hosting live music most nights.

Smugglers
Marine Walk, Lower Promenade, Roker
11-11;
12-10.30 Sun
Beer range varies Ⓗ
Next to the beach with a single lounge bar serving ale from local Darwin Brewery.

SUNNISIDE
Potters Wheel
Sun Street
11-11; 11-3, 5.30-11 Mon;
12-3, 7-10.30 Sun
Beer range varies Ⓗ
Fine pub, with a spacious, divided bar. Children's certificate until 8.30pm. Wheelchair WC. Good food and three guest beers.

TYNEMOUTH
Cumberland Arms
12-11; 12-10.30 Sun
Courage Directors; McEwan 80/-; Theakston Best Bitter, Cool Cask; guest beers Ⓗ
Small public bar and comfortable upper room, used mainly for food. Guest beers are usually from Mordue.

WASHINGTON
Sandpiper
Easby Road, Biddick
11-11; 12-10.30 Sun
Boddingtons Bitter; Castle Eden Ale; guest beers Ⓗ
Two-roomed modern estate pub, with a public bar and lounge with stone flooring. Up to five beers usually available.

WHITLEY BAY
Fat Ox
278 Whitley Road
12 (11 Sat)-11;
12-10.30 Sun
Black Sheep Best Bitter; Courage Directors Ⓗ
This pub situated on a corner site has one large room offering various areas for drinking, chat and pool.

NORTH HYLTON

Shipwrights Hotel
Ferryboat Lane (300 yds from A19)
✪ 11-4, 5-11; 12-3, 7-10.30 Sun
☎ (0191) 549 5139
Marston's Pedigree; guest beers Ⓗ
Old-style country pub on the river bank, located in a 350-year-old listed building that was once a coaching house on the Durham coast road. From the 17th to 19th century, it was a ship's chandlers and used by the press gang to recruit for the Navy. Serving traditional as well as more exotic food, such as kangaroo steaks, it is a comfortable, friendly pub well worth a visit for a quiet pint. Note the impressive collection of chamber pots.
🏭Q🖛◖P

NORTH SHIELDS

Magnesia Bank
Camden Street
✪ 11-11; 12-10.30 Sun
☎ (0191) 257 4831
Durham Magus; guest beers Ⓗ
Winner of many awards for food and music as well as beer, and a frequent local CAMRA *Pub of the Year*, this is a friendly, family-run pub. The recently refurbished bar has three areas: two raised seating areas, popular with diners and aficionados of live music plus a third, smaller area. The garden's view of the Tyne is now somewhat restricted by housing developments, signifying the growing popularity of the area. Food is largely organic and sourced locally; guest beers are from local micros.
🕸◖⊖

Prince of Wales
2 Liddell Street (follow signs for fish quay)
✪ 12-3.30 (4.30 Sat; not Tue), 7-11; 12-4.30, 7-10.30 Sun
☎ (0191) 296 2816
e-mail: sherron@princeofwales.fsnet.co.uk
Samuel Smith OBB Ⓗ
Dating from 1927, the exterior is faced with green glazed bricks; the premises were empty for some years before being restored by Samuel Smith's in traditional style, including embossed windows. The bar and pool room are both served from the central bar, the sitting room from a hatch on the corridor. Pool, darts and dominoes are played and the pub runs its own football and angling clubs. The brewery's organic beers are also available.
🏭Q⭆🕸◖⊟⊖♣

Tap & Spile
184 Tynemouth Road
✪ 12 (11.30 Sat)-11; 12-10.30 Sun
☎ (0191) 257 2523
Draught Bass; Theakston Black Bull; guest beers Ⓗ
A Tap & Spile that maintains the original concept of the chain, despite regular changes of ownership. It has, unusually, been refurbished back into a multi-roomed pub with a small bar with darts and TV and a larger, comfortable lounge. The manager regularly hosts themed beer festivals featuring beers not normally available as guest beers. Eve meals finish at 7pm.
◖⊟⊖♣🐕

PENSHAW

Grey Horse Inn
Old Penshaw Village Green
✪ 11-11; 12-10.30 Sun
☎ (0191) 584 4882
Tetley Bitter Ⓗ
Friendly local, a long-standing *Guide* entry, located in Penshaw old village, close to the popular local tourist attraction, Penshaw Monument. Families are more than welcome, and it makes a convenient place to rest after climbing the hill to the monument. The recent addition of a ramp to the front door allows easy wheelchair access. 🏭Q🕸◖⊟🖕♿▲♣P

RYHOPE

Ryhope Catholic Club
Dinsdale Cottages, Dinsdale Street
✪ 7-11 (not Tue-Thu); 12-2, 7-10.30 Sun
☎ (0191) 521 3437
Castle Eden Ale; guest beer Ⓗ
The club, comprising a simple, comfortable lounge bar and a small games room, is run entirely by volunteers. Despite the limited opening hours it has a good reputation for the quality of its cask beers and was selected local CAMRA *Club of the Year* 2000. Both regular and guest beers represent excellent value; an oasis in a cask beer desert. Contact the club for admission details. ♣⊟

SHIREMOOR

Shiremoor Farm
Middle Engine Lane
✪ 11-11; 12-10.30 Sun
☎ (0191) 257 6302
Mordue Workie Ticket; Taylor Landlord; guest beers Ⓗ
Fitzgerald's award-winning conversion of derelict stone farm buildings by designer Alan Simpson has been recently extended. It retains the original conical raftered former 'gingang' which now serves as the highly recommended restaurant. A thriving lunchtime trade means it can get busy but never overcrowded. The pub is, happily, free of distractions – no juke box, gambling machines or pool tables. Designated smoke-free areas, coupled with an efficient air extraction system guarantee comfort; two changing guest ales guarantee variety.
Q⭆🕸◖P🖕

SOUTH GOSFORTH

Victory
Killingworth Road
✪ 11-11; 12-10.30 Sun
☎ (0191) 285 1254
Courage Directors; Taylor Landlord; Theakston Best Bitter; guest beers Ⓗ
Although not separate rooms this pub has three distinct areas: a lounge, a raised area and the bar with seating at either end. There is much use of wood panelling, and heavy wooden furniture, including benches around the lounge walls. There is an ever-changing range of guest beers and food is available most of the day. Established in 1861, and named after Nelson's flagship, it enjoys a loyal local following. An outdoor drinking area fronts on to the main road. 🕸◖⊖P

Come Back to the Inn

Come back to the inn, love,
and the lights and the fire,
And the fiddler's old tune and
the shuffling of feet;
For there in a while we shall
rest and desire,
And there shall the morrow's
uprising be sweet.

William Morris,
The Message of the March Wind,
1891.

SOUTH SHIELDS ✣

Alum Ale House
River Drive
◷ 11-11; 12-10.30 Sun
☎ (0191) 427 7245
Banks's Bitter; Camerons Strongarm; Marston's Pedigree; guest beers Ⓗ
Small pub on the bank of the River Tyne, next to the ferry landing for North Shields. The single room comprises two contrasting areas: around the bar panelled walls, bare floorboards and bench seating feature. The second, quieter area is carpeted with more comfortable seating. Events include quiz nights, Sun and buskers' nights Thu. Up to six beers are usually available. The house beer Alum Ale is brewed by Durham Brewery.
⊖▯

Chichester Arms
Chichester Road (outside metro station)
◷ 11-11; 12-10.30 Sun
☎ (0191) 420 0127
Federation Buchanan's Best Bitter; Ind Coope Burton Ale; Tetley Bitter Ⓗ
Spacious three-roomed local convenient for buses. The staff are friendly and helpful – a prominently displayed notice advises drinkers that the staff will gladly top up a glass if the head on the beer is too large. The beer range does not vary but the Buchanan's is often sold at 'happy hour' prices. It attracts a mostly mature clientele.
⧖ⓄⰁ⊖ (Chichester)

Dolly Peel
Commercial Road
◷ 11-11; 12-10.30 Sun
☎ (0191) 427 1441
Courage Directors; Taylor Landlord; guest beers Ⓗ
Originally called the Earl Grey, the Dolly Peel was renamed to commemorate a local fishwife, famous for smuggling and following her husband to sea when he was press ganged into the Navy during the Napoleonic Wars. It is a quiet two-roomed pub on the river road to South Shields, where everyone can be sure to find at least one beer to their liking from the six handpulls on the bar. Very traditional – no large-screen TV, pool table or bandits disturb customers.
Q ❀ ⅋ ⊖ (Chichester) ●

Riverside
3 Commercial Road
◷ 12-11; 12-3, 7-10.30 Sun
☎ (0191) 455 2328
Black Sheep Special; Courage Directors; Taylor Landlord; Theakston Cool Cask; guest beers Ⓗ
Formerly a seaman's mission, then briefly a fun pub, it was sold in the mid-1990s and became the traditional, friendly pub it is today. With six handpulls, real ale has always been top priority, recognised by its quick entry into this *Guide*. Voted local CAMRA *Pub of the Year* 1999 and 2000, when it was also awarded regional *Pub of the Year*. ⊖ ♣

Stag's Head
45 Fowler Street (400 yds N of Town Hall)
◷ 11-11; 12-10.30 Sun
☎ (0191) 456 9174
Draught Bass; Stones Bitter; Worthington Bitter Ⓗ
Thriving pub in the town centre, handy for the metro and bus station. Dating back to the 19th century, its comfortable unspoilt interior displays photographs of old South Shields and is a very popular venue for many drinkers. The bar can get very busy, but there is an upstairs room which is normally quieter. Themed music nights, such as 70s and 80s, are always popular and attract a good crowd.
⚞ ⊖

Steamboat
51 Mill Dam
◷ 12-11; 12-10.30 Sun
☎ (0191) 454 0134
Stones Bitter; Greene King Old Speckled Hen; guest beers Ⓗ
Hostelry on Mill Dam overlooking the River Tyne, decorated with old photographs, flags and ensigns of the mercantile trade; most of the memorabilia relates to the pub and the surrounding area. The main bar is always busy but is complemented by a quieter lounge. ⊖

SUNDERLAND ✣

Fitzgerald's
10-12 Green Terrace
◷ 11-11; 12-10.30 Sun
☎ (0191) 567 0852 website: www.sjf.co.uk
Beer range varies Ⓗ
Large, open-plan pub, with a small, quieter chart room featuring a nautical theme and a large-screen TV, mainly used for sport. Popular with students from the university, it attracts a varied range of customers. Fitzgerald's offers the biggest range of beers in town, up to 10, often including beer from the local Darwin Brewery. It can be lively at weekends when door control staff are employed. A quiz night is held Tue in the chart room. Eve meals finish at 6.30 (not served Sun).
❀Ⓞⅅ⇌

King's Arms
Farringdon Row, Deptford
◷ 4.30 (12 Sat)-11; 12-10.30 Sun

☎ (0191) 567 9804

Beer range varies H

Single-roomed pub bearing a fine wood-panelled exterior, the King's Arms is one of the oldest pubs in Sunderland. The bar has bare floorboards, wood-panelled walls and partitions; a small games area has table football. The back bar and window screens are original and the pub is one of the few in town that have not been spoilt by 'progress'. Under the same management as the Ropery and Saltgrass, free transport runs between the three pubs at weekends. It stages live music weekends. Well worth a visit. ♨️⛲

Saltgrass

36 Ayres Quay, Deptford

✪ 11-11; 12-10.30 Sun

☎ (0191) 565 7229

Draught Bass; Marston's Pedigree; guest beers H

This two-roomed pub, set off from the main road, maintains a regular custom, despite the closure of local shipyards and Vaux Brewery. The bar is crowded with ship's furnishings such as brass diving helmets, fancy knotted rope and other salvaged parts. An open fire blazes on cold evenings, giving an instant feeling of a welcome. The lounge is the larger of the two rooms, and is quieter. Free transport to other local pubs is available at weekends. ♨️◖🍺

William Jameson

30-32 Fawcett Street

(2 minutes' walk from station)

✪ 11-11; 12-10.30 Sun

☎ (0191) 514 5016

Boddingtons Bitter; Castle Eden Nimmos XXXX; Courage Directors; Shepherd Neame Spitfire; Theakston Best Bitter; Wadworth 6X; guest beers H

Spacious, one-roomed, glass-fronted Wetherspoon's pub on the site of the former Binns department store. It serves food all day and takes part in all the usual Wetherspoon's promotions, including cheap drinks and beer festivals. In the city centre, on a main road, it is convenient for buses and trains. It serves up to eight real ales at any time. Q◖🍺♿⚓🔅✓⬤

TYNEMOUTH ✣

Copperfields

Hotspur Street

✪ 12-11; 12-10.30 Sun

☎ (0191) 293 6666

website: www.grand-hotel.demon.co.uk

Durham Magus; Theakston Best Bitter; guest beers H

Cosy bar, a short distance from the circuit pubs of Front Street, lightly themed on characters from Dickens' novel. Drawings and photographs show local scenes from the past. It forms part of the aptly-named

Fizz warning

Some national breweries produce both cask-conditioned and 'nitro-keg' versions of their beers. Boddingtons Bitter, John Smith's Bitter, Tetley's Bitter and Worthington fall into this category. Nitro-keg beers, often promoted as 'smooth' or 'cream-flow' products, are filtered and pasteurised in the brewery, and served in pubs by a mix of applied carbon dioxide and nitrogen gases. They are bland, served extremely cold, and any hop character is lost by the use of applied gas.

To add insult to injury, the keg founts that serve such beers are often topped by small dummy handpumps. As a result of lobbying by CAMRA, some producers of cask and nitro versions of the same beer now include the word 'cask' on pump clips for the genuine article. For example, both John Smith's Bitter and Tetley's Bitter now carry the word 'cask' on pump clips for the real thing. For the sake of brevity, and as the Good Beer Guide lists only cask-conditioned beers, we refer simply to John Smith's Bitter and Tetley Bitter. The Bass/Interbrew brand, Worthington, is labelled Worthington Bitter in cask form, and – bizarrely – Worthington Best Bitter in the nitro-keg version. Always choose the living rather than the dead.

Grand Hotel, built as an imposing clifftop home for a 19th-century Duchess of Northumberland. Renowned for its stunning sea views over a magnificent coastline (clearly visible from the plush lounge at the front – drinks from the bar may be taken in), it is now gaining a reputation for real ales. Eve meals finish at 7pm. ⊷◑✦⊖P

Tynemouth Lodge Hotel
Tynemouth Road
✪ 11-11; 12-10.30 Sun
☎ (0191) 296 3433
website: www.tynemouthlodgehotel.co.uk
Draught Bass; Belhaven 80/-; Caledonian Deuchars IPA; guest beer (occasional) Ⓗ
Built in 1799, next to the former Tynemouth House of Correction and Justices Room, this is a comfortable single-roomed bar. This free house has been a *Guide* entry since 1984, shortly after being bought by the present owners. Unusual for the area, in specialising in Scottish real ales, it also boasts the highest Draught Bass sales on Tyneside. It is next to Northumberland Park and near to the Coast-to-Coast cycle route.
🏰Q❀⊖♣P

WARDLEY

Green
White Mare Pool
(A184/B1288 jct)
✪ 11.30-11; 12-10.30 Sun
☎ (0191) 495 0161 website: www.sjf.co.uk
Black Sheep Best Bitter; Courage Directors; Taylor Landlord; guest beers Ⓗ
Part of the Sir John Fitzgerald's chain, easily accessible by road, and built to a design based on golfer Gary Player's house in South Africa, the pub overlooks an 18th green. The plush public bar has a Victorian feel and is often busy in eves (closed daytimes). Its design contrasts well with the New England atmosphere of the dining room, and whitewashed walls and glass in the lounge. There are always three guest beers available, many from local micros, plus quarterly mini beer festivals.
❀◑⊟✦P

WASHINGTON ❄

Steps
47-49 Spout Lane
(next to Washington Old Hall)
✪ 11-11; 12-10.30 Sun
☎ (0191) 415 0733
Beer range varies Ⓗ
Warm, friendly bar/lounge in old Washington village, recently extended and refurbished. All live football matches are shown on a large-screen TV. Wed eve is quiz night with free finger buffet. Every Tue there is 30p off a pint of cask ale. Bar snacks are usually available. ◑

WEST BOLDON

Black Horse
Rectory Bank
(100 yds from A184 on road to Boldon Colliery)
✪ 11-11; 12-10.30 Sun
☎ (0191) 536 1814

Castle Eden Ale; Flowers Original; Greene King Old Speckled Hen; guest beer Ⓗ
Pleasing pub, conveniently situated just off the main Sunderland-Newcastle road, close to the parish church. The pub specialises in good quality, value-for-money meals. The bar is on the small side and can get busy, particularly at weekends.
❀◑⊟♣P

WEST MOOR

George Stephenson
Great Lime Road
✪ 12-11; 12-10.30 Sun
☎ (0191) 268 1073
e-mail: richard@thegeorgestephenson.sagehos
John Smith's Magnet; guest beers Ⓗ
Much altered over its 100 years, this pub is now split into two areas that, when required, can become a single room by opening the dividing doors. An established music venue, it hosts live bands Wed, Thu and Sat, plus a weekly quiz (Mon) and other occasional events. The frequently changing guest beer is usually from one of the country's smaller (often local) breweries. Unashamedly a drinkers' pub, but a wide range of take-away food is available locally. The railway bridge that carries the East Coast mainline passes right by the patio.
❀P🍴

WHITLEY BAY ❄

Briar Dene
71 The Links
✪ 11-11 (public bar may close afternoons); 12-10.30 Sun
☎ (0191) 252 0926
Black Sheep Best Bitter; Fuller's London Pride; Mordue Workie Ticket; Theakston Cool Cask; guest beers Ⓗ
Formerly known as the Culvert Inn, when an embankment was constructed over the nearby steep-sided Briar Dene burn, this large Fitzgerald's pub is split into an attractive lounge bar, with sea views to the links and St Mary's Island and lighthouse, and a more compact rear bar with wide-screen TV, pool and darts. An indoor children's play area, with adjoining seating is well used by families. This free house is well known for its food (fish and chips a speciality). Guest beers change regularly and it hosts beer festivals featuring beers not normally found locally.
🛏❀◑⊟✦P🍴

Rockcliffe Arms
Algernon Place
✪ 11-11; 12-10.30 Sun
☎ (0191) 253 1299
Beer range varies Ⓗ
Compact Fitzgerald's one-roomed community pub, offering drinking in pleasant surroundings. Enter by the snug or the lounge doors, attractively decorated with stained glass. The single bar is partitioned to serve two distinct drinking areas: the snug with leather seating, and the lounge with tables and chairs. A mix of images is provided by the old photographs of Cullercoats, nautical prints and photographs. Regular darts and dominoes nights are held, plus a quiz night.
❀⊖♣

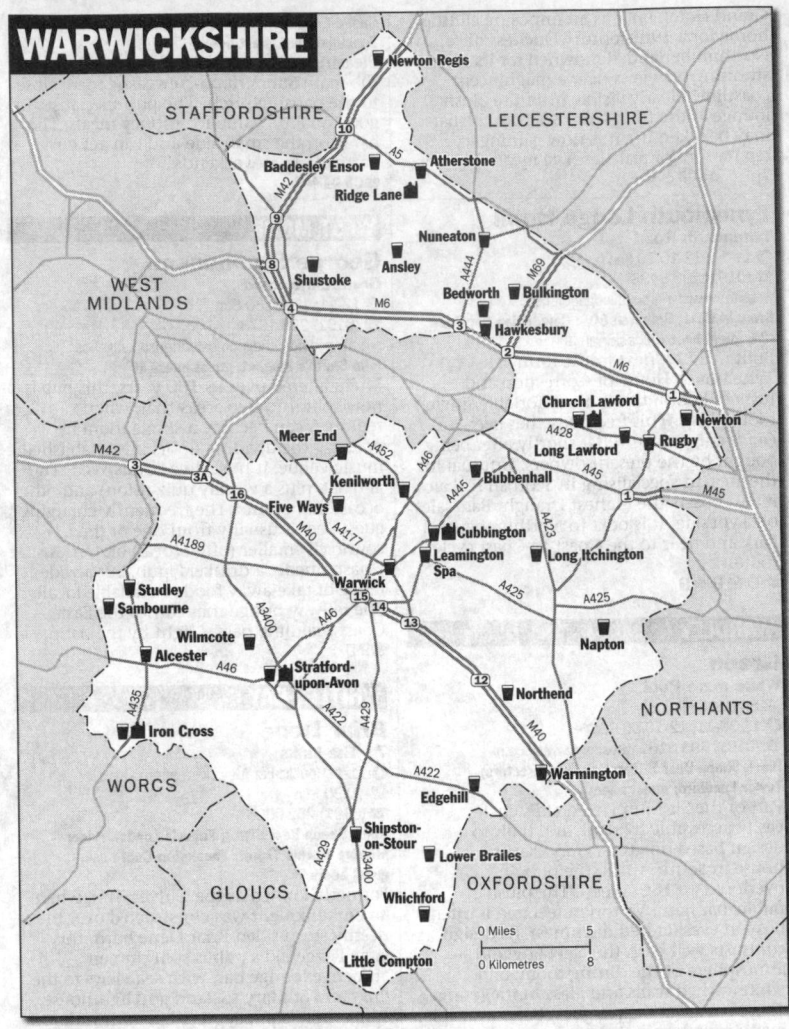

WARWICKSHIRE

ALCESTER

Holly Bush
37 Henley Street
⊕ 12-11; 12-10.30 Sun
☎ (01789) 762482 e-mail: hollybushpub@aol.com
Black Sheep Best Bitter; Cannon Royall Fruiterer's Mild; Uley Bitter; guest beers ℍ
Former market town hotel, where a sympathetic refurbishment has increased the number of rooms from two to five, including a games-mad public bar and a no-smoking room. Oak and pine wall panelling and bare wood or flagstone floors are the keynotes here. The function room is used for beer festivals. It supports the Alcester and Arden Folk Festival fringe, and hosts regular folk sessions. A selection of home-made bar lunches is supplemented by a more substantial lunch and eve menu. At least three guest beers are supplied by micros. Large garden. ♨Q♥❀◑ꔹ♣⊁

Three Tuns
High Street
⊕ 12-11; 12-10.30 Sun

☎ (01789) 762626
Goff's Jouster; Hobsons Best Bitter; guest beers ℍ
Single-bar pub where small-paned bull's-eye windows make it look like an antique shop. Inside, among the low beams and flagstone floor, the antiquity of the building is revealed by a glass panel in one wall showing the wattle and daub construction. No piped music, no pool table, no food – just how pubs used to be. It serves up to eight independent ales (many from local micros) and fruit wines. Look out for occasional issues of its newspaper/scandal sheet, *The Tumbler*. Q♣

ANSLEY

Lord Nelson Inn
Birmingham Road
⊕ 12-2.30, 5.30-11; 12-11 Sat; 12-10.30 Sun
☎ (024) 7639 2305
Draught Bass; M&B Brew XI; guest beers ℍ
Something for everyone in this large, family-run free house with two restaurants. The Victory is fully air-conditioned and offers an excellent choice of both English

and French cuisine, or try the Mary Rose Bar for a good choice of informal meals. Maintaining a nautical theme, the popular bar displays a fine collection of pump clips, mementos of past guest beers. For that special occasion a chauffeur-driven Rolls Royce is available for hire. ♨ ❀ ◑ ⌂ ♣ P

ATHERSTONE ❖

Redding's Bar
66 Long Street
❂ 5 (12 Thu & Sat)-11; closed Mon; 7-11 Sun
☎ (01827) 714348
Everards Tiger; ⒣ guest beers ⒣/⒢
Un-typical Everards' house, in a narrow building, formerly a wine bar. Do not be misled by the illuminated Stella sign – the bar provides a changing selection of guest beers, often showcasing the local Church End Brewery; the friendly tenants are receptive to beer suggestions. It can be noisy eves, but is frequented by all ages. Games are tucked away in small rear room. See if you recognise anyone in the photographic rogues' gallery. ⇌ ☐

BADDESLEY ENSOR

Red Lion
The Common
❂ 12-3 (not Mon-Fri), 7-11; 12-3, 7-10.30 Sun
☎ (01827) 713009
Banks's Original; Marston's Pedigree; guest beers ⒣
Traditional, one-roomed village local. This friendly pub is clearly a focus for village life, fielding its own football team. Up to three guest beers are sourced from a variety of independent breweries. It is well worth finding, but note the restricted weekday opening hours. ♨ Q ❀

BEDWORTH ❖

Old Goose
27 Orchard Street, Collycroft
❂ 12-4 (not Tue or Wed), 7-11; 12-4, 7-10.30 Sun
☎ (0204) 7631 3266
Ansells Mild; Tetley Bitter; guest beers ⒣
There is always something happening at this lively, friendly public house. The large single room, that includes a well-equipped games areas, provides the best in entertainment. At weekends it hosts discos and Karaoke, with new acts and old favourites. On quieter weekday eves darts and dominoes are played and there's Roy's prize bingo on Tue. Monthly entertainment guides are available from the bar. ❀ ♣ P

White Swan
All Saints Square
❂ 11-11; 12-10.30 Sun
☎ (0204) 7631 2164
Wells Eagle, Bombardier ⒣
Ideally situated, at the top of the traffic-free shopping area, and handy for the Mill Street bus stops, this large corner pub has a small traditional bar with a games area to one side. The larger refurbished lounge is also popular with shoppers, as are the good value bar meals (not served Sun). In the eves and at weekends the pub is busy with entertainment, such as discos, attracting both locals and visitors to the area.
❀ ◑ ⌂ ⇌ ♣ ♠

BUBBENHALL

Malt Shovel
Lower End
❂ 12 2.30, 6-11; 12-3, 7-10.30 Sun
☎ (024) 7630 1141
Ansells Bitter; Draught Bass; M&B Brew XI; Tetley Bitter; guest beer ⒣
Extended village local, built around the original timber-framed building. This comfortable pub has a large L-shaped lounge bar, complemented by a smaller, slightly more basic public. Traditional bar food is available at lunchtime, with roasts on Sun. Substantial eve menu is available until 9.30 (not served Sun). To the rear there is a pleasant garden and, more unusually, a small bowling green. It is handy for the Ryton Pools Country Park.
❀ ◑ ⌂ P

BULKINGTON ❖

Old Chequers Inn
Chequers Street
❂ 12-3, 7-11; 12-11 Thu-Sat; 12-10.30 Sun
☎ (024) 7631 2182
Draught Bass; M&B Mild, Brew XI; guest beers ⒣
Thriving village free house that looks very picturesque in summer, with hanging baskets and flower tubs. The interior is split into three drinking areas, all served from one central bar. It retains much character, and is well worth a visit. A recent addition is the restaurant extension to the rear (opening is imminent, so ring for menu details and opening times). ♨ ❀ ♣ P

Weavers Arms
12 Long Street, Ryton (off Wolvey Rd)
❂ 12-3.30 (3 Fri), 5-11; 12-11 Sat; 12-10.30 Sun
☎ (024) 7631 4415
Draught Bass; M&B Mild, Brew XI; guest beers ⒣
Row of cottages built in 1841, converted in 1891. On arrival, take a look at the humorous pub sign. The present owners took over 12 years ago and revitalised this one-time keg pub. Joining in is what this pub is all about, with lively conversation and light-hearted banter; the regulars take part in games leagues, and in July enter a float in the local carnival. Thu eve is well known for the Pork Pie Club. Drop in and experience the delights of this family-run free house. Lunches served Tue-Sat.
♨ ❀ ◑ ♣ ♠

CHURCH LAWFORD

Old Smithy
1 Green Lane (off A428, 4 miles from Rugby)
❂ 11-3, 5.30-11; 11-11 Sat; 12-10.30 Sun
☎ (024) 7654 2333 website: www.theold-smithy.com
Ansells Mild; Greene King IPA, Abbot; Tetley Bitter; guest beers ⒣
This large, friendly village pub caters for just about everybody. A traditional bar area is complemented by a no-smoking restaurant

INDEPENDENT BREWERIES

Church End Ridge Lane
Cox's Yard Stratford-upon-Avon
Frankton Bagby Church Lawford
Queen's Head Iron Cross
Warwickshire Cubbington

serving high quality food. A games room is unobtrusively hidden at one end of the bar; it also has an outdoor children's play area. Upwards of seven real ales are usually available with at least two from Frankton Bagby Brewery situated behind the pub. A thriving food trade does mean that getting a table is difficult at busy times.
🏮 Q ⊛ ◑ 🌢 ♣ P ⌁

CUBBINGTON

Queen's Head
20 Queen Street
🕐 12-11; 12-10.30 Sun
☎ (01926) 429949
Ansells Mild, Bitter; Draught Bass; guest beer Ⓗ
Typical, cosy Victorian village pub with a public bar, pool room and comfortable lounge. This is a real, living community local where young and old alike meet and where often the loudest noise is conversation. The vast display of pump clips testifies to the range and popularity of guest beers, while a blackboard lists upcoming guests already in the cellar. A fishing club, golf society and darts team all use the pub, and major sports events are shown on a large-screen TV. Q ⊛ ⊕ ♣ P

FIVE WAYS

Case is Altered ☆
Case Lane (off Claverdon road at A4141/A4177 island) OS225701
🕐 12 (11.30 Sat)-2.30, 6-11; 12-2, 7-10.30 Sun
☎ (01926) 484206
Brains Dark; Greene King IPA; Hook Norton Old Hooky Ⓖ **guest beer** Ⓗ
Superb, traditional, rural pub that has remained unaltered throughout its 350 years. The bar is a blend of wood, bricks and tiles, enhancing the relaxed atmosphere, and contains a framed poster from the defunct Lucas, Blackwell & Arkwright brewery of Leamington Spa. The entrance

HAWKESBURY

Elephant & Castle
Aldermans Green Road (N of M6)
🕐 12-11; 12-10.30 Sun
☎ (024) 7636 4606
Hardys & Hansons Best Mild; M&B Brew XI; Wells Eagle Ⓗ
Situated next to Tusses Bridge, No. 4 on the Oxford Canal, and close to the famous Hawkesbury Junction, it is always frequented by a good mix of regulars and canal-trippers that come to savour the pleasure of this unspoilt two-roomed local. Both rooms are attractively furnished, the larger having a well-used games area. This all adds to a relaxed and friendly atmosphere. A high fence separates the canal from the children's play area.
🏮 ⊛ ⊕ ♣ P

IRON CROSS

Queen's Head & Fat God's Brewery
🕐 11 (12 winter)-11; 12-10.30 Sun
☎ (01386) 871012 website: www.fatgodsbrewery.co.uk
Fat God's Mild (occasional)**, Bitter, Morris Dancer, Porter of the Vale, Thunder & Lightning, guest beers** (occasional) Ⓗ
Home of the Fat God's Brewery, which can be seen at the rear of the pub, this was the local CAMRA *Pub of the Year* 1999 and 2000, and West Midlands *Community Pub of the Year* 1998. It holds a 10-day beer festival in late June, with 25-plus beers from independents, as well as the Fat God's

INN BRIEF

ATHERSTONE
Old Swan
175 Long Street
12-4, 6-11; 11.30-11 Fri & Sat;
12-3.30, 7-10.30 Sun
Banks's Original, Bitter Ⓟ
No food is served in this old, attractive, timber-framed pub.

BEDWORTH
Traveller's Rest
Bulkington Road
12-5, 7-11; 12-11 Fri & Sat;
12-5, 7-10.30 Sun
Worthington Bitter; guest beers Ⓗ
Near the station, a free house that lives up to its name. A large traditional bar and small lounge adorned with football pictures.

BULKINGTON
War Memorial Club
Sandpits New Street
11-2.30 (not Mon), 7-11;
12-3, 7-10.30 Sun
Tetley Bitter; guest beers Ⓗ
Well-used, friendly, three-roomed club with a pleasant, comfortable atmosphere and well-appointed decor. Guests are from Tapster's Choice.

EDGEHILL
Castle
11-2.30, 6-11;
12-3, 6-10.30 Sun
Hook Norton Best Bitter, Old Hooky, seasonal beers; guest beers Ⓗ
70ft high round tower overlooking the Civil War battlefield. A pleasant garden affords panoramic views. Guest beers are from independents. B&B.

MEER END
Tipperary Inn
11.30-11;
12-10.30 Sun
Courage Directors; Tetley Bitter; guest beers Ⓗ
Welcoming country inn serving good food (no meals Sun eve). Regularly changing guest beers come from small independents. Pleasant garden.

RUGBY
William Webb Ellis
22 Warwick Street
11-11; 12-10.30 Sun
Banks's Original, Bitter; Marston's Pedigree Ⓗ
Friendly, comfortable pub serving good value bar meals all day, until 9pm.

SHIPSTON-ON-STOUR
Black Horse
Station Road
12-2.30, 7-11; 12-3.30, 7-10.30 Sun
Greene King Abbot; Tetley Bitter; guest beers Ⓗ
Ancient stone and thatch pub where drink, conversation and amusement hold sway. Food served.

WARWICK
New Bowling Green Inn
13 St Nicholas Church Street
12-2.30, 5-11; 12-11 Fri & Sat; 12-3,
7-10.30 (12-10.30 summer) Sun
Wells Eagle, Bombardier, seasonal beers Ⓗ
500-year-old pub with low ceilings in its two bars and folk music room. Boules played in a walled garden. No food available.

WILMCOTE
Mason's Arms
Aston Cantlow Road
11-3, 5.30-11 (11-11 summer); 12-4,
7-10.30 (12-10.30 summer) Sun
Black Sheep Best Bitter; Brakspear Bitter; Hook Norton Best Bitter; guest beers Ⓗ
Welcoming pub, 400 yards from canal, station and Mary Arden's house. Reasonably priced beer. Conservatory restaurant

range. It has special offers on food weekday eves, and a take-away service for beer and food. Cream teas are available. The mild is occasionally on handpump, but is otherwise served through a pressure fount.

ᐧ🅑🍴🕒♿♣🐾

KENILWORTH

Clarendon House Hotel
6 High Street (near A429/A452 jct)
🕐 11-11; 12-10.30 Sun
☎ (01926) 857668
Greene King IPA, Abbot; Hook Norton Best Bitter; guest beers Ⓗ

Comfortable hotel bar, recently refurbished where an abundance of sofas give it a chic, café-bar ambience. In the centre of old Kenilworth, the bar is very much open to the public as well as hotel residents. Bar food is available all day and a brasserie serves more substantial meals. Two guest beers are always available, including ales from local breweries. Just beyond the main bar area an old well houses a resident skeleton. The patio garden is heated.
🏵🛏🕒P

Earl Clarendon
127 Warwick Road (A452)
🕐 12-2, 4-11; 12-11 Sat; 12-10.30 Sun
☎ (01926) 854643
Marston's Bitter, Pedigree Ⓗ

Last bastion of the traditional local on a High Street otherwise colonised by theme bars. This friendly pub, known locally as Bottom Clad, has two drinking areas – a comfortable public bar to the front and a quieter lounge to the rear – served from a central bar. Fund-raising quizzes are held alternate Wed eves. The doorstep sandwiches at lunchtime are renowned (no food Sun). In summer the recently expanded garden provides a haven from the busy road. 🏵🕒

Old Bakery Hotel
12 High Street (near A429/A452 jct)
🕐 12-2.30 (not Mon-Fri), 5-11; 12-2.30, 7-10.30 Sun
☎ (01926) 864111
Hook Norton Best Bitter; Taylor Landlord; guest beer Ⓗ

In the old, and most picturesque, part of this small town, close to the Abbey Fields recreation grounds and the castle ruins, this is a sympathetically restored and extended, family-run hotel, parts of which date from the 17th century. A peaceful bar, free from music, TV or games machines, welcomes residents and visitors alike. Outside, a small patio area has a few seats around the covered 17th-century well.
Q🏵🛏♿P

LEAMINGTON SPA

Red House
113 Radford Road
🕐 11.30-11; 12-10.30 Sun
☎ (01926) 881725
Draught Bass; Greene King Abbot; M&B Brew XI; Worthington Bitter; guest beer Ⓗ

This fine, Victorian brick pub, on the south-eastern side of town, is a very popular community tavern that draws a diverse and friendly clientele. The weekly Cheese Club is an unusual feature, while the framed

collection of bottle labels from the former Thornley's Brewery of Radford Semele (closed in the 1960s) is even rarer. Look out for the old coloured handpulls on the bar. The pleasant enclosed garden at the rear is safe for children.
ᐧQ🏵♣

Somerville Arms
4 Campion Terrace
🕐 11-3 (not winter Mon-Wed), 5.30-11; 11-11 Sat; 12-10.30 Sun
☎ (01926) 426746
Adnams Broadside; Ansells Mild, Bitter; Greene King IPA, Abbot; Ind Coope Burton Ale Ⓗ

A welcome return to this *Guide* for this unspoilt, traditional pub which has been re-established as one of the finest locals in town by new licensees, following its acquisition by Punch Taverns in 1999. A thriving drinkers' pub with a large busy bar at the front and a smaller cosy lounge at the rear, both enjoy a friendly atmosphere. Each room has its own drinking motto displayed: 'Real ale for your health' and 'Abound in hops all ye who enter here'. The pub is named after Captain Somerville, a local magistrate in Victorian times.
Q🏵🔲♣

LITTLE COMPTON

Red Lion
Signed from A44
🕐 12-2.30, 6-11; 12-3, 7-10.30 Sun
website: www.redlioninn.com
Donnington BB, SBA Ⓗ

This Cotswold-stone local, in Warwickshire's most southerly village, boasts a strong community involvement, an Aunt Sally pitch and, unusually, a real public bar. It serves good food and is renowned for the quality of its steaks and fresh fish. Set in beautiful countryside, it is handy as a touring base (always fully booked during the Cheltenham National Hunt Festival) and is only a couple of miles from the megalithic Rollright Stones.
ᐧQ🏵🛏🕒🔲♿▲♣P

LONG ITCHINGTON

Harvester Inn
Church Road
🕐 11-3, 6-11; 12-10.30 Sun
☎ (01926) 812698
Hook Norton Best Bitter, Old Hooky; guest beer Ⓗ

Note: This is The Harvester, not to be confused with the restaurant chain of the same name. An unpretentious village local, this is a good value free house with favourably priced beers and food in the restaurant that seats 30. A side room houses the pool table. Dating from the early 1800s, when it was built as two separate houses, the pub overlooks the village pond. It is a few minutes' walk from the nearest moorings on the Grand Union Canal.
Q🕒▲♣P

LONG LAWFORD

Country Inn
29 Main Street
🕐 12-3, 7-11; 12-11 Fri & Sat: 12-2.30, 7-10.30 Sun
☎ (01788) 565188
Greene King IPA; M&B Brew XI; guest beers Ⓗ

Single bar village free house, that is a pleasure to drink in. It boasts oak beams and a flagstone floor in both the bar and games room where cheese skittles can be played. A log fire enhances the relaxed ambience of the bar area. A quality restaurant is situated at the rear, next to a pleasant lawned garden. Up to five real ales are usually available and often come from micro-breweries unusual for the area. Eve meals are served Wed–Sun. ⚲Q☸♣♣P

Sheaf & Sickle
Coventry Road (A428, 1$1/2$ miles from Rugby)
⚙ 12-2.30, 6-11; 12-11 Sat; 12-10.30 Sun
☎ (01788) 544622
Ansells Bitter; Tetley Bitter; guest beers Ⓗ
Friendly local with a quiet snug and a busier bar. A restaurant, scrving excellent food at competitive prices, is open Wed–Sun. Excellent value bar meals are available in the bar and snug. A comfortable outdoor seating area is popular in fine weather. It is the only pub in the area to boast its own cricket pitch. A good choice of guest beers is supplemented by occasional beer festivals. ⚲Q☸♣♣P

LOWER BRAILES

George Hotel
High Street
⚙ 11-11; 12-10.30 Sun
☎ (01608) 685223
Hook Norton Mild, Best Bitter, Old Hooky, Generation, seasonal beers Ⓗ
This sympathetically refurbished, Grade II coaching inn incorporates elements from the 16th to 18th centuries. An extensive garden and patio area includes an enclosed Aunt Sally pitch. It hosts frequent live music. A coin-operated internet terminal is available on the upstairs landing. The restaurant often stages themed eves and costume dinners, while a take-away service is available for curries (Mon eve) and fish and chips (Wed). ⚲Q☸☸♣♣P

NAPTON

King's Head
Southam Road
⚙ 12-3, 5.30-11; 12-11 Fri & Sat; 12-10.30 Sun
☎ (01926) 812202
Hook Norton Best Bitter, Old Hooky; guest beers Ⓗ
A new landlord, and a new owner, Oxfordshire brewer, Hook Norton, have revived this spacious roadside pub. Beside the regular beers there is usually a seasonal ale from Hook Norton and their mild, plus a guest from elsewhere. A restaurant (closed Mon), accommodates parties of up to 50. The no-smoking lounge is decorated with canal maps. Darts and pool are played in the bar, which also has a TV. Children can play in the garden where barbecues are held in summer. ⚲☸♣♣P⚥

NEWTON

Stag & Pheasant
27 Main Street (off Newton Manor Lane)
⚙ 12-2 (3 Sat), 6-11; 12-4, 7-10.30 Sun
☎ (01788) 860326
Banks's Original, Bitter; guest beers Ⓗ
Lovely village local with a real community spirit, this former farmhouse has a thatched

roof. Heavily beamed, it is reputedly the oldest A-frame building in Warwickshire – the original beam is still visible in the bar. It fields various games teams and is the focal point for villagers, who often run fêtes and outside games in the car park and garden. Traditional pub fare includes pies made on the premises. Strange noises are often heard coming from the cellar, which is supposedly haunted. ☸♣♣P⚀

NEWTON REGIS

Queen's Head
Main Road
⚙ 11-2.30, 6-11; 12-2.30, 7-10.30 Sun
Draught Bass; Highgate Dark; M&B Brew XI; guest beer Ⓗ
16th-century village local, with a garden. Guest beers from both local and regional micro-breweries change roughly every fortnight. Games are played in the traditional bar and food is served in the lounge (booking advisable). ⚲☸♣♣P

NORTHEND

Red Lion
Bottom Street (signed off the B4001, former A41)
⚙ 11.30-2.30 (3 Sat), 6-11 (closed winter Mon); 12-3, 6-10.30 Sun
☎ (01295) 770308
Taylor Landlord; guest beer Ⓗ
Saved from extinction, following closure after a failed application for change of use, this idyllic, one-bar country pub at the foot of the Burton Dassett Hills has a warm, friendly atmosphere. Very popular with locals, ramblers and cyclists, this genuine free house keeps a constantly changing guest ale. The garden affords panoramic views. The dining room serves excellent, freshly-prepared food to order by the resident chef, from a varied menu. Traditional pub games are played eves. ⚲Q☸♣♣P

NUNEATON

Bull Inn
Bull Street, Attleborough
⚙ 12-11; 12-10.30 Sun
☎ (024) 7638 6626
Beer range varies Ⓗ
At the very hub of the village, this one-time Ansells Heritage pub attracts a broad selection of customers. It retains its local charm and appeal, as little has changed. The one large room has it all: a bar, lounge and, to one side, a popular games areas. At weekends the pub comes alive with music, discos, quiz nights and other activities, but the most important reason for a visit has to be the ever-changing guest ale from small micro-breweries. ⚲☸☸♣P

Fox Inn
11a The Square, Attleborough
⚙ 11-11; 12-10.30 Sun
☎ (024) 7638 3290
Mansfield Dark Mild, Cask Ale; Marston's Pedigree Ⓗ
Once three cottages, great changes have taken place in the last 200 years at this well-known village local. Over the years it has been sympathetically refurbished and extended to give a deceptively spacious, attractive public house. The busy bar, with a

tiled floor and carpeted games area, generates an excellent friendly feeling; the lounge has a relaxed atmosphere in which to drink and enjoy the food. From this room large doors lead to the garden where high walls are adorned with flowers in summer – it makes a very pleasant extra eating/drinking area.
🐕🍴🛏️🍺🚃♣️●

RUGBY ✿

Alexandra Arms
James Street (behind multi-storey car park)
🕐 12-3.30, 5-11; 12-11 Fri & Sat; 12-3, 5-10.30 Sun
☎ (01788) 587660
website: www.rugbycamra.org.uk/alexandraarms
Ansells Bitter; Greene King Abbot; Marston's Pedigree; guest beers Ⓗ
Rugby CAMRA *Pub of the Year* 1998, '99 and 2000. The comfortable L-shaped lounge, benefiting from a sensitive refurbishment, can be busy and lively debate is guaranteed with locals. The games room at the rear is popular with youngsters playing pool and rock fans attracted by the well-stocked juke box. The garden used to be a bowling green and now hosts an annual beer festival. Good value bar food is available until 9pm. Two ever-changing guest beers are stocked often from Wye Valley and Beowulf, as well as other micros.
Q🐕🍴🛏️🍺🚃♣️🐾

Raglan Arms
30 Dunchurch Road
🕐 12-3 (not Thu), 7-11; 12-11 Fri; 11-11 Sat; 12-10.30 Sun
☎ (01788) 544441
Banks's Hanson's Mild; Greene King Abbot; Marston's Bitter, Pedigree; guest beers Ⓗ
Small, friendly, traditional pub, close to the town centre. Of interest locally are the Rugby School and the Rugby Football Museum, both close by. This is one of the best pubs in the area for both the range and quality of real ale, and has twice been Rugby CAMRA *Pub of the Year*. There are three guest beers in addition to the regular ales. The pub has a no-nonsense traditional bar to the rear and a more comfortable lounge at the front.
Q🐕🛏️♣️P

Three Horseshoes Hotel
22 Sheep Street
🕐 11-2.30, 7-11; 7-11 Sun
☎ (01788) 544585
Greene King IPA, Abbot; guest beers Ⓗ
Just off one of the main pedestrian areas of Rugby, the 'Three Shoes' offers an oasis of calm. This spacious 18th-century former coaching inn is divided into a variety of drinking areas: the front room with bar and real fire, a small side room with TV, and a quiet room (no bar, no TV, no music). It stocks two guests in addition to the Greene King. As well as an extensive fixed menu, it offers up to five specials, advertised as GM free. Parking is limited.
🏨Q🍴🍴P

Victoria
1 Lower Hillmorton Road
🕐 12-2.30, 6-11; 12-11 Sat; 12-2.30, 7-10.30 Sun
☎ (01788) 544374
Cottage Champflower; guest beers Ⓗ

This triangular-shaped local is on the edge of the town centre, but well worth a visit. The public bar at the front is where pool and darts are played; for a more comfortable drink, try the lounge. Decorated in a Victorian style, it provides a good environment to enjoy the guest beers. Recently, the landlord has heavily promoted beers from the local breweries: Church End, Frankton Bagby and Warwickshire. This range makes it a worthy stop on any Rugby pub crawl. No food Sun.
🍴🍺🚃

SAMBOURNE

Green Dragon
The Village Green (between A435 and A441)
🕐 11-3, 6 (5.30 Fri)-11; 12-3, 7-10.30 Sun
☎ (01527) 892465
Draught Bass; Hobsons Best Bitter; M&B Brew XI Ⓗ
17th-century inn in an attractive position overlooking the village green. Oak beams, brasses and pewter add to the character of the two bars and restaurant. It enjoys a reputation for good food and boasts connections with comedian, Tony Hancock. Modern en-suite accommodation completes the picture.
🏨Q🐕🛏️🍴P

SHUSTOKE

Griffin Inn
Church Road (B4116)
🕐 12-2.30, 7-11; 12-2.30, 7-10.30 Sun
☎ (01675) 481205
website: www.midlandspubs.co.uk/warwickshire/griffin
Highgate Dark; Marston's Pedigree; RCH Pitchfork; Theakston Old Peculier; Wells Bombardier; guest beers Ⓗ
Renowned countrywide for the number and variety of its guest beers – normally nine are on tap. This 360-year-old country village inn is situated on a dangerous bend in the road; there is an ample car park and garden. A conservatory provides an ideal area for children and can be booked for meetings. The pub has real fires for comfort, and alcoves for privacy; the seating is generous. With delicious food and the excellent range of beers – what more could one ask?
🏨Q🐎🐕🍴🛏️🐾P

STRATFORD-UPON-AVON

Jester at Cox's Yard
Bridgefoot (N end of bridge)
🕐 11-11; 12-10.30 Sun
☎ (01789) 404600 website: www.coxsyard.co.uk
Cox's Yard Jester, Juggler, seasonal beers Ⓗ
Formerly the timber yard that supplied the coopers at Flowers Brewery, Charles Wells have turned it into a leisure experience. As well as the pub there is an adjacent micro-brewery in the old engine house, a teashop, restaurant, art gallery, the *Stratford Tales* (an audio-visual odyssey through Stratford's history), and conference facilities. A large terrace beside the Avon makes a pleasant summer drinking spot. The brewer gives regular talks and tours. It hosts a beer festival and frequent live music, including jazz, Sun eve. Wheelchair lift links the pub to the first-floor restaurant.
🐎🐕🍴🛏️🍴

Pen & Parchment

Bridgefoot (between High St and bridge)

✪ 11-11; 12-10.30 Sun

☎ (01789) 297697

Brakspear Bitter; Taylor Landlord; guest beers Ⓗ

Originally part of a boatbuilder's yard then the Unicorn and later the Navigation, this old pub is now part of the Heritage Hogshead chain. It offers eight real ales and four real ciders – you can try before you buy, or have a 'bat' of four one-third pints of different ales. The pub features pictures of old Stratford and the Flowers Brewery and some timbers from a wooden warship. A no-smoking area is available until 9pm. Belgian bottled beers and an extensive menu add to its appeal. Four real ale/lager/cider festivals are held annually. ❀⇋◑♣✁

STUDLEY

Little Lark

108 Alcester Road (A435/Tom's Town Lane jct)

✪ 12-3, 6-11; 12-11 Sat; 12-3, 6.30-10.30 Sun

☎ (01527) 853105

Usher's Best Bitter, Founders Ale, seasonal beers Ⓗ

Friendly, street-corner pub, that retains its newspaper theme from the time when it belonged to the Little Pub Company. Popular with local workers and residents, its central bar serves three rooms, one of which has an open fire; the pub has a cosy atmosphere. Good quality food is available from a varied menu, which includes excellent sandwiches and baguettes, all at very reasonable prices. It stocks an extensive selection of country wines. ▨◑♣●

WARMINGTON

Plough

Church Hill

✪ 12-3, 5.30-11; 12-3, 7-10.30 Sun

☎ (01295) 690666

Greene King Abbot; Hook Norton Best Bitter; Marston's Pedigree; guest beer Ⓗ

This fine old country inn is almost 400 years old. Built of local ironstone, it stands on the face of the Edgehill Escarpment; soldiers retreating from the Battle of Edgehill passed through the village on their way to Oxfordshire. The pub has low-beamed ceilings and a large inglenook with a copper hood. The cosy interior creates a welcoming, friendly atmosphere. No food Sun eve. The village boasts a fine duckpond. ▨❀◑♣P

WARWICK ❖

Globe Hotel

10 Theatre Street

✪ 11-11; 12-10.30 Sun

☎ (01926) 492044

website: www.globehotel.demon.co.uk

M&B Brew XI; guest beers Ⓗ

This Grade II listed pub dates back to the mid-18th century. Although once described as a commercial inn and posting house, and located near the market place, it was never a busy coaching inn. Until the 1960s it was reached by an iron bridge across the deep ravine of the street known as The Holloway. A spacious, comfortable lounge usually has two guest beers available. A restaurant with

its own bar offers Italian specialities. Some of the en-suite guest rooms have four-poster beds. Q⇋◑●⇌P

Old Fourpenny Shop Hotel

27 Crompton Street

✪ 12-2.30 (3 Fri & Sat), 5.30 (5 Fri; 6 Sat)-11; 12-3, 6-10.30 Sun

☎ (01926) 491360

M&B Brew XI; guest beers Ⓗ

Near the Warwick racecourse, officially the Warwick Tavern; its present name derives from around 1800 when navvies building the Warwick canals were attracted by cheap tots of rum sold at 4d a tot. Now it is best known for the ever-changing range of five guest beers, boasting 11 consecutive entries in this *Guide* and Warwickshire's CAMRA Pub of the Year 2000 award. The single bar uses warm shades to create a cosy, relaxed atmosphere in an uncluttered contemporary style. It offers upmarket pub food and en-suite guest rooms in converted stables. ⇋◑P

Simple Simon

105 Emscote Road (main road to Leamington)

✪ 11-3, 6-11; 12-3, 6-10.30 Sun

☎ (01926) 774078

Flowers IPA, Original; Fuller's London Pride; Wadworth 6X; guest beer Ⓗ

Warm, friendly pub with two bars, called the Elephant and Castle until 1970, when a pie factory along the street caused the change of name. Although the factory no longer exists, it is remembered by a plaque inside the pub. Pool and darts are played in the public bar which bears a sports theme, with photographs and autographed shirts. The lounge bar displays photographs of steam engines and scenes of Warwickshire. An unusual game called Shut the Box is often played. ◑♣●

WHICHFORD

Norman Knight

✪ 12-2.30, 7-11; 12-2.30, 7-10.30 Sun

☎ (01608) 684621

website: www.thenormanknight.co.uk

Hook Norton Best Bitter; guest beers Ⓗ

Traditional village pub, with a stone-flagged floor and exposed timbers, in an idyllic setting facing the extensive village green. Its name commemorates Sir John De Mohun, a Knight of the Garter, who is buried in the nearby parish church. Popular with visitors and locals, the pub has its own caravan site and two holiday cottages. Eve meals are served Fri and Sat (no food Tue). Aunt Sally, dominoes and shove-ha'penny are played enthusiastically. The two or three guest beers show an adventurous variety – almost always from micros. ▨❀⇋◑▲♣P

Good beer guides

These latest titles from CAMRA Books enable you drink some fine real ales in bottles and discover the history of India Pale Ale ... and how to brew it.

Good Bottled Beer Guide

In the third edition of his guide, Jeff Evans lists all the bottle-conditioned beers brewed in Britain, along with tasting notes and information about the ingredients used by each brewery. This has become the seminal work on the subject and Jeff Evans is now recognise as the authority on real bottled beer. Sponsored by Safeway. £8.99

Homebrew Classics: India Pale Ale

In the first of a series, writer Roger Protz and brewer Clive La Pensee combine their talents to bring you the history of the great 19th-century beer style that revolutionised brewing on a world scale, along with recipes that will enable keen home brewers to recreate IPAs. The book contains original and fascinating information on the origins of the style in London. £8.99

WEST MIDLANDS

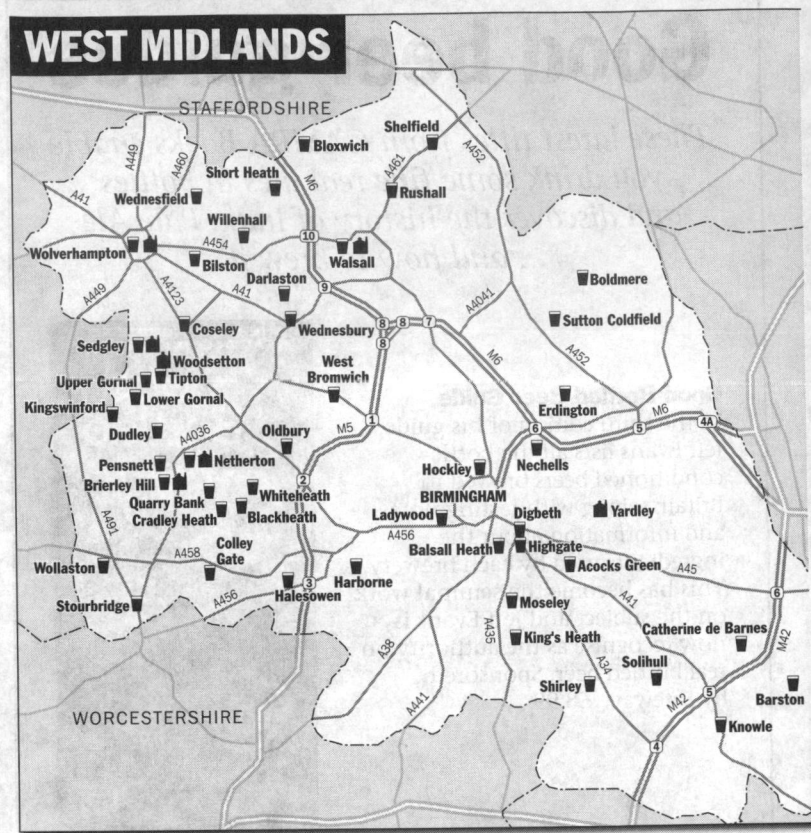

ALLESLEY

Rainbow Inn
73 Birmingham Road (off A4114)
🕐 11-11; 12-10.30 Sun
☎ (024) 7640 2888 e-mail: irothers@aol.com
Courage Best Bitter, Directors; Greene King IPA; Rainbow Piddlebrook Ⓗ
On the western side of Coventry, this has been a busy village local since the 17th century. In earlier times it served as a court and Post Office, while still serving beer. Rainbow Brewery, to the rear, opened in 1994 and supplies the pub with 50% of its beer. Lunches (not Sun) are served in the bar and lounge; eve meals in the lounge only Tue-Fri, plus themed food monthly Sat eve. Car park access is tricky. The Coventry-Birmingham bus stops outside. ❁◗ ♿P

BARSTON

Bull's Head
Barston Lane
🕐 11-2.30, 5.30-11; 11-11 Sat; 12-10.30 Sun
☎ (01675) 442830
Draught Bass; Fuller's London Pride; M&B Brew XI; guest beer Ⓗ
Beamed country pub, partly dating back to 1490, a genuine village local, offering a warm welcome to passers-by. This loyal supporter of independent breweries won the local CAMRA *Pub of the Year* award 1998 and 2000. Split into three rooms, including a restaurant in the original part of the building, it offers excellent home-cooked food, Mon-Sat. Log fires dominate, together with horse-racing memorabilia. Upstairs (out of view) is a priest's hole dating from Cromwell's time. ﹫Q❁◗P

BERKSWELL

Railway
547 Station Road, Balsall Common
🕐 12-2.30, 5-11; 12-11 Sat; 12-3, 7-10.30 Sun
☎ (01676) 533284
Draught Bass; M&B Brew XI; Tetley Bitter; guest beers Ⓗ
The Railway Inn has recently undergone refurbishment, and has been styled to resemble a station buffet bar. This one-roomed pub features a section for pool and darts at one end and a comfortable seated area for the remainder, with a real fire providing a focal point in winter. The pub hosts occasional food-themed nights. On the main line for local trains between Coventry and Birmingham, this pub is a deserving new entry to the *Guide*.
﹫❁◗≠♣P

BILSTON

Olde White Rose
20 Lichfield Street
🕐 12-11; 12-4, 7-10.30 Sun ☎ (01902) 498339
Beer range varies Ⓗ
A listed frontage leads to a long, narrow interior, with an eating area to the side.

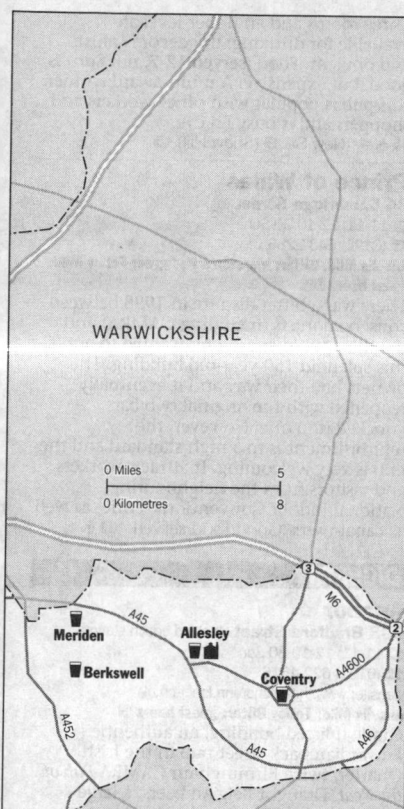

WARWICKSHIRE

0 Miles 5
0 Kilometres 8

Meriden · Allesley
Berkswell
Coventry

☺ 12-11; 12-10.30 Sun
☎ (0121) 440 1954

Ansells Bitter; Enville Ale; Marston's Pedigree; guest beer Ⓗ

Pub with two ground-floor rooms and an upstairs room with pool table. The public bar walls are covered with framed cuttings describing various exploits of its regulars. The pub fields a cricket team, although the only obvious evidence is the club noticeboard and a tendency for the public bar to fill up with cricketers and cricket gear on match days. The pub is also a short walk from Edgbaston Cricket Ground. ✿⊟

CITY CENTRE ✿

Briar Rose
25 Bennetts Hill
☺ 11-11; 12-10.30 Sun
☎ (0121) 634 8100

Shepherd Neame Spitfire; Theakston Best Bitter; Wadworth 6X; guest beers Ⓗ

Wetherspoon's third city-centre opening. The pub is a plush, smart affair decorated in Art Deco style. The furniture has a curious brown and fawn check design and the walls are bedecked with pictures describing the history of the area and the building's history as a financial institution. It can get very busy at weekends. Food is typical Wetherspoon's fare (served all day). Reasonably priced accommodation is available in the adjacent Wetherlodge. Winner of *Best Loos* award 2001.
Q🛏◖► ⑤⇌ (New St) ⊖ (Snow Hill) ●

Figure of Eight
236 Broad Street
☺ 11-11; 12-10.30 Sun
☎ (0121) 633 0917

Courage Directors; Fuller's London Pride; Shepherd Neame Spitfire; Theakston XB; guest beers Ⓗ

Typical city-centre Wetherspoon's in the heart of the lively Broad Street pub, club and restaurant area. The pub has a collection of books and an outdoor drinking area. Food is served daily until 10pm. Always a good selection of guest beers on tap that change frequently. Popular with local office workers, it is busy lunchtimes, early eve and weekends.
✿◖► ⑤⇌ (Five Ways) ⊖ (Snow Hill) ⚡ ●

Hogshead
29a Newhall Street
☺ 12-11; closed Sun
☎ (0121) 200 2453

Boddingtons Bitter; Enville Bitter; Flowers IPA; guest beers Ⓗ

Hogshead whose friendly landlord takes a real interest in his beers, sourced from predominantly regional brewers; the Enville

---

Continuing improvements, including a *Bierkeller*, conservatory and garden, are due to be completed by summer 2001. Up to 12 beers on tap, many are unusual for the area; an extensive menu serves good value, home-cooked food 12-9 Mon-Sat, plus a popular Sun lunch. Convenient for Bilston bus station, it was local CAMRA *Town Pub of the Year* in 1999. Beer discount for CAMRA members showing a card. ✿◖► ⊖ (Central)

Trumpet
58 High Street
☺ 12-2.30, 7-11; 12-2.30, 7-10.30 Sun
☎ (01902) 493723 website: www.trumpetbilston.co.uk

Holden's Mild, Bitter, Golden Glow, Special Bitter; guest beers Ⓗ

Over the past 30 years, this small, single-roomed pub has established itself as a superb jazz venue – free entry, but please support the collection. Surprisingly good jazz is played every night, and Sun lunch, showcasing different jazz styles. Look for the monthly list – or visit the website. Local caricatures and celebrity photographs cover the walls. The monitored parking is not the pub's own. Note the two contrasting pubs opposite – one dates from 1642 and was a manor house, the other is a Wetherspoon's conversion of a supermarket. ✿⊖ (Central)

BIRMINGHAM: *BALSALL HEATH*

Old Mosely Arms
Tindal Street

INDEPENDENT BREWERIES

Banks's Wolverhampton
Batham Brierley Hill
Beowulf Yardley
Goldthorn Wolverhampton
Highgate Walsall
Holden's Woodsetton
Hughes Sedgley
Old Swan Netherton
Rainbow Allesley

range can vary. Popular with the office set at lunchtime and Fri eve; students are regulars during term-time. Note the splendid choice of Belgian bottled beers, but beware that all beers are expensive. Recently refurbished, the various drinking areas on different levels are decorated in pastel shades of green and yellow imparting a relaxed, comfortable atmosphere. Food served 12-9 (8 Sat).
⊕ 🚻 ♿ ⇌ (Snow Hill) ⊖ ♣ ♠ ✂

Old Fox
54 Hurst Street
✪ 11.30-11; 12-10.30 Sun
☎ (0121) 622 5080
Ansells Mild; Greene King Old Speckled Hen; Marston's Pedigree; Tetley Bitter; guest beers Ⓗ
This traditional pub, opposite the Birmingham Hippodrome, is very popular with theatre-goers. It is recorded that Charlie Chaplin and other stars would use the pub when appearing at the theatre. There are at least two, and sometimes four, guest beers. Good value home-cooked meals are served lunchtime and early eve (not Sun eve). Two rooms are served from an island bar; the walls are adorned with theatrical posters and photographs. Tables and chairs are put out on the pavement weather permitting. ❀⊕ ♿ ⇌ (New St)

Old Joint Stock
4 Temple Row West (opp. Cathedral)
✪ 11-11; closed Sun
☎ (0121) 200 1892
Beowulf Beorma; Fuller's Chiswick, London Pride, ESB; guest beer Ⓗ
Grade II listed building displaying pictures showing the building's previous use as a bank; the palatial façade is an impressive sight when illuminated. The graceful interior mixes Victorian gothic and classical styles with Roman statuettes, colonnades and a cupola, set around an island bar.

Three rooms and an upper-level are available for drinking: the decor is plush and opulent. Food (served 12-7, not Sun) is good, but expensive. A multi-award winner, this pub is popular with office workers and shoppers and is busy Fri eve.
⊕ ♿ ⇌ (New St) ⊖ (Snow Hill) ●

Prince of Wales
84 Cambridge Street
✪ 11-11; 12-10.30 Sun
☎ (0121) 643 2286
Ansells Mild, Bitter; Marston's Pedigree; Tetley Mild; guest beers Ⓗ
There was a bitter dispute in 1998 between conservationists (including CAMRA) and the then pub-owners who wanted to gut this splendid 150-year-old building. The owners had their way and it eventually reopened with the original two bars knocked into one. However, the refurbishment is to a high standard and the pub is very welcoming. It attracts workers and visitors from the neighbouring National Indoor Convention Centre, as well as canal-users. Good food served. ⊕ ♿

Anchor ☆
308 Bradford Street (behind coach station)
✪ 11-11; 12-10.30 Sun
☎ (0121) 622 4516
website: www.the-anchor-inn.fsnet.co.uk
Ansells Mild; Tetley Bitter; guest beers Ⓗ
Grade II listed building, an authentic Edwardian back-street pub in the Irish Quarter, twice Birmingham CAMRA *Pub of the Year*. Draught Belgian beers, a large selection of international bottled beers, regular beer festivals and themed weekends add to its appeal. It stocks up to seven guest beers at weekends. Sporting events are shown on TV. Meals are served until 6pm.
⊕ ⇌ (New St) ♠

BIRMINGHAM: ACOCKS GREEN

Spread Eagle
1146 Warwick Road
11-11; 12-10.30 Sun
Boddingtons Bitter; Courage Directors; Shepherd Neame Spitfire; Wadworth 6X; guest beers Ⓗ
Wetherspoon's pub giving a good choice of ales to a part of the city where there was little real ale. *Cask Marque* accredited.

CITY CENTRE

Gunmakers Arms
12 Bath Street
11-3, 5-11; 11-11 Fri; 12-9 Sat; 12-3 (closed eve) Sun
Draught Bass; M&B Mild Ⓗ
Comfortable, two-roomed pub, one of the few in the city centre to serve a mild.

Tap & Spile
Regency Wharf Gas Street (off Broad St) 12-11; 12-10.30 Sun
Bateman XB; Everards Tiger; Fuller's London Pride; Highgate Dark; Hook Norton Old Hooky; Tap & Spile Premium Ⓗ
Attractive canalside pub near the Convention Centre and Symphony Hall. Busy lunchtime and early eve.

Victoria
48 John Bright Street (behind Alexandra Theatre) 11-11; 12-10.30 Sun
Fuller's London Pride Ⓗ
'Thespian' pub divided into two drinking areas served by a single bar. Good quality meals come in generous portions.

KING'S HEATH

Pavilions
229 Alcester Road South
12-3, 5-11; 12-11 Fri & Sat; 12-10.30 Sun
Banks's Bitter; Ⓟ **Marston's Pedigree** Ⓗ
Modern, two-roomed pub with a stylish interior and traditional ambience, popular with all ages.

NECHELLS

Villa Tavern ☆
307 Nechells Park Road
11.30-2.30, 5.30-11; 11.30-11 Fri & Sat; 12-2.30, 7-10.30 Sun
Adnams Broadside; Ansells Mild, Bitter; Marston's Pedigree Ⓗ
Victorian-style pub with a superb Grade II listed interior. Food is served at lunchtime.

BLOXWICH

Sir Robert Peel
104 Bell Lane
12-11; 12-10.30 Sun
Badger Tanglefoot; Ⓗ **Banks's Mild, Bitter;** Ⓟ **Boddingtons Bitter; Greene King Abbot; John Smith's Bitter; guest beer** Ⓗ
Large pub with a friendly atmosphere, serving food and drink at competitive prices (no food Sun eve). Families are welcome.

BOLDMERE

Bishop Vesey
Boldmere Road
11-11; 11-10.30 Sun
Boddingtons Bitter; Courage Directors; guest beers Ⓗ
Long room with an ample bar, plus an upstairs drinking area, selling a good range of ales at reasonable prices. *Cask Marque* accredited.

BRIERLEY HILL

Waterfront
6-7 Waterfront, Merry Hill
11-11; 12-10.30 Sun
Banks's Original; Courage Directors; Shepherd Neame Spitfire; Theakston Best Bitter; guest beers Ⓗ
Canalside Wetherspoon's with a café-bar feel. Surrounding bars and clubs make it a lively nightspot. *Cask Marque* accredited.

White Swan ☆
276 Bradford Street
✪ 11-3, 4.15-11; 12-3, 7-10.30 Sun
☎ (0121) 622 2586
Banks's Original, Bitter Ⓗ

Unspoilt pub in the Irish Quarter, divided into a bar and lounge with tiled ceiling and walls. It retains the original bar with the brewery's etched glass. A small collection of books helps while away the time.
≠ (Moor St)

Woodman ☆
106 Albert Street
✪ 11-11; 12-10.30 Sun
☎ (0121) 643 1959
Ansells Mild; Tetley Bitter; guest beers Ⓗ

Seemingly one of the few buildings not to be razed to the ground during the rebuilding of Birmingham city centre. A rare example of a virtually completely unspoilt pub, its friendly atmosphere makes it popular. A bit off the beaten track, but it is well worth the effort to find it.
◖◗ ⊟≠ (Moor St)

ERDINGTON

Charlie Hall
49 Barnabas Road (opp. little market)
✪ 11-11; 12-10.30 Sun
☎ (0121) 384 2716
Boddingtons Bitter; Courage Directors; Theakston Best Bitter; Wadworth 6X; guest beers Ⓗ

Charlie Hall was a locally-born actor who appeared in about 30 Laurel and Hardy films. The pub that bears his name is a fine refurbishment of a former bingo hall. Many photographs of Laurel and Hardy are displayed on the walls. The pub consists of one room, but the rear section has a much higher, decorated ceiling. The pub is wood-panelled all the way through and there are a number of alcoves for privacy. The rear section features a huge, double-sided open fireplace. A patio provides outside drinking space. ❀◖◗ ⅋≠ (Erdington) ⅍●

Lad in the Lane
28 Bromford Lane (400 yds N of A38)
✪ 11-11; 12-3, 7-10.30 Sun
☎ (0121) 377 7471
Ansells Mild; Marston's Pedigree; Tetley Bitter Ⓗ

This splendid building was originally constructed in 1306 and has been magnificently renovated. From the outside, one can see that it is a timber-framed building with leaded windows; the immediate visual impact on entering the lounge is the sight of the black exposed joints and rafters. The lounge is in three distinct sections on two levels and with differing heights. Various memorabilia include a wooden bicycle. The large garden is very popular with regulars and visitors in summer. No food Sun. ❀◖◗♣P

HARBORNE

Bell Inn
11 Old Church Road
✪ 12-11; 12-10.30 Sun
☎ (0121) 427 0934
Beer range varies Ⓗ

Plush, 18th-century pub, popular with affluent locals. Two pumps dispense a constantly changing range of guest ales, which are of good quality, but expensive. The setting is peaceful, almost like a village. The pub is built on consecrated ground opposite a church. The small bar is surrounded by a small snug and a large dining/drinking area. The outside area can be very pleasant, complete with a bowling green. A very cosy, homely pub, note the quaint outside toilets.
Q❀◖◗♿P

White Horse
2 York Street
✪ 11-11; 12-10.30 Sun
☎ (0121) 427 2063
Greene King Abbot; Marston's Pedigree; Tetley Bitter; guest beers Ⓗ

Typical Tetley Festival Ale House, opened four years ago, rejuvenating a local side-street pub. A curious mish-mash of styles abound, reflecting a mixed clientele of students and affluent locals alike. The choice has been less adventurous recently, with larger regionals dominating the guest range, which is very expensive. A snug is tucked away around the side of the island bar. Sky TV with live football and unobtrusive music blend to make a lively, busy, atmosphere in this thriving community local. No food Sun. ◖◗♣●

HIGHGATE

Lamp Tavern
257 Barford Street
✪ 12-11; 12-6 Sun
☎ (0121) 622 2599
Church End Gravediggers; Everards Tiger; Greene King Old Speckled Hen; Marston's Pedigree; Stanway Stanney Bitter; guest beer Ⓗ

Popular, back-street pub near the city centre. Often packed eves, some drinkers travel a fair distance to drink here. It offers an excellent choice of real ales and is the only regular local outlet for Stanway beers. The large function room at the back often hosts live music. Former Birmingham CAMRA *Pub of the Year*. ◖♿

HOCKLEY

Black Eagle
16 Factory Road
✪ 11.30-3, 5.30-11; 11.30-11 Fri; 12-3, 7-11 Sat; 12-3 (closed eve) Sun
☎ (0121) 523 4008
Ansells Mild, Bitter; Marston's Pedigree; Taylor Landlord; guest beers Ⓗ

Friendly pub, three times winner of Birmingham CAMRA *Pub of the Year*. Rebuilt in 1895, it retains most of the original features, including Minton tiles. One of the few pubs selling Beowulf beers from Birmingham's only brewery, it is Birmingham's only entry in CAMRA's *Good Pub Food*. Close to the Soho House Museum, the famous Jewellery Quarter, and Jewellery Museum, this pub is an ideal destination for the ale connoisseur and sightseer. It holds beer festivals and quiz nights.
❀◖◗ ⊟≠ (Benson Rd)⊖ (Soho Rd)

Church Inn
22 Great Hampton Street (A41 from centre)
✪ 11.45-11; 12-3, 6-11 Sat; closed Sun
☎ (0121) 515 1851

website: communities.msn.com/thebestpubinbirmingham
Batham Best Bitter; Burton Bridge Old Expensive; Greene King Old Speckled Hen; guest beer H
Excellent, old-fashioned pub near the city centre. Over 160 years old, it enjoys a warranted reputation for its excellent food – there is an extensive menu and the portions are huge. Choose from over 80 whiskies, mostly single malts. The bar is divided into two and shares one serving bar; many superb old photographs adorn the walls. Another small bar, with its collection of film star photographs, is opened on request.
◖◗ 咠⇌ (Jewellery Qtr/Snow Hill) ⊖ (St Pauls)

Red Lion ☆
94-95 Warstone Lane
✪ 12-11 (8.30 Mon-Wed winter); 12-10.30 (5 winter) Sun
☎ (0121) 236 8371
Beer range varies H
Old-fashioned, two-bar local boasting an elaborate mirrored bar-back and etched windows. Situated in Birmingham's famous Jewellery Quarter, the bar features a collection of drinking vessels and books behind the bar. The public bar floor has a noticeable slope. 咠&⇌ (Jewellery Qtr) ⊖

White House
99 New John Street West (off A41 near Hockley Circus)
✪ 11-11; 12-10.30 Sun
☎ (0121) 523 0782
Beer range varies H
Unusual to find a real ale pub on a council estate, but this is no ordinary pub. It has one bar, divided into two: one half is a carpeted lounge and the other half is a typical public bar with basic furniture. The pub has no handpumps, except for the one guest beer that changes frequently and is always from local independent brewers. The pub is almost exclusively used by estate residents and can be difficult to find.
◖⇌ (Jewellery Qtr) ⊖ ♣

KINGS HEATH ❄

Station
7 High Street
✪ 11-11; 12-10.30 Sun
☎ (0121) 444 1257
Ind Coope Burton Ale; Tetley Bitter; guest beer (occasional) H
Friendly and comfortably-furnished local on the edge of a busy shopping area. The pub draws a mixed crowd and is in an area with a high student population. Generous portions of food are served. Live music is sometimes performed, and a room is set aside for sporting events.
◖咠

LADYWOOD

Fiddle & Bone
4 Sheepcote Street
✪ 11-11; 12-10.30 Sun
☎ (0121) 200 2223 website: www.fiddle-bone.co.uk
Marston's Pedigree; Theakston Bitter; guest beer H
Old school house, renovated by two ex-Birmingham City Symphony Orchestra musicians, into a popular two-storey pub, with a total music theme in its four bars. The lower level opens on to the canal, with a patio and courtyard; the

upper level has wooden floorboards and hosts free live music nightly (jazz, blues, even skiffle). Note the Trombone lights above the bar. An artists' residence next door has craft workshops and it is handy for the National Indoor Arena. An excellent range of meals is served in the restaurant (not Sun eve). Fiddler's Pluck is Courage Directors rebadged.
❀◖◗ &⇌ (New St/Five Ways) P

MOSELEY

Prince of Wales
118 Alcester Road
✪ 11-11; 12-10.30 Sun
☎ (0121) 449 4198
Ansells Mild; Marston's Pedigree; Ind Coope Burton Ale H
Cosy, unspoilt, three-roomed pub in a cosmopolitan and youthful district of Birmingham. A popular community local, largely unchanged since the turn of the last century, it is one of a dwindling band of pubs serving Ansells Mild on handpump.
Q ❀ 咠 ♣

BLACKHEATH

Bell & Bear Inn
71 Gorsty Hill Road, Rowley Regis (A4099)
✪ 11-11; 11-3, 6-11 Sat; 12-3, 7-10.30 Sun
☎ (0121) 561 2196
Greene King Old Speckled Hen; Highgate Dark; Ind Coope Burton Ale; Taylor Landlord; Tetley Bitter; Wood's Special H
The entrance of this 400-year-old listed building leads, via a stuffed bear, into one large irregular area for drinks and meals. In an alcove is an area licensed for children's meals (till 9pm) and one for non-smoking drinkers alongside. To the rear of the pub lies a terrace, complemented by an extensive garden affording views out over the Black Country – as far as Wenlock Edge on a clear day. No food on Sun eve.
⛺ ❀ ⌂ ◖◗ ⇌ (Old Hill) P ⌿

Lighthouse
153 Coombes Road, Halesowen (A4009, ½ mile from A45 jct)
✪ 12-11; 12-10.30 Sun
☎ (0121) 602 1620
Enville Ale; Greene King IPA, Abbot H
Eye-catching pub one entire end wall is painted to depict a lighthouse. The L-shaped bar is extended by a lower level row of alcoves, with tables: usually live music is performed here Wed eve, and a monthly blues night (first Sun). Numerous wall-hangings bear a nautical flavour; note, too the ship's figurehead and the lighthouse pictured on a stained glass window. This 18th-century pub was known as the Throttler, having once been run by the local hangman. No food Mon or Sat eves. A portable skittle alley is for hire. Wheelchair WC.
❀◖◗ &⇌ (Old Hill) ♣ 🐾 P

Waterfall
132 Waterfall Lane, Rowley Regis
✪ 12-3, 5-11; 12-11 Fri & Sat; 12-10.30 Sun
☎ (0121) 561 3499
Batham Best Bitter; Cains FA; Enville Ale; Holden's Special Bitter; Hook Norton Old Hooky; Marston's

Pedigree; guest beers Ⓗ

Regular *Guide* entry and former local CAMRA *Pub of the Year*, the Waterfall is situated on a steep hill. It has had a varied past, and for a period in the 1970s lay derelict. Happily, a change of ownership, plus greater emphasis on real ales (three guests) has transformed the pub into a thriving hostelry. The bar has a popular dartboard, the lounge is complemented by a no-smoking area, and the garden offers views over the Black Country. It is noted locally for the quality of its home cooking.
✿◑▶ ⊖♣ ♠P✂

BLOXWICH ✤

Turf Tavern ☆
13 Wolverhampton Road
✿ 12-3, 7-11; 12-3, 7-10.30 Sun
☎ (01922) 407745

Highgate Mild or Holden's Mild, Bitter; RCH Pitchfork; guest beer Ⓗ

Known locally as Tinky's after the current licensee's grandfather, this Grade II listed, three-roomed unspoilt gem has been owned by the same family for 130 years. The last major refurbishment was in 1921 when the outside toilet block was built. Unusual seating in the bar and smoke room, plus William Morris-style wallpaper, underseat heating pipes and a tiled floor add to the genuine character of this terraced pub, a quiet haven from the hustle and bustle of modern life. The two milds are alternated – Walsall CAMRA *Pub of the Year* 2000.
⌂Q✿⊖≠

BRIERLEY HILL ✤

Bell
172 Delph Road (off A4100)
✿ 12-11; 12-3, 7-10.30 Sun
☎ (01384) 572376

Draught Bass; Greene King Abbot; Taylor Landlord; Tetley Bitter; guest beer Ⓗ

Traditional two-roomed local at the foot of the eight locks on the Dudley Canal, known as the Delph Nine. The bar to the right of the front entrance still bears remnants of the period in the recent past when the pub was part of the now defunct Holt, Plant & Deakin chain. A blackboard behind the bar indicates the choice of snacks available. There is also a comfy lounge. The pleasant garden hosts barbecues in summer.
⌂✿⊖♣P

Vine (Bull & Bladder)
10 Delph Road (off A4100)
✿ 12-11; 12-10.30 Sun
☎ (01384) 78293

Batham Mild, Best Bitter, XXX Ⓗ

Famous Black Country brewery tap at the top of the Delph Run, whose imposing frontage proclaims the Shakespearian quotation: *'Blessing of your heart, you brew good ale'*. The unspoilt front bar lies on the right of the central passageway, while on the left is the extension into the former butcher's shop that won CAMRA's *Joe Goodwin* award for refurbishment in 1996, when the pub also took the local CAMRA *Pub of the Year* award. The small family room doubles as a food service area for the excellent snacks and meals available weekday lunchtimes. ⌂✿◑▶⊖♣P

CATHERINE DE BARNES

Boat Inn
222 Hampton Lane
✿ 11.30-11; 12-10.30 Sun
☎ (0121) 705 0474

Courage Directors; Tetley Bitter; Theakston Best Bitter; guest beers Ⓗ

Part of the Miller's Kitchen chain, the Boat originally stood next to the Grand Union Canal, but after a fire it was relocated further up the road, although it is still ideally situated for boaters. Local CAMRA *Pub of the Year* 2001, the pub hosts a wide range of activities including food theme nights and race nights and has a large family dining area, catering well for children. Look out for regular promotions including reduced price meals.
▷✿◑▶♣♠P

COLLEY GATE

Why Not
Why Not Street (½ mile from A458, Windmill Hill)
✿ 12-3, 6-11; 12-11 Sat; 12-3, 7-10.30 Sun
☎ (01384) 561019

Banks's Original; Batham Best Bitter; guest beers Ⓗ

Rambling, pleasant local tucked away in a side street on the edge of the Black Country. Refurbished in 1999, the pub comprises a front lounge favoured by drinkers and several smaller areas popular with diners. The lounge benefits from a real fire and houses two large glass cabinets, one containing a bottle collection, the other miniatures. Copperware, bric-à-brac and pot plants combine to make the dining areas a pleasant environment in which to enjoy the excellent menu.
⌂✿◑▶♣♠

COSELEY ✤

White House
1 Daisy Street (B4163)
✿ 11-3, 6-11; 12-3, 7-10.30 Sun
☎ (01902) 402703

Ansells Mild; Greene King Abbot; Tetley Bitter; guest beers Ⓗ

Well off the beaten track, this cosy, family-run free house lies in the now suburban hinterland between Dudley, Wolverhampton and Bilston. An imposing structure, dominating the crossroads, on entering you experience a kind of reverse-Tardis effect, the interior consisting of a tiny snug/bar and a slightly larger lounge. Behind the pub is a pleasant garden. Two proper guest ales supplement the regular range. Good value food is available lunchtime and early eve (not Sun).
⌂✿◑▶≠⊖(Loxdale St)♣

COVENTRY ✤

Biggin Hall
214 Binley Road (A427, 2½ miles E of centre)
✿ 10.30-11; 12-10.30 Sun
☎ (024) 7645 1046

Banks's Original, Bitter; Marston's Bitter, Pedigree; guest beer Ⓗ

Prominent roadside, community pub, built in the 1920s in mock-Tudor style. In the front bar darts, cards and dominoes are played regularly, and a large-screen TV shows major sporting events; the games room houses a pool table. The back lounge, apart from redecoration, has been practically untouched since the pub opened and has wooden panelled walls. The locally famous central table has 'seating rights' which have been respected over the years. Good value Sun lunches served. An upstairs room hosts regular jazz eves. Q✿❀◖◗⊞♣P

Chestnut Tree

113 Craven Street, Chapelfields (vehicle access is from Hearsall Lane, B4101)
✪ 12 (11 Sat)-11; 12-10.30 Sun
☎ (024) 7667 5830

Courage Directors; John Smith's Bitter; guest beers Ⓗ

Popular drinking pub on the famous Craven Street crawl in the former watch-making district. Regularly changing guest beers from independent brewers, a traditional cider and a choice of some 200 malt whiskies add to its appeal. Breakfast is served, plus an excellent Sun lunch (no meals Sun eve). The pleasant lounge is used primarily for food on Sun lunchtimes, the traditional bar has a pool table in the games area, and a big-screen TV for sport. The pleasant back patio is shaded by a chestnut tree – hence the name.

✿◖◗⊞♣◗P

Craven Arms

58 Craven Street, Chapelfields (1 mile from centre, off B4106)
✪ 11 (4 Tue)-11; 12-4, 7-10.30 Sun
☎ (024) 7671 5308

Flowers Original; guest beers Ⓗ

Popular community pub with friendly bar staff, in the old watch-making area of the city, where some of the buildings retain their original 'top shops'. The area was featured in a *Time Team* TV programme. Live entertainment is provided Sun eve and a quiz Thu. There is a welcoming fire in winter and an outdoor barbecue on the patio in summer, with food provided. Pool and darts are played in a games area.

🏨✿◖♣

Flying Standard

2-10 Trinity Street
✪ 11-11; 12-10.30 Sun
☎ (024) 7655 5723

Banks's Bitter; Boddingtons Bitter; Courage Directors; Shepherd Neame Spitfire; Theakston Best Bitter; guest beers Ⓗ

This large Wetherspoon's pub is one of the latest additions to the city's real ale scene. Its decor is mainly based on Coventry memorabilia including the legendary Lady Godiva. There are two no-smoking areas, one is upstairs, where a reduced choice of beer is available. There is also a small outside terrace on the upper floor. However this gets very busy weekend eves. Coventry City FC home matches add to the crowd Sat afternoons. It is near Coventry's two cathedrals and the Transport Museum.

Q✿◖◗⚲✄●

Gatehouse Tavern

46 Hill Street (near Belgrade Theatre)
✪ 11-3, 5-11; 11-11 Thu-Sat; 12-4, 7-10.30 Sun
☎ (024) 7663 0140

Draught Bass; Fuller's London Pride; guest beer Ⓗ

Built in 1866 as the former gatehouse of the

Leigh Mill, home to the North Warwickshire Worsted and Woollen Spinning Co, it was rebuilt to the original design by the landlord and opened as a pub in 1995. The rugby-mad boss has incorporated windows featuring the emblems of the Six Nations. This free house (rare in Coventry) boasts one of the few pub gardens in the centre; it can get busy in summer. Guest beers are usually from the extensive Church End range. No food Sat, or Sun eve.

✿◖◗

Malt Shovel

93 Spon End, Chapelfields (B4101, off inner ring road, jct 7)
✪ 12 (4 winter Mon-Tue)-11; 12-10.30 Sun
☎ (024) 7622 0204

Donnington SBA; Tetley Bitter; guest beers Ⓗ

Traditional pub circa 1800: a wood-panelled, four-roomed pub, where three of the rooms are served by a central bar; the fourth room is upstairs and opens Fri and Sat eves, concentrating on continental beers. The pub's guest beers include at least two from the local Church End Brewery, it is also the only outlet in the area for Donnington SBA. The decor reflects the pub's long history and features paintings by the landlord. Enormous roast dinners are available Sun lunchtime. 🏨✿◖P

Nursery Tavern

38-39 Lord Street, Chapelfields (1 mile W of centre)
✪ 11-11; 12-10.30 Sun
☎ (024) 7667 4530

Banks's Bitter; Courage Bitter; Greene King Abbot; John Smith's Bitter; Wells Bombardier; guest beers Ⓗ

Family-run pub where the bar and lounge are served by a central bar, the third room is quieter, welcomes families, and doubles as a restaurant Sun lunchtimes. Full breakfasts are available at weekends (11-12); traditional Sun roasts (12-2.30) are excellent value. Diverse activities include the Formula 1 Club and a fanatical rugby supporters' association; monthly quiz nights and 'free and easy' nights are held and regular brewery trips are organised. Q⚯✿◖♣●

Old Windmill

22-23 Spon Street
✪ 11-11; 12-3, 7-10.30 Sun
☎ (024) 7625 2183

Banks's Bitter; Courage Directors; Greene King Old Speckled Hen; Marston's Pedigree; Wells Bombardier; guest beers Ⓗ

One of the oldest pubs in Coventry, at the heart of medieval Spon Street. The original bar has been converted into a snug, with the old brewery now a back room retaining its brewing vessel as a main feature. The flagstone floor between the bar and toilets is all that remains of the old courtyard. Popular with the Coventry folk scene, it stages regular music nights. Close by is the newly-opened Skydome Complex, with a multi-screen cinema and ice-skating rink. This makes the pub very busy at weekends. 🏨Q◖

Royal Oak

28 Earlsdon Street, Earlsdon
✪ 5-11; 12-3, 7-10.30 Sun
☎ (024) 7667 4140

Ansells Mild; Draught Bass; Tetley Bitter; guest beers ⊞

Busy, popular pub. Note the bar top and large clock in the front bar that are both made from slate. No need to queue at the bar during busy periods as table service is provided. The spacious back bar has a fireplace based on an original at the Dutch Oranjeboom Brewery. The award-winning rear patio is festooned with magnificent hanging baskets and has been canopied to provide a pleasant drinking area in summer irrespective of the weather. ♨Q❀

Town Wall Tavern
Bond Street (behind Belgrade Theatre)
✪ 11-11; 12-10.30 Sun
☎ (024) 7622 0963
Draught Bass; M&B Brew XI; guest beers ⊞
Friendly, three-roomed pub comprising a public bar, lounge (both with real fires) and the smallest snug in the city which is known to everyone as the 'Donkey Box'. The landlord has taken out the nitro-keg fonts as a matter of principle. A guest beer policy introduced when he took over has proved so successful that a second guest beer has now been made available. Several windows bear the crest of the long-defunct Atkinson's Brewery. ♨Q❂◁⊟♣

CRADLEY HEATH

Moon Under Water
164-166 High Street (A4100)
✪ 11-11; 12-10.30 Sun
☎ (01384) 565419
Banks's Original; Courage Directors; Shepherd Neame Spitfire; Theakston Best Bitter; Wadworth 6X; guest beers ⊞
Traditional-style Wetherspoon's at the centre of a busy shopping area. The decor includes many items of local historical interest, mostly celebrating the town's chain-making industry. A paved outdoor drinking area with a water feature, ivy-clad wall and rustic furniture add to its appeal. The standard Wetherspoon's menu, plus daily specials are served until 10pm daily.

There are good bus links, and the pub is only 10 minutes' walk from the station. Q❀◁▷&≠⚥✦●

DARLASTON

Fallings Heath Tavern
248 Walsall Road (A4038)
✪ 12-3, 7.15-11; 12-2.30, 7.30-10.30 Sun
☎ (0121) 526 3403
Ansells Mild, Bitter; guest beer ⊞
Three-roomed roadside pub, built in 1937, between Darlaston and Walsall. The bar is noted for its pig memorabilia. A family room adjoins the garden. The lounge is quiet and comfortable. There is also an off-licence at the front of the pub.
Q⛟❀⊟♣P⊟

DUDLEY ❖

Full Moon
58-60 High Street
✪ 10-11; 12-10.30 Sun
☎ (01384) 212294
Banks's Original; Enville Ale; Shepherd Neame Spitfire; Theakston Best Bitter; Wadworth 6X; guest beers ⊞
Wetherspoon's pub in the town centre, five minutes' walk through the market place from the bus station. Many framed articles and pictures illustrating local history decorate the walls. Food, from the standard Wetherspoon's menu, plus specials are served until 10pm. Converted from a former Pizzaland restaurant in 1996, it has become a very popular venue for drinkers of all ages. Q◁▷⚥✦●

HALESOWEN

Hawne Tavern
76 Attwood Street (off A458 near football ground)
✪ 12-2.30, 5-11; 12-11 Sat; 12-10.30 Sun
☎ (0121) 602 2601
Banks's Original, Bitter; Ⓟ **guest beers** ⊞
Now a regular in this *Guide*, the Hawne is a traditional local situated down a side street off the main Birmingham-Stourbridge bus route, one mile out of the town. Up to six

INN BRIEF

COSELEY
Painters Arms
Avenue Road
11-midnight;
12-3, 7-10.30 Sun
Holden's Mild, Bitter, Ⓟ
Special Bitter ⊞
Popular community pub handy for the station and Wolverhampton Canal. Lunchtime food available (not Sun).

COVENTRY
Alexander Wines (off-licence)
112 Berkeley Road South
10-2, 5.30-10.30;
11.30-2.30,
7-10.30 Sun
Independent off-licence stocking over 200 beers, about 50 of which are bottle-conditioned.

Boat
31 Shilton Lane
12-3, 5-11; 12-11 Sat; 12-10.30
(12-3.30, 7-10.30 winter) Sun
Draught Bass; M&B Brew XI ⊞
Old-fashioned, three-roomed pub, set back from the road in a semi-rural location, enjoying a loyal following. Well worth a visit.

Herald
Sir Henry Parkes Road, Canley
11-11; 12-10.30 Sun
Tetley Bitter; guest beer ⊞
Local with a comfortable lounge and a sports-orientated bar. Food is available lunchtime and eves (not Sun eve).

Whitefriars Olde Ale House
114-115 Gosford Street
11-11; 3-10.30 Sun
Greene King Old Speckled Hen; Marston's Pedigree; Tetley Bitter; guest beers ⊞
One of Coventry's oldest buildings, circa 1335, recently restored and opened as a pub. A gem. Simple food is available weekdays 12-7.

DUDLEY
Lamp Tavern
116 High Street
12-11;
12-10.30 Sun
Batham Mild, Best Bitter, XXX ⊞
Lively, two-roomed local, offering weekday lunches, regular live music and accommodation. The front bar has been sympathetically refurbished.

PENSNETT
Fox & Grapes
176 High Street
12-11; 12-10.30 Sun
Batham Mild, Best Bitter, XXX ⊞
Recent addition to the Batham's Nine, replacing the nearby Hollybush, an open-plan boozer near the hospital.

QUARRY BANK
Nailmakers Arms
36 High Street
11-11; 12-10.30 Sun
Banks's Bitter, Cains Dr Duncan's IPA; guest beers ⊞
A former HP&D pub known as the Church Tavern. Remains as lively and unpretentious as ever.

SOLIHULL
Hogshead
28-30 Station Road
11-11; 12-10.30 Sun
Boddingtons Bitter; Brakspear Bitter; Marston's Pedigree; Wadworth 6X; guest beers ⊞/Ⓖ
Modern Hogshead, serving a good selection of wines and Belgian beers. Gets busy late eves.

real ales are dispensed in the games-orientated bar and comfortable small lounge. Regular beer festivals are organised by the landlord who obviously takes pride in his work. The area around the pub (Short Cross) is steeped in history especially mining and button-making.
Q ❀ ◑ ♣ P

Somer's Sports & Social Club
The Grange, Grange Hill (B4551/A456 jct)
❀ 12-2.30, 6-11; 12-2, 7-10.30 Sun
☎ (0121) 550 1645
Banks's Original, Bitter; Batham's Mild, Best Bitter; Tetley Bitter; guest beers Ⓗ
2001 CAMRA National *Club of the Year,* it occupies a large house on the edge of town, providing tennis courts and a football pitch. The drinking area is served by a long bar, off which is a large, comfortable alcove adorned with pictures of old local pubs and cases of sports trophies. To gain admission, visitors should immediately identify themselves to the steward or his staff, producing this *Guide* or CAMRA their membership card. Groups of five or more should phone first. ☙ ❀

Waggon & Horses
21 Stourbridge Road (A458. 1/4 mile from bus station)
❀ 12-11; 12-10.30 Sun
☎ (0121) 550 4989
Batham Best Bitter; Enville Ale; guest beers Ⓗ
Every day is a beer festival here, with 15 real ales on tap, constantly changing with some rarely seen beers. Situated between Birmingham and Stourbridge, on the main bus route, just out of the town centre, it is a must to be included on any Black Country crawl and is handy for the town's football ground. Three distinct drinking areas are served from the long bar. A local skiffle group, which includes the licensee, performs here occasionally. A selection of fruit wines supplements the ales.
♣ ●

KINGSWINFORD

Park Tavern
182 Cot Lane (1/2 mile from Kingswinford Cross)
❀ 12-11; 12-3, 7-10.30 Sun
☎ (01384) 287178
Ansells Bitter; Batham Best Bitter; guest beers Ⓗ
Former Ansell's house, now part of the Pubmaster group, it has two good-sized rooms – a comfy lounge and not-so-basic bar where televised sporting events are enthusiastically followed. This pub caters for all types of drinker. For those taking an interest in glass-making history, the Broadfield House Glass Museum is close by, part of the region's Black Country tour.
❀ ⊟ ♣ P

Union
Water Street (off A4101/A491)
❀ 12-3 (4.30 Sat), 7-11; 12-4, 7-10.30 Sun
☎ (01384) 830668
Banks's Original, Bitter Ⓟ
This old, established, late Victorian local is well worth seeking out, roughly 10 minutes' walk from the centre of Kingswinford, which is served by several bus routes from Dudley, Stourbridge and Wolverhampton. There is just one L-shaped room where crib

and dominoes are played. The traditional walled garden has regularly won the brewery's *Best Garden* award. The present licensee was born in the pub and took over the licence from her father in 1962.
❀ ♣ P ⊟

KNOWLE

Vaults
St John's Close
❀ 12-2.30, 5-11; 11-11 Sat; 12-10.30 Sun
☎ (01564) 773656
Ansells Mild; Greene King IPA; Ind Coope Burton Ale; Tetley Bitter; guest beers Ⓗ
Traditional pub, just off the picturesque High Street, one of the few in the area offering real cider (Weston's) and the increasingly rare Burton Ale. Oak beams, horse brasses and old settles give a cosy, old-fashioned atmosphere; note the collection of breweriana. The bar at the rear is favoured by many regulars and houses the bar billiards table and dartboard. In the 1990s the pub was the venue for two local CAMRA beer fests, and now hosts occasional festivals of its own.
❀ ◑ ♣ ●

LOWER GORNAL

Black Bear
86 Deepdale Lane
❀ 5-11; 12-4.30, 7-11 Sat; 12-3.30, 7-10.30 Sun
☎ (01384) 253333
Shepherd Neame Best Bitter; guest beers Ⓗ
This community pub has been untouched by brewery or pub co for over 20 years, and has evolved, through private ownership, into a drinking establishment of diverse character. Originally an 18th-century farmhouse it has been integrated into the built-up area behind the Milking Bank estate. It offers two to four guest beers, depending on demand. There is also a good whisky selection. Ten minutes' uphill walk from Gornal bus station, buses from Dudley, Woverhampton and Stourbridge stop here.
🚗 ❀ ●

Fountain
8 Temple Street (A4175, off A459)
❀ 12-3, 6-11; 12-11 Fri & Sat; 12-4, 7-10.30 Sun
☎ (01384) 242777
Enville Ale; Everards Original; Holden's Golden Glow, Special Bitter; guest beers Ⓗ
Genuine Black Country free house offering up to nine real ales, at least two real ciders, bottled Belgian classics and numerous fruit wines. A sympathetic extension at the rear of the pub has added a new kitchen and dining area, enabling the provision of a wide range of meals and snacks, including vegetarian options (no food Sun eve). It organises two beer festivals each year (Easter and Oct). It stands on the 257 bus route from Dudley.
❀ ◑ ♣ ●

MERIDEN

Queen's Head
Old Road (off Coventry road, 1/2 mile E of town)
OS250820
❀ 12-11; 12-3, 7-10.30 Sun
☎ (01676) 522256

Draught Bass; M&B Brew XI; guest beer [H]

Large, single-roomed pub on the old main road to Coventry, now a single track lane. It claims to be the oldest recorded inn in Meriden, the town that is reputed to be at the very heart of England. Popular with locals, this traditional country pub is adorned by many horse brasses, early pictures of the pub and other memorabilia. One regularly changing guest beer is always available.

❀◖P

NETHERTON

Old Swan

89 Halesowen Road (A459)

✪ 11-11; 12-10.30 Sun

☎ (01384) 253075

Old Swan Dark Swan, Entire [H]

After many troubled years this classic pub is once again flourishing and the bar has been returned to its former glory, retaining an enamelled ceiling and etched mirrors depicting swans. The rear snug is cosiness itself. The newly refurbished brewery is recreating Mrs Pardoe's home brew, in addition to a premium bitter, also based on a much-missed local favourite. Black Country humour is the order of the day, and be prepared for a singalong when the landlord plays the piano. On the 247 bus route from Dudley.

▲Q◖◖◖P

OLDBURY

Waggon & Horses ☆

Church Street

(off A4034, 3/4 mile from M5 jct 2)

✪ 12-3, 5-11; 12-3, (closed eve) Sun

☎ (0121) 552 5467

Enville White; Holden's Mild, Special Bitter; Marston's Pedigree; Weatheroak Ale; guest beers [H]

Late Victorian, Grade II listed town-centre pub a few minutes' walk from the bus station, it is also close to the Birmingham Canal. The main bar boasts its original tiled interior, panelled copper ceiling (which is painted), and mirrored shelving behind the bar. A further drinking area where children are welcome also bears original features. Locals use the tiled passageway for drinking too.

Look out for Holt Brewery etched windows. A large selection of meals and snacks is available (no food Sun, or Mon eve). The pub is popular with the local business community.

▲◔◖◖⇌ (Sandwell & Dudley)

RUSHALL

Farmer's Boy

Barns Lane (from Walsall along A461 to Birds timber yard, right for 1/4 mile)

✪ 12-11; 12-10.30 Sun

☎ (01922) 629660

Ansells Mild, Bitter; guest beers (occasional) [H]

Occasional guest ales complement the regular Ansells' beers at this genuine estate pub where locals meet. It does not get a lot of passing trade, but there is always a warm welcome for a new face. It fields darts, pool, crib and domino teams and also adult and children's football teams. Quiz is held every Fri; entertainment staged on Sat eve.

SEDGLEY

Beacon Hotel ☆

129 Bilston Street (A463)

✪ 12-3, 6-11; 12-3, 7-10.30 Sun

☎ (01902) 883380

Hughes Pale Amber, Surprise, Dark Ruby, Snowflake; guest beer [H]

Faithfully restored Victorian brewery tap where four rooms surround an island bar, cloaked in snob screens. A door from the large lounge leads to a well-stocked conservatory, beyond which lies Sarah Hughes' Brewery. A single guest ale supplements the brewery's full range, along with a couple of bottled Belgian ales. The walled garden is popular with families, who are also welcome in an annexe at the rear of the pub. It is accessible by 558/545 bus.

Q◔❀◖P

SHELFIELD

Four Crosses

1 Green Lane (off A461)

Banks's Original, Bitter; [P] **guest beers** [H]

Imposing free-standing pub over 200 years old; part of the building was once a blacksmith's. On entering the pub the visitor will find mosaic flooring and stained glass, remnants of a bygone age of pub construction. The traditional saloon bar is warmed by a coal fire, the guest beers are dispensed in the quieter comfortable lounge. Children, accompanied by adults, may use the passageway.

▲❀◖P

SHIRLEY

Bernie's Real Ale Off-Licence

266 Cranmore Boulevard

(just off A3400)

✪ 12-2 (not Mon), 6-10; 12-2, 7-9.30 Sun

☎ (0121) 744 2827

Beer range varies [H]/[P]

In an area that often disappoints for beer range and quality, this refreshingly different off-licence is an oasis for beer lovers. Run by father and son, who have an infectious enthusiasm and knowledge about ale, the draught beer range varies, and you are encouraged to try before you buy! Among the regulars are superb beers from the likes of Slaters, Timothy Taylor, Oakham, Rooster's, Hop Back and RCH, plus bottled beers. Bernie's has enjoyed 18 consecutive years in this *Guide*.

Red Lion

171 Stratford Road

✪ 11-3, 5.30-11; 11-11 Sat; 12-3, 7-10.30 Sun

☎ (0121) 744 1030

Ansells Mild; Boddingtons Bitter; Marston's Pedigree; Tetley Bitter; guest beer [H]

Do not be put off by the exterior of this boxy 1960s pub (the original Red Lion was a coaching inn). The interior of this Red Lion was refurbished some time ago and is no longer 60s plastic. The front room is divided into three distinct areas – one no-smoking. The back room has a pool table, juke box and six-foot TV screen for sports events. The single guest beer is usually either Hydes' Light or Slaters', although a beer from a local brewery is sometimes available. No food Sun. ◖✄

SHORT HEATH

Duke of Cambridge
82 Coltham Road
✪ 12-3.30 (4 Sat), 7 (7.30 Sat)-11; 12-3.30,
7.30-10.30 Sun
☎ (01922) 408895
Draught Bass; Greene King Old Speckled Hen; ⊞
Highgate Mild; Worthington Bitter; ℗ **guest beers** ⊞
This three-roomed, family-run, free house,
originally a farm cottage, has been a pub
since the 1820s. The public bar has a wood-
burning fire and a display of commercial
vehicle models. The lounge is split into two
halves, with an aquarium in the dividing
wall and original beams exposed in the
front half. Both bar and lounge have an
electronic air cleaner. There is a pool table
in the spacious family room. Bar snacks
(rolls) are available lunchtime. ⌷Q❀⌷♣P

STOURBRIDGE ❄

Hogshead
21-26 Foster Street (off ring road, near bus and
rail stations)
✪ 12-11; 12-10.30 Sun
☎ (01384) 370140
**Boddingtons Bitter; Enville White; Marston's Pedigree;
guest beers** ⊞
Formerly a newspaper office, this large,
single-roomed pub has a long bar, where
various seating areas on two levels and
wood floors add character. There is a TV for
live sporting events, and low background
music; it hosts a regular quiz on Tue. A 20p
per pint reduction on beer for card-carrying
CAMRA members is a bonus. The cider
range varies with two choices usually
available. A well-priced menu includes
adventurous specials as well as standard
Hogshead fare. ❀◖❀⌷≠♦⌕

New Inn
2 Cherry Street (off B4186, via Glebe Lane)
✪ 2 (12 Sat)-11; 12-10.30 Sun
☎ (01384) 393323 e-mail: rjvickers@msm.com
**Adnams Bitter; Ansells Mild; Draught Bass; Enville Ale;
Greene King Abbot** ⊞
It is worth finding this gem, situated in a
quiet residential area, for its range of beers.
Choice is the landlord's watchword and he
keeps an enviable selection of single malt
whiskies and vodkas. The food on offer
(Tue-Fri) is based on international cuisine;

one example, resulting from a customer
request, was a 'curry and fresh mussel
night', which has since been repeated.
There are good quality sound systems in
both rooms and a TV in the bar.
❀◖⌷♣P

Shrubbery Cottage
28 Heath Lane, Oldswinford (B4186, ¼ mile W
of A491 jct)
✪ 12-11; 12-3, 7-10.30 (12-10.30 summer) Sun
☎ (01384) 377598
Holden's Mild, Bitter, Special Bitter; guest beer ⊞
A *Guide* regular, dedicated to good ale and
conversation – no juke box or dartboard to
detract from the friendly atmosphere.
Situated near the town's college, it is
frequented by all ages who mix well. The
landlord is keen on golf as the pub's
artefacts reveal. Occasional quizzes are held.
The rear room can be hired. The guest beer
may be replaced by Holden's XB.
Q❀◖≈ (Junction) ♦P

SUTTON COLDFIELD

Duke Inn
Duke Street, Maney (off Birmingham road)
✪ 11-11; 12-10.30 Sun
☎ (0121) 355 1767
**Ansells Mild, Bitter; Greene King Abbot; Ind Coope
Burton Ale; Tetley Bitter;** ⊞
Excellent, traditional back-street local,
unspoilt, except for Sky TV in the bar, but
in need of refurbishment. Frequented by a
cross-section of regulars and visitors, it is
the only pub in the town where chat is not
drowned by music. The large garden at the
rear is well used, and enjoyed by young and
old alike. The beer quality is not
compromised by food odours; the range
includes the popular Ansells Mild, not
found now in town pubs.
Q❀⌷♣

Laurel Wines
63 Westwood Road (near Sutton Park)
✪ 12-2, 5.30-10.30; 12-10.30 Sat; 12-2, 7-10 Sun
☎ (0121) 353 0399
Batham Bitter; guest beers ⒢
Real ale off-licence; a frequently changed
selection and taste samples make this
strongly recommended. There is also a wide
range of British and European bottled beers.
♦P

INN BRIEF

STOURBRIDGE
Red Lion
Lion Street
12-3.30, 7-11; 12-11 Sat;
12-3, 7-10.30 Sun
**Draught Bass; Enville White;
guest beer** (occasional) ⊞
Well-established pub, just off the
ring road. Good quality food is
served in a designated
dining area.

Royal Exchange
75 Enville Street (A458)
1 (12 Sat & summer)-11;
12-10.30 Sun
**Batham Mild, Best Bitter;
seasonal beers** ⊞
Terraced pub on a busy road, with
a basic, lively bar and a small, quiet
lounge.

WALSALL
Lane Arms
169 Wolverhampton Road West
12-3, 5-11; 12-11 Fri & Sat;
12-11 Sun
**Highgate Dark, Bitter, Saddlers; guest
beer** (occasional) ⊞
Large, multi-roomed 1930s
roadhouse, with a small
comfortable snug, sports-orientated
bar and a large lounge hosting
entertainment. No food Sun.

Red Lion
69 Park Street
10.30-11; 12-3 (closed eve) Sun
Banks's Bitter; Marston's Pedigree ⊞
Town-centre pub near the bus and
rail stations, built in 1815 with a
listed exterior. Lunches served
Mon-Sat. Summertime pavement
tables.

WEDNESBURY
Old Blue Ball
19 Hall End Road
12-3, 5-11; 12-11 Fri; 11.15 5, 7-11 Sat;
12-3, 7-10.30 Sun
Draught Bass; Everards Original; ⊞
Highgate Dark; Stones Bitter; ℗ **guest
beer** ⊞
Friendly, traditional local, with a
bar, snug and family room. The
garden is ideal for summer. Sky TV.

WILLENHALL
Malthouse
The Dale, New Road
11-11; 12-10.30 Sun
**Banks's Original, Bitter; Courage Directors;
Theakston Best Bitter; guest beers** ⊞
Former cinema/bingo hall, given
the Wetherspoon's treatment;
friendly atmosphere. Meals served
all day. *Cask Marque* accredited.

TIPTON

Port 'n' Ale

178 Horseley Heath (A461, 300 yds from Gt Bridge bus station)

⏵ 12-3, 5-11; 12-11 Fri & Sat; 12-4.30, 7-10.30 Sun

Greene King Abbot; RCH Pitchfork, Double Header; guest beers H

Three-roomed free house on the main Dudley-West Bromwich road, where the clientele ranges from 18 to 80. Biker-friendly, the pub is a base for a local motorcycle action group and a bike club, the Moonshiners. The pub offers three guest ales, plus two real ciders, while connoisseurs of the hard stuff will find a range of 20 malt whiskies. A computer is available for customers to use. It is accessible by 74 bus from Birmingham or Dudley.
❀⌂≠(Dudley Port) ♣P

Rising Sun

116 Horseley Road (1/4 mile from Gt Bridge bus station)

⏵ 12-2.30 (3 Sat), 5-11; 12-3, 7-10.30 Sun

☎ (0121) 520 7033

Banks's Original, Bitter; Burton Bridge Bridge Bitter; guest beers H

CAMRA National *Pub of the Year* 1999 and local award-winner three years running, this superb free house is a must for any discerning drinker visiting the Black Country. It boasts an airy, high-ceilinged main bar and a cosier lounge. Out the back is a secluded courtyard which stages live music, theatrical events and an August Bank holiday beer festival. Excellent weekday lunches are available. Take bus 74 from Birmingham or Dudley and alight at Gt Bridge. ⚏❀⌂≠(Dudley Port) ♣♠⊟

UPPER GORNAL

Britannia Inn

109 Kent Street (A459)

⏵ 12-3 (4 Fri), 7-11; 12-11 Sat; 12-4, 7-10.30 Sun

☎ (01902) 883253

Batham Mild, Best Bitter, XXX H

Built in 1780, the pub boasts an unspoilt late 19th-century tap room where beer is served from pumps set against the wall. Only jovial banter disturbs the peaceful, smoke-free atmosphere of this room; like the livelier front bar, it is heated by coal fires in winter. The landlord regularly organises the famous 'Batham's Nine' outing – a must for Batham's lovers, visiting in one day all the brewery's nine tied pubs. The garden is a riot of colour in summer – an ideal place to enjoy the occasional barbecue. It stands on the 558 Dudley-Wolverhampton bus route. ⚏Q❀⌂♣≠

Jolly Crispin

Clarence Street (A459)

⏵ 12-3, 7-11; 12-3, 7-10.30 Sun

☎ (01902) 672220

Banks's Original; Courage Directors; Wells Bombardier; guest beers H

Comfortable free house, serving a wide range of guest ales. The public bar has a dartboard right by the door, beyond that a real fire banishes the winter cold from an imposing Gornal stone fireplace. The lounge, at the rear, offers a panoramic view of the Black Country. The 558 bus from Wolverhampton stops right outside the pub. ⚏Q⌂⌂♣P

WALSALL ❉

Hogshead

9-19 Leicester Street

⏵ 11.30-11 (1am Fri & Sat); 11.30-10.30 Sun

☎ (01902) 616963

Boddingtons Bitter; Fuller's London Pride; Greene King Old Speckled Hen; Marston's Pedigree; Wadworth 6X; guest beer H

A preserved red sandstone frontage hides a modern building right opposite the entrance to Walsall Town Hall, the current venue for Walsall's beer festival held in April. Although the interior is spacious, it can get very crowded, especially at weekends, and it is popular with the young. Eve meals finish at 8pm. ❀⌂♿≠

Rose & Crown

55 Old Birchills (off A34, near Canal Museum)

⏵ 11-11; 12-10.30 Sun

☎ (01922) 720533

Highgate Dark, Saddlers, seasonal beers H

This imposing Edwardian pub occupies a corner site. Restored a few years ago by Highgate Brewery, the long bar features an attractive bar-back incorporating a clock, some nice tiled friezes and other period details. There is a pool table in the lounge plus a corridor drinking area. It hosts live music Thu and Karaoke at weekends. Very

WOLLASTON

Princess

115 Bridgnorth Road

11-11;

12-3.30, 7-10.30 Sun

Banks's Original; Wadworth 6X; Wells Bombardier; guest beers H
Former M&B pub, now owned by Enterprise Inns, refurbished in traditional manner to appeal to all ages.

WOLVERHAMPTON

Clarendon Hotel

Chapel Ash

11-11;

12-10.30 Sun

Banks's Original, Bitter; P Marston's Pedigree; guest beer H
The imposing façade of this turn of the century Banks's brewery tap masks a much renovated interior.

Mitre

Lower Green, Tettenhall

12-2.30, 5.30-11; 12-11 Sat;

12-10.30 Sun

Banks's Original; Draught Bass; Greene King IPA H
Friendly and spacious pub off the A41 at the bottom of the 'rock'. A chalkboard shows food, steaks, etc, served weekdays.

Shoulder of Mutton

62 Wood Road, Tettenhall Wood

11.30-3, 5.30-11; 11-11 Sat;

12-3, 7-10.30 Sun

Banks's Original, Bitter; P Marston's Pedigree H
Large, modern pub with a beamed interior. Food is available lunchtime and eve Mon-Sat.

Wheatsheaf Hotel

Market Street

11-11 10.30-11 Sat;

12-3, 7-10.30 Sun

Banks's Original, Bitter P
Traditional, city-centre pub, the last in the centre to retain a public bar.

❉ symbol next to a main entry place name indicates there are Inn Brief entries as well.

much a lively local where you can experience a real slice of Walsall life, the pub is a short walk from an interesting little canal museum situated in an old boatman's chapel.
🏛⌂♣

Royal Oak
81 Lord Street
🕐 12-2.30, 5-11; 11-11 Fri & Sat; 12-10.30 Sun
☎ (01922) 645913 e-mail: fraank@talk21.com
Banks's Original; ℗ **Highgate Dark; Thwaites Daniel's Hammer, guest beers** Ⓗ
Three-roomed community pub, built in the 1930s: a lounge with a pool table, a quiet snug room at the front, and a spacious main bar. There is also a corridor bar. Entertainment is staged most weekends and barbecues held in summer.
🏛Q❀⌂≠ (Bescot Stadium) ♣

Tap & Spile
John Street (off B4210)
🕐 11-3, 5.30-11; 11-11 Fri & Sat; 12-3, 7-10.30 Sun
☎ (01922) 627660
Wells Eagle; guest beers Ⓗ
Friendly, Victorian, two-roomed pub with tiled frontage, known locally as the Pretty Bricks. Good value food is offered, with occasional 'gourmet' eves; no meals Sun, or Mon eve. Up to seven guest beers are stocked. It is convenient for the Magistrates' Court.
🏛Q◐⌂≠

Victoria
23 Lower Rushall Street
🕐 11-11; 12-3.30, 7-11 Sun
☎ (01922) 725848
Brains SA; Burton Bridge XL; Everards Tiger; Greene King IPA, Abbot; Marston's Pedigree; guest beers Ⓗ
Small, comfortable two-roomed ale house, totally free of tie, at the edge of the town centre. The landlord prides himself on serving 10 good honest cask ales from all around the country. Known locally as the Cats, it dates from the 1800s and retains the old brewhouse at the rear, now used for accommodation. This traditional public house has no juke box, gaming machines, dartboard (or lager louts). 🏛Q❀◐⌂

Walsall Arms
17 Bank Street (off A34 behind Royal Hotel)
🕐 12-3 (4 Sat)l 5 (6 Sat)-11; 12-5, 7-10.30 Sun
☎ (01922) 626660
Camerons Strongarm; Mansfield Dark Mild, Bitter; Marston's Bitter Ⓗ
A hidden gem, this terraced pub is hidden by industrial buildings. This three-roomed pub has a traditional quarry-tile floored saloon bar; the lounge, small and intimate, is popular with office staff at lunchtime. It also has an unusual back bar servery. The skittle alley doubles as a meeting room. All in all, it is an excellent back-street boozer.
◐⌂

Walsall Cricket Club
Gorway Road
🕐 7.30-11; 12-midnight Sat; 12-midnight (varies winter) Sun
☎ (01922) 622094
Adnams Bitter; Banks's Original; Marston's Bitter Ⓗ
Established in 1830, Walsall Cricket Club has occupied this site since 1907. It is affiliated with Walsall hockey, bowls and

bridge clubs. The comfortable lounge has a friendly, sporting atmosphere. For a large part of the week the bar is manned by members themselves. Four cricket teams, plus juniors, are supported and for matches in good weather the lounge is opened on to a patio area affording a view right across the green. Emphasis is placed on socials for the family. ❀♣P⊟

White Horse
Green Lane, Birchills (A34, 1 mile N of centre)
🕐 12-3, 5-11; 12-11 Fri; 11.30-11 Sat; 12-4, 7-10.30 Sun
☎ (01922) 631272
Banks's Original, Bitter ℗
The pub's regulars are heavily into social activities such as darts, crib, dominoes and weekly Karaoke nights. At least 100 years old, it boasts a comfortable bar with a surprisingly low ceiling. A tiny intimate snug can be found at the rear. The pub has developed a reputation for no-nonsense traditional food – the home-made steak and kidney pies are particularly popular.
❀◐P

White Lion
150 Sandwell Street (off A34 at Five Ways)
🕐 12-3, 6-11; 12-11 Sat; 12-5, 7-10.30 Sun
☎ (01922) 628542
Adnams Bitter; Ansells Mild, Bitter; Ind Coope Burton Ale; guest beers Ⓗ
Imposing Victorian street-corner pub, it features a traditional saloon bar with a sloping floor. The L-shaped room has a servery with a mahogany front and mirrored bar-back. The bar is the most popular room in the pub by far, where the art of conversation is practised. The lounge is more plush, featuring traditional red leather upholstery. The games room has two pool tables. ❀◐⌂♣

WEDNESFIELD

Pyle Cock
Rookery Street
🕐 10.30-11; 12-4, 7-10.30 Sun
☎ (01902) 732125
Banks's Original, Bitter, ℗ **seasonal beers** Ⓗ
Splendid 130-year-old local retaining its traditional bar with wooden settle backs, together with the etched windows depicting a Pyle Cock. The corridor from the entrance door leads to a serving hatch used by customers of the small room to the right and the back lounge. The pub has no food, frills or fads, just excellent beer and conversation. Visiting is easy by public transport – on a major bus route from the city, it enjoys a frequent service.
❀⌂P

Vine Inn
35 Lichfield Road (A4124, over canal bridge from centre)
🕐 11-3, 7-11; 12-3, 7-10.30 Sun
☎ (01902) 733529
Burton Bridge Stairway to Heaven; Flowers IPA; guest beers Ⓗ
Not far from the main shopping centre, this three-roomed pub has changed little since being built in 1938. In the bar note the collection of miniature cars and vans and the ballad to Blackbeard. The regularly changing guest beers frequently include

milds and dark beers. Convenient for the Wyrley and Essington Canal, it stands on the bus route between Wolverhampton and Bloxwich, featured in the local CAMRA guide to the best pubs on the route.
ᴁ❀🕭P

Billiard Hall
St Michael's Ringway
✪ 10-11; 12-10.30 Sun
☎ (0121) 580 2892
Banks's Original, Bitter; Theakston Best Bitter; guest beers Ⓗ
One of the few buildings remaining after St Michael's Street was obliterated by the new ring road, the relief stone lettering on the pediment is all that remains of the premises' former use. Wetherspoon's refurbishment won the CAMRA/English Heritage *Conversion to Pub Use* award in 1999. The open-plan interior features a barrel-vaulted ceiling above natural wood floors with a raised area at the rear and plain walls displaying a design of simulated snooker balls. Two banks of handpumps atop a polished whitewood bar dispense up to six guests. Q◖❀✦●

Churchfield Tavern
18 Little Lane (by Sandwell Hospital)
✪ 11-11; 12-10.30 Sun
☎ (0121) 588 5468
Banks's Original, Bitter; ℗ seasonal beers; Marston's Pedigree (summer) Ⓗ
Thriving, community-minded pub, where four rooms are connected by a central corridor. The basic bar and smarter lounge both have Sky TV; there is a dining room and a family room with novelty and fruit machines. The garden has a children's play area, and the very popular bowling green is used by 11 teams. A much-needed car park is soon to be built. Marston's Pedigree is available March-October. A carvery on Sun is served 1-4pm.
ᗡ❀◖🕭¿♣

Old Crown
56 Sandwell Road (near A41/A4031 jct)
✪ 12-4, 5 (6 Sat)-11; 12-4, 7-10.30 Sun
☎ (0121) 525 4600
Beer range varies Ⓗ
Tiny side-street pub, not far from the town centre, with one L-shaped compartmentalised room, this fine establishment shows how well drinkers and diners can occupy the same limited space without undue friction. For, while its fame has been built on its tasty Indian food, you never feel that you are in a restaurant rather than a pub. Three ever-changing guest ales whizz through the pumps, some favourites lasting only a couple of hours. No meals Sat lunch, or Sun. ◖❀ (Dartmouth St) 🖥

Vine
Roebuck Street (near M5 jct 1)
✪ 11.30-3.30, 5-11; 11.30-11 Fri; 12-11 Sat; 12-10.30 Sun
☎ (0121) 553 2866
Beer range varies Ⓗ
Entering this apparently small back-street local you'll find a traditional layout of three small rooms and a bar. This, however, is only the beginning: continue into the widened passageway (with lots more seating); knock here on the kitchen door to order a curry. Further still, there is a cafeteria-style room, complete with an indoor barbecue serving a variety of Tandoori starters. Beyond this is a marquee-covered family area with children's play equipment. An English menu is also available at lunchtime. The single real ale changes regularly and is usually from an independent brewer. ❀◖❧ (Galton Bridge) ❧ (Kenrick Pk) 🖥

Wheatsheaf
379 High Street
✪ 11-11; 12-3, 7-10.30 Sun
☎ (0121) 553 4221
Holden's Mild, ℗ Bitter; ℗/Ⓗ Golden Glow, Special Bitter; seasonal beers; guest beers Ⓗ
This Holden's pub bears a wonderful traditional exterior; inside the bar runs across the front of the pub with a lounge behind. A tiled passageway leads to a patio drinking area. The lounge is popular with local office workers lunchtime; the bar has a TV for the regulars to watch sport, especially horse-racing. The traditional menu offers excellent value (no food Sun eve). The pub is served by a number of bus routes.
❀◖🕭❀ (Dartmouth St/Guns Village) ♣ 🖥

Whiteheath Tavern
400 Birchfield Lane (near M5 jct 2)
✪ 12-3.30 (not Tue-Fri), 8-11; 12-3.30, 8-10.30 Sun
☎ (0121) 552 3603
Ansells Mild; Banks's Original: ℗ Boddingtons Bitter Ⓗ
Friendly, old-fashioned local on the main road from Oldbury-Blackheath. The bright, spacious front bar is a mecca for darts and dominoes-players. The pub can reached by rail or the 404 bus.
🕭❧ (Rowley Regis) ♣

Falcon Inn
77 Gomer Street West (off B4464 behind flats)
✪ 12-11; 12-10.30 Sun
☎ (01902) 633378
Greene King Abbot; Hydes Dark, Bitter; RCH Pitchfork; guest beers Ⓗ
Large,1930s pub, handy for the town centre and the Lock Museum, it stands to the west of town, near a high-rise block. The bustling bar boasts 10 handpumps, serving a selection of up to nine good value beers, in the quieter lounge the beers are listed on a blackboard. There is normally also a good selection of malt whiskies. The pub fields its own darts and cricket teams. 🕭♣🖥

Robin Hood
54 The Crescent (off B4464, 100 yds from McDonald's)
✪ 12-3; 5 (7 Sat)-11; 12-3, 7-10.30 Sun
☎ (01902) 608006
Ind Coope Burton Ale; Tetley Bitter; guest beers Ⓗ
Small single-roomed pub near the railway line. Up to two guest beers are featured, together with a good selection of country wines. Regular quiz nights are held Mon; Tue is crib night. Archers practise their art on the adjacent field on Sun before opening time. ❀P

WOLLASTON ❊

Foresters Arms
Bridgnorth Road (A458, towards Bridgnorth)
🕐 12-2.30, 6 (5 Fri)-11; 12-3, 7-10.30 Sun
☎ (01384) 394476
Enville Ale; Wadworth 6X; guest beers Ⓗ
Popular pub, renowned for its good value food which includes lunchtime specials and traditional roasts on Sun (no food Sun eve). The T-shaped room conveniently provides an area for dining; children are welcome to eat here during eve. Commonly known as the Ridge, the pub is situated on the outskirts of Wollaston next to rolling countryside.
🏦❊🛏◑ P

Unicorn
145 Bridgnorth Road (A458)
🕐 12 (11 Fri & Sat)-11; 12-4, 7-10.30 Sun
☎ (01384) 394823
Batham Mild, Best Bitter, seasonal beers Ⓗ
This former brewhouse was purchased by Batham's some six years ago and has earned a reputation of serving one of the best pints in the estate. The old brewhouse remains at the side of the pub, but would require much restoration to brew again. The house itself is very much a basic, two-roomed traditional drinkers' pub, popular with all ages. A sandwich may be ordered at lunchtime. This is a pub which is genuinely unspoilt.
Q❊◫P

WOLVERHAMPTON ❊

Chindit
113 Merridale Road
🕐 11-11; 12-10.30 Sun
☎ (01902) 425582
Draught Bass or John Smith's Bitter; guest beers Ⓗ
Popular, two-roomed local serving three guest ales – tasting notes are supplied for the week's beers. Acoustic music nights are held every Fri and a beer festival is staged over May Day weekend. Buses from the city to Bradmore and Castlecroft stop outside. The pub was built in the late 1940s, and named in honour of the soldiers of the Staffordshire Regiment who served in the Chindit Campaign in Burma during WWII. The history of the Chindits and the pub are displayed on a wall in the lounge.
◫♣P

Combermere Arms
90 Chapel Ash (A41, near A454)
🕐 11-3, 5.30-11; 12-11 Fri & Sat; 12-10.30 Sun
☎ (01902) 421880
Banks's Hanson's Mild, Bitter, Mansfield Bitter; guest beer Ⓗ
This pub has now reverted to its original name; General Combermere was a senior figure in the Crimean War. Set in an attractive terrace, the pub boasts three rooms and a covered patio, plus a small garden with a barbecue area. This is a drinkers' pub, serving rather special lunchtime sandwiches, and is one of the few places in the newly-designated city where you can drink Hanson's Mild. A tree is growing in the gents' toilet.
❊P⊟

Great Western
Sun Street
🕐 11-11; 12-3, 7-10.30 Sun

☎ (01902) 351090
Batham Best Bitter; Holden's Mild, Bitter, Golden Glow, Special Bitter; guest beer Ⓗ
Past national CAMRA *Pub of the Year* winner, selling beers from two small local breweries. Hidden behind, and well below, the current Wolverhampton Station, it used to serve the now-derelict low level station and can be accessed from the new station by subway into the old station yard. The Western boasts a major collection of railway memorabilia and its excellent home-cooked food is served so fast it has often arrived before you get back from the bar. Very busy on Wolves match days.
❊◑≠P

Hogshead
186 Stafford Street (near rail and bus stations)
🕐 11-11; 12-10.30 Sun
☎ (01902) 717955
Boddington Bitter; Brakspear Bitter; Marston's Pedigree; Wadworth 6X Ⓗ **guest beers** Ⓗ/Ⓖ
Town-centre pub, serving a large choice of cask ales and Belgian beers. It has three no-smoking areas. It serves good value meals and is popular with all ages, but 18-25 year-olds dominate on Fri and Sat eves. Originally called the Vine, it was built to serve the soldiers of the South Staffs Regiment whose drill hall stood behind the pub. It closed in the late 1970s and was used as offices until reborn as the Hogshead four years ago. Note the leaded skylight above the bar of this local CAMRA *Pub of the Year* 2000.
❊◑♿≠⊖ (St George's) ♣⌇

Homestead
Lodge Road, Oxley (off A449 at Goodyear island)
🕐 12-2.30, 6-11; 12-3, 7-11 Sat; 12-3, 7-10.30 Sun
☎ (01902) 787357
John Smith's Bitter; Tetley Bitter; guest beers Ⓗ
Large, two-roomed pub in what was previously a farmhouse. It is accessible from the main Stafford road on foot; vehicles via the local estate roads. The pub consists of a sizeable bar, popular with darts players and a comfortable lounge. Families are well catered for with a large outdoor children's play area. Popular with canal-users, the pub is about 10 minutes' walk from Autherley Junction and is one of the few Wolverhampton pubs to offer accommodation. Well known for good home-cooked food, it regularly offers two guest beers.
❊🛏◑◫♣P

Newhampton
Riches Street, Whitmore Reans (off A41)
🕐 11-11; 12-10.30 Sun
☎ (01902) 745773
Courage Best Bitter, Directors; Marston's Pedigree; Wells Bombardier; guest beer Ⓗ
Deceptively large, street-corner local with three bars and a bowls pavilion bar serving an extensive outdoor area of garden, bowling green and children's play area. Particular care has been taken to preserve historical features such as the Atkinson's Brewery door and stained glass windows. The Newhampton is also noted for its home-cooked food; the 'smoke room' is smoke-free at lunchtimes only. The 'hot pot' option is served Sun. The function room is a major local venue for folk and

jazz. The guest beer and cider usually change at least daily.
♨Q❀◑🅱️➊●

Posada
48 Lichfield Street (opp. art gallery)
✪ 11-11; 12-2.30, 7.30-10.30 Sun
☎ (01902) 711304
Tetley Dark Mild, Bitter; Wells Bombardier; guest beer Ⓗ

The narrow, tiled frontage of this 1875 Grade II listed building sets the tone for the interior. A sympathetic renovation some years ago by Holt, Plant and Deakin retained a number of features (fireplace, large screen and moulded ceiling) and some original tiling, recently rediscovered, is to be renovated and displayed. The three rooms and cosy nook produce a Tardis-like effect, but even so it can be crowded on match days. Try the 'doorsteps' – hot beef/vegetarian sausages weekday lunchtimes. Tea and coffee are always available.
⇌ ⊖ (St George's)

Royal Oak
7 School Road, Tettenhall Wood
✪ 12-11; 12-10.30 Sun
☎ (01902) 754396
Banks's Original, Bitter Ⓟ

Grade II listed building in a conservation area, this small pub is over 200 years old. It has an attractive exterior and was runner-up in the National *Hanging Baskets* competition 2000. The bar has cable TV for sport, and its dominoes team plays in the local league. The cosy lounge seats just 12. A large fenced garden contains a function room for cabarets or children's parties, a volleyball/five-a-side football pitch, and a children's play area; it hosts occasional barbecues. Eve meals served in summer.
❀◑🅱️♣🅰️

Swan
Bridgnorth Road, Compton
✪ 11-11; 12-10.30 Sun
☎ (01902) 754736
Banks's Original, Bitter Ⓟ

This coaching inn is one of the oldest pubs in Wolverhampton; the faded painting of a swan and the legend dated 1777 on the chimney breast in the public bar attest to its age. The Grade II listed building features a public bar, with old settles and beams, an L-shaped snug and a larger lounge that doubles as a games room. This unspoilt pub offers a friendly and convivial atmosphere in the Compton area of the city. Buses stop nearby. ❀🅱️♣P

Tap & Spile
35 Princess Street
✪ 11-11; 12-10.30 Sun
☎ (01902) 713319
Banks's Original, Bitter; guest beers Ⓗ

Small, three-roomed, city-centre pub, comprising an open bar area with a large-screen TV for Sky Sports and two snugs, the rear one exhibiting a collection of old bottles. It is popular for Wolves home games and handy for Fri and Sat night clubbers. Good home-cooked food is available Mon-Fri (and sometimes Sat) lunchtimes – try the hot steak baguettes when available. An enterprising range of ever-changing guest beers is offered at inviting prices.
◑♿⇌⊖ (St George's) ♣●

The Roadside Inn

All passing men, with beast or wagons,
Draw in, draw up, and call for flagons.
And say it's cold, or say it's hot,
Or will be shortly, like as not;
Or say it's time we'd sun, or rain,
Or Mrs Jones has twins again;
Or Rector's dead, or that girl Ann
Has gone off with a soldier man.
Or we remember old things, we;
Or tidden like it used to be.

Five hundred years this talk has gone
Then they have drained their mugs and paid,
And slowly watch the summer fade,
And see the evening star and gone.

John Masefield, *The Country Scene,* 1938.

WILTSHIRE

BOWDEN HILL

Bell
1/2 mile E of Lacock
☼ 11 (11.30 Fri & Sat)-2.30, 7 (6.30 Fri & Sat)-11;
12-3, 7-10.30 Sun
☎ (01249) 730308
Beer range varies H
Genuine free house in 140-year-old former canal cottages. The canal was the former Wilts and Berks now long-closed and difficult to trace although some brave souls hope to reopen it. The pub is in the attractive setting of Bowden Hill, a hamlet between the National Trust-owned village of Lacock and the village of Sandy Lane, where the majority of the cottages are thatched. There is a single bar with separate no-smoking restaurant *(à la carte)*, serving excellent meals. The extensive garden has a children's play area. Beers include Wickwar Coopers' WPA.
⌂❀◑▲♣P

Rising Sun
32 Bowden Hill (1 mile E of Lacock)
☼ 11.30-3, 6-11; 12-10.30 Sun
☎ (01249) 730363

Mole's Tap Bitter; Best Bitter; Molennium, seasonal beers; guest beer H
Attractive, 17th-century single-bar inn with traditional flagstones. There are spectacular views over the Avon Valley from the large garden which has a children's play area. This is Mole's Brewery tap and it stocks their whole range. The pub hosts live music every Wed eve and alternate Sun afternoons and has a quiz on Mon eve. Lacock (the nearby National Trust village) is the scene of many film and TV productions, when a period set is required. All Lacock pubs serve real ale. The interesting Fox-Talbot Museum of Photography is in the old abbey buildings.
⌂Q❀◑▲♣P

BOX

Quarryman's Arms
Box Hill (off A4)
☼ 11-3, 6-11; 11-11 Fri-Sat; 12-10.30 Sun
☎ (01225) 743569
Butcombe Bitter; Mole's Best Bitter; Wadworth 6X; H **guest beer** G
Excellent village pub, well-hidden in a maze of small lanes. Many people have got lost trying to find it, so ring for directions. The

main bar is decorated with maps of the old stone mines that riddle the hill underneath the village. Enjoy the superb views over the Box Valley from the dining area while you tuck into the delicious food served. Pleasant patio area. ⚲✵☻✍◑▣♣P

Beehive

263 Trowbridge Road (by canal bridge)
✪ 12-2.30, 7-11; 12-3, 7-10.30 Sun
☎ (01225) 863620
Butcombe Bitter; Ⓗ guest beers Ⓗ/Ⓖ
Situated close to the Kennet and Avon Canal, this former brothel(!) stocks an ever-changing range of five guest beers. The pub was built in the early 19th century to provide refreshment for the canal trade. The large garden to the rear hosts not only a children's play area but a brood of chickens. Beers are served on gravity or from two genuine Victorian handpumps. Old CAMRA stalwarts will feel a rush of nostalgia when they see the Watney's Red Barrel pump on the bar! No lunchtime meals on Tue or eve meals on Sun. ⚲Q☻◑♣P

Bunch of Grapes

14 Silver Street
✪ 12-11; 12-10.30 Sun
☎ (01225) 863877
Smiles Best; Young's Bitter, Special Ⓗ
Town-centre pub near the antique shops, easily recognised by the grapevine growing over the front (it fruits in summer). A welcoming pub with wooden floors and panelled walls painted soft peach. There are three levels creating separate drinking areas, plus a restaurant upstairs (advisable to book). The whole pub has an air of good taste, from the decor to the wall prints. It can get very busy at times and can appear crowded as it is not very large. The bar also hosts a Sun quiz and occasional soft live music. ☻◑≠

BRATTON

Duke

Near Westbury
✪ 11.30-3, 7-11.30; 11.30-11.30 football season only; 12-3, 7-10.30 Sun
☎ (01380) 830242
Mole's Best Bitter; guest beers Ⓗ
Situated in an interesting village at the base of Westbury White Horse it has won many accolades, most recently *Sunday Roast Pub of the Year*. During the present landlord's era it began as an Usher's house but is now affiliated to Mole's. Guest beers have been introduced to support Mole's. A cosy lounge bar/restaurant and a friendly public bar, cater for a wide range of customers. The landlord is an excellent chef, producing an interesting and varied menu. ☻✍◑▣♣P⚏

BROUGHTON GIFFORD

Bell on the Common

2 miles W of Melksham, off B3107
✪ 11-11; 12-10.30 Sun
☎ (01225) 782309
Wadworth IPA, 6X, seasonal beers Ⓗ
This handsome, old pub overlooks the village green. There are two contrasting

beers; one smart bar/restaurant, the other is very much the locals' meeting place with wooden settles, old tables and a games room attached. A warm welcome is assured in both bars. Large, pleasant garden which is safe for children, where boules is played and barbecues held in summer. The restaurant food is highly rated and the 'Waddies' is some of the best you will find. ⚲✵☻◑▣♣P●

CHARLTON

Horse & Groom Inn

The Street (B4040, Malmesbury-Cricklade road)
✪ 12-3, 7-11; 12-11 Sat; 12-10.30 Sun
☎ (01666) 823904
Archers Village; Wadworth 6X; guest beer Ⓗ
16th-century coaching inn with a unique rustic charm. Attractive setting in a small village, welcoming log fires in winter and a pleasant private garden to enjoy in summer. Good selection of real ales from Wiltshire breweries. Excellent food ranges from simple bar snacks to a full *à la carte* menu. The accommodation has been sensitively refurbished and bedrooms look out over the Cotswold countryside. Full English breakfast is included in the tariff. Bath, the Cotswolds and Malmesbury are all nearby. ⚲☻✍◑▣☺♣P

CHIPPENHAM

Old Road Tavern

Old Road (next to station)
✪ 11-4, 5.45-11; 11-11 Fri & Sat; 12-10.30 Sun
☎ (01249) 652094
Courage Best Bitter; Greene King Ruddles County; Wadworth 6X Ⓗ
Basic, unpretentious local in a 130-year-old Grade II listed building. The pub has separate bar and lounge areas, a large function room, family area, pool room and a floral garden with ample seating. It won *Chippenham in Bloom* 1999. Darts are played and the pub is home to the Chippenham Morris Men. Plenty of live music to entertain; traditional folk (first and third Sun of month), French music (second Sun) and bands play regularly on Sat night. Excellent value food at lunchtime (not Sun). ✵☻◑▣♣

CLYFFE PYPARD

Goddard Arms

Wood Street OS074769
✪ 12-2.30, 7-11; 11-11 Sat; 12-10.30 Sun
☎ (01793) 731386
Wadworth 6X; guest beers Ⓗ
This is a picturesque village pub with a traditional skittle alley. The pub is on split levels, with the pleasant dining area on the higher level. Quality food is served at all sessions. There is an interesting range of

INDEPENDENT BREWERIES

Archers Swindon
Arkell's Swindon
Hop Back Downton
Mole's Melksham
Stonehenge Netheravon
Heritage Ales Dinton
Wadworth Devizes

guest ales which regularly change and are mainly from smaller breweries. The homely atmosphere in the Goddard Arms is enhanced by real wood fires in winter.
🏃◖🌗⊟♣P

COMPTON BASSETT

White Horse
The Street (take A4 E of Calne or A3102 N of Calne)
☼ 11-3, 5-11; 12-3, 7-11 Sun
☎ (01249) 813118
Wadworth 6X; guest beers 🅗
This is the village where, a few years ago, a disgruntled resident hacked down the church belfry door and cut the bell ropes because she objected to the noise. But don't let that put you off! Despite the pub name the chalk white horse is in the next village. This pub has been greatly improved in recent years and now serves superb food and a range of beers mostly from the independent sector. The skittle alley is popular. The pub has pointed gables, characteristic of the older buildings here; the village was once part of a landed estate.
🏃Q❀🏨◖🌗⊟🕭▲♣P

CORSHAM

Two Pigs
38 Pickwick
☼ 7-11; 12-2.30, 7-10.30 Sun
☎ (01249) 712515
website: www.twopigs.freeserve.co.uk
Stonehenge Pigswill; guest beers 🅗
Lively, stone-built, single-bar pub at the side of the old coach road between London and Bath. The pub has a strong commitment to real ale and offers an ever-changing range of at least three guest beers. Pigswill, the house beer, is brewed by Stonehenge Brewery especially for the pub. There is a long, rustic bar with flagstone floor and wood-panelled walls. In summer outside seating is provided (under cover) in an area called the Sty at the rear. Live blues music on Mon eve. Regular

local CAMRA *Pub of the Year*. Caters for over 21s only. Closed lunchtimes (except Sun).
🏃◖🌗&

CORSTON

Radnor Arms
Off A429, 3 miles N of jct 17, M4
☼ 11-3, 5.30-11; 12-4, 7-10.30 Sun
☎ (01666) 823389 e-mail: fujimo@onetel.net.uk
Archers Best Bitter; RCH Pitchfork; guest beers (summer) 🅗
Welcoming freehold pub in the village centre: a single bar with dining area and a real fire in winter. A blackboard lists daily specials, salad baguettes and fresh fish, as well as locally-produced steaks. At least two real ales are always available. The Radnor Arms is frequented by a friendly mix of local people, employees of nearby Telecoms plant and midlanders heading for the south coast. The pub dates from the late 18th century and is built of locally quarried stone. A pig roast usually takes place on summer bank holidays. 🏃❀🏨◖🌗▲♣P

CORTON

Dove Inn
Off A36 OS934406
☼ 12-3 (3.30 Sat), 6.30-11; 12-4, 7-10.30 Sun
☎ (01985) 850109 website: www.thedove.co.uk
Oakhill Best Bitter; guest beers 🅗
Welcoming village pub in the heart of the Wylye Valley. The candlelit conservatory and separate restaurant (where children are served) leaves drinkers with a dedicated bar area which has a polished wood floor and open fire. Usually three ales on handpump, Oakhill and two guests. Food is excellent with a varied lunchtime menu and a more sophisticated eve choice using, where possible, local ingredients including game and fish. There is a large, pleasant garden. The new car park eases parking problems. Corton is situated on the Wiltshire cycle way. 🏃Q❀🏨◖🌗&P✂

INN BRIEF

BISHOPSTONE
Three Horseshoes
The Alley
11-2.30 (not Mon-Wed or Fri), 6-11;
12-2.30, 7-10.30 Sun
Wadworth 6X 🅗
Known locally as 'Freda's' after the long-serving landlady. A quiet pub ideal for conversation and a visit to the nearby kingfisher stream.

BRADFORD ON AVON
Rising Sun
231 Winsley Road
12-11;
12-10.30 Sun
Archers Village, Best Bitter, Golden 🅗
Friendly two-bar local, one area is quiet, the other lively. Cosy and relaxing, a good outlet for Archers.

BROKERSWOOD
Kicking Donkey
11.30-2.30 (3 Sat); 6.30-11;
12-10.30 Sun
Oakhill Bitter; Stonehenge Danish Dynamite; Wadworth 6X; guest beers 🅗
17th-century inn with exposed beams and brasses. Comprises three drinking areas and a separate restaurant. Close to woodland park.

HEDDINGTON
Ivy
Stockley Road
12-3, 6.30-11; 12-11 Sat;
12-10.30 Sun
Wadworth IPA, 6X, seasonal beers 🅖
At the heart of the village this picturesque thatched pub has a reputation for good food and a relaxed atmosphere. *Cask Marque* accredited.

LOWER CHUTE
Hatchet
11.30-3, 6.30-11;
12-4, 7-10.30 Sun
Greene King IPA; guest beers 🅗
14th-century thatched village pub near Hampshire border. Busy bar area with inglenook. Good food and a real pub atmosphere.

MALMESBURY
Three Cups
90 The Triangle
11-2.30, 6-11; 11-11 Sat;
12-10.30 Sun
Brakspear Bitter; guest beers 🅗
Two-bar pub with lively public bar and more intimate lounge. Large selection of malt whiskies. Close to historic abbey and market cross.

MARKET LAVINGTON
Green Dragon
26-28 High Street
12-2.30 (not Mon), 6.30 (5.30 Mon)-11;
12-2.30, 7-10.30 Sun
Wadworth IPA, 6X, JCB 🅗
Village pub on the edge of Salisbury Plain, five miles south of Devizes. A 17th-century listed building.

NORTH NEWNTON
Woodbridge Inn
Next to roundabout on A345 Pewsey-Upavon road
12-11; 12-10.30 Sun
Wadworth IPA, 6X, JCB 🅗
16th-century inn set in the Vale of Pewsey, on the banks of the River Avon. Enclosed children's play area and a pétanque piste.

SALISBURY
Queen's Arms
9 Ivy Street
11-3.30, 5.30-11; 11-11 Mon, Fri & Sat;
12-10.30 Sun
Banks's Bitter; Greene King IPA; Ushers Best Bitter 🅗
This reputedly haunted 14th-century pub claims the city's longest continuous licence. Named after Queen Elizabeth I.

CRICKLADE

Red Lion
74 High Street
☼ 12-11; 12-10.30 Sun
☎ (01793) 750776 c mail: redlioninn@fsbdial.com.uk
Archers Best Bitter; guest beers Ⓗ

This is a friendly, traditional local. The building dates back to the 16th century and the bar walls are adorned with stuffed animals and other bric-à-brac. There is a wide range of real ales on offer with eight regularly changing beers available at any one time. The pleasant walled garden and patio at the rear is ideal in summer. The River Thames is nearby, so ask the bar staff about borrowing a canoe! ♨Q✿Ⓓ&♣●P

DEVIZES

British Lion
Estcourt Street (A361)
☼ 11-11; 12-10.30 Sun
☎ (01380) 720665
Beer range varies Ⓗ

Basic, down-to-earth pub offering a varied selection of ever-changing beers. During the course of a week you can sample at least 10 different ales. The same landlord has been resident for 10 years. Traditional games such as darts, dominoes, pool, crib and cards are played. The British Lion attracts a very mixed range of customers. If you like a good discussion over an excellent pint then this pub is worth a visit.
✿♣●P

Cavalier
1 Eastleigh Road
☼ 11-11; 12-10.30 Sun
☎ (01380) 723285
Wadworth IPA, 6X, JCB, seasonal beers Ⓗ

Until recently this was a not-so-special, two-bar estate pub. It was also the only 'Gay Cavalier' pub in the country. Following complete refurbishment and a name change it is the comfortable, single-bar pub that we see today. The bar is split into different eating and drinking areas. The enterprising licensee tries to cater for a wide range of tastes and appetites. Enjoy the steak and kidney pies – they're home-made with 6X and were recently nominated for a national award. ✿Ⓓ♣P●

Hare & Hounds
Hare & Hounds Street
☼ 11-2.30, 7-11; 12-3, 7-10.30 Sun
☎ (01380) 723231
Wadworth IPA, 6X, JCB, seasonal beers Ⓗ

Regular readers of this *Guide* will need no introduction to this first-rate, back-street local. A friendly welcome is guaranteed and for the past 10 years, the pub has sold the most consistently good Wadworth's in town. If you want to know what Wadworth beers should taste like, then this is the place to come. Lunchtime food is served on Fri and Sat only. ♨✿Ⓓ♣P●

DILTON MARSH

Prince of Wales
94 High Street
☼ 11.30 (12 Fri)-2.30 (3 Sat; not Mon or Tue); 7-11; 12-3, 7-10.30 Sun
☎ (01373) 865487

Fuller's London Pride; Wadworth 6X; Wells Eagle; guest beer Ⓗ

Friendly, welcoming village local. A single bar serves two drinking areas plus a small pool table annexe and a large skittle alley. The pub participates in local skittles, crib and pool leagues. In addition a quiz is held every Sun eve. (Why not field a team and see if you can beat the 'Bar Flies'?) Please note that the Prince is not normally open Mon and Tue lunchtimes. The factually incorrect pub sign (can you spot the error?) has featured in a Japanese pub sign guide! Eve meals served Tue–Sat.
Q✿Ⓓ⇌♣P

EASTERTON

Royal Oak
11 High Street (B3098)
☼ 11-3, 5.30-11; 12-3, 7 10.30 Sun
☎ (01380) 812343
Wadworth IPA, 6X; JCB, seasonal beers; guest beer (occasional) Ⓗ

Very popular, thatched pub, pleasantly decorated with much local memorabilia. There is a separate public bar and two dining areas leading off the main bar. Excellent home-cooked meals are served (not Sun eve). The enthusiastic landlord stocks all the Wadworth seasonal brews and a good range of wines.
♨Q✿✿Ⓓ&♣P

EASTON ROYAL

Bruce Arms ☆
Easton Road (B3087)
☼ 11-2.30 (3 Sat), 6-11; 12-3, 7-10.30 Sun
☎ (01672) 810216 website: www.brucearms.co.uk
Butts Bitter; Wadworth 6X; guest beer Ⓗ

Traditional pub, nestling in the countryside some distance outside the village of Easton Royal in the Vale of Pewsey. Little has changed since it was established in the 1840s. The coat of arms belongs to the local aristocracy, the Earls of Cardigan, whose family name is Brundenell-Bruce. The pub is also known as 'The Gammon' (ask when you go there). The friendly locals don't seem to live nearby (there are no buildings around the pub) but are willing to travel some distance, a tribute to the character of the pub. It boasts its own cricket team and pitch on the opposite side of the road. The large back room features a skittle alley and pool table. The front room is more akin to a private living room. Guest beer served Fri–Sun. ♨Q✿✿A♣P

FONTHILL GIFFORD

Beckford Arms
Midway between Hindon and Tisbury OS931312
☼ 11.30-11; 12-10.30 Sun
☎ (01747) 870385
Greene King Abbot; guest beers Ⓗ

You need to hunt for the Beckford Arms, hidden in beautiful south Wiltshire countryside between the A30 and A303. This large 17th-century building of local stone is on a small crossroads near the mile-long Fonthill Lake. The high-ceilinged public bar and lounge have open log fires and are attractively furnished. The pub is spacious yet intimate; the lounge leads to a series of small, cosy dining areas and to a

larger room overlooking the peaceful garden. Greene King Abbot is on regularly, supported by two or three local guest ales.
🏠🌲�"🌙🖤♣P

FOVANT

Pembroke Arms
On A30, 5 miles W of Wilton
☼ 12-2.30, 5-11; 12-11 Sat; 12-10.30 Sun
☎ (01722) 714201
Ringwood Best Bitter; guest beers Ⓗ
This family-run pub is a genuine free house. The regularly changing guest beers are supplemented by an annual beer festival in August. Attractive 17th-century, ivy-clad building which is close to WWI regimental badges that are cut into the Downs. Good quality food. 🏠🌲🚃🌙🖤♣P✗

GRITTLETON

Neeld Arms
The Street
☼ 5.30-11; 11-3.30, 5.30-11 Sat; 12-3.30, 6-10.30 Sun
☎ (01249) 782470 e-mail: neeldarms@genie.co.uk
Archers Best Bitter; Brains Buckley's Best Bitter; Wadworth 6X; guest beer Ⓗ
17th-century inn set in a beautiful and ancient landscape where the Cotswolds meet the Wiltshire Downs. The range of real ales includes local brews and new guest beers are introduced frequently. A good selection of home-made food is offered. A log fire is always welcoming in winter. Within easy reach of many picturesque villages such as Castle Combe, Lacock and historic towns like Bath and Malmesbury. Take A420 from Chippenham, signposted right fork to Yatton Keynell and right turn to the attractive, unspoilt village of Grittleton.
🏠Q🌲🚃🌙P

HAMPTWORTH

Cuckoo
1 mile from A36 at Landford jct
☼ 11.30-2.30, 6-11; 11.30-11 Sat; 12-10.30 Sun
☎ (01794) 390302
Badger Tanglefoot; Cheriton Pots Ale; Hop Back GFB, Summer Lightning; Wadworth 6X; guest beers Ⓖ
On the edge of the New Forest, this rustic, thatched pub has a genuine and friendly atmosphere. Four small bars cater for all and excellent beer, conversation and traditional pub games are the priorities. The large, attractive garden has several pétanque terrains, an area for children and a peaceful area for adults. Wessex CAMRA *Pub of the Year* 1999. Not to be missed.
🏠Q🌲🌙♣🖤P✗

HAYDON WICK

Manor Farm
Near Swindon
☼ 11-11; 12-10.30 Sun
☎ (01793) 705222
Banks's Original, Bitter; Marston's Pedigree Ⓗ
This inn is an old farmhouse that has been sympathetically converted and extended. It is now surrounded by new housing. In 2000, the old part of the building was severely damaged by fire. It has been rebuilt and restored to the same high standards.

The Manor Farm is a quiet pub, with an emphasis on the enjoyment of food, drink and conversation. Oversized, lined glasses are used. It offers a wide food menu.
Q🌲🌙🖤P🍽

HIGHWORTH

Wine Cellar
10 High Street
☼ 7 (5.30 Wed & Thu; 1 Fri; 12 Sat)-11; 12-5, 7-10.30 Sun
☎ (01793) 763828
Archers Village, Best Bitter; guest beer Ⓖ
A well-hidden cellar bar next to the Indian takeaway opposite the market square. As the name implies, there is an extensive range of wines, also 55 different malt whiskies. The cellar used to be the kitchen for one of the houses above. It is said that there was a tunnel leading from the cellar to the other side of the square. A discount is offered to CAMRA members on production of a membership card. Thatcher's Black Rat cider is stocked. 🍷✗

HODSON

Calley Arms
Off B4005
☼ 12-2.30 (not Mon; 11.30-3 Sat), 6.30-11 Tue-Sat; 12-3, 7-10.30 Sun
☎ (01793) 740350
Wadworth IPA, 6X, seasonal beer; guest beer Ⓗ
Welcoming pub set in a pleasant rural setting high above the edge of Swindon, near the village of Chiseldon. A large board outside the pub gives the directions for a 2½ mile walk down to Coate Water Country Park. There is a large bar with a real fire and a raised dining area. An interesting menu includes plenty of changing specials. No food Sun eve. For those whose thirst is not quenched by the range of Wadworth real ales there are over 60 malt whiskies to try and a wide selection of English country wines. Weston's Scrumpy is also served.
🏠🌲🌙🍷P🌑

HOLT

Tollgate Inn
Ham Green
☼ 11.30-2.30, 6.30-11; 12-2.30 (closed eve) Sun
☎ (01225) 782326
e-mail: tollgatefood@care4free.co.uk
Beer range varies Ⓗ
Old village inn, well-known for its excellent food and beer. The range of four to five ales varies from day to day and is an imaginative selection from local and more distant small brewers. Good, wholesome food is served in the restaurant and bar, while the garden overlooks the pretty valley (though rather spoilt by the Nestlé factory!). The pub as a whole has an upmarket feel, though drinkers are always made very welcome. Boules sometimes played in summer.
🏠Q🌲🌙P

IDMISTON

Earl of Normanton
Tidworth Road (A338, 3 miles S of A303 jct)
☼ 12-3, 6-11; 12-3, 7-10.30 Sun
☎ (01980) 610251
Cheriton Pots Ale, Best Bitter; guest beers Ⓗ

This popular, lively village local was once owned by Strongs Brewery who changed its name to the Plough. The present owners obtained permission from the current Earl of Normanton to use the pub's original name. Its elevated garden has superb views over the Bourne valley and chalk escarpments. The B&B accommodation is in a separate annexe. Locally renowned for excellent food, it makes a perfect stop on the busy A338.
🏨⊛🛏◗P

KILMINGTON

Red Lion Inn
On B3092, 2½ miles N of A303 near Mere
🕐 11.30-3, 6.30-11; 12-3.30, 7-10.30 Sun
☎ (01985) 844263
Butcombe Bitter; Butts Jester; guest beers Ⓗ
This 400-year-old former farmworker's cottage retains the timeless characteristics of a bygone age. It nestles in the lee of the South Wilts Downs, near Stourhead Gardens. Walking sticks are on sale for visiting ramblers. No music and no machines, this pub has a single bar with flagstone floors, two large open fires and a small no-smoking area. Darts and shove-ha'penny played (challenge the landlord if you dare). He has been resident for 23 years and is only the third landlord here in the past 100 years. Large garden and good-value food.
🏨Q⊛🛏◗♣♠P✗●

LIMPLEY STOKE

Hop Pole
Woods Hill
🕐 11-3, 6-11; 12-3, 7-10.30 Sun
☎ (01225) 723134
Draught Bass; Butcombe Bitter; Courage Best Bitter Ⓗ
Charming village local overlooking the beautiful Limpley Stoke valley. A cosy wood-panelled public bar has an open wood fire in winter and a larger lounge is set out with tables for dining. A very small family room doubles up as the darts area. The unusual, long, thin garden is great for train spotting! In summer boules is played. Shove-ha'penny is also popular.
Q🕙⊛◗🚃≠(Freshford)♣P

MELKSHAM

Red Lion
3 The City (on one-way system, close to Avon tyre factory)
🕐 11-2.30, 5 (6 Sat)-11; 11-11 Fri; 12-3, 7-10.30 Sun
☎ (01225) 702960
Draught Bass; Bath Gem; Church End Gravediggers; guest beer Ⓗ
Popular, friendly local, claimed to be the oldest pub in Wiltshire, dating back to the 13th century. Close to the town centre, it is a rare local outlet for mild ales, Church End Gravedigger's Mild is always available. The pub is split into two with a chimney breast screening the serving area from a larger, but intimate, lounge. The lunchtime food (served Mon–Fri) represents very good value for money, and the prices of the beers are competitive with ales served in local clubs. With the guest beers changing regularly, this is a veritable gem. Q⊛◗&≠P

NORTH WROUGHTON

Check Inn
79 Woodland View (from Swindon follow signs for Wroughton, first right once over M4)
🕐 11.30-3.30, 6.30-11; 11.30-11 Sat; 12-10.30 Sun
☎ (01793) 845584
Beer range varies Ⓗ
Genuine free house serving six real ales, imported lagers and bottled beers. This ex-roadside stop has been cut off by the M4 and isolated in a cul-de-sac. It would have been closed had it not been purchased as a tree house in 1996. The pub has flourished, now extended, it retains an open, friendly atmosphere and attracts visitors and locals. A community feel is reinforced by the regular quiz and crib nights. Guest beers constantly change and Leffe Blonde is stocked. 🏨⊛◗♣♠P

OGBOURNE ST GEORGE

Old Crown
Marlborough Road (signed off A346)
🕐 12-3 (not Mon), 6-11; 12-3, 7-9 Sun
☎ (01672) 841445
webste: www.theinnwiththewell.com
Wadworth 6X; guest beer Ⓖ
Cosy 300-year-old pub near the now disused railway line. Despite the handpumps, every pint is drawn straight from the barrel in the small cellar. The changing guest beer means there is always something of interest. A 90ft well is featured in the separate dining area. Good food and a comprehensive menu make this pub a favourite with visitors to the nearby Ridgeway path. The new purpose-built accommodation block makes it a good base to explore the countryside. Or, if you prefer, camping facilities are close at hand.
🏨Q⊛🛏◗♠♣P✗

PEWSEY

Coopers Arms
37-39 Ball Road (off B3087) OS170595
🕐 6-11; 12-2, 7-11 Sat; 12-4, 7-10.30 Sun
☎ (01672) 562495
Butts Barbus Barbus; Wadworth 6X; guest beers Ⓗ
This back-street pub is full of character. It is difficult to find but well worth the effort. Splendid, thatched building with a wealth of entertainment offered. Live music, comedy and quiz nights are hosted regularly. There is a pool table in a separate room. Real cider is stocked in summer. 🏨🕙⊛♣≠●P

ROWDE

George & Dragon
High Street (A342, in village centre)
🕐 12-3 (not Mon), 7-11; 12-3, 7-10.30 Sun
☎ (01380) 723053 e-mail: gd-rowde@lineone.net
Beer range varies Ⓗ
Dominant in the High Street, this imposing pub has an attractive exterior and wonderful interior with beams, large stone fireplaces and real log fires in winter. Well-known for its award-winning food, the George & Dragon specialises in seafood and fish. No food on Mon, but for the rest of the week lunchtime and eve meals are served (booking advisable). It is now primarily a restaurant with well-kept beers. Pleasant, friendly staff. 🏨Q⊛P●

SALISBURY ❖

Deacon's Alms
118 Fisherton Street
✪ 5 (12 Fri & Sat)-11; 12-10.30 Sun
☎ (01722) 504723
Cheriton Village Elder, Best Bitter; Hop Back GFB, Summer Lightning; guest beers (occasional) Ⓗ
Unusual split-level pub, five minutes' walk from the city centre. There are two bars; the small front area has bare boards and a collection of old photographs and adverts. The larger rear bar has table football and a TV showing sporting events. In addition to the regulars from Cheriton and Hop Back, there are occasional guest beers.
≠ ♣ ☐

Royal George
17 Bedwin Street
✪ 11-11; 12-10.30 Sun
☎ (01722) 327782
Adnams Bitter; Wadworth 6X; guest beer Ⓗ
Originally a 15th-century inn, this Grade II listed pub is named after the sister ship of *HMS Victory* and has a beam purported to be from the ship. The low-beamed bar is decorated with pictures of ships and sea battles and gives this city pub a country feel. The pub is well-known locally, particularly for its involvement in crib, darts, pool and football leagues. Lunchtime meals are served Mon-Sat. The pub offers accommodation and has its own car park.
❀ ⇔ ◖ ♣ P

Tom Brown's
225 Wilton Road
✪ 12-3 (not Mon-Fri), 6-11; 12-3, 7-10.30 Sun
☎ (01722) 335918
Goldfinch Tom Brown, Midnight Sun Special, Midnight Blinder Ⓗ
This Goldfinch Brewery house has a strong community spirit, it is popular with locals and enters teams in several leagues. Pool and darts are played and other games are available on request. There is a TV for sporting events such as the Grand Prix races and rugby internationals. At other times there is background music and the buzz of conversation. The pub lies midway between London and Exeter and was originally called the Halfway House. ♣

Village Free House
33 Wilton Road (A36, near St Pauls roundabout)
✪ 12 (4 Mon)-11; 12-5, 7-10.30 Sun
☎ (01722) 329707
Abbey Bellringer; Taylor Landlord; guest beers Ⓗ
Friendly city local with a large collection of railwayana including a pair of locomotive horns on which 'time' is called. It specialises in beers unusual for the area – the three ever-changing guests regularly include a mild or a stout. There is a separate cellar bar available for functions. Pub games are popular here. ≠ ♣

Wig & Quill
1 New Street
✪ 11-11; 12-3, 7-10.30 Sun
☎ (01722) 335665
Wadworth IPA, 6X; guest beers Ⓗ
This 16th-century building has only been a pub for 25 years. It opened as Wadworth's first pub in Salisbury. There is a long bar

500

Cask Marque

The Cask Marque symbol with a pub entry indicates that the licensee has successfully passed a number of tests concerning beer quality, and can display a plaque to this effect. However, the choice of all pubs in the guide is made by CAMRA independently of Cask Marque. The Cask Marque symbol is added during the editing process, and Cask Marque has no say in the selection of pubs.

split into drinking areas with a viewing window into the ground level cellar. The attractive garden backs on to the Cathedral close. The 6X and IPA are served from wood. Regular live music is performed.
❀ ◖ ♣ ●

Winchester Gate
113 Rampart Road
✪ 3 (12 Thu-Sat)-11; 12-10.30 Sun
☎ (01722) 322834
website: www.milkstreetbrewery.co.uk
Crouch Vale Brewers Gold; Milk Street Beer; guest beer Ⓗ
Welcoming pub taken over by Milk Street Brewery in 2000. A 16th-century building (former coaching inn) it was extended in the 18th-century and again in the 1950s. It has now been totally refurbished inside and out and is gaining a flourishing local trade. It serves Sun lunch only and booking is advised. Guest beers are from small southern breweries. An October hop festival is held and live music and barbecues are planned. ⇔ ⊟ ♣ P

Wyndham Arms
27 Estcourt Road (off ring road near swimming pool)
✪ 4.30 (3 Fri; 12 Sat)-11; 12-10.30 Sun
☎ (01722) 331026
Hop Back GFB, Best Bitter, Crop Circle, Thunderstorm, Summer Lightning, seasonal beers Ⓗ
Home of the original Hop Back Brewery since 1986, this city pub attracts people from all walks of life. The head of Bacchus greets you in the front, no-smoking room. There is a long, narrow bar with brewery awards on the walls and blackboards above the bar, listing future events. A bridge club is held on Sun. Lunchtime meals are served Mon-Sat. This pub was built as a hotel in 1860 and first owned by Folliotts Brewery.
Q ❀ ◖ ♣ ⊬

SHAW

Golden Fleece
Folly Lane
✪ 11-2.30 (3 Sat), 6-11; 12-3, 7-10.30 Sun
☎ (01225) 702050

Butcombe Bitter, Gold; Marston's Pedigree; Wickwar BOB H

This old coaching inn is on the main road from Bath. There is a comfortable bar and a restaurant in the new, stylish extension. The large, pretty garden overlooks the village cricket pitch. At the front of the pub is the skittle alley. Beers include Wickwar Brand Oak Bitter, more popularly known as BOB and quite rare in this area. The bar food is simple and filling while the restaurant offers normal pub fare.
❀◗♣P

STAPLEFORD

Pelican Inn
Warminster Road
(A36)
✪ 11-2.30 (3 Sat), 6-11; 12-3, 7-10.30 Sun
☎ (01722) 790241 website: www.pelican-inn.co.uk
Greene King Abbot; Otter Bitter; Ringwood Best Bitter; guest beer H

This 18th-century pub takes its name from a galleon which later became Drake's *Golden Hind*. A recent extension of the bar exposed a large inglenook. Serving excellent value food and beer, it retains a true pub feel. It was Wessex CAMRA *Pub of the Year* 2000. It has a quiet area for a peaceful drink and a wealth of amenities including the large, safe garden, which has swings and a slide.
🏨Q❀⇆◗♿♣P

SWINDON ❖

Duke of Wellington
27 Eastcott Hill
(just outside town centre, up into old town)
✪ 12-3 (not Mon-Thu), 6.30-11; 11-11 Sat; 12-10.30 Sun
☎ (01793) 534180
Arkell's 2B, 3B, seasonal beers G

The only pub in Swindon where Arkell's is served on gravity. Typical back-street local, consisting of a bar and a very cosy snug. Named after the famous duke, not for his exploits at Waterloo, but as a tribute to his 1830 Beer House Act. This allowed private houses to sell beer. It was about to be repealed but Arkell's bought two houses and converted them into this unspoilt pub. It opened in March 1869 just before the law changed in October that year. Crib is played Wed eve. Lunchtime meals served Fri–Sun.
🏨Q❀◗♣

Foresters Arms
Common Platt (between west Swindon and Cricklade)
✪ 11-3, 6-11; 12-3, 7-10.30 Sun
☎ (01793) 770615
Courage Best Bitter; Greene King Ruddles Best; Wadworth 6X H

This pub was in no man's land but, following recent building development, it now stands as part of the town. It is a very popular place, attracting customers from miles around. There are two bars, one of which concentrates on food, bookings are advisable. The beer garden has an adjacent children's play area. The staff are very pleasant and friendly.
Q⚲❀◗⊟♿♣P

Plough
26 Devizes Road (at jct of Devizes and Croft Road)
✪ 12-2.30, 6-11; 11 (12 Fri)-11 Sat; 12-3, 7.30-10.30 Sun
☎ (01793) 535603
Arkell's 2B, 3B H

Traditional inn bought by local brewers, Arkell's, in 1867. In 1881 part of the garden was sold to the Swindon and Marlborough railway. The pub has outlasted the railway and is now perched above the cutting which marks the divide between Croft Road and Devizes Road. The former railway track is now a footpath and cycle way. This is a friendly local with a small bar and lounge. Ideal for a quiet, relaxing drink, it is a peaceful contrast to the larger, noisier pubs in Newport Street. ♣

TISBURY

Boot Inn
High Street
✪ 11-2.30, 7-11; 12-2.30, 7-10.30 Sun
☎ (01747) 870363
Thomas Hardy Hardy Country; Greene King Ruddles County; Wells Bombardier G

Popular pub with locals and visitors wanting a chat and drink in a friendly atmosphere. This traditional inn has had a licence since 1768, although parts of the building are older. Beers are served on gravity behind the bar and include a variety of ales in addition to the regulars listed. The spacious garden is a definite bonus. Meals are served lunchtime and eve (not Tue eve).
🏨❀◗⇌♣♣

INN BRIEF

SWINDON

King's Arms Hotel
20 Wood Street
11 (12 Sat)-3, 5.30 (6 Sat)-11; 12-3, 7-10.30 Sun
Arkell's 2B, 3B, Kingsdown, seasonal beers H
An Arkells pub since 1885, this fine Victorian building is a hotel with a busy public bar. Music every Fri, Sat and Sun eve.

Rifleman's Hotel
42 Regent Street
11-11;
12-10.30 Sun
Banks's Original, Bitter H
A large Victorian pub whose exterior has not been altered significantly. It gets quite busy in the evening.

UPTON LOVELL

Prince Leopold
Nr Warminster
12-3 (not Mon), 7-11;
12-3 (closed eve) Sun
Ringwood Best Bitter, XXXX Porter; guest beers (summer) H
Welcoming pub, good food, lovely riverside garden. Built in 1887 and named after Queen Victoria's youngest son, a regular visitor

WOOTTON BASSETT

Five Bells
Wood Street
11-11; 12-10.30 Sun
Courage Directors; John Smith's Bitter; guest beer H
Old-fashioned thatched pub in busy village. Roaring fire in winter. Pleasant beer garden.

Check it out

Pubs in the Good Beer Guide may change ownership and the facilities listed could alter. If a visit to a pub in the guide involves a lengthy journey, it is advisable to check before leaving that full meals, family facilities, accommodation or camping sites are still available.

WANBOROUGH

Plough
High Street
☼ 12-2.30, 5-11; 12-11 Fri; 12-3, 7-10.30 Sun
☎ (01793) 790523
Archers Village; Draught Bass; Fuller's London Pride; Wadworth 6X; guest beer Ⓗ

Attractive thatched Grade II listed building. It was opened as a beer house after 1830. In 1854 the local constable commented that it was the most disorderly house in the village, and it narrowly escaped closure in 1906. Despite this, it remained open and is the only Wanborough pub to have always sold real ale. The present licensee, a noted local character, gutted the bland 1950s interior with his own hands, exposing the beams, bare stone walls and open fireplaces. It is now a cosy, warm pub with much character, serving quality bar meals and ale. Food served Mon–Fri lunchtime and Mon–Sat eves. The walls are adorned with old artefacts and pictures. There is a separate area with bar billiards and darts. The clientele is mainly local, but being near Swindon, the conversation is more likely to be of computers than cattle. Do not be surprised to find vintage car parts or mechanical gadgets on the bar. The landlord sometimes brings his hobbies to work! ⅏Q❀◑Ⓓ╄♣P

True and Proper Drunk

Oh genial and gladdening is the power of good ale, the true and proper drink of an Englishman. He is not deserving of the name of Englishman who speaketh against ale, that is good ale...and yet there are beings, calling themselves Englishmen, who say that it is a sin to drink a cup of ale, and who, on coming to this passage, will be tempted to fling down the book and exclaim, 'The man is evidently a bad man, for behold, by his own confession, he is not only fond of ale himself, but is in the habit of tempting other people with it'.

George Borrow,
Lavengro, 1851.

WHITEPARISH

King's Head
The Street
☼ 12-3, 6.30-11; 12-3.30, 7-10.30 Sun
☎ (01794) 884287
Fuller's London Pride; Ringwood Best Bitter; Wells Bombardier; guest beer Ⓗ

Delightful 16th-century pub on the main street through the village. A quiet, friendly pub with one large bar and a separate games room. This characterful inn has a number of amenities, a large pleasant garden with its own duck pond, a real fire in winter, car parking and good, wholesome food served lunchtime and eve.
⅏Q❀◑Ⓓ⏶P

WILTON

Bear
12 West Street
☼ 11-2.30 3 Sat), 4.30 (5.45 Sat)-11; 12-3, 5.45-10.30 Sun
☎ (01722) 742398
Badger Best Ⓗ

This warmly decorated single bar dates from the 16th century. It features beams and a cosy real fire (in winter). There is a separate area with a pool table and a pleasant beer garden. The landlord has been at the pub for 25 years and offers a friendly welcome to regulars and visitors alike.
⅏❀♣

WINTERBOURNE MONKTON

New Inn
High Street
(follow signs for village off A4361 N of Avebury)
☼ 11-3, 6-11; 12-3, 7-10.30 Sun
☎ (01672) 539240
Archers Village; Wadworth 6X; guest beer Ⓗ

Friendly local with a cosy bar and restaurant area. Note the large display of china plates. Huge children's play area in the garden which, not surprisingly, is very busy in the summer months. This is a pleasant stop-off point if visiting Avebury. Real cider is stocked in summer. Camping facilites are available nearby. Good food served (no meals Sun eve).
⅏❀╊◑Ⓓ⏶♣◍P

WOOTTON BASSETT ❖

Town Local
51 Station Road
(near old railway station)
☼ 11-3, 5-11; 11-11 Sat; 12-10.30 Sun
☎ (01793) 852480
Archers Best Bitter; Fuller's London Pride; guest beer Ⓗ

The landlord has built up a steady trade in the short time he has been resident in this one-bar pub. Much regular entertainment has been laid on; music quiz nights (first and third Thu of month), a trivia quiz (every Tue) and a jazz group playing (first Sun of month). There are plans to install an old railway carriage at the rear of the pub to create an extra room. Good value food is served; two people can eat for £4.99 between 11.30–2 and 5–7, from a selected menu. 'Happy hour' specials are offered between 11–1 and 5–7. Q◑Ⓓ⏶⏶♣P

ARELEY KINGS

King's Arms
19 Redhouse Road (off B4196)
⏰ 12-3, 6-11; 12-11 Fri & Sat; 12-10.30 Sun
☎ (01299) 827132
Banks's Original, Ⓗ Bitter; Ⓟ guest beer Ⓗ
Old, friendly village local with an L-shaped bar and a restaurant. The bar is decorated with jugs hanging from the ceiling beams, old golf clubs on the walls and several 1930s-style mantle clocks. The guest beers come from the current Banks's range. Outside is a garden area, with tables and chairs, and a well-kept bowling green.
⚅◑♣Pⓣ

BEWDLEY ❄

Black Boy
50 Wyre Hill (follow Sandy Bank from B4194 at Welch Gate)
⏰ 12-3, 7-11; 12-3, 7-10.30 Sun
☎ (01299) 403523
Banks's Original, Bitter; Marston's Pedigree, seasonal beers Ⓗ
Not to be confused with the Black Boy Hotel, in nearby Wribbenhall, this comfortable, well-cared for local calls for a steep, but worthwhile, climb from the town – it is only a few minutes' walk for the fit. Dating back several hundred years, the pub has three rooms. Well-behaved children may be allowed in the games room when it is not in use, but check first. ⚏Q⚅⊞♣

Cock & Magpie
Severnside North (N side of River Severn near the bridge)
⏰ 11-11; 12-10.30 Sun
☎ (01299) 403748
Banks's Original, Bitter Ⓟ

Small, two-roomed local, the Cock appeared in the background of many news bulletins during the severe flooding in Nov 2000. Now redecorated, it has lost none of its traditional style, with a central bar serving a basic, tiled public bar and the newly carpeted lounge. A regular *Guide* entry for over 10 years, the Cock is home to thriving dominoes, darts, cribbage and quiz teams, which all compete in local leagues.
Q⊞⇌(SVR)♣ⓣ

Little Pack Horse
31 High Street (near Lax Lane)
⏰ 12-3, 6-11; 12-11 Sat; 12-10.30 Sun
☎ (01299) 403762
website: www.bewdley.actinet.net/startup.htm
Ind Coope Burton Ale; Ushers Best Bitter, seasonal beer Ⓗ
One of Bewdley's oldest pubs, dating back to the 15th century, the Pack Horse has a central bar serving three cosy drinking areas, replete with exposed beams. The first of the defunct Little Pub chain it retains the Mad O'Rourke style – its walls covered with memorabilia and eccentric artefacts and Desperate Dan Cow Pie still on the menu (now joined by more varied meals including

vegetarian options). A no-smoking area is available weekday lunchtimes.

🏠 Q ⌇ ◁ ◑ ⇌ (SVR) ✻

Woodcolliers Arms
76 Welch Gate (foot of Wyre Hill)
⊕ 12-11; 12-10.30 Sun
☎ (01299) 400589
Enville White; Wells Bombardier; guest beers ⒣
A change of ownership at the Woodcolliers in 2000 brought some welcome variety for Bewdley drinkers. Although the previous omnipresent Theakston's still sometimes appears as a guest, it is now augmented by an impressive selection of local and not-so local brews including Hobsons', Wood's, Adnams' and many more. Four comfortable drinking areas surround a central bar, with a food servery at one end. At time of survey meals were only available at weekends, but this may be extended in summer. Slightly off the beaten track, but perseverance will bring its reward.
🏠 ❀ ◁ ◑ ⇌ (SVR)

BIRTSMORTON

Farmers Arms
Birts Street
(off B4208) OS791363
⊕ 11-2.30, 6-11 (11 -11 summer Sat); 12-3, 7-10.30 Sun (12-10.30 summer) Sun
☎ (01684) 833308
Hook Norton Best Bitter, Old Hooky; guest beer ⒣
Black and white pub, tucked away down a country lane. The large bar area, with a real fire, is joined by a small lounge where the warm atmosphere is typically interrupted only by the crack of foreheads against low beams (you have been warned). Home-made traditional food includes classic desserts such as spotted dick. The guest beer is usually from local independents and can be enjoyed in the large safe garden, with swings and fine views of the Malvern Hills.
🏠 Q ❀ ◁ ◑ ⊟ P

BOURNHEATH

Nailers Arms
Doctors Hill
⊕ 12-11; 12-10.30 Sun
☎ (01527) 873045 e-mail: nailersarms@junglelink.com
Enville White; Greene King Old Speckled Hen; guest beers ⒣
Whitewashed, three-gabled building housing a traditional quarry-tiled bar with a real fire, stripped pine furniture and dartboard. The lounge has a distinctly Mediterranean feel to it: raised areas have comfortable armchairs and sofas but the decor is very striking and contemporary. A restaurant, serving an interesting and imaginative menu, is off the lounge. Normally two guest beers are available, often showcasing local breweries.
🏠 ❀ ◁ ◑ ⊟ ♣ ♠ P ✻

BROADWAY

Crown & Trumpet
Church Street
⊕ 11-2.30 (3 summer Mon-Thu), 5-11; (11-11 summer Fri & Sat); 12-4, 6-10.30 (12-10.30 summer) Sun
☎ (01386) 853202
website: www.cotswoldholidays.co.uk
Boddingtons Bitter; Flowers IPA, Original (summer);

Greene King Old Speckled Hen; Stanway Stanney Bitter, guest beers ⒣
17th-century Cotswold inn, just behind the green in the picturesque village of Broadway. A perfect watering-hole for walkers on the Cotswold Way, it boasts many period features – beams, a settle and open fires. It hosts live acoustic music Sat – feel free to give the piano a tinkle. A wide variety of traditional games are played; the locals take part in cribbage, darts, dominoes and quiz leagues. Good grub – try the bangers and mash with onion gravy – excellent! Look out for the Mummers performing at Christmas.
🏠 ❀ ⇌ ◁ ◑ ♣ ♠ P

BROMSGROVE

Golden Cross
20 High Street
⊕ 11-11; 12-10.30 Sun
☎ (01527) 870005
Draught Bass; Courage Directors; Highgate Dark; Shepherd Neame Spitfire; Theakston Best Bitter; guest beers ⒣
This former town-centre hotel was the first to be opened by Wetherspoon's in the area. The interior is very spacious, with a lengthy bar serving around 12 ales. The walls display interesting snippets of local history. At the far end of the building steps lead up to a no-smoking area. In spring and autumn the pub hosts its beer festivals, with an extensive range on offer, some brewed especially for the occasion. Use the Pay and Display parking to the rear.
❀ ◁ ◑ & ♠ ●

Ladybird
2 Finstall Road, Aston Fields (A448 by station)
⊕ 11-11; 12-10.30 Sun
☎ (01527) 878014 website: www.ladybirdinns.co.uk
Batham Best Bitter; Hobsons Best Bitter; guest beers (occasional) ⒣
Formerly the Dragoon, this pub has been redecorated since it was saved from closure in 1997. The use of pine gives a light, airy feel to the bar and lounge. The no-smoking dining area retains its no-smoking rule when no food is served (no meals Sun). There are three function rooms, the largest is on the ground floor, while the other two are upstairs; all of them can be booked, with catering for up to 120 people.
❀ ◁ ◑ ⊟ & ⇌ P

CHADDESLEY CORBETT

Swan
High Street
⊕ 11-3, 6-11; 11-11 Sat; 12-3, 7-10.30 Sun
☎ (01562) 777302
website: www.midlandspubs.co.uk
Batham Mild, Best Bitter, XXX ⒣
Circa 1606, this comfortable village pub is set in a picturesque black and white timbered village. The excellent traditional bar enjoys a good atmosphere, while the comfortable large lounge to the side has a rustic feel. There is also a small drinking area to the rear and a restaurant on the other side (no food Sun eve or Mon). A jazz band plays every Thu eve and it hosts occasional Irish bands. A large garden to the rear offers summer barbecues.
🏠 Q ❀ ◁ ◑ ⊟ ♣ ♠ P

DODFORD

Dodford Inn

Whinfield Road (off A448, near Bournheath)
OS939729

✪ 12-3, 6.30-11; 12-3, 7-10.30 Sun

☎ (01527) 832470 e-mail: larry.dodfordinn@virgin.net

Banks's Original; Flowers IPA; guest beers Ⓗ

Small, country pub set in beautiful rolling countryside, the Dodford can be difficult to find, but the views from the garden are quite magnificent. The pub is popular with ramblers and there are camping and caravanning facilities on site. A single room, with a real fire in the centre, the bar is to one side. A good range of food always includes daily specials. Biddenden cider is stocked. A popular folk and beer festival is held in July.

曲⊛◑Å♣♠P⊁

DRAYTON

Robin Hood

Drayton Road

(off B4188, between Belbroughton and Chaddesley) OS906758

✪ 12-3, 5-11; 12-11 Sat; 12-10.30 Sun

☎ (01562) 730255

Ansells Bitter; guest beers Ⓗ

Friendly pub serving excellent, reasonably priced food to complement the equally superb range of beers (four guests). Inside, several stained glass windows depict Robin Hood and his Merry Men. With a real fire, it is a very cosy place to spend an hour or three. The small beamed bar is decorated with caricatures of customers, bar staff and darts players; the lounge is equally inviting. Outside there is a playground, and a miniature zoo; tethering posts and dog bowls are provided.

曲Q⊛◑⊟♠P

DROITWICH ❖

Railway Inn

Kidderminster Road (from A38, Westlands island next to canal) OS896636

✪ 12-11; (10.30 summer); 12-10.30 Sun

☎ (01905) 770056

Banks's Mild; Marston's Bitter, Pedigree; guest beers Ⓗ

Small, basic, two-roomed pub by the Droitwich barge canal, within easy reach of the old market town centre. A friendly atmosphere can be enjoyed among the railway memorabilia. Bar food is good value and freshly prepared (not served Sun). A rooftop patio overlooks the restored canal basin. Quiz nights, dominoes and regular beer festivals, with a variety of musical traditions, provide entertainment. The guest beers are from Banks's range.

⊛◑⊟≢♠P

ELDERSFIELD

Greyhound

Lime Street (off B4211) OS815304

✪ 11.30-2.30 (3 Sat), 6 (7 Mon)-11; 12-3, 7-10.30 Sun

☎ (01452) 840381

Butcombe Bitter; Wadworth 6X; guest beer Ⓖ

Set in a labyrinth of winding lanes and toying with the border of Gloucestershire (it has a Gloucester postcode and telephone number), the Greyhound is far from the easiest prey to chase. The maze is well worth navigating. With stone flags, bentwood benches, log fires, a tranquil garden, on-site camping and gravity-dispensed beer, the pub has all of the trappings of an unspoilt rural watering-hole (check availability of food before setting off). A small, but busy beer festival is held in June.

曲Q⊛◑⊟ÅP⊁

EVESHAM ❖

Trumpet

Merstow Green (near library)

✪ 11-11; 12-10.30 Sun

☎ (01386) 446227

Hook Norton Best Bitter, Old Hooky, Generation, seasonal beers; guest beers Ⓗ

Next to the fire station, the pub was acquired by Hook Norton in 1999 and has gone from strength to strength. The burnt orange walls, redwood slatted blinds and cane furniture give it a Mediterranean feel, but the cuisine is predominantly English – it offers sausages of the day, and liver and bacon with black pudding. No accommodation at the pub, but it operates a nearby B&B (with 10% discount on pub meals to guests). Live music is staged alternate Wed eves. 曲⊛≢◑&≢

GREAT MALVERN

Great Malvern Hotel

Graham Road

✪ 10-11; 11-10.30 Sun

☎ (01684) 563411

Fuller's London Pride; Wood Shropshire Lad; guest beer Ⓗ

Victorian hotel built during Malvern's heyday as a spa, with a friendly public bar used by residents and visitors alike. Near Malvern's theatre and cinema complex, the hotel goes out of its way to enhance your evening – meals and a pint of real ale can be enjoyed in the bar, or adjoining brasserie, before or after a performance. The actors often stay at the hotel. A comprehensive menu uses fresh local produce wherever possible, and features award-winning sausages with bubble and squeak. Limited parking.

Q⊱≢◑≢P

Malvern Hills Hotel

Wynds Point

(A449/B4232 jct, British Camp)

✪ 11-11; 12-10.30 Sun

☎ (01684) 540690

Fuller's London Pride; Greene King Abbot; Hobsons Best Bitter; Malvern Hills Black Pear; guest beer Ⓗ

Oak-panelled bar in an upmarket, recently refurbished hotel on the ridge of the Malvern Hills, directly opposite the British Camp hill fort (constructed for 2nd-century BC feuds) and the Red Earl's dyke (built for 14th-century feuds – this time between landowners). The long-distance Worcestershire Way passes within a few hundred yards. Usually two guest beers are stocked in summer, when visitors can enjoy the patio, with views to the Black Mountains in Wales. Live music is staged Tue and Sun.

曲⊛≢◑♠P⊁

HANLEY CASTLE

Three Kings Inn ☆
Church End (off B4211)
🕑 12-3 (can vary), 7-11; 12-3, 7-10.30 Sun
☎ (01684) 592686
Butcombe Bitter; Thwaites Bitter; guest beers Ⓗ
Traditional black and white 15th-century gem that celebrated 90 years with the same family in 2001. An intimate snug combines with the larger Nell's Bar, both with log fires, and a family room with no bar. It won national CAMRA *Pub of the Year* awards in 1993 and '97. Nearly 2,000 different ales have been served since counting began in the early 1990s, a figure which is boosted by a beer festival (Nov). Organised musical performances (Sun and some Sat eves) are often supplemented by informal jamming sessions at other times. ▲Q☽🏠🛏️◑♣♠

ISMERE

Old Waggon & Horses
Stourbridge Road (A451)
🕑 11.30-3.30, 6-11; 12-3, 7-11 Sun
☎ (01562) 700298
Banks's Original, Bitter; Ⓟ **Marston's Pedigree; guest beer** Ⓗ
Early 19th-century former brewhouse where the bar, with its old-fashioned, panelled bar front, etched windows and quarry-tiled floor has a basic, but homely feel. The L-shaped lounge, with exposed beams and two fireplaces has a comfy air. The dining area admits children and offers a varied menu with a good choice of vegetarian dishes; Thai food is served Sun. The guest beer comes from the Banks's range.
▲Q🏠◑🍴♣P🍽️

KEMPSEY

Walter de Cantelupe
Main Road
🕑 12-2, 6-11; closed Mon; 12-2, 7-10.30 Sun
☎ (01905) 820572 e-mail: walter.depub@fsbdial.co.uk
Malvern Hills Black Pear (winter)**; Taylor Landlord; guest beers** Ⓗ
Attractive free house in a large village three miles south of Worcester and only 10 minutes' walk from the River Severn. The bar has an inglenook and, for the summer, there is an attractive walled garden. A wide selection of beers and wine is complemented by an ever-changing, high quality food menu. The ploughmans and doorstep sandwiches, made with local bread, are specialities. Look out for the annual outdoor paella party and the biennial 'beer elections'. Rich's Farmhouse cider served in summer ▲★🏠🛏️◑♠P

KEMPSEY GREEN STREET

Huntsman Inn
Green Street (from A38 at Kempsey, via Post Office Lane, 2 miles) OS868491
🕑 12-3 (not Mon), 6-11; 12-4, 7-10.30 Sun
☎ (01905) 820336
Batham Best Bitter; Everards Beacon, Tiger Ⓗ
Comfortable free house offering a homely atmosphere that is popular with locals. Not content with being the only regular outlet for Everards for miles, the owners go out of their way – literally, requiring close on a 100-mile round trip – to pick up the Batham's. Covering several rooms, the bar and restaurant areas have exposed beams and open fires throughout – all of which contribute to a strong food trade. Impressive skittle alley has its own bar.
▲Q☽★◑🍴♣P

KIDDERMINSTER

Boar's Head (Tap House)
39 Worcester Street (near Glades Arena Sports Centre)
🕑 12-11, 12-3, 7-10.30 Sun
☎ (01562) 862450
Banks's Original, Bitter; Camerons Strongarm; Marston's Pedigree; guest beers Ⓗ
Red-brick Victorian, town-centre pub boasting two bars and a small garden. The small lounge is comfy, with part oak-panelled walls, settles and subdued lighting. The bar has a more basic feel with bar stools and tables. An open passageway leads to a covered courtyard where tables and chairs are warmed by overhead gas heaters in cold weather. A working red telephone box is built into the wall between the bar and courtyard. No food Sun. ▲★◑🍴≠🍽️

Hare & Hounds
120 Stourbridge Road
(A449, 1½ miles from centre)
🕑 11-11, 12-10.30 Sun
☎ (01562) 753897

INN BRIEF

BASTONFORD
Halfway House
12-3 (not Mon), 6-11; 12-10.30 Sun
Marston's Pedigree; guest beers Ⓗ
Between Worcester and Malvern on the A449; one drinking bar, one for dining. Guests come from local micros. Real cider and extensive food menu.

BEWDLEY
Tipplers
70 Load Street
10-10; 12-10 Sun
Hook Norton Old Hooky, Best Bitter, guest beers Ⓗ
Town-centre off-licence stocking a wide range of bottled and foreign beers and cider. Will order beers not usually stocked if possible.

DROITWICH
Gardeners Arms
47 Vines Lane
12 (11 summer Fri & Sat)-11; 12-10.30 Sun
Banks's Hanson's Mild, Original, Bitter; Ⓟ **guest beer** Ⓗ
Cosy, two-roomed pub, near Vines Park, and Droitwich Barge Canal. Garden with children's play area. Traditional Sun lunch.

EVESHAM
Old Swanne Inne
66 High Street (by bus station)
11-11; 12-10.30 Sun
Banks's Original; Shepherd Neame Spitfire; Theakston Best Bitter; Wadworth 6X; guest beers Ⓗ
Former coaching inn converted by Wetherspoon's; the cheapest and quietest pub in the town centre. *Cask Marque* accredited.

MALVERN LINK
New Inn
105 Lower Howsell Road
12-2, 6-11; 12-3, 7-11 Sat; 12.30-3, 7-10.30 Sun
Banks's Original, Bitter; Ⓟ **Marston's Pedigree** Ⓗ
Genuine, two-roomed, basic bar and a plush lounge. Very strong community spirit, with several events staged annually.

PEBWORTH
Masons Arms
Broad Marston Road
12-2, 6-11; 12-3, 7-11 Sat; 12.30-3, 7-10.30 Sun
Draught Bass; Hook Norton Bitter; guest beers Ⓗ
Friendly village pub with a skittle alley; families welcome. No food Tue. Weekly guest beers.

Enville Ale; Highgate Dark; Theakston Best Bitter;
guest beers ⒣

Large, main road pub, refurbished by
Wetherspoon's after a period of closure.
This bright and airy local now sports a
single bar with a number of drinking areas
around it, some on different levels. Outside
the small patio and enclosed garden area
share a single exit – ideal for families – no
children are allowed inside. The pub offers
all the usual Wetherspoon's features and is
close to the Rose Theatre. Meals available all
day (until 9.30pm Sun).
Q❀⟨❶&P↦●

King & Castle
SVR Station, Comberton Hill (next to mainline
station)
◷ 11-3, 5-11; 11-11 Sat; 12-10.30 Sun
☎ (01562) 747505
**Ansells Mild; Batham Best Bitter; Wyre Piddle Royal
Piddle; guest beers** ⒣

This elegant pub, a recreation of a typical
Great Western Railway refreshment room of
the 1930s, is at the Kidderminster terminus
of the Severn Valley Railway. The GWR
association is commemorated by two
station clocks, numerous photographs of
railways and a carpet, with its original GWE
pattern, reproduced by a local carpet
factory. It welcomes children (away from
the bar) until 9pm. Shops (open when
trains are running) and a wheelchair WC
are on the concourse. It hosts live music
and occasional private parties.
🏮Q❀⟨❶&⇌●

KNIGHTWICK
Talbot
On B4197, 400 yds from A44 jct
◷ 11-11; 12-10.30 Sun
☎ (01886) 821235 e-mail: teme_valley@aol.com
**Hobsons Best Bitter; Teme Valley T'Other, This, That,
seasonal beer** ⒣

In an idyllic setting, next to the old coach
road bridge over the River Teme, this is a
family-owned hotel, partly dating back to
the 14th century. At the rear of the building
is the Teme Valley Brewery, also owned by
the family, which uses only locally-grown
hops. The restaurant offers imaginative
good quality food, made wherever possible
from local (some home-grown) organic
produce. Meals can be taken in the bar or

oak-panelled dining room; a take-away
menu is available. 🏮Q❀⇌⟨❶ ⊟P

MALVERN LINK ❉
Nag's Head
21 Bank Street, Link Top
(uphill from station)
◷ 11-11; 12-10.30 Sun
☎ (01684) 574373
e-mail: duncanironmonger@woolpackinn.fsnet.co.uk
Marston's Pedigree; guest beers ⒣

Usually serving six different cask ales, this
traditional pub is popular with all ages.
Recently redecorated and refurbished in
keeping with the original style, it has a
function room (the Nag's Tail) with a bar
for private hire. The main pub is open plan
with differing floor levels and archways;
plants are a feature. Games are played and
two morris dancing sides meet here to
practise Mon and Tue. Within 10 minutes'
walk are the hills and Great Malvern town
centre.
🏮❀⟨❶⇌♣P

Swan
Newland (off A449)
◷ 12-3, 7 (6 summer)-11; 12-3, 7-10.30 Sun
☎ (01886) 832224
e-mail: johnlhuillier.swan@virgin.net
**Hobsons Best Bitter; Hook Norton Best Bitter;
Shepherd Neame Spitfire; guest beer** (summer) ⒣

Unusual long bar in a creeper-clad old brick
building situated on common land, close to
Madresfield Court with its gardens and
maze. Exposed beams, hops, brasses and an
eclectic range of prints and pictures feature.
An extensive menu can be enjoyed in the
bar or dining area; oriental food is a
speciality (no meals winter Tue eve).
Visitors can watch cricket on the
neighbouring picturesque ground.
🏮Q❀⟨❶&P

MAMBLE
Sun & Slipper
Signed on A456, approx ¼ mile
◷ 12-3 (not Mon), 6.30-11; 12-3, 7-10.30 Sun
☎ (01299) 832018
**Banks's Original, Bitter; Hobsons Best Bitter; guest
beer** ⒣

Comfortable, two-roomed village pub with
a pool table in the bar and hops decorating

POUND GREEN
Olde New Inn
12-4, 6-11;
12-10.30 Sun
**Draught Bass; Theakston Mild; guest
beer** ⒣
Olde-worlde country pub with a
restaurant. Several beamed areas
surround a central bar. 15 minutes'
walk from SVR Arley station.

REDDITCH
Brodies
163 Evesham Road, Headless Cross
5.30 (4 Fri, 12 Sat)-11;
12-3, 7-10.30 Sun
Beer range varies ⒣
Friendly weekday local becomes
crowded and boisterous weekend
eves. A regular bitter is
supplemented by a changing guest.
Bizarre curios, a pool table and
garden complete the picture.

STOURPORT-ON-SEVERN
Wheatsheaf
39 High Street
10.30-11;
12-10.30 Sun
Banks's Hanson's Mild, Original, Bitter Ⓟ
Town-centre pub, with a bar and
lounge, close to the river.
Lunchtime snacks available, plus
Sun lunches.

WEST MALVERN
Lamb Inn
87 West Malvern Road
12-2 (not Mon-Wed; 2.30 Sat), 6 (7 Sat)-
11 (seasonal variations);
12-3, 7-10.30 Sun
Beer range varies ⒣
Revitalised village local thriving
under new owners. Spacious bar
and eating areas serving high
quality cuisine. Rare bar billiards
table.

WORCESTER
Bush
4 The Bull Ring, St John's
11-3, 5.30-11; 11-11 Sat;
12-3, 7-10.30 Sun
**Banks's Original, Bitter; Fuller's London
Pride; M&B Brew XI; guest beer** ⒣
Traditional, multi-roomed pub,
served from a delightful Victorian
bar. The upstairs restaurant serves
food every day.

Lamb & Flag
30 The Tything
11-2 (2.30 Fri; 3 Sat), 5.30 (6 Sat)-11;
12-2.30, 7-10.30 Sun
**Mansfield Riding Bitter; Marston's Bitter,
Pedigree** ⒣
Two small rooms off a narrow
entrance alleyway. Its size is
inversely proportional to its iconic
status among pub-goers.

the ceiling. By a small green in the village centre, it stands opposite a craft centre, which is also well worth visiting. The small, cosy bar is frequented by local drinkers, while the restaurant attracts diners from further afield (no meals Sun eve).

ᴁ❀◑Ⅰ▲♣P🖰

MONKWOOD GREEN

Fox Inn
Follow signs to Wichenford, off A443 at Hallow
OS803601
☼ 12-2, 6.30-11; 12-3, 6.30-10.30 Sun
☎ (01886) 889123
Cannon Royall Fruiterer's Mild, Arrowhead, Buckshot Ⓗ

Traditional, one-bar country pub, little changed in over 30 years, it comprises two distinct drinking areas, one with an inglenook and beamed ceiling. Popular with walkers and cyclists due to its proximity to Monkwood Nature Reserve, the pub is set back from the road, bordering common land, with views of the Malvern Hills. Watch out for the assorted fowl that patrol the parking area. Informal folk music sessions are held monthly (last Fri). It is a rare outlet for locally-produced Barker's farmhouse cider and perry.

ᴁQ❀◑Ⅰ▲♣P

OFFENHAM

Bridge Inn
Boat Lane (follow signs for river)
☼ 11-11; 12-10.30 Sun
☎ (01386) 446565
Bateman XB, seasonal beers; Caledonian Deuchars IPA; Greene King Ruddles Best; guest beers Ⓗ

Ancient riverside inn, with its own moorings and a patio garden leading down to the Avon. The eponymous bridge was washed away in the 17th century and replaced by a ferry, so it is often called the Boat locally. Devastated by the floods of Easter 1998, it has since been completely refurbished, and retains a vibrant public bar. The favoured watering-hole of several local clubs and sports teams, no intrusive music invades the lounge. A courtesy minibus is available to collect and deliver groups.

ᴁQ❀◑Ⅰ▣♣P

PENSAX

Bell
On B4202, S of village
☼ 12-2.30 (not Mon), 5-11;
12-10.30 Sun
☎ (01299) 896677
Archers Golden; guest beers Ⓗ

Comfortable, solid, mock-Tudor pub and former shooting lodge. The L-shaped bar features cushioned, pew style setting, wood panelling, pendulous hops and collections of beer mats and cockerels. These, combined with the wood-burning stove, give a traditional feel. Off the quarry-tiled entrance hall is a smaller, quieter room; the no-smoking dining room welcomes children. Guest beers often hail from local independents, two are normally under 4% ABV.

ᴁQ❀◑Ⅰ🐷P

PERSHORE

Brandy Cask
25 Bridge Street
☼ 11.30-2.30 (3 Sat), 7-11; 12-3, 7-10.30 Sun
☎ (01386) 552602
Brandy Cask Whistling Joe, Brandysnapper, John Baker's Original, Ale Mary, Courage Directors; Greene King Ruddles Best; guest beer Ⓗ

On the main drag of a bustling market town, this is a deservedly popular local. From brewing its own beer – yet still offering up to four others – to landscaping a long, attractive garden stretching down to the Avon, lavish attention has been paid to the entire drinking experience. An added attraction is the August bank holiday beer festival, when around 70 firkins are somehow accommodated. A mooring point is available for rivercraft.

ᴁQ❀◑Ⅰ

REDDITCH ✣

Sportsman's Arms
Peakman Street (opp. library)
☼ 11-11; 12-10.30 Sun
☎ (01527) 62518
Banks's Original; M&B Brew XI; guest beer Ⓗ

The Sportsman is an unpretentious town boozer, in the centre of Redditch. It comprises a comfortable lounge, boasting sporting prints and trophies, and a small public bar at the front. Both rooms have their own bars to serve the friendly, lively clientele. Situated across from the main shopping centre, many weary shoppers find a welcome rest from their exertions here. Parking space is available for orange badge holders at the back of the pub, which is not easy to find the first time.

▣≈♣

Woodland Cottage
102 Mount Pleasant
☼ 12-3, 5.30-11; 12-11 Fri & Sat; 12-3, 7-10.30 Sun
☎ (01527) 402299
Boddingtons Bitter; Fuller's London Pride; guest beers Ⓗ

Situated at one of the highest points in Redditch, the car park affords spectacular views over the town. Parts of the building are believed to be Elizabethan. A large open-plan lounge, with a single long bar, is divided into smaller areas. Frequent events such as Karaoke, quiz nights, live bands (Thu eve) and occasional folk bands (Fri and Sat eve) all contribute to the pub's lively, convivial atmosphere. Two guest beers often showcase local breweries. ❀P

RIPPLE

Railway Inn
Station Road OS874377
☼ 11 (6 Mon)-11; 12-3, 7-10.30 Sun
☎ (01684) 592225
Malvern Hills Black Pear; guest beers Ⓗ

Busy, community village pub half a mile from the Severn where walkers and anglers are regular, and appreciated, visitors. A restaurant area is to the front, with further seating areas all around. To the rear, a large function room houses a skittle alley and pool tables. The capacious car park has room for coaches, that are always welcome.

⛼❀◑Ⅰ▣♣P

SHENSTONE

Plough

Off A450/A448 OS865735
12-3, 6-11; 12-3, 7-10.30 Sun
☎ (01562) 777340
Batham Mild, Best Bitter, XXX H
One of the 'Batham's Nine'; a pleasant popular country pub off the beaten track, comprising a bar and a divided lounge. A homely, cosy pub with a real fire where one section of the lounge displays a collection of pictures of the Falklands War. Outside is a covered, enclosed courtyard where children are allowed. A small grassed area at the front has tables and benches. Well worth seeking out for excellent ale at excellent prices. Q P

STONEHALL COMMON

Fruiterer's Arms

From Norton, first left after garden centre OS882489
12-2, 6-11; 12-10.30 Sun
☎ (01905) 820462
Worthington Bitter; guest beers H
Large country inn, with a new restaurant and conservatory blending in behind the much older original house. It attracts a strong food trade due to its extensive menu. The bar area is welcoming, with wood panelling and an open fire. Three guests are the norm, with micros strongly supported. In summer the large garden is a treat, affording views of the Malverns and Bredon Hill. Children can play in the impressive adventure area. Good access and wheelchair WC. P

STOURPORT-ON-SEVERN

Old Crown

9 Bridge Street (main street, near river bridge)
11-11; 12-10.30 Sun
☎ (01299) 825693
Banks's Original; Courage Directors; Shepherd Neame Spitfire; Theakston Best Bitter; guest beers H
Close to the riverside and amusement park, the pub is the latest Wetherspoon's to open in the area. Following refurbishment, having been opened out inside, it has a large drinking area with the bar down one side and plenty of tables and chairs. It is light and airy, displaying pictures of old Stourport on the walls. A patio area overlooks the River Severn and one of James Brindley's historic river basins. Meals are served all day until 10pm (9.30 Sun).
Q P

TENBURY WELLS

Ship Inn

Teme Street
11-3, 7-11; 12-3, 7-10.30 Sun
☎ (01584) 810269
Hobsons Best Bitter; guest beer H
Whitewashed town house, easily recognisable from its impressive, overflowing window baskets in which the landlord takes great pride (to the extent that they are monitored by CCTV). The interior is almost Tardis-like, with a small but comfortable bar area, a larger dining area and an even larger garden. Renowned for its food, the blackboard lists mouth-watering meals – duck à l'orange, salmon in dill – with prices to match. The restaurant is no-smoking and drinkers are welcome to sup there during quiet periods. P

Star pubs

Pubs with a star symbol next to their names are listed in CAMRA's National Inventory of pubs with interiors of outstanding interest. The full list is printed in the guide.

UPHAMPTON

Fruiterer's Arms

Uphampton Lane (off A449 at Reindeer Pub, near Ombersley)) OS839649
12.30 (12 Sat)-3, 7-11; 12-3, 7-10.30 Sun
☎ (01905) 620305
Cannon Royall Fruiterer's Mild, Arrowhead, Buckshot; John Smith's Bitter, seasonal beers H
This unspoilt country pub, the home of Cannon Royall Brewery, has a cosy, homely lounge and a public bar, both friendly and welcoming. The lounge, with half-timbered walls and a wood-panelled bar, boasts a grandfather clock and the walls are decorated with old local pictures, antique sporting guns and horse harnesses. Basic home-cooked food, includes excellent sandwiches and baguettes, with, unusually, freshly-made mustard. The approach to the pub is down a short country lane; local produce is often on sale. Q P

UPTON UPON SEVERN

White Lion Hotel

High Street
11-11; 12-10.30 Sun
☎ (01684) 592551
website: www.whitelionhotel.demon.co.uk
Beer range varies H
16th-century hotel in a riverside town with Civil War connections, including the site of the Battle of Upton Bridge. The drinking area is divided in two: one part given over to comfy sofas, the other more bar-like with bench seats and tables. Beers on offer all come from micro-brewers, with usually at least one from the local region. Fine food is served in the Pepperpot Brasserie. Those arriving by boat can use one of the hotel's mooring points.
P

WEATHEROAK

Coach & Horses

Weatheroak Hill (Alvechurch-Wythall road)
11.30-2.30, 5.30-11; 11.30-11 Fri & Sat; 12-10.30 Sun
☎ (01564) 823386
Black Sheep Best Bitter; Weatheroak Light Oak, Weatheroak, Redwood; Wood Special; guest beers H
Attractive pub, near a disused windmill and next to a Roman road, comprising a characterful, stone-flagged public bar and a

split-level lounge. To the side is a modern restaurant serving a full range of food to accompany the eight real ales on tap. Gardens surrounding the pub are popular in the summer. Home of the Weatheroak Brewery, it hosts frequent beer festivals, often accompanied by local morris groups. Local CAMRA *Pub of the Year* 1999 and 2000. ⚜Q❄🌙🍽♿🅰♣P

WORCESTER ❄

Bell
35 St John's
🔵 11-3, 5.30-11; 11-4, 7-11 Sat; 12-3, 7-10.30 Sun
☎ (01905) 424570
Fuller's London Pride; M&B Brew XI; guest beer ⊞
Friendly, traditional drinkers' pub, comprising a main bar and two small side rooms, one of which is designated a family room. Pub games play an important rôle here with darts, dominoes and cribbage being enjoyed regularly; several trophies are on display in the bar. There is a skittle alley at the rear of the pub. The guest beer is usually from a local brewery and changes every other month. 🌿♣

Berkeley Arms
School Road, St John's (off Bransford Rd, A4103)
🔵 11-2.30, 5-11; 11.30-11 Fri, Sat & summer; 12-3, 7-10.30 Sun
☎ (01905) 421427
Banks's Hansons Mild, Original, Bitter; ℗ **Marston's Pedigree** ⊞
No-nonsense, traditional local where beer – not food – is the order of the day. Two distinctly separate rooms are served from a single bar. TV is restricted to the bar, leaving the lounge as a comfortable place to chat. The new handpump usually serves Pedigree but may serve different beers from the Banks's stable. A third room, at the back of the pub, is used for darts matches (Tue) but on other nights doubles as a family room. A popular quiz is held Sun eve. 🌿❄🍽♣P🅳

Dragon Inn
51 The Tything
🔵 12-11; 12-10.30 Sun
☎ (01905) 25845
Beer range varies ⊞

Georgian listed building, dating from around 1750, the pub is full of character – and CAMRA awards, including local *Pub of the Year* 1999 and 2000, and Herefordshire and Worcestershire winner 2000. Numerous others from the '80s and '90s, establish the pub as a long-standing haven for ale enthusiasts. The usual range of six ales and two ciders all come from independents and micros. Stouts and porters feature in winter. ❄≢ (Foregate St) ♠

Plough
23 Fish Street, Deansway
(next to fire station)
🔵 12-3, 8-11; closed Mon & Tue; 8-10.30 Sun
☎ (01905) 21381
Shepherd Neame Spitfire; guest beers ⊞
Historic, listed, two-roomed pub with hidden priest holes and rumoured smuggling tunnels to the Severn from the cellar. The landlord is proud of his Basque origins and his nickname of 'Tony Never Opens' (a result of the slightly idiosyncratic opening hours). Other quirks to watch for are the mobile phone fines (donated to charity) and a portable TV that appears for important football matches. This enthusiastic supporter of local breweries serves good value, simple bar snacks at lunchtime, when an area is set aside for non-smokers.
Q❄◖≢ (Foregate St) ✂

Swan with Two Nicks
28 New Street (by Cornmarket)
🔵 11-11; 7-10.30 Sun
☎ (01905) 28190
Boddingtons Bitter; guest beers ⊞
Vibrant, multi-level free house with extensive oak fittings and beams, common in this historic part of Worcester. Watch your head as you explore its various nooks and crannies. Three ever-changing guest beers usually include an offering from a local micro; it also stocks a huge selection of malts. Look out for the many assorted old tin signs. The upstairs restaurant is especially popular for lunch, but meals can be taken in the bar (eve meals Thu–Sat). Quizzes, crib and bridge are regular events. 🌿◖≢ (Shrub Hill/Foregate St) ♣

Choosing Pubs

CAMRA members and branches choose the pubs listed in the Good Beer Guide. There is no payment for entry, and pubs are inspected on a regular basis by personal visits; publicans are not sent a questionnaire once a year, as is the case with some pub guides. CAMRA branches monitor all the pubs in their areas, and the choice of pubs for the guide is often the result of democratic vote at branch meetings. However, recommendations from readers are welcomed and will be passed on to the relevant branch: write to Good Beer Guide, CAMRA, 230 Hatfield Road, St Albans, AL1 4LW; or send an e-mail to camra@camra.org.uk

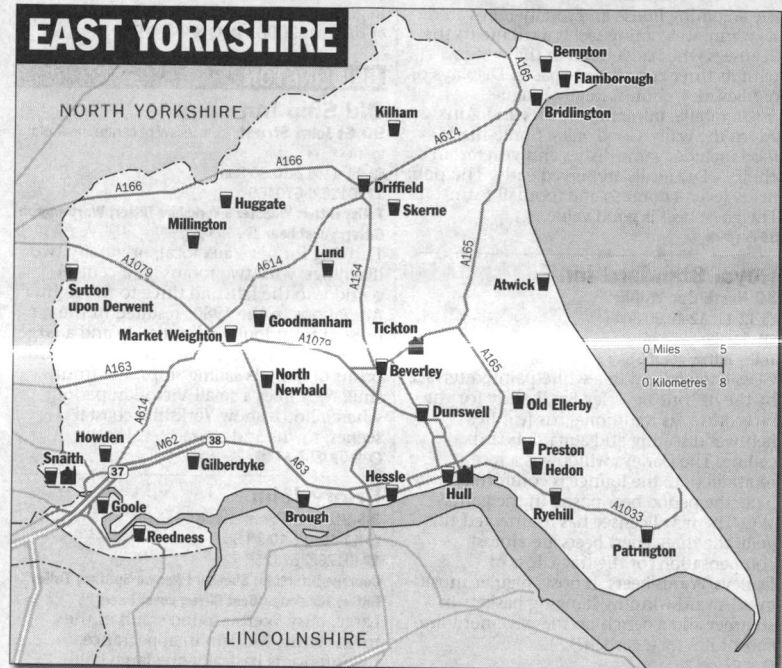

EAST YORKSHIRE

Yorkshire (East)

ATWICK

Black Horse
Church Street
☎ 11.30-3, 6-11; 11.30-11 Sat; 12-10.30 Sun
☎ (01964) 532691 e-mail: jac.thompson@lunie.net
John Smith's Bitter; guest beers Ⓗ

Two miles north of Hornsea, overlooking the village green, this building dates from the mid-18th century and has one room plus a restaurant area. The traditional cottage-style decor is enhanced by old pictures and prints and low beamed ceilings. Unusual guest beers are occasionally available. Food come in generous portions with a specials board, and curry nights as added attractions. It fields a darts, dominoes and cricket team. Many local footpaths pass nearby, including one to a memorial of a WWII bomber crew. Listen carefully for the footsteps of a previous landlord. ✿◖◗▲♣P

BEVERLEY ✣

Corner House
2 Norwood
☎ 12-2.30, 5-11; 12-11 Fri; 11-11 Sat; 12-10.30 Sun
☎ (01482) 882652
Greene King Abbot; Taylor Landlord; Tetley Bitter; Rooster's Yankee; guest beers Ⓗ

Former Tetley pub, known as the Valiant Soldier, this historic building was gutted by the previous owners as a Firkin identikit pub for youngsters. Fortunately this gimmick did not last and Corner House has quickly become a well-respected pub/café bar serving quality fare in colourful surroundings. The licensee, a former Tynemill manager, offers varied guest beers plus 50 single malts, vodkas, gins and cocktails. Food is a speciality, mostly home made with vegetarian and vegan choices. Various teas and coffee are available and English breakfast is served weekends 10am-1pm. Eve meals finish at 8pm. ✿◖◗P

Dog & Duck Inn
33 Ladygate
☎ 11-4; 7-11; 11-11 Sat; 12-3, 7-10.30 Sun
☎ (01482) 862419 website: www.dog&duckinn.co.uk
Greene King Abbot; John Smith's Bitter; guest beer Ⓗ

Solid public house down a side street off the main Saturday market and next to the historic picture playhouse; built in the 1930s this John Smith's house has been in the same family for 30 years and features an imposing entrance lobby with stained glass fanlight. The interior comprises a former tap room with period painted brick fireplace and bentwood seating, a lounge and a rear snug area, but dividing walls have been removed. The good value home-cooked lunches are popular and include pensioners specials. The guest beer changes fortnightly. ⌂♫◗♣

Moulders Arms
32 Wilbert Lane (off New Walkergate, near Safeway)
☎ 11-11; 12-10.30 Sun
☎ (01482) 867033 website: http://come.to/moulders
Stones Bitter; Worthington Bitter; Theakston Cool Cask; guest beer Ⓗ

Street-corner former Worthington house near the station. In 1996, the building, now owned by Century Inns, was extended into

INDEPENDENT BREWERIES

Hull Hull
Old Mill Snaith
Wawne Tickton

the adjoining house and totally renovated. Its warm, welcoming feel is a tribute to the licensees who had a hand in the design, with its three connecting spaces. Displays of old Beverley photos, Rugby League memorabilia, miniature bottles and guns adorn the walls. Good value home-made food includes game dishes and vegetarian choices. Eve meals are served early. The pub fields several domino and football teams. The guest beer is good value.
◑ ⑤ ⮂ ♣

Royal Standard Inn
30 North Bar Within
☼ 12-11; 12-10.30 Sun
☎ (01482) 882434
Tetley Bitter; guest beers Ⓗ

Classic town local in a white-painted terrace by the historic Beverley Bar, handy for the racecourse. Its traditional bar features bentwood seating and a matchboard ceiling. The Darleys window is a recent reproduction; the lounge is comfortable. Note the period beer poster in the gents' WC. The new licensee has resurrected this gem; the three guest beers are almost compensation for the tragic loss of Darleys/Wards beers. It hosts regular music eves. Award-winning hanging baskets in summer and a bench on the pavement are substitutes for a garden.
Q ❀ ⮰

Sun Inn
1 Flemingate
☼ 12-11; 12-10.30 Sun
☎ (01482) 881547
Greene King IPA; guest beers Ⓗ

Medieval timber-framed building, set opposite the east front of Beverley Minster, and reputed to be the town's oldest pub. Its spartan interior, with flagstone floors, bare brick walls and wooden seating, dates from 1994 when it became a Tap & Spile outlet serving up to eight guest beers. The welcome change back to the Sun Inn took place in 2000, but the guest beers remain as popular as ever. This is an acoustic music venue with sessions Tue eve and open mike/folk Sun from 3.30 till late. Good value home-made meals (served 12-7 Fri-Sun). Fare from the Beverley Mustard Co. is on sale.
❀ ◑ ⮂ ♣ ♠ ⠧

White Horse Inn (Nellies) ☆
22 Hengate (by bus station)
☼ 11-11; 12-10.30 Sun
☎ (01482) 861973 website: www.nellies.co.uk
Samuel Smith OBB Ⓗ

One of Beverley's landmarks, this historic inn offers a multi-roomed interior with gas lighting, stone-flagged and quarry-tiled floors; all five rooms often have coal fires. In its heyday in Victorian times farmers attending the cattle market were offered stabling for up to 70 horses in the stables and yard, now the car park and garden. It was owned by the Collinson family from the 1920s until the death of Miss Nellie in 1976, when it was acquired by Sam Smith's who made minimal changes. Good value home-cooked lunches (not served Mon) include Sunday roasts. Folk and jazz eves are held upstairs.

Regional winner of CAMRA's National *Pub of the Year* 2000. ⚏ Q ❀ ◑ ⮰ ♣ P ⠧

Old Ship Inn
90 St John Street (1 mile NW of centre, near old town)
☼ 11-11; 12-10.30 Sun
☎ (01262) 670466
Tetley Bitter; Webster's Yorkshire Bitter; Worthington Bitter; guest beer Ⓗ

Thriving former Vaux local, originally two dwellings, with two rooms off a central corridor to the left, and three to the right. Alterations in the 1980s resulted in the present front lounge, front snug and a large rear bar. The lounge walls are adorned with prints of famous sailing ships; the front snug resembles a small Victorian parlour where photos show Yorkshire coastal scenes, towns and characters.
Q ❀ ◑ ⮰ ♣ ⠧ ●

Priory John
34-36 The Promenade
☼ 11-11; 12-10.30 Sun
☎ (01262) 674256
Courage Directors; Shepherd Neame Spitfire; Tetley Bitter; Theakston Best Bitter; guest beers Ⓗ

Large, busy Wetherspoon's pub in the town centre. Modern in appearance, the interior is basically one large half-moon shape. To the left of the serving area is a first-floor gallery, reached by a sweeping metal staircase. The fabric of the downstairs room is a clever mix of metal and wood with a segmented ceiling supported by steel pillars. The decor is plain and bright using mainly pastel colours. Two guest beers.
Q ❀ ◑ ⑤ ⮂ ⠧ ●

Seabirds
6 Fortyfoot (1 mile N of centre, near railway bridge)
☼ 12-11; 12-10.30 Sun
☎ (01262) 674174
Camerons Bitter, Strongarm; Marston's Pedigree Ⓗ

Large pub that was extended in the 1990s and now consists of a spacious rear lounge with a smaller front bar. The lounge, which doubles as a restaurant lunchtime and early eve, bears a boating theme, while the front bar is more basic with leather-backed seating and old photos of Bridlington's promenade and harbour areas. Children's certificate.
❀ ◑ ⮰ ⑤ ⋏ ♣ P ⠥

Buccaneer
47 Station Road
☼ 12-2.30, 5-11; 12-11 Fri & Sat; 12-10.30 Sun
☎ (01482) 667435
Draught Bass; Black Sheep Best Bitter; Tetley Dark Mild, Bitter; guest beer Ⓗ

Popular village pub, renovated in 2000 to provide a comfortable front lounge and a rear 45-seat dining room. It dates back to 1870 when it was known as the Railway Tavern. It was renamed in 1968 after the aircraft built by the nearby Blackburn Aircraft Company, now British Aerospace. The lounge is comfortably furnished and has historic photographs of Brough. The bar itself is decorated with whisky and water jugs while the dining room displays farm implements.

⌘⌂◑⟐♣P

DRIFFIELD

Bell Hotel
Market Place
✪ 10-2.30, 6-11; 10-11 Thu; 12-3, 7-10.30 Sun
☎ (01377) 256661
Beer range varies Ⓗ

Historic coaching inn situated in the town centre. The entrance hall opens on to a long, wood-panelled bar to the right featuring red leather seating, substantial fireplaces, antiques and paintings which lend a quality feel. Four guest beers, some from Yorkshire micros, are usually available, plus a choice of some 250 malt whiskies. A covered courtyard has bistro seating and old photographs of Driffield. The restaurant opens 7-9.30. Q⌂◑⟐&P

Mariner's Arms
47 Eastgate South (near cattle market)
✪ 3-11; 12-11 Sat; 12-4.30, 7-10.30 Sun
☎ (01377) 253708
Burtonwood Bitter, seasonal beers; guest beers Ⓗ

This traditional, street-corner local is well worth seeking out as an alternative to the John Smith outlets that dominate the 'Capital of the Wolds'. Formerly part of the original Hull Brewery estate, the pub has retained two rooms. It is situated in a residential terraced side street, it has a basic bar and a more comfortable lounge. The long-standing licensees create a very friendly amtosphere. ⌘⟐≠♣P

DUNSWELL

Ship Inn
Beverley Road (A1174)
✪ 11-11; 12-10.30 Sun
☎ (01482) 859160
Ind Coope Burton Ale; John Smith's Bitter; Tetley Bitter; guest beer (occasional) Ⓗ

This white-painted inn, fronting the old Hull-Beverley road, once served traffic on the nearby River Hull. Two log fires warm the welcoming interior which is partly divided to form a dining area with church pew seating. Formerly a Worthington house, it is a rare local outlet for Ind Coope Burton Ale; beers from the local Wawne Brewery are also occasionally available. Barbecues and special events are held in the adjoining paddock. ⌘⌘◑♣P

FLAMBOROUGH

Seabirds
Tower Street
✪ 11.30-2.30, 7 (6.30 Sat)-11; 12-3, 8-10.30 Sun
☎ (01262) 850242
John Smith's Bitter; guest beer Ⓗ

Just inside this pleasant seaside village pub stands a cabinet full of stuffed seabirds. The bar to the right bears a fishing theme, plus a collection of pump clips detailing the many guest beers previously offered. There is an emphasis on seafood and the specials board changes daily. All food is home cooked. The Seabirds is popular with walkers and bird enthusiasts: spectacular cliffs and Bempton RSPB Sanctuary are close by.
⌘◑▲P

GILBERDYKE

Cross Keys
Main Road (B1230, W edge of village)
✪ 12 11; 12-10.30 Sun
☎ (01430) 440310
Black Sheep Best Bitter; John Smith's Bitter; Tetley Bitter; guest beers Ⓗ

This pub on the old A63 (now bypassed by the M62) enjoys strong local support and draws visitors from near and far. A listed building, dated 1750, it was originally known as Mook's Inn after its Dutch owners. Around 1800 it changed to its current name, derived from the nearby crossroads. It has a pool/bar room and bar/lounge with a split-level snug displaying a selection of traditional brewery mirrors. Three rotating guest beers and usually two draught ciders are available.
⌘⌘♣♣P

GOODMANHAM

Goodmanham Arms
Main Street
✪ 8 (7 Fri)-11; 12-5; 7-11 Sat; 12-10.30 Sun
☎ (01430) 873849
e-mail: geoff.cawthray@goodmanhampubco.fsnet.co.uk
Black Sheep Best Bitter; Theakston Best Bitter; guest beer Ⓗ

This pleasant inn is popular with walkers due to its proximity to the Wolds Way footpath. The two bars both boast red and black chequered tiled floors; the main bar has a coal fire, the other bar has a seating area warmed by a log burner. At the front is a small garden. The gents' WC is outside. Planning permission for a micro-brewery was granted in January 2001.
⌘Q♣P

GOOLE

Macintosh Arms
13 Aire Street
✪ 11-11; 12-10.30 Sun
☎ (01405) 763850
e-mail: the macgoole@netscapeonline.co.uk
Greene King Old Speckled Hen; Tetley Dark Mild, Bitter; guest beer Ⓗ

Traditional pub, dating from the 1820s, and named after Sir Hugh Macintosh who commissioned the building of the adjacent Goole docks. Formerly part of a courthouse, this is a real community pub which is deservedly popular and can be very lively weekend eves. Home of Goole and District Motorcyle Club, it hosts Karaoke Sun eve and live music the last Thu of the month. The guest beers are from independent breweries. No garden, but pavement tables for outdoor drinking.
⌘≠♣P

HEDON

Shakespeare Inn
9 Baxtergate
✪ 12-11; 12-10.30 Sun
☎ (01482) 898371
Tetley Bitter; Theakston Best Bitter; Worthington Bitter; guest beers Ⓗ

Popular, friendly, one-roomed local in large village, east of Hull. Noted for food, eve meals include tea-time specials, served 5-7 Tue-Fri. Brewery memorabilia are displayed everywhere, including the ceiling. Compare the photographs of old Hedon with others taken more recently. 🏚✿◖♣P

HESSLE ✤

Hase
5-7 Swinegate
✪ 11-3, 5-11; 11-11 Sat; 12-10.30 Sun
☎ (01482) 648559
Black Sheep Best Bitter; Flowers IPA; Taylor Landlord; Tetley Dark Mild; guest beers ℍ

Set in the shadow of the Humber bridge, Hase is the Anglo-Saxon name for Hessle. Once inside this period property you can relax in a warm, friendly environment. The split-level restaurant area serves a full range of quality home-made dishes, including vegetarian and speciality fish dishes. An archway leads to the 'gatehouse' area that features a Yorkshire stone floor and Hessle memorabilia. It plays host to a computer club, darts, Celtic folk music and quiz nights. ✿◖➤

HOWDEN

Barnes Wallis
Station Road (B1228)
✪ 12-2 (not Mon & Tue), 5 (7 Mon & Tue)-11; 12-11 Sat; 12-10.30 Sun
☎ (01430) 430639 website: www.barneswallis.co.uk
Black Sheep Best Bitter; Hambleton Bitter; guest beers ℍ

The pub stands next to Howden station, about a mile north of this small market town with a fine 14th-century minster, which is worth a visit in its own right. The great inventor, after whom the Barnes Wallis is named, had local associations and the pub sports an extensive display of photographs dedicated to him and local wartime airfields. A friendly, open-plan hostelry, it features the best range of beers for miles around, with guests from independent breweries changing frequently. Regular live music is performed, and barbecues are held in the sheltered garden. 🏚✿◖♿➤♣P🍴

HULL ✤

Bay Horse
115-117 Wincolmlee
✪ 11-11; 12-10.30 Sun
☎ (01482) 329227
Bateman Mild, XB, XXXB, seasonal beers ℍ

Cosy, street-corner local, purchased by Bateman's in 1990. The spectacular lofty stable lounge is the result of an extension into the adjoining building (formerly a garage and once a blacksmith's and smelting foundry). The bar has historical photographs of the city's two Rugby League teams, while the lounge, which doubles as a dining room, displays brewery photographs. Home-cooked food is a speciality. CAMRA's Hull *Pub of the Year* 1998 and joint winner 1999. 🏚✿◖🍴♿♣P

Courts Bar
11 Bowlalley Lane, Lowgate, Old Town
✪ 11-11; 12-10.30 Sun
☎ (01482) 226543
Camerons Bitter, Strongarm ℍ

Formerly the Varsity, it was converted in 1997 from the Law Society's hall (Imperial Chambers) and is situated at the heart of the Old Town. A large circuit pub, its high turnover is boosted by the remarkably low prices which, combined with oversize glasses, guarantee excellent value. On its west side the building fronts on to the Land of Green Ginger and overlooks the George Inn, one of Hull's oldest established pubs. ♣⌀🍴

Editorial Inn
48 Spring Bank
✪ 11-11; 7-10.30 Sun
☎ (01482) 327738
Draught Bass; Tetley Bitter; guest beers ℍ

Converted former shop premises which opened in August 2000 as a cosy, privately-owned free house, run by experienced licensees. Situated next to the Hull Daily Mail premises, the pub features memorabilia and newspaper articles of both local and national significance. The narrow downstairs bar features a Chinese slate floor. An upstairs room, with its own bar, is available for functions. ✿◖➤(Paragon) ♣

Gardeners Arms
35 Cottingham Road
✪ 11-11; 12-10.30 Sun
☎ (01482) 342396
Tetley Bitter; guest beers ℍ

Popular and at times busy pub near the university. The ale house style in the front of the building is popular with locals and students. Its friendly, convivial atmosphere is enhanced by dark wood, subdued lighting, original matchboard ceiling and

INN BRIEF

BEMPTON

White Horse
30 High Street
11-4, 7-11; 12-3, 7-10.30 Sun
Draught Bass; Theakston Best Bitter; guest beer ℍ
Former Moors & Robsons house built in 1938. Note the interesting blue tiled roof.

BEVERLEY

Grovehill
183 Holmechurch Lane
12-2 (not winter Mon-Thu), 4.30-11; 11-11 Sat; 12-10.30 Sun
Marston's Bitter ℍ
Built in the 1920s by Moors & Robsons, this roadside pub has a public bar and well furnished lounge.

HESSLE

Darleys
312 Boothferry Road (A1105/B1232 jct)
11-11; 12-10.30 Sun
Black Sheep Best Bitter; Marston's Pedigree; Whitbread Trophy ℍ
Substantial mock-Tudor pub on the old western approach to Hull, recently refurbished. Good food.

HUGGATE

Wolds Inn
Driffield Road
12-2, 7 (6.30 Sat)-11; closed Mon; 12-2.30, 6.30-10.30 Sun
Greene King Old Speckled Hen; Taylor Landlord; Tetley Bitter ℍ
Family-run inn, dating back to the 16th century, with a wood-panelled restaurant and bar.

HULL

Doodlebugs
22 Witham
12-3 (not Mon or Sat), 7.30-11 (not Mon-Wed); 8-10.30 Sun
Tetley Bitter; guest beer (occasional) ℍ
Closed since 1968, now restored and reopened with many original features and layout retained. A WWII theme includes period music.

Eagle
283-285 Anlaby Road
11-11; 12-10.30 Sun
Banks's Original; Camerons Bitter; Marston's Pedigree ℍ
Basic, street-corner, two roomed pub handy for Hull Rugby League ground.

bare brick walls. The rear room attracts younger drinkers. Up to six guest ales are mainly sourced from independents; regular beer festivals are held. Good value meals; eve meals served 5-7, food available 12-6 Sat and Sun. ✿◗▯♣P

Kingston Hotel
25 Trinity House Lane, Old Town
✪ 11-4.30, 7-11; 11-11 Fri & Sat; 12-4.30; 7-10.30 Sun
☎ (01482) 223993
Banks's Original, Bitter Ⓗ

Historic, Grade II listed, basic town pub, dating from 1882, overlooking Holy Trinity Church, the former market place and Trinity House. Notable features are the decorative exterior, front door glass etched 'Kingston Hotel Spirit Stores', and the superb original carved wooden bar back, made from Canadian pine, with an off-centre clock. A minor bastion for dark mild drinkers, its main bar attracts a mixed clientele. Can get very busy on weekends with younger circuit drinkers. ♣

Minerva Hotel
Nelson Street, Old Town
✪ 11-11; 12-10.30 Sun
☎ (01482) 326909 website: www.hull-local.co.uk
Taylor Landlord; Tetley Bitter; guest beers Ⓗ

Famous pub, built in 1835, overlooking the River Humber estuary and Victoria Pier – a great place to watch the ships going by on the tide. Superb photographs and memorabilia serve as a reminder of the area's maritime past. The central bar serves a variety of rooms including a tiny snug. Regular beer festivals include a sea shanty festival in Aug/Sept. Evening meals served Mon-Thu – home-made food and huge haddocks complete an enticing menu. Local CAMRA *Pub of the Year* 2000.
▥✿◗♣♣

Olde Black Boy
150 High Street, Old Town
✪ 11-11; 12-10.30 Sun
☎ (01482) 326516
Tetley Bitter; guest beers Ⓗ

In the heart of the Old Town, this 14th-century building has been a pub for over 200 years. The black front room snug and window with carved head over the fireplace are worth a look. The rear bar has recently returned to rich chestnut varnished panelled walls. Up to five guest ales are

stocked, plus unusually for the area, three ciders/perries from the Weston's range.
▥◗♣♣♣

Olde White Harte
25 Silver Street, Old Town
✪ 11-11; 12-10.30 Sun
☎ (01482) 326363
McEwan 80/-; Theakston Best Bitter, Old Peculier; guest beer Ⓗ

Historic 16th-century courtyard pub, once the residence where the Governor of Hull resolved to deny Charles I entry to the city. Award-winning floral displays, superb dark woodwork, stained glass windows and sit-in fireplaces feature. Situated down an alleyway at the heart of the commercial centre, it boasts a covered, heated outdoor drinking area. An impressive staircase leads to the upstairs rooms including the 'Plotting Room'. The guest beer is often from Hull Brewery. No music or TV.
Q❧✿◗♣

St John's Hotel
10 Queens Road (off Beverley Road, 1 mile N of centre)
✪ 12-11; 12-10.30 Sun
☎ (01482) 343669
Banks's Original, Bitter; Mansfield Dark Mild, Riding Bitter; Marston's Pedigree Ⓗ

Victorian pub, the epitome of a street-corner local that retains its separate rooms and community focus. The friendly down-to-earth front corner bar still has the old gaslight pipes across the windows; the quiet back room boasts original bench seating. A basic side room, with a popular juke box, doubles as a family room (until 8pm). A pleasant secluded garden has seats and tables. Run by long-established licensees and faithful, efficient bar staff, it is loved by its regulars. ❧✿▯♣♣P

Tap & Spile
169-171 Spring Bank
✪ 12-11; 12-10.30 Sun
☎ (01482) 323518
Cains Mild; Greene King IPA Ⓗ

Formerly the Eagle, this Victorian street-corner local was associated with the Botanical and Zoological Gardens. Converted and extended, it is now a themed ale house serving Hull's largest selection of cask ales, plus Lindisfarne fruit wines and Hoegaarden wheat beer. Now a well-established live music venue, it hosts

---

Mission
11-13 Posterngate
11-11;
12-3, 7-10.30 Sun
Old Mill Bitter, Old Curiosity Ⓗ
Converted seamen's mission, resembling a baronial hall, it includes a minstrel's gallery and deconsecrated chapel.

Station Inn
202 Beverley Road
12-11;
12-10.30 Sun
Old Mill Bitter Ⓗ
Two-roomed pub, north of the city centre: a basic front bar with tiled floor and a lounge/pool room.

KILHAM
Star Inn
Church Street
11-2, 7-11; 11-11 Sat; 12-10.30 Sun
John Smith's Bitter; Theakston XB; guest beer Ⓗ
Traditionally renovated four-roomed pub with a central bar, it boasts a piano and high quality restaurant.

MARKET WEIGHTON
Half Moon
39 High Street
5 (12 Fri & Sat)-11; 12-10.30 Sun
Burtonwood Bitter Ⓗ
Former coaching inn, offering a friendly welcome. One long room has a bar area at the rear with pool table.

SNAITH
Brewers Arms
10 Pontefract Road
11.30-2.30, 5-11;
12-3, 6-10.30 Sun
Old Mill Bitter, Bullion, Blackjack Ⓗ
Old Mill Brewery flagship, carrying the full portfolio of its beers in a well-furnished interior.

> ✳ **symbol next to a main entry place name indicates there are Inn Brief entries as well.**

folk sessions Sun eve, acoustic Mon and blues Tue. Two comfortable areas for non-smokers include the old smoke room that retains a superb fireplace and mirror. Sun lunch is served until 6pm otherwise sandwiches are usually available. ⚘👜✄

LUND

Wellington Inn
19 The Green
✪ 12-3 (not Mon), 6.30-11; 12-3, 7-11 Sun
☎ (01377) 217294 e-mail: thebestboot@901.com
Black Sheep Best Bitter; John Smith's Bitter; Taylor Dark Mild, Landlord; guest beer (occasional) Ⓗ
Five miles north of Beverley, just off the B1248, Lund is an award-winning Wolds village with the Wellington situated on the green. Most of the trade comes from the local farming community. It was totally renovated by the present licensee in 1995, with stone-flagged floors and beamed ceilings. There is a no-smoking room, games room and a candlelit restaurant, serving an *à la carte* menu (eve meals Tue-Sat). There are real fires in three rooms. ▲⚘◑💧♣P✄

MILLINGTON

Gate Inn
Main Street
✪ 12-4 (not Mon-Fri), 7-11 Sat; 12-5, 7.30-10.30 Sun
☎ (01759) 302045
Black Sheep Best Bitter; Old Mill Bitter; John Smith's Bitter; Tetley Bitter Ⓗ
Millington may well have been the Roman village of Delgovicia as this area has been inhabited since ancient times. Plenty of people still pass through on long-distance footpaths, the Wolds Walk and Minster Walk. At the centre of the village, the Gate has a single, comfortable bar with an adjoining pool room. If you're lost, plot your way home with the aid of the old Yorkshire map on the bar ceiling! No eve meals Sun. ▲⛵⚘◑♣P

NORTH NEWBALD

Tiger Inn
The Green
✪ 12-11; 12-10.30 Sun
☎ (01430) 827759
Black Sheep Best Bitter; John Smith's Bitter; Taylor Landlord; guest beer Ⓗ
Old pub overlooking the village green; its refurbished interior includes ceiling beams and polished brasses. There is a public bar, lounge bar and games room. Popular with diners, it offers a substantial home-cooked menu, the house specialities being beef pies and haddock fried in beer and lemon batter. Close to the Wolds Way footpath, it offers a warm welcome to walkers; picnic tables are set outside in summer. ▲Q⚘◑⊟P

OLD ELLERBY

Blue Bell
Crabtree Lane (off A165)
✪ 12-4.30 (not Mon-Fri), 7-11; 12-4.30, 7-10.30 Sun
☎ (01964) 562364
Black Sheep Best Bitter; Ind Coope Burton Ale; Tetley Bitter; guest beers Ⓗ
Previously owned by Burton Constable estate, this 16th-century one-roomed inn has a games area to the rear, beamed

ceilings, and stone floors. CAMRA East Yorkshire *Pub of the Year* 1998 and 2000, it serves two rotating guest beers. A patio area features hanging baskets while the large garden has a children's play area and bowling green. It supports the local community by holding a country show and various fund-raising events. Morris dancers visit in summer and before Christmas. ▲⚘♣P

PATRINGTON

Hildyard Arms
1 Market Place
✪ 12-11; 12-10.30 Sun
☎ (01964) 630234
e-mail: eileenshildyard@yahoo.co.uk
Draught Bass; Highgate Dark; Tetley Bitter; guest beer Ⓗ
Refurbished former coaching inn that once served as a corn exchange for local farmers. A central bar serves all rooms: a public bar, lounge bar/restaurant area and games room, all with real fires. There is a pleasant outdoor patio drinking area. The pub offers an array of games and fields teams. Food is of a very high standard. It is convenient to Patrington Haven and the Holderness Rail Trail. ▲Q⚘◑⊟♣P

PRESTON

Cock & Bell
1 Main Street
✪ 6 (11.30 Fri & Sat)-11; 12-10.30 Sun
☎ (01482) 899345
Castle Eden Ale; guest beer Ⓗ
200-year-old village pub in traditional cottage style comprising a main bar, no-smoking games room and a no-smoking restaurant (only open Sun). It hosts community meetings and is a base for local sports teams. The large outdoor drinking area has children's play facilities. The guest beer is supplied direct from the West Midlands and Worcester area; the pub acts as a wholesale and distribution point for other local free houses, hence the low beer prices.
⚘♣P✄

REEDNESS

Half Moon Inn
Main Street
✪ 7 (11 Sat)-11; 12-10.30 Sun
☎ (01405) 704484
Old Mill Bullion; Greene King Old Speckled Hen; guest beers Ⓗ
Remote village pub with a well appointed public bar and lounge/restaurant. Its appealing interior features dark wood beams and red leather seating. An extensive home-cooked food selection includes specials on Thu and Fri eves. Caravan and camping facilities at rear of pub are handy for the Blacktoft Sands RSPB site. Guest beers mainly come from independent brewers, often Cottage Brewery. Well worth it, it opens lunchtime summer weekdays.
▲Q⚘◑⊟💧▲♣P🍴

RYEHILL

Crooked Billet
Pitt Lane (400 yds off A1033, E of Thorngumbald)

✪ 11-11; 12-10.30 Sun
☎ (01964) 622303

Burtonwood Bitter, Top Hat, guest beer Ⓗ

Oasis in a quiet country hamlet, the guest beer is from Burtonwood's monthly rotating list. This 17th-century coaching inn is wonderfully unspoilt with a stone-flagged floor, comfortable upholstered seating areas, horse brasses and historical pictures of the pub, it is home to cricket and darts teams and a Scrabble club. Good value, freshly-prepared home-cooked food (not served Tue eve) is an added attraction.
🏚Q◖♣P

SKERNE

Eagle Inn ☆
Wandsford Road
✪ 12-2 (not Mon-Fri), 7-11; 12-3, 7-10.30 Sun
☎ (01377) 252178
Camerons Bitter Ⓗ

Plain, white-painted village local surrounded by mature trees. The unspoilt homely interior consists of a public bar with coal fire and matchboard ceiling, and a more comfortable front parlour. Drinks are brought to your table from a cellar off the entrance corridor. Beer is dispensed from a Victorian cash register beer engine which delivers a spectacular cone head above the glass. Outside WCs complete this timewarp pub.
🏚Q❀🖺♣P

SNAITH ❄

Downe Arms
15 Market Place
✪ 12-11; 12-10.30 Sun
☎ (01405) 860544
Banks's Bitter; Camerons Bitter; Marston's Pedigree; guest beer Ⓗ

Named after Lord Downe, a local landowner, it is known that a pub existed on this site from about 1500. Note the front market place façade with its rounded sash bay windows. Inside a three-sided bar, attentive staff, unusual whiskies and a fine collection of jugs add atmosphere. Excellent food includes a Sunday carvery. On Sun eve join in the singalong with organ accompaniment.
❀◖♣P↙

SUTTON UPON DERWENT

St Vincent Arms
Main Street (follow B1288 past Elvington)
✪ 11.30-3, 7-11; 12-3, 7-10.30 Sun
☎ (01904) 608349
Banks's Bitter; Fuller's Chiswick, Ⓗ **ESB;** Ⓖ **John Smith's Bitter; Taylor Landlord; Wells Bombardier; guest beer** Ⓗ/Ⓖ

Close to the old, stone bridge linking Sutton with its neighbour Elvington, the pub consists of an L-shaped bar and small lounge that leads to two dining area. A long-time entry in this *Guide*, it has a firm commitment to beer. Unusually for the area two of the beers are drawn directly from the cask in the cellar. The reputation for quality extends to the food, too, and it get very busy eves with diners.
🏚Q🖦❀◖P

Yorkshire (North)
(Including parts of Cleveland)

APPLETREEWICK

New Inn
✪ 12-3 (not Mon), 7-11; 12-3, 7-10.30 Sun
☎ (01756) 720252
John Smith's Bitter; Theakston Black Bull; guest beer Ⓗ

Walkers, (motor)cyclists, and tourists are all welcome at this family-run 'small pub with a big heart'. Also enjoys a good local trade. The emphasis on foreign beer with three draught Belgian beers always available, alongside a wide range of bottled beers from around the world. The landlord is a keen mountain-biker and can offer information on routes both on- and off-road. A 'bike livery' behind the pub provides a workshop, bike-wash and changing facilities. Good value home-cooked food is served. The guest beer is from Daleside.
🏚Q❀🖺◖♣P

BECK HOLE (NEAR GOATHLAND)

Birch Hall Inn ☆
1 mile N of Goathland OSNZ8202
✪ 11-3, 7.30-11 (not Mon eve), 11-11 Sat & summer; 12-10.30 Sun
☎ (01947) 896245 website: www.beckhole.com
Black Sheep Best Bitter; Theakston Black Bull; guest beers Ⓗ

Not to be missed, this gem dates back to before the 1860s. It has had only two licensees in the last 78 years. The current licensee clocked up 20 years in 2001 and has deliberately kept the pub unchanged. A small shop separates the bar from the snug which is serviced through a hatch. With a strong local patronage, it can also get very busy with walkers. A large painting of the beck by Algernon Newton (RA) has hung outside for many years. It is located approx. 1 mile from Goathland (Aidensfield in *Heartbeat*) and the North York Moors Railway.
🏚Q❀🖺♣

BEDALE

Three Coopers
2 Emgate
✪ 11-11; 12-10.30 Sun
☎ (01677) 422153
Black Sheep Best Bitter; Jennings Bitter, Cumberland Ale, Cocker Hoop, Sneck Lifter Ⓗ

Just off the main street and down hill from the market cross, this is not a typical Yorkshire town pub. The style here is timber floors, distressed plaster walls in brown and green, and wooden furniture, including some adapted from barrels. Converted from several rooms on different levels, the effect is very cosy. The excellent chalkboard all-day menu is novel and reasonably priced; look out for occasional special deals such as steak nights. Often quite quiet during the week, it can be busy at weekends.
🏚◖

BILBROUGH

Three Hares
Main Street (off A64, York-Leeds road)

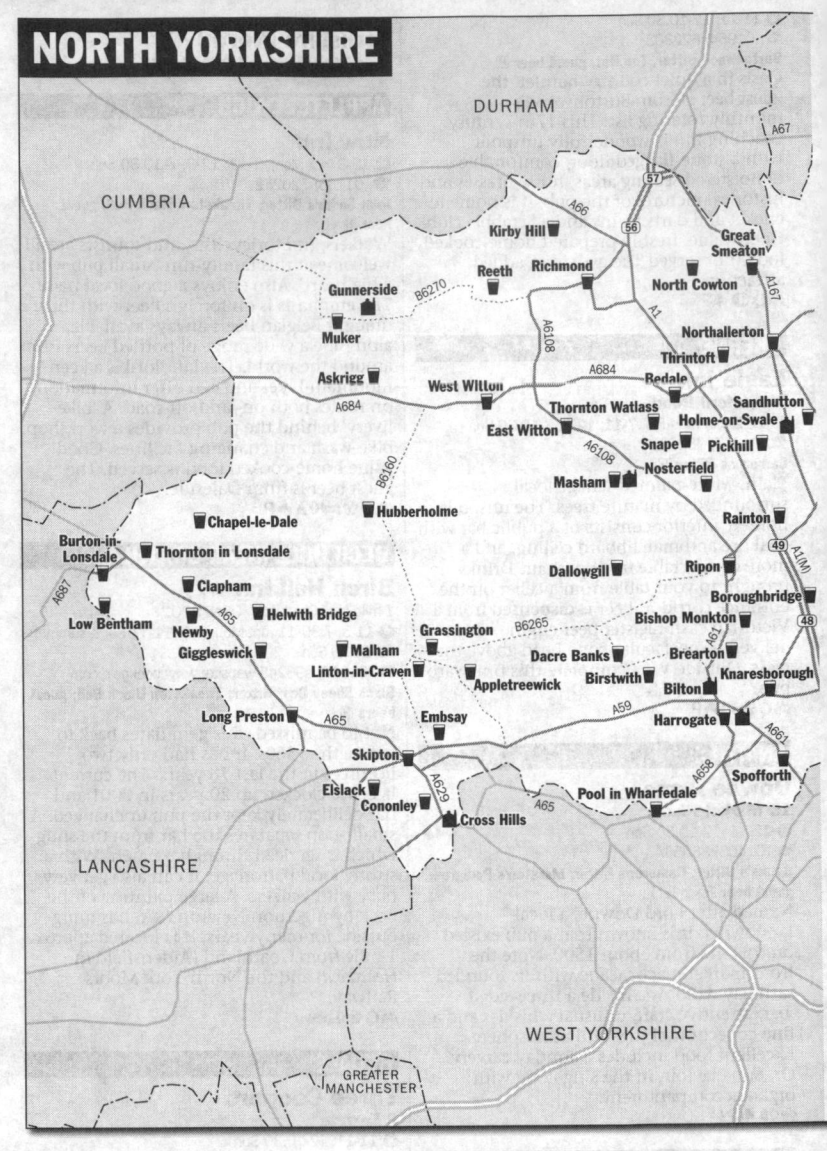

NORTH YORKSHIRE

DURHAM

CUMBRIA

Kirby Hill
Reeth
Richmond
Great Smeaton
North Cowton
Gunnerside
Muker
Northallerton
Thrintoft
Askrigg
West Witton
Redale
Sandhutton
Thornton Watlass
Holme-on-Swale
East Witton
Snape
Pickhill
Masham
Nosterfield
Hubberholme
Rainton
Chapel-le-Dale
Burton-in-Lonsdale
Thornton in Lonsdale
Dallowgill
Ripon
Clapham
Boroughbridge
Low Bentham
Helwith Bridge
Bishop Monkton
Newby
Grassington
Giggleswick
Malham
Dacre Banks
Brearton
Linton-in-Craven
Appletreewick
Birstwith
Knaresborough
Long Preston
Bilton
Embsay
Harrogate
Skipton
Spofforth
Eslack
Cononley
Pool in Wharfedale
Cross Hills

LANCASHIRE

WEST YORKSHIRE

GREATER MANCHESTER

✪ 12-3, 7-11 (closed Mon); 12-3 (closed eve) Sun
☎ (01937) 832128 website: www.thethreehares.co.uk
Black Sheep Best Bitter; Taylor Landlord; guest beers Ⓗ
An effort to discover this village pub will be rewarded by the award-winning food or simply a pint of the latest guest beer. A *Country Pub of the Season* award from York CAMRA testifies to the beer quality and food awards from the AA, *Yorkshire Life, The Publican* and the British Cheese Board assures an excellent meal, served in the no-smoking restaurants or the bar. This 200-year-old converted blacksmith's shop has a central servery to the bar and eating areas.
Q ✿ ◑ ♣ P

BIRSTWITH

Station
Station Road OSSE2459

✪ 11.30-2.30 (not Mon), 5.30-11; 11.30-11 Sat; 12-5, 7-10.30 Sun
☎ (01423) 770254
Black Sheep Best Bitter; Rudgate Viking; Tetley Bitter Ⓗ
Delightful village pub displaying framed drawings of Yorkshire village scenes and Staffordshire pottery in the small L-shaped bar. An attractive restaurant and a cosy snug room, free from background music and TV, complete the picture. Well worth a visit.
Q ✿ ⇔ ◑ P

BISHOP MONKTON

Lamb & Flag
Boroughbridge Road (off A61)
✪ 12-3, 5.30-11; 12-3, 7-10.30 Sun
☎ (01765) 677322
Black Sheep Best Bitter; Tetley Bitter Ⓗ
Two-roomed traditional village pub, full of

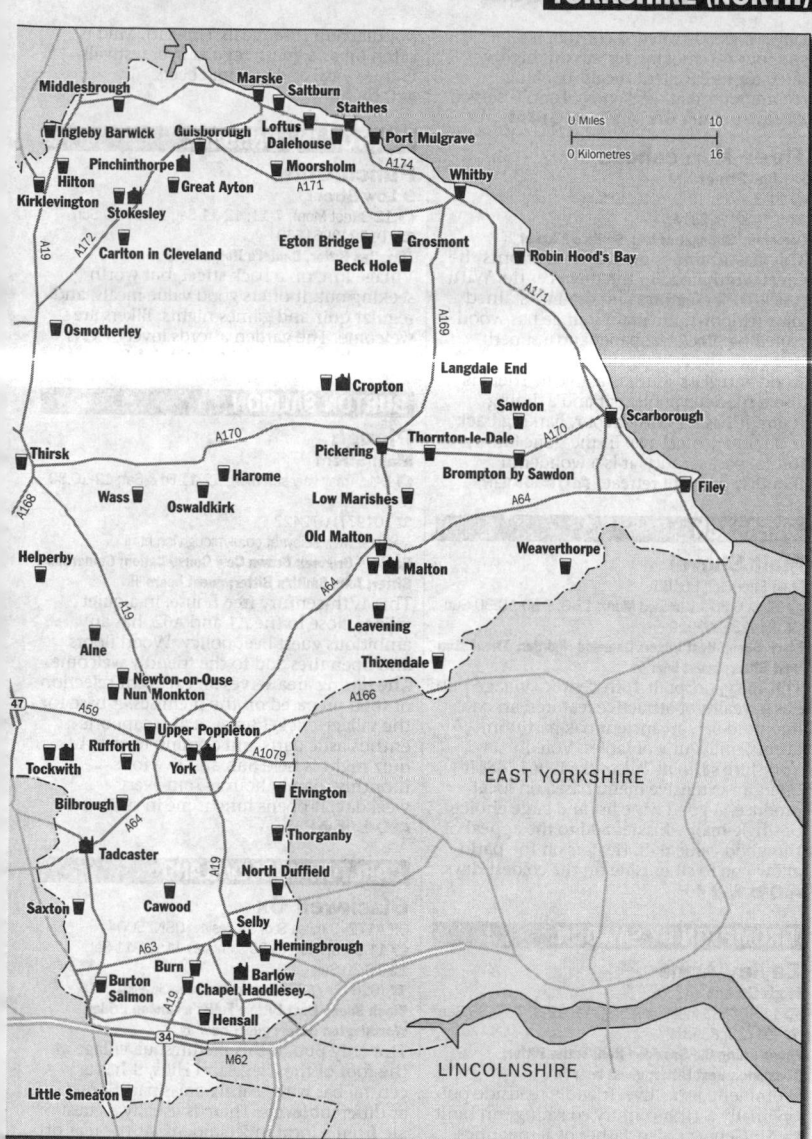

U Miles 0 — 10
0 Kilometres — 16

Middlesbrough
Marske • Saltburn
Ingleby Barwick • Staithes
Guisborough • Loftus • Port Mulgrave
Pinchinthorpe • Dalehouse
Hilton • Moorsholm
Kirklevington • Great Ayton
Stokesley • Whitby
Carlton in Cleveland
Egton Bridge • Grosmont
Beck Hole • Robin Hood's Bay
Osmotherley
Cropton
Langdale End
Sawdon
Thirsk • Thornton-le-Dale • Scarborough
Pickering
Harome • Brompton by Sawdon
Wass • Low Marishes • Filey
Oswaldkirk
Old Malton
Helperby • Weaverthorpe
Malton
Leavening
Alne • Thixendale
Newton-on-Ouse
Nun Monkton
Upper Poppleton
Rufforth • York
Tockwith • Elvington
Bilbrough • Thorganby
Tadcaster • North Duffield
Saxton • Cawood
Selby • EAST YORKSHIRE
Hemingbrough
Burn • Barlow
Burton • Chapel Haddlesey
Salmon • Hensall
Little Smeaton • LINCOLNSHIRE

knick-knacks and unusual brasses. It has a peaceful garden at the rear and tables in a suntrap at the front. It supports the village cricket team with fund-raising throughout the year. The village stages an annual Duck Race on Aug bank holiday on the picturesque stream. It is close to Ripon Cathedral, the Racecourse, Studley Royal and Fountains Abbey. A Daleside and a Jennings beer are usually added to the list in summer. ♒Q✿⊕♣P

Masons Arms
St John's Road (off A61)
✪ 12-3, 6.30-11; 12-3, 6.30-10.30 Sun
☎ (01765) 677427
Black Sheep Best Bitter; Tetley Bitter Ⓗ
Set in a delightful village, the pub overlooks a stream which is home to some unusual species of ducks. The pub, which made an appearance in TV's *Touch of Frost*, has a cosy

interior with beamed ceilings and open fires. An extensive *à la carte* menu is served in the restaurant. Various Rudgate and Daleside beers are usually on tap.
♒Q✿☜⊛⊕ᵭ♣⚫P

BOROUGHBRIDGE

Black Bull
6 St. James Square
✪ 11-11; 12-10.30 Sun
☎ (01423) 322413
Black Sheep Best Bitter; John Smith's Bitter; guest beer Ⓗ
This historic inn at the centre of the market town is very attractive – white painted with Georgian-style bay windows and bedecked with hanging baskets in summer. The main bar is cosy, with a brick inglenook, low beamed ceiling and copper-topped tables; the adjacent snug has another open fire.

Down a wood-panelled corridor is a spacious no-smoking restaurant, highly rated for its excellent meals (booking recommended at weekends). Food is served all day summer weekends. 🏤Q🚫🍴🍺

Three Horseshoes ☆
Bridge Street
🕐 11-3, 5-11; 12-3, 6-10.30 Sun
☎ (01432) 322314
Camerons Strongarm; John Smith's Magnet Ⓗ
This classic, imposing roadhouse fronts the Great North Road in the town centre. With mock-Tudor features and original stained glass windows, the main lounge has wood panelling, flock wallpaper and a superb fireplace. The bar counter features unusual wood and glass shutters above it. There is also a spacious public bar and a dining room. It has a 1930s flavour, harking back to a more genteel age. In the same family for the past century, it is a wonderful friendly, peaceful retreat. 🏤Q🚫🍴🍺🅿

BREARTON

Malt Shovel
Main Street (off B6165)
🕐 12-3, 6.30-11 (closed Mon); 12-3, 7.30-10.30 Sun
☎ (01423) 862929
Black Sheep Best Bitter; Daleside Nightjar; Theakston Best Bitter; guest beer Ⓗ
This busy, unspoilt 16th-century village pub has a wealth of attractive features: an oak linenfold bar, an ancient oak partition, beams, and a mix of tables. Voted Yorkshire's *Dining Pub of the Year* 1988, it offers an extensive menu based on local produce. A good wine list and large choice of single malt whiskies add to the appeal of this good value pub. Heaters on the patio allow you to sit outside on the coldest days. 🏤Q🌳🚫🍴♣🅿

BROMPTON BY SAWDON

Cayley Arms
High Street (A170)
🕐 11.30-2.30 (not Mon); 5.30-11; 12-3, 7-10.30 Sun
☎ (01723) 859372
Greene King Old Speckled Hen; Tetley Bitter; Theakston Best Bitter; guest beer Ⓗ
Prominent, attractive, friendly roadside pub, originally a 19th-century coaching inn built by Sir George Caley, father of aeronautics. The excellent food includes local specialities. A children's play area is available. The guest beer is usually from the Tapster's Choice range. 🏤Q🌳🚫🍴♣🅿🍴

BURN

Wheatsheaf
Main Road (A19, 3 miles S of Selby)
🕐 12-11; 12-10.30 Sun
☎ (01757) 270614
John Smith's Bitter; Taylor Landlord; Tetley Bitter; guest beers Ⓗ
Roadside inn, built in 1896, on the site of a pub called the Boy and Barrel. Although opened out, it retains a narrow bar passage and pool room. Agricultural and aeronautical memorabilia reflect the rural and WWII associations of the village (Burn aerodrome was a bomber base). See, too, the large collection of Dinky toys and huge open fire. Home-cooked food is especially

popular Sun (eve meals Thu-Sat). Mild is often on as a guest; regular beer festivals feature local and regional beers. 🏤Q🚫🍴♣🅿

BURTON-IN-LONSDALE

Punch Bowl
9 Low Street
🕐 12-3 (not Mon), 7-11; 12-11 Sat; 12-10.30 Sun
☎ (015242) 61568
Thwaites Bitter, Daniel's Hammer Ⓗ
Village inn, on a back street, but worth seeking out. It offers good value meals, and regular quiz and games nights. Bikers are welcome. The garden affords lovely views across the valley. 🏤Q🌳🚫🍴♣🅿

BURTON SALMON

Plough
Main Street
🕐 5-11 (may vary summer); 12-11 Fri & Sat; 12-10.30 Sun
☎ (01977) 672422
website: www.selbynet.co.uk/plough/inn.html
Banks's Original; Brown Cow Constellation; Camerons Bitter; John Smith's Bitter; guest beers Ⓗ
This 17th-century free house, in a quiet village close to the A1 and A62, has an ambitious guest beer policy. Wood floors and open fires add to the friendly welcome. The dining area serves an excellent selection of food prepared on the premises. A base for the village cricket team, it also supports enthusiastic darts and domino teams. A quiz night is held Sun and live folk monthly; happy hour 6-7pm every weekday. It opens lunchtime in summer. 🏤Q🚫🍴♣🅿

CARLTON IN CLEVELAND

Blackwell Ox
Off A172, 3 miles S of Stokesley OSNZ5004
🕐 11.30-3, 6.30 (5.30 summer)-11; 11-11 Sat; 12-10.30 Sun
☎ (01642) 712287 website: theblackwellox.co.uk
Black Sheep Best Bitter; Fuller's London Pride; Worthington Bitter; guest beer Ⓗ
The only pub in this picturesque village at the foot of the Cleveland Hills, it has a central bar with seating areas partitioned off at different levels. There is usually a guest ale from a local independent. At the rear of the pub there is a small caravan park and a children's play area at the front. Popular with locals, campers and walkers, it enjoys a good reputation for food, particularly the Thai dishes. Well worth a visit. 🏤Q🌳🚫🍴♣🅿🍴

CAWOOD

Ferry Inn
2 King Street (S side of river, near swing bridge)
🕐 12-3 (not Mon or Tue), 5-11; 12-11 Fri & Sat; 12-10.30 Sun
☎ (01757) 268515 website: www.ferryinn.f9.co.uk
Black Sheep Special; Camerons Bitter; Mansfield Bitter; Taylor Landlord; guest beers Ⓗ
Probably one of the most historic pubs in the district; low ceilings and inglenooks give a cosy charm to this friendly village inn. The terrace and garden overlook the River Ouse. The village has connections with Cardinal Wolsey, whose residence as

Archbishop of York was Cawood Castle. Although the menu today is not as sumptuous as the great feast of 1464 (see details in the bar) it still offers exceptional value; try the chilli and curry specials (curry night Sun). The guest beer is often local. ♨Q≿❀✍◑▷▲♣P

CHAPEL HADDLESEY

Jug Inn
Main Street
✪ 12-3, 6-11; 12-11 Sat; 12-10.30 Sun
☎ (01757) 270307
website: www.selbynet.co.uk/jug/inn.html
Beer range varies Ⓗ

300-year-old, award-winning village pub on the River Aire. It once had a blacksmith's shop, but now has a friendly ghost. Family-owned, it is renowned for its guest beers, which always include a Brown Cow-brewed house beer. A small bar serves both the front lounge and the public bar; both rooms feature a collection of jugs hanging from the beams. Local folk groups meet here on Wed nights for impromptu entertainment. Good home-made meals include Desperate Dan cow pie. Beer festivals, concentrating on local breweries, are held in a garden marquee. ♨Q❀◑⊟♣P

CHAPEL-LE-DALE

Hill Inn
✪ 12-3, 6-11 (closed winter Mon; 12-11 summer); 12-10.30 Sun
☎ (015242) 415256
Black Sheep Best Bitter, Riggwelter; Dent Aviator; Theakston Best Bitter; guest beers Ⓗ

Beloved of generations of hikers and potholers – well-worn paths lead from here to both Whernside (Yorkshire's highest peak) and Ingleborough (its best-known). New owners have smartened the place up considerably and added a restaurant but the bars remain unaltered; soft furnishings are eschewed in favour of woodwork and some exposed limestone stonework. Guest beers come from Dent and Black Sheep. ♨❀◑▲♣P

CLAPHAM

New Inn
✪ 11-3, 7-11; 11-11 Sat; 12-10.30 Sun
☎ (015242) 51203
website: www.newinnclapham.co.uk
Black Sheep Best Bitter; Dent Bitter; Tetley Bitter; guest beers Ⓗ

Large, 18th-century coaching inn comprising two lounge bars with oak panelling. Photos and cartoons depicting caving and (less predictably) cycling adorn the walls. Popular with all kinds of tourist; children are welcome in the no-smoking restaurant. Felbeck Bitter is Flying Firkin Aviator rebadged. ♨Q❀✍◑▷♿▲♣P

CONONLEY

New Inn
Main Street
✪ 12-3, 5.30-11; 12-10.30 Sun
☎ (01535) 636302
Taylor Golden Best, Best Bitter, Landlord, Ram Tam Ⓗ

Attractive, low-beamed Taylor's tied house at the centre of a quiet Dales village. The

traditional exterior, with stone-mullioned windows, compliments the well-laid-out, recently refurbished interior. There is a small, but pleasant garden. If catching the train south allow plenty of time to get over the level crossing. ♨❀◑▷≼♣

CROPTON

New Inn
Woolcroft
✪ 11-3, 6-11; 11-11 Fri, Sat & summer; 12-10.30 Sun
☎ (01751) 417330
Cropton Two Pints, Monkmans Slaughter; Thwaites Best Bitter; guest beers Ⓗ

The village stands at the southern edge of the North York Moors close to popular Rosedale. Cropton Brewery, behind the pub, has a visitor centre. The inn comprises a comfortable main bar with a small residents' lounge and pool room. A large family room on a lower level is the venue for the annual beer festival – usually late Nov. Guest beers are often others from Cropton's own range; the cider is Saxon Golddigger. ≿❀✍◑▷▲♣P⊬⊟

DACRE BANKS

Royal Oak
Oak Lane
✪ 11-3, 5.30-11; 12-3, 7-10.30 Sun
☎ (01423) 780200 e-mail: royaloakdacre@aol.com
Black Sheep Best Bitter; Daleside Old Legover; Rudgate Battleaxe; John Smith's Bitter Ⓗ

Family-run Grade II listed pub built in 1752 affording fine views over the River Nidd (fishing tickets available) close to Fountains Abbey, Brimham Rocks and the Dales, it makes a popular venue for locals, holidaymakers and ramblers. There are open fires, cosy bars and panelled walls; note the beamed ceilings painted with anagrams about food and drink. It has a garden and cobbled seating area. One bar and the restaurant are no-smoking, other areas are air filtered. Extensive menus feature local produce and a wide selection of fish. ♨Q≿❀✍◑▷♿♣P⊬

DALLOWGILL

Drovers' Inn
Minor road about 2 miles W of Laverton OS210720
✪ 12-3 (3.30 Fri, Sat & summer), 7 (6.30 Fri, Sat &

INDEPENDENT BREWERIES

Black Sheep Masham
Brown Cow Barlow
Captain Cook Stokesley
Cropton Cropton
Daleside Harrogate
Franklin's Bilton
Hambleton Holme-on-Swale
Malton Malton
North Yorkshire Pinchinthorpe
Old Bear Crosshills
Rooster's Harrogate
Rudgate Tockwith
Selby Selby
Samuel Smith Tadcaster
Swaled Ale Gunnerside
York York

summer); closed Mon; 12-3 (3.30 summer), 6.30-10.30 Sun

☎ (01765) 658510

Black Sheep Best Bitter; Hambleton Bitter; Old Mill Bitter H

This homely, single-roomed wayside country pub stands in the very attractive surroundings of Lower Nidderdale. Simply furnished, the small bar counter is tucked away in one corner. The very reasonably-priced food is highly regarded. The clientele are mainly from the local farming community, but it gets busy with ramblers in season, with plenty of excellent local walks. Well worth a visit to sample rural Yorkshire conviviality.

🏚Q🌮◑Å♣P

EAST WITTON

Cover Bridge Inn

On B6108, Leyburn-Ripon road, 1½ miles from Middleham

☀ 11-11; 12-10.30 Sun

☎ (01969) 622115

website: www.thecoverbridgeinn.co.uk

Black Sheep Best Bitter; Taylor Landlord; Theakston Best Bitter, Old Peculier; guest beers H

Historic, 16th-century inn on the River Cover; don't be fooled by the escutcheon lift latch on the entry door, it is open. You are met by a cosy atmosphere, open log fire and olde-worlde bench seating in the main bar. The pub offers excellent food all day, in a quiet environment (children welcome in the no-smoking dining room). Well used by locals and ramblers alike, good walks in all directions allow you to work up a thirst for the large selection of real ales including seasonal beers. Enjoy the excellent views through the bay windows in winter, or from the garden.

🏚Q🌮◑⏚Å♣P

EGTON BRIDGE

Horseshoe Hotel

Approx. ¼ mile from station, over the river bridge OSNZ8005

☀ 11.30-3, 6.30-11 (11-11 Sat & summer); 12-3, 7-10.30 (12-10.30 summer) Sun

☎ (01947) 895245

John Smith's Bitter; Theakston Best Bitter; guest beers H

18th-century country house, with later additions, in an idyllic setting, this ivy-covered hotel stands in its own gardens on the River Esk. Egton Bridge was the 17th-century home of Nicholas Postgate, the last of the English martyrs. The hotel has a reputation for good food. The beamed bar features old pews and a stone floor. In summer it can get busy, but the large gardens have tables and chairs. The licensee supports cask ale from the Durham Brewery, one of only a few outlets in this area.

🏚Q🌮◑⏚◑≈♣P

ELSLACK

Tempest Arms

☀ 11-11; 12-10.30 Sun

☎ (01282) 842450

Jennings Bitter; Cumberland Ale, Cocker Hoop, Sneck Lifter; guest beer H

Traditional South Craven pub, extended and converted into a hotel and restaurant in the early 1990s and purchased by Jennings in 1996. The bar is one large room, divided into several distinct areas, with cosy log fires. The emphasis is on food, both in the bar and restaurant. Breakfasts are served from 7.30. A regular daytime bus service runs from Skipton.

🏚Q🌮◑⏚◑♣P●

ELVINGTON

Grey Horse

Main Street

☀ 12-2.30 (not Mon, Tue or Thu); 5.30-11; 12-11 Sat; 12-10.30 Sun

☎ (01904) 608335

Black Sheep Best Bitter; John Smith's Bitter; Taylor Landlord; Tetley Bitter; guest beers H

Small pub, opposite the green in this expanding village. The innocent-looking beck on the other side of the street can become a 'raging torrent' in wet weather and occasionally necessitates the use of rowing boats to ferry in thirsty locals. The two comfortable rooms both have wood-burning stoves and one features attractive African 'hand' stools by the bar. Indoor sportsmen favour this pub – the many trophies testify to their prowess. Others come for the quiz (Thu eve) of the live music (Fri). Guest beers change frequently. No eve meals Mon.

🏚◑Å♣P

INN BRIEF

ALNE
Blue Bell
Main Street
7 (6 Tue)-11; 12-6, 7-10.30 Sun
Beer range varies H
Traditionally decorated village inn with three constantly changing guest beers. Thai food is a speciality.

ASKRIGG
Crown Inn
Main Street
11-3, 6-11; 11-11 Sat & summer; 12-10.30 Sun
Black Sheep Best Bitter, Special; John Smith's Bitter; Theakston Best Bitter, Cool Cask H
Large bar area serving several rooms, popular with locals and visitors, especially for the meals based on fresh produce.

DALEHOUSE
Fox & Hounds
12-3 (not winter Mon or Tue), 7-11; 12-3, 7-10.30 Sun
Greene King Old Speckled Hen; Marston's Pedigree; Theakston XB H
Cosy, hospitable country pub enjoying a reputation for good food, served in the bar or no-smoking diner.

GIGGLESWICK
Hart's Head
Belle Hill
12-3, 5.30-11; 11-11 Sat; 12-10.30 Sun
Black Sheep Best Bitter; Jennings Cumberland Ale; Tetley Bitter; Theakston Black Bull; Taylor Landlord; guest beer H
Welcoming, 17th-century coaching inn, modernised but retaining four drinking areas, and offering an imaginative menu.

HAROME
Star Inn
High Street
11.30-3 (not Mon); 6.30-11; 12-10.30 Sun
Black Sheep Special; John Smith's Bitter; Theakston Best Bitter; guest beer H
Historic thatched inn with a formidable reputation for excellent food; a single, characterful lounge bar and a restaurant.

HARROGATE
Shepherd's Dog
141 Otley Road
11-11;
12-10.30 Sun
Draught Bass; Stone's Bitter H
Large, community-orientated pub serving traditional pub food. It hosts many activities and fields football teams.

EMBSAY

Elm Tree
Elm Tree Square
☼ 11.30-3, 5.30-11; 12-3, 7-10.30 Sun
☎ (01756) 790717
Goose Eye No-Eyed Deer; Tetley Bitter; guest beers Ⓗ
Popular with locals and visitors for both the ale and food, the large main bar has an open fire, a collection of polished brass curios and horse-brasses on the ceiling beams. A smaller side room features pew seating and photos of bygone Embsay. This former coaching inn is ideally situated for exploring the nearby moors of the National Park and is only minutes away from the Embsay and Bolton Abbey Steam Railway. Note the worn mounting steps at the front. Three guest beers normally available.
▯ ❀ ▱◖◗ P

FILEY

Imperial Vaults
20-22 Hope Street
☼ 11-11; 12-10.30 Sun
☎ (01723) 512185
John Smith's Bitter; Greene King Old Speckled Hen; Tetley Bitter; guest beer Ⓗ
Popular, town-centre pub, sympathetically restored with wooden floors. Aspects of local history adorn the walls. Food is served in the summer season, April-Sept.
◖◗ ♿ ▲ ♣ ♠

GRASSINGTON

Foresters Arms
20 Main Street
☼ 11-11; 12-10.30 Sun
☎ (01756) 752349 e-mail: theforesters@totalise.co.uk
Black Sheep Best Bitter; Taylor Best Bitter; Tetley Mild, Bitter; guest beers Ⓗ
Very popular village-centre local that also welcomes tourists. On entering, the bar is to the left, beyond is the pool area and a TV, which is often on for major sporting events. Another large seating area leads to the dining room; home-cooked food includes a take-away menu. Join in the quiz (Mon). The accommodation is all en-suite with colour TVs. Up to three guest beers are stocked.
▯ ▱◖◗ ♣ ●

GREAT AYTON

Buck
1 West Terrace (A173, near river bridge)
☼ 11-11; 12-10.30 Sun
☎ (01642) 722242
Black Sheep Special; Boddingtons Bitter; Flowers Original; guest beers Ⓗ
Pleasant, bay-windowed coaching inn, dating from the 1700s, overlooking the River Leven in the village where Captain Cook went to school (now a museum). The pub has recently been refurbished to provide four partitioned seating areas around the central bar. It enjoys a strong local patronage, and the pub organises charity events and beer festivals. Good value bar meals served. A great place to go on a summer's day, with tables outside the front. Q ❀ ◖◗ ♣ P

GREAT SMEATON

Bay Horse
Northallerton Road (A167)
☼ 12-2 (not Mon or Tue), 6-11; 11-11 Sat; 12-10.30 Sun
☎ (01609) 881466
John Smith's Bitter; guest beers Ⓗ
Small 18th-century free house in the middle of a row of roadside cottages in an attractive village setting comprising three linked rooms: a soft-furnished lounge, with central fireplace and beams, a bustling little bar, and a games area behind. Former local CAMRA *Rural Pub of the Year* it has an attractive, enclosed garden to the rear with a small play area. ▯ ❀ ◖◗ ♣ ▯

GROSMONT

Crossing Club
Front Street (off A171, 5 miles SW of Whitby)
☼ 7-11; 7-10.30 Sun
☎ (01947) 895040
Beer range varies Ⓗ
Brilliant, comfortable conversion of a former Co-op delivery bay, undertaken by village volunteers, complete with its own level crossing gate inside – Grosmont station is next door. Usually at least four real ales from independents are available, with a mild regularly on tap, due to popular demand. Members are proud of their club, as shown in their hospitality – and rightly so. Non-members are welcome – just ring

---

HELWITH BRIDGE
Helwith Bridge Hotel
11-11; 12-10.30 Sun
Greene King Old Speckled Hen; Marston's Pedigree; Theakston Best Bitter; Webster's Yorkshire Bitter; guest beers Ⓗ
Characterful, cosy free house, backing onto the river, decorated with railway paraphernalia. Two guest beers on tap.

HEMINGBROUGH
Crown
Main Street
12 (2 Mon)-11;
12-10.30 Sun
John Smith's Bitter; Tetley Bitter; guest beer Ⓗ
Comfortable village pub near the 12th-century Minster. Folk night is first Sun of month. No food Mon.

HENSALL
Anchor
Main Street
5.30 (3 Sat)-11;
12-10.30 Sun
John Smith's Bitter; Taylor Landlord; guest beer Ⓗ
Well refurbished village pub, family friendly, with a separate dining area. Meals served Tue-Sat eve, plus Sun lunch.

HUBBERHOLME
George Inn
11.30-3, 6-11 (11-11 summer); 12-3, 6-10.30 (12-10.30 summer) Sun
Black Sheep Best Bitter, Special; Tetley Bitter; guest beer (summer) Ⓗ
Stone-flagged, unspoilt inn, with oak beams and an open stove, offering wholesome bar food. It has a pleasant outdoor area.

LANGDALE END
Moorcock Inn
7 (11 summer)-11 (closed winter Mon-Tue); 11-3, 7-11 (11-11 summer) Sat; 12-3, 7-10.30 Sun
Beer range varies Ⓗ
Remote stone pub. Sympathetically renovated, near Dalby Forest. Welcoming and friendly, it serves home-cooked food.

LINTON-IN-CRAVEN
Fountaine
The Green
11-11;
12-10.30 Sun
John Smith's Bitter; Taylor Landlord; Tetley Bitter; Theakston Best Bitter; guest beers Ⓗ
Low-beamed, 17th-century inn serving food all day, idyllically set on the green in this historic village.

the bell and push the door. Weekend lunchtime opening in summer is likely, please check. Children are not allowed inside, but can use the garden. ✿▲≄♣⊟

GUISBOROUGH

Tap & Spile
11-13 Westgate
✪ 11.30-11; 12-3, 7-10.30 Sun
☎ (01287) 632778
Big Lamp Bitter; guest beers ⊞
Old pub on the main street of this historic market town (once the capital of Cleveland), now a Tap & Spile with a wooden-floored bar area and beamed ceilings. A no-smoking room/family room at the rear opens on to a small yard with tables in summer. It stocks a good range of guest beers and one guest traditional cider. A quiz night is held Tue, music Wed. Can be busy on market days (Thu and Sat). No food served Sun. ☸✿⊕(♣●½

HARROGATE ❋

Coach & Horses
16 West Park
✪ 11-11; 12-10.30 Sun
☎ (01423) 568371
Black Sheep Best Bitter; Tetley Bitter; guest beer ⊞
Popular pub on the edge of the town centre where a U-shaped bar serves three areas. The split-level interior has a narrow area along two sides of the bar used mainly by standing drinkers; the front rooms have comfortable seating, and the rear room has a TV, tables and chairs. Framed caricatures of past and present members of the pub's golfing society adorn one wall. Other artefacts include brass barrel taps. A regularly changing guest beer has replaced a national brew.
(≄

Gardener's Arms ☆
Bilton Lane (1 mile from A59)
✪ 12-3, 6-11; 12-3, 7-10.30 Sun
☎ (01423) 506051
Samuel Smith OBB ⊞
Built in the 1500s, with thick stone walls and wooden panelling. This totally unspoilt pub has a large stone fireplace and a tiny snug. A little gem, it is very popular in summer with an excellent garden by a stream that attracts much wildlife. It stands

on the route of a bridle path said to have been used by Oliver Cromwell after destroying Knaresborough Castle. Fishing tickets are available for the River Nidd. No eve meals winter Sun or Wed.
🏨Q☸✿⊕(▲P

Old Bell Tavern
6 Royal Parade
✪ 12-11; 12-10.30 Sun
☎ (01423) 507930
Black Sheep Best Bitter; Caledonian Deuchars IPA; Taylor Landlord; guest beers ⊞
This former restaurant opened as a pub in 1999. An L-shaped bar serves the single drinking area where old brewery adverts adorn the walls. Note, too, the framed history of the premises. It enjoys a good trade from the nearby conference centre. Eight real ales include one or more from local craft breweries. Two draught foreign beers and a good selection of Belgian bottled beers are also available. Good quality food is served in the bar and restaurant.
Q(▮≄

Tap & Spile
Tower Street
✪ 11-11; 12-10.30 Sun
☎ (01423) 526785
Beer range varies ⊞
A former Camerons' house, this pub was 'mothballed' for a time and re-opened as one of the early Tap and Spiles in the late 1980s. Three separate drinking areas (one designated a no-smoking room) are served by a central bar. Local breweries are well represented on the regularly changing beer menu and a draught foreign beer is available. The bus and rail stations are both just five minutes' walk away. No food Sun.
✿(≄♣●½

HELPERBY

Golden Lion
Main Street
✪ 12 (3 winter Mon-Fri)-11; 12-10.30 Sun
☎ (01423) 360870
website: www.goldenlion.free-online.co.uk
Black Sheep Best Bitter; Hambleton Bitter; Robinson's Best Bitter; Tetley Bitter; guest beers ⊞
Despite being a small village, Helperby boasts four pubs. The hub of the village, the

INN BRIEF

LOW MARISHES (NEAR MALTON)
School House Inn
11.30-3, 6-11; 11.30-11 Sat;
12-10.30 Sun
Black Sheep Bitter; Hambleton Stallion; Tetley Bitter; guest beers ⊞
Cosy, wood-panelled pub with open fire in the bar offering home-cooked food and a large selection of malt whiskies.

MASHAM
White Bear
12 Crosshills
11-11; 12-10.30 Sun
Caledonian Deuchars IPA; Theakston Best Bitter, Cool Cask, Old Peculier; guest beer ⊞
Popular, stone-built two-roomed pub, recently refurbished. Good food and occasional live music. Outside patio.

MIDDLESBROUGH
Lingfield Farm
Parkway Court (off Stainton Way), Coulby, Newham
11-11; 12-10.30 Sun
Banks's Bitter; Camerons Strongarm; Marston's Pedigree ⊞
Welcoming, comfortable, new suburban pub. Single room, divided into bar/lounge areas. Excellent beer and food – bargains in both.

NEWBY
Goat Gap Inn
12-3, 5.30-11; 11-11 Sat & summer; 12-10.30 Sun
Black Sheep Best Bitter, Special ⊞
Old farmhouse with rambling, low-beamed bar. It has a dining area and galleried function area but the whole pub is really for diners.

NORTH COWTON
Blacksmith's Arms
Myton Terrace
12-3 (not Mon-Fri), 7-11;
12-3, 7-10.30 Sun
Black Sheep Best Bitter; guest beers ⊞
Busy pub with an emphasis on meals but a distinct bar area with a fine old fireplace. Guest beers come from local independents.

OLD MALTON
Royal Oak
47 Town Street
12-2.30 (not Mon), 5-11; 12-11 Sat;
12-10.30 Sun
Tetley Bitter; guest beers ⊞
Traditional two-roomed pub: a low-beamed bar with open fire and quiet wood-panelled lounge. Home-cooked food.

Golden Lion was saved from closure and developed into a thriving free house only a few years ago by the previous licensees. The present incumbents are working hard to keep it that way. A good range of beers and live music Sat eve, have maintained its reputation. Log fires and stone-flagged floors add atmosphere, while outdoor tables and chairs let you watch rural life go by.
🅰Q🌣❄◑◗

HILTON

Falcon
2 miles off A1044 at High Leven crossroads
🕓 11.30-11; 12-10.30 Sun
☎ (01642) 592228
Flowers Original; Marston's Pedigree; guest beers Ⓗ
This extended pub in the village centre is at last enjoying some stability of ownership after a rather chequered history. A few years ago it was voted *Pub of the Year* by readers of the local evening newspaper, as much for its food as anything, for then it was all keg. Its current licensee has a long record of serving good real ale in the area. The pub still has a strong emphasis on food; guest ales come from local independents including the North Yorkshire Brewery.
Q🌣◑◗♣P

INGLEBY BARWICK

Myton House Farm
Ingleby Way (access from A1044 roundabout, High Leven)
🕓 11-11; 12-10.30 Sun
☎ (01642) 751308
Camerons Bitter, Strongarm; guest beer Ⓗ
Impressive farmhouse-style pub in what has been dubbed 'the largest village in Europe', and all built in the last 15 years. The rural theme is emphasised by the flagstoned floors and old farming artefacts and pictures. Several drinking areas surround the central bar. The Strongarm is chilled, and guest beers are taken from the Wolverhampton & Dudley Festival Ales range. It hosts weekly quiz nights, occasional live music and mini-beer festivals, as well as being a focus for local charitable fund-raising initiatives.
🌣◑◗&♣P

KIRBY HILL

Shoulder of Mutton
4 miles NW of Richmond OS140067
🕓 12-2 (not winter Mon-Fri; 3 Sat), 6-11; 12-3, 7-10.30 Sun
☎ (01748) 822772 website: www.@holmedale.com
Black Sheep Best Bitter; Jennings Cumberland; John Smith's Bitter Ⓗ
Ivy-fronted country inn in a beautiful hillside setting, overlooking lower Teesdale and the ruins of Ravensworth Castle. It stands opposite the church and the narrow entrance to the historic, enclosed village green. Carpeted and cosy throughout, the opened-out front bar, which is traditionally decorated with old brasses and plates links through to the lounge bar and no-smoking restaurant to the rear. The pub's owners know the area as 'Holmedale' and have their own house bitter brewed for them by Darwin. The five guest bedrooms have en-suite facilities. 🅰Q🌣🛏◑◗&♣P

KIRKLEVINGTON

Crown
Thirsk Road (A67, near Crathorne A19 interchange)
🕓 5 (12 Sat)-11; 12-10.30 Sun
☎ (01642) 780044
Boddingtons Bitter; Castle Eden Ale; John Smith's Magnet; Ⓗ
Pleasant old pub dominating the village road junction. Two drinking areas: the bar area with a pool table attracts a younger clientele, while the lounge features a massive fireplace and is used by diners as well as drinkers. All meals are prepared and cooked using only fresh ingredients and are deservedly popular (lunches served Sat). The pub-owning company does not permit a wide range of real ales. Despite its rather remote setting, this unspoilt pub is well worth seeking out for its warm, friendly atmosphere. 🅰🌣◗&♣P

KNARESBOROUGH

Blind Jack's
19 Market Place
🕓 4 (5.30 Mon; 12 Fri & Sat)-11; 12-10.30 Sun
☎ (01423) 869148
Black Sheep Best Bitter; Daleside Greengrass; Taylor Landlord; Village White Boar; guest beers Ⓗ
Veritable gem of an ale house with bare boards, exposed brickwork and wood

OSWALDKIRK

Malt Shovel
11.30-3, 6.30-11; 12-3, 7-10.30 Sun
Samuel Smith OBB Ⓗ
Built around 1610 as a manor house, but an inn for 300 years, it is multi-roomed and full of character.

RAINTON

Bay Horse Inn
12-3 (not Mon), 6-11; 12-11 Sat; 12-10.30 Sun
Hambleton Bitter; Tetley Bitter; guest beer Ⓗ
Multi-roomed, open-plan pub in a quiet village close to the A1 and A19, offering good quality food and locally-brewed ales.

RIPON

Golden Lion
69-70 Allhallowgate
12-3, 7-11; 12-11 Thu-Sat; 12-10.30 Sun
Draught Bass; Black Sheep Best Bitter; John Smith's Bitter; Theakston Best Bitter Ⓗ
L-shaped lounge bar and a no-smoking dining room in a pub with a strong nautical theme, provided by shipping memorabilia.

Wheatsheaf
Harrogate Road
12-3 (not Mon), 7-11; 12-3, 7-10.30 Sun
Tetley Bitter; guest beer Ⓗ
Quiet, relaxing, traditional inn near the city bypass, away from the busy city centre pubs. Guest beer at weekends.

SCARBOROUGH

Jolly Roger
27-31 Eastborough
12-11; 12-10.30 Sun
Banks's Bitter; Camerons Strongarm; guest beer Ⓗ
Near the beach and town centre, a pub with accommodation, live music (twice weekly) and good value food (summer) plus a resident ghost.

Scarborough Arms
1 North Terrace
11-11; 12-10.30 Sun
Camerons Bitter; guest beers Ⓗ
Attractive, friendly local near the castle; two rooms. Excellent value meals served until 8pm; big screen TV for sports.

panelling, at the centre of this historic town, overlooking the pedestrianised area around the market cross. Converted from two shops in 1991, now a venue for real ale drinkers from far and wide, it is consequently busy at most times. No pool table, juke box or gaming machines, just lively conversation. Four guest ales are always available. Winner of CAMRA's *Best New Pub* 1992 award, it comprises a bar and snug downstairs, plus three rooms upstairs. Q ≠ ⚡

Marquis of Granby

31 York Place (A59, York Road 600 yds E of bus station)

☼ 11.30-3, 5.30-11; 11.30-11 Wed, Fri & Sat; 12-10.30 Sun

☎ (01423) 862207

Samuel Smith OBB H

Comfortably furnished Victorian pub, within easy walking distance of the town centre, it was recently completely renovated. Popular with locals and visitors, it stands opposite the swimming pool, and quite close to holiday caravan sites. The interior is divided into a pleasant lounge and a traditional tap room, used for games. It organises an annual golf tournament and an in-house cribbage league. It sells some of the cheapest beer in town.
❀◑Ɖ♣P

Mitre Hotel

4 Station Road

☼ 4 (3 Fri; 11 Sat)-11; 12-3, 7-10.30 Sun

☎ (01423) 863589 website: the-mitre.bizhosting.com

Tetley Bitter; guest beers H

Almost impossible to miss when you get off the train, this imposing pub boasts a large split-level bar with two smaller snugs where pool and darts are played. A regular outlet for nearby Daleside and Roosters' beers, the pub is a true supporter of Yorkshire ale. A lower level bar, the Trapdoor opens occasionally; in summer it becomes a tea-room and also hosts impromptu jam sessions.
❀≠◑♣♣

LEAVENING

Jolly Farmers

Main Street

☼ 12-3 (not Mon), 7-11; 12-3, 7-10.30 Sun

☎ (01653) 658276

John Smith's Bitter; Taylor Landlord; Tetley Bitter; guest beesr H

In rolling countryside between York and Malton, the village is on the edge of the Yorkshire Wolds, an area popular for outdoor pursuits. A recent York CAMRA *Pub of the Year*, this 17th-century village local has been extended, but retains the cosiness of its original multi-rooms. The restaurant offers a varied menu, specialising in locally-caught game in season. The changing guest beers often include strong ales from independent breweries. An annual themed beer festival is held in the family room.
🏠⅍❀◑♣P♿

LITTLE SMEATON

Fox

Main Street

☼ 7-11; 12-5, 7-10.30 Sun

☎ (01977) 620254

Black Sheep Best Bitter; John Smith's Bitter; Taylor Landlord H

This cosy, comfortable free house, on the outskirts of a tiny village offers a splendid view of the Went Valley. It now consists of a single L-shaped room, having been converted from a traditional three-roomed local, but retains its homely atmosphere. Despite its rural location, access by public transport is easy (no. 412 and 413 Doncaster-Pontefract buses stop at the doorstep). The decor reflects the area's horse-racing traditions.
❀♣P

LOFTUS

White Horse

73 High Street

☼ 12-11; 12-10.30 Sun

☎ (01287) 640758

John Smith's Bitter; guest beer H

Long-established, terraced pub on the main street at the east end of town, just off the market place. Refurbished, it has a large L-shaped room with a central bar and a real fire; beamed ceilings complete the atmosphere. It enjoys a strong local patronage, with darts and pool teams competing in the local league. No food, unless you are a B&B guest. 🏠❀≠♣P

LONG PRESTON

Maypole Inn

☼ 11-3, 6 (5 Sat)-11 (11-11 summer Sat); 12-10.30 Sun

☎ (01729) 840219 website: www.maypole.co.uk

INN BRIEF

Albion Vaults

1 The Crescent

12-11; 12-10.30 Sun

Old Mill Bitter, seasonal beers H

Small, interesting town pub, near the swing bridge; two rooms with Edwardian decor. Food served from midday daily.

THIRSK

Golden Fleece

Market Square

11-2.30, 6-11; 12-3, 7-10.30 Sun

Hambleton Bitter, Goldfield, Stud H

In the market place, the cosy lounge and paddock bar serve a selection of local ales and traditional bar meals.

WHITBY

Endeavour Hotel

66 Church Street

11-11; 12-10.30 Sun

Tetley Bitter; guest beer H

One-roomed bar enjoying a strong local patronage; a place for a drink and socialising – no food.

Little Angel Hotel

18 Flowergate

11-11; 12-10.30 Sun

Black Sheep Best Bitter; Tetley Bitter; guest beer H

Grade II listed building, dating back to 1823, incorporating a 14th-century window and two rooms with low-beamed ceilings.

Carlton Tavern

140 Acomb Road, Acomb

11-11; 12-10.30 Sun

Camerons Bitter, Strongarm; Marston's Pedigree H

First-class, former hotel set in beautiful, enclosed gardens, offering a good range of beers, quality food and a warm welcome.

YORK

York Beer & Wine Shop

28 Sandringham Street

11 (6 Mon; 10 Sat)-10; 6-10 Sun

Taylor Landlord; guest beers H

Draught beer and cider in any quantity and many bottle-conditioned beers. Mouth-watering cheeses and ice-cream too.

Castle Eden Ale; Moorhouse's Premier; Taylor Landlord; Tetley Bitter H
On the village green, opposite the maypole, this welcoming village local has won many awards. The tap room boasts carved bench seating dating from 1875. The cosy lounge has a list of the pub's licensees since 1695 and old local photos showing an idyllic A65. Good value food (served all day Sun) – can be eaten in the bar or the no-smoking dining room. Dogs are welcome in the tap room. The cider is Ruby Tuesday from Saxon.
🏨Q🕮🍴◑≠♣P

LOW BENTHAM

Sun Dial
✪ 11-3, 5-11, 11-11 Fri & Sat; 12-10.30 Sun
☎ (015242) 65132 website: www.sundialinn.co.uk
Tetley Mild, Bitter; guest beers H
The Sun Dial remains what it has always been, a local pub for local drinkers. The small homely bar is complemented by an even smaller games room. Note the old Sun Dial functioning as an inn sign. Seats outside are on the roadside. A quiz night is held Wed. Guest beers are often from Jennings. Sandwiches and soup are available weekday lunchtime; main meals are served at weekends, including Fri eve.
🕮◑♣P

MALHAM

Listers Arms
✪ 12-3, 7-11 (12-11 summer Sat); 12-3, 7-10.30 (12-10.30 summer) Sun
☎ (01729) 830330 www.listersarms.co.uk
Black Sheep Special; Boddingtons Bitter; guest beers H
Homely pub dating from 1702, popular with locals and visitors alike. A tiled entrance leads to a wood-panelled bar area with solid wooden seating. A second room, with a large inglenook, overlooks the village. There is also a restaurant seating up to 70. The garden is large and sheltered. A range of foreign bottled beers and one draught Belgian beer are stocked, alongside usually two guest beers; a cider is added in summer. Both the food and guest accommodation are of a high standard.
🏨Q🛏🕮🍴◑♨♣P

MALTON

Crown Hotel (Suddaby's)
12 Wheelgate
✪ 11-11; 12-4, 7-10.30 Sun
☎ (01653) 692038
website: www.suddabyscrown.co.uk
Malton Golden Chance, Pickwick's Porter, Ryedale Champion, Auld Bob, seasonal beers; guest beers H
Five generations of the Suddaby family have run the hotel since 1879. The building's façade is Grade II listed and many architectural and historic features have been conserved. The hotel has seven bedrooms, plus nine rooms in the brewery annexe. Malton Brewery, in the courtyard, regularly supplies several other outlets in the area. Live music eves, including jazz, folk and piano recitals, are staged regularly in the conservatory and seasonal beer festivals are held. Lunches served Fri and Sat. 🏨🛏🍴◑♨≠♣P

MARSKE

Frigate
Hummers Hill Lane (opp. cricket club)
✪ 1 (12 Fri & Sat)-11; 12-10.30 Sun
☎ (01642) 484302
John Smith's Magnet H
Well-established, friendly, local estate pub with a lounge, bar and snug. A general knowledge quiz is held Thu eves, and a pop music quiz Sun. Live music is performed in the lounge. Pool and darts are played in the bar. Q🕮🍴≠♣P🚭

MASHAM ❖

Black Sheep Brewery Visitors Centre
Wellgarth, Crosshills
✪ 11-11 (closed Mon); 12-6 Sun
☎ (01765) 689227 website: www.blacksheep.co.uk
Black Sheep Best Bitter, Special, Riggwelter, seasonal beer H
This popular attraction is based in a former maltings. Apart from regular brewery tours, there is a split-level bistro, serving quality meals, coffee and snacks, a bar area that boasts a selection of unusual table-top games, and a 'sheepy' gift shop. The small garden affords pleasant views over Lower Wensleydale. An interesting few hours can be spent in this historic building, filled with fascinating brewery artefacts; families are welcome during the day. Special events feature throughout the year (booking is necessary for some functions). 🕮◑♿P

MIDDLESBOROUGH ❖

Doctor Brown's
135 Corporation Road
✪ 11-11; 12-10.30 Sun
☎ (01642) 213213
Beer range varies H
Large, comfortable, end-of-terrace pub in an area where traffic is restricted with shady outside seating for balmy summer drinking. Beers are sourced from all over the country so, for a Teesside pub, be prepared to be pleasantly surprised, with usually three, ever-changing guest beers on tap. Live music is a regular feature weekend eves. It is the closest town-centre pub to the football ground, so gets busy on match days.
🕮◑≠

Hogshead
14 Corporation Road (near Town Hall)
✪ 11-11; 12-10.30 Sun
☎ (01642) 219320
Boddingtons Bitter; guest beers H
Standard, ex-Whitbread, Hogshead pub, comfortably fitted out, including settees in a former shop in the pedestrianised part of the town centre. Popular with office workers during the day, it attracts older (25+) customers eves. Low fencing outside encloses a pavement café-style area. An ever-changing, wide selection of beers available, usually includes four guests, with good value, four-pint jug offers and bottled Belgian beers. It stages regular beer festivals, and usually at least one annual real cider/perry festival. No children allowed.
Q🕮◑♿≠¼

Isaac Wilson
61 Wilson Street
✪ 11-11; 12-10.30 Sun
☎ (01642) 247708
Courage Directors; Worthington Bitter; guest beers H
Handy for the station, buses and shops, it has a spacious ground-floor lounge bar with panelled walls displaying pictures of old Middlesbrough. Divided up by pillars and partitions, to include a no-smoking area, a single long bar serves drink and food. A wide range of drinks at competitive prices means it can get busy, especially on match days and weekends; no under-18s allowed. Formerly the old county court, it was converted by J D Wetherspoons. Good value meals are served all day.
Q ◑ & ⇌ ⅙ ●

Star & Garter
14 Southfield Road
✪ 11-11; 12-10.30 Sun
☎ (01642) 245307
Black Sheep Special; Boddingtons Bitter; guest beers H
Excellent conversion of a former dockers' club, which deservedly won a CAMRA *Pub Preservation* award. A large public bar, with pool table is situated below a raised lounge which has a large screen TV and is always busy when the local team is featured. Being near the university, it is often busy, but one end of the lounge is normally peaceful. Two guest beers are usually available, mostly from small independents, and the pub regularly holds beer festivals. The public bar has no handpulls; real ale is served from the lounge. ◑ ● ⊟ & ♣ P

MOORSHOLM

Jolly Sailor
Whitby Moor Road (A171)
✪ 11-3, 6-11; 11-11 Fri, Sat & summer; 12-.10.30 Sun
☎ (01287) 660270
Black Sheep Best Bitter; guest beers H
Old coaching inn on the main moors road to Whitby. In severe winters it has been a welcome refuge for stranded travellers who have reputedly drunk the inn dry while being marooned. The bar is a long room with low beamed ceilings; good food is available here or in the dining room. Mon eve is 'sizzling steak night' – well worth the visit; on Sun there is a carvery. The guest beers, from local breweries, are competitively priced. Live music is staged regularly. The garden, with children's area is an added attraction.
🏚 ✿ ◑ P

MUKER

Farmers Arms
✪ 11-3, 7-11 (opens afternoons in summer); 12-3, 7-10.30 Sun
☎ (01748) 886297
Castle Eden Nimmo's XXXX; John Smith's Bitter; Theakston Best Bitter, Cool Cask, Old Peculier; guest beer (summer) H
Cold and wet from a walk in picturesque Swaledale? Then visit the Farmers Arms for a warm welcome. No excuse is really necessary to visit this quiet establishment that maintains an impressive range of cask

beers throughout the year. If you do need warming up, hot drinks are also available and tasty home-made meals are served. The pub is child, dog and muddy boot friendly (part of the bar being stone-flagged). Afternoon opening hours to lengthen with increased custom in the summer.
🏚 Q ✿ ◑ ▲ ♣ P

NEWTON-ON-OUSE

Blacksmith's Arms
Cherry Tree Avenue (head for RAF Linton, 3 miles off A19)
✪ 12-3 (not Mon-Thu), 5.30-11, 12-11 Sat; 12-10.30 Sun
☎ (01347) 848249
Banks's Bitter; Camerons Bitter, Strongarm; Marston's Pedigree H
Busy pub, despite being tucked away and surrounded by housing. The building was erected in 1850 as the blacksmith's shop for nearby Beningbrough Hall – a popular attraction in its own right. The original corridor linking three rooms was removed in the recent past, leaving an essentially open-plan layout and a pool room added to the rear. The Lebanese chef is famous locally for his pizzas. If you visit in June you may catch the annual Newton Feast.
🏚 ✿ ⊟ ◑ ▲ ♣ P ⊟

NORTH DUFFIELD

King's Arms
Main Street (off A163)
✪ 4 (12 Sat)-11; 12-10.30 Sun
☎ (01757) 288492 e-mail: kingsarms@barbox.net
Black Sheep Best Bitter; John Smith's Bitter; Theakston Cool Cask; guest beers H
Exactly what a village pub should be – an old building in an idyllic situation, by the green and duck pond offering a warm, friendly welcome, and quality food and drink. With the large garden-cum-children's play area, there's something here for everyone. A single, spacious bar is complemented by a no-smoking dining area (eve meals Wed-Sat). A long-standing entry in this *Guide*, it stocks draught cider in summer. 🏚 ✿ ◑ ♣ ● P ⅙ ●

NORTHALLERTON

Station Hotel
2 Boroughbridge Road
✪ 12-3, 5 (6 Sat)-11; 12-3, 7-10.30 Sun
☎ (01609) 772053
website: www.stationhotel.northallerton.com
Tetley Bitter; guest beers H
The Station Hotel has a fine Edwardian frontage and, as the etched window to the main bar proclaims, was once known as the Railway Hotel. The bar is light, airy and comfortable; a second quiet, bar lies to the rear, while the third room is used for the Fri eve folk club and meetings. Two beer festivals are held every year, and the main bar typically hosts a couple of live music eves a month.
🏚 ⅚ ✿ ⊟ ◑ ⊟ & ⇌ ♣ P ⅙

NOSTERFIELD

Freemasons Arms
On B6367
✪ 12-3, 6-11 (closed Mon); 12-3, 7-10.30 Sun

☎ (01677) 470548

Black Sheep Best Bitter; Taylor Landlord; Tetley Bitter; Old Mill Bitter; guest beer Ⓗ

This old stone inn is a prominent feature on the main road through the village. It has a stone-flagged bar area, low, heavily beamed ceilings and two open fires. Opened up long ago, it retains the feeling of separate areas. A plethora of fascinating memorabilia mainly relate to the Great War and motorcycling. It attracts customers from far and wide because of its reputation for quality cuisine, but it's definitely a pub with food rather than a restaurant with beer. ᛘQ✿◖Ɪ)P🖸●

NUN MONKTON

Alice Hawthorn
The Green (off A59, York-Harrogate road)
✪ 11-2, 6-11; 12-10.30 Sun
☎ (01423) 330303

Camerons Bitter; Castle Eden Ale; John Smith's Bitter; guest beers Ⓗ

At the end of a country lane, this cosy country pub offers an excellent range of home-cooked food. Enjoy the view of the maypole and the duck pond on the village green, or huddle around a log fire in winter. Named after a famous racehorse of the 1840s, it had previously been known as the Blue Bell until around 1900. The pub is a firm favourite with the fishing fraternity from the nearby Rivers Ouse and Nidd. Outside are patio tables and a children's playground. ᛘ✿◖Ɪ)🖸ᛘ♣P

OSMOTHERLEY

Golden Lion
6 West End, Village Square (1 mile E of A19 at Northallerton jct)
✪ 12-4, 6-11; 12-11 Sat; 12-10.30 Sun
☎ (01609) 883526

Hambleton Bitter; John Smith's Bitter; North Yorkshire Fools Gold; Tetley Bitter; guest beer (occasional) Ⓗ

The Golden Lion is renowned for the quality and range of its food – everything except the bread is home made – but the drinker is as welcome as the diner. Similarly, the dinner suit is just as welcome as the wellied and jerseyed local. All the real ales are from Yorkshire breweries. The decor is simple, with the accent on fresh flowers outside and in. This free house is equally popular with locals and the walkers who frequent this part of Yorkshire. ᛘ◖Ɪ)ᛘ♣

PICKERING

White Swan Hotel
Market Place
✪ 11-3, 6-11; 11-11 Mon & Sat; 11-3, 7-10.30 Sun
☎ (01751) 472288 website: www.white-swan.co.uk

Black Sheep Best Bitter, Special; guest beers Ⓗ

Family-run historic former coaching inn with a cosy, beamed bar and open fire. Choose from the excellent bar menu or dine in the restaurant that prides itself on the quality of its cuisine. A relaxed, informal atmosphere is enhanced by friendly, attentive staff. Situated in a scenic part of the North York Moors it was Yorkshire Tourist Board's Hotel of the Year 2000. Guest beers are sourced from local breweries.
ᛘQ✥✿🖨⛐◖Ɪ)ᛘ🚂(North Yorks Moors Rlwy)P✂🖸

PICKHILL

Nag's Head
1½ miles off A1 between Bedale and Masham exits
✪ 11-11; 12-10.30 Sun
☎ (01845) 567391
website: www.nagsheadpickhill.co.uk

Black Sheep Best Bitter, Special; Hambleton Bitter; John Smith's Bitter; guest beer Ⓗ

Off the A1, near Thirsk, this lovely small country coaching inn has a well-founded reputation for good food and hospitality. The lounge bar and restaurant are separate from the cosy bar which is decorated with a frieze of ties. Traditional bar games include the unusual bar draughts. It offers good en-suite accommodation and has seasonal outdoor games facilities: quoits, boules and a nine-hole putting green. Children are welcome until 7.30, but only with well-behaved parents. ᛘ✿🖨◖Ɪ)🖧ᛘ♣P

POOL-IN-WHARFEDALE

Hunters Inn
Harrogate Road (½ mile E of village)
✪ 11-11; 12-10.30 Sun
☎ (0113) 284 1090

Tetley Bitter; Theakston Best Bitter; guest beers Ⓗ

Single-room on a split level, with a real fire at one end and a pool table and juke box at the other. A very popular venue for real ale enthusiasts; seven guest ales are regularly changed and come from all over the country. Prices are very reasonable. No food Tue. Well worth a visit. ᛘ✿◖Ɪ)P

PORT MULGRAVE

Ship
20 Rosedale Lane (off A174 at Hinderwell)
✪ 11-11; 12-10.30 Sun
☎ (01947) 840303

Black Sheep Best Bitter; John Smith's Magnet; guest beers Ⓗ

Popular local in a clifftop village overlooking the cove which once was a busy port for the export of iron ore from local mines that have all disappeared. Opened in 1896 to serve the mining community, it now serves locals and walkers from the nearby Cleveland Way (clean feet please). The lounge/bar displays numerous artefacts and memorabilia. Quiz nights are held Thu and themed eves monthly. The pub serves food from 12-9 daily, plus Sun lunch. ᛘQ✥🖨◖Ɪ)ᛘ♣P

REETH

King's Arms
✪ 11-11; 12-10.30 Sun
☎ (01748) 884259 website: www.thekingsarms.com

Black Sheep Best Bitter; John Smith's Bitter; Taylor Landlord; guest beers Ⓗ

Known by many as the Middle House, it is the middle one of Reeth's three pubs facing the broad village green. The bar is warm and comfortable with a large inglenook. The King's Arms enjoys a good reputation for its fine food, cooked from fresh ingredients, including game in season. Popular with both locals and tourists, it holds frequent and varied live music eves. Reeth is a good base for a holiday and the King's Arms an excellent place to stay. ᛘ✿🖨◖Ɪ)ᛘ♣🖸●

RICHMOND

Holly Hill Inn
Sleegill (Hudswell road)
✪ 12-11; 12-10.30 Sun
☎ (01748) 822192
Black Sheep Best Bitter; Taylor Landlord; guest beer (occasional) Ⓗ

On a hill, across the river from Richmond, the pub affords impressive panoramic views of Richmond Castle. With a warm split-level bar, where games are played, on the upper level and a comfortable lounge, the interior has been nicely refurbished. It is very popular for its interesting and reasonably-priced food; the restaurant and accommodation block are new features.
▲Q❀☎◑♣♠P✗●

RIPON ✤

One-Eyed Rat
51 Allhallowgate
✪ 12-3.30 (not Mon-Wed), 6 (5.30 Fri)-11; 12-11 Sat; 12-3, 7-10.30 Sun
☎ (01765) 607704
website: www.oneeyedrat.homestead.com
Black Sheep Best Bitter; Taylor Landlord; guest beers Ⓗ

Traditional, popular pub without TV or juke box, close to the city centre, stocking a selection of Belgian, Czech and German bottled beers, a vast selection of fruit wines and Biddenden cider. A German beer festival is held each May. Play bar billiards or pool (in summer – the table is in the excellent garden). Four ever-changing guest beers all come from independent brewers. Added attractions are the wood floor, a black-leaded range, brewery memorabilia, old mirrors and hops over the bar.
▲Q❀♣♠

ROBIN HOOD'S BAY

Dolphin
22 King Street
✪ 11 (12 winter)-11; 12-10.30 Sun
☎ (01947) 880337
John Smith's Bitter; Theakston XB, Old Peculier; guest beer Ⓗ

The pub lies near the bottom of the village, just above the harbour. The extensive collection of pump clips behind the bar bears testimony to the range of guest beers over the past few years. A good selection of home-cooked food includes a children's menu, plus snacks and sandwiches. A single central bar serves a small bar and lounge areas, both featuring old beer bottles; note the bottle from Roses of Malton.
▲Q☎◑Å♣

Victoria Hotel
Station Road
✪ 11-3, 6.30-11; 11-11 Fri, Sat & summer; 12-10.30 Sun
☎ (01947) 880205
e-mail: victoriahoteluk@yahoo.co.uk
Banks's Bitter, Camerons Bitter, Strongarm; guest beers Ⓗ

Impressive hotel built in 1897 on the cliff overlooking the bay and village; the views are especially fine from some of the nine en-suite bedrooms. The comfortable bar displays a collection of guest ale pump clips. There is a no-smoking/family room and a

dining room, serving high quality home-cooked food. Cleveland CAMRA *Pub of the Year* 1999 – do not miss it. ▲Q☎❀☎◑♣

RUFFORTH

Tankard Inn
Main Street (B1224, 4 miles W of York)
✪ 11.30-3, 6-11; 11.30-11 Sat; 12-4, 7-10.30 Sun
☎ (01904) 738621
Samuel Smith OBB Ⓗ

The 1930s remodelling of this outstanding local gives visitors an opportunity to see how a pub can retain the essential elements of a past era and continue to be a popular village inn. Two delightful rooms, in which the original small, curved counter in the public bar has been successfully replicated in the lounge. Both have leaded windows, bench seating and open fire. A daily specials board of home-cooked food is available (no food Sun eve or Mon). A pleasant, large grassed area has tables and children's play equipment. ▲☎◑🍴♣P

SALTBURN

Saltburn Cricket, Bowls and Tennis Club
Marske Mill Lane (next to Leisure Centre)
✪ 8 (2 summer Sat)-11; 12-3, 8-10.30 Sun
☎ (01287) 622761
Tetley Bitter; guest beer Ⓗ

Friendly, private sports club, fielding cricket, tennis and bowls teams. It has a spacious well-furnished lounge and a games room; both areas afford a magnificent view of the cricket field. Casual visitors are welcome, without joining. It stocks a large selection of guest beers, sometimes local brews, and hosts occasional beer festivals. Cleveland CAMRA *Pub of the Season* winner 1997 and 1999.
❀Å⇌♣P

SANDHUTTON

King's Arms
On A167, 4 miles W of Thirsk
✪ 12-2.30 (4 Sat), 6.30-11; 12-4, 6.30-10.30 Sun
☎ (01845) 587263
John Smith's Bitter; Taylor Landlord; Theakston Cool Cask; Village Brewers White Boar; guest beer (occasional) Ⓗ

Delightful traditional village inn in rural North Yorkshire, with easy access to the moors and dales. Well-used by locals, it offers a good selection of real ales. The popular dining room serves an extensive menu and meals can also be taken in the comfortable lounge or the public bar where pool and darts are played. No food Mon.
▲Q❀◑🍴♣P

SAWDON

Anvil Inn
Main Street (off A170)
✪ 11-11; 12-10.30 Sun
☎ (01723) 859896
Theakston Best Bitter; guest beers Ⓗ

Friendly, restored blacksmith's shop with original anvils proudly displayed. Handy for picturesque forest drives and the moors. The dining area serves excellent value meals.
▲Q☎❀☎◑Å♣P🍴

SAXTON

Greyhound Inn
Main Street
🕓 11.30-3, 5.30-11, 11-11 Sat; 12-10.30 Sun
☎ (01937) 557202
Samuel Smith OBB Ⓗ
Small, 13th-century village inn nestling by the church – it is said that more than one of the occupants of the graveyard still pops in for a quick one! This Grade II listed building was an old teasle barn before becoming an inn. Enter through the garden into a low-ceilinged, stone-flagged corridor leading to the tiny, cosy bar. Real fires blaze in two of the three rooms in winter. The walls are covered with an extensive, colourful plate collection. Popular with locals and a few walkers in summer.
🏚Q🕮🏠♣

SCARBOROUGH ✤

Cellars
35-37 Valley Road
🕓 3 (12 Sat)-11 (11-11 summer); 12-10.30 Sun
☎ (01723) 367158 website:
www.spiderweb.co.uk/brialene
Black Sheep Best Bitter; Tetley Bitter; guest beers Ⓗ
Small, cosy family-run pub in the cellars of an elegant Victorian building, converted to self-contained holiday flats, a short walk from the south side beach. The comfortable lounge area features sporting memorabilia. Bar meal are served from midday to early eve, as well as traditional lunch on Sun. Above the bar is a well-appointed restaurant offering fine cuisine. Prize-winning gardens and patio area provide pleasant outdoor drinking. Two ever-changing guest beers are stocked. 🕮🏠◑ㅊ🅰⇌P

Highlander
15-16 The Esplanade
🕓 11-11; 12-10.30 Sun
☎ (01723) 373426 website: highlandhotel.com
McEwan 80/-; Tetley Bitter; Webster's Green Label; guest beers Ⓗ
Part of the Stressa hotel, a one-roomed pub with patio providing superb views of the South Bay and sporting a huge range of malt whiskies and Tartan decor. Showcased in a new extension to the bar is a steam engine, Island Chief. A cellar bar, with two snooker tables, is planned to open by the time this *Guide* goes to press. Wm Clark's Mild, brewed in Wakefield, is available throughout the year, as well as two guest ales.
🏚Q🕮◑🅰⇌🍴

Hole in the Wall
26-32 Vernon Road
🕓 11.30-2.30 (3 Sat), 7-11; 12-3, 7-10.30 Sun
☎ (01723) 373746
Fuller's ESB; guest beers Ⓗ
Built in the 1840s, the pub has a split-level interior with three seating areas. This busy, friendly, conversational pub is handy for the town centre and spa complex. The lunch menu always offers a selection of vegetarian options (no food Sun). Frequent winner of local CAMRA's *Town Pub of the Year* award, it has appeared in the last 18 editions of this *Guide*. Weston's Old Rosie cider is served straight from the cask.
Q◑🅰⇌♣♠●

Indigo Alley
4 North Marine Road
🕓 3 (12 Sat)-11; 12-10.30 Sun
☎ (01723) 381900
e-mail: graham@indigoalley.freeserve.co.uk
Beer range varies Ⓗ
Lively, popular pub situated between the North Bay and the town centre. Five constantly changing guest ales and Belgian Leffe beer are available on draught. Fruit beers and fruit wines are also stocked. The house beer Indigo Ale is from Daleside Brewery in Harrogate. Live music is performed four nights a week at this local CAMRA Joint *Town Pub of the Year 2000*. ⇌

Old Scalby Mills Hotel
Scalby Mills Road
🕓 11-11; 12-10.30 Sun
☎ (01723) 500449
Daleside Nightjar, Old Lubrication, Monkey Wrench; guest beers Ⓗ
Popular with walkers and tourists in a seafront location, the hotel was originally a watermill, but the buildings have seen many uses over the years. Old photographs and prints in the larger of the two bars chart their history. This bar also benefits from a superb view across North Bay to the castle; outside is a sheltered patio. The Cleveland Way joins the sea front at this point. There is a Sea-life Centre very close by, so a children's certificate covers the main bar, while the small bar is quieter. Q🕮◑ㅊ🅰♣

Scholar's
Somerset Terrace
🕓 12-3, 6-11; 12-11 Fri, Sat & summer; 12-10.30 Sun
☎ (01723) 360084
website: www.yorkshirecoast/bedfordhotel.co.uk
Beer range varies Ⓗ
Large, single-roomed, purpose-built pub, part of the Bedford Hotel, offering affordable accommodation. The building is situated in an elegant Regency crescent and was the birthplace in 1897 of Sir Sacheverell Sitwell, poet and art critic. Two constantly changing guest beers are currently offered (more are planned). Good quality, reasonably-priced food is available until early eve. Live jazz music is performed Tue and occasional music Thu eve. Q🕮◑ㅊ⇌

Tap & Spile
94 Falsgrave Road
🕓 11-11; 12-10.30 Sun
☎ (01723) 363837
Big Lamp Bitter; Black Sheep Special; Everards Tiger; Theakston Cool Cask, Old Peculier; guest beers Ⓗ
Thriving local, formerly a coaching inn, just off the town centre. Enjoy the friendly service and the wide choice of ales, cider and fruit wines; the chilli is not to be missed. Live music is performed Thu eve and Sun afternoon. Local CAMRA Joint *Town Pub of the Year 2000*.
🏚Q🍃🕮ㅊ⇌♣●P🍴

SKIPTON

Narrow Boat
38 Victoria Street (alleyway off Coach St, near canal bridge)
🕓 12-11; 12-10.30 Sun
☎ (01756) 797922
website: www.thewaterweb.force9.co.uk

Black Sheep Best Bitter; Taylor Landlord; guest beers Ⓗ

Skipton's permanent beer exhibition, housed in a former wine bar, is furnished with old church pews and decorated with old brewery posters, mirrors and two eye-catching canal-themed murals. Piped music, gaming machines and juke boxes are conspicuous by their absence. Smoking is only permitted in the upstairs minstrels' gallery. Live jazz (Tue eve) and folk or Irish traditional music (Sun eve) are popular. Six handpumps dispense ever-changing guests from northern and Scottish independents while a good selection of Belgian and German bottled beers are served in appropriate glasses. Q ❀ ◖ ≉ ♣ ✒

Railway
13-15 Carleton Street (opp. Tesco)
✪ 11-11; 12-10.30 Sun
☎ (01756) 793186

Tetley Mild, Bitter; John Smith's Bitter; guest beer Ⓗ

Sadly one of a fast-disappearing breed, this friendly two-roomed street-corner boozer has a strong local following and is popular with sports fans, local workers and shoppers. Both rooms are decorated with railway photos and prints and the recently-refurbished lounge has a collection of water jugs. The pub fields teams in the local dominoes league and supports thriving golfing and racing societies. The guest beer is from the Tapster's Choice range. ⊟ ≉ ♣

SNAPE

Castle Arms
✪ 12-3, 6-11; 12-3, 6.30-10.30 Sun
☎ (01677) 470270

Black Sheep Best Bitter; Hambleton Bitter; John Smith's Bitter; guest beer Ⓗ

The beautiful village of Snape is situated between Bedale and Masham, near the famous Thorpe Perrow Arboretum. Its castle, once the home of Catherine Parr, is still inhabited. Built in the 14th century, the spacious bar has a splendid flagged floor and free-standing fireplace. A comfortable restaurant provides a wide choice of tasty home-cooked meals. The pub's camping and caravan facilities are only open to CC members. Quoits played.
🛏 Q ❀ ⋈ ◖ ⅃ ♣ ▲ ♣ ♠ P ●

SPOFFORTH

King William IV
Church Hill
✪ 12-3 (not Mon or Tue), 5-11; 12-11 Sat; 12-10.30 Sun
☎ (01937) 590293

John Smith's Bitter; guest beers Ⓗ

Delightful local, tucked away from the main road, by the village green. The single bar served three rooms – a traditional tap room with old settles and tiled floor, a comfortable extended lounge where food is served, but there is a always room for drinking, and a small, intimate dining room. French windows lead from the lounge to a new patio area (barbecues held in summer). Spofforth was the birthplace of Harry Hotspur, and the pub is reputedly haunted, although the landlord claims no knowledge of this.
🛏 Q ❀ ◖ ⊟ ♣ P

STAITHES

Captain Cook Inn
60 Staithes Lane (200 yds from A174)
✪ 11-11; 12-10.30 Sun
☎ (01947) 840200
website: www.captaincookinn.co.uk

John Smith's Magnet; Tetley Bitter; Theakston Cool Cask; guest beer Ⓗ

Built in the late 19th century as the Station Hotel, it was renamed in the 1960s after the closure of the railway line. This lovely olde-worlde fishing village was the home of Captain Cook and has a museum dedicated to him. The pub affords good views across Staithes Beck towards Boulby Cliffs, which at 660 feet are the highest in England. Guest beers mostly come from East Midlands micro-breweries. Children are welcome in the games room of this local CAMRA *Pub of the Year 2000.*
🛏 Q ➳ ❀ ⋈ ◖ ⅃ ▲ P ✐

Cod & Lobster
Slip End (Harbour's edge)
✪ 12-11; 12-10.30 Sun
☎ (01947) 840295

Camerons Bitter, Strongarm; Ind Coope Burton Ale Ⓗ

Harbourside pub set in a traditional fishing village. The single room displays nautical pictures and watercolours by a local artist, Lucy Wilson (for sale). Popular with locals and visitors, children are welcome until 9.30. An apt place to end a day's walking, beachcombing or rockpooling, there is no vehicular access to the pub; park at the top of the bank and walk down.
🛏 ❀ ◖ ♣

STOKESLEY

Spread Eagle
39 High Street (close to Town Hall)
✪ 11-11; 12-10.30 Sun
☎ (01642) 710278 e-mail: jeanspread@hotmail.com

Banks's Original; Cameron Strongarm; Marston's Pedigree Ⓗ

Small, unspoilt, town-centre pub drawing a friendly, local clientele. Originally a coaching inn, it serves excellent, home-cooked food all day from an interesting menu, with meat, poultry and game from the family butcher, and imaginative salads (booking advisable). An enclosed rear garden leads down to the River Leven. In the front room, only the real fire is permitted to smoke. Live music Tue eve, otherwise a quiet pub with occasional subdued piped music. Local CAMRA *Pub of the Year 1997.* 🛏 Q ❀ ◖ ♣ ✒ ✐

White Swan
1 West End
✪ 11.30-3, 5.30 (7 Sat)-11; 12-3, 7-10.30 Sun
☎ (01642) 710263 e-mail: joonanbri@aol.com

Captain Cook Sunset, Slipway, Porter; Castle Eden Ale; guest beers Ⓗ

This town pub, built 1705, smart and cosy, decorated with agricultural memorabilia, was a recent local CAMRA *Pub of the Year.* The Captain Cook beers, brewed on the premises, are well worth trying. National winner of the *Perfect Ploughmans* award 1997, choose from a wide range of traditional cheeses or patês, served with granary bread. Regular beer festivals are held Easter and Oct. No piped music, no juke box, just good beer and conversation and some unusual pub games. No children permitted. ♨Q◗♣✂

THIXENDALE

Cross Keys
✪ 12-3, 6-11; 12-3, 7-10.30 Sun
☎ (01377) 288272
Jennings Bitter; Tetley Bitter; guest beer Ⓗ
Thixendale lies in the heart of the Yorkshire Wolds at the junction of several dry valleys. The surrounding area was inhabited way back in the stone-age and many tracks and roads, used so enthusiastically by walkers today on their way to the Cross Keys, were well established by Roman times. An unspoilt, award-winning unpretentious village local, it has a single bar where good value, home-cooked food is available daily. Children are welcome in the garden.
♨❀◗▲♣

THORGANBY

Ferryboat Inn
1 mile NE of Thorganby OS697426
✪ 12-3, 7-11 (closed winter Wed; extended hours in summer); 12-3, 7-10.30 Sun
☎ (01904) 448224
Old Mill Bitter; guest beers Ⓗ
Quiet, remote, family-run pub, in the same hands for over 50 years; for most of that time it had a six-day licence and Sunday opening returned only recently. Give the pub's position, close to the River Derwent, it is popular with anglers. The public rooms comprise a single bar – featuring a beam which was once a ship's mast – and an attractive family room, added during a recent refurbishment. A pleasant garden slopes down to the river. Guest beers are from small breweries – often Rooster.
♨Q✿▲P🏠

THORNTON-IN-LONSDALE

Marton Arms
¼ mile N of A65/A687 jct
✪ 12-11; 12-10.30 Sun
☎ (015242) 41281 website: www.martonarms.co.uk
Black Sheep Best Bitter; Dent Bitter; Oakhill Best Bitter, Mendip Gold; Taylor Golden Best; guest beers Ⓗ
In a hamlet containing an old parish church, stocks and little else, it relies almost entirely on tourists and trippers, attracted mainly by the 18 handpumps, though there are several other interesting beverages, notably Belgian specialities. The 1679 datestone, old oak door and flagged passage belie the modernised bar, one corner of which has recently been fitted out with settles. The front patio has picnic tables. Ten minutes' walk from the start of the Ingleton Waterfalls Walk, it opens weekday lunchtimes June-Aug. ❀◗▲♣P●

THORNTON-LE-DALE

New Inn
The Square
✪ 12-2.30, 6.30-11; 12-3, 6.30-10.30 Sun
☎ (01751) 474226 e-mail: newinntld@aol.com
Black Sheep Best Bitter; John Smith's Bitter; Taylor Landlord Ⓗ
Family-owned and -run inn, restored to

create the feel of yesteryear. Dating to around 1720, when it was a coaching house, the ancient village stocks and market cross can be seen from the inn. An ideal touring base for the North York moors, countryside and coast, it prides itself on freshly-cooked food, with a wide range of ever-changing specials. All bedrooms are en-suite and feature hand-made pine furniture.
♨Q❀🛏◗▲♣P✂🏠

THORNTON WATLASS

Buck Inn
Village green
✪ 11-11; 12-10.30 Sun
☎ (01677) 422461
website: www.smoothhound.co.uk/hotels/buckinn
Black Sheep Best Bitter; John Smith's Bitter; Tetley Bitter; Theakston Best Bitter; guest beer Ⓗ
This delightful Wensleydale inn overlooks the village green and its 100-year-old cricket pitch with unusual boundaries: outside the front door acts as position for deep third man. A small comfortable bar has settles, a collection of old bottles and a gem of a bar servery. A full choice of food from an excellent menu is served in the bar and informal no-smoking dining area. Sunday lunch trad jazz is performed fortnightly. The large garden has a children's play area and quoits pitches. ♨❀🛏◗♣P

THRINTOFT

New Inn
1 mile from A684
✪ 12-3, 7-11; closed Mon; 12-3, 7-10.30 Sun
☎ (01609) 777060 e-mail: new.inn@lineone.net
Black Sheep Best Bitter; Fuller's London Pride; Worthington Bitter; guest beer Ⓗ
Village pub and restaurant, with a good reputation, run by a brother and sister team. The pub is new in name only, having been built in 1776 as a small bar and extended into two adjoining cottages in the early 1900s. With low, beamed ceilings and real fires it is set in beautiful countryside. The four ales are complemented by a varied home-cooked menu. Local legend has it that the pub is haunted by an old lady, seen by locals late at night. ♨❀◗♣P

TOCKWITH

Spotted Ox
Westfield Road (off B1224 York-Wetherby road)
✪ 11-3, 5.30-11; 11-11 Fri & Sat; 12-10.30 Sun
☎ (01423) 358387
Tetley Bitter; guest beers Ⓗ
Situated in a village in the area famed for the Battle of Marston Moor in 1644, the Spotted Ox is a perfect example of a community local attracting visitors from the greater York area. An extensive, varied menu of home-cooked food includes daily specials. The range of guest beers contributed to the licensee being presented with a York CAMRA *Pub of the Season* award. ❀◗♣P

UPPER POPPLETON

Lord Collingwood
The Green (off A59, York-Harrogate road)
✪ 12-3, 6-11; 12-3, 7-10.30 Sun
☎ (01904) 794388

Banks's Bitter; Mansfield Bitter; Marston's Pedigree Ⓗ

The dormitory York villages of Upper Poppleton and its neighbour Nether support four pubs. The attractive Tudor-styled Lord Collingwood overlooks the village green with its traditional maypole. This olde-worlde pub has a single, pleasant, L-shaped bar providing comfortable areas for eating and drinking. Locals, commuters and visitors from the greater York area come for the pub's friendly atmosphere and quality food. Travel by rail is still possible; Poppleton is on the York-Harrogate line.
▲ ❀ ◑ ≥ (Poppleton) ♣ P

WASS

Wombwell Arms
OS555793
☼ 11-11, 12-10.30 Sun
☎ (01347) 868280
Black Sheep Best Bitter; Taylor Landlord; guest beer Ⓗ

Wass stands at the foot of the Hambleton Hills in a much-visited part of Yorkshire. The ruins of Byland Abbey are close by, on the way to Newburgh Priory – home of the Wombwell family, in whose honour the pub is named. A whitewashed building, dating back to the 1600s, it was originally a grain store. The small, cosy bar boasts a stone-flagged floor and beamed ceiling. Highly-regarded for its extensive menu; one dining room is for non-smokers. Opening hours are reduced in winter phone before travelling. ▲Q❀≈◑▲P

WEAVERTHORPE

Star Inn
Main Street (off A64 at Sherburn traffic lights)
☼ 12-4 (not Mon-Fri), 7-11; 12-4, 7-10.30 Sun
☎ (01944) 738273 website: www.starinn.net
Camerons Bitter; Tetley Bitter; guest beers Ⓗ

This Wolds village inn is also listed in CAMRA's *Good Pub Food* and *Room at the Inn*. There are always interesting regional guest beers on offer. Three-diamond rated by the English Tourist Board, en-suite rooms are available for around £25 per person B&B and make an ideal touring base for the East Coast, York and the North Yorkshire Moors National Park. It holds a late supper licence – no meals Tue eve. ▲Q❀≈◑▲♣P↙

WEST WITTON

Fox & Hounds
Main Street (A684)
☼ 12-4, 7-11 (may vary summer); 12-4, 7-10.30 Sun
☎ (01969) 623650
Black Sheep Best Bitter; Ind Coope Burton Ale; Theakston Old Peculier (summer); guest beer Ⓗ

On the main Wensleydale route, this 15th-century outpost of Jervaulx Abbey has been a pub for 300 years. Inside the Grade II listed building a stone chimney breast divides the cosy drinking area into a games area and bar, which hosts a weekly quiz (Fri) and fortnightly piano sessions (Sat). Wholesome bar meals are served in a tiny dining room boasting an impressive inglenook. Each Aug West Witton celebrates the 'Burning of Bartle', when a straw effigy is paraded from the village to be burned on nearby Penhill.
▲❀≈◑▲♣♠P□

WHITBY ✲

Duke of York
Church Street (at foot of 199 steps)
☼ 11-11; 12-10.30 Sun
☎ (01947) 600324
Black Sheep Special; Courage Directors; John Smith's Bitter; guest beer Ⓗ

Busy, unspoilt pub with a nautical theme. Established in 1851 it has been the haunt of seafarers, locals, visitors and even Bram Stoker, author of *Dracula*. Very popular, especially in Regatta Week, it affords fine views over the river and harbour. Food is served 12-9 daily. The large single lounge bar has a partitioned no-smoking area. It hosts a quiz Tue eve and live music nights.
◑▶≈↙

Tap & Spile
New Quay Road (opp. bus and rail station)
☼ 12-11 (midnight Fri & Sat summer); 12-10.30 (11 summer) Sun
☎ (01947) 603937
Black Sheep Best Bitter; Courage Directors; Theakston Cool Cask; guest beers Ⓗ

Benefitting from views over the quayside and River Esk in the popular historic port of Whitby, this red-brick pub was once called the Cutty Sark. Now a Tap & Spile in Victorian style with wooden floors, it has a snug on the other side of the central bar and a no-smoking room that is suitable for families. The pub stocks a varying range of up to five guest ales and two ciders. It hosts live music regularly and is a mecca in folk week. Q꒰◑≈♣♠↙

YORK ✲

Ackhorne
St Martins Lane
☼ 12-11; 12-10.30 Sun
☎ (01904) 671421 website: www.ackhorne.com
Black Sheep Best Bitter; Rooster's Yankee; guest beers Ⓗ

A true oasis, just off busy Micklegate, it provides a haven from the bustle of the city centre. Although recently modernised, it retains some original stained-glass windows. The spacious bar boasts bare boards and comfortable bench seating, complemented by a small, intimate, area dedicated to local Civil War hero, Sir Thomas Fairfax. Interesting guest beers change with reassuring speed; a cider and perry are also stocked. York CAMRA *Pub of the Year* 2001; don't miss the tiny garden. Lunches served Mon-Sat; eve meals Tue-Fri. Q❀◑≈♣♠

Blue Bell ☆
53 Fossgate
☼ 11-11; 12-10.30 Sun
☎ (01904) 654904
Camerons Strongarm; Greene King Abbot; Marston's Pedigree; Tetley Bitter; guest beers Ⓗ

York's only pub of truly national historic importance and one of the country's few pubs to have Grade II* listed status. It boasts a perfect Edwardian interior courtesy of a 1903 refurbishment by then owners C J Melrose. It has more recently been the local CAMRA *Pub of the Year* and runner-up in the national competition. These words don't adequately do justice to what is a compact, cosy, welcoming, city-centre local. Its two small rooms and drinking corridor are beloved by regulars and visitors alike. Good-value sandwiches available 11-6, Mon-Sat. ✿♣

Last Drop
27 Colliergate
✿ 11-11; 12-10.30 Sun
☎ (01904) 621951 website: www.thelastdropinn.co.uk
York Stonewall Bitter, Yorkshire Terrier, seasonal beers; guest beers Ⓗ

York Brewery's first tied house is a skilful conversion of a former solicitor's office on a busy thoroughfare. The building dates back to the 17th-century and its refit was accomplished using local materials. The owners have eschewed most modern gimmickry and are to be applauded for bucking current trends by creating a new pub on a more modest and intimate scale than is the norm. One modern pub idiom, though, is the large, plain-glass windows. Food, made mostly from local ingredients, is served daily 12-4. Q✿Ⓓ

Maltings
Tanners Moat (below Lendal Bridge)
✿ 11-11; 12-10.30 Sun
☎ (01904) 655387 website: www.maltings.co.uk
Black Sheep Best Bitter; guest beers Ⓗ

It is not just its proximity to the station that makes the Maltings the first and last port of call for so many visitors to York. Twice local CAMRA *Pub of the Year* and twice national *Cask Ale Pub of the Year*, it is a great supporter of micro-breweries from whom the six guest beers are usually drawn. Twice-yearly beer festivals are extremely popular and the lunches (served until 4pm at weekends) are recommended. The cider varies. Ⓓ≈♣

Minster Inn
24 Marygate (behind Museum Gardens)
✿ 11.30 (11 Thu-Sat)-11; 12-10.30 Sun
☎ (01904) 624499 e-mail: howardtreed@supanet.com
Hambleton Bitter; John Smith's Bitter; guest beers Ⓗ

Edwardian period local near the ruins of St Mary's Abbey, it retains the original layout of four rooms – one recently converted into a drinking room from a private kitchen – off a central corridor. Very much a community pub, hosting regular varied events, the friendly service helps create the atmosphere of a pub they used to be, enhanced by a selection of guest beers. Sandwiches are available on request. Q⏱✿✿≈♣✄

Royal Oak
18 Goodramgate
✿ 11-11; 12-10.30 Sun
☎ (01904) 653856
website: www.royal-oak-pub-york.co.uk
Ind Coope Burton Ale; Tetley Bitter; guest beers Ⓗ

Small, stylish town pub with three rooms off a staggered corridor. There has been a pub on this site since 1783, but known as the Royal Oak since 1819. The current mock-Tudor look was created in a 1934 revamp by then owners John J Hunt, whose brewery was close by on Aldwark. Cosy and welcoming, it is a *Guide* regular. It is very widely known for its food – including home-baked bread – available from 11 (12 Sun) until 8 daily. Q⏱Ⓓ✄

Swan Inn
16 Bishopgate Street
✿ 4 (12 Thu-Sat)-11; 12-10.30 Sun
☎ (01904) 634968 website: www.swanyork.com
Black Sheep Best Bitter; Greene King Abbot; Jennings Cumberland Ale; Taylor Landlord; Tetley Bitter; Ⓗ

Classic street-corner local with a 'West Riding' layout, unusual for the city. The entrance corridor leads to a drinking lobby with a servery, and two rooms also served from the main bar. One of only two Tetley Heritage inns in York, this popular local gets extremely busy most eves with the younger generation. The beers (which include a York brew) are perhaps best sampled during relaxed daytime periods. A paved, walled garden (large by York's standards) has a pleasant, sunny aspect. ⌂✿✿♣♣

Tap & Spile
29 Monkgate
✿ 11.30-11; 12-10.30 Sun
☎ (01904) 656158
Black Sheep Best Bitter; guest beers Ⓗ

The former Black Horse was one of the very first Tap & Spile outlets more than a decade ago. Its Flemish-style frontage dates back to 1897 and the building is thought originally to have been a school. It has a single, high-ceilinged room with a raised, partitioned darts/TV area. A second, carpeted room – which may be used for functions – has been re-introduced via some skilful partitioning. The seven guest beers usually include one from Rooster. ✿Ⓓ♣♣P

Victoria
1 Heslington Road
✿ 12-11; 12-10.30 Sun
☎ (01904) 622295
Old Mill Mild, Bitter, Bullion, seasonal beers Ⓗ

The only Old Mill tied house in York is a revitalised, street-corner pub. Although now opened out into a single, L-shaped room, the comfortable interior is broken up into distinct areas by pillars and partitions. From being rather run-down and unappealing it has blossomed into a real asset to the area and is deservedly popular with students and locals. The only regular outlet for Mild in York, it is handy for the Barbican Centre and recommended for overnight stays. ✿⌂ⓄP

Wellington Inn
47 Alma Terrace
✿ 11-3 (not Mon), 6-11; 11-5, 7-11 Sat; 12-4, 7-10.30 Sun
☎ (01904) 645642
Samuel Smith OBB Ⓗ

This classic, back-street, mid-terrace local is Grade II listed and was purpose-built in the mid-19th-century. The brewery's refurbishments have been admirably low-key and helped preserve the pub's atmosphere. The central corridor is flanked on one side by the public bar and on the other by two small lounges, one with a pool table. The frontage always has a splendid floral display in the summer, as does the suntrap backyard. Utterly traditional in every way, it is well worth seeking out. ⌂Q⏱✿✿♣

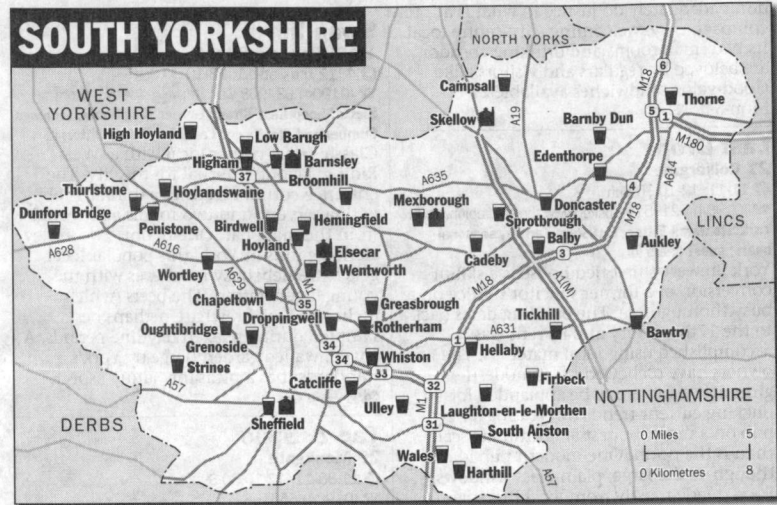

Yorkshire (South)

Eagle & Child
24 Main Street
✪ 11.30-3, 5-11; 11.30-11 Sat; 12-4, 7-10.30 Sun
☎ (01302) 770406 e-mail: eagleauckley@aol.com
Barnsley Bitter; John Smith's Bitter; Theakston Cool Cask; guest beers Ⓗ
Unspoilt, traditional village local that has steadily enhanced its reputation. Two guest beers complement the regular choice, one usually from the Darwin range. Meals are served in a no-smoking area. Regular events include a quiz (Mon eve) and twice-monthly Investment Club meetings. Local CAMRA *Pub of the Year* 2000 runner-up. ✿◑P✣

Gateway Inn
Station Road
✪ 12-3, 6-11; 12-3, 6.45-10.30
☎ (01302) 882849 website:
www.gatewayinnandrestaurant.co.uk
Barnsley Bitter; John Smith's Bitter; Theakston Cool Cask Ⓗ
This establishment consists of an excellent restaurant, a lounge bar, a function suite and hotel accommodation. The bar has a comfortable, friendly atmosphere where locals make visitors feel welcome. Although there is occasional background music or a small TV for the big match, conversation is the norm here. The bar lunches are recommended (no food Sun eve). Quizzes are held Wed and Sun. ✿⊨◑&P

Courthouse Station
24 Regent Street (opp. rail/bus interchange)
✪ 11-11; 12-10.30 Sun
☎ (01226) 779056
Tetley Bitter; Theakston Best Bitter; guest beers Ⓗ
Built as a courthouse in 1861, it was a railway station from 1870 to 1960, and eventually a Wetherspoon's outlet for the last three years. Thankfully giving Barnsley a choice of real ales from smaller breweries,

this busy pub has recently started offering real cider on gravity. One floor has a raised drinking area and small no-smoking corner, the toilets upstairs give a grand view of the interchange and a chance to check which bus/train you've just missed. Occasional beer festivals are held and there is a bargain curry and beer offer Thu eve.
Q✿◑⇌●P✣●

Keresforth Hall
Keresforth Hall Road, Kingstone (800 yds off
A6133 down narrow lane)
✪ 11-2, 7-11; 12-3, 7-10.30 Sun
☎ (01226) 284226 website: www.keresforthhall.co.uk
Beer range varies Ⓗ
About 1/2 mile from nearest bus stop and 11/2 miles from the town centre, the walk is very worthwhile to this pleasing quarter of Barnsley. With open rural views across to Stainborough Low and Wentworth Castle, the main 1930s rebuilt house provides for all: dining room to right; lounge bar with usually two real ales on left and conservatory attached; plus a large function hall. Familes are well catered for with slide, swings and playhouses in a split-level garden. Q☃✿◑⊟&P✣⑃

Turnpike
High Street (A638)
✪ 11-11; 12-10.30 Sun
☎ (01302) 711960
Greene King Ruddles County; John Smith's Bitter; guest beer Ⓗ
Formerly a wine bar, the Turnpike became a pub in 1986. The three-level layout owes more to the original architecture than fashion. Flagstone floors, glass and wood panelling add to the appeal. Three times winner of local CAMRA's *Pub of the Season* award, it stands opposite the market place, convenient for buses and as a meeting place for Bawtry's restaurant-goers. Now celebrating 15 consecutive years in this *Guide*, it has a steadily growing golf society. A 'Kleenair' machine and extractors ensure a smoke-free atmosphere. Eve meals served Wed and Thu. ✿◑

BIRDWELL

Cock Inn

Pilley Hill (off A61)

☼ 11-3, 7-11; 12-3, 7-10.30 Sun

☎ (01226) 742155

Barnsley Bitter; Draught Bass H

A popular village local, the Cock is stone built and traditional in style with two main rooms, the larger featuring a slate floor, exposed beams, brassware and an open fire, the smaller room is comfortable and quieter. Popular bar menu which includes daily specials (no meals Sun eve; book Sun lunch). Quiz nights are held Mon and Thu. In summer the garden is put to good use and there are Fri eve barbecues.
▲ ✿ ◑ P

BROOMHILL

Old Moor Tavern

Everilgate Road

☼ 11-11; 12-10.30 Sun

☎ (01226) 755455

Banks's Bitter; Courage Directors; Marston's Pedigree; John Smith's Bitter H

Just off the A1/M1 link road, this is an easily accessible village pub. In the middle of the developing Wetlands Project, it makes a useful watering-hole for bird-watchers, naturalists, walkers and of course locals. The provision of good honest food is an art which has been honed by the landlord and his wife over many years. Guest beers are frequently from Yorkshire independents, such as Black Sheep, Timothy Taylor, Wentworth and Glentworth.
Q ✿ ◑ ♿ P

CADEBY

Cadeby Inn

Main Street

☼ 11-11; 12-10.30 Sun

☎ (01709) 864009

John Smith's Bitter; Samuel Smith OBB; Tetley Bitter; Theakston Cool Cask; guest beers H

Converted from an old farmhouse in 1975 the pub retains much of its original character with open fires, flagged floors and exposed beams. With extensive outdoor drinking areas both front (with children's play area) and back, it is the perfect place for a pint on a warm summer eve. Famed for its carvery (available all week), it is very popular with diners. Denaby Ings Nature Reserve is a short walk away, and the Earth Centre is nearby at Conisbrough.
▲ ✿ ◑ ♱ ♣ P ⌀ ⌂

CAMPSALL

Old Bells

High Street

☼ 11.30-2, 6-11; 12-3, 7-10.30 Sun

☎ (01302) 700423

Black Sheep Special; John Smith's Bitter H

In the tiny hamlet of Old Campsall, the Old Bells, at 150-plus, is the oldest pub in Doncaster Borough. It consists of a small, traditional, wood-panelled and exposed stone smoke room, a tiny snug, lounge and two restaurants, specialising in good quality, fresh food. It is popular for wedding receptions and other special celebrations. Although food is obviously at the top of the agenda, this is definitely a pub that sells food; drinkers are made just as welcome as diners. Q ◑ ♿ P

CATCLIFFE

Waverley

Brinsworth Road (B6067, 1 mile from M1 jct 33)

☼ 12-4, 6-11; 11-11 Sat; 12-4, 7-10.30 Sun

☎ (01709) 360906

Beer range varies H

Modern stone pub, opened in 1984, by the present licensees, it has three rooms: a small traditional tap, a spacious lounge and a large children's room. Set back from the road it also has a large patio and outside play area. Four ever-changing ales are always available, sourced from brewers large and small, with at least one from Glentworth usually available. Local CAMRA *Pub of the Year* 2000. ⌀ ✿ ◑ ♱ ♿ ♣ P

CHAPELTOWN ✤

Commercial

107 Station Road

☼ 12-3, 5.30-11; 12-11 Sat; 12-10.30 Sun

☎ (0114) 246 9066

e-mail: paul@the-commercial.freeserve.co.uk

Wentworth WPA, Oatmeal Stout; guest beers H

Imposing roadhouse, built as a combined hotel and ale house in 1890 by the former Stroutts Brewery. Also on the original site were a butcher's shop and a confectioner's, now long gone. The island bar serves three distinct drinking areas: a comfortable lounge, a large, more basic public bar with a pool table, and a small no-smoking snug. The landlords' involvement with the nearby Wentworth Brewery means that their beers are always available. Beer festivals are held in May/June and Nov.
▲ Q ✿ ◑ ♱ Å ⇌ ♣ ● P ⌀ ⌂

DONCASTER ✤

Corner Pin

145 St. Sepulchre Gate West

☼ 11-11; 12-10.30 Sun

☎ (01302) 323159

John Smith's Bitter; guest beers H

Old-style, street-corner boozer. A rare remnant from a once-busy quarter of the town. It has been revitalised by sympathetic redecoration, an enlightened change in beer policy and the return of capable former licensees. A central bar serves a basic bar and more cosy lounge areas. Two constantly changing guest beers come from independent brewers, that CAMRA members help select. This local CAMRA *Pub of Season*, spring 2001, is now a regular stop on the west end real ale circuit. A parrot provides entertainment!
◑ ⇌ ●

INDEPENDENT BREWERIES

Abbeydale Sheffield

Barnsley Elsecar

Concertina Mexborough

Glentworth Skellow

Kelham Island Sheffield

Oakwell Barnsley

Orchard Barnsley

Wentworth Wentworth

Leopard
1 West Street
✪ 11-11; 12-10.30 Sun
☎ (01302) 363054 website: www.thegigguide.co.uk
John Smith's Bitter; guest beer H

Imposing, street-corner pub boasting a superb tiled exterior recalling its former ownership by Warwicks and Richardsons' brewery. A wide variety of music is played on the juke box in both the lively bar/games room and the more comfortable and subdued lounge. An upstairs music room hosts regular gigs, featuring both local and nationally-known bands, and a comedy club (Thu eve). The only regular outlet in town for local Glentworth beers, one of which is always available. Local CAMRA *Pub of the Year* 2000. ⊛☉❤♣Ⓟ

Mason's Arms
Market Place
✪ 12 (11.30 Mon)-4.30, 7.30-11; 10.30-11 Tue, Fri & Sat; 12-5, 8-10.30 Sun
☎ (01302) 364391
Taylor Landlord; Tetley Bitter; guest beer (occasional) H

Traditional market place pub, a *Guide* regular in recent years, where once only a superb pint of Tetley's was on offer, the expanded range has proved popular. Just over 200 years old, it has maintained its multi-roomed layout. The outstanding public bar has occasional background music and a TV for sport (horse-racing being particularly popular). The other two rooms are for quiet conversation except when the local morris men take over the back room for a session. The garden is a riot of colour in summer. Q⊛☉≉

Plough
8 West Laithe Gate
✪ 11-11; 12-3, 7-10.30 Sun
☎ (01302) 738310
Barnsley Bitter; Draught Bass; guest beer (occasional) H

Possibly the least altered pub in the town centre, boasting many original features, such as the stained glass windows in the cosy lounge bar at the rear. To step into the tap room is to enter another world; yes, there is often background music, but it is never obtrusive. The noise you hear is that of people talking to each other, often arguing over the horse-racing or other sport on the TV. The garden is probably the smallest in town. Entertainment is home-grown: quizzes, darts and dominoes. ⊛☉≉♣

Salutation
14 South Parade
✪ 11-11, 12-10.30 Sun
☎ (01302) 340705
Marston's Pedigree; Tetley Dark Mild, Bitter; guest beers H

Originally a coaching inn on the Great North Road, on the way to the famous racecourse, the pub has seen many transformations over the years. Its current configuration is that of a large open room, but broken into cosier drinking areas by wood and glass screens. There is a large function room, with its own bar, upstairs. The patio is used for outside drinking in summer. Entertainment comes in the form of big-screen sport (Rugby Union internationals draw a good crowd) and a quiz (Tue). No eve meals at weekends. ⊛☉≉♣

DROPPINGWELL

Effingham Arms
Upper Wortley Road (2 miles W of M1 jct 35)
✪ 11-11, 12-10.30 Sun
☎ (01709) 382094
Draught Bass; Tetley Bitter H

Opposite Grange Park Golf Course, this imposing building stands back from the main road. Open plan, it has a central island bar, a no-smoking area and pool table. Food-orientated, this Big Steak pub has a children's/function room (due for refurbishment); a small area near the bar, without tables, is for drinkers. An extensive wine selection and special food offers add to its appeal. Close to Keppels Column Monument, it is fairly modern yet retains a traditional atmosphere. Wheelchair WC. ⊛☉♿♣Ⓟ✗

DUNFORD BRIDGE

Stanhope Arms Inn
✪ 12-3 (not Mon), 7-11; 12-11 Sat; 12-10 Sun
☎ (01226) 763104 e-mail: stanhope.arms@virgin-net
Black Sheep Best Bitter; Taylor Landlord H

Built as a shooting lodge for the Spencer-Stanhope family of Cannon Hall, Cawthorne (open to visitors), the inn stands in a quiet moorland village of the northern

---

INN BRIEF

BALBY
Winning Post
Warmsworth Road
12 (11 Sat)-11;
12-4, 7-10.30 Sun
1950s roadhouse, barely altered, that serves a local housing estate; games in the lounge, quizzes in the lounge. Sun lunch served.
John Smith's Bitter; guest beer H

CHAPELTOWN
Wharncliffe Arms
365 Burncross Road
3 (1 Fri; 11 Sat)-11;
12-10.30 Sun
Stones Bitter; guest beer H
Small, unpretentious, former Strouts's local, comprising a 'best' room and a public bar; large garden at the rear.

DONCASTER
Tut'n'Shive
6 West Laithe Gate
11-11 (midnight Fri & Sat); 12-10.30 Sun
Black Sheep Best Bitter; Boddingtons Bitter; Marston's Pedigree; guest beers H
Eccentric decor, but excellent ale and cider, recently recognised by *Cask Marque*. The food, music and TV sports are popular with young drinkers.

HEMINGFIELD, BARNSLEY
Lundhill Tavern
Beechhouse Road
12-11; 12-10.30 Sun
Barnsley Bitter; John Smith's Bitter; Samuel Smith OBB; guest beers H
Split-level, early 19th-century pub serving excellent food. Hosts a popular May Day rock concert.

HOYLANDSWAINE
Rose & Crown
Barnsley Road
4 (12 Sat)-11; 12-10.30 Sun
Marston's Pedigree; Theakston Best Bitter; guest beers H
Truly traditional village local: a lounge, a public bar with real fire and dining areas.

ROTHERHAM
Limes
38 Broom Lane
11-11; 12-10.30 Sun
Banks's Original, Bitter; Cameron's Strongarm; guest beer H
Having dropped 'Hotel' from its name, it remains a popular local pub with rooms. The comfortable bar area serves an exceptional menu.

Peak District National Park. Convenient for the Upper Don section of the Trans-Pennine Trail, it is popular with hikers and bikers. Spacious and comfortable, it offers restaurant food as well as bar meals (food served 12-8 Sun). Coach parties are welcomed by arrangement. ✿⋈♿▲♣P

EDENTHORPE

Beverley Inn
117 Thorne Road
☼ 12-3, 5 (6 Sat)-11; 12-3, 7-10.30 Sun
☎ (01302) 882724
Barnsley Bitter; John Smith's Bitter; Theakston XB; guest beers Ⓗ
A deceptively modern exterior hides the fact that the heart of this building dates back over 200 years. Popular with all, young and old, diners and drinkers. The hum of conversation strikes you as you enter this friendly pub. The spacious comfortable lounge (whose shape defies description) features a large collection of framed cigarette cards. There is also a pleasant restaurant. The accommodation (14 rooms) is very popular, so book well ahead. ✿⋈◑▷♿P

FIRBECK

Black Lion
9 New Road
☼ 11.30-3.30, 5.30-11; 11-11 Sat; 12-10.30 Sun
☎ (01709) 812575 e-mail: blacklion@amserve.com
John Smith's Bitter, Magnet; Stones Bitter; guest beers Ⓗ
Dating back to the 17th-century, this pleasantly modernised village pub specialises in good food, while regularly changing guest beers ensure a good choice for the ale enthusiast. The large main bar displays hundreds of photos of local characters and famous visitors. The restaurant has an excellent *à la carte* menu, and hosts occasional cabaret nights. A quiz takes place Tue eve and Thu is Karaoke night. The ancient monument of Roche Abbey stands nearby. ⋈Q✿⋈◑P🍴

GREASBROUGH

Prince of Wales
9 Potter Hill (B6089)
☼ 11-4, 7-11; 12-3, 7-10.30 Sun
☎ (01709) 551358
John Smith's Bitter; Ⓟ **guest beer** Ⓗ

Friendly, street-corner local serving a low-priced, ever-changing guest beer in its traditional tap room and comfortable lounge. China plates depict the local mining industry, alongside a large collection of jugs. Up to 50 malt whiskies are stocked, as well as beers that are unusual for the area. This *Guide* regular has twice been voted local CAMRA *Pub of the Season*. A chip shop next door is one of four local take-aways. ✿⊟♣🍴

GRENOSIDE

Cow & Calf
88 Skew Hill Lane (½ mile of A61)
☼ 11.30-3, 6-11 (11.30-11 summer Sat); 12-5, 7-10.30 (12-10.30 summer) Sun
☎ (0114) 246 8191
Samuel Smith OBB Ⓗ
This spacious former farmhouse was converted to a pub in 1978 by the owners, Sam Smith's. There is a comfortable lounge area to the right of the entrance, while to the left is a stone-flagged drinking area by the bar, leading to another seating area and a no-smoking room. There is outside drinking in the courtyard, next to the children's play room. The brewery's organic ale is available in bottles. No eve meals Sun. Q🛏✿◑♣P🍴

HARTHILL

Beehive
16 Union Street
☼ 12-3 (not Mon), 6 (7 Sat)-11; 12-3, 7-10.30 Sun
☎ (01909) 770205 e-mail: the.beehive@talk21.com
Taylor Landlord; Tetley Bitter; guest beer Ⓗ
Lively, traditional pub in a historic village, well served by public transport. The bar is run by Hilary, while husband Jim runs the kitchen. There are two rooms for drinking and dining, served by a central bar. A room at the rear houses a full-sized snooker table, one of only three locally. It is home to the famous Harthill morris dancers. The Rother Valley Country Park is close by offering camping and very good walks. A Braille menu is available (no lunches Sun). Q✿◑▷♿▲🚲♣P🍴

HELLABY

Stockyard – Harry's Bar
Hellaby Lane (1 mile from Denby Way/A631 jct)
Hellaby Lane (1 mile from Denby Way/A631 jct)

SHEFFIELD: *CENTRAL*
Red Deer
18 Pitt Street
11.30 (11 Fri)-11; 12-3, 7-11 Sat; closed lunch, 7.30-10.30 Sun
Black Sheep Best Bitter; Greene King Abbot, Old Speckled Hen; Tetley Bitter; Wentworth WPA; guest beers Ⓗ
Tucked behind West Street, this is a refuge of fine ale away from the circuit. Good value food.

Red Lion
109 Charles Street
11.30-11; closed lunch, 7.30-10.30 Sun
John Smith's Magnet; Stones Bitter; Theakston Cool Cask Ⓗ
Comfortable pub, tucked behind the National Centre for Popular Music. Food at lunchtimes. Conservatory for summer eve pint.

NORTH
Rock House
168-172 Rock Street, Pitsmoor
1-4 (not Mon-Thu), 8-11; 1-4, 8-10.30 Sun
Draught Bass; John Smith's Bitter Ⓗ
Friendly, family-run, two-roomed local; its cheery Scottish landlord has brought a Caledonian theme along with a wide range of whiskies.

SOUTH
Millhouses
951 Abbeydale Road
11-11; 12-10.30 Sun
Boddingtons Bitter; Kelham Island; Pride of Sheffield; Tetley Bitter; guest beer Ⓗ
Traditional local, serving Sheffield ales and food based on Yorkshire recipes in a warm, friendly, fun atmosphere.

WEST
Bell Hagg Inn
3 Manchester Road
12-11; 12-10.30 Sun
Banks's Bitter, seasonal beers Ⓗ
Comfortable free house, on the edge of the city, affording spectacular views over the Rivelin Valley. Breakfast is served 7.30-11am.

> ✲ **symbol next to a main entry place name indicates there are Inn Brief entries as well.**

⊕ 12-11; closed Sat & Sun
☎ (01709) 700200
Taylor Landlord H

Opened in 1999, it's a truck stop! However the truck stop image ends in the car park. Built mainly from reclaimed materials, the impressive brick and pantile building houses an unusual foyer, superb bar and carvery. Harry's Bar features real beams, an open log fire, yorkstone flags, antique board floors and pews. The atmosphere is cosy, relaxed, and very friendly. A stylish carvery offers food to a very high standard at reasonable prices. ▲Q❀&P

HEMINGFIELD ❋

Elephant & Castle

Tinglebridge Lane (off M1 jct 36, at B6096)
⊕ 11-4, 5-11; 11-11 Sat; 11-10.30 Sun
☎ (01226) 755986

Barge & Barrel Nettlethrasher, Black Stump; John Smith's Bitter; Tetley Bitter H

Set by the canal, you are welcomed to this 17th-century village inn by the sight of a delightful seating area arranged around a fountain complete with the elephants of the pub's name. Inside is a split-level seating area, the upper level being no-smoking. A large bar front area has window seats overlooking the fountain. To the right is a more traditional area with football memorabilia. Twice local CAMRA *Pub of the Season* in 2000. Good value meals are freshly prepared.
❀❶&❀♣P✦

HIGH HOYLAND

Cherry Tree

Bank End Lane OS410026
⊕ 12-3 (4 Sat), 7-11; 12-5, 6-10.30 Sun
☎ (01226) 382541

Barge & Barrel Nettlethrasher; John Smith's Bitter H

Elongated pub with beamed ceilings, a semi-circular central bar and open fires on both sides. Truly magnificent views look out to Cawthorne Park and far beyond. Used by walkers and cyclists, it is near Cannon Hall Park. Inside, one of the wall decorations to be admired is a large collage of the parish of High Hoyland, showing the buildings and the names of the residents when it was made in 1999. No meals Mon eve.
▲Q❀❶P

HIGHAM, BARNSLEY

Engineers Inn

Higham Common Road (off A635)
⊕ 12-3, 7-11; 12-3, 7-10.30 Sun
☎ (01226) 384204

Samuel Smith OBB H

Just set back from the main road, the Engineers offers good value for money. The lounge bar has a pool table with a red cloth which is in marked contrast to the rest of the decor; the walls are mainly covered with large framed pictures of characters from *Last of the Summer Wine*. It has a small, but comfortable seating area. Up a couple of stairs and to the left is the public bar.
❀❺♣P

HOYLAND

Furnace Inn

163 Milton Road
⊕ 12-4, 6.30-11; 12-3, 7-10.30 Sun
☎ (01226) 742000

Stones Bitter; Tetley Bitter H

Recently redecorated, this pub has kept all its charm and character. Once part of a row of back-to-back workers' houses, it is close to the Forge Waggonway and the old site of Milton Forge. The garden overlooking Milton pond is a perfect place to relax on a sunny afternoon. Divided into two rooms, a games room and a large bar area, the pub boasts a large collection of jugs and commemorative colliery plates. It has won more awards from Barnsley CAMRA than any other pub.
▲❀≠(Elsecar & Hoyland)♣P❒

LAUGHTON-EN-LE-MORTHEN

St Leger Arms

4 High Street
⊕ 12-11; 12-10.30 Sun
☎ (01909) 562940

Barnsley Bitter; Boddingtons Bitter; Whitbread Trophy H

Friendly village pub, popular with locals and hikers, it has a small bar area for drinkers, and a games area to the side, with a pool table, dartboard and TV. Good, moderately-priced, food is served in the recently extended carvery (which can be very busy Sun, when service is 12-9). An

INN BRIEF

WEST
Cobden View
40 Cobden View Road
5 (2 Sat)-11;
2-10.30 Sun
Barnsley Bitter; Castle Eden Ale; guest beers H
Popular community pub with a lounge and pool room to the right of the bar and a larger seating area at the rear.

THORNE
Punch Bowl
Fieldside
12-3, 7-11;
12-3, 7-10.30 Sun
Old Mill Bitter H
Imposing early 1900s building; ask where the bell-call signals are. No food Tue and Sun eves.

WENTWORTH
Rockingham Arms
8 Main Street
11-11; 12-10.30 Sun
Theakston Best Bitter, XB, Old Peculier; guest beer H
Cosy pub in a charming village, with multi-room layout and good food. A barn hosts live music. Bowling green and cricket pitch adjacent; large garden.

WHISTON, ROTHERHAM
Sitwell Arms
Pleasley Road (A618)
11-11; 12-10.30 Sun
Tetley Bitter; guest beers H
Village local/restaurant, originally a farm and ale house, with wheelchair access, centuries old in parts. Up to three guest beers on tap; good food.

Guide site

Keep your copy of the Good Beer Guide up-to-date by contacting the CAMRA website where you will find information about changes to pubs and breweries

www.camra.org.uk/gbg

outside drinking area has a grassed play area for children, sited well away from the main road. ✿◑♣P☐

LOW BARUGH

Millers

Dearne Hall Road (off M1 jct 37 or 38)
✪ 11 (5 Tue)-11; 11-3, 5-11 Wed & Thu; 12-4, 7-10.30 Sun
☎ (01226) 382888 e-mail: millers@hotmail.com
Barnsley Bitter; Taylor Landlord; Theakston Cool Cask; guest beers Ⓗ

Free house by the River Dearne – watch out for the goose that lives in the car park. A smaller room leads off the lounge through an arch; the public bar boasts an unusual mural of a clay pigeon shooter with gun dogs, done in raised brickwork between two open fireplaces. A popular venue for meetings of various clubs and societies, it fields darts and football teams and is home to a clay pigeon shooting club. Eve meals served Fri and Sat. Wheelchair WC.
🏰Q✿◑☐≠♣P

MEXBOROUGH

Concertina Band Club

9a Dolcliffe Road
✪ 12-4, 7-11; 12-2, 7-10.30 Sun
☎ (01709) 580841
Concertina Club Bitter, Bengal Tiger; John Smith's Bitter; guest beer (occasional) Ⓗ

Off the High Street, the 'Tina' is a small, friendly club with an on-site brewery. A large bar area leads to a small games room and a pleasant lounge. The club is steeped in local history and there are pictures of the prize-winning Concertina Band after which it is named. Visitors will find a warm welcome and a choice of guest beers, as well as other ales in the Concertina range. Brewing started in 1992 and the beers have won many awards. ≠♣☐

Falcon

12 Main Street
✪ 11.30-11; 12.30-3.30, 7-10.30 Sun
☎ (01709) 513084
Old Mill Bitter; guest beers Ⓗ

Double-fronted pub, with original leaded windows, at the town centre, with a paved seating area at the front. Originally called the Old Masons Arms, it closed for some time, and after being bought by Old Mill Brewery in 1990, it was refurbished and reopened as the Falcon. A lively pub, it has a large lounge with raised areas and a smaller tap room offering traditional pub games. Guest beers are from the Old Mill range. ✿☐≠♣

George & Dragon

81 Church Street (off A6023, near River Don)
✪ 12-11; 12-10.30 Sun
☎ (01709) 584375
John Smith's Bitter; Stones Bitter; Tetley Bitter; guest beers Ⓗ

The earliest known reference to the George & Dragon is 1822. This three-roomed pub, with its central bar, set in a quiet part of town, offers a good rotation of quality guest ales. It has won many awards, including local CAMRA *Pub of the Season*, Ward's *Cellarman* and *Pub in Bloom* for its attractive garden and play area that is popular with

families. The pub can be reached by road or from the station, via a pleasant walk along the canal towpath. ✿&♣P

OUGHTIBRIDGE

Travellers Rest

93 Langsett Road South
✪ 12-3, 7-11; 12-3, 7-10.30 Sun
☎ (0114) 286 2221
Samuel Smith OBB Ⓗ

This pub definitely lives up to its name. On entering to the right is a small tap room, with bare floorboards and a dartboard, featuring the original etched glass Str,outts Brewery window; the bar is small and unpretentious. A pool area, a small corridor drinking area and a modest, yet comfortable, lounge complete the picture. Regular folk sessions are held. ☐♣

PENISTONE

Cubley Hall

Mortimer Road, Cubley (²/₃ mile S of centre)
✪ 11-11; 12-10.30 Sun
☎ (01226) 766086 e-mail: cubley.hall@ukonline.co.uk
Greene King Abbot; Ind Coope Burton Ale; Tetley Bitter; guest beer Ⓗ

Originally a moorland farm on the Pennine packhorse routes of the 1700s, Cubley Hall evolved into a fine Victorian gentleman's residence. It became a children's home after the war, when resident ghost Flora was said to appear at the bedside of sick children. It has been refurbished sympathetically under the present owners, with the original mosaic tiles, oak panelling, stained glass and elaborate ceiling mouldings creating a rich ambience. The guest rooms are new. Extremely family-friendly, ample grounds include a children's play area. The area is criss-crossed with footpaths. ⬗✿🛏◑P⅄●

ROTHERHAM ❀

Moulders Rest

110-112 Masbrough Street (near Millmoor football ground)
✪ 12-4 (5 Sat), 6 (7 Fri & Sat)-11; 12-5, 7-10.30 Sun
☎ (01709) 560095
John Smith's Bitter; guest beer Ⓗ

Built in the early 1800s the Moulders Rest occupies a prominent corner position, within easy walking distance of the town centre, and is well served by public transport. This traditional local comprises a busy tap room, popular for pub games, and a spacious lounge. Good value food is served weekdays and accommodation is available. This regular *Guide* entry has twice been local CAMRA *Pub of the Season*.
✿🛏◑☐≠(Central)♣P

Rhinoceros

35-37 Bridgegate (near bus station)
✪ 11-11; 12-10.30 Sun
☎ (01709) 361422
Courage Directors; Shepherd Neame Spitfire; Theakston Best Bitter; guest beers Ⓗ

Open-plan, town-centre pub, close to All Saints Square. Good value beer and food, as standard in Wetherspoon's pubs, this is a typical conversion from a former furniture salesroom. No music, but conversation is appreciated. Beer festivals are held April and

Oct. The no-smoking area is extensive. The food is recommended and good value. See old pictures of Rotherham on the way to the toilets. Nearby is the Chapel of Our Lady on the Bridge, one of only three in Britain, built in the 15th century.
◑▯♿♣✦●

Woodman
Midland Road, Masbrough (off A269, opp. bus garage)
◐ 12-3, 7-11; 12-3, 7-10.30 Sun
☎ (01709) 512128
Draught Bass; Stones Bitter; guest beer Ⓗ
This former Bentley's pub, built in 1853, is a traditional local, comprising a tap room, a snug lounge and a full size snooker table upstairs, for hire. Close to Rotherham FC, the Woodman has good public transport links. In the *Guide* for 19 years, it has twice won Rotherham CAMRA's *Pub of the Season* award. ❀▱♣

SHEFFIELD: CENTRAL ✣

Banker's Draft
1-3 Market Place
◐ 11-11; 12-10.30 Sun
☎ (0114) 275 6609
Boddingtons Bitter; Courage Directors; Tetley Bitter; Theakston Best Bitter; guest beers Ⓗ
This converted banking house is large without being cavernous, spread over two levels, each with its own bar. Along with the usual Wetherspoon niceties, including no-smoking areas and attention to architectural detail, there is always space to just drink, even at peak mealtimes. Alongside beer festivals and promotions, a range of local and regional guest beers is maintained. A convenient place to meet in the city centre. Q◑♿⇌(Midland) ⊖(Castle Sq) ✂●

Fat Cat
23 Alma Street
◐ 12-3, 5.30-11; 12-3, 7-10.30 Sun
☎ (0114) 249 4801 website: www.thefatcat.co.uk
Kelham Island Bitter, Pale Rider, seasonal beers; Taylor Landlord; guest beers Ⓗ
The motto on the sign outside proclaims 'ferociously independent' and it is, unless you count the Kelham Island Brewery that grew out of a shed in the back yard to a full size brewhouse next door. As well as 10 handpumps, you will often find another beer on gravity next to the real cider and the ever-changing draught Belgian beer (check out the bottles in the fridge too). Other high points are the large collection of country wines and the award-winning food, including a varied choice of vegetarian meals (eve meals weekdays). ⚲Q❀◑⊖(Shalesmoor) ●P✂

Hogshead
25 Orchard Street, Orchard Square
◐ 9-11; 12-10.30 Sun
☎ (0114) 275 5016 website: www.hogshead.co.uk
Boddingtons Bitter; Wentworth WPA, Oatmeal Stout, Gryphon, Rampant Gryphon; Ⓗ **guest beers** Ⓖ
This is a shining example of how a chain-owned pub can be, hosting two beer festivals a year (April and Oct), a summer cider festival, year-round support of a local micro plus four guest beers. Light and airy with a lively atmosphere, staging live music

some nights, it offers a good food menu (9-9 daily), special offers on cask ales and a growing range of Belgian beers. The continental-style outdoor seating in Orchard Square gives an opportunity to watch the shoppers go by.
❀◑♿⇌(Midland) ⊖(Cathedral) ●✂

Rutland Arms
86 Brown Street (near station)
◐ 11.30 (12 Sat)-11; 12-10.30 Sun
☎ (0114) 272 9003
website: www.rutlandarms-sheffield.co.uk
Adnams Bitter; Barnsley Bitter; Black Sheep Best Bitter; Greene King Abbot; Marston's Pedigree Ⓗ
Attractive, traditional ex-Gilmour's house, filling an odd-shaped corner, this friendly watering-hole boasts not only a solid range of real ale (including Wentworth's seasonal brews), but an award-winning garden to enjoy them in. The pub itself has also earned numerous awards from the local CAMRA branch. As well as good bed and breakfast accommodation, there is an ample menu of home-cooked food including vegetarian choices and a specials board. Meals served 11.30-8 weekdays; no food Sat or Sun eves. ❀▱◑⇌(Midland) ⊖P

Ship Inn
312 Shalesmoor
◐ 12-3, 7 (5 Fri, 7.30 Sat)-11; 12-3, 7.30-10.30 Sun
☎ (0114) 281 2209
website: www.theshipinn.co.uk/sheffield
Hardys & Hansons Best Bitter, guest beer Ⓗ
The tiled frontage proudly proclaims Tomlinson's Anchor Ales in broad sweeping lettering, while a plaque informs punters as they enter that the pub may be haunted by two seamen drowned in the flood of 1864. The interior is slightly lower key, decorated with a mix of pub and nautical memorabilia. Only a short walk from the centre, but maintaining a more congenial atmosphere than the city pubs; sink into one of the plush bench seats and relax. Weekday lunches served.
◑⊖(Shalesmoor) ♣P▯

Three Cranes Hotel
74 Queens Street (behind the Anglican Cathedral)
◐ 11.30-11; closed Sun
☎ (0114) 273 1415
Stones Bitter; guest beers Ⓗ
Tucked among legal firms and estate agents, this intriguing pub retains the Wm Stones' frosted glass windows. Unsurprisingly popular with local professionals at lunchtime, evenings draw a more eclectic mix. Arranged around a central bar, two-thirds of the floor space is a comfortable lounge while the remainder is a smoke room. Reasonably-priced food and a wide range of guest ales, plus an upstairs function room, makes this a popular venue for meetings. Eve meals can be booked.
◑⊖(Cathedral)

Three Tuns
Silver Street Head
◐ 11.30-11; 12-3, 7.30-11 Sat; closed Sun
☎ (0114) 272 0646
Greene King Abbot; Tetley Bitter; guest beers Ⓗ
Thrusting into the developing technology West Bar sector, this prow-shaped drinking establishment uses an odd corner to good effect. The addition of blue mood lighting

to highlight the lowered ceiling does not detract from the mainly traditional decor. The lively lunchtime crowd gives way to a more serious set. Comfortable, both in terms of furniture and atmosphere, it feels as if it has been given new life while retaining an air of the familiar. Weekday lunches served. ◑⊖(Cathedral)

Wetherspoons
Cambridge Street
☼ 11-11; 12-10.30 Sun
☎ (0114) 263 9500
Buddingtons Bitter; Courage Directors; Shepherd Neame Spitfire; Tetley Bitter; Theakston Best Bitter; guest beers Ⓗ

This purpose-built establishment manages to mix the modern with 1970s retro: glass and steel intermingle with wood panelling and back-lit features in yellow and brown. A bar on each of two floors, combined with energetic staff, means that even when at its busiest, there is excellent service. The outdoor drinking area is a terrace on the first floor. Subscribing to most of the Wetherspoon standard offers, this is a popular spot to meet before going to the nearby City Hall. Q✿❋◑&⊖(City Hall) ●

SHEFFIELD: EAST

Carlton
563 Attercliffe Road
☼ 11 (11.30 Fri)-3, 7 (7.30 Fri & Sat)-11; (closed lunch), 7.30-10.30 Sun
☎ (0114) 244 3287
John Smith's Bitter, Magnet; Theakston Cool Cask Ⓗ

Dating from 1862, this former Gilmour's pub has a deceptively small frontage. A free house for the last 12 years, with a friendly atmosphere, a comfortable lounge around the main bar is complemented by a pool room at the rear. Weekend entertainment may be a singalong with the landlord at the organ or Karaoke. Once at the heart of a busy shopping area, it is handy for the Don Valley Stadium. This community pub is redolent of a bygone era and still boasts a swear box. Beer is reduced by 10p a pint at lunchtimes.
🚶Q⊖(Attercliffe/Woodbourne Rd) ♣ ☐

Cocked Hat
75 Worksop Road
☼ 11-11; 11-3, 7-11 Sat; 12-2, 7-10.30 Sun
☎ (0114) 244 8332
Banks's Bitter; Marston's Bitter, Pedigree, seasonal beers Ⓗ

Street-corner pub, dating from the 1840s, taken over by Marston's in the mid-1980s and completely refurbished in traditional style. Stalled seating at the end of the bar is reserved for diners weekday lunchtimes (no eve or weekend meals). A raised area to the left of the entrance has a bar billiards table. The decor features old bottles and jars, an impressive collection of bottled beers, and pictures of old Attercliffe. Lying in the shadow of the Don Valley Stadium, it is patronised by sports personalities and is handy for the Five Weirs walk.
🚶✿◑⊖(Attercliffe) ♣

SHEFFIELD: NORTH ❋

Cask & Cutler
1 Henry Street, Shalesmoor

☼ 12-2 (not Mon), 5.30-11; 12-11 Fri & Sat; 12-3, 7-10.30 Sun
☎ (0114) 249 2295
Beer range varies Ⓗ

This genuine free house, twice winner of Sheffield CAMRA *Pub of the Year* and 1999 runner-up in Yorkshire, offers a variety of real ales on seven handpulls, plus a large choice of Belgian bottled beers. Since 1993 when it was bought from Whitbread, over 3,000 different real ales have been served from small independents. Minor structural changes have seen the pub redivided into two rooms. A house brewery is close to completion, next to the secluded garden. A popular annual beer festival is held (Nov). Home-made sandwiches are available Fri and Sat. 🚶Q✿⊖(Shalesmoor) ♣ ●⊬☐

Gardeners Rest
105 Neepsend Lane
☼ 12-11; 12-10.30 Sun
☎ (0114) 272 4978
Taylor Golden Best, Porter, Best Bitter, Landlord, guest beers Ⓗ

Re-opening as a free house in 1998, this friendly pub in the shadow of the now-closed Stone's Brewery quickly established itself and was awarded Sheffield CAMRA's *Pub of the Year* award 2000. Guest beers come from a monthly-changing featured brewery, alongside a selection of draught and bottled Belgian beers. A new conservatory and the redesigned secluded garden overlooking the River Don add to its appeal. Full wheelchair access and facilities have been included. The Dram Shop, a quiet no-smoking room, displays local brewery memorabilia. The main room, featuring one of only two bar billiard tables in Sheffield, hosts regular live music eves.
Q✿&⊖(Infirmary Rd) ♣ ●⊬☐

Hillsborough Hotel
54-58 Langsett Road
☼ 5-11; 5-10.30 Sun
☎ (0114) 232 2100
website: www.hillsboroughhotel.com
Beer range varies Ⓗ

Hotel opened in 1999, following thorough refurbishment, retaining many original Victorian features. The bar is only open to the public from Thu-Sun, but this can mean a bargain for the late Sun real ale drinkers. Eight handpulled beers are available at any one time, with others in jugs direct from the cask, often from a weekly featured guest micro-brewery; the house beer is from Rooster's. Bar meals are home made and of generous proportions; children are welcome on the sun terrace.
✿⊨◑⊖(Langsett/Primrose View) ●P⊬

New Barrack Tavern
601 Penistone Road, Hillsborough
☼ 12-11; 12-10.30 Sun
☎ (0114) 234 9148
Abbeydale Moonshine; Barnsley Bitter; John Smith's Magnet; Wentworth WPA; guest beers Ⓗ

Award-winning roadside pub retaining many original Gilmour's features, close to the remains of the Dearden Brewery. Its three rooms comprise a public bar, a no-smoking room and a large lounge featuring mirrors from bygone brewing days. Five changing guests come from small independents; more than 30 bottled continental beers are stocked, with a further seven on draught and a varying guest cider; up to 70 malt whiskies are available. Renowned for its good food, it hosts a popular speciality eve Wed with world cuisines. Live music is staged three nights a week. Handy for discerning football fans. ♨Q✿◑ ⌷⊟ (Bamforth St) ♣♠✦✄

SHEFFIELD: *SOUTH* ✿

Archer Road Beer Stop (off-licence)
57 Archer Road (opp. Esporta)
✿ 11-10; 12-2, 6-10 Sun
☎ (0114) 255 1356
Beer range varies Ⓗ
Small, real ale off-licence stocking up to four draught beers, mainly from local breweries, plus an extensive range of bottle-conditioned beers and world classics. Originally known as Small Beer, opened in 1982 by CAMRA enthusiasts, it provided an oasis in an area considered a real ale desert. The management may have changed but the commitment to provide the best ales from around the world is as strong as ever. ♠⎕

Castle Inn
1 Castle Row, Twentywell Road
✿ 12 (11 Fri & Sat)-11; 12-10.30 Sun
☎ (0114) 236 2955
Black Sheep Best Bitter; Boddingtons Bitter; Fuller's London Pride; Marston's Pedigree; Taylor Landlord; Tetley Bitter Ⓗ
Stone-fronted pub at the end of a row of cottages, built in the 1860s as a dormitory and ale house for the workers who built the Bradway rail tunnel. Originally two cottages, now one building consisting of a lounge with adjoining restaurant and a tap room. Very much a pub that serves food rather than a restaurant serving beer. Worth seeking out for its friendly, relaxed atmosphere. ✿◑ ⌷⎕▲➔ (Dore) ♣P

Old Mother Redcap
Prospect Road, Bradway
✿ 11.30-3.30, 5.30-11; 11-11 Sat; 12-10.30 Sun
☎ (0114) 236 0179
Samuel Smith OBB Ⓗ
Modern, stone pub in the style of an old Yorkshire farmhouse. A single large L-shaped lounge is divided into small areas, served by a large central bar. One quiet end, the other end has TV and games; plenty of comfortable seating throughout. This community local offers a full social calendar including regular trips and charitable events. The unusual name refers to an elderly 'buffer girl', but the sign depicts a witch believed to have lived in the woods nearby. It serves the cheapest real ale in the city. ✿◑♣P

Prince of Wales
150 Derbyshire Lane
✿ 11-11; 12-10.30 Sun
☎ (0114) 255 0960
Flowers Original; Greene King Abbot; guest beers Ⓗ
Traditional local, with a single L-shaped lounge split into small areas. Strong emphasis is placed on family entertainment: special events often centre on children's activities usually held in the garden. A children's favourite is 'Piggy', a

300lb English White who loves the real ales on offer which include two constantly changing beers, usually from small independent brewers. Recently refurbished, it now has good wheelchair access. Entertainment most nights includes quizzes and Karaoke. ✿◑♿♣P

Sheaf View
25 Gleadless Road
✿ 12 (5 Mon)-11; 12-10.30 Sun
☎ (0114) 249 6455
Abbeydale Mooshine; Barnsley Bitter; John Smith's Magnet; Wentworth WPA; guest beers Ⓗ
Standing derelict since the early 1990s the pub reopened following extensive refurbishment by the owners of the city's award-winning New Barrack Tavern. Where previously managements have failed, new owners have introduced four constantly changing guest beers complemented by cider and a range of draught and bottled continental ales. Choice, reasonable prices and friendly, helpful staff have brought the crowds in. A genuine free house where future awards seem certain. Over-sized glasses are available on request. Q✿♿♣♠P⎕

SHEFFIELD: *WEST* ✿

Ball Inn
171 Crookes
✿ 11-11; 12-10.30 Sun
☎ (0114) 266 1211
Boddingtons Bitter; Castle Eden Ale; Marston's Pedigree; guest beers Ⓗ
Large, suburban pub with a bay-windowed frontage and entrance porch approached across a cobbled forecourt that provides an outdoor seating area. The two rooms at the front are in typical ale house style, with bare floorboards, exposed brick walls and wood panelling. To the rear is a further seating area and a large games room with two pool tables. Up to five guest beers are served from the central bar, mostly from established regional brewers. A popular community pub, it also attracts students. ✿◑♣♠

Noah's Ark
94 Crookes
✿ 12 (11 Sat)-11; 12-10.30 Sun
☎ (0114) 266 3300
Boddingtons Bitter; Castle Eden Ale; Marston's Pedigree; John Smith's Magnet; Tetley Bitter; guest beers Ⓗ
Busy community pub in a popular student area. Recently extended, it now has a central bar with a variety of seating areas. Dark wood and warm red in the exposed brickwork are set off by a large display of pictures, including some of bygone Crookes. One of the first Whitbread pubs to reintroduce real ale in the early 1980s, it now offers an impressive range, including two guests, usually from established regionals. Although it has a pool table and TV, it is more of a pub for quiet conversation, appealing to all ages. ✿◑♣

Old Heavygate
114 Matlock Road
✿ 2-4 (12-5 Sat), 7-11 (12-11 winter Sat); 12-4, 7-10.30 Sun

☎ (0114) 234 0003

Hardys & Hansons Best Bitter; seasonal beers Ⓗ

Occupying a former tollhouse and adjoining cottage dating from 1696, because of the hillside location the two rooms arc on different levels, so unusually the tap room customers can look down on those in the lounge. A pub for over 100 years, it is a popular meeting place for sports teams and offers a varied social calendar for the local community. One of only a handful of the brewery's pubs in the city, their current seasonal brew is usually available. ✿♣Ⓟ⊟

Plough Inn
268 Sandygate Road

✪ 11-11; 12-10.30 Sun

☎ (0114) 230 1802

Barnsley Bitter; Black Sheep Best Bitter; Boddingtons Bitter; Kelham Island Golden Eagle; guest beers Ⓗ

After the indignity of a spell as a Whitbread theme pub in the 1980s, the Plough has been restored to suit the upmarket suburb it serves. A long bar serves raised seating areas at either end and a pool area. The wood-panelled walls are decorated with local pictures and bric-à-brac. One of the four pubs forming the Sheffield Pubco division of Whitbread, usually has seven real ales on tap, mostly from local breweries, including at least one from Wentworth.
Q✿◑♿♣Ⓟⓧ

Porter Brook
565 Ecclesall Road

✪ 11-11; 12-10.30 Sun

☎ (0114) 266 5765

Boddingtons Bitter; Greene King Abbot; Wadworth 6X; Ⓗ **guest beers** Ⓗ/Ⓖ

Opened in a converted house on the banks of the River Porter about four years ago, this Whitbread Hogshead has quickly established itself as the leading real ale pub on the Ecclesall Road scene, with up to 14 cask beers available. Guest beers are mainly from regional brewers, although micros are featured fairly regularly. Furnished in typical ale house style with bare boards and exposed brickwork, it attracts a wide ranging clientele, and can be crowded, especially weekend eves. Meals served all day until 9pm. ✿◑ⓧ

Walkley Cottage
46 Bolehill Road

✪ 11-11; 12-10.30 Sun

☎ (0114) 234 4968

Marston's Pedigree; Taylor Landlord; Tetley Bitter; guest beer Ⓗ

Large roadhouse-style, suburban pub of two rooms: a good-sized tap room with snooker table, and a spacious L-shaped lounge. Built for Gilmour's between the wars, on a spacious site with an extensive garden, it usually stocks three or four guest beers from both regional and local micros. A lively local, it hosts a popular quiz and games eves. Situated on top of a hill, it benefits from good views over the Rivelin Valley.
Q✿◑♣Ⓟ

SOUTH ANSTON

Loyal Trooper
34 Sheffield Road (3 miles from M1 jct 31)

✪ 12-3, 6-11; 12-11 Sat; 12-3, 7-10.30 Sun

☎ (01909) 562203

Draught Bass; Taylor Landlord; Tetley Bitter; guest beer Ⓗ

Traditional, friendly village local in old part of Anston, reputedly named after being used to house soldiers. The former stables now house kitchens and stores. A beam in the stables is dated 1690. Three rooms: a lounge, known as the Dragoons Room, public bar (with TV) and a snug. The upstairs function room regularly caters for various local groups. It hosts regular quiz nights, and has been home to the Anston Folk Club for years. Anston Stones Nature Reserve is close by, as is Lindrick Golf Course. No food Sun; eve meals Mon-Thu.
Q✿◑♿⊟♣Ⓟ

SPROTBROUGH

Ivanhoe Hotel
Melton Road

✪ 11-11; 12-10.30 Sun

☎ (01302) 853130

Samuel Smith OBB Ⓗ

Popular community pub in an idyllic setting next to the village cricket pitch. It has a large lounge with adjoining conservatory where children are welcome and very reasonably-priced meals can be enjoyed. Sun lunch is particularly popular and a specials board lists a good choice of food; no meals Sun eve or winter Mon eve. The public bar has TV, snooker and pool tables; weekly quizzes held. The attractive garden includes a children's play area.
♿▣◑⊟♣Ⓟ☙

STRINES

Strines Inn
Mortimer Road, Bradfield (signed 2 miles from A57) OS222906

✪ 10.30-3, 5.30-11; 10.30-11 Sat & summer; 12-10.30 Sun

☎ (0144) 285 1247

Banks's Bitter; Camerons Strongarm; Marston's Pedigree; guest beer (summer) Ⓗ

Built as a manor house for the local Worral family in 1275, most of the current Grade II listed buildings date from the 1550s. It has been an inn since 1771 and has never been owned by a brewery. An isolated country pub, set in walking country, its three drinking areas include a no-smoking room. A small farm for rescued animals stands at the rear. *Coffee Pub of the Year* 2001 in the pub food awards, meals are served all day at weekends and in summer. ♿✿▣◑♣Ⓟⓧ

THORNE ✿

Canal Tavern
South Parade (town side of flyover bridge, A614)

✪ 11.30-3, 5.30-11; 11.30-11 Fri & Sat; 12-10.30 Sun

☎ (01405) 813688

Flowers Original; John Smith's Bitter; Tetley Bitter; Theakston Cool Cask; guest beer Ⓗ

Dating back to 1822, this hostelry stands on the Stainforth and Keadby canal, which is popular with boaters. Pictures of old Thorne and maps of its windmills line the pub walls and there are 69 items on the menu to line your stomach walls. This is a true free house – the number of pump clips behind the bar

WEST YORKSHIRE

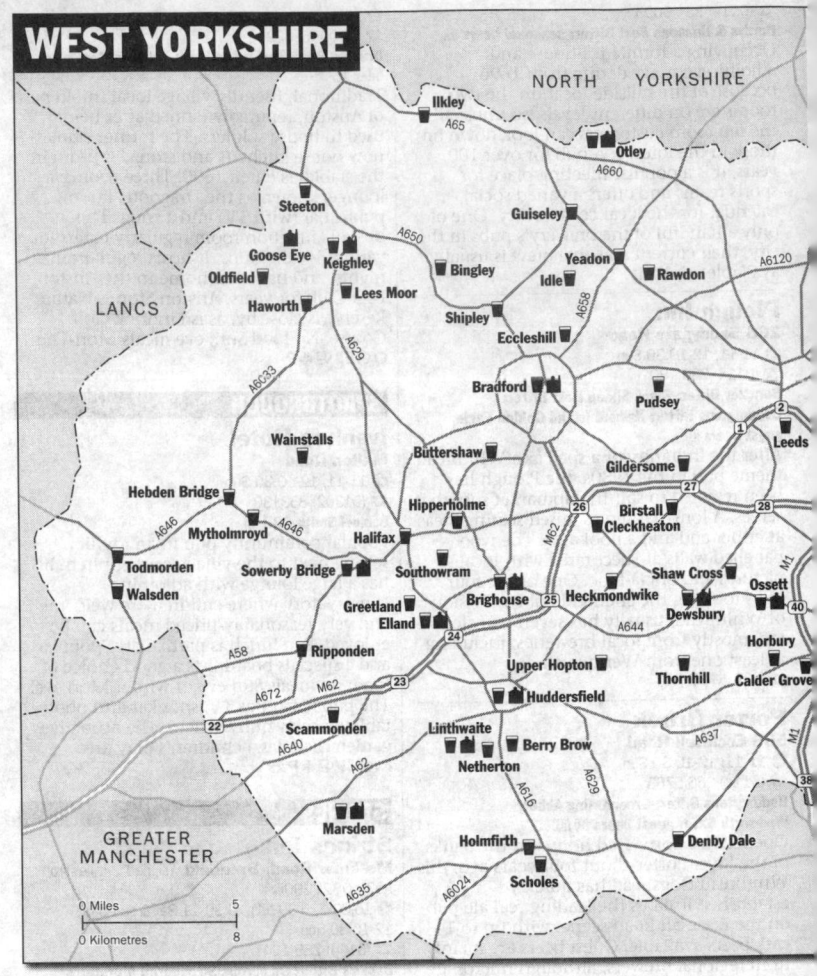

give some idea of the variety and popularity of its guest beers. Country and Western devotees congregate here every Sun eve.
❀◑▶ ⊕≠(South) ♣P

THURLSTONE

Huntsman
136 Manchester Road
⊙ 6 (12 Fri & Sat)-11; 12-10.30 Sun
☎ (01226) 764892
Clark's Traditional, seasonal beers; guest beers H
The plain exterior of this Clark's terrace pub belies the quality inside, where something is bound to delight you. It could be the real fires, the excellent home-cooked food, or the variety of the guest beers, with six handpumps in regular use and many more on the pub's beer festival weekends. Meals are served all day Fri and Sat (12-8) and until 5pm Sun, no lunches Mon-Thu.
⋈Q◑▶❀✦

TICKHILL

Scarbrough Arms
Sunderland Street
⊙ 11-3, 6-11; 12-3, 7-10.30 Sun
☎ (01302) 742977

Greene King Abbot; John Smith's Bitter, Magnet; guest beers H
Close to the centre of historic Tickhill, in sight of the ancient Buttercross, the Scarbrough (note the spelling) is a large stone pub that adopted its unusual name in the 1830s in deference to its then owner, a prominent local landowner. It consists of three rooms: a lively traditional tap with games; a cosy, wood-panelled middle room where most of the furniture is made from old wooden barrels; and a more spacious lounge, used as a dining area (lunches served Tue-Sat). Two rotating guest beers are always available.
⋈Q❀◑▶♣P▯

ULLEY

Royal Oak
12 Turnshaw Road (near M1 jct 31)
⊙ 11-3, 6-11; 12-3, 6-10.30 Sun
☎ (0114) 287 2464
Samuel Smith OBB H
Over 300 years old, in a picturesque village, the pub is replete with brasses, saddles and beams. Popular with local farmers, walkers and diners, this large country pub has extensive gardens and good children's

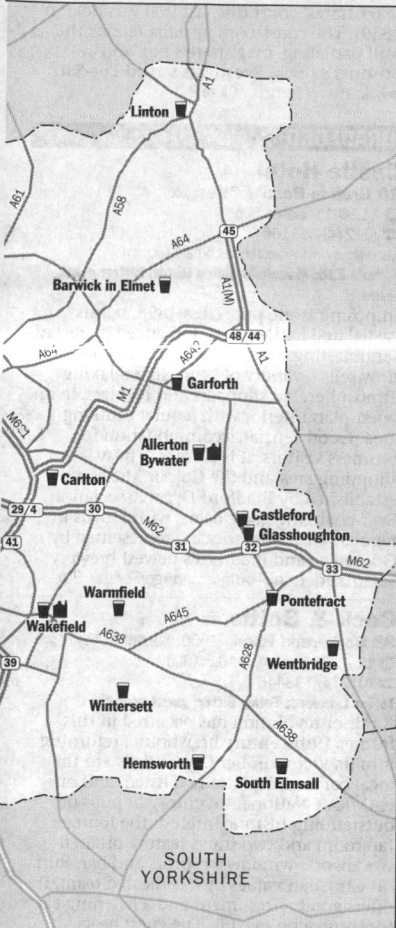

WENTWORTH ☀

George & Dragon

85 Main Street (B6090, approx. 1½ miles from M1 jct 35)

☼ 11 (10 Sat & summer)-11; 12-10.30 Sun

☎ (01226) 742440

Stones Bitter; Taylor Landlord; Wentworth WPA; guest beers Ⓗ

Traditional pub at the heart of a conservation village. Popular with drinkers and diners it opens 10am for breakfast. A choice of nearby Wentworth's beers includes Black Zac, named after a former landlord's dog; the village shop sells Wentworth bottled beers. Wentworth Woodhouse (18th century) has the longest frontage of any house in the country; the park contains many deer. Children welcome in the pub garden. Rotherham CAMRA *Pub of the Season* winter 2000. ♨ ⛭ ◑ ♣ P

WHISTON ☀

Golden Ball

7 Turner Lane (1½ miles from M1 jct 33, off A618)

☼ 12-11; 12-10.30 Sun

☎ (01709) 726911

Taylor Landlord; Tetley Bitter; guest beers Ⓗ

Originally a coaching inn, the oldest parts are nearly 500 years old. Renowned for a good range of cask beers, but prices can be high. Extensions during the 1970s and 80s used traditional materials to retain its olde-worlde character. In a conservation area, it stands close to the village dyke and an historic thatched manorial barn. The licensees were formerly singers on the club circuit and stage occasional cabaret nights at the pub, which has been three times Rotherham CAMRA *Pub of the Season*. Good food. ♨ Q ⛭ ◑ ♣ P⅟

WORTLEY

Wortley Arms

Halifax Road (A629)

☼ 12-11; 12-10.30 Sun

☎ (0114) 288 2245

Barnsley Bitter; John Smith's Magnet; Taylor Landlord; Theakston Old Peculier, guest beers Ⓗ

Cosy, rambling, multi-roomed (including a tiny 'no-dogs' room) old village hostelry, oozing with understated character and charm, boasting an enormous inglenook, wood panelling and exposed stonework, inlaid with a coat of arms. It stocks a wide range of malt whiskies and a selection of bottled Belgian beers. The house beer is light and refreshing but its origin is a closely-guarded secret. Half a mile (uphill) from the Trans-Pennine Trail, in excellent walking country, it is served by buses from Penistone and Sheffield. ♨ Q ⛭ ☞ ⋈ ◑ 🍴 A P⅟

Yorkshire (West)

ALLERTON BYWATER

Boat Inn

Boat Lane (off Main Street)

☼ 11.45-3.30, 6-11; 11.45-11 Sat & summer; 12-10.30 Sun

☎ (01977) 552216 website: www.boatpub.co.uk

Tetley Bitter; guest beers Ⓗ

Old pub at the site of a ferry service (closed

facilities. It offers good value beer and excellent home-cooked food. It is close to Ulley Reservoir Country Park, good for walks and water sports. The main bar stands on site of a well; the beams in the extension came from the home of notorious murderer, Charlie Peace. This regular *Guide* entry sells the only real Sam Smith's in the area. ☞ ⛭ ◑ P⅟

WALES

Duke of Leeds

16 Church Street (½ mile off Rotherham road)

☼ 12-2 (Mon & Tue), 7-11 closed lunch, 7-10.30 Sun

☎ (01909) 770301

Boddingtons Bitter; Castle Eden Ale; Greene King Abbot; guest beers Ⓗ

This former coaching inn dates from around 1700. It is situated on the old coach road to Chesterfield that runs parallel to the M1 motorway. Two areas near the entrance are for drinking, while the area to the rear is reserved for diners, all served by a central bar. The exposed beams lend character to the building. Close to the Rother Valley Country Park, camping is also available. ◑ ♿ A ☞ P⅟

in 1954) that transported miners and horses across the River Aire. Run by Brian Lockwood, former British Rugby League captain, mementos of his playing days decorate the three rooms, a lounge, restaurant/function room and a family room that leads to the large fenced garden. There is seating on the river bank and moorings nearby. Up to three guest beers; two come from the Boat Brewery, situated in the car park. A recent extensive refurbishment has provided the family room and wheelchair WCs. Note the etched glass window in the front entrance porch of a canal boat in a lock. Good food. ⌣❀◑ ⊟⌶ ▲P⌿

BARWICK IN ELMET

New Inn
17 Main Street (Garforth Rd jct)
☼ 12-11; 12-3, 7-10.30 Sun
☎ (0113) 281 2289
John Smith's Bitter; guest beer Ⓗ
Benches by the pantiled porch make an ideal place to watch the bustle of this active village, once the capital of the Celtic kingdom of Elmet. From a cottage tavern 240 years ago, it has been extended over the years but retains much of its character with beams, settles in inglenooks, and its low-ceilinged bar, one of the smallest in England. The tap room and snug are retained; the large lounge is comfortable and relaxed. Leeds CAMRA *Pub of the Summer* 1999, it serves an imaginative choice of rapidly-changing guest beers, that tend to be rare for the area; the food's good, too (eve meals Tue-Thu; book Sun lunch).
Q❀◑ ⊟♣

BERRY BROW, HUDDERSFIELD

Railway Hotel
2 School Lane (100 yds from Birch Rd halt on 306/308 bus route)
☼ 3-11; 12-11 Sat; 12-10.30 Sun
☎ (01484) 318052
e-mail: margery.woodcock@virgin.net
Black Sheep Best Bitter; Tetley Bitter; guest beers Ⓗ
Traditional, small, village free house that actively supports the micro-breweries of Huddersfield and the surrounding area. The pub is open-plan, with areas for all the usual pub games, including a side room with a pool table. Entertainment ranges from quiz nights to very lively Karaoke eves. Small patio is very popular in summer, as it offers a pleasant view overlooking the Holme Valley. Situated on a very good bus route, just 100 yards from the stop. ❀⇌♣

BIRSTALL

Black Bull
5 Kirkgate (off A652/A643)
☼ 12-11; 12-3.30; 7-10.30 Sun
☎ (01274) 873039
Boddingtons Bitter; Whitbread Trophy; guest beer Ⓗ
Dating from the 17th century, this lively inn has played an important part in the history of the district. St. Peter's church opposite stands at the centre of a large parish, so parishioners came some distance to worship or marry and the inn became the natural place for other functions such as auctions, local elections and as the local

magistrates' court (the last trial was held in 1839). The courtroom upstairs retains the wall panelling, magistrate's box and prisoner's dock. Eve meals served Tue-Sat; book at weekends. ◑ ▶P

BRADFORD ☀

Castle Hotel
20 Grattan Road (off Westgate)
☼ 11.30-11; closed Sun
☎ (01274) 393166
website: www.thecastlehotel.britain-uk.com
Fuller's ESB; Mansfield Riding Bitter, Bitter; guest beers Ⓗ
Imposing stone pub, circa 1898, boasts castellated battlements, enhanced by recent sandblasting. Formerly a Webster's house it now sells a variety of beers, in a relaxing atmosphere, to shoppers and regulars, in an open-plan interior with a quiet drinking area. Good central accommodation for business visitors. It is close to a busy shopping area and the Colour Museum, established by Bradford Dyers Association. Ever-changing guest beers, with Lloyds a regular; local breweries are represented by Goose Eye and Bradford's newest brewery, Salamander. ⇑⇌ (Interchange/Forster Sq)

Cock & Bottle ☆
93 Barkerend Road (A650, inner ring/Otley rd jct)
☼ 12-4, 7-11; 12-4, 8-10.30 Sun
☎ (01274) 738446
Taylor Landlord; Tetley Bitter; guest beer Ⓗ
A minor revolution has occurred in this former 19th-century brewhouse, returning it to its Victorian heritage and also to the local community. Grade II listed, and on CAMRA's National Inventory of pubs of outstanding historic interest, the lounge, tap room and two snugs feature original woodwork, windows, mirrors and bar. Run on Christian values by a dedicated team, it offers good refreshment and a listening ear for those who need it. The guest beers mainly come from Yorkshire micros. No food Sun. ◑⇌ (Forster Sq/Interchange) ♣P⌿

Corn Dolly
110 Bolton Road
☼ 11.30-11; 12-10.30 Sun
☎ (01274) 720219
Black Sheep Best Bitter; Everards Tiger; Taylor Landlord; guest beers Ⓗ
Opened in 1834 as the Wharfe Hotel, by Bradford's canal, Warwick & Co's ales from Boroughbridge flowed on tap from the 1890s, until they fell to John Smith's. The 1980s saw the house become free, with a name change and country-style decoration. Though now open plan, there are distinct lounge and games areas. Popular with Bradford City supporters on match days, occasionally the juke box can be loud. Guest beers are usually available, plus a house ale from Moorhouses. 2001 Bradford CAMRA *Pub of the Year*.
⇑❀⇌ (Forster Sq/Interchange) ♣P

Fighting Cock
21-23 Preston Street
☼ 11.30-11; 12-10.30 Sun
☎ (01274) 726907
Black Sheep Special; Greene King Abbot; Old Mill Bitter; Taylor Golden Best, Landlord; Thwaites Mild; guest beers Ⓗ

Drinkers' oasis in an industrial neighbourhood, 15 minutes' walk from the city centre. This is a popular, unpretentious pub that attracts a mixed clientele. The juke box with nothing post 1990 gives the feeling of a place stuck in time. Always 12 ales, plus real cider, Belgian bottled beers and fruit wines are stocked. The pub divides into three areas, so, although it can be a crush at the bar, it is possible to avoid this and the TV. Legendary dockers' wedge sandwiches and hot lunches are served weekdays. ⚲ ◖ ♣ ♠ ●

Goldsborough
118 Bolton Road
✪ 11.30-11; 12-10.30 Sun
☎ (01274) 740138
e-mail: commer.goldsborough@virgin.net
Old Mill Bitter; Taylor Landlord; Tetley Bitter; guest beers Ⓗ

Pleasant single-roomed pub in a relatively quiet area, but not far from centre and transport links. The L-shaped room divides the pub conveniently in two and provides distractions such as evocative rock music posters and a large old map of the city's pubs and ale houses. The floor is plain wood but many sofas ensure a comfortable stay. A strong Bradford City connection boosts trade at times, and the big screen TV is used for sporting events. No food Sun (in winter opening may be nearer 1pm). Good wine list. ⊛◖⇌ (Forster Sq/Interchange) ♣ P

Haigy's
31 Lumb Lane
✪ 5 (12 Fri & Sat)-1am; closed Sun
☎ (01274) 731644
Black Sheep Best Bitter; Greene King Abbot; Tetley Bitter; guest beers Ⓗ

Welcoming pub, despite its location. Built in an unusual style, note the claret and amber painted stripes, colours of Bradford City FC whose ground is nearby. It was acquired as the Flying Dutchman in 1895 by former local brewer J Hey. Inside a video wall complements the small dance floor, which is in complete contrast to a comfortable lounge and large pool room, divided by a lobby. Busy on match days and late eves. It opens on Sun when the Bradford Bulls Rugby League team play at home. The guest beer comes from Ossett Brewery.
⊛◗⇌ (Forster Sq/Interchange) ♣ P

Melborn Hotel
104 White Abbey Road (B6144)
✪ 12 (4 Wed-Fri, 2 Sat)-11; 12-10.30 Sun
☎ (01274) 726867
Moorhouse's Premier; Tetley Bitter; guest beers Ⓗ

Fine example of 1930s pub design, this former Melbourne Brewery house comes alive through the commitment of the owner/landlord to live music. Stepping into the large traditional tap room or even larger lounge and music room, one gets a distinct Irish feel, reflecting the landlord's roots. Live blues and folk music are performed six nights a week, with the long-established Topic Folk Club every Thu. This genuine free house features a changing range of guest beers from Yorkshire and northern small brewers.
⊛⇔◻⇌ (Forster Sq) P

New Beehive Inn ☆
171 Westgate (B6144)
✪ 12-11; (2am Fri & Sat); closed lunch, 6-10.30 Sun
☎ (01274) 721784 e-mail: newbeehiveinn.amservenett
Kelham Island Bitter; Taylor Landlord; guest beers Ⓗ

Genuine, traditional 1901 Edwardian gaslit inn serving at least three guest beers in a multi-roomed interior with wood panelling and floors. The pool room has walls decked with breweriana, the comfortable 'pink room' with portraits. The front bar boasts 12 handpumps and a collection of Toby jugs. The back bar displays large paintings of pub scenes and opens on to the tidy walled back yard, with an opened-up stable to shelter from summer showers. It hosts a variety of live music in the cellar Wed, Fri and Sat.
⚲⊛⇔◻⇌ (Forster Sq) ♣ ♠ P

Old Bank
69 Market Street (near City Hall)
✪ 11-11; 12-10.30 Sun
☎ (01274) 743680
Boddingtons Bitter; Castle Eden Ale; Marston's Pedigree; Tetley Bitter; Ⓗ **guest beers** Ⓗ/Ⓖ

Barclays Bank conversion, now well established and popular with office workers and shoppers. Recently refurbished, but retaining the two-level layout, the ground floor has a long bar with numerous handpumps and gravity dispense facility. Upstairs contains a small bar, used at busy periods. A number of settees add comfort. The pub stocks a large range of real ales and bottled Belgian beers. Meals are served 12-9 (until 7pm Fri and Sat).
⚲◖⇔ & ⇌ (Interchange/Forster Sq) ✂

Queen Hotel
863 Thornton Road, Fairweather Green (B6145)
✪ 12-11; 12-10.30 Sun
☎ (01274) 542898
e-mail: vodkamartini@theboozer2000.freeserve.co.uk
Beer range varies Ⓗ

This was a smart private house, converted to a pub in the early 1900s, now a two-roomed free house with local stone and slate flooring adding character. This busy local was Bradford CAMRA *Pub of the Year* 1997, under previous ownership, but the present

INDEPENDENT BREWERIES

Anglo Dutch Dewsbury
Barge & Barrel Elland
Boat Allerton Bywater
Briscoe's Otley
Clark's Wakefield
Fernandes Wakefield
Goose Eye Keighley
Halifax Steam Brewing Co. Brighouse
Linfit Linthwaite
Ossett Ossett
Rat & Ratchet Huddersfield
Riverhead Marsden
Ryburn Sowerby Bridge
Salamander Bradford
Sunset Dewsbury
Taylor Keighley
Tigertops Wakefield
Turkey Inn Goose Eye

licensees have kept up the tradition of serving a range of ever-changing guest ales, regulars include Ringwood, Taylors, Goose Eye and Salamander. Pub memorabilia decorate the walls, especially mirrors and pictures. It hosts a quiz Wed and live bands Thu.

🏚️⏣◑▶♣P

Sir Titus Salt

Windsor Baths, Morley Street (by Alhambra Theatre)
🟢 11-11; 12-10.30 Sun
☎ (01274) 732853
Black Sheep Special; Taylor Landlord; Theakston Best Bitter; guest beers Ⓗ

Wetherspoon's conversion from the old Windsor Baths, providing plenty of seating and standing space, with a mezzanine for further seating away from the bar. The single bar stretches along one wall and offers up to six guest beers. Situated in Bradford's lively West End, this pub is excellent for theatre-goers and clubbers. Meals are typical Wetherspoon fare, but keenly priced to attract students from the nearby university.

Q◑▶♿⇌(Interchange)✂●

Steve Biko Bar

D Floor, Richmond Building, University, Richmond Road
🟢 11 (7 Sat)-11; 7-10.30 Sun
☎ (01274) 233257
Courage Directors; John Smith's Bitter; Theakston Cool Cask, XB, Old Peculier; guest beers Ⓗ

Open-plan, with a new longer bar added in a summer refit two years ago, it now offers snacks, coffee and soft drinks. Evening promotions are popular, with cheap prices from 7-11. Four ever-changing guest beers, from independent breweries, are always sold at reasonable prices. Although run by the Students' Union, the bar is open to the general public at all times and draws a good mixed clientele; can be noisy at times.

⇌(Interchange) P

BRIGHOUSE

Red Rooster

123 Elland Road, Brookfoot (A6025)
🟢 5 (4 Fri)-11; 12-11 Sat; 12-10.30 Sun
☎ (01484) 713737

Black Sheep Best Bitter; Moorhouse's Pendle Witches Brew; Rooster's Yankee; guest beers Ⓗ

Small, roadside pub on the inside of a sharp bend on the main road. Although opened out, the former four-room layout is discernible by variation in decor and fittings. Quiz night is Wed and live bands are a monthly feature on summer Sunday afternoons. Popular with real ale drinkers, it stocks six changing guest beers and Saxon Gold Digger cider. Glasses holding two pints are available for the seriously thirsty (or the Cropton drinker).

⏣♣♠P

CALDER GROVE

Navigation

Broad Cut Road (near M1 jct 39)
🟢 12-11; 12-10.30 Sun
☎ (01924) 274361
Barge & Barrel Best Bitter, Nettlethrasher; Tetley Bitter; guest beers (occasional) Ⓗ

Split-level pub; the lower level houses the public bar and a no-smoking family room with soft play adventure playground. On the upper level is the lounge bar (no children allowed), featuring a beamed ceiling and a large coal fire. The garden has picnic tables and an adventure playground for children; the grassed area leads down to the Calder and Hebble Canal with mooring facilities. It is very popular with families, ramblers and boaters. Eve meals available in summer.

🏚️Q🛏️⏣◑♿♣P✂

CARLTON

Rosebud

22 Westfield Road
🟢 5 (11 Fri & Sat)-11;
12-4.30, 7-10.30 Sun
☎ (0113) 282 2236
John Smith's Bitter; guest beer Ⓗ

Two-roomed pub, served from a central bar area: the comfortable lounge has bric-à-brac and banquette seating; the public bar has more basic furnishings, with a dartboard and TV. It hosts occasional live music and a quiz Sun and Thu eves. The guest beer is usually, but not always, from the pub company's approved list.

🏚️⏣⏥♣P

INN BRIEF

Myrtle Grove
141 Main Street
11-11;
12-10.30 Sun
Black Sheep Special; Shepherd Neame Spitfire; Taylor Landlord; Theakston Best Bitter; guest beers Ⓗ
Recent Wetherspoon's conversion, in a former cinema, then supermarket. A popular venue for all ages. *Cask Marque* accredited.

BRADFORD

Shoulder of Mutton
28 Kirkgate
11-11;
12-10.30 Sun
Samuel Smith OBB Ⓗ
Town-centre pub with a large garden. Lunch served Mon-Sat. Comfortable, with several rooms, it is handy for Foster Square Station.

BUTTERSHAW

Barley Mow
536 Halifax Road
11-11;
12-10.30 Sun
Fuller's ESB; Tetley Bitter; guest beer Ⓗ
Popular traditional pub with a regularly changing guest beer and a lively atmosphere, especially in the games room.

Beehive Inn
583 Halifax Road
11-11;
12-10.30 Sun
Ansells Bitter; Tetley Bitter; guest beers Ⓗ
Lively, homely local where children are welcome until 7.30pm. Disco every Fri eve, Karaoke Sat eve and Sun lunch.

CASTLEFORD Ⓗ

Garden House
Wheldon Road
11.30-11; 12-10.30 Sun
John Smith's Bitter; Tetley Bitter; Theakston Best Bitter; guest beers Ⓗ
Friendly, two-roomed pub, very close to Castleford RL ground. Cheap and wholesome pub food served 12-8. Safe children's play area outside.

Glass Blower
15 Bank Street
11-11; 12-10.30 Sun
Shepherd Neame Spitfire; Taylor Landlord; Theakston Best Bitter; Wadworth 6X; guest beers Ⓗ
Typical Wetherspoon's conversion of post office, very keen on real ale from micros and regional breweries. Good value food served all day. *Cask Marque* accredited.

CLECKHEATON

Marsh
28 Bradford Road (A638)
☼ 12-3 (4 Sat; not Wed), 7-11; 12-11 Fri; 12-5, 7-10.30 Sun
☎ (01274) 872104
Old Mill Mild, Bitter, Bullion, seasonal beers Ⓗ

A quiet, triangular-shaped keg Tetley house, with dwindling trade, until Old Mill bought and refurbished it in their house style, with some exposed brickwork decorated with bottles, a dais and a sprinkling of attractive woodwork. Now a lively focal point for the community, with quiz nights (Tue) and games, a friendly welcome is assured. There is a tempting array of country wines. Leave the car at home; you may stay longer than planned, and the bus station is nearby.
❀♣P

DENBY DALE

Dunkirk Inn
231 Barnsley Road (A635, midway between Holmfirth and Barnsley)
☼ 12-3 (not Mon, or winter Tue & Wed), 5.30-11; 12-11 Sat; 12-10.30 Sun
☎ (01484) 862646 website: www.dunkirkinn.co.uk
Black Sheep Best Bitter; John Smith's Bitter; Theakston Cool Cask; Taylor Landlord; Tetley Bitter; guest beers Ⓗ

Country local, commanding extensive views over countryside, converted from three buildings, it now consists of linked areas: a restaurant, lounge, tap room (board games, dominoes, etc) and a games area with a pool table. It serves eight ales, including three guests from the Tapster's Choice range. Frequented by walkers and cycle club members, it stands on the 236 Huddersfield-Barnsley bus route. Well worth a visit, particularly for the home-made traditional meals. ⚏❀◖◗♣P

DEWSBURY ✼

Gate Inn
50 Thornhill Road (B6117, S of A644 jct)
☼ 4 (12 Fri & Sat)-11; 12-10.30 Sun
☎ (01924) 461897
Barnsley Bitter; Tetley Bitter Ⓗ

Three independent rooms offer a choice of atmosphere in this traditional local, in the shadow of a railway bridge and textile mills. The landlord, Roy Ellam, is a former Huddersfield Town and Leeds United star, so it comes as no surprise that the pub fields strong sporting teams. The Huddersfield Town Supporters Club meets monthly in one of the function rooms which have seen more use since other pubs in the area have been opened out, as per the recent trend.
❀⌂♣P

Leggers
Robinsons Boatyard, Savile Town Wharf, Mill Street East
☼ 12-11; 12-10.30 Sun
☎ (01924) 502846
Everards Tiger; guest beers Ⓗ

This first-floor bar, with a very low-beamed ceiling, was once the hayloft of the stables where horses rested after pulling barges along the Calder and Hebble Navigation. It still overlooks a busy canal basin, now with residential moorings and home to the Calder Lady trip boat. The Sunset Cider and Wine Company brews downstairs and two of its beers are on tap, alongside three guests that change daily and a selection of continental beers. Pie and peas and sandwiches are available all day. Local CAMRA *Pub of the Year 2000.*
⚏❀P

West Riding Licensed Refreshment Rooms
Railway Station, Wellington Road (ring road)
☼ 11-11; 12-10.30 Sun
☎ (01924) 459193
Black Sheep Best Bitter; Taylor Landlord; guest beers Ⓗ

Created from part of a Grade II listed station building (1848), it now usually has eight beers on tap, mostly from small breweries including its own Anglo Dutch beers brewed elsewhere in the town. Access is from the station platform or car park. There is regular live music and a charity music festival is held in July. Fresh coffee is always available, as are some bottled Belgian specialities. Railway paintings by local artist, Malcolm East, are on display alongside many railway artefacts. This is a popular stop on the Trans-Pennine Ale Rail route.
⚏❀◖◗ঌ⇌P✂

DEWSBURY

John F Kennedy
2 Webster Hill
8 (7 Fri & Sat)-11;
8-10.30 Sun
Taylor Landlord; guest beers Ⓗ
Quiet pub: a cosy lounge with a real fire, plus a pool room, good juke box. The guest beer is from Glentworth.

HALIFAX

Big Six
10 Horsfall Street, King Cross
5 (11 Fri; 12 Sat)-11;
12-4.30, 7-10.30 Sun
Tetley Bitter; guest beers Ⓗ
Multi-roomed, Victorian local between back-to-back terraces, close to Tesco's at the top end of Savile Park.

Sportsman
Bradford Old Road, Swalesmoor, Ploughcroft
12-2.30, 6-11 (midnight Fri); 12-midnight Sat; 12-10.30 Sun
Marston's Pedigree; Taylor Landlord; Tetley Bitter; Theakston Old Peculier; guest beer (occasional) Ⓗ
Hilltop family leisure centre with a dry ski-slope, karting and adventure playground. Folk club and quiz nights held. No food Mon.

HORBURY

Caldervale Hotel
Millfield Road
12-4, 7-11; 12-3, 7-10.30 Sun
John Smith's Bitter; guest beer (occasional)
Large, three-roomed local, built in 1884 by the original Fernandes Brewery family; a local venue for Coutry and Western music.

IDLE

New Inn
58 High Street
12-11;
12-10.30 Sun
Black Sheep Best Bitter; Taylor Landlord; Tetley Mild, Bitter Ⓗ
At the top of an aptly named street, the pub serves lunchtime food. Big screen TV for Sky Sports.

LEEDS: *CITY*

George
67-69 Great George Street
11-11;
12-10.30 Sun
Tetley Bitter Ⓗ
Small, open-plan pub with a cellar bar used for functions. Popular with hospital workers, it is known as Ward 13.

ECCLESHILL

Royal Oak
39 Stony Lane
✪ 11-11; 12-10.30 Sun
☎ (01274) 639182 e-mail: alanroyaloakbd2@aol
Taylor Landlord; Tetley Mild, Bitter Ⓗ
Popular local with a separate public
bar that was built behind the old inn in
1976 when the rest of the building was
modernised. The landlord has been
Vanguard Cellarman of the Year twice in
recent times. It stages regular promotions
and the beer quizzes are popular (Tue and
Fri eves). The tap room has darts and
dominoes, but no pool table.
⌘⌂♣P

ELLAND

Barge & Barrel
10-20 Park Road (A6025)
✪ 12-11; 12-10.30 Sun
☎ (01422) 373623
**Barge & Barrel Best Bitter, Nettlethrasher, Black
Stump, Leveller; guest beers** Ⓗ
Large canalside pub with a central
horseshoe-shaped bar; most of the interior
walls have been removed but some have
been replaced by glazed screens. The decor
features Victoriana and breweriana.
It hosts a quiz night (Mon) and is the
meeting place for the Canal Society and
ramblers. John Eastwood's brewery is
located in the former children's room. Two
regular and three changing guest beers are
available, together with Saxon cider or
perry.
⌘⌘⌂♣▲♣♠P♠♠

GARFORTH

Gaping Goose
41 Selby Road (A63, 200 yds E of A642 jct)
✪ 11.30-11; 12-10.30 Sun
☎ (0113) 286 2127
Tetley Mild, Bitter Ⓗ
Old roadside pub in the former
mining town of Garforth. Renowned
for its beers, it is a welcome outlet for mild,
and survives, indeed thrives, as a drinkers'
pub rather than by extraneous activities
such as food or entertainment. It
comprises a single saloon, with two
adjacent rooms – a basic tap room and the
more opulent Tudor Room. A popular

meeting place for many groups, it has its
own golfing society and holds a quiz night
(Tue).
Q⌘♣P

GILDERSOME

New Inn
Church Street
✪ 12-3.30, 5.30-11; 11-11 Fri & Sat; 12-10.30 Sun
☎ (0113) 253 4821
Samuel Smith OBB Ⓗ
Recent refurbishment has not altered the
classic 1930s Art Deco feel of this pub,
indeed in some respects it has augmented it.
A mature locals' pub, its four rooms are
served from two central bars. The plainer
tap room has its own entrance and contains
the TV and dartboard. On the lounge side, a
small drinking area, with a parquet floor,
gives way to two comfortable rooms – the
front has an intimate feel while the rear
looks out over the garden and children's
play area. No food Tue. ⌘⌂♣P

GLASSHOUGHTON

George V WMC
Holliwell House, 124 Front Street
(A639/B6136 jct, near Freeport Designer Outlet)
✪ 11-11; 12-10.30 Sun
☎ (01997) 552775
John Smith's Bitter; Tetley Bitter; guest beer Ⓗ
CAMRA members showing their card can be
signed in at this popular working men's
club which has a large concert room and a
bar lounge. The board placed at the busy
junction attracts attention to the changing
guest beers, and thereby, the real ale cause.
Frequently these are from the nearby Boat
Brewery. There are events most nights, with
live entertainment Fri and Sat. At the rear is
a large, secure children's play area.
⌘⌂P

GREETLAND

Druids
2-4 Spring Lane off Rochdale Road (B6113)
✪ 5 (12 Sat)-11; 12-10.30 Sun
☎ (01422) 372465
**Taylor Golden Best, Best Bitter, Landlord; guest
beers** Ⓗ
Popular village free house, known to the
locals as the Rat. Speak to the regulars to
hear the many tales of how the pub

INN BRIEF

Palace
Kirkgate
11-11; 12-10.30 Sun
**Draught Bass; Ind Coope Burton Ale;
Tetley Bitter; guest beers** Ⓗ
Ex-Festival Ale House, serving up to
seven, frequently changing, guest
ales. Lunches daily, eve meals
weekdays. *Cask Marque* accredited.

Scarbrough Hotel
Bishopgate Street
11.30-11; closed Sun
**Black Sheep Best Bitter; Taylor Landlord;
Tetley Bitter; guest beers** Ⓗ
Ex-Festival Ale House, by the
station, serving up to eight guest
beers plus a cider and occasional
perry.

Victoria Family &
Commercial Hotel
28 Great George Street
11-11 12-10.30 Sun
**Black Sheep Best Bitter; Tetley Bitter;
guest beers** Ⓗ
Restored to its former glory in
1997, it bills itself as a traditional
oasis among the new bars of Leeds.

LEEDS: *NORTH*
Woodies
104 Otley Road, Headingley
11-11; 12-10.30 Sun
**Black Sheep Best Bitter, Special;
Boddingtons Bitter; Taylor Landlord; Tetley
Bitter; guest beer** Ⓗ
Large, mock-Tudor pub with a
single U-shaped room, drawing a
mix of locals and students. Meals
include vegetarian options.

MYTHOLMROYD
Shoulder of Mutton
38 New Road
11-3, 7-11; 11-11 Sat; 12-10.30 Sun
**Black Sheep Best Bitter; Boddingtons
Bitter; Castle Eden Ale; Flowers IPA;
Marston's Pedigree; Taylor Landlord** Ⓗ
Long bar, facing two rooms, one
extending along the frontage. No
food Sun eve or Mon.

NETHERTON
Beaumont Arms
396 Meltham Road (nr. Huddersfield)
12-2, 4-11; 2.30-11 Sat; 12-10.30 Sun
**Boddingtons Bitter; Tetley Mild, Bitter;
guest beer** Ⓗ
Traditional village pub with a
garden to the rear. The landlord
has won Tetley *Grandmaster of Mild*
award. Lunches Mon-Fri.

acquired its nickname. In winter, the bar is heated by two open fires, while in summer an outdoor drinking area offers impressive views. The pub serves three ever-changing guest beers, concentrating on small independent brewers. Local CAMRA *Pub of the Season* award winter 2000/01. 🏚🏮♣P

GUISELEY

Ings

Ings Lane (½ mile from A65 jct)
🕓 11-11; 12-10.30 Sun
☎ (01943) 873315

John Smith's Bitter; Taylor Landlord; Tetley Bitter Ⓗ
Prominent 1930s public house on the edge of rolling countryside close to Otley Chevin, named after an area of adjacent wetland. The building replaced an earlier hostelry, a photograph of which is on display. A large, well-appointed L-shaped open plan lounge provides comfortable surroundings and a relaxed atmosphere, appealing to the more mature drinker. Weekday lunches served; quiz nights Tue and Thu. 🏚🏮◖♣P

Regent

16 Otley Road
🕓 11-11; 12-10.30 Sun
☎ (01943) 877795

John Smith's Bitter; Tetley Bitter Ⓗ
Victorian roadside local where a long narrow lounge area has been extended into the former stable yard entrance. Old photos of Guiseley, including the pub, adorn the walls. An unpretentious games room is hidden behind the bar, where darts and pool are played; the pub team competes in the local pool league. The lounge gets busy at weekends, with a mixed clientele; a quiz is held Thu and Sun. Convenient for main bus routes. 🏮◖♣♠

HALIFAX ❄

Commercial

23 Lower Skircoat Green
🕓 12-2, 5-11; 12-3, 7-10.30 Sun
☎ (01422) 365078

Tetley Bitter; guest beer Ⓗ
Small, unpretentious free house, enjoying a good local following. A former Whitaker's house, run by the same licensees now for 30 years – they bought the pub from Whitbread and introduced real ale. Originally two rooms, it has been partially opened up, but has retained the 1950s style fireplace. The juke box plays classic pop records selected by the regulars. A small walled garden affords fine views across the Calder Valley. On-street parking is possible at the top of the steep hill where the pub stands. 🏮

Shears Inn

Paris Gates, Boys Lane (behind flats opp. football ground)
🕓 11.45-11; 12-10.30 Sun
☎ (01422) 362936

Taylor Golden Best, Best Bitter, Landlord; Ram Tam; Theakston Best Bitter; guest beer Ⓗ
Overlooked by wooded slopes on one side and overshadowed by the huge Shaw Lodge Mill with its awesome chimney on the other, the tiny Shears Inn has served the local community for several centuries. With its cosy, low-ceilinged interior, it is a popular venue for lunch with its varied menu of good value, hearty, home-cooked food – it gets especially crowded Thu and Fri (no meals Sun). Home of the Kestrels footballers and the Paris Gates cricket team, it is also handy for the Shay football ground. 🏚🏮◖≈♣P

Three Pigeons

South Parade
🕓 12-11; 12-10.30 Sun
☎ (01422) 347001
website: www.threepigeons.demon.co.uk

Barge & Barrel Best Bitter; Black Sheep Best Bitter; Taylor Best Bitter, Landlord; guest beers Ⓗ
An award-winning free house (local CAMRA *Pub of the Year* and Yorkshire runner-up, 2000), this 1930s Art Deco pub offers a friendly welcome, with real fires lit during winter. A few minutes' walk from bus and rail stations, it consists of an octagonal drinking area (note the ceiling mural) with three rooms radiating off, and a private meeting/buffet room to the rear. Home-made food is served weekdays, plus an excellent cheap and cheerful curry night, Mon. Always three guests available, a mild being pretty regular. 🏮◖≈●

West End

216 Parkinson Lane, Highroad Well
🕓 11-30-11; 12-10.30 Sun
☎ (01422) 250559

Boddingtons Bitter; Old Mill Bitter; guest beers Ⓗ
Community local of imposing Gothic appearance; once a flourishing hotel, the bedrooms have been converted into a large function room with a bar, home to many local societies. Enjoy unspoilt conversation without the intrusion of loud music; darts, dominoes and pool are complemented by a rarity for these parts, bar billiards. Two ever-changing guests augment the regular beers. Limited parking. 🏚♿♣P

HAWORTH

Haworth Old Hall

Sun Street (opp. park)
🕓 11-11; 12-10.30 Sun
☎ (01535) 642709
website: www.jenningsbrewery.co.uk

Black Sheep Special; Jennings Bitter, Cocker Hoop, Cumberland Ale, Sneck Lifter; Tetley Bitter Ⓗ
Circa 1612, this former manor house, with mullioned windows and low ceilings, is warm and comfortable. Children are welcome throughout the three rooms; the Tudor Room is no-smoking. Pictures show views of the surrounding area; two rooms have large inglenooks while the bar area is wood panelled with a stone-flagged floor. Toilets, including a wheelchair WC, are in the former stables (indoors). Good quality home-cooked food includes steaks and seasonal specials that change monthly. Meals are served all day Sat and Sun (12-9). 🏚♿🏮◖♿Å≈(K & WV LR) P✂

HEBDEN BRIDGE

Fox & Goose

9 Heptonstall Road (A646 jct)
🕓 11.30-3, 7-11; 12-3, 7-10.30 Sun
☎ (01422) 842649
e-mail: maureen.aris@btinternet.com

Daleside Blonde; guest beers 🄷
Traditional, sociable pub, free from juke box or bandits, where conversation comes second only to the appreciation of the ever-changing ales from independent breweries. Recorded as the Fox & Goose since at least 1777, its three rooms include a pool table, small bar and huge pump clip collection. Twelve consecutive years in this *Guide*, Czech and German bottled beers and over 30 malt whiskies are also stocked. Parking is difficult, but this pub is a mecca for ale lovers.
Q❀⇌♣▯

Hare & Hounds

Billy Lane, Chiserley, Old Town (off A6033 at Pecket Well, 1 mile) OS005280
7(12 Sat)-11; 12-10.30 Sun
☎ (01422) 842671
website: www.hare.and.hounds.connectfree.co.uk
Taylor Golden Best, Best Bitter, Landlord 🄷
Perched on a hillside giving superb views of the Calder Valley, this stone pub, known locally as the Lane Ends, shows farmhouse origins. The bar is flanked by two lounge areas, one with a traditional stone fireplace, a surther seating area looks out on to a patio, popular in summer. There is also a cosy pool room. This Taylor's house serves good value food, Sat and Sun lunch, plus Tue-Sun eves. The Calderdale Way, the pretty village of Wadsworth and the Pennine Way long distance footpath are all close by. ❀⇆◐♣P

Stubbing Wharf

King Street (A646)
12-11; 12-10.30 Sun
☎ (01422) 844107
Boddingtons Bitter; Flowers Original; Greene King IPA; Taylor Landlord; guest beers 🄷
Sandwiched between river and canal, this spacious pub offers four guest ales, a cloudy cider on handpump and good home-made food. The picturesque towpath, with boat moorings and canalside seating, is popular with walkers and forms part of the valley cycle route. The large car park once housed a cattle market – note the iron tethering rails. Regular events include local motorcycle club meetings, story tellings and Indian buffets. The original rooms have been knocked through, but distinct seating areas remain. ⛼Q❀◐◑♣●P

White Lion

Bridge Gate (A6033)
11-11; 12-3, 7-10.30 Sun
☎ (01422) 842197
website: www.whitelionhotelhb.co.uk
Boddingtons Bitter; Castle Eden Ale; Flowers Original; Taylor Landlord; guest beers 🄷
This 1657 coaching inn is family run, with a relaxed atmosphere in historic surroundings. The Grade II listed, town-centre building has been extensively refurbished, uncovering many original features. Of the two guest ales, one is usually from a small independent. It is known for good food served informally in the bar areas. There are two good-sized no-smoking areas and accommodation, with full English breakfast, is available in ten en-suite bedrooms. The garden overlooks the river. ⛼❀⇆◐♿⇌P⚟

HECKMONDWIKE

Old Hall

New North Road
11.30-11; 12-10.30 Sun
☎ (01924) 404774
Samuel Smith OBB 🄷
Built in 1472 as a timber structure, with stone walls added in the 16th century, this Grade I listed building is one of only four remaining aisled manor houses in the county. Many original timbers may still be seen, including the Queen's trusses in the upstairs gallery. This part of the building once housed the Black Cow Inn, evidenced by the sculpture built into the wall. In the reputedly haunted main hall, with 16th-century royalist acorn ceiling, portraits of Tudor royalty adorn the walls; the

INN BRIEF

OTLEY

Whitakers
47 Kirkgate
11.30 (11 Fri & Sat)-11; 12-10.30 Sun
Black Sheep Best Bitter; Tetley Bitter; guest beer 🄷
Refurbished, late 18th-century town-centre pub. The house beer is from Goose Eye.

PUDSEY

Butchers Arms
30 Church Lane
11-11; 12-10.30 Sun
Samuel Smith OBB 🄷
Chunky, stone pub on the main road close to Pudsey Park. Warm and welcoming in winter; popular for its outside tables in summer.

SCHOLES

Boot & Shoe Inn
St George's Road (nr. Holmfirth)
12 (7 Tue)-11; 12-11 Sun
Taylor Best Bitter, Landlord; Tetley Bitter; guest beer 🄷
Traditional, friendly local, in the same family for 31 years, warmed by a roaring fire in winter. Snacks available.

SOUTHOWRAM

Shoulder of Mutton
14 Cain Lane
12 (2.30 Wed)-11; 12-11 Sun
Greene King Ruddles Best Bitter, Abbot; guest beer 🄷
Stone-built pub, dating from the 1790s serving the community, with local history presentations, themed eves and charity quizzes.

WAKEFIELD

Moon under Water
2 Batley Road, Alverthorpe
11-11; 12-10.30 Sun
Black Sheep Special; Theakston Best Bitter; guest beers 🄷
Large, one-room Wetherspoon's estate pub, with one central bar. Half of pub is no-smoking. Good choice of food available every day, 11-10. *Cask Marque* accredited.

Six Chimneys
41-43 Kirkgate
11-11; 12-10.30 Sun
Boddingtons Bitter; Taylor Landlord; Tetley Bitter; Theakston Best Bitter; guest beers 🄷
City-centre pub with a large no-smoking area (no children allowed), free from music and fruit machines. Six guest beers; curry night Thu. *Cask Marque* accredited.

WALSDEN

Cross Keys
649 Rochdale Road
12-11; 12-10.30 Sun
Black Sheep Best Bitter; Taylor Landlord; Theakston Mild; Wells Bombardier; guest beers 🄷
The bar faces in turn a lounge, conservatory, and a small canalside garden. Food is served 12-2, 4-8.

discoverer of oxygen, Joseph Priestley, once made his home here. Sun meals are served 12-5. ⌂◑♣P⚲

HEMSWORTH

Melbourne Arms
140 Barnsley Road
✆ 5.30 (12.30 Fri & Sat)-11; 12-4, 7-10.30 Sun
☎ (01977) 617235
John Smith's Bitter; Tetley Bitter; Ⓗ
Former Melbourne Brewery house on the south-western outskirts of the town, it is comfortably furnished with settees and easy chairs as well as ordinary tables and chairs. It is an outpost of real ale in the area, a fact which is proudly announced as you enter. Good range of food is served Tue-Sat eves and Sun lunches. ⌂⊛⛺◑P

HIPPERHOLME

Brown Horse
Denholme Gate Road, Coley (A644)
✆ 11-11; 12-3, 7-10.30 Sun
☎ (01422) 202112
Boddingtons Bitter; Taylor Landlord; Webster's Yorkshire Bitter; guest beer Ⓗ
The pub affords impressive views down the valley; inside two distinct areas surround a semi-circular bar while an adjoining room leads to a conservatory and garden. The walls and ceilings are covered with collectables: water jugs grace the bar area and smokers' pipes and golf memorabilia decorate other rooms. The pub prides itself on serving good food (daily at lunchtime, and early eve Mon-Fri). The guest beers are from small independent breweries. ⊛◑P⚲

HOLMFIRTH

Rose & Crown (Nook)
7 Victoria Square
✆ 11.30-11; 12-10.30 Sun
☎ (01484) 683960
Samuel Smith OBB; Taylor Best Bitter, Landlord; Tetley Bitter; Theakston Best Bitter; guest beer Ⓗ
Sound, traditional local in every way, this family-owned free house has a phenomenal record in the *Guide*, appearing every year since 1976. Several cosy rooms adjoin the main bar. Occasional live music may be heard, and the local folk group meets here monthly. Typically eight beers are available including a mild, either Tetley or Moorhouses Black Cat. ⌂⛺♣

HORBURY ✲

Boon's
6 Queen Street (1½ miles from M1 jct 40)
✆ 11-3, 5-11; 11-11 Fri & Sat; 12-10.30 Sun
☎ (01924) 280442
Clark's Traditional; John Smith's Bitter; Taylor Landlord; Tetley Bitter; guest beers Ⓗ
Just off the High Street, this pub was for many years a keg-only outlet, until bought by Clark's Brewery around six years ago, who renamed it. Sympathetically refurbished in traditional style, Clark's added a central bar and a real fire, however their most important innovation was the introduction of cask ale. ⌂⊛◐♣

Cherry Tree
Church Street

✆ 3 (7 Tue)-11; 12-10.30 Sun
☎ (01924) 274875
Black Sheep Best Bitter; John Smith's Bitter; Tetley Bitter; guest beer Ⓗ
Cosy local, consisting of a tap room, lounge and downstairs games room, situated opposite Horbury's historic parish church. There are plans to introduce live music eves. ⛺⊛⛩♣P

HUDDERSFIELD

County Hotel
4 Princess Street
✆ 11-11; 7-10.30 Sun
☎ (01484) 300494
John Smith's Bitter; Wells Bombardier; guest beers Ⓗ
Deceptively large pub with a narrow façade, hidden behind the Town Hall, a refuge from the hustle and bustle of town-centre life and the trauma of shopping, offering good, traditional food. Three well-appointed areas, served by a central bar, are popular with all, particularly shoppers and music students who come to play pool and occasionally entertain. Guest beers are sourced from the Unique Pub Company approved list. A happy hours policy operates. ⊛◑⇌⚲

Fieldhead
219 Quarmby Road, Quarmby
✆ 4 (12 Fri & Sat)-11; 12-10.30 Sun
☎ (01484) 654581 e-mail: russrogue@aol.com
Stones Bitter; guest beer Ⓗ
In a suburban housing estate, this remarkably prominent building is unmistakable from any angle. To the front, an imposing stone façade dominates; at the back there are good views across to the Colne Valley. Smart, comfortable, and well-furnished, an unusual horseshoe-shaped bar is the most obvious feature. There is a lounge and pool room, and a former tap room is now used for games. Regular live entertainment is staged Tue and Fri eves. ⊛♣P

Marsh Liberal Club
Glenfield, 31 New Hey Road, Marsh (A640)
✆ 12-2, 7-11; 12-11 Sat; 12-10.30 Sun
☎ (01484) 420152
Taylor Golden Best, Dark Mild, Best Bitter; Theakston Best Bitter; guest beers Ⓗ
Imposing Grade II listed building, that has undergone sympathetic alterations. Three guest beers are on offer, often from Glentworth or Phoenix. As well as the bar area, there is a lounge, a new no-smoking family room (children welcome until 9pm), snooker room and an upstairs function room. A wheelchair WC and access are provided. At the rear is a bowling green, where you can sit and watch games in summer. Show this *Guide* or a CAMRA membership card to be signed in. ⛺⊛♣P⚲

Rat & Ratchet
40 Chapel Hill (A616, below ring road)
✆ 12 (3.30 Mon & Tue)-11; 12-10.30 Sun
☎ (01484) 516734 website: www.ratandratchet.co.uk
Greene King Abbot; Taylor Dark Mild, Landlord, Ram Tam Ⓗ
Popular with local drinkers and students, this highly-regarded brew-pub has featured in this *Guide* for over 10 years. Usually one beer brewed on the premises is available, as

well as up to 13 guests – the largest selection of real ale in Huddersfield – and it is a rare outlet for Pictish Ales. A collection of memorabilia and an interesting juke box add to its appeal. Served from one bar, the split-level interior provides several seating areas. Lunches served Wed-Sat; Wed eve is curry night.
❀◖≈♣P

Sygenta Sports & Leisure Club
509 Leeds Road (A62)
❂ 11.30-11; 11.30-10.30 Sun
☎ (01484) 421784 e-mail:trevort@linone-net
Taylor Best Bitter; Tetley Bitter; guest beer Ⓗ
Formerly known as the Zeneca Recreation Club, this CAMRA award-winning club, set back off the main road, is well worth the short trip from the town centre (on the Leeds bus route). It has a spacious bar, a large, no-smoking area, a snooker hall, and a patio for outside drinking. Excellent value food is served at lunchtimes. The guest beers come from independent breweries. Even when the club is busy, you can find a quiet corner. Show this *Guide* or CAMRA membership card to gain entry. ❀◖♣P⊭

IDLE ❊

Albion Inn
25 New Line, Greengates (A657)
❂ 12-11; 12-4, 7-10.30 Sun
☎ (01274) 613211
Taylor Landlord; Tetley Mild, Bitter Ⓗ
Popular local on the main Leeds-Keighley road, a former Whitaker's house until 1919, its L-shaped lounge is adorned with photos of old Bradford. The small tap room is just large enough for a game of darts. The landlord is very keen to promote real ale and may try to introduce guest beers and real cider. ◖♣

Idle Working Men's Club
23 High Street
❂ 12-3 (4 Fri & Sat), 7.30 (7 Fri & Sat)-11; 12-3, 7-10.30 Sun
☎ (01274) 613602 website: idleworkingmensclub.com
Tetley Mild, Bitter; guest beers Ⓗ
Popular working men's club that attracts members because of its name! Souvenir merchandise is available to buy. The club comprises a concert room, lounge and games room. The concert room hosts live entertainment Sat and Sun eves and bingo (Thu). The lounge offers a quieter alternative. The downstairs games room has two full-sized snooker tables, plus big screen TV; a different guest beer is usually available here. Parking is difficult. Show this *Guide* or CAMRA membership to be signed in. ♣

ILKLEY

Bar T'at
7 Cunliffe Road
❂ 12-11; 12-10.30 Sun
☎ (01943) 608888
website: www.markettowntaverns.co.uk
Black Sheep Best Bitter; Caledonian Deuchars IPA; Taylor Landlord; guest beers Ⓗ
Popular, two-level bar converted from a china shop in 1999, in a central location behind Betty's Tea Rooms, near a large Pay and Display car park. A wide range of bottled and draught continental beers

complement the six real ales; the guest beers usually promote small Yorkshire breweries, such as Daleside, Ossett and Rooster's, and a stout is often available. The bar is decorated with brewery memorabilia. Newspapers are available and dogs are welcome. No eve meals Tue or Sun.
Q❀◖▷≈⊭

Riverside Hotel
Riverside Gardens, Bridge Lane
❂ 11-11; 12-10.30 Sun
☎ (01943) 607338
Samuel Smith OBB; Tetley Bitter; Thwaites Bitter Ⓗ
Smart hotel in a parkland setting, with a popular riverside patio. The two roomed bar is comfortable and welcoming to families; there is also an outdoor play area. The hotel has a fish and chip shop attached, with additional ice cream sales although opening is limited in winter months. An ideal halt for local walks, it opens daily at 10am for tea and coffee; eve meals finish at 6pm winter. ⊭❀⊨◖▷≈P

KEIGHLEY

Boltmakers Arms
117 East Parade
❂ 11-11; 12-10.30 Sun
☎ (01535) 661936
Taylor Golden Best, Best Bitter, Landlord Ⓗ
Small, one-roomed, very popular local on two levels, it features pictures of Victorian pub interiors and from brewing and distilling processes. As there is little space, games are limited, but the pub fields a football team in the local league. The TV in the back area shows major sporting events, while the open fire in the front is cosy on cold winter eves. Over 50 malt whiskies are stocked, usually one at a reduced price. Sandwiches available. ⊭≈♣

Cricketers Arms
23 Coney Lane
❂ 11.30-11; 12-10.30 Sun
☎ (01535) 669912
Moorhouse's Black Cat, Premier; Taylor Golden Best; guest beers Ⓗ
Originally three cottages, built in 1828, this compact, friendly, single-room free house was imaginatively refurbished by the former Worth Brewery in 1999. The walls have been taken back to the original stone, brass ship's port-holes adorn the doors and the part-carpeted, part-polished floor interior features tram-style seating complete with luggage racks. Note the Worth Brewery windows and Len Hutton on the pub sign. The two guest beers come mostly from local micros and often include a beer from Rooster's or Durham.
&≈♣

Friendly
2 Aireworth Street
❂ 12-11; 12-5, 7-11 Sat; 12-10.30 Sun
☎ (01535) 672136
Taylor Golden Best, Best Bitter Ⓟ
Friendly by name, friendly by nature, this two-roomed local is one of Keighley's several small terraced pubs. No theme needed here, just good Yorkshire hospitality – if this pub did not exist, it would probably not be built today. A bright,

relaxed place with 1960s background music, this Taylor's tied house serves the beers in oversized glasses. The view from the upstairs ladies is awesome, owing to the steep stairs. ⊓

Globe Inn
2 Parkwood Street
✪ 11.30-11; 12-10.30 Sun
☎ (01535) 610802
Taylor Golden Best, Dark Mild (winter)**; Best Bitter, Landlord** Ⓗ
Genuine community pub, comfortably furnished, friendly and catering for all tastes in three open rooms and a bar area. It is home to a local sub aqua club, swimming club and pigeon club. The Keighley and North Valley steam railway passes close to the lounge bar window. Weekly entertainment includes a quiz, Karaoke and bingo; eve meals can be booked.
ऄQ◑Ġ☞♣P

KEIGHLEY TO OXENHOPE AND BACK

Keighley & Worth Valley Railway Buffet Car
Stations at Keighley, Ingrow West, Oakworth, Haworth & Oxenhope
✪ Sat, Sun & Bank Hols, March-Oct; Dec 26th-Jan 1st
☎ (01535) 645214 talking timetable (01535) 647777
website: www.kwvr.co.uk
Beer range varies Ⓗ
Steam railway buffet car giving changing views of the Worth Valley. The line has been run by volunteers for over 30 years – far longer than it was run by British Rail. The railway, and particularly Oakworth station, were used as the location for the original film version of *The Railway Children*. The round trip, Keighley-Oxenhope and return, takes about 90 minutes, or passengers can buy a Day Rover and spend all day on the train. It usually sells two beers from independent breweries.
Q▲⧴(Keighley)⊬⊓

LEEDS: CITY ❄

City of Mabgate
45 Mabgate
✪ 11-11; 12-3, 7-10.30 Sun
☎ (0113) 245 7789
Adnams Bitter; Boddingtons Bitter; Taylor Landlord; Whitbread Trophy; guest beers Ⓗ
Regular award-winner for the quality of its ales, including up to four guest beers, the pub recently secured its future with a long-term tenancy agreement, after the previous pub company went into receivership. The superb glazed tiles outside invite you into a two-roomed hostelry that has a comfortable, busy lounge and a rear smoke room where the landlord watches live Rugby League games – woe betide anyone who disturbs him! See, too, the collection of Leeds RLFC Rhino models. Weekday lunches served. ❀◑Ġ♣

Prince of Wales
Mill Hill
✪ 11-11; 12-10.30 Sun
☎ (0113) 245 2434
Barnsley Bitter; Black Sheep Best Bitter; John Smith's Bitter; guest beers Ⓗ
Bustling, traditional pub in the shadow of Leeds station, local CAMRA summer *Pub of*

the Season 2000. An eclectic mix of artefacts adorn the lounge with its four banqueting tables. The games room, designed by Andy Gibney, defies description – it is unique! The two guest beers usually include a Barnsley seasonal brew; it is the only regular Leeds outlet for Barnsley Brewery, and has a 'Happy Hour' for Barnsley Bitter Mon-Thu 2-6pm. ❀◑Ġ⧴♣

Whip Inn
Bowers Yard (alleyway off Duncan St)
✪ 11-11; 12-3, 8-10.30 Sun
☎ (0113) 242 7246
Tetley Mild, Bitter Ⓗ
Classic, award-winning city-centre boozer, this uncompromising drinking establishment is Leeds' oldest traditional courtyard pub. Wooden-floored throughout, the drinking area is on two levels with the bar in the centre. There is a small outdoor yard at the back. Featuring a collection of Tetley memorabilia, it is popular with the staff of the nearby brewery, and is one of the few outlets in Leeds to stock the light version of Tetley Mild. It can be very busy when major sporting events are shown on the big screen TV. ❀♣♠

LEEDS: NORTH ❄

Black Horse
58 Mabgate
✪ 11-11; 12-10.30 Sun
☎ (0113) 242 5177
Tetley Dark Mild, Bitter Ⓗ
Back-street local, popular with a varied clientele, this converted one-roomed bar boasts an authentic 1950s decor, giving the impression of a time when life was simpler, the pubs were peoples' homes and beer was all one needed for contentment. Certificates for its many fund-raising activities for cancer research, etc are displayed. Disco and Karaoke nights are regular events, as are 'Happy Hours' Mon, Tue and Thu (4-8pm) and Wed (4-11). ♣

Eldon
190 Woodhouse Lane
✪ 11-11; 12-10.30 Sun
☎ (0113) 245 3387
Black Sheep Best Bitter; Marston's Pedigree; Tetley Dark Mild; guest beers Ⓗ
Former Tetley Festival Ale House, rebadged as a Festival Inn, popular with staff and students from the university (and proof that students will drink real ale when on offer). Formerly a multi-roomed corner local, refurbishment saw the removal of the internal walls and expansion into an adjoining shop (now the raised area at one end). The decor is bare boards and bric-à-brac. Internet access is available. One of the guest beers is usually a mild and there are often two ciders during term time.
◑Ġ♣♠●

Fenton
161 Woodhouse Lane
✪ 11-11; 12-10.30 Sun
☎ (0113) 245 3908
Black Sheep Best Bitter; Brains SA; Marston's Pedigree; Tetley Bitter; guest beer Ⓗ
Typical ex-Tetley pub that lost its multi-room layout in a 1980s refurbishment.

Popular with university staff and students, it is busy at lunch times and reputedly has the best juke box in Leeds. The central bar serves one large room and a side games room with a pool table. The original public bar survives (but no longer separate) and the former lounge area still has the old bell pushes (not connected). A music venue is upstairs. The only regular outlet for Brains SA in Leeds. Eve meals end at 6pm. ◖▮

New Roscoe
Bristol Street
☼ 11.30-11; 11.30-midnight Thu-Sat; 12-10.30 Sun
☎ (0113) 246 0778
Tetley Bitter; guest beers Ⓗ
Formerly a club, then an Indian restaurant, transformed in 1988 into a three-roomed modern pub in the style of the late lamented Old Roscoe – demolished for the Sheepscar interchange. *Farewell and Hail*, written by CAMRA's Barrie Pepper, chronicles the history of both houses. The large concert room gets very busy with live bands; the back room is quieter and more comfortable. The lively front bar opens up on to a games area with three pool tables. Up to seven guest beers may be on sale. Weekday lunches are all under £2.
❀◖P

LEEDS: SOUTH

Blooming Rose
19 Burton Row, Hunslet Moor
☼ 11-11; 12-10.30 Sun
☎ (0113) 270 0426
Black Sheep Best Bitter; Tetley Bitter; guest beer Ⓗ
Popular with locals and office/factory workers alike, the pub overlooks Hunslet Moor and provides a quiet haven away from the M621. A vibrant tap room, with pool room off, is home to local football and Rugby League teams. The cosy, split-level lounge incorporates a no-smoking area. Good value food is served weekdays. The guest beer is usually from a large regional brewer. ❀◖▣♣P⚡

Garden Gate ☆
3 Whitfield Place, Hunslet (pedestrian precinct)
☼ 12-11; 12-10.30 Sun
☎ (0113) 270 0379
Tetley Bitter Ⓗ
Magnificent drinking establishment, it has been a pub since 1833, deriving its name from bygone market gardens. An elaborate façade leads into a long drinking corridor with four rooms off; the tap room is a real gem with its mahogany panelling and tiled bar. A comfortable lounge with hatch access to the bar is at the rear. The pub is predominantly frequented by locals, but all are made welcome. It can be difficult to find, but well worth the effort. ♨▣♣

Grove Inn
Back Row, Holbeck
☼ 12-11; 12-4, 7-11 Sat; 12-10.30 Sun
☎ (0113) 243 9254
e-mail: rachel@thegroveinn.go-legend.net
Adnams Broadside; Courage Directors; John Smith's Magnet; guest beers Ⓗ
Unspoilt hostelry set among modern office blocks; first mentioned in a survey of the City of Leeds in 1850, it was later extended

to include two attached terraced cottages. Between the wars an extension was added that now houses the concert room where bands play and impromptu jam sessions take place (a young Mark Knopfler of Dire Straits fame once played here). There are three other rooms off a traditional West Riding corridor, the tap room, a quiet front room and a side room with pews. Leeds CAMRA winter *Pub of the Season* 2000/2001. ♨❀◖▣≈♣

LEEDS: WEST

Beech Hotel
8 Tong Road, Lower Wortley
☼ 11-11; 12-3, 7-10.30 Sun
☎ (0113) 263 8659
Tetley Bitter Ⓗ
Community local with genuine Irish connections and a friendly atmosphere, the Melbourne Brewery exterior features fine etched windows and a mosaic pub sign. The main bar area has a tiled floor and is decorated with a vast array of brassware, including an extensive collection of blowlamps, many sports trophies and photos of the pub's various sports teams. To the rear of the bar are two further rooms, a basic smoke room and a games room with a pool table. ▣♣

Highland
36 Cavendish Street (down steps to left of Sentinel Towers on Burley Road)
☼ 11.30-11; 12-10.30 Sun
☎ (0113) 242 8592
Tetley Mild, Bitter Ⓗ
Known locally as the Highland Laddie, this wedge-shaped local would have once been at the end of a terrace, but now nestles among commercial buildings and student flats. The narrow main room has a curved wood-panelled bar and attractive leaded stained glass windows. The decor includes old photographs of trams, both horse-drawn and electric. At the wider end of the pub a second area contains a large TV. ♣

Old Vic
17 Whitecote Hill, Bramley (400 yds from A657/B6157 jct)
☼ 4 (2 Fri, 11 Sat)-11; 12-3, 7-10.30 Sun
☎ (0113) 256 1207
Black Sheep Best Bitter; Taylor Landlord; Tetley Bitter; guest beers Ⓗ
Friendly, suburban local, originally a vicarage, hence the name. A comfortable lounge and two large games rooms are served by a central bar. The function room is popular with local clubs; dominoes are a popular past-time and Thu quiz eves can be busy. A changing guest beer is available, plus a house beer from Coach House named after the licensee. Leeds CAMRA *Pub of the Year* 1999/2000. ♨Q❀♣♣P

LEES MOOR

Quarry House Inn
Bingley Road (roundabout junction of A629/A6033)
☼ 12-2.30, 7-11.30; 12-2.30, 7-10.30 Sun
☎ (01535) 642239
Taylor Golden Best, Landlord; Tetley Bitter Ⓗ
Family-run converted farmhouse, set in open countryside, benefitting from extensive views. The bar is a former pulpit,

set in a small cosy area. Twice local CAMRA *Pub of the Season*, it welcomes families at all times; coaches are accommodated by appointment. The restaurant provides a 'global' menu, with excellent soups; mixed grill is a speciality Wed eve. Meals reflect seasonal availability, including game (booking is advisable Sun lunch). ⊛ⓒⅅ ᴕ ▲P

LINTHWAITE

Sair Inn

139 Lane Top (top of Hoyle Ing, off A62)
OS100143
☼ 7 (5 Fri; 12 Sat)-11; 12-10.30 Sun
☎ (01484) 842370
Linfit Mild, Bitter, Cascade, Special, English Guineas Stout, seasonal beers Ⓗ

Noteworthy as CAMRA's national *Pub of the Year* in 1997, this brewpub's origins go back to the 19th century, with local memorabilia much in evidence. Four rooms radiate from the bar area, complete with roaring fires in winter; one room is no-smoking. Up to ten beers are available, often including seasonal specials. A popular meeting-place, a friendly local, a focus for visitors, and those merely curious, this pub's appeal is widespread and legendary. Its distinctive siting on the steep slopes of the Colne Valley adds to its renown. ᴀᴀQ✴⊛♣●⅄

LINTON

Windmill

Main Street (99 bus route Leeds-Wetherby)
☼ 11-3, 5-11; 11-11 Sat & summer; 12-10.30 Sun
☎ (01937) 582209
John Smith's Bitter; Theakston Best Bitter; guest beers Ⓗ

Linton's only pub, the honey-coloured stone building is over 700 years old and was once the village blacksmith's. Reputedly haunted, the pub is on two levels, with sometimes three roaring fires, and comfortable seating. The two guest beers mainly come from Yorkshire craft breweries at this genuine free house. An old pear tree in the car park was planted by a soldier with seed brought back from the Napoleonic Wars. The inn sign, of a windmill that used to stand nearby, also acts as the No. 99 bus stop. The popular Linton Room serves an extensive home-cooked menu. ᴀᴀ⊛ⓒⅅ ᴕP

MARSDEN

Riverhead Brewery Tap

2 Peel Street (off A62)
☼ 5 (4 Thu; 11 Sat)-11; 12-10.30 Sun
☎ (01484) 841270
Riverhead Sparth Mild, Butterley Bitter, Deer Hill Porter, Cupwith Light, March Haigh Special Ⓗ

This brew-pub opened in 1995 after its conversion from a grocery store. The result is a popular and lively pub with a wide-ranging appeal, and an interesting range of beer styles. There's plenty for visitors to enjoy in the surrounding area – the Pennine Way, Standedge Tunnel and Huddersfield Narrow Canal. As well as the permanent beers – named after local landmarks, mainly reservoirs – there are additional brews at Christmas and other times, plus Saxon Ruby cider. The bar serves a single large room. Q⇌●

MYTHOLMROYD ✴

Hinchliffe Arms

Cragg Vale (off B6138)
☼ 12-2.30, 6-11; closed Mon; 12-10.30 Sun
☎ (01422) 883256 website: www.hinchliffearms.com
Greene King Old Speckled Hen; Taylor Landlord; Theakston Best Bitter, Black Bull, Old Peculier Ⓗ

In a narrow valley in attractive countryside, the Hinchliffe is especially popular with hikers and diners. Gold coins were manufactured locally in the 18th century from clippings of coins circulating throughout northern England, hence the large replica Portuguese doubloons on the bar front. The spacious lounge has panelled walls and there is a cosy no-smoking restaurant offering freshly produced food from a varied menu (Sun meals served 12-8). The Calderdale Way passes the door, and the Pennine Way is nearby. ᴀᴀ⊛⇌ⓒⅅ ▲P

OLDFIELD

Grouse Inn

Harehills Lane
☼ 11.30-3, 5.30-11; 11.30-11 Sat; 12-11 Sun
☎ (01535) 643073 website: thegrouseinn.co.uk
Taylor Golden Best, Best Bitter, Landlord Ⓗ

A gem in open countryside where the silence is only disturbed by conversation. One room serves as a tap room/games room with a bar, tiled floor, bare stone walls, and a wood-burning stove. The oak-panelled lounge has a bar, and a display of pictures, some for sale. It offers extensive views across open moorland and the reservoir to 'Wuthering Heights' of Brontë fame. The restaurant with a coffee/smoking lounge off, serves a good, weekly changed menu; meals served all day Sun until 9pm. Children are welcome throughout this quiet, comfortable inn. ᴀᴀQ⊛ⓒⅅ ⊟ᴕ♣P

OSSETT

Brewers Pride

Low Mill Road (off Healey Rd)
☼ 12-3, 5.30-11; 12-11 Fri & Sat; 12-10.30 Sun
☎ (01924) 273865
Ossett Excelsior; Taylor Landlord; guest beers Ⓗ

Popular free house next to Ossett Brewery, offering a choice of eight beers, it is within five minutes' walk of the Calder and Hebble Canal, or can be reached by bus No. 121 from Wakefield. Home-cooked food, including vegetarian dishes, is served Mon-Sat lunch, plus Wed eve. A beer festival is staged late in the year, with over 30 beers on sale. The local folk club meets every Thu. Local CAMRA *Pub of the Season* winner, 1999 and 2000. ᴀᴀQ⊛ⓒ●

OTLEY ✴

Bowling Green

18 Bondgate (near bus station)
☼ 12-4, 7-11; 12-3, 7-10.30 Sun
☎ (01943) 461494
Beer range varies Ⓗ

This fine public house was originally built as the town's courthouse in 1757. It was subsequently used as Assembly Rooms, prior to becoming a pub in 1825. The L-shaped main bar is full of bizarre items – beware the skeleton by the pool table. Beers

from Briscoe's, now brewed in converted outbuildings behind the pub, are always available. No children permitted.
ᴔ❀♣

Junction
44 Bondgate
✪ 11-11; 12-10.30 Sun
☎ (01943) 463233
website: www.otley.com/junction
Black Sheep Best Bitter; Taylor Best Bitter, Landlord; Tetley Bitter; Theakston Old Peculier; guest beer Ⓗ
Vibrant, one-roomed, street-corner beer drinkers' haven with friendly welcoming staff. A central stone fireplace, settles and benches add to the ambience of this fine establishment, close to public car parks and the bus station. Acoustic musicians are welcome Mon; live music is staged Tue. A regular *Guide* entry for well over 20 years, it was Leeds CAMRA *Pub of the Year* 1998/99. Weekday lunches served. ᴔ♣♣

Red Lion
43-45 Kirkgate (near market square)
✪ 11-11; 12-4, 7-10.30 Sun
☎ (01943) 462226
Courage Directors; Greene King Ruddles County; John Smith's Bitter; guest beer Ⓗ
Comfortable, late 19th-century town-centre pub: an open-plan lounge provides three quiet drinking areas, served by a small rear bar. Locals watch TV and play dominoes in the room beyond the bar. The upstairs meeting room plays host to local clubs during the week. The guest beer changes weekly. Q♣♣

PONTEFRACT

Golden Lion
Sessions House Yard (top end of Cornmarket)
✪ 11 (7 Tue)-11; 12-10.30 Sun
☎ (01977) 702915
e-mail: squintymcginty@goldenlion.org.uk
John Smith's Bitter; guest beers Ⓗ
This pub has just been refurbished to a very high standard, and the old sign, a reclining golden lion, is now in the local museum. It is an unusual pub with a central servery, but the public and lounge bars have their own separate entrances. Darts, dominoes and pool are played in the public bar. Live music is staged in the lounge Fri eve; a weekly quiz is held Wed eve. ❀⍾≈(Tanshelf) ♣

Robin Hood
4 Wakefield Road (off A645)
✪ 11.30-3.30 (4.30 Fri & Sat), 7-11; 12-3.30, 7-10.30 Sun
☎ (01977) 702231
John Smith's Bitter; Tetley Bitter; guest beer Ⓗ
Friendly pub overlooking 'Jenkins Folly'; aka the Town End traffic lights, comprising a busy public bar and three other drinking areas, it fields pool, darts and dominoes teams and holds quizzes on Tue and Sun eves. This local CAMRA *Pub of the Year* 1998 holds regular beer festivals.
ᴔ❀⍾≈(Tanshelf/Baghill) ♣

PUDSEY ❉

Worlds End
Booths Yard, Lowtown
✪ 11-11; 12-10.30 Sun
☎ (0113) 255 1634

Theakston Best Bitter, Old Peculier; guest beers Ⓗ
Access is via two yards off the main shopping street: the upstairs Overworld Bar from one, the smaller downstairs Underworld from the other. The pub was constructed in 1983, when Booth's Yard was rebuilt in a style redolent of an earlier era. Downstairs, there are three main drinking areas, stone-flagged, with bare stone walls where live jazz is performed Mon and Folk Sun. The larger upstairs bar is on three levels, bare-boarded and simply decorated and has a gallery for watching the musicians below. Guest beers come mostly from Daleside and other Yorkshire breweries. ❀◑

RAWDON

Emmott Arms
Town Street
✪ 11-11; 12-10.30 Sun
☎ (0113) 250 6036
Samuel Smith OBB Ⓗ
Comfortable pub favoured with good views across Airedale – on a fine summer's day the tables and benches out front prove popular. Inside, the lounge and tap room are decorated in Sam Smith's understated style. The lounge is well appointed; its two large bay windows act as a suntrap. The tap room is more traditional – bare floors and settles – with TV, dartboard, and dominoes. The function room/restaurant upstairs does not serve real ale. Q❀◑⍾P

Princess
Apperley Lane
✪ 11-11; 12-10.30 Sun
☎ (0113) 250 2495
Tetley Mild, Bitter Ⓗ
Cracking little pub, slightly off the beaten track. The views from the car park are worth a second look. Largely unaltered the pub retains a small no-smoking room (during meal times at least) which has the original bell pushes in the walls above comfortable settles. The rest of the pub is largely open plan around the bar. Mon is quiz night and Tue is folk night. The Black Sheep Bitter and Taylor Landlord can be served using cask breathers. Sun meals are served 12-7. ◑P

RIPPONDEN

Butchers Arms
143 Rochdale Road (off A58)
✪ 12-3 (not Mon), 5-11; 11-11 Sat; 11-10.30 Sun
☎ (01422) 823100
Banks's Bitter; Mansfield Bitter; Orkney Red MacGregor; Taylor Landlord; Theakston Best Bitter Ⓗ
Traditional, stone house with mullioned windows; beside a trans-Pennine road affording fine views across the Ryburn Valley to the High Pennines beyond. Much of the original stone flagging has been retained internally, where several rooms are sited at differing levels. The dining room is highest, and there are three comfortably furnished areas, including the bar, descending to the more spartan pool room at the lowest level. Local CAMRA *Summer Pub 2000*. ❀◑P

Old Bridge
Priest Lane (off A58, near B6113 jct)
✪ 12-3, 5.30-11; 12-11 Sat; 12-10.30 Sun

☎ (01422) 822595

Black Sheep Best Bitter; Moorhouse's Premier; Taylor Golden Best, Best Bitter, Landlord Ⓗ

Picturesque free house by the old packhorse bridge. The building itself dates from the 14th century, and is divided into three interconnecting rooms on two levels, heated by open fires. The Pork Pie Appreciation Society holds its meetings and an annual competition at the pub. A guest beer is often available in summer; note that the beer pumps are not always labelled. Eve meals served Mon-Fri.

🏚️Q◖❙P

SCAMMONDEN

Brown Cow

Saddleworth Road, Deanhead (B6114, 2½ miles S of Barkisland)

☀ 12-3 (not Mon-Thu), 7-11; 12-3, 7-10.30 Sun

☎ (01422) 822227 website: browncow@totalise.co.uk

Beer range varies Ⓗ

Located high on the moorland overlooking Scammonden Water, this ex-coaching house is popular with cross-Pennine travellers and cyclist groups. Kevin – the 24th licensee here – has documented the history of the pub, dating back to 1838, under the Blackburn Brewery Company Ltd. The walls are adorned with old firefighting memorabilia and a collection of unusual clocks. There is a main bar and a seating area, plus a restaurant with ample seating and good food (no meals Mon eve). Two permanent beers (usually John Smith's) are complemented by two guests.

🏚️Q⤳❀◖▲P●

SHAW CROSS

Huntsman

Chidswell Lane (near Dewbury, 400 yds from A653/B6128 jct)

☀ 12-3, 5 (5 Fri)-11; 12-3, 7-10.30 Sun

☎ (01924) 275700

Black Sheep Special; Taylor Landlord; guest beer Ⓗ

Originally two 17th-century farm cottages, the pub has recently been extended and has three distinct, but linked, rooms furnished with agricultural and rural memorabilia and a Yorkshire range. Being on the urban fringe, close to a working farm, it offers extensive views to the north towards the rhubarb fields. The house beers are brewed by Highwood. Lunch is served Tue-Sat.

🏚️❀◖P●

SHIPLEY

Fanny's Ale & Cider House

63 Saltaire Road (A657)

☀ 11.30 (5 Mon)-11; 12-10.30 Sun

☎ (01274) 591419 e-mail: fannys@aleslfd.fsat.co.uk

Moorhouse's Premier; Taylor Landlord; guest beers Ⓗ

Formerly a pet shop and a beer shop, before becoming a pub, it has a cosy nostalgic atmosphere enhanced by gaslights, log fires and old brewery memorabilia. It stocks an excellent range of Belgian and Czech bottled beers; Hoegaarden and Dortmunder German beer are regularly available on draught. Normally six guest beers are on offer, with Old Mill as a regular. Biddenden's is the usual farm cider. The pub is near the historic village of Saltaire with its classical

Victorian buildings, Organ Museum and the 1853 Exhibition Hall, displaying paintings by David Hockney.

🏚️Q➹(Saltaire) ♣P

Shipley Pride

1 Saltaire Road (A657)

☀ 11.30 (11 Sat)-11; 12-3, 7-10.30 Sun

☎ (01274) 585341

Taylor Landlord; Tetley Bitter; guest beers Ⓗ

Built 1870 as the Beehive Hotel, the Shipley Pride is a genuine free house and friendly local. Its two traditional rooms are linked by a central bar. The rectangular lounge features wood panels, stained glass windows and a semi-circular bar; the games room has two pool tables that are popular with locals, and a display of plates from around the world. Quiz nights are held every Thu. Guest beers include ales from Clarks and Salamander. Home-made food is a speciality, served weekday lunchtimes.

❀◖➹(Saltaire/Shipley) ♣P

Sun Hotel

3 Kirkgate

☀ 11-11; 12-10.30 Sun

☎ (01274) 580757

Black Sheep Special; Taylor Landlord; Theakston Best Bitter; guest beers Ⓗ

19th-century Grade II listed building, formerly a residential hotel, now a town-centre pub. Set on two levels, linked by a central staircase, the bottom bar is triangular in shape with three small drinking areas (one no-smoking) served by an L-shaped bar. Upstairs, a modern, open-plan interior features turquoise wood panels, white walls and a red ceiling with a secluded no-smoking area, leading to the garden. Guest beers are from the Wetherspoon's guest list. Food is served daily until 10pm.

Q❀◖&⚬✕●

Victoria Hotel

192 Saltaire Road (A657)

☀ 11.30-11; 12-10.30 Sun

☎ (01274) 585642

Boddingtons Bitter; Taylor Landlord; Whitbread Trophy; guest beers Ⓗ

Two-roomed, friendly local featuring a Victorian-style decor of stained glass and wood in the lounge. The lively tap room is popular with younger customers. Quiz nights are held every Tue and Thu. Guest beers are often from Cropton, Ryburn, Slaters and Springhead. Meals are served weekdays, 12-3. The historic village of Saltaire is a few minutes' walk away.

❀◖➹(Saltaire) ♣P

SOUTH ELMSALL

Brookside Commercial Social Club

35 Barnsley Road (near bus and rail stations)

☀ 11-3.30, 6-11; 11-2, 7-10.30 Sun

☎ (01977) 643530

John Smith's Bitter; Barnsley Bitter or IPA; guest beer Ⓗ

An oasis for cask beer in the town centre, taking great pride in its championing of the real ale cause and support for smaller brewers. It is also a thriving centre for social activity, popular with all ages. CIU-affiliated, but

CAMRA members can be signed in on production of a membership card. Parking is limited.
&⭍♣P

SOWERBY BRIDGE

Alma Inn
Cottonstones, Mill Bank (1¼ miles off A58 at Triangle pub) OS 028215
✪ 5.30 (12 Sat)-11; 12-10.30 Sun
☎ (01422) 823334
Taylor Landlord; Tetley Bitter; Theakston Best Bitter H
The last remaining of three pubs in the area, all named after Crimean battles. This popular, family-friendly inn, with stone-flagged floors, provides excellent views of the surrounding countryside. Over 80 Belgian beers are stocked, and specialist beer evening are occasionally hosted, often with appropriate food. Tutored tastings can be arranged. Extremely busy during 'Rushbearing' (first weekend in Sept) when the rush cart visits. A regular bus service from Halifax stops at the door. No meals Mon/Tue eves. ♨✿◑⚫♠♣P

Ram's Head
26 Wakefield Road
✪ 12-2.30 (3.30 Sat), 6-11; 12-3.30, 7-10.30 Sun
☎ (01422) 835876
Ryburn Best Mild, Best Bitter, Rydale Bitter, Luddite, Stabbers; guest beer H
Home to Ryburn Brewery, located in the cellar, offering probably the cheapest permanently available beers in the area. Wood panelling and ceiling beams create a homely atmosphere and, although open plan, the pub has four distinct drinking areas. The frontage retains its original Webster's Brewery windows and door. Home-cooked, reasonably priced three-course meals are available (no food Sat). Popular with all ages, particularly senior citizens, as it is not a town-centre 'circuit' pub, and hosts singalongs Sat and Sun eves. ♨✿◑P⚇

White Horse
Burnley Road, Friendly (A646, ½ mile from centre)
✪ 12 (11.30 Sat)-11; 12-10.30 Sun
☎ (01422) 831173
Barge & Barrel Nettlethrasher; Tetley Mild, Bitter H
Now run by White Rose, this end of terrace pub has expanded into the adjoining cottages. The main bar faces a smart lounge, while a side bar serves the smaller, more basic tap. This lively pub enjoys a strong local following; two soccer teams are based here and it also fields dominoes, cards, and quiz teams. The present tenants have won several *Pub in Bloom* awards, which is easy to understand if you pass by in summer – the window-box displays are splendid.
✿♣P

STEETON

Steeton Hall
Station Road
✪ 11-11; 12-10.30 Sun
☎ (01535) 655676
website: www.steetonhallhotel.co.uk
Jennings Bitter; Taylor Best Bitter; guest beers H
Part of the Honeycombe Leisure Group, this

16th-century house has a glass conservatory and several other public rooms decorated with a mix of old photographs and paintings of the local area. This comfortable pub/restaurant also has nine recently refurbished bedrooms, and serves excellent food at reasonable prices.
✿⌂◑&⭍(Steeton & Silsden) P

THORNHILL

Savile Arms (Church House)
Church Lane (B6117, 2½ miles S of Dewsbury)
✪ 5-11; 12-4, 7-11 Sat; 12-4, 7-10.30 Sun
☎ (01924) 463738
Black Sheep Best Bitter; Tetley Bitter; guest beer H
Mentioned in the *Domesday Book*, Thornhill is the site of an important Civil War battle. 600 years old, the pub shares consecrated ground with St Michael's Church, which contains Savile family tombs and 15th-century stained glass. Once tied to Kirkstall Brewery, then Duttons of Blackburn, the 'Church House' is now free of tie. The tropical fish tank is eye catching as is the display of local art. The oldest part of the pub is the tap room. A fine village local, but it is unsuitable for children. Q✿♣P●

TODMORDEN

Masons Arms
1 Bacup Road (A6033/A681 jct)
✪ 3 (12 Fri, Sat & summer)-11; 12-10.30 Sun
☎ (01706) 812180
Barnsley Bitter; Tetley Bitter; guest beers H
Locals' pub, nestling beside a railway viaduct: two comfortable lounge areas lie either side of the corridor entrance, leading to the bar. Unusual tables in one lounge are believed to date back to when the pub doubled as a mortuary. Read about the Summit Tunnel fire, of 1984, and of slavering dogs, who died in 1840, after falling in the nearby canal; the towpath makes an interesting walk from Todmorden to Walsden and beyond. The guest ales are mostly from small breweries. ♨✿⭍♣

Top Brink
Top Brink, Lumbutts OS957235
✪ 12-3 (not Mon-Fri), 6-11; 12-10.30 Sun
☎ (01706) 812696
Boddingtons Bitter; Castle Eden Ale; Flowers Original; Taylor Landlord; guest beer H
In a rural area overlooked by moorland hills, the Top Brink is especially popular with diners. Set around the bar are a dark-panelled lounge with attractive brassware, and other lounge areas. A conservatory provides more space and there is a small room with gaming machines. In summer, there is plenty of outdoor seating, in the attractive sloping garden. Handy for the Pennine Way, the Calderdale Way passes the door. ✿◑♠P

WAINSTALLS

Cat i' th' Well Inn
Wainstalls Lane
✪ 12-3 (not winter Mon-Fri); 7 (6 Sat & summer)-11, 12-3, 7 (6 summer)-10-30 Sun
☎ (01422) 244841
Castle Eden Bitter; Taylor Golden Best, Best Bitter, Landlord H
Delightfully situated in the wooded valley

of the Catywell Brook, it makes a popular stopping-off point for ramblers. The pub is open plan, featuring oak panelling that used to adorn a local folly, Castle Carr. The absence of a pool table, music and gambling machines makes it a pleasant place for a quiet drink, but there is a quiz on Mon eve. It has a garden, and children have access to a two-acre field. Q✿♣P

WAKEFIELD ❄

Fernandes Brewery Tap
5 Avison Yard, Kirkgate (500 yds from Kirkgate Station)
🕑 5 (11 Fri & Sat)-11; 12-10.30 Sun
☎ (01924) 369547
Fernandes Maltshovel Mild, Oddfellows; guest beers Ⓗ
Housed in the original malt kiln, built in 1822 by Louis Fernandes (closed 1929), the premises became the malt store and conditioning room for Beverley's Brewery until 1968. It was bought in 1994 by the James family, when they transferred their home-brew shop. In 1997, a micro-brewery was installed using the Fernandes name and the brewery tap opened in 1999. Local CAMRA *Pub of the Year* 1999 and 2000 it has also won many seasonal awards. The pub features an extensive collection of brewery memorabilia. ⚒Q◖≠(Westgate/Kirkgate) P

Harry's Bar
107b Westgate
🕑 5-11; closed Sun
☎ (01924) 373773 e-mail: mbateson@telinco.co.uk
Taylor Landlord; Tetley Bitter; guest beers Ⓗ
Small, one-roomed pub, hidden just off Westgate, but certainly not aimed at the 'Westgate Run' crowd. The pub was named after the landlord's father-in-law Harry Murphy who played rugby for Great Britain and Wakefield Trinity in the 1940s and '50s; the walls display memorabilia from his playing days. No one-armed bandits or juke box, but it hosts live music twice monthly. A must for those who enjoy a quiet drink. ⚒✿&≠(Westgate)

King's Arms
Heath Common, Heath (off A6555)
🕑 11-3, 5.30-11; 12-10.30 Sun
☎ (01924) 377527
Clark's Traditional; Taylor Landlord; Tetley Bitter; guest beer Ⓗ
Built in the early 1700s and converted into a public house in 1841, the King's Arms became part of the Clark's brewery chain of ale houses in 1989. The pub comprises three oak-panelled rooms with gas lighting, extensive gardens to the rear, and a family conservatory. Surrounded by 100 acres of common grass land, the King's Arms offers an excellent choice of traditional ales, superb food and a friendly welcome – all that is needed for an enjoyable visit to the heath. ⚒Q✿❦◖&P

O'Donoghues
60 George Street
🕑 5-11; 1-10.30 Sun
☎ (01924) 291326
Black Sheep Special; Hop Back Summer Lightning or Winter Lightning; Ossett Excelsior; guest beers Ⓗ
Only 200 yards off Westgate, but not aimed at the 'Westgate Crowd', this pub is a traditional ale house with a reputation as an outlet for Ossett Brewing Company. Live music eves are a regular feature. On Sun a selection of newspapers are provided for drinkers to read at their leisure. ⚒&≠(Westgate/Kirkgate)

Redoubt ☆
28 Horbury Road
🕑 11.30-11; 12-10.30 Sun
☎ (01924) 377085
Taylor Landlord; Tetley Mild, Bitter Ⓗ
This four-roomed Tetley Heritage pub is one of the oldest in town, and has probably altered little in the last 150 years. With strong sporting connections, it fields its own football and cricket teams. The pub has two rooms available mid-week for private functions at no charge. It has been presented with local CAMRA's *Pub of the Season* award in 1995, 1999 and 2000. Because no meals are served the landlord allows people to bring their own food in. ✿&≠(Westgate) ♣P

Wakefield Labour Club (Red Shed)
18 Vicarage Street (by market car park)
🕑 11-4 (not Mon-Thu), 7-11; 12-4, (closed eve) Sun
☎ (01924) 215626
Barnsley Bitter; guest beers Ⓗ
A base for Wakefield's labour movement for many years, unlike other labour clubs, it has maintained its traditions and been the backbone of organisational support for workers involved in a whole range of industrial struggles, playing a vital part in the lives and history of the people of Wakefield. This small, friendly wooden club has become a favourite with ale drinkers from far and wide, stocking a variety of beers from independent breweries (over 190 in 12 months). It holds several CAMRA *Club of the Year* awards. ✿≠(Westgate/Kirkgate) P⃫

White Hart
77 Westgate End
🕑 12-11; 12-10.30 Sun
☎ (01924) 375887 website: www.whitehartwfd.co.uk
Hop Back Summer Lightning; Taylor Landlord; Tetley Bitter; Theakston Best Bitter; guest beers Ⓗ
Flowers brighten the front of this traditional pub with stone floors and coal fires. The covered garden is heated and hosts barbecues in summer, as well as other events. Sat is party night, with hot pork sandwiches, free suppers are served late Sun, Tue and Wed. There is 'happy hour' every day between 5 and 7pm. ⚒⛱✿⋈≠(Westgate)

WARMFIELD

Plough
45 Warmfield Lane (400 yds from A655)
🕑 12-3, 5-11; 12-11 Sat; 12-10.30 Sun
☎ (01924) 892007 e-mail: jeanette.plough@virgin.net
John Smith's Bitter; Theakston Best Bitter, Cool Cask; guest beer Ⓗ
Unspoilt, 18th-century inn overlooking the Lower Calder Valley, with a low, beamed ceiling and a huge open fireplace. It has been extensively, yet sympathetically refurbished by the owner. Good quality bar meals and snacks are served. A

rotating guest beer from local breweries is stocked. A paved seating area at the front of the pub has an adjacent children's play area.

🏛Q🍽🌞🚮◑&♣P

WENTBRIDGE

Bluebell
Great North Road
✪ 11.30-3, 5-11; 12-10.30 Sun
☎ (01977) 620697
Taylor Landlord; Tetley Bitter Ⓗ
In the picturesque village of Wentbridge, on the old A1, this former coaching inn was rebuilt in 1633. An old pub sign hangs in the entrance. It stands at the head of Brockadale, the smallest of the Yorkshire Dales. Noted for its excellent range of food, with several vegetarian options, it is comfortably furnished with Mousey Thompson tables and chairs in a warm, friendly atmosphere.

Q🌞🚮◑&P✄

WINTERSETT

Angler's Retreat
Ferrytop Lane (between the villages of Crofton and Ryhill) OS382157
✪ 12-3, 7-11; 12-3, 7-10.30 Sun
☎ (01924) 862370
Barnsley Bitter; John Smith's Bitter; Samuel Smith OBB; Theakston XB; guest beer (summer) Ⓗ
Cosy, two-roomed rural pub with the smaller of the two rooms warmed by a real fire. The bar stands mainly in the right-hand half of the pub, but can be accessed from the larger room on the left, which contains old photographs, a plate collection and two stuffed birds in glass cases. It is handy for birdwatchers, anglers, ramblers and other visitors to the nearby reservoirs and country park.

🏛🌞P

YEADON

Albert Inn
High Street
✪ 12-11; 12-10.30 Sun
☎ (0113) 250 0420
Black Sheep Best Bitter; Taylor Landlord; Tetley Bitter Ⓗ
Long, thin, two-roomed pub: the larger lounge is comfortably furnished, displaying plenty of photographs, prints and paintings; note the old brass taps over the bar. The smaller tap/games room is traditionally furnished with wooden seating and panelling, a pool table, dartboard and dominoes table. Weekly events include quiz night Wed, singles night Thu and Golden Oldies night Sun. No food Mon.

◑🍽♣

New Inn
Cemetery Road
✪ 11-11; 12-10.30 Sun
☎ (0113) 250 3220
John Smith's Bitter, Magnet Ⓗ
Quiet local near the High Street, but far enough away to avoid the more boisterous elements. The two rooms are served from a central bar area; the front room is a comfortably furnished lounge with banquette seating and the usual pub paraphernalia – old pictures, brasses, jugs, porcelain, etc. The public bar is similarly furnished, but with wooden seating. Mon is darts and doms league night; a quiz is held Thu. Yeadon Tarn is nearby.

🌞🍽♣

Woolpack
18 New Road
✪ 11-11; 12-10.30 Sun
☎ (0113) 250 6079 website: punchonline.com
Draught Bass; Marston's Pedigree; Shepherd Neame Spitfire; Taylor Landlord; Tetley Bitter; guest beers Ⓗ
Yorkshire stone pub fronting on to the A65. One large room has several distinct drinking areas furnished in typical Festival Ale House style – bare boards, wood panelling and nicotine-coloured walls. The licensee has won various *Cellarmanship* awards, and usually stocks three rotating guest beers as well as a cider and, occasionally, a perry. Traditional Sunday lunch is served between 12-4; vegetarians are catered for. Senior citizens get a special lunch deal Mon-Thu. Eve meals end at 8pm (not served Sun).

🌞◑♣●P

A Quart a Day

A judicious labourer would probably always have some ale in his house, and have small beer for the general drink. There is no reason why he should not keep Christmas as well as the farmer; and when he is mowing, reaping, or is at any other hard work, a quart, or three pints, of really good fat ale a-day is by no means too much.

William Cobbett, *Cottage Economy*, 1822.
(Small beer indicates a beer with a low alcohol content.)

Flying Under False Colours

Several beers listed in the Good Beer Guide give the impression they come from living, independent brewers when in fact the breweries have been closed and the brands moved elsewhere. In some cases, the current brewers of these brands are misleading the public by suggesting the original breweries still exist.

Take the case of the pub group Morrells. Morrell's Oxford brewery closed in 1998, yet a full-colour brochure produced by the pub group declares it offers 'Three classic ales with the real taste of Oxford'. Warming to the theme, the brochure goes on, 'There's more to Oxford than its famous dreaming spires, noble lawns and ancient, honey-coloured colleges. Real Oxford life blends a rich cultural heritage with the here and now...with Eights Week rowing on the Isis in May, languid punting on the meandering Cherwell and the clamour of a Varsity match, and a pint or two of Morrells in celebration. Morrells have been part of Oxford life since 1782, so there's not much they don't know about the city, past and present. Today's "silicon generation" of sporting, fun-loving students, thronging the city's bars, are equally well informed. They know that classic Morrells beers are an essential part of real Oxford life'.

What this risible hyperbole doesn't tell the well-informed, silicon-enhanced students is that Morrell's beers are now brewed a fair punt from Oxford – in Dorchester, the capital of Dorset, to be precise. The Thomas Hardy Brewery, since its divorce from Eldridge Pope in 1996, is now a contract brewery, producing beers for all and sundry. As well as Morrells of Oxford's brands, Thomas Hardy also produces 'Ushers' beers for a retail company called Refresh UK. The Usher's brewery in Trowbridge, Wiltshire, closed in 2000, and its large pub estate is now run by a company called InnSpired. Drinkers who, understandably, are not up to speed on all the rapid changes in the brewing industry could be forgiven for thinking they are consuming genuine Wiltshire beers brewed in Trowbridge when they frequent pubs badged as Ushers.

As the Guide swent to press, there were fears for the future of Thomas Hardy. Eldridge Pope appears to have lost interest in Royal Oak and its other brands, and prefers to offer the ubiquitous joys of Tetley Bitter to its pub customers. If the brewery were to close, we assume that Morrells and Ushers beers would move to Thomas Hardy's partner, the Burtonwood Brewery in Warrington, Cheshire. Now there's a real taste of Oxford...

The most high-profile offender in the passing-off business is Greene King. The Suffolk brewer, as a result of the closure of both Ruddles of Rutland and Morland of Abingdon, now owns the Ruddles and Old Speckled Hen brands. There is no mention of Greene King on or labels for these brands: they are labelled respectively 'Ruddles Brewing' and 'Morland Brewing': the unitiated could draw the conclusion the beers are brewed by existing companies bearing those names. Such is the affection for Ruddles County among the older generation of cask beer drinkers that many may think they are getting a true Rutland beer. But in its region of origin, Ruddles County was 5 per cent alcohol. The Greene King version is 4.3 per cent, an alcohol rating that conveniently plugs the gap between the company's IPA and Abbot Ale.

There is a similar problem with the former King & Barnes brands now owned by Hall & Woodhouse's Badger Brewery. 'Sussex Bitter' brewed in Blandford Forum, Dorset? Odd things appear to be happening to English geography. And did you know that the revered home of pale ale brewing, Burton-on-Trent, is now part of West Yorkshire? For Draught Burton Ale, a former CAMRA Champion Beer of Britain, has moved from Burton and is now produced by Tetley in Leeds.

Our opposition to misleading brands is not based on pedantry. It is about authenticity. If we are to convince both current and future drinkers of cask beers that they should treat them as seriously as French wines, then authenticity and place of origin are of great importance. Of course, beers can be matched: the Greene King 'Ruddles' beers taste fine, but that misses the point. A Rutland beer cannot be brewed in Suffolk, any more than an Oxford beer can be brewed in Dorset, or a proud Burton pale ale be removed to Yorkshire.

It couldn't happen to a chateau-bottled French claret. But French wines are protected by appellations – guarantees of place of origin as well as quality. Think on, as they say in West Yorkshire. Or, perhaps, Burton-on-Humber.

GLAMORGAN

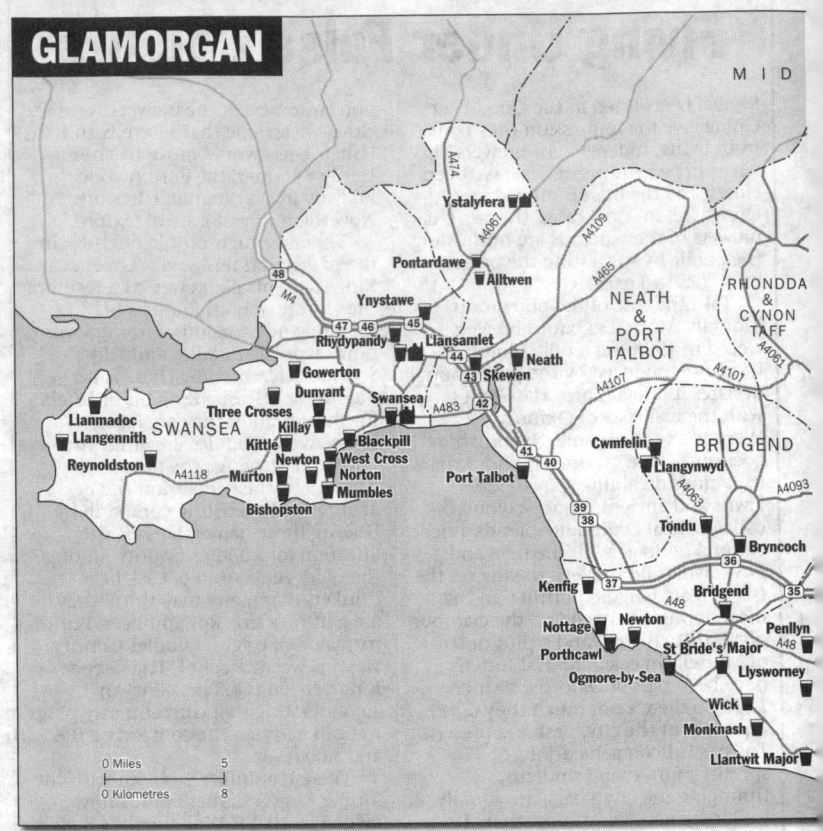

Authority areas covered: Bridgend UA, Caerphilly UA, Cardiff UA, Merthyr Tydfil UA, Neath & Port Talbot UA, Rhondda, Cynon, Taff UA, Swansea UA, Vale of Glamorgan UA

ABERAMAN

Blaengwawr Inn
373 Cardiff Road
✪ 11-11; 12-10.30 Sun
☎ (01685) 871706
Cains Bitter; guest beers Ⓗ
Lively, bustling single-bar village pub situated on a busy main road. Supporting more than a few pub teams, the fireplace displays the many trophies won. Live entertainment is on offer most weeks, with local as well as some national acts appearing. A pool table and TV dominate one side of the mock-Tudor bar while comfortable seating is arranged on the other, one corner by the fireplace bearing the sign for 'The Hernia Club'. ♣♣

ABERCARN

Old Swan
55 Commercial Road
✪ 12.30 (11.30 Fri & Sat); 12-10.30 Sun
☎ (01495) 243161
Courage Best Bitter; Ⓗ/Ⓖ **guest beer** Ⓗ
Welcoming, roadside village pub with a well-refurbished bar area, real fire and comfortable lounge. Courage Best on gravity is a popular choice, known by the locals as 'cold tea'. A great supporter of a local charity, the pub has a strong community spirit and friendly atmosphere.

It is reputed to be haunted by a soldier from WWI. The relatively local game of corks is played here, among the usual pub games. 🏚♣

ABERDARE ❋

Whitcombe Inn
Whitcombe Street
✪ 3 (12 Sat)-11; 12-10.30 Sun
☎ (01685) 875106
Beer range varies Ⓗ
Small, pleasant street-corner pub, just off the town centre, offering a warm welcome. Behind the sombre exterior with its etched windows, the interior is basically furnished with bare-brick walls and floorboards, made cosy by the real fire. Something of a real ale oasis in the town, Fuller's London Pride is a welcome regular accompanied by a good range of guest beers. Darts and pool are available in the back room and live music on Wed and Fri nights. 🏚≉♣

ALLTWEN

Butchers Arms
Alltwen Hill (in village just off main road to Neath, A474)
✪ 12-3, 6.30-11; 12-3, 7-10.30 Sun
☎ (01792) 863100
Courage Directors; Everards Original; John Smith's Bitter; Wadworth 6X; guest beer Ⓗ

Open-plan, traditional village pub with separate restaurant attracting a mixture of diners and locals. In addition to the regular beers a guest ale is available at all times but is not prominently displayed so ask for details. There is also a large range of malt whiskies. The pub is well-known in the area for its food, offering a wide range of dishes including vegetarian options (no food Sun eve). The pub has been run by the same landlord for 10 years. 🏰Q🅱🕒P

BISHOPSTON

Joiners Arms
50 Bishopston road
🕐 11.30-11; 12-10.30 Sun
☎ (01792) 232658
Courage Best Bitter; John Smith's Bitter; Swansea Bishopswood Bitter, Three Cliffs Gold, Original Wood; guest beers Ⓗ

This former wheelwright's and blacksmith's shop has been licensed since the 1860s and is now home to the popular Swansea Brewing Company. Well-known for its real ales among locals and visitors alike, it was the South and Mid Wales CAMRA *Pub of the Year* 1999. Attractive, stone-built village pub with a dartboard and TV in the front bar and an interesting spiral staircase. There is also a rear lounge and good value food is served in both bars. Popular venue for CAMRA visits and occasional beer festivals are held. Bus stop outside the pub.
🏰Q🅱🕒🅱♣P

BLACKPILL

Woodman
120 Mumbles Road
🕐 11-11; 12-10.30 Sun
☎ (01792) 402700
Boddingtons Bitter; Marston's Pedigree; Wadworth 6X Ⓗ

House situated at the side of the main road dating from Victorian times, which has been extended over the years to become a pleasantly-appointed, mainly food-orientated pub/restaurant. The restaurant area includes a conservatory and offers reasonable prices with various special deals. Meals are also served in the bar area which includes a dartboard and big-screen TV for sporting events. Quizzes are held on Wed eve. The pub is located at the entrance to Clyne Gardens, a popular local beauty spot, and the beach is just across the road.
🏰🕒🅱P

BLACKWOOD

Rock & Fountain
St David's Avenue, Woodfieldside (from High St take turn opp. Argos, follow road to river)
🕐 12 (3 Mon)-11; 12-10.30 Sun
☎ (01495) 223907
Beer range varies Ⓗ

Small, characterful pub next to the river and close to the town centre. The building dates from the 1820s and was originally a counting house for the coal-mining industry. The bar is divided into three areas, one of which is for non-smokers. Wooden floors and a real fire enhance the atmosphere. Good quality and reasonably priced pub food is served including 'real chips'. No food on Sun eve or Mon. Up to four well-kept real ales are on offer. The Sirhowy Valley walk runs close to the pub.
🏰🕒P⚅

BONVILSTON

Red Lion
On A48
🕐 11.30-3, 5-11; 12-3, 7-10.30 Sun
☎ (01446) 781208
Brains Bitter, SA Ⓗ

Easy to find on the main A48 between Cardiff and Cowbridge with an ample car park. This 17th-century pub is open-plan with one bar catering for three separate drinking areas plus a neat garden. It has been a regular entry in the *Guide*. Pictures of the pub, past and present, fill the walls and beams alongside the many brasses. No food served on Sun or Mon eves.
Q🕒🅱♣P●

INDEPENDENT BREWERIES

Brains Cardiff
Bryn Celyn Ystalyfera
Bullmastiff Cardiff
Lord Raglan Cefn Coed y Cymmer
Swansea Swansea
Tomos Watkin Llansamlet
White Hart Machen

BRIDGEND ✣

Wyndham Arms
Dunraven Place
✪ 11-11; 12-10.30 Sun
☎ (01656) 663608
Brains SA; Courage Directors; Theakston Best Bitter; guest beers Ⓗ

Wetherspoon's revival of an old town-centre hotel. The comfortable interior has much original wood panelling and displays interesting photographs and paintings of old Bridgend and district. Wetherspoon's curry club range and other meals are available daily 11–10 (12–9.30 Sun). An occasional cider, such as Addlestone's, is stocked. Wheelchair WC.
Q ⒶⒹ & ♣ ✦ ●

CARDIFF ✣

Black Lion
Cardiff Road, Llandaff (A4119/High St. jct)
✪ 12-2.30, 4.30-11; 12-11 Fri & Sat; 12-3, 7-10.30 Sun
☎ (029) 2056 7312
Brains Dark, Bitter, SA; guest beer Ⓗ

Long-established, traditional pub on busy junction. The Victorian half-timbered exterior is complemented by classic Brains windows. The public bar is simply furnished and is pleasant and welcoming. The lounge bar is spacious and comfortable with a good range of malt whiskies. The landlord has won several Brains *Cellarmanship* awards and is a former Cardiff CAMRA *Pub of the Year* winner. Llandaff Cathedral and village green are close by. Buses stop close to the pub or parking is available just off the High Street. Q ⒶⒹ ➔ ≈ (Fairwater) ♣ ●

Cayo Arms
36 Cathedral Road, Pontcanna
✪ 12 (11 Sat)-11; 12-10.30 Sun
☎ (029) 2039 1910
Tomos Watkin Whoosh, BB, Merlin's Stout, OSB, seasonal beers Ⓗ

Opened in July 2000, Cardiff's first Tomos Watkin pub quickly gained in popularity to become local CAMRA *Pub of the Year* 2001. Named after Julian 'Cayo' Evans – notorious founder of the Free Wales Army – its single-bar interior has a homely atmosphere appealing to locals, business people and ale lovers alike. Well-appointed patio area and a fully-equipped function room are available. Conveniently located for the Millennium Stadium and Glamorgan County Cricket ground; can get busy on match days. No food Fri–Sun eves; chef's specials include imaginative fish and game dishes.
✤ ⋈ ⒶⒹ & Å ≈ (Central) P ✂

Ernest Willows
2-12 City Road
✪ 11-11; 12-10.30 Sun
Brains SA; Theakston Best Bitter; Tomos Watkin BB; Worthington Bitter Ⓗ

Named after a local aviation pioneer (1886–1926), this is a busy Wetherspoon's pub near the city centre. It has one very long bar, but the seating has been carefully arranged in different styles to avoid an 'airport lounge' feel. There are two raised areas as well as some partitioned seating, plus an outside terrace for warmer days. It has ridiculously large ladies' toilets.
Q ✤ ⒶⒹ & ≈ ✂ ●

Fox & Hounds
Old Church Road, Whitchurch
✪ 12 (11 Sat)-11; 12-10.30 Sun
☎ (029) 2069 3377
Brains Dark, Bitter, SA, seasonal beers; guest beers Ⓗ

Large, recently refurbished local close to Whitchurch village, serving the usual Brains range plus a Buckley's seasonal ale and one guest ale. The pub is divided into a drinking or 'village' area and a dining area. A large beer garden makes an ideal spot for a quiet drink on a balmy summer day. Note the old photographs of Whitchurch village dotted around the pub, and become versed in the history of north Cardiff by reading the short guides placed on each table. Meals served 12–9.30; specialities include Welsh curries.
✤ ⒶⒹ & ≈ (Whitchurch) P ✂

Glass Works
Wharton Street
✪ 12-11; closed Sun
☎ (029) 2022 2114
Greene King IPA, Abbot, Old Speckled Hen; guest beers Ⓗ

This popular venue is now part of the Greene King empire. One of many in the former Morland chain known as 'Newt & Cucumber', it is a converted city-centre, street-corner shop. Visit during 'happy hour' (weekdays 5–7) when there is a 25 per cent reduction in price on all cask beers. A two-for-one price offer on meals is also

INN BRIEF

ABERDARE

Cambrian Inn
Seymour Street
11-4, 7-11; 11-11 Fri & Sat;
12-10.30 Sun
Worthington Bitter; guest beer Ⓗ
Town-centre, single-bar pub, well-decorated and pleasantly furnished. Food available lunchtimes all week. No food eves.

BRIDGEND

Coach
37 Cowbridge Road
11.30-11;
12-10.30 Sun
Draught Bass; Worthington Bitter Ⓗ
Friendly, quiet, award-winning pub near Bridgend College. No meals served Sun eve.

Five Bells Inn
Ewenny Road
11.30-4, 6-11; 11.30-11 Wed-Sat;
12-10.30 Sun
Draught Bass; Worthington Bitter Ⓗ
Cosy pub at a busy road junction. Spacious bar with adjoining games area, and a quiet lounge on upper level.

Haywain
Coychurch Road, Brackla
11.30-11; 12-10.30 Sun
Greene King Old Speckled Hen; Worthington Bitter; guest beers Ⓗ
Large, bustling estate pub decorated with old farming implements. Popular for lunches.

Old Castle – Yr Hen Gastell
Nolton Street
11-11; 12-10.30 Sun
Hancock's HB; Worthington Bitter; guest beer Ⓗ
Old-fashioned town pub with a bar and separate lounge.

BRYNOCH

Dyffryn Arms
Neath Road
12-3, 7-11;
12-3, 7-11 Sun
Boddingtons Bitter; Wadworth 6X; Worthington Bitter Ⓗ
Comfortable pub in a rural setting where the emphasis is on food. Children welcome until 9pm if eating. *Cask Marque* accredited.

available between 3–8. Invariably an interesting rotation range of up to four guest beers at any time, which is quite remarkable considering the somewhat restricting range which owners Greene King would apparently wish to impose.

◑ ⇌ (Central) ✂

Griffin
Church Road, Lisvane

✪ 11-11; 12-10.30 Sun
☎ (029) 2074 7399

Flowers IPA; Fuller's London Pride; Marston's Pedigree; Robinson's Best Bitter; Wadworth 6X Ⓗ
Comfortable pub comprising a bar area with flagstones, large fireplace and TV. Two raised dining areas are linked by a long, central bar. A guest beer complements a range of well-known real ales. A local reputation for good food combined with a relaxed atmosphere makes this a popular pub. Small patio for outdoor drinking at the rear.

Q ✿ ◑ ₤ P

New Dock Tavern
188 Broadway

✪ 12-11; 12-4, 7-10.30 Sun
☎ (029) 2047 1221

Brains Dark, Bitter, SA Ⓗ
Locals' pub, suitably named since the landlady has recently moved from a *Guide* pub near the docks. Unusual angular layout, with a main bar, a snug, and a separate room for meetings or small functions. Simply furnished, but model ships, nautical artefacts and pictures of naval vessels give the pub its character. About one mile from the city centre, just off Newport Road.

Olde Butchers Arms
22 Heol y Felin, Rhiwbina

✪ 12-11; 12-10.30 Sun
☎ (029) 2069 3526

Brains Bitter; Greene King Old Speckled Hen; Marston's Pedigree Ⓗ
Lively pub with a large central bar rejuvenated by the new landlord back to a deserved popularity. There is a regular quiz night and live jazz on Thu. Under 21s restricted at weekends. With a pool table and TV in one area, a more peaceful drink can be had in the quieter section. Amenities include a separate skittle alley, pleasant beer garden and large car park.

✿ ◑ ₤ ♣ P

Owain Glyndwr
St John's Square

✪ 12-11 (usually extends to midnight Fri & Sat); 12-10.30 Sun
☎ (029) 2022 1980

Beer range varies Ⓗ
Split-level smallish Hogshead in the shadow of St John's church. With up to six guest beers, the occasional appearance of local micro-brewery beers enhances an already enterprising choice. A real cider is frequently available from a variety of small producers. There is usually a quiet ambience, although it can get busy at weekends and live music is performed on Tue eve. Welcome haven for shoppers and city-centre workers, out of the hustle and bustle. Avoid match days at the nearby national stadium of Wales as beer prices have been known to be inflated.

✿ ◑ ₤ ⇌ (Central) ♣

Vulcan
10 Adam Street
(outside the prison)

✪ 11-7 (5 Sat); (may stay open later for darts, etc); 12-5 Sun
☎ (029) 2046 1580

Brains Dark, Bitter Ⓗ
Although close to the city centre the pub has little passing trade hence the unusual opening hours. It is just over five minutes' walk from central station, by the prison. Characterful, teetotal landlord. The main bar is the public bar and has sawdust on the floor and unusual artefacts such as a ship's compass. The quieter, smaller lounge bar is served by a hatchway. Excellent lunchtime food (Mon–Fri) although a limited menu. Former Cardiff CAMRA *Pub of the Year*.

◑ ⇌ (Central)

CRAIG PENLLYN

Barley Mow
1½ miles N of A48 OS978773

✪ 12-3 (not Mon), 6-11; 12-3, 7-10.30 Sun
☎ (01446) 772558

Hancock's HB; guest beer Ⓗ
A true commitment to real ale has been evident at this fine old hostelry along with good food since the current owner arrived 10 years ago. Popular with all ages, families are welcome but beware the licensee's sense

---

CARDIFF
Cornwall
92 Cornwall Street, Grangetown
12-11; 12-10.30 Sun
Brains Dark, Bitter, SA; guest beer Ⓗ
Refurbished community pub, L-shaped public area comprises lounge and bar as two distinct areas. Guest beer is from Brains' range. *Cask Marque* accredited.

Westgate Hotel
49 Cowbridge Road
12-11; 12-10.30 Sun
Brains Dark, Bitter, SA Ⓗ
Landmark 1930s, red-brick public house at busy road junction just off city centre, near Millennium Stadium. Food served weekdays.

COWBRIDGE
Edmondes Arms
Cardiff Road
3-11; 12-11 Sat; 12-10.30 Sun
Hancock's HB; guest beer Ⓗ
Small local with lounge and bar, recently refurbished by new owners incorporating new accommodation. Pool and darts played.

CWMFELIN
Cross Inn
Maesteg Road
11.45-11; 12-10.30 Sun
Brains Bitter, Buckley's Best Bitter, Wye Valley Butty Bach Ⓗ
Friendly local on a busy road with a traditional benched public bar and a smart lounge. Near Garth railway station.

GELLIHAF
Coal Hole
Bryn Road
11-3.30; 11-11 Fri & Sat; 12-3, 7-10.30 Sun
Hancock's HB; guest beers Ⓗ
Popular, friendly, one-bar pub where the dining area offers good value food. Children's play area and accommodation.

GOWERTON
Commercial Hotel
Station Road
12-11; 12-3, 6-10.30 (12-10.30 summer) Sun
Brains Buckley's Best Bitter, SA, seasonal beers Ⓗ
This renovated Victorian local near the station serves weekday bar meals.

of humour. A large car park is situated across the road. Roaring log fires keep out the winter chill. Beer garden at rear. No food Sun eve. ⚲Q🐾⬦⬥⬤♣P

CWMAMAN

Falcon Inn
1 Incline Row OS008998
☼ 11-11; 12-10.30 Sun
☎ (01685) 873758
website: www.thefalconinn.net
Beer range varies Ⓗ
Nestled at the bottom of the Aman Valley, this pub is close to the village but feels almost isolated. The picturesque setting by the river, ensures its popularity in the summer. At least three beers are on offer at any one time, Robinson's Old Tom is a particular favourite in the winter. The extension, using wood and stone from a local chapel, progresses at a leisurely pace, but is a good example of painstaking work. The pub is quite hard to find but well worth the effort. Once visited, never forgotten. 🐾⬦⬥⬤P

DUNVANT

Found Out Inn
Killan Road (up hill towards Three Crosses)
☼ 12-3.30, 5.30-11; 12-11 Sat; 12-3, 7-10.30 Sun
☎ (01792) 203596
Flowers Original; Greene King Old Speckled Hen Ⓗ
Village local which was rebuilt in the 1960s when the old inn was demolished. The old pub was originally called the Dunvant Inn but was nicknamed the Found Out from the time when local colliers went straight from work to the pub on pay-days, only to be found there by their wives and chased home! The pub is immaculately kept and the bar has darts, pool table, juke box and TV while the lounge is comfortable with memorabilia of the Dunvant Male Choir on display. Good value food is served and a quiz held each Tue. Ramp available for wheelchair access.
Q🐾⬦⬤⬥♣P

EGLWYS BREWIS

Carpenters Arms
Eglwys Brewis Road
☼ 6.30 (11 Thu-Sat)-11; 12-10.30 Sun
☎ (01446) 792063
Brains Bitter, SA; guest beer (occasional) Ⓗ
Stone-built roadside pub with a car park either side of the road, transformed by an enthusiastic new owner committed to cask ale who carried out the alterations himself. To complement the family room a children's farm is a recent addition as is self-catering accommodation. A wide range of high quality meals are served all sessions. Full wheelchair facilities from a ramp entrance, through well-spaced tables to toilets and low-handled doors make this a pub for all. Late opening for entertainment on Fri and Sat. ⚲Q🐾🐾⬦⬤⬦♣♣P

GILFACH FARGOED

Capel
Park Place
☼ 12-4, 7-11; 11-11 Fri & Sat; 12-10.30 Sun
☎ (01443) 830272

Brains SA; John Smith's Bitter; guest beers Ⓗ
Large, friendly traditional Valleys pub retaining many original features including a long bar and extensive wood panelling; there's even a gaslight. The pub offers a comfortable, no-smoking room, together with accommodation. Look out for the large, decorated cast-iron weighing scales in the lobby. Focus of the local community with pool and bar skittles. The pub is a rare surviving example of a style once common in the former mining valleys. As well as the regular beers there is a guest beer usually from small independent regional and craft brewers. Lunches are served at weekends.
Q⬤⬦⬤≢⅄

GILFACH GOCH

Griffin Inn
Hendreforgan (1/2 mile off A4093) OS988875
☼ 7 (12 Sat)-11; 12-10.30 Sun
☎ (01443) 672247
Brains SA; guest beers Ⓗ
Traditional, unspoilt three-bedroomed pub, known locally as 'the Bog'. It nestles in an isolated valley, now a developing area, with its large car park accessed by an uneven road. The rooms are filled with china, brass, mining, military and hunting artefacts while some of the furniture is period. The patio has benches for summer use where customers can catch a glimpse of the pair of roving peacocks and other wildlife. The customers, mainly locals with some visitors, combine with the friendly family (who have run the pub for 40 years) to make a lively atmosphere.
🐾⬤♣P

GROESFAEN

Dynevor Arms
Llantrisant Road, Pontyclun (A4119)
OS061810
☼ 11-11; 12-3, 7-10.30 Sun
☎ (029) 2089 0530
Draught Bass; Hancock's HB; guest beer Ⓗ
Popular, welcoming roadside village pub. It is comfortable and well-decorated on the inside, while on the outside it is colourfully signposted and painted in traditional pub colours. Ever-changing guest beer, the brewer and brew varies. An area is set aside for darts, cards and dominoes and either live music or a quiz is held on Sun eve. A dining area enhances the open-plan bar facilities and a varied menu offers good-value meals with special prices for senior citizens on Mon (no food Sun eve).
🐾⬦♣⬤P

GROESWEN

White Cross
On mountain between Caerphilly and Eglwysilan
☼ 11-11; 12-10.30 Sun
☎ (029) 2085 1332
Hancock's HB; Ⓗ **guest beer** Ⓗ/Ⓖ
Comfortable local on the eastern side of Eglwysilan mountain. Enjoy panoramic views over the town of Caerphilly with the historic castle dominating the skyline. Traditional games are played in the small bar with an open fire in winter. There is a separate dining/function room and an

external canopied patio. Next to the pub is an old cemetery known as the 'Westminster Abbey' of Wales – it dates back to 1724. Many preachers, poets and bards were buried here, including James James, who composed the Welsh national anthem.
🏚❀◑♣P

HOPKINSTOWN

Hollybush
Ty Mawr Road
🕓 11-11; 12-10.30 Sun
☎ (01443) 402325
Hancock's HB; guest beer Ⓗ
Three times mid-Glamorgan CAMRA *Pub of the Year*, this friendly roadside inn is justifiably popular with locals and visitors. The sports-orientated bar has racing and boxing memorabilia and a large screen descends for televised sporting events. However, matters cerebral are not forgotten as testified by the well-used reference library. The comfortable (and quieter) lounge, where lunchtime and eve meals are served, is the venue for live entertainment on Sun nights and a quiz on Mon. As well as the constantly changing guest beer, real cider such as Thatcher's or Inch's is stocked.
◑🞄🏚♣P🝙

KENFIG

Prince of Wales
Maudlam OS804818
🕓 11.30-4, 6-11; 11.30-11 Fri & Sat; 12-10.30 Sun
☎ (01656) 740356
Draught Bass; Brains Bitter; Worthington Bitter; guest beer Ⓖ
Historic pub nearly four centuries old with exposed stone walls and a large open fireplace. Former town hall (upstairs, complete with ghostly harmonium player) of the drowned city of Kenfig. It is believed that the Maid of Sker first met her harpist lover here. Renowned for Bass on gravity, no handpumps are used. The pub may stay open throughout the afternoon if busy. Meals served 12–2.30 and 7–9.30 Tue–Sat. The pub is next to a nature reserve.
🏚Q❀◑P

KILLAY

Railway Inn
553 Gower Road, Upper Killay
🕓 11-11; 12-10.30 Sun
☎ (01792) 203946
Greene King Old Speckled Hen; Swansea Deep Slade Dark, Bishopwood Bitter, Original Wood; Theakston Old Peculier; guest beers Ⓗ
The pub was built in 1864 when the railway was constructed through the Clyne Valley. The railway closed in the 1960s but happily the pub still stands. An unspoilt gem with railway memorabilia and a good selection of ales. The pub is a major outlet for the Swansea Brewing Company and holds occasional beer festivals. It was Swansea CAMRA *Pub of the Year* 2000. The pub is currently threatened by a plan to redevelop the site and there is a very active campaign to save it. The old railway route is now a popular walk and cycle track.
🏚🝙❀🝙♣P

KITTLE

Beaufort Arms
18 Pennard Road
🕓 11.30-11; 12-10.30 Sun
☎ (01792) 234521
Brains Buckley's Best Bitter, SA, Rev. James, seasonal beers Ⓗ
Reputedly the oldest pub in Gower, this popular, community village local has won some local awards. A Brains tenanted house with three bars and a function room, the oldest part of the pub has a beamed ceiling and some early stone work. There is a large car park and seating area plus a children's play area, well used in summer. Piped music is played and juke box provided. Mon is a regular quiz night and the pub hosts the local ladies darts team. Extensive menu served 11–3, 5–9.30 Mon–Thu and 11.30–9.30 Fri–Sun.
🝙❀◑🝙P

LLANGENNITH

King's Head
🕓 11-11; 12-10.30 Sun
☎ (01792) 386212
Tomos Watkin BB, OSB; guest beers Ⓗ
Historic, stone-walled pub on the village green near the church, extended over the years as adjoining farm buildings have been incorporated. There are splendid views of the nearby beaches which are within walking distance for the energetic. The pub is popular with visitors to nearby caravan and camping sites, and a games room is available. Note the old pictures displayed in the bar, including those of Phil Tanner, the legendary Gower folk singer. The guest beers are usually Welsh and food is served all day.
🏚Q❀◑🝙🞄♣P

LLANGYNWYD ❉

Old House (Yr Hen Dŷ)
Opp. church on top of the hill, W of A4063 OS858889
🕓 11-11; 12-10.30 Sun
☎ (01656) 733310
Flowers IPA, Original; Worthington Bitter; guest beer Ⓗ
Extremely popular, atmospheric thatched pub, one of the oldest in Wales (circa 1147). Much extended with spacious windows affording views across the Bryncynan Valley. Advisable to book for Sun and eve meals in the excellent restaurant. The festive tradition 'Mari Lwyd' is depicted on the pub sign and performed each New Year. Locals dress up (in a horse's head, for example) and visit houses, singing and drinking on the way. Wil Hopcyn (1701–41), the poet, used the pub and courted Ann Thomas (1704–27), the maid of Cefn Ydfa, read about them in the pub.
🏚Q🝙❀◑AP●

LLANMADOC

Britannia Inn
🕓 11-11; 12-10.30 Sun
☎ (01792) 386624
Marston's Pedigree; Wadworth 6X; guest beer (occasional) Ⓗ

The last pub surviving in a village which was once a thriving little port. There are ships' timbers in the construction and two old bread ovens retained. 'The Mapsant', an ancient annual religious festival celebrating the patron saint of the parish, is still celebrated here every November. The pub benefits from excellent views and good walks nearby. It has a good range of facilities for families including a menagerie in the grounds. Guest beers are available in the holiday periods and food is served all day in the season. 🏚Q🏚🕭🕭🍴🖶🖪♿🍴

LLANSAMLET

Plough & Harrow
57 Church Road (next to church)
🕓 12-11; 12-10.30 Sun
☎ (01792) 772263
Tomos Watkin Whoosh, Merlin's Stout, OSB, seasonal beers 🅷

Recently reopened as the brewery tap for Tomos Watkin ales. First Watkin's pub in Swansea, situated just off the busy road at the junction of Llansamlet lights. The Plough nestles in the shadow of the parish church. A bright, cheery, open-plan pub with a large, cosy log fire at one end which adds to the warmth of the welcome. As well as the Brewery beers, the pub sells a tempting menu for the weary traveller with a restaurant upstairs (bookable for parties of 10 or more). A pleasant alternative to the town pubs. 🏚🕭&≠P

LLANTWIT FARDRE

Bush Inn
Main Road
🕓 4 (12 Sat)-11; 12-4, 7-10.30 Sun
☎ (01443) 203958
Hancock's HB; guest beers 🅷

Small, single-bar village local, popular with its loyal, mostly mature clientele. Generally a quiet pub with side room, TV for major sports events, darts and cards available and a garden. Trips/tours to sports events are regularly organised and in-house sports competitions frequently run. Small car park. 🕭♣P

LLANTWIT MAJOR

King's Head
East Street (in the centre of the old town)
🕓 11-11; 12-10.30 Sun

☎ (01446) 792697
Brains Dark, Bitter, SA, seasonal beers; Worthington Bitter 🅷

Warm, friendly welcome awaits in this local. There is a largish bar with a roaring fire and traditional pub games. A big-screen TV is used for sports events and there is music played in the bar (mainly) at weekends. In the refurbished lounge, good bar meals and snacks are served (12–2) at reasonable prices. There is a children's menu and a separate dining area. 🏚🕭🕭🍴♿♣

Llantwit Major Social Club
The Hayes, Colhugh Street (entrance on main beach road)
🕓 11.30-3.30 (not Wed), 6.30-11; 12-2, 7-10.30 Sun
☎ (01446) 792266
Hancock's HB; Worthington Bitter; guest beer 🅷

Large, imposing building dating from the late 19th century, close to the historic town hall and St Illtyd's church. Set in its own grounds there is a huge car park at the front and back of the building. The club offers pool, darts and two snooker tables. Teams are entered in many local fundraising events. Regular activities include Sat night entertainment and Tue afternoon line dancing for older patrons. Thu has line dancing; lunchtime beginners, early eve for children and all ages and abilities later eve. Wye Valley and Eccleshall feature regularly among the guest beers. Q🕭♿🍴♣P

MACHEN

White Hart Inn
Nant Ceisiad (100 yds N of A468 under railway bridge) OS203892
🕓 12-3, 6.30-11; 12-11 Sat; 12-10.30 Sun
☎ (01633) 441005
Hancock's HB; guest beers 🅷

Convivial country inn enjoyed by drinkers and diners alike. Fine wood panelling (much salvaged from the luxury liner *Empress of France*) adorns the walls throughout. One particularly impressive circular panel is on the ceiling of the main bar. This room also has a welcoming real fire in the corner. There is a cosy ante-room off the bar and a large function room, opened for Sun diners and the regular mini beer festivals. The catholic range of guest beers is ever-changing and may include an offering from the embryonic in-house brewery. 🏚🕭🍴🕭P

INN BRIEF

LLANGYNWYD
Corner House
11-11;
12-10.30 Sun
Brains Bitter, SA; guest beer 🅷
Comfortable, traditional country pub in a small historic village. Food available.

LLANTRISANT
New Inn
26 Swan Street
12-11;
12-10.30 Sun
Worthing Bitter; guest beer 🅷
Traditional pub serving an ever-changing, well-kept guest beer. Food available on weekdays and Sun lunchtimes only.

LLYSWORNEY
Carne Arms
12-11; 12-10.30 Sun
Ushers Best Bitter, Founders Ale 🅷
On B4268. The pub has a floral entrance area and inglenooks in both bars. Meals in lounge bar. Local community pub.

MERTHYR TYDFIL
Tregenna Hotel
Park Terrace
12-3, 5.30-11; 12-4, 7-10.30 (eves-summer only) Sun
Draught Bass; guest beer 🅷
Pleasant lounge bar in a family-run three-star hotel, ideally placed for exploring the nearby Brecon Beacons National Park.

NEATH
Liberal Club
18 Orchard Street
12-3, 6-11; 11.30-11 Sat;
12-3, 6.30-10.30 Sun
Tomos Watkin BB; guest beer 🅷
Friendly, lively atmosphere. Ideal for town-centre shoppers. Thu is curry and pint night.

NOTTAGE
Farmer's Arms
Lougher Row
11.30-11; 12-10.30 Sun
Greene King Ruddles County; Worthington Bitter; guest beer 🅷
Popular, rambling pub by the village green. Live music most nights in one bar.

MERTHYR TYDFIL ✧

Dic Penderyn
102-103 High Street
✪ 11-11;
12-10.30 Sun
☎ (01685) 385786
**Brains SA; Theakston Best Bitter;
Worthington Bitter; guest beer** Ⓗ
This busy Wetherspoon's pub is named after one of the leaders of the Merthyr riots of 1833. He was later executed and has become a local hero. The premises have been converted from what was a very large 19th-century general store. There is a pleasant room dedicated to the famous Welsh composer Joseph Parry, where his family records and photographs are displayed. There are also many historic photographs of Merthyr when it was a major iron-producing town. The railway and bus stations and a large car park are nearby.
Q ◑ ♿ ⧖ ♣ ♠ ✗ ●

MISKIN

Miskin Arms
Hensol Road
(150 yds off B4264 and opp. war memorial)
✪ 11-11; 12-10.30 Sun
☎ (01443) 224346
e-mail: miskinarms@aol.com
Hancock's HB; guest beer Ⓗ
Pleasant, village-centre one-bar pub opposite St David's church and war memorial. Extensive refurbishment in 2000, now incorporates the Mayfields restaurant with two full-time chefs preparing Thai food, daily 'around the world' curries, and some very fine, adventurous menus (food not served Sun eve). It is well-decorated throughout with several old settles in bar. A wooden decking area outside the lounge doors leads on to the sunken garden, children's play area and car park. Has regular rotating menu of guest ales. The proprietors are willing to order any real ale suggested.
❀ ◑ ♿ ▲ P

MONKNASH

Plough & Harrow
Off B4265
✪ 12-11;
12-10.30 Sun
☎ (01656) 890209 website:
www.theploughandharrow.com
Draught Bass; Ⓖ **Cottage Golden Arrow; Hancock's HB; Shepherd Neame Spitfire; Taylor Landlord;** Ⓗ **guest beers** Ⓗ/Ⓖ
Local CAMRA *Pub of the Year* 2000. Ancient country pub serving up to 10 beers and a cider in two bars with real fires. Range of guest beers constantly changes. Now also selling a wide range of bottle-conditioned beers. Excellent food served every lunchtime and weekday eves. This pub oozes character and is popular with locals, walkers and cyclists. Summer beer garden with children's swings. The pub hosts a variety of special events throughout the year. Live music on Sun eves. Limited parking but on local bus route No. 145 between Bridgend and Llantwit Major.
🚶 ❀ ◑ ♣ ♠ P

MOUNTAIN ASH

Jeffreys Arms
Jeffrey Street
✪ 12-11 (may vary in winter); 12-10.30 Sun
☎ (01443) 472976
Worthington Bitter; guest beers Ⓗ
Popular and lively village pub, set in a quiet side street not far from the main road. Photographs of Mountain Ash in bygone times adorn the walls of the basically-furnished public bar, while the plush, well-appointed lounge allows customers a greater degree of comfort. Having recently been refurbished, the pub now boasts a beer garden. Upstairs is a pleasant function room and restaurant, the latter offering a good menu of home-cooked food (booking is advisable). ❀ ❑ ≷ ♣

MUMBLES

Park Inn
23 Park Street
✪ 12-2.30, 4.30-11; 12-11 Sat; 12-10.30 Sun
☎ (01792) 366738
Swansea Three Cliffs Gold; Tomos Watkin OSB; Worthington Bitter; guest beers Ⓗ
Perennial back-street local, where conversation is the order of the day. The beer range (three guests) features beers from local brewers. A splendid collection of pump clips decorate the bar. Popular with locals and visitors alike, the meals are all home-cooked, with daily specials always available. Current Swansea CAMRA *Pub of the Year*, this pub is a must during any visit to the area. A quiz is held each Thu eve. The street in which the pub is situated is a regular winner of the *Mumbles In Bloom* competition. Q ◑ ♣ ♠ 🖥

Victoria Inn
21 Westbourne Place
✪ 12 (11.30 Sat)-11; 12-10.30 Sun
☎ (01792) 360111
Draught Bass; Worthington Bitter; guest beer Ⓗ
Lovely old back-street, corner local dating from the mid-19th century, as the name implies. The pub has been stylishly renovated, retaining the stained glass windows and making a feature of the old pub well which was undoubtedly the water source in the days when the pub brewed its own beer. The pub is a single room although there are two distinct areas – the bar area has darts and TV while the other end is a little quieter. Note the collection of photographs of 'Victoria Inn local heroes' which include many famous sporting celebrities. ❀ ♣

MURTON

Plough & Harrow
88 Oldway
✪ 11-11; 12-10.30 Sun
☎ (01792) 234459
e-mail: plough&harrow@hotmail.com
Courage Best Bitter, Directors; guest beer Ⓗ
Historic village inn reputed to be one of the oldest in Gower, which has been enlarged and renovated recently. It still retains its character, however, and manages to combine its popular food trade with its tradition as a village local. The bar has darts, TV and a pool table, popular with younger

customers, while the lounge is a comfortable place to enjoy a quiet chat or a bar meal. The present licensee has brought a reputation for quality beer with him from the Park Inn, Mumbles, which he previously managed. Quiz night is Tue.
Q ⊛◑ ♣ P

MWYNDY

Barn at Mwyndy

Down lane opp. corner Park Garage on A4119
OS056816
✪ 11-3, 5-11; 11.30-11 Sat; 12-10.30 Sun
☎ (01443) 222333
Worthington Bitter; guest beers Ⓗ
Converted 16th-century Welsh long barn with an intriguing array of farming and fishing memorabilia, note the coracle. There is a split-level bar, the lower area has a thatched canopy and the upper area a log fire in winter. Reputed sightings of a female ghost upstairs. Excellent restaurant with a no-smoking room, reservations advised for Sun lunch (no food Sun eve). Amenities include conference facilities, a beer garden, children's play area and a large car park. Regular beer festivals hosted and an enthusiastic pétanque team plays frequently. Up to six guest beers are served. Local CAMRA *Pub of the Year* 2001.
♨ ⊛◑ ♿ P

NEATH ✿

Highlander

2 Lewis Road (on Stockhams roundabout on A474)
✪ 12-2.30, 6-11; 12-11 Sat; 12-3.30, 7-10.30 Sun
☎ (01639) 633586
Draught Bass; Worthington Bitter; guest beers Ⓗ
Genuine free house, this imposing building is situated between the British Legion and the Methodist church, about 200 yards from Neath river bridge. Comfortable one-bar town pub with lots of wood, and an elevated eating area downstairs plus an upstairs restaurant which enjoys a well-deserved reputation locally for its good-value food. Free buffet provided Sun eve. Wide variety of guest ales served from all over the country (and occasionally further afield), three of which are usually on offer. Not a pub for binge drinkers.
◑ ≠

Star Inn

83 Pen-y-dre (near Neath RFC ground)
✪ 12-11; 12-2.30, 7-10.30 Sun
☎ (01639) 637745 website: star-inn-neath.co.uk
Draught Bass; Hancock's HB; Tomos Watkin OSB; guest beer Ⓗ
Popular back-street local near the Neath Canal and national cycleway, where strangers don't feel out of place and where the landlord runs a splendid pub and cooks the food. The beer is handpumped from 1940s beer engines – no swan-necks or sparklers here. Star Bitter comes from Wye Valley Brewery. It is wonderfully mad on match days (Neath RFC) and Six Nations Tournaments. Boules played and pub competitions held in summer. The historic building dates from about 1700. A trouble-free, genuine free house. Local CAMRA *Pub of the Year* 2001.
Q ⊛◑ ≠ P ⚹

574

NEWTON (Porthcawl)

Jolly Sailor

Church Street
✪ 11-11; 12-10.30 Sun
☎ (01656) 782403
Brains Dark, Bitter, SA; guest beers (summer) Ⓗ
Fine old nautical pub decorated with ships' fittings, note the fine bell behind the bar. The smuggler's tunnel has now been bricked up. The pub overlooks the village green and the ancient defensive church. Live music is performed on Sun eve in the lounge. Parking is very limited outside the pub, please park behind the Ancient Briton (also a Brains house). ♨ Q ⊛◑ ⊟ ♣ P

NEWTON (Gower)

Newton Inn

New Well Lane (opp. garage)
✪ 12-11; 12-10.30 Sun
☎ (01792) 365101
Draught Bass; Ⓗ/Ⓖ **Fuller's London Pride; Worthington Bitter; guest beer** (occasional) Ⓗ
Popular village local refurbished about 10 years ago but still retaining bar and lounge areas in a semi open-plan layout. The pub offers very competitively priced meals with wine included and is popular with diners at lunchtimes and early eves. The bar has a big-screen TV which is much-used for sporting events. The draught beers, particularly the Bass, can be drawn straight from the cask on request. Quizzes are held on Mon and Wed. Tables are set outside the pub, alongside the road.
⊛◑ ⊟

NORTON

Beaufort

1 Castle Road (turn by Norton House Hotel, off Mumbles road)
✪ 11.30-11; 12-10.30 Sun
☎ (01792) 407001
Draught Bass; Fuller's London Pride; Worthington Bitter Ⓗ
Old-fashioned locals' pub dating from the 18th century, with traditional public bar and smaller, comfortable lounge; both have real fires. The bar has darts and a TV, a quiz is held every Tue. There are photographs of the annual Mumbles Raft Race on the walls including one splendid picture of a raft built to replicate the pub itself! The Beaufort still has its characters and retains its friendly charm. ♨ Q ⊛ ⊟ ♣

OGMORE BY SEA

Pelican In Her Piety

Ewenny Road
✪ 11.30-11; 12-10.30 Sun
☎ (01656) 880049 website: www.pelicanpub.co.uk
Draught Bass; Fuller's London Pride; Greene King Old Speckled Hen; Wadworth 6X; Wells Bombardier; Young's Special Ⓗ
A splendid refurbishment has been carried out (see website) since the new regime took over in autumn, 1999. High standards and superb quality with a top chef and the finest ingredients to work with. A log fire in winter creates a very cosy atmosphere. Now truly a village local once more, where non-locals are very welcome and lots of charity events are run for an autistic children's

hospice. Cask ale is a sparkler-free drink (they will not put them on). Ogmore Castle is nearby. ♨Q☼❄☺◖♠P

PANT

Pant-Cad-Ifor
By mountain railway
☼ 12-11 (12-3, 7-11 winter Mon); 12-10.30 Sun
☎ (01685) 723688
Hancock's HB; Worthington Bitter; guest beers Ⓗ

The Pant-Cad-Ifor (Ivor's Chair in the Hollow) is a plush, bustling village pub situated near the Brecon mountain railway and makes an ideal starting or finishing point for rail enthusiasts. Popular with locals and visitors alike, it offers a fine range of guest ales, a real cider and good food from the restaurant. Pleasant decor and a real fire welcome people in. The beams are festooned with a bewildering array of pump clips showing past guest beers and an extensive collection of water jugs.
♨❄◖♣P

PENARTH

Royal Hotel
1 Queen Street
☼ 11-11; 12-10.30 Sun
☎ (029) 2025 6888
Bullmastiff Gold Brew, Son of a Bitch, seasonal beers Ⓗ

Street-corner pub with friendly locals and plenty of interesting characters. This is the brewery tap for Bullmastiff beers (CAMRA National *Champion Bitter* 2000), there are twice-yearly beer festivals featuring the whole range of Bullmastiff beers plus guests. The beers are very moderately priced. An occasional disco or Karaoke is staged at weekends and hog roasts, etc. are available on request. Supporters of rugby events are welcome. A maritime theme reflects Penarth's proud seafaring tradition.
❄♐❄⇄(Dingle Rd) ♣

PENLLYN

Red Fox Inn
Off A48
☼ 12-3, 6-11; 12-3, 7-10.30 Sun
☎ (01446) 772352
Tomos Watkin Whoosh, BB, OSB, seasonal beers Ⓗ

A warm welcome awaits in this lovely, family-run village pub. The bar boasts a roaring log fire. The charming restaurant (no-smoking) has a fine menu. Food is also served in the bar, the menu and prices are the same. The cuisine is varied and of first-class quality. Children are welcome. Regular summer barbecues are held in the large orchard beer garden. Saved from closure and conversion to houses by locals in 2000 and bought by Tomos Watkin, this is the sort of pub that one enters as a stranger and leaves as a friend. ♨Q❄◖♣P

PONTARDAWE

Pontardawe Inn
123 Herbert Street
☼ 12-11; 12-10.30 Sun
☎ (01792) 830791
e-mail: peter@acres2000.freeserve.co.uk
Brains Buckley's Best Bitter, Rev. James; guest beers Ⓗ

Attractive, two-bar, village inn, with a riverside location. Interesting selection of local history displayed in the bar. Large car park and outside family area with attractive hanging baskets during summer periods. Home to Pontardawe Music Festival, it also hosts live music Fri and Sat eves. Regular beer festivals held. There is a boules court at the rear. Good food served (no meals Tue or Sun eves). The pub is known locally as the Gwachel. It is served by local bus route.
❄◖⊟&♣P

PONTLLANFRAITH

Crown
Bryn View
☼ 12-3, 5-11; 12-11 Fri & Sat; 7-10.30 Sun
☎ (01495) 223404
Courage Best Bitter; John Smith's Bitter; guest beers Ⓗ

Two-roomed pub surrounded by roads on all sides. A basic public bar and a spacious lounge and dining area. A haven for both locals and golfers alike. Large car park, outside drinking area and children's play equipment in the garden. It can get busy with families at weekends and on fine summer eves. Regular quiz nights on Tue are hosted by the landlord.
❄◖♣P⅄

PONTYCLUN ❋

Windsor Hotel
Llantrisant Road
(centre of town near the railway station)
☼ 11-11, 12-10.30 Sun
☎ (01443) 223800
e-mail: jarretlisa@supanet.com
Hancock's HB; guest beers Ⓗ

Fairly large, town-centre pub with the bar catering for the sports-orientated locals. The lounge has been recently renovated and redecorated; it is the quiet area of the pub. The reasonably-priced meals are very popular here. In summer the attractive patio is excellent for *al fresco* activities, together with a new children's play area. A function room is available for private meetings.
Q❄◖⊟&⇄♣P

PONTYPRIDD

Llanover Arms
Bridge Street
☼ 12-11; 12-3, 7-10.30 Sun
☎ (01443) 403215
Brains Dark, Bitter, SA; Worthington Bitter; guest beer Ⓗ

To the north of town, opposite the renowned Ynysynhard Park, this 18th-century free house has been kept by the same family for over 100 years. Once slaking the thirst of chainmakers and bargees, it now attracts discerning drinkers of all ages and from all walks of life. Consisting of a small bar, snug and vestry, each area has its devotees who appreciate the timeless feel of the pub and its convivial atmosphere. Interesting artefacts on display include old enamel signs, photographs and maps. Two mirrors advertise the delights of Dunvilles Irish whisky and Worthington IPA.
❄⊟⇄♣P

PORTHCAWL ❄

Lorelei Hotel
36-38 Esplanade Avenue
☼ 5 (4 Fri; 12 Sat)-11; 12-10.30 Sun
☎ (01656) 788342
Draught Bass; ⑤ Shepherd Neame Spitfire; Ⓗ Wye Valley Butty Bach; ⑤ guest beers Ⓗ
Enterprising bar in a small hotel that runs several beer festivals each year. Situated just off the seafront, the bar is small but comfortable with a dining area to the rear of the premises. Meals served 12–3 Sun and 6–9 Mon–Sat. Cider is stocked occasionally. Neath and Bridgend CAMRA *Pub of the Year* 2000. Well worth visiting this oasis of real ale in a mainly keg seaside town.
❀🏠◑Ⓐ♣

PORT TALBOT

Lord Caradoc
69-72 Station Road
☼ 11-11; 12-10.30 Sun
☎ (01639) 896007
Draught Bass; Brains SA; Theakston Best Bitter; Worthington Bitter; guest beers
Spacious, open-plan Wetherspoon's pub with a large L-shaped bar. Close to the railway station. Excellent selection of beers offered. It has an outdoor drinking area, wheelchair facilities and a no-smoking area. Good value meals; chips, burgers, vegetarian dishes, desserts, tea and coffee are served at all sessions. All staff are friendly and efficient. Q❀◑🔥♿✕✘●

QUAKERS YARD

Glan Taff
Cardiff Road (on A4054 between Abercynon and Treharris)
☼ 12-4, 7-11; 12-4, 7-10.30 Sun
☎ (01443) 410822
Cain's Bitter; Courage Best Bitter, Directors; John Smith's Bitter; Wells Bombardier; guest beers Ⓗ
Comfortable inn displaying a large collection of water jugs, boxing memorabilia and photographs of local and historical interest. A well-appointed pub which enjoys a warm and friendly atmosphere on the side of the River Taff and close to the Taff Trail. Walkers and cyclists break their journey for refreshments to sample a cool, refreshing glass of beer and enjoy the good food that is served (no eve meals Sun). This is a long-standing *Guide* entry and well worth a visit. Q❀◑P

REYNOLDSTON

King Arthur Hotel
Higher Green
☼ 12-11; 12-10.30 Sun
☎ (01792) 390775
Draught Bass; Felinfoel Double Dragon; Worthington Bitter; guest beer (summer) Ⓗ
Imposing village pub and hotel/restaurant popular with both locals and tourists. The King Arthur is named after Arthur's Stone, a prehistoric monument standing on the nearby Cefn Bryn Hill, which is well worth a visit. The hotel is situated in a pleasant spot in the middle of the Gower Peninsula and has a large outdoor drinking area. It is reputedly haunted with not one, but two ghosts. Meals from varied menus are served in the bar as well as the restaurant and family room and outside.
🛏Q🛌❀🏠◑🍴Ⓐ♣P

RHYDYPANDY

Masons Arms
Rhydypandy Road, Morriston (follow signs to hospital then Rhydypandy road for 1½ miles)
OSSN6602
☼ 12-11; 12-10.30 Sun
☎ (01792) 842535
Draught Bass; Courage Best Bitter, Directors; guest beers (occasional) Ⓗ
17th-century inn with two bars; now owned by the Unique Pub Co. Watch out for the low-beamed ceiling in the lounge and the wood panelling in the bar. Diners travel for miles to enjoy the good value food served (12–2.30 and 7–9.30) daily. The lounge is a no-smoking area during Sun lunches. There is a juke box and live music every Wed plus monthly Sat Karaoke night. The darts team plays on Sun. The pub has plenty of seating outside and enjoys a thriving local following. 🛏❀◑🍴♣P

RHYMNEY

Farmers Arms
Brewery Row
☼ 12-11; 12-10.30 Sun
☎ (01685) 840257
Boddingtons Bitter; Brains Bitter; Fuller's London Pride; guest beer Ⓗ
Friendly, spacious, comfortable pub and restaurant, traditionally furnished. Originally a farmhouse, taken over by the former Rhymney Brewery which opened in 1839. Extended to provide a function room for up to 40 people. Furnishings and bric-à-brac reflect a farming theme together with Rhymney Brewery memorabilia and interesting old photographs. Popular with locals and train-spotters alike, the nearby railway (Valley Lines–Rhymney Valley) frequently runs diesel locomotive-hauled services. Traditional card games are popular, especially cribbage. Good, reasonably priced food and a separate dining area. Regular guest beer is usually from small independent micros. Beer garden. ❀◑🍴♣●

RISCA

Fox & Hounds
Park Road
☼ 11-11; 12-10.30 Sun
☎ (01633) 612937
Beer range varies Ⓗ
Bustling village pub situated away from the main road, overlooking the park. Pleasantly decorated, the single bar offers guest ales from predominantly local micro-breweries, with the next beers due to arrive displayed on a blackboard. A pool table at one end and a large TV screen at the opposite end cater for all sports fans. A good range of bar meals is available and a beer festival is usually held between Christmas and New Year. ❀◑♣P

RUDRY

Maenllwyd Inn
At crossroads SE of Rudry
☼ 11-11; 12-10.30 Sun

☎ (029) 2088 2372
Courage Best Bitter, Directors; Theakston XB; guest beer Ⓗ

Sympathetically extended 400-year-old country inn. With low-beamed ceilings and grey stone walls (the Welsh equivalent being maenllwyd), it was originally a farmhouse at the time of the Civil War and has possible links with the mighty Caerphilly Castle. There have been reported sightings of two ghosts, one is a legless cavalier (not due to drink, but the original floor level was lower). Well-kept beers and an extensive, varied menu offered daily. 'Hops and turkey, carp and beer, came into Wales all in one year' (1520) is one of the old sayings displayed in the pub.
🏚Q🛇🏵🌑P

ST BRIDE'S MAJOR

Farmers Arms
Wick Road (B4265)
🕓 12-2.30, 6-11; 12-3.30, 6-10.30 Sun
☎ (01656) 880224 e-mail: nigel@pubonthepond.co.uk
Courage Best Bitter; John Smith's Bitter; Ushers Best Bitter, Founders Ale Ⓗ

Busy, welcoming bar and restaurant at the eastern end of the village opposite the village pond, locally known as 'the pub on the pond'. China plates adorn the walls and plinths and assorted water jugs hang from the ceiling. There is a water feature in the doorway. A justifiably regular entry in the *Guide*, with customers treated to a friendly atmosphere with good beer and food served in an old-fashioned, farmhouse-style setting. 🏚Q🏵🌑P

ST HILARY

Bush Inn
½ mile off A48 near TV mast
🕓 11.30-11; 12-10.30 Sun
☎ (01446) 772745
Draught Bass; Greene King Old Speckled Hen; Ⓖ **Hancock's HB** Ⓗ

Stunningly attractive, thatched inn dating from the 16th century and sympathetically extended. Award-winning restaurant meals are all home-made under the auspices of one French and one Welsh chef (no food Sun eve). Families welcome and high chairs provided. The bar features a stone-flagged floor, low beams and hops on the wall. The Weston's Old Rosie cider is always in residence as is the ghost of a highwayman who usually stays upstairs. Tables available for outside drinking and car parks at front and rear. There should be more pubs of this quality.
🏚Q🏵🌑🍴P

SIGINGSTONE

Victoria Inn
🕓 11.45-3, 6.30-11; 12-3, 7-10.30 Sun
☎ (01446) 773943
Tomos Watkin Whoosh, OSB, seasonal beer Ⓗ

This busy pub was renamed during Victoria's jubilee year, previously called the Moor's Head. In the past little attention was seemingly paid to beer quality, but things have changed dramatically since Tomos Watkin's takeover. Still keeping its high standards in food, the beer quality has risen sharply, coming very close to winning the vale's *Most Improved Pub of the Year* award. The large, well-decorated lounge serves bar meals with a bust of Queen Victoria looking on. A small front bar has a large print of Victoria's coronation. There is a separate beamed restaurant upstairs.
Q🏵🌑P

SKEWEN

Crown
216 New Road
🕓 12-11; 12-10.30 Sun
☎ (01792) 411270
Brains Dark, Bitter, SA Ⓗ

Village-centre pub with a comfortable locals' bar, plus a split-level modern lounge. Upstairs is a snooker room with a bar. The pub sells the best range of Brains beers in the area.
🏵🚲🍺♣

INN BRIEF

NOTTAGE
Rose & Crown
Heol y Capel
11-11; 12-10.30 Sun
Courage Best Bitter, Directors; guest beers Ⓗ
Smartly-kept old pub with a rustic ambience, 'Dickensian' but pleasantly modernised.

PONTYCLUN
Pontyclun Rugby & Sports Club
Windsor Park
11.30-11; 12-10.30 Sun
Hancock's HB; John Smith's Bitter; guest beer Ⓗ
Well-appointed club, offering guest beers. Occasional beer festivals held. Bar meals available Tue-Sat.

PORTHCAWL
Royal Oak
1 South Road
11.30-11; 12-10.30 Sun
Draught Bass; Worthington Bitter; guest beer (occasional) Ⓗ
Comfortable pub on the fringe of the shopping area. A pub of character.

SWANSEA
Potter's Wheel
85-86 Kingsway
11-11; 12-10.30 Sun
Courage Directors; Theakston Best Bitter; Worthington Bitter; guest beers Ⓗ
Large Wetherspoon's city-centre outlet serving meals all day. Real cider and up to three guests. *Cask Marque* accredited.

SWANSEA
Red Lion
49 Sway Road, Morriston
11-11; 12-10.30 Sun
Beer range varies Ⓗ
The pub has one cask ale available at any time, supplied by the Valley Brewery. Meals available 12-2.30 and 5.30-9.30 Mon-Sat, 12-2 Sun.

SWANSEA
Singleton Hotel
1-2 Dillwyn Street
11-11; 12-10.30 Sun
Wadworth 6X; guest beers Ⓗ
City-centre pub with live music Sat and Karaoke Fri and Sun. Lunches only. Guest beers change regularly in this Unique Pub Co. outlet.

TREFOREST
Otley Arms
Forest Road
11-11; 12-10.30 Sun
Bullmastiff Gold Brew; Cains Bitter; Hancock's HB; guest beer Ⓗ
Multi-roomed pub, popular with both students and locals for its keenly priced ales and lunchtime food. Good venue for TV sport.

WEST CROSS
West Cross Inn
43 Mumbles Road
11-3.30, 5.30-11; 11-11 Sat; 11-10.30 Sun
Flowers Original; Wadworth 6X; Worthington Bitter Ⓗ
Popular pub and restaurant in a splendid position on the edge of Swansea Bay, on the route of the old Mumbles railway.

> ✳ symbol next to a main entry place name indicates there are Inn Brief entries as well.

SWANSEA ❖

Brynymor Hotel
Brynymor Road
☼ 11.30–11; 12–10.30 Sun
☎ (01792) 466650
Draught Bass; Ind Coope Burton Ale Ⓗ
Well-established outlet on fringe of city
centre, now operates as a Punch Retail
Taverns 'Mr Q's' with one large bar. Caters
mainly for the local student population
with pool tables, juke box, large-screen TV
and occasional discos, but still retains a
significant number of local regulars of
mixed age. It is a rare local outlet for Burton
Ale. Meals served 12–8 Mon–Sat and
12–3.30 Sun. There is a front patio for
outdoor drinking.
🏠◑

Eli Jenkins Ale House
24 Oxford Street (near bus station)
☼ 11–11; 12–10.30 Sun
☎ (01792) 630961
**Badger Tanglefoot; Draught Bass; Worthington Bitter;
guest beers** Ⓗ
Large, modern city-centre Bass Taverns
outlet named after a character in *Under
Milkwood* by Dylan Thomas. Much wood
throughout with wooden alcoves and
niches. The walls are adorned with
memorabilia, old books, etc. and some
references to Dylan Thomas. Good value
meals served 11.30–7 Mon–Sat and 12–3.30
on Sun. Very popular with city-centre
diners and gets very busy during weekday
lunchtimes. The guest beer is changed
frequently. Wheelchair WC. ◑◔ ♿

Queen's Hotel
Gloucester Place
☼ 11–11; 12–10.30 Sun
☎ (01792) 521531
**Brains Buckley's Best Bitter; Theakston Best Bitter,
Old Peculier; guest beers** (occasional) Ⓗ
Well-established, genuine free house on the
edge of the city centre and marina. High-
ceilinged, one-bar outlet with strong local
support. The walls have many photographs
depicting the maritime history of the area
and the pub co-hosts the sea shanty festival
in the first week of July. Quizzes every Sun
and Wed with monthly Karaoke and live
music on bank holiday Mon. Selective juke
box music. Meals served 12–2.30 daily with
Sun lunches a speciality. Rare regular outlet
for Old Peculier. Small TV room at back for
sport. 🏠◑

Vivian Arms
6 Gower Road, Sketty
☼ 12–11; 12–10.30 Sun
☎ (01792) 516914
Brains Bitter, SA, Rev James Ⓗ
Long-standing *Guide* entry: situated on
Sketty Cross, a Brains-managed house.
Recently sympathetically refurbished and
now a one-bar pub. Lots of wood and walls
adorned with a mixture of modern art and
pictures of old Swansea, still retains some
stained glass windows. Lunches 12–3 daily
and eve meals 6–8 Mon–Fri. Large-screen TV
for sport. Small, walled, pretty beer garden
to rear. Piped music only and quiz night
held on Mon. Wheelchair WC.
🏠◑♿●

Westbourne Hotel
1 Bryn-y-mor Road
☼ 12–2.30, 5.30–11; 12–11 Fri & Sat; 12–2.30,
7–10.30 Sun
☎ (01792) 476637
Draught Bass; Hancock's HB; guest beer Ⓗ
This recently well-refurbished pub is now an
Enterprise Inn free house. Still retains two
bars and the large slate Bass wall plaque, but
a much improved internal layout. Good
value meals served 12–2 daily and 6–8
Mon–Fri. No-smoking area during meal
times. Sporting pictures and a few
interesting brewery mirrors hang on the
walls. Guest beer changes weekly and the
pub boasts over 270 guest ales in the last
five years. Also retains its dartboard. Piped
music is played and quizzes held (Mon).
The pub is handy for both the football and
rugby grounds. Regular *Guide* entry.
🏠◑♣♠

THREE CROSSES

Poundffald Inn
☼ 12–11; 12–10.30 Sun
☎ (01792) 873428
**Greene King Abbot, Old Speckled Hen; Marston's
Pedigree; Worthington Bitter** Ⓗ
Welcoming village local on the edge of
Gower. Traditional public bar with log fire
and big-screen TV for sporting events. There
is an interesting collection of horse bits, old
kettles and other rural implements. The
name Poundffald refers to the old circular
animal pound that has been incorporated
into the lounge bar. The 'ffald' half of the
name is the Welsh word for pound and so
we have the name in both languages
together. The lounge is mainly orientated
towards food and the reasonably priced
menu includes hot Welsh curries. *Swansea
in Bloom* award-winner 1999 and 2000.
🛏🏠🏠◑♣♠P

TONDU

Llynfi Arms
Maesteg Road
☼ 12 (1 Mon & Tue)–4, 7–11; 12–3, 7–10.30 Sun
☎ (01656) 720010
Draught Bass; Worthington Bitter Ⓗ
Roadside pub with a lively bar and a
comfortable lounge with a railway theme. It
is encircled by a working model railway.
Beers are always in perfect condition. Hosts
a quiz and live music eve on Fri, there are
quiz, pool and darts teams. Meals are served
12–2 Wed–Sun and 7–9.30 Wed–Sat.
Booking is advised for eve meals.
◑◔♣♿≠

UPPER CHURCH VILLAGE

Farmers Arms
St Illtyd's Road
☼ 11–11, 12–10.30 Sun
☎ (01443) 205766
Draught Bass; Brains Bitter; Hancock's HB Ⓗ
Oldest pub in the parish, dating from 1703.
Its plain white walls still give it the
appearance of a country pub. The one long
bar is more modern, but has touches of an
earlier age, such as the fireplaces.
Decorations include photographs of the
pub, plus an eclectic collection of plates and

rugby memorabilia. The history of the village on one wall is worth reading, and one can check how many of St Illtyd's five keys are represented among the customers. Warm welcome for everyone. Sat breakfast sessions, with traditional fry-up, are always popular. Lunches served Mon–Sat.
❁◖P

WICK

Star Inn
Ewenny Road (B4265)
◷ 2-3.30 (not winter), 6 (7 Sat) 11; 12-10.30 Sun
☎ (01656) 890519
Hancock's HB; Worthington Bitter; guest beer Ⓗ
Friendly, quiet roadside pub close to the Bristol Channel beaches and St Donats. It has a spacious bar and a smaller lounge. Rescued from closure by an excellent, conscientious husband and wife ownership eight years ago, they have maintained the same high standards ever since. The guest beer changes regularly and the only noise is the pleasant sound of conversation (the piano does not work). Deservedly won a CAMRA special award for being the only pub in the area to always serve all cask ale in oversized lined glasses.
ᨇQ❁◖ 🏠♣P🍴

YNYSTAWE

Millers Arms
634 Clydach Road (next to school)
◷ 11.30-3, 6-11; 11.30-11 Sat; 12-3, 7-10.30 Sun
☎ (01792) 842614
Flowers Original; Wadworth 6X; guest beers Ⓗ
Welcoming pub enjoying a reputation for good food both in the bar and adjoining restaurant. Visitors should note the unusual teapot collection. It is handy for bus routes into the city and there is a car park at the

rear. The guest beer sometimes comes from the local Tomos Watkin Brewery, now a thriving Welsh independent. Q◖P🍴

YSTALYFERA

Wern Fawr Inn
47 Wern Road
◷ 7-11; 1-3, 7-10.30 Sun
☎ (01639) 843625 website: trust.ystalyfera.org
Bryncelyn Buddy Marvellous, Oh Boy, Buddy's Delight, Ⓗ
Cosy two-roomed brew-pub consisting of a lounge and bar heated by an old stove. The bar displays a large collection of bygone domestic and industrial curios and 1960s music is regularly played. The owner of the local Bryn Celyn Brewery is a big fan of Buddy Holly. Bryncelyn translates as Holly Hill and even the two house dogs are named Buddy and Holly. Popular with local CAMRA members, well worth finding but check the opening hours.
ᨇ🏠♣🍴

YSTRAD MYNACH

Royal Oak
Commercial Street
◷ 12-3, 5.30-11; 12-11 Sat; 12-3, 7-10.30 Sun
☎ (01443) 862345
Draught Bass; Hancock's HB Ⓗ
Unmistakable 'Brewers Tudor' style pub on a busy road junction. There are some noteworthy examples of acid-etched windows, displaying the former owners – Giles & Harrap, the long-defunct Merthyr Tydfil brewers. Separate dining area with good food and a busy public bar which includes discrete areas. Interesting selection of old photographs of the area. Outside drinking area available.
❁◖ ⇌♣P

Fishy business

CAMRA and the Good Beer Guide probably receive more enquiries concerning beers suitable for vegetarians and vegans than any other subject. Brewers use isinglass to 'fine' or clear cask-conditioned beers of yeast. Isinglass is made from the swim bladders of the sturgeon. Its use dates from the 18th century and it is high time that the brewing industry found a better method, especially as the sturgeon is in danger of being fished to extinction as a result of the demand for caviar. Irish moss is used to clarify the 'hopped wort' in the brewing copper prior to fermentation, and, along with other natural plants and herbs, could be a substitute for isinglass. The problem is that publicans are under intense pressure to serve and empty casks as fast as possible, and isinglass works more quickly than other clearing agents. However, by the time a cask of beer has 'dropped bright' in a pub cellar, isinglass, dead yeast cells and other detritus will have settled in the belly of the cask, and will not be served in the glass along with the beer. Most producers of bottle-conditioned beers also use isinglass, though a few do use Irish moss or other forms of what are called 'auxiliary finings'. As a small step forward, it would be useful if brewers indicated on bottle labels whether or not they use isinglass. Better still, the industry should look at less environmentally harmful methods of clearing both cask- and bottle-conditioned beers.

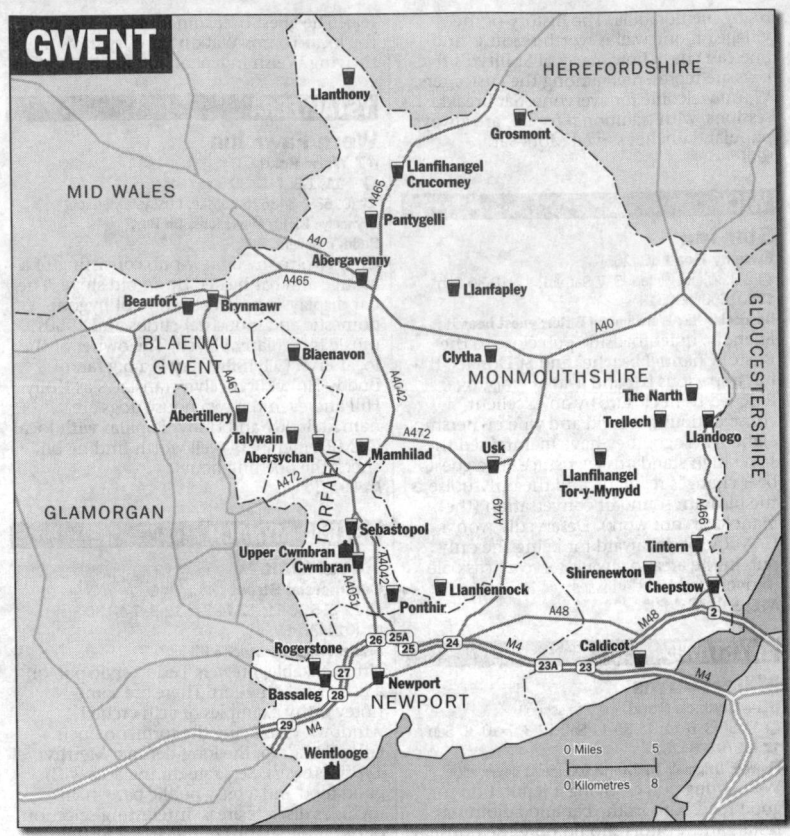

GWENT

(Map of Gwent showing locations including Llanthony, Grosmont, Llanfihangel Crucorney, Pantygelli, Abergavenny, Llanfapley, Beaufort, Brynmawr, Blaenavon, Clytha, Abertillery, The Narth, Trellech, Talywain, Abersychan, Mamhilad, Usk, Llandogo, Upper Cwmbran, Sebastopol, Llanfihangel Tor-y-Mynydd, Tintern, Cwmbran, Llanhennock, Ponthir, Shirenewton, Chepstow, Rogerstone, Caldicot, Bassaleg, Newport, Wentlooge. Surrounding areas: Herefordshire, Mid Wales, Gloucestershire, Blaenau Gwent, Monmouthshire, Glamorgan, Torfaen.)

ABERGAVENNY ✤

Somerset Arms
Victoria Street (on jct with Merthyr Rd)
☼ 12-11; 12-10.30 Sun
☎ (01873) 852158
Draught Bass; Worthington Bitter; guest beer Ⓗ
Make the short walk from the town centre to this traditional pub, with public bar and separate, comfortable lounge. On summer days the patio provides another pleasant area. Since becoming a free house the pub's popularity has increased dramatically. The bar is far from the traditional male-only environment. Music from the landlord's extensive CD collection plays unobtrusively, while prominent sports fixtures feature on TV. Choose the lounge for a quieter atmosphere. Delicious, home-cooked meals are excellent value. Book for Sun lunch. Two en-suite rooms available.
❀⇌◑🖟♣

ABERSYCHAN

Buck Inn
8 Station Street
☼ 12-11; 12-10.30 Sun
☎ (01495) 772152
Greene King Abbot Ⓗ
Popular pub on the main Pontypool-Blaenavon road (handy for local bus services). An open-plan bar leads to a function/games room on a higher level at the rear. Here there is a pool table and skittle alley; teams compete in local leagues. While there is only one cask beer available, it has a good following and some devotees swear it is the best Abbot Ale for miles around, a fine compliment to a landlord with a good track record. ♣

White Hart
Broad Street
☼ 12-11; 12-10.30 Sun
☎ (01495) 772924
Beer range varies Ⓗ
A former hotel, this pub retains features such as an old serving hatch. Friendly locals gather in the small front bar which serves as a base for the 'temperance' hillwalking club. Another more spacious bar and a pool room are at the rear, past the fruit machines, a popular haunt for younger folk. The cellar ovens are reputed to have been used by the Chartists to store gunpowder prior to their ill-fated march to Newport. One or two guest beers are available, usually from independent breweries. 🖟♣

ABERTILLERY

Commercial
Market Street (off High St)
☼ 12-3 (not Mon), 6.30-11 (12-11 Fri & Sat); 12-10.30 Sun
☎ (01495) 212310
Worthington Bitter; guest beer Ⓗ
Popular town-centre pub where cask ale has

held its own against the 'cream-flow' onslaught. The large public bar has plenty of standing room, an indication of how busy it can get when sports fans gather to watch major events on the large TV screen. The front and rear lounge bars offer quieter and more comfortable surroundings. Food served lunchtime (not Mon), advisable to book for Sun. Handy for local shopping and main bus routes. ◑ ⌓ ♣

BASSALEG

Tredegar Arms
4 Caerphilly Road (1 mile N of M4, jct 28)
◑ 11-11; 12-10.30 Sun
☎ (01633) 893247
Brains Bitter; Fuller's London Pride; Greene King Abbott; guest beers Ⓗ/Ⓖ
Large cask ale house prominently positioned in a residential village on the outskirts of Newport. A traditional-style pub, the spacious interior has several linked areas on different levels, although the public bar is separate. A no-smoking area accommodates families and gives access to a large garden play area. It is popular with diners and a major attraction for cask ale lovers as it offers the widest selection in the area. The range is dominated by independent breweries with many different styles represented during the course of a year, particularly at the occasional beer festivals. ⋈ ❀ ❁ ◑ ⌓ ♣ P ⚲

BLAENAVON

Castle Hotel
94 Broad Street
◑ 11-11; 12-3.30, 7-10.30 Sun
☎ (01495) 792477
Beer range varies Ⓗ
Town-centre pub (with accommodation) where a friendly dog extends a canine greeting on entry. The interior has wooden beams, a bar decorated with humorous posters and many handpump stickers, a games room and a separate dining area. The one guest ale is on sale at a single competitive price, regardless of strength (always ABV 4% plus). A handy base for exploring local heritage sites, the old iron works, Big Pit Mining Museum, or the Pontypool & Blaenavon Railway. Advance notice required for eve meals. The town of Blaenavon has been designated a World Heritage Site by the United Nations. ⋈ ◑ ♣ P ⎚

Pottery
Llanover Road (off Ton Mawr Rd)
◑ 12-3 (not Mon & Tue), 6.30 (not Mon)-11, 12-11 Fri & Sat; 12-10.30 Sun
☎ (01495) 790395
Brains Bitter; guest beer Ⓗ
Formerly called the Oak, this pleasant, comfortable pub is thought to have taken its present name from the Blaenavon Blue pottery, once made locally. Split-level public bar has lovely mountainside views from the higher level at the rear and overlooks the garden and children's play area. The front bar is popular with diners, endorsing the pub's reputation for good home-made food (not served Mon & Tue, book on Sun). The low-priced Brains Bitter ensures a good throughput to maintain quality and is joined by a frequently-changing guest from another independent brewery. ❀ ◑ ⌓ & ♣ P

CALDICOT

Cross Inn
1 Newport Road
◑ 11-11; 12-10.30 Sun
☎ (01291) 420692
Draught Bass; Courage Best Bitter; guest beer Ⓗ
Busy, whitewashed pub at the old crossroads in the village centre. The wooden-floored lounge is based around a central fireplace and has a raised area where live bands play every Thu eve. The smaller public bar is popular for games with a pool table, dartboard and a collection of sporting trophies. A steady local trade, especially at weekends when it can become quite busy, ensures a good turnover of guest beers, which tend to lean towards higher gravities. Cider in summer. ⋈ ❀ ⌓ ♣ ♠ P

CHEPSTOW ❖

Castle View Hotel
16 Bridge Street
◑ 12-11; 12-10.30 Sun
☎ (01291) 620349
website: www.hotelschepstow.co.uk
Wye Valley HPA Ⓗ
Upmarket 350-year-old hotel, which used to be the home of the local mill-owner. Converted to a hotel 55 years ago, it is ideally situated opposite the oldest (1067) stone-built castle in Europe, which is often used in film locations. Note also the nearby 18th-century iron bridge over the River Wye. The pub does not have its own car park, but there is a large public one opposite. Good quality meals are served lunchtimes and eves. Only a small lounge bar, adventurously maintaining an excellent cask ale. ❀ ⇌ ◑ ⇌

CLYTHA

Clytha Arms
On B4598
◑ 12-3.30 (not Mon), 6-11; 12-11 Sat; 12-3, 7-10.30 Sun
☎ (01873) 840206
Draught Bass; Caledonian Deuchars IPA; Felinfoel Double Dragon; guest beers Ⓗ
Award-winning, rural pub, local CAMRA *Pub of the Year*. Superb old dower house, set in extensive grounds making it popular with families. It offers an attractive package for those seeking top-quality cask ales, real draught cider, excellent home-produced food (not Sun eve or Mon) and very comfortable accommodation. Traditional decor (check out the toilets!) and pleasant ambience. The range of beer styles showcased comes mainly from independent breweries, and Welsh beer and cheese festival is held in summer. ⋈ Q ❀ ⇌ ◑ ⌓ & ♠ P ⎚

INDEPENDENT BREWERIES

Cottage Spring Upper Cwmbran
Warcop Wentlooge

CWMBRAN ✲

Commodore Hotel
Mill Lane, Llanyravon (off Llanfrechfa Way, behind Crow's Nest pub)
🕐 11-3, 6-11; (Mary O'Brien's: 2-11, 12-11 Sat); 7-10.30 Sun (Mary O'Brien's 12-10.30)
☎ (01633) 484091
Beer range varies Ⓗ
Well-established, plush residential hotel run by the same family for 30 years. Excellent base for local attractions. The Pilliners Lounge is perfect for a relaxing drink and a good value bar meal. Tasty à la carte dishes are served in the Willows Restaurant. Downstairs, the more traditional Mary O'Brien's bar, named after the owner's late mother, offers a livelier atmosphere, and is particularly popular for eve entertainment. One or two cask beers are usually selected from the Brains range or the local micro-brewery, Cottage Spring.
❀⇔◑◲P

GROSMONT

Angel Inn
High Street
🕐 12-(3.30 Sat) 2.30, (not Thu); 6 (5.30 Sat)-11 (12-11 summer Sat); 12-10.30 Sun
☎ (01981) 240646 website: www.angel-inn.co.uk
Tomos Watkin Whoosh; guest beers Ⓗ
The village of Grosmont was once the third largest town in Gwent. Owain Glyndwr fought battles against the English nearby. The pub is a listed building, dating from the late 16th century. There is an unusual small town hall/market hall next door, and the 12th-century castle and church are close by. Beers are from small/micro-breweries, and are delivered direct from the brewery. There is a summer beer festival, and an annual sausage competition. Accommodation is available from April to August. Pétanque played. No meals served Wed eve.
❀⇔◑Å♣♦●

LLANDOGO

Sloop Inn
On A466
🕐 12-2.30, 5.30-11 (12-11 summer); 11.30-11 Sat; 12-10.30 Sun
☎ (01594) 530291
Wye Valley Dorothy Goodbody Traditional Bitter; guest beers Ⓗ
Traditional roadside pub taking its name

from the sloops that used to ply their trade between Bristol and Hereford. Standing below steep wooded slopes in a picturesque Wye Valley village, it makes an excellent base, having a comfortable standard of accommodation, for exploration of historic sites such as Tintern Abbey. The large public bar has a welcoming fire in cold weather and features large wooden masts between ceiling and floor. Good views of the River Wye can be had from the lounge, while the garden play area is popular with families.
🏚❀⇔◑◲P

LLANFAPLEY

Red Hart Inn
Old Monmouth Road (B4233 E of Abergavenny)
🕐 12-3, 7-11; closed Mon; 12-3 Sun
☎ (01600) 780227 website: www.redhartinn.co.uk
Draught Bass; Cottage Golden Arrow; guest beer Ⓗ
Welcoming old pub in a small village set in rolling countryside. Two generations of the same family work together here. An annexe off the bar has a pool table. The excellent food can be eaten in the restaurant or bar (eve meals Tue-Sat). During the winter months there is a blazing log fire. Cottage Ales are a rarity for the area, however, at least one is always on sale. Very pleasant garden; enjoy the view with a pint.
🏚Q❀◑♣P

LLANFIHANGEL CRUCORNEY

Skirrid Inn
Hereford Road (off A465, 4 miles N of Abergavenny)
🕐 12-3, 6-11; 12-11 Sat & summer; 12-10.30; 12-3, (7-10.30 winter) Sun
☎ (01873) 890258
Draught Bass; Ushers Best Bitter, seasonal beers Ⓗ
This famous pub is reputedly the oldest in Wales. Once a court as well as a hostelry, locals were sentenced to be hanged by judges, including Judge Jeffreys, after the Monmouth Rebellion (you can still see the beam allegedly used for hangings). Impressive in scale and solidly-built, this pub has immense stone flags on the floors, powerful beams, bare brick walls and a large fireplace dominating the main room. As a modern pub, its good quality beers are complemented by excellent accommodation and highly-praised food (eve meals Tue-Sat) and a pleasant garden.
🏚Q❀⇔◑◲P

INN BRIEF

ABERGAVENNY
Coach & Horses
41 Cross Street
11-11; 12-3, 7-10.30 Sun
Brains SA; Flowers IPA; Wadworth 6X Ⓗ
Near the bus station. A rare local outlet for Flowers and Wadworth beers. Features quality jazz sessions.

Station
37 Brecon Road
5-11 (Mon-Wed); 12-11 (Thu-Sat); 12-3, 7-10.30 Sun
Draught Bass; Freeminer Bitter; Hancock's HB; Tetley Bitter Ⓗ
Central feature of the real ale scene in town – a rare outlet for Free-miner beer. Traditional interior.

BEAUFORT
Rhyd-y-Blew
Rassau Road, Carmeltown
11.30-3, 6.30-11; 12-3, 7-10.30 Sun
Brains SA; Gales HSB; guest beer Ⓗ
Community focused pub with a multi-level interior and a name meaning 'Ford of the Hairs' – best ask!

BRYNMAWR
Gold Diggers Arms
122 King Street
12-11; 12-4, 7-10.30 Sun
Beer range varies Ⓗ
Traditional-style, two-roomed pub that has carved out a niche for itself among cask ale drinkers in the area.

CHEPSTOW
Coach & Horses Inn
Welsh Street
12-11; 12-10.30 Sun
Brains Buckley's Best Bitter; Rev James Ⓗ
Convenient central pub, inexpensive accommodation and good food. Occasional guest beer.

CWMBRAN
Bush Inn
Graig Road, Upper Cwmbran
12-3, 7-11;
12-3, 7-10.30 Sun
Cottage Spring Crow Valley Bitter Ⓗ
Cosy and very popular hillside pub giving far-reaching views on a good day. Unofficial brewery tap of Cottage Spring micro-brewery.

LLANFIHANGEL TOR-Y-MYNYDD

Star Inn

Follow Llansoy signs OS459023
🌣 11.30-3, 6.30-11; 12-3, 7-10.30 Sun
☎ (01291) 650256

Ind Coope Burton Ale; Marston's Pedigree; guest beer Ⓗ

Large inn with an unusually friendly atmosphere. An impressive, ornately carved reception desk faces visitors on entry. Large, separate dining area and a smaller lounge with an enormous log fire, usually jealously guarded by a huge dog. A bar runs off the lounge. Extensive menu of delicious, home-cooked food offered. Cottage to let in grounds with comfortable accommodation for five people; camping and caravan site also available. John Wesley visited in 1748 describing it as 'a good though small inn'.
🏚Q✿🛏�🍴🕭♣P

LLANHENNOCK

Wheatsheaf Inn

Approx 1 mile off main Caerleon-Usk road OS353927
🌣 11-11 (11-4, 6-11 Mon & Wed in summer); 12-4, 7-10.30 Sun
☎ (01633) 420468

Draught Bass; Worthington Bitter; guest beer Ⓗ

Charming pub, with a strong community focus, situated on a hill with superb views overlooking the Usk Valley and south Gwent. A huge crest of arms, of unknown origin, dominates one wall and there is an old Rhymney Brewery hobby horse model. Resident pets seek fuss and attention while darts and boules are played enthusiastically. Outside, admire the ornate hedge trimming and iron rings once used for tethering horses. An old railway semaphore signal sits uncomfortably in the car park though the village was never served by the railway. Worth a visit.
🏚✿🕭♣P

LLANTHONY

Half Moon Inn

Off A465(T) at Llanfihangel Crucorney (Skirrid Inn)
OS288279
🌣 12-4 (not Mon-Fri), 7 (6 Sat Apr-Oct)-11 (not Mon-Thu Nov-Mar); 12-3, 7-10.30 Sun
☎ (01873) 890611

Bullmastiff Gold Brew, Son of a Bitch, seasonal beer Ⓗ

Fine, traditional pub and restaurant

providing an opportunity to sample award-winning Bullmastiff ales; a brewery to which it has remained steadfastly loyal for many years. The bar has several original features such as a flagstone floor. The bar billiards table is a rare sight these days. Set beneath a challenging high ridge that is popular with walkers, and in the heart of peaceful countryside, it is a short stroll from the magnificent ruins of Llanthony Abbey. Advisable to ring and check opening times and the availability of food.
🏚Q✿🛏🕭🌖🍴♣🕭P⚬

MAMHILAD

Star Inn

Folly Lane (off A4042 at roundabout)
🌣 11.30-3, 6-11; 11-11 Sat & summer; 12-10.30 Sun
☎ (01495) 785319

Draught Bass; Hancock's HB; guest beers Ⓗ

Popular, country pub with hop-adorned beams, 100 yards from the Monmouthshire & Brecon Canal (down Folly Lane at Bridge No. 62). Two guest beers usually available. A large log fire ensures a warm welcome in winter months. The picturesque churchyard opposite is reputed to contain the oldest yew trees in the county. Good food available from a varied menu; see blackboard for daily specials. No food Mon Jan-April. There is a children's play area in the beer garden and ample parking available. Cottage to let.
🏚✿🛏🕭🌖P

THE NARTH

Trekkers

2 miles E of Trellech, off B4293 OS525064
🌣 11-3.30, 6-11; 11-11 Sat; 12-10.30 Sun
☎ (01600) 860367

Felinfoel Best Bitter; Freeminer Bitter; guest beer Ⓗ

Built in the style of a log cabin, this pub is situated on the Wye Valley ridge. Originally a pony-trekking centre; hence the name. The large garden and play area at the rear boast fine views of the surrounding area. Ideally placed for exploring the picturesque countryside, a large stock of guide books and maps of walks are available. Home-cooked local and British dishes are a speciality, booking is strongly recommended. The skittle alley doubles as a family room.
🏚🛏✿🕭🌖🍴♣P

Mount Pleasant Inn
Wesley Street
12-3, 7-11;
12-3, 7-10.30 Sun
Ushers Best Bitter, Founders Ale Ⓗ
Homely pub with a comfortable split-level interior, set in a terrace in the heart of old Cwmbran.

NEWPORT
Handpost
2 Bassaleg Road
11-11; 12-10.30 Sun
Ansells Bitter; Draught Bass; Ind Coope Burton Ale; guest beer Ⓗ
Popular roadside pub with a spacious open-plan interior that still gives an impression of discreet areas.

PONTHIR
Ponthir House Inn
Candwr Road
11.30-11; 12-4, 7-10.30 Sun
Draught Bass; Hancock's HB; guest beer Ⓗ
Attractive, whitewashed village inn with a well-decorated interior. The dining area has an unusual teapot collection.

SHIRENEWTON
Tredegar Arms
The Square
12-3 (may vary), 6-11; 12-11 Sat;
12-4, 7-10.30 Sun
Greene King Ruddles Best; Hancock's HB; guest beers Ⓗ
Village-centre, locals' pub with a public bar and games area and small lounge/restaurant.

Guide site

Keep your copy of the Good Beer Guide up-to-date by contacting the CAMRA website where you will find information about changes to pubs and breweries

www.camra.org.uk/gbg

NEWPORT ❄

Godfrey Morgan
158 Chepstow Road, Maindee
☺ 11-11; 12-10.30 Sun
☎ (01633) 221928
Brains Dark, SA; Theakston Best Bitter; Tomos Watkin BB; Worthington Bitter; guest beer Ⓗ
Since opening in 1999 this Wetherspoon's outlet has encouraged many people back to drinking in Maindee. The Godfrey Morgan (named after a local family member who rode in the Charge of the Light Brigade) is always busy. This conversion of a former cinema and bingo hall looks deceptively small from the outside, however, the interior opens out into a large, pleasantly decorated multi-level pub. Memorabilia of Newport celebrities and long forgotten cinemas are displayed. Two separate no-smoking areas are available. Wheelchair access is via the car park entrance.
Q ◑ ▶ & P ⌿ ●

Hornblower
126 Commercial Street
☺ 11-11; 12-10.30 Sun
☎ (01633) 668001 e-mail: andrew.bates@virgin.net
Brains SA; Young's Bitter; guest beers Ⓗ
Busy, one-bar ale house in the town centre. An extensive juke box caters for rock'n'rollers. Live music every Thu night, usually blues and rock bands. A small wall plaque gives a potted history of the pub. One of the three guests is always a mild, a beer style which it champions. Others include a premium ale and a best bitter. The walls abound with bikers' memorabilia. No children admitted. Five real ales and a guest cider are always available. ≈ ♣ ◉

Red Lion
47 Stow Hill (500 yds from train and bus stations)
☺ 11-11; 12-10.30 Sun
☎ (01633) 264398
Draught Bass; John Smith's Bitter; Ushers Best Bitter; seasonal beer Ⓗ
Unspoilt pub just outside the centre of Newport, five minutes from the museum and art gallery. Basic one-roomed bar, with a coal fire in winter. Shove-ha'penny is played by the locals, and a pool table is available. A large TV screen is rolled out for sports events. Note the old-style beer pumps on display by the bar. Live music performed every Fri, and the local folk club meet upstairs on Thu. Founding place of Gwent CAMRA branch. No children admitted.
▲ ⊛ ◁ ≈ ♣

St Julian Inn
Caerleon Road (outskirts of Caerleon)
☺ 11.30-11; 12-10.30 Sun
☎ (01633) 243523 e-mail: swill96340@aol.com
Courage Best Bitter; John Smith's Bitter; guest beer Ⓗ
Popular, CAMRA award-winning pub, a former coaching inn dating back to 1836. Panoramic views from the wood-panelled lounge, and the attractive verandah overlooks the River Usk. The remains of the Roman amphitheatre in Caerleon are almost opposite. Large pub divided into several distinct areas; sketches of Welsh castles are displayed around the bar. Pool and darts are played and there is a skittle

alley downstairs. Hosts occasional league quiz nights and sporting events are shown on the large screen TV. Families are welcome. ⊛ ◑ ▶ ♣ P

PANTYGELLI

Crown Inn
Old Hereford Road (off A465, 4 miles N of Abergavenny)
☺ 11.30-3 (not Mon), 6.30-11; 12-3, 7-10.30 Sun
☎ (01873) 853314 e-mail: yeoldcroen@aol.com
Draught Bass; Fuller's London Pride; Hancock's HB; guest beers Ⓗ /Ⓖ
Thriving pub with attached restaurant in a hamlet near Abergavenny, nestling between the Sugar Loaf and Skirrid Mountains. Fine views from the flower-decked patio. Good beer and food (no meals Sun eve), plus live music, quizzes, treasure hunts and barbecues help to explain its popularity. Interesting, often unusual guest beers supplement the regular ales, while the way that the open-plan bar is divided creates a feeling of smaller, intimate drinking areas. Two miles off the main road, this pub is well worth a detour. ▲ ⊛ ⌂ ◑ ▶ ⚓ ♣ P

ROGERSTONE

Tredegar Arms
157 Cefn Road (approx 1 mile from M4 jct 27)
☺ 12-3, 6.30-11; 12-11 Thu-Sat; 12-4, 7-10.30 Sun
☎ (01633) 664999
Draught Bass; Courage Best Bitter; guest beer Ⓗ
Traditional roadside pub, very popular with locals and ramblers. The Sirhowy Valley walk, 14 locks and the Cwmcarn Forest drive are all close by. Dating from before 1860, the pub has maintained many original features including the flagstone floors and ceiling beams. It boasts a sun terrace and garden area, with barbecues in the summer. The award-winning restaurant provides an excellent traditional Sun lunch (booking advisable). Sports coverage is provided by large TV in the bar. There is an under 14s indoor area. ⊛ ◑ ▶ ⊟ P ⌿

SEBASTOPOL

Open Hearth
Wern Road (access via South St or Station Rd/Austin Rd)
☺ 11.30-4, 6-11; 11-11 Sat; 12-4, 7-10.30 Sun
☎ (01495) 763752
Archers Golden; Greene King Abbot; Hancock's HB; RCH Pitchfork; Wye Valley Bitter; guest beers Ⓗ
CAMRA award-winning, canalside favourite. Eight beers are usually on tap including unusual guests. The towpath is popular in fine weather, look out for the resident wildfowl. The large enclosed beer garden has a children's play area. A cribbage tournament is an annual event. Well-behaved dogs are welcome in the bar, also families in the adjoining room. Excellent and varied menu available – large parties (up to 56) catered for in the downstairs restaurant. Ample car parking. ⊛ ◑ ▶ ♣ P

SHIRENEWTON ❄

Carpenters Arms
Usk Road (B4235)
☺ 11-2.30; 6-11; 12-3, 7-10.30 Sun
☎ (01291) 641231

website: www.chepstow.co.uk/adverts/carps

Flowers IPA; Fuller's London Pride; Marston's Pedigree; Theakston Old Peculier; Wadworth 6X; guest beer Ⓗ

Attractive 400-year-old pub which boasts seven different rooms, flagstone floors and low wooden beams. The building used to be three separate businesses – a blacksmith's and a carpenter's shop were once on either side, now merged into the pub. Antiques and memorabilia adorn the walls and ceilings. Enjoy the two log fires in winter, while in summer hanging baskets provide a blaze of colour outside. Popular with locals and tourists. High quality home-cooked food served (not Sun eve). Over 50 malt whiskies are available. ♨Q℃⊛◖♣P

TALYWAIN

Globe Inn
Commercial Road
✪ 7 (12 Sat)-11; 12-4, 7-10.30 Sun
☎ (01495) 772053
Brains Dark, Bitter; guest beer Ⓗ

A cask ale oasis in a locality where other pubs have given up the cause. It is a traditional locals' pub with a distinctive and colourful 'Globe' sign hanging over the entrance. The intimate public bar has a cosy, real fire while the lounge plays host to live entertainment at weekends and has a pool table situated unobtrusively at the rear. A real hub of the community, it has a good local trade and thriving sports teams that compete in local leagues. Popular mini beer and cider festival held in spring. ♨⊞♣⛴

TINTERN

Cherry Tree Inn
Devauden Road (off A466 at Royal George Hotel)
OS526001
✪ 12-2.30, 6-11; 12-11 Sat; 12-10.30 Sun
☎ (01291) 689292
website: www.thecherry.co.uk
Greene King Old Speckled Hen; Hancock's HB Ⓖ

The only Welsh pub to appear in every edition of this *Guide*, it is starting to rival the ancient abbey ruins as the village's major attraction. Found in a tranquil spot, this small, cosy pub still displays the handsome original Hancock's Toastmaster sign. The new owners have made a couple of significant changes: there is now a second cask beer on sale, and excellent food is available at all reasonable times. A philosophy circle meets on the third Tue of the month. Quizzes and dominoes are popular. Limited parking. ♨⊛◖♣⛴P

TRELLECH

Lion Inn
On B4293, Chepstow-Monmouth road
✪ 11-3, 6 (7 Mon, 6.30 Sat)-11; 12-3 (closed eve) Sun
☎ (01600) 860322
Bath SPA; Wadworth 6X; guest beers Ⓗ

Close to the historic Trellech Standing Stones ancient monument, this popular village pub runs quizzes, cribbage teams and a whisky club. Split-level, it has a raised dining area and a lower public bar. Bath Ales are frequent guests. Regulars can request their choice of future beers on a blackboard. The prize-winning food includes some unusual and exotic dishes.

One corner of the pub displays award certificates from local competitions. ♨℃⊛◖⊞♣

USK

Greyhound Inn
1 Chepstow Road
✪ 12-3, 6-11; 12-3, 7-10.30 Sun
☎ (01291) 672074
website: www.greyhoundinn.freeserve.co.uk
Hancock's HB; guest beers Ⓗ

Cosy pub with a single, L-shaped room, decorated with old photographs and other items of local interest. A pub has been on the site for about 450 years; once it was a major junction serving Monmouth and Chepstow, now a peaceful location on the edge of town. Popular with local regulars who appreciate good conversation in quieter surroundings – this is definitely not a young persons' pub with vibrant nightlife! Three guest ales are normally on sale to wash down the tasty home-cooked food. ⊛◖P

King's Head Hotel
18 Old Market Street
✪ 11-11; 12-10.30 Sun
☎ (01291) 672963
Badger Tanglefoot; Fuller's London Pride; Taylor Landlord; guest beers Ⓗ

Fine, town-centre hotel which is something of a mecca for local real ale enthusiasts. Cask beer is served only in the split-level lounge, a pleasant place to relax with a huge log fire and comfortable armchairs. It is decorated with many items connected with the landlord's passion for fly-fishing. A small alcove off the lounge is used mainly as a dining area. The food is of a very high standard and, unsurprisingly, fish features prominently on the menu. Trade is a good mix of locals and visitors. ♨⇆◖♣P

Nag's Head
Twyn Square
✪ 11-3, 5.30-11; 12-3, 6.30-10.30 Sun
☎ (01291) 672820
Brains Buckley's Best Bitter, SA, Rev James Ⓗ

Centrally-located pub, probably better-known for its fine food. Many visitors travel a considerable distance to dine here. It has been run by the same family for 35 years. Delightful 500-year-old building, the main bar has original wooden beams and an intimate snug with a fine set of etched windows. To the rear is a cosy, no-smoking family room. Tables on the pavement outside are ideal for sunny, summer days. Virtually all the produce served is of Welsh origin (including the beer), with game a speciality. Booking is advisable for weekend meals. Q℃⊛◖✗●

Star pubs

Pubs with a star symbol next to their names are listed in CAMRA's National Inventory of pubs with interiors of outstanding interest. The full list is printed in the guide.

MID WALES

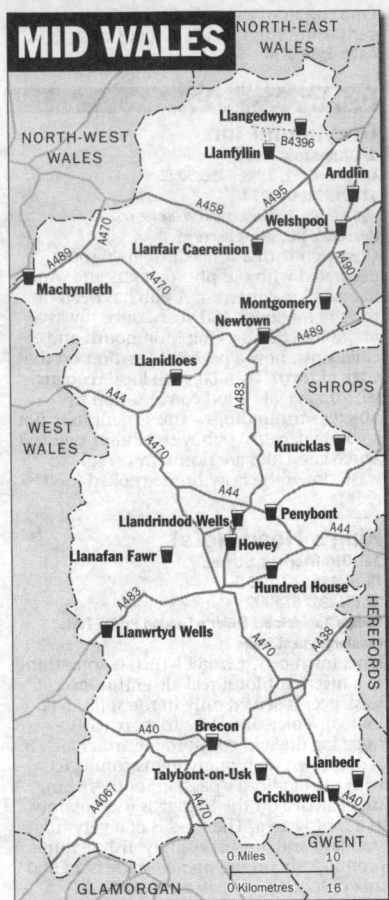

NORTH-EAST WALES

NORTH-WEST WALES

WEST WALES

Llangedwyn
Llanfyllin · B4396
Arddlin
A458 · A495
Welshpool
Llanfair Caereinion
A489 · A470
Machynlleth
Montgomery
Newtown
A489
Llanidloes
A483 · SHROPS
A44 · A470
Knucklas
A44
Penybont
Llandrindod Wells
Howey · A44
Llanafan Fawr
Hundred House
A483 · HEREFORDS
Llanwrtyd Wells · A470 · A438
A40
Brecon
Lianbedr
Talybont-on-Usk
Crickhowell · A40
A4067 · A470 · GWENT
GLAMORGAN

0 Miles 10
0 Kilometres 16

BRECON

Bull
86 The Struet
☼ 12-2.30, 7-11; 12-3, 7-10.30 Sun
☎ (01874) 622044
Beer range varies Ⓗ
Alongside the river, just below the cathedral, the Bull offers the best choice of real ale in Brecon. A constantly changing range of guest beers and foreign and British bottled beers are stocked. Addlestone's cider and a decent lager (Budvar) are served. There are two bars but three distinctive drinking areas. The pub publishes its own monthly magazine. Well worth visiting while in the town. ⚫◑ ⊟⚫

George
George Street (off The Struet)
☼ 11-11; 12-10.30 Sun
☎ (01874) 623422
Greene King Abbot; Ind Coope Burton Ale; guest beers Ⓗ
Smartly refurbished family-run hotel with an upmarket bar, separate bistro and a conservatory giving a splendid view of old Brecon. The bistro is only open eves and serves bottle-conditioned beers. The extensive and imaginative menu uses local ingredients and offers vegetarian and children's choices. ⚫◑P

Old Boar's Head
14 Ship Street (by the river)
☼ 11.30-2.30, 5.30-11 (longer in summer); 11-11 Fri & Sat; 12-4.30, 7-10.30 Sun
☎ (01874) 622856
Everards Tiger; Fuller's London Pride; guest beers Ⓗ
Old riverside pub with two bars, a spacious rear one for the younger set and a smart, modern bar at the front. Photographs of flooded Brecon adorn the walls of the front bar. The pub may open longer in summer, when lunches are also available. ⚫⚫◑⊟⚫P

CRICKHOWELL

Bear Hotel
High Street
☼ 11-3, 6-11; 12-3, 7-10.30 Sun
☎ (01873) 810408 website: www.bearhotel.co.uk
Draught Bass; Greene King Old Speckled Hen; Hancock's HB; guest beer (occasional) Ⓗ
Originally a 15th-century coaching inn, now a hotel that has won numerous awards. The attractive wood-panelled bar has a lovely olde-worlde atmosphere. It is universally popular and has an extensive, inventive menu. Crickhowell is an ideal base for exploring the Black Mountains. The Monmouthshire–Brecon Canal passes close by. Bus No. 21, Abergavenny to Brecon, serves the town (not Sun or eves). ⚫Q⚫⚫⚫◑ ⊟P

HOWEY

Drovers Arms
Off A483, 1½ miles S of Llandrindod Wells
☼ 12-2.30 (not Tue), 7-11; 12-2.30, 7-10.30 Sun
☎ (01597) 822711 website: www.drovers-arms.co.uk
Beer range varies Ⓗ
Stylish, red-brick Victorian building housing this pleasant two-bar inn. It is on the original drovers' route, with a 13th-century cellar. Some woodcarving in the charming bar is reputedly part of a staircase from Penybont Hall. The exclusive house beer, Drovers Ale, is brewed by Wood of Wistanstow, Shropshire, but may on occasion be replaced by ales from other small breweries. Excellent, traditional food is served using Welsh produce where possible. Home-made puddings accompany main courses with Welsh and English cheeses. Booking advisable for Sun lunch. This pub has won a huge array of awards and has been a regular entry in this *Guide* since 1987. ⚫Q⚫⚫◑ ⊟Å⚫P

HUNDRED HOUSE

Hundred House Inn
Near Llandrindod Wells
☼ 11-11 (Easter to late autumn); 12-10.30 Sun
☎ (01982) 570231
Draught Bass; guest beers Ⓗ
Former drovers' inn set in a prominent roadside position with fine views of the surrounding upland scenery. The ground floor is a series of connected rooms. The public bar and lounge retain original fireplaces. The games room and no-smoking restaurants (supper licence) are later additions, but the joins don't show too much! The pub has its own fishing club – Rainbow Trout Fishery nearby, ample

parking and en-suite accommodation. The Hundred was an ancient Anglo-Saxon administrative subdivision of the shire or county, their origins now lost in the mists of time.

⚒Q☆◑◧⬚&♣♠P

KNUCKLAS

Castle Inn
100 yds off B4355 in village centre
✪ 12-2.30, 6.30-11; 12-2.30, 7-10.30 Sun
☎ (01547) 528150 e-mail: inncastle@aol.com
Draught Bass; guest beer H

Prominent building in the centre of the village, dating back to the 16th century and once home to one of Oliver Cromwell's generals. It retains original stonework, exposed wooden beams and an inglenook in the main bar. A snug-cum-dining area doubles as a Post Office on Tue and Thu mornings. A larger restaurant and guest accommodation can be found behind the pub. Knucklas lies in beautiful and serene border countryside. Memories of its less peaceful past abound, however; Offa's Dyke is two miles away and there are several castles nearby including one overlooking the pub.
⚒☆❀◑◧Å⇌♣P

LLANAFAN FAWR

Red Lion
On B4358, Newbridge on Wye to Beulah road
✪ 12-2 (closed Jan-Mar), 6-11; 12-2; 6-10.30 Sun
☎ (01597) 860204
website: www.homepages.which.net/~adrian.f
Worthington Bitter; guest beers H

Dating from 1472, or possibly earlier, this pub retains an olde-worlde character with huge beams, despite being in place for over 500 years they are thought to be secondhand. Other materials have been recycled; the shaped stones around the fireplace and the large floor slates probably come from Llanafan church. A booklet describing the history of the pub and local area is on sale (produced by the current owners). A yew in the village churchyard is one of the oldest trees in Britain, thought to be 2,200 years old. The pub offers an excellent, varied menu and live outdoor music.
⚒Q☆❀◑◧⬚&♣P⤧

LLANBEDR

Red Lion
OS241204
✪ 12-2.30 (not winter Mon & Tue), 7-11; 12-11 Sat; 12-3, 7-10.30 Sun
☎ (01873) 810754
Brains Buckley's Best Bitter; guest beers H

Set in a small village in the scenic Black Mountains, this pub was originally owned by local brewers Facey's of Abergavenny, then Roberts of Aberystwyth, then Hancock's of Cardiff before finally becoming a free house. Situated next to the church, this charming pub is the heart of the small community as well as being popular with hillwalkers. It may open longer in summer. Winter weekday lunchtime hours may vary, so please ring first to check if travelling far.
⚒Q☆❀◑◧Å♣P

Conservative Club
South Crescent
✪ 11-2, 5.30-11; 11-11 Fri & Sat; 12-10.30 Sun
☎ (01597) 822126
Worthington Bitter; guest beers H

The club occupies much of what was the Lansdowne, a hotel with 19th-century links. This was when the development of Llandrindod Wells took off with the coming of the railway to the town and the 'taking of the waters' – a fashionable part of Victorian life. The club, centrally placed in the town, has a large lounge, TV room, smaller games bar, snooker (2) and pool tables, a small patio at the front and a larger, enclosed garden with seating on the opposite side of the road. The ever-present Worthington Bitter is accompanied by a constantly changing guest beer – up to four most weeks. Occasional entertainment and cooked lunches on offer. Non-members must be signed in to this quiet and comfortable club. Q❀◑&⇌♣♠

Llanerch 16th-Century Inn
Llanerch Lane (by police station)
✪ 11.30-2.30, 6-11; 11.30-11 Sat; 12-10.30 Sun
☎ (01597) 822086 e-mail: llanerchinn@ic24.net
Hancock's HB; guest beers H

Originally Llanerchderion – 'resting place by the glade for coaches' – the 16th-century Llanerch was built as a staging post, and still retains many of its original features such as a Jacobean staircase and an inglenook in the lounge bar. With large garden and orchard at the front and views of the Cambrian foothills at the rear, it has easy access to the railway station and town centre. A vigorous guest beer policy is operated, with many from smaller craft breweries. The inn, with its many-roomed, split-level interior, has a no-smoking lounge up to 8pm. A comprehensive menu of snacks and home-made meals is available. Dining room opens eves only. Quizzes and live music are hosted occasionally, with boules in summer and the Llanerch boules league. The inn has its own drive, car park and secure storage for cycles. Limited wheelchair access. Q⬚❀◑◧&⇌♣♠P⤧

Royal British Legion
Tremont Road (A483, between hospital and fire station)
✪ 7 (12 Sat)-11; 12-10.30 Sun
☎ (01597) 822558
Ansells Bitter; Draught Bass; Worthington Bitter; guest beers H

This friendly club is just outside the town centre. It offers a comfortable lounge and a games room with snooker, pool, darts, quoits, dominoes and now skittles after the purchase of a portable mat, which is available for hire. Non-members must be signed in. Coaches welcome. South and Mid Wales CAMRA *Club of the Year* 1999 and 2000. ⬚◑&⇌♣♠P

Goat Hotel
High Street (A458)
✪ 11-11; 12-10.30 Sun
☎ (01938) 810428
Brains Rev James; Hancock's HB; guest beer H

Delightful beamed inn with a welcoming atmosphere, popular with locals. The comfortable lounge has plush leather armchairs and settees. Old Weston's cider photographs are displayed. A large inglenook and fire dominate the lounge. The public bar offers a pool table and there is a separate restaurant area. Home-cooked food and excellent accommodation provided. ♨☆⇔◖◗✑♣P

LLANIDLOES ❋

Mount Inn
China Street
🕐 11-11; 11-3, 5.30-11 Sat; 12-10.30 Sun
☎ (01686) 412247
Draught Bass; Worthington Bitter Ⓗ
Excellent town-centre inn with two basic public bars, a separate TV and games room, and a plush, comfortable lounge. One bar has a tiled floor while the other has a listed stone floor, originally from a castle which stood on this site. This bar also has an attractive stove and two settles. Food is served in the lounge. ♨Q☆⇔◖◗✑♣P

LLANWRTYD WELLS

Neuadd Arms Hotel
The Square (A483, Builth Wells-Llandovery road)
🕐 11.30-11 (may close afternoons); 12-3, 7-10.30 Sun
☎ (01591) 610236
website: www.s-h-systems.co.uk/hotels/neuaddarms
Felinfoel Double Dragon; Hancock's HB; guest beers Ⓗ
Situated on the picturesque 'Heart of Wales' railway line, the smallest town in Wales offers regular beer festivals in Jan (Saturnalia) and Nov (Mid-Wales) as well as hosting the world Bog-Snorkelling Championships in Aug. The Neuadd Arms is a large, imposing Georgian hotel, extended in Victorian times. The bar and lounge provide distinct drinking areas. The menu has a good choice of curries available. ♨Q☆⇔◖◗✑▲✦♣P✂

Stonecroft Inn
Dolecoed Road (off A483)
🕐 12 (5 winter Mon-Thu)-11; 12-10.30 Sun
☎ (01591) 610332
website: www.s-h-systems.co.uk/hotels/stonesra
Brains SA; guest beers Ⓗ
Open-plan Victorian pub, popular with locals and visitors alike; a good base for touring the area. The attractive patio garden has a barbecue area. Families are welcome at this Mid-Wales beer festival venue. Food is available all day. Accommodation is

in the adjoining independent youth hostel. The song 'Sospan Fach' was composed nearby. ♨☆⇔◖◗▲✦♣P

MACHYNLLETH

Skinners Arms
Main Street (A487)
🕐 11-11; 12-10.30 Sun
☎ (01654) 702354
Burtonwood Bitter; guest beer Ⓗ
Town-centre, timbered local, with a plush, comfortable, stone-walled lounge bar and a no-smoking eating area. This is set around an impressive stone inglenook. The public bar has a friendly, comfortable feel with a wood floor, subdued lighting and a pool table. A good selection of food is available in the lounge, and bar snacks in the public bar. Meals are served 12–2 and 6–9 daily. The pub attracts a wide range of customers. ☆◖◗✑≠♣

Wynnstay Arms Hotel
Maengwyn Street (off A487)
🕐 11-11; 12-10.30 Sun
☎ (01654) 702941 website: www.wynnstay-hotel.com
Brains Bitter; guest beers Ⓗ
Very friendly, small bar in a town-centre hotel. The main room is beamed with a large open log fire creating an excellent setting. Small rooms off to the side are quiet and offer a relaxing retreat if you want to get away from the crowd. A new bar and games area with a pool table is being built to the rear of the hotel. Guest beers are served from a wide range of breweries. ♨Q☆⇔◖◗≠♣P✂

MONTGOMERY

Dragon Hotel
Off B4385
🕐 11-3, 6-11; 12-3, 7-10.30 Sun
☎ (01686) 668359 website: www.dragonhotel.com
Beer range varies Ⓗ
Excellent plush bar in a 17th-century coaching inn. This hotel is a two-star establishment in the town centre. The bar walls are covered with bric-à-brac and the beams and masonry are reputedly from the local castle which was destroyed by Oliver Cromwell. The hotel has good facilities, including an indoor, heated swimming pool and a function room catering for 20–100 people. The bar stages jazz Wed eve and the beer range includes guests from independent breweries including Wood's. Q⇔◖◗♣P

INN BRIEF

Horseshoe Inn
A483
12-3, 5.30-11; 12-10.30 Sun
Worthington Bitter; guest beer Ⓗ
Pleasant village pub with a public bar and a lounge/restaurant. Real fire and a garden with a games area.

LLANFYLLIN
Cain Valley Hotel
High Street
11.30-11; 12-10.30 Sun
Ansells Bitter; Worthington Bitter Ⓗ

Long-running *Guide* entry, with a public bar, a long back bar and a plush wood-panelled lounge.

LLANGEDWYN
Green Man
On B4396
11-3, 6-11; 11-11 Sat; 12-10.30 Sun
Tetley Bitter; guest beer Ⓗ
Imposing food-orientated pub set back from the B4396. Wonderful views of the Tanat Valley.

LLANIDLOES
Crown & Anchor
41 Long Bridge Street
11-11; 12-10.30 Sun
Hancock's HB; Worthington Bitter Ⓗ
Traditional, no-frills, beamed local in the town centre. The pub has many rooms including a public bar, lounge, pool room and snug.

NEWTOWN

Bell Hotel
Commercial Street (B4568)
☼ 12-2 (2.30 Fri), 5-11; 12-midnight Sat;
12-10.30 Sun
☎ (01686) 625540
Six Bells Big Nev's; Tetley Bitter; guest beer Ⓗ
Edge-of-town local hosting live music at
weekends. The Bell is popular with a wide
range of customers. Six Bells beers are
supplied to the hotel without fish finings,
making them vegetarian. The comfortable
lounge is separate from the more basic
public bar which has a pool table. The pub
is the home of the Dragonfire Rocket
project which explains some of the cartoons
on the bar. ✦✿ⓓ♣P

Cross Guns
32 Park Street (off A483)
☼ 11-3, 7-11; 11-midnight Fri & Sat; 12-10.30 Sun
☎ (01686) 625546
Theakston Best Bitter; guest beer Ⓗ
Many-roomed, beamed pub, offering guest
beers from independent breweries. A large
patio and courtyard offers a pleasant
environment for summer drinking. A huge
function room, with a capacity of 200
people, is a venue for regular live
entertainment. Meals include Indian dishes;
these have won local awards. This
traditional inn displays a large jug
collection. ✿✿ⓓ✉✿♣P

Railway Tavern
Old Kerry Road (off A483)
☼ 12-2.30, 6.30-11; 11-11 Tue, Fri & Sat; 12-4,
7-10.30 Sun
☎ (01686) 626156
Draught Bass; Worthington Bitter; guest beer Ⓗ
Unspoilt, small, one-bar local near the
railway station. This characterful pub has
beams and a stone wall. It is very popular
with darts and dominoes players and can
get very busy at weekends and on match
nights. Beware of the cellar hatch which is
in front of the darts area. ✿♣♣

Sportsman
Severn Street (off A483)
☼ 11-2.30, 5-11; 11-11 Tue, Fri & Sat; 12-10.30 Sun
☎ (01686) 625885
Brains SA; Tetley Bitter; guest beer Ⓗ
Friendly, town-centre local popular with a
wide range of customers. It stages Celtic
music jam sessions every Tue night. It also
hosts a Welsh-speaking eve. The guest beer
is from the Tapster's range. The pub
consists of three drinking areas, all of which
are quiet and conducive to conversation. There
is a patio for outdoor drinking. Q✿ⓓ≋

PENYBONT

Severn Arms
At A44/A488 jct
☼ 11-2.30, 6-11; 12-3, 7-10.30 Sun
☎ (01597) 851224
e-mail: owen@severnarms.fsnet.co.uk
**Draught Bass; Brains SA; Hancock's HB; guest
beers** Ⓗ
18th-century coaching inn and a stop-off
point between Aberystwyth and Hereford. It
is named after John Cheesment Severn,
second squire of Penybont Hall. He married
Mary Price, the daughter of the first squire.

It was he who had the first pub built in the
village. The Severn Arms has a spacious
public bar, which has access to a large rear
garden sloping down to the River Ithon. A
games room, quiet secluded lounge and a
restaurant, the Cheesments, complete the
picture. The guest beers appear infrequently
in winter. The pub has six miles of fishing
rights on the River Ithon, a major tributary
of the River Wye (free to residents, modestly
priced permits are available to non-
residents). Wales and Border Counties
trotting racing takes place twice yearly on a
nearby course. ✿✿✿ⓓ✉✿AP

TALYBONT-ON-USK

Star
On B4518
☼ 11-3, 6-11; 11-11 Sat; 12-10.30 Sun
☎ (01874) 676635
Beer range varies Ⓗ
Attractive pub on the Brecon-
Monmouthshire Canal. Up to 12 real ales
served in summer (fewer in winter).
Theakston Old Peculier and beers from
Bullmastiff Brewery feature regularly on the
beer blackboard. A large fireplace in the
main bar adds to the cosy atmosphere of
this excellent rural pub. Very reasonably
priced accommodation available. The pub is
served by the Abergavenny–Brecon bus (No.
21), the bus stop is close by. No eve or Sun
service. ✿✿✿ⓓA✿

WELSHPOOL

Royal Oak Hotel
Severn Street (off A483)
☼ 11-3, 5.30-11; 11-11 Fri & Sat; 12-10.30 Sun
☎ (01938) 552217
Worthington Bitter; guest beers Ⓗ
Plush, town-centre, 300-year-old coaching
inn, which was formerly the manor house
of the Earls of Powys. There are two bars;
the comfortable, quiet Oak bar with a real
fire and relaxing atmosphere and the Ostler
bar with pool, music and TV. Two guest
beers are offered and the hotel has a
separate restaurant. ✿Q✿ⓓ≋

NORTH-EAST WALES

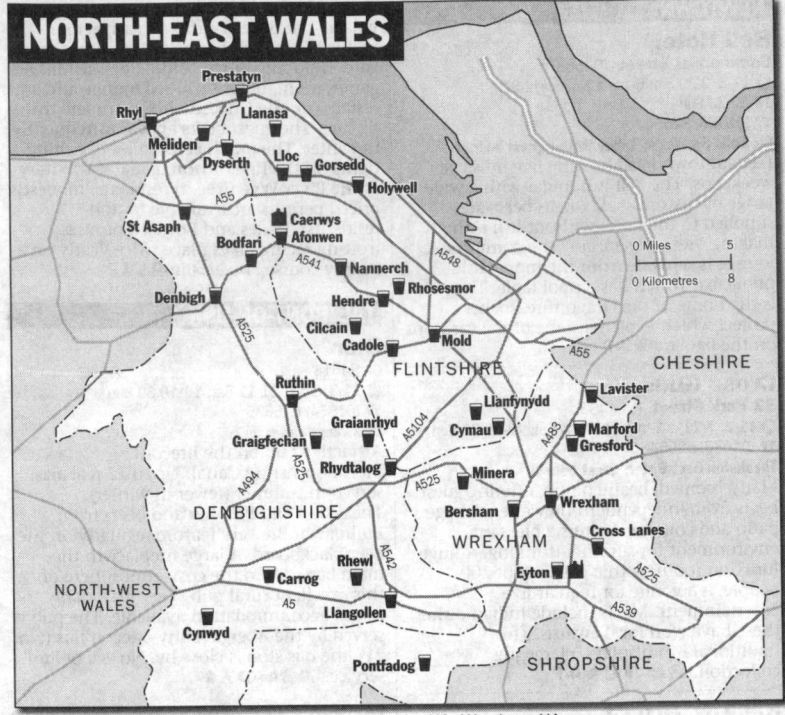

Authority areas covered: Denbighshire UA, Flintshire UA, Wrexham UA

Denbighshire

BODFARI

Dinorben Arms

On B5429, 100 yds from A541 OS093701
☼ 12-3, 6-11; 12-11 Sat; 12-10.30 Sun
☎ (01745) 710309
Greene King Old Speckled Hen; Tetley Bitter; guest beer Ⓗ

Early 17th-century inn, overlooking the Vale of Clywd, that has grown over the years. Fortunately the extensive rebuilding has succeeded in maintaining its olde-worlde charm. There are numerous water jugs hanging from the ceiling, old dinner plates line the walls and a suit of armour is displayed in the bar. The dining area has many nooks and crannies. The lounge has two settles and what is thought to be an old Roman well that has been renovated; plate glass covers the shaft. There is a large patio area. ♨❀◑ ♣P✸

CARROG

Grouse Inn

On B5437, 3/4 mile from A5 OS112436
☼ 12-11; 12-10.30 Sun
☎ (01490) 430272
Lees Bitter, seasonal beers Ⓗ

Comfortable village inn a short walk from the western terminus of the historic, preserved Llangollen Railway. Passsengers find it a refreshing watering-hole before making their return journey. The bar and patio have superb views of the Dee Valley. There is a separate pool room and also a family room. The main bar has a display of old school photographs. Food is served all day (12-10). Although the pub has no accommodation, there are several holiday cottages to let nearby in this delightful village. ♨❀◑ ▲P

CYNWYD

Blue Lion

On B4401, 2 miles S of Corwen OS057411
☼ 12-3, 6-11; 12-11 Sat; 12-10.30 Sun
☎ (01490) 412106
Jennings Bitter; Marston's Bitter Ⓗ

Friendly, traditional village pub situated near Cynwyd Forest and Waterfall, popular attractions for hikers and summer visitors. The building was part of the Rûg estate owned by Lord Newborough, but was sold in 1912. There is a public bar with a painted stone floor and a peaceful rear lounge where a fine selection of old dinner plates line the walls. The River Dee lies 400 yards away and is spanned by a narrow road bridge. Youth hostel nearby. The pub has one guest room. Meals are served in the lounge.
♨╘◑ ⬕

DENBIGH

Old Vaults

40-42 High Street (signed from A525)
☼ 11-11 (1am Thu-Sat); 12-10.30 Sun
☎ (01745) 815142
Draught Bass; Brains SA; Greene King Abbot Ⓗ

Popular town-centre pub close to town hall and library. Single L-shaped room has a bar to the front. The walls are adorned with pictures of local places and people and there are a number of nooks containing bric-à-brac. There is a pool table. Denbigh Castle is nearby. ♣

DYSERTH

New Inn

Waterfall Road (5 miles S of Rhyl)
☼ 12-11; 12-10.30 Sun
☎ (01745) 570482
e-mail: geoff.hughes@valeofclwyd.freeserve.co.uk
Banks's Original, Bitter; Mansfield Riding Bitter;
Marston's Pedigree Ⓗ

Brewery memorabilia is much in evidence in this welcoming old inn, situated in the lower part of town (opposite the historic church) and close to the attractive Dyserth Waterfall. This natural feature supplies the roadside stream across the road. Recently this pub has been very fully but sympathetically refurbished and remains popular with a good reputation for quality food and well-kept beers. A large and secluded garden with children's play area can be enjoyed. Regular bus service passes the inn from Rhyl and Prestatyn.
Ⅲ Q ⚲ 🕮 ◖ ♣ P

GRAIGFECHAN

Three Pigeons

On B5429, 3 miles S of Ruthin OS147544
☼ 12-3, 5.30-11; 12-3, 7-10.30 Sun
☎ (01824) 703178
Draught Bass; guest beer Ⓗ

Spacious, rural pub in a fine setting with panoramic views over the Vale of Clwyd. There are separate rooms for dining and pub games plus a tiled public bar area. The exterior is an interesting shade of green. There is easy access for the less able. Secluded camping site, with toilets and shower facilities, to rear. Extensive menu and specials board with filled baguettes a speciality. The children's menu includes half-portions. Country fruit wines are available by the bottle or glass. Live music Sun eve. The guest beer includes local independents such as Plassey or Weetwood. No food Sun eve or Mon.
Ⅲ Q ⚲ ⚇ ◖ ⊟ ♿ ▲ ♣ P

LLANGOLLEN ❈

Sun

49 Regent Street
☼ 12-11; 12-10.30 Sun
☎ (01978) 860233
e-mail: sunllangollen@ukonline.co.uk
Beer range varies Ⓗ

Award-winning free house boasting a continuously changing range of five real ales, plus draught and bottled continental beers and a traditional cider. The Grade II listed exterior has been recently restored, while work inside has uncovered the original slate floor and oak beams. The oak-panelled main room with open fireplaces is the venue for regular live music (folk Wed, jazz Sun and more general bands, Fri and Sat). Can get very busy. A quieter, small snug is accessed from the garden. Food range changes daily, may include guest chef days. Accommodation may be available – contact pub for details. ⅢⓃ◖ ⊟▲♣

Wynnstay Arms

20 Bridge Street
☼ 12-3 (4 Sat), 7 (6 Fri & Sat)-11 (may extend if busy);
12-3, 7-10.30 Sun
☎ (01978) 860710

Greene King IPA, Abbot; Ind Coope Burton Ale Ⓗ
Popular, 400-year-old coaching inn with an impressive façade and various small drinking areas. The timber-framed main room is bedecked with locally-made brasses. The cosy wooden-floored bar boasts a large open fire and a selection of antique firearms. Enjoy the intimate, little dining room, separate games room with juke box and large beer garden. Meals are good value and include daily specials. Comfortable accommodation makes this an ideal base for Llangollen, water sports on the River Dee or visiting local attractions. ⅢQ ⚲ 🕮◖ ⊟♿ ♣

PRESTATYN

Royal Victoria

Sandy Lane (near station)
☼ 11.30-11; 12-3, 7-10.30 Sun
☎ (01745) 854670
Burtonwood Bitter; guest beer Ⓗ

This popular town local has a frequently changing guest beer plus one from Draught Bass, Flowers or Worthington. Catering possible for parties and meetings (max 60 people). The pub was originally wired for electricity in 1897, 10 years before it became available. It is the first/last pub on the popular Offa's Dyke footpath to the cliffs at Sedbury. All the usual pub games are offered plus backgammon, draughts and Scrabble. Quiz every Sun. Lunches available in summer. ⚇◖▲≢♣

RHEWL (LLANGOLLEN)

Sun Inn

Off B5103 OS178449
☼ 12-3, 6-11; 12-11 Sat; 12-10.30 Sun
☎ (01978) 861043
Beer range varies Ⓗ

Splendid, 14th-century Grade II listed drovers' inn located in the picturesque Dee Valley. With the Horseshoe Falls nearby and Llantysilio Mountain behind it is popular with walkers and fell-runners. A small bar and side hatch serve the two rooms and a snug. Beers come from local independents and, depending on the season, two may be available. Thre is a cosy atmosphere with beamed ceiling, horse brasses and old pictures. Beer garden and separate games room outside. Home-cooked food is a speciality, but booking is advised.
ⅢQ ⚲ ⚇◖▲♣P

RHYL

Swan

13 Russell Road
☼ 11-11; 12-10.30 Sun
☎ (01745) 336694
e-mail: noel@maggies.freeserve.co.uk
Thwaites Mild, Bitter; Daniel's Hammer; guest beer Ⓗ
This welcoming, two-roomed pub is close to Rhyl town centre. The bar features a display of electric sub-station nameplates. Homely lounge with pictures of historic Rhyl. The frontage has the name of Wilderspool Ales which no longer exists. It is a former local

INDEPENDENT BREWERIES

Plassey Eyton
Travellers Inn Caerwys

CAMRA *Pub of the Year*. Reputed to be the oldest pub in town and the first to obtain a public TV licence in 1951. ♣♠

RUTHIN

Wine Vaults
2 Castle Street
☼ 11-11; 11-10.30 Sun
☎ (01824) 702067
Robinson's Best Bitter Ⓗ

Previously unchanging and gimmick-free, this two-roomed pub in the heart of Ruthin is undergoing something of a transformation. A new licensee is imposing his own identity and a genuine Irish atmosphere is being developed. This is a tasteful conversion to an Irish theme, unlike those often undertaken by the big pub-owning companies. The clientele is sports-orientated, and there are regular special promotional events. The lounge bar houses a pool table and original Guinness advertising posters. A verandah overlooks the historic courthouse (AD1401), now converted into a bank. No food is available. ❀ ⚅ Å ♣ P

ST ASAPH ❋

Kentigern Arms
High Street (A525, close to A55)
☼ 12-3, 7-11; 12-3, 7-10.30 Sun
☎ (01745) 584157
Courage Directors; John Smith's Bitter; Theakston Best Bitter; guest beer Ⓗ

Two-roomed, 17th-century free house close to the cathedral (home to the North Wales Music Festival each September). The River Elwy gives the place its Welsh name of 'Llanelwy'. The pub has a pool table room and a lounge which often has a real fire. A quiz team of doctors play home league games (they go under the name 'quacks') during winter. A no-smoking area is set aside. Lunchtime meals are served. ❀ ⚅ ◖ ⚅ Å ♣ P ✍

Flintshire

AFONWEN

Pwll-Gwyn
On A541 OS127717
☼ 12-2, 7-11; 12-3, 6-11 Sat; 12-3, 7-10.30 (12-10.30 summer) Sun
☎ (01352) 720227
Tetley Bitter; guest beers Ⓗ

Popular roadside pub. This 18th-century coaching inn has an early 20th-century façade and was an upmarket hotel owned by Chester Northgate brewery. Now a free house there is a good, ever-changing choice of draught beer. The landlord is a real ale fan and does not intend to sell smooth-flow beer. There is one large bar with brasses galore and two dining rooms, both no-smoking. ❀ Q ❀ ♣ P

CADOLE

Colomendy Arms
Village Road (off A494)
☼ 7 (6 Thu; 4 Fri; 12 Sat)-11; 12-10.30 Sun
☎ (01352) 810217
Shepherd Neame Master Brew Bitter; guest beers Ⓗ

It is unusual to find a little piece of Kent in Flintshire but Shepherd Neame beers are a particular favourite in this friendly, unpretentious local. The name Cadole comes from the unpromising 'Cat's Hole', the lead mine from which the village took its name. This brick-built, 19th-century single-bar pub supplies up to four changing guest beers. The simple, pine-panelled bar has old photos and a hearty fire; a piano graces the smaller lounge. Marvel at the 5000-year-old jaw bone of a wild boar! Convenient for Loggerheads Country Park. ❀ ❀ ◖ ₺ Å ♣ P

INN BRIEF

Denbighshire
GRAIANRHYD
Rose & Crown
4 (12 Fri & Sat); 12-11 Fri & Sat; 12-10.30 Sun
Flowers IPA; Marston's Pedigree; guest beer Ⓗ
Dating from the 1820s this cosy, basic village local is the heart of the community.

LLANGOLLEN
Bridge End
Mill Street
12-11; 12-10.30 Sun
Robinson's Best Bitter Ⓗ
Locals' pub, convenient for Steam Railway and canal.

MELIDEN
Melyd Arms
23 Talargoch Road
11.30-11; 12-10.30 Sun
Marston's Pedigree, Pedigree Ⓗ
Friendly village pub with two bars and dining area, built as miners' pay office in 1735. 'Happy hour' 4-6. Traditional pub games available.

ST ASAPH
Plough
The Roe
11-11; 12-10.30 Sun
Plassey Bitter; guest beers Ⓗ
Large pub/restaurant with a racing theme, the bar has tables named after racehorses and the restaurant tables are after racecourses.

Flintshire
HENDRE
Royal Oak
Denbigh Road
7 (12 Sat)-11; 12-3, 7-10.30 Sun
Black Sheep Best Bitter; Worthington Bitter Ⓗ
300-year-old coaching inn, in an old mining area, with bar, lounge and pool room. Lounge has mugs from around the world hanging from the ceiling.

LLOC
Rock Inn
St Asaph Road
12-11; 12-10.30 Sun
Burtonwood Bitter; guest beer Ⓗ
Two-roomed inn with separate restaurant, the last orders traffic-light fixture is an unusual feature. Beware of mild handpump – only keg.

MOLD
y Pentan
3 New Street
11-11; 12-10.30 Sun
Marston's Pedigree Ⓗ
Run by the former brewer from Flannery's, this bustling town-centre pub caters for all tastes.

RHOSESMOR
Red Lion
Rhosesmor Road
7-11; 11-10.30 Sun
Tetley Bitter; guest beer Ⓗ
Formerly owned by Burtonwood brewery this free house remains unspoilt by modernisation. A real local with bar and separate lounge.

Wrexham
PONTFADOG
Swan
On B4500
12-3, 7-11; 12-4, 7-11 Sat; 12-3, 7-10.30 Sun
Brains SA; guest beer Ⓗ
Whitewashed pub. One old bar serves restaurant and lively public bar. Table football machine is available.

Cask breather

Where an entry states that some beers in a pub are served with the aid of cask breathers, this means that demand valves are connected to both casks and cylinders of gas; as beer is drawn off, it is replaced by applied gas (either carbon dioxide, nitrogen or both) to prevent oxidation. The method is not acceptable to CAMRA as it does not allow beer to condition and mature naturally. The Campaign believes brewers and publicans should use the size of casks best suited to the turnover of beer in order to avoid oxidation. If a pub in the Good Beer Guide uses cask breathers, we list only those beers that are free of the device.

CILCAIN

White Horse
The Square (1 mile S of A541) OS177652
✪ 12-3, 6.30-11; 12-11 Sat; 12-10.30 Sun
☎ (01352) 740142
Banks's Bitter; guest beers Ⓗ
Whitewashed village pub near Moel Famau Country Park, popular with walkers and mountain-bikers. Dogs are welcome in the public bar which has a traditional quarry-tiled floor. Meals are served in the cosy, split-level lounge between 12-2 and 7-9 from a wide menu and specials board. Old photographs of Cilcain village and interesting exterior signs from long-defunct breweries are displayed. The guest beer often includes the latest selection from Banks's seasonal range. Cilcain is on the Holywell to Mold bus route.
ᛗQ❀ⅅ⌸♣P

CYMAU

Talbot
Cymau Lane
✪ 12-4 (not Mon-Thu); 7-11; 12-4, 7-10.30 Sun
☎ (01978) 761410
Hydes Bitter; Ⓟ seasonal beers Ⓗ
19th-century former coach house, the Talbot is an unpretentious, friendly, well-run pub. Whitewashed with contrasting black window and door frames, the pub commands spectacular views over the Cheshire Plain. For a quiet drink choose the plush, cosy lounge. The bustling, tiled-floored public bar offers darts, dominoes and a TV. This pub is a long-standing *Guide* entry. It lies close to the Hope Mountain Country Park
Q♣⌸♣P

GORSEDD

Druid Inn
The Village (200 yds from A5026, 2 miles W of Holywell) OS152767
✪ 7-11; 12-3, 7-10.30 Sun
☎ (01352) 710044
Boddingtons Bitter; Taylor Landlord Ⓗ
Multi-roomed, 12th-century Grade III listed Welsh longhouse, it was originally a toll house. Old prints hang on the walls including a Burton Union System in relief, also on display are a brace of old handpumps. Meals are served in the conservatory or the separate restaurant (Sun lunchtimes and Tue-Sat eves). An old disused inglenook now houses a large comfortable sofa. Three real fires make it very cosy on winter nights. ᛗ❀ⅅ⌸♣P

HOLYWELL

Glan-yr-Afon Inn
Milwr (off A5026, follow signs) OS195739
✪ 12-3, 5.30-11; 12-10.30 Sun
☎ (01352) 710052
Tetley Bitter; guest beers Ⓗ
Sympathetically extended Welsh longhouse, recently renovated to include accommodation (seven bedrooms, some with disabled facilities). The same family ran the inn from 1559-1977 and features in the *Guinness Book of Records*. Regular mini-beer festivals are held. Food is excellent but it is advisable to book. Pepe, the Spanish landlord, hosts a Spanish circle every last Thu of the month. Quiz held every Wed eve. The pub has a football team plus darts and pool teams.
ᛗ⛉❀⌸⌸♣P

LLANASA

Red Lion
Off A5151
✪ 12-11; 12-10.30 Sun
☎ (01745) 854291
Courage Directors; Webster's Yorkshire Bitter; guest beer Ⓗ
Delightful, 17th-century building, a former police station complete with cells. Picturesque village in summer bedecked with colourful hanging baskets, a glorious sight to see, with beautiful views over hills and farmland. There are two bars and a restaurant with beamed ceilings, open fires and exposed stone walls. The restaurant has *table d'hôte* and *à la carte* menus. Traditional Sun lunch and bar snacks served. Booking is advisable, especially at weekends. Accommodation now available.
ᛗ❀⌸ⅅ⌸♣P

LLANFYNYDD

Cross Keys
On B5101
✪ 12-3 (not Mon-Fri), 7-11; 12-3, 7-10.30 Sun
☎ (01978) 760333
Beer range varies Ⓗ

There has been a pub on this site for over 300 years. The original pub has expanded into the former blacksmith's shop and farm buildings either side. The quarry-tiled public bar is basic, while the lounge with its unusual raised area has a stone-clad fireplace and superbly carved settles. A comfortable, unpretentious, traditional local where the beer policy has done away with the previous national bland choice, and now features constantly changing beers from independent breweries. Parking is only accessible from direction of Ffrith.
🏰Q❀❀◐ ⊟♣P

MOLD ❖

Griffin
41 High Street
❀ 12-11; 12-10.30 Sun
☎ (01352) 750697
Burtonwood Bitter; guest beer Ⓗ
Located by the dominant church of St Mary's, built by Margaret Beaufort to celebrate her son Henry Tudor's victory at the battle of Bosworth (1485), there has been a pub on the site since 1760. Also known as 'The Long Pull' and as The Griffin since 1763 it is now a friendly, lively, bare-boarded Forshaw's ale house, rejuvenated and renovated from the gloomy bar it replaced. The big screen is occasionally drawn over the windows for sporting events. Thu is quiz night. ❀◐♣

NANNERCH

Cross Foxes
Village Road (off A541) OS167695
❀ 6-11; 1-11 (Sat & summer); 12-10.30 Sun
☎ (01352) 741293
Beer range varies Ⓗ
Traditional village pub with open fires, low-beamed ceilings and a welcoming atmosphere. The public bar area boasts a tiled floor and an extended wood-panelled lounge, with a piano, is decorated with brassware. Restaurant, lounge and dining area with different menus in each. Food is only available at weekends. The bar displays a Wrexham lager brewery mirror – founded in 1882 but cynically closed by Carlsberg-Tetley over 100 years later. There are fly fishing facilities nearby.
🏰❀◐ ⊟💄♣P

RHYDTALOG

Liver Inn
On A5104
❀ 12-3 (not Mon), 7-11; 12-3, 7-10.30 Sun
☎ (01824) 780244
Tetley Bitter; guest beer Ⓗ
This impressive building stands at crossroads on the edge of the Llandegla Moors. A 17th-century former coaching inn: a cosy lounge with pictures of old Rhydtalog, separate function room available for hire and a pool room with free games on Mon. Next to the Offa's Dyke path it can get busy at weekends. A meeting place for local clubs it is also popular with horse riders and golfers from the nearby course. The guest beer changes every two weeks. Food is served at lunchtimes Tue-Sun, bank holidays and eves except Sun and Mon.
🏰◐ Å♣P

Wrexham

BERSHAM

Black Lion Inn
Y Ddol (off B5097)
❀ 12-11; 12-10.30 Sun
☎ (01978) 365588
Hydes Light, Bitter, seasonal beers Ⓗ
Known locally as the 'Hole-in-the-Wall', the pub stands below road level in an attractive hamlet on the bank of the Clywedog (next to Bersham Heritage Centre). The latter is on the site of the 18th-century Wilkinson's ironworks. Sympathetic renovation of a parlour-style pub with a side off-shoot and a separate pool room with darts. Convivial and cosy, popular with hikers in the summer as it is halfway along the Clywedog Valley Industrial Trail. The garden overlooks the wooded riverside. Runner-up in the 1999 Hydes *Best-Kept Cellar* competition.
🏰❀♣P

CROSS LANES

Cross Lanes Hotel (Kagan's Brasserie)
Bangor Road, Marchwiel (A525)
❀ 11-11; 12-10.30 Sun
☎ (01978) 780555 website: www.crosslanes.co.uk
Plassey Bitter Ⓗ
Large, stately lounge set around a central bar in a mansion formerly known as Maes-y-Nant ('house-by-a-stream'). Attached to an upmarket hotel in six acres of beautiful gardens, it is reached via a grand entrance hall containing fine panelling and a 1618 staircase, rescued from Emral Hall, Worthenbury. Old prints and paraphernalia include an unusual photo of the last survivor of the Charge of the Light Brigade. Interesting layout, with a formal magenta-papered drawing room through a small, varnished-floored barside to the bare-flagged dining area. A thoroughly relaxing atmosphere with stunning rural views.
🏰❀🛏◐♣P

Kiln Inn
Cross Lanes On B5130, off A525, signed Cock Bank
❀ 12-3 (not Mon-Fri), 7-11; 12-3, 7-10.30 Sun
☎ (01978) 780429
Plassey Bitter; guest beer Ⓗ
Three-storey, red-brick building, a former malt kiln, converted to a pub about 1800. A small central servery, cramped by the stairway, is surrounded by three small rooms including a characterful front parlour. There are impressive fireplaces, belching heat in the winter months. An old photo shows former incumbents Enoch and Charlotte Brookfield, great-great grandparents of the current landlady; the pub has been in the same family for over a century. Booking is advised for the little restaurant (no food Mon eve).
🏰❀◐♣P

EYTON

Plassey Leisure Park
The Plassey
(off B5426, signed from A483)
❀ 11-11 (may vary winter); 12-10.30 Sun
☎ (01978) 780905
Plassey Bitter, Cwrw Tudno, Dragon's Breath Ⓗ

Prosperous, Victorian dairy farm that has diversified into the leisure industry. There is a golf course, caravan park (tents by arrangement), swimming pool and craft centre. The Haywain golf club bar is open all year, but has restricted opening hours in winter. The Treetops bar is by the caravan park and literally at treetop level (open all day during summer). The restaurant sells Plassey beers and a small brewery shop usually has beer to take away. Situated in a pleasant rural environment there is plenty of interest at the Plassey, including brewery tours when available.
🍺🅿 ⚓

GRESFORD

Griffin
Church Green
✪ 1.30-4.30, 7-11; 1.30-4.30, 7-10.30 Sun
☎ (01978) 852231
Greenalls Mild, Bitter Ⓗ

Whitewashed village pub standing next to the impressive 15/16th-century All Saints parish church with its old yew trees and famous bells. Irregular, open-plan layout, with the TV tucked away almost as an afterthought, this is a rare relic of pre-electronic days, conversational, convivial and relaxed with none of the muzak, games machines or food obtrusiveness of many modern establishments. The friendly landlady has been here for the last 28 years. The huge village pond down the hill is worth a look.
Q🕮♣🅿

LAVISTER

Nag's Head
Chester Road (B5445)
✪ 12-3, 5.30-11; 11-11 Sat; 12-10.30 Sun
☎ (01244) 570486
Boddingtons Bitter; Taylor Landlord; Thwaites Bitter; guest beer Ⓗ

This pub claims to have been the birthplace of CAMRA in 1971; a plaque on the bar commemorates this event. On the old Chester road, this extended pub is popular

Cask Marque

The Cask Marque symbol with a pub entry indicates that the licensee has successfully passed a number of tests concerning beer quality, and can display a plaque to this effect. However, the choice of all pubs in the guide is made by CAMRA independently of Cask Marque. The Cask Marque symbol is added during the editing process, and Cask Marque has no say in the selection of pubs.

with locals and tourists. Children's play area, camping facilities and bowling green provided. Beer is dispensed from a central bar, with pool table, dartboard and a display of the trophies won by the pub teams. Comfortable seating area next to one of the two real fires. Separate dining area. Food is served weekend eves.
🍺Q🕮🍴& ⚓🅿

MARFORD

Red Lion
Marford Hill
✪ 12-3 (not Mon & Tue), 5-11; 12-11 Sat; 12-10.30 Sun
☎ (01978) 853562
Burtonwood Bitter; guest beer Ⓗ

Former coaching inn on the old Chester-Wrexham road now a pleasantly renovated two-roomed pub. There is a comfortable, split-level lounge compartmentalised by iron and wood dividers. The large TV and pool room is backed by a lovely brick fireplace, tastefully enhanced, the half-wood fittings matching the lounge. Outside is a little courtyard suntrap and a small raised lawn. Various trips are organised by the landlord in his minibus and apparently Gordon the Ghost insists on inverting the lightshades!
🕮🍴🍴♣🅿

MINERA

Tyn-y-Capel
Church Road (off B5426 from Coedpoeth)
✪ 11.30-3.30 (not Mon or Tue); 6.30-11 (midnight Fri & Sat; not Mon); 12-3.30, 6.30-10.30 Sun
☎ (01978) 757502
Tetley Bitter; guest beer Ⓗ

Former drovers' pub, with whitewashed walls and sturdy, stone-flanked windows of ancient origin and translating as 'house-by-the-church' (referring to neighbouring St Mary's, originally a chapel of ease). It dates back to 1597 when it was a farmhouse attached to nearby Plas Gwyn. Renovated recently, it is now semi-open plan and split-level with a pool table at the top end and a bare-boarded, spacious area below. There is a separate restaurant area. Superb views of Esclusham Mountain and the Clywedog Valley, close to the northern end of the latter's Industrial Trail.
🕮🍴♣🅿

WREXHAM

Albion Hotel
1 Pen-y-Bryn (down Town Hill from town centre)
✪ 12-4, 7-11; 12-4, 7-10.30 Sun
☎ (01978) 364969
Lees Bitter, seasonal beers Ⓗ

Impressive town-centre Edwardian pub. Spacious lounge retains its original frosted glass windows, while the more basic lively back bar with domino tables and dartboard is the focal point for many pub games. Both these rooms are served from a central bar, while one has one of the few pool tables in the town centre. Good-value accommodation makes an ideal base from which to explore this area rich in industrial heritage. This is a traditional community pub in a town desperately in need of such venues. 🛏🍴♣

NORTH WEST WALES

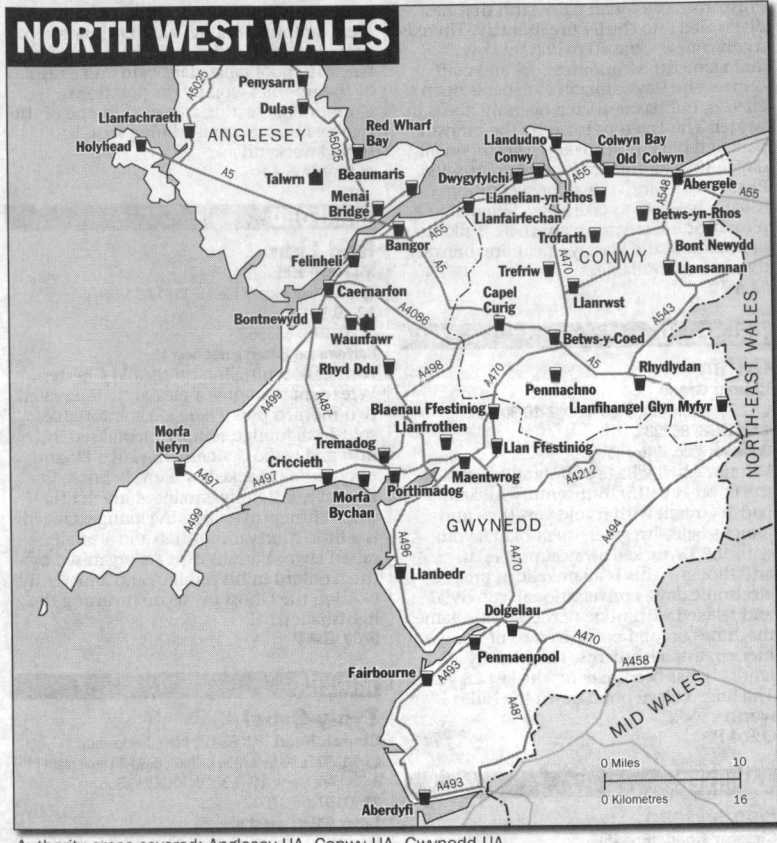

Authority areas covered: Anglesey UA, Conwy UA, Gwynedd UA

Anglesey/Ynys Môn

BEAUMARIS ✤

George & Dragon
Church Street (B5109)
☼ 11-11; 12-10.30 Sun
☎ (01248) 810491
Robinson's Best Bitter; seasonal beers Ⓗ
A welcoming local in the centre of the town
and a short walk from the Menai Straits,
castle and other historic buildings.
According to tradition this timber-framed
inn was built in 1410 but architectural
detail suggests a date in the more settled,
prosperous days of Queen Elizabeth I. In the
1970s a remarkable series of wall paintings
came to light during repair work, these have
been restored and can be viewed on request.
☎◖♣✔

Olde Bull's Head Inn
Castle Street
☼ 11-11; 12-10.30 Sun
☎ (01248) 810491 e-mail: info@bullsheadinn.co.uk
**Draught Bass; Hancock's HB; Worthington Bitter;
guest beer** (summer) Ⓗ
Grade II listed building that was the original
posting house of the borough. In 1645
General Mytton, a Parliamentarian,
comandeered the inn while his forces lay
siege to the castle which is a mere stone's
throw away. The Royalists surrendered on
25th June 1646. Dr Samuel Johnson and

Charles Dickens were famous guests and
each individually designed bedroom is
named after a Dickens' character. The
beamed bar has a large open fire and many
antiques combining to create a genuine,
olde-worlde atmosphere. Excellent
restaurant and brasserie (with wheelchair
access). Limited parking available.
☎Q☞☞▭◖◑⬚♿P

DULAS

Pilot Boat Inn
On A5025 OS477873
☼ 11-11; 12-10.30 Sun
☎ (01248) 410205
Robinson's Best Bitter, seasonal beers Ⓗ
Friendly, rural family pub with a play area
and converted double-decker bus to keep
the children amused. Originally a cottage-
type building now much extended. The
lounge has an unusual boat-shaped bar and
a coal fire in winter. The pub is much used
by walkers, the Anglesey coastal path passes
through the car park. There are many
worthwhile places to visit in the area
including Mynydd Bodafon for its
spectacular views and Traethlligwy for the
sands. ☎⛺◑⬚♿▲♣P

HOLYHEAD

79
79 Market Street

✪ 11-11; 12-10.30 Sun
☎ (01407) 763939 e-mail: glyn79@aol.com
Beer range varies Ⓗ

Smart, popular town-centre pub with comfortable seating and three distinct drinking areas, two of which have their own bars. The third section doubles as a drinking and dining area, which can be partitioned off for private functions. A free house with regularly-changing beers supplied by a local wholesaler, the pub is often busy with holidaymakers and rugby fans on their way to Ireland. The dining area overlooks the Irish ferry port, and has interesting aerial photographs of Holyhead, showing the changes in recent years.
◑ ≢ ≋

LLANFACHRAETH

Holland Hotel
Cemaes Road (A5025)
✪ 11-3.30 (except Wed in winter); 7-11 (11-11 Sat & summer); 12-10.30 Sun
☎ (01407) 740252 website: www.holland-hotel.co.uk
Lees GB Mild, Bitter, seasonal beers Ⓗ

Welcoming, little country pub, runner-up in local CAMRA *Pub of the Year*. A central bar area serves a basic public bar and passageway. Well-furnished dining room and separate pool room. Near the newly built A5 dual carriageway across Anglesey, giving quick access to Holyhead and Irish ferries, the mainland and Snowdonia. The Anglesey coastal path, freshwater and sea fishing, golf and horseriding are all nearby. Many historic and pre-historic sites to visit. An extensive menu features home-cooked local produce.
Q ❀ ✍ ◑ ⊟ ♣ P

MENAI BRIDGE

Liverpool Arms
St Georges Road (between PO and pier)
✪ 11-3, 5-11; 12-3, 7-10.30 Sun
☎ (01248) 713335
Flowers Original; John Smith's Bitter; guest beers Ⓗ

This 150-year-old pub has several rooms and a conservatory all served from one bar. Popular with locals, the sailing fraternity and students. There is a choice of four different guest beers every week. The pub enjoys an excellent reputation for home-cooked food. Old maps, antiquities and photos bedeck the walls. Recently extended accommodation offers excellent bed and breakfast (from £30pp/pn), making a good base for touring Anglesey and Snowdonia. The new narrow-gauge Welsh Mountain Railway from Caernarfon to Waunfawr in Snowdonia is within easy reach.
Q ❀ ✍ ◑

Victoria Hotel
Telford Road (over suspension bridge towards town centre)
✪ 11-11; 12-10.30 Sun
☎ (01248) 713335
Draught Bass; guest beers Ⓗ

Comfortable residential hotel (19 rooms) overlooking the beautiful Menai Straits from the garden and patio. A large function room is licensed to midnight. Regular live music. Easy access to Snowdonia and the North Wales coast and the Welsh Mountain Railway. Licensed for weddings. The local

independent brewery Bragdy Ynys Môn supplies the hotel on a regular basis with excellent Welsh bitters. The beaches of Anglesey are all within easy reach, sailing on the Menai Straits and more than a dozen golf courses close at hand.
Q ♿ ❀ ✍ ◑ ⊟ & P

RED WHARF BAY

Ship Inn
1½ miles off A5025, near Benllech
✪ 11-3.30, 6.30-11; 11-11 summer; 12-10.30 Sun
☎ (01248) 852586
Friary Meux Bitter; Ind Coope Burton Ale; guest beers Ⓗ

A warm, cosy old pub with stone walls, exposed beams and log fires (in the winter) adding to the character. Good food is served in all bars. The blackboard menu changes daily. Red Wharf Bay was once a busy port in the days of sailing ships and the main cargoes were fertiliser and coal. The port also saw some boat building between 1700 and 1820. The Ship Inn was then known as the 'Old Quay'. Today it is bustling with locals and holidaymakers. Extensive views can be enjoyed across the bay from the beer garden.
🏚 Q ♿ ❀ ◑ ⊟ & A P ⚹

Conwy

BETWS-Y-COED

Glan Aber Hotel
Holyhead Road
✪ 11-11; 12-10.30 Sun
☎ (01690) 710505 website: www.betws-y-coed.co.uk
Marston's Pedigree; Tetley Dark Mild, Bitter; guest beer Ⓗ

Traditional Welsh stone-built hotel located in the middle of the picturesque village of Betws-y-Coed. The bar is open to visitors as well as residents. There are a number of lounge areas, each with interesting features and located on several levels. There is also a separate games room with many unusual plaques displayed. In addition to their regular beers there is always one guest ale available and it is the aim of the hotel to provide this from one of the Welsh independent breweries whenever possible.
🏚 Q ♿ ✍ ◑ A ≋ ♣ P

Pont-y-Pair
Holyhead Road
✪ 11-11; 12-10.30 (11 summer) Sun
☎ (01690) 710407
Greene King Abbot; Marston's Pedigree; Tetley Bitter Ⓗ

A comfortable, family-run hotel opposite the famous bridge (from which the hotel gets its name) over the Afon Llugwy. At certain times of the year the river is renowned for its leaping salmon. A warm welcome is offered to visitors, many of whom use the hotel as a base for their varied activities around Snowdonia. A good selection of freshly-cooked meals are served in the bar and lounge and there is a separate pool room to the rear. Tiny car park.
Q ❀ ✍ ◑ A ≋ ♣ P

INDEPENDENT BREWERIES

Bragdy Ynys Môn Talwrn
Snowdonia Waunfawr

BETWS-YN-RHOS

Wheatsheaf Inn
✪ 12-3, 6.30-11; 12-3, 6.30-10.30 Sun
☎ (01492) 680218
Courage Directors; Greene King IPA; Wadworth 6X Ⓗ
Situated in an award-winning picturesque village between coast and mountains, the Wheatsheaf was originally built in the 13th century, and licensed in 1640 as a coaching inn. The main features of this free house are brass-strewn oak beams, stone pillars and an original hayloft ladder. Light snacks and bar meals are served in a cosy lounge and there's a separate public bar. Extended to the rear on split-levels is an *à la carte* restaurant and function room (with bar and dance area). Four en-suite rooms are available for bed and breakfast accommodation.
Q ⊛ ⇔ ◑ ⅏ ♣ P

BONT NEWYDD

Dolben Arms
3 miles S of St Asaph OS013708
✪ 7-11 (midnight supper licence), 12-10.30 Sun
☎ (01745) 582207
Theakston XB; guest beer Ⓗ
Narrow, single-track country lanes lead to this charming, family-run 16th-century inn and restaurant, a true free house (locally known as 'The Bont'). Located in remote countryside where a narrow bridge crosses the River Elwy. A small bar serves the lounge, with piano and TV. The adjacent restaurant is popular for traditional Sun lunch, and eve meals. There is a separate games/family room. Outside seating is provided at the front of the pub. Open all day Sun. Guest beers are selected mainly from independent regional breweries.
Q ⊛ ◑ ♣ P

CAPEL CURIG

Cobdens Hotel
OS731576
✪ 11-11; 12-10.30 Sun
☎ (01690) 720243 website: www.cobdens.co.uk
Brains SA; Greene King Old Speckled Hen; Tetley Bitter Ⓗ
Situated on the main A5 trunk road at the eastern edge of Snowdonia this is an informal 200-year-old hotel. There is a welcoming lounge, restaurant and climbers' bar which features a natural rock face (created from the adjoining hillside). In addition to the real ale it serves, the hotel prides itself on being a member of the Campaign for Real Food and the excellent food it provides can cater for most tastes. The hotel is popular all-year round.
⇔ Q ⅏ ⊛ ⇔ ◑ ⌐ A ♣ P

COLWYN BAY

Wings Social Club
Station Square
✪ 11-3, 7-11; 11-11 Sat; 12-3, 7-10.30 Sun
☎ (01492) 530682
Lees GB Mild, Bitter Ⓗ
Social club offering a welcome to visitors and their families with CAMRA members being made especially welcome. The large L-shaped lounge has a raised stage area for live entertainment. The club also has a billiards, pool and darts room in addition to a separate TV room. Proud winner of CAMRA's *Regional Club of the Year* 2000. Across the road from the resort's mainline rail station and within two minutes' walk of the main coast road bus services, it is very easy to access. Small charge for admission.
Q ⇌ ♣

CONWY

Bridge Inn
Rose Hill Street
✪ 11-11; 12-10.30 Sun
☎ (01492) 573482 website: www.bridge-conwy.co.uk
Banks's Bitter; Mansfield Dark Mild; guest beers Ⓗ
Traditional-style inn opposite Conwy Castle. The open-plan lounge with coal fire in the colder months surrounds a central bar. The pub displays a collection of beer badges and pump clips and there are framed caricatures of Victorian politicians together with interesting artefacts highlighting the town's history. There is an annual beer festival in autumn, details on website. Two guest ales from independent breweries are regularly offered. Bar meals are available, lunchtimes and Fri and Sat eves. Excellent accommodation is offered. ⇔ ⇔ ◑ ⇌

George & Dragon
Castle Street
✪ 12-11; 12-10.30 Sun
☎ (01492) 592305
Draught Bass; Cains Bitter; Greene King Old Speckled Hen; M&B Mild; Worthington Bitter Ⓗ
Centrally-located, this family-run pub is owned by Punch Taverns. A small, narrow frontage among the old terraced buildings disguises the fact that inside there is a long, pleasant lounge, which provides popular, comfortable surroundings for locals and visitors. A good range of food is served, to complement the interesting choice of beers. In summer additional seating is available in the enclosed rear beer garden, of which the famous town walls form the rear boundary. Three rooms available for overnight stays.
⊛ ⇔ ◑ ⇌ ♣

DWYGYFYLCHI

Dwygyfylchi Hotel
Capelulo
✪ 12-3, 5.30-11; 11-11 Sat & Mon-Fri summer); 12-10.30 Sun
☎ (01492) 623395
Burtonwod Bitter, Top Hat Ⓗ
Situated about only one mile from the busy A55, the quiet community of Capelulo is well worth the detour. Here is a traditional popular pub attracting visitors, and friendly locals. The lounge is cosy and quiet, whereas the busier adjoining public bar area has a TV. A separate dining room has a no-smoking area. For the summer, a beer garden and sun patio can be enjoyed. Inside, note the gents' toilet adjacent to the rock face. ⊛ ⇔ ◑ ⌐ ♣ P

LLANDUDNO

King's Head
Old Road (above the tram station)
✪ 11-11; 12-10.30 Sun
☎ (01492) 877993
Tetley Dark Mild, Bitter; guest beers Ⓗ

Reputedly the oldest pub in Llandudno: nestling on the lower slopes of the Great Orme next to the Orme Railway station. An olde-worlde bar dates back to the 16th century, with slate floor and large stone fireplace. The accommodation has been extended to three levels with two lounge areas, one of which on the second level has comfortable seating and is decorated with half-timbered panelling and Victorian photographs. An unobtrusive third level is a restaurant. Two guest ales are usually provided from independent breweries.
🏨❀◑▶P

London Hotel

131 Mostyn Street
✪ 11-11; 12-10.30 Sun
☎ (01492) 876740
Burtonwood Bitter, Top Hat; guest beer Ⓗ

Large, popular town pub with a very friendly atmosphere. There are two distinct features to the pub. The front room is based on a London theme to reflect the pub's name. Here you will see an original red telephone-box, a cased dummy of a Chelsea pensioner and a collection of jugs. The rear room provides a large TV screen to show sporting events and other entertainment. There is pavement seating in summer months. ❀◑≈♣

Snowdon Hotel

11 Tudno Street
✪ 12-11; 12-10.30 Sun
☎ (01492) 872166 website: www.snowdonhotel.co.uk
Courage Directors; Ind Coope Burton Ale; Theakston Best Bitter; guest beers Ⓗ

A popular free house just off the main shopping area. A lounge area, with open coal fire and TV, surrounds a central bar. A separate pool area has another TV. Pump clips, posters and signs from independent breweries are displayed. A games room offers darts, dominoes and cards and has historic shipping memorabilia from the age of the tall ships. The regular beers include Weetwood ales and two guest ales from independent breweries are supplied. 'Happy Hour' is 4-7pm and a Doubles Bar is 12-9pm. 🏨❀≈♣

White Lion Inn

Off B5383
✪ 11-3, 6-11; 12-3, 6-10.30 Sun
☎ (01492) 515807 website: www.whitelioninn.co.uk
Marston's Bitter, Pedigree; seasonal beers Ⓗ

Located in rolling hills near the coast, next to St Elian's church, this is an attractive, traditionally-furnished, Welsh village inn. A tasteful extension provides a no-smoking area for diners. The slate-floored bar, tiny snug and lounge partly date back to the 16th century. White Lion pottery lamps adorn all windows and two lions guard the door. A collection of jugs hang from the ceiling beams. The comfortable leather suite in front of a real log fire is especially inviting in winter. 🏨Q❀⇔◑▶ＡP

Llanfair Arms

Mill Road
✪ 11-11; 12-10.30 Sun

☎ (01248) 680521
Greene King IPA; guest beer Ⓗ

Purpose-built in the mid-19th-century as a multi-roomed pub and off-licence, this is a pleasant and typical local. There is one large room plus a small front lounge and a rear pool room. The pub is based in the upper village across the road from the fast flowing river. A beer garden and children's play area are available. A shelf of old bottles in the entrance catches the eye, as does the bright red cloth on the pool table. Sky TV for those interested in sport and a real fire for those who enjoy a warm welcome. 🏨❀⊞≈♣

Crown Inn

Off B5105
✪ 7 (12 Sat)-11; closed Mon; 12-5; 7-10.30 Sun
☎ (01490) 420209
Beer range varies Ⓗ

Lovely old inn beside the Afon Alwen. The front bar has an open fire and slate floor. There is a pool room (with a portable TV) and rear room where children are welcome. There is an attractive terraced gardens beside the river, where in the summer bar meals are served. Permits for trout fishing are available from the pub. The beers are from breweries in the principality, or independents. Three en-suite rooms for a longer stay. A true free house.
🏨Q❀⇔◑Ａ♣P

New Inn

Dinbych Steet
✪ 11-11; 12-10.30 (11 summer) Sun
☎ (01492) 640476
Banks's Original; Marston's Bitter, Pedigree, seasonal beers Ⓗ

Popular, terraced, traditional, town pub. One bar serves the comfortable long lounge and rear games area that has a pool table, and juke box (this reaches amazing volumes on busy eves). Small, cosy front snug boasts an open fire, and occasional TV. Local CAMRA members regularly gather here. Outside there is a small rear partially-covered courtyard, with picnic tables. Friendly welcome assured.
🏨❀Ａ♣♣

Red Lion (Llew Coch)

✪ 5 (12 Sat)-11; 12-10.30 Sun
☎ (01745) 870256
Lees GB Mild, Bitter, seasonal beers Ⓗ

Old village pub, popular with local farmers and visitors. An unusual layout, with original 14th-century secluded bar area around a stove, a raised lounge with large stone fireplace and old seating. The lower public bar has TV, pool table, dartboard and juke box. Totally separate dining rom, normally no-smoking. Large rear garden with picnic tables beyond the courtyard. Good-value food available at most times. Freshly-prepared Welsh meat pies and curries are the specialities (generous portions). Four simply but comfortably furnished rooms available. Large cooked breakfast included for under £20.
🏨Q❀⇔◑⊞♣P

OLD COLWYN ✵

Plough
282 Abergele Road
☼ 12-3, 6-11; 12-4, 7.30-10.30 Sun
☎ (01492) 515387
Boddingtons Bitter; Greenalls Bitter; guest beers Ⓗ
A traditional pub. A one-level lounge
surrounds the bar, with cosy, quiet areas.
Two guest ales are usually provided from
independent breweries, there is a separate
games room with TV. Traditional pub quiz
on Thu eve which is very popular with
locals. Furthermore, the pub is the
quenching-place for the local Colwyn male
choir and the pub walls proudly display a
pictorial account of the choir's history.
Lunchtime meals with Sun lunch a
speciality. Concessions to senior citizens.
Convenient access to local bus services.
Q ◖ ♣

Red Lion
385 Abergele Road
☼ 5 (4 Fri, 12 Sat)-11; 12-10.30 Sun
☎ (01492) 515042
**Boddingtons Bitter; Flowers IPA; Theakston Mild;
guest beers** Ⓗ
Popular town pub with a sprawling lounge,
one area of which contains a welcoming
real coal fire in the colder months. The
walls are almost completely covered with
framed photographs depicting the
interesting history of the local area,
including a description of the origins of the
pub. There is a separate games room with
TV, stables at rear and a yard with picnic
tables. With up to four guest ales, including
seasonals, from independent breweries it
boasts many CAMRA awards for dedication
to real ale. Convenient for all local bus
services.
🏠 Q ✿ ⊟ ♣

PENMACHNO

Eagles (Ty Uchaf)
4 miles SE of Betws-y-Coed on B4406, off A5
OS790506
☼ 7 (1 Sat)-11; 1-10.30 Sun
☎ (01690) 760177
website: www.eaglespenmachno.co.uk
**Greene King Ruddles Best; John Smith's Bitter;
Theakston Mild, Cool Cask; guest beer** Ⓗ
On the edge of the Gwydyr Forest in the
Snowdonia National Park this is a delightful

two-roomed country pub/hotel, recently
tastefully redecorated. With a wood-burning
stove in the lounge, a warm welcome awaits
visitors. The pub is also the centre of many
village activities and fills a role as a focal
point for the community in this isolated
area. Moreover, this hostelry is one of the
very few pubs in the Conwy area to offer
their real ale in lined glasses, thus
promoting the CAMRA ideals of fair
measures to drinkers. Sun lunch served, plus
eve meals Thu-Sun.
🏠 Q ✿ 🛏 ◖ ♣ ✂ ⊟

RHYDLYDAN

Giler Arms Hotel
Near A5, 1 mile E of Pentrefoelas
☼ 11-11; (11-2.30, 6.30-11 winter); 12-10.30 Sun
☎ (01690) 770612
Marston's Pedigree; Tetley Bitter; guest beers Ⓗ
Friendly country hotel with seven
bedrooms in the Hiraethog, the hidden
heart of North Wales. Set in seven acres of
grounds it offers a lake for coarse fishing, a
small campsite and pleasant gardens beside
the River Merddwr. The comfortable lounge
has a large open stove. The separate public
bar is popular with locals, with dartboard
and TV. A small pool room is also well used.
The 60-seater restaurant overlooks the lake.
Children are welcome. A genuine free house
with interesting guest beers and an annual
beer festival. 🏠 Q ✿ 🛏 ◖ ⊟ Å ♣ P

Gwynedd

ABERDOVEY/ABERDYFI

Penhelig Arms Hotel
The Promenade, Terrace Road
☼ 11-3.30, 6-11, (11-11 summer); 12-3.30, 6-10.30
Sun
☎ (01654) 767215
e-mail: penheligarms@saqnet.co.uk
Draught Bass; Tetley Bitter; guest beer Ⓗ
Archetypal, small, friendly seaside hotel
standing beside the Penhelig harbour, with
superb views across the Dyfi Estuary. The
hotel is of historical interest, mainly built in
the 1700s and known then as 'y Dafarn
Fach'. Today the 'Little Inn' has grown into
a delightful hotel with an excellent
reputation. Located in a self-contained part
of the building is the stylish, nautically-
themed fisherman's public bar. Good food
including fish specialities served in the

INN BRIEF

Anglesey/Ynys Môn

BEAUMARIS
Bulkeley Hotel
Castle Street
11-11; 12-10.30 Sun
**Courage Directors; Theakston Cool
Cask** Ⓗ
Old, well-established hotel
overlooking the Menai Straits and
the mountains of Snowdonia. Ideal
for travelling around Anglesey.

PENYSARN
Bedol
12-11; 12-3, 7-10.30 Sun
Robinson's Hartleys XB; seasonal beers Ⓗ
Purpose-built in 1984. This is very
much a community pub with
regular functions for locals and
visitors.
12-10.30 Sun

Conwy

LLANFAIRFECHAN
Virginia Inn
Mill Road
11-11;
12-2, 7-10.30 Sun
Theakston Mild Ⓗ
Quarry-tiled hallway leads to small
bar, and three rooms, all furnished
with period items. Basic, busy
village pub.

OLD COLWYN
Sun
Abergele Road
12-3; 5-11 (Mon-Thurs); 12-11 Fri & Sat;
12-10.30 Sun
**Mansfield Dark Mild, Bitter; Marston's
Bitter, Pedigree** Ⓗ
Small pub with public bar, lounge,
and rear games room.

TREFRIW

Fairy Falls Hotel
11-11;
12-10.30 Sun
**Banks's Bitter; Marston's Bitter, Pedigree;
seasonal beer** Ⓗ
Public bar, lounge, and rear
restaurant. Popular for diners.

Old Ship Hotel
12-3; 6-11; 12-11 Sat & summer
weekdays; 12-10.30 Sun
**Banks's Bitter; Marston's Pedigree;
guest beer** Ⓗ
Refurbished roadside pub, front bar
with open fire, and rear dining
room. Free house.

restaurant. The hotel has 10 bedrooms, all but one having stunning views. Comfortable and homely accommodation. ♨Q❀♿◑ Å≂P

BANGOR ❖

Belle Vue
Holyhead Road
☼ 11 (12 Sat)-11; 12.30-10.30 Sun
☎ (01248) 364439
Boddingtons Bitter; Bragdy Ynys Môn Medra; Flowers IPA; Marston's Pedigree Ⓗ
Traditional town pub situated near Bangor University, frequented by students, lecturers and locals. Good range of beers featuring Welsh breweries including Bragdy Ynys Môn. There is a wood-panelled lounge, and the bar boasts a traditional Welsh range. Regular quiz nights and outdoor summer music events are a recent feature of the pub. Generous helpings of home-made food are served at lunchtimes when a no-smoking area is available. ❀◑🅐Å≂✦

Globe Inn
Albert Street, Upper Bangor (off Holyhead road near Post Office)
☼ 11-11; 12-10.30 Sun
☎ (01248) 362095
Boddingtons Bitter; Bragdy Ynys Môn Wennol; Flowers IPA Ⓗ
Small, traditional pub full of local characters and students. This is a family-run pub with good value, home-made food with plenty of variety. There is a wood-panelled bar, pool room and a cosy snug. Guest beers are usually Welsh, often from Bragdy Ynys Môn – the local brewery. Pool, dominoes and backgammon are played. ◑Å≂✦

Castell
Off High Street, Glanrafon (opp. Cathedral)
☼ 12-11; 12-10.30 Sun
☎ (01248) 355866
Boddingtons Bitter; Marston's Pedigree; Tetley Bitter; guest beers Ⓗ
Hogshead pub: recently refurbished, a spacious one-roomed house offering the widest range of real ales (up to 12) in the area to a good mix of locals and students. The menu, served 12-9 (7 Fri-Sat) includes specials. Newspapers available. Four cask ciders on tap. No-smoking area available at lunchtime. ◑≂❀✦

BONTNEWYDD

Newborough Arms
On A487, Porthmadog-Caernarfon road
☼ 11-11; 12-10.30 Sun
☎ (01286) 673126
Marston's Pedigree; Tetley Dark Mild, Bitter; guest beers Ⓗ
Busy, often crowded, village pub on the main holiday route to Porthmadog and the Lleyn Peninsula. Enjoys a good reputation for food. Very friendly staff. Multi-roomed pub with separate restaurant served by a regular bus service from Caernarfon. ♨❄❀◑Å✦P✦●

CAERNARFON ❖

Black Boy Inn
Northgate Street (opp. castle entrance)
☼ 11-11; 12-10.30 Sun

☎ (01286) 673023
Draught Bass; guest beers Ⓗ
16th-century pub within the town walls near the castle. A public bar and small lounge are both warmed by roaring fires. Good-value food served. Limited parking. The Welsh Highland Railway recently opened nearby. This historic town is well worth a visit, ending with a welcome pint at the Black Boy Inn. ♨Q♿◑⊟≂✦P

CRICCIETH

Prince of Wales Hotel
High Street
☼ 11-3, 6-11; 12-3, 7-10.30 Sun
☎ (01766) 522556
Boddingtons Bitter; Greene King Old Speckled Hen Ⓗ
Busy local in the centre of town, opposite a village green where two annual fairs are held in May and June. The pub consists of one central bar with a large lounge and several cosy drinking areas. There is also a split-level family area. A wide selection of good-value food is available. It is very popular with locals and tourists and very busy in summer. A guest ale is usually available. Well served by rail and bus routes. ◑Å≂

DOLGELLAU

Stag Inn
Bridge Street
☼ 12-11; 12-10.30 Sun
☎ (01341) 422533
Burtonwood Bitter Ⓗ
Close to the 17th-century bridge over the River Wnion, the Stag is a pub well-known to regular travellers. There is a small central single bar, with a tiled floor one side and a comfortable section on the other. Honest, no-frills pub with a juke box, TV and two dartboards, plus upstairs pool room. The pub is a popular meeting place for the locals. Inside only a few benches and tables can fit in the small space, outside there is a small patio at the rear. Open all day. ❀

FAIRBOURNE

Fairbourne Hotel
☼ 11-3, 6-11; 11-11 Sat; 12-10.30 Sun
☎ (01341) 250203
McEwan 80/-; John Smith's Bitter; Theakston Cool Cask Ⓗ
Situated on the Mawddach Estuary commanding views of Cardigan Bay, this large, 17th-century residential hotel is renowned for excellent food and a friendly atmosphere. There are 20 comfortable bedrooms. Attractive lounge bar has subdued lighting and plenty of quiet corners, where bar meals can be enjoyed. The terrace bar (no-smoking until 9pm) provides an ideal area for families. The restaurant has beautiful views over the hotel gardens and out to sea, and offers an extensive menu. The only outlet for McEwan's beers in the county. Full disabled facilities are provided. ♨Q♿◑⊟♿P✦

FELINHELI

Gardd Fôn
Beach Road (off main road, by the Menai Straits)
☼ 11-11; 12-10.30 Sun

☎ (01284) 670359
Burtonwood Bitter; guest beers Ⓗ
Nautically-themed, 18th-century, friendly pub, busy in summer when locals are joined by numerous visitors. The new bistro restaurant (no-smoking) offers excellent food, booking advisable at weekends. Wonderful views over the Menai Straits can be enjoyed from the grassed drinking area in the front of the pub. Note the lovely brasses and church pews. ▲Q❀◁▯ ⇦▵♣

LLANBEDR

Tŷ Mawr Hotel

❂ 11-11; 12-10.30 Sun
☎ (01341) 241440
e-mail: tymawrhotel@netscapeonline.co.uk
Draught Bass; Worthington Bitter; guest beers Ⓗ
Small country hotel set in its own grounds. Modern lounge bar with slate-flagged floor and cosy wood-burning stove in winter. A long room has a corner bar with occasional unobtrusive background music. Interesting flying memorabilia points to connections to a local airfield nearby. French windows lead on to verandah and landscaped terrace and gardens with outdoor seating. Popular with locals, walkers and real ale enthusiasts. Dogs and children are welcome. Good value meals with occasional themed nights. Interesting range of guest beers stocked.
▲❀▱◁▯⇥P

LLANFROTHEN

Brondanw Arms

On A4085
❂ 12-3, 6 (12 Sat)-11; 12-3, 6-10.30; (12-10.30 summer) Sun
☎ (01766) 770555
Robinson's Best Bitter; Frederics Ⓗ
Comfortable, end-of-terrace country pub near village war memorial. Families made welcome; well-behaved children allowed in bar areas until 9.30pm. Good outdoor play area. Good value, reasonably priced meals (no lunches Mon or Tue). Occasional live music. Within the Snowdonia Park, it is popular with tourists and locals alike. Plas Brondanw, the ancestral home of Sir Clough Williams-Ellis, lies opposite the pub. It is open to the public in summer and has marvellous gardens. (Sir Clough Williams-Ellis began

Portmeirion in 1926; it was built to resemble the Italian village of Portofino). ▲❀◁▯⇦P

MAENTWROG

Grapes Hotel

On A496 towards Harlech
❂ 11-11; 12-10.30 Sun
☎ (01766) 590208 e-mail: grapeshotel@aol.com
Beer range varies Ⓗ
Welcoming, 13th-century former coaching inn, a Grade II listed building. Spacious public bar, large verandah/diner and smaller lounge with real fire. A dining/drinking room is no-smoking and doubles as a family room. Quiet atmosphere apart from juke box in public bar. Wheelchair WC and wide doors allow access to all. Stone walls and furnished with pitch-pine pews and settles mainly salvaged from chapels. Excellent value home-cooked food with seafood specialities – but try the ultimate challenge of house spare ribs! Popular central point for hillwalking; on a bus route. Regular changing beers, often Wye Valley. Not far from the Ffestiniog Railway.
▲Q⅁▱◁▯⇦▵♣P⅄

MORFA BYCHAN

Tafarn Glanaber

Beach Road
❂ 12-3, 6.30-11; (11-11 summer); 12-10.30 Sun
☎ (01766) 514917
Draught Bass; Greene King Ruddles Best; Theakston Best Bitter, Cool Cask Ⓗ
Large free house situated among the Black Rock Sands Morfa Buchan camp sites. Ideal location close to the beach and golf course. Caters for all; there is a beer garden and children's play area outside plus family area inside. With a varying beer range, occasional live music and extensive menu of good value food, this pub is popular with tourists. Function facilities are available.
▲⅁❀◁▯▵♣P

MORFA NEFYN

Cliffs Inn

Beach Road
❂ 12-3, 6 (7 winter)-11; 6-11 (not winter) Sun
☎ (01758) 720356
Greene King Old Speckled Hen; guest beer Ⓗ

INN BRIEF

Holland Arms
Llanrwst Road
12-3, 7-11; 12-3, 7-10.30 Sun
Tetley Bitter; guest beer Ⓗ
18th-century coaching house, with pleasantly furnished bar, lounge and restaurant. Popular for good-value meals.
Gwynedd

BANGOR
Eryl Môr Hotel
2 Upper Garth Road
11-11; 12-10.30 Sun
Greene King Old Speckled Hen; Theakston Cool Cask Ⓗ
Residential hotel overlooking Bangor pier and the Menai Straits. Lunches and eve meals served.

Tap & Spile
Garth Road
12-11; 12-10.30 Sun
Draught Bass; Greene King IPA, Old Speckled Hen Ⓗ
Very popular, multi-levelled pub overlooking the pier and Menai Straits. Be prepared for very large TV (sport) and fruit machines.

BLAENAU FFESTINIOG
Queen's Hotel/Gwesty r Frenhines
High Street
11-11; 12-10.30 Sun
Tetley Bitter; guest beer Ⓗ
Large, refurbished (in 1996) residential hotel beside the railway stations. with 12 en-suite bedrooms. and 'Buffers' bistro restaurant.

CAERNARFON
Alexandra Hotel
North Road
11-11; 12-10.30 Sun
Draught Bass; Boddingtons Bitter; Flowers Original; guest beers Ⓗ
Free house of original style near the town centre. Note the mirrors. This friendly local offers a variety of beers – try the Flowers.

LLAN FFESTINIOG
Pengwern Arms Hotel
Church Square
12-3; 6 (12 Sat)-11; 12-10.30 Sun
Draught Bass; Theakston Cool Cask Ⓗ
Three-bar, 14th-century village hotel, popular with the locals, and walkers and anglers. Separate family room.

Large, friendly pub with the added attraction of a sun lounge overlooking the bay. As it is very close to the beach, it gets very busy in the summer. Good-value food is served. A favourite with locals and tourists. Families are welcome; accommodation is available. Q✿⊨◑ÅP

PENMAENPOOL

George III Hotel
☉ 11-11; 12-10.30 Sun
☎ (01341) 422525
Greene King Ruddles Best; John Smith's Bitter; guest beer (summer) Ⓗ

Family-run hotel beside the toll-bridge crossing of the Mawddach Estuary. The main hotel was built in 1650. The 'cellar bar' with slate floor, oak-beamed ceiling, and panelled benches is ideal for families. The pub has a children's certificate, children's menu and no-smoking policy. Home-made bar food is served. Could hardly be closer to the estuary and the old railway line (the signal box is now a RSPB hide). The hotel has a separate 'dresser bar' lounge, and restaurant, on upper floor, with fine views. ⋈Q✿⊨◑⊟⅋P⅌

PORTHMADOG

Royal Sportsman Hotel
131 High Street (200yds from station)
☉ 11-11; 12-10.30 Sun
☎ (01766) 512015 website: www.royalsportsman.co.uk
Tetley Bitter; guest beer (summer) Ⓗ

Real ale is served in the bar of this family-run hotel; non-residents made very welcome. Popular with locals and tourists. Bar food available and good-value, quality home-prepared food served in separating dining room and function room. Good quality 3 crown Welsh Tourist Board accommodation with some ground-floor accommodation for the less mobile, all with en-suite facilities. ⋈⅄⊨◑⊟⇌P

Ship Inn/Llong
14 Lombard Street (near park and harbour)
☉ 11-11; 12-4 (not winter) Sun
☎ (01766) 512990
Greene King IPA, Old Speckled Hen; Ind Coope Burton Ale; Marston's Pedigree; Tetley Bitter; guest beers Ⓗ

Local CAMRA *Pub of the Year* 1999. Two-roomed local with public bar and no-smoking lounge, with further separate dining area at rear. Both bars are attractively adorned with nautical memorabilia, and early photographs and prints. The landlord has several awards for cellarmanship and stocks a large range of beers. An annual beer festival is staged in March. Excellent food menu, good-value meals, children welcome if dining. Selection of over 70 malt whiskies offered. ⋈Q◑⊟⅊Å⇌♣⅌

Spooner's Bar
Harbour Station (part of Ffestiniog Railway)
☉ 11-11; 12-10.30 Sun
☎ (01766) 512340 website: www.festrail.co.uk
Banks's Original; Mansfield Bitter; Marston's Pedigree; guest beers Ⓗ

Relaxed, comfortable café-bar situated on the platform of the Ffestiniog Railway, popular with tourists and locals. Excellent range of home-cooked food, vegetarians and children catered for (no food served Mon-Wed eves in winter). Reasonably-priced snacks available all day in café area. Wheelchair WC on station platform. Occasional beer festivals organised. ✿◑⅊⇌P⅌

RHYD DDU

Cwellyn Arms
On A4085, Caernarfon-Beddgelert road
☉ 11-11; 11-10.30 Sun
☎ (01766) 890321 website: snowdoninn.com
Draught Bass; Stones Bitter; Worthington Bitter; guest beers Ⓗ

This beamed, 200-year-old pub at the foot of Snowdon, serving an extensive menu of good food, is open 365 days a year. It offers large bunkhouse accommodation in a beautiful National Park location 15 minutes' walk from the pub; ideal for climbers and walkers. Up to six guest beers on tap. The Welsh Highland Railway is due to reach Rhy Ddu around summer 2002. Served by Sherpa bus route 95. ⋈Q⅄✿⊨◑⊟ÅP

TREMADOG

Golden Fleece
The Square (A487, 1 mile N of Porthmadog)
☉ 11.30-3, 6-11; 12-3, 6-10.30 Sun
☎ (01766) 512421
Draught Bass; guest beer Ⓗ

Situated in the old market square of Tremadog, this old coaching inn is now a friendly local. On the main bus routes, local attractions range from rock climbing to narrow-gauge railways. The large lounge has a no-smoking area at the rear, and there is a snug which may be reserved for local regulars on occasion. There is also a large covered area at the rear with tables and benches. Additional bistro upstairs. Children welcome; good value food. ⋈Q✿⊨◑⊟⅊⅌

WAUNFAWR

Snowdonia Parc
On A4085, Caernarfon-Beddgelert road
☉ 6 (12 Sat & summer)-11; 12-10.30 Sun
☎ (01286) 650409
website: www.snowdonia-park.co.uk
Mansfield Dark Mild; Marston's Bitter, Pedigree; Snowdonia Experimental Ale; guest beers Ⓗ

Brew-pub located in the heart of Snowdonia with its own campsite (reduction for CAMRA members). It offers good food and home-brewed beers, plus live entertainment Sat eves. The Welsh Highland Railway stops outside the pub. The garden has a children's play area and there's a play room inside the pub. Served by Sherpa bus from Caernarfon (nos 89 & 95). Q⅄✿◑⊟Å⇌♣P⅌

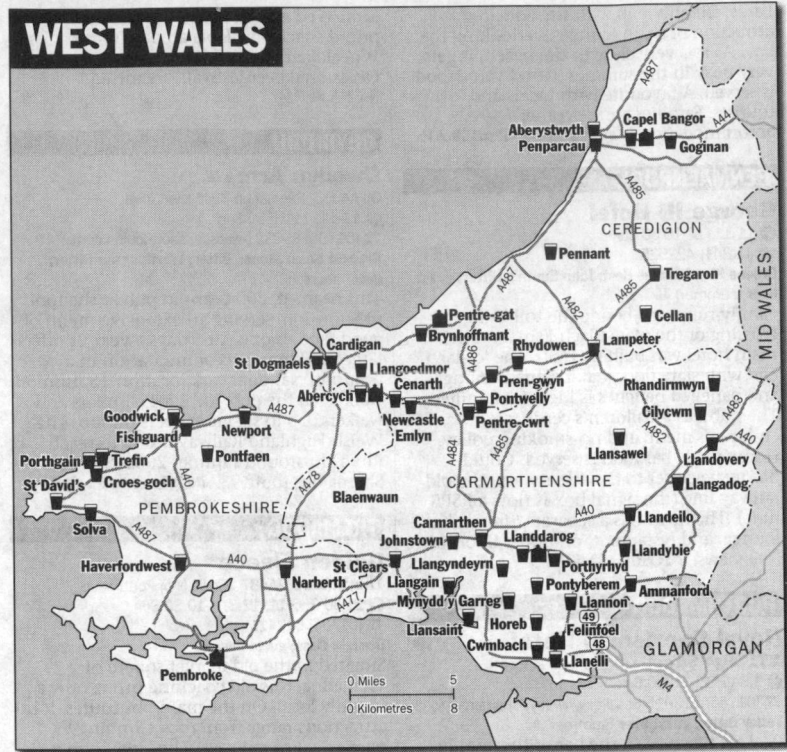

WEST WALES

Authority areas covered: Camarthenshire UA, Ceredigion UA, Pembrokeshire UA

Carmarthenshire

AMMANFORD

Wernolau

31 Pontamman Road (from Ammanford-Neath road, 50 yds past Murco garage on right)
✆ 5.30-11; 12-10.30 (7 winter) Sun
☎ (01269) 592598
Brains Buckley's Best Bitter; guest beers Ⓗ
A wide range of beers (five guests) often rotate here. If the locals make a request, the proprietors try their best to accommodate the choice. Originally a mine manager's house, it was built in the 17th century and extended later. Five acres of splendid grounds include a landscaped area and woodland. It is a residential hotel (open to non-residents) and has a Victorian theme, with open fires in winter. There is a large function room catering for weddings, etc. Meals are available and families are welcome. The Lions club and Round Table meetings are held here. ⌂Q🏠➥D▲

BLAENWAUN

Lamb Inn

8 miles N of St Clears on road to Tegryn OS237271
✆ 5.30 (12 Sat)-11; 12-10.30 Sun
☎ (01994) 448440
Brains Rev. James; guest beer Ⓗ
Interesting pub, definitely worth finding. Recently refurbished, the pub displays some entertaining bric-à-brac and check out the parrot. The landlord or locals will answer any queries about the pub. Live music performed and morris dancing in the summer. Very friendly country inn, dogs are welcome. A hairdresser calls on first Mon of each month for those customers wanting a trim. 'Happy hour' is held 5.30-6.30, Mon-Fri. Limited food currently available. The landlord has plans for future improvements. 🏵▲♣P

CENARTH

Three Horseshoes

On A484
✆ 11-11; 12-10.30 Sun; closed every afternoon in winter
☎ (01239) 710119
Ansells Mild; Brains Buckley's Best Bitter; Ⓗ
Greene King Abbot; Ⓖ **Tetley Bitter; guest beer** Ⓗ
Picturesque riverside inn popular with anglers and tourists. The beer garden overlooks the famous Cenarth Falls. The pub doubles as the HQ of the Teifi Valley Trout Association which explains the display of fly rods and reels hanging from the bar ceiling. The thatched former brewhouse is worth a visit and hosts beer festivals (with music) on bank holidays. Beware of the beams, this is a low-ceilinged pub. Excellent, tasty food served lunchtime and eve. ⌂Q🏵◑▲♣P

HOREB

Waunwyllt

Horeb Road
(off B4309 at Five Roads, 3 miles from Llanelli)
✆ 12-3, 7 (6.30 Fri & Sat)-11 (12-11 summer); 12-3, 7-11 Sun
☎ (01269) 860209

Beer range varies H

Families are welcome at this popular pub that lies close to the new cycle path from Llanelli. Many customers are passing cyclists, and the landlord and some locals are also keen – they have taken part in several charity bike rides. This superb country pub has a genuine warm welcome and was local CAMRA *Pub of the Year* 2000. A good choice of beers come from large and small breweries. It offers excellent, reasonably priced food from a varied menu and specials board. En-suite accommodation provided but booking is advisable. Outside seats at the front of the pub and a beer garden to the rear.
Q ❀ ♙ ◖ Å P

JOHNSTOWN

Friends Arms

St Clears Road (on jct of Johnstown-Picton Hill)
🕐 11-11; 12-3, 7-10.30 Sun
☎ (01267) 234073
Ansells Mild; Ind Coope Burton Ale; Tetley Bitter H

Large, inviting bar with low beams and much decorative brassware. The landlord is a member of the Guild of Master Cellarmen; the only one in the area. For 400 years there has been a pub on this site, before that it was a blacksmith's with stables attached. The consecutive owners have shared the same names, Thomas, Lewis and Owens. The current landlord is a Lewis, but not related to the original family. This is a community local which raises a great deal for charity. Q ❀ ♣

LLANDEILO

Castle Hotel

113 Rhosmaen Street (main street)
🕐 11-11; 12-10.30 Sun
☎ (01558) 823446
e-mail: simonwilliams@llandeilo.plus.com
Tomos Watkin Whoosh, BB, Merlin's Stout, OSB, seasonal beers H

This was the original home of Tomos Watkin Brewery and remains at the heart of the expanding business. It is a multi-roomed pub with an increasing reputation for good food. There is live music performed each Fri eve. For drivers, beer can be bought to take home in four-pint containers. Locals are very friendly and will make all visitors welcome. There is a large free council car park at the back of the hotel where the local tourist information office is located. The pub is handy for attractions such as the National Botanical Gardens.
Q ❀ ◖ ⇌ (Llandovery)

White Horse

125 Rhosmaen Street
🕐 11-11; 12-10.30 Sun
☎ (01558) 822424
Wadworth IPA; Wells Bombardier; guest beers H

Situated through an arch just off the main street in the town, this multi-roomed pub is a 16th-century, Grade II listed coaching inn. Amusing caricatures of locals decorate the bar front. Enjoy a pint in one of the two beer gardens, front or rear. The pub is close to the tourist information office; there are numerous places of interest to visit in the vicinity. No food is served. The White Horse is popular with all ages. ♨ ❀ ⇌ ♣ ●

LLANDYBIE

Ivy Bush

18 Church Street (centre of village near church)
🕐 12-4 (not Mon or Tue), 6-11; 11-11 Fri; 12-4.30, 6.30-11 Sat; 12-2 (closed eve) Sun
☎ (01269) 850272
Ind Coope Burton Ale; guest beer H

Recently refurbished open-plan pub near the station. It is the oldest pub in the village, dating back nearly 300 years. A priest's hole that connected the local church to the pub has now been sealed. There is an interesting collection of cigarette cards on display as well as militaria. Children and dogs are welcome and Boris, the pub's Boxer dog, is a favourite. No food is served here, just good honest ale. It is a real local, housing a darts team and 9 Card Don is played on a Wed eve. ⇌ P

LLANELLI

Baldy's Bar

2 Prospect Place (off A476, near jct with A484)
🕐 11.30-11; 12-10.30 Sun
☎ (01554) 755121 e-mail: www.baldysbar.co.uk
Brains Buckley's Best Bitter; Tomos Watkin Whoosh; guest beer H

Popular pub with many sport-loving customers. Previously called the Lemon Tree, it is now named after the shaven heads of its new owners. Interesting art work on the exterior and there used to be a bowling green at the back. The pub has recently been refurbished and given an open-plan layout, but the feeling of separate bars is retained. The locals make this a very friendly pub. ❀

Union

Bryn Road, Seaside (off western end of bypass)
🕐 11-11; 12-10.30 Sun
☎ (01554) 759514
Brains Buckley's IPA, Best Bitter H

Originally named after the Union Castle shipping line, which used the nearby docks (now closed). It was rebuilt in the 1930s on the site of a much older pub. Currently undergoing refurbishment, on completion the Union will again have a nautical theme. This pub is a friendly locals' pub and appeals to all ages. Benches are set out at the front for outdoor drinking. It is close to Llanelli Rugby Ground and the new Millennium Coastal Project. ❀ ♙ ⇌ P

LLANGADOG

Telegraph

Station Road (near railway line on road to village)
🕐 12-3 (not Mon-Fri), 5.30 (6 Sat)-11; 12-3, 7-10.30 Sun
☎ (01550) 777727
e-mail: davenport@bushinternet.com
Beer range varies H

On the edge of the village, this pub is close

to Llangadog Station, which is on the Heart of Wales line. Basic, no-frills inn with one rotating guest beer primarily from the smaller breweries. The landlord is also committed to selling good traditional cider, such as Black Rat. There is a very small cellar which you can see, if interested. Beware of the chimes on entering the lounge from the car park. Built around 1830, this pleasant pub has limited accommodation but the landlord has a good relationship with the nearby campsite.
🏠Q🛏🚶♣♥P

LLANGAIN

Tafarn Pantydderwen
Old School Road (near golf course)
☻ 12-3, 6-11; 12-3, 6-10.30 Sun
☎ (01267) 241560
Flowers Original; guest beers Ⓗ
This pub has a good location on the edge of a golf course. The restaurant dominates the pub, but the landlord makes every effort to accommodate real ale drinkers by providing a range of guest beers. The food is excellent and inexpensive. It is situated just off the main road between Carmarthen and Llanstephan. The golf course to the rear of the pub uses the premises as its 19th hole.
Q◑🍴P

LLANGYNDEYRN

Tafarn y Gof/Smith's Arms
OSN148458
☻ 7-11; 7-10.30 Sun
☎ (01269) 842213
Worthington Bitter; guest beer Ⓗ
Delightful 18th-century coaching inn, set in beautiful countryside. The pub is the focal point of the village which is situated between Carmarthen and Pontyberem. Splendid views of the river (the Gwendraeth Fawr) and ample car parking here. In summer there is a beer garden, while you can warm yourself by a real fire in winter.

Very friendly pub, offering a pool table and traditional games such as tippit, cards and darts.
🏠Q🌸♣

LLANNON

Red Lion
3 Heol y Plas (Tumble-Llanelli road)
☻ 5 (12 Sat)-11; 12-3, 7-10.30 Sun
☎ (01269) 841276
Felinfoel Dragon Bitter Ale, Double Dragon Ⓗ
The Red Lion is reputed to have a secret tunnel linking it to the nearby church. Dating back to the 17th century, the pub is rumoured to have a ghost and apparently, Oliver Cromwell was once a visitor. It boasts a well and a fine collection of Toby jugs. Situated on the main road between Cross Hands and Llanelli, the Red Lion has a good menu, including some unusual dishes. Limited parking.
🏠Q🍴P

LLANSAINT

King's Arms
13 Maes yr Eglwys
☻ 12-2.30, 6.30-11; 12-2.30, 6.30-10.30 Sun
☎ (01267) 267487
e-mail: johnmorris@bradpole.freeserve.co.uk
Worthington Bitter; guest beers Ⓗ
Welcoming pub hidden behind the village's 11th-century church. Rumour has it that it was partly built from stone recovered from the lost village of St Ishmael – ask the landlord for more details. Handy for the Carmarthen Bay holiday park, the pub is family-friendly, has a log fire and offers good food (not Tue lunch). Plenty of entertainment provided at weekends. The King's Arms has been a pub for over 200 years. The fine interior boasts a large collection of jugs, hanging from the beams, and some fascinating old photographs of the locality.
🏠🌸🛏◑🅰♣♥P

INN BRIEF

Carmarthenshire
CARMARTHEN

Stag & Pheasant
34 Spilman Street
11-11; 12-10.30 Sun
Worthington Bitter; guest beers Ⓗ
Popular pub especially with local office workers. Once part of a stable block belonging to local hotel.

CILYCWM

Neuadd Fawr
11-3, 6-11 (can vary);
12-10.30 Sun
Beer range varies Ⓗ
Map ref 753401, four miles north of Llandovery. A traditional local pub with an interesting interior.

CWMBACH

Farriers
Trimsaran Road
11-11;
12-10.30 Sun
Draught Bass (winter)**; Worthington Bitter; guest beers** Ⓗ
Small pub with attractive garden and good food. The landlord is a keen golfer and the interior reflects this.

LLANDDAROG

White Hart Inn
11.30-3, 630-11;
12-3, 7-10.30 Sun
Beer range varies Ⓗ
14th-century thatched inn with small brewery attached. Stocks Cwrw Blasus and rotates own beers which are brewed to distinctive recipes.

LLANDOVERY

Castle Hotel
King's Road
11-11;
12-3, 7-11 Sun
Wadworth IPA; Worthington Bitter; guest beer Ⓗ
Recently refurbished hotel in the town centre, it was built in the 18th century. Excellent food.

ST CLEARS

Corvus
Station Road
11-11; 12-10.30 Sun
Courage Best Bitter; Worthington Bitter; guest beers Ⓗ
Busy two-bar locals' pub at the centre of the village. It is thought to be haunted.

Ceredigion
ABERYSTWYTH

Downies Vaults
Eastgate
11-11; 12-10.30 Sun
Banks's Original, Bitter; Ⓟ **Marston's Pedigree** Ⓗ
Modernised, town-centre pub with good atmosphere and well-presented, inexpensive pub grub (not weekend eves).

Fountain
Trefechan
12 (2 Mon-Fri, Jan-Mar)-11; 12-10.30 Sun
Boddingtons Bitter; Brains Dark; guest beer Ⓗ
Charming two-roomed local in the town's old industrial/brewing quarter – note the old photographs.

LAMPETER

King's Head
14 Bridge Street
11-11; 12-10.30 Sun
Beer range varies Ⓗ
The best beer selection in town, usually an enterprising choice. Beers not visible from front bar, so ask what's available. Friendly, two-roomed pub.

LLANSAWEL

Black Lion

OS619364

✪ 5 (11 Sat)-11; 12-10.30 Sun

☎ (01558) 685263

Beer range varies Ⓗ

Focal point in the community, this pub doubles as HQ for the rugby club. It is situated in a quiet village off the beaten track. The Black Lion is a two-storey building with a traditional black and white façade. The main bar is on two levels with stone walls, a large fireplace, and ancient meat hooks. The friendly landlord runs the pub single-handed and personally cooks the reasonably priced food. The guest beers are usually from Cottage Brewery.

◑♣

MYNYDD Y GARREG

Prince of Wales

1¹/₂ miles from Kidwelly bypass

✪ 7 (5 Sat)-11; 12-3 Sun

☎ (01554) 890522

Beer range varies Ⓗ

Small, isolated pub that is worth finding. Extensive movie memorabilia covers the walls. There is a cosy, no-smoking restaurant serving splendid food, Sun lunch and Mon–Sat eves. The Prince of Wales does a good trade in take-home beer – bring your own containers. There is an ever-changing list of beers available, many from small local breweries; the pub offers the most extensive range of real ale in the area. Children under 14 years are not allowed in. This comfortable, welcoming pub is close to Pembrey Country Park, Kidwelly Castle and Kidwelly Industrial Museum.

🏚Q❀◑Å

NEWCASTLE EMLYN

Bunch of Grapes

Bridge Street

✪ 12-11; 12-10.30 Sun

☎ (01239) 711185

Courage Best Bitter, Directors; guest beer Ⓗ

Attractive, 17th-century listed town pub retaining many original features and a traditional ambience with exposed oak beams, timber floors, a huge inglenook and stone walls. Delicious home-made food is served Thu–Sun lunchtimes (all week in summer) at reasonable prices. The traditional Sun roast is a speciality. Live music played on Thu and Celtic folk on Mon in summer. It carries a wide range of guest ales from independent brewers.

🏚❀◑Å♣

Coopers Arms

Station Road (A484, E end of town)

✪ 12-3.30, 5.30-11; 12-3, 7-10.30 Sun

☎ (01239) 710323

Draught Bass; Bragwr Arbennig o Ceridigion Barcud Coch; Ⓗ **guest beer** Ⓖ

Local legend has it that the last dragon in Wales was slain close to this edge-of-town pub. It is the only *Guide* pub that has a regular beer from Ceredigion Brewery. Offers an excellent choice of food and wine, plus take-away containers for real ale. See the permanent exhibition by local artists.

Q❀◑Å♣P⊬

PENTRE-CWRT

Plas Parke Inn

On A484 near Newcastle Emlyn OS388387

✪ 2.30-11; 2.30-10.30 Sun

☎ (01559) 362684

Draught Bass; guest beer Ⓗ

Lively, cosy, three-roomed country pub and restaurant on the outskirts of a rural village. The name roughly translates as 'the mansion in the parkland', and is said to derive from the 13th-century property dealings between the church and the local chieftain. The pub has a pleasant enclosed beer garden, ideal for summer afternoons and eves, with a large car park to the rear. It is close to the popular fishing and canoeing facilities of the River Teifi and the steam railway at Henllan. 🏚❀◑Å♣P

PONTWELLY

Half Moon Inn

✪ 11-11; 11-10.30 Sun

☎ (01559) 362131

Beer range varies Ⓗ

The enthusiastic young landlord here keenly promotes a range of three to four different beers a week, plus a good selection of bottled beers. The unusual shape of the games room is due to the pub's location in a fork in the road. Handy for Llandysul, a pretty tourist town, that has a large park and riverside walks. It is a renowned canoeing centre which attracts competitors from all over Britain. ◑♣P

PONTYBEREM

Pontyberem Workingmen's Club

Furnace Terrace (just off main road road between Pontyberem and Drefach)

✪ 3-5, 7-11; 12-11 Sat; 12-3, 7-10.30 Sun

☎ (01269) 870214

Worthington Bitter; guest beers Ⓗ

Friendly workingmen's club situated in a pretty Welsh village. The club has a lounge and a public bar. The latter has a full-sized snooker table, pool and table tennis. Both areas welcome children, allowing them to stay until 9.30pm. There is a new guest beer every week as well as Worthington on draught. The bar staff and steward are very friendly, as are the locals. CAMRA members are very welcome but need to produce their membership cards.

Q❄&♣

PORTHYRHYD

Mansel

Banc y Mansel (off A48, Drefach-Llanddarog road)

✪ 6 (2 Sat)-11; 12-4 (closed eve) Sun

☎ (01267) 275305

Beer range varies Ⓗ

Welcoming local pub with wood fires in each room. It is an 18th-century former coaching inn. The pool room was once a slaughter room for pigs, with slate limestone slabs which have been broken up and used in the fireplace. The pig sty used to be at the end of the building. Low beams have been added to create atmosphere. A collection of jugs hang from the beams and are set behind the bar. In 1827 R Mansel Phillip who was the High Sheriff, was dragged from his carriage by his tenants, to the pub, where he entertained them to a fine dinner. 🏚Q🅿🍴🛏♣P

RHANDIRMWYN

Royal Oak

Signed from A483 in Llandovery

✪ 11.30-3, 6-11 (times can vary); 12-2, 7-10.30 Sun

☎ (01550) 760201 website: www.rhandirmwyn.com

Beer range varies Ⓗ

Remote inn with excellent views of the valley. Close to Llyn Brianne Dam and the RSPB sanctuary. It was originally built for the local landowner as a hunting lodge. The stone-flagged bar has an open fire. There is a separate pool room. Popular with ramblers and birdwatchers, the pub is dog-friendly. It is worth finding for its beer choice (up to six guests in summer and three to four in winter), good food and extensive selection of whiskies. 🏚Q🕭🍴🛏♣P

Ceredigion

ABERYSTWYTH ✣

Ship & Castle

1 High Street (near market hall)

✪ 12-11; 12-10.30 Sun

☎ (01970) 612334

Beer range varies Ⓗ

This is definitely the number one pub for real ale enthusiasts in the Aberystwyth area. It has six beers to choose from, combining Flannery's beers (now brewed by the Spinning Dog Brewery in Hereford) and interesting guest ales. It is unpretentious and friendly, and although having some of the trappings of an Irish-style pub, it avoids the obtrusiveness of many other examples of this genre. There is Irish music held on a Wed night and Sun lunch is available (12–4). Beer festivals are hosted (April and Oct). Families are welcome. CAMRA *Pub of the Year* 1999 (Ceredigion area). Recently reverted to its original name (from Flannery's). 🛏⇌♣

BRYNHOFFNANT

Brynhoffnant Inn

10 miles N of Cardigan at A487/B4334 jct

✪ 12-3 (summer only), 5 (7 winter)-11; 12-10.30 Sun

☎ (01239) 654961

Felinfoel Best Bitter; Worthington Bitter Ⓗ

Quiet, rural free house only two miles from attractive beaches. It is very popular with locals and tourists. The large L-shaped bar has separate areas for dining (seating for 16) and games; darts, pool and shove-ha'penny are played. The open fires, beams and timber walls create a homely atmosphere. Apart from the excellent beer, tea and coffee are served on request. 🏚🕭🍴🛏♣P

CAPEL BANGOR

Tynllidiart Arms

On A44, 5 miles E of Aberstwyth

✪ 12-11; (12-3, 6.30-11 winter); 12-10.30 Sun

☎ (01970) 880248

Spinning Dog Top Dog, Flannery's Harvest Moon, Flannery's Rheidol Reserve Ⓗ

This village-centre pub survived the troubles that beset the local Flannery's micro-brewery in early 2001 and continues to showcase the now Hereford-brewed beers. Other Spinning Dog/Flannery's beers (and guests) may appear, while Bragdy Ty Bach, the tiny brewery based in a converted outside lavatory, still stands in the pub grounds. It is used for occasional brews, often to recipes suggested by pub regulars. The one-roomed interior has an ale house look, with bare boards and exposed stonework. Good emphasis on food but it doesn't dominate, an upstairs restaurant is available. New car park in progress, otherwise space in the lane opposite. 🏚🕭🍴🛏♣

CARDIGAN

Black Lion

High Street

✪ 10-11; 12-10.30 Sun

☎ (01239) 612532

Tomos Watkin Whoosh, BB, OSB, seasonal beers Ⓗ

Historic coaching inn in a busy, characterful town. It dates back to the 12th century, but the present building is 18th century and comprises a main drinking area, small panelled snug and a rear dining area. A welcome outpost for this ambitious brewery. The variety of seasonal ales is always increasing. 🛏🍴🛏♣

Red Lion/Llew Coch

Pwllhai (near Finch Square bus terminus)

✪ 11-11; 12-5.30 (may open eve summer) Sun

☎ (01239) 612482

Brains Buckley's Best Bitter, Rev. James, seasonal beers Ⓗ

Warm-hearted town local whose skilful 1980s refurbishment is wearing well. The

INN BRIEF

Pembrokeshire

FISHGUARD

Fishguard Arms

11-3, 6-11;

12-3, 7-10.30 Sun

Beer range varies Ⓖ

Small locals' pub. Welcoming bar with an open fire. Two rotating real ales are served and no keg beer.

GOODWICK

Rose & Crown

11-11; 12-10.30 Sun

Worthington Bitter; guest beer Ⓗ

Picturesque pub close to ferry and enjoying harbour views. It has a small but welcoming no-smoking restaurant.

HAVERFORDWEST

George's

Market Street

10.30-10.30; closed Sun

Marston's Pedigree; Wye Valley Bitter; guest beer Ⓗ

Reached through a small Celtic Arts shop at the front. Enjoy a relaxing atmosphere, fine ales and excellent food.

NARBERTH

Angel Inn

High Street

11-3, 5.30-11; 7-10.30 Sun

Worthington Bitter; guest beer Ⓗ

Cosy, modernised town-centre pub, popular for food. Separate public bar.

TREFIN

Ship Inn

12-3, 6-11;

11-10.30 Sun

Worthington Bitter; guest beer Ⓗ

Village local with separate dining area, situated on unclassified road through village OS838325.

> ✣ symbol next to
> a main entry place
> name indicates there
> are Inn Brief entries
> as well.

large tiled main drinking area, with darts, table skittles and animated conversation in both Welsh and English, is joined by a lounge area and a pool room. Recorded Welsh music sold; C&W performed Fri eves. The town's longest-serving licensee presides over a vibrant mix of customers. Food is available all day (not Sun).
Q❄️◑⊟A♣

CELLAN

Fishers Arms
On B4343
✪ 4.30 (11 Sat)-11; 12-10.30 Sun
☎ (01570) 422895 e-mail: fishers@barbox.net
Tomos Watkin OSB Ⓗ
Friendly, village-centre pub, just two miles from the university town of Lampeter. The village is positioned alongside the River Teifi, one of the premier trout and salmon rivers in Wales. It is the venue for a famous raft race each summer. The Fishers has a main bar with open fire and fly rods and shotguns hanging from the beamed ceiling. A family room and eating room complete the pub. Fishers Bitter is a house beer by Brains. Camping facilities are available.
🚶Q🛏️❄️◑A♣P

GOGINAN

Druid
On A44, 7 iles E of Aberystwyth
✪ 11-11; 12-10.30 Sun
☎ (01970) 880650
Banks's Bitter, Brains Bitter; guest beer (occasional) Ⓗ
Strategically located on a main trunk route across the spine of Wales, this roadside free house is in an old lead-mining village. Visit Llywernog Mining Museum, a couple of miles east, to appreciate the industrial heritage. The L-shaped main bar is pleasantly decorated, with plenty of bench seating and a display of locally-made love spoons (a traditional love token). Reference books behind the bar, on hand to settle pub arguments, include Welsh and English dictionaries, a bible, bird books and many more. Check the village's website (www.goginan.co.uk) for guest beers and events. Guest ales are usually available in summer and at other busy periods, and generally come from an established regional brewer. Separate pool room.
❄️◑A♣P

LLANGOEDMOR

Penllwyndu
On B4570, 4 miles E of Cardigan OS241458
✪ 3-11; 3-10.30 Sun
☎ (01239) 682533
Brains Buckley's Best Bitter; Ind Coope Burton Ale; guest beer Ⓗ
Quiet, friendly, country pub with a good atmosphere. The public bar has a traditional slate floor and is oak beamed with a large open inglenook log fire. The games room (pool and darts) is down steps from the public bar. The delightful pub garden has views extending to the Preseli Hills. Popular locally, the pub reopened in 1985 after many years' closure – proving that old-style, non-food-led country pubs still have a future, if capably run. 🚶Q🛏️❄️♣P

PENNANT

Ship Inn
300 yds S of B4577 OS513631
✪ 6 (12 Sat)-11; 12-3, 7-10.30 Sun
☎ (01545) 570355
Beer range varies Ⓗ
For most of the 20th century this was a timeless, unchanged rural ale house – one licensee spent 60 years here – and those days are recalled by a newspaper cutting in the bar (in Welsh, but with photographs). The present owners have extended and altered the pub, creating a large, new games-cum-family room, but much of the place's character remains. Built 1754 (see beam over fireplace) and claiming smuggling connections with the former port of Aberarth, two miles downstream, it is a locals' pub, although customers from a nearby caravan site find their way here in summer. Just one real ale at a time, sourced from a reputable West Wales wholesaler – the choice spans regionals and micros, largely, although not exclusively, from South Wales or the west of England, and leans towards beers of session rather than premium strength. No full meals, but sandwiches always available in summer.
🚶Q🛏️❄️A♣P

PENPARCAU

Tollgate
Piercefield Lane (off A487 near A4120 roundabout)
✪ 12-11 (11.45 Fri); 11-11.45 Sat; 12-10.30 Sun
☎ (01970) 615016
Brain's Dark, SA, seasonal beer Ⓗ
Bustling, enthusiastically-run estate pub, situated on the outskirts of Aberystwyth, it is friendly and welcoming. Serves a keen local clientele in its two linked, spacious rooms. The recently refurbished lounge also provides space for eating and entertainment. There is a big-screen TV for major sporting events, and trophies and photos of the local football, pool and darts teams. The food served includes a popular Sun lunch and breakfast from 10.30 on a Sat morning. There is also a senior citizens' lunchtime special, Mon–Fri. Families are welcome, with a children's play area at the rear.
❄️◑⊟A♣P⚥

PREN-GWYN

Gwarcefel Arms
Crossroads of A475 and B4476
✪ 11-11; 12-3 (closed eve) Sun
☎ (01559) 362720
Brains Buckley's Best Bitter; Worthington Bitter; guest beer Ⓗ
The Gwarcefel Arms is a very popular eating place for locals throughout the year. The restaurant caters for parties and functions as well as normal trade. The bar has a cosy open fire and a relaxed, friendly atmosphere. Stunning location with the village nestled in the beautiful Teifi Valley, the pub is a welcome watering-hole for the many visitors to the area. Children welcome.
🚶❄️◑P

RHYDOWEN

Alltyrodyn Arms
At A475/B4459 crossroads
✪ 12-11; 12-4 (closed eve) Sun
☎ (01545) 590319
Cains Doctor Duncans IPA; Fuller's London Pride; guest beers Ⓗ
Named after a local landed estate, this village pub traces its history to Elizabeth times, though the present building is largely 18th century. The heart of the pub is the main bar, with roaring fire and beams from which dangle hundreds of mugs. A pool room and dining room complete the picture. The area's history, remarkably turbulent in the 19th century, is well described by a Victorian society sheet in the bar. Today's customers are a mix of domino-playing farmers, discerning tourists, and beer fans from a wide area of west Wales. Latin scholars can read the inscription on the barn; public transport users can now get here by bus from neighbouring market towns – but you can't get back! Still, a cab to nearby Llandysul shouldn't break the bank. South and Mid-Wales CAMRA *Pub of the Year* 2000, it stocks up to three guest beers, well chosen from a mix of micros and the better regionals – though far from home, the glorious Oakham beers have proved a favourite. No food Sun eve. Cider served in summer. ⚒✿≠◖♣♠P

TREGARON

Talbot Hotel
The Square
✪ 11-11; 12-10.30 Sun
☎ (01974) 298208 e-mail: talbot.hotel@btinternet.com
Boddingtons Bitter; Felinfoel Double Dragon; Marston's Pedigree Ⓗ
This old drovers' inn stands at the hub – both geographically and socially – of this small upland market town. The public bars, adjacent to the main hotel building, comprise three linked rooms – two front bars featuring old beams, stone-flagged floors, and open fires, plus a larger room, perhaps with more of a locals' character, to the rear (well-behaved children are welcome in the right-hand front bar). There is a fascinating array of drawings, photographs and press cuttings of local interest (yes, there really is an elephant buried out the back!), plus a display of paintings (for sale) by local artists. The function room hosts regular live gigs, and is central to local arts festivals. Pony-trekking, birdwatching (this is Red Kite country), and fishing can all be enjoyed locally. A splendid example of a community-based, Welsh-speaking local, extending a warm welcome to everyone. ⚒Q✿≠◖♠P

Pembrokeshire

ABERCYCH

Nag's Head
✪ 11-3, 5.30-11; 11-11 Sat; 12-10.30 Sun
☎ (01239) 841200
Flowers Original; Nags Head Old Emrys; Worthington Bitter; guest beers Ⓗ
Well-restored old smithy, boasting a beamed bar, riverside garden and a micro-brewery. Its Old Emrys ale is not always available. The bar area is furnished with an interesting collection of old medical instruments, railway memorabilia and a range of timepieces giving the time in different parts of the world. ⚒Q♿✿❀◖P

CRESSWELL

Cresselly Arms
✪ 12-3, 5-11; 7-10.30 Sun
☎ (01646) 651210
Worthington Best; guest beers Ⓖ
Unspoilt riverside pub where the beer is served from jugs. The pub is at the centre of the local community with strong hunting and cricketing traditions. The river has been known to reach the door at spring tides (dripping frogmen have been served!) Pembrokeshire CAMRA *Pub of the Year* 2001. ⚒QP

CROES-GOCH

Artramont Arms
On A487
✪ 7-11 (12-3, 6-11 summer); 12-3, 6-10 Fri & Sat; 12-3, 7-10.30 Sun
☎ (01348) 831309
Brains SA; guest beer Ⓗ
Friendly village local with a large public bar and a separate lounge with dining area. There is a no-smoking area for drinkers and a pleasant garden. Interesting, varied menu; food is served lunchtime and eve. ⚒✿◖⊟P⌇

FISHGUARD ✣

Royal Oak Inn
Market Square (A482)
✪ 11-11; 12-10.30 Sun
☎ (01348) 872514
Hancock's HB; guest beer Ⓗ
Charming, friendly, comfortable pub claiming historic connections (French forces surrendered here following the last invasion of mainland Britain in 1797). Some fascinating memorabilia dates back to this time. This pub is full of character and offers a separate public bar and pleasant garden. Home-cooked meals are served at affordable prices from a varied menu. Camping facilities are available nearby. ❀◖⊟♠♣

HAVERFORDWEST ✣

Pembroke Yeoman
St Thomas's Green, Hill Street
✪ 11-11; 12-3, 7-10.30 Sun
☎ (01437) 762500
Flowers IPA; Worthington Bitter; Ⓗ **guest beers** Ⓗ/Ⓖ
This well-supported, comfortable town local attracts a wide range of customers. It is very popular with all age groups and is a meeting place for a variety of local organisations. The guest ale can be served on gravity and the sparkler will be removed on request. Enjoy a very relaxing atmosphere, fine beers and traditional pub games. The pub offers an interesting menu. ⚒◖♣

NARBERTH ✣

Kirkland Arms
East Gate, St James Street
✪ 11-11; 11-10.30 Sun
☎ (01834) 860423

Felinfoel Best Bitter, Double Dragon; guest beer H
Comfortable, two-bar local on the edge of a one-way system. No food is served, but enjoy the excellent beers. There is a separate public bar and the pub has its own car park. Alternatively, if walking, it is the first stop-off point for a pint after a lengthy trek from the railway station. Camping facilities are available nearby. ⊕Å⇌P

NEWPORT

Castle Hotel
Bridge Street (A487)
✪ 11-11; 12-10.30 Sun
☎ (01239) 820742
Wadworth 6X; Worthington Bitter; guest beer H
Friendly, popular local: an attractive bar with a real fire and a wealth of wood panelling. There is an extensive separate dining area serving food all sessions. A large off-street car park is situated behind the hotel. ▲↘❀◁①Å P

Llwyngwair Arms
Bridge Street (on A487 through town)
✪ 11-11; 12-10.30 Sun
☎ (01239) 820267
Worthington Bitter; guest beer H
This popular local has not been altered for some considerable time. It has a separate dining area that serves inexpensive food all day in summer (more restricted hours in winter). Car parking is through an archway on the opposite side of the road. Friendly, unspoilt pub. ▲Q①Å P

PONTFAEN

Dyffryn Arms ☆
Off B4313, Gwaun Valley road OS027341
✪ hours vary
☎ (01348) 881305
Draught Bass or Ind Coope Burton Ale G
This bar resembles a 1920s front room where time has stood still. The beer is still served by the jug through a sliding hatch.

Children's certificates

When pubs are described as having 'children's certificates', this indicates that local licensing authorities are satisfied that the pubs in question have environments suitable for children under 14, and that meals and non-alcoholic drinks are available. Some authorities demand more wide-ranging facilities – such as non-smoking areas, an absence of gaming machines, nappy-changing provision, junior WCs and basins, and furniture suitable for small children — before granting certificates, which must be prominently displayed.

Conversation is the main form of entertainment. The landlady is in her eighties and there is a superb, relaxed atmosphere in this pub. It lies in the heart of the scenic Gwaun Valley between the Preseli hills and Fishguard (Abergwaun). ▲Q❀Å♣

PORTHGAIN

Sloop Inn
Near quay in village
✪ 11.30-3, 6-11 (11-11 summer); 12-4, 6-10.30 Sun
☎ (01348) 831449
Brains SA; Felinfoel Double Dragon; Worthington Bitter H
This sympathetically modernised old inn has served both the locally-based fishing industry and the now-defunct quarrying industry. The pub features quarrying and shipping ephemera in its decor. Holding hoppers for stone can be seen on the opposite side of the harbour. Very popular pub with a good variety of beers and well-priced food. ▲❀①♣P

ST DAVID'S

Farmers Arms
12-14 Goat Street (on road from old cross towards cathedral) OS751253
✪ 11-11; 12-10.30 Sun
☎ (01437) 720328
Felinfoel Double Dragon; Flowers Original; Wadworth 6X; Worthington Bitter H
19th-century stone hostelry retaining many old features. It is popular with local farmers and fishermen, and many tourists visit during the summer season. The pub serves an interesting range of good, wholesome, home-cooked food. Definitely worth a visit. ▲Q❀①⊕Å

ST DOGMAELS

White Hart
Finch Street (on B4546)
✪ 12-2.30 (not Tue), 7-11; 12-3, 7-10.30 Sun
☎ (01239) 612099
Wadworth IPA; guest beers H
Cheery, welcoming small village pub with a good local following. It is on the right-hand side of the road when entering St Dogmaels from Cardigan. The guest beers change on a regular basis and are often from breweries not represented locally. Three guest ales are served in summer and two in winter. The landlord is a great rugby enthusiast. Opening hours extend in the summer and the pub is a good stop-off point if walking the Pembrokeshire Coast Path. ▲①⊕Å♣

SOLVA

Harbour Inn
On A487 through road adjoining harbour car park
✪ 11-11; 12-10.30 Sun
☎ (01437) 720013
Draught Bass; Worthington Bitter; guest beer H
This delightful seaside hostelry retains a traditional atmosphere, having remained unaltered for a considerable time. It is used as a base for many community activities and is very popular with locals. Camping facilities are close by for caravans and tents. Enjoy a quiet, relaxing pint in this attractive, unspoilt local. ▲Q❀◁①Å

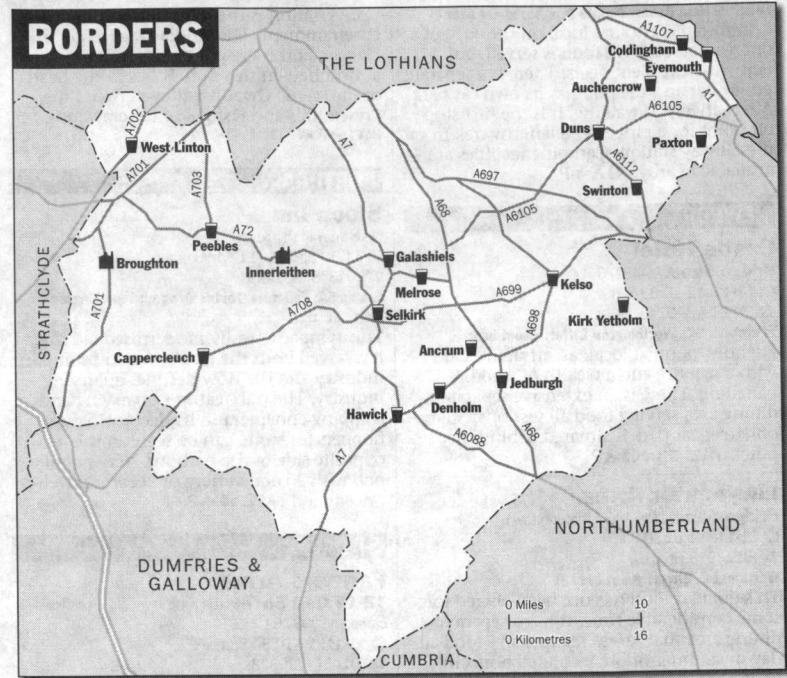

BORDERS

(Map of the Borders area showing: THE LOTHIANS, A1107, Coldingham, Eyemouth, Auchencrow, A6105, Duns, Paxton, A6112, Swinton, A6105, West Linton, A702, A701, A703, A7, A697, A68, Peebles, A72, Broughton, Innerleithen, Galashiels, Kelso, A699, Melrose, A698, Kirk Yetholm, A708, Selkirk, STRATHCLYDE, A701, Cappercleuch, Ancrum, Jedburgh, Hawick, Denholm, A6088, A68, A7, NORTHUMBERLAND, DUMFRIES & GALLOWAY, CUMBRIA)

0 Miles 10 / 0 Kilometres 16

Authority area covered: The Borders UA

ANCRUM

Cross Keys Inn ☆
The Green (B6400, off A68)
⏰ 6-11 (midnight Thu); 5-1am Fri; 12-midnight Sat;
12.30-11 Sun
☎ (01835) 830344 e-mail: crossxkeys@ukgateway.net
Caledonian Deuchars IPA; guest beers Ⓗ
Friendly village local with a cosy, olde-
world feel. The bar remains nearly
untouched from the refurbishment by
Jedburgh Brewery in 1908, retaining the
half-pine panelling through into the gantry.
A conversation piece by the fireplace is a
primitive painting by Wally Turnbull, a
local artist. The seating is compact but
comfortable and tables have been made
from old sewing machine stands. The
spacious back lounge has been tastefully
renovated and retains overhead tram lines
from the former cellar. A good varied menu
is supplemented by daily specials. A patio is
used for outdoor drinking. Children's
certificate. 🏚Q❄◖◑🍴♣P

AUCHENCROW

Craw Inn
On B6438, follow signs from A1
⏰ 12-2.30, 6-11 (midnight Fri); 12-midnight Sat;
12.30-11 Sun
☎ (01890) 761253
Beer range varies Ⓗ
Welcoming and recently renovated village
inn, circa 1680. The original beamed bar
has bench seating at one end and wooden
tables and chairs at the other. A log-burning
stove creates a cosy atmosphere. Numerous
pump clips indicate the superb, ever-
changing range of beer served on the two
handpumps. The no-smoking area of the
inn has views to the surrounding
countryside and is divided into a lounge-
cum-eating area and restaurant. Traditional
furniture gives a select feel. Many meals on
the wide-ranging menu are based on local
produce. A small room is available for
private functions. 🏚Q❄🐾◖◑🍴&♣P✗

DENHOLM

Auld Cross Keys Inn
Main Street (A698)
⏰ 11-2.30 (not Mon), 5-11 (midnight Fri); 11-midnight
Sat; 12.30-11 Sun
☎ (01450) 870305
Beer range varies Ⓗ
Picturesque, 18th-century inn by the village
green. The main bar has a low ceiling, false
panelling, a real fire and a pool table at one
end. The presence of a scarlet macaw and a
full-sized Robertson's Golly are conversation
pieces in this cosy bar. The recently
refurbished upmarket lounge and dining
area, in Tardis tradition open through to a
large function room. Quizzes, folk music
sessions and concerts are regular features.
Those not wishing to dine could try the
cheesy eggs or high teas. No food Mon.
Children's certificate in lounge.
🏚❄🐾◖◑🍴♣P

Fox & Hounds Inn
Main Street (A698)
⏰ 5-midnight (1am Fri); 11-1am Sat; 12.30-midnight
Sun
☎ (01450) 870247 e-mail: vigstow@vista.net
Beer range varies Ⓗ
Village local, dating from the 1750s,
overlooking the village green. The main bar
is light and comfortable and retains the
original beams. The real fire gives it a warm,
welcoming feel in winter. Above the fire is
the odd stuffed animal head and other

memorabilia including a photograph of Rubstik, a local horse that won the Grand National in the 1970s. Separate dining area has a coffee-house atmosphere. There is a wind-up gramophone with a selection of 78s. The courtyard is sheltered for outdoor drinking. The interesting beer range is limited, but frequently changes. Children's certificate. 🏠♿🍴◑☐🅰♣P

DUNS

Whip & Saddle
Market Square
☼ 11-11 (midnight Fri & Sat); 12.30-11.30 Sun
☎ (01361) 883215
Caledonian Deuchars IPA; Theakston XB; guest beer (summer) Ⓗ

Town-centre bar, dating from 1790, has an airy interior with light wooden floors and distinctive leaded windows, giving views across the square. The pub has modern decor, which contrasts with the 1950s photos of local interest. One photo was taken in exceptionally snowy weather, conditions which recurred last winter. The dining room upstairs doubles as a family room and is pleasantly decorated. No food Sun. River Whiteadder angling permits are available. Darts, dominoes and Shut the Box are played. 🚭🅰♣

EYEMOUTH

Ship Hotel
Harbour Road
☼ 11-midnight (1am Fri & Sat); 12-midnight Sun
☎ (01890) 750224
Caledonian 80/-; guest beer Ⓗ

Family-run hotel by the harbour. The functional bar is a vibrant fisherman's haunt with more trawlers than cars parked outside, a point to bear in mind when you leave! A warm fire, a selection of rums and a wide range of maritime memorabilia add to the character. It can be smoky and the pool table is well used. The lounge is a contrast, being comfortable, bright and much quieter. It is mainly used for eating. The menu is reasonably priced and is supplemented by daily specials. Many dishes feature locally caught fish. An upstairs dining room is also open eves. Children's certificate.
🏠♿🍴◑☐🅰♣P

GALASHIELS

Ladhope Inn
33 High Buckholmside
(A7, ½ mile N of centre)
☼ 11-3, 5-11; 11-11 Wed; 11-midnight Thu-Sat; 12.30-midnight Sun
☎ (01896) 752446 e-mail: ladhopeinn@fsnet.co.uk
Caledonian Deuchars IPA; guest beer Ⓗ

Comfortable, friendly locals' bar with a vibrant Borders atmosphere. Part of a terraced row built into the hillside, dating from 1792, it has been altered considerably inside. A single room houses the main bar with TVs and modern slot machines, it is decorated with whisky jugs. An additional alcove area has old photographs and a large inked map of the Borders region. The guest beer changes regularly and toasties are available. Only well-behaved children are welcome. ♿🅰♣

HAWICK

High Level Bar
11 Green Terrace (Hope St, on SW edge of town)
☼ 11-2.30 (not Tue), 5-11 (midnight Thu); 11-1am Fri & Sat; 12.30-11 Sun
☎ (01450) 377469
Mansfield Cask Ale Ⓗ

Popular community local nestled on a hillside above the town in the heart of the residential area. The fine public bar has wood-panelled walls, wooden floors, bar and gantry. The clientele has a strong interest in horses and rugby, making it a haven for those with a similar interest. A vibrant atmosphere can be found on most race days. More reminiscent of a games room is the lounge, which is half-filled by a pool table and where darts, cards and dominoes are played. The small bar counter has mock panels and horsey memorabilia. ☐♣

KIRK YETHOLM

Border Hotel
The Green
☼ 11-midnight (11 winter); 11-1am (midnight winter) Fri & Sat; 12-midnight (11 winter) Sun
☎ (01573) 420237 website: theborderhotel.co.uk
Beer range varies Ⓗ

17th-century hotel just over a mile from the English border. Standing at the end of the Pennine Way and on the route of St Cuthbert's Way, it attracts many walkers. The main bar, which was originally the stables, is decorated in tartan, boasts wooden beams and has a large hunting mural running round the walls. The small dining area is in the original thatched part of the building. Diners congregate in the elegant conservatory and there is a games room. Children's certificate. A second beer is added in summer. 🏠Q♿🍴◑☐🅰P⚲

MELROSE

Burt's Hotel
Market Square
☼ 11-2, 5-11; 12-2, 6-11 Sun
☎ (01896) 822285
Caledonian Deuchars IPA, 80/-; guest beer Ⓗ

Elegant, well-appointed, family-run hotel and restaurant in the main square. The decor of the plush lounge bar reflects the hunting and fishing interests of many of the regulars. The restaurant is expensive but serves award-winning food. The bar menu offers a wide choice of cheaper meals. A comfortable seating area by the entrance is available for non-smokers. Close by is Melrose Abbey and the Teddy Bear Museum. Real ale may not be available during the Melrose 7s week. Children's certificate. 🏠Q🍴◑🅰P⚲

PAXTON

Cross Inn
Off B6460
☼ 11-2.30 (not Mon), 6.30-midnight; 12.30-2.30, 6.30-midnight ☎ (01289) 386267

INDEPENDENT BREWERIES

Broughton Broughton
Traquair Innerleithen

Orkney Dark Island; guest beer Ⓗ
Comfortable village pub, circa 1870s. It has now reverted to its original name following the restoration to former glory of an old cross outside the front. Until recently, it was the Hoolit's Nest which reflected the vast number of owls, in all sorts of guises, which watch the bar and seating areas. The bar counter has a mahogany top and wood-panelling. The walls are decorated with an unusual art collection. There is a small, pleasant dining room. The guest beer is often from Broughton. Fishing permits are available and historic Paxton House is nearby. ⚜️◑♿♣P

PEEBLES

Bridge Inn
Portbrae (W end of town centre)
🕐 11 (12 Sun)-midnight
☎ (01721) 720589
Caledonian Deuchars IPA; Courage Directors; guest beer (summer) Ⓗ
Cheerful and welcoming town-centre local, conveniently situated by a church and the police station. The ground floor of the Tudor-style building contains a bright single-roomed bar. The mosaic-floored entrance bears the pub's original name of the Tweedside Inn. It is also known as the Trust. The comfortable bar is decorated with memorabilia relevant to the outdoor life. An interesting selection of jugs and bottles also catch the eye. ▲♣

Neidpath Inn
27-29 Old Town (A72, W of town centre)
🕐 11-midnight (11 Mon); 12.30-midnight Sun
☎ (01721) 721721
Caledonian Deuchars IPA; guest beer Ⓗ
On the quieter west side of town, this airy L-shaped bar provides a contrast for drinkers. The front bar area with a real fire provides a cosy area to enjoy a relaxing drink in traditional surroundings. The back bar area is popular with the younger clientele with a pool table and juke box. In contrast the quieter lounge bar provides a safe haven away from distractions. The wood, glasswork and musical instruments throughout are noteworthy. Local folk, chess and fishing clubs meet here. Awarded Vanguard *Best Cellarman* 1999 and 2000. Children welcome in lounge or garden until 7pm. ⚜️⚛️⏚▲♣

SELKIRK

Heatherlie House Hotel
Heatherlie Park (off A708 near town centre)

🕐 11-11 (midnight Fri & Sat); 12.30-11 Sun
☎ (01750) 721200
Beer range varies Ⓗ
Family-run hotel set in tranquil surroundings. Originally a Victorian villa it retains a stately air of grandeur with a magnificent hand-carved fireplace depicting barn owls in the entrance and a beautiful cornice in the bar. The bar, which is also a dining area, is comfortable and airy. It has views through the large bay windows to the gardens, popular with drinkers in the summer. Old photos in the bar are of the owners and the bar is inlaid with old wine boxes. In winter the single real ale is often from Broughton. In the summer a choice is available.
🏨⚜️🛏️◑▲♣P

SWINTON

Wheatsheaf Hotel
Main Street
🕐 11-2, 6-11 (not Mon eve);
11.30 Fri & Sat;
12.30-3.30, 6.30-10.30 Sun (not winter eve)
☎ (01890) 860257 website: wheatsheaf-swinton.co.uk
Caledonian 80/-; guest beer Ⓗ
Well-appointed hotel, with an award-winning restaurant, situated on the main street overlooking the village green. Originally dating from the 1850s this coaching inn has evolved considerably. There are three large comfortable dining and lounge areas, one being a conservatory. The food is not cheap but is excellent. The menu offers an extensive choice, much of which uses local produce. A small dimly lit snug bar has an oak-topped counter, church pews and photos of local legend Jim Clark, the Formula 1 racing driver. The guest beer is often from Broughton. Children's certificate.
🏨Q⚜️🛏️◑⏚♣P

WEST LINTON

Gordon Arms Hotel
Dolphinton Road (on A702)
🕐 11-midnight (1am Fri & Sat); 11-midnight Sun
☎ (01968) 660208
Caledonian Deuchars IPA; guest beer Ⓗ
Situated in a commuter village close to the Pentland Hills and a short drive from Edinburgh. Airy-L-shaped, homely public bar with stone walls and a fine cornice. Entertainment includes a juke box, TV, radio and piano. The attractive restaurant has a continental feel and there is a small beer garden.
🏨⚜️◑⏚▲♣P

INN BRIEF

COLDINGHAM
Anchor Inn
School Road
12-2.30 (closed winter), 5-midnight;
12-midnight Sat, Sun and summer
Beer range varies Ⓗ
Cosy village inn with wood-panelled bar and comfortable lounge. The menu is extensive. Be prepared for humour that prevails.

CAPPERCLEUCH
Tibbie Shiels Inn
St Mary's Loch
11-11 (midnight Fri & Sat);

closed Mon-Wed; 12.30-11 (6 winter) Sun
Belhaven 80/-; Broughton Greenmantle Ⓗ
Cosy, remote, historic inn in an idyllic setting between two lochs in the Yarrow Valley. Ideal for peace, solitude and good food.

JEDBURGH
Cannon
8 Exchange Street
11-midnight (1am Fri); 12.30-11 Sun
Theakston Best Bitter; guest beer Ⓗ
Small public house, reminiscent of a traditional ale house and popular with local sportsmen. The walls are decorated with rugby memorabilia.

KELSO
White Swan
Abbey Row
11-midnight (1am Thu-Sat); 11-midnight Sun
Caledonian Deuchars IPA; guest beer Ⓗ
An often lively, modernised old pub with a single bar near Kelso Abbey. The back area is for pool and a real fire warms the central part.

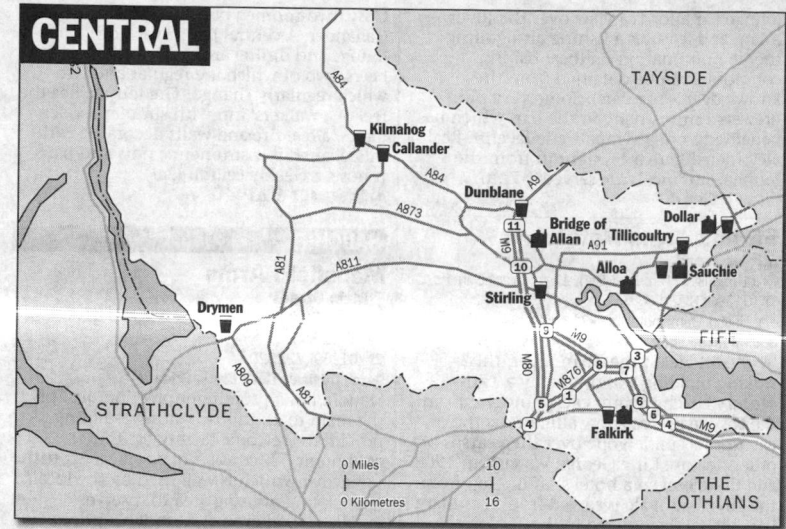

Authority areas covered: Clackmannan UA, Falkirk UA, Stirling UA

CALLANDER

Waverley Hotel
Main Street
⊙ 11-midnight (1am Fri & Sat); 11-midnight Sun
☎ (01877) 330245
website: www.thewaverleycallander.com
Arran Dark; Harviestoun Wee Stoater; guest beers Ⓗ
Beside the Waverley Hotel, in this popular
tourist town, the Claymore Bar has two
drinking areas: a large main bar with a
wrought iron screen and a smaller TV room.
Stocking three beers in winter, the range
increases to four or five during the summer,
plus a cask cider. Two beer festivals are held
annually, one in Sept and a second around
Christmas with a seasonal theme. A great
place for a refreshing pint after a walk in the
Trossachs, lunches are always served, but
check availability of eve meals in winter.
🛏◑♠♨

DOLLAR

Castle Campbell
13 Bridge Street
⊙ 11-11.30 (1am Fri & Sat); 12.30-midnight Sun
☎ (01259) 742519
website: www.castle-campbell.co.uk
Fuller's London Pride; Harviestoun Bitter & Twisted Ⓗ
Friendly, family-run hotel on the main
street through the town, with a resident
ghost, according to staff and locals.
Originally a coaching inn dating back to
1822, it is named after the local NT-owned
castle, which stands on a nearby hillside.
Real ale is only served in the lounge bar,
which is themed on golf and whisky. Food
and guest accommodation are of a high
standard. Q🛏◑⊟P

Strathallan Hotel
Chapel Place
⊙ 12-2.30 (not Mon or Tue), 5-midnight (1am Fri &
Sat); 12-3, 6-midnight Sun
☎ (01259) 742205
**Fuller's London Pride; Harviestoun Wee Stoater, Bitter
& Twisted** Ⓗ
Traditional country hotel with a bistro
restaurant and a small bar run by cheerful
staff. Note the extensive collection of jugs
hanging from the ceiling. An outlet for local
Harviestoun beers, the pub may stock
special brews when available. The National
Trust's Castle Campbell is a short walk
away. Dating back to the 15th century, it
was burned by Cromwell's troops in the
mid-17th century, but is still worth a visit,
and the surrounding Dollar Glen offers
pleasant walks. Q🛏◑P

DRYMEN

Winnock
The Square
⊙ 11-midnight (1am Fri & Sat); 12-midnight Sun
☎ (01360) 660245 website: www.winnockhotel.com
Broughton Merlin's Ale; Tetley Bitter; guest beers Ⓗ
Pleasant, 300-year-old, 48-roomed hotel at
the centre of a village near the eastern side
of Loch Lomond. There are five handpumps
in the main stone-walled lounge bar from
which the restaurant leads off. No real ale is
dispensed in the public bar. It is well known
for food, Sun night ceilidhs and Murder
Mystery weekends. There is a pétanque
pitch in the grounds. 🛏Q❀🛏◑⊟♣P

DUNBLANE

Dunblane Hotel
10 Stirling Road
⊙ 11-midnight (1am Fri & Sat); 11-midnight Sun
☎ (01786) 822178
**Courage Directors; Greene King Abbot, Old Speckled
Hen; Ind Coope Burton Ale; guest beer** Ⓗ
This well-appointed village pub and hotel
offers a warm welcome to both locals and
tourists alike. The pleasant, comfortable

INDEPENDENT BREWERIES

Bridge of Allan Bridge of Allan
Devon Sauchie
Eglesbrech Falkirk
Forth Alloa
Harviestoun Dollar

lounge bar affords a view over the River Allan, and features a fishing and golfing theme (information on local fishing conditions can be obtained from the knowledgable regulars). Some very old brewery mirrors hang in the bar, which has benefited from a sympathetic facelift. Real ale ordered here is brought in from the lounge. Sun meals are served 1-7pm.
🏠🛏️◑🚮♿♣P

Stirling Arms Hotel
Stirling Road
☼ 11-midnight (1am Fri & Sat); 12-midnight Sun
☎ (01786) 822156
e-mail: stirlingarmshotel@talk21.com
Greene King Abbot; Taylor Landlord Ⓗ
By the bridge on the Allan River, this striking building was originally a 17th-century coaching inn. Old photographs in the cosy main bar show alterations the exterior has undergone over the years; others feature King George V's visit in 1908 and there is even a hotel staff line-up from the 1870s. Real ale is served from this main bar, but can be ordered in the TV lounge; there is also a small side bar. Eve meals are served in the Oak Room Restaurant, downstairs in what were once the staff quarters. The garden overlooks the river.
🏠🛏️◑♿P

Tappit Hen
Kirk Street
☼ 11-midnight (1am Fri & Sat); 11-midnight Sun
☎ (01786) 825226
Belhaven 70/-, 80/-; guest beers Ⓗ
A fine collection of pump clips adorns the walls, together with a definition of the pub's name: a Tappit Hen is a jug or pitcher. This traditional one-roomed local caters for a wide cross-section of drinkers; the range of guest beers is ever changing, up to five being available at any one time. There are pictures of old Dunblane to peruse in this comfortable pub, situated directly opposite the imposing cathedral. ♿♣

Wheatsheaf Inn
16 Baxter's Wynd (off High St)
☼ 11-11 (12.30am Fri & Sat); 12.30-11 Sun
☎ (01324) 623716
Belhaven 80/-; Caledonian Deuchars IPA; guest beers Ⓗ
Coaching inn, over 200 years old, consisting of a single-storey building housing only a bar with stools, and tables with chairs around the walls. The bar stocks an excellent selection of whiskies and is decorated with brewery mirrors and caricatures of the town's worthies. The pub is very popular with the locals and has a welcoming atmosphere, enhanced by being conveniently located in the town centre, but in a quiet spot away from the traffic and shops. Q♿(Grahamston & Falkirk High)

Lade Inn
At A84/A821 jct, 1 mile W of Callander
☼ 12-3, 5.30-11; 12.30-8.30 Sun
☎ (01877) 330152 website: www.theladeinn.com
Broughton Greenmantle; Orkney Red MacGregor; guest beers Ⓗ

Cosy, two-roomed pub on the outskirts of Callander. A central bar serves both a lounge and dining area with a range of four beers, two of which are regular and two which regularly change. The lounge has the feel of a walkers' inn with simple wooden tables, a real fire and walls decorated with miscellaneous instruments, pots and pans. It hosts a weekly ceilidh (Sat).
🏨🛏️🏠◑♿▲P✂️🍴

Mansfield Arms
7 Main Street
☼ 11-11.30 (11 Tue & Wed; 12.30am Fri & Sat); 12.30-11 Sun
☎ (01259) 722020
Devon Original, Thick Black, Pride Ⓐ
Standing in a prominent position, just off the main road, this two-storey building provides a welcome facility for the community. It consists of a typical Scottish public bar, which is well used by the locals, and a lounge/dining area that serves excellent food at very reasonable prices. Behind the pub is a small brewery where the publican makes three ales which are sold only in his own premises. ◑🚮♿♣P

Choosing Pubs

CAMRA members and branches choose the pubs listed in the Good Beer Guide. There is no payment for entry, and pubs are inspected on a regular basis by personal visits; publicans are not sent a questionnaire once a year, as is the case with some pub guides. CAMRA branches monitor all the pubs in their areas, and the choice of pubs for the guide is often the result of democratic vote at branch meetings. However, recommendations from readers are welcomed and will be passed on to the relevant branch: write to Good Beer Guide, CAMRA, 230 Hatfield Road, St Albans, AL1 4LW; or send an e-mail to camra@camra.org.uk.

Fizz warning

Some national breweries produce both cask-conditioned and 'nitro-keg' versions of their beers. Boddingtons Bitter, John Smith's Bitter, Tetley's Bitter and Worthington fall into this category. Nitro-keg beers, often promoted as 'smooth' or 'cream-flow' products, are filtered and pasteurised in the brewery, and served in pubs by a mix of applied carbon dioxide and nitrogen gases. They are bland, served extremely cold, and any hop character is lost by the use of applied gas. To add insult to injury, the keg founts that serve such beers are often topped by small dummy handpumps. As a result of lobbying by CAMRA, some producers of cask and nitro versions of the same beer now include the word 'cask' on pump clips for the genuine article. For example, both John Smith's Bitter and Tetley's Bitter now carry the word 'cask' on pump clips for the real thing. For the sake of brevity, and as the Good Beer Guide lists only cask-conditioned beers, we refer simply to John Smith's Bitter and Tetley Bitter. The Bass/Interbrew brand, Worthington, is labelled Worthington Bitter in cask form, and – bizarrely – Worthington Best Bitter in the nitro-keg version. Always choose the living rather than the dead.

STIRLING

Birds & Bees
Easter Cornton Road (turn off the Stirling-Causewayhead road)
☼ 12-3, 5-midnight, 12-1am Fri & Sat; 12.30-midnight Sun
☎ (01786) 473663
Caledonian 80/-; guest beers Ⓗ
Converted from an old farm building, the Birds & Bees is a popular pub, mainly with locals, being located in a residential area on the outskirts of Stirling. The pub has a very open and bright interior; its semi-rural location is reflected in the interior with stuffed sheep and fleece-covered seats scattered around the lounge/bar. Outside there is an extensive seating area and ample parking. ☼Ⓞ◐ &

Hogshead
2 Baker Street
☼ 11-midnight (1am Fri & Sat); 12-30-midnight Sun
☎ (01786) 448722
Boddingtons Bitter; Caledonian Deuchars IPA, 80/-; Flowers IPA; guest beers Ⓗ
Friendly pub, that usually has a selection of eight ales, where helpful staff are willing to provide a sample of beer to try. Very popular with locals, students and tourists, situated close to the high street and town centre. An interesting walk, along cobbled streets, takes you up to the castle, passing many historic buildings. The bar is a typical ale house, with a somewhat rustic theme, making it a comfortable drinking spot. ◐ & ≈

Portcullis
Castle Wynd
☼ 11.30 (12.30 Sun)-midnight
☎ (01786) 472290 website: www.portcullishotel.com
Orkney Dark Island; guest beer Ⓗ
Originally a grammar school, the Portcullis is a popular, friendly hotel situated at the foot of Stirling Castle Esplanade, next to the old town jail. It has a nice outdoor area for eating and drinking in ancient surroundings. It enjoys a good reputation for quality meals – booking is recommended, particularly in the tourist season when busloads of visitors descend on the town. No meals Mon eve. Parking can be a problem. Accommodation is in four rooms with en-suite facilities. ⚌ ✿ ⋈ ◐ ≈ P

TILLICOULTRY

Woolpack Inn
Glassford Square
☼ 11-midnight (1am Fri & Sat); 12.30-11 Sun
☎ (01259) 750332
Beer range varies Ⓗ
Old drovers' inn dating back to 1748 with a basic bar area and a small public bar area with a lounge to the rear. This cheerful pub is very popular with hillwalkers in the summer, and tends to get busy at weekends. It has a high turnover of beer, so you are guaranteed a fresh pint. The beers are sourced from all over the UK, from small and larger breweries and you will often find ales from Scottish brewers such as Aviemore and Isle of Skye. ♣

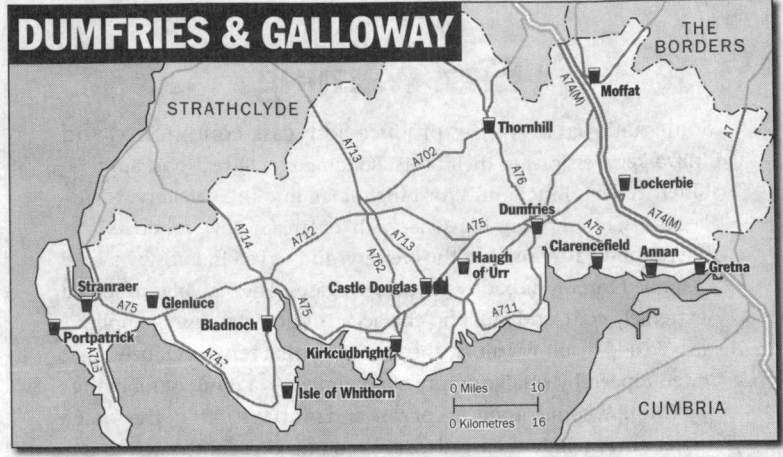

DUMFRIES & GALLOWAY

Authority area covered: Dumfries & Galloway UA

ANNAN

Blue Bell Inn
10 High Street
⏰ 11-11 (midnight Thu-Sat); 12.30-11 Sun
☎ (01461) 202385
Theakston Best Bitter; guest beers Ⓗ
Former coaching inn, built in 1770 of local red sandstone. The leftover stone was used as ballast by ships sailing to New York and incorporated in the construction of Grand Central Station and the base for the Statue of Liberty. The pub is ex-State Management scheme, and has changed little, retaining its fine wood panelling. Note the prints of local scenes and characters, and quotations from local literary luminaries such as Thomas Carlyle and Edward Irving. This lively, friendly local usually has up to three guest beers. Å❀≈♣

BLADNOCH

Bladnoch Inn
On A714, 6 miles S of Newton Stewart
⏰ 11 (12.30 Sun)-11
☎ (01988) 402200
website: www.bladnochinngalloway.co.uk
Beer range varies Ⓗ
In a picturesque riverside setting, the pub stands opposite the Bladnoch Distillery which has a visitors' centre and offers tours. The pub is an ideal base for anglers, and is close to the local rugby union club ground; both sports are reflected in the decor. The bar area comprises two rooms, and meals may be taken there or in the restaurant. One beer, usually a national brand, is offered in winter, two in summer.
🚶Q❀🛏◑ÅP

CASTLE DOUGLAS

Douglas Arms Hotel
King Street
⏰ 10.30-midnight (including Sun)
☎ (01556) 502231
website: www.first-inn-scotland.co.uk/douglas.htm
Beer range varies Ⓗ
A former coaching inn, dating back to 1779, the hotel has been sympathetically modernised. The beers come from the Sulwath Brewery across the street, and there is a choice of over 100 whiskies. The St Andrews Restaurant features fresh local produce, and more relaxed meals can be taken in the adjoining bar. The hotel has 24 en-suite bedrooms. Nearby are Threave Gardens (NTS) and Castle (situated on an island in the middle of the river). Castle Douglas, an attractive town makes a good touring centre.
🚶Q🛏◑&♣P

CLARENCEFIELD

Farmers Inn
Main Street (B724, halfway between Dumfries and Annan)
⏰ 11-2.30, 6-11.30 (12.30am Fri); 12-12.30am Sat; 12.30-11.30 Sun
☎ (01387) 870675
website: www.smoothhound.co.uk/hotels/farmersinn.html
Beer range varies Ⓗ
Late 17th-century coaching inn, formerly the Castle Inn after nearby Comlongon Castle. The inn has had a varied history: it was the Post Office, housed the village's first telephone exchange and, in 1896, became the Temperance Castle Hotel. There are three internationally important historic sites within walking distance: the 8th-century Ruthwell Cross, the world's first savings bank at Ruthwell and Brow Well where Robert Burns (a customer at the inn) died. 🚶Q❀🛏◑&♣♠P

DUMFRIES

Globe Inn
56 High Street
⏰ 11-11 (midnight Thu-Sat); 12.30-11 Sun
☎ (01387) 252335
Caledonian Deuchars IPA Ⓗ
This town-centre inn is internationally famous for its Robert Burns connections. Established in 1610, tucked away in a narrow wynd, Burns' favourite chair still rests by the fireplace and his handwriting is etched on a bedroom window; presumably the bedroom where his affair with barmaid Anna Park, resulted in a daughter. The Globe retains all its original features; it is not, however, a museum, but a friendly place to soak up the atmosphere. Don't miss it! 🚶❀◑≈

New Bazaar
39 Whitesands
✪ 11-11 (midnight Thu-Sat); 11-11 Sun
☎ (01387) 268776
Belhaven St Andrew's Ale; McEwan 80/-; Sulwath Knockendoch; guest beers Ⓗ
Traditional pub, affording excellent views across the River Nith to the Camera Obscura at Dumfries Museum. Dating from 1836, the Camera Obscura is located in a converted windmill and offers a panoramic view of Dumfries. An absolute must is a walk over the superb 15th-century Devorgilla Bridge, where you can visit the Old Bridge Museum and Robert Burns Centre. But, do return to the Bazaar and enjoy good company in its superb Victorian bar. 🏚Q≷♣

Ship Inn
97 St Michael Street
✪ 11-2.30, 5-11; 12-2.30; 6.30-11 Sun
☎ (01387) 255189
Greene King Abbot; Ⓗ **McEwan 80/-;** Ⓐ **Marston's Pedigree; Taylor Landlord; Theakston XB; guest beers** Ⓗ
Welcoming, two-roomed free house that keeps to 'traditional' opening hours and retains traditional fonts for the McEwan's. A varied clientele enjoys the friendly atmosphere in this local CAMRA former *Pub of the Year*. The Ship is opposite St Michael's churchyard where you will find the Robert Burns Mausoleum, close to the Burns House Museum and River Nith. Q≷♣

Tam O'Shanter
113 Queensbury Street
✪ 11-11 (midnight Fri & Sat); 12.30-11 Sun
☎ e-mail: flomasterales@ukonline.uk
Belhaven 80/-; Caledonian Deuchars IPA; guest beers Ⓗ
The 'Tam' is a 17th-century former coaching inn, named after one of Rabbie Burns' famous poems. Recent refurbishments have brightened the place up and the words of the Bard feature in a few places. The bar is small, decorated with prints of old Dumfries and even a couple of books by the editor of this *Guide!* A corridor leads to the small no-smoking room that retains the original hearth. The back room displays a number of brewery mirrors. Q❀Ⓒ◖≷♣✄

Kelvin House Hotel
53 Main Street (off A75)
✪ 11-11 (midnight Fri & Sat); (12-3, 6-midnight winter); 12-11.30 Sun
☎ (01581) 300303 website: www.kelvin-house.co.uk
Orkney Red MacGregor; guest beers Ⓗ
Small, friendly, hotel, circa 1790, near Luce Bay in a bypassed village, that dates back to Roman times; Robert the Bruce is known to have stayed locally. The hotel is renowned for traditional Scottish food, including seafood, venison and salmon. Of local interest is Luce Abbey and there are good walks and golf courses nearby. TV fans will recognise scenes from the BBC series *2,000 Acres of Sky*. The range of guest beers is evident from the pump clips above the bar; local Sulwath ales are featured regularly. 🏚≷❀◖Ⓐ♣✄

Solway Lodge Hotel
Annan Road (½ mile from the border)
✪ 11-11; 12-11 (3 winter) Sun
☎ (01461) 338266
Tetley Bitter Ⓗ
Comfortable, family-run hotel on the main road, on the bus route between Carlisle, Annan and Dumfries. Gretna is known as the Gateway to Scotland and the Solway Lodge is less than 10 minutes' walk from the border. It is popular with wedding parties, in keeping with Gretna's reputation as Scotland's 'Love Town', and the famous old blacksmith's shop and museum are within walking distance at Gretna Green. Good value bar meals are served, and a no-smoking restaurant opens eves.
≷❀🛏Ⓒ♿Å≷(Gretna Green)

Laurie Arms Hotel
On B794, 1 mile S of A75
✪ 11.45-2.30, 5.30-midnight (11 Mon-Wed winter); 11.45-3.30; 6-midnight Sun
☎ (01556) 660246
Beer range varies Ⓗ
Attractive country inn, set in a quiet village in the Urr Valley. The wood-panelled bar boasts a large fireplace of local Dalbeattie granite. The pub is a family business and all aspects are given the same care as the real ales, of which up to four are normally available – a board outside lists those on tap and future treats. The restaurant and bar meals include local game. Twice local CAMRA *Pub of the Year*, it has also held the Scottish title. 🏚❀Ⓒ P

Steampacket Inn
Harbour Row (A750)
✪ 11-11 (11-2.30, 6-11 Mon-Thu winter); 12-11 Sun
☎ (01988) 500334
Theakston XB; guest beer Ⓗ
This harbourside inn has a small public bar with stone-clad walls, a large stone fireplace and flagstone floor. There is a larger lounge, with a pool room off, plus a new conservatory. Picture windows give good views of the harbour which attracts sailing craft from Ireland and beyond, and from where both the Lake District and Isle of Man are visible. The historic village has a chapel on a former island (now linked by a causeway); it is handy for St Ninian's Cave and Whithorn dig. Local produce features on the menu. 🏚Q≷❀Ⓒ◖Ⓑ♣

Masonic Arms
19 Castle Street
✪ 11 (12.30 Sun)-midnight
☎ (01557) 330517
e-mail: jackson.masonic@barbox.net
Beer range varies Ⓗ
Small, friendly bar with a pool table. The tables, stools and bar-front are shaped like barrels. A good local, it is also welcoming to

Sulwath Castle Douglas

visitors. There are over 85 whiskies on offer. Between July and Sept the pub features jazz and folk (Sun). McLellan's Castle is close by, at the side of the Dee Estuary, and the town is very picturesque with a reputation for attracting artists. ♨ ♣

Selkirk Arms Hotel
High Street
✪ 11 (12 Sun)-midnight
☎ (01557) 330402
website: www.selkirkarmshotel.co.uk
Draught Bass; Sulwath Criffel; guest beers Ⓗ
Situated in the historic High Street of this picturesque town, the Selkirk Arms is a lovely hotel stocking local and guest beers. The comfortable lounge features a plaque depicting the life of John Paul Jones, the founder of the US Navy, who was born locally, and paintings by local artists for sale. Although the ales are not on display in the public bar, staff are happy to bring them through. Robert Burns is reputed to have written his *Selkirk Grace* in the hotel.
♨ ✿ ⊯ ⊲❺ ♿❺

LOCKERBIE

Somerton House Hotel
Carlisle Road
✪ 11-11 (midnight Thu-Sat); 11-11 Sun
☎ (01576) 202583/4
website: www.somertonhotel.co.uk
Beer range varies Ⓗ
Very comfortable hotel close to M74, but within walking distance of the town centre. A sympathetically converted Victorian mansion, it was designed by Alexander Thomson whose hallmark remains in the very rare Kauri timber panelling and fine fireplaces. It is highly recommended for food, with an emphasis on Scottish fare and local produce, and elegantly-furnished accommodation. Places of interest nearby include Lochmaben Castle, and Ecclefechan, birthplace of Thomas Carlyle. The guest beer is usually from Caledonian or Fuller's. Children are welcome in the dining room. ✿ ⊯ ⊲❺ ♿P

MOFFAT ❊

Black Bull Hotel
Church Gate
✪ 11-11 (midnight Thu-Sat); 12.30-11 Sun
☎ (01683) 220206
e-mail: hotel@blackbullmoffat.co.uk
McEwan 80/-; Theakston Best Bitter; guest beers Ⓗ
Comfortable hotel and bar, the Black Bull

dates from 1568 and was used by the infamous Graham of Claverhouse, in the 1680s, as his HQ. The Railway Bar occupies former stables and houses old railway relics and memorabilia. The Robert Burns Room, in the main hotel, commemorates the poet's visits; always with an eye for a lady, Burns etched *Epigram to a Scrimpit Nature* on a window. Alas only a replica is on show now; it is rumoured the original was given as a present to a Tsar of Russia!
✿ ⊯ ⊲❺ ⊯❺ ♣ ♨

STRANRAER

Ruddicot Hotel
London Road
✪ 12-2.30, 5-11 (midnight Thu-Sat); 12-2.30, 6.30-11 Sun
☎ (01776) 702684
Beer range varies Ⓗ
Small, family-run hotel in a detached sandstone building which was formerly a girls' school. The small bar features wooden screens which divide the bar seating from the eating area. The beers tend to be national brands. Handy for football and rugby grounds, and also for the ferry terminal where ferries leave for Belfast. Stranraer is also the gateway for the scenic Rhinns of Galloway. ♨ ✿ ⊯ ♣ P

THORNHILL

Buccleuch & Queensberry Hotel
112 Drumlanrig Street (A76)
✪ 11-midnight (1am Thu-Sat); 12.30-midnight Sun
☎ (01848) 330215 website: www.buccleuchhotel.co.uk
Caledonian 80/-; guest beers Ⓗ
Attractive, stone hotel in the centre of this small country town, with its unusually wide main street. The very comfortable lounge bar offers a varied menu, with a specials board nearly always available. It has very friendly regulars and the chat is often about fishing, and sometimes, shooting; you may find yourself in conversation with tourists from Europe and beyond. A good stopping-off point between Dumfries and Ayrshire, it is handy for historic Drumlanrig Castle.
♨ Q ⊯ ⊲❺ ⊯❺ ♣ P

Beer site
Keep in touch with CAMRA:
www.camra.org.uk

INN BRIEF

GRETNA
Crossways Inn
Glasgow Road
11-11 (midnight Fri & Sat); 12-11 Sun
Marston's Pedigree; Theakston Best Bitter Ⓗ
Lively pub – the first in Scotland, just a few minutes' walk from the border. Real ale is served in the lounge.

❊ **symbol next to a main entry place name indicates there are Inn Brief entries as well.**

ISLE OF WHITHORN
Queen's Arms Hotel
22 Main Street
12-3; 7-11 (midnight Fri); (12-11, [midnight Fri] summer); 12-midnight Sat; 12-11 Sun
Beer range varies Ⓗ
Modernised bar with stone-clad walls, plus a pool room and lounge bar. It hosts folk music Fri. One beer is usually from Sulwath. Good food.

MOFFAT
Balmoral Hotel
High Street
11-11 (midnight Thu-Sat); 12.30-11 Sun
Broughton Greenmantle (summer);

Caledonian 80/- Ⓗ
Friendly, comfortable, traditionally decorated hotel, serving good value meals.

PORTPATRICK
Downshire Arms Hotel
Main Street
11-12.30 (1am Thu-Sat); 12-12.30 Sun
Beer range varies Ⓗ
Traditional coaching inn with real ale in the public bar, dominated by a pool table and large-screen TV. Food and accommodation available.

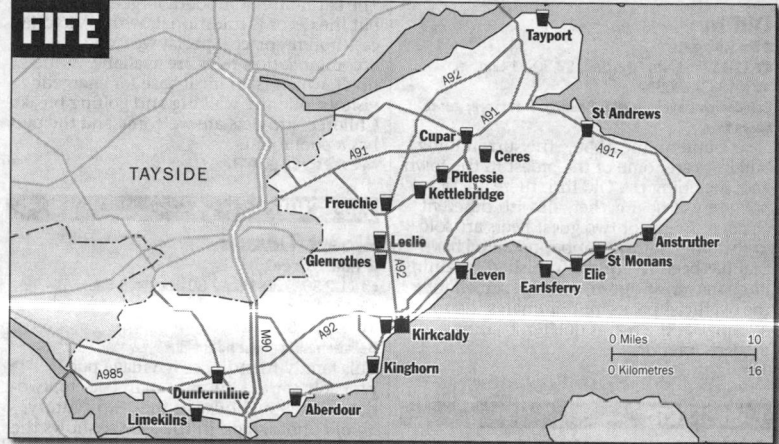

Authority area covered: Fife UA

ABERDOUR

Aberdour Hotel
38 High Street
⊕ 4-11; 3-11.45 Fri; 11-11.45 Sat; 12-11 Sun
☎ (01383) 860325 website: www.aberdourhotel.com
Caledonian Deuchars IPA; Taylor Landlord; guest beers Ⓗ
Family-run, traditional small hotel in a popular tourist and commuter area, with public and lounge bars, the latter is used more as a restaurant (6-9 eves) offering a seafood menu. It started life as a coaching inn and despite extensive modernisation, many original features remain. One handpump in winter is increased to two in spring, sometimes four during summer. The proprietor runs a small beer festival (Aug) to coincide with the village Gala Week. Wheelchair access is from the rear courtyard. Lunches are served at weekends.
🏚🍴🛏️◑❄✦🅿

Cedar Inn
20 Shore Road
⊕ 11-2.30, 5-midnight; 11-midnight Sat; 12-midnight Sun
☎ (01383) 860310
Caledonian Deuchars IPA; guest beers Ⓗ
In a village on the north shore of the River Forth which is popular with tourists and renowned for its 'silver sands', this small hotel is a short walk from the scenic harbour. Facilities include a public bar with mega TV and pool table, a quiet side bar, a conservatory, a quiet lounge and no-smoking restaurant. Photographs in the main bar suggest long-standing links with nearby Rosyth naval base. Four handpumps dispense ales from all over Britain.
🛏️❄🍴◑❄🅿✓

ANSTRUTHER

Dreel Tavern
16 High Street
⊕ 11-midnight; 12.30-11 Sun
☎ (01334) 310727
Orkney Dark Island; guest beers Ⓗ
In the scenic East Neuk of Fife, this old stone building features crow step gables and a pantile roof. The pub was previously called the Railway Tavern, but the station

disappeared in the 1960s thanks to Dr Beeching. It started life as a 16th-century coaching inn, reputedly visited by James V and the low-beamed ceiling certainly looks old. The intimate public and lounge bars are separated by an open fire; a conservatory provides dining/family space. Very busy lunchtime and early eve, it serves good quality meals. Joint winner Fife CAMRA *Pub of the Year* 2001. 🏚🛏️◑

CUPAR

Golf Tavern
11 South Road
⊕ 11.30-midnight (1am Fri & Sat); 12-11.30 Sun
☎ (01334) 654233
Beer range varies Ⓗ
Small traditional bar, with a modern interior, it forms part of a terrace on the main road south out of town. This large single-roomed bar, the only real ale outlet in Cupar, has one ale on during the week and sometimes two at the weekend. Home-cooked lunchtime bar meals including a dish of the day, are a recent innovation. The pub has a small function room.
🏚◑❄

DUNFERMLINE

Commercial Inn
13 Douglas Street
⊕ 11-2.30, 5.30-midnight; 11-midnight Fri & Sat; 11-midnight Sun
☎ (01383) 733876
Courage Directors; McEwan 80/-; guest beers Ⓗ
Busy, town-centre T&J Bernard's which gets very busy Fri and Sat eves, with bouncers on the door. The interior is typical of the genre, with a wooden floor, simulated distemper on the walls and a multitude of blackboards listing the cask and bottled beer ranges. There are regularly eight ales on tap, mainly from the ScotCo range, augmented by a variety of guest ales. Good value meals are served throughout the day. A large-screen TV caters for the sporting enthusiast. ◑❄

INDEPENDENT BREWERY

Fyfe Kirkcaldy

Old Inn
15a Kirkgate
◆ 11-11 (midnight Fri & Sat); 12.30-11 Sun
☎ (01383) 736652
Caledonian Deuchars IPA; Courage Directors; guest beers Ⓗ

Near Dunfermline Abbey, the surrounding buildings are some of the oldest in the town and, including the Old Inn, there are four pubs very close together, all with different characters. One or two guest beers are sold in the long, narrow, timber-panelled bar that has been recently refurbished, retaining its character; at one end a large screen for the overhead projector dominates the space. A lounge at the rear is quieter, bearing a modern interior.
◖≉

EARLSFERRY

Golf Tavern (19th Hole)
5 Links Road (on the S edge of Elie golf course)
◆ 11-midnight (1am Fri & Sat); 12.30-1am (hours vary winter) Sun
☎ (01333) 330610
Caledonian 80/-; guest beers Ⓗ

The tavern's plain exterior belies a superb timber-panelled public bar boasting old-fashioned gas lamps and gas cigar lighter on the bar; note the two magnificent etched mirrors, advertising soft drinks and whisky. The lounge bar, in contrast, features exposed stonework and, not unsurprisingly, a golfing theme with old photographs and memorabilia. A small room to the rear is used for pool and darts. The map beside the bus stop in the centre of Elie opposite the Victoria Hotel shows the pub's location.
♨Q

ELIE

Braid's Bar at the Victoria Hotel
High Street
◆ 11 (12 Sun)-1am
☎ (01333) 330305
Caledonian Deuchars IPA, 80/-; guest beers Ⓗ

Narrow, timber-panelled bar in a popular hotel, a few yards from the north shore of the River Forth, beside the Fife coastal path.

The bar houses a modern large-screen TV, but the decor is traditional, with a Victorian cast-iron fireplace. Special weekend accommodation rates are available in the hotel, which is an ideal base for energetic visitors, offering walking and golfing breaks. Children and pets are welcome and the pub has a pool room.
♨☞✿⚲◖◗♿♣P

FREUCHIE

Albert Tavern
2 Main Street
◆ 11-2.30, 5.30-11; 12.30-1am Fri & Sat; 12.30-11 Sun
☎ (01337) 857192
Belhaven 80/-; guest beers Ⓗ

This family-friendly, cosy village pub probably started life as a small two-up, two-down dwelling house in the 18th century; an old photograph in the lounge shows the Albert Tavern in Victorian times. The 'two down' are now the bar and lounge, retaining original beamed ceilings, the former with wainscot panelling. One room on the upper floor has been converted into a small intimate restaurant. Two guest beers are available at the weekends (one during the week). Pump clips on the beams in the bar testify to the 300-plus guest beers sold in the past 12 months.
♨☞✿◖◗

GLENROTHES

Glenrothes Snooker Club
Plot 7, Caskiebarren Road
◆ 11-11 (midnight Thu-Sat); 12.30-11 Sun
☎ (01592) 642083
Draught Bass; guest beers Ⓗ

Situated in a bland modern building, beside some small business units, to the south of the town centre, the club is quite difficult to find, in a maze of new town roads. Primarily the bar is for the snooker players to whet their whistle before and after matches, but visitors are welcome, especially CAMRA members. The lounge area sports some comfortable leather chesterfields, in a reasonably quiet area with subdued lighting. ♿P

INN BRIEF

CERES
Ceres Inn
The Cross
12-3, 5-midnight; 11-1am Thu & Fri; 11-midnight Sat; 12.30-midnight Sun
Beer range varies Ⓗ
Low-ceilinged bar, restored in the 1990s to its original state with exposed beams and stone walls. Meals are served in the restaurant.

LEVEN
Hawkshill Hotel
Hawkslaw Street
11-2.30, 6-midnight, 11-1am Fri & Sat; 11-midnight Sun
Taylor Landlord Ⓗ
Comfortable, friendly hotel where a pleasant west-facing garden has benches, and a children's play area. It hosts an annual beer festival, with competitions and quizzes. Meals available.

LIMEKILNS
Ship Inn
Halketts Hall
11-11 (midnight Thu-Sat), 12.30-midnight Sun
Belhaven 80/-; Orkney Dark Island; guest beers Ⓗ
Single-roomed white-painted village pub with a rather unexpected interior where the colours are more typical of a bistro. It offers two guest beers and meals. Outside benches are beside the River Forth.

LST MONANS
Mayview Hotel
40 Station Road
11-midnight (1am Fri & Sat); 12.30-midnight Sun
Caledonian 80/- Ⓗ
Quiet hotel in a residential street on the main street in St Monans from the A917 coast road. Meals are available in the bar of the adjacent restaurant, which can also be used as a family room.

KETTLEBRIDGE

Kettlebridge Inn
9 Cupar Road
🕐 11.30-2.30, 5-11; (4.30-midnight Fri & Sat);
12.30-11 Sun; hours may vary
☎ (01337) 830232
Belhaven 80/-; guest beers Ⓗ
Small, one-roomed local beside a busy trunk road in the scenic Howe of Fife. The three guest beers are sourced from a variety of independent brewers. Opening hours can vary depending on trade, particularly in winter so it is worth checking by phone. Excellent meals are served in the small restaurant: the bar has a quiet and relaxed atmosphere. Tayside CAMRA *Pub of the Year* 1999.
🏮🏵️◑▶

KINGHORN

Auld Hoose
6-8 Nethergate
🕐 12 (12.30 Sun)-midnight
☎ (01592) 891074
Broughton Ghillie; Caledonian 80/-; guest beer Ⓗ
Busy local situated on a very steep side street, just south of Kinghorn main street, it is accessed via a flight of steps. It is popular with locals and visitors alike, handy for the station and the beach. The main bar has a TV and pool table to keep the sports fans happy and hosts dominoes competitions at weekends. The lounge is more comfortable with a relaxed atmosphere.
🏮🥢♣

Ship Tavern
2 Bruce Street (E end of town)
🕐 12 (12.30 Sun)-midnight
☎ (01592) 890655
Inveralmond Independence; Orkney Dark Island; guest beer Ⓗ
One of the older buildings in Kinghorn, with the stone walls and pantile roof that are common along the Forth Estuary in Fife. A rather unobtrusive entrance door, facing the main road, opens into a fine timber-panelled interior with a long bar counter and ornate gantry. The small jug bar is probably one of the finest surviving traditional interiors in Fife. Very good value bar meals are available lunchtime and early eve.
◑▶🥢

KIRKCALDY

Betty Nicol's
297 High Street (N end of the High St shopping area)
🕐 11-11 (midnight Wed-Sat); closed Sun
☎ (01592) 642083
Caledonian Deuchars IPA; Harviestoun Bitter & Twisted; guest beers Ⓗ
Two-roomed town-centre bar which is popular for live music (jazz, blues and folk). The main front room has been beautifully restored and has a relaxed atmosphere with easy chairs and sofas; a large room at the rear provides space for meetings, functions and live music. The beer range varies; there are presently five handpumps on the corner bar offering two regular beers and three from the Carlsberg-Tetley guest range.
🏮◑🥢♣

Harbour Bar
471-473 High Street
🕐 11-2.30, 5-11; 11-midnight Fri & Sat; 12.30-midnight Sun
☎ (01592) 264270
Beer range varies Ⓗ
At the north end of the High Street in a tenement building, the pub is a quiet, unspoilt local where bar and lounge areas feature timber panelling and large murals depicting the town's whaling history. The bar's ornate gantry is stocked with a fine range of malt whiskies. The beer range, on six handpumps, continually changes, featuring some from the Fyfe Brewing Company, housed in premises to the rear, as well as small breweries in northern England and from as far apart as Orkney and Kent. CAMRA Scottish *Pub of the Year* 2000, it was joint Fife winner 2001.
🥢

LESLIE

Burns Tavern
184 High Street
🕐 12 (11 Fri & Sat)-midnight;
12.30-midnight Sun
☎ (01592) 741345
Caledonian 80/-; Taylor Landlord; guest beers Ⓗ
A typical, Scottish two-roomed main street pub, popular with locals who enjoy good cask ale. The public bar is lively and noisy with a TV and pool table, while the lounge bar is quieter and more spacious. Basic bar snacks are available at lunchtimes but there is no set menu, so it is pot luck as to what is available. The guest beer is generally from a small independent brewery.
🏮🛏️🍺♣

PITLESSIE

Village Inn
Cupar Road
🕐 11-midnight (1am Fri & Sat); 11-2.30, 5-midnight (1am Fri & Sat) winter; 12.30-1am (12.30-2.30, 5-1am winter) Sun
☎ (01337) 842156
Caledonian Deuchars IPA; guest beers Ⓗ
Looks just like a traditional Scottish village pub from the outside, with painted stonework, but inside the public bar is quite a surprise, featuring bare stonework and an open fire. The overall feel, with the

623

artefacts, is bothy-like with large bare wooden tables just right for dining. The pub has several other small rooms, one featuring a range cooker, providing additional space for families and games. Good value food is cooked to order. Two guest beers are on offer. ♨ ☎ ◑ ♣ P

ST ANDREWS

Aikman's Cellar Bar
32 Bell Street
✪ 11 (11.30 Sun)-midnight; hours may vary
☎ (01334) 477425
Beer range varies H

Small basement lounge bar below a continental-style bistro, mainly frequented by students. Opening hours outside term times can vary, but if the bar is closed and the bistro is open the staff are happy to bring cask ale upstairs if asked. The rolled copper bar top was salvaged from the White Star liner *Oceanic* (same shipping line as the *Titanic*). Around 200 real ales are sold each year, together with a variety of European bottled beers. ◑

Whey Pat Tavern
1 Bridge Street
✪ 11-midnight; 12-11.30 Sun
☎ (01334) 477740
Beer range varies H

Town-centre pub on a busy road junction, just outside the old town walls. Unusually for St Andrews, it is popular with students, academics, golfers and locals, unlike other bars where an unofficial segregation policy seems to operate. The beer range often features small Scottish independent breweries, such as Harviestoun, Inveralmond and Orkney.
◑ ♣

TAYPORT

Bell Rock Tavern
4-6 Dalgliesh Street
✪ 11-midnight (1am Thu & Fri); 12.30-midnight Sun
☎ (01382) 552388
Taylor Landlord; guest beer (summer) H

Small local, tucked away from the centre, close to the harbour. The main bar is on three levels each bearing a different theme in its artefacts and old photographs, which include charts of the River Tay, and photographs of old Dundee, Tayport and the Tay Ferries which last ran in 1966. Close to the Fife coastal path, it is ideally situated for walkers. A guest beer is available in summer and at Christmas. Excellent value home-cooked meals, such as mince and tatties are served.
♨ ◑ ♣

Fizz warning

Some national breweries produce both cask-conditioned and 'nitro-keg' versions of their beers. Boddingtons Bitter, John Smith's Bitter, Tetley's Bitter and Worthington fall into this category. Nitro-keg beers, often promoted as 'smooth' or 'cream-flow' products, are filtered and pasteurised in the brewery, and served in pubs by a mix of applied carbon dioxide and nitrogen gases. They are bland, served extremely cold, and any hop character is lost by the use of applied gas. To add insult to injury, the keg founts that serve such beers are often topped by small dummy handpumps.

As a result of lobbying by CAMRA, some producers of cask and nitro versions of the same beer now include the word 'cask' on pump clips for the genuine article. For example, both John Smith's Bitter and Tetley's Bitter now carry the word 'cask' on pump clips for the real thing. For the sake of brevity, and as the Good Beer Guide lists only cask-conditioned beers, we refer simply to John Smith's Bitter and Tetley Bitter. The Bass/Interbrew brand, Worthington, is labelled Worthington Bitter in cask form, and – bizarrely – Worthington Best Bitter in the nitro-keg version. Always choose the living rather than the dead.

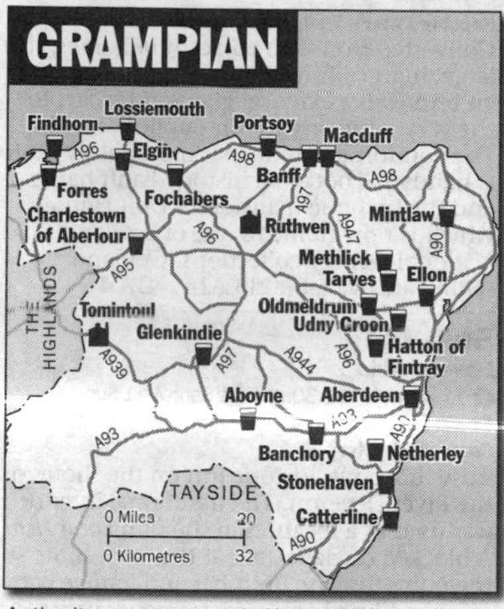

Authority areas covered: Aberdeenshire UA, City of Aberdeen UA, Moray UA

ABERDEEN ❄

Atholl Hotel

54 Kings Gate

✪ 11.30-2.30, 5-11 (11.30 Fri & Sat); 12-2.30, 5-11 Sun

☎ (01224) 323505 website: www.atholl-aberdeen.com

Courage Directors; Taylor Landlord; guest beer Ⓗ

Traditional lounge bar in a handsome granite building in the residential heartland of the West End. It could be the quiet, subtly-lit, well-appointed lounge that appeals to the predominantly middle-aged business clientele or maybe it is the good-value bar food that complements the two regular beers and the occasional guest beer. Non-smokers may prefer to eat in the dining room where smoking restrictions apply. Q⇆◑P

Carriages

101 Crown Street (below Brentwood Hotel)

✪ 11-2.30, 5-midnight; 6-11 Sun

☎ (01224) 595440

website: www.brentwood-hotel.demon.co.uk

Boddingtons Bitter; Caledonian Deuchars IPA; Castle Eden Ale; Courage Directors; Flowers Original; guest beers Ⓗ

Friendly, busy, city-centre basement bar offering an excellent choice of 10 ales, including some from the smaller micro-breweries. It also stocks bottled Belgian and German Weiss beers. As the adjoining hotel's guests account for a large part of its trade, the bar tends to be busier midweek than at weekends. Food is served in the bar and restaurant (open eves). Car parking is very limited. ⇆◑⇌P

Globe

13 North Silver Street (off Golden Sq)

✪ 12-midnight (11 Sun, Mon & Wed)

☎ (01224) 624258

Houston Peter's Well; guest beer Ⓗ

Bright, airy bar that has recently been sympathetically extended, embracing a strong music theme, and hosting live music on Tue, Fri, Sat and Sun. It is decorated with enough musical instruments to start an orchestra. The coloured glass feature in the ceiling must be unique, and the loos with fireplaces must be rare too! Good value bistro-style bar food, free newspapers and chess sets make it a haven within the city. Convenient for the Theatre and Music Hall. ❀⇆◑⇌♣▯

Moorings

2 Trinity Quay (harbour front)

✪ 11-midnight; 12.30-11 sun

☎ (01224) 587602

Harviestoun Bitter & Twisted; Isle of Skye Red Cuillin; Orkney Dark Island; guest beers Ⓗ

One-roomed dockside haven, mainly catering for rock 'n' real ale fans, with one of the most varied guest ale policies in the city, and always a good showing of Scottish independents' beers, backed up by occasional beer festivals. Live music, mostly on Sat eve, can be very loud. It is convenient for the Maritime Museum, multiplex cinema and the ferry terminal. ◑⇌♣

Old Blackfriars

52 Castle Street

✪ 11-midnight; 12.30-11 Sun

☎ (01224) 581922

Belhaven 80/-, St Andrew's Ale; Caledonian Deuchars IPA, 80/-; Inveralmond Ossian's Ale; guest beers Ⓗ

Split-level bar in historic Castlegate on the site where it is said Mary, Queen of Scots, witnessed the execution of Sir John Gordon, her alleged lover, at the Tolbooth opposite. This CAMRA award-winning pub gets the balance right between bar and restaurant, with all tables free for supping or dining. The low-ceilinged downstairs room features some backlit stained glass (from Dunecht House) while an enormous solid wooden door greets you at the top bar. Food is served all day until 9pm (8pm Fri and Sat). Wheelchair WC and baby-changing facilities available. Hosts an annual Czech beer festival. ◑♿⇌

Prince of Wales

7 St Nicholas Lane

✪ 11-midnight; 12.30-11 Sun

☎ (01224) 640597

Draught Bass; Caledonian 80/-; Theakston Old Peculier; guest beers Ⓗ

This fine old pub boasts an impressive long bar with a bank of eight handpumps, and two old gantries, one of which was inherited from the long-vanished Lemon Tree pub. A seated lounge area at the front complements a large stone-floored area at the back where separated seating areas offer a degree of privacy. It runs regular promotions on selected Scottish independent's beers. Sun breakfast is served (12.30–3) and sandwiches and toasties are available all day. The house beer is from Inveralmond. Q⇌♣●

Under the Hammer

11 North Silver Street (off Golden Sq)

✪ 12-midnight (1am Thu-Sat); 5-11 Sun

☎ (01224) 640253

Beer range varies Ⓗ

One-room cellar bar underneath the city's auction rooms. The candlelit tables produce a very intimate atmosphere in what is

INDEPENDENT BREWERIES

Borve Ruthven

Tomintoul Tomintoul

essentially a wine bar. The severity of the bare granite walls is broken by an ever-changing exhibition of paintings, all of which are for sale. Of the three real ales, there is usually something from Caledonian and Inveralmond. Convenient for both the Theatre and Music Hall, the pub's extensive 'What's On' board is a good guide to local events. ◖≈

ABOYNE

Boat Inn
Charleston Road   (north bank of River Dee)
☼ 11-2.30, 5-11; 11-midnight Sat; 11-11 Sun
☎ (013398) 86137 e-mail: boatinnltd@aol.com
Draught Bass; guest beers H
Popular riverside inn where the emphasis is on food in the lounge, which features a log-burning stove and a spiral staircase leading to the upper drinking area and a dining room. Junior diners can request to see the model train traverse the entire pub at picture-rail height, upon completion of their meal. The guest beer is usually from a Scottish independent. Accommodation is in a self-catering flat. ﹏Q❀✿☎◖◗ ⌺♿♣P

BANCHORY

Ravenswood Club (Royal British Legion)
25 Ramsay Road
☼ 11-2.30, 5-midnight; 11-midnight Sat & Sun
☎ (01330) 822347
Beer range varies H
Extremely large club with extensive accommodation and function rooms, where members always make visitors welcome; bring this *Guide* with you. The lounge and patio overlook the Deeside hills. The restaurant and guest accommodation (15 rooms) are open to the public (temporary membership being granted). Snooker and pool are played. The single beer varies – it may be a Scottish brew from Houston or Inveralmond, or perhaps an English import. Real ale is only served in one bar in the club. Q❧❀✿◖◗♿♣P

Scott Skinner's
North Deeside Road   (A93, 1 mile E of centre)
☼ 11-2.30, 5-11 (midnight Tue-Sat); 11-2.30, 5-11 Sun
☎ (01330) 824393
Beer range varies H
Converted Victorian house whose Tardis-like interior includes a restaurant, games room, children's play area, snug and a public bar. Children are welcome in the restaurant; meals can also be eaten in the bar. It stocks a varied choice of up to three guest ales, covering breweries in Scotland and those further afield. Scott Skinner was a noted fiddler, who is remembered in Banchory Museum (in the Library Complex) which also houses a collection of Royal commemorative china and a display of Highland dress. ﹏❧❀◖◗♿♣P

BANFF

Castle Inn
47 Castle Street
☼ 11 (12.30 Sun)-12.30am
☎ (01261) 815068

Houston Peter's Well; guest beer H
Converted from two adjacent buildings, this large, high-ceilinged, two-roomed pub bears an impressive exterior, giving little clue to the very basic brightly-lit public bar within. The comfortable lounge is more subtly lit. It is handy for both the historic Banff harbour and the baroque mansion of Duff House, which is now home to one of Scotland's National Gallery collections. Golf and sailing are available close by. ◖♿♣

Ship Inn
Deveronside
☼ 11-midnight (12.30am Fri & Sat); 7-11 Sun
☎ (01261) 812620
Courage Directors H
Cosy, unspoilt, historic inn on the shores of the River Deveron. The traditional interior was used as a location in the film *Local Hero*. A blocked carriage-arch at the front hints at the pub's history. Both bar and lounge bar are wood-lined and offer tremendous sea views, although the windows are small. Note the ship-shaped bar counter in the public bar. It stands very close to the historic harbour and the National Gallery's Duff House, with golf and sailing facilities nearby. ﹏◖♿♣

CATTERLINE

Creel Inn
By harbour OS868781
☼ 12-2.30, 6-11 (midnight Fri & Sat); closed Tue; 12-2.30, 6-11 Sun
☎ (01569) 750254
Caledonian Deuchars IPA; guest beer H
Village local in a single-storey whitewashed cottage on a clifftop, close to the harbour. It is divided into three areas: a bar, lounge and a restaurant. The traditional construction, with low ceilings and small windows, together with the wood-burning stove in the lounge, give an intimate atmosphere. Excellent food is served in both the lounge and highly-praised restaurant, where lobster is a speciality. ﹏❀✿◖◗ ⌺P

CHARLESTOWN OF ABERLOUR

Mash Tun
8 Broomfield Square   (signed from main town square)
☼ 12-11 (11.45 Thu; 12.30am Fri & Sat); (11-2.30, 5-11 winter Mon-Fri); 12.30-11.45 Sun
☎ (01340) 881771
Beer range varies H
Dating from 1896 as the former Station Bar, this round-ended building is a former local CAMRA *Country Pub of the Year*, and offers one beer in winter and up to three in summer, including a regular brew from Belhaven. It also stocks draught continental lagers, small malts and some unusual bottled beers. On the Speyside Way long distance footpath, its good value food includes Mexican dishes as a speciality. The disused railway station platform, with its views of the River Spey, makes an ideal location for an *al fresco* pint. Children's certificate. ❀◖◗ ♿P

ELGIN ❀

Flanagan's
Shepherds Close, 48a High Street

✪ 11-11; (11.45 Wed & Thu; 12.30am Fri & Sat); 6-11 Sun
☎ (01343) 549737
Beer range varies Ⓗ
Partially hidden, down a small alleyway leading off the main shopping street, this long, narrow, dimly-lit but lively town-centre bar is decked out with all manner of Irish memorabilia. Up to three real ales are on offer in the bar, regularly featuring Scottish brews. They are also available on request in the Tapas restaurant upstairs. Children are welcome. The ruins of Elgin Cathedral, considered in its day to be the most beautiful in Scotland, are open to the public. ⏣≋

ELLON

Station Hotel
Station Brae
✪ 11-11 (11.45 Thu & Sat; 1am Fri); 11-11 Sun
☎ (01358) 720209 e-mail: stathotel@aol.com
Beer range varies Ⓗ
This family-run hotel, built in 1891, comprises a comfortable lounge bar, an attractively decorated Arches Restaurant and a basic public bar that stocks two regularly changing guest beers. Children are welcome in the no-smoking lounge and restaurant. Overnight accommodation is provided in eight guest rooms with en-suite facilities. Q✲⏴◑♿♣P⊁

Tolbooth
21-23 Station Road
✪ 11-2.30, 5-11 (midnight Thu & Fri); 11-11.45 Sat; 6.30-11 Sun
☎ (01358) 721308
Draught Bass; guest beers Ⓗ
Pub converted from two semi-detached houses, with a large conservatory on the lower section of the split-level. Up to three guest beers complement the regular Bass on tap in the main bar. No food is served, other than lunchtime sandwiches. Attracting a predominantly mature clientele, children are not allowed in at any time. Many pictures of local historical interest are displayed. There is also a small attic lounge bar which is open to the public on Fri eve. Q❀♿♣♠

FINDHORN

Crown & Anchor Inn
✪ 11-11 (11.45 Wed & Thu; 12.30am Fri & Sat); 12-11 Sun
☎ (01309) 690243
Beer range varies Ⓗ
Listed building in a picturesque bay, the inn dates from 1739 when Findhorn was a busy port and staging post on the Edinburgh–Inverness route. It now attracts naturalists and water sports enthusiasts who take advantage of its six pleasant en-suite guest rooms. This beamed two-bar free house stocks four real ales – beers from Orkney, Caledonian and Taylor's are usually available. A children's certificate applies until 9pm and the pub has an enclosed garden. Reasonably-priced meals are offered on a very varied menu. ✲⌛❀⏴◑♿Ⓐ♣P

Kimberley Inn
✪ 11-11 (11.45 Thu & Fri; 12.30am Sat); 12.30-11.45 Sun

☎ (01309) 690492
Tetley Bitter; guest beers Ⓗ
Popular, friendly bar with two no-smoking areas; the patio affords fine views over the lovely Findhorn Bay, popular for water sports. Famed for its food, it has a children's certificate until 8pm. Orkney, Fuller's and Marston's beers feature regularly on the guest list. ✲Q❀⏴◑♿Ⓐ♣⊁

GLENKINDIE

Glenkindie Arms Hotel
OS442138
✪ 11-11 (1am Fri; 11.45 Sat); (11-2.30, 5-11 winter Mon-Fri); 12-11 Sun
☎ (01975) 641288 website: www.glenkindiearms.co.uk
Beer range varies Ⓗ
400-year-old, listed, tiny drovers' inn, known locally as the Lodge, due to its former Masonic use, stocks two real ales in summer and one in winter. An impressive coat of arms hangs over the main entrance to the cosy bar and small dining room. An enormous range of food is served, with the emphasis on local game, steaks and curries with always a vegetarian choice. All food is locally sourced. Convenient for the Lecht ski area, and the 'Castle Trail' (Kildrummy Castle is only three miles away). Check winter hours, particularly Mon. ✲❀✪⏴◑P

HATTON OF FINTRAY

Northern Lights
Station Road
✪ 11-1am (12.30am Sat); 12.30-11 Sun
☎ (01224) 791261
Beer range varies Ⓗ
Almost hidden down a back lane between houses in the village centre, this small pub, converted from a pair of cottages, offers three guest beers all year round. The wood-lined bar is heated by a large log fire. The lounge is predominantly used as a restaurant, hosting occasional live music Fri eve. The quiet conservatory is used as an overspill drinking/dining area. It offers a wide range of food and a take-away service is available. It stages an annual summer folk music festival. ✲Q❀✪⏴◑♿♣P⊟

MACDUFF

Knowes Hotel
78 Market Street
✪ 12-midnight (12-2, 5-midnight winter Mon-Fri); 12.30-11 Sun
☎ (01261) 832229
Beer range varies Ⓗ
Family-run hotel on an elevated site, enjoying panoramic views of the Moray Firth from most drinking areas. The building dates from 1879, but numerous extensions and a conservatory have been added. Two handpumps normally offer a favourite such as Bass, plus maybe a Scottish beer. The family room is upstairs; children may like to visit Macduff's aquarium nearby with its unusual open-air central tank. Q⌛❀✲⏴◑♣P⊁

METHLICK

Gight House Hotel
Sunnybrae (B9170, ½ mile N of river)
✪ 12-2.30, 5-midnight; 12-midnight Sat; 12-11 Sun

☎ (01651) 806389
website: www.gight-house@freeuk.com
Beer range varies Ⓗ
Built in 1850, this former free kirk manse, reputedly haunted by a former minister, has an attractive beamed lounge bar offering at least two guest beers. Two conservatories overlook the colourful one-acre garden, complete with putting green and pétanque pitch. It has a well-deserved reputation for home-cooked meals, made with predominantly local produce. As well as supporting local football, cricket and darts teams, pheasant shooting, a clay pigeon lodge, fishing and golf facilities are all nearby.

🏨❀🅿🍴◖👌♣🅿

Ythanview Hotel
Ellon Road
🕐 11-2.30; 5-11 (1am Fri); 11-11.45 Sat; 12.30-11 Sun
☎ (01651) 806235 e-mail: angjallan@aol.com
Beer range varies Ⓗ
Family-run hotel, overlooking the river, with a smart lounge and a cheery public bar. An impressive display of sports trophies shows support for local football, cricket and fishing teams, together with the intriguing *Mountain Man of the Year* award. Good value home-cooked food is on offer and the landlord's extra-hot curry is challenging. The pub is on the 'Castle Trail', with Fyvie Castle and Haddo House both nearby. Children's certificate.

🏨Q👌❀🅿🍴◖👌♣

MINTLAW

Country Park Inn
Station Road (A950, 1/2 mile W of village)
🕐 11-11.30 (midnight Fri; 12.30am Sat); 12.30-11 Sun
☎ (01771) 622622 e-mail: cpiboss@aol.com
Beer range varies Ⓗ
Well-appointed country inn with a large lounge bar and a small bar that forms part of the conservatory restaurant. The single cask ale tends to be a Scottish brew. Good value bar food is served all day from an extensive menu. It has a large children's play area and its own nightclub for the young (and young-at-heart). It is convenient for Aden Country Park and the newly-extended Formartine long distance walkway, which follows the old

Aberdeen–Peterhead railway line.
🏨Q👌❀🅿◖👌♣🅿 Å♣🅿

NETHERLEY

Lairhillock Inn
Off B979, 3 miles S of B9077 OS855952
🕐 11.30-2.30, 5-11 (midnight Fri); 11-midnight Sat; 12-11 Sun
☎ (01569) 730001 website: www.lairhillock.co.uk
Courage Directors; Fuller's London Pride; Marston's Pedigree; Taylor Landlord; guest beers Ⓗ
Set in the heart of beautiful countryside, with the emphasis on quality, friendliness and families. The public bar, with its log fire, is ideal for a convivial drink, while both the lounge and conservatory tend to be used by diners. The conservatory, where the views are breathtaking, whatever the season, is also a popular choice for families with children; the lounge has a more intimate atmosphere. Look out for the 'inn' on the roof. Lairies Ale is brewed by the Isle of Skye brewery.

🏨Q👌❀◖👌👌♣🅿🍴

OLDMELDRUM

Redgarth Hotel
Kirk Brae (off A947, towards golf course)
🕐 11-2.30, 5-midnight; 12-2.30, 5-11 Sun
☎ (01651) 872353
Beer range varies Ⓗ/Ⓖ
Traditional, wood-panelled lounge bar, in an imposing position at the top of the village enjoying panoramic views of the eastern Grampian mountains. It offers an imaginative selection of seasonal guest ales and a varied menu of home-cooked food. Occasional 'brewer-in-residence' eves are an added attraction. A room is available for families, diners or meetings. Local CAMRA *Pub of the Year* 2001. Q👌❀🅿◖👌♣🅿🍴●

PORTSOY

Shore Inn
Church Street (harbour front)
🕐 11 (10 summer)-11 (midnight Thu; 12.30am Fri & Sat); 11-11 Sun
☎ (01261) 842831
Beer range varies Ⓗ
18th-century seafarers' inn, nestling in the oldest harbour on the Moray Firth. Decorated with paraphernalia from the owner's brewing background, it offers up to

INN BRIEF

ABERDEEN

Blue Lamp
121 Gallowgate
11-midnight (lounge 1am Fri & Sat); 12.30-2.30, 6.30-11 Sun
Caledonian 80/-; Ⓟ guest beers Ⓗ
Small public bar stocks guest beers only; the cavernous lounge has regular beers and guests, and hosts live bands.

Cameron's Inn (Ma's)
6-8 Little Belmont Street
11-midnight;
closed Sun
Orkney Dark Island;
guest beers Ⓗ
Oldest inn in the city; a small public bar, unchanged for decades, a tiny listed snug, and contrasting large, modern, open-plan lounge.

Macandrews
6 Crown Street
11-midnight; 12.30-11 Sun
Caledonian Deuchars IPA, 80/-; guest beers Ⓗ
Large one-roomed bar specialising in beers from Scottish independents; can be noisy. Snacks always available; handy for Music Hall.

Old Town School
Little Belmont Street
11-midnight;
12.30-11 Sun
Boddingtons Bitter; Caledonian Deuchars IPA, 80/-; Greene King Old Speckled Hen; Marston's Pedigree; Ⓗ guest beers Ⓗ/Ⓖ
Former school, with an upstairs cellar, balconied drinking area, and a flagged patio out front. Food served until 9pm.

ELGIN

Sunninghill Hotel
Hay Street
11-2.30, 5-11 (12.30am Fri & Sat); 12.30-2.30; 6.30-11 Sun
Beer range varies Ⓗ
Hotel with balanced mix of diners and drinkers in the large conservatory, inner bar and cocktail bar. Five beers; children's certificate.

FOCHABERS

Red Lion Tavern
67 High Street
11-11.30 (1am Fri & Sat); 12.30-midnight Sun
Beer range varies Ⓗ
Village-centre local with up to two ales in the bar which can be taken into the lounge. Handy for fishermen, and Speyside Way walkers.

Long, narrow pub, built in 1771, on the picturesque harbour. Divided into three sections: bar, lounge and family room, all bear a distinct nautical feel, with brass fittings, wood panelling and old photographs of the harbour area. The tiny patio makes an ideal location for a summer pint, and the large picture windows enable you to enjoy the spectacular views when the weather is more inclement. Good value meals (not served Sun eve).
Q ☕ ⛱ ◐ ⌂ ♣

TARVES

Aberdeen Arms Hotel
The Square
✪ 12-2.30 (closed Mon), 5-11; 12-midnight Fri & Sat; 12-11 Sun
☎ (01651) 851214
Caledonian 80/-; Courage Directors; guest beer Ⓗ
Small, family-run hotel in the village conservation area. Note the fine mirrors in the public bar where a children's certificate operates until 8pm. Regular folk music eves feature bagpipes and a zither! Food ranges from the cuisine of the north-east to that of the Far East. It is handy for Tolquhon Castle and Pitmedden Gardens which were laid out in the 17th century by Sir Alexander Seddon, with elaborate flower beds, fountains and pavilions.
🏠 Q ☕ ⛱ ◐ ⌂ ♣ P ⅟

UDNY GREEN

Udny Green Hotel
Opp. village green
✪ 12-3, 6-11 (1am Fri, 11.45 Sat); closed Mon; 12-3, 5.30-11 Sun
☎ (01651) 842337
Beer range varies Ⓗ
This small inn, fronted with undressed granite blocks, forms the major part of the buildings on the main side of the large village green. The village itself is part of a conservation area at the gates of Udny Castle. The hotel has a public bar and a pleasant, family-friendly, pine-clad lounge bar with a children's play area accessible via french doors. Local musicians occasionally hold sessions eves. A children's certificate, a reduced-price pensioner's menu, up to two ales and good value home-cooked food ensure it appeals to all ages.
Q ⛱ ◐ ⌂ ♣ P ⅟

three real ales, including the occasional house beer, Smugglers Ale, which is brewed by Aviemore. The evening *à la carte* menu replaces the more standard lunchtime selection. It has a small family room upstairs, and a children's certificate applies until 8pm. 🏠 Q ☕ ⛱ ◐ ⌂ A ♣

STONEHAVEN

Marine Hotel
9-10 Shorehead (harbour front)
✪ 11 (12 Sun)-midnight
☎ (01569) 762155
Beer range varies Ⓗ
Former Scottish CAMRA *Pub of the Year* whose picturesque harbour-front location makes it a must, particularly in summer. Downstairs consists of a simple, wood-panelled bar with six ever-changing ales selected from both micro-breweries and the more enterprising regionals. The adjacent lounge, furnished with armchairs and settees, together with a huge fire in winter, makes a comfortable contrast to the bustle of the small bar. Upstairs, the main eating area (children admitted) specialises in fresh local produce, particularly fish dishes.
🏠 Q ☕ ⛱ ◐ ⌂ A ♣ ⊕ ⊟

Ship Inn
5 Shorehead (harbour front)
✪ 11 (12.30 Sun)-midnight
☎ (01569) 762617
Caledonian Deuchars IPA; Orkney Dark Island; guest beer Ⓗ

FORRES

Carisbrooke Hotel
Drumduan Road
11-11 (11.45 Tue & Thu); 12.30am Fri & Sat); 11-11 Sun
Boddingtons Bitter; Marston's Pedigree; guest beer Ⓗ
Small, extended hotel on outskirts of town with small bar and larger lounge. Families welcome; summer barbecues held. Good quality accommodation.

LOSSIEMOUTH

Clifton Bar
4 Clifton Road
11-2.30, 5-11 (11.45 Wed & Thu); 11-12.30am Fri & Sat; 12.30-11 Sun
McEwan 80/-; Tetley Bitter; Theakston Old Peculier; guest beer Ⓗ
Long-established free house on the east side of town, near the beach and harbour. No food served.

Skerry Brae Hotel
Stotfield Road
11-11 (11.45 Wed; 12.30am Thu-Sat); 12-11 Sun
Beer range varies Ⓗ
Good food and accommodation, and fine views over golf course to the sea. Three ales available in the bar with conservatory extension and a large balcony.

HIGHLANDS & ISLANDS

Authority areas covered: Highland UA, Orkney Islands UA, Shetland Islands UA, Western Islands UA

ARDGOUR

Inn at Ardgour

On A861, at the Corran ferry
☼ 10-11 (1am Fri & Sat); 12-11 Sun
☎ (01855) 841225 website: www.ardgour/innatardgour
Beer range varies Ⓗ
18th-century, family-run village inn at the entrance to the Great Glen. The 10 en-suite rooms all benefit from sea views. Popular with locals, it is ideally located for walking, fishing, climbing, sailing, wildlife-watching, and a good base for touring the West Highlands. Bar meals are served all day. The beers are from the Isle of Skye Brewery and more than 100 malts are on offer in 35ml measures. A book swap library operates in the bar; take a book to read in the comfortable lounge by the open fire.
🏨🛏ⓘⒹ🅰♣P

AVIEMORE

Old Bridge Inn

Dalfaber Road (100 yds from Cairngorm ski road jct)
☼ 11-midnight (1am Fri-midnight Sat); 12.30-8 Sun
☎ (01479) 811137
Aviemore Highland IPA; Tomintoul Wild Cat Ⓗ
Converted cottage, recently enlarged, situated just south of the village, on the road leading to the Strathspey Steam Railway. It is popular with walkers, climbers and skiers. The beer range varies, but Highland IPA from the nearby Aviemore Brewery is normally available. The house ale is Alba, specially brewed for the inn by the Isle of Skye Brewery. No-smoking dining room open eves. The pub holds a children's certificate, but is free from the intrusions of

TV or fruit machines.
🏨Q🕸ⒾⒹ🅰🅰≠P

AVOCH

Station Hotel

Main Street
☼ 11-2.30, 5-11 (midnight Fri); 11-11.30 Sat (11-11 summer Mon-Fri); 12.30-11.30 Sun
☎ (01381) 620246
Beer range varies Ⓗ
This large family-run pub, a meeting place for many village clubs, has had only two owners in the last 75 years. Regular beers are Taylor Landlord and Greene King Abbot, and a spacious conservatory provides an attractive environment to enjoy the extensive, popular menu. Red kites (RSPB's big success story) can often be seen from the child-friendly garden; other local attractions include dolphin-watching at Chanory Point, a spectacular golf course by the Moray Firth and many well-signed walks.
🏨🕸ⒾⒹ🍴♣P✄

CARRBRIDGE

Cairn Hotel

Main Road (B9153, the old A9)
☼ 11.30-midnight (1am Fri & Sat); 12.30 (12 summer)-11 Sun
☎ (01479) 841212
e-mail: cairncarrbridge@talk21.com
Beer range varies Ⓗ
Busy pub with an adjoining hotel, situated in the centre of the village, catering for locals as well as skiers, walkers and birdwatchers: the two beers on offer are mainly Scottish, from the Isle of Skye,

Aviemore and Black Isle breweries. In addition to bar meals (served 12-2 and 6-8) soup and toasties are available all day.
🏨🍴♿◐≈P✓

FORT WILLIAM

Grog & Gruel
66 High Street
☼ 11 (12 winter)-midnight (1am Thu-Sat); 5-midnight Sun
☎ (01397) 705078 website: www.grogandgruel.co.uk
Beer range varies Ⓗ

In the shadow of Britain's highest mountain, at the cente of one of Scotland's main tourist areas, this bare-floored ale house, with church pew seating, has up to six beers in summer, reducing to two in winter. Owned by the same family that owns the famous Clachaig Inn, it holds beer festivals at Easter, Oct and Christmas, often specialising in Highland beers. Busy with tourists in summer, it is popular with locals. Home-cooked meals are available all day in the upstairs dining room or from the more limited bar menu. ❀◐♿▲≈

GAIRLOCH

Old Inn
The Harbour
☼ 11-1am (11.30 Sat); 12.30-11 Sun
☎ (01445) 712006 website: www.theoldinn.co.uk
Beer range varies Ⓗ

This family-run hotel is popular with walkers and climbers. In a truly delightful setting on the magnificent Wester Ross coast at the foot of Flowerdale Glen, it is convenient for major climbing areas. There is a pottery, a walkers' lodge and a natural climbing wall in the grounds. Two bars stock eight beers, mainly Scottish, in summer (falling to three in winter). Don't miss the murals in the main bar and the spectacular painting by Lincoln Rowe. A bistro and restaurant offer a home-cooked menu specialising in seafood and game.
🏨🛏❀🍴◐🅿♣P☐

GLENCOE

Clachaig Inn
On A82, almost 2 miles SE of village OSNN1256
☼ 11-11 (midnight Fri; 11.30 Sat); 11-11 Sun
☎ (01855) 811252
website: www.glencoe-scotland.co.uk
Ind Coope Burton Ale; guest beers Ⓗ

18th-century coaching inn, amid Glencoe's steep-sided mountains, at the site of the 1692 Massacre. Popular with walkers and climbers, the spacious bar has a pool table and rustic wood furniture. Low, slate room-dividers offer a precarious perch for drinks, while corner areas provide more privacy. There is a side room for non-smokers, and a comfortable lounge. The long, straight bar counter serves ale at one end and food at the other. It stocks bottled beers (especially from Scottish independents), and a good range of malts. 🏨🛏❀🍴◐🅿♿P✓

King's House
Off A82, 12 miles E of village
☼ 11-midnight (1am Fri & Sat); 11-midnight Sun
☎ (01855) 851259 website: www.kingy.co.uk
Caledonian 80/-; Orkney Dark Island; guest beer (summer) Ⓗ

Licensed since the 17th century, the hotel takes its name from the time when it housed soldiers guarding the road to the north of Rannoch Moor before it descends through Glen Coe. The isolated building, extended and modernised over the years, now has a large comfortable lounge and the aptly-named, basic Climbers Bar to the rear. The hotel is frequented by walkers, some trekking the West Highland Way, climbers and skiers, all enjoying the spectacular mountain scenery. 🛏❀🍴◐♿▲P✓

HOSWICK

Barclay Arms Hotel
OS416240
☼ 12.30-3, 6-1am (including Sun)
☎ (01950) 431226
Beer range varies Ⓗ

Friendly, coastal village inn, built into the hillside. The 1970s-style lounge bar, with its floor to ceiling windows, overlooks a Shetland rarity – a stand of trees. It hosts live music most weekends. The family-run hotel offers a convenient base to explore the archaeology at Jarlshof, Mousa and Scatness. A low-cost bed (and no breakfast) arrangement operates for enthusiastic drinkers. It maintains a very varied guest beer policy and displays a rare collection of old drinks trays. 🍴◐🅿♣P

INVERIE

Old Forge
By ferry from Mallaig
☼ 11-midnight (including Sun)
☎ (01687) 462267 website: www.theoldforge.co.uk
Beer range varies Ⓗ

Most remote pub in mainland Britain, reached only by ferry from Mallaig or a 15-mile hilly walk from the road end at Kinloch Hourn. In a spectacular setting on the shore of Loch Nevis, it provides an ideal location for walking the 'rough bounds' of Knoydart, while its moorings welcome waterborne visitors. The essential hub of the local community, the one handpump serves mainly Isle of Skye beers. Food is served all day; specialities include locally-caught seafood. It has an informal atmosphere, the dress code being wellies, waterproofs, and midge cream. 🏨Q❀◐▲

INVERNESS

Blackfriars
93-95 Academy Street
☼ 11-midnight (12.30 Fri; 11.45 Sat); 12.30-11 Sun
☎ (01463) 233881
website: www.blackfriars@50megs.com
Black Isle Red Kite; Courage Directors; McEwan 80/-; Marston's Pedigree; Theakston Best Bitter, Old Peculier; guest beers Ⓗ

Traditional, town-centre pub: one spacious room has a large standing area at the bar

INDEPENDENT BREWERIES

Aviemore Aviemore
Black Isle Taeblair
Far North Melvich
Isle of Skye Uig
Orkney Quoyloo
Valhalla Baltasound

and ample seating in comfortable alcoves around the room. The guest beer range regularly showcases Black Isle, Isle of Skye and Orkney breweries; bottled beers from Belgium and Germany are available. Food is served all day until 9pm; meals are inexpensive and home cooked, using local produce (vegetarian choice always available). Children are welcome. Live music most nights features traditional music and local bands; there is Scottish country dancing Wed eve. ◖▷≈

Clachnaharry Inn
17-19 High Street (A862, Beauly Road, on outskirts of town)
✪ 11-11 (midnight Thu-Sat); 12.30-11.45 Sun
☎ (01463) 239806
Adnams Broadside; Courage Directors; Isle of Skye Red Cuillin Ⓗ **Blaven;** Ⓗ/Ⓖ **McEwan 80/-; guest beers** Ⓗ
Friendly, family-run, 17th-century coaching inn overlooking Caledonian Canal sea lock to the Beauly Firth beyond. The lounge and garden afford fine views of Ben Wyvis to the north, and the Glen Affric and Strathfarrar Hills to the west. The garden was once the platform of the old station. Families are always welcome and good value bar meals are served all day. Up to three beers are dispensed by gravity; house beers are from the Isle of Skye Brewery. Local CAMRA *Town Pub of the Year* 2000 and 2001.
🏚Q✿◖▷⊖▣Å

Heathmount Hotel
Kingshills Road
✪ 11-midnight (1am Thu & Fri; 12.30am Sat); 12.30-11 Sun
☎ (01463) 235877 website: www.heathmountinn.co.uk
Beer range varies Ⓗ
More of an inn than a hotel, it has seven rooms, but most of the business is from the two bars and restaurant featuring fish, game and other traditional Scottish dishes. Situated between the city centre and the quiet Crown residential area, it is popular with locals and professionals. Usually two handpumps dispense national brands, with a third reserved for a local Scottish beer. The public bar has pool, darts and a large-screen TV, while the lounge has plenty of tables.
✿🛏◖▷⊖Å≈✦P

Number 27
27 Castle Street
✪ 11-11 (midnight Thu; 1am Fri; 11.45 Sat); 12.30-11 Sun
☎ (01463) 241999
Beer range varies Ⓗ
Bright, friendly, modern pub in the shadow of Inverness Castle. The bar has a comfortable seating area, where beers on tap usually include an English bitter and a local ale often from Black Isle or Isle of Skye. Food, served in the attractive dining area (no wheelchair access) and main bar is prepared using fresh local produce, including game and salmon in season. A large-screen TV shows sporting events. It received the Scottish Tourist Board's *Best Customer Service* award 2000. ◖▷ᄒ≈

Phoenix
108 Academy Street
✪ 11-11 (12.30am Fri; 11.45 Sat); 12.30-11 Sun
☎ (01463) 245991

Draught Bass; Caledonian Deuchars IPA, 80/-; Taylor Landlord; guest beers Ⓗ
Established 1894, the public bar has changed little, with wooden floor, wood-panelled walls and the original island bar with granite trough around the base, it is a gem. A glass case displays the water engine once used to pump the beers from the cellar. Guests include beers from the Inveralmond and Heather breweries. Two ales are available in the lounge. Good value food is served in the lounge bar (12-5, extended hours in summer). Children are welcome. It hosts live music most weekends and a large-screen TV is used for football matches.
◖▷⊖ᄒ

KINGUSSIE

Royal Hotel
High Street
✪ 11-midnight (1am Thu-Sat); 12.30-midnight Sun
☎ (01540) 661898
Beer range varies Ⓗ
This family-run, 52-bedroom hotel specialises in coach parties and is located in a popular holiday area. It was the main outlet for the attached Iris Rose Brewery that has closed. An ideal base for hillwalking/climbing in the Cairngorms, other local attractions include the Highland Folk Museum and the Wildlife Park at Kincraig. Up to 12 handpumps are in use in summer and at the beer festival in Nov, reducing to three in winter. The large bar/dining area is popular with locals and provides an extensive menu (all day in summer); regular live music.
✿🛏◖▷ᄒÅ≈P⅒

KIRKWALL

Bothy Bar (Albert Hotel)
Mounthoolie Lane
✪ 11-11 (1am Thu-Sat); 12-1am Sun
☎ (01856) 876000 e-mail: enquiries@alberthotel.co.uk
Orkney Raven, Red MacGregor, Dark Island Ⓗ
Public bar in a town-centre hotel, situated behind Woolworth's. It has a low-beamed ceiling and a massive open fire. Seafood is a speciality – try the local scallops. It provides a convenient overnight stop for the ferry terminal, when island hopping.
🏚🛏◖▷Å

NAIRN

Invernairne Hotel
Thurlow Road
✪ 11-11.30 (1am Thu-Sat); 11-11.30 Sun
☎ (01667) 452039 website: www.golf-vacations.co.uk
Beer range varies Ⓗ
Family-owned hotel, with reasonably-priced accommodation, tucked away in the acres of secluded gardens overlooking the Moray Firth. The baronial-style lounge bar has cosy nooks, oak panelling and a roaring log fire in winter. The real ale is usually supplied by the Isle of Skye Brewery. Excellent cuisine is based on fresh, local produce. The garden path leads to a beach. An ideal base for the 'Whisky Trail', it is close to Nairn's two championship golf courses. Children's certificate.
🏚Q⛟✿🛏◖▷ᄒÅP

ROSEMARKIE

Plough Inn
High Street
🕐 11-midnight (1am Fri; 11.45 Sat); 12.30-11.30 Sun
☎ (01381) 620164
Black Isle Golden Eagle, Red Kite, Yellow Hammer, Wagtail Ⓗ

Beautiful old country pub, in a pretty seaside village on the old coaching route to the famous Duthas Stone in Tain. This gem is the tap for Black Isle Brewery. Unmissable, with its distinctive leaning gable, it has a cosy wood-lined bar, with an ancient marriage stone lintel, dated 1691, over the fireplace. Two attractive gardens lead to a sandy beach, with signposted walks on the shore and through the local beauty spot, Fairy Glen. The menu specialises in seafood and game.
🏚Q⊛◑⊟🛆♣P

ROUSAY

Taversoe Hotel
Gripps OS406274
🕐 12-4, 7-midnight (6.30-1am Fri & Sat); closed Mon; 12-4, 6.30-midnight Sun
☎ (01856) 821325
Orkney Red MacGregor, Dark Island Ⓖ

The only bar on the island of Rousay, two miles west of the ferry terminal. The beer is brought from the cellar, situated in an adjacent outbuilding to the main single-storey hotel, which overlooks the Eynhallow Sound, separating Rousay from the 'mainland'. An ideal base to explore the island, with its many burial chambers; cycles can be hired at the ferry terminal if you do not want to walk. All meals must be booked in advance.
🏚◑🛆P

SCOUSBURGH

Spiggie Hotel
🕐 11-11 (midnight Wed-Sat); 12.30-11 Sun
☎ (01950) 460409 website: www.spiggie.co.uk
Valhalla Simmer Dim; guest beers Ⓗ

Recently refurbished, family-run hotel, with a children's certificate, situated above the Spiggie trout loch. The traditional public bar has a stone and wood floor. Food is prepared from local produce, with a vegetarian option always available. It is convenient for exploring the important archaelogical sites of Jarlshof and Scatness. The summer guest beer is usually from Valhalla while winter guests come from further afield. A cask cider is also occasionally stocked in summer.
🏚⊛◑♣🍺P

SLIGACHAN

Sligachan Hotel
At A850/A863 jct
🕐 9am-midnight; 9am-11 Sun
☎ (01478) 650204
website: www.sligachan.demon.co.uk
Beer range varies Ⓗ

Superb, family-run, 19th-century hotel on the main road at the head of Sea Loch and the foot of the Cuillin Hills, which offer some of the most spectacular walking and climbing in Britain. Golf and fishing are also available close by. Children are welcome; there is a well-equipped campsite opposite. Eight ales are stocked in season with a reduced winter range, many from the island's brewery, while Seumas' Bar boasts 80 malt whiskies. It hosts an autumn real ale and music festival. Loal CAMRA *Country Pub of the Year* 2001.
🏚🛏⊛⊛◑⊟🛆♣P

STRATHCARRON

Strathcarron Hotel
🕐 11-11 (including Sun)
☎ (01520) 722227
website: www.strathcarronhotel.com
Beer range varies Ⓗ

This traditional, small 10-roomed hotel enjoys a spectacular situation at the head of Loch Carron. Right next door to a station on the Inverness-Kyle railway, it is an ideal base for touring Wester Ross. On the road to Skye, Plockton and Eilean Donan Castle, it is popular with visitors from Britain and abroad who enjoy beers from Highland breweries in Skye, Black Isle, Aviemore and Orkney. The food is home cooked; seafood is a speciality in summer.
🏚⊛◑⊟🛆⇌♣P

STROMNESS

Ferry Inn
John Street
(near ferry terminal)
🕐 11-midnight (1am Thu-Sat); 11-midnight Sun
☎ (01856) 850280 website: www.ferryinn.com
Orkney Dark Island Ⓗ

Nestling in the heart of the town, only a few strides from the ferry terminal, this hotel keeps beer in summer only. The clientele is predominantly made up of visiting divers wanting to come to explore the wrecks in nearby Scapa Flow. Ironically, it was previously a Temperance hotel, endorsed by the Cyclists Touring Club.
🏚◑🛆

Stromness Hotel
15 Victoria Street (near ferry terminal)
🕐 11-11 (1am Fri & Sat); 12-11 Sun
☎ (01856) 850298 website: www.stromnesshotel.com
Beer range varies Ⓗ

In a prominent position at the pierhead, the hotel is clearly visible from approaching ferries. Avoid the street-level Flatty Bar; beer is only available in the spacious first-floor lounge bar. It gets packed with visiting divers in summer and locals throughout the year. Families are welcome. It hosts jazz and folk music festivals and holds its own beer festival every August. The beer selection is usually from Orkney with up to three on tap at any one time.
🏚Q⊛🏚◑♣P

THURSO

Central Hotel
Traill Street
🕐 11-11.45 (1am Fri & Sat); 12.30-11.45 Sun
☎ (01847) 893129
e-mail: central.hotel@btinternet.com
Caledonian Deuchars IPA; guest beers Ⓗ

Town-centre hotel, two miles from the ferry terminal at Scrabster, on the spectacular Pentland Firth coast. It specialises in welcoming families with children; a soft

play area and bouncy castle are accessed from the large upstairs bar/restaurant, but no children are allowed in the downstairs bar, popular with locals, which has a large-screen Sky TV. Beers are mainly from the Caledonian Brewery. The popular menu is mainly home made and is available from 9am-8.30pm; takeaways are also available.
🍴◐⊖🚻♿🌲♣✂

ULLAPOOL

Ferry Boat Inn
Shore Street
✪ 11-11; 12.30-11 Sun
☎ (01854) 612366 website: www.ferryboat-inn.com
Beer range varies Ⓗ
Small, comfortable, 18th-century inn on the shore of Loch Broom. The bar has an old-fashioned style and the atmosphere is friendly and informal. The bar and restaurant afford glorious views across the loch to the mountains of Wester Ross. Local fresh produce is served in the bar (all year) and restaurant (open spring-late autumn). Close to the Western Isles ferry terminals, this was the local CAMRA *Country Pub of the Year* 2000. 🏚Q🌲🍴◐♣

WATERNISH

Stein Inn
North of Dunvegan, on B886, 4¹/₂ miles from Fairy Bridge

✪ 4-11 (midnight Fri; 12-midnight summer); 12-12.30am Sat; 12.30-11 Sun
☎ (01470) 592362 website: www.steininn.co.uk
Isle of Skye Red Cuillin; guest beers Ⓗ
This traditional Highland hostelry, in a picturesque setting on the shores of Loch Bay, is the oldest inn on the Isle of Skye. The small bar has recently been extended. House beers are from the island's brewery. Local seafood is served (Easter-Oct) in the bar and restaurant, both boasting fine views over the loch to Rubha Mol. The large garden is on the shore. Facilities for seafarers include council moorings, showers, food supplies (by arrangement), and message relay services.
🏚Q🏡🍴♣P

WORMADALE

Westings Inn
On A971, 10 miles NW of Lerwick OS402464
✪ 12.15-2.15 (2.30 Sat); 12-2.30, 5-11 Sun
☎ (01595) 840242
website: www.westings.shetland.co.uk
Beer range varies Ⓗ
Situated close to the summit of Wormadale Hill, and surrounded by Whiteness Valley Moors at the head of Weisdale Voe, this family-run hotel offers up to three guest beers, with either Valhalla or Greene King regularly stocked in the Palm Shack. It has a restaurant, and the green room holds a children's certificate. ⚲🍴◐♿♣P

Fizz warning

Some national breweries produce both cask-conditioned and 'nitro-keg' versions of their beers. Boddingtons Bitter, John Smith's Bitter, Tetley's Bitter and Worthington fall into this category. Nitro-keg beers, often promoted as 'smooth' or 'cream-flow' products, are filtered and pasteurised in the brewery, and served in pubs by a mix of applied carbon dioxide and nitrogen gases. They are bland, served extremely cold, and any hop character is lost by the use of applied gas. To add insult to injury, the keg founts that serve such beers are often topped by small dummy handpumps. As a result of lobbying by CAMRA, some producers of cask and nitro versions of the same beer now include the word 'cask' on pump clips for the genuine article. For example, both John Smith's Bitter and Tetley's Bitter now carry the word 'cask' on pump clips for the real thing. For the sake of brevity, and as the Good Beer Guide lists only cask-conditioned beers, we refer simply to John Smith's Bitter and Tetley Bitter. The Bass/Interbrew brand, Worthington, is labelled Worthington Bitter in cask form, and – bizarrely – Worthington Best Bitter in the nitro-keg version. Always choose the living rather than the dead.

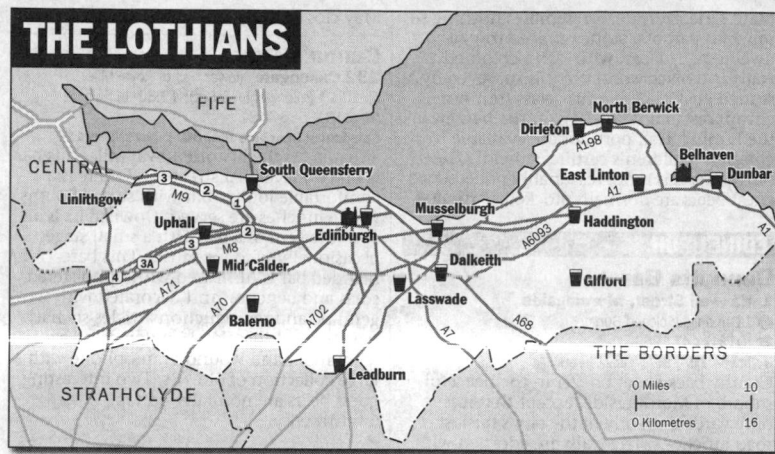

THE LOTHIANS

Authority areas covered: City of Edinburgh UA, East Lothian UA, Midlothian UA

BALERNO

Johnsburn House
64 Johnsburn Road (off A70, NW side of village)
✪ 12-3, 6.30-midnight (1am Fri); 12-1am Sat; closed Mon; 12.30-midnight Sun
☎ (0131) 449 3847 e-mail: johs1760@aol.com
Caledonian Deuchars IPA; guest beers Ⓗ
Baronial mansion dating from 1760 and now Grade B listed, originally owned by Professor Adam Fergusson who reputedly brought together the two great men of Scottish literature, Robert Burns and Sir Walter Scott. The low-ceilinged, cosy bar has a convivial atmosphere and varied memorabilia decorating the walls and wooden beams. A passageway leads to a dark, wood-panelled dining room beyond which is the service corridor and further rooms for diners. Its reputation for meals is well deserved. It holds a children's certificate. ♨Q❀◑◖♣P

DALKEITH

Black Bull
1 Lothian Street
✪ 11-11.30 (midnight Thu-Sat); 12.30-11.45 Sun
☎ (0131) 663 2095
Caledonian Deuchars IPA; guest beers Ⓗ
Close to the busy centre of Dalkeith, at the back of the Jarnac Court shopping precinct, this busy, vibrant public bar has fine arched windows, cornice work and a well-crafted gantry; a large TV makes it a popular venue for sporting events. The more modern lounge (where children are allowed) is popular at lunchtimes and can be a welcome refuge from the bar at busy times. Wheelchair access is via the side door. A pool room and honest, inexpensive food complete the picture. ❀◑◖♿♣♠

DUNBAR

Volunteer Arms
17 Victoria Street (between harbour and swimming pool)
✪ 11-11 (1 am Thu-Sat); 12.30-midnight Sun
☎ (01368) 862278
Belhaven 80/-; guest beer (summer) Ⓗ
The history of the lifeboat and Dunbar adorn the walls of this oak-beamed, wood-panelled, friendly, boisterous bar, near the harbour. A local calligrapher's representations of Scottish *bon mots* also hang on the walls. Church pew banquettes and candle-effect sconces add a twinkle to the dark interior with its tiled floor and plaid curtaining. Old lobster pots, floats and a short wave radio complete a nautical theme. The RNLA flag flies proudly in the garden. There is a restaurant upstairs (meals served April–Oct). Children are welcome. ❀◑♿⩲≈♣

EAST LINTON

Bridgend Hotel
3 Bridge End (off A1)
✪ 12-2, 7-11 (midnight Thu); 12-midnight Fri & Sat; 12-midnight Sun
☎ (01620) 860202
website: www.scoot.co.uk/bridgend_hotel/
Hadrian & Border Rampart; guest beer Ⓗ
Village pub with a public bar and comfortable lounge. Connections with the Hadrian & Border Brewery mean their beers usually feature on the bar. The stained glass windows and rooftop statue reveal the pub's previous identity as the Red Lion. The bar, with a tiled floor, houses a pool table and musical instruments hang on the wall as decoration. The lounge-cum-dining room has a banquette running three-quarters of the way around the room. Eve meals are served Fri–Sun. The ensuite accommodation has recently been refurbished. Children welcome. ⇆◑⩲♣🖵

Drovers Inn
5 Bridge Street (off A1)
✪ 11.30-midnight (1am Fri & Sat); 11.30-2.30, 5-11 Mon; 12.30-1am Sun
☎ (01620) 860298
Adnams Broadside; Caledonian Deuchars IPA; guest beers Ⓗ
An oasis, just off the A1, formerly called the Railway, it stands close to the East Coast

INDEPENDENT BREWERIES

Belhaven Belhaven
Caledonian Edinburgh
Fisherrow Edinburgh

Main Line. Outside, it resembles nothing so much as part of a stone terraced row of dwellings. The bar, with claret-coloured walls and black wood decor is surveyed by a stuffed goat's head. A first-class (but not cheap) restaurant, leading off the bar, awaits the hungry. Half portions are available for children (children's certificate held). The bistro menu is more reasonably priced. Two guest beers are normally stocked. 🚻🏮🕪🍴♣

EDINBURGH ✣

Bennetts Bar ☆
1 Maxwell Street, Morningside
🕐 11-midnight; closed Sun
☎ (0131) 447 1903
Belhaven 70/-, 80/-; guest beers Ⓐ
Couthy back-street boozer in the peaceful suburb of Morningside, except that it is only yards from one of the city's busiest road junctions. The walls are adorned with photographs of old Edinburgh, including one of the eponymous family's first pub, now demolished, in Market Street. In summer you can sit outside and watch the traffic at the aforementioned junction going, well, nowhere actually. Can be smoky when busy. It stocks up to four guest beers; bar snacks available. 🏮

Bow Bar
80 West Bow (between George IV Bridge and Grassmarket)
🕐 12-11.30; 12.30-10 Sun
☎ (0131) 226 7667
Caledonian Deuchars IPA, 80/-; Taylor Landlord; guest beers Ⓐ
One-room drinking shop in the heart of the historic old town, dedicated to the peculiar Scottish art of perpendicular drinking and traditional air pressure dispense. Rare old brewery mirrors, cigarette advertisements and a map showing old Scottish county boundaries adorn the walls. It is a favoured watering-hole for members of the Scottish Parliament, whose temporary home is close by. Up to five interesting guest beers and a superb range of malt whiskies are on offer.

May close early Sun if quiet. **Q**🚻(Waverley)

Canon's Gait
232 Canongate (lower half of Royal Mile)
🕐 12-11 (midnight Fri & Sat); 12.30-11 Sun
☎ (0131) 556 4481
Caledonian Deuchars IPA, 80/-; guest beers Ⓗ
Situated on the historic Royal Mile, this bar is on two levels. At street level there is a comfortable lounge bar with seated booths where lunches are served. Downstairs is an absolute gem of a bar with a small stage occasionally used for music. This bare-boarded bar is furnished with upholstered sofas and benches, and decorated with genuine and reproduction articles such as sewing machines, kitchen items and a (genuine) hand-wound gramophone with a large collection of old 78s. Two interesting guest beers are normally on tap.
🕪🚻(Waverley)
♣

Cask & Barrel
115 Broughton Street
🕐 11-12.30am (1am Thu-Sat); 12.30-12.30am
☎ (0131) 556 3132
Draught Bass; Boddingtons Bitter; Hadrian & Border Special; Caledonian Deuchars IPA, 80/-; Flowers IPA; guest beers Ⓗ
Spacious, and extremely busy, urban ale house, with a mainly local clientele, including all ages and ranging from business people to football fans. The interior features an imposing horseshoe bar, wooden floorboards, a splendid cornice and a collection of brewery mirrors, some quite rare. Old barrels act as tables for those who wish to stand up, or can't find a seat. Pavement tables are put outside in summer. 🏮🕪🚻

Cloisters
26 Brougham Street
🕐 11-midnight (12.30am Fri & Sat); 12.30-midnight Sun
☎ (0131) 221 9997
Caledonian Deuchars IPA, 80/-; Taylor Landlord; Thwaites Bitter; Ⓐ **guest beers** Ⓗ

INN BRIEF

DIRLETON
Castle Inn ☆
11.30-midnight (1am Fri & Sat)
Orkney Dark Island; guest beer Ⓗ
Attractive inn, with a cosy bar and games room. The comfortable lounge/dining room is popular for food. En-suite accommodation.

EDINBURGH
Abbey Festival Ale House
65 South Clerk Street
11-1am; 12.30-midnight Sun
Caledonian Deuchars IPA, 80/-; Taylor Landlord; guest beers Ⓗ
Bare-boarded ale house divided into two halves by the island bar. Decor is typical of the chain. Good range of guest beers.

Clark's Bar
142 Dundas Street
11-11 (11.30 Thu-Sat);
12.30-11 Sun
Caledonian Deuchars IPA, 80/- Ⓐ
Traditional tenement bar, popular with male locals and workers. The internal layout is interesting with two private rooms off the bar. *Cask Marque* accredited.

HADDINGTON
Pheasant
72 Market Street
11-11 (midnight Thu; 1am Fri & Sat);
11-midnight Sun
Ind Coope Burton Ale; Tetley Bitter; guest beers Ⓗ
Attracting a mixed clientele, a long thin bar snakes through to a pool area where Basil the African Grey parrot oversees events.

Tyneside Tavern
10 Poldrate
11-11 (midnight Thu; 12.45am Fri & Sat);
12.30-midnight Sun
Courage Directors; guest beer Ⓗ
Cosy, convivial local displaying X-rated rugby photos and rustic woodwork; comfortable lounge. Children's certificate; good food.

LINLITHGOW
Black Bitch
14 West Port, High Street
11 (12.30 Sun)-midnight
Beer range varies Ⓗ
Named after the town crest, it is one of the oldest pubs in the town. Real ale in lounge only.

MID CALDER
Torphichen
36 Bank Street
11-11 (midnight Thu-Sat); 12.30-midnight
Caledonian Deuchars IPA, 80/-; Ind Coope Burton Ale; guest beers Ⓗ
Village local where several rooms, with original cornices, now form one L-shaped bar with public and lounge areas. Lunches daily, eve meals Sat and Sun.

Star Bar
1 Northumberland Place
12-1am (including Sun)
Caledonian Deuchars IPA, 80/- Ⓗ
Split-level, New Town local: the upper level serves food The lower part has the bar and table football.

> ✣ symbol next to a main entry place name indicates there are Inn Brief entries as well.

Situated in the former All Saints parsonage between Tollcross and the Meadows, this ale house reverberates to the sound of contented drinkers. Some rare old Scottish brewery mirrors adorn the walls and the large selection of malt whiskies does justice to the impressive gantry, which was built with wood from a redundant church. Good quality, and good value, lunches are served and traditional Scottish and vegetarian breakfasts are available Sun lunchtime. The four interesting guest beers change regularly.
Q◁

Golden Rule
30 Yeaman Place
✪ 11-11.30 (midnight Fri); 12.30-11 Sun
☎ (0131) 229 3413
Caledonian Deuchars IPA, 80/-; Harviestoun Bitter & Twisted; guest beers Ⓗ

Tucked away in a late Victorian tenement, just around the corner from the Scottish Courage beer factory, this pub has been a regular in this *Guide* since reopening as an ale house in 1990. While offering a wide range of beers, it remains, in essence, a local boozer. The atmosphere is now much less smoky since the installation of powerful extraction equipment. The downstairs lounge, Rule 2, is aimed at the trendier end of the market. Of the four guest beers, one is always either Harviestoun Ptarmigan or Schiehallion.
⇌ (Haymarket) ♣ ●

Guildford Arms
1 West Register Street
✪ 11-11 (midnight Fri & Sat & summer Thu); 12.30-11 Sun
☎ (0131) 556 4312
Caledonian Deuchars IPA, 80/-; Ⓟ **Harviestoun Bitter & Twisted; Taylor Landlord; Orkney Dark Island; guest beers** Ⓗ

Busy, but orderly, city-centre pub, notable for its ornate plasterwork. The high ceiling, cornices and friezes are spectacular, as are the window arches and screens. There are areas for standing and others with comfortable seating. An unusual wood-panelled gallery above the main bar is used as a lounge and dining area at lunchtimes. The seven regularly-changing guests usually include beers from Haviestoun and other smaller breweries. Themed beer festivals are held twice a year. No food Sun.
◁⇌ (Waverley) ♣ ●

Leslie's Bar ☆
45 Ratcliffe Terrace
(Newington, 2 miles S of centre)
✪ 11-11 (11.30 Thu; 12.30am Fri & Sat); 12.30-11.30 Sun
☎ (0131) 667 5957
Caledonian Deuchars IPA, 80/-; Taylor Landlord; guest beers Ⓗ

Busy, cheery, community pub on Edinburgh's Southside split into two by a spectacular snob screen at the back of the island bar. Small hatches allow the customers in the snug and saloon to order drinks away from the sight of *hoi polloi* in the bar. Over 100 years old, and in impeccable condition, it was designed by Peter Lyle Henderson, in the golden age of late Victorian pub design. A true local, it has

been run by the same family for 40 years. One of the two guest beers is often from Harviestoun.
🏛Q Ⓔ♣ ●

Malt & Hops
45 The Shore, Leith
✪ 12-midnight (1am Fri & Sat); 12.30-11 Sun
☎ (0131) 555 0083
website: www.spidacom.co.uk/edg/malthops/
Tetley Bitter; Marston's Pedigree; guest beers Ⓗ

One-roomed public bar dating from 1749 and almost certainly the oldest pub in Leith. Now in the heart of the riverside restaurant district, it stands close to the Water of Leith. The superb collection of pump clips, many from now deceased breweries, indicate the ever-changing range of guest beers served (usually six). Note the oil painting above the fire, showing Leith around 50 years ago and the old local wooden bus sign. Children are welcome until 6pm. Tables are put out on the pavement in summer. 🏛Q◁◁♣ ●

Old Chain Pier
32 Trinity Crescent
(foreshore between Leith and Granton)
✪ 12-11 (midnight Thu-Sat); 12.30-11 Sun
☎ (0131) 552 1233 website: www.oldchainpier.co.uk
Caledonian Deuchars IPA; Ind Coope Burton Ale; Taylor Landlord; guest beers Ⓗ

This is the place to go if you want great beer, imaginative food (including tripe for Tue lunch), superb sea views across the Firth of Forth to Fife and sunny seats outside in the summer. The pub is on the site of the booking office for the pier, which was destroyed in 1898. The new conservatory is perfect for family meals, with a children's certificate until 7pm. The manager is one of Edinburgh's long-serving local ale champions. In addition to a full, non-formula menu, unusual snacks are available, such as superbly ripe Stilton.
🌠◁◁ ♣

Spylaw Tavern
27 Spylaw Street. Colinton
✪ 11-11 (11.30 Thu-Sat); 12.30-11 Sun
☎ (0131) 441 2783
Caledonian Deuchars IPA, 80/-; guest beer Ⓗ

Set in historic Colinton village this attractive bar, lounge and restaurant conveys an airy atmosphere, enhanced by the light-coloured wood used for the bar, gantry and decor. A 'no smoking' policy is upheld in the restaurant and all food is freshly prepared on the premises; home-made pies are a speciality. Meals are served all day until 8pm (5.30 Sun). Children are welcome if dining. The Spylaw makes an ideal stopping point for walkers on the Water of Leith walkway but dogs are not admitted.
Q🌠◁◁ ♿ ●

Starbank Inn
64 Laverockbank Road
(foreshore between Leith and Granton)
✪ 11-11 (midnight Thu-Sat); 12.30-11 Sun
☎ (0131) 552 4141
Belhaven Sandy Hunter's Ale, IPA, 80/-, St Andrew's Ale; Taylor Landlord; guest beers Ⓗ

Bright, airy, bare-boarded ale house, with an extended U-shaped layout, the Starbank is proud that it does not sell any keg ales and the three guest beers are usually Scottish. Why not try a pint of prawns with your beer? The uncluttered walls sport several rare brewery mirrors. A no-smoking restaurant serves food until 9pm (children are welcome until 8.30pm). Superb views across the Firth of Forth to Fife can be enjoyed and Newhaven harbour is just along the road. Occasional jazz is staged Sun. Q ◖◗ ♣

Thomsons
182-4 Morrison Street
✪ 12-11.30; closed Sun
☎ (0131) 228 5700
Caledonian Deuchars IPA, 80/-; Taylor Landlord; guest beers Ⓐ
This former, grotty local was stripped back to the bricks to allow the design team to start again from scratch. The result pays homage to the underrated Glasgow architect, Alexander 'Greek' Thomson, and traditional air pressure dispense. Around the walls, rare old brewery mirrors provide a history lesson on the subject of Scottish brewing. It is very handy for the Edinburgh International Conference Centre and Haymarket station. The five guest beers usually include one from Arran.
Q ≠ (Haymarket)

Winston's
20 Kirk Loan, Corstophine (off A8
✪ 11-11.30 (midnight Thu-Sat); 12.30-11 Sun
☎ (0131) 539 7077
Caledonian Deuchars IPA; Ind Coope Burton Ale; Orkney Dark Island; guest beer Ⓗ
Run by the same licensee for many years, this comfortable lounge bar is situated off the main road in Corstorphine, a busy area of west Edinburgh, just over a mile from Murrayfield stadium and near the zoo. This small modern building hides a warm, active community pub. The one room is used by old and young alike, with children welcome until 3pm. The decor features golfing and rugby themes. Its popularity is due not only to the consistent quality of the three regular and single guest beers, but also to its wonderful home-made pies (no food Sun).
◖●

Goblin Ha' Hotel
Main Street
✪ 11-2.30, 4.30-11; 11-midnight Fri & Sat; 11-11 Sun
☎ (01620) 810244
Caledonian Deuchars IPA; Hop Back Summer Lightning; Taylor Landlord; guest beer Ⓗ
Large village hotel, with a children's certificate in a picturesque hamlet. The public bar contains a mixture of church pews and mock-leather covered banquettes. The ceiling is low, of painted wood, while the gantry is a mix of glass and wood. There is a pool room and a comfortable lounge, mainly laid out for eating, also a conservatory and dining room – these can be busy weekend lunchtimes. The garden is popular with families in summer and has an outdoor play area.
⚐ ❁ ⇔ ◖◗ ⊟ ▲ ♣

Tweeddale Arms Hotel
High Street (off Main St)
✪ 11-11 (midnight Fri & Sat); 11-11 Sun

☎ (01620) 810240 e-mail: info@tweeddalearms.co.uk
Caledonian Deuchars IPA; Greene King Abbot; guest beer Ⓗ
Attractive hotel overlooking the village green and a 300-year-old avenue of lime trees. The public bar boasts an impressive collection of spirit miniature bottles, a sandstone fireplace and pictures of George IV reviewing troops in Edinburgh. The L-shaped lounge is modern and very comfortable. The quality menu is supplemented with daily specials; high teas are served at weekends. A children's certificate covers the lounge and restaurant. Ask staff which real ales are on as there are two pumps in the lounge and two in the bar.
⚐ Q ⇔ ◖◗ ⊟ ♣

Laird & Dog Hotel
5 High Street (A768 near river bridge)
✪ 11-11.30 (11.45 Thu; 12.30am Fri & Sat); 12.30-11.30 Sun
☎ (0131) 663 9219
Beer range varies Ⓗ
Comfortable village local, comprising several areas: music and pool at one end of the bar contrast with quieter seating areas at the other (children welcome until 8pm). A conservatory extension is used as a no-smoking restaurant, serving a good quality varied menu and daily specials. A simpler bar menu is also available; food is served all day. Another room, with armchairs around a fire, boasts an interesting bottle-shaped well, with display cases of items found in it. Up to three real ales, usually from smaller breweries, are on tap.
⚐ ❁ ⇔ ◖◗ ♣ P

Leadburn Inn
At A701/A703/A6094 jct.
✪ 11-11 (11.45 Fri & Sat; midnight summer); 12-11 (midnight summer) Sun
☎ (01968) 672952
Caledonian Deuchars IPA, 80/-; guest beer Ⓗ
Established in 1777, this large food-oriented hostelry, with a children's certificate, has a converted railway coach that serves as a function room. The plain public bar has a pot-bellied stove and a picture window looking to the Pentland Hills. A conservatory, inhabited by a mighty grapevine, links the bar to the plush lounge, where shelving displays books and ornaments. The guest beers are usually from smaller Scottish breweries. The two pumps in the bar offer different beers to those in the lounge.
⚐ Q ❁ ⇔ ◖◗ ♣ P ⊁

Four Marys
65-67 High Street
✪ 12-11 (midnight Thu-Sat); 12.30-11 Sun
☎ (01506) 842171
Belhaven 80/-; St Andrew's Ale; Caledonian Deuchars IPA; Harviestoun Schiehallion; Taylor Landlord; guest beers Ⓐ
The Four Marys was named after the four ladies-in-waiting of Mary Queen of Scots, who was born in the nearby Linlithgow

Palace. Originally built around 1500 as a dwelling, the pub has seen several uses throughout the years. It was once a chemist's shop run by the Waldie family, whose most famous member, David Waldie, established the anaesthetic properties of chloroform in 1847. It only opened as a pub in 1975, and hosts beer festivals twice a year (May and Oct) when 18 handpumps are in use.

❶▶≉✲

Platform 3
1a High Street
✪ 11 (12.30 Sun)-midnight
☎ (01506) 847405
Caledonian Deuchars IPA; Courage Directors; guest beer 🅷

Small, friendly pub on the railway station approach. Originally the public bar of the hotel next door, it was purchased and renovated in 1998 as a pub in its own right. Occasional live music is staged. The third handpump on the bar is used for guest beers, usually from the Caledonian Brewery range. Some interesting memorabilia is displayed around the walls. ≉

MUSSELBURGH

Levenhall Arms
10 Ravensheugh Road (B1348, near racecourse roundabout)
✪ 11 (3 Mon-Thu winter)-11 (midnight Thu; 1am Fri & Sat); 12.30-midnight Sun
☎ (0131) 665 3220
Caledonian Deuchars IPA; 🅿 **Ind Coope Burton Ale;** 🅷 **guest beer** 🅿

Busy pub, popular with locals, racegoers and visitors to the nearby golf course. The building dates from 1830 and houses three public rooms. Once a stopping point on the Edinburgh–London stagecoach run, more recently it had a tram terminus outside. The public bar is partly timber panelled and carpeted; at the rear, is the games room with a pool table and dartboard. To the right of the entrance, is the lounge with vinyl banquettes and tables. An additional guest beer is stocked in summer.
Q 🏠🚻≉ (Wallyford) ♣P

Volunteer Arms (Staggs)
81 North High Street (behind Brunton Hall)
✪ 11-11 (11.30 Thu; midnight Fri & Sat); 11-2.30, 5-11 Tue & Wed; closed Sun
☎ (0131) 665 9654
Caledonian Deuchars IPA, 80/-; guest beer 🅷

Three-room pub, run by the same family since 1858; the main bar is traditional with a tiled floor, dark wood panelling, wood and glass screens and advertising mirrors from defunct local breweries. A superb gantry is topped with old casks and vinyl banquettes provide seating. In the snug, peruse the beginnings of a history collection about local breweries. The lounge opens at weekends. The single guest beer changes frequently (up to four times on a Sat). A one-day real ale festival is held on Remembrance Sunday at this 1998 national CAMRA *Pub of the Year*. ❀🏠♣●

NORTH BERWICK

Nether Abbey Hotel
20 Dirleton Avenue (A198, ½ mile W of centre)

✪ 11-11 (midnight Thu; 1am Fri & Sat); 12-11 Sun
☎ (01620) 892802 website: www.netherabbey.co.uk
Caledonian Deuchars IPA; Courage Directors; guest beers 🅿

On the eastern Scottish Riviera, this comfortable family-run hotel in a Victorian villa boasts an L-shaped bar and a bistro; the bar is carpeted and the bistro bare-boarded and dark wood features in the decor. In good weather the bar expands into a sizeable outdoor area, with a retractable canvas roof. However, all may change with refurbishment planned in 2001. An annual real ale festival is held in Feb. Handy for some legendary golf courses, rounds can be arranged by staff. Meals are served all day in summer; children's certificate.
🏨❀🛏❶▶ 🅰≉♣P

SOUTH QUEENSFERRY

Ferry Tap
36 High Street
✪ 11.30-11.30 (midnight Thu; 12.30am Fri & Sat); 12.30-11.30 Sun
☎ (0131) 331 2000
Caledonian Deuchars IPA, 80/-; Orkney Dark Island; guest beers 🅷

Ground-floor bar in a 300-year-old building in the old part of a village, dominated by bridges. It comprises an intriguing, comfortable, one-roomed L-shaped bar, with an unusual barrel-vaulted ceiling. Dark wood gives an intimate feel and numerous artefacts, many from bygone breweries, add interest. A varied selection of meals is served at lunchtime; on Wed, Fri and Sat eves, basket meals are available. Parking is difficult, but there is plenty of space near the railway bridge.
❶▶≉ (Dalmeny) ♣●

UPHALL

Oatridge Hotel
2-4 East Main Street
(at A899/B8046 jct)
✪ 11 (12.30 Sun)-midnight
☎ (01506) 856465
Beer range varies 🅷

Originally a 19th-century coaching house, the hotel still serves the modern traveller as well as locals. Run by the same family for 28 years, real ale is served in the public bar – up to four beers regularly feature Caledonian, Arran and Heather ales. Note the large collection of ceramic vessels behind the bar, which once held various refreshing liquids. Pool can be played and TV sports are popular. Weekday lunches served and eve meals Fri–Sun.
❀🛏❶▶ 🏠♣ 🅰P

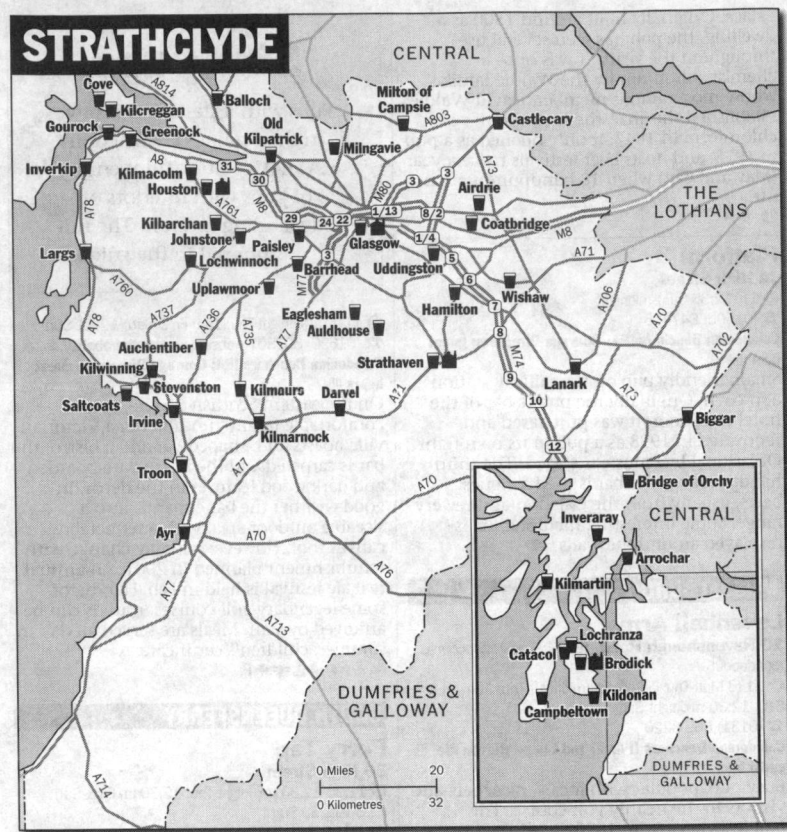

STRATHCLYDE

Strathclyde comprises Argyllshire, Ayrshire and Arran, Dunbartonshire, Glasgow, Lanarkshire and Renfrewshire.

Argyllshire

ARROCHAR

Village Inn

On A814, 1/2 mile S of A83 jct
11-midnight (1am Fri & Sat); 12-midnight Sun
☎ (01301) 702279 website: www.maclay.com
Orkney Dark Island; guest beers Ⓗ

A warm, friendly atmosphere awaits at this idyllic lochside inn. Originally built in 1827 as the local manse, it is situated on the east shore of Loch Long, offering breathtaking views over the Arrochar Alps and the famous Cobbler Mountain. Wooden floorboards and furniture create a rustic feel. The fireplaces are constructed from stone from Greenock Esplanade with a one-foot-thick section of local oak used as a mantelpiece. An ideal base for hillwalkers, also good stop-off point on the West Highland circuit. ♨❀⇔◗ ♣P

BRIDGE OF ORCHY

Bridge of Orchy Hotel

11-11 (midnight Fri & Sat); 12-11 Sun
☎ (01838) 400208
Caledonian Deuchars IPA, 80/- Ⓗ

Roadside hotel south of Rannoch Moor and Glencoe, built 40 years ago to replace an old coaching inn on the same site which burnt down. For many years this hotel and its predecessor have catered for travellers and those indulging in various outdoor pursuits such as climbing, hillwalking and even rafting in nearby Glen Fruin. It is ideally situated on the West Highland Way, Scotland's best-known long distance footpath. Bar service is in the recently modernised wood-panelled Caley Bar. ♨Q❀⇔◗⇔P●

CAMPBELTOWN

Commercial Inn
Cross Street
11 (12.30 Sun)-1am
☎ (01586) 553703
Caledonian Deuchars IPA; guest beers (occasional) Ⓗ

Busy, family-run town bar, located in a quiet pedestrianised square off the main streets. Distinctive decorative wood panels, wooden bench seating and a large Aitchison's of Edinburgh Brewery mirror are found in the L-shaped main room and bar. The separate lounge is soft-furnished, with tartan carpets and subdued lighting. It also has bar stools, ceiling fans and most unusual wallpaper; gold flies(!) on a dark green background. The separate pool room is plainly furnished and has a TV. ⚑

COVE

Knockderry Hotel

204 Shore Road (B833)
🕐 11.30-midnight; 12.30-11 Sun
☎ (01436) 842283 website: www.knockderry.co.uk
Beer range varies Ⓗ

'Ruritanian hunting lodge' boasting excellent examples of work by William Leiper, Daniel Cottier and Thomas Jekyll. It is a stunning building with a recurring theme of the four seasons, with examples in both stained glass and wood. This former Glasgow merchant's house is situated on the picturesque Rosneath Peninsula, offering superb views over Loch Long towards Benmore and Strone. The hotel boasts a safe anchorage, large garden and snooker room, as well as open fires for roasting toes. Jamming session on Thu night. Beers from Maclay's guest list. Local CAMRA *Pub of the Year* 2000. 🏚️❄️🛏️◖ 🐕P

INVERARAY

George Hotel
Main Street East
🕐 11 (12 Sun)-12.30am
☎ (01499) 302111 website: www.thegeorgehotel.co.uk
Beer range varies Ⓗ

Long-established hotel (built 1775) at the heart of this historic conservation town and next to the old jail. The main bar has been well-restored keeping the original flagstone floors, stone walls and welcoming log and peat fires. The lively public bar is off to one side and has restricted opening hours. Two guest beers are offered in summer (generally reduced to one in winter), often including Caledonian Deuchars IPA. The hotel has been owned by the same family for five generations. Excellent meals are prepared using local produce. 🏚️❄️🛏️◖🍽️&ÅP

KILCREGGAN

Kilcreggan Hotel
Argyll Road (from B833 on to Argyll road 500 yds on left)
🕐 12-midnight (1am Fri & Sat); 12.30-midnight Sun
☎ (01436) 842243
Theakston Best Bitter; guest beers Ⓗ

Stone-built Victorian mansion, in the heart of Kilcreggan village on the southern tip of the Rosneath Peninsula, overlooking the Clyde estuary. Stunning views south to Arran. Built by Robert Donaldson of Glasgow Shipping Line fame, the hotel contains fine wood panelling with stained glass windows and ornate bargeboards and balconies. It features a curious gabled and battlemented tower. Close to the pier with regular passenger-only ferry to Gourock and hourly bus service to Helensburgh. The paddle-steamer 'Waverley' calls on Fri in summer. Guest beers from smaller Scottish breweries and English standards. 🏚️⏳❄️🛏️◖🍽️P

KILMARTIN

Kilmartin Hotel
On A816
🕐 11-1am (winter 12-2.30, 5-1am); 12-1am Sun
☎ (01546) 510250 e-mail: kilmartinhotel@aol.com
Caledonian 80/-; guest beer (summer) Ⓗ

Whitewashed building among attractive hills on the main road. Close to an ancient site; there is evidence of Neolithic and Bronze Age settlements. Standing stones and a stone circle can be seen nearby. The long, rectangular bar has cushioned bench seating, bare-stone walls and a fireplace. The L-shaped wooden counter and gantry with brewery mirrors leads through to a semi-divided pool room and a cosier lounge/dining room. The football pitch opposite is also used at weekends for the traditional Scottish game of Shinty. 🏚️Q⏳❄️🛏️◖ÅP🍽️

Ayrshire & Arran

AUCHENTIBER

Blair Country Restaurant
A736/B778 jct
🕐 11-3, 5-11; 11-11 Sat & Sun
☎ (01294) 850237
Arran Dark; guest beers Ⓗ

Pleasant country inn on the Glasgow–Irvine road, six miles from both Irvine and Kilwinning. There are few houses nearby so it concentrates on food. There is limited space for drinkers during main meal times, but it does have a pub licence. The two rooms have traditional decor, one of them is no-smoking. One guest beer is on at most times, often from Belhaven. The food makes it well worth the journey to visit this attractive hostelry. Q❄️◖P🍽️

AYR ☼

Chestnuts Hotel
52 Racecourse Road (A719, 1 mile S of centre)
🕐 11 (12 Sun)-midnight
☎ (01292) 264393 website: chestnuts.hypermart.net
Beer range varies Ⓗ

Comfortable, family-run hotel once owned by the town's Jewish community. The wood-panelled lounge bar features a large collection of water jugs and, reflecting its proximity to local courses, golfing prints are also prominent. The three real ales are usually from the larger regional brewers, but occasionally beers are offered from the local Arran and Houston breweries. High quality meals can be eaten in the bar area or restaurant. 🏚️❄️🛏️◖P

Geordie's Byre
103 Main Street (over river towards Prestwick)
🕐 11-11 (midnight Thu-Sat); 12.30-11 Sun
☎ (01292) 264925
Caledonian Deuchars IPA; guest beers Ⓐ

The rather ordinary exterior hides an Aladdin's cave of memorabilia, especially in the lounge bar which is open Thu–Sat eves. Regularly awarded local CAMRA *Pub of the Year*, it is also a former winner of the Scottish award. The four guest beers come from far and wide with over 300 beers featured throughout a typical year. To the landlord spirits are a hobby as well as a profession, and well over 100 malt whiskies and 28 rums are on offer. The home-made pickled eggs are a house speciality. 🍽️≠ (Newton-on-Ayr)

INDEPENDENT BREWERIES

Arran Brodick
Clockwork Glasgow
Heather Strathaven
Houston Houston
Millers Thumb Glasgow

Market Inn
2 Castlehill Road
✪ 11-12.30am; 12.30-midnight Sun
☎ (01292) 280391
Draught Bass; guest beers Ⓗ

Once an integral part of the cattle market, this prominent sandstone building, opposite the rear exit of Ayr railway station, was earmarked for demolition. However, it was saved after a campaign involving the local CAMRA branch. The refurbishment has retained the listed horseshoe bar and gantry, along with the original tiled floor, fireplaces and stained glass windows. The guest beer is often from the local Arran Brewery. Meals are served in the upstairs lounge where a function suite can also be found.
◑⍃≷

Old Racecourse Hotel
2 Victoria Park (A719, 1 mile S of centre)
✪ 11-midnight (12.30am Fri & Sat); 12-midnight Sun
☎ (01292) 262873
Tetley Bitter; guest beers Ⓗ

Large, comfortable lounge featuring an unusual fire as a centrepiece. The racecourse in the name refers to the former horse-racing venue nearby, now sports pitches and a golf course. The three guest ales are mainly from the larger regional breweries, but the local Arran and Houston breweries are sometimes represented. Excellent meals can be eaten in the bar area or in the more formal setting of the adjacent restaurant. A separate pool/TV room is an added attraction.
🏕Q❀⌂◑♿P

Wellington's
17 Wellington Square (next to County buildings)
✪ 11-12.30am; 12.30-midnight Sun
☎ (01292) 262794
Beer range varies Ⓗ

Welcoming basement bar situated in a Georgian square just behind the seafront. Sky TV is the only evidence that time does not stand still. The beers are mainly from Scottish breweries, and bar food is served all week, 12–7. A venue for quizzes (Wed) and a DJ (Sat). The pub dog is well-trained at spotting local CAMRA members! ◑

BRODICK

Brodick Bar
Alma Road (off Shore Road)
✪ 11-midnight; 12.30-midnight (summer only) Sun
☎ (01770) 302169
Arran Ale; guest beers Ⓟ

Once described as the only pub in Arran (the others were all hotel bars), this long, white building next to the Post Office has two bars. The main bar has been transformed, replacing a rather dark 1970s style with a lighter, more airy and contemporary look. Much of the woodwork is reclaimed material, including church pews and a fanlight, all stripped and polished. The other bar is similar but more food-orientated. The extensive menu is chalked on blackboards in both bars. This is the only real ale daytime winter choice in Brodick. 🏕Q◑⍃

Duncan's Bar
Kingsley Hotel, Shore Road (on seafront)
✪ 11-2.30, 6-midnight (11-midnight summer; closed mid-Oct – mid-March) 6 (11 summer)-midnight Sun
☎ (01770) 302531
Arran Ale, Blonde; Ⓗ **McEwan 80/-** Ⓟ

Large, comfortable bar at the side of one of the main seafront hotels. Serves the nearest real ale to the ferry terminal. It attracts a wide variety of locals and visitors, and the view across the bay to Goat Fell from the front garden is spectacular. A popular eating place, it also hosts regular music sessions in summer, particularly during the Arran folk

INN BRIEF

Ayrshire & Aran

AYR
West Kirk
Sandgate
11-midnight (12.30am Fri & Sat); 12.30-midnight Sun
Caledonian 80/-; Courage Directors; Theakston Best Bitter; guest beers Ⓗ
Wetherspoon's conversion of a former church. Access to the toilets is through the pulpit. *Cask Marque* accredited.

DARVEL
Loudounhill Inn
12-2.30 (not Wed), 5-11 (not Tue); 12-midnight Sat; 12.30-2.30, 4.30-11 Sun
Beer range varies Ⓗ
Family-owned, old coaching inn near Loudoun Hill, three miles east of Darvel on main road. Small, cosy bar and large lounge-cum-restaurant.

KILMARNOCK
Hunting Lodge
14-16 Glencairn Square
11-3, 5-midnight; 11-1am Thu-Sat; 12.30-midnight Sun
Beer range varies Ⓗ
Mock-Tudor, free-standing pub opposite retail park. Large bar area divided into distinct areas for games and dining.

KILWINNING
Dalgarven House Hotel
Dalry Road
12-11 (midnight Wed & Thu; 1am Fri & Sat); 12-midnight Sun
Beer range varies Ⓗ
Small bar in a riverside hotel two miles north of Kilwinning on A737. Next to Dalgarven Mill/Museum. Beer is usually from Houston Brewery.

TROON
Piersland House Hotel
Craigend Road
11-midnight, including Sun
Beer range varies Ⓗ
Quality hotel next to Royal Troon golf course. The bar is wood-panelled with comfy chairs and a log fire. Beer can be expensive.

Renfrewshire
KILBARCHAN
Glenleven Inn
25 New Street
11-11.30 (midnight Fri & Sat); 12.30-11 Sun
Houston Barochan Ⓗ
Traditional village local on a terraced residential street. Pool table at rear with plusher, comfortable area at the front.

KILMACOLM
Pullman Tavern
Lochwinnoch Road
11-11.30 (12.30 Thu-Sat); 11.30-11.30 Sun
Draught Bass Ⓗ
Converted railway building with family restaurant, two real fires and outside drinking area. On Paisley-Greenock cycle track.

PAISLEY
Bull Inn ☆
7 New Street
11-11.30 (midnight Fri & Sat); 12.30-11 Sun
Houston Barochan; Orkney Dark Island; Taylor Landlord; guest beer Ⓗ
Former coaching inn, one-roomed pub and three snugs in rear. Historic feel spoilt by too much bric-à-brac.

> ✳ symbol next to a main entry place name indicates there are Inn Brief entries as well.

festival. The hotel has been owned and run by the Duncan family for 50 years.
🏨Q❀🚲🍴◑P

Ormidale Hotel

Knowe Road (off A841, W end of village)
☼ 12-2.30 (not winter); 4.30-midnight; 12-midnight Sat & Sun
☎ (01770) 302293 website: www.ormidale-hotel.co.uk
Arran Ale, Blonde Ⓐ

Fine sandstone building with a small, friendly bar plus a large conservatory which is a real suntrap. The original tall founts on the boat-shaped bar serve two beers from the nearby Arran Brewery. It was built in the 1850s as a summerhouse for the painter, Herring, and converted to a hotel in 1935 by the present owner's grandparents. It has never stopped selling real ale. In summer a relaxed pint on the sheltered lawns surrounded by an arboretum is a real treat. Discos and folk music at weekends, and quizzes held Tue and Thu. Accommodation available in summer. 🏨Q❀🚲◑ⓒ♣P

Catacol Bay Hotel

☼ 11 (12.30 Sun)-1am
☎ (01770) 830231 website: www.catacol.co.uk
Arran Blonde; Draught Bass Ⓗ

Free-standing, white building nestling among the hills opposite the shore, with grand views across the Kilbrannan Sound to Kintyre. It is adjacent to the Twelve Apostles, a listed terrace of former estate houses. It was originally a manse and has been run by the present owner for 21 years. Ideally situated for walking or climbing, and for lovers of natural history, there is a richness of flora and fauna; glimpses of red deer and golden eagles are not unusual.
🏨❀🚲◑♣P

Marina Inn

110 Harbour Street
☼ 11.45-3, 5.45-midnight (11.45-midnight summer); 11.45-1am Fri & Sat; 12.30-midnight Sun
☎ (01294) 274079
Belhaven St Andrew's Ale Ⓗ

Attractive harbourside lounge bar ideally placed for tourist attractions; next to the Magnum Leisure Centre, the Scottish Maritime Museum, the Big Idea Inventor Centre and the beach park. Irvine was originally the main port for Glasgow and, dating from 1821, this was a lodging inn. The emphasis is on food at lunchtime and early eve. Folk jam sessions are held on Tue eve, and during August's Marymass Festival there is daily folk music. ❀◑≠

Breadalbane Hotel

On loop road through village OS022220
☼ 11-midnight (1am Thu-Sat); 11-midnight Sun
☎ (01770) 820284
Beer range varies Ⓗ

White-painted hotel near the shore at the southern end of the island. Spectacular views, especially from the front sun lounge, to Pladda and its lighthouse, Ailsa Craig, and, on clear days, south Ayrshire and Loch Ryan. The main bar has a large stone

fireplace, a corner bar and a pool table. Ales are usually from Arran and Houston breweries, and food is served all day. En-suite rooms and self-catering flats available. The hotel is named after a sailing ship which sank in the Northwest Passage. Seal spotting possible on nearby beaches. Closed first two weeks in January. Q❀🚲◑♣P

Wheatsheaf

Unit 5, Portland Gate
☼ 11-midnight (1am Thu-Sat); 12.30-midnight Sun
☎ (01563) 572483
Caledonian 80/-; Courage Directors; Theakston Best Bitter; guest beers Ⓗ

Unusually for a Wetherspoon's pub this is largely a new building, although the shell of the original Wheatsheaf Inn can be seen outside at the rear. The interior is modern with Robert Burns connections and local history displayed on the walls. Children are allowed in the rear area until 6pm. Tends to be busy Thu-Sat eves. The pub is close to both railway and bus stations and lies at the north end of the main shopping street in a new development. Q❀◑🚲♿≠⚲●

Weston Tavern

27 Main Street (A735, at the cross)
☼ 11 (12.30 Sun)-midnight
☎ (01563) 538805
Beer range varies Ⓗ

Historic pub with a chequered history, having been a school, a manse and a blacksmith's; part of the latter can still be seen at the rear. The public bar has craggy stonework and an original tiled floor which is a listed feature. There is usually beer from the Houston Brewery. Outside the pub is the landmark 'Jougs' where criminals used to be shackled and, sometimes, hanged. The rear lounge is used by various clubs. ⓒ≠♣

Clachan

14 Bath Street (B7025, off Main Street)
☼ 11-midnight (1am Thu-Sat); 12.30-midnight Sun
☎ (01475) 672224
Beer range varies Ⓗ

Single-bar, town-centre pub normally featuring Belhaven ales, and also a good selection of whiskies. Hosts live music on Fri eve and a quiz on Mon eve. The back door leads to the seafront opposite the pier, from where the Cumbrae car ferry leaves; the paddle-steamer 'Waverley' also calls in summer. Largs is one of the main 'Costa Clyde' resorts and boasts two good golf courses and the Vikingar Centre. ♿≠

Lochranza Hotel

☼ 11 (5 winter)-1am; 11.30-1am Sun
☎ (01770) 830223 website: www.lochranza.co.uk
Arran Ale; guest beers Ⓗ

Traditional hotel located in a very tranquil village with spectacular views to Lochranza Castle and across the sea loch. The bar comprises two interconnecting rooms and stocks over 100 single malt whiskies. The front of the hotel has a large, grassed area

with tables, an ideal place to watch the varied local wildlife, including red deer, seals and golden eagles. There are plenty of good walks in the area, and the hotel is handy for the summer car ferry to Kintyre.
🏨🐕🍴♿🌳▲♣✁

SALTCOATS

Salt Cot
7 Hamilton Street
❂ 11-midnight (1am Thu-Sat); 12.30-midnight Sun
☎ (01294) 465924
Courage Directors; Theakston Best Bitter, Old Peculier; guest beers Ⓗ

Attractive conversion of a former cinema by Wetherspoon's. The cinema opened in 1913 and featured live entertainment and films. Built by premier showman, GH Kemp, it was managed by his son, Harry, and was famous throughout Scotland. The pub is decorated with photos of the cinema in its heyday, old Saltcoats and the Kemp family entertainments. Children are welcome in one area and there is a family menu. The pub's name comes from the original cottages at the salt pans. Q❂♿≈✁●

STEVENSTON

Champion Shell Inn
5 Schoolwell Street (off A738)
❂ 11-midnight (1am Thu-Sat); 12.30-midnight Sun
☎ (01294) 463055
Beer range varies Ⓗ

This old pub is a listed building – the oldest inhabited building in the 'Three Towns'. The attractive lounge bar has one stone-clad wall featuring a large fireplace and there is a small separate dining room. The bar can get smoky despite good ventilation. In the 18th century the building was inhabited by monks and was a popular stop-off point for travellers, providing food, shelter, entertainment and stables. The pub's name derives from a contest for drinking from a carved pect/shell goblet (an old-fashioned yard of ale contest). ❂♿♣

TROON ❉

Ardneil Hotel
51 St Meddans Street
❂ 11-12.30am; 12-midnight Sun
☎ (01292) 311611
Draught Bass; guest beers Ⓗ

Popular hotel adjacent to Troon railway station, with a bar that attracts all generations, locals and tourists alike. It has two restaurant areas and a cocktail bar, while the main bar includes a lower level pool and darts area. The guest ales usually come from the local Arran and Houston breweries. The bar hosts a popular Wed eve quiz. Troon is famous for golf – the main public courses are close to the hotel
🌯🛏❂≈♣✁

Dan McKay's Ale House
69 Portland Street (A759)
❂ 11-12.30am; 12.30-midnight Sun
☎ (01292) 311079
Beer range varies Ⓗ

Comfortable, one-roomed town-centre lounge bar with three real ales in the winter months and four the rest of the year; one is

always from the Caledonian Brewery range. The pub hosts occasional live music on Sun and a pub quiz on Thu. A display of pump clips and beer mats shows the variety of ales sold over the years. A rare Lorimer & Clark print hangs on the wall. The number of foreign bottled beers has increased recently. There is a 'happy hour' between 5–7 Mon–Fri eves. 🌯❂≈

Dunbartonshire

BALLOCH

Balloch Hotel
Balloch Road
❂ 11-midnight (1am Fri & Sat); 11-midnight Sun
☎ (01389) 752579
Beer range varies Ⓗ

150-year-old white building on the banks of Loch Lomond across the bridge from Balloch rail station. The large, rectangular, utilitarian lounge has tartan carpets and curtains, a long counter with ales and dining tables. There is also a formal restaurant and a comfortable lounge. Ale can be ordered at 5p cheaper in the rear bar, which has a pool table and TV, but no view to the loch. On sunny days the outside tables with parasols offer views of the grassy banks, boats and people feeding swans and ducks. Popular with locals, tourists, walkers and waterfowl. Four real ales normally available.
🌯🛏❂♿▲≈♣P

CASTLECARY

Castlecary House Hotel
Main Street
❂ 11-11 (11.30 Thu-Sat); 12.30-11 Sun
☎ (01324) 840233
Draught Bass; Stones Bitter; guest beers Ⓗ

Private hotel, in a village on the site of one of the major forts on the Antonine Wall. It has three distinct drinking areas (most real ales are served in the Castle Lounge). The main bar, known as the Poachers, has a central stone fireplace with a roaring real fire in winter. The guest beer list often features beers from the Belhaven and Caledonian ranges. A large extension has recently been completed providing a new lounge bar and restaurant; the high teas are highly recommended.
🌯🛏❂◻P

MILNGAVIE

Talbot Arms
30 Main Street
❂ 11-11 (midnight Thu & Fri; 11.45 Sat); 12.30-11 Sun
☎ (0141) 955 0981
Draught Bass; Caledonian Deuchars IPA; guest beers Ⓗ

Recently renovated Bass-owned former Festival Ale House located in the pedestrianised centre of a small commuter town on the edge of Glasgow at the southern end of the West Highland Way footpath. The single, large bar is divided by stained glass partitions, one half being carpeted and lounge-style and the other fitted out with wooden floorboards, old brewery pictures and a pool table. There are usually two or three guest ales available.
❂♿≈

MILTON OF CAMPSIE

Kincaid House Hotel
Birdston Road (off B757, at end of long drive)
🕐 12-midnight (1am Fri; 11.45 Sat);
12.30-midnight Sun
☎ (0141) 776 2226 website: www.kincaidhouse.com
Taylor Landlord; guest beer Ⓗ
This bar lies behind the impressive pale stone castle-like hotel. Inside are dark wooden tables, beams and trellis dividers separating the lounge with an imitation (gas) fireplace, horse brasses and upholstered furniture, left of the long bar. There is a fine Alloa Brewery mirror. A pool table occupies the other end of the room. Ale and food can be ordered in the garden and large conservatory/diner, best accessed via a rear door opened on fine days.
🏨🅰️🛏️🍴◑🚻♿🅿️

OLD KILPATRICK

Ettrick
159 Dumbarton Road
🕐 11-11.45 (12.45am Fri & Sat); 12.30-11.45 Sun
☎ (01389) 872821 website: www.theettrick.com
Caledonian Deuchars IPA Ⓗ
Late Victorian village local named after James Hogg, the Ettrick shepherd, a friend of Sir Walter Scott. The lively public bar, where the handpump is located, has a mainly nautical theme, as might be expected being so close to the River Clyde and the newly reopened Forth and Clyde Canal. Televised sporting events are shown and there are quiz nights on Fri and Sun, Karaoke on Thu and live bands on Sat afternoon or eve. The lounge is a bright, modern café-style bar with minimalist decor and CD music. Smoking is not permitted while food is served. 🅰️◑🚉 (Kilpatrick) 🅿️✂

Glasgow

GLASGOW

1901 Bar & Bistro
1534 Pollokshaws Road, Shawlands (Haggs Rd jct)
🕐 11.30-11 (midnight Fri & Sat); 12.30-midnight Sun
☎ (0141) 632 0161
Caledonian Deuchars IPA; guest beers Ⓗ
Situated on the ground floor of one of the first red, sandstone tenement blocks to be built in the area. Originally called the Old Swan Inn, it was opened by Sir John Stirling Maxwell and the provost of Pollokshaws in 1901. The wooden floored bar area provides ample seating and standing room, while the old lounge bar has been converted into a bistro with a food and wine list to match. The house beer, 1901 Swan Ale, is from the Houston Brewery and a good selection of bottled German Weiss beers is also available. Children are welcome until 8pm.
◑🚉♿ (Shawlands/Pollokshaws W) 🍴

Allison Arms
720 Pollokshaws Road
🕐 11-11 (midnight Fri & Sat); 12.30-11 Sun
☎ (0141) 423 1661
Belhaven 80/-; Ⓗ **guest beers** Ⓗ/Ⓟ
Southside suburban local public bar alongside a recently renovated lounge bar. Open-plan, the two sit side by side without destroying the traditional feel of the public

bar with its large solid gantry incorporating an old brewery mirror and original guttering round the foot of the bar. As well as four guest ales, one on handpump and three on tall fount supplied by electric pump, there is a large selection of foreign (especially German) bottled beers and draught Hoegaarden.
🚉(Queen's Pk) ♣

Babbity Bowster
16-18 Blackfriars Street, Merchant City (between Albion St and High St)
🕐 11 (12.30 Sun)-midnight
☎ (0141) 552 5055 website: www.babbity.com
Caledonian Deuchars IPA, 80/-; Houston St Peter's Well; guest beer Ⓟ
Hotel? Pub? Café-Bar? The unique, light, simple decor in this 18th-century building, named after a dance of the time, defies categories. Away from roads, the only sounds are conversation and quiet Sat folk sessions. In winter, the peat fire has the aroma and warmth of an Islay malt. In summer, the patio has barbecues and a movable canvas roof. Over the window boxes, pétanque can be watched. The good bar food reflects the high-quality restaurant upstairs, with the emphasis on Scottish fare. Frequented by local residents, city and media professionals and academics, it is excellent for visitors. 🏨Q🅰️🛏️◑🚉(High St) 🚇(Buchanan St) ♣🍴🅿️

Blackfriars
36 Bell Street, Merchant City (corner of Bell St and Albion St)
🕐 12 (12.30 Sun)-midnight
☎ (0141) 552 5924 e-mail: blackfriars2000@aol.com
Ind Coope Burton Ale; Tetley Bitter; guest beers Ⓗ
Split-level, corner, metropolitan bar. The cosy main area has subdued lighting, fine, large, brass-framed wall mirrors and free live jazz Sat and Sun eves. The raised corner café-bar area has windows on to Merchant City life. Candles are placed on tables in both areas in the eve. The downstairs venue has a weekly comedy club and jazz concerts. The range of three guest beers usually includes a Houston brew, the other two from Scottish micros, plus a good selection of bottled and draught foreign beers. Food served all day until 11pm.
◑🚉(High St/Argyle St) 🚇(Buchanan St) 🍴

Clockwork Beer Co.
1153-1155 Cathcart Road (King's Park Road jct)
🕐 11-midnight (11 Mon; 11.30 Tue); 11-11 Sun
☎ (0141) 649 0184
Caledonian Deuchars IPA, 80/-; guest beers Ⓟ
Open-plan, modern bar not far from Hampden Park, Scotland's national football stadium. It was completely rebuilt in 1997 to include a brewery (visible behind plate glass windows opposite the bar). A spiral staircase leads to a mezzanine level where live music and quiz nights are held. An extensive range of drinks include German and Belgian bottled beers, draught Belgian and Czech beers and their own ales, including fruit beers, brewed on-site, are available. Children's certificate.
🛏️◑♿🚉(Mt Florida) 🍴🅿️✂📺

Hogshead
14-16 West George Street
🕐 11 (12.30 Sun)-12

☎ (0141) 353 6082
Boddingtons Bitter; guest beers Ⓗ
Two-storied Hogshead offering contrasting decor. Downstairs is all light pine, betraying its origin as a coffee bar while upstairs is the more traditional Hogshead mock-Tudor. Cider is only available in the upstairs bar which is closed Sun–Tue. Despite the steep stairs, wheelchair access is available to all parts via ramp and lift. The pub is conveniently located, immediately outside Queen Street Station and right next to George Square, in the heart of the city. Religiously offers drinkers 'try before you buy' samples of all real ales.
◖◗ ♿ ≎ (Queen St/Central) ⊖ (Buchanan St) ♣

Lismore
206 Dumbarton Road
☼ 11-11 (midnight Fri & Sat); 12.30-11 Sun
☎ (0141) 576 0103
Arran Dark; Caledonian Deuchars IPA; guest beer Ⓗ
Extensively and expensively refurbished five years ago, the Lismore features a Scottish baronial interior with superb art deco lamps. It was designed in part by the owner, Colin Beattie. The leaded glass windows are of a quality that harks back to a bygone age and were designed by local artists, Joe Boyle and Yvonne Smith. Local craftsmen were involved throughout. Folk music sessions at least four nights a week and over 100 whiskies are offered. An unusual feature in the gents' toilet is that each urinal is dedicated to one of the villains of the Highland clearances.
Q ❀ ◖◗ ♿ ≎ (Partick) ⊖ (Kelvin Hall)

Mitre Bar
12 Brunswick Street, Merchant City (off Trongate)
☼ 11-midnight; 12.30-8 Sun
☎ (0141) 552 3764
Belhaven 60/-; guest beers Ⓗ
Possibly Glasgow's smallest bar, it is hidden in a passageway and has a Victorian mini-horseshoe bar, glass snob screens and gantry; unchanged since 1866. A regulars' pub with a football theme, displaying a 'Belhaven Bill' brewery mirror, old photographs of players and teams, and scarves from around the world. Good selection of bottled and draught foreign beers enhances the international flavour. An oasis providing an alternative to standardised pub chains, where shoppers escaping busy Trongate and city workers can come for a pint of scarce 60/- and an inexpensive lunch. TV for sports and regular darts nights.
◖≎ (Argyle St) ⊖ (Buchanan St) ♣

Station Bar
55 Port Dundas Road
☼ 11 (12.30 Sun)-midnight
☎ (0141) 332 3117
Caledonian Deuchars IPA; guest beers Ⓗ
Superb city-centre local just north of Glasgow's two rail termini and 200 yards from Buchanan bus station, it takes its name from the now-demolished Buchanan Street railway station. It is the last survivor in an area which once accommodated many small pubs. The gantry includes a glass frieze celebrating local trades such as the police, fire brigade, civil service, press and universities, that provide much of the

varied clientele. Close to Glasgow Royal Concert Hall you will often find dozens of drinkers in full evening dress downing pints. Don't worry, it is just the orchestra between movements.
◖⊞≎ (Queen St) ⊖ (Cowcaddens) ♣

Stravaigin
28 Gibson Street
☼ 11-11 (midnight Fri & Sat); 12.30-11 Sun
☎ (0141) 334 2665 website: www.stravaigin.com
Caledonian Deuchars IPA, 80/- Ⓗ
'Think global, eat local' is the motto of the pub. It lives up to this by providing a bar menu of varying dishes from around the world, plus Scottish fare, in a down-to-earth atmosphere. The pub is quite small and often busy, needing the ingenious extra seating area above the bar. Furnishing is spartan with wooden seats and tables and the unobtrusive decorations have a maritime flavour to complement the seafood dishes. A larger restaurant downstairs provides extra seating and a more extensive menu.
Q ◖◗ ⊖ (Kelvinbridge) ● ●

Tennents
191 Byres Road
☼ 11-11 (midnight Fri & Sat); 12.30-11 Sun
☎ (0141) 341 1021
Broughton Old Jock; Caledonian Deuchars IPA; Fuller's London Pride; Orkney Dark Island; Taylor Landlord; Tomintoul Wild Cat; guest beers Ⓗ
Large, Victorian pub situated at the heart of the west end of the city. The high ceiling still has the original cornice work around the pillars and beams. A U-shaped bar provides space to stand and be served. Seating is arranged around the dark wood-panelled walls which are adorned with old photographs and pictures. A total of nine permanent and three guest beers are available. Eve meals served until 9pm.
◖◗ ♿ ⊖ (Hillhead) ●

Three Judges
141 Dumbarton Road (Byres Road jct)
☼ 11-11 (midnight Fri ; 11.45 Sat); 12.30-11 Sun
☎ (0141) 337 3055
Beer range varies Ⓗ
Traditional west-end tenement corner local. An oasis of good old-fashioned Glasgow friendliness at the southern end of trendy Byres Road. The pub name refers to the three judges in a boxing bout, a legacy of its earlier days as a boxing theme pub. There are nine handpumps which have served over 2,000 different British beers, plus, on occasion, an additional fount supplied by a restored Albany water engine. The pub and its licensee have been frequent winners of local CAMRA awards during the last 10 years. Live trad jazz every second Sun.
≎ (Partick) ⊖ (Kelvin Hall)

Windsor Tavern
471 Dumbarton Road
☼ 11-11 (midnight Fri & Sat); 12.30-11 Sun
☎ (0141) 569 1011
Belhaven 80/- Ⓗ
The Windsor Tavern is a lively and friendly Partick institution and very much a community pub. It is one of the very few tenancies in Scotland exercising its right under the beer orders to offer a beer not from the owning brewery's range, in this

case Belhaven 80/- which is, these days, a rare beer in Glasgow. The landlord took a leading role in a successful campaign which denied a megapub chain its intention to disrupt an area currently well-served by long-established local pubs.
&≈(Partick)⊖♣

Lanarkshire

AIRDRIE

Cellar Bar
79 Stirling Street
○ 11 (12.30 Sun)-12.15am
☎ (01236) 764495
Beer range varies Ⓗ
Small pub with a single bar split into two levels and a pleasant beer garden at the back. The present owners took it over in 1998 and have maintained the previous high standards. It sells 340 malt whiskies and there are regular whisky-tasting nights each month. Folk music held on Mon. The pub also celebrates annual events such as Burns' Night and St Patrick's Day. ❀≈♣

AULDHOUSE

Auldhouse Arms
6 Langlands Road
○ 12.30-11 (midnight Thu-Sat); 12.30-11 Sun
☎ (01355) 263242
Belhaven 80/- Ⓗ
Excellent example of an unspoilt village pub. The small public bar has remained unchanged for decades, with varnished wooden beer barrels, copper kettles and jugs behind the wooden gantry. Old plates, mirrors and photographs give the bar the look and feel of times gone by. Both snugs off the bar have real log fires. Mon is quiz night and a local folk band play on Tue. The lounge bar only opens at weekends, and the lack of public transport requires a visit by car. ▲Q🛏🍴P

BIGGAR

Crown Hotel
109 High Street
○ 11 (12.30 Sun)-1am
☎ (01899) 220116
Beer range varies Ⓗ
16th-century coaching inn in the centre of an attractive Borders village. The stone walls are adorned with pictures and artefacts of old Biggar and blend in well with the fireplace at the lounge end of the single, large room. The two handpumps serve beers from Belhaven or their guest list. Popular with locals so can get very busy. ▲Q❀◖▲

COATBRIDGE

St Andrews
37-38 Sunnyside Road (between Sunnyside railway station and town centre)
○ 11-midnight; 11-5, 8-midnight Sun
☎ (01236) 423773
Beer range varies Ⓗ
Small, wood-panelled public bar with an even smaller snug. Two original Fowlers adverts, a 1910 local map and other pictures decorate the bar. The pub, which is over 100 years old, was formerly called the Saloon Bar. The present owners took over in 1998 and subsequently changed the name. It has undergone restoration several times, in the 1930s art deco features were added and again in the 1960s when the main legacy was Formica. In time this will be replaced with mahogany. Large selection of malt whiskies available.
≈(Coatbridge Sunnyside/Central)♣

HAMILTON

George
18 Campbell Street
○ 11 midnight (1am Fri & Sat); 12.30-midnight Sun
☎ (01698) 424225
Beer range varies Ⓗ
This family-run pub is a frequent winner, and the current holder, of CAMRA's Lanarkshire *Pub of the Year* award. Once known as the Thistle, it is located in the Old Town. The present owners took it over in 1991 and immediately restored its reputation as a first-class local after a couple of years in the doldrums. Very popular so tends to be extremely busy on Fri eve. Camping available at Strathclyde Park.
◖▲≈(Central)🍴●

LANARK

Horse & Jockey
56 High Street
○ 11-1am (11.45 Sat); 12.30-11 Sun
☎ (01555) 664825
Beer range varies Ⓗ
Public bar, with a lounge/diner at the rear, on the main street of this historic market town. A pub has stood on this site since 1740. It received an award from CAMRA's Scottish Pubs Group in 1999 in appreciation of a fine refurbishment. Although there are two handpumps at the bar, only one is usually on in winter. The pub name and some of the decor recalls the town's connection with the sport of kings, though the nearby racecourse is now disused. ◖◗≈

STRATHAVEN

Weavers
3 Green Street
○ 12 (4.30 Tue-Thu)-midnight; 12-1am Fri & Sat; 7-1am Sun
☎ (01357) 522648 website: www.strathaven.com
Beer range varies Ⓗ
Listed building in the centre of this attractive, small town. Formerly the Crown Hotel, it was reopened as the Weavers in 1980. The wood panelling came from the beams that originally supported the Crown's roof. The bar is decorated with pictures of Hollywood stars ranging from the unmistakable (Marilyn Monroe, Laurel and Hardy) to some that the pub's owner cannot identify. A range of Belgian bottled beers is sold. The licensee likes to support local micros but the customers seem to prefer the standard guest beers found all over the country. Q🍴🍴

UDDINGSTON

Rowan Tree ☆
60 Old Mill Road (next to Tunnocks bakery)
○ 11 (12.30 Sun)-11.45
☎ (01698) 812678
Beer range varies Ⓗ

Grade B listed building with superb wood-panelled interior, two fireplaces and some fine, rare mirrors (including one from Whitelaws Brewery). Reputedly the oldest pub in Lanarkshire, possibly a former staging inn, it has a genuine olde-worlde feel that no modern fake could ever emulate. Since the present owners bought it from Maclay's in 1998, it has concentrated on selling beers from local micros although the actual beer range at any time is customer-driven.
ⓂⒺ◑⊑P

WISHAW

Wishaw Malt
62-66 Kirk Road
⊙ 11 (12.30 Sun)-midnight
☎ (01698) 358806
Caledonian Deuchars 80/-; guest beers Ⓗ
Former furniture store, Wetherspoon's opened it as a pub in October 1999 and overnight Wishaw was changed from one of the country's most dismal beer deserts into a town worth drinking in. The bar is a large, single room but is sectioned in such a way as to give each area of the pub its own distinct feel. Decorated with pictures reflecting local history including Keir Hardie, the Lanarkshire man who managed the curious feat of being both leader of the Labour Party and a socialist. Usually at least one beer from a Scottish micro-brewery among the guests.
Q❀◑Ⓖⓐ≠⅄●

Renfrewshire

BARRHEAD

Waterside Inn
Glasgow Road, The Hurlet
⊙ 11-11 (midnight Fri; 1am Sat); 12.30-11 Sun
☎ (0141) 881 2822
Beer range varies Ⓗ
Popular establishmen among families with young children, even well into the eve. Pleasant outside drinking area in the summer with tables and umbrellas. Relax in easy chairs round a real fire in winter. Choice of two beers usually sees one national brand and one Scottish independent. Food in the restaurant is excellent, driven more by what is freshly available locally than a set menu. Theme nights held: St Valentine's, Easter, etc. More of a drinking area attached to a restaurant than a pub in its own right.
Ⓜ❀◑ⒶⓅP

EAGLESHAM

Cross Keys
1 Montgomery Street
⊙ 11-midnight; 12.30-11 Sun
☎ (013553) 302356 e-mail: pepper.pot@barbox.net
Beer range varies Ⓗ
Scottish independent breweries provide the beer range served in the comfortable lounge. The adjacent bar has no handpumps but beer is served from the lounge which features a gantry with exceptional whisky collection, some fine prints of rural life on the walls, sherry casks on shelves by the windows and historical artefacts such as the constitution for the local farmers' society. Food served in the

lounge is both varied and of a high quality. Upstairs restaurant focuses on fresh, Scottish fare. First Fri of the month sees live entertainment/Karaoke until 1am in the lounge. ◑⅄⊑

GOUROCK

Spinnaker Hotel
121 Albert Road
⊙ 11-11.45 (midnight Thu; 1am Fri & Sat); 12.30-11.45 Sun
☎ (01475) 633107 website: www.spinnakerhotel.co.uk
Beer range varies Ⓗ
Regular *Guide* entry; the two handpumps dispense guest ales that change frequently. Bar meals are good and typical of this type of establishment. Splendid views over the Firth of Clyde towards the Holy Loch and Loch Long. Enjoy a drink while you watch the Gourock to Dunoon car ferry crossing in front of the pub on its 20-minute voyage. The Spinnaker Hotel has eight bedrooms and is an ideal base for exploring the area.
Q❀⇔◑

GREENOCK

James Watt
80-92 Cathcart Street
⊙ 11-11 (midnight Thu; 1am Fri & Sat); 12.30-11 Sun
☎ (01475) 722640
Caledonian 80/-; Courage Directors; Theakston Best Bitter; guest beers Ⓗ
Large Wetherspoon's free house built into the former Post Office. The pub is named after one of Greenock's famous sons, James Watt. This pub is a welcome sight in a large beer desert. The beer range varies frequently. The food is good, standard Wetherspoon's fare. Greenock used to be the home of shipbuilding. The yards are all closed now and the whole riverside area has been redeveloped. Q◑≠ (Central) ⅄●

HOUSTON

Fox & Hounds
South Street
⊙ 11-midnight (1am Fri & Sat); 12.30-midnight Sun
☎ (01505) 612448
Houston Killellan, Barochan, Peter's Well, Teuchter; seasonal beers; guest beers Ⓗ
The Houston Brewery is attached to this country pub and their beers are served in all three bars. The Fox & Vixen bar is comfortable and quiet with five handpumps dispensing four Houston beers and one guest. A bar menu is available. The livelier Stables bar has a large-screen TV, pool table, juke box and pinball machine. Upstairs, the Huntsman lounge is used for bar meals and as a waiting area for the first-class restaurant. Former local CAMRA *Pub of the Year* and highly commended in the Scottish *Pub of the Year* competition. Food is available all day at weekends. Q◑⊑P

INVERKIP

Inverkip Hotel
Main Street
⊙ 11-2.30, 5-11 including Sun
☎ (01475) 521478 website: www.inverkip.co.uk
Belhaven St Andrew's Ale; guest beer Ⓗ
Old-fashioned hotel in the unspoilt village of Inverkip on the Clyde coast. The hotel is

situated between two car ferry terminals: a few miles to the west is Wemyss Bay where the ferry for the island of Bute leaves and a few miles to the east, past the impressive Cloch lighthouse, is McInroy's Point, where a ferry leaves for Dunoon. Real ale is sold in the lounge only. St Andrew's is standard and the other pump serves a frequently changing guest.
Q ⇔ ◑ ⇌ P

JOHNSTONE

Coanes
26 High Street
✪ 11-11.30 (1am Fri; 11.45 Sat); 6.30-11.30 Sun
☎ (01505) 322924
Boddingtons Bitter; Caledonian Deuchars IPA, 80/-; Houston Barochan; Orkney Dark Island; guest beers Ⓗ
Lounge and bar housed in a townhouse-style building where the doors open straight on to the main street. Up to five guest beers are served in the bar which has the feel of a great 'wee' local with fake beams and bric-à-brac. The lounge is more spacious and popular with coffee-drinking shoppers on Sat afternoons. There is a comfortable eating area with full menu. The layout means drinkers are spared food odours and diners afforded a degree of privacy.
◑ ⊟ ⇌ ●

KILBARCHAN ✣

Trust Inn
8 Low Barholm
✪ 11-11.30 (midnight Fri & Sat); 12.30-11 Sun
☎ (01505) 702401
Caledonian Deuchars IPA; Ind Coope Burton Ale Ⓗ
Lounge bar with low-beamed ceiling, intimate recesses and decorative brasses. Situated in a conservation village steeped in weaving heritage where single-storey, Tudor-style architecture predominates. The weaver's cottage is nearby as is the Glasgow–Irvine cycle path. A large TV projection screen can dominate the premises during big football and rugby matches. When folded away, the pub's quiet, village local character is restored. At one stage in the building's history it was run by the Temperance Society when nothing stronger than tea was on offer. Varied menu served (snacks only Sun).
◑ ⇌ (Milliken Pk)

LOCHWINNOCH

Brown Bull
33 Main Street (Largs Road, off A737)
✪ 12-11 (midnight Fri; 11.45 Sat); 12.30-11 Sun
☎ (01505) 843250
Belhaven Sandy Hunter's Traditional Ale; Caledonian 80/-; Orkney Dark Island; guest beers Ⓗ
Unspoilt, classic country pub where low ceilings, a real fire and friendly staff make for a welcoming atmosphere. There is a fruit machine and audio speakers, but their positioning is so unobtrusive that you could have stepped back to the 1930s. Hop bines adorn the gantry, paintings by local artists depicting farming and rural scenes are featured and a vast 72-gallon barrel serves as a drinking table. Quizzes and folk music eves are popular. The upstairs restaurant has a growing reputation and Castle Semple Nature Reserve is nearby. 🛏Q 🍴 ৬ ⇌

PAISLEY ✣

Gabriel's
33 Gauze Street (Silk St jct)
✪ 11-midnight (1am Fri & Sat); 12.30-midnight Sun
☎ (0141) 887 8204
Caledonian Deuchars IPA; Ind Coope Burton Ale; guest beers Ⓗ
Comfortable town-centre pub with an oval-shaped bar and a raised dining area. Its annual spring beer festival is now in its seventh year. Food served daily except Sun eve. Children's certificate. Well-attended quiz is held each Tue eve at 9pm.
◑ ৬ ⇌ (Gilmour St)

Hogshead
45 High Street
✪ 11-midnight (1am Fri & Sat); 12.30-midnight Sun
☎ (0141) 840 4150
Boddingtons Bitter; Caledonian 80/- Ⓗ
This town-centre lounge is comfortable and open-plan with a raised dining area. Meals are popular all day. The lounge is spacious and attracts customers of all ages during the week, and mainly students at weekends. There is always one beer from Houston available. ◑ ৬ ⇌ (Gilmour St) ⊬

Last Post
2 County Square (outside main entrance of railway station)
✪ 11-midnight (1am Fri & Sat); 12.30-11.30 Sun
☎ (0141) 848 0353
Caledonian 80/-; Courage Directors; Theakston Best Bitter; guest beers Ⓗ
Typical Wetherspoon's conversion of the old Post Office. There is a split-level drinking area (no bar on upper level). Watch out for the steep stairs. The wheelchair access is from the station entrance of the building. Service can be slow when the local football team play.
Q ◑ ৬ ⇌ (Gilmour St) ⊬ ●

Wee Howff
53 High Street
✪ 11-11 (11.30 Wed & Thu; 12.30am Fri; 11.45 Sat); closed Sun
☎ (0141) 889 2095
Caledonian Deuchars IPA; Ind Coope Burton Ale; guest beers Ⓗ
Small town-centre pub near the University. It has a warm and friendly atmosphere. Guest beers are usually from the Arran and Houston breweries. The pub used to be called the Market Bar. The landlord was the first Burton *Master Cellarman* in Scotland.
⇌ (Gilmour St)

UPLAWMOOR

Uplawmoor Hotel
66 Neilston Road (off A736, Barrhead-Irvine Road)
✪ 12-2.30, 5-11 (midnight Fri & Sat); 12-midnight Sun
☎ (01505) 850565
Beer range varies Ⓗ
Patronised by locals and visitors to the quality restaurant. The choice of three beers has one Houston ale alternating with two others. Beer is served in a large, spacious lounge where basic pub grub and a juke box (featuring soft rock compilations) create a relaxed atmosphere. This is in contrast to the more sophisticated cocktail bar. Acclaimed restaurant with a large central open fire form a focal point. 🍴⇔◑ ৬ P

TAYSIDE

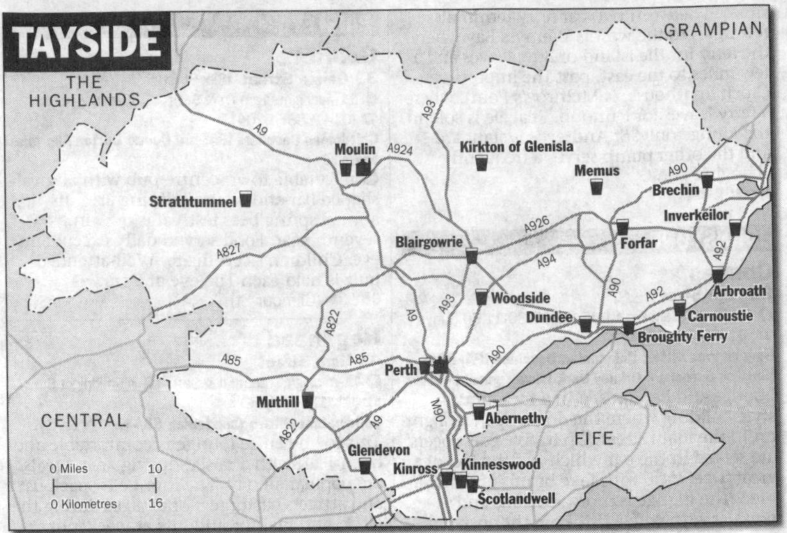
TAYSIDE
THE HIGHLANDS
GRAMPIAN
Moulin
A924
Kirkton of Glenisla
Memus
Brechin
A90
Strathtummel
A9
Inverkeilor
A926
Blairgowrie
Forfar
A92
A94
A827
Woodside
Arbroath
Dundee
Carnoustie
Broughty Ferry
A822
A93
A85
Perth
Muthill
Abernethy
CENTRAL
FIFE
M90
Glendevon
Kinross
Kinnesswood
Scotlandwell
0 Miles 10
0 Kilometres 16

Authority areas covered: Angus UA, City of Dundee UA, Perth & Kinross UA

ABERNETHY

Cree's Inn

Main Street

⏲ 11-2.30, 5-11; 11-11 Sat; 12.30-11 Sun

☎ (01738) 850714

Beer range varies Ⓗ

Located in what was the ancient Pictish capital of Scotland, lying in the shadow of a 12th-century round tower, this former farmhouse is now a homely village pub. Recent renovations have extended the lounge bar area that boasts a mix of natural stone and oak beams. The former snug has been converted into a restaurant area. A varied menu, based on fresh local produce, complements the choice of up to four real ales which frequently change – usually two are Scottish, and the locals' favourite is Marston's Pedigree.

♨Q⇔◑P⊬

ARBROATH ❊

Lochlands Bar

14 Lochland Street

⏲ 11-11; (12.30am Fri & Sat); 12.30-11.30 Sun

☎ (01241) 873286

Beer range varies Ⓗ

Classic, street-corner local with strong sporting associations; the large public bar displays a case of trophies, and the large TV set dominates when football matches are on. If you are not a fan, do not despair – peace can be found in the small lounge where ale orders are brought through from the bar, which usually has two or three cask beers on tap. Five or ten minutes' walk takes you to both rail and bus stations.

⊟⇌♣

BLAIRGOWRIE

Ericht Alehouse

13 Wellmeadow

⏲ 11-11 (11.45 Fri & Sat); 12.30-11 Sun

☎ (01250) 872649

Beer range varies Ⓗ

Traditional, friendly town-centre pub (established 1802) run by an enthusiastic landlord. It is full of local character. A large single-roomed pub, its two seating areas are split by a small, well-stocked bar, with an ever-changing range of beers from all over Britain. As well as up to six ales on tap, it offers Addlestone's draught cider and Hoegaarden from Belgium. Occasional live music is performed at weekends.

Q⊟●⊽

Rosemount Golf Hotel

Golf Course Road

⏲ 11-11 (11.45 Fri & Sat); 12-11 Sun

☎ (01250) 872604

Caledonian Deuchars IPA; guest beer Ⓗ

Friendly traditional hotel where a comfortable lounge is warmed by an open fire. An unusual array of golf club tags hangs above the bar. Very close to the golf course, as its name suggests, makes it an ideal base for golfers, but also for walkers. It also enjoys a good local following. Meals are served in a designated restaurant area.

♨❀⇔◑♿P⊽

BROUGHTY FERRY ❊

Fisherman's Tavern

10-12 Fort Street (beside lifeboat station)

⏲ 11-midnight (1am Fri & Sat); 12.30-midnight Sun

☎ (01382) 775941

website: www.fishermans-tavern-hotel.co.uk

Belhaven St Andrew's Ale; Boddingtons Bitter; guest beers Ⓗ

Situated in a row of terraced ex-fishermen's houses, this pub has been in every *Guide* since 1975, and has won numerous awards. Ale is kept in the public bar, but is readily available in the no-smoking side, and rear lounges. Now much extended, changes are generally in keeping with the low-ceilinged public bar. It was one of only two or three pubs in Scotland to continuously employ handpump dispense, as opposed to air pressure, during the Scottish real ale revival.

♨Q❧❀⇔◑⊟⇌(limited service)♣⊬

CARNOUSTIE

Stag's Head Inn
61 Dundee Street
☼ 11-11 (midnight Fri; 1am Sat); 12.30-11 Sun
☎ (01241) 858777
Beer range varies Ⓗ

Large bar and lounge/function room in a totally renovated building, to the west of the town centre. Popular with locals and visiting golfers, it sometimes hosts live music and Karaoke. Note the tribute in the corridor, in the form of portrait and plaque, to comedian/actor Billy Connolly who drank here in his youth while on TA exercises at Barry Buddon army range. Three or four ales are normally stocked. ✿P

DUNDEE ❄

Drouthy Neebors
142 Perth Road (opp. Art College)
☼ 11 (12.30 Sun)-midnight
☎ (01382) 322392
Belhaven 80/-, Caledonian Deuchars IPA; guest beer Ⓗ

Scottish theme pub courtesy of Belhaven. Once a car showroom, this hostelry began life as a shrine to Dundee's anti-poet William McGonagall, but now celebrates Scotland's real bard, Robert Burns. The split-level bar features much dark wood, and quotes from Rabbie's works. The name comes from the famous *Tam o' Shanter*, itself a glorification of the inn, where 'drouthy' (thirsty) neighbours enjoy good fellowship and foaming pints ('reaming swats') of ale. The basement bar often stages live music. ◖▯≢

Hogshead
7-9 Union Street (opp. city churches)
☼ 11 (12.30 Sun)-midnight
☎ (01382) 205039
Boddingtons Bitter; guest beers Ⓗ

Usual Hogshead ale house decor, with memorabilia, hops and pictures hung around, but on a more intimate level than most, with a low ceiling and several booths and alcoves. These make it a popular place to meet and provide a more cosy atmosphere than so many barn-like city-centre pubs. The food is reasonably priced which means mealtimes are busy, although food is available until early eve. New management has promised to lay an emphasis on local beers – Perth's Inveralmond is usually represented.
Q◖▯♿≢

Mickey Coyle's
21-23 Old Hawkhill
☼ 11-3, 5.30-midnight; 11-midnight Fri & Sat; 7-11 Sun
☎ (01382) 225871
Caledonian Deuchars IPA, 80/- Ⓗ

Long, split-level bar, popular for meals with university folk, named after a late 19th-century owner, who also ran a spirits business – some rare examples of 'MC' rum and whisky jars and bottles stand behind the bar. Closed for many years, the pub was reopened as a students' club, then to the public as the Blue Mountains (a nearby tenement area). Its abbreviated title 'MC' once appeared in the *Guinness Book of Records* as the shortest pub name, but it has now adopted the full version. Eve meals finish at 7.45pm.
◖▯≢✿

Phoenix
103 Nethergate
☼ 11-midnight; 12.30-11 Sun
☎ (01382) 200014
Caledonian Deuchars IPA; Orkney Dark Island; Taylor Landlord; guest beer Ⓗ

Busy pub, between the university and shopping areas – hence its 1980s nickname, Town and Gown, which does reflect the clientele. The present owner did a splendid job in converting a rather basic street-corner local into the impressive place it has become. The bar fittings came from a condemned Cardiff pub, the old ceiling has been restored and stained glass panels and partitions introduced. There are a few private nooks, pillars and a wealth of adverts – look out for the shoe leather one – and local memorabilia.
◖▯≢

Tavern
168 Perth Road
☼ 11-midnight; 12.30-11 Sun
☎ (01382) 227135
Orkney Dark Island Ⓗ

Taking its name from a legendary pub in Hawkhill, the 'Tav' was thus renamed by the owner who took over the pub when the legend was reduced to dust for a new road. A well-run local, it is a cosy, L-shaped lounge with a concealed niche for meetings or assignations. A comfortable howff for town and gown. ◖

FORFAR

O'Hara's
41 West High Street (opp. Post Office)
☼ 11-2.30, 5.30-11 (midnight Fri & Sat); closed Sun
☎ (01307) 464350
Beer range varies Ⓗ

This attractive, first-floor lounge is more a bistro than a pub, but attracts visitors through the quality of its two beers, as well as its culinary efforts. Wood-panelled, with beams and an open fire in winter, several windows give views of a preserved part of old Forfar as well as the High Street. Food is of above-average quality and ranges from Scots to oriental dishes. Downstairs to the rear is an overflow extension for busy times. Occasional live music is staged in the lounge.
♨Q◖▯

Queen Street Bar
45a Queen Street (between East Street and Castle Street)
☼ 11-midnight; 12.30-7 Sun
☎ (01307) 462722
Inveralmond Lia Fail Ⓗ

Cosy, popular local, just off the town centre. The comfortable bar has a low ceiling, soft lights and panelled walls, which are covered with old prints and memorabilia. The lounge doubles as a function room. Try the famous Forfar

INDEPENDENT BREWERIES

Inveralmond Perth
Moulin Moulin

bridies (like a Cornish pasty without the potato) that are available in a nearby baker's. If you are hungry though, lunch in the pub's own restaurant, off the bar. ◀P

GLENDEVON

Tormaukin Hotel
☼ 11 (12 Sun)-11
☎ (01259) 781252 website: www.tormaukin.co.uk
Beer range varies Ⓗ

In a peaceful rural setting surrounded by the Ochil Hills, this was originally an 18th-century drovers' inn. Natural timbers and stone enhance the warm, welcoming atmosphere. Two comfortable lounge bars have plush seating and log fires. Bar meals, on an extensive menu, offer an interesting choice of traditional Scottish and international dishes. Three real ales are served in the rear lounge – two are usually from Harviestoun. An ideal base for golf, walking and fishing; Tormaukin means 'hill of the mountain hare' in old Scots.
🏨Q🍽🌫◀P

INVERKEILOR

Chance Inn
Main Street (off A92, halfway between Arbroath and Montrose)
☼ 12-2.30, 5-11; 12-11 Sat; 12.30-11 Sun
☎ (01241) 830308 e-mail: chanceinn.comatbarbox.net
Beer range varies Ⓗ

Small bar in old coaching inn with a lounge/restaurant to the rear. This is a cask ale outpost, where a really friendly atmosphere is created by both the landlord and locals alike. If you cannot tear yourself away there are four bedrooms; it is well worth breaking your journey to stay here. One of the three ales available is normally a mild or light ale. The large garden is an added attraction. 🌫🍽◀🍺♣P

KINNESSWOOD

Lomond Country Inn
☼ 11-11 (midnight Fri & Sat); 11-11 Sun
☎ (01592) 840693
website: www.smoothhound.co.uk/hotels/lomond1
Caledonian Deuchars IPA; guest beers Ⓗ

Set on the slopes of the Lomond Hills, within the village of Kinnesswood, this popular and informal country inn affords fine views over Loch Leven from the open-plan bar/restaurant. A suitable base for cycling, fishing and walking, and you can visit Loch Leven Castle. The hotel offers an interesting menu based on good local produce. Guest ales regularly on offer are Marston's Pedigree and Jennings' beers.
🏨Q🌫🍽◀🍺P✠

KINROSS

Kirklands Hotel
20 High Street
☼ 11-2.30, 5-11; 11-11.45 Sat; 3.45-11 Sun
☎ (01577) 863313 website: www.kirklandshotel.com
Beer range varies Ⓗ

Traditional, small town hotel, now fully refurbished with a comfortable bar and lounge area. It is one of the original coaching inns in Kinross. Note that the Sun opening hours will be reviewed during the currency of this *Guide*. Eve meals are served

6-8.30pm. Its nine guest rooms all have en-suite facilities and B&B is reasonably priced. By Loch Leven, a five-minute boat trip takes you to Loch Leven Castle where Mary, Queen of Scots was imprisoned by the Earl of Bothwell; naturalists will enjoy a visit to the RSPB's Vane Farm reserve. 🏨Q🍽◀🍺

KIRKTON OF GLENISLA

Glenisla Hotel
On B591, 10 miles N of Alyth
☼ 11-11 (12.30am Fri; midnight Sat; 12.30-11 Sun
☎ (01575) 582223
Inveralmond Independence, Lia Fail; guest beer Ⓗ

The 'Inn in the Glen' is a warm, friendly, former 17th-century coaching inn. The small village of Kirkton is about a third of the way up the glen. The oak-beamed bar, with log fire and half-panelled walls, is furnished with oak and pine tables and chairs. The bar area is on two levels with access to a large garden. Hearty bar meals make use of fresh local produce. An adjoining renovated stable block houses a games room. An ideal base for touring, there are good surrounding walks and fishing nearby. 🏨🌫🍽◀🍺♿▲♣P

MEMUS

Drovers' Inn
5 miles N of Forfar, off B957
☼ 12-2.30, 6-midnight; (12-1am Fri & Sat; closed winter Mon); 12.30-11 Sun
☎ (01307) 860322
Beer range varies Ⓗ

Pleasant and welcoming bar/lounge featuring pine panelling, flagstones and framed country scenes and newspapers. It boasts a large garden and car park, and an adjoining restaurant. Formerly the village Post Office, the refurbishment has been sympathetic and effective, including the addition of a conservatory. Opening times may vary, it generally opens all day in the summer months, but phone to check. Two cask ales are usually stocked. 🏨🌫◀P

MOULIN

Moulin Inn
11-13 Kirkmichael Road
(³⁄₄ mile NE of Pitlochry)
☼ 11-11 (11.45 Fri & Sat); 12-11 Sun
☎ (01796) 472196 website: www.moulin.u-net.com/
Moulin Light, Braveheart, Ale of Atholl, Old Remedial Ⓗ

In the village square of Moulin, an ancient Scottish crossroads, this country inn was established in 1695. Although extended into a hotel, it retains much character and charm. The oldest part of the building is the original Moulin Inn, furnished in traditional pub style, with two log fires. A good choice of home-prepared local fare is available, along with its own beer, provided by the brewery in the old coach house behind the hotel. An ideal base for a walking holiday, up to 16 routed walks pass nearby.
🏨Q🌫🍽◀🍺▲P

MUTHILL

Muthill Village Hotel
6 Willoughby Street

11-11 (11.45 Fri & Sat); 12.30-11 Sun
(01764) 681451
Orkney Dark Island; guest beers H
Friendly village local in the conservation village of Muthill. Originally an 18th-century coaching inn on the old drovers' road from the Highlands, the comfortable public bar, the Bothy, has traditional bare boards and a real fire; the walls are adorned with farming implements and old livestock catalogues. An adjoining restaurant bears a hunting theme. Up to four real ales are served in the public bar (two in winter). Do not miss nearby Drummond Gardens one of the finest formal gardens in Europe.
Q P

PERTH

Capital Asset
26 Tay Street
11-11 (11.45 Fri & Sat);
12.30-11 Sun
(01738) 580457
Caledonian Deuchars IPA, 80/-; Theakston Best Bitter; guest beers H
Large, open-plan Wetherspoon's house with modern decoration and a small split-level seating area. It draws a varied clientele, and can be very busy at weekends. It offers standard Wetherspoon's fare, plus up to five real ales on tap. It takes its name from the fact that it used to be a bank and Perth was once the ancient capital of Scotland. The building overlooks the River Tay.
Q

Greyfriars
15 South Street
11-11 (11.45 Fri & Sat); 7-11 Sun
(01738) 633036
Caledonian Deuchars IPA; Taylor Landlord; guest beer H
Cosy, but vibrant, city-centre lounge bar with a friendly atmosphere. Lunches are served in the bar and a small upstairs seating area. Up to four beers are usually available; the house beer, Friar's Tipple, is brewed by Inveralmond. It is just a short walk to the River Tay. Other attractions in Perth include the Victorian theatre, art gallery and an award-winning leisure pool, with no less than four pools offering a multitude of activities.

Old Ship Inn
Skinnergate
11-2.30, 5-11; 11-11.45 Fri & Sat; closed Sun
(01738) 624929
Caledonian Deuchars IPA; Greene King Abbot; guest beers H
One of the oldest licensed houses in Perth, circa 1665, it stands on part of the old Blackfriars monastery grounds. For many years the building's exterior was a landmark, with a painting showing ships of Nelson's time; unfortunately, the painting has faded, although an outline of one of the 'Hearts of Oak' is still discernible – the original oil painting can be seen in the public bar. The Ship is traditional and basic, but a welcome retreat in the heart of the city, with great local character. It hosts regular dominoes nights.
Q

SCOTLANDWELL

Well Country Inn
Main Street
11-11 (11.45 Fri & Sat); 12-11 Sun
(01592) 840444
website: www.s-h-systems.co.uk/hotels/wellcountry
Belhaven 80/-; guest beers H
Country inn, in a tranquil village that dates back to 84AD, when the Romans were in occupation. An ideal location for outdoor pursuits, including golf, gliding and hill walking, the famous 'Tetley tea trail' is only yards from the inn. Also nearby is one of the last natural underground spring-water wells still working in Scotland. The main lounge area has a warm, relaxed atmosphere; there is a smaller public bar, plus two restaurant areas (one no-smoking). Snacks and meals are based on fresh local produce.
Q P

INN BRIEF

ARBROATH

Old Brewhouse
3 High Street
11 (12.30 Sun)-11
Orkney Dark Island H
Small bar and lounge/restaurant on the seafront, refurbished in traditional style. Watch out for waves in stormy weather!

Viewfield Hotel
1 Viewfield Road
Beer varies H
Popular bar of a small hotel, stocking a single cask ale. A long room houses a pool table and juke box; also a spacious lounge.

BRECHIN

Dalhousie
1 Market Street
11-midnight (1am Fri & Sat)
Beer range varies H
Corner local with a horseshoe bar, high ceiling and memorabilia on display. Often busy, it stocks just one real ale.

BROUGHTY FERRY

Old Anchor Inn
48 Gray Street
11-midnight; 12.30-11 Sun
Caledonian Deuchars IPA; Courage Directors H
Modernised, wide bar with partitions and nautical decor. Very busy late eves and weekends. No-smoking areas available at meal times.

DUNDEE

Frew's
117 Strathmartine Road
Draught Bass; McEwan 80/-; guest beer (occasional) H
Fine Victorian pub, well refurbished with a notable gantry and fireplace in the bar; two lounges

Speedwell ☆
165-167 Perth Road
11-midnight; 12.30-11 Sun
Beer range varies H
Superbly preserved Edwardian bar with two sitting rooms (one no-smoking), known as Mennie's. Up to four ales on tap.

PERTH

Ring o' Bells
6 St John's Place
11-11 (11.45 Fri & Sat); 12.30-11 Sun
Beer range varies H
Large, friendly, central lounge bar with ramps for wheelchair access, plus children's certificate. Changing beers showcase Scottish micros.

Guide site

Keep your copy of the Good Beer Guide up-to-date by contacting the CAMRA website where you will find information about changes to pubs and breweries

www.camra.org.uk/gbg

STRATHTUMMEL

Loch Tummel Inn
On B8019, approx. 3 miles W of Queen's View
✪ Mid-March-Oct: 11-11 (may close afternoons); 12.30-11 Sun
☎ (01882) 634272
Moulin Braveheart Ⓗ
On the B8019, west from Pitlochry – part of the romantic road to the isles – this old coaching inn is located in an idyllic rural setting. It boasts magnificent scenery (none more so than the panorama provided by Queen's View nearby) overlooking Loch Tummel. The bar area is in the former stables, the restaurant is in a converted hayloft. Look out for the inn's own smoked salmon on the menu. The inn closes in winter from Oct to mid-March
⚅ Q ⊛ ⊨ ◖ P

WOODSIDE

Woodside Inn
Main Street (A94 S of Coupar Angus)
✪ 11-2, 5-11 (11.45 Fri); 11-11.45 Sat; 12.30-11 Sun
☎ (01828) 670524
**Caledonian Deuchars IPA;
guest beers** Ⓗ
Small village pub at the north-east end of Burrelton/Woodside, formerly used as a convalescent home for WWI casualties. It has a small, but comfortable, public bar serving up to four real ales, including favourites such as Taylor Landlord and Marston's Pedigree; other guest beers change frequently. Excellent food is served in the adjacent restaurant (children welcome), which can be busy at weekends.
⚅ ⊛ ◖ P

Hold the front page...

Members of CAMRA receive a free monthly newspaper, What's Brewing. It is packed with up-to date information about beer, brewing and pubs, and will keep you informed about all the latest developments in the beer world. What's Brewing also lists CAMRA beer festivals throughout the country, along with CAMRA branch and regional activities.

What's Brewing has the best and most authoritative writers. It is edited by Ted Bruning, and regular columnists include Jeff Evans, Lynne Pearce, Good Beer Guide editor Roger Protz, and Arthur Taylor. John Reynolds surveys the City scene while laughter is provided by veteran cartoonist Bill Tidy with his Kegbuster strip.

What's Brewing is worth the price of CAMRA membership alone. To receive your monthly copy, sign up for membership by using the form at the back of the Guide.

NORTHERN IRELAND

BALLYMENA

Spinning Mill
17-21 Broughshane Street
🕐 11.30-11; 12-10 Sun
☎ (028) 256 38985
Courage Directors; Hilden Molly Malone's Porter, Scullion's Irish; Theakston Best Bitter; Whitewater Belfast Special Bitter Ⓗ
The first Wetherspoon's pub in Northern Ireland, this large building has three bars, split on lower floors by a passage used as an outside drinking area. Real ale is served in the ground floor and first floor bars in the main building only. Excellent value meals are available at all times. It stocks five real ales at all times and hosts occasional beer festivals. This is a welcome oasis in a real ale desert. 🏚Q🌠🕪👌🛇≢✄

BANGOR

Esplanade
12 Ballyholme
🕐 11.30-11; 12.30-10 Sun
☎ (028) 912 70954
website: www.gillespie-esplanade.com
Whitewater Glen Ale; guest beers Ⓗ
Comfortable, quiet, seaside pub in a converted three-storey house, affording commanding views over Ballyholme Bay from the patio and lounge. Handpumps are in the public bar only, but lounge staff will fetch real ale on request. The beer range has recently been increased. Excellent food is served in the bar and lounge as well as the upstairs dining room which offers an *à la carte* menu. Wheelchair WC. Q🌠🕪🛒👌

BELFAST ✣

Beaten Docket
48 Great Victoria Street (opp. Europa Hotel)
🕐 11.30-midnight (1am Thu-Sat); 11.30-midnight Sun
☎ (028) 902 42986

Beer range varies Ⓗ
Opened in the early 1980s, this city-centre bar is at one end of Belfast's 'Golden Mile'. The black and white tiled floor contrasts with the brass on the bar and glasswork on the ceiling; find the snug in the corner. It tends to attract a very mixed crowd. On Fri and Sat live music is staged downstairs, and a club night (with DJs) is held in the large function room upstairs. Beers from Whitewater are always available, plus guest beers from the mainland. Meals are served 11.30 (12 Sun)-6. 🏚🕪≢(Gt Victoria St)

Botanic Inn
23 Malone Road (500 yds from Queens University)
🕐 11-midnight (1am Wed-Sat); 11-midnight Sun
☎ (028) 905 09740
Cains Bitter, FA; Whitewater Belfast Special Bitter; guest beers Ⓗ
One of Belfast's busiest pubs, the Botanic attracts a mainly student crowd. It is very large, with the bar split into a modern and a more traditional one. Real ale (which can be pricey) is available from four handpumps, two in the old bar and two tucked away in the modern side. Entertainment plays a large part in the pub's popularity; DJs host the upstairs disco Wed-Sun and live bands play Mon. Football and rugby games are shown live on a large screen, when the pub is often packed. 🏚🕪👌≢(Botanic)

Kitchen Bar
16-18 Victoria Street
🕐 11.30-11 (1am Fri); 12-7 Sun
☎ (028) 903 24901
Beer range varies Ⓗ
Long-established, family-run pub, now under threat from developers. It has a long narrow bar in the old tradition, opening into the parlour. The Kitchen is held dear by CAMRA Northern Ireland, being among the first to sell real ale in the province. Popular for home-cooked food weekdays, and traditional music (Fri eves). Horse-racing pictures feature behind the public bar, while photos of the stars from the old Empire Music Hall decorate the parlour. The pub's future is precarious. See this old treasure before it goes. It always stocks beers from Whitewater plus guest beers from the mainland. 🛒🕪🍴≢(Central)

McHugh's
29-31 Queen's Square (near Albert Clock)
🕐 11.30-1am (midnight Mon); 12-midnight Sun
☎ (028) 902 47830 e-mail: info@botanic-inns.com
Whitewater Belfast Special Bitter; guest beers Ⓗ
Busy, city-centre pub recently restored and extended to preserve Belfast's oldest building (dating from 1711). A range of bars and seating areas combine with a restaurant floor serving modern menus. The basement bar hosts live bands, jazz and other entertainment Wed-Sat. Families are welcome in this attractive, stylish pub near Laganbank bus station. 🏚🕪👌≢(Central)

Rotterdam Bar
52-54 Pilot Street

INDEPENDENT BREWERIES

Hilden Lisburn
Whitewater Kilkeel

655

11.30-1am (midnight Mon & Wed); 4-1.30am Sat;
4-midnight Sun
☎ (028) 907 46021
Whitewater Belfast Special Bitter H

Very old-fashioned dockside bar; a listed building with rough walls, tiled floor and low ceiling. Hard-to-find, a mile from the city centre, it is located off Corporation Street, between modern apartment blocks and Clarendon Docks. Renowned for its music, a variety of acts are featured nearly every day of the week. Recently, the Performing Rights Society voted it *Music Pub of the Year*. Children are allowed in before 7pm, and the bar has a great atmosphere. Weekday lunches served. ⚏❀◐⇌ (Yorkgate)

COMBER

North Down House
Belfast Road (Castle St roundabout)
12-midnight (1am Fri & Sat); 12.30-midnight Sun
☎ (028) 918 72242
Beer range varies H

The pub is over 100 years old, yet manages to combine the old with the new. The lively main bar area has been extended, hosting a disco Fri eve and live entertainment Sat eve. The modern, cosy, quieter lounge is decorated with memorabilia of the old Comber Whiskey Distillery. It is popular with young and old alike, who are served by friendly staff. Pool played in the bar.

HILLSBOROUGH

Hillside
21 Main Street
12-11 (1am Fri & Sat); 12-10 Sun
☎ (028) 926 82765
Beer range varies H

In a picturesque, English-style village, the public bar houses four handpumps offering Whitewater beers and guests. Good food is available in the bar, the Refectory and the award-winning restaurant upstairs. Food and ale can be consumed in the outside area, which is the venue for the Hillsborough beer festival in July. The bar is generally quiet, with a fairly well-heeled clientele; occasionally Ministers of State drop in. On Sun eve entertainment is laid on, with local jazz bands. ⚏Q❀◐▭⅋Å

HOLYWOOD

Dirty Duck
2 Kinnegar Road
11-midnight (1am Fri & Sat); 12.30-midnight Sun
☎ (028) 905 96666
Beer range varies H

Friendly pub on the seafront, enjoying excellent views over Belfast Lough. Four beers at all times fully justifies winning the

Children's certificates

When pubs are described as having 'children's certificates', this indicates that local licensing authorities are satisfied that the pubs in question have environments suitable for children under 14, and that meals and non-alcoholic drinks are available. Some authorities demand more wide-ranging facilities – such as non-smoking areas, an absence of gaming machines, nappy-changing provision, junior WCs and basins, and furniture suitable for small children — before granting certificates, which must be prominently displayed.

Northern Ireland CAMRA *Pub of the Year* on several occasions. High quality food is available all day, and regular live music attracts a wide range of clientele. The family room is open in the daytime and the upstairs restaurant is busy eves. It hosts occasional beer festivals when the seated area outside is served by a temporary covered bar. ⚏▭❀◐⇌

KILLINCHY

Daft Eddie's
Skettrick Island (Whiterock Road, 1 mile N of Killinchy)
11.30-11.30 (1am Fri & Sat); 11.30-10 Sun
☎ (028) 975 41615 website: www.dafteddies.co.uk
Whitewater Belfast Special Bitter H

A gem, set in beautiful surroundings, on an island in Whiterock Bay, formerly used by smugglers. It can be difficult to find but is well worth a visit to see the recently restored remains of Skettrick Castle and the lounge/restaurant with its maritime theme. The whole area is dedicated to seafaring with a yachting centre and sailmakers in the pub's grounds. The food is highly recommended and can be eaten on the patio, (booking advised). The public bar has a pool table and a pianist plays Sat eve. ⚏Q❀◐▭⅋P

INN BRIEF

BELFAST
Bonaparte's
192 Cavehill Road
11.30-midnight Wed; 1am Thu-Sat);
12.30-midnight Sun
Beer range varies H
Sister pub to the Dirty Duck. Excellent food includes a children's menu. Three handpumps serve real ale in an oasis in North Belfast.

COLERAINE
Old Courthouse
Castlerock Road
11.30-12; 12.10 Sun
Courage Directors; Hilden Molly Malone's Porter; Theakston Best Bitter; Whitewater Belfast Special Bitter; guest beer H
Wetherspoon's first Northern Ireland conversion, a spacious, one-bar pub in a former county courthouse. Food served all day.

✳ **symbol next to a main entry place name indicates there are Inn Brief entries as well.**

LISBURN

Taproom
Hilden Brewery

✪ 12-2.30; Tue-Sat eves by appointment; closed Sun
☎ (028) 926 63863 website: www.hildeninshbeers.com

Hilden Ale, Molly Malone's Porter, Scullion's Irish Ⓗ

Award-winning licensed restaurant in the courtyard of Hilden Manor, about one mile from the centre of Lisburn. Formerly the seat of linen barons, it now belongs to the Scullion family who started brewing real ale in 1981. Brewery tours take place at 11.30 and 2.30, or by arrangement. The visitor's centre houses a brewing exhibition and a history of Hilden's past as a linen village. Hilden revived their much-missed beer festival in 2000. ♨Q☕⌂♿P

SAINTFIELD

White Horse
49 Main Street (16 miles SE of Belfast)

✪ 11-11; closed Sun
☎ (028) 975 10417 website: www.white-horse-inn.com

Whitewater Best Bitter, Mountain Ale, Belfast Special Bitter; guest beers Ⓗ

Five handpumps are constantly in action in this family-run pub, one of the busiest outlets for real ale in the Province. Ales can also be bought in the adjoining off-licence, with carryout containers. Good food can be purchased in the bar or in the downstairs restaurant. At the centre of Saintfield's village life, it hosts social and charity events nearly every night. The weekends tend to be so busy that the pub's annual beer festival sometimes has to be held midweek. ♨Q☕◑☕✂

WHITEABBEY

Woody's Lounge
607 Shore Road
(off A2, Belfast-Carrickfergus road)

✪ 11.30-11; 1-10 Sun
☎ (028) 908 63206

Beer range varies Ⓗ

Comfortable, cosy lounge bar on a slip road off the A2 Belfast to Carrickfergus road. Food is available weekday lunchtimes. Children are not admitted and the pub operates a ban on football gear. The bar is decorated with fine prints of the village and surrounding area. It also has off-sales for its good range of beers; an excellent choice of wines and malts is also stocked.
Q◑⌂P

Fizz warning

Some national breweries produce both cask-conditioned and 'nitro-keg' versions of their beers. Boddingtons Bitter, John Smith's Bitter, Tetley's Bitter and Worthington fall into this category. Nitro-keg beers, often promoted as 'smooth' or 'cream-flow' products, are filtered and pasteurised in the brewery, and served in pubs by a mix of applied carbon dioxide and nitrogen gases. They are bland, served extremely cold, and any hop character is lost by the use of applied gas.

To add insult to injury, the keg founts that serve such beers are often topped by small dummy handpumps. As a result of lobbying by CAMRA, some producers of cask and nitro versions of the same beer now include the word 'cask' on pump clips for the genuine article. For example, both John Smith's Bitter and Tetley's Bitter now carry the word 'cask' on pump clips for the real thing.

For the sake of brevity, and as the Good Beer Guide lists only cask-conditioned beers, we refer simply to John Smith's Bitter and Tetley Bitter. The Bass/Interbrew brand, Worthington, is labelled Worthington Bitter in cask form, and – bizarrely – Worthington Best Bitter in the nitro-keg version. Always choose the living rather than the dead.

Good beer guides

*Two new guides from CAMRA books
will help you find some of the finest pubs in
London and recreate great pub meals in
your own kitchen*

London Pub Guide

Top beer writer Lynne
Pearce has travelled the
capital to choose the finest
pubs – pubs with
fascinating histories,
architecture and anecdotes,
along with information
about the food available
and, of course, the beer.
With maps and transport
information, you're never
lost for a capital pint.
£9.99.

Pub Superchefs

Award-winning food writer
Susan Nowak has followed
the success of her Good Pub
Food series by presenting
some of the best recipes
created by her favourite pub
chefs. They range from
'gastropubs', with exotic
menus, to ones offering
more homely and
traditional fare. £7.99

The books are available from good bookshops or direct from CAMRA (post free),
230 Hatfield Road, St Albans AL1 4LW; cheques or postal orders made out to 'CAMRA'.
To order by Access or Visa, phone 01727 867201 between 9am and 5pm, Monday to
Friday (answerphone outside office hours). Allow 28 days for delivery.

CHANNEL ISLANDS

CASTEL

Guernsey

CASTEL

Fleur du Jardin
Kings Mills
☼ 10.30-11.45; 12-3.15 Sun
☎ (01481) 257996
Guernsey Sunbeam, seasonal beers Ⓗ

Country pub, with a good-sized garden, in an attractive setting. There is ample parking on site, spread over three areas. This hotel is popular with tourists and locals alike. There are two bars: one small and cosy, attached to the restaurant and the other large and airy. The larger bar closes during the winter. Real ale can be obtained in either. The restaurant and bar menus feature fresh local produce and daily changing specials.
Q ❀ ⊭ ◑ P

FOREST

Venture Inn
New Road (2 minutes' drive from the airport)
☼ 10.30-midnight; closed Sun
☎ (01481) 263211
Randalls Patois Ⓗ

Popular, traditional Guernsey hostelry where the visitor is made welcome in either the lively public or the cosy lounge bar. The latter serves excellent food, with eve meals available Mon–Sat during the summer and on Fri and Sat in winter. Very occasionally a real mild is served. Well worth a visit.
▥ ❀ ◑ ◑ ⊟ P

ST MARTIN

Ambassador Hotel
Route de Sausmarez
☼ 12-3, 6-11.45; 12-3.30 Sun
☎ (01481) 238356
Beer range varies Ⓗ

This hotel bar is popular with locals and visitors alike. Situated just down from Sausmarez Manor, it features a large lounge bar that has undergone recent changes to the bar layout; further expansion is planned. An excellent range of bar meals is available either in the bar area or the conservatory. Quiz nights are organised during the winter. The bar is closed Sun eve except to hotel residents. The beer is mainly supplied by the Guernsey Brewery. ❀ ⊭ ◑ ◑ P

ST PETER PORT

Cock & Bull
Lower Hauteville
☼ 11.30-2.30, 4-11.45; 11.30-11.45 Fri & Sat; closed Sun
☎ (01481) 722660
Beer range varies Ⓗ

Popular pub, up the hill from the town church. Five handpumps provide a changing range of beers which include Ringwood brews. It hosts live music twice a week (Tue and Thu after 9pm). A big-screen TV shows sports events, but as the pub is on three levels, there is plenty of room for non-sports fans to enjoy a visit. The lower level houses a pool table. Regular beer festivals are held throughout the year; half of them are run as charity events. Snacks are usually available at lunchtime (not Sat).

Doghouse
The Rohais (main route out of town, 200 yds from Safeway's)
☼ 10.30-11.45, 12-3.30 (6.30-11.45 for diners) Sun
☎ (01481) 721302
Badger Tanglefoot; Courage Directors Ⓗ

Free house on the edge of town, specialising in live music each eve and some lunchtimes. Comfortable seating and walls painted with attractive murals on a music theme add to its appeal. It has a cosy wood-panelled dining area, on Sun eve a meal must be consumed to comply with Guernsey law – alcohol cannot be served without food. The small patio has tables and seating. ❀ ◑ ◑ ⊛ P

Drunken Duck
Le Charroterie (1/2 mile SW of town church)
☼ 11-11.45; 12-3.30 (closed eve) Sun
☎ (01481) 725045
Badger Best, Tanglefoot; guest beers Ⓗ

Cosy, friendly two-roomed free house situated almost opposite the States of Guernsey building. Beers are usually from the Badger stable, plus two guest beers, usually a choice of Courage Directors, Wadworth 6X or Theakston Old Peculier. Lunchtimes can be quiet but eves tend to be popular, especially at weekends when live music is performed or wide-screen TV sport is showing; it gets packed for rugby internationals. ◑

Ship & Crown
North Esplanade (just across from the Crown Pier car park)
☼ 10-11.45; 12-3.30, 6-10 Sun
☎ (01481) 721368
Guernsey Pirates Ale, Sunbeam, seasonal beers Ⓗ

Providing picturesque views of the harbour, this pub is popular with locals and tourists alike. There is a convenient public car park opposite. It appeals to all ages at different times of the day; popular eves with the younger crowd, being part of the 'town crawl'. The walls are decorated with pictures from the WWII occupation and local shipping disasters. Guernsey Braye is

INDEPENDENT BREWERIES

Guernsey St Peter Port
Randalls St Peter Port
Tipsy Toad St Peter

rebadged as Three Crowns. The pub serves a varied range of good value meals, in generous portions, and plenty of daily specials. ◖

ST SAMPSON

Pony Inn
Les Capelles
✪ 10.30-11.45; 12-3, 6-10 Sun
☎ (01481) 244374
Guernsey Sunbeam or Pirates Ale Ⓗ

Real family pub, with a quiet, child-free zone. The main area includes a large bar with plenty of seating. If you like your food this is the place to come. A small patio area is reached through French doors from the main bar. There is an outdoor and indoor play area for children. The ale alternates between Sunbeam and Pirates via the single handpump. The pub tends to quieten down a bit after meals end at 9.30, except Fri eve when live music is staged. ✤✿◖◗&P

VALE

Houmet Tavern
La Route du Picquerel
✪ 10-11.45; closed Sun
☎ (01481) 242214
Guernsey Braye Ⓗ

Very popular pub with the locals and visitors. The friendly public (Anchor) bar is a favourite for the younger generation, with darts, pool and bar billiards. The lounge bar at the front affords spectacular views across Grande Havre Bay from its recently-added conservatory. An excellent range of bar meals is available in the lounge (eve meals served Tue, Wed, Fri and Sat, 7–8.45). Q✿◖◗&P

Jersey

GROUVILLE ✿

Pembroke Inn
La Grande Route des Sablons
✪ 11-11, including Sun
☎ (01534) 855756
Draught Bass; Courage Directors Ⓗ

By the entrance to the Royal Jersey Golf Club in Grouville Bay, the Pembroke is a large friendly pub, making a welcome return to this *Guide*. Real ale is served in the public bar; ask if you cannot see it. Food is popular and booking is advised for groups (no eve meals Sun). Games are played in the public bar which houses a pool table and a vast TV screen. The car park is small but there is plenty of safe parking on the road nearby. ✤Q✿◖◗&P

ROZEL

Rozel Bay Inn
La Vallée de Rozel

✪ 11-11, including Sun
☎ (01534) 863438
Draught Bass; Courage Directors; Wadworth 6X Ⓗ

The Rozel Bay has become very popular, and deservedly so, with one of the cosiest lounge bars imaginable, three real ales on the small corner bar, and a public bar with pool table and TV. A good bar menu is supplemented by an *à la carte* restaurant upstairs (no meals Sun eve). The garden is being enlarged and is one of few in Jersey. ✤Q✿◖◗&♣P

ST BRELADE

Old Smugglers' Inn
Ouaisne Bay
✪ 11-11, including Sun
☎ (01534) 741510
Draught Bass; guest beers Ⓗ

Historic pub, nestling at the bottom of Ouaisne Bay, home of the 'Agile Frog'. A cosy, but busy, local, the Smugglers' is a stalwart of real ale, being until 2001, Jersey's only surviving free house. Bass is a constant feature, with the other two handpumps often promoting beers from Ringwood and other independents. The Smugglers' specialises in good food; the large eating areas serve a comprehensive menu. A fine beach is less than 100 yards away. ✤Q✤◖♣P

ST HELIER ✿

Lamplighter
Mulcaster Street (near bus station)
✪ 11-11, including Sun
☎ (01534) 723119
Draught Bass; Boddingtons Bitter; Marston's Pedigree; Theakston Old Peculier; guest beer Ⓗ

The Lamplighter is an institution in the Jersey real ale scene. Unashamedly a drinkers' pub, this was Jersey CAMRA's *Pub of the Year* 1999 and 2000. It is the only pub in Jersey to serve five real ales, and to serve real cider. This is also Jersey's only gaslit pub, giving it an intimate atmosphere in which to relax and chat. If you can tear yourself away from the bar, have a look at the top of the pub from outside.
◖♣☙

Original Wine Bar
Bath Street
✪ 11-11; 4.30-11 Sun
☎ (01534) 871119
Beer range varies Ⓗ

Relaxed drinking and dining environment, enhanced by pastel colours, soft furnishings and a variety of different drinking areas, it is very popular with town workers, especially women. Although designated a wine bar, on account of its great choice of wines, it stocks a good real ale range too, usually as many as

INN BRIEF

Jersey
GROUVILLE

Seymour Inn
La Rue du Puits Mahaut
11-11, including Sun
Tipsy Toad Jimmy's Bitter Ⓗ
Friendly, coastal pub with a separate real ale bar in summer. Excellent for pub games.

ST HELIER
Dog & Sausage
Halkett Street
11-11, including Sun
Draught Bass Ⓗ
Small pub in the main shopping area opposite McDonald's. Note the interesting railway features. A second bar is upstairs.

TRINITY
Trinity Arms
La Rue des Picots
11-11, including Sun
Guernsey Sunbeam Ⓗ
Local in northern Trinity, near the zoo. Recently refurbished.

four, sourced from Brains and the local Tipsy Toad Brewery. It won the local CAMRA *Best Newcomer* award 1999. Do not be put off by doormen eves.
Q◑&✚

Prince of Wales
Hilgrove Street
✪ 10-11; 11-2 Sun
☎ (01534) 737378
Draught Bass; John Smith's Bitter; guest beer Ⓗ
Busy, one-bar town pub, next to the central market. An impressive bar with stained glass insets dominates the room and frames a classic six-pump beer engine (only three work). The back yard is a super sun terrace, surrounding a little fountain, offering a welcome sanctuary from busy St Helier. The pub provides refreshment for town workers and, as such, is very busy lunchtime, but less so eves. It always has three real ales on tap. Q◑

ST MARTIN

Royal Hotel
La Grande Route de Faldouet (by church)
✪ 9.30 (11 lounge)-11; 11-11 Sun
☎ (01534) 856289
Boddingtons Bitter; guest beer Ⓗ
Large, popular pub, opposite the church in the village. It successfully combines a variety of drinking and dining areas, including a large public bar with games and TV, a comfortable lounge with armchairs and a roaring fire, a large family dining area, sun terrace, and an upstairs restaurant. It is one of the most wheelchair-friendly pubs in Jersey, and also very good for children. The food is from a good menu, comes very fast and in generous portions; no meals Sun eve.
🏠Q≿❀◑&♣P

ST OUEN

Moulin de Lecq
Grève de Lecq
✪ 11-11, including Sun
☎ (01534) 482818
Draught Bass; Guernsey Sunbeam; guest beers Ⓗ
One of Jersey's most picturesque pubs, a must for tourists; it is a converted 12th-century water mill with a working drive wheel behind the bar. The mill was used to generate power by the Germans during the occupation. The cosy lounge bar has a roaring fire in winter, while the large outdoor area hosts barbecues in summer. It has a great children's playground and is very family-friendly. In 2001, the Moulin was refurbished and became a free house, serving guest beers and hosts annual mini-beer festivals.
🏠Q≿❀◑Å P

ST PETER

Star & Tipsy Toad Brewery
La Route de Beaumont
✪ 9-11.30; 11-11.30 Sun
☎ (01534) 485556
Tipsy Toad Ale, Jimmy's Bitter; guest beer Ⓗ
Home of Jersey's only remaining real ale producer, the Star, refurbished and reopened in late 2000, is smart and bright. A variety of drinking and dining areas surround a central bar. All the Tipsy Toad beers are served, but the brewery is not large, and sometimes there may only be the award-winning Jimmy's Bitter available. Live music is staged Sat eve. Tours of the brewery, which is clearly visible at the side of the lounge bar, are available on request. Check out the stained glass roof of the main bar! 🏠Q≿❀◑&♣P

Choosing Pubs

CAMRA members and branches choose the pubs listed in the Good Beer Guide. There is no payment for entry, and pubs are inspected on a regular basis by personal visits; publicans are not sent a questionnaire once a year, as is the case with some pub guides. CAMRA branches monitor all the pubs in their areas, and the choice of pubs for the guide is often the result of democratic vote at branch meetings.

However, recommendations from readers are welcomed and will be passed on to the relevant branch: write to Good Beer Guide, CAMRA, 230 Hatfield Road, St Albans, AL1 4LW; or send an e-mail to camra@camra.org.uk.

ISLE OF MAN

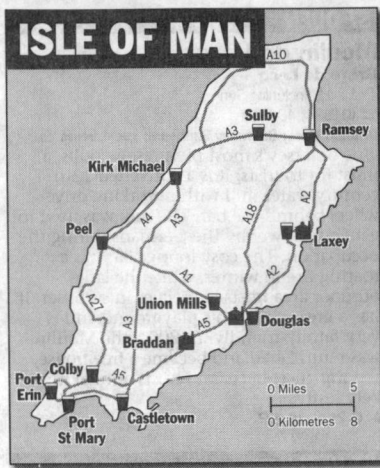

room (pool played), a lounge/dining area with a stone fireplace, and a large, well-kept garden drinking area to the rear. It stocks the widest range of guest beers in Castletown (seven). Economical lunchtime snacks are served Mon–Sat.
❀◖▲⇌(IMR)♣

CASTLETOWN

Castle Arms (Gluepot)
The Quay (opp. Castle Rushen and harbour)
✪ 12-10.45 (midnight Fri & Sat); 12-3, 7-10.30 Sun
☎ (01624) 824673
Cains Bitter; Okells Bitter Ⓗ
Small, picturesque harbourside pub, circa 1760, in the shadow of Castle Rushen where two small rooms display an abundance of nautical memorabilia. The nickname derives from the days when glue was made in the pub's cellar for use in repairing the boats in the nearby harbour. Food is served 12–3, plus Thai cuisine on Fri and Sat eves, 6.30–10. There is a pleasant outdoor seating area, and a private function room on the first floor. Handy for nearby Ronaldsway Airport, it lies on the Douglas–Port Erin bus route. ◖▶▲⇌(IMR)

Ship
Hope Street (opp. inner harbour)
✪ 12-11 (midnight Fri & Sat); 12-3, 7-10.30 Sun
☎ (01624) 824959
Okells Bitter Ⓗ
The large basic bar acts as a lounge/games room, where darts and pool are played. A corridor leads to the first-floor Chart Room bar, affording views of the inner harbour. It has a smart wood and tiled bar and a raised seating area for dining; an extensive lunchtime bar menu is served. Prints of sailing ships adorn the walls. Across the harbour you can see the closed Castletown Brewery, now private accommodation. From the rear the pub resembles a ship (hence its name), complete with a large red funnel. ❀◖▲⇌(IMR)

Sidings
Victoria Road (by steam railway station)
✪ 12-10 (midnight Fri & Sat); 12-3, 7-10.30 Sun
☎ (01624) 823282
Bushy's Manannan's Cloak; Marston's Pedigree; Theakston Mild, Best Bitter; guest beers Ⓗ
Large, black and white free house, next to Castletown narrow gauge steam railway station, on the edge of town. The line runs a regular service in summer from Douglas to Port Erin. A handsome carved wood long bar with old church pews is the dominant feature of the pub. It also boasts a games

COLBY

Colby Glen Hotel
Main Road (A7)
✪ 12-11 (midnight Fri & Sat); (closed winter afternoons); 12-3, 7-10.30 Sun
☎ (01624) 834853
Okells Mild, Bitter Ⓗ
This spacious pub sits by the main road of a rural village. Its rooms include a wood-panelled bar, a games room at the rear with pool and darts and a comfortable lounge with a central stone fireplace. Diners can choose between the restaurant, which incorporates a raised carvery area and a no-smoking section, or the quaint Colby Diner attached to the pub, serving an excellent, varied choice of food. There is also an extensive outdoor dining area. The No.1 bus from Douglas to Port St Mary stops nearby every half hour. ❀◖▶ ⬚⬚⇌P

DOUGLAS

Albert Hotel
3 Chapel Row (next to bus station)
✪ 10-11 (midnight Fri & Sat); 12-3, 7-10.30 Sun
☎ (01624) 673632 e-mail: geoffjonghin@manx.net
Okells Mild, Bitter Ⓗ
Typical, back-street, busy Manx pub, full of character, where two rooms are set around a central bar: a lounge and a basic vault housing a pool table and Sky TV. Photographs of former Isle of Man Steam Packet Co. boats and TT riders adorn the wood-panelled walls. It boasts a well-run social club with over 100 members, and holds local charity nights including an auction. Joughs house bitter is brewed specially for the pub by Okells. Very handy for the bus station.
▥Q◖⬚⇌(IMR)

Foresters Arms
St Georges Street (near steam railway station)
✪ 12-11 (midnight Fri & Sat); 12-3, 7-10.30 Sun
☎ (01624) 676509
Okells Mild, Bitter Ⓗ
Excellent street-corner local, a traditional characterful Manx pub, this former Castletown house retains its original brewery windows. A central bar serves several small rooms including an old-fashioned snug. The pub is just off the central downtown area of Douglas in the finance district. The IOM Tourist Minister and Mayor of Douglas number among its clientele, which includes office workers weekday lunchtimes. It hosts lively social activities. Basic sandwiches and toasties are available during the day. But… this typical drinking-man's pub is soon to be altered – pay a visit before it's too late.
▥⬚⇌(IMR)♣

Old Market Tavern
2 Chapel Row (near bus station)
✪ 12-11 (midnight Fri & Sat); 12-3, 7-10.30 Sun
☎ (01624) 675202

Bushy's Bitter; Okells Bitter Ⓗ
Eye-catching blue tiles clad the exterior of this old-fashioned back-street local. A central bar serves two wood-panelled rooms. Very popular with visitors to the island, it has so far resisted selling food. The friendly licensee and locals are keen supporters of local charities. Situated next to the Albert, the two pubs complement one another, and are handy for the bus station. It stays open until midnight every night during TT fortnight. The hallway often becomes crowded eves and weekends.
⛫⊟⇌ (IMR)

Rovers Return

11 Church Street (behind town hall)
⏲ 12-11 (midnight Fri & Sat); 12-3, 7-10.30 Sun
☎ (01624) 676459
Bushy's Bitter, seasonal beers; guest beers Ⓗ
Previously the Albion Hotel, belonging to Castletown Brewery, this back-street local is the only tied Bushy's pub on the island. A cobbled drinking area at the front has tables and chairs. Named after the owner's favourite Blackburn football team, a small bar serves a large basic room, and three other smaller rooms, one of which is a shrine to the Lancashire club. The main room displays photographs of old Manx hotels and a collection of English football club badges, while another room bears fire brigade memorabilia; note the unusual handpumps (fire brigade brass branch pipes) which came from the former fire station nearby.
⛫ᘓ◖⇌ (IMR)

Saddle Inn

2 Queens Street
(on harbour)
⏲ 10-11 (midnight Fri & Sat) 12-4, 7-10.30 (12-10.30 summer) Sun
☎ (01624) 673161
Cains Bitter; Okells Mild, Bitter; guest beers Ⓗ
Small, single-roomed bar, just off the quay; recently refurbished, it retains the bare-boards character of a local fishermen's haunt. This lively, friendly local can get very busy. Racing silks adorn the walls, alongside a large photo of Joey Dunlop, a tribute to this famous adopted son of the Isle of Man. Joey was an Irish motorcycle champion, who, having won the TT races on several occasions, was worshipped the world over. He died in 2000, doing what he loved, and will be sadly missed. The pub hosts Karaoke (Thu eve) and, in winter, Manx pool (Tue), men's darts (Mon) and ladies' (Wed).
⇌ (IMR) ♣

Terminus Tavern

Strathallan Crescent
(N end of promenade)
⏲ 12-11 (midnight Fri & Sat); 12-3, 7-10.30 Sun
☎ (01624) 624312
Okells Mild, Bitter; guest beers Ⓗ
This spacious, multi-roomed black and white pub boasts bay windows overlooking the promenade at the termini of the horse tram/Manx Electric Railway. With a large outdoor seating area at the front, the accommodation includes a no-smoking family room; old photographs feature many of Stan Laurel and Oliver Hardy. The Huddersfield group, Storm, performs live music during TT fortnight. In summer just sit outside and watch the world go by, and enjoy the panoramic views across Douglas Bay.
ᘓ❀◖⊟♿⇌ (MER) ⚟

Waterloo Hotel

77 Strand Street
(behind Loch Promenade in shopping street)
⏲ 12-11 (midnight Fri & Sat); 12-3, 7-10.30 Sun
☎ (01624) 677468
Okells Mild, Bitter Ⓗ
Small, very basic, tiled-fronted, typical Manx pub, tucked away in the Strand pedestrian shopping street. Long and narrow, its two rooms (one housing a pool table) are joined by a narrow drinking corridor displaying horse-racing photographs. A collection of water jugs and plates feature in the front bar. Basic sandwiches and toasties are sold at lunchtime. This unspoilt pub is welcoming and friendly, and can get very busy; it hosts Karaoke on Fri eve.
♣

Woodbourne Hotel

Alexander Drive
(off Woodbourne Road)
⏲ 12-11 (midnight Fri & Sat); closed winter afternoons; 12-3, 7-10.30 Sun
☎ (01624) 676754
Okells Mild, Bitter Ⓗ
Large, Victorian suburban multi-roomed former hotel in a residential area; worth finding for a friendly quiet drink, among customers of all ages. Three bars serve the various rooms, which include a games room for darts and dominoes, a gentlemen's-only bar (rules tend to be relaxed at times), and a large, comfortable front lounge. The licensee, who has won a *Customer Care* award, describes the Woodbourne as three pubs in one, with three different sets of clientele, who all get on with one another.
Q⊟

INDEPENDENT BREWERIES

Bushy's Bradden
Okells Douglas
Old Laxey Laxey

KIRK MICHAEL

Mitre Hotel
Main Road (A3)
☼ 12-11 (midnight Fri & Sat); 12-3, 7-10.30 Sun
☎ (01624) 878244
Okells Mild, Bitter; guest beers Ⓗ

Large roadside village pub with a restaurant, said to be the oldest on the island (circa 1789), the Mitre is an ideal spot for watching the TT races, as it is fronted by a large car park. A large garden and safe children's play area to the rear afford a fine panoramic view towards Snaefell. A split bar serves both the lounge and dining area, and is wheelchair friendly. An unusual pub game, 'Shulbac', which originated in Holland, was introduced here and has been taken up by other island pubs. The adjacent old village fire station is now the function room. ⛺☙❀◑⊟♣♠P

LAXEY

Mines Tavern
Captains Hill (Douglas/Ramsey/Snaefell station interchange)
☼ 12-11 (midnight Fri & Sat); 12-3, 7-10.30 Sun
☎ (01624) 861484
Bushy's Bitter; Okells Bitter Ⓗ

Adjacent to the delightful Laxey electric tram station and Snaefell mountain railway terminus, the Douglas–Ramsey bus stops close by. This popular family-run tourist pub is also favoured by locals. The pub layout must be unique: enter the public bar from the garden and you will find a counter resembling a Manx electric railway tramcar; railways and mining are emphasised in the decor. A safe children's play area is another feature. Speciality 'sizzling platers' and home-cooked food are served daily. A trip to the summit of Snaefell (2,000 feet) and a visit to the local Lady Isabella Waterwheel, are recommended.
❀◑⊟≠⊖(MER)

PEEL

Royal Hotel
25 Atholl Street (opp. bus station)
☼ 12-11 (midnight Fri & Sat); 12-3, 7-10.30 Sun
☎ (01624) 842217
Okells Mild, Bitter Ⓗ

Faded, red-brick three-storey pub, sandwiched between a church and a pharmacy in the town centre, it stands just off the main street, leading to Peel Harbour and promenade. This cosy, back-street, L-shaped local has a comfortable, attractive outdoor eating area that hosts barbecues summer weekends, while live music nights are held in the rear lounge occasionally. A feature of the pub is a serving hatch from the bar to the small front room. The pub fields a football and rugby team, two darts and dominoes teams, and three pool teams.
Q❀♠

White House
2 Tynwald Road
☼ 12-11 (midnight Fri & Sat); 12-3, 7-10.30 Sun
☎ (01624) 842252
Bushy's Bitter; Okells Mild, Bitter; guest beers Ⓗ

Currently five real ales are stocked at this multi-roomed town pub with a snug, a public bar, music room and pool room, all surrounding a central bar counter. Local musicians meet most Sat eves to play Gaelic music at this popular pub that enjoys substantial local support. A genuine free house, one of very few on the island. It also hosts occasional Karaoke and 'poetry & pint' nights. Serving one of the best pints on the island, this family-run pub serves lunchtime snacks, and is a gem. ⛺❀⊟⌖♠P●

PORT ERIN

Falcon's Nest Hotel
Station Road (Spaldrick Promenade jct)
☼ 12-11 (midnight Fri & Sat); 12-3, 7-10.30 Sun
☎ (01624) 834077
Okells Bitter; guest beers Ⓗ

Splendid, spacious seafront hotel with two public bars (real ale in the front lounge bar only), it commands a fine view of Port Erin's small harbour. Run by the same family for almost 20 years, it provides comfort and a relaxing atmosphere with superb service. During the last century the hotel was the most prestigious on the island with such distinguished patrons as Prime Minister WE Gladstone and is being restored to its former elegance. Children are made more than welcome. Good food is served in the bar or restaurant.
⛺⊨◑≠(IMR)

PORT ST MARY

Albert Hotel
Athol Street (overlooking harbour)
☼ 12-11 (midnight Fri & Sat); 12-10.30 Sun
☎ (01624) 832118
Draught Bass; Okells Bitter; guest beers Ⓗ

Harbourside pub that has been free of tie for four years. Recently sympathetically refurbished and extended, a wood-blocked floor and wrought iron tables enhance its smart new appearance. The extension includes a raised games area for pool and darts, and a bistro has been created in the former pool room. Two guest beers are always available; it can get very busy at weekends. It has five letting bedrooms, and enjoys a panoramic view of the small harbour. The Douglas bus stops outside.
⛺Q◑⊟♣

RAMSEY

Swan Hotel
Parliament Square
☼ 12-11 (midnight Fri & Sat);12-3, 7-10.30 Sun
☎ (01624) 814236
Okells Mild, Bitter, seasonal beers Ⓗ

Large, town-centre modern local that attracts visitors. On the TT course, a central bar serves a large, comfortable lounge and a games room that supports darts and pool teams. It runs a winter quiz league and a social club for its regulars. Lunches are served Mon–Sat. It is wheelchair-friendly, including designated WCs. It has a spacious garden at the rear and is convenient for the MER terminus. ◑⊖(MER)

Trafalgar
West Quay
☼ 12-11 (midnight Fri & Sat); closed lunch, 7-10.30 Sun
☎ (01624) 801624

Draught Bass; Bushy's Bitter; Cains Bitter; guest beer Ⓗ

Laid-back quayside local that caters for visitors as well; no gimmicks, no frills, just good real ale, with usually one guest. The good food, with seafood meals a speciality, should not be missed. The friendly licensees run a homestead nearby, housing a menagerie of assorted animals and birds. They also provide free food for local sports teams at weekends. This local CAMRA *Pub of the Year* in 1996/97 benefits from harbour views.

🏠🛏🍴⊖ (MER) ♣ ●

SULBY

Sulby Glen Hotel
Sulby Crossroads (A3)

🕙 12-11 (midnight Fri & Sat); 12-3, 7-10.30 Sun

☎ (01624) 897240

Bushy's Bitter, seasonal beers; Okells Bitter; guest beers Ⓗ

Pleasant, spacious, roadside pub, situated in the centre of the village by the picturesque Sulby Straight on the famous TT course. The hotel, with 11 guest rooms, is ideally placed for motorcycle fans or those who simply appreciate the attractive rural surroundings.

Its two public bars display much TT memorabilia, including signed photographs. Manx CAMRA *Pub of the Year* 1998, it hosts a 'Battle of the Pubs' challenge each year, where games include wellie-throwing and canoeing. No Sun eve meals, except in summer.

🏠Q🐕🛏⊙◑🚶♿♣♠P

UNION MILLS

Railway Inn
Union Mills, Braddan (A1)

🕙 12-11 (midnight Fri & Sat); 12-3, 7-10.30 Sun

☎ (01624) 853006

Boddingtons Bitter; Cains Bitter; Okells Mild, Bitter; guest beers Ⓗ

Village pub, a hive of social activity, serving up to three guest beers. A true free house, this former Castletown Brewery tied pub has been in the same family for over 100 years, and has never had a man's name over the front door. One central bar serves the main lounge and several small rooms. Its former names include the Grapes and the Prince of Wales; look out for original memorabilia. It closed for a period for extensive refurbishment, but reopened in Aug 1998. 🏠Q♣❀♣P

Hop Picking

As summer grew middle-aged and a little grey, the season of hop-picking arrived with unfailing activity and excitement, in the local sense of the word. Our meadows and copses, even some of the lairs of the redoubtable anglers, were then invaded by the annual tribes from the East End of London or the slums of Brighton; no place was too venerable for these joyful and blasphemous marauders. However, the actual business of hop-picking, which occupies almost all of daylight, kept them from taking us, and our damsons, entirely by storm. They came in families, and alliances of families, to 'take on' as last year the farmer whose mien and pay pleased best. It must have been a wonderful holiday, hop-picking, for those who ordinarily have to fight for a little sun and air in mean streets, and there used to be many a smile as the measurer and the book-keepers moved among the bins of the hop-pickers...The same old fellows as ever in football jerseys and patchwork trousers appeared opposite the village stores to do a roaring trade in dried fish, clothing, gaudy sweets, bottled mysteries; the same brawls outside the Two Brewers...Besides these personal differences occasionally the pickers at some of the farms would strike, but how gently! A few hours, and all was proceeding as before, nor would any graver disturbance usually interrupt the ingathering of hops, until at length the special train with cushionless seats carried back the Londoners to their homes.

Edmund Blunden, *The Face of England, 1932.*

How to use The Breweries section

Breweries are listed in alphabetical order. The Independents (regional, smaller craft brewers and brew-pubs) are listed first, followed by the Nationals and finally the major non-brewing Pub Groups. Within each brewery entry, beers are listed in increasing order of strength. Beers that are available for less than three months of the year are described as 'occasional' or 'seasonal' brews. Bottle-conditioned beers are also listed: these are beers that have not been pasteurised and contain live yeast, allowing them to continue to ferment and mature in the bottle as a draught real ale does in its cask.

Symbols

♀ A brew-pub: a pub that brews beer on the premises.

◆ CAMRA tasting notes, supplied by a trained CAMRA tasting panel. Beer descriptions that do not carry this symbol are based on more limited tastings or have been obtained from other sources. Tasting notes are not provided for brew-pub beers that are available in fewer than five outlets, nor for other breweries' beers that are available for less than three months of the year.

🗗 A CAMRA Beer of the Year in the past three years.

🛆 One of the 2001 CAMRA Beers of the Year, a finalist in the Champion Beer of Britain competition held during the Great British Beer Festival at Olympia in August 2001, or the Champion Winter Beer of Britain competition held earlier in the year.

⊛ The brewery's beers can be acceptably served through a 'tight sparkler' attached to the nozzle of the beer pump, designed to give a thick collar of foam on the beer.

⊠ The brewery's beer should NOT be served through a tight sparkler. CAMRA is opposed to the growing tendency to serve southern-brewed beers with the aid of sparklers, which aerate the beer and tend to drive hop aroma and flavour into the head, altering the balance of the beer achieved in the brewery.

Abbreviations

OG stands for original gravity, the measure taken before fermentation of the level of 'fermentable material' (malt sugars and added sugars) in the brew. It is a rough indication of strength and is no longer used for duty purposes.

ABV stands for Alcohol by Volume, which is a more reliable measure of the percentage of alcohol in the finished beer. Many breweries now only disclose ABVs but the Guide lists OGs where available. Often the OG and the ABV of a beer are identical, ie 1035 and 3.5 per cent. If the ABV is higher than the OG, ie OG 1035, ABV 3.8, this indicates that the beer has been 'well attenuated' with most of the malt sugars turned into alcohol. If the ABV is lower than the OG, this means residual sugars have been left in the beer for fullness of body and flavour: this is rare but can apply to some milds or strong old ales, barley wines, and winter beers.

*The Breweries Section was correct at the time of going to press and every effort has been made to ensure that all cask-conditioned and bottle-conditioned beers are included.

The Independents

*Indicates new entry since last edition

ABBEY ALES

**Abbey Ales Ltd, The Abbey Brewery,
2 Lansdown Road, Bath, Somerset, BA1 5EE
Tel (01225) 444437 Fax 01225 443569
E-mail am@abbeyales.co.uk
Website www.abbeyales.co.uk**
Tours by arrangement

Abbey Ales is the first and only brewery in Bath for more than 40 years. Bellringer was launched at the Bath Beer Festival in 1997 and is the only beer produced on a regular basis. It has won three CAMRA festival awards: Cotswolds 1998, Devizes 1999 and Bath 2000. Seasonal beers: Bath Star (ABV 4.5%,autumn); and Twelfth Night (ABV 5%, winter). A spring beer is planned. The brewery supplies more than 80 regular accounts within a 20-mile radius of Bath; Bellringer is available nationally through selected wholesalers. One tied house, the Star Inn, Bath, is listed on CAMRA's National Inventory of Heritage Inns.

Bellringer *(OG 1042, ABV 4.2%)*
A notably hoppy ale which is light to medium-bodied, clean-tasting, refreshingly dry, with a balancing sweetness. Citrus, pale malt aroma and dry, bitter finish. Consistent. Amber-gold in colour.

Chorister *(OG 1048, ABV 4.8%)*

ABBEYDALE

**Abbeydale Brewery, Unit 8, Aizlewood Road,
Sheffield, S Yorkshire, S8 0YX
Tel (0114) 281 2712
Fax (0114) 281 2713**

Started in 1996 by Patrick Morton, previously of Kelham Island. 100 pubs are supplied with guest beers. Occasional/seasonal/special commission beers: Steamhammer (ABV 4.7%), White Christmas (ABV 5.2%), Black Lurcher (ABV 7.2%), James I (ABV 7.2%).

Matins *(OG 1035, ABV 3.6%)*

Bitter *(OG 1038, ABV 4%)*

Moonshine *(OG 1041, ABV 4.3%)*

Archangel *(OG 1047, ABV 4.7%)*

Dark Angel *(OG 1047, ABV 4.7%)*

Black Mass *(OG 1062, ABV 6.6%)*

Last Rites *(OG 1105, ABV 11.5%)*

ADNAMS

**Adnams PLC, Sole Bay Brewery,
Southwold, Suffolk, IP18 6JW
Tel (01502) 727200
Fax (01502) 727201
E-mail info@adnams.co.uk
Website www.adnams.co.uk**
Shop 9.30-6.30 Mon-Sat
Tours by arrangement

The earliest recorded brewing on the site of Adnams was in 1345 by Johanna de Corby. The present brewery was taken over by George and Ernest Adnams in 1872 and turned into a public company in 1890. The Adnams family was joined by the Loftus family in 1902, and Adnams still has three members of the family working within the company: John Adnams, president, chairman Simon Loftus, and Jonathan Adnams, managing director. Adnams remains committed to brewing cask ale and unthemed pubs. Real ale is available in 87 of its 88 pubs, and it also supplies some 750 other outlets direct. New fermenting vessels were installed in 2001 to cope with increased demand. Seasonal beers are now available for longer periods: Regatta (ABV 4.3%, spring/summer), Fisherman (ABV 4.5%, autumn/winter), Tally Ho (ABV 7%, Christmas).

Bitter *(OG 1036, ABV 3.7%)*
An excellent drinking beer, with the characteristic Adnams' aroma of hops, citrus fruits and sulphur. The flavour is dry and hoppy, with some fruit. The finish is long, dry and hoppy.

Regatta *(OG 1042, ABV 4.3%)*
Light, bright and crisp in flavour with a refreshing touch of bitterness.

Fisherman *(OG 1047, ABV 4.5%)*
Rich and complex but clean and refreshing deep copper-red ale. Roasted nuts and dark chocolate dominate the aroma, with lingering flavours of liquorice and dried fruits.

Broadside *(OG 1049, ABV 4.7%)*
A mid-brown beer with a well-balanced flavour of fruit, malt and hops on a bitter-sweet base. The aroma is fruity, with some underlying malt and hops. Bitter fruit finish.

ALCAZAR

**Alcazar Brewing Company at the
Fox & Crown brew-pub, 33 Church Street,
Old Basford, Nottingham, NG6 0GA**

Tel (0115) 942 2002 Fax (0115) 978 2282
E-mail dallen@alcazar.freeserve.co.uk
Tours by arrangement

Alcazar Brewing Company (ABC) was
established in 1999 and is located behind
its brewery tap. The name Alcazar is
Spanish for 'palace', which relates to the
crown in the pub's name. The brewery is
full mash with a 12-barrel brew-length.
Production is primarily for the pub plus
CAMRA beer festivals. Plans are in hand to
expand the brewing operation for regular
sales to the free trade as well as bottling a
range of new beers for the local and export
markets. Visitors are welcome and regular
tours are conducted on Saturdays by prior
arrangement. Seasonal ales: Black Fox Mild
(ABV 3.9%, spring); Maple Magic Winter
Ale (ABV 5%, winter).

Ale *(OG 1038, ABV 3.7%)*
A traditional session ale, full flavoured with
a fruity aroma and fruit-hoppy finish.

New Dawn Millennium Ale
(OG 1045, ABV 4.5%)
A light coloured ale, full-bodied with a
crisp, clean finish.

Brush Bitter *(OG 1050, ABV 4.9%)*
A deep red bitter with a well-rounded
flavour, maltiness on the palate and a
distinctive hoppy finish.

Vixen's Vice *(OG 1052, ABV 5.2%)*
A pale, full malt beer with distinctive
flavour and a crisp, hoppy finish.

ALES OF KENT

**Ales of Kent Brewery Ltd, The Old Stables,
Boxley Grange, Grange Farm, Lidsing Road,
Boxley, Maidstone, Kent, ME14 3EL
Tel/Fax (01634) 669296
E-mail info@alesofkentbrewery.co.uk
Website www.alesofkentbrewery.co.uk**
Tours by arrangement

The brewery moved in 2000 after 15
months in an industrial unit. It is now on
a farm in a former stable block; farm and
buildings were once associated with the
former Style & Winch brewing company.
A third fermenter will be added to increase
production. 60 outlets are supplied direct.
Bottle-conditioned beers: Stiltman (ABV
4.3%), Smugglers Glory (ABV 4.8%).
Seasonal beer: Defiance (ABV 4.1%,
spring/autumn).

Old Ma Weasel *(OG 1035, ABV 3.6%)*
A pale, hoppy session beer.

Wealden Wonder *(OG 1035, ABV 3.7%)*
A smooth, citrus ale with hoppy aroma.

Smugglers Mild *(OG 1036.5, ABV 3.8%)*
A dark mild ale. Lightly hopped with Kent-
grown hops.

Stiltman *(OG 1041, ABV 4.3%)*
Rich fruity notes and aroma from First Gold
and Fuggles hops.

Smugglers Glory *(OG 1046, ABV 4.8%)*
A dark smooth ale with chocolate
undertones.

Contraflow *(OG 1048.5, ABV 5%)*
A strong, pale beer with a smooth finish.

ALEWIFE*

**Alewife Brewery, Starston, Harleston,
Norfolk, IP20 9NN
Tel (01379) 855267
E-mail AlewifeBrewery@yahoo.co.uk
Website www.alewifebrewers.co.uk**

A small brewery set up in October by Jane
Taylor, who had been home-brewing for 20
years. Her friends so admired her Xmas
brew in 1999 that they encouraged her to
brew commercially. At present she produces
only bottle-conditioned beers as casks are
too heavy for her to handle, though she
hopes to brew cask ales sometime in 2002.
She supplies one pub, several off-licences
and also sells by mail order.

Harvest Ale *(ABV 4.5%)*

Dark Skies *(ABV 4.6%)*

Festival Ale *(ABV 6.5%)*

ALL NATIONS

**◻ All Nations, 20 Coalport Road, Madeley,
Telford, Shropshire, TF7 5DP
Tel (01952) 585747**

Brewing ceased in December 2000 at this
famous brew-pub, which first opened in
1789. The licensee is due to retire and the
pub is up for sale.

ALTRINCHAM

**Altrincham Brewing Company,
Old Market Tavern, Old Market Place,
Altrincham, Cheshire, WA14 4DN
Tel (0771) 2033886 (mobile)
(0161) 9277062 (pub)
E-mail dave_ward@connectfree.co.uk**
Tours by arrangement

The beers are available at the pub and in
free houses around Manchester.

Timperley Mild Man *(ABV 3.8%)*

Agent X *(ABV 4.1%)*

Coal Porter *(ABV 4.8%)*

ANGLO DUTCH*

**The Anglo Dutch Brewery, Unit 12,
Savile Bridge Mills, Mill Street East,
Dewsbury, W Yorkshire, WF13 6QQ
Tel (01924) 457772**

Dewsbury's first new commercial brewery
was set up in November 2000 by Mike Field
(Anglo) and Paul Klos (Dutch). Mike also
runs the buffet bar at Dewsbury Railway
Station, where the beers are on sale; they are
occasionally sold at the famous Stalybridge
Station buffet as well, plus free houses in the
area. Both beers use wheat in the recipes;
more beers are due to be added to the range.
Kletswater is Dutch for 'waffle water', which
begs the question 'What is waffle water?'

Kletswater *(ABV 3.9%)*
Pale, full-bodied session bitter.

Grizzly Ghost *(ABV 4.3%)*
Full-bodied pale bitter.

Ghost on the Rim *(ABV 4.5%)*
Pale, dry and fruity.

*Whitterus Organicus is an organic version
of Kletswater.

ANN STREET

See Jersey.

ARCHERS

**Archers Ales Ltd,
Penzance Drive,
Swindon, Wiltshire, SN5 7JL
Tel (01793) 879929
Fax (01793) 879489
Website www.archers-brewery.co.uk**
Shop 9-5 Mon-Fri; 9-12 Sat
Tours occasionally, by arrangement, with a charge

⊗ Founded in 1979 in Swindon, the home of the Great Western Railway, Archers is in the former Weigh House, used for weighing and balancing steam engines of a bygone age. Archers has become one of the premier regional breweries in the south. The beers have won many prizes including a Gold Medal at the Brewing Industry International Awards. The company supplies three tied houses and another 200 free trade outlets direct and via wholesalers. The brewery was bought by a pub group, Burns Leisure, in August 1999, which then bought and closed Tom Hoskins of Leicester in 2000. Occasional/seasonal beers: Marley's Ghost (ABV 7%, Dec-Jan), Black Jack Porter (ABV 4.6%, Oct-Jan). Bottle-conditioned beer: Golden Bitter (ABV 4.6%).

Village Bitter *(OG 1035, ABV 3.5%)* 🗂️🌿
A dry, well-balanced beer, with a full body for its gravity. Malty and fruity in the nose, then a fresh, hoppy flavour with balancing malt and a hoppy, fruity finish.

Tom Hoskins Bitter *(OG 1037, ABV 3.7%)*
A light, golden bitter.

Best Bitter *(OG 1040, ABV 4%)* 🌿
Slightly sweeter and rounder than Village, with a malty, fruity aroma and a pronounced bitter finish.

Golden Bitter *(OG 1046, ABV 4.7%)* 🌿
A full-bodied, hoppy, straw-coloured brew with an underlying fruity sweetness. A gentle aroma, but a strong, distinctive bitter finish.

Churchill's Pride *(OG 1049, ABV 4.9%)*
A beer from the former Tom Hoskin's portfolio.

ARKELLS

**Arkell's Brewery Ltd, Kingsdown, Swindon, Wiltshire, SN2 6RU
Tel (01793) 823026**
**Fax (01793) 828864
Website www.arkells.co.uk**
Tours by arrangement

⊗ Established in 1843 and now one of the few remaining breweries whose shares are all held by one family. Managing director James Arkell is a great-great-grandson of founder John Arkell. Gradually expanding its tied estate, mainly along the M4 corridor, the brewery is committed to a continual programme of upgrading and refurbishment for its pubs. All 96 tied pubs serve real ale, which is also supplied direct to around 200 free trade accounts. Some of the malt comes from James Arkell's own farm. Fuggles and Goldings hops are used, with pale ale malt and crystal malt. There is a higher proportion of crystal malt in 3B and Kingsdown, which are 'parti-gyled', i.e. made from the same mash but then reduced with 'liquor' [water] to the required strength. Occasional/seasonal beers: Yeomanry (ABV 4.5%), Peter's Porter (ABV 4.8%), Noel Ale (ABV 5.5%, Christmas).

2B *(OG 1032, ABV 3.2%)* 🌿
Light brown in colour, malty but with a smack of hops and an astringent aftertaste. An ideal lunchtime beer, it has good body for its strength.

3B *(OG 1040, ABV 4%)* 🌿
A medium brown beer with a strong, sweetish malt/caramel flavour. The hops come through strongly in the aftertaste, which is lingering and dry.

Kingsdown Ale *(OG 1052, ABV 5%)* 🌿
A rich deep russet-coloured beer, a stronger version of 3B. The malty/fruity aroma continues in the taste, which has a hint of pears. The hops come through in the aftertaste where they are complemented by caramel tones.

ARRAN

**Isle of Arran Brewery Co Ltd, Cladach, Brodick, Isle of Arran, KA27 8DE
Tel (01770) 302353
Website www.arranbrewery.com**
Visitor centre

A brewery opened in 2000 by Richard and Elizabeth Roberts. The brewing plant was bought from the Tipsy Toad Town House brew-pub in St Helier, Jersey, a move that brings a new meaning to 'island hopping'. It is a 20-barrel plant arranged on two floors, with the mash tun based above the copper and fermenters. The three cask beers are also available in carbonated bottled form. Arran Ale is sold as Arran Light in bottle.

Ale *(ABV 3.8%)* 🌿
A deep amber summer ale, typical of new wave Scottish beers. The predominance of the hop produces a bitter beer with a subtle balancing sweetness of malt and fruit.

Dark *(4.3%)* 🌿
A well-balanced malty beer with a distinctive taste and a dry, bitter finish.

Blonde *(ABV 5%)* 🌿
A hoppy beer with substantial fruit balance. The taste is bitter-sweet and the finish increasingly bitter and dry. An aromatic strong bitter that drinks below its weight.

ARUNDEL

**Arundel Brewery Ltd,
Unit 7C, Ford Airfield Industrial Estate,
Ford, Arundel, W Sussex, BN18 0BE
Tel (01903) 733111
Fax (01903) 733381
E-mail arundelbrewery@telinco.co.uk**

⊠ Set up in 1992, the town's first brewery in
60 years, Arundel now supplies around 100
outlets. Under new ownership from
September 1998, Arundel continues to serve
and increase its range of occasional and
seasonal beers. Occasional ales are on sale
for one month each. Seasonal beers: Old
Knucker (ABV 5.5%, Sept-April), Summer
Daze (ABV 4.7%).

Gauntlet *(OG 1035, ABV 3.5%)*

Castle *(OG 1038, ABV 3.8%)* ◆
A pale tawny beer with fruit and malt
noticeable in the aroma. The flavour has a
good balance of malt, fruit and hops, with a
dry, hoppy finish.

Gold *(OG 1042, ABV 4.2%)* ◆
A light golden ale with a malty, fruity
flavour and a little hop in the finish.

Classic *(OG 1045, ABV 4.5%)*
A golden brown beer with roast malt and
hop flavour giving way to a fruity, hoppy,
bitter-sweet finish.

Black Beastie *(OG 1049, ABV 4.9%)*

Stronghold *(OG 1050, ABV 5%)*

For Beards:

Best Bitter *(OG 1040, ABV 4%)* ◆
Hints of fruit and hops in the aroma lead
into a sweet, malty beer, with a dry, hoppy
aftertaste.

ASH VINE

**Ash Vine Brewery,
Unit F, Vallis Trading Estate, Robins Lane,
Frome, Somerset, BA11 3DT**

The brewery ceased trading early in 2001.
The company's four pubs are still in
operation and it is hoped to find a buyer for
the brewery.

ASTON MANOR

**Aston Manor Brewery Co Ltd,
173 Thimble Mill Lane, Aston, Birmingham,
W Midlands, B7 5HS
Tel (0121) 328 4336
Fax (0121) 328 0139**
Shop 10-6 Mon-Fri; 10-1 Sat

Aston Manor owns the Highgate Brewery in
Walsall (qv). Its own plant concentrates on
packaged beers, lagers and cider in plastic
bottles.

AVIEMORE

**The Aviemore Brewery Co Ltd, Unit 12,
Dalfaber Ind Estate, Aviemore, PH22 1PY
Tel (01479) 812222
Fax (01479) 811465
E-mail aviemore.brewery@dial.pipex.com**
Shop. Tours by arrangement

Aviemore started brewing in July 1997 and
bottling followed in November that year.

Four regular cask-conditioned beers are
produced and 253 outlets are supplied
direct. The company also owns and brews
for Tomintoul Brewery.

Highland IPA *(OG 1036, ABV 3.6%)* ◆
A light ale with a crisp freshness.

Ruthven Brew *(OG 1039, ABV 3.8%)* ◆
A copper-coloured ale that is malt-accented
with a hoppy aroma but without a
particularly bitter taste.

Cairngorm Gold *(OG 1046, ABV 4.5%)* ◆
A golden beer with a good balance between
continental hops and fine Scottish malt.

Wee Murdoch *(OG 1048, ABV 4.8%)* ◆
A strong, robust, deep copper-coloured beer.

Tomintoul beers:

Stag *(ABV 4.1%)* ◆
A powerful malty nose with less hop
character on the palate than in early brews.
This tawny brew has a lingering malty,
gently bitter aftertaste.

Nessie's Monster Mash *(ABV 4.4%)* ◆
A mahogany-coloured, full malty brew with
a creamy mouthfeel leading to a satisfying,
fruity finish. ◆

Wild Cat *(ABV 5.1%)* ◆
A fruity aroma leads to a sweetish fruity
beer with much malt in evidence. Hops and
caramel add complexity to this pale brown
ale.

B&T

**B&T Brewery Ltd, The Brewery, Shefford,
Beds, SG17 5DZ
Tel (01462) 815080
Fax (01462) 850841**
Tours by arrangement

⊠ Banks & Taylor, founded in 1981, was
restructured in 1994 under the name B&T
Brewery and has continued to produce an
extensive range of beers, including monthly
special brews together with contract
brewing for wholesalers and individual
public houses. 60 outlets are supplied direct
and three pubs are owned. Bottle-
conditioned beer: Dragonslayer (ABV 5%) ⊡

Shefford Bitter *(OG 1038, ABV 3.8%)*
A pleasant, predominantly hoppy session
beer with a bitter finish.

Shefford Dark Mild
(OG 1038, ABV 3.8%) ◆
A dark beer with a well-balanced taste.
Sweetish, roast malt aftertaste.

Dragonslayer *(OG 1045, ABV 4.5%)* ◆
A straw-coloured beer, dry, malty and
lightly hopped.

Edwin Taylor's Extra Stout
(OG 1045, ABV 4.5%) ◆
A pleasant, bitter beer with a strong roast
malt flavour.

Shefford Pale Ale (SPA)
(OG 1045, ABV 4.5%) ◆
A well-balanced beer with hop, fruit and
malt flavours. Dry, bitter aftertaste.

Shefford Old Strong (SOS)
(OG 1050, ABV 5%) ◆
A rich mixture of fruit, hops and malt is
present in the taste and aftertaste of this

beer. Predominantly hoppy aroma.

Shefford Old Dark (SOD)
(OG 1050, ABV 5%)
SOS with caramel added for colour. Often sold under house names.

Black Bat *(OG 1060, ABV 6%)* ◆
A powerful, sweet, fruity and malty beer for winter. Fruity, nutty aroma; strong roast malt aftertaste.

2XS *(OG 1060, ABV 6%)* ◆
A reddish beer with a strong, fruity, hoppy aroma. The taste is full-flavoured and the finish strong and sweetish

Old Bat *(OG 1070, ABV 7%)* ◆
A powerful-tasting, sweet winter beer, with bitterness coming through in the aftertaste. Fruit is present in both aroma and taste.

BADGER

Hall & Woodhouse Ltd, The Brewery, Blandford St Mary, Dorset, DT11 9LS
Tel (01258) 452141
Fax (01258) 459528
E-mail tim.morris@hall-woodhouse.co.uk
Website www.badgerbrewery.com
Shop 9-5 Mon-Sat. Tours by arrangement

⊗ The company was founded in 1777 as the Ansty Brewery by Charles Hall. Charles's son took George Woodhouse into partnership and formed Hall & Woodhouse. They moved to their present site at Blandford St Mary in 1899. Now a well-established brewer trading under the Badger name, it owns 250 pubs in the south of England including the Gribble Inn brew-pub at Oving, West Sussex (qv), and supplies 700 outlets direct. In 2000, Hall & Woodhouse bought King & Barnes of Horsham and closed the brewery. It matched some of K&B beers, which will be available throughout the Badger estate as well as the former Horsham company's 57 pubs. Seasonal ale: King & Barnes Old Ale (ABV 4.5%, winter). Bottled-conditioned beers: K&B Faygate Dragon (ABV 4.7%), Cornucopia (ABV 6.5%).

Sussex Bitter *(OG 1033, ABV 3.5%)*
A smooth bitter, well-hopped and full-bodied. A former King & Barnes beer.

IPA *(OG 1034, ABV 3.6%)*
A pale beer, light, refreshing and pleasantly hoppy. Served with a creamy head.

Best Bitter *(OG 1039, ABV 4%)* ◆
A fine best bitter whose taste is strong in hop and bitterness, with underlying malt and fruit. Hoppy finish with a bitter edge.

Champion Ale *(OG 1043, ABV 4.6%)*
A golden ale with a distinctive floral, elderflower character. Lightly bittered to give a clean, fresh finish.

Tanglefoot *(OG 1047, ABV 5.1%)*
A full-bodied beer, pale straw in colour with a characteristic fruitiness, medium bitterness and a slightly spicy finish.

BALLARD'S

Ballard's Brewery Ltd, The Old Sawmill, Nyewood, Petersfield, GU31 5HA
Tel (01730) 821301/821362
Fax (01730) 821742

E-mail carola@ballards24.freeserve.co.uk
Website www.real-ale-guide.co.uk/ballards
Shop 8.30-4.30 Mon-Fri, by appointment Sat-Sun
Tours by arrangement

⊗ Founded in 1980 at Cumbers Farm, Trotton, Ballard's has been trading at Nyewood (in W Sussex, despite the postal address) since 1988 and now supplies around 70 free trade outlets. Occasional/seasonal beers: Golden Bine (ABV 4.2%, spring), On the Hop (ABV 4.5%, September), Wild (ABV 4.7%). Bottle-conditioned beers: Nyewood Gold (ABV 5%), Wassail (ABV 6%), Trout Tickler (ABV 9.9%).

Midhurst Mild *(3.5%)*

Trotton Bitter *(OG 1036, ABV 3.6%)* ◆
Amber, clean-tasting bitter. A roast malt aroma leads to a fruity, slightly sweet taste and a dry finish.

Best Bitter *(OG 1042, ABV 4.2%)* ◆
A copper-coloured beer with a malty aroma. A good balance of fruit and malt in the flavour gives way to a dry, hoppy aftertaste.

Nyewood Gold *(OG 1050, ABV 5%)* ⬡◆
Robust golden brown strong bitter, very hoppy and fruity throughout, with a tasty balanced finish.

Wassail *(OG 1060, ABV 6%)* ◆
A strong, full-bodied, fruity beer with a predominance of malt throughout, but also an underlying hoppiness. Tawny/red in colour.

BANFIELD

Correspondence to: Banfield Ales, Wingfield Farm, Wing, Leighton Buzzard, Beds, LU7 0LD
Brewery located at: The Brewery, 6 Main Street, Burrough-on-the-Hill, Leicestershire
Tel (07956) 246215
Fax (01296) 682632
E-mail steve@banfield-ales.co.uk
Website www.banfield-ales.co.uk
Tours by arrangement for small parties

Brewing suspended while new premises sought. Consult the website for latest information.

BANK TOP

Bank Top Brewery, Unit 1, Back Lane, off Vernon Street, Bolton, Lancs, BL1 2LD
Tel (01204) 528865
Tours by arrangement Mon-Fri evenings

⊗ Bank Top was established in 1995 by John Feeney. The brewery has enjoyed gradual expansion and there are plans to relocate to the Bank Top area of Bolton. The beers are supplied to 50-60 outlets locally. Seasonal/occasional beers: Satanic Mills II Judgement Day (ABV 5%), Santa's Claws (ABV 5%, Christmas).

Brydge Bitter *(OG 1038, ABV 3.8%)*

Flat Cap *(OG 1040, ABV 4%)*

Gold Digger *(OG 1040, ABV 4%)* ◆
Golden coloured, with a citrus aroma, grapefruit and a touch of spiciness on the palate and a fresh, hoppy citrus finish.

Dark Mild *(OG 1040, ABV 4%)*

Samuel Cromptons Ale
(OG 1042, ABV 4.2%) ◆
Amber beer with a fresh citrus-peel aroma.
Well-balanced with hops and zesty
grapefruit flavour and a hoppy, citrus finish.

The Haka *(OG 1042, ABV 4.2%)*

Old Slapper *(OG 1042, ABV 4.2%)*

Cliff Hanger *(OG 1045, ABV 4.5%)* ◆

Smoke Stack Lightning
(OG 1050, ABV 5%)

BANKS'S

**Wolverhampton & Dudley Breweries plc,
Park Brewery, Bath Road, Wolverhampton,
W Midlands, WV1 4NY
Tel (01902) 711811
Fax (01902) 329136
Website www.fullpint.co.uk**
Tours by arrangement

⊛ The future of Wolverhampton & Dudley
Breweries, Britain's biggest regional brewer,
was thrown into doubt in 2001 when the
Pubmaster group made a hostile, £453
million bid in June. The bid was defeated in
August 2001. Pre-empting the bid, W&D's
management decided to appease the City of
London in April 2001 with its own get-
tough stance. It announced that Camerons
of Hartlepool would be sold to the
neighbouring Castle Eden Brewery, while
Mansfield Brewery would close at the end of
the year. Mansfield brands will be switched
to Wolverhampton, where capacity will be
increased. Marston's of Burton-on-Trent will
remain in production, though a distribution
facility will close and some land will
be sold off. W&D will also sell most of its
managed pubs, and in total some 200 jobs
will disappear. See the separate entries for
all the breweries mentioned. Banks's was
formed in 1890 by the amalgamation of
three local companies. Hanson's was
acquired in 1943, but its Dudley brewery
was closed in 1991 and its beers are now
brewed at Wolverhampton, though
Hanson's pubs maintain their own livery. In
1992, W&D bought Camerons Brewery and
51 pubs from Brent Walker. In 1999 W&D
turned itself into a 'super regional' through
the acquisition of Marston's and Mansfield.
The W&D estate numbers 1,763, which
makes it tempting for companies interested
only in profitable retail outlets. Almost all
W&D pubs serve traditional ales and they
offer a 'full pint guarantee' by serving the
beer in oversized glasses. There is also
extensive free trade throughout the
country, particularly in pubs and clubs.
W&D, if it survives the predators, will
concentrate on such key brands as Banks's
Original and Bitter, and Marston's Pedigree.

Hanson's Mild *(OG 1034, ABV 3.3%)* ◆
A mid-to dark brown mild with a malty
roast flavour and aftertaste.

Banks's Original *(OG 1036, ABV 3.5%)* ◆
An amber-coloured, well-balanced,
refreshing session beer.

Banks's Bitter *(OG 1038, ABV 3.8%)* ◆
A pale brown bitter with a pleasant balance
of hops and malt. Hops continue from the
taste through to a bitter-sweet aftertaste.

BARGE & BARREL

**Barge & Barrel Brewery Co,
10-20 Park Road, Elland,
W Yorkshire, HX5 9HP
Tel/Fax (01422) 375039**

The brewery, owned by White Rose Inns,
was set up in a large ex-children's room in
the Barge and Barrel pub. It brews in 4-
barrel batches and there are plans to
enlarge the plant. The beers have won
awards at CAMRA beer festivals in Barnsley,
Bradford, Huddersfield, Leeds, Stockport
and Wakefield. The company supplies
some of its own pubs and free trade
throughout Yorkshire and in Lancashire.
Rotating special beers, including
Old Gimmer (ABV 5%), and Coronation
Class (ABV 6%).

Bargee *(OG 1038, ABV 3.8%)* ◀◆
Pale bitter with a well-balanced malt, fruit
and hoppy character, and slightly sweet
citrus taste.

Best Bitter *(OG 1040, ABV 4%)* ◆
A straw-coloured bitter with a strong hoppy
aroma and taste. Fruity and malty in
character, the dry citrus, bitter flavour
lingers to the end.

Nettlethrasher *(OG 1044, ABV 4.4%)*
A premium bitter brewed with three
different malts and English and American
hops.

Black Stump *(OG 1050, ABV 5%)* ◆
Strong black porter with a smooth roasted
malt and chocolate flavour, and bitter
character.

Leveller *(OG 1057, ABV 5.7%)* ◆
A copper-coloured strong bitter with good
malt and hop balance. Slightly sweet and
fruity.

BARNGATES

**Barngates Brewery Ltd,
Barngates, Ambleside,
Cumbria, LA22 0NG
Tel/Fax (015394) 36575
E-mail
barngatesbrewery@drunkenduckinn.co.uk
Website www.drunkenduckinn.co.uk**
Tours by arrangement

Barngates Brewery began operating a 1-
barrel brewplant within the Drunken Duck
Inn in 1997. Expansion came in 1999 when
a brand-new 5-barrel plant was installed,
and the brewery became a separate limited
company. At present the brewery supplies
60 local outlets throughout Cumbria.
Bottle-conditioned beer: Tag Lag.

Cracker Ale
(OG 1038, ABV 3.9%)
Subtle hoppy aroma, clean, smooth and
refreshing, developing into a lingering
malty finish.

Tag Lag *(OG 1044, ABV 4.4%)*
A copper-coloured beer with a fruity aroma.
It has a sweet underlying bitterness, which
ends in a long-tasting bitter finish.

Chester's Strong & Ugly
(OG 1050, ABV 5.2%)
Slightly fruity, well-balanced, with roasted
malt and hop flavours.

BARNSLEY

Barnsley Brewery Co Ltd, Wath Road, Elsecar, Barnsley, S Yorkshire, S74 8HJ
Tel (01226) 741010 Fax (01226) 741009
Tours by arrangement

⊛ Established in 1994 as the South Yorkshire Brewing Co at the purpose- built brewery in Elsecar, Barnsley Bitter was reintroduced using the original yeast culture used by the old Barnsley Brewery at Oakwell, closed by John Smiths in the 1970s. In 1996, South Yorkshire won the right to use the name Barnsley Brewery and changed its name. The company has welcomed Robert Umbers as company chairman, whose family ran the original Barnsley Brewery for three generations. Demand continues to grow, with more than 200 local outlets taking the beer direct, while others are supplied by national distributors. It is planned to reintroduce Barnsley Bitter in bottle and to buy some tied houses. Seasonal beers: Mayflower (ABV 4.5%), Ey-Up! It's Christmas (ABV 4.7%), Ginger Tom (ABV 3.9%).

Bitter *(OG 1038, ABV 3.8%)* ⬧
A pale brown, creamy and smooth bitter with a hoppy and fruity aroma, and an even balance of hops and malt in the taste and in the long, dry and bitter finish.

IPA *(OG 1041, ABV 4.2%)*
A beer dominated by fruit and hops, leading to a hoppy finish. Light golden in colour with a flowery aroma.

Black Heart Stout *(OG 1044, ABV 4.6%)* ⬧
A black stout with a hoppy aroma, and roasted malt flavour throughout. Chocolatey, bitter finish.

Glory *(OG 1048, ABV 4.8%)*
A stronger version of Barnsley Bitter.

BARTRAMS

Bartrams Brewery, 8 Thurston Granary, Thurston, Suffolk, IP31 3QU
E-mail captainbill@lineone.net
Tours by arrangement

Marc Bartram started his brewery in 1999 and has built up a good trade with locals. Thirty outlets are supplied direct. He uses a 5-barrel plant purchased from Buffy's Brewery. He currently produces 10 barrels a week but hopes to double the amount. There was a Bartrams Brewery between 1894 and 1902 run by Captain Bill Bartram and his image graces the pump clips. Occasional beers: Trial & Error (ABV 3.5%), Beer Elsie Bub (ABV 4.8%), Xmas Holly Daze (ABV 7%).

Marld *(OG 1034, ABV 3.4%)*
A traditional mild.

Premier Bitter *(OG 1037, ABV 3.7%)*

Red Queen *(OG 1039, ABV 3.9%)*

Green Man *(ABV 4%)*
An organic beer, using West Country floor-malted Maris Otter malt, New Zealand hops and coriander.

Bees Knees *(OG 1042, ABV 4.2%)*

Jester Quick One *(OG 1044, ABV 4.4%)*
A darker than average best bitter that is more malty than hoppy, with hints of fruit in the aroma.

Captain's Stout *(OG 1048, ABV 4.8%)*

Captain Bill Bartrams Best Bitter
(OG 1048, ABV 4.8%)

BARUM

Barum Brewery Ltd, c/o The Reform Inn, Pilton, Barnstaple, Devon, EX31 1PD
Tel (01271) 329994
Fax (01271) 321590
Website www.barumbrewery.co.uk
Tours by arrangement

⊗ In 1996 the Combe Brewery in Ilfracombe was purchased and relocated to the Reform Inn in Barnstaple, where the name was changed. As Barum, it supplies some 60 pubs as well as Barnstaple Rugby Club. The company is building a new 5-barrel plant at the Castle Inn, George Nympton, South Molton, to cope with demand. Seasonal beer: Gold (ABV 4%, summer). Bottle-conditioned beers: Breakfast, Barnstablasta.

XTC *(OG 1040, ABV 3.9%)*

Original *(OG 1044, ABV 4.4%)*

Breakfast *(OG 1050, ABV 5%)*

Challenger *(OG 1056, ABV 5.6%)*

Barnstablasta *(OG 1066, ABV 6.6%)*

BATEMAN

George Bateman & Son Ltd, Salem Bridge Brewery, Wainfleet, Lincolnshire, PE24 4JE
Tel (01754) 880317 Fax (01754) 880939
E-mail jaclynbateman@bateman.co.uk
Website www.bateman.co.uk
Visitor centre and shop 11-4 daily

⊗ A family-owned brewery established in 1874 by the present chairman's grandfather, Batemans is committed to brewing cask-conditioned beers that have won many CAMRA awards. Beer was first brewed for local farmers but now the full range can be found in pubs throughout the country. A visitor centre was opened in 2000. Batemans owns 70 pubs and all serve cask ales. Seasonal ales: Loxley's Liquor (ABV 4.7%, Jan/Feb), Excalibur (ABV 4.4%, March/April), Godiva's Gold (ABV 4%, May/June), Marie Celeste (ABV 4.6%, July/Aug), Blackbeerd (ABV 3.6%, Sept/Oct), Owd Nessie (ABV 5%, Nov/Dec). Speciality Beers: Hooker (ABV 4.5%, Feb), Victory Ale (ABV 5.2%, April and Oct), Miss Whiplash (ABV 4.2%, June), Summer Swallow (ABV 3.9%, Aug), Rosey Nosey (ABV 4.9%, Dec). Bottled-conditioned beer: Pour With Care (for Booths supermarkets: 4.5%)

Dark Mild *(OG 1032, ABV 3%)* ▥▢⬧
Characteristic orchard fruit and roasted nut nose with hops evident. One of the classic mild ales, although the lasting bitter finish

673

may not be entirely true to type; nevertheless, a ruby-black gem.

XB *(OG 1037, ABV 3.7%)* ◈
A mid-brown balanced session bitter with malt most obvious in the finish. The taste is dominated by the house-style apple hop, which also leads the aroma.

Lincolnshire Yella Belly Organic Bitter *(OG 1042, ABV 4.2%)*
A seasonal beer that immediately became so popular it is now brewed on a regular basis.

Salem Porter *(OG 1048, ABV 4.7%)* ⬚◈
Ruby black with a brown tint to the head. The aroma is of liquorice with a subtle hint of dandelion and burdock; the initial taste is hoppy and bitter, with a mellowing of all the elements in the finish.

XXXB *(OG 1048, ABV 4.8%)* ◈
A brilliant blend of malt, hops and fruit on the nose with a bitter bite over the top of a faintly banana maltiness that stays the course. A russet-tan brown classic.

BATH

Bath Ales Ltd, The Old Barn, Siston Lane, Webbs Heath, Bristol, BSW30 5LX
Tel Brewery (0117) 9615122
Office (0117) 9071797
Fax Brewery (0117) 9615122
Office (0117) 9095140
E-mail Hare@bathales.co.uk
Website www.bathales.com
Tours by arrangement

⊗ Bath Ales began in 1995, formed by two former Smiles brewers and a Hardington brewer. They started with rented equipment at the Henstridge Brewery, near Wincanton and moved premises and upgraded to a full steam, 15-barrel plant in 1999. Situated between Bath and Bristol, all beer deliveries are direct to 100-plus outlets. Wholesalers are used in a limited way. Four pubs are owned, all serving cask ale.
Bottle-conditioned beer: Gem (ABV 4.8%).
Seasonal/occasional beers: Spa Extra (ABV 5%), Festivity (ABV 5%), Rare Hare (ABV 5.2%).

Special Pale Ale (SPA) *(OG 1038, ABV 3.7%)* ◈
Light-bodied, dry bitter beer. Pale and lager malts and citrus hop aroma. Lots of malt and citrus floral hops. Long, pale, malty, bitter finish with some fruit and slight sweetness. Gold/yellow colour. Refreshing, clean and complex.

Gem Bitter *(OG 1041, ABV 4.1%)* ◈
Malty (pale and crystal with a tiny hint of chocolate), fruity and hoppy throughout. Drier and more bitter at the end, this amber-coloured, medium-bodied bitter is well-balanced and complex.

Barnstormer *(OG 1050, ABV 4.5%)* ◈
Mid-brown, well-balanced and smooth. Malt (roast and chocolate), hop and fruit aroma, with similar taste, with a complex malty and bitter, dry finish.

BATHAM

Daniel Batham & Son Ltd, Delph Brewery, Delph Road, Brierley Hill, West Midlands, DY5 2TN

Tel (01384) 77229 Fax (01384) 482292
E-mail bathams@cableinet.co.uk
Website www.bathams.co.uk

⊗ A small brewery established in 1877 and now in its fifth generation of family ownership, run by Tim and Matthew Batham. Batham's sympathetic programme of upgrading and refurbishment in its tied estate has been rewarded by winning CAMRA's 1996 Joe Goodwin Award for pub refurbishment for the Vine, one of the Black Country's most famous pubs and the site of the brewery. The company has nine tied houses and supplies around 25 other outlets.
Seasonal beer: XXX (ABV 6.3%, winter).
Bottle-conditioned beer: Best Bitter ⬚

Mild Ale *(OG 1036.5, ABV 3.5%)* ◈
A fruity, dark brown mild with a malty sweetness and a roast malt finish.

Best Bitter *(OG 1043.5, ABV 4.3%)* ⬚◈
A pale yellow, fruity, sweetish bitter, with a dry, hoppy finish. A good, light, refreshing beer.

BEARDS

See Arundel and Pub Groups.

BEARTOWN

Beartown Brewery Ltd, Unit 9, Varey Road, Eaton Bank Industrial Estate, Congleton, Cheshire, CW12 1UW
Tel (01260) 299964
Fax (01260) 278895
E-mail steve@beartown42.co.uk
Website www.beartownbrewery.co.uk
Tours by arrangement

Congleton's links with brewing can be traced back to 1272, when the town received charter status. Two of its most senior officers at the time were Ale Taster and Bear Warden, hence the name of the brewery. During 1999/2000 the brewery acquired two pubs, the Beartown Tap in Congleton and the White Bull in Rossendale. The brewery also operates a private members' club at Holmes Chapel, Cheshire, where a range of the brewery's ales are served. Beartown supplies 50 outlets direct.

Ambeardextrous *(ABV 3.5)*
A new dark mild.

Bear Ass *(OG 1038, ABV 4%)* ◈
Dark ruby-red, malty bitter with good hop nose and fruity flavour with dry, bitter, astringent aftertaste.

Kodiak Gold *(OG 1038, ABV 4%)* ⬚◈
Well-balanced, straw-coloured and very drinkable with citrus fruit and hops aroma, and sharper bitter, clean, astringent aftertaste.

Bearskinful *(OG 1040, ABV 4.2%)* ◈
A tawny, malty beer, with a clean hop finish.

Polar Eclipse *(OG 1046, ABV 4.8%)* ◈
A smooth and roasty dark stout, with light hoppy notes and dry, bitter finish.

Wheat Beer *(OG 1050, ABV 5%)* ◈
A dry and bitter wheat beer. Initial fruitiness in aroma and taste with good wheat malt flavours. Long-lasting dry aftertaste.

Black Bear *(OG 1048, ABV 5%)* ◆
Dark brown strong mild, some roast and malt flavours, with a mellow sweetish finish.

BECKETT'S

Beckett's Brewery Ltd, 8 Enterprise Court, Daneshill, Basingstoke, Hampshire, RG24 8GE
Tel (01256) 472986
Fax (01256) 703205
E-mail beer@beckettsbrewery.co.uk
Tours by arrangement

⊗ Founded in 1997, Beckett's now brews 40 barrels a week, double its initial capacity. Seasonal ale: Whitewater (ABV 4.3%, summer). Bottle-conditioned beer: Fortress Ale (ABV 5%). Beckett's also brews a range of occasional beers under the Porterquack label; they include milds, porters and a strong winter beer.

Old Town Bitter *(OG 1038, ABV 3.7%)* ◆
An intensely bitter, amber-coloured session beer with some pale malt, fruit and butterscotch notes. Finishes uncompromisingly bitter and dry.

Original Bitter *(OG 1041, ABV 4%)* ◆
A refreshing copper-coloured bitter with hints of fruit and a rounded hop character. Slightly vinous for its strength, with a suggestion of crystal malt and a long bitter finish.

Stoke Ale *(OG 1043, ABV 4.2%)*

Golden Grale *(OG 1046, ABV 4.5%)*

Fortress Ale *(OG 1052, ABV 5%)*

BEECHAM'S

Beecham's Bar & Brewery, St Helen's College, Town Centre Campus, Brook Street, St Helens, Merseyside, WA10 1PZ
Tel (01744) 623420
Fax (01744) 623400
Tours by arrangement

Beecham's Brewery is a training establishment within St Helens College of Further Education. The brewing course has a recognised certificate validated by the National Open College Network. Seasonal brews are produced.

Mild *(ABV 4.1%)*

Original Bitter *(OG 1044, ABV 4.4%)*

Epiphany *(ABV 4.8%)*

Stout *(OG 1048, ABV 5%)* ◆
Thick, creamy, silky stout with roasty and caramel aroma and flavours, some balancing hop and a residual roastiness.

Crystal Wheat Beer *(OG 1048, ABV 5%)* ◆
Light, fruity wheat beer with an aroma of citrus fruits, clean, hoppy palate, and a dry finish.

BEER ENGINE

⌂ **Beer Engine, Newton St Cyres, Exeter, Devon, EX5 5AX**
Tel (01392) 851282
Fax (01392) 851876
E-mail peterbrew@aol.com
Tours by arrangement

Beer Engine, run by Peter and Jill Hawksley, started brewing in 1983 next to the Barnstaple branch railway line, and the brewery is visible behind glass in the rear lobby. It uses the finest malts from Tuckers of Newton Abbot and quality English hops from Charles Faram of Newland. Two other outlets are supplied regularly and the beers are also distributed via agencies. Seasonal beers vary from year to year, but include Porter (ABV 4.6%, early December) and Whistlemas (ABV 6.4%, Christmas).

Rail Ale *(OG 1037, ABV 3.8%)* ◆
A straw-coloured beer with a fruity aroma and a sweet, fruity finish.

Piston Bitter *(OG 1043, ABV 4.3%)* ◆
A mid-brown, sweet-tasting beer with a pleasant, bitter-sweet aftertaste.

Sleeper Heavy *(OG 1052, ABV 5.4%)* ◆
A red-coloured beer with a fruity, sweet taste and a bitter finish.

BELHAVEN

Belhaven Brewing Co Limited, Dunbar, East Lothian, EH42 1RS
Tel (01368) 864488
Fax (01368) 865640
E-mail info@belhavenbrewery.demon.co.uk
Website www.belhaven.co.uk
Shop open during tours. Tours by arrangement

⊕ With a tradition of brewing going back almost 800 years, Scotland's oldest brewery supplies all its 39 houses, and an extensive free trade, with cask beer. 80/- was second in the Champion Beer of Scotland award in 1997. Belhaven has installed a 5-barrel brew plant for experimental beers. It also has an arrangement to brew and market the Maclay range of beers. The brewery now uses brewing liquor from a well and says that the famous Belhaven sulphury note on the aroma of its beers has gone. Seasonal beers: Festival (ABV 4%), Special Cargo (ABV 4.5%), Rudolph's Revenge (ABV 5.5%, brewed for Maclays), 90/- Ale (ABV 8%), Five Nations.

60/- Ale *(OG 1030, ABV 2.9%)* ▱◆
A fine, but sadly rare, example of a Scottish light. This bitter-sweet, reddish-brown beer is dominated by fruit and malt with a hint of roast and caramel, and increasing hop bitterness in the aftertaste.

70/- Ale *(OG 1035, ABV 3.5%)* ◆
A fine Scottish ale. This pale brown beer has malt and fruit and some hop throughout, and is increasingly bitter-sweet in the aftertaste.

Sandy Hunter's Traditional Ale
(OG 1038, ABV 3.6%) ◆
A distinctive, medium-bodied beer named after a past chairman and head brewer. An aroma of malt and hops greets the nose. A hint of roast combines with the malt and hops to give a bitter-sweet taste and finish.

Belhaven IPA *(OG 1038, ABV 4%)* ◆
An amber ale with fruit and malt throughout. A pleasant session ale, but too lightly hopped to be a true IPA.

80/- Ale *(OG 1040, ABV 4.2%)* ◆
The last of a noble breed of Scottish 80/-s, with malt the predominant flavour

characteristic, though it is balanced by hop and fruit. Those used to hops as the lead to a beer's taste might find this complex ale disconcerting. The soubriquet 'the claret of Scotland' hints at the depth and complexity of the flavours.

St Andrew's Ale *(OG 1046, ABV 4.9%)* ◆
A bitter-sweet beer with lots of body. The malt, fruit and roast mingle throughout with hints of hop and caramel.

For Maclay:

70/- *(ABV 3.6%)*

80/- *(ABV 4%)*

Kane's Amber Ale *(ABV 4%)*

Wallace IPA *(ABV 4.5%)*

BELVOIR

Belvoir Brewery Ltd, Woodhill, Nottingham Lane, Old Dalby, Leicestershire, LE14 3LX
Tel/Fax (01664) 823455
Website www.belvoirbrewery.co.uk
Tours by arrangement

⊗ Belvoir (pronounced 'beaver') Brewery was set up in 1995 by Colin Brown, who had brewed with Shipstone and Theakston. The brewery has been lovingly constructed using mostly original equipment and artefacts recovered from traditional cask ale breweries all over the country. Time-honoured brewing methods are used incorporating only the finest ingredients. These include traditional floor-malted Maris Otter malts, and four varieties of Worcester whole hops (Bramling Cross, Challenger, Goldings and Progress). A refrigerated cold store/cellar was added in 2000. A bottled beer, Melton Red, was launched in November 1999 and the acquisition of the Kitchen Brewery's bottling line will enable Belvoir to produce bottle-conditioned beers. Plans are in hand to expand to a 20-barrel capacity brewhouse. 80-100 outlets are supplied direct. Occasional/seasonal beers: Mild Ale (ABV 3.4%), Peacock's Glory (ABV 4.7%), Old Dalby (ABV 5.1%).

Whippling Golden Bitter
(OG 1036, ABV 3.6%)

Star Bitter *(OG 1039, ABV 3.9%)*
A beer designed to replicate the bitter flavour of the old Shipstone's Bitter.

Beaver Bitter *(OG 1043, ABV 4.3%)* ◆
A light brown bitter that starts malty in both aroma and taste, but soon develops a hoppy bitterness. Appreciably fruity.

BEOWULF

Beowulf Brewing Company, Waterloo Buildings, 14 Waterloo Road, Yardley, Birmingham, W Midlands, B25 8JR
Tel (0121) 706 4116
Fax (0121) 706 0735
E-mail cheers@beowulf.co.uk
Website www.beowulf.co.uk
Tours for small groups by arrangement

In its fifth year of production, Beowulf is well-established throughout central England. It remains Birmingham's only independent brewery. Close to 200 outlets serve Beowulf beers, from Scotland to southern England, usually as a guest ale. There are expansion plans in hand and bottled beers will be added. Seasonal beers: Finn's Hall Porter (ABV 4.7%, autumn/winter), Dragon Smoke Stout (ABV 4.7%, autumn/winter), Grendel's Winter Ale (ABV 5.8%), Blizzard (ABV 5%, winter), Wergild cask-conditioned lager (ABV 4.3%, spring/summer), Fifty Winters (ABV 4.4%, spring/summer), Wuffa (ABV 4.5%, spring/summer), Gold Work wheat beer (ABV 5.1%, summer), Hurricane (ABV 4%, winter), Glutlusty (ABV 4.7%, autumn).

Beorma *(OG 1038, ABV 3.9%)*
A pale session ale with a malty hint of fruit giving way to a lingering bitterness.

Noble Bitter *(OG 1039, ABV 4%)* ◆
Gold colour, fruity aroma, hoppy taste with a dry finish.

Wiglaf *(OG 1043, ABV 4.3%)*
A golden bitter, with a malty flavour married to a pleasing bitterness, with three hop varieties used.

Swordsman *(OG 1045, ABV 4.5%)* ◆
Pale gold, light fruity aroma, tangy hoppy flavour. Faintly hoppy finish.

Heroes *(OG 1046, ABV 4.7%)*
Gold colour, malt aroma, hoppy taste but sweetish finish.

Mercian Shine *(OG 1048, ABV 5%)* ◆
Pale gold colour, citrus flavour with a full body and hoppy, dry finish.

BERROW

Berrow Brewery, Coast Road, Berrow, Burnham-on-Sea, Somerset, TA8 2QU
Tel (01278) 751345
Shop 9-9
Tours by arrangement

⊗ The brewery started brewing in 1982. Its success was boosted when Topsy Turvy was added to the range and rapidly became a favourite. In recent years Porter was added. Berrow supplies 12 outlets direct. Seasonal beers: Porter (ABV 4.6%, autumn/winter), Christmas Ale (ABV 4.6-4.7%).

Berrow Brewery Best Bitter/4Bs
(OG 1038, ABV 3.9-4%) ◆
A pleasant, pale brown session beer, with a fruity aroma, a malty, fruity flavour and bitterness in the palate and finish.

Topsy Turvy *(OG 1055, ABV 6%)* ◆
A gold-coloured beer with an aroma of malt and hops. Well-balanced malt and hops taste with a hoppy, bitter finish with some fruit notes.

Millennium Mash *(OG 1047, ABV 4.6-4.7%)*
Available during 2000 and 2001 and may be extended.

BIG LAMP

Big Lamp Brewers, Grange Road, Newburn, Newcastle upon Tyne, NE15 8NL
Tel (0191) 2671689
Fax (0191) 2677387
Tours by arrangement

⊛ Big Lamp Brewers started in 1982 and relocated in 1996 to a 55-barrel former water pumping station. Thirty outlets are supplied and two pubs are owned. Seasonal/occasional beers: Sunny Daze (ABV 3.6%), Embers (ABV 5.5%, winter), Old Genie (ABV 7.4%).

Bitter *(OG 1039, ABV 3.9%)* 🍴❧
A clean-tasting bitter, full of hops and malt, a hint of fruit and a good hoppy finish.

Double MM *(OG 1043, ABV 4.3%)*

Summerhill Stout *(OG 1046, ABV 4.4%)* ❧
A tasty, rich, ruby stout with a lasting rich roast feel and character. A malty mouthfeel with a lingering finish.

Prince Bishop Ale
(OG 1048, ABV 4.8%) 🍴❧
A refreshing, easy-drinking bitter, golden in colour, full of hops. Strong bitterness with a spicy dry finish.

Premium *(OG 1052, ABV 5.2%)* ❧
A well-balanced, flavoursome bitter with a big nose full of hops. The sweetness lasts into a mellow, dry finish.

Blackout *(OG 1100, ABV 11%)* ❧
A strong bitter, fortified with roast malt character and rich maltiness. Try it for its mouthfeel and lasting bitterness.

BIRD IN HAND

🗋 Wheal Ale Brewery, Nr Paradise Park, Trelissick Road, Hayle, Cornwall, TR27 4HY
Tel/Fax (01736) 753974

Founded 1980 as Parkside Brewery, the small brewhouse is behind a large pub, the Bird in Hand, converted from Victorian stables and coach house by the entrance to the Paradise Park Bird Sanctuary. The two brews are brewed regularly and a winter warmer is available in season.

Miller's Ale *(OG 1045, ABV 4.3%)*

Old Speckled Parrot *(OG 1052, ABV 5.5%)*

BITTER END

🗋 Bitter End Brew-pub, 15 Kirkgate, Cockermouth, Cumbria, CA13 9PJ
Tel/Fax (01900) 828993

Brew-pub founded in 1995. The beers are now brewed by Derwent (qv).

Cockersnoot *(ABV 3.8%)*

Cuddy Luggs *(ABV 4.2%)*

Skinners Old Strong *(ABV 5.5%)*

BLACK BULL

🗋 Black Bull (Haltwhistle Brewery), Market Square, Haltwhistle, Northumberland, NE14 0BL
Tel (01434) 320463

Seasonal beers: Dark Mild (ABV 3.5%), Fat Boys Bitter (ABV 3.7%), Captain O'Neills Intrepid Stout (ABV 3.8%), 1555 (ABV 4.4%), Special (ABV 4.6%), ESB (ABV 5.5%).

Bitter *(ABV 3.8%)*

Beastly Bitter *(ABV 4.5%)*

Bishop Ridley's Ale *(ABV 4.7%)*

BLACK DOG

**Black Dog Brewery,
St Hilda's Business Centre,
The Ropery, Whitby,
N Yorkshire, YO22 4EU
Tel (01947) 821467
Fax (01947) 603301
E-mail black_dog@lineone.net**

⊛ Black Dog's beers are currently brewed by Hambleton Ales of Thirsk (qv) but it is hoped to restart brewing at Whitby in the near future. Black Dog opened in 1997 and takes its name from the vampire who transformed himself into a black dog to land in Whitby in Bram Stoker's novel Dracula. It supplies 30-40 outlets, mainly in the north of England, and three distributors on an occasional basis. All beers are suitable for vegetarians. Seasonal beers: Synod (ABV 4.2%, spring), Schooner (ABV 4.2%, autumn), Whitby Jet (ABV 5%, winter).

Scallywag *(OG 1036, ABV 3.6%)*
A light, hoppy summer session beer.

Whitby Abbey Ale *(OG 1036.7, ABV 3.8%)*
A light, hoppy bitter.

First Out *(OG 1038.8, ABV 4%)*
A light, hoppy bitter.

Rhatas/Black Dog Special
(OG 1043.2, ABV 4.6%)
A dark, malty bitter.

BLACK ISLE

**Black Isle Brewery, Old Allangrange, Munlochy, Ross-shire, IV8 8NZ
Tel (01463) 811871
Fax (01463) 811875
E-mail djg@blackislebrewery.com
Website www.blackislebrewery.com**

Launched in December 1998, Black Isle Brewery is a small, intensely independent brewery, in the heart of the Scottish Highlands. The 5-barrel plant is based in converted farm buildings on the Black Isle. It supplies casks to pubs locally and sells direct from the brewery through the brewery shop. The beer is also sold in bottles (including three organic brands) throughout Scotland. One pub is owned. Bottle-conditioned beer: Organic Wheat Beer (ABV 5%).

Golden Eagle *(OG 1039, ABV 3.8%)* ❧
A surprisingly robust beer for its strength. A sweetish Scottish 70/- style golden amber beer bursting with malt in the nose and taste leading to a satisfying astringent bitter finish.

Red Kite *(OG 1041, ABV 4.2%)* ◆
A sweet, typically Scottish 80/- with an abundance of berry fruit aroma and taste. Hints of plum and mango lead to a classic bitter aftertaste.

Yellow Hammer *(OG 1042, ABV 4.3%)* ◆
A classic summer ale, this straw-coloured brew has an intense aroma of citrus fruits and hops, which is maintained through to the dry, bitter finish.

Wagtail *(OG 1045, ABV 4.5%)* ◆
A glorious ruby-red beer bursting with berry fruits and roast malt, and with some coffee notes in the nose. The dark fruit flavours also prevail in the typically dry, bitter finish.

BLACK SHEEP

Black Sheep Brewery plc, Wellgarth, Masham, Ripon, N Yorkshire, HG4 4EN
Tel (01765) 689227 (brewery)
680100 (visitor centre)
Fax (01765) 689746
E-mail visitor.centre@blacksheep.co.uk
Website www.blacksheep.co.uk
Shop 10-5 Wed-Sun Jan/Feb; Tue-Sun and Bank
Holidays from March; every day July/Aug
Tours by arrangement on shop opening days

⊛ Set up in 1992 by Paul Theakston, a member of Masham's famous brewing family, in the former Wellgarth Maltings, Black Sheep has enjoyed continued growth and now supplies a free trade of around 600 outlets in the Yorkshire Dales and in an 80-mile radius of Masham, but it owns no pubs. A limited number of wholesalers is also supplied. All the output is fermented in Yorkshire Square vessels; there are six slate ones and eight stainless steel Yorkshire 'round' squares. The Black Sheep complex includes video shows of the brewing process, a brewery shop, and a bistro open for snacks, lunches and evening meals every day (Wed-Sun only Jan to March). Seasonal beer: Yorkshire Square Ale (ABV 5%).

Best Bitter *(OG 1039, ABV 3.8%)* ▢◆
A hoppy and fruity beer with strong bitter overtones, leading to a long, dry, bitter finish.

Special Ale *(OG 1046, ABV 4.4%)* ◆
A well-rounded and warming bitter beer with a good helping of hops and fruit in the taste and aroma, leading to a moderately dry, bitter aftertaste.

Riggwelter *(OG 1056, ABV 5.9%)* ◆
A fruity bitter, with complex underlying tastes and hints of liquorice and pear drops leading to a long, dry, bitter finish.

BLACKAWTON*

Blackawton Brewery, Unit 14, Saltash Business Park, Moorlands Trading Estate, Forge Lane, Saltash, Cornwall, PL12 6LX
Tel(01752) 848777 Fax (01752) 848999
E-mail blackawtonbrewery@talk21.com

Blackawton was Devon's oldest operating brewery when it stopped production in 2000 at its Washbourne site near Totnes. All the brewery equipment and recipes were sold to a new buyer, who relocated to a site near Saltash and brewing started again in the autumn of 2000. Blackawton is flourishing to such an extent that a further move was made in the same area in February 2001. Seasonal beers: West Country (ABV 4.1%, Easter), Shepherds Delight (ABV 4.6%, spring), Nell Gwynn (ABV 4.7%, autumn), Winter Fuel (ABV 5%).

Best Bitter *(OG 1038, ABV 3.8%)*

44 Special *(OG 1044, ABV 4.5%)*

Exhibition *(OG 1045, ABV 4.7%)*

Headstrong *(OG 1048, ABV 5.2%)*

BLACKPOOL*

Blackpool Brewery Co Ltd, The Old Dairy, George Street, Blackpool, FY1 3RP.
Tel (01253) 304999
Fax (01253) 304868
Tours by arrangement

Blackpool was the first brewery in the town for 28 years when production started in November 2000. Owner Kean Brown produces 80 barrels a week. Seasonal beers: Lights Out (ABV 4.4%), Black Diamond (3.4%), Sweet FA (3.9%), Christmas Lights (ABV 3.9%).

Golden Smile *(OG 1036.5, ABV 3.7%)*
Gold-coloured beer with a hoppy aroma; well-balanced with a fruity flavour.

Bitter *(OG 1039, ABV 4%)*
A golden beer with great depth of flavour.

BPA *(OG 1041, ABV 4.2%)*
A full-bodied, malty bitter with an agreeable flowery aroma.

BLANCHFIELDS

Blanchfields Brewery, The Bull, Bridge Street, Fakenham, Norfolk, NR21 9AG
Tel (01328) 862560
E-mail sales@blanchfields-brewery.co.uk
Website www.blanchfields-brewery.co.uk
Tours by arrangement

⊠ Blanchfields has been brewing since 1997 at the Bull with a 2.5 barrel plant. It has won a gold medal at the Peterborough Beer Festival for its mild and a medal at Norwich for its Best Bitter. It brews mainly for its own pub but sometimes has a little spare to sell to a couple of other local pubs. Seasonal/occasional beers: High Hop Bitter (ABV 4.1%, April-Aug), White Bull Wheat Beer (ABV 4.4%, April-Nov), Winter Warmer (ABV 5.9%, Dec-Feb). Bottle-conditioned beer: Raging Bull.

Black Bull Mild *(OG 1040, ABV 3.6%)* ◆
A reddish-brown beer with a distinct roasted malt aroma. This translates into a dark, dry roasty beginning with a supporting malty undertone. The powerfully beefy flavour continues to a grainy, arid end.

Bull Best Bitter *(OG 1040, ABV 3.9%)* ◆
A gentle hoppy aroma befits this amber-coloured brew. An even blend of bitter-sweet hoppiness backed up a vanilla fruitiness slowly fades to a Pandora's box of flavours. A memory of citrus fruit remains.

Raging Bull Bitter *(OG 1048, ABV 4.9%)* ◆
Blackberry bouquet and a heavy malty beginning gives this tawny-coloured ale a warm fruity feel. A lack of balance gives the sugary, bitter-sweet finish an almost cough-sweet feel.

BLENCOWE

Blencowe Brewing Company, c/o Exeter Arms, Barrowden, Rutland, LE15 8EQ
Tel (01572) 747247
Website www.exeterarms.co.uk
Tours by arrangement

The brewery was set up in 1998 in a barn adjacent to the pub. The 2-barrel plant was bought with the intention of supplying traditional beers for sale in the Exeter Arms bar and festivals only. Seasonal beers: Lover Boys (ABV 3.9%, St Valentine's), Spice Boys (ABV 6%, Easter and Xmas), Fruit Beer (ABV 3.6%, spring).

Best Boys *(OG 1038, ABV 3.6%)*
A hoppy, dry and bitter ale.

Beach Boys *(OG 1040, ABV 3.8%)*
Fruit on the aroma; hoppy with a bitter finish.

Danny Boys *(OG 1046, ABV 4.5%)*
A rich, dark and creamy stout.

BLEWITTS

Blewitts Brewery, Sorley Tunnel Adventure Farm, Loddiswell Road, Kingsbridge, Devon, TQ7 4BP
Tel (01548) 852485 (number for Ship & Plough: no phone at brewery)
Tours as part of Sorley Tunnel attraction

⊗ Established in 1991 as a brew-pub at the Ship & Plough, owner Steve Blewitt moved the plant in 1999 to the Sorley Tunnel Adventure Farm where visitors can watch the brewing process. Joined by brewer John Benford, quality has steadily risen. All the output now goes to the Ship & Plough, the brewery tap.

Best *(OG 1040, ABV 4%)*

Wages *(OG 1045, ABV 4.5%)*

Head Off *(OG 1050, ABV 5%)*

BLUE ANCHOR

▢ **Blue Anchor Inn, 50 Coinagehall Street, Helston, Cornwall, TR13 8EX**
Tel (01326) 562821
Tours by arrangement

Historic thatched brew-pub, possibly the oldest in Britain, originating as a monks' resting place in the 15th century. It produces powerful ales known locally as Spingo. The brewery has undergone complete refurbishment and the pub is also due for improvement, with careful attention to preserving its special character. Two outlets are supplied direct.

Spingo Middle *(OG 1050, ABV 5%)*

Spingo Best *(OG 1053, ABV 5.3%)*

Special *(OG 1066, ABV 6.6%)*

Easter and Christmas Special
(OG 1076, ABV 7.6%)

BLUE BELL*

Blue Bell Brewery Ltd, Blue Bell Inn, Cranesgate South, Whaplode St Catherine, Holbeach, Lincs, PE12 6SN
Tel (01406) 540300

The brewery opened in 2000 behind the Blue Bell pub in a former potato store. The 7-barrel plant was bought second-hand from Oxford. The partnership is run by Mike Pilkington, the landlord of the inn for 33 years, and Ken Dixon, a former brewer with several national and regional companies. 30 outlets are supplied direct.

Olde Honesty *(ABV 4.1%)*

Olde Fashioned *(ABV 4.8%)*

BLUE COW

▢ **Blue Cow Inn and Brewery, South Witham, Nr Grantham, Lincs, NG33 5QB**
Tel/Fax (01572) 768432
E-mail bluecow@btclick.com
Website www.thebluecowinn.co.uk
Tours by arrangement

The Blue Cow opened in 1997 and is run by Dick Thirlwell, who brews only for the pub.

Thirlwell's Cuddy *(OG 1040, ABV 3.8%)*

Thirlwell's Best Bitter
(OG 1040, ABV 3.8%)

BLUE MOON

Blue Moon Brewery, 15 Market Place, Hingham, Norfolk, NR9 4AF
Tel (01953) 851115

Originally sited at Pearces Farm, Hingham, in a converted manger, the farm has been sold and the beers are currently brewed at Buffy's Brewery, Tivetshall (qv), until new premises are ready. Blue Moon owns one pub and 60 outlets are supplied direct.

Easy Life *(OG 1040, ABV 3.8%)* ◗
A light, well-balanced session beer that greets you with a solid malty aroma. This translates into a hoppy beginning with toffee and vanilla overtones. An underlying maltiness continues throughout this golden beer.

Sea of Tranquillity *(OG 1042, ABV 4.2%)* ◗
A copper-coloured brew with a thin feel and a delicate, malt-enhanced aroma. Malt continues to dominate throughout as a hoppy bitterness recedes to an abrupt, dry finish.

Dark Side *(OG 1048, ABV 4.5%)*

Hingham High *(OG 1050, ABV 5.2%)* ◗
Hints of malt and hop aroma give a good indication of the basis of this well-rounded, full-bodied ale. A nectarine sweetness stays as bitterness recedes to leave a dominant hoppy maltiness befitting a tawny-coloured ale.

Milk of Amnesia *(OG 1055, ABV 5.2%)*

Liquor Mortis *(OG 1065, ABV 6.5%)*

BOAT

Boat Brewery, Boat Inn, Boat Lane, Main Street, Allerton Bywater, W Yorkshire, WF10 2BX
Tel (01977) 667788
Fax (0113) 2267593
Website www.theboatbrewery.co.uk
Tours by arrangement

Established in 1999 in premises behind the Boat Inn on the banks of the River Aire,

Boat is run by retired chemical worker and CAMRA activist Ron Ridout. At first he supplied only the inn, but his production has expanded and he now supplies the free trade nationally. Man in the Boat Mild has won several CAMRA awards. Brewery trips are highly entertaining. Nevisons Leap is named after a local highwayman, Jim Nevison. Occasional beers: If Thy Bob Doesn't Give Our Bob That There Bob Thy Bob Owes Our Bob Our Bob'll Give Thy Bob A Bob On't Nose (ABV 5.9%: thought to be the longest beer name in the world), ELB/Evil Little Bastard (4.7%).

Man in the Boat
(OG 1037, ABV 3.5%) 🏴🍷🥄
A smooth, dark mild. Full in flavour for its strength. Chocolate and dark fruit in the aroma and taste lead to a satisfying dry, fruity finish.

Bomber's Moon *(OG 1038, ABV 3.8%)*

Rattler *(OG 1041, ABV 4.3%)*

Nevisons Leap *(OG 1050, ABV 5%)*

BOGGART HOLE CLOUGH*

Boggart Hole Clough Brewing Co, Unit 13, Brookside Works, Clough Road, Moston, Manchester, M9 4FP
Tel (0161) 277 9666

Set up by Mark Dade, former brewer at Marble, next to Boggart Hole Clough Park in North Manchester, brewing started in February 2001. With 80 or 90 free houses taking the beer, Mark increased the brew length from 2.5 barrels to 8 in July.

Boggart Bitter *(ABV 3.8%)*

Logend *(ABV 4%)*

Angel Hill *(ABV 4.2%)*

Boggart Brew *(ABV 4.3%)*

Dark Side *(ABV 4.4%)*

BORDER

See Hadrian & Border.

BORVE

⌂ **Borve Brew House, Ruthven, Huntly, Aberdeenshire, AB54 4SG**
Tel (01466) 760343
Tours by arrangement

⊛ Established in 1983, Borve moved from its original site on the Isle of Lewis five years later to a former school on the mainland. The school is now a pub, with the brewhouse adjacent. The cask beers are also available in bottle-conditioned form; Extra Strong (ABV 10%) is bottle-conditioned only. All the beers are suitable for vegetarians. Brewing is currently suspended due to illness but the family hopes to start again soon.

Borve Ale *(ABV 3.9%)*

Tall Ships *(ABV 5%)*

BOSTON EXPERIENCE

⌂ **Boston Experience Ltd, 1-3 Church Path, Woking, Surrey, GU21 1EL**

Tel (01483) 598586
Fax (01483) 599201
E-mail gary@boston-experience.co.uk
Website www.boston-experience.co.uk
Tours by arrangement

The Boston Experience produces three beers brewed to American recipes. All the beers are chill-filtered and dispensed from cellar tanks to the bar. Beers: Babe Ruth (ABV 3.8%), Bunker Hill (ABV 4.3%), Boston Strangler (ABV 5.3%).

BRAGDY CEREDIGION

Bragdy Ceredigion Brewery, Brynderwen, Llangranog, Llandysul, Ceredigion, SA44 6AD
Tel (01239) 654099/888
Fax (01239) 654099
E-mail brian@ceredigionbrewery.fs.business.co.uk
Website www.tavernontap.co.uk
www.bestofruralwales.co.uk
Shop due to open summer 2001. Tours by arrangement

Bragdy Ceredigion Brewery is situated on the coastal belt of West Wales and housed in a converted barn on Wervil Grange Farm. A family-run craft brewery established in 1997 by Brian and Julia Tilby, it produces bottle-conditioned and cask-conditioned ales. No chemical additives are used. The bottle-conditioned beers are suitable for vegans. The full-mash, 5-barrel plant uses Maris Otter floor-malted barley, with Challenger, First Gold and Fuggles hops. An organic beer with certified pale malt and organic hops was added in 2001 and a range of organic fruit beers is planned. Bottle-conditioned beers: as for cask beers, save for the Spirit of the Forest. Occasional beer: Honey Beer (ABV 5%).

Ysbryd O'r Goeden/Spirit of the Forest
(OG 1036, ABV 3.8%)

Gwrach Ddu/Black Witch
(OG 1038, ABV 4%)

Draig Aur/Gold Dragon
(OG 1039, ABV 4.2%)

Barcud Coch/Red Kite
(OG 1040, ABV 4.3%)

Blodeuwedd/Flowerface organic beer
(OG 1043, ABV 4.5%)

Cwrw 2000/Ale 2000 *(OG 1049, ABV 5%)*

Yr Hen Darw Du/Old Black Bull
(OG 1058, ABV 6.2%)

BRAGDY TY BACH

⌂ **Tynllidiart Arms, Capel Bangor, Aberystwyth, Ceredigion, SY23 3LR**
(a subsidiary of Spinning Dog Brewery)
Tel (01970) 880248

Claimed to be the smallest commercial brewery in the world, with a brew length of just 9 gallons, the plant is housed in the fomer gents lavatory by the side of the pub. (Ty Bach is colloquial Welsh for the 'little house' – the brick building usually found at the bottom of most cottage gardens during the 19th century.) The full-mash plant is used only occasionally for one-off experimental brews that are then available in the pub. It's best to check before visiting the pub to sample a brew. The beers are brewed by Chris Giles, ex-Flannery's.

BRAGDY YNYS MON

Cae Cwta Mawr, Talwrn, Anglesey, LI77 7SD
Tel (01248) 723801
E-mail martyn@caecwtamawr.freeserve.co.uk

Martyn Lewis started brewing in 1999 on a 5-barrel plant acquired from Cambrinus in Liverpool. In 2001, he built a bottling line in an old stables and plans to produce bottle-conditioned beers.

Medra *(ABV 4%)* ◈
Attractive-looking, copper-coloured, soft, malty bitter with hints of berries in the short, dry finish.

Wennol *(ABV 4.1%)*
The name means Swallow.

Enlli *(ABV 4.4%)*
A strong mild: the name is the Welsh version of Bardsey Island.

Tarw Du *(ABV 4.5%)* ◈
The name means Black Bull. Inviting black porter-style beer that has an earthy flavour with some chocolate/coffee notes and a long, dry aftertaste.

Amnesia *(ABV 4.9%)*

BRAINS

SA Brain & Company Ltd,
The Cardiff Brewery, PO Box 53,
Crawshay Street, Cardiff, CF10 5TR
Tel (029) 2040 2060 Fax (029) 2038 3127
Website www.sabrain.co.uk
Shop 9.15-5 Mon-Sat
Tours by arrangement

SA Brain began trading at the Old Brewery in Cardiff in 1882 when Samuel Arthur Brain and his uncle Joseph Benjamin Brain puchased a site founded in 1713. The company has remained in family ownership ever since and in 1997 it bought South Wales' other leading independent brewery, Crown Buckley, formed from the merger of the Crown Brewery of Pontyclun with Buckleys of Llanelli. The full range of Brain's and Buckley's ales are now produced at the company's Cardiff Brewery (formerly Hancock's) bought from Bass in 1999. The company owns 200 pubs, as well as having a sizeable free trade, plus interests in hotel and leisure projects in Wales and the West Country. 1,000 outlets are supplied direct. A range of seasonal and occasional ales includes Saint David's, Hat Trick, Merlin's Oak, Fresh Hop and the Rev's Cracker. Brains brews the cask version of M&B Brew XI for Bass/Interbrew.

Buckley's IPA *(OG 1033.5, ABV 3.4%)*

Brains Dark *(OG 1035.5, ABV 3.5%)* ▣▣◈
A dark brown mild with a pleasant, bitter-sweet mix of caramel, roast and malt flavours. A good traditional mild.

Brains Bitter *(OG 1036, ABV 3.7%)* ◈
A pale beer, low aroma, with malt and hops in the taste, leading to a clean, bitter finish. Known locally as 'Light'.

Buckley's Best Bitter
(OG 1036.5, ABV 3.7%)

Arms Park Ale *(OG 1040, ABV 4%)*
Brewed to support Cardiff Rugby Club, this is now regular beer.

SA *(OG 1042, ABV 4.2%)* ◈
A moderately bitter, amber beer with a rounded mix of flavours, mellowed for wider appeal.

Rev James Original Ale
(OG 1045.5, ABV 4.5%) ◈
Pale brown with a gentle aroma and flavour of malt, with a weak hop/fruit mix dominated by a moderate bitterness. Aftertaste fades

BRAKSPEAR

WH Brakspear & Sons plc, The Brewery,
New Street, Henley-on-Thames,
Oxon, RG9 2BU
Tel (01491) 570200
Fax (01491) 410254
E-mail peterscholey@brakspear.co.uk
Website www.brakspear.co.uk
Shop 9-6 Mon-Sat (9-7 Fri). Tours by arrangement

⊠ Brewing took place before 1700 on the Henley site. The 19th-century brewhouse and Tun Room still incorporate the unique two-tier 'dropping system' of fermentation: once fermentation starts, the fermenting wort is dropped from the first tier to the second, leaving dead yeast cells and other detritus behind. This encourages a more powerful, clean fermentation to continue, with a sparkling clear beer at the end. Maris Otter malt, whole hops and Brakspear's own well water form the heart of the company's beers. A managed house venture, Honeypot Inns, came to an end in 2000. Brakspear currently owns or leases 105 pubs, two of which are to be sold. Only one of its pubs does not offer cask ale. Seasonal beers: Ted & Ben's Organic Beer (ABV 4.7%, March-April), Henry on Thames (ABV 4.6%, May/June), Downpour (ABV 4.5%,July/Aug). Bottle-conditioned beers: Coniston Bluebird (ABV 4.2%: brewed for Coniston Brewery), Vintage Henley (ABV 5.5%), Vintage Ale (ABV 5.5-6.5%: varies annually). Organic beers (not bottle-conditioned): Naturale and Live Organic (both ABV 4.6%).

2.5 *(ABV 2.5%)*
A low alcohol beer.

Mild *(OG 1032, ABV 3%)* ▣◈
A dry, red-brown mild with a good balance of chocolate malt and roast barley. A hint of sweetness gives way to a dry, bitter finish.

Bitter *(OG 1035.5, ABV 3.4%)* ▣◈
This copper-coloured bitter is well hopped, moderately fruity and unpretentious, with a spicy bitterness and good mouthfeel. It ends fruity, dry and pungently hoppy, and can be sulphurous at times.

Old Ale *(OG 1043.5, ABV 4.3%)* ◈
Red/brown in colour with good body. The strong, fruity aroma is well complemented by malt, hops and caramel. Its pronounced taste of malt, with discernible sweet, roast malt and caramel flavours, gives way to fruitiness. The aftertaste is of bitter-sweet chocolate, even though chocolate malt is not used.

Special *(OG 1043.5, ABV 4.3%)* ▣◈
A honey-coloured bitter, well-balanced with

fruit and a good bitter hop character. Pale malt and hops lead through to an astringent finish.

Contract beer:

Bluebird (for Coniston Brewery)
(OG 1036, ABV 3.6%)

BRANDY CASK

⌂ Brandy Cask Pub & Brewery,
Bridge Street, Pershore,
Worcs,WR10 1AJ
Tel/Fax (01386) 552602
Tours by arrangement

Brewing started in 1995 in a refurbished bottle store in the garden of the pub. It was run as a separate business until the retirement of the brewer in 1998. Brewery and pub now operate under one umbrella, with brewing carried out by the owner/landlord. Since the change, brewing is restricted to the Brandy Cask but a return to supplying other outlets in the future is anticipated. Occasional beer: Ale Mary (ABV 4.8%).

Whistling Joe *(ABV 3.6%)* ❧
The dominant taste of malts does allow the fruity hops to come through to produce a beer that is a treat.

Brandy Snapper *(ABV 4%)* ❧
A dry aftertaste is testament to the strong flavours of malts and hops that are available in this complex bitter.

John Baker's Original *(ABV 4.8%)* ❧
A sweet malty memory is left by this contrasting array of tastes where the roast notes refuse to be outdone by the hops or malt. The battle to come is not revealed in a very subdued nose.

Ale Mary *(ABV 4.8%)* ❧
A premium bitter that allows the bitterness prevalence over the malty and fruit flavours. Its drinkability belies its strength and should be treated with respect.

BRANSCOMBE VALE

Branscombe Vale Brewery,
Branscombe, Seaton,
Devon, EX12 3DP
Tel/Fax (01297) 680511
Tours by arrangement, winter only

⊠ The brewery was set up in 1992, in two cowsheds owned by the National Trust, by former dairy workers Paul Dimond and Graham Luxton, who converted the sheds and dug their own well. The NT has built an extension for the brewery to ensure future growth. Branscombe Vale currently supplies 60 regular outlets. Seasonal beers: Anniversary Ale (ABV 4.6%, January), Hells Belles (ABV 4.8%, winter), Summa That (ABV 5%, summer), Yo Ho Ho (ABV 6%, Christmas).

Branoc *(OG 1037, ABV 3.8%)* ❧
A pale brown session ale. Fruit and malt predominate with a very bitter taste and finish.

BVB *(OG 1045, ABV 4.6%)* ❧
Reddy/brown-coloured beer with a fruity aroma and taste, and bitter/astringent finish.

Summa That
(OG 1049, ABV 5%) ❧
Highly drinkable, golden fruity beer with a bitter finish

BREWERY ON SEA

See Spinnaker

BREWSTER'S

Brewster's Brewing Co Ltd, Penn Lane,
Stathern, Nr Melton Mowbray,
Leicestershire, LE14 4HR
Tel (01949) 861868 Fax (01949) 861901
E-mail sara@brewsters.co.uk
Website www.brewsters.co.uk
Tours by arrangement

Brewster is the old English term for a female brewer and Sara Barton is a modern example A Master of Brewing trained at Heriot Watt Brewing School in Edinburgh, she worked with Courage before striking out alone. In 2000, she won the Small Business category of Country Living magazine's Enterprising Rural Women awards. Brewster's Brewery was set up in the heart of the Vale of Belvoir in January 1998 with a 5-barrel plant. There are plans to upgrade to cope with increased demand. Beer is supplied direct to some 200 pubs throughout central England and further afield via wholesalers. Seasonal/occasional beers: Claudia Wheat Beer (ABV 4.5%, summer), Brewster's Stocking (ABV 5.5%, Christmas), Frau Brau Lager (ABV 5%, summer). Serendipity experimental beer range: Serendipity Bellydancer (ABV 5.2%).

Hophead *(OG 1036, ABV 3.6%)*
A pale and hoppy brew, a very refreshing session beer with a fresh floral hop character.

Marquis *(OG 1038, ABV 3.8%)*
A pleasant quaffing beer with a light maltiness, balanced by a dry hoppy finish.

Monty's Mild *(OG 1040, ABV 4%)*
A full-bodied dark mild made with a blend of pale, chocolate and crystal malts as well as torrefied wheat. Lightly hopped with Progress.

Bitter *(OG 1042, ABV 4.2%)*
A well-balanced red ale with nutty malt character and aromatic hop flavour.

Vale Pale Ale (VPA) *(OG 1045, ABV 4.5%)*
A golden ale with a subtle biscuit malt flavour and citrus hop notes.

BRIDGE OF ALLAN

Bridge of Allan Brewery Ltd, The
Brewhouse, Queens Lane, Bridge of Allan,
Stirlingshire, FK9 4NY
Tel (01786) 834555
Fax (01786) 833426
E-mail brewery@bridgeofallan.co.uk
Website www.bridgeofallan.co.uk
Shop 10-5 daily. Tours by arrangement

Bridge of Allan Brewery was founded in 1997 and is located in the leafy Victorian spa town in the Forth Valley, with Stirling Castle, the Wallace Monument and the nearby Trossochs. The 5-barrel custom-built brewery, run by Douglas Ross, also owns two local village pubs and sells to more than 50 pubs in Scotland and also distributes to England via agencies. Seasonal/occasional beers: Summer Breeze (ABV 4%), Wild Oats Stout (ABV 4.8%), Sporran Warmer (ABV 4.8%), Spring Ale (ABV 4.2%), Golden Harvest (ABV 4%), Chicken Ale (ABV 4.4%). Other seasonals are available throughout the year on a monthly basis. Ben Nevis, Glencoe Stout and Lomond Gold are organic beers.

Stirling Bitter *(OG 1038, ABV 3.7%)*

Ben Nevis *(ABV 4%)*

Stirling Brig *(OG 1042, ABV 4.1%)*

Bannock Burn *(OG 1044, ABV 4.2%)*

Glencoe Stout *(ABV 4.5%)*

Lomond Gold *(ABV 5%)*

BRIDGE of ALLAN BREWERY

BRISCOE'S

Briscoe's Brewery,
16 Ash Grove, Otley,
W Yorkshire, LS21 3EL
Tel/Fax (01943) 466515
E-mail briscoe.brewery@virgin.net

The brewery was launched in 1998 by microbiologist/chemist Dr Paul Briscoe in the cellar of his house with a 1-barrel brew length. A new 3-barrel brewery at the rear of the Bowling Green public house in Otley opened in 2000. The existing 1-barrel plant has been retained for special/occasional bottled beers. The beers are full mash, most being all malt. Eleven outlets are supplied direct. Most of the beer names are related to the brewer's other passion – long distance running. Occasional beers: Rombalds Reviver (ABV 3.8%), Runner's Ruin (ABV 4.3%), Shane's Shamrock Stout (ABV 4.6%), Chevinbrau Pilsner-style lager (ABV 5.2%), Puddled and Barmy Ale (ABV 5.8%).

Littondale Light *(OG 1039, ABV 4%)*
A pale and refreshing beer brewed in the style of lager.

Burnsall Classic Bitter *(OG 1040, ABV 4%)*
A full-flavoured, reddish coloured bitter with a good hop flavour.

Chevin Chaser *(OG 1043, ABV 4.3%)*
A refreshing, pale-coloured, all-malt bitter with a distinct hop finish.

Dalebottom Dark *(OG 1043, ABV 4.3%)*
A smooth and malty strong dark mild with a good hop character.

Badger Stone Bitter *(OG 1044, ABV 4.4%)*
A classic English bitter, packed with the flavour of malt and hops.

Three Peaks Ale *(OG 1045, ABV 4.5%)*
A strong, pale premium bitter brewed with only pale malt and traditional hops.

BROADSTONE

Broadstone Brewing Company Ltd,
Rum Runner, Wharf Road,
Retford,
Notts, DN22 7ZJ
Tel (01777) 719797
Fax (01777) 719898
E-mail broadstone.brewery@virgin.net
Website www.broadstonebrewery.com
Tours by arrangement

Alan Gill, who founded Springhead Brewery, set up Broadstone in Retford in 1999 and in the spring of 2001 moved the brewery to the same site as his Rum Runner pub. Seasonal beers: March Ale (ABV 5%, March-April), War Horse (ABV 5.8%).

Best Bitter *(OG 1037.5, ABV 3.8%)*

Stonebridge Mild *(OG 1041, ABV 4%)*

Fletcher's Ale *(ABV 4.2%)*

Charter Ale *(OG 1047, ABV 4.6%)*

Gold *(OG 1049.5, ABV 5%)*

Black Stout *(ABV 5%)*

BROUGHTON

Broughton Ales Ltd, Broughton,
Peeblesshire, ML12 6HQ
Tel (01899) 830345
Fax (01899) 830474
E-mail bro-ales@dircon.co.uk;
beer@BroughtonAles.co.uk
Website www.broughton-ales.co.uk
Shop 9-5 Mon-Fri. Tours by arrangement (evenings)

☺ Founded in 1979, the company went into receivership in 1995 and was taken over by Whim Brewery's owner Giles Litchfield. 70 per cent of production is bottled (not bottle-conditioned), much of it for export. A single tied house and 200 outlets in Scotland are supplied direct from the brewery, while other customers throughout Britain are served by wholesalers. Expansion into new markets in England is going well. Seasonal/occasional beers: Winter Fire (ABV 4.2%), First Foot Ale (ABV 4.2%), Bramling Cross (ABV 4.2%, summer), Match Ale (ABV 3.9%), Black Douglas (5.2%, spring and autumn), Reeket Yill (ABV 4.8%), Brewer's Gold (ABV 4.2%).

Greenmantle Ale *(ABV 3.9%)* ❧
A fruity beer with a sweet malty taste and a hint of hop.

Broughton Special Bitter *(ABV 3.9%)* ❧
An aroma of hop, with malt and fruit, leads into a pleasingly bitter beer, balanced with more malt and fruit, with the bitterness and fruit lasting into the aftertaste. Slightly lacking in body.

Scottish Oatmeal Stout *(ABV 4.2%)* ❧
A rare pleasure, this wonderfully dry stout has a bitter aftertaste dominated by roast malt. A distinctive malt aroma is followed by a prominent roast taste. Fruit is evident throughout.

Merlin's Ale *(ABV 4.2%)* ❧
A well-hopped, fruity flavour is balanced by malt in the taste. The finish is bitter-sweet, light but dry.

80/- *(ABV 4.2%)* ◆
A typical Scottish 80/- session ale.

The Ghillie *(ABV 4.5%)* ◆
A full-bodied ale. Hops, malt and fruit dominate the palate. The finish is dry and dominated by hops.

Old Jock *(ABV 6.7%)*
Strong, sweetish and fruity in the finish. A classic Scottish strong ale.

BROWN COW

**Brown Cow Brewery, Brown Cow Road, Barlow, Selby, N Yorkshire, YO8 8EH
Tel/Fax 01757 618947
E-mail k.simpson@btconnect.com
Website www.browncowbrewery.f9.co.uk**

Brewing takes place in a converted outbuilding at the brewer's riverside home (the former Brown Cow Inn). The brewery is run by Susan Simpson, who brews 5-7.5 barrels a week on the 2.5-barrel plant. The beers are always available as three local outlets and as guest ales to free houses in the area. 75 outlets are supplied direct. Seasonal beers: Maiden Century (ABV 4%, spring/summer), Cockle Warmer (ABV 5%, winter).

Mistle Mild *(OG 1037, ABV 3.7%)* ◆
Dark, malty and softly rounded.

Bitter *(OG 1038, ABV 3.8%)* ◆
A well-hopped traditional session bitter.

Just 4U *(OG 1038, ABV 3.9%)*
A pub house beer with individual recipes.

Constellation *(OG 1042, ABV 4.2%)*
A pub house beer with individual recipes.

Simpsons No. 4
(OG 1043, ABV 4.4%) ◆
Dark and bitter-sweet, full of roast barley character.

Wolfhound *(OG 1043, ABV 4.5%)* ◆
Straw-coloured, full and rounded palate of malt and traditional English hops.

How Now *(OG 1044, ABV 4.5%)* ◆
Pale, fruity and single hopped.

BRUNSWICK

⚲ **Brunswick Brewing Co,
1 Railway Terrace, Derby,
DE1 2RU
Tel (01332) 290677
Fax (01332) 370226**
Tours by arrangement

⊠ A purpose-built tower brewery attached to the Brunswick Inn, the first railwaymen's hostelry in the world, partly restored by the Derbyshire Historic Building Trust and bought by the present owners in 1987. Brewing began in 1991 and a viewing area allows pub-users to watch production. The beers are supplied to the inn and 13 other outlets. Numerous one-off beers are also produced.

Triple Hop *(OG 1040, ABV 4%)*
A straw-coloured ale with a slightly sulphury aroma. An overtly bitter beer with pleasant mouth-puckering dryness.

Second Brew *(OG 1042, ABV 4.2%)*
A dark copper colour, it drinks vinously with a lot of mouthfeel round the rich,

clean malt. Dry aftertaste with a dash of orange.

Coming of Age *(OG 1041, ABV 4.1%)*
A tawny ale with little aroma. After initial sweetness, a lasting bitterness and a dry finish.

Railway Porter *(OG 1045, ABV 4.3%)*
Chocolate aroma with spicy fruit notes. A complex, full-bodied brew with distinct coffee and fruity after character.

Old Accidental *(OG 1050, ABV 5%)*
A light vinous floral hop aroma with underlying malt notes. Well-balanced, malty beer leading to a bitter finish with warming aftertaste.

BRYN CELYN

**Bryn Celyn Brewery, Wern Fawr,
47 Wern Road, Ystalyfera, Swansea, SA9 2LX
Tel (01639) 843625**

Will Hopton, owner of the Wern Fawr pub, opened Bryn Celyn (Holly Hill) Brewery in his cellar in 1999 and upgraded to 1-barrel brews in 2000. He plans to increase to 2.5-barrel capacity. Will's theme for the brewery is Buddy Holly: he even got married on Buddy Holly's birthday. He hopes to install a bottling plant. Seasonal beers: May B Baby (ABV 4%), That Will Be the Sleigh (ABV 7.1%, Christmas).

Feb 59 *(ABV 3.8%)*

Buddy Marvellous *(ABV 4%)*

Oh Boy *(ABV 4.5%)*

CHH *(ABV 4.5%)*

Buddy's Delight *(ABV 4.5%)*

Rave On *(ABV 5%)*

Buddy Confusing *(ABV 5%)*

BRYSON'S*

**Bryson's Brews, c/o Summerside,
25 Oxcliffe Road, Heysham, Lancs, LA3 1PU
Tel (01524) 852150**

George Palmer, a mechanical engineer, had been a keen home-brewer for 30 years before deciding to brew commercially, though he didn't give up the day job until the summer of 2001 after opening his 4.5-barrel plant the previous December. The brewing kit was supplied by Moss Brew and is based on a business park near George's house. He supplies pubs in Morecambe and Lancaster, including student bars at Lancaster University, and wholesalers are now distributing the beers to a wider area. The beers are named after local landmarks and features: a 'wammell' is a type of fishing boat. Seasonal beer: Patrick's Porter (ABV 4.3%, winter).

Wammellers Wheat *(ABV 4%)*

Barrows Bitter *(ABV 4.2%)*

Acre Moss Amber *(ABV 4.5%)*

BUFFY'S

**Buffy's Brewery, Rectory Road,
Tivetshall St Mary, Norwich, NR15 2DD
Tel/Fax (01379) 676523**

E-mail buffysbrewery@lineone.net
Website www.buffys.co.uk
Tours by arrangement

⊗ Established in 1993, the brewing capacity stands at 45 barrels, but plans are in hand to move to bigger premises and to buy a second pub. Blue Moon beers are currently brewed at Buffy's until the brewery finds new premises. Seasonal beer: Hollybeery, Christmas: recipe and ABV change every year.

Norwich Terrier *(OG 1036, ABV 3.6%)*
Clean honey-blossom aroma gives an indication of the light refreshing hoppiness of the initial taste of this amber beer. A fruity bitterness augments the flavour. The finish is long as the bitter edge develops intensity.

Bitter *(OG 1039, ABV 3.9%)* ✦
A well-balanced beer with a distinct spectrum of flavours. A malty nose with hoppy overtones leads to a similar first taste. Bitterness matches the initial maltiness as a consistent hop background remains in hand.

Mild *(OG 1042, ABV 4.2%)* ✦
A reddish-brown brew with a gentle roast malt aroma. A dark chocolate beginning with some sweet, fruity hints. Easy drinking with a long, smooth roast, hoppy finish. An old-fashioned, soft-drinking mild.

Polly's Folly *(OG 1043, ABV 4.3%)* ✦
A full-flavoured bitter with malt the dominant flavour in both taste and nose. Hops, noticeable in the bouquet, provide a counter to the maltiness as the long finish develops a bitter-sweet fruitiness.

Hopleaf *(OG 1044.5, ABV 4.5%)* ✦
Hops and caramel mix in the nose to introduce a gentle mix of flavours from which fruit and hops emerge in their own right. Hops continue to influence the finish as the fruitiness subsides into a sweetish light background.

India Pale Ale *(OG 1046, ABV 4.6%)* ✦
Hops, malt and bitterness blend to give a full-flavoured but well-balanced beer. The light malty/hop nose belies the robustness of the taste. The bitterness and hops continue to a clean, dry and lingering finish.

Norwegian Blue *(OG 1049, ABV 4.9%)* ✦
Hints of malt and hops give this copper bitter a soft nose. This is at odds with a strong, smooth taste, with equal amounts of malt and hops balancing a bitter-sweet gooseberry body. Short malty, bitter end.

Ale *(OG 1055, ABV 5.5%)* ✦
A tawny, old-fashioned Christmas pudding beer. Rich, plummy aroma emerges from a sweet fruity flavour laced with a malty platform. The finish continues through to a smooth malty flavour abetted by sweet bitterness.

BULLMASTIFF

Bullmastiff Brewery, 14 Bessemer Close, Leckwith, Cardiff, CF11 8DL
Tel (029) 20665292
Website www.bullmastiffbrewery.com

An award-winning small craft brewery run by the brothers Bob and Paul Jenkins. The name stems from their love of the bullmastiff breed. They have won many awards for the beers, including Champion Beer of Wales 1999 and 2000 and joint gold medal for bitter at the 2000 Great British Beer Festival, but have no ambitions for expansion or owning any pubs, preferring to concentrate on quality control. 30 outlets are supplied direct. Seasonal beers: Summer Moult (ABV 4.3%), Mogadog (ABV 10%, winter).

Gold *(OG 1038, ABV 3.8%)* 🍺✦
Champion Beer of Wales 1999 and 2000. A hoppy aroma invites you into a fine blend of hops, fruit and malt. Bitterness balances the taste with a refreshing, lasting finish.

Best Bitter *(OG 1042, ABV 4%)* ✦
A balanced beer with a hoppy, bitter and fruity finish. A good example of a tasty best bitter.

Thoroughbred *(OG 1047, ABV 4.5%)* ✦
A tasty, premium bitter with hops strong on the aroma and flavour balanced by fruit and malt with a bitter finish.

Snarlsberg Llager *(OG 1045, ABV 5%)*
A break from tradition, a cask-conditioned Welsh 'llager'.

Brindle *(OG 1051, ABV 5%)* ✦
A full-bodied, flavoursome pale beer. Good hop aroma with a mix of malt, hops, fruit and bitterness in the taste. A lasting and satisfying finish.

Son of A Bitch *(OG 1059, ABV 6%)* ✦
A powerful amber beer with a complex mix of hops, malt and fruit with balancing bitterness. Slightly lighter of late but still warming, tasty and drinkable.

BURTON BRIDGE

**Burton Bridge Brewery,
24 Bridge Street, Burton upon Trent,
Staffs, DE14 1SY**
Tel (01283) 510573
Fax (01283) 515594
Tours Wednesday evenings

⊗ A craft brewery established in 1982 by Bruce Wilkinson and Geoff Mumford, two refugees from Allied Breweries who finished up at Ind Coope of Romford. Burton Bridge now has three pubs in the town including an enlarged brewery tap. It supplies 300 outlets direct. Bottle-conditioned beers: Burton Porter (ABV 4.5%), Bramble Stout (ABV 5%), Empire Pale Ale (ABV 7.5%)🍺, Tickle Brain (ABV 8%). Seasonal beer: Old Expensive (ABV 6.5%)🍷, Top Dog Stout (ABV 5%), Hearty Ale (ABV 5%), Battle Brew (ABV 5%), Knot Brown Ale (ABV 4.8%), Spring Ale (ABV 4.7%). Gold Medal Ales (ABV 4.5%, a range of monthly beers).

Golden Delicious *(ABV 3.8%)*

XL Bitter *(OG 1040, ABV 4%)* ✦
A golden, malty bitter, with a faint, hoppy and fruity aroma. An excellent mix of flavours follows, with fruitiness dominating.

Bridge Bitter
(OG 1042, ABV 4.2%) ✦
Amber-coloured and malty. Clean tasting with little aroma but a superb, bitter, hoppy aftertaste.

Porter *(OG 1045, ABV 4.5%)*
Dark red, with a faint roast aroma. The taste combines some liquorice flavour with hops and fruit; slightly sweet. A dry, astringent aftertaste.

Festival Ale *(OG 1055, ABV 5.5%)*
A full-bodied, tawny-coloured, strong but sweet beer. The aroma is hoppy, malty and slightly fruity. Malt and hops in the flavour give way to a fruity finish. Tremendous sparkling mouthfeel.

BURTONWOOD

Thomas Hardy Burtonwood Ltd, Bold Lane, Burtonwood, Warrington, Cheshire, WA5 4PJ
Tel (01925) 220022
Tours by arrangement (charge)

☺ A family-run brewery that merged its brewing operation in 1998 with Thomas Hardy of Dorchester (qv) to form Thomas Hardy Burtonwood Ltd. The brewery is still 40% owned by Burtonwood Brewery plc, which is now a pub-owning group. The other 60% is owned by Thomas Hardy. Occasional beers: Black Parrot (ABV 4%), Forshaws Bitter (ABV 4%), Hoppers (ABV 4.2%).

Bitter *(OG 1036.8, ABV 3.7%)*
A well-balanced, refreshing, malty bitter, with good hoppiness. Fairly dry aftertaste.

Top Hat *(OG 1046, ABV 4.8%)*
Soft, nutty, malty and a little sweet. Fairly thin for its gravity.

BUSHY'S

The Mount Murray Brewing Co Ltd, Mount Murray, Castletown Road, Braddan, Isle of Man, IM4 1JE
Tel (01624) 661244
Fax (01624) 611101
Website www.bushys.com
Tours by arrangement

☺ Set up in 1986 as a brew-pub, Bushy's moved to its present site in 1990 when demand outgrew capacity. It owns four tied houses and the beers, all brewed to the stipulations of the Manx Brewers' Act of 1874, are also supplied to 20 other outlets. Occasional/seasonal beers: Summer Ale (ABV 3.6%, July), Celtibration Ale (ABV 4%), Piston Brew (ABV 4.5%, for the TT races in May-June), Old Bushy Tail (ABV 4.5%), Old Shunter (ABV 4.5%, Aug-Sept), Lovely Jubbely Christmas Ale (ABV 5.2%). Bottle-conditioned beer: Bushys (ABV 4.5%).

Ruby (1874) Mild *(OG 1035, ABV 3.4%)*

Castletown Bitter *(OG 1035, ABV 3.5%)*

Export Bitter *(OG 1038, ABV 3.8%)*
An aroma full of pale malt and hops introduces you to a beautifully hoppy, bitter beer. Despite the predominant hop character, malt is also evident. Fresh and clean-tasting.

Manannan's Cloak *(OG 1038, ABV 3.8%)*

BUTCOMBE

Butcombe Brewery Ltd, Butcombe, Bristol, BS40 7XQ
Tel (01275) 472240
Fax (01275) 474734

E-mail butcombebrewery@talk21.com
Tours by arrangement (trade only)

⊗ One of the most successful of the newer breweries, set up in 1978 by a former Courage Western director, Simon Whitmore. During 1992-93, the brewery virtually doubled in size (for the third time) and, after 18 years of brewing just a single beer, a second ale went into production in 1996 after further plant development. Butcombe has bought a further two pubs, bringing its estate up to six houses (although none is tied) and it also supplies 350 other outlets within a 50-mile radius of the brewery.

Bitter *(OG 1039, ABV 4%)*
Amber-coloured, malty and notably bitter beer, with subtle citrus fruit qualities. Hoppy, malty, citrus and very slightly sulphur aroma, and a long, dry, bitter finish with light fruit notes. Consistent and refreshing.

Gold *(OG 1047, ABV 4.7%)*
Aroma of pale malt, citrus hops and fruit. Medium bodied, well-balanced, with good pale malt, hops and bitterness. Yellow-gold in colour, it is quite fruity, slightly sweet, with an abiding dryness.

BUTTS

Butts Brewery Ltd, Northfield Farm, Great Shefford, Hungerford, Berkshire, RG17 7BY
Tel (01488) 648133
Fax (0118) 375 9341
Tours by arrangement

⊗ The brewery, established in 1994, is housed in an old Dutch barn on a farm. The 18-barrel brewery supplies some 200 pubs as far afield as Dartford and Taunton, with an emphasis on direct supply to ensure that high quality standards are maintained. Barbus Barbus has won the Champion Beer of the Festival award three years running at the Steventon (Oxfordshire) Beer Festival. Seasonal beer: Golden Brown (ABV 5%, spring and autumn). Bottle-conditioned beers: Blackguard (ABV 4.5%), Barbus Barbus (ABV 4.6%).

Jester *(OG 1035, ABV 3.5%)*
This amber-coloured beer is fruity and slightly buttery, with an excellent hop aroma supported by pale malt. Aroma and bittering hops balance in the mouth, leading to a dry, hoppy finish.

Bitter *(OG 1040, ABV 4%)*
A traditional southern-style bitter, pale brown in colour with a good bitter hop character and some fruity tendencies.

Blackguard *(OG 1045, ABV 4.5%)*
A rich, fruity red-brown porter with hints of crystal and chocolate malt in the mouth. A blackcurrant aroma and taste are well-balanced with bitterness and malt characters, followed by a dry, bitter and roast finish.

Barbus Barbus
(OG 1046, ABV 4.6%)
The pale malt in this amber beer is tempered with a hint of crystal malt, well balanced by hops and fruit, leading to a long, complex and bitter-sweet finish. Very drinkable.

CAINS

Robert Cain Brewery Ltd, Stanhope Street, Liverpool, Merseyside, L8 5XJ
Tel (0151) 709 8734
Fax (0151) 708 8395
E-mail info@cainsbeers.com
Website www.cainsbeers.com
Tours by arrangement Mon-Thu evenings

☺ The Robert Cain Brewery was first established on the site in 1850, but was bought by Higsons in the 1920s, then by Boddingtons in 1985. Whitbread took control of the Boddingtons' breweries in 1990 and closed the site. It reopened as Robert Cain Brewery, now a division of Brewery Group Denmark A/S. Cain's has nine tied houses and 313 outlets are supplied direct. Occasional/seasonal beers: Dragon Heart (ABV 5%, Jan/Feb), Dr Duncans Elixir (ABV 4.5%, March/April), Sundowner (ABV 4.5%, May/June), Triple Hop (ABV 4.5%, July/Aug), Cains Red (ABV 4.5%, Sept/Oct), First Class Ale (ABV 4.3%, Nov/Dec).

Dark Mild *(OG 1033.5, ABV 3.2%)* 🍺🏠🍷
A smooth, dry and roasty dark mild, with some chocolate and coffee notes.

Dr Duncans IPA *(OG 1036, ABV 3.5%)*

Traditional Bitter *(OG 1038.5, ABV 4%)* 🍷
A darkish, full-bodied and fruity bitter, with a good hoppy nose and a dry aftertaste.

Formidable Ale *(OG 1048, ABV 5%)* 🍷
A bitter and hoppy beer with a good dry aftertaste. Sharp, clean and dry.

CALEDONIAN

Caledonian Brewing Company Ltd, 42 Slateford Road, Edinburgh, EH11 1PH
Tel (0131) 337 1286
Fax (0131) 313 2370
E-mail info@caledonian-brewery.co.uk
Website www.caledonian-brewery.co.uk
Shop 9-5 Mon-Fri. Tours by arrangement

☺ Established in 1869, the brewery was bought by Vaux in 1919 and saved from closure by a management buy-out in 1987. Caledonian still brews in three direct-fired open coppers and uses open fermentation. It supplies 500 outlets but does not own any pubs or bars of its own. Monthly seasonals are brewed.

Murrays Summer Ale
(OG 1036, ABV 3.6%) 🍷
A clean-tasting, thirst-quenching, golden session beer, with hop and fruit evident throughout. A bitter beer, balanced by malt in the taste and aftertaste.

Deuchars IPA *(OG 1038, ABV 3.8%)* 🍺🏠🍷
At its best, an extremely tasty and refreshing amber-coloured session beer. Hops and fruit are very evident and are balanced by malt

throughout. The lingering aftertaste is delightfully bitter and hoppy.

80/- *(OG 1042, ABV 4.1%)* 🏠🍷
A predominantly malty, copper-coloured beer with hop and fruit. A Scottish heavy that now lacks the complex taste and hoppiness of old.

Golden Promise *(OG 1045, ABV 4.5%)* 🍷
The original organic beer, pale in colour, with pronounced hop character. Floral and fruity on the nose.

Lorimers IPA *(OG 1054, ABV 5.2%)*

CAMBRINUS

Cambrinus Craft Brewery, Home Farm, Knowsley Park, Knowsley, Merseyside, L34 4AQ
Tel (0151) 546 2226
E-mail cambrinus@talk21.co.uk
Tours by arrangement

Cambrinus has had a helter-skelter history: it opened in July 1997, closed in January 1999 and re-opened in October 1999 and is now run by John Aspinall. Approximately 30 outlets are supplied direct. Seasonal beers: Lamp Oil (ABV 4.5%, late autumn), Boot Strap (ABV 4.5%, early spring), Epoch (ABV 5%), Celebrance (ABV 6.5%, Christmas).

Herald *(OG 1036, ABV 3.7%)*

Yardstick *(OG 1040, ABV 4%)*

Deliverance *(OG 1040, ABV 4.2%)*

Endurance *(OG 1045, ABV 4.5%)*
An India Pale Ale.

CAMERONS

Camerons Brewery Company, Lion Brewery, Hartlepool, Co Durham, TS24 7QS
Tel (01429) 266666
Fax (01429) 868198
E-mail martindutoyek@bankss.co.uk
Website www.fullpint.co.uk
Tours by arrangement

☺ This major regional brewer, established in 1865, is once again facing an uncertain future. It went through a period of neglect for 17 years when it was owned by Ellerman Shipping lines and then the Brent Walker property group. In 1992, Camerons was bought by Wolverhampton & Dudley Breweries in a deal that included the brewery, 51 pubs and the brands. The company has 172 tied houses, all of which use lined glasses to ensure a full pint. The brewery is operating at full capacity as it also brews Harp and (for Scottish Courage) Kronenbourg lagers. But in April 2001 W&D announced it planned to sell Camerons to the owners of the nearby Castle Eden Brewery (qv). Castle Eden will close and its brands will be transferred to Camerons.

Bitter *(OG 1036, ABV 3.6%)* 🍷
A light bitter, but well-balanced, with hops and malt.

Strongarm *(OG 1041, ABV 4%)* 🍷
A well-rounded, ruby-red ale with a distinctive, tight creamy head; initially fruity, but with a good balance of malt, hops and moderate bitterness.

CANNON

**The Cannon, Parker & Sons Brewers Ltd,
71 Cannon Street, Wellingborough,
Northants, NN8 4DJ
Tel (01933) 279629**

The brewery ceased trading in March 1999 and re-opened in 2000. But in June 2001 the Cannon pub was sold and the brewery closed again.

CANNON ROYALL

**◊ Cannon Royall Brewery, Fruiterer's Arms,
Uphampton, Nr Droitwich, Worcs, WR9 0JW
Tel (01905) 621161
Fax (01562) 743262**
Tours by arrangement (occasional)

The first brew was in 1993 in a converted cider house behind the Fruiterer's Arms pub. It has increased capacity from five barrels to more than 16 a week. The brewery has a tied house, the Fox at Monkwood Green. Cannon Royall supplies a number of outlets in the West Midlands and Worcestershire.

Fruiterer's Mild *(ABV 3.7%)* ◗
There is just enough sweetness and fruitiness to bring out and complement the chocolate and roasted malts in this black, luxuriant mild.

Muzzle Loader *(ABV 3.8%)* ◗
A fruity nose disguises the attack of bitter hops that follows. A dry, bitter beer that leaves a lingering aftertaste.

Arrowhead *(ABV 3.9%)* ◗
The strong hoppy presence is evident throughout, leaving a clean, dry finish in the mouth.

Buckshot *(ABV 4.5%)*
The balance of hop and malt flavours with a hint of fruitiness are just right in this premium bitter.

Heart of Oak *(ABV 5.4%)* ◗
The accent is on malt in this strong ale with a plum fruitiness on the palate.

CAPTAIN COOK

**◊ Captain Cook Brewery Ltd,
White Swan, 1 West End, Stokesley,
Middlesbrough, TS9 5BL
Tel (01642) 710263 Fax (01642) 714245
E-mail Joonanbri@aol.com**
Tours by arrangement

The 18th-century White Swan concentrated on promoting real ale for 10 years before taking on the challenge of becoming a brew-pub. The Captain Cook Brewery, with a 4-barrel plant, started brewing in 1999 and was opened by White Swan regular James Cook on his 79th birthday. The beer range is now supplied to other pubs and bottled beer production will begin this year.

Sunset *(OG 1040, ABV 4%)*
An extremely smooth light ale with a good balance of malt and hops.

Slipway *(OG 1042, ABV 4.2%)*
A light-coloured hoppy ale, with bitterness coming through from Challenger hops. A full-flavoured ale with a smooth malt aftertaste.

Red Gold *(OG 1044, ABV 4.4%)*
A premium bitter with a smooth balance of malt and hops. The initial flavour has hints of mellow toffee followed by the smooth bitterness of Fuggles and Goldings hops.

Black Porter *(OG 1044, ABV 4.4%)*
A dark beer with a slightly sweet, malty start, counter-balanced by a sharp bitterness and a noticeable roast barley character.

CASTLE EDEN

**Castle Eden Brewery Ltd,
PO Box 13, Castle Eden, Hartlepool,
Co Durham, TS27 4SX
Tel (01429) 836007
Fax (01429) 839292
E-mail enquiries@castleedenbrewery.com
Website www.castleedenbrewery.com**
Tours by arrangement

The threat of closure hangs over this much-loved, historic brewery following the announcement in April 2000 by Wolverhampton & Dudley that it planned to sell Camerons of Hartlepool to David Soley, the owner of Castle Eden. If the deal goes ahead, Castle Eden will close and its brands will transfer to Camerons (qv). The Castle Eden Inn started trading in 1758. In 1826 John Nimmo bought the site, leasing the inn and adjoining buildings and expanding the brewery to produce mild, bitter and Scotch ales. The brewery remained in the Nimmo family until 1963 when Whitbread bought the company with 125 tied houses. The Nimmo's brands were phased out and the company was renamed Whitbread East Pennines. In 1998 Whitbread announced its intention to close or sell Castle Eden. After a vigorous campaign by CAMRA, trade unions and the local council, Whitbread sold the brewery to two local businessmen, David Soley and David Beecroft, with manager Jim Kerr staying on as operations director (Jim Kerr is now operations director of Brain's of Cardiff) and the beers listed below may be reduced if production moves to Camerons. Seasonal beers: Spring Knight, Summer Knight, Autumn Knight and Winter Knight.

Nimmo's 3X *(ABV 3.6%)*

Bitter *(ABV 3.9%)*

Classic *(ABV 4%)*

Ale *(ABV 4.2%)* ▣◗
Amber, fruity premium ale, usually dry-hopped. Bitter flavours with a lingering aftertaste. Slight maltiness develops as cask empties.

Nimmo's 4X *(ABV 4.4%)* ◗
A smooth golden, fruity bitter. Full-bodied but not as bitter as might be expected. Lingering and satisfying aftertaste.

CASTLE ROCK

**Castle Rock Brewery Ltd,
Queens Bridge Road, The Meadows,
Nottingham, NG2 1NB
Tel/Fax (0115) 985 1615
E-mail Castlerock@Tynemill.co.uk
Website www.tynemill.co.uk/castle**
Shop. Tours by arrangement

Castle Rock Brewery started life as the Bramcote Brewing Company in 1996. A reputation for quality beers soon grew, and came to the attention of the East Midlands pub chain, Tynemill. A partnership between Tynemill and Bramcote created the Castle Rock Brewery at the present site close to Nottingham's historic castle rock. In 2001, Tynemill bought out the original partners and the brewery became a wholly-owned subsidiary of the pub group. Following the success of the World Cup cricket special brew Middle Wicket, Castle Rock has created a Rugby World Cup brew named Rolling Ruck. Seasonal beers: Daze Collection (ABV 3.8%, summer, autumn, winter and Christmas).

Nottingham Pale Ale *(ABV 3.6%)*

Hemlock *(ABV 4%)*

Snowhite *(ABV 4.2%)*

Bendigo *(ABV 4.5%)*

Salsa *(ABV 4.5%)*

Elsie Mo *(ABV 4.7%)*

Trentsman *(ABV 4.8%)*

Black Jack Stout *(ABV 4.9%)*

Stairway *(ABV 5.2%)*

CAYTHORPE

**Caythorpe Brewery,
3 Gonalston Lane, Hoveringham,
Nottingham, NG14 7JH
Tel/Fax (0115) 966 4376**
Tours by arrangement

Set up in 1997 by an ex-Home Brewery employee, Geoff Slack, and his wife Pam, Caythorpe's beers are brewed at the Black Horse pub. It supplies some 50 local outlets. A third fermenter is now operational, increasing the brewery's capacity by 50 per cent. Demand is high from local outlets. The brewery survived the floods of 2000 and 2001, when the River Trent burst its banks. Occasional/seasonal beers: Dark Horse Bitter (ABV 4.3%), Too Grand (ABV 4.8%), Crazy Horse Bitter (ABV 5%), Top Cat (ABV 4.7%).

Light Horse Bitter *(OG 1034.7, ABV 3.7%)*
Light in strength but richly coloured. A malty-flavoured session bitter with a dry finish. Dry hopped in cask for aroma.

Leading Light Bitter
(OG 1035.5, ABV 3.8%)
A golden brown bitter with just a hint of roast malt. Dry hopped with Challenger for aroma.

Dover Beck Bitter *(OG 1037, ABV 4%)*
A light, dry, well-hopped beer, dry hopped in cask. The house beer at the Black Horse.

Old Nottingham Extra Pale Ale
(OG 1038.6, ABV 4.2%)
The recipe comes from a Home Brewery brewing book of 1914 and offers a taste of old Nottingham. Very light in colour, hoppy and crisp.

Landlady Bitter *(OG 1038.6, ABV 4.2%)*
A light golden coloured bitter, well hopped and fairly dry tasting. Dry hopped with Challenger for aroma.

Birthday Brew Bitter *(OG 1040, ABV 4.5%)*
A golden-coloured bitter with a full malt feel. Late hopping in the copper using Styrian Goldings gives a pleasant aroma.

CHALK HILL

**Chalk Hill Brewery, Rosary Road,
Norwich, Norfolk, NR1 4DA
Tel/Fax (01603) 477078**
Tours by arrangement

⊗ Run by former Reindeer brew-pub owner Bill Thomas and his partners Tiny Little and Dave Blake, Chalk Hill began production with a 15-barrel plant in 1993. It has taken on award-winning David Winter (ex-Woodforde's) as head brewer, and is developing plans for expansion and new brews. Chalk Hill supplies its own two pubs and 20 local free trade outlets. The beers are also available nationwide via beer agencies. Occasional beer: IPA (ABV 5.3%).

Brewery Tap *(OG 1036, ABV 3.6%)* ✦
A tawny-coloured brew with a gentle aroma based on hops and malt. Easy on the palate, with a caramel-backed hoppiness throughout. Traces of bitterness remain as the initial maltiness fades.

CHB *(OG 1042, ABV 4.2%)* ✦
An aroma based on a fruity/malty blend gives a hint of the delicate flavours to follow. Malt provides the base from which bitterness and a light flowery hoppiness are sustained to a quick, bitter finish.

Dreadnought *(OG 1050, ABV 4.9%)* ✦
Only a hint of malt and hops in the nose of this mid-brown, full-bodied ale. A dry bitterness and malt taste provide a smooth introduction. This evolves into a bitter follow-through with hoppy notes.

Flintknapper's Mild *(OG 1050, ABV 5%)* ✦
A strong coffee/roasty aroma introduces this red-brown strong mild. A full-bodied, smooth roast malt backbone dominates throughout. A sweet, grapey background fades to a short hoppy finish with caramel.

Old Tackle *(OG 1056, ABV 5.6%)* ✦
Reddish-brown with a moderate malt nose. Hops join the roast malt initiation into a complex old ale. A bitter-sweet hoppiness can be detected throughout but only the malt retains its initial impact.

CHERITON

⚲ **Cheriton Brewhouse, Cheriton, Alresford,
Hampshire, SO24 0QQ
Tel (01962) 771166 Fax (01962) 771595
E-mail bestbeer1@aol.com**
Tours by arrangement

⊗ A purpose-built brewery, opened in 1993 by the proprietors of the Flower Pots Inn next door. The brewery is now working close to its weekly capacity of 50 barrels to supply 30-40 outlets as well as a second tied house. Occasional/seasonal beers: Beltane (ABV 4.5%, spring), Flower Power (ABV 5.2%, summer), Turkey's Delight (ABV 5.9%, Christmas).

Pots Ale *(OG 1036.5, ABV 3.8%)* ✦
Pale brown, with a hoppy nose. A well-balanced bitter and hoppy taste leads through to the aftertaste.

Village Elder *(OG 1038.5, ABV 3.8%)* ▯

Cheriton Best Bitter
(OG 1043, ABV 4.2%) ▮◗
A malty and fruity taste continues into the aftertaste. A dark brown beer with a malty and fruity nose.

Diggers Gold
(OG 1044.5, ABV 4.6%) ▯◗
A golden beer with a citric, hoppy aroma; bitter and hoppy in all respects. A dry finish.

CHILTERN

Chiltern Brewery, Nash Lee Road, Terrick, Aylesbury, Bucks, HP17 0TQ
Tel (01296) 613647
Fax (01296) 612419
E-mail info@chilternbrewery.co.uk
Website www.chilternbrewery.co.uk
Shop 9-5 Mon-Sat. Tours by arrangement (individual tour most Saturdays at noon)

⊗ Established by Richard and Lesley Jenkinson in 1980, the first brew, Chiltern Ale, was followed in 1982 by Beechwood Bitter. Three Hundred Old Ale joined the ranks in 1988 to celebrate the eighth anniversary, with Bodgers Barley Wine in 1990 for the 10th, and John Hampden's Ale in 1995 for the 15th anniversary. A brewery shop opened in 1989, followed by a small museum in 1994. Buckinghamshire County Celebration Ale has been replaced with Lord Lieutenant's Ale. Bottle-conditioned beer: Bodgers Barley Wine (ABV 8.5%). The brewery now offers Own Label bottled beers for customers who choose a name or supply a design.

Chiltern Ale *(OG 1038, ABV 3.7%)* ◗
A refreshing session bitter, amber in colour, with a predominantly malty character. The aroma is of pale malt with a hint of grape, with some sweetness in the mouth and a short finish.

Beechwood Bitter *(OG 1043, ABV 4.3%)* ◗
A pale brown, refreshing beer with a rich butter-toffee aroma, lots of pale malt and fruit in the mouth and a finish that is more sweet and fruity than bitter.

Three Hundred Old Ale
(OG 1049/50, ABV 4.9%) ◗
A strong old ale with some crystal malt and roast character plus hints of liquorice. Deceptively strong.

CHURCH END

Church End Brewery Ltd,
109 Ridge Lane, Nr Atherstone,
Warwickshire, CV10 0RD
Tel (01827) 713080
Fax (01827) 717328
Tours by arrangement

Church End opened as a small brewery in a 350-year-old stable workshop with a 4-barrel capacity in 1994 and moved to new premises in 2001 with 10-barrel equipment and the potential for building a tap room on site. The brewery produces unusual beers (banana, lemon, spices and herbs) made at different times of the year. It also brews two of the beers from the closed Judges Brewery in Birmingham, Barrister's Bitter and Old Gavel Bender. Church End supplies 50-100 outlets. Occasional beers: Mild Quaker (ABV 3.4%), Anchor Bitter (ABV 4%), Hooker Ale or Rusty Dudley (ABV 4.5%), Pews Porter (ABV 4.5%), Silent Night (ABV 4.5%, Christmas), Willie Brew'd (ABV 4.5%, Burns Night), Stout Coffin (ABV 4.6%), Shustoke Surpryes (ABV 4.8%), Cracker or Four King Ale (ABV 5%, Christmas), Father Brown (ABV 6%), Rest in Peace (ABV 7%). Bottle-conditioned beer: Ruby Ale (ABV 5%).

Barrister's Bitter *(ABV 3.5%)*

Cuthberts *(OG 1038, ABV 3.8%)* ◗
A refreshing, hoppy beer, with hints of malt, fruit and caramel taste. Lingering bitter aftertaste.

Gravediggers *(OG 1038, ABV 3.8%)* ◗
A premium mild. Black and red in colour, with a complex mix of chocolate and roast flavours, it is almost a light porter. Available in spring and summer.

Wheat-a-Bix *(OG 1042, ABV 4.2%)* ◗
A wheat beer; clear, malty and pale, combining German hops and English wheat.

What the Fox's Hat *(OG 1043, ABV 4.2%)* ◗
A beer with a malty aroma, and a hoppy and malty taste with some caramel flavour.

Pooh Beer *(OG 1044, ABV 4.3%)* ◗
A bright golden beer brewed with honey. Sweet, yet hoppy; moreish.

Vicar's Ruin *(OG 1044, ABV 4.4%)* ◗
A straw-coloured best bitter with an initially hoppy, bitter flavour, softening to a delicate malt finish.

Old Pal *(OG 1055, ABV 5%)* ◗
A strong, copper-coloured ale, full of rich, malty flavours. Three different types of hops are used; dry finish.

Old Gavel Bender *(ABV 5%)*

CITY OF CAMBRIDGE

City of Cambridge Brewery,
19 Cheddars Lane, Cambridge, CB5 8LD
Tel (01223) 353939
Website www.cambridgebrewery.co.uk
Tours by arrangement

⊗ Opened in May 1997 with a 5-barrel brew plant, the company supplies 70 outlets direct. Bottle-conditioned beer: Hobson's Choice (ABV 4.1%). Seasonal beer: Michaelmas (ABV 4.6%, Christmas).

IPA *(ABV 3.6%)*
A fresh amber-coloured session bitter, using Target hops. A blend of two yeasts gives the beer its unique dry, bitter finish.

Boathouse Bitter *(OG 1038, ABV 3.8%)* ◗
Copper-brown and full-bodied session bitter, starting with impressive citrus and floral hop; grassy, fruity notes and cooked vegetables are present with finally a fading, gentle bitterness.

Hobson's Choice *(OG 1041, ABV 4.1%)* ▯◗
A highly-drinkable, golden brew with a pronounced hop aroma and taste, and a fruity, bitter balance in the mouth, finishing gently dry. Vegetable notes occur when young.

Atom Splitter *(OG 1047, ABV 4.7%)* ◗
Robust copper-coloured strong bitter with hop aroma and taste, and a distinct vegetably sulphur edge.

Darwin's Downfall *(ABV 5%)*
A blended, ruby-golden coloured beer. Hoppy with a fruity character and a refreshing citrus aftertaste.

Parkers Porter *(ABV 5.3%)* ◆
Impressive reddish brew with a defined roast character thoughout, and short, fruity, bitter-sweet palate.

Bramling Traditional *(OG 1055, ABV 5.5%)*
Made with Bramling Cross hops; fruity and delicious.

CLARK'S

HB Clark Co (Successors) Ltd, Westgate Brewery, Westgate, Wakefield, W Yorkshire, WF2 9SW
Tel **(01924) 373328** Fax **(01924) 372306**
Shop (cash and carry) 8-5 Mon-Fri; 8-1pm Sat-Sun
Tours by arrangement

☺ Founded in 1905, Clark's ceased brewing during the keg revolution of the 1960s and 1970s. It resumed cask ale production in 1982 and now supplies by direct delivery to more than 150 outlets, in addition to wholesalers and distributors throughout England and Scotland. Clark's has five tied houses, four of which serve cask-conditioned beer. Seasonal and monthly beers are produced. Clark's T'owd Dreadnought is brewed specifically for beer festivals.

Traditional *(OG 1038, ABV 3.8%)* ◆
A copper-coloured, well-balanced, smooth beer, with a malty and hoppy aroma, leading to a hoppy, fruity taste and a good, clean, strong malt flavour. Bitterness and dryness linger in the taste and aftertaste.

Festival Ale *(OG 1042, ABV 4.2%)* ◆
A light, fruity, pleasantly hopped premium bitter with a good fruity, hoppy nose. Moderate bitterness follows, with a dry, fruity finish. Gold in colour.

Burglar Bill *(OG 1044, ABV 4.4%)* ◆
A good hoppy, fruity aroma precedes an enjoyable, strongly hoppy and fruity taste, with moderate bitterness and good malt character. A lingering, dry, hoppy finish follows. Dark brown in colour.

Rams Revenge *(OG 1046, ABV 4.6%)* ◆
A rich, ruby-coloured premium ale, well-balanced with malt and hops, with a deep fruity taste and a dry hoppy aftertaste, with a pleasant hoppy aroma.

Golden Hornet *(OG 1050, ABV 5%)* ◆
A crisp golden premium beer with a full fruity taste, with full hop aroma and dry hop aftertaste.

T'owd Dreadnought *(OG 1090, ABV 9%)* ◆
An exceptionally strong nut-brown super premium ale with a full malt flavour. Not too sweet, with a lingering full hop character.

CLEARWATER

Clearwater Brewery, 2 Devon Units, Hatchmoor Industrial Estate, Torrington, Devon, EX38 7HP
Tel **(01805) 625242**
Tours by arrangement

Brian Broughton, formerly of Barum, took over the closed St Giles in the Wood Brewery in January 1999 and has continued with many improvements since. 70 outlets in the West Country are supplied direct.

Cavalier *(ABV 4%)* ◆
Mid-brown, full-bodied best bitter with a burnt, rich malt aroma and taste, leading to a bitter, well-rounded finish.

Beggars Tipple *(ABV 4.2%)*

1646 *(ABV 4.8%)*

Oliver's Nectar *(ABV 5.2%)*

CLOCKWORK

⚲ **RH & JG Graham t/a Graham Enterprises, The Clockwork Beer Co, 1153/55 Cathcart Road, Glasgow, G42 9HB**
Tel/Fax **0141 6490184**
E-mail rhg@talk21.com
Tours by arrangement

Robin and Gay Graham, a husband-and-wife partnership, purchased a Glasgow pub in 1997, gutted it and rebuilt it to include a micro-brewery in the middle of the bar. They started brewing in December 1997. Beers (which use primarily American Hops): Amber IPA (ABV 3.8%), Red Alt Beer (ABV 4.4%), either Oregon IPA (ABV 5.5%) or Thunder and Lightning (ABV 6%) – the uncut versions of the Amber IPA and Red Alt Beer, Original Lager (ABV 4.8%), Hazy Daze fruit range (ABV 5%): Seriously Ginger is permanent, with others produced as the fruit is available (eg Kiwi, Raspberry and Banana). A German Weisse [wheat] Beer and a Raspberry Weisse Beer (both ABV 5%) are also produced. A Monthly Special (ABV 4.1/4.2%) is always available and uses European/British hops for customers who are not keen on the more flowery American hops. The Specials tend to be quite eclectic, ranging from Original Kelpie [seaweed] Ale, Scottish Oatmeal Stout to Organic Rowan Ale. They are on sale for approximately four weeks at a time. The ales are only available in the pub itself. All the beers are cold conditioned and are kept under a blanket of carbon dioxide; in the case of Alt and Amber, only the natural gas produced by fermentation is used.

COACH HOUSE

Coach House Brewing Company Ltd, Wharf Street, Howley, Warrington, Cheshire, WA1 2DQ
Tel **(01925) 232800**
Fax **(01925) 232700**

☺ The brewery was founded in 1991 by four ex-Greenall Whitley employees. In 1995 Coach House increased its brewing capacity to cope with growing demand and it now

delivers to outlets throughout England, Wales and Scotland, either direct or via wholesalers. The brewery also produces specially commissioned beers.
Seasonal beers: Ostlers (ABV 4%, summer), Squires Gold (ABV 4.2%, spring), Taverners (ABV 5%, autumn), Blunderbus (ABV 5.5% winter).

Coachman's Best Bitter
(OG 1037, ABV 3.7%) ◆
A well-hopped, malty bitter, moderately fruity with a hint of sweetness and a peppery nose.

Honeypot Bitter *(OG 1038, ABV 3.8%)*

Gunpowder Strong Mild
(OG 1039, ABV 3.8%)
Dark brown, lightly hopped, malty mild with faint roast undertones. Easy drinking but not as characterful as it once was.

Dick Turpin *(OG 1042, ABV 4.2%)* ◆
Malty, hoppy pale brown beer with some initial sweetish flavours leading to a short, bitter aftertaste. Also sold under other names as a pub house beer.

Flintlock Best Bitter *(ABV 4.4%)*

Innkeeper's Special Reserve
(OG 1045, ABV 4.5%) ◆
A darkish, full-flavoured bitter. Quite fruity, with a strong, bitter aftertaste.

Gingernut Premium *(OG 1050, ABV 5%)*

Posthorn Premium Ale
(OG 1050, ABV 5%) ◆
Well-hopped and fruity, with bitterness and malt also prominent. Hoppy aroma and fruity aftertaste.

Coach House also brews several beers for a non-brewing company, John Joule of Stone (01785 814909).

COLES

◻ **Coles Family Brewery, White Hart Inn, Llanddarog, Nr Carmarthen, SA32 8NT**
Tel/Fax (01267) 275395

Coles was started by Cain, one of the sons, in 1999. Cwrw Blasus, meaning 'tasty beer', was the first brew and has continued to be the main ale.

Mild *(OG 1037, ABV 3.8%)*

Beetroot *(OG 1040, ABV 4%)*

Nettle *(OG 1040, ABV 4%)*

Twrogs Golden Summer Ale
(OG 1040, ABV 4.2%)

Cwrw Blasus *(OG 1042, ABV 4.5%)*

Spiced Cwrw Nadolig *(OG 1042, ABV 4.5%)*

Stout *(OG 1045, ABV 4.5%)*

CONCERTINA

◻ **Concertina Brewery, 9A Dolcliffe Road, Mexborough, S Yorkshire, S64 9AZ**
Tel (01709) 580841
Tours by arrangement

A club once famous for its concertina band, where brewing started in its cellar in 1992. The plant is continuously upgraded and produces eight barrels a week and supplies 25 outlets.

Club Bitter *(ABV 3.9%)* ◆
A fruity session bitter with a good bitter flavour.

Old Dark Attic *(OG 1038, ABV 3.9%)*
A dark brown beer with a fairly sweet, fruity taste.

Best Bitter *(OG 1038.5, ABV 3.9%)* ◆
This mid-brown bitter has lots of hops on the nose, a hoppy taste and a dry finish, plus gentle fruitiness throughout.

One-eyed Jack *(OG 1039, ABV 4%)*
Fairly pale in colour, with plenty of hop bitterness. Brewed with the same malt and hops combination as Bengal Tiger, but more of a session beer. Also known as Mexborough Bitter.

Bengal Tiger *(OG 1043, ABV 4.6%)* ◻◆
Light amber ale with an aromatic hoppy nose followed by a wonderful combination of fruit and bitterness. A very smooth finish.

New Imperial *(ABV 4.6%)*
An amber malty-flavoured beer with an aromatic nose. The flavour is complemented by fruity overtones.

Dictators *(OG 1044, ABV 4.7%)*

Ariel Square Four *(OG 1046, ABV 5.2%)*

CONISTON

◻ **Coniston Brewing Co Ltd, Coppermines Road, Coniston, Cumbria, LA21 8HL**
Tel (015394) 41133
Fax (015394) 41177
E-mail i.s.bradley@btinternet
Website www.conistonbrewery.com
Shop 11-11. Tours by arrangement.

☺ A 10-barrel brewery set up in 1995 behind the Black Bull inn, it achieved national fame when it won the Champion Beer of Britain competition in 1998 for Bluebird Bitter. It is now brewing 30 barrels a week and supplies 20 local outlets direct. Brakspear brews and bottles Bluebird for Coniston in bottle-conditioned form at ABV 4.2%. Seasonal beer: Blacksmith's Ale (ABV 5%, Dec-Feb).

Bluebird Bitter *(OG 1036, ABV 3.6%)* ◻◆
A yellow-gold, predominantly hoppy and fruity beer, well-balanced with some sweetness and a rising bitter finish.

Opium *(OG 1040, ABV 4%)* ◆
Copper-coloured with distinctly fruity, hoppy aromas; a well-balanced flavour with malt, hops and fruit, and more bitter and astringent in the aftertaste.

Old Man Ale *(OG 1042.5, ABV 4.4%)* ◆
Delicious fruity, winey beer with complex, well-balanced richness.

CORVEDALE

◻ **Corvedale Brewery, Sun Inn, Corfton, Craven Arms, Shropshire, SY7 9DF**
Tel (01584) 861503
E-mail thesun@corfton.co.uk
Tours by arrangement

Brewing started in 1999 in a building behind the pub. Landlord Norman Pearce is also the brewer and he uses only British malt and hops, with water from the local borehole. Corvedale swaps its beer with those of other small craft breweries, making them available in many parts of the country. The three beers are also on sale in the pub in bottle-conditioned form.

Norman's Pride (*OG 1043, ABV 4.3%*)
A golden amber beer with a refreshing, slightly hoppy taste and a bitter finish.

Secret Hop (*OG 1045, ABV 4.5%*)
A clear, ruby bitter with a smooth malty taste. Customers are invited to guess the hop!

Dark and Delicious (*OG 1046, ABV 4.6%*)
A dark ruby beer with hops on the aroma and palate, and a sweet aftertaste.

COTLEIGH

**Cotleigh Brewery, Ford Road, Wiveliscombe, Somerset, TA4 2RE
Tel (01984) 624086 Fax (01984) 624365
E-mail cotleigh@cloveruk.net**
Tours by arrangement

⊗ Situated in the historic brewing town of Wiveliscombe, Cotleigh Brewery is one of the oldest and most successful small breweries in the West Country. The brewery, which started trading in 1979, is housed in specially converted premises with a modern brew plant capable of producing 140 barrels a week. 150 pubs, mostly in Devon and Somerset, are supplied direct from the brewery and the beers are also widely available across the country via selected wholesalers. A number of beers are produced on a monthly guest beer rota: Nutcracker Mild (ABV 3.6%), Kiwi Pale Ale (ABV 3.9%), Harvest Ale (ABV 4%), Blue Jay Bitter (ABV 4.2%), Hobby Ale (ABV 4.2%), Goshawk (ABV 4.3%), Kookaburra Bitter (ABV 4.4%), Peregrine Porter (ABV 4.4%), Golden Eagle (ABV 4.5%), Merlin Ale (ABV 4.8%), Old Buzzard (ABV 4.8%, winter), Osprey (ABV 5%), Snowy Ale (ABV 5%), Hawkshead (ABV 5.5%), Red Nose Reinbeer (ABV 5%, Christmas).

Harrier SPA (*OG 1035, ABV 3.6%*) ◆
A straw-coloured beer with a hoppy aroma and taste, followed by a hoppy, bitter finish. Plenty of flavour for a light beer.

Tawny Bitter (*OG 1038, ABV 3.8%*) ◆
A mid-brown coloured beer with a hoppy aroma, a hoppy but well-balanced flavour, and a hoppy, bitter finish.

Barn Owl Bitter (*OG 1045, ABV 4.5%*) ▯◆
A dark amber beer with a malty aroma backed by hops; smooth, full-bodied taste with hops dominating, followed by malt. The finish is hoppy balanced with a little malt.

COTTAGE

**Cottage Brewing Co Ltd,
The Old Cheese Dairy, Hornblotton Road, Lovington, Somerset, BA7 7PS
Tel (01963) 240551
Fax (01963) 240383
Website www.cottagebrewing.com**
Tours by arrangement

⊗ The brewery was founded in West Lydford in 1993 and upgraded to a 10-barrel plant in 1994. Owned by former airline pilot Chris Norman and his wife Helen, the company got off to a flying start with Norman's Conquest winning the Champion Beer of Britain title at the 1995 Great British Beer Festival. Other awards followed and, on the strength of this success, the brewery moved to larger premises in 1996, doubling the brewing capacity at the same time. In early summer 2001, Cottage installed a 30-barrel plant, which will enable head brewer Daren Godfrey to brew four times a week, instead of six or seven times a week on the previous 20-barrel kit. The malt used in Maris Otter and hops come mainly from Kent. In 1997 Golden Arrow won the silver medal for Best Bitter at the Great British Beer Festival. In January 1999 Norman's Conquest won the Gold Medal for strong beers at the Great British Winter Beer Festival. No pubs are owned but the beers are supplied as far away as Liverpool and Yorkshire. The names of beers mostly follow a railway theme. Seasonal beers: Goldrush (ABV 5%), Santa's Steaming Ale (ABV 5.5%, Christmas). Occasional beer: Broadgauge Bitter (ABV 3.9%).

Southern Bitter (*OG 1037, ABV 3.7%*) ◆
Gold-coloured beer with malt and fruity hops on the nose. Malt and hops in the mouth with a long fruity, bitter finish.

Champflower Ale (*OG 1043, ABV 4.2%*) ◆
Amber beer with fruity hop aroma, full hop taste and powerful bitter finish.

Golden Arrow (*OG 1044, ABV 4.5%*) ◆
Golden beer with powerful floral hoppy aroma, a fruity, full-bodied taste with a dry, bitter finish.

Somerset & Dorset Ale
(*OG 1044, ABV 4.4%*) ◆
A well-hopped, malty brew, with a deep red colour.

Norman's Conquest
(*OG 1066, ABV 7%*) ▯◆
A dark strong ale, with plenty of fruit in the aroma and taste; rounded vinous, hoppy finish.

COTTAGE SPRING

**Cottage Spring Brewery, Gorse Cottage, Graig Road, Upper Cwmbran, Cwmbran, Torfaen, NP44 5AS
Tel (0780) 346 6346**

Cottage Spring is a craft brewery on the slopes of Mynydd Maen in Upper Cwmbran in Gwent's Eastern Valley. With an output of up to 20 barrels a week, the brewery takes its name from the cottage where it was built, and the local spring that supplies the water used for brewing liquor. The brewer produces three regular cask beers (plus Drayman's Gold for spring and summer) that are all produced using traditional methods and ingredients. Ten outlets are supplied direct. Seasonal/occasional beer: Drayman's Gold (ABV 3.8%, spring/summer).

Drayman's Choice (*OG 1038, ABV 3.8%*)

Crow Valley Bitter (*OG 1042, ABV 4.2%*) ◆
Faint hop and malt aroma followed by a crisp, clean mix of malt, hops and fruit in the taste. Bitterness builds, leaving a lasting dry finish.

The Full Malty (*OG 1050, ABV 5.2%*)

COUNTRY LIFE

Country Life Brewery, Pig on the Hill,
Pusehill, Westward Ho!, Devon, EX39 5AH
Tel (01237) 477615, (07971) 267790 (m)
Fax (01237) 425979
E-mail simon@countrylife.freeserve.co.uk
Website
www.pigonthehill.co.uk/clbframeindex.htm
Shop open during pub hours. Tours by arrangement

The original 2.5-barrel plant was bought
from the Lundy Island brewery in the
Bristol Channel and set up by Simon Lacey
at the Pig on the Hill pub. Due to popular
demand for Old Appledore, the plant was
upgraded in 2001 to 5-barrel production.
The brewing process can be seen from the
pub through large viewing screens. More
than 15 outlets are supplied direct.

Old Appledore (OG 1036, ABV 3.7%)

Wallop (OG 1043, ABV 4.4%)

Golden Pig (OG 1047, ABV 4.7%)

Country Bumpkin (OG 1059, ABV 6%)

COX & HOLBROOK

Cox & Holbrook, Manor Farm,
Brettenham Road, Buxhall, Suffolk,
Tel/Fax (01449) 770682
Tours by arrangement

David Cox, an accountant by profession,
bought his 5-barrel plant in 1997. It's one of
the most travelled micro-breweries, having
started life as Mackintosh Croft Head Brewery,
and became Sutherland's of Edinburgh
before journeying south to Suffolk. The
emphasis is on dark ales, stouts and porters.
The short-term plan is to concentrate on
free trade outlets and to expand the range
of products in bottle and cask. Bottle-
conditioned beers: Albion Pale Ale, East
Anglian Pale, Stowmarket Porter, Iron Oak,
Remus, and Uncle Stan: strengths as below.

Crown Dark Mild (OG 1032, ABV 3.2%)
Malty and full bodied for its strength.

Old Mill Bitter (OG 1036, ABV 3.8%)
A good, middle of the road, session bitter.

Albion Pale Ale (OG 1047, ABV 5%)

East Anglian Pale Ale
(OG 1050, ABV 5%) ◆
A very drinkable pale beer with a hoppy
taste and fruit to follow.

Stormwatch (OG 1050, ABV 5%) ◆
An amber, fruity beer with a bitter
aftertaste. Does not taste as strong as it
really is: beware.

Stowmarket Porter (OG 1050, ABV 5%)
Keeping tradition alive: a soft, well-rounded
example of this enigmatic style, which is
full of both body and malty, chocolate
flavours.

Remus (OG 1050, ABV 5%)
A complex, malty amber ale.

Uncle Stan (OG 1050, ABV 5%)
A single brown stout, a rare and possibly
unique example of a late 19th-century style.
It is rich, malty and firm bodied.

Iron Oak (OG 1050, ABV 5%)
A luscious, full-flavoured stout in the
Victorian style.

COX'S YARD

⛏ Cox's Yard (Charles Wells Ltd),
Bridge Foot, Stratford-on-Avon,
Warwickshire, CV37 6YY
Tel (01789) 404600
Fax (01789) 263212
E-mail Info@coxsyard.co.uk
Website www.coxsyard.co.uk
Shop 9-5 summer; 9-4 winter. Tours by arrangement

The brewery, part of a development by
Charles Wells of Bedford, is housed in the
old engine shed of a sawmill and a timber
yard. The brewery can be seen through large
windows at the Jester pub, which overlooks
the River Avon. There's a restaurant, gift
shop and the Stratford Tales attraction, in
addition to the micro-brewery. The site was
opened in August 1998 and the first brew
left the brewery, which uses equipment
from the Ancient Druids at Cambridge, in
October that year. Brewery tours are always
welcome. Future plans include a beer
festival and the production of bottle-
conditioned ales. Approximately 47 outlets
are supplied direct. Occasional beers: Old
Timber (ABV 5%), Cox's Millennium Mash
(ABV 5.2%) and other regular seasonal
brews. Seasonal ales: Mild (ABV 4%), Blitzen
(ABV 5.2%, December).

Jester Best Bitter (OG 1038, ABV 3.8%)
A light best bitter, well balanced with malt
and Fuggles hops.

Juggler Strong Bitter (OG 1046, ABV 4.6%)
A copper-coloured strong bitter with
caramel malt in the mouth, leading to a
hoppy finish.

CREWKERNE

⛏ Crewkerne Brewery, c/o Crown Inn,
34 South Street, Crewkerne,
Somerset, TA18 8DB
Tel (01460) 72464
Tours by arrangement

A pub brewery set up in 1997, it brews three
beers, one of which won CAMRA's Best
Somerset Beer award in 1998. Ten outlets
are currently supplied.

Crew Brew (OG 1040, ABV 4%)

Mainsail (OG 1045, ABV 4.5%)

Jack Tar (OG 1052, ABV 5%)

CROPTON

⛏ Cropton Brewery, Woolcroft,
New Inn, Cropton, Nr Pickering,
N Yorkshire, YO18 8HH
Tel (01751) 417330
Fax (01751) 417310
E-mail newinn@cropton.fsbusiness.co.uk
Website www.croptonbrewery.co.uk
Shop 10-4 summer. Tours by arrangement

⊛ Brewing returned to Cropton in 1984
when the cellars of the pub were converted
to accommodate a 5-barrel plant. The plant
was extended in 1988, but by 1994 it had
outgrown the cellar and a purpose-built
brewery was installed in the grounds of
Woolcroft Farm behind the pub. Production
fluctuates between 35 and 50 barrels a week
according to the season. Cropton's seven
additive-free beers are supplied to more

than 100 independent outlets direct and nationwide through wholesalers. All the beers, with the exception of Balmy Mild and Yorkshire Moors Bitter are available bottle-conditioned and can be purchased from the visitor centre attached to the pub. The bottled beers are suitable for vegetarians and vegans. Special brew: Rudolph's Revenge (ABV 4.6%).

King Billy (OG 1039, ABV 3.6%) ✦
A refreshing, straw-coloured bitter, quite hoppy, with a strong, but pleasant, bitter finish that leaves a clean, dry taste on the palate.

Two Pints (OG 1040, ABV 4%) ✦
A good, full-bodied bitter. Malt flavours initially dominate, with a touch of caramel, but the balancing hoppiness and residual sweetness come through.

Honey Gold Bitter (ABV 4.2%) ✦
A medium-bodied beer, ideal for summer drinking. Honey is apparent in both aroma and taste but does not overwhelm. Clean finish with a hint of hops.

Scoresby Stout
(OG 1044, ABV 4.2%) ✦
A classic of the style. A jet-black stout whose roast malt and chocolate flavours contrast with a satisfying bitter finish.

Balmy Mild (ABV 4.4%) ✦
Dark and full-flavoured with a malty aroma and taste. Milk chocolate and slight coffee notes. Moreish.

Uncle Sam's (OG 1044, ABV 4.4%) ✦
A clean-tasting and refreshing premium pale ale. The overriding characteristic is the fruity bouquet yielded by authentic American ingredients.

Yorkshire Moors Bitter (ABV 4.6%)

Backwoods Bitter
(OG 1049, ABV 4.7%) ✦
A malty premium bitter, tawny-coloured and full-bodied. A long and satisfying, sweet finish contains an abundance of fruit flavours.

Monkmans Slaughter
(OG 1060, ABV 6%) ▱✦
Rich-tasting and warming; fruit and malt in the aroma and taste, with dark chocolate, caramel and autumn fruit notes. Subtle bitterness continues into the aftertaste. Winner of the Strong Beer category in Champion Beer of Britain competition 2000.

CROUCH VALE

**Crouch Vale Brewery Limited,
12 Redhills Road,
South Woodham Ferrers,
Chelmsford, Essex, CM3 5UP
Tel (01245) 322744
Fax (01245) 329082
E-mail info@crouch-vale.co.uk
Website www.crouch-vale.co.uk**
Tours by arrangement

⊗ Founded in 1981, Crouch Vale has grown to be one of the longest-established craft breweries in the eastern counties. In addition to its brewing operation, the company is a major wholesaler of guest cask ales and a supplier to regional beer festivals. 250 outlets are supplied direct. Two tied

houses are owned, both serving cask-conditioned beer. Seasonal beers: Snowdrop (ABV 4.1%, February), Topsail (ABV 4.3%, March), Fireball (ABV 4.5%, April), Golden Duck (ABV 3.8%, August), The Conkeror (ABV 4.2%, October), Santa's Revenge (ABV 5%, December), Willie Warmer (ABV 6.4%, winter).

Woodham IPA Bitter
(OG 1036, ABV 3.6%) ✦
A dry, amber beer with a hoppy aroma followed by a more fruity taste.

Blackwater Mild
(OG 1037, ABV 3.7%) ✦
A fruity mild with a full body, in spite of its name.

Best Bitter (OG 1040, ABV 4%) ✦
Clean-tasting, tawny bitter with a fruity aroma, followed by a taste that balances malt and hops, leading to a dry finish.

Brewers Gold (OG 1040, ABV 4%) ▱✦
An impressive, refreshing, grapefruity, hoppy beer with soapy undertones.

Millennium Premium
(OG 1044, ABV 4.4%) ✦
A golden, easy-drinking premium ale, notably bitter at the end but with a balance of malt, hops and fruit in the mouth after a light malty aroma.

SAS (OG 1048, ABV 4.8%) ✦
A dry, astringent, mid-brown beer with aggressive bitterness.

Anchor Street Porter (OG 1049, ABV 4.9%)
A strong and substantial dark ale, flavoured with roast barley and primed for a fuller flavour.

CROWN

⊽ Munslow, nr Craven Arms,
**Shropshire, SY7 9ET
Tel (01584) 841205
Fax (01584) 841255
E-mail v.clandlord@tinyworld.uk**
Tours during business hours

Pub with one of the country's smallest breweries, a 2-barrel plant based in a large cupboard to the side of the bar. Brewing started in 1994. The owner has taken over the Dog at Worfield and is now brewing for both pubs. One other local outlet is supplied. Ironmaster (ABV 4.2%) is brewed solely for the Golden Ball in Ironbridge. Seasonal beer: Butcher's Baubles (ABV 5.8%, Christmas).

Butcher's Best (OG 1038, ABV 3.8%)

CUCKMERE HAVEN

**Cuckmere Haven Brewery,
Golden Galleon, Exceat Bridge,
Cuckmere Haven,
East Sussex, BN25 4AB
Tel (01323) 892247 or 899261
Fax (01323) 892555
E-mail alan@goldengalleon.co.uk**
Tours by arrangement

⊠ Brewing started in 1994, using yeast supplied by Harveys of Lewes. The brewery has moved to a new extension to the pub conservatory and now has a 5-barrel mash tun and three fermenters. As a result of the height of the building, the brewhouse is designed as a mini-tower brewery with a shop. Seasonal/occasional beers: Swallows Return (ΛBV 1%, spring), Saxon King Stout (ABV 4.2%), Dark Velvet (ABV 4.7%, autumn), Saxon Berserker (ABV 7.4%, spring).

Downland Bitter *(ABV 3.4%)*

Best Bitter *(OG 1040, ABV 4.1%)* ✎
Malty overtones in the aroma are joined by a hoppy bitterness in the flavour.

Guvnor *(OG 1046, ABV 4.7%)*

Golden Peace *(OG 1054, ABV 5.5%)*
An amber-coloured, strong beer.

DALESIDE

**Daleside Brewery Ltd, Unit 1,
Camwal Road, Starbeck, Harrogate,
N Yorkshire, HG1 4PT
Tel (01423) 880022
Fax (01423) 541717
E-mail dalesidebrewery@hotmail.com
Website www.dalesidebrewery.co.uk**
Tours by arrangement

⊛ Formerly Big End Brewery, founded in 1987, the company moved to new premises and changed its name in 1992. After years of gradual expansion, capacity was greatly increased in October 2000 when plant was bought from Vaux. Around 200 barrels a week are brewed, half of which is cask beer. Daleside has no tied pubs but the beers are available nationwide. Occasional beers: Christmas Classic (ABV 4.5%), Auld Lang Syne (ABV 4.1%), Ripon Jewel (ABV 5.8%)

Bitter *(ABV 3.7%)*
New beer introduced in 2001.

Nightjar *(OG 1038, ABV 3.7%)* ✎
A fruity, amber-coloured, medium-hopped beer with some sweetness. Leads to a sharp, slightly subdued, long, bitter finish.

Blonde *(OG 1039, ABV 3.9%)*

Old Legover *(OG 1042, ABV 4.1%)* ✎
A well-balanced, mid-brown, refreshing beer that leads to an equally well-balanced, fruity and bitter aftertaste.

Old Lubrication *(OG 1042, ABV 4.1%)* ✎
Plenty of malt, fruit and hops with a hint of sweetness leading to a moderate-to-strong bitter aftertaste in this complex dark ale.

Greengrass Old Rogue Ale
(OG 1046, ABV 4.5%) ⌂✎
A well-balanced, robust, tawny bitter with strong hop and fruit overtones, with a long, dry finish.

Crack Shot *(OG 1047, ABV 4.5%)*
Strong mid-brown ale with a reddish hint. Well balanced and full bodied.

Monkey Wrench *(OG 1056, ABV 5.3%)* ⌂✎
A powerful strong ale, mid-brown to ruby in hue. Aromas of fruit, hops, malt and roast malt give way to well-balanced fruit, malt and hoppiness on the tongue, with some sweetness throughout. A very flavoursome beer.

Morocco Ale *(ABV 5.5%)* ⌂✎
A powerful, dark brew with malt and fruit in the taste. A spicy beer in which ginger predominates and can at times overpower. Brewed to an Elizabethan recipe found at Levens Hall in Cumbria and using a 'secret' spice, the beer is becoming increasingly more widely available.

**For AVS Wholesalers of Gravesend:
Shrimpers** *(ABV 4.1%)*
An amber to dark amber bitter with a malty nose and a hint of fruitiness. Hops and malt carry over to leave a clean, hoppy aftertaste.

DARK HORSE

**Dark Horse Brewery Ltd, Adams Yard,
Maidenhead Street, Hertford, SG14 1DR
Tel/Fax (01992) 509800
E-mail dhb@beerline.co.uk
Website www.beerline.co.uk/darkhorse**

⊠ Since 1994, the brewery has evolved from a small-scale hobby to a succesful producer of quality ales distributed countrywide through wholesalers. The strategy of offering pubs and the public the opportunity to collect beer from the brewery or by post at a vastly-reduced price has also resulted in increased production. No pubs are owned but dozens of outlets are supplied direct, as far away as Liverpool and Manchester. Seasonal beers: Maybee Mild (ABV 3.9%, spring), Brand X (ABV 4%, summer).

Ale *(OG 1038, ABV 3.6%)*
A tasty bitter, with a hint of roast grain.

Moonrunner *(OG 1040, ABV 3.8%)*

Sunrunner *(OG 1042, ABV 4.1%)*
A well-balanced, full-flavoured bitter, with fruit notes and a strong, bitter finish.

Fallen Angel *(OG 1042, ABV 4.2%)* ⌂

Black Widow *(OG 1047, ABV 4.4%)*

Death Wish *(OG 1053, ABV 5%)*

DARK STAR

**Dark Star Brewing Co Ltd, Moon Hill Farm,
Burgess Hill Road, Ansty, Haywards Heath,
W Sussex, RH17 5AH;
and Evening Star, 55 Surrey Street,
Brighton, E Sussex, BN1 3PB
Tel (01273) 701758 or 328931:
number for the Evening Star, no number yet
available for Moon Hill Farm.
Website www.real-ale-guide.co.uk/dark-star**
Tours by arrangement

⊠ The Brighton brewery started life in 1995, run by Rob Jones (ex-Pitfield) and Peter Skinner, in the cellar of the Evening Star. Peter Skinner, with his beer range, left the business in 2001 to go solo. Dark Star embarked on a major expansion in May

2001, with a brand-new 15-barrel plant in a converted dairy near Burgess Hill. The Brighton brew-pub continues to brew low-volume beers, such as seasonal beers, experimental brews and one-off specialities. Seasonal beers: Star Porter (ABV 5%, winter) and Critical Mass (ABV 7%, Christmas).

Mild *(OG 1038, ABV 3.8%)*
A traditional, flavoursome mild ale.

Hophead *(OG 1036-1040, ABV 3.8%)*
A light, hoppy, refreshing bitter.

English Wheat Beer
(OG 1039-1043, ABV 4.1%)
Delicately spiced, cask-conditioned wheat beer.

Meltdown *(OG 1048, ABV 4.8%)*
Well-balanced and smooth, flavoured with genuine Chinese stem ginger.

Sunburst *(OG 1048, ABV 4.8%)*
Strong, full-flavoured golden ale.

Red Ale *(OG 1050, ABV 5%)*
Malty, full-flavoured, dry-hopped red ale.

Dark Star *(OG 1050, ABV 5%)* ◆
Dark full-bodied ale with a roast malt aroma and a dry, bitter stout-like finish.

DARKTRIBE

DarkTribe Brewery, 25 Doncaster Road, Gunness, Scunthorpe, Lincs, DN15 8TG
Tel (01724) 782324
E-mail dixie@darktribe.co.uk

⊗ The small brewery was built during the summer of 1996 in a workshop at the bottom of the garden by Dave 'Dixie' Dean. The beers generally follow a marine theme, recalling Dixie's days as a marine engineer in the Merchant Navy and his enthusiasm for sailing. DarkTribe merged with Duffield of Harmston, Lincs: at present, the Duffield beers are not being brewed.
Occasional/seasonal beers: Gunness Stout (ABV 4.1%), Futtocks (ABV 4.2%), Dixie's Bollards (ABV 4.5%), Sixteen Bells (ABV 6.5%, Christmas/New Year), Dixie's Midnight Runner (ABV 6.5%), Dark Destroyer (ABV 9.7%).

Dixie's Mild *(OG 1036, ABV 3.6%)*

Honey Mild *(OG 1036, ABV 3.6%)*

Full Ahead *(OG 1037, ABV 3.8%)* ◆
A malty smoothness backed by a slightly fruity hop give a good bitterness to this amber-brown bitter.

Albecore *(ABV 4%)*

Dr Griffin's Mermaid
(OG 1043, ABV 4.5%)

Galleon *(OG 1044, ABV 4.7%)* ▯◆
A tasty, golden, smooth, full-bodied ale with fruity hops and consistent malt. The thirst-quenching bitterness lingers into a well-balanced finish.

Old Gaffer *(ABV 4.5%)*

Aegir Ale *(OG 1044, ABV 4.7%)*

Twin Screw *(OG 1047, ABV 5.1%)* ◆
A fruity, rose-hip tasting beer, red in colour. Good malt presence with a dry, hoppy bitterness coming through in the finish.

DARWIN

Darwin Brewery Ltd,
63 Back Tatham Street, Sunderland,
SR1 2QE
Tel (0191) 514 4746
Fax (0191) 515 2531
E-mail darwinbrewery@sunderland.ac.uk
Website www.darwinbrewery.co.uk
Tours by arrangement (including tasting at local venue)

⊛ The Darwin Brewery first brewed beers in 1994 and expanded with the acquisition of the Hodges Brewery in Crook, County Durham. Hodge's Brewery beers are still brewed in the plant, which also produces dedicated Darwin Brewery beers as well as specialist trial beers from Brewlab at the University of Sunderland. The brewery produces a range of high-quality beers with the strong individual character of the North-east region, and specialises in historical recreations of past beers such as Flag Porter, a beer produced with a yeast rescued from a shipwreck in the English Channel. Future plans are to develop retail sales and commission further historical research for lost beers. 40 outlets are supplied direct. Occasional beers: Prof's Pint, Siddeley's Purge, Wheatfield Ale.

Darwin's Bitter *(OG 1038, ABV 3.8%)*

Hodge's Original *(OG 1040, ABV 4%)* ◆
Smooth, with a soft, bitter taste and generally light character. Ending with a stronger, slightly fruity and bitter aftertaste.

Evolution Ale *(OG 1042, ABV 4%)*
A dark amber, full-bodied bitter with a malty flavour and a clean, bitter aftertaste.

Durham Light Ale *(OG 1042, ABV 4%)*

Richmond Ale *(OG 1048, ABV 4.5%)*

Saints Sinner *(OG 1052, ABV 5%)*
A rich, smooth-tasting, ruby-red ale with a fruity aroma and hop character in the taste.

Killer Beer *(OG 1054, ABV 6%)*
A strong beer made with honey.

Extinction Ale *(OG 1086, ABV 8.3%)*

DENT

Dent Brewery, Hollins, Cowgill, Dent,
Cumbria, LA10 5TQ
Tel (01539) 625326
Fax (01539) 625033
E-mail martin@dentbrew.u-net.com
Tours by arrangement (minimum six people)

⊛ A brewery set up in a converted barn in the Yorkshire Dales in 1990, originally to supply just three local pubs. It now has two tied houses and supplies 50 free trade outlets direct. Its own distribution company, Flying Firkin (01282 865923), delivers all over northern England and is making some inroads into the south. All Dent's beers are brewed using the brewery's own spring water.

Bitter *(OG 1036, ABV 3.7%)* ◆
Fruity throughout and lightly hopped. This beer has a pervading earthiness that is evident to a lesser extent in other Dent beers. A short, bitter finish.

Rambrau *(OG 1039, ABV 4.2%)*
A cask-conditioned lager.

Ramsbottom Strong Ale
(OG 1044, ABV 4.5%) 🍷
This complex, mid-brown beer has a
warming, dry, bitter finish to follow its
unusual combination of roast, bitter, fruity
and sweet flavours.

T'Owd Tup *(OG 1058, ABV 6%)* 🍷🍷
A rich, fully-flavoured, strong stout with a
coffee aroma. The dominant roast character
is balanced by a warming sweetness and a
raisiny, fruit-cake taste that linger on into
the finish.

For Flying Firkin:

Aviator *(OG 1038, ABV 4%)* 🍷🍷
This medium-bodied amber ale is
characterised by strong citrus and hoppy
flavours that develop into a long bitter
finish.

Kamikaze *(OG 1048, ABV 5%)* 🍷🍷
Hops and fruit dominate this full-bodied,
golden, strong bitter, with a dry bitterness
growing in the aftertaste. While still
enjoyable, this beer has lost the sparkle it
once had.

DERWENT

**Derwent Brewery, Units 2a/2b Station Road
Industrial Estate, Silloth, Cumbria, CA5 4AG
Tel (016973) 31522 Fax (016973) 31523**
Tours by arrangement

⊛ Set up in 1997 in Cockermouth by Hans
Kruger and Frank Smith, both ex-Jennings,
together with Mike Askey, as the Bitter End
Brewing Co. In December 1996 it moved to
Silloth as Derwent Brewery. It supplies beers
throughout the north of England and
organises the Silloth Beer Festival in August.
It now brews the beers formerly brewed at
Bitter End.

Bitter *(OG 1036, ABV 3.6%)* 🍷
Very malty amber beer with a distinct roast
flavour and a very dry aftertaste.

Mutineers Ale *(OG 1041, ABV 4.1%)* 🍷
Aromas of roast and fruit. A sweet, light
brown bitter with some roast in the middle
and a rising bitter finish.

Hansi's Oktober Fest
(OG 1042, ABV 4.2%)

Dozy Brewer *(OG 1042, ABV 4.4%)*

Bill Monks *(OG 1045, ABV 4.5%)* 🍷
A mid-brown ale with a faintly flowery and
fruity aroma. Fruity in the mouth and then
a quickly arriving intense bitterness.

Old Cocker *(OG 1050, ABV 5%)*
A pale brown beer with some initial fruit
and malt, turning quickly into a lingering
bitterness.

DERWENT ROSE

**▯ Derwent Rose Brewery, Grey Horse,
115 Sherburn Terrace, Consett,
Co Durham, DH8 6NE
Tel (01207) 502585
E-mail paul@thegreyhorse.co.uk
Website www.thegreyhorse.co.uk**

A micro-brewery based in Consett's oldest
surviving pub, 154 years old in 2000. It
produced its first brew in a former stable
block behind the pub in 1997.

3 Giants *(ABV 3.2%)*

Mutton Clog *(ABV 3.8%)*

Paddy's Delight *(ABV 3.8%)*

Steel Town *(ABV 3.8%)*

Target Ale *(ABV 4%)*

Conroy's Stout *(ABV 4.1%)*

Red Dust *(ABV 4.2%)*

Swordmaker *(ABV 4.5%)*

Angel Ale *(ABV 5%)*

Coast 2 Coast *(ABV 5%)*

Derwent Deep *(ABV 5%)*

Devil's Dip *(ABV 9%)*

DEVON

**▯ Devon Ales Ltd, 7 Main Street,
Sauchie, Alloa, FK10 3JR
Tel (01259) 722020**
Tours by arrangement

The brewery was set up in outbuildings at
the rear of the Mansfield Arms in Sauchie
for the pub and in The Inn at Muckhart.

Original *(OG 1037, ABV 3.7%)*

Thick Black *(OG 1041, ABV 4.2%)*

Pride *(OG 1046, ABV 4.8%)*

DOLPHIN*

**Dolphin Brewery, Dolphin Inn,
48 St Michael's Street,
Shrewsbury, SY1 2EZ
Tel (01743) 350419**

Nigel Morton is a French-trained chef who
ran a pub for 16 years, 'got bored and
decided to brew as the next logical step'.
The brewery is behind the pub and came on
stream at Xmas 2000. It was upgraded to 4.5
barrels in June 2001. Two of the beers listed
are always available in the pub.

Best Bitter *(ABV 4%)*

Amber Ale *(ABV 4.2%)*

Brew *(ABV 4.6%)*

Double Dolphin *(ABV 4.6%)*

Fuggles Special *(ABV 4.9%)*

ESB *(ABV 5.2%)*

DONNINGTON

**Donnington Brewery, Stow-on-the-Wold,
Gloucestershire, GL54 1EP
Tel (01451) 830603**

⊗ Thomas Arkell bought a 13th-century
watermill in idyllic countryside in 1827,
and he began brewing on the site in 1865. It
is owned and run by a direct family
descendant, Claude Arkell, and the
millwheel is still used to drive small pumps
and machinery. Donnington supplies its
own 15 tied houses and a number of free
trade outlets.

XXX *(OG 1035, ABV 3.6%)* 🍷
Thin in aroma but very flavoursome. More
subtle than others in its class, it has some
hops and traces of chocolate and liquorice
in the taste and a notably malty finish.

BB *(OG 1035, ABV 3.6%)* ◥
A pleasant amber bitter with a slight hop aroma, a good balance of malt and hops in the mouth and a bitter aftertaste.

SBA *(OG 1045, ABV 4.6%)* ◥
Malt dominates over bitterness in the subtle flavour of this premium bitter, which has a hint of fruit and a dry malty finish.

DONOGHUE*

⬓ Donoghue Brewing Co, Black Horse Inn, Mill Lane, Grainthorpe, Louth, Lincs, LN11 7HU
Tel (01472) 388229

Experimental brews were conducted in 1999 but brewing did not start on a regular basis until 2001. In June the kit was upgraded from 2 barrels to 5 and other pubs may be supplied.

Fiddlers Elbow *(ABV 3.5%)*

The Pipes *(ABV 3.7%)*

Danny Boy *(ABV 4%)*

DRIFTWOOD

⬓ Driftwood Spars Hotel, Trevaunance Cove, St Agnes, Cornwall, TR5 0RT
Tel (01872) 552428/553323
Fax (01872) 553701
E-mail driftwoodspars@hotmail.com
Tours by arrangement

Gordon and Jill Treleaven started brewing in 2000 in this famous Cornish pub and hotel that dates from the 17th century. The brewery is based in the former Flying Dutchman fish and chip shop across the road from the hotel. The 1-barrel plant was bought from the Royal Inn, Horsebridge, in Devon. Pale malt comes from Tuckers of Newton Abbot and the hops are Fuggles and Goldings.

Cuckoo Ale *(OG 1045, ABV 4.5%)*

DUNN PLOWMAN

Dunn Plowman Brewery,
The Brewhouse, Bridge Street, Kington,
Herefordshire, HR5 3DL
Tel (01544) 231993
Fax (01544) 231985
E-mail dunnplowman.brewery@talk21.co

The brewery was established in 1987 as a brew-pub, moved to Leominster in 1992, and to its present site in 1994. The brewery supplies the Queen's Head, its brewery tap, and 18 other outlets within a 30-mile radius. It is run by husband and wife team Steve and Gaye Dunn. Seasonal beer: Crooked Furrow (ABV 6.5%, Nov-Jan, all year in bottle), Parsons Nose (ABV 5.5, Nov-Jan). Bottle-conditioned beers: Old Jake Stout (ABV 4.8%), Kyneton Ale (ABV 5%), Crooked Furrow (ABV 6.5%).

Brewhouse Bitter *(OG 1037, ABV 3.8%)*

Early Riser *(OG 1039, ABV 4%)*

Kingdom Bitter *(OG 1043, ABV 4.5%)*

DURHAM

Durham Brewery, Unit 5A,
Bowburn North Industrial Estate, Bowburn,
Co Durham, DH6 5PF
Tel (0191) 3771991
Fax (0191) 3770768
E-mail gibbs@durham-brewery.co.uk
Website www.durham-brewery.co.uk
Shop open during business hours. Tours by arrangement

A brewery established in 1994 and upgraded to a 10-barrel plant. 100 outlets are supplied direct. Production of bottle-conditioned ales started in 1999. Production capacity was increased to 40 barrels a week in 2000. Seasonal beers: Sunstroke (ABV 3.6%, summer), Frostbite (ABV 3.6%, winter). Bottle-conditioned beers (suitable for vegetarians): Bede's Chalice (ABV 4.8%), Cloister (ABV 4.5%), Durham Helles (ABV 4.6%), Black Bishop, Sanctuary, St Cuthbert (ABV 6.5%).

Magus *(OG 1037.5, ABV 3.8%)* ◥
Golden, refreshing dry bitter. An excellent session and summer ale, with a medium fruity/dry aftertaste.

Green Goddess *(OG 1037.5, ABV 3.8%)*

Black Velvet *(OG 1038, ABV 4%)*

White Gold *(OG 1039, ABV 4%)*
Pale and aromatic, mouth-filling and thirst-quenching with citrus aromas and flavours.

White Velvet *(OG 1040.5, ABV 4.2%)* ◥
Smooth, golden bitter with a tangy hop and fruit taste. The aftertaste lingers with a pleasant fruitiness.

Celtic Gold *(OG 1041, ABV 4.3%)*

NeueSchloss *(OG 1041.6, ABV 4.6%)* ▣
A pale continental-style beer. Saaz hops and a special lager yeast make for plenty of body and a pleasant hint of banana in the finish.

White Bishop
(OG 1042.5, ABV 4.8%) ▢◥
Excellent golden strong ale. Bags of hoppiness in aroma and taste, with a complex of flavours in the aftertaste.

White Sapphire *(OG 1043, ABV 4.5%)*
Light and easy, aromatic and refreshing, it fills the mouth with a zesty tang and leaves a hint of spice in the finish.

Prior's Gold *(OG 1043, ABV 4.5%)*
A very round, full hop aroma and flavour.

Canny Lad *(OG 1043, ABV 4.5%)*
A complex background with six different malts. A rounded and satisfying bitter that is balanced with American Liberty hops for aroma. Light chestnut in colour.

Invincible (OG 1043, ABV 4.5%)
A strong version of Magus. Very pale with a clean rounded bitterness. Created to commemorate the visit of the aircraft carrier HMS Invincible to the North-east in 1996.

Cuthberts Ale (OG 1046.5, ABV 5%)
Pale gold in colour but rich and fruity. Strong in alcohol and flavour, yet is thirst-quenching and easy to drink. Named after St Cuthbert, who is buried in Durham Cathedral.

Black Bishop (OG 1050.6, ABV 5.5%)
Truly black with roast malts, this stout manages to be smooth and eminently drinkable, with a dry finish.

Sanctuary (OG 1055, ABV 6%)
Sanctuary is not too sweet, but remains a well-rounded, ruby-coloured old ale. It is named after the sanctuary door knocker at Durham Cathedral.

Millennium City (OG 1058, ABV 6.5%)
A rich, golden, original style IPA. Despite being strong, this beer is not too sweet, but has a luscious malty base over which a complex bitterness gives balancing, thirst-quenching properties.

EARL SOHAM

⚲ Earl Soham Brewery, The Old Forge, The Street, Earl Soham, Suffolk, IP13 7RL
Tel (01728) 684097
E-mail fram.station@btinternet.com &
malc@walker173.freeserve.co.uk

⊠ The brewery, initially set up behind the Victoria pub in 1984 to supply just that outlet, moved 200 yards down the road in 2001 to bigger, purpose-built premises in an old converted garage. The building also houses the village sub-post office. The new plant has five times the capacity of the old site. Earl Soham owns a second pub, the Framlingham Station, and enjoys healthy sales to the free trade. The tied estate expanded to a second pub in Cambridge (since sold to Everards). Seasonal beer: Jolabrugg (ABV 5%, Christmas).

Gannet Mild (OG 1034, ABV 3.3%)
An unusual, full-tasting mild with a bitter finish and roast flavours that compete with underlying maltiness.

Victoria Bitter (OG 1037, ABV 3.6%)
A characterful, well-hopped, malty beer with a tangy, hoppy aftertaste.

Low House Bitter (OG 1040, ABV 3.9%)
First brewed for the King's Head (Low House) in Laxfield, but now available to other pubs.

Sir Roger's Porter (OG 1043, ABV 4.2%)
Full-flavoured dark brown malty beer with bitter overtones, and a fruity aftertaste.

Albert Ale (OG 1045, ABV 4.4%)
Hops dominate every aspect of this beer, but especially the finish. A fruity, astringent beer.

ECCLESHALL

Slaters Eccleshall Brewery, George Hotel, Castle Street, Eccleshall, Stafford, ST21 6DF

Tel (01785) 850300
Fax (01785) 851452
Tours by arrangement

⊠ The brewery was set up by Ged Slater in out buildings behind the George Hotel. The first three beers, Bitter, Original and Premium, were launched in 1995. They became so popular that the brewery was extended twice and bigger premises are now being considered. Ged's son, Andrew, is head brewer and there are three other staff. Slaters Bitter was Champion West Midlands Beer of the Year 2000, with Slaters Supreme as runner-up. The company also owns the Monkey at Crewe. Seasonal beer: High Duck (ABV 4.1%, spring).

Monkey Magic (ABV 3.4%) ✦
Dark brown/red beer with liquorice and caramel aroma; tastes sweet and malty with some hops to start. Fruit comes through later as bitterness develops.

Slaters Bitter (ABV 3.6%) ✦
Golden bitter with full fruit flavour combined with hops and malt. The fruit lingers, the hops develop later.

Slaters Original (ABV 4%) ⬠✦
Well-balanced hops and fruit with a hint of caramel. The sweet and bitter mix leads to an astringency difficult to resist.

Slaters Top Totty (ABV 4%) ⬠✦
A light, straw-coloured, fruit-flavoured beer.

Slaters Premium (ABV 4.4%) ✦
Creamy start to this pale brown beer. Quite bitter and fruity, with an astringent finish. Subtle flavours come and go.

Slaters Supreme (ABV 4.7%) ◧✦
A well-hopped, golden bitter. Fresh and fruity with a hoppy aroma; the hops linger through the developing bitterness to a moreish finish.

EGLESBRECH*

Eglesbrech Brewing Co,
Eglesbrech at Behind the Wall,
14 Melville Street, Falkirk, FK1 1HZ
Tel (01324) 633338

Scott Robertson brews for the Ale House section (upstairs) of this large pub, using a 4.5-barrel plant. Brewing started in June 2000. He brews a new seasonal beer every six weeks and also plans a Czech-style Pilsner for what he calls 'the other side' of the pub, where lager drinkers congregate.

Falkirk 400 (ABV 3.8%)

Antonine (ABV 3.9%)

Tall Blonde (ABV 4%)

ELGOOD'S

Elgood & Sons Ltd, North Brink Brewery, Wisbech, Cambridgeshire, PE13 1LN
Tel (01945) 583160
Fax (01945) 587711
E-mail info@elgoods-brewery.co.uk
Website www.elgoods-brewery.co.uk
Shop 1-5 Wed, Thur, Fri & Sun and Bank Holiday Mondays; closed Sat (May-Sept). Tours by arrangement

⊠ A 200-year-old Georgian riverside brewery where a visitor centre and gardens are open from 1 May to 31 October. Elgood's is committed to producing a range of quality real ales, including the award-winning Black Dog Mild, Champion Beer of East Anglia 1999. 43 pubs are owned, all are tied, all but one serving cask-conditioned beer. 300-400 outlets are supplied direct. Seasonal beers: Old Black Shuck (ABV 4.5%, winter), Barleymead (ABV 4.8%, September), Reinbeer (ABV 5.9%, December), Wenceslas Winter Warmer (ABV 7.5%, December), North Brink Porter (ABV 5%), Double Swan (ABV 4.5%, April-May).

Black Dog Mild
(OG 1036.8, ABV 3.6%) 📠🍴🍷
Muscular ruby/black, dry mild with a defined liquorice character. Raisin fruit, malt and hops are in balance, and the dry, bitter finish does not fade.

Cambridge Bitter
(OG 1038.5, ABV 3.8%) 🍷
Impressive copper-coloured session bitter with a light fruity aroma, a malty palate and a long bitter, dry aftertaste.

Pageant Ale *(OG 1043.8, ABV 4.3%)*

Golden Newt *(OG 1044.5, ABV 4.6%)* 🍷
Fragrant hops and orange fruit aromas introduce this golden bitter. Citrus, resiny hop fills the mouth, and the finish is delightfully bitter, with hops and fruit persisting.

Greyhound Strong Bitter
(OG 1052.8, ABV 5.2%) 🍷
Full-bodied, tawny brew, with a mouth-filling blend of malty sweetness and fruit. Starts with berry fruits on the nose and ends surprisingly bitter.

ENVILLE

Enville Ales, Enville Brewery, Cox Green, Enville, Stourbridge, W Midlands, DY7 5LG
Tel (01384) 873728
Fax (01384) 873770
E-mail info@envilleales.com
Website www.envilleales.com

⊗ A brewery on a picturesque Victorian farm complex. Using the same water source as the original village brewery (closed in 1919), the beers also incorporate more than three tons of honey annually (produced on the farm), using recipes passed down from the proprietor's great-great aunt. Enville's owner, H Constantine-Cort, had originally intended to go into full-time beekeeping with brewing as a sideline, but the position is now reversed. The brewery grows its own barley, too. Seasonal beer: Phoenix IPA (ABV 4.8%, April-Sept).

Chainmaker Mild *(OG 1036-38, ABV 3.6%)*

Bitter *(OG 1036-38, ABV 3.8%)* 🍷
A straw-coloured, hoppy and bitter beer that leaves a malty, moreish aftertaste.

Simpkiss Bitter *(OG 1036-38, ABV 3.8%)* 🍷
A medium-bodied, golden bitter. The refreshing, hoppy taste lingers.

Nailmaker Mild *(OG 1040-42, ABV 4%)*

Enville White *(OG 1040-42, ABV 4.2%)* 🍷
A clean, well-balanced, golden, sweet bitter, light in flavour. An appealing beer.

Czechmate Saaz *(OG 1041-43, ABV 4.2%)*

Enville Ale *(OG 1044-45, ABV 4.5%)*
A pale gold, medium-bodied bitter. Light hops and sweet fruit in the taste; a hint of honey in the aroma and aftertaste.

Enville Porter *(OG 1044-1045, ABV 4.5%)*

Ginger Beer *(OG 1044-46, ABV 4.6%)*

Gothic *(OG 1050-52, ABV 5.2%)* 🍷
Malt, hops and caramel combine with a strong roast malt taste in this dark, stout-like beer. Well-balanced, with lurking hints of honey. Available Oct-March.

EVERARDS

Everards Brewery Ltd, Castle Acres, Narborough, Leicester, LE9 5BY
Tel (0116) 201 4100
Fax (0116) 281 4199
E-mail mail@everards.co.uk
Website www.everards.co.uk
Tours by arrangement (CAMRA branches)

⊗ An independent, family-owned brewery run by the great-great grandson of the founder. Based at Narborough on the outskirts of Leicester, Everards celebrated its 150th anniversary in 1999. A developing estate of 154 high-quality pubs is based largely in Leicestershire and surrounding counties. Nearly all the pubs serve a full range of cask-conditioned ales and many serve guest ales. Everards ales are all brewed to individual recipes using only the finest English hops and barley. The principal ales are all dry-hopped and conditioned for a week prior to dispatch from the brewery. Tiger Best Bitter is the most widely distributed ale and can be found all over Britain. Daytime weekday tours can be arranged for CAMRA branches. 500 outlets are supplied direct. Seasonal beers: Perfick (ABV 4.5%, spring), Equinox (ABV 4.8%, autumn).

Beacon Bitter *(OG 1036, ABV 3.8%)* 🍷
The sulphurous aroma of this copper-coloured session beer presages a malty-hop bitterness that continues into a long bitter-sweet finish. Sulphur present throughout – a typical Burton snatch.

Tiger Best *(OG 1041, ABV 4.2%)* 🍴🍷
Mid-brown in colour, this somewhat unexciting brew has a sulphurous malty nose and a well-balanced palate that continues into a long, bitter-sweet finish.

Original *(OG 1050, ABV 5.2%)* 🍷
Beautifully full-bodied, the sulphurous hop-malt aroma of this red-brown strong beer is followed by a malty bitterness that continues into a late finish. Very smooth and well-balanced.

EVESHAM

🚪 **SM Murphy Associates Ltd, Evesham Brewery, r/o Green Dragon, 170 Oat Street, Evesham, Worcestershire, WR11 4PJ**
Tel/Fax (01386) 443462
E-mail evesham@brewery98.freeserve.co.uk
Tours by arrangement

⊗ A brewery set up in 1992 in the old bottle store at the Green Dragon Inn in Evesham. The owner and licensee, Steve Murphy, currently supplies another four outlets direct. The brewery has become a tourist attraction, drawing thousands of visitors each year. 'Asum' in the beer names is the local pronunciation of Evesham. Seasonal beer: Santa's Nightmare (ABV 6%, Christmas).

Asum Ale *(OG 1038, ABV 3.8%)* ◥
A very hoppy nose and an array of flavours in the palate in this very good example of a fairly weak beer being able to deliver in the flavour stakes.

Asum Gold *(OG 1050, ABV 5.2%)* ◥
A well-balanced premium ale that has all the range of tastes from malt to a fruity hoppiness that make it a very satisfying drink.

EXE VALLEY

**Exe Valley Brewery, Silverton, Nr Exeter, Devon, EX5 4HF
Tel (01392) 860406
Fax (01392) 861001
Website www.execamra.freeserve.co.uk /brewery/exe**
Brewery tours not available except to pre-arranged groups – charge made

⊠ The brewery was set up in a redundant barn in 1984 as Barron's Brewery by former publican Richard Barron. Richard was joined by former brewers' agent Guy Sheppard and the name was changed to Exe Valley. The beers are brewed traditionally from their own spring water, using Devon malt and English hops. Approximately 50 outlets are supplied direct. Occasional/seasonal beers: Devon Summer (ABV 3.9%, June-Aug), Barron's Dark (4.1%, occasional), Spring Beer (ABV 4.3%, March-May), Autumn Glory (ABV 4.5%, Sept-Nov), Devon Dawn (ABV 4.5%, December-New Year), Curate's Choice (ABV 4.8%, occasional), Winter Glow (ABV 6%, Dec-Feb).

Bitter *(OG 1036, ABV 3.7%)* ◥
Mid-brown bitter, pleasantly fruity with underlying malt through the aroma, taste and finish.

Barron's Hopsit *(OG 1040, ABV 4.1%)* ◥
Straw-coloured beer with strong hop aroma, hop and fruit flavour and a bitter hop finish.

Dob's Best Bitter *(OG 1040, ABV 4.1%)* ⌂◥
Malt and fruit aroma with a pleasant fruity taste and bitter finish.

Devon Glory *(OG 1046, ABV 4.7%)*
Mid-brown, fruity-tasting pint with a sweet, fruity finish.

Mr Sheppard's Crook *(OG 1046, ABV 4.7%)* ◥
Smooth, full-bodied, mid-brown beer with a malty-fruit nose and a sweetish palate leading to a bitter, dry finish.

Exeter Old Bitter *(OG 1046, ABV 4.8%)* ◥
A well-balanced beer with a malt/fruit aroma and taste, and a complex, sweet, fruity finish.

EXMOOR

**Exmoor Ales Limited, Golden Hill Brewery, Wiveliscombe, Somerset, TA4 2NY
Tel (01984) 623798
Fax (01984) 624572
Website www.exmoorales.co.uk**
Tours by arrangement

⊠ Somerset's largest brewery was founded in 1980 in the old Hancock's plant, which had been closed since 1959. It quickly won national acclaim, as its Exmoor Ale took the Best Bitter award at CAMRA's Great British Beer Festival that year, the first of many prizes. The brewery has enjoyed many years of continuous expansion and steadily increasing demand. Around 250 pubs in the South-west are supplied direct, and others nationwide via wholesalers and pub chains. Seasonal/occasional beers: Hound Dog (ABV 4%, March-May), Wild Cat (ABV 4.4%, Sept-Nov), Beast (ABV 6.6%, Oct-April) ⌂, Exmas (ABV 5%, Nov-Dec).

Ale *(OG 1039, ABV 3.8%)* ◥
A pale brown beer with a malty aroma, a malty, dry taste, and a bitter and malty finish.

Fox *(OG 1043, ABV 4.2%)*
Crafted from a special blend of several malts and hops to produce a mid-brown beer of unusual subtlety and taste. The slight maltiness on the tongue is followed by a burst of hops with a lingering bitter-sweet aftertaste.

Gold *(OG 1045, ABV 4.5%)* ◥
Yellow/golden in colour, with a malty aroma and flavour, and a slight sweetness and hoppiness. Sweet, malty finish.

Hart *(OG 1049, ABV 4.8%)* ◥
Mid-brown beer with a hoppy aroma, rich malty, full-bodied palate, following through to a sharp, hoppy finish.

Stag *(OG 1050, ABV 5.2%)* ◥
A pale brown beer, with a malty taste and aroma, and a bitter finish.

FAR NORTH

**⌂ Far North Brewery, Melvich by Thurso, Sutherland, KW14 7YJ
Tel (01641) 531206 Fax (01641) 531347**

Peter Martin was born in Scotland but lived in London for 18 years. He moved to Sutherland in spring 1996, a real ale desert. He is currently brewing one cask at a time for the weekly consumption of the predominantly English guests working at the nuclear power site at Dounreay. Seasonal beer: Old Mackay (ABV 6.5%, winter).

Real Mackay *(OG 1042, ABV 4.1%)*

FEATHERSTONE

Featherstone Brewery, Unit 3, King Street Buildings, King Street, Enderby, Leicestershire, LE9 5NT
Tel (0116) 275 0952
Mobile 0966 137762

⊠ Small brewery that specialises in supplying custom-brewed beers to pubs for sale under house names. Personalised beers are brewed to order, minimum volume four barrels.

Howes Howler *(OG 1035, ABV 3.6%)*

Best Bitter *(OG 1041, ABV 4.2%)*

Vulcan Bitter *(OG 1048, ABV 5.1%)*

FEDERATION

Federation Brewery Ltd, Lancaster Road, Dunston, Tyne and Wear, NE11 9JR
Tel (0191) 460 9023 Fax (0191) 460 1297
Production (0191) 460 8853
Website www.federation-brewery.co.uk
Tours by arrangement

☺ Brewery owned by working-men's clubs that produces only bright beers. The Buchanans range of cask beers is now produced under licence by Robinson's of Stockport.

Buchanan's Best Bitter
(OG 1035.5, ABV 3.6%)

Buchanan's Original
(OG 1044.5, ABV 4.4%)

FELINFOEL

Felinfoel Brewery Co Ltd, Farmers Row, Felinfoel, Llanelli, Carmarthenshire, SA14 8LB
Tel (01554) 773357 Fax (01554) 752452
E-mail enquiries@felinfoel-brewery.com
Website www.felinfoel-brewery.com
Shop 9-5 Mon-Fri; 10-12 Sat

☺ Founded in 1830 by David John, the company is still family-owned and is now the oldest brewery in Wales. The present buildings are Grade II listed and were built in the 1870s. Felinfoel was the first brewery in Europe to can beer in the 1930s. It supplies cask ale to 50% of its 84 houses – though some use top pressure – and to approximately 350 free trade outlets.

Dragon Bitter Ale *(OG 1034, ABV 3.4%)*

Best Bitter *(OG 1038, ABV 3.8%)* ◆
A well-balanced session bitter, light on aroma with some sweetness in the mouth and building in the finish.

Double Dragon Ale *(OG 1042, ABV 4.2%)* ◆
A malty bitter with fruit/apple flavours. Sulphur noticeable in aroma and taste. Bitterness builds, leading to a crisp finish.

FENLAND

Fenland Brewery, Unit 4, Prospect Way, Chatteris, Cambridgeshire, PE16 6TZ
Tel (01354) 695776 (brewery);
(01354) 695852 (office)
Fax (01354) 695852
(ansaphone ((01354) 695692
E-mail fenland@users.breworld.net
Website www.fuggle.demon.co.uk/fenland
Tours by arrangement

⊠ Fenland Brewery has been brewing its award-winning ales in Chatteris since 1997. Head brewer and owner Rob Thomas uses skills learnt over 11 years in chemical research to formulate his beers while co-owner Liz Thomas counts the money and occasionally mucks in with deliveries. Beers are supplied throughout Bedfordshire, Cambridgeshire, Lincolnshire, Norfolk, and Northamptonshire, and have been steadily winning both awards and customer loyalty. It was the first brewery in the town for 65 years. More than 50 outlets are supplied direct. Occasional/seasonal beers: Rudolph's Rocket Fuel/Winter Warmer (ABV 5.5%, Nov-Jan), Sparkling Wit (ABV 4.5%, May-Sept).

Codename Roz *(ABV 3.8%)*
The use of a new breed of hop, Roz, adds a special character to this refreshingly bitter pale ale.

Paranoia *(ABV 4.2%)*
A beautiful balance of first grade hops and several rare malts give this beer a complex flavour.

Doctor's Orders *(ABV 5%)*
A russet best bitter with a ruby glint and a complex malty fruit aroma, with a blend of First Gold hops and three varieties of Norfolk malts.

FERNANDES

Fernandes Brewery, The Old Malt House, 5 Avison Yard, Kirkgate, Wakefield, W Yorkshire, WF1 1UA
Tel (01924) 291709
Shop (and off-licence) 10-6. Tours by arrangement

☺ The brewery opened in 1997 and is housed in a 19th-century malthouse. It incorporates a home-brew shop and Fernandes Brewery Tap which opened in July 1999, winning Wakefield CAMRA's Pub of the Year in its first year of opening. Seasonal beer: 12 monthly special beers, named after the months, are brewed, all ABV 3.9%.

Shakespeare Special Bitter
(OG 1037, ABV 3.4%)
A light, hoppy and refreshing bitter beer with plenty of hop and malt flavours, ending with a long, dry aftertaste.

Malt Shovel Mild *(OG 1040, ABV 3.8%)*
A dark, full-bodied, malty mild with an abundance of roast malt and chocolate flavours, leading to a lasting, dry, malty finish.

Ale to the Tsar *(OG 1042, ABV 4.1%)*
A pale, smooth, well-balanced beer with some sweetness and a delicate blend of malt and hop flavours, leading to a satisfying malty finish with some fruit.

Green Bullet *(OG 1042, ABV 4.1%)*
A pleasant and quaffable hoppy bitter with a lingering, fresh hoppy aftertaste.

Lord Rodney Porter *(OG 1048, ABV 4.1%)*
A dark, rich and robust bitter beer with a complex dark malt taste, leading to a lingering, smooth, bitter and dry finish with some fruitiness.

Oddfellows Premium Bitter
(OG 1046, ABV 4.3%)
A pale, well-hopped, dry and astringent beer with plenty of fruit and malt flavours. A hoppy aroma and a long lasting fruity aftertaste.

Wakefield Pride
(OG 1045, ABV 4.5%)
A light-coloured and intensely fruity beer with a clean, bitter and hoppy palate, leading to a long fruity finish.

Empress of India *(OG 1055, ABV 6%)*
A strong, light-coloured and dangerously drinkable fruity and malty beer with a complex bitter palate. Fruit and malt dominate the aftertaste.

Double Six *(OG 1057, ABV 6%)*
A powerful, dark and rich strong beer with an array of malt, roast malt and chocolate flavours and a strong, lasting malty finish, with some hop character.

FILO

⌂ **First In Last Out Brewery,**
14-15 High Street, Old Town, Hastings,
E Sussex, TN34 3EY
Tel (01424) 425079
Tours by arrangement

The Filo Brewery (previously named St Clements Brewery) has been running since 1985, brewing the same two ales, Crofters and Cardinal. The pub brewery is still run by the owner, Mike Bigg. A new brewhouse was installed in 2000. A third beer, ABV 5.1%, has been added but had not been named when the guide went to press.

Crofters *(ABV 4%)*

Cardinal *(ABV 4.6%)*

FISHERROW

Fisherrow Brewery Limited,
Unit 12, Duddingston Yards,
Duddingston Park South,
Edinburgh, EH15 3NX
Tel (0131) 621 5501
Fax (0131) 621 9552
E-mail sales@fisherrow.co.uk
Website www.fisherrow.co.uk
Tours by arrangement

The brewery – pronounced 'Fisher Row' – is based in a council-owned industrial unit and the plant is made from converted dairy equipment. The three owners made history by putting pictures of the construction on the brewery website each evening so progress could be monitored. The first brew was in October 1999 and progress has been good, with 100 outlets supplied direct. Two strengths are given for Porter as it is occasionally brewed as stronger version as a special. Seasonal/occasional beers: Autumn Ale (ABV 4.2%), Porter (ABV 4% or 8%), Bears Ale (ABV 3.8%), Mick the Tick's 12,000th Tick (ABV 5.8%).

India Pale Ale *(ABV 3.8%)*

Burgh Bitter *(ABV 4.2%)*

Portobello Porter *(ABV 4.5%)*

Nut Brown Ale *(ABV 4.8%)*

Export Pale Ale *(ABV 5.2%)*

FLAGSHIP

Flagship Brewery Ltd,
Unit 2 Building 64, The Historic Dockyard,
Chatham, Kent, ME4 4TE
Tel (01634) 832828
Website www.real-ale-guide.co.uk/flagship
Tours by arrangement

⊠ The brewery was established in 1995 by home-brewing enthusiast Andrew Purcell in partnership with his father-in-law. It became a limited company in 2000. It is located in Chatham's Historic Dockyard, a uniquely preserved Georgian dockyard, now promoted as the South-east's premier tourist attraction. Production has steadily increased with at least 70 regular outlets served direct and further outlets supplied by wholesalers and other breweries. The brewery now has its own tap house in the dockyard. Named the Harbourmasters Club, the building was formerly the Assistant Queen's Harbourmaster's Office, built in 1808. It has a single bar with a lounge above and is open to visitors between 11am to 6pm, and private members thereafter until 2300. Occasional/seasonal beers: Victory Mild (ABV 3.5%), Spring Pride (ABV 4.4%), Frigging Yuletide (ABV 5.5%), Old Sea Dog Stout (ABV 5.5%), Nelson's Blood (ABV 6%), Powder Monkey (ABV 4.4%), Moby Dick (ABV 4.4%).

Paddle Steamer Bitter
(OG 1038, ABV 3.8%)

Destroyer *(OG 1039, ABV 4%)*

Trafalgar Bitter *(OG 1040, ABV 4.1%)*

Ensign *(OG 1042, ABV 4.2%)*
A fruity ale, with a good balance of malt and hops.

Spanker *(OG 1042, ABV 4.2%)*
A version of Ensign.

Friggin in the Riggin
(OG 1045, ABV 4.7%)
A premium bitter with a smooth malt flavour and a bitter-sweet aftertaste.

Crow's Nest *(OG 1048, ABV 4.8%)*
A straw-coloured, sweet and fruity ale with a hoppy aroma.

Shipwrecked *(OG 1048, ABV 5%)*

Futtock Ale *(OG 1050, ABV 5.2%)*
A fruity, ruby-coloured ale, with a roast malt aftertaste.

FLANNERY'S
See Spinning Dog

FORGE
See Sussex Brewery

FORTH

Forth Brewery Co Ltd, Eglinton,
Kelliebank, Alloa, FK10 1NU
Tel (01259) 725511
Fax (01259) 725522

A brewing company set up by former partners when Maclay stopped brewing in 1999. Forth's beers are distributed by Belhaven, Caledonian, Beer Seller, Flying Firkin and Maclay.

Steamboat Ale *(ABV 4%)*

Puffer Ale *(ABV 4.1%)*

FOUR RIVERS

See Hadrian & Border

FOXFIELD

Foxfield Brewery, Prince of Wales Hotel, Foxfield, Broughton in Furness, Cumbria, LA20 6BX
Tel (01229) 716238

A 3-barrel plant run by Stuart and Lynda Johnson in old stables attached to the Prince of Wales inn. A few other outlets are supplied direct. The Johnson's also own Tigertops in Wakefield (qv). There are many occasional and seasonal beers.

Black Hoad *(OG 1036, ABV 3.5%)*
A dark roast mild with a fruity nose and a sweet finish.

Sands *(OG 1038, ABV 3.6%)*
A pale, light, aromatic quaffing ale.

Brief Encounter *(OG 1042, ABV 4.1%)*
A fruity beer with a long, bitter finish.

Foxfield Flyer *(OG 1048, ABV 4.6%)*
A full-flavoured bitter with loads of middle.

Black Coombe *(OG 1048, ABV 5%)*
A bitter stout.

FRANKLIN'S

Franklin's Brewery, Bilton Lane, Bilton, Harrogate, N Yorkshire, HG1 4DH
Tel/Fax (01423) 322345
E-mail Tommy2Tom@yahoo.co.uk

⊛ A brewery set up in 1980 by Sean Franklin and run by Leeds CAMRA founder-member Tommy Thomas and stepson Tim Osborne. 10-20 outlets are supplied direct. Seasonal beers: Summer Blotto (OG 1047, ABV 4.7%), Winter Blotto (ABV 4.7%).

Bitter *(OG 1038, ABV 3.8%)* ◆
A tremendous hop aroma precedes a flowery hop flavour, combined with malt. Long, hoppy, bitter finish. A fine, unusual amber bitter.

DT's *(OG 1045, ABV 4.5%)*

My Better Half *(OG 1060, ABV 5%)*

FRANKTON BAGBY

Old Stables Brewery, Green Lane, Church Lawford, Rugby, Warwickshire, CV23 9EF
Tel (02476) 540770
Tours by arrangement

Frankton Bagby was set up in 1999 by three local families. The 5-barrel plant is housed in a small, 18th-century stable block that has been carefully renovated by Warwickshire craftsmen. A specialist micro-brewery engineer undertook the design and installation of the equipment for the brewhouse. Frankton Bagby is passionately committed to brewing a range of top-quality beers and has already achieved considerable success in the area. More than 150 outlets are supplied direct. Seasonal beers: Midsummer Madness (ABV 3.8%), Christmas Pud (ABV 7%).

Barnstormer *(OG 1037, ABV 3.7%)*
A light golden bitter that is easy on the palate with a slightly flowery taste and a good nose followed by a dry bitter aftertaste.

Old Chestnut *(OG 1040, ABV 4%)*
A chestnut-coloured bitter brewed using a combination of Green Bullet and Fuggles hops that give the beer a distinctive mellow flavour; the late addition of Styrian Goldings adds a fruity nose.

Squires Brew *(OG 1042, ABV 4.2%)*
A straw coloured best bitter, smooth on the palate with a good, hoppy aftertaste. A mix of Challenger and Fuggles hops are used in the main brew and Styrian Goldings are added for late hopping.

Rugby Special *(OG 1045, ABV 4.5%)*
A reddy-brown, full-bodied, well-balanced and pleasantly hoppy best bitter. First brewed in the borough of Rugby to celebrate Rugby Union's World Cup, the beer proved so popular with drinkers that it became necessary to extend the season to all-year-round.

Old Retainer *(OG 1050, ABV 5%)*
Rich in colour and taste, this is a traditional strong bitter, smooth and fruity on the palate with a long, dry aftertaste.

FREEDOM

Freedom Brewing Company Ltd, The Coachworks, 80 Parsons Green Lane, Fulham, London, SW6 4HU
Tel (020) 7731 7372
Fax (020) 7731 1218
E-mail info@freedombrew.com
Website www.freedombrew.com
Tours by arrangement

⊠ The brewery opened in 1995 in Fulham as the first dedicated lager micro-brewery in Britain. It has outgrown the site, which is now the headquarters and office; the beers are produced at Meantime in Greenwich (qv) and Freedom's two brew-restaurants in Earlham Street, Covent Garden, WC2, and Ganton Street, W1. An organic version of Freedom Pilsener is produced for the Duke of Cambridge in Islington and the Crown, Victoria Park, Bethnal Green. All the beers are kept and served by gas pressure. Pale (ABV 4.3%), Soho Red (ABV 4.4%), Organic Pilsener (ABV 4.8%), Wheat Beer (5%), Pilsener Lager (ABV 5%).

FREEMINER

Freeminer Brewery Ltd, Whimsey Road, Steam Mills, Cinderford, Gloucestershire, GL14 3JA
Tel (01594) 827989
Fax (01594) 829464
E-mail sales@freeminer.com
Website www.freeminer.com
Tours by arrangement

⊠ Freeminer Brewery was established in the Forest of Dean in 1992 and has expanded from a 5-barrel to a 40-barrel plant. The expansion was due to national sales and increased bottle production, especially new export orders. There are plans to fit a 5-barrel plant in the outbuildings of a local public house, to create the Forest of Dean's first brew-pub. Even though it has a rural location, the brewery makes great efforts through a network of national distributors to ensure that its beers can be enjoyed nationwide. Occasional/seasonal beers: Gold Standard (ABV 5%, summer/autumn), Strip and At It (ABV 4%, spring), Iron Brew (ABV 4.2%, spring/summer), Celestial Steam Gale (ABV 5%, summer), Slaughter Porter (ABV 5%, winter), Deep Shaft Stout (ABV 6.2%, autumn/winter), Northern United (ABV 7%, winter). Bottle-conditioned beers: Bitter, Speculation Ale, Deep Shaft Stout, Shakemantle Ginger Ale, Speculation Ale, Trafalgar IPA 🍾, and Slaughter Porter are bottled-conditioned versions of the cask ales. Shakemantle Ginger Ale and Deep Shaft Stout are suitable for vegetarians.

Bitter *(OG 1038, ABV 4%)* ◥
A light, hoppy session bitter with an intense hop aroma and a dry, hoppy finish.

Speculation Ale *(OG 1047, ABV 4.8%)* ◥
An aromatic, chestnut-brown, full-bodied beer with a smooth, well-balanced mix of malt and hops, and a predominantly hoppy aftertaste.

Shakemantle Ginger Ale
(OG 1050, ABV 5%) 🚱◥
A refreshing ginger ale. Unfined, with a high wheat content, it is like a European-style wheat beer. Ginger dominates throughout, mingled with a light hoppiness. Champion Beer of Britain Speciality Beer 1998.

Trafalgar IPA *(OG 1060, ABV 6%)* ◥
Pale, heavily hopped traditional IPA with a pronounced bitterness; hoppy nose, malt and hops on the palate and a dry, hoppy finish.

FROG ISLAND

Frog Island Brewery, The Maltings, Westbridge, St James' Road, Northampton, NN5 5HS
Tel (01604) 587772 Fax (01604) 750754
E-mail beer@frogislandbrewery.co.uk
Website www.frogislandbrewery.co.uk
Tours by arrangement

⊠ Started in 1994 by home-brewer Bruce Littler and business partner Graham Cherry in a malt house built by the long-defunct brewery Thomas Manning & Co, Frog Island expanded from a 5-barrel plant to 10 barrels in 1998. It specialises in personalised beer bottles, available by mail order. 40 free trade outlets supplied. Seasonal beers: Fuggled Frog (ABV 3.5%, May), Head in the Clouds (ABV 4.5%, August). Bottle-conditioned beers: Fire Bellied Toad (ABV 5%), Croak & Stagger (ABV 5.6%).

Best Bitter *(OG 1040, ABV 3.8%)* ◥
A complex beer, with malt, roast malt and fruit, plus a hint of sulphur, before a powerful kick of hop bitterness and astringency in the aftertaste. Pale brown in colour, and light on the tongue.

Shoemaker *(OG 1043, ABV 4.2%)* ◥
The Cascade hop citrus notes on the tongue are preceded by a huge malty aroma with passion fruit and roast characteristics. The malty aftertaste fades into a dry, nuttiness. Rich, pale brown and complex.

Fire Bellied Toad *(OG 1044, ABV 4.4%)*

Natterjack *(OG 1048, ABV 4.8%)* ◥
Deceptively robust, golden and smooth. Fruit and hop aromas fight for dominance before the grainy astringency and floral palate give way to a long, strong, dry aftertaste with a hint of lingering malt.

Croak & Stagger *(OG 1056, ABV 5.8%)* ◥
The initial honey/fruit aroma is quickly overpowered by roast malt then bitter chocolate and pale malt sweetness on the tongue. Gentle, bitter-sweet finish. A winter brew.

FROME VALLEY

Frome Valley Brewery, Mayfields, Bishop's Frome, Herefordshire, WR5 5AS
Tel (01531) 640321

Brewery founded in 1997 and established in a former 18th-century hop kiln in the depth of the Frome Valley. It supplies local pubs and also supplies bottled beers to local craft shops. All the beers are made with spring water.

Frome Valley Premium Bitter
(OG 1038, ABV 3.8%)
A traditional beer, good bitterness, with a light aroma. Local hops and spring water are used.

Tawny Ale *(OG 1041, ABV 4.2%)*

Pale Ale *(OG 1041, ABV 4.2%)*

Blackmoor Stout *(OG 1042, ABV 4.3%)*

Naughty Noughty *(OG 1061, ABV 6.4%)*

FULLER'S

Fuller, Smith and Turner PLC, Griffin Brewery, Chiswick Lane South, Chiswick, London, W4 2QB
Tel (020) 8996 2000
Fax (020) 8995 0230
E-mail fullers@fullers.co.uk
Website www.fullers.co.uk
Shop 10-6 Mon-Fri; 10-5 Sat. Tours by arrangement

⊠ Fuller, Smith & Turner's Griffin Brewery in Chiswick has stood on this same site for more than 350 years. Messrs Fuller, Smith & Turner formed their partnership in 1845 and direct descendants of the founding families are still involved in the running of the company. In spite of technical advances, traditional brewing methods have been maintained. In the 24 years that CAMRA has held the Champion Beer of Britain competition, Fuller's has won the Beer of the Year award five times. The beers have been Best in Class no less than nine times and ESB has been voted Best Strong Ale an unprecedented seven times. All but one of Fuller's 234 pubs serves cask ales. Fuller's also supplies close to 500 free trade accounts. Fuller's Organic Honey Dew (cask and bottle), is the world's first honey-flavoured organic ale and its winter ale, Jack Frost, is made with the addition of blackberries. Occasional/seasonal beers: Summer Ale (ABV 3.9%, May-Aug), Organic Honey Dew (ABV 4.3%, March-May), Red Fox (ABV 4.3%, Sept-Nov), Jack Frost (ABV 4.5%, Nov-Jan). Bottle-conditioned beers: 1845 Celebration Ale (ABV 6.3%) 🍂, Vintage Ale (ABV 8.5%).

Chiswick Bitter (OG 1034.5, ABV 3.5%) 🍂
A refreshing, hoppy amber beer with some malt notes throughout, and a fruity, bitter, dry aftertaste.

London Pride (OG 1040.5, ABV 4.1%) 🍂
Well-balanced, golden brown best bitter, with a hoppy aroma, a sweetish fruity palate, and a persistent malty, dryish finish.

ESB (OG 1054.8, ABV 5.5%) 🍂
A strong pale brown ale of great character. The immediate full-bodied maltiness gives way to a rich hoppiness in the finish.

FYFE

🏠 Fyfe Brewing Company, 469 High Street, Kirkcaldy, Fife, KY1 2SN
Tel/Fax (01592) 646211
Tours by arrangement

⊗ Established in 1995 behind the Harbour Bar, it was Fife's first brew-pub in the 20th century. Most of the output is taken by the pub, the remainder being sold direct to 20 local outlets and to the free trade via wholesalers. Seasonal beer: Cauld Turkey (OG 1060, ABV 6%, winter).

Rope of Sand (OG 1037, ABV 3.7%) 🍂
A quenching bitter. Malt and fruit throughout, with a hoppy, bitter aftertaste.

Auld Alliance (OG 1040, ABV 4%) 🍂
A very bitter beer with a lingering, dry, hoppy finish. Malt and hop, with fruit, are present throughout, fading in the finish.

Lion Slayer (OG 1042, ABV 4.2%)

Fyfe Fyre (OG 1048, ABV 4.8%)

GALE'S

George Gale & Co Ltd, The Hampshire Brewery, Horndean, Hampshire, PO8 0DA
Tel (02392) 571212
Fax (02392) 598641
E-mail gales@mcmail.com
Website www.gales.co.uk
Shop 10-5 Mon-Fri; 10-2 Sat. Tours by arrangement

⊗ Richard Gale bought the Ship & Bell inn and its small brewery in 1847. His youngest son, George, expanded the business by buying local inns and the farm buildings next to the Ship & Bell, which he developed into a substantial brewery. In 1869 the brewery was destroyed by fire, but by the end of the year had been rebuilt; much of the present building results from that time. In 1896 George Gale sold his major share in the brewery to the Bowyer family, who still control the company today. All 112 tied houses serve cask ale. Gale's also supplies 650 free trade outlets direct.

Seasonal/occasional beers: Trafalgar Ale (ABV 4.2%, October), Happy Hog (ABV 4.4%, February), Frolic Bitter (ABV 4.4%, April), Hampshire Glory (ABV 4.3%, June), Summer Hog (3.8%), Hogy Bear (ABV 4.5%, September), Christmas Ale (ABV 5%, December). Bottle-conditioned beers: HSB, Festival Mild, Christmas Ale (ABV 8%), Trafalgar Ale (ABV 9%), Prize Old Ale (ABV 9%) 🍂, Conquest (9%, export only), Milestones Ale (ABV 9%).

Butser Bitter (OG 1034, ABV 3.4%) 🍂
A mid-brown chestnut beer. A slightly malty and fruity aroma preludes a sweet taste, with some fruit and malt. The aftertaste is sweet and fruity with a little bitterness.

GB (OG 1040, ABV 4%) 🍂
A medium-bodied, deep golden brown brew that is initially malty sweet, has a fruity middle period with a hint of burnt orange and a dry hop flower-tasting bitter finish. Several of the characteristics are ruined if served through a sparkler.

Winter Brew (OG 1044, ABV 4.2%) 🍂
A rich winter ale, containing Prize Old Ale. Almost black in colour, it has a roast malt aroma with fruit and caramel, all of which are echoed in the taste and finish. Available Nov-March.

HSB (OG 1050, ABV 4.8%) 🍂
A mid-brown beer with a fruity aroma. The full-bodied, sweet and fruity taste, with some maltiness, follows through to the aftertaste. For those with a sweet tooth.

Festival Mild (OG 1052, ABV 4.8%) 🍂
Black in colour, with a red tinge. The aroma is fruity. A sweet, fruity and malty taste, with some caramel, carries through to the aftertaste, but with more bitterness.

GLENTWORTH

Glentworth Brewery, Glentworth House, Crossfield Lane, Skellow, Doncaster, S Yorkshire, DN6 8PL
Tel (01302) 725555
Fax (01302) 724133

⊗ Glentworth started in 1996 in buildings behind a former dairy, with a 5-barrel plant and a maximum of two brews a week. More than 120 outlets are supplied direct. Seasonal beer: At least two new beers every month.

Easy Goer (OG 1035.5, ABV 3.7%)

Lightyear (OG 1037, ABV 3.9%) 🍂

Ghost (OG 1037.5, ABV 4%)

Oasis (OG 1038.5, ABV 4.1%)

Mirage (OG 1042, ABV 4.5%)

Whispers (OG 1042, ABV 4.5%)

Yorkshire Grit (OG 1045.5, ABV 5%)

GOACHER'S

P&DJ Goacher, Unit 8, Tovil Green Business Park, Maidstone, Kent, ME15 6TA
Tel (01622) 682112
Tours by arrangement

⊗ Kent's oldest small independent brewer, set up in 1983 by Phil and Debbie Goacher, producing all-malt ales with only local

Kentish hops for two tied houses and around 30 free trade outlets in the mid-Kent area. Special, a mix of Light and Dark ales, is also available to pubs for sale under house names.

Real Mild Ale *(OG 1033, ABV 3.4%)* ⌂
A full-flavoured malty ale with a background bitterness.

Fine Light Ale *(OG 1036, ABV 3.7%)* ⌂◆
A pale, golden brown bitter with a strong, floral, hoppy aroma and aftertaste. A hoppy and moderately malty session beer.

Special *(OG 1037, ABV 3.8%)*

Best Dark Ale *(OG 1040, ABV 4.1%)* ◆
An intensely bitter beer, balanced by a moderate maltiness, with a complex aftertaste.

Crown Imperial Stout
(OG 1044, ABV 4.5%)
A classic Irish Stout with a clean palate and satisfying aftertaste from Kent Fuggles.

Gold Star Ale *(OG 1050, ABV 5.1%)* ◆
A strong pale ale brewed from 100% Maris Otter malt and all Kent hops.

Maidstone Porter *(OG 1050, ABV 5.1%)*
A dark ruby winter beer with a roast malt flavour.

Old Ale *(OG 1066, ABV 6.7%)*
A black, potent old ale, produced in winter only.

GODDARDS

Goddards Brewery Ltd, Barnsley Farm, Bullen Road, Ryde, Isle of Wight, PO33 1QF
Tel (01983) 611011
Fax (01983) 611012
E-mail office@goddards-brewery.co.uk
Website www.goddards-brewery.co.uk

⊗ Housed in a converted 18th-century barn on a farm near Ryde, the brewery went into production in 1993. Sales of its award-winning beers have been rising steadily. Around 40 outlets are supplied and Goddards owns two pubs, the Wishing Well at Pondwell, Ryde, and Billy Bunter's at Shanklin. There are plans to add a further two or three pubs. Occasional/seasonal beers: Ale of Wight (ABV 4%, spring), Duck's Folly (ABV 5%, early autumn), Inspiration (ABV 5.2%), Winter Warmer (ABV 5.2%).

Special Bitter *(OG 1038.5, ABV 4%)* ⌂◨◆
A refreshing, straw-coloured, easy-drinking bitter with a wonderfully flowery hop aroma that carries right through to a satisfying aftertaste.

Fuggle-Dee-Dum *(OG 1048.5, ABV 4.8%)* ◆
Tawny, full-flavoured, rich malty ale with a pleasing consistency of malty sweetness complemented by a hoppy bitterness that produces that essential bite that makes you want more.

Iron Horse *(OG 1049, ABV 4.8%)* ◆
Superb roast old ale/porter style beer with complex roast malty-fruity bitterness consistent through the tasting experience – and what an experience. Available late autumn.

Inspiration Ale *(OG 1050, ABV 5.2%)* ◆

Straw-coloured pale strong ale with a predominantly bitter fruity flavour balanced by a sweet undertone.

Winter Warmer *(OG 1052, ABV 5.2%)* ◆
Good example of a winter ale with a refreshing bitterness that cleans the palate of the sweetness inherent in this style of beer.

GOFF'S

Goff's Brewery Ltd, 9 Isbourne Way, Winchcombe, Gloucestershire, GL54 5NS
Tel (01242) 603383
Fax (01242) 603959
E-mail goffsbrewery@lineone.net
Tours by arrangement

⊗ Goff's is a family concern that started brewing in 1994, using plant purchased from Nethergate Brewery. Now brewing to capacity, it supplies beer direct to 200 outlets and through wholesalers. One pub is owned in Cheltenham.

Jouster *(OG 1040, ABV 4%)* ⌂◆
A drinkable, tawny-coloured ale, with a light hoppiness in the aroma. It has a good balance of malt and bitterness in the mouth, underscored by fruitiness, with a clean, hoppy aftertaste.

Tournament *(OG 1040, ABV 4%)*

Fallen Knight *(OG 1044, ABV 4.4%)* ◆
A tawny-coloured premium bitter, dry hopped for a delicate floral aroma. A good balance of malt and fruit in the mouth with a bitter-sweet finish. Autumn ale now brewed all year round.

White Knight *(OG 1046, ABV 4.7%)* ◆
A well-hopped bitter with a light colour and full-bodied taste. Bitterness predominates in the mouth and leads to a dry, hoppy aftertaste. Deceptively drinkable for its strength.

Black Knight *(OG 1053, ABV 5.3%)* ◆
A dark, ruby-red tinted beer with a strong chocolate malt aroma. It has a smooth, dry, malty taste, with a subtle hoppiness, leading to a dry finish. A classic winter porter.

GOLDFINCH

Goldfinch Brewery, 47 High East Street, Dorchester, DT1 1HU
Tel (01305) 264020

⊗ A brewery established in 1987 at the rear of Tom Brown's public house in Dorchester. Originally a 1-barrel plant, it has been increased to four barrels. The brewery supplies Tom Brown's (Dorchester) and Tom Brown's (Salisbury) and free trade outlets direct, plus others via wholesalers. Occasional beer: Mayor J Porter (ABV 4.5%, Nov-Feb).

Tom Brown's Best Bitter
(OG 1039, ABV 4%) ◆
Clean, refreshing session beer. Moderate fruit and hops in the aroma and taste, balanced well with a little caramel sweetness.

Midnight Sun Special Pale Ale
(OG 1045, ABV 4.5%) ◆
A well-balanced golden bitter, light in body

with hops, fruit and bitterness in moderation.

Flashman's Clout Strong Ale
(OG 1045, ABV 4.5%) ◆
A tawny/mid-brown beer with an attractive, honeyed aroma, and a bitter-sweet taste with malt and some hops. Hoppiness continues through to give a bitter edge to the aftertaste.

Midnight Blinder *(OG 1050, ABV 5%)* ◆
A reddish brown, full-bodied strong bitter. Dark malts dominate the bitter-sweet flavour, continuing into the hoppy aftertaste.

GOLDTHORN*

Goldthorn Brewery Co Ltd, Imex Unit 60, Sunbeam Street, Wolverhampton, WV2 4NU
Tel (01902) 756920 Fax (01902) 579108
E-mail paul@goldthornbrewery.co.uk
Website www.goldthornbrewery.co.uk
Tours by arrangement

A 5-barrel plant set up in the former Sunbeam car and motorcycle factory. Brewing started in January 2001. 30 outlets are supplied and there are plans for seasonal and occasional beers.

Ge It Sum Ommer *(OG 1039, ABV 3.8%)*

Wulfrun Gold *(OG 1043, ABV 4.3%)*

GOOSE EYE

Goose Eye Brewery, Ingrow Bridge, South Street, Keighley, W Yorkshire, BD22 5AX
Tel (01535) 605807 (07768) 20026
Fax (01535) 605735
E-mail enquiries@goose.eye.brewery.co.uk
Website www.goose-eye-brewery.co.uk
Tours by arrangement

⊛ Goose Eye supplies 50-60 regular outlets, mainly in West and North Yorkshire, and Lancashire. Its beers are also available through national wholesalers and pub chains. It produces an ever-expanding and diverse range of occasional beers, sometimes brewed to order, and is diversifying into wholesaling and bottled beers (filtered but not pasteurised). No-Eyed Deer is often rebadged under house names. Occasional/seasonal beers: Spellbound (ABV 4%, Halloween), Summer Jack's (ABV 4.2%, summer), Wandy Wabbit (ABV 4.2%, Easter), Cockeyed Goose (ABV 6.2%, Christmas), Christmas Goose (ABV 5.2%).

Barmpot *(OG 1038, ABV 3.8%)* ▦◆
A golden, citrus-hoppy quaffing ale with a dry, bitter finish.

No-Eyed Deer *(OG 1038, ABV 3.8%)* ◆
A faint fruity and malty aroma, hoppy fruit flavours, and a long, bitter finish characterise this refreshing, copper-coloured beer.

Bronte *(OG 1040, ABV 4%)* ◆
A pale brown beer with a faint fruity aroma. Fruit and bitterness dominate the taste with some background malt and hops. The lingering aftertaste is dry and bitter.

Wharfedale *(OG 1045, ABV 4.5%)* ◆
Malt and hops dominate the taste of this copper-coloured premium bitter. Bitterness comes through into the finish.

Pommies Revenge *(OG 1052, ABV 5.2%)*
A light-coloured, full-bodied and fruity, strong bitter.

GRAINSTORE

Davis'es Brewing Company Ltd, The Grainstore Brewery, Station Approach, Oakham, Rutland, LE15 6RE
Tel (01572) 770065
Fax (01572) 770068
E-mail hopsdavis@aol.com
Tours by arrangement

⊗ Grainstore, the smallest county's largest brewery, has been brewing since 1995. The brewery's curious name comes from the fact that it was founded by Tony Davis and Mike Davies. After 30 years in the industry, latterly with Ruddles, Tony decided to set up his own business after finding a derelict Victorian railway grainstore building. The brewing is designed traditionally, relying on whole hops and Maris Otter barley malt. 60 outlets are supplied direct. Seasonal beers: Springtime (ABV 4.5%, March-May), Gold (ABV 4.5%, May-Oct), Harvest IPA (ABV 4.5%, Sept-Oct), Three Kings (ABV 4.5%, Nov-Dec), Winter Nip (ABV 7.3%, Nov-Dec).

Grainstore Dark Mild *(OG 1034, ABV 3.4%)*
Smooth and well-rounded with a balance of hop and malt.

Cooking Bitter *(OG 1036, ABV 3.6%)* ◆
A smooth, copper-coloured beer, full-bodied for its gravity. Malt and hops on the nose; malt and fruit to taste, with a malty aftertaste.

Triple B *(OG 1042, ABV 4.2%)* ◆
Initially, hops dominate over malt in both the aroma and taste, but fruit is there, too. All three linger in varying degrees in the sweetish aftertaste of this tawny brew.

Steamin' Billy Bitter
(OG 1043, ABV 4.3%)

Ten Fifty *(OG 1050, ABV 5%)* ◆
This full-bodied, tawny beer is hoppy and fruity right into the aftertaste. A little malt on the nose and in the initial taste, with an underlying sweetness and an increasing bitterness.

GREEN DRAGON

Green Dragon Free House & Brewery, Broad Street, Bungay, Suffolk, NR35 1EE
Tel/Fax (01986) 892681
Tours by arrangement

⊗ The Green Dragon was purchased from Brent Walker in 1991 and the buildings at the rear converted to a brewery. In 1994 the plant was expanded and moved into a converted barn across the car park. The doubling of capacity allowed the production of a larger range of ales, including seasonal and occasional brews. The beers are available at the pub and in six other outlets. The company is owned by the Pickard brothers and brewer Rob Pickard is planning a buy-out. If he is successful, a new cask beer is planned and the bottled range will be expanded. Bottle-conditioned beers: Dragon (ABV 5.5%), Wynter Warmer (ABV 7%).

Mildew *(ABV 3.4%)*

Chaucer Ale *(OG 1037, ABV 3.8%)*

Bridge Street Bitter *(OG 1046, ABV 4.5%)*

Green Dragon Lager *(ABV 4.5%)*

Dragon *(OG 1055, ABV 5.5%)*

Wynter Warmer *(ABV 7%)*

GREEN JACK

Green Jack Brewing Co, Harbour Road Industrial Estate, Oulton Broad, Lowestoft, Suffolk, NR32 3LZ
Tel (01502) 587905
Fax (01502) 583387
Tours by arrangement

⊗ A brewery that started in 1993 on the old Forbes Brewery site with a capacity of 900 barrels a year. Green Jack hopes to increase to 1,200 barrels to meet pub demand and also for bottling. Two fermenting tanks and a mash tun have been purchased to allow for expansion. 20-25 outlets supplied direct, as well as its own three pubs. Wholesalers also take the beers. Seasonal beers: Honey Bunny (ABV 4%, spring), Summer Dream (ABV 4%, summer), Old Thunderbox (ABV 4%, autumn), Norfolk Wolf Porter (ABV 5.2%, autumn), Ripper (ABV 8.5%). Mild (ABV 3%) is brewed occasionally.

Green Jack *(OG 1037, ABV 3.5%)* ◆
A hoppy, pale brown light bitter with an underlying malty sweetness and a long, dry aftertaste.

Canary *(OG 1039, ABV 3.8%)* ◆
Golden yellow, fruity pale ale with a clean, hoppy-fruity palate ending dry and hoppy.

Grass Hopper *(OG 1043, ABV 4.2%)* ◆
Copper-coloured hoppy bitter with balancing malt throughout and a developing fruitiness.

Orange Wheat *(OG 1043, ABV 4.2%)*

Gone Fishing *(OG 1051, ABV 5%)*

GREENE KING

Greene King PLC, Abbot House, Westgate Brewery, Bury St Edmunds, Suffolk, IP33 1QT
Tel (01284) 763222
Fax (01284) 706502
Website www.greeneking.com
Shop/museum 1-4 Weekdays; 11-4 Sat & peak season Sun. Tours by arrangement (01284 714382)

⊗ Founded in 1799, Greene King celebrated its 200th birthday in 1999 and transformed itself into a 'super regional' with the acquisition of Morland and Ruddles brands. It closed the Morland Brewery in Abingdon. Greene King now owns 1,600 pubs in East Anglia, the Thames Valley and South-east England, 99 per cent of them serving cask beer. 3,500 free trade outlets are supplied direct. A brewery museum opened in 2001 and it includes a new oak vat that stores 5X, a 12% beer that is blended with a 5% BPA to form Strong Suffolk Ale (ABV 6%), a bottled beer that is available on draught in the winter. Seasonal beers: Black Baron (ABV 4.3%, Sept-Oct), The Sorcerer (ABV 4.5%, March-April). Bottle-conditioned beer: Hen's Tooth (ABV 6.2%).

XX Dark Mild *(OG 1035, ABV 3%)* ◆

Smooth and sweet, with a bitter aftertaste. The beer is enjoying greater promotion and has increased sales.

IPA *(OG 1036, ABV 3.6%)* ◆
An easy-drinking, amber-coloured session bitter. Bitterness predominates throughout, leading to a somewhat astringent finish. Sweetness and hoppiness can be variable, depending on age.

Ruddles Best Bitter *(OG 1037, ABV 3.7%)* ◆
An amber/brown beer, strong on bitterness but with some initial sweetness, fruit and subtle, distinctive Bramling Cross hop. Dryness lingers in the aftertaste.

Morland Original Bitter *(OG 1039, ABV 4%)*

Triumph Ale *(OG 1042, ABV 4.3%)* ◆
Sweetish fresh bitter with a complex and pleasing hop character in the aroma and on the palate. Initially fruity, well-balanced, and with a moreish dry aftertaste.

Ruddles County Ale *(OG 1048, ABV 4.3%)* ◆
Richer and slightly darker than Ruddles Best, this premium ale shares similar characteristics. Sweetness and fruit on the palate give way to bitterness and a distinctive hoppy, dry finish. Good body for its strength.

Abbot Ale *(OG 1049, ABV 5%)* ◆
A full-bodied, very distinctive beer with a bitter-sweet aftertaste.

Old Speckled Hen *(OG 1050, ABV 5.2%)* ◆
This full-flavoured, smooth strong ale has a good sweetness/bitterness balance, and rich fruit, particularly on the nose. The finish is dryish and very pleasant.

GREEN TYE

Green Tye Brewery, Green Tye, Much Hadham, Hertfordshire, SG10 6JP
Tel/Fax (01279) 841041
E-mail enquiries@gtbrewery.co.uk
Website www.gtbrewery.co.uk
Tours by arrangement

A brewery set up in October 1999 by William Compton and Gary Whelan. It currently produces eight barrels a week, supplying direct to nine local outlets and nationally via a wholesaler. As well as seasonal beers, other beers, including a dark mild, are brewed occasionally throughout the year. Seasonal beers: Snowdrop (ABV

3.9%, spring), Mad Morris (ABV 4.2%, summer), Autumn Rose (ABV 4.2%, late autumn), Conkerer (ABV 4.7%, early autumn), Coal Porter (ABV 4.5%, winter).

Shot in the Dark *(OG 1036, ABV 3.6%)*
A dark, hoppy bitter, with a pleasant, lingering aftertaste. A stronger flavour than its strength suggests.

IPA *(OG 1036, ABV 3.7%)*
A copper-coloured bitter. A hoppy aroma, with strong hops in the mouth and finish. Clean tasting, with a dry finish.

Wheelbarrow *(OG 1044, ABV 4.3%)*
A soft, fruity nose and taste. Gentle malt, with underlying hop bitterness, with a fruity and slightly dry finish.

GRIBBLE INN

Gribble Brewery, Gribble Inn, Oving, nr Chichester, W Sussex, PO20 6BP
Tel/Fax (01243) 786893
E-mail elderflower@msn.co.uk
Tours by arrangement

A micro-brewery owned by Hall & Woodhouse (Badger qv) on the site of the Gribble Inn, which has expanded its portfolio of beers and ales and now supplies in excess of 30 outlets along the south coast from London to Taunton and Exeter.

King & Barnes Mild Ale
(OG 1032, ABV 3.5%)
Matched beer from the former Horsham brewery.

Fursty Ferret *(OG 1045, ABV 4%)*

Ale *(OG 1047, ABV 4.1%)*

Oving Bitter *(OG 1048, ABV 4.5%)*

Reg's Tipple *(OG 1050, ABV 5%)*

Porterhouse *(OG 1050, ABV 5.1%)*

Plucking Pheasant *(OG 1048, ABV 5.2%)*

Pig's Ear *(OG 1060, ABV 5.8%)*

Wobbler *(OG 1075, ABV 7.2%)*

GRIMSDALES

GBC (Kent) Ltd, t/a Grimsdales Brewery Co, Park Barn Oast, Canterbury Road, Boughton Aluph, Nr Ashford, Kent, TN25 4EW
Tel (01233) 630900
Fax (01233) 633990
Website www.gbckent.co.uk

Not currently brewing; beer is contract-brewed by Pilgrim Brewery, Reigate and Thomas Hardy. 13 pubs are owned serving cask-conditioned beer. 100 outlets are supplied direct. Seasonal beers: Lightning Strike (ABV 4.9%, summer), Grumpys Gripewater (ABV 5%, winter). Beers: Mr Grimsdales Bitter (ABV 3.6%), AKB (ABV 3.7%), Becketts Best Bitter (ABV 4.2%), Grim Reaper (ABV 4.6%), Apocalypse (ABV 5%).

GUERNSEY

Guernsey Brewery Co (1920) Ltd, South Esplanade, St Peter Port, Guernsey, Channel Isles, GY1 1BJ
Tel (01481) 720143
Fax (01481) 710658
Website www.bucktrouts.com

One of two breweries on the island, serving its stronger than average real ales in 13 of its 33 pubs. Originally opened as the London Brewery in 1856, it became a Guernsey registered company in 1920 on the introduction of income tax on the mainland. It was acquired in 1978 by Bucktrout, a Guernsey wine and spirit company that owns several pubs on the island. In 1988 Bucktrout merged with Ann Street, now Jersey Brewery; Guernsey cask ale is available in selected Jersey Brewery houses. 11 outlets are supplied direct.

Braye Mild *(OG 1037, ABV 3.8%)*
Copper-red in colour, with a complex aroma of malt, hops, fruit and toffee. The rich, mellow flavour combines malt, fruit, hops and butterscotch, while the finish has malt and hops. Full-flavoured, surprisingly dry and hoppy.

Pirates Ale *(OG 1042, ABV 4%)*

Sunbeam Bitter *(OG 1045, ABV 4.2%)*
Golden in colour, with a fine malt aroma. Malt and fruit are strong on the palate and the beer is quite dry for its strength. Excellent, dry malt and hop finish.

Millennium Ale *(OG 1050, ABV 4.6%)*

HADRIAN & BORDER*

Hadrian & Border Brewery, Unit 10, Hawick Crescent Industrial Estate, Newcastle upon Tyne, NE6 1AS
Tel (0191) 276 5302 Fax (0191) 265 5312
Tours by arrangement

Hadrian & Border is the result of a merger between Border Brewery of Berwick-on-Tweed and Four Rivers of Newcastle. Shona and Andy Burrows of Border joined forces with Trevor Smith of Four Rivers (and formerly of Hadrian) and the new company is based at the ex-Four Rivers 20-barrel site in Newcastle. Border's Noggins Nog, SOB and Old Kiln Ale have been de-listed while Hadrian's Emperor Ale may be revived. The new company's brands are available from Glasgow to Yorkshire, and nationally through wholesalers. They are hard to find on Tyneside, though the Sir John Fitzgerald group stocks them from time to time. Seasonal beer: Yule Fuel (ABV 5%, December).

Vallum Bitter *(OG 1034, ABV 3.6%)*
A well-hopped, amber-coloured bitter with a distinctive dry refreshing taste.

Special Bitter *(OG 1036, ABV 3.8%)*
Straw-coloured, delicately hopped, well-balanced bitter.

Gladiator *(OG 1038, ABV 3.8%)*
A deep copper-coloured bitter with a soft malt palate.

Farne Island *(OG 1038, ABV 4%)*
An amber/mid-brown bitter with a refreshing hop/malt balance.

Flotsam *(OG 1038, ABV 4%)*
A deep bronze colour with a clean citrus bitterness and a distinctive hoppy/flowery aroma.

Legion Ale *(OG 1042, ABV 4.2%)*
Well-hopped and full-bodied beer with a rounded malt flavour.

Centurion Bitter (OG 1045, ABV 4.5%)
A light-coloured bitter with a distinctive
hop palate, pleasantly fruity, smooth, clean-
tasting and refreshing.

Rampart (OG 1046, ABV 4.8%) ◆
Golden bitter, well-balanced with clean,
refreshing taste. However, the finish lacks
depth.

Jetsam (OG 1046, ABV 4.8%)
Pale golden bitter, clean and fresh with a
flowery palate and hoppy nose.

HAGGARDS

Haggards Brewery Limited,
c/o 577 King's Road, London, SW6 2EH
Tel (020) 7731 3845
E-mail:
andrewhaggard@haggardsbrewery.fsnet.co.uk
Tours by arrangement

The brewery was set up in 1998 to supply
beer to the Imperial pub on King's Road. It
is owned and run by the Haggard brothers,
who worked in the City of London but gave
up their jobs to run the pub and establish
the brewery. The brewery has a 5-barrel
capacity, and was designed by Rob Jones of
Dark Star in Brighton. Haggards supplies
other pubs only on request. Only one beer
is brewed: it is sold as Haggards Horny Ale
to other pubs.

Imperial Best Bitter
(OG 1043, ABV 4.2%) ◆
Tawny beer that is fruity and sweet with
little hop character.

HALIFAX*

Halifax Steam Brewery, 173 Healey Wood
Road, Brighouse, W Yorkshire, HD6 3RW
Tel (01484) 715074

David Earnshaw started brewing in April
2001, in a converted garage, inspired by
CAMRA's series of home-brewing books. He
learnt his brewing skills at Barge & Barrel,
and now produces one regular beer from a
7-barrel plant. He supplies 12 pubs and
plans to add other beers to his range.

Cock o' t' North (ABV 4.7%)

HAMBLETON

Nick Stafford Hambleton Ales, Holme-on-
Swale, Thirsk, N Yorkshire, YO7 4JE
Tel (01845) 567460
Fax (01845) 567741
E-mail sales@hambletonales.co.uk
Website www.hambletonales.co.uk
Shop 9-4. Tours by arrangement

⊛ Established in 1991 by Nick Stafford on
the banks of the River Swale in the heart of
the Vale of York. The bottling line caters for
micro and large brewers, handling more
than 20 brands. New brewing equipment
was installed in 2000, doubling capacity to
100 barrels a week. A mail-order service for
all bottle brands is available from the
brewery or its website. 100 outlets are
supplied direct. Hambleton brews beers
under contract for the Village Brewer
wholesale company (01325) 374887, and
Black Dog of Whitby (qv).

Bitter (OG 1036.5, ABV 3.6%) ◆

Rich, hoppy aroma rides through this light
and drinkable beer. Taste is bitter with
citrus and marmalade aroma and solid
body. Ends dry with a spicy mouthfeel.

Goldfield (OG 1040, ABV 4.2%) ◆
A light amber bitter with good hop
character and increasing dryness. A fine
blend of malts gives a smooth overall
impression.

Stallion (OG 1040, ABV 4.2%) ◆
A premium bitter, moderately hoppy
throughout and richly balanced in malt and
fruit, developing a sound and robust
bitterness, with earthy hop drying the
aftertaste.

Stud (OG 1042, ABV 4.3%) ◆
A strongly bitter beer, with rich hop and
fruit. It ends dry and spicy.

Nightmare (OG 1050, ABV 5%) ❑◆
Fully deserving its acclaim, this impressively
flavoured beer satisfies all parts of the
palate. Strong roast malts dominate, but
hoppiness rears out of this complex blend.

For Village Brewer:

White Boar (OG 1037.5, ABV 3.7%) ◆
A light, flowery and fruity ale; crisp, clean
and refreshing, with a dry-hopped, powerful
but not aggressive, bitter finish.

Bull (OG 1039, ABV 4%) ◆
A fairly thin, but well-hopped bitter, with a
distinct dryness in the aftertaste.

Old Ruby (OG 1048, ABV 4.8%) ◆
A full-bodied, smooth, rich-tasting dark ale.
A complex balance of malt, fruit character
and creamy caramel sweetness offsets the
bitterness. A classic old ale.

HAMPSHIRE

Hampshire Brewery Ltd,
6-8 Romsey Industrial Estate,
Greatbridge Road,
Romsey, Hampshire, SO51 0HR
Tel (01794) 830529
Fax (01794) 830528
E-mail online@hampshire-brewery.co.uk
Shop 9-5.30 Mon-Fri 9-12 Sat. Tours by arrangement.
CAMRA groups/customers only

⊠ Set up in 1992, the brewery outgrew its
capacity in Andover and moved in 1997 to
a larger site in Romsey. Pride of Romsey was
launched to celebrate the move and has
already won several awards in both cask and
bottle-conditioned form. In May 1999 the
brewery started to brew Strong's Best Bitter,
to the old Romsey Brewery's original recipe,
by arrangement with Whitbread, who
bought and closed Strong's. In 2000,
Hampshire entered a sales and distribution
agreement with the pub group Morrells of
Oxford. Hampshire Brewery Direct, despite
the name, is wholly owned by Morrells, but
the company distributes the Romsey
company's brands. Bottle-conditioned
beers: King Alfred's, Pendragon, Pride of
Romsey ❑, 1066. Occasional beers:
Pendragon (ABV 4.8%), 1066 (ABV 6%).
Seasonal ales: Temptation (ABV 4.2%) and
Californian Red (ABV 5%, both October);
Wild Thing (ABV 4.2%) and Penny Black
Porter (ABV 4.5%, both November); Good
King 'Censlas (ABV 5%, December).

King Alfred's *(OG 1038, ABV 3.8%)* ◆
A mid-brown beer, featuring a malty and hoppy aroma. A malty taste leads to a hoppy, malty and bitter finish.

Strong's Best Bitter
(OG 1038, ABV 3.8%)
A deep copper-coloured bitter with rich malt complexity brewed with classic English aroma hops.

Ironside *(OG 1042, ABV 4.2%)* ◆
A beer with little aroma, but some malt. The taste has solid fruit with lasting hops and malt. The aftertaste is more bitter and malty. Pale brown in colour.

Lionheart *(OG 1045, ABV 4.5%)*
A golden ale with fresh fruit and malt fragrance. Full drinking with a subtle hop finish.

Pride of Romsey *(OG 1050, ABV 5%)*
Abundant aroma of the fruit of the hop, citrus and fragrant with orange, grapefruit and lemon hints. Powerful hop aroma through to the aftertaste with distinctive bitterness complemented by good strength of malt character.

HANBY

Hanby Ales Ltd, New Brewery, Aston Park, Soulton Road, Wem, Shropshire, SY4 5SD
Tel/Fax (01939) 232432
E-mail hanby@dial.pipex.com
Tours by arrangement

⊗ Hanby was set up in 1990 by three partners. The 12-barrel plant was upgraded to 20 barrels in 2000 to cope with demand. Hanby supplies some 200-300 pubs direct and others via wholesalers. Bottle-conditioned beers: Hanby Premium (ABV 4.6%), Rainbow Chaser and Cherry Bomb.

Black Magic Mild *(OG 1033, ABV 3.3%)* ◆
A dark, reddish-brown mild, which is dry and bitter with a roast malt taste.

Drawwell Bitter *(OG 1039, ABV 3.9%)* ◆
A hoppy beer with excellent bitterness, both in taste and aftertaste. Beautiful amber colour.

All Seasons Bitter *(OG 1042, ABV 4.2%)*

Rainbow Chaser *(OG 1043, ABV 4.3%)*
A pale beer brewed with Pioneer hops.

Wem Special *(OG 1044, ABV 4.4%)*
A pale, smooth, hoppy bitter.

Cascade *(OG 1045, ABV 4.5%)*

Golden Honey *(OG 1045, ABV 4.5%)*
A beer made with the addition of Australian honey.

Premium Bitter *(OG 1046, ABV 4.6%)* ◆
Formerly Treacleminer, a pale brown beer that is sweeter and fruitier than most of the beers above. Slight malt and hop taste.

Old Wemian Ale *(OG 1049, ABV 4.9%)*
Golden-brown colour with an aroma of malt and hops and a soft, malty palate.

Taverners Ale *(OG 1053, ABV 5.3%)*

Cherry Bomb *(OG 1060, ABV 6%)*
Beer made with the addition of cherries.

Nutcracker *(OG 1060, ABV 6%)*

Joy Bringer *(OG 1060, ABV 6%)*
Beer made with the addition of ginger.

HANSON'S
See Banks's.

HAPPY HOOKER*

Happy Hooker Beers, 30 St Edmunds Road, Sleaford, Lincs, NG34 7LS
Tel (01529) 307499

A small brewery launched in May 2001 by Brent Day, a CAMRA member from the early 1970s who home-brewed with enthusiasm when stationed abroad with the RAF. His other passion is Rugby Union, hence the name of the company. He bought a 2.5-barrel plant with the aid of his RAF pension and is currently based in the back garden of his home, but plans to move either to an industrial unit or a pub. Seasonal beer: Stay On Your Feet (ABV 5.8%, Rugby season).

Up And Under *(ABV 3.9%)*
A hoppy session beer.

Loosehead *(ABV 4.2%)*
A tawny-coloured, malty brew.

Tighthead *(ABV 4.8%)*
A darker, stronger, full-flavoured ale.

THOMAS HARDY

Thomas Hardy Burtonwood Brewery, Weymouth Avenue, Dorchester, Dorset, DT1 1QT
Tel (01305) 250255   Fax (01305) 258381

⊗ The Thomas Hardy Brewery is the result of a management buy-out in 1997. Eldridge Pope is now a pub retailing group (see Pub Groups). In 1998, the brewery company set up a joint venture with Burtonwood Brewery (qv) to form Thomas Hardy Burtonwood Brewery. The Dorchester brewery brews Eldridge Pope brands under contract, and also brews and packages for other companies. Tragically, the classic bottle-conditioned Thomas Hardy's Ale (ABV 12%) has been discontinued.

For Eldridge Pope:

Pope's Traditional *(OG 1038, ABV 3.8%)* ◆
Formerly Eldridge Pope Best Bitter. A mixture of malt and hop with a hint of fruit.

Hardy Country *(OG 1040, ABV 4.2%)* ◆
A dry, hoppy beer with faint undertones of malt and fruit. The taste is smooth despite a bitter edge that continues into the finish.

Royal Oak *(OG 1048, ABV 5%)* ◆
A full-bodied beer with a distinctive banana aroma and a mainly sweet, fruity taste. This is balanced by malt and some hops, and there is a fruity finish to this smooth, well-rounded brew.

For Morells pubs:

Oxford Blue *(ABV 3.7%)*
A rebranding of Oxford Bitter.

Varsity *(ABV 4.3%)*

Graduate *(ABV 4.8%)*
Plus the following seasonal beers: Old Don (ABV 4.6%, Jan-Feb), Blustering Bursar (ABV 4.3%, March-April), Trinity (ABV 4.1%, May-June), Scorcher (ABV 3.8%, July-Aug), Pickled Proctor (ABV 4%, Sept-Oct), Advent (ABV 4.4%, Nov-Dec).

For Refresh, a beer-marketing company set up to sell the Usher's beer range:

Best Bitter *(ABV 3.8%)*

Founders Ale *(ABV 4.5%)*

Bishop's Tipple *(ABV 5.2%)*

Spring Fever, Summer Madness, Autumn Frenzy and Winter Storm (all ABV 4%).

HARDYS & HANSONS

Hardys & Hansons PLC, Kimberley Brewery, Nottingham, NG16 2NS
Tel (0115) 938 3611 Fax (0115) 945 9055
Tours by arrangement

⊛ Established in 1832 and 1847 respectively, Hardys & Hansons were two competitive breweries until a merger in 1931 produced the present company. The brewery is still run by descendants of the original families. The majority of its 246 tied houses take its award-winning real ales, mostly drawn by metered dispense into oversized glasses, although Kimberley Classic, and increasingly the Bitter, are served by handpumps. Around 100 other outlets are also supplied direct. A range of seasonal ales, with a rotation or new beer every month under the Cellarman's Cask banner, has extended Hardys & Hansons' geographical availability and reputation. Occasional/seasonal beers: Frolicking Farmer (ABV 4.2%), Peddler's Pride (ABV 4.3%), Guzzling Goose (ABV 4.4%), Rocking Rudolph (ABV 5%), Guinea Gold (ABV 4.5%).

Kimberley Best Mild
(OG 1035, ABV 3.1%) ◗
A deep ruby mild dominated by chocolate malt. The fruitiness and caramel sweetness are well balanced in the taste, with a faintly hoppy finish.

Kimberley Best Bitter
(OG 1039, ABV 3.9%) ◗
A beer with a flowery, hoppy and fruity nose, although malt is never far away. Fruity hop is evident in the taste and there is a consistent bitterness.

Kimberley Classic *(OG 1047, ABV 4.8%)* ◗
A light brown beer with an amber hue. Bitter throughout, it has a fruity hop nose, with malt behind the hops in the taste and aftertaste. It is not always easy to find (occasionally alternating with seasonals).

HART

⌂ **Hart Brewery, Cartford Hotel, Cartford Lane, Little Eccleston, Lancs, PR3 0YP**
Tel (01995) 671686
Fax (01772) 797069
Tours by arrangement

714

Brewery founded in 1994 in a small private garage, it moved to premises at the rear of the Cartford Hotel in 1995. With a 10-barrel plant, Hart now supplies direct to 200 outlets nationwide. A monthly beer is available alongside the regular range.
Seasonal beers: Andrew's Cobblestone Stout (ABV 5%), Old Ram (ABV 5%), Criminale Porter (ABV 4%), No Balls (ABV 4.5%), Amethyst (ABV 4.2%), Jade (ABV 4%), Amber (ABV 3.8%), Chinook (ABV 4.7%), IPA (ABV 4.4%), Dishie Debbie (ABV 4%), Valediction (ABV 4.2%).

Gold Beach *(OG 1038, ABV 3.8%)*

Squirrels Hoard *(OG 1042, ABV 4%)*
Brewed for the Cartford Hotel and CAMRA festivals.

Nemesis *(OG 1046, ABV 4.5%)*
A light amber-coloured beer with a refreshing flavour.

Ricketts 7X *(OG 1048, ABV 4.7%)*

HARVEYS

Harvey & Son (Lewes) Ltd, The Bridge Wharf Brewery, 6 Cliffe High Street, Lewes, E Sussex, BN7 2AH
Tel (01273) 480209 Fax (01273) 483706
Website
www.freepages.pavilion.net/users/harveys
Shop 9.30-4.45 Mon-Sat
Tours by arrangement (two-year waiting list)

⊠ Established in 1790, this independent family brewery operates from a superb site on the banks of the River Ouse in Lewes. The brewery was rebuilt in 1881 and is a classic Victorian 'tower' plant, with the brewing process flowing by gravity from floor to floor. A major development in 1985 doubled the brewhouse capacity and subsequent additional fermenting capacity has seen production rise to more than 34,000 barrels a year. The brewery was badly flooded during the storms of autumn 2000 but was quickly back in production. Harveys supplies real ale to all its 43 pubs and 600 free trade outlets in Sussex and Kent.
Seasonal beers: Knots of May Light Mild (ABV 3%, May), Sussex XXXX Old Ale (ABV 4.3%, Oct-May), Kiss (ABV 4.8%, February), Southdown Harvest Ale (ABV 5%, September), 1859 Porter (ABV 4.8%, March), Tom Paine (ABV 5.5%, July), Copperwheat (ABV 4.8%, June), Bonfire Boy (ABV 5.8%, November), Christmas Ale (ABV 8.1%, December). Bottle-conditioned beers: Imperial Extra Double Stout (9%); annual vintages in limited supply.

Sussex XX Mild Ale
(OG 1030, ABV 3%) ▢◗
A dark copper-brown colour. Roast malt dominates the aroma and palate leading to a sweet, caramel finish.

Sussex Pale Ale *(OG 1033, ABV 3.5%)* ◗
An agreeable, light bitter with malt and hops dominating the aroma, while a hoppy bitterness develops throughout the taste, to dominate the finish.

Sussex Best Bitter
(OG 1040, ABV 4%) ▣▢◗
Full-bodied brown bitter. A hoppy aroma leads to a good malt and hop balance and a dry aftertaste.

Sussex XXXX Old Ale
(OG 1043, ABV 4.3%) 🍺❧
A rich, dark beer with a good malty nose, with undertones of roast malt, hops and fruit. The flavour is a complex blend of roast malt, grain, fruit and hops with some caramel. Malty caramel finish with roast malt.

Armada Ale *(OG 1045, ABV 4.5%)* 🍺❧
Hoppy amber best bitter. Well-balanced fruit and hops dominate throughout with a fruity palate.

HARVIESTOUN

Harviestoun Brewery Ltd, Devon Road, Dollar, Clackmannanshire, FK14 7LX
Tel (01259) 742141
Fax (01259) 743141
E-mail harviestoun@talk21.com

☺ Hand-built in a 200-year-old stone byre by two home-brew enthusiasts in 1985, this small brewery operates from a former dairy at the foot of the Ochil Hills, near Stirling. A new custom-built brewing plant was installed in 1991 and Harviestoun now serves 70 outlets in central Scotland as well as wholesalers' customers throughout Britain. Harviestoun bottles a range of beers (not bottle conditioned). Occasional beers: Spring Fever (ABV 3.8%, March), Fresher's Bitter (ABV 3.9%, October), Cutlass Sharp (ABV 4%, August), Lochinvar (ABV 4%, April), American Red (ABV 4.1%, September), Belgian White (ABV 4.3%, July), Mayfest Wheat Beer (ABV 4.4%, May), Old Engine Oil (ABV 4.4%, November), Black Lager (ABV 4.5%, February), Good King Legless (ABV 4.5%, December), Burn's Ale (ABV 4.6%, January), Auld Lang Syne (ABV 4.7%, December), Natural Blonde (ABV 4%), Gremlin (ABV 4.3%), Hitchhiker Bitter (ABV 3.9%), Sandpiper (ABV 3.9%, June), Storm Force (ABV 4.2%, February), Liberation (ABV 4.5%, January).

Wee Stoater *(OG 1034, ABV 3.6%)*

Brooker's Bitter & Twisted
(OG 1038, ABV 3.8%) 🍺🍴❧
Refreshingly hoppy beer with fruit throughout. A bitter-sweet taste with a long, dry, bitter finish. A golden session beer, 1999 Champion Beer of Scotland.

Turnpike *(ABV 4.1%)*

Ptarmigan 80/- *(OG 1045, ABV 4.5%)* ❧
A well-balanced, bitter-sweet beer in which hops and malt dominate. The blend of malt, hops and fruit produces a clean, hoppy aftertaste.

Schiehallion *(OG 1048, ABV 4.8%)* 🍺🍴❧
A Scottish cask lager, brewed using a lager yeast and Hersbrucker hops. A hoppy aroma, with fruit and malt, leads to a malty, bitter taste with floral hoppiness and a bitter finish.

HEATHER

Heather Ale Ltd, Craigmill Brewery, Craigmill, Strathaven, Lanarkshire, ML10 6PB
Tel (01357) 529529
Fax (01357) 522256
E-mail fraoch@heatherale.co.uk

Website www.heatherale.co.uk
Shop 12-6 Mon-Sat, opening June 2001
Tours by arrangement

Bruce Williams started brewing Fraoch (Gaelic for heather and pronounced 'Frook') in 1992 at the now closed West Highland Brewery in Argyll. Production moved to Maclay's brewery in Alloa the following year and when that company closed Heather moved to its own plant in an old grain mill on the banks of the River Avon in the Clyde Valley. All cask beers are made in Strathaven while the bottled products are brewed and bottled at Forth Brewery. Heather Ale is made with flowering heather, while Pictish is a stronger version for the dark winter months. The Strathaven Brewery is also producing a couple of conventionally hopped ales. 30 outlets are supplied direct. Seasonal beers: Grozet Gooseberry Wheat Ale (ABV 4.5%, Sept-Feb), Pictish Heather Ale (ABV 5.4%, Dec-April), Ebulum Elderberry Black Ale (ABV 5.6%, Oct-Jan).

Paley Aley *(OG 1038, ABV 3.9%)*

Swallow IPA *(OG 1041, ABV 4%)*

Fraoch Heather Ale
(OG 1043, ABV 4.1%) 🍺🍴❧
A beer with a floral, peaty aroma, a spicy, herbal, woody flavour and a dry finish.

Grozet Gooseberry Ale
(OG 1044, ABV 4.5%)

A.T. Bob *(OG 1044, ABV 4.2%)*

Kelpie Organic Seaweed Ale
(OG 1044, ABV 4.4%)
Suitable for vegetarians and vegans.

HENRY'S BUTCHER'S YARD*

Henry's Butcher's Yard Brewery, c/o 25 High Street, Chipping Norton, Oxon, OX7 5AD
Tel (01608) 645334

Neil Henry opened his 2.5-barrel plant in June 2000, stopped for a while and re-opened in June 2001. The brewery stands behind a butcher's shop. He supplies 30 pubs in West Oxfordshire. A summer ale was planned but the name had not been finalised.

Chippy Best *(ABV 3.8%)*

HEPWORTH*

Hepworth & Co, The Beer Station, Railway Goods Yard, Nightingale Road, Horsham, W. Sussex, RH12 2NW
Tel (01403) 242901
E-mail ray@weltons.co.uk
Tours by arrangement

Andy Hepworth, former head brewer at King & Barnes, has joined forces with Ray Welton, who closed his brewery in Dorking and moved the equipment to Horsham. Andy is brewing beers for Ray and will develop his own range of bottled beers (including some bottle-conditioned ones). He has no plans to brew his own cask beers.

For Weltons:

Pride & Joy *(ABV 2.8%)*

Kid & Bard *(ABV 3.5%)*

Old Cocky *(ABV 4.3%)*

HERITAGE*

Heritage Ales Ltd, Oakley Business Park, Dinton, Salisbury, Wilts, SP3 5EU
Tel (01722) 716622
Fax (01722) 716644
E-mail mail.enquiries@heritageales.com

Andre Selwood and Phil Downer bought the former Tisbury Brewery in 2001. Since 2000, the brewery has been in modern buildings between Dinton and Wylye; the historic brewery in Tisbury has been sold for redevelopment. The new owners hope to increase production and distribute beer through other regional brewers. The beer range will be developed with new seasonal beers, including a porter in winter. Bottle-conditioned beers: Stonehenge, Ale Fresco and Nadderjack. Seasonal beers: Ale Fresco (ABV 4.5%, June-Aug), Hob Nob (ABV 4.5%, Feb-April), CSB (ABV 4.3%, Aug-Oct), Woodford Dark (ABV 4.3%, Oct-Feb).

Stonehenge *(ABV 3.8%)*
A golden/amber-coloured beer with a malty nose. The malty taste has hints of fruit and hop. Full-bodied for its strength.

Avebury Ale *(ABV 4.3%)*

Old Wardour *(ABV 5%)*

HESKET NEWMARKET

Hesket Newmarket Brewery Ltd, Old Crown Barn, Back Green, Hesket Newmarket, Cumbria, CA7 8JG
Tel/Fax (016974) 78066
E-mail breweryhesket&talk21.com
Website www.bdksol.demon.co.uk/hesket
Tours by arrangement (016974) 78288

⊕ A brewery run as a co-operative by the villagers. Hesket Newmarket was set up in 1988 in a converted barn behind the Old Crown pub by Jim and Liz Fearnley. In 1999 they said they planned to retire. The villagers, anxious to save the brewery as a community resource, raised the funds to buy the site. The beers are named after local fells, with the notable exception of Doris's 90th Birthday Ale (Doris died in 1995, aged 96). Around 20 pubs take the beers regularly and many more on an occasional basis.

Great Cockup Porter *(OG 1035, ABV 3.1%)*
A refreshing, dark and chocolatey porter with a dry finish.

Blencathra Bitter *(OG 1035, ABV 3.3%)* ◄
A malty, tawny ale, mild and mellow for a bitter, with a dominant caramel flavour.

Skiddaw Special Bitter
(OG 1035, ABV 3.5%) ◄
An amber session beer, malty throughout, thin with a dryish finish.

Pigs Might Fly *(OG 1041, ABV 4.3%)* ◄
Roast, chocolate and malt dominate this full-tasting, well-balanced tasty ale.

Doris's 90th Birthday Ale
(OG 1045, ABV 4.4%) ◄
Golden brown with a caramel and barley sugar aroma. Full tasting and satisfying, drying in the aftertaste to a more balanced finish.

Catbells Pale Ale
(OG 1050, ABV 5.1%) ◄
A powerful golden ale with a well-balanced malty bitterness, ending with a bitter and decidedly dry aftertaste.

Old Carrock Strong Ale
(OG 1060, ABV 5.6%)
A dark red, powerful ale.

Ayala's Angel *(OG 1075, ABV 7.1%)*
A black, dark, strong beer, with a complex, nutty character.

HEXHAMSHIRE

Hexhamshire Brewery, Leafields, Ordley, Hexham, NE46 1SX
Tel (01434) 606577

⊗ Brewing started in 1992 and the company is now family-owned. A small producer with an annual output of around 250 barrels, its beers can occasionally be found as far away as Worcester and Sheffield. No adjuncts are used in the beers, which are produced for its single tied house, the Dipton Mill Inn, and 10-20 other outlets. Seasonal beer: Old Humbug (ABV 5.5%).

Devil's Elbow *(OG 1036, ABV 3.6%)* ◄
Satisfying robust, dark amber brew full of hops leading to a bitter finish.

Shire Bitter *(OG 1037, ABV 3.8%)* ◄
Good balance of hops with fruity overtones, this amber beer makes an easy-drinking session bitter.

Devil's Water *(OG 1041, ABV 4.1%)* ◄
Copper-coloured best bitter, well-balanced with a slightly fruity, hoppy finish.

Whap Wheasel *(OG 1048, ABV 4.8%)* ▣◄
An interesting smooth, hoppy beer with a fruity flavour. Amber in colour, the bitter finish brings out the fruit and hops.

HIGH FORCE

High Force Hotel and Brewery, Forest-in-Teesdale, Barnard Castle, Co Durham, DL12 0XH
Tel (01833) 622222
Shop 11-11. Tours by arrangement

⊕ Founded in 1995, High Force Brewery claims to be the highest in Britain at 1,060 feet, next to England's highest waterfall, High Force. In the spring of 2001, High Force stopped brewing: the beers are now brewed under licence by Darwin (qv).

Teesdale Bitter *(OG 1040, ABV 3.8%)* ◄
A well-balanced session ale with lingering fruit character and spicy aftertaste.

Forest XB *(OG 1044, ABV 4.2%)* ◄
A smooth malty flavoured beer, with a solid bitterness and almond undertones to a spicy finish.

Cauldron Snout *(OG 1056, ABV 5.6%)*
A dark and creamy ale with a smooth roasted taste and a rich, solid body. Deceptively drinkable.

HIGHGATE

**Highgate & Walsall Brewing Company Ltd,
Sandymount Road, Walsall,
W Midlands, WS1 3AP**
A subsidiary of Aston Manor of Birmingham
Tel (01922) 644453
Fax (01922) 644471
Tours by arrangement

☺ Highgate, which celebrated its centenary in 1998, was an independent brewery until 1938 when it was taken over by Mitchells & Butlers, and subsequently became the smallest brewery in the Bass group. It had been under threat of closure for some years until a management buy-out brought it back into the independent sector in 1995. Some of the original equipment in the traditional Victorian tower brewery is still in use. Highgate now has 10 tied houses and is aiming for an estate of 50. All the tied houses supply real ale and Highgate has an expanding free trade, with more than 200 outlets in the Midlands supplied direct and further afield via wholesalers. The company also has a contract to supply Bass. It was bought by Aston Manor in 2000. Seasonal/occasional beer: Black Pig (ABV 4.4%).

Dark Mild *(OG 1036.7, ABV 3.4%)*
A dark brown Black Country mild with a good balance of malt and hops, and traces of roast flavour following a malty aroma.

Fox's Nob *(OG 1039.7, ABV 3.6%)*

Bitter *(OG 1039.7, ABV 3.7%)*

Saddlers Best Bitter
(OG 1044.7, ABV 4.3%)
A fruity, pale yellow bitter with a strong hop flavour and a light, refreshing bitter aftertaste.

Breacais *(OG 1044.7, ABV 4.6%)*
A beer made with whisky malt.

Old Ale *(OG 1053.7, ABV 5.1%)*
A winter beer (Nov-Jan): a dark brown/ruby-coloured old ale, full-flavoured, fruity and malty, with a complex aftertaste with hints of malt, roast, hops and fruit.

A honey beer was due to be added to the regular cask beers during 2001 (ABV 3.8%).

For Bass:

M&B Mild *(OG 1034.7, ABV 3.2%)*

HIGHWOOD

**Highwood Brewery Ltd,
Melton Highwood, Barnetby,
Lincs, DN38 6AA**
Tel (01652) 680020
Fax (01652) 680010
E-mail tomwood@users.breworld.net
Website www.tom-wood.com
Tours by arrangement

☒ Highwood started brewing in a converted Victorian granary in 1995 and now uses malt made from barley grown on the family farm. More than 100 outlets are supplied direct. Seasonal beers: Mill Race (ABV 4.2%, Jan-Feb), Wagoners Ale (ABV 4.8%, March-April), Barndance (4.2%, June-July), Summer Days (ABV 4.4%, July-Aug), Lincolnshire Longwool (4.4%, Sept-Oct), Jolly Ploughman (ABV 4.4%, Oct-Nov), Christmas Cheer (ABV 4.5%, December).

Tom Wood Dark Mild
(OG 1035, ABV 3.5%)

Tom Wood Best Bitter
(OG 1035, ABV 3.5%)
A good citric passion fruit hop on the nose and taste, which dominates the background malt. A lingering hoppy and bitter finish makes this amber bitter very drinkable.

Tom Wood Shepherd's Delight
(OG 1040, ABV 4%)
Malt is the dominant taste in this amber brew, although the fruity hop bitterness complements it all the way.

Tom Wood Lincolnshire Legend
(OG 1041, ABV 4.2%)
An orange fruity hop is balanced by malt on the nose and taste, where there is also a good bitter bite lingering into the aftertaste of this copper chestnut beer.

Tom Wood Harvest Bitter
(OG 1041.5, ABV 4.3%)
A well-balanced amber beer where the hops and bitterness just about outdo the malt.

Tom Wood Old Timber
(OG 1043, ABV 4.5%)
Hoppy on the nose, but featuring well-balanced malt and hops otherwise. A slight, lingering roast/coffee flavour develops, but this is generally a bitter, darkish brown beer.

Tom Wood Bomber County
(OG 1046, ABV 4.8%)
An earthy malt aroma but with a complex underlying mix of coffee, hops, caramel and apple fruit. The beer starts bitter and intensifies but all its mahogany characteristics stay on until the end.

HILDEN

**Hilden Brewing Company,
Hilden House, Hilden, Lisburn,
Co Antrim, BT27 4TY**
Tel (028 92) 663863
Fax (028 92) 603511
E-mail hilden.brewery@uk.gateway.net
Website
www.networkpersonnel.org.uk/hilden
Shop 11.30-5. Tours 11.30 & 2.30 Tue-Sat

☺ Hilden was established in 1981 by Ann and Seamus Scullion in stables alongside a Georgian country house. It supplies Hilden Ale to a handful of pubs in Northern Ireland, with the full range exported to some pubs in England. The beers are available in a visitor centre at Hilden House. Bottle-conditioned beer: Original (ABV 4.6%).

Hilden Ale *(OG 1038, ABV 4%)*
An amber-coloured beer with an aroma of malt, hops and fruit. The balanced taste is slightly slanted towards hops, and hops are also prominent in the full, malty finish. Bitter and refreshing.

Molly Malone's Porter
(OG 1048, ABV 4.6%)
Dark ruby-red porter with complex flavours of hop bitterness and chocolate malt.

Scullion's Irish *(OG 1048, ABV 4.6%)*
Initially smooth on the palate, it finishes with a clean, hoppy aftertaste.

HOBSONS

Hobsons Brewery & Co Ltd, Newhouse Farm, Tenbury Road, Cleobury Mortimer, nr Kidderminster, Worcestershire, DY14 8RD
Tel (01299) 270837
Fax (01299) 270260
E-mail beer@hobsons-brewery.co.uk
Shop 8-5 weekdays. Tours by arrangement

⊗ Established in 1993, Hobsons moved to its current premises in 1996. Production has grown to 75 barrels a week. An extension was built in 2001 that allowed production to grow by 50% and to include a bottling plant. 92 outlets are supplied direct.

Best Bitter *(OG 1038.5, ABV 3.8%)* ◆
A pale brown to amber, medium-bodied beer with strong hop character throughout. It is consequently bitter, but with malt discernible in the taste.

Town Crier *(OG 1045, ABV 4.5%)*
A straw-coloured bitter.

Old Henry *(OG 1051, ABV 5.2%)*

HOGS BACK

Hogs Back Brewery, Manor Farm, The Street, Tongham, Surrey, GU10 1DE
Tel (01252) 783000
Fax (01252) 782328
E-mail info@hogsback.co.uk
Website www.hogsback.co.uk
Shop 10-6 Mon-Tue; 10-8.30 Wed-Fri; 9-6 Sat; 10-4.30 Sun. Tours by arrangement 6.30 Wed-Fri; 11am and 2.30 Sat; 2.30 Sun

⊗ The purpose-built brewery was set up in a restored, 18th-century farm building in 1992 and the popularity of its ales – particularly the award-winning TEA – resulted in a major plant change to double production capacity. From small beginnings, with just a single beer, Hogs Back now brews nearly 20 beer types on a regular or occasional basis. The brewery has undergone another major expansion programme, installing a new conditioning/racking room and cask cellar. Two new 40-barrel fermentation vessels have been installed, and the company has bought a 500-year-old barn to house a new brewery shop and off-licence. A new bottling and labelling system has been installed to meet the demand for bottled beers. Hogs Back exports cask ales to the US and sells through e-commerce, with mail order on its website. The brewery has a ghost, known to walk the brewery gallery, and believed to be a former local vicar. Occasional/seasonal beers: Dark Mild (ABV 3.4%), APB or A Pinta Bitter (ABV 3.5%), Spring Call (ABV 4%), Summer Capers (ABV 4%), Easter Teaser (ABV 4.2%), Friday 13th (ABV 4.2%), Blackwater Porter (ABV 4.4%), BSA or Burma Star Ale (ABV 4.5%), Autumn Seer (ABV 4.8%, autumn), Tattoo (ABV 4.8%), Arena (ABV 4.8%), YES or Your Every Success (ABV 5%), Fuggles Nouveau (ABV 5%), Goldings Nouveau (ABV 5%), Utopia (ABV 5.4%), OTT or Old Tongham Tasty (ABV 6%), Brewster's Bundle (ABV 7.6%),

Santa's Wobble (ABV 7.5%, Christmas), A over T or Aromas over Tongham (ABV 9%), Wheat Your Whistle (4.8%, for the summer). Bottle-conditioned beers: TEA (ABV 4.2%), BSA (ABV 4.5%), Vintage Ale (ABV 6%), Brewster's Bundle (ABV 7.4%), Wobble in a Bottle (ABV 7.5%), A over T (ABV 9%), OTT (ABV 6%).

Hair of the Hog *(OG 1038, ABV 3.5%)* ◆
An honest, refreshing pale brown session beer with a good bitter hop character balanced with pale malt and fruit. A dry, bitter finish.

Legend *(OG 1038, ABV 4%)* ◆
Complex and drinkable, this golden coloured beer contains both wheat and lager malts, and has a dry, malty and bitter taste that lingers. Available September.

TEA or Traditional English Ale *(OG 1044, ABV 4.2%)* 📷🍴◆
The brewery's flagship beer is pale brown, with a hoppy and slightly fruity aroma, supported by malt in the taste. A well-crafted, bitter-sweet beer with a long dry finish.

Advent Ale *(OG 1046, ABV 4.6%)* ◆
Dark red-brown in colour, this easy-to-drink winter ale tastes of dark malts and roast barley, with liquorice hints in the finish. Available Christmas.

Hop Garden Gold *(OG 1048, ABV 4.6%)* ◆
A malty, pale golden beer with hints of banana and pineapple, with a good balance of aroma and bittering hops and a long dry finish.

Rip Snorter *(OG 1052, ABV 5%)* ◆
A strong, malty and fruity, reddish-brown bitter with a slight hop flavour.

HOLDEN'S

Holden's Brewery Ltd Co, Hopden Brewery, George Street, Woodsetton, Dudley, W Midlands, DY1 4LN
Tel (01902) 880051
Fax (01902) 665473
E-mail hbrewery@aol.com
Website www.holdensbrewery.co.uk
Shop 11-9 Mon-Sat; 12-3, 7-9 Sun
Tours by arrangement

☺ A family brewery going back five generations, Holden's began life as a brew-pub when Edwin and Lucy Holden took over the Park Inn (now the brewery tap) in the 1920s; the inn has been refurbished to its former Victorian heritage. With 21 pubs, the tied estate is continuing to grow. Some 45 other outlets are also supplied with Holden's cask ales. Occasional/seasonal beer: Old XL Ale (ABV 7.2%, Christmas).

Black Country Mild
(OG 1037, ABV 3.7%) ✵
A good, red/brown mild; a refreshing, light blend of roast malt, hops and fruit, dominated by malt throughout.

Black Country Bitter
(OG 1039, ABV 3.9%) ✵
A medium-bodied, golden ale; a light, well-balanced bitter with a subtle, dry, hoppy finish.

XB *(OG 1042, ABV 4.1%)* ✵
Named after founder Lucy Blanche Holden, this is a sweeter, slightly fuller version of the Bitter. Sold in different outlets under different names.

Golden Glow *(OG 1044, ABV 4.4%)*
A pale golden beer, with a subtle hop aroma plus gentle sweetness and a light hoppiness.

Special Bitter *(OG 1052, ABV 5.1%)* ✵
A sweet, malty, full-bodied amber ale with hops to balance in the taste and in the good, bitter-sweet finish.

HOLLAND*

Holland Brewery, 5 Brown Flatts, Brewery Street, Kimberley, Notts, NG16 2JU
Tel (0115) 938 2685

Len Holland, a keen home-brewer for 30 years, went commercial in April 2000, cheek-by-jowl with mighty Hardys & Hansons. He has a 9-gallon plant, which is based in his back yard. Seasonal beers: Holly Hop (ABV 4.7%, Xmas), Dutch Courage (ABV 5%, winter).

Golden Blond *(ABV 4%)*

Lip Smacker *(ABV 4%)*

Cloghopper *(ABV 4.2%)*

Double Dutch *(ABV 4.5%)*

HOLT

Joseph Holt Group Ltd,
Derby Brewery, Empire Street,
Cheetham, Manchester, M3 1JD
Tel (0161) 834 3285
Fax (0161) 834 6458
Tours 10-11.15am Sat, £10 per person donation to Holt Radium Institute at the Christie Hospital. Groups of 12-15 only. Tours may be restricted in 2001 and 2002 to March–May only.

⊛ A family brewery established in 1849 by Joseph Holt, it celebrated 150 years in brewing in 1999. In recent years new equipment for the brewing process has been installed to cope with demand for the ever-expanding estate of pubs. Bitter is often delivered in 54-gallon hogsheads and the brewery hopes that one day there will be a demand for Mild in hogsheads, too. 127 pubs are owned, all serving cask-conditioned beer. Holts became a limited company in 1951 and was quoted on the Stock Exchange but in March 2000 the

company applied to re-purchase all the shares and to become de-listed. This will make the company even more secure from takeovers, being family-run and truly independent once more.

Mild *(OG 1032, ABV 3.2%)* ✵
A dark brown beer with a fruity, malty nose and taste. Strong in bitterness for a mild, with a dry, hoppy finish.

Bitter *(OG 1040, ABV 4%)* ⌂✵
A tawny beer with a good hop aroma. Although balanced by malt and fruit, the uncompromising bitterness can be a shock to the unwary.

HOME COUNTY

Home County Brewers, The Old Brewery, Station Road, Wickwar Trading Estate, Wickwar, Gloucestershire, GL12 8NB
Tel/Fax (01454) 294045
Shop working hours, 6.30 Fri. Tours by arrangement

Home County was set up in 1997 with a 5-barrel brew length. The brewery was badly flooded in the October 2000 storms but owner Maurice Beezer had the brewery functioning again by June 2001. There are plans to expand the premises, once the trade lost has been made up. 24 outlets are supplied direct. Seasonal beer: Pit Orchard (ABV 4.5%, summer).

Golden Brown *(OG 1035, ABV 3.5%)* ✵
Gentle and clean-tasting ale. Golden brown in colour, this is a light malty ale with a very subtle aroma. Moderately bitter and slightly dry. Malty and dry finish.

Wichen *(OG 1042, ABV 4.2%)* ✵
Pale brown, this has a malty and fruity aroma with a little hop. Medium bodied, with a good, malty taste throughout, some hops and complex fruit, and a slightly dry, bitter finish.

Old Tradition *(OG 1048, ABV 4.8%)* ✵
Malty throughout, but with balancing fruit and hops. Mid to full-bodied, brown in colour, and bitter-sweet. Predominantly malty aroma.

County Pride *(OG 1050, ABV 5%)* ✵
Pale and crystal malts and fruit aroma. Mid-brown and bitter-sweet tasting, with a slightly dry, malty aftertaste. Medium-bodied for its strength.

HOOK NORTON

Hook Norton Brewery Co Ltd, Brewery Lane, Hook Norton, Banbury, Oxon, OX15 5NY
Tel (01608) 737210
Fax (01608) 730294
E-mail info@hooknorton-brewery.co.uk
Website www.hook-norton-brewery.co.uk
Shop in visitor centre with a small museum 10-4.30 Mon-Fri. Tours by arrangement

⊠ The Hook Norton Brewery can trace its origins back to 1849 when John Harris set up in business as a maltster. He soon started brewing and in 1872 built a small, three-storey brewery. In 1896 major building work started with new stables and offices, followed by the six-storey tower brewery still in use today. Much of the original brewing equipment is still in use, including a 25hp steam engine that provides nearly all the motive power. Hook Norton owns 39 pubs and supplies approximately 250 free trade accounts. All Hook Norton draught beers are cask conditioned and dry hopped. All the beers use water drawn from wells beneath the brewery, Maris Otter malt and English Challenger, Fuggles and Goldings hops. Seasonal beers: First Light (ABV 4.3%, May-June), Steam Ale (ABV 4.4%, Sept-Oct), Copper Ale (ABV 4.8%, March-Apr), Double Stout (ABV 4.8%, Jan-Feb), Haymaker (ABV 5%, July-Aug), Twelve Days (ABV 5.5%, Nov-Dec).

Best Mild *(OG 1032, ABV 3%)* ◆
A dark, red/brown mild with a malty aroma and a malty, sweetish taste, tinged with a faint hoppy balance. Malty in the aftertaste.

Best Bitter *(OG 1035, ABV 3.4%)* ◻◆
A fruity and hoppy aroma introduces this complex, well-crafted amber bitter. Moderate maltiness underpins the hops, leading to a long, bitter-sweet finish.

Generation *(OG 1041, ABV 4%)* ◆
A pale brown best bitter, predominantly hoppy but balanced with moderate malt and banana fruit. The fruit and malt decline to a relatively short, hoppy finish.

Old Hooky *(OG 1048, ABV 4.6%)* ◆
A well-balanced and full-bodied pale copper beer that is fruity with pale and crystal malt and hops on the aroma and taste. The hoppy character gives way to a sweet and fruity finish.

Double Stout *(OG 1050, ABV 4.8%)* ◆
This dry, dark red-brown stout has masses of roast malt flavour but not too much depth of character. The finish is dry and powdery.

HOP BACK

Hop Back Brewery PLC, Units 20-25 Batten Road Industrial Estate, Downton, Salisbury, Wilts, SP5 3HU
Tel (01725) 510986
Fax (01725) 513116
E-mail sales@hopback.co.uk
Website www.hopback.co.uk
Tours by arrangement

⊠ Started by John Gilbert in 1985 at the Wyndham Arms in Salisbury, the brewery has expanded steadily ever since. It went public via a Business Expansion Scheme support plan in 1993 and has enjoyed rapid continued growth. Summer Lightning has won many awards. The brewery has eight tied houses, including the Hop Leaf in Reading (see Reading Lion Brewery) and Hop Back also sells directly to 200 other outlets. Seasonal beers are produced on a monthly basis. Bottle-conditioned beers: Thunderstorm (ABV 5%), Summer Lightning (ABV 5%) ◻◼, Taiphoon (ABV 4.2%), Crop Circle (ABV 4.2%).

GFB/Gilbert's First Brew
(OG 1034, ABV 3.5%) ◻◆
A golden beer, with the sort of light, clean quality that makes it an ideal session ale. A hoppy aroma and taste lead to a good, dry finish. Refreshing.

Best Bitter *(OG 1040, ABV 4%)*

Crop Circle *(OG 1041, ABV 4.2%)*

Entire Stout *(OG 1043, ABV 4.5%)* ◻◆

A rich, dark stout with a strong roasted malt flavour and a long, sweet and malty aftertaste. A beer suitable for vegans. Also produced with ginger.

Thunderstorm *(OG 1048, ABV 5%)* ◻◆
A softly bitter, easy-drinking wheat beer.

Summer Lightning
(OG 1049, ABV 5%) ◼◻◆
A pleasurable pale bitter with a good, fresh, hoppy aroma and a malty, hoppy flavour. Finely balanced, it has an intense bitterness leading to a long, dry finish. Though strong, it tastes like a session ale.

HOPDAEMON*

**Hopdaemon Brewery Co,
18a-18b Canterbury Hill, Tyler Hill, Canterbury, Kent CT2 9LS**
Tel (01227) 784962
E-mail hopdaemon@supanet.com

Tonie Prins, former brewer at Swale Brewery, opened a 12-barrel plant in January 2001 and within six months was supplying more than 30 pubs in the area, as well as exclusive bottled-conditioned, own-label beers for the British Museum and Southwark Cathedral, named Beer and Pilgrim's Pleasure respectively, both 5% ABV. Seasonal beers: Changeling (ABV 5.3%), Leviathan (ABV 6%), both winter. Bottle-conditioned beers: Skrimshander, Leviathan.

Golden Braid *(ABV 3.7%)*

Skrimshander IPA *(ABV 4.5%)*

Dominator *(ABV 5.1%)*

HOSKINS & OLDFIELD

Hoskins & Oldfield Brewery Ltd, North Mills, Frog Island, Leicester, LE3 5DH
Tel (0116) 262 3330
E-mail HOB@neptunegroup.demon.co.uk
Website www.neptunegroup.demon.co.uk/hob

The brewery was set up by Philip and Stephen Hoskins, two members of Leicester's famous brewing family, in 1984, after the sale of the old Hoskins Brewery. They opened their first tied house in 1999, the Ale Waggon, in Leicester city centre. The company supplies more than 15 outlets direct, and others nationwide via wholesalers. Occasional/seasonal beers: Midnight Express (ABV 5%), Tom Kelly's Christmas Pudding Porter (ABV 5%, Christmas), Reckless Raspberry (ABV 5.5%, a wheat beer with raspberries), Petulant Peach (ABV 5.5%), Pioneer Gold (ABV 4.8%).

HOB Best Mild *(OG 1036, ABV 3.5%)* ◆
An almost black coloured beer, with malt and hops in the taste.

Brigadier Bitter *(OG 1036, ABV 3.6%)*

HOB Bitter *(OG 1041, ABV 4%)* ◆
A copper-coloured best bitter with a hoppy-malty nose and dominated by hop bitterness throughout.

Little Matty *(OG 1041, ABV 4%)*
A complex brown/red beer.

White Dolphin *(OG 1041, ABV 4%)*
A fruity wheat beer.

IPA *(OG 1042, ABV 4.2%)*

A well-hopped pale ale.

Tom Kelly's Stout *(OG 1043, ABV 4.2%)*
A dark, dry stout.

Supreme *(OG 1045, ABV 4.4%)*
A pale gold best bitter.

Grandad Tom's Porter
(OG 1050, ABV 4.8%)
Brewed using honey and oats.

EXS Bitter *(OG 1051, ABV 5%)*
A malty, full-bodied premium bitter.

O4 Ale *(OG 1052, ABV 5.2%)*
A red/brown coloured, full-flavoured ale.

Ginger Tom *(OG 1053, ABV 5.2%)*
A ginger beer.

Old Navigation Ale *(OG 1071, ABV 7%)* 🏠◆
A strong ruby/black beer.

Christmas Noggin *(OG 1100, ABV 10%)*
A potent barley wine. Despite the name, available all year.

HOUSTON

Houston Brewing Company, South Street, Houston, Renfrewshire, PA6 7EN
Tel (01505) 614528
Fax (01505) 614133
E-mail ale@houston-brewing.co.uk
Website www.houston-brewing.co.uk
Shop open all day, every day. Tours by arrangement

Brewing since 1997, Houston has expanded rapidly and the beers are now available throughout Britain. Silver Medal winner, Champion Beer of Scotland and Bronze Medal winner, Best Bitter category, Champion Beer of Britain 2000, for Peter's Well, which is now available in bottle but not bottle conditioned. Seasonal beers: Champion (ABV 4%, summer), Formakin (ABV 4.3%, spring), Jock Frost (ABV 4.5%, winter), Teuchter (ABV 4.8%, autumn).

Killellan *(OG 1037, ABV 3.7%)* ◆
Light session ale, with a floral hop and fruity taste. The finish of this amber beer is dry and quenching.

Barochan *(OG 1041, ABV 4.1%)*
A red, malty beer, in which fruit is balanced by roast and hop overtones; dry, bitter-sweet finish.

Peter's Well *(OG 1042, ABV 4.2%)* 🏠◆
Well-balanced fruity taste with sweet hop, leading to an increasingly bitter-sweet finish. Formerly St Peter's Well, excommunication has not affected the taste of this golden ale.

Texas *(OG 1045, ABV 4.5%)* ◆
Named Texas in honour of Houston, Texas; brewed with American hops that merge with pale chocolate malt to produce an amber, full-bodied ale.

SARAH HUGHES

🛒 **Sarah Hughes Brewery, Beacon Hotel, 129 Bilston Street, Sedgley, W Midlands, DY3 1JE**
Tel (01902) 883380
Tours by prior arrangement

⊛ Opened originally in the 1860s behind the Beacon Hotel, Sarah Hughes bought the brewery in 1921 and started to brew the

beer now called Dark Ruby. After lying idle for 30 years, the brewery was re-opened in 1987 by John Hughes, who continued the tradition and recipe of his grandmother. One pub is owned and more than 100 outlets are supplied direct. The beers are now exported to the United States. Seasonal beer: Snow Flake (ABV 8%). Bottle-conditioned beer: Dark Ruby Mild (ABV 6%).

Pale Amber *(OG 1038, ABV 4%)*
A well-balanced beer, initially slightly sweet but with hops close behind.

Sedgley Surprise *(OG 1048, ABV 5%)* ◆
A bitter-sweet, medium-bodied, hoppy ale with some malt.

Dark Ruby Mild *(OG 1058, ABV 6%)* 🍾🏠◆
A dark ruby strong ale with a good balance of fruit and hops, leading to a pleasant, lingering hops and malt finish.

HULL

Hull Brewery Company Limited, 144 English Street, Hull, Yorkshire, HU3 2BT
Tel (01482) 586364
Fax (01482) 586365

⊛ The name of the closed Hull Brewery was resurrected after a 15-year absence when a new brewery opened in 1989. It was forced into liquidation in 1994 and the assets taken over by local businessman Dieter Ellwood, who formed a new company. It acquired its first tied house in 1995 from Bass, now has three, and supplies 20 outlets direct. A bottling plant was added in 1997.

Mild *(OG 1036, ABV 3.6%)* ◆
Roasted malt dominates this very good example of a dark mild. Dark red/black in colour, it has a good balance of fruit and hop flavours with a smooth finish.

Ellwood's Best Bitter
(OG 1038, ABV 3.8%) ◆
A golden, straw-coloured session bitter, smooth and rounded, with subtle hints of hops and malt and a refreshing aftertaste.

Bitter *(OG 1038, ABV 3.8%)* ◆
A refreshing copper bitter, with a predominantly hoppy aroma. The initial bitter aftertaste leads to a pleasant, lingering maltiness. Complex.

Northern Pride *(OG 1042, ABV 4.2%)*
A distinctive, full-bodied beer, with a malty aroma.

The Governor *(OG 1044, ABV 4.4%)*
A full-bodied, amber-coloured premium ale; a deceptively powerful brew with a malty taste and a distinctive hop aroma.

Mickey Finn *(OG 1052, ABV 5.2%)*

HUMPTY DUMPTY

Humpty Dumpty Brewery, Church Road, Reedham, Norfolk, NR13 3TZ
Tel (01493) 701818
E-mail mick@humptydumptybrewery.com
Website www.humptydumptybrewery.com
Tours by arrangement

Humpty Dumpty Brewery was opened in 1998 by Mick Cottrell. He sells to the Railway Tavern in Reedham and some 150 pubs nationwide. Seasonal/occasional beers:

Lemon & Ginger Ale (ABV 3.8%), Swingbridge (ABV 4%), Tender Behind ABV 4%), Brief Encounter (ABV 4.3%), Reed Cutter (ABV 4.2%), Christmas Chuckle (ABV 4.1%).

Nord Atlantic *(ABV 3.7%)* ◈
A dark, copper-coloured bitter with little aroma. A sweet malty taste develops toffee overtones. A long, bitter-sweet finish for a beer that has a surprising lightness of body.

Little Sharpie *(ABV 3.8%)* ◈
A delicate hoppy aroma is a forerunner to a sweet hoppy lagerish flavour. A clean golden yellow bitter with a finish in which bitterness grows.

Claud Hamilton *(ABV 4.3%)* ◈
With its dark brown coloration, this old style oyster stout is a stirring mix of roast fruity sweetness. The bitter-sweet finish draws out a hint of caramelised toffee.

Butt Jumper *(ABV 4.8%)* ◈
Toffee and malt dominate the aroma of this tawny-hued ale. Full-flavoured, with malt vying with a fruity bitterness for dominance. Long, lingering finish does not fade as a nutty bitterness becomes prevalent.

Railway Sleeper *(ABV 5%)* ◈
A sweet plummy fruitiness blankets an underlying malty bitterness. Full and rich in flavour, the aftertaste develops an increasing malt bias that does not fade.

HYDES

Hydes' Brewery Ltd, 46 Moss Lane West, Manchester, M15 5PH
Tel (0161) 226 1317
Fax (0161) 227 9593
E-mail mail@hydesbrewery.com
Website www.hydesbrewery.com
Shop 9-5. Tours by arrangement

⊛ A family-controlled brewing company marrying traditional and state of the art techniques, Hydes was first established at the Crown Brewery, Audenshaw, Manchester, in 1863 and on its present site, the former Greatorex Brothers Brewery, since the turn of the century. It supplies cask ale to all but one of its 69 tied houses, and direct to more than 80 free trade outlets. 1999 saw the rebranding of the company and products, with the introduction of a new premium ale, Jekyll's Gold, to the cask portfolio. Brewery volumes doubled in 2000. In order to cope with increased demand for Hydes' products, the brewery has drawn up plans to increase capacity by a further 50%. A successful programme of seasonal cask ales sees a new beer appearing every two months. Seasonal beers: A Quick One (ABV, 4.8%, Jan-Feb), Down the Hatch (ABV 4.2%, March-April), The Usual (ABV 4.4%, May-June), Hits the Spot (ABV 4%, July-Aug), One to Unwind (ABV 4.5%, Sept-Oct), Dutch Courage (ABV 5%, Nov-Dec).

Light *(OG 1033.5, ABV 3.5%)* ◈
A lightly-hopped, amber-coloured session beer with a refreshing lemon fruitiness and a brief but dry finish.

Traditional Mild *(OG 1033.5, ABV 3.5%)* ◈
A mid-brown beer with malt and citrus fruit

on the aroma and taste. Quite sweet in the mouth but drier in the aftertaste.

Dark Mild *(OG 1033.5, ABV 3.5%)* ◈

Traditional Bitter *(OG 1036, ABV 3.8%)* ◈
A good-flavoured bitter, with a malty and fruity nose, malt and hop in the taste, with a fruity background, and good bitterness through into the aftertaste.

Jekyll's Gold Premium Ale *(OG 1042, ABV 4.3%)* ◈
Pale gold in colour, fruity nose with a touch of sulphur. A well-balanced beer with hops, fruit and malt all in evidence, and a dry, hoppy finish.

XXXX *(OG 1070, ABV 6.8%)*

ICENI

Iceni Brewery, 3 Foulden Road, Ickburgh, Norfolk, IP26 5BJ
Tel (01842) 878922
Fax (01842) 879216
Website www.stevedunks.demon.co.uk/iceni
Tours by arrangement

⊠ Iceni Brewery started in 1995 and for four years grew slowly, mainly supplying guest beers. From mid-1998 the beer range has been produced in bottle-conditioned form. In 1999 Iceni Brewery produced LAD Lager in cask and bottle-conditioned versions. In 2000, Iceni joined with nine other East Anglian breweries to form the East Anglia Brewery Trail. 33 outlets are supplied direct. Special beers are brewed for festivals.

Fine Soft Day *(OG 1038, ABV 4%)* ◈
Full-bodied and hoppy amber ale with a lingering aftertaste of hops and malt.

Celtic Queen *(OG 1038, ABV 4%)*
A light summer ale, packed with flavour.

Boadicea Chariot Ale *(OG 1038, ABV 3.8%)*
A well-balanced session bitter.

Deirdre of the Sorrows *(OG 1042, ABV 4.4%)*
A gold-coloured ale with a distinctively pleasant taste that lingers.

Roisin Dubh *(OG 1042, ABV 4.4%)*
The name means 'Dark Rose': a sweet, smooth dark ale.

Gold *(OG 1045, ABV 5%)*
A strong ale, sun gold in colour. Crisp taste; smooth and deceptive for its strength.

LAD Lager *(OG 1048, ABV 5%)*

Raspberry Wheat *(OG 1048, ABV 5%)*

INVERALMOND

Inveralmond Brewery Ltd,
1 Inveralmond Way, Perth, PH1 3UQ
Tel/Fax (01738) 449448
E-mail info@inveralmond-brewery.co.uk
Website www.inveralmond-brewery.co.uk
Shop 9-5

◎ Established in April 1997, the Inveralmond Brewery was the first brewery in Perth for more than 30 years. Set up by Heriot-Watt trained, ex-Ruddles, Courage and S&N brewer Fergus Clark and his wife Ailish, the brewery supplies more than 150 outlets direct, with wholesalers supplying pubs nationwide. Ossian's Ale and Lia Fail are now also available in bottle (not bottle conditioned). Seasonal ales: Inkie Pinkie (ABV 3.7%), Amber Bead (ABV 4.1%), Pint Stowp (ABV 4.2%), Pundie (ABV 5%).

Independence *(OG 1040, ABV 3.8%)* ◆
A well-balanced Scottish ale with fruit and malt tones. Hop provides an increasing bitterness in the finish.

Ossian's Ale *(OG 1042, ABV 4.1%)* 🍴🍷
Well-balanced, moreish best bitter with a dry finish. This full-bodied amber ale is dominated by fruit and hop with a bitter-sweet character.

Thrappledouser
(OG 1043, ABV 4.3%) ◆
A refreshing amber beer with reddish hues. The crisp, hoppy aroma is finely balanced with the tangy but quenching taste.

Lia Fail *(OG 1048, ABV 4.7%)* ◆
The name is the Gaelic title of the Stone of Destiny; a dark, robust, full-bodied beer with a deep malty taste. Smooth texture and balanced finish.

ISLE OF SKYE

**Isle of Skye Brewing Company
(Leann an Eilein), The Pier, Uig,
Isle of Skye, IV51 9XY
Tel (01470) 542477
Fax (01470) 542488
E-mail info@skyebrewery.co.uk
Website www.skyebrewery.co.uk**
Shop 10-6 Mon-Sat; 12-5 Sun Apr-Oct
Tours by arrangement

☺ Established in 1995, Isle of Skye's trade continues to expand steadily, both directly and via wholesalers, to cover most of mainland Britain. The island now has 11 hotels serving cask ale from the brewery and many others stock the bottled range. The company serves 60 outlets direct.

Young Pretender *(OG 1039, ABV 4%)* ◆
Golden amber ale with hop and fruit on the nose. The bitter taste is dominated by fruit and hop, the latter lingering into the dry, bitter finish.

Red Cuillin *(OG 1041, ABV 4.2%)* ◆
A burst of fruit with malt and hop notes introduce this tawny reddish beer. These characteristics continue into the wonderful bitter-sweet taste. A very dry and bitter finish.

Hebridean Gold
(OG 1041.5, ABV 4.3%) 🍷◆
A superb golden coloured beer that is brewed using oats. Hops and fruit dominate the bitter taste and increasingly dry, citrus finish.

Black Cuillin *(OG 1044, ABV 4.5%)*

Blaven *(OG 1047, ABV 5%)* ◆
An amber-coloured, bitter-sweet beer dominated by fruit and hop throughout. There is also malt in the taste and increasing bitterness in the long, dry finish.

ITCHEN VALLEY

**Itchen Valley Brewery Ltd, Shelf House,
New Farm Road, Alresford, Hampshire,
SO24 9QE**

**Tel (01962) 735111
Fax (01962) 735678
E-mail info@itchenvalley.com
Website www.itchenvalley.com**
Shop 9-3.30 Mon-Fri. Tours by arrangement

✗ The brewery, founded in 1997, had a fine first year culminating in winning a Bronze award at the Great British Beer Festival in 1998, barely a year after starting brewing. The brewery now has more than 150 regular account customers taking the full range of beer in casks, and the brewery is expanding to meet demand. In late 1999 the brewery installed a bottling plant. Pure Gold, introduced during 2000, has been a run-away success and the brewery is working hard to satisfy demand. Further expansion is planned. Seasonal beers: Easter Bunnies (ABV 3.9%, Easter), Red Roses (ABV 4%, Valentine's week), Broomstick Bitter (ABV 4%, Halloween), Father Christmas (ABV 5%).

Godfathers *(OG 1042, ABV 3.8%)* 🍷
A pale brown beer with a hoppy aroma. A malty and bitter taste leads through to the finish.

Fagin's *(OG 1041, ABV 4.1%)*
Light brown, well-balanced bitter. Late hopping with First Gold gives this beer a distinctive, dry citrus aftertaste.

Wykehams Glory *(OG 1045, ABV 4.3%)*
A nut brown, malty flavoured ale, with a hoppy nose.

Judge Jeffreys *(OG 1048, ABV 4.5%)*
A copper-coloured premium bitter with a hoppy nose.

Pure Gold *(OG 1048, ABV 4.8%)*
A lightly effervescent beer with initial bitterness coming from the choicest Czech hops, leading to sweet aromatic hop notes, gathered from American speciality hops.

Wat Tyler *(OG 1057, ABV 5%)*
A dark brown hoppy ale, bitter sweet with an aromatic nose.

JENNINGS

**Jennings Bros PLC, Castle Brewery,
Cockermouth, Cumbria, CA13 9NE
Tel (01900) 823214
Fax (01900) 827462
Website www.jenningsbrewery.co.uk**
Shop 9-5 Mon-Sun summer
Tours by arrangement 11-2 spring/summer

☺ Founded in 1828, Jennings moved to its present idyllic site by the River Derwent and at the foot of Cockermouth Castle in 1874, where it still uses its own well water. Although there is no longer any family involvement, many of the company's shares are owned by local people. Around 200 free trade outlets are supplied direct with many more via a network of wholesalers throughout the country. A £1 million investment programme was launched in 1999 to upgrade the brewery and increase output. Real ale is available in most of Jennings's 111 tied houses. The company is committed to an integrated pub and brewery business. Seasonal beers: Cross Buttock Ale (ABV 4.5%, autumn), La'al Cockle Warmer (ABV 6.5%, winter).

Dark Mild *(OG 1031, ABV 3.1%)* ◆

723

A well-balanced dark brown mild with malty aroma, strong roast taste, not over-sweet, with some hops and slightly bitter finish.

Bitter (OG 1035, ABV 3.5%) ◈
A mid-brown bitter with pronounced malt and roast flavours and aftertaste. Some hoppiness and a rising bitter, dry finish. Good mouth-feel.

Cumberland Ale (OG 1040, ABV 4%) ◈
A creamy amber-gold malty ale with hop resin and fruity notes; rising bitterness balances well.

Cocker Hoop (OG 1047, ABV 4.8%) ⬚◈
A rich, creamy, copper-coloured beer with raisiny maltiness balanced with a resiny hoppiness, with a developing bitterness towards the end.

Sneck Lifter (OG 1055, ABV 5.1%) ◈
A strong, dark brown ale with a complex balance of fruit, malt and full roast flavours right through to the finish.

JERSEY

Ann Street Brewery Co Ltd,
t/a Jersey Brewery, 57 Ann Street,
St Helier, Jersey, JE1 1BZ
Tel (01534) 31561
Fax (01534) 67033
Tours by arrangement

Jersey, better known as Ann Street, phased out cask ale after a brief flirtation in the 1980s and 90s. It has 50 tied houses, of which 12 take real ale, including beers from its sister company, Guernsey Brewery. Jersey Brewery also has an interest in the Tipsy Toad brew-pub (qv).

JOHN O'GAUNT

John O'Gaunt Brewing Co Ltd, Fox Inn,
13 Main Street, Melton Mowbray,
Leicestershire, LE14 2DQ
Tel/Fax (01664) 840257
Tours by arrangement

⊠ The brewery was set up by Celia Atton in 1997 next to the Stag and Hounds pub at Borough on the Hill and moved in 1998 to share the equipment of the Parish Brewery (qv). Celia took over the Old Brewery Inn in 1998. Her first beer, Robin a Tiptoe, was named after a local landmark. She left the Old Brewery Inn and bought her own pub, the Fox, in 2000. Some 20 local outlets are supplied but brewing is low-key as most effort goes into running the inn.

Robin a Tiptoe (OG 1043, ABV 3.9%)

Cropped Oak (OG 1047, ABV 4.4%)

Coat O' Red (OG 1052, ABV 5%)

JOLLYBOAT

Jollyboat Brewery (Bideford) Ltd,
the Coach House, Buttgarden Street,
Bideford, Devon, EX39 2AU
Tel (01237) 424343
Tours by arrangement

⊠ The brewery, named after sailors' leave boats, was established in 1995 by Hugh Parry and his son Simon. The brewery went into receivership in 2000 but brewing didn't stop, and the new company is now in the sole hands of Hugh. It currently supplies some 50 local outlets. Seasonal beer: Contraband (ABV 5.8%, Nov-March). Bottle-conditioned beers: Privateer (ABV 4.8%), Contraband (ABV 5.8%).

Buccaneers (OG 1036, ABV 3.7%)
A pale brown summer bitter with a pleasant presence of hops and bitterness from the nose through to the aftertaste.

Freebooter (OG 1039, ABV 4%)

Mainbrace Bitter (OG 1041, ABV 4.2%) ◈
Pale brown brew with a rich fruity aroma and a bitter taste and aftertaste.

Plunder (OG 1046, ABV 4.8%) ⬚◈
A good balance of malt, hops and fruit are present on the aroma and palate of this red/brown-coloured beer with a bitter finish.

JOLLYBOAT BREWERY

JUWARDS

Juwards Brewery, Unit 14G,
Tonedale Business Park, Wellington,
Somerset, TA21 0AW
Tel (01823) 667909

⊠ A brewery founded in 1994 in an old woollen mill to produce 10 to 12 barrels a week maximum, using plant with a 6-barrel brew length. Trading started by going far and wide but is gradually becoming more localised: 14 outlets are supplied direct. A 10-barrel plant was bought in 1999 to increase production. Occasional/seasonal beers: Golden (ABV 4.2%), Winter Brew (ABV 4.3%).

Bitter (OG 1038, ABV 3.8%) ◈
Amber-coloured bitter, hoppy aroma, well-balanced malt and hops on the palate with hints of honey. Hoppy, bitter finish, again with honey notes.

Premium (OG 1044, ABV 4.3%) ◈
Full-bodied, mid-brown beer. Fruit and hops on the nose. Malt and fruit taste with fruity, hoppy finish.

KELHAM ISLAND

Kelham Island Brewery Ltd, 23 Alma Street,
Sheffield, S Yorkshire, S3 8SA
Tel (0114) 249 4804
Fax (0114) 249 4803
E-mail enquiries@kelhambrewery.co.uk
Website www.kelhambrewery.co.uk
Tours by arrangement

⊛ Kelham Island Brewery was formed in 1990 in the backyard of the Fat Cat pub. In 1999 the brewery moved 100 yards up the street to new, purpose-built premises capable of taking the company well into the 21st century. The old brewery site now houses a visitor centre; pre-arranged tours are welcome. 150 outlets are supplied direct.

Seasonal beers: Wheat Bier (ABV 5%, summer), Bete Noire (ABV 5.5%, winter), Grande Pale (ABV 6.6%, winter). Disappointingly, Kelham Island has discontinued its bottle-conditioned beers.

Bitter *(OG 1038, ABV 3.8%)* ☐◆
A clean, characterful, crisp, pale brown beer. The nose and palate are dominated by refreshing hoppiness and fruitiness, which, with a good bitter dryness, lasts in the aftertaste.

Easy Rider *(OG 1044.5, ABV 4.5%)* ◆
A pale, straw-coloured beer with a sweetish flavour and delicate hints of citrus fruits. A beer with hints of flavour rather than full-bodied.

Pride of Sheffield *(OG 1045, ABV 4.5%)*
A full-flavoured, amber-coloured, premium strength bitter.

Pale Rider *(OG 1052, ABV 5.2%)* ◆
A full-bodied, straw pale ale, with a good fruity aroma and a strong fruit and hop taste. Its well-balanced sweetness and bitterness continue in the finish.

KELTEK

Keltek Brewery, Unit 3A, Restormel Industrial Estate, Liddicoat Road, Lostwithiel, Cornwall, PL22 0HG
Tel/Fax (01208) 871199
Tours by arrangement

⊗ Keltek Brewery moved to Lostwithiel in 1999 and started brewing again in March of that year. Monthly specials and house beers for pubs are brewed. 50 outlets in Cornwall and North Devon are supplied direct. Seasonal/occasional beers: Olde Smugglers Ale (ABV 4.2%, September), Olde Pirates Ale (ABV 4.8%, March). Bottle-conditioned beers: King (ABV 5.1%), Revenge (ABV 7%).

4K Mild *(OG 1038, ABV 3.8%)*
Dark and fruity.

Golden Lance *(OG 1038, ABV 3.8%)*
Light golden, refreshing brew.

Magik *(OG 1042, ABV 4.2%)*
Good balance of malt and hops. Tawny red in colour.

King *(OG 1051, ABV 5.1%)*
A light brown beer with a bitter taste, then a sweetness through the middle.

Revenge *(OG 1066, ABV 7%)*
Dark ruby in colour; sweetish with a bitter edge.

KEMPTOWN

⌂ **Kemptown Brewery Co Ltd, 33 Upper St James's Street, Brighton, E Sussex, BN2 1JN**
Tel (01273) 699595   Fax (01273) 696483
E-mail kemptownbrewery@btinternet.com
Website www.kemptownbrewery.com
Tours by arrangement

⊗ Brewery established in 1989 and built in the tower tradition behind the Hand in Hand, which is possibly the smallest pub in England with its own brewery. It takes its name and logo from the former Charrington's Kemptown Brewery 500 yards

away, which closed in 1964. Six free trade outlets are supplied.

Black Moggy Mild *(ABV 3.6%)*

Brighton Bitter *(ABV 3.6%)* ◆
A refreshing, dry beer, with malt and hops in the flavour and a dry, hoppy finish.

Ye Old Trout Ale *(OG 1045, ABV 4.5%)*

Kemptown *(ABV 4%)*

SID/Staggering in the Dark *(ABV 5.2%)* ◆
A dark, almost black beer with a vinous nose and a complex flavour, with roast and bitterness giving way to a dry finish.

Old Grumpy *(ABV 6.2%)*

KING*

W J King & Co (Brewers), 3-5 Jubilee Estate, Foundry Lane, Horsham, W Sussex, RH13 5UE
Tel (01403) 272102
Fax (01403) 754455
E-mail sales@kingfamilybrewers.co.uk
Website www.kingfamilybrewers.co.uk

Bill King, former managing director of King & Barnes of Horsham, is back in business, using an ex-Firkin brew-pub kit that produces 20 barrels a week. Brewing started on 1 May 2001 and by June Bill had six accounts with local pubs. His former salesman at K&B is working for him and is clocking up six new accounts a week. Bill says his beers, in the Horsham fashion, are bitter and full-bodied, but he is not attempting to replicate the beers from his former brewery.

Horsham Best Bitter *(ABV 3.8%)*

Red River *(ABV 4.8%)*

KINGS HEAD

Kings Head Brewing Co, Kings Head, 132 High Street, Bildeston, Ipswich, Suffolk, IP7 7ED
Tel/Fax (01449) 741434
E-mail kingshead-brewery@yahoo.net

⊗ Kings Head has been brewing since 1996, originally as Brettvale Brewing Co. A 5-barrel plant is based in an old stable block behind the pub. Brewing takes places two or three times a week and six other outlets are supplied direct. Seasonal beers: Blondie (ABV 4%, summer), Crowdie (ABV 5%, winter).

Best Bitter *(OG 1037, ABV 3.8%)*

First Gold *(OG 1043, ABV 4.3%)*

Apache *(OG 1045, ABV 4.5%)*

Billy *(OG 1048, ABV 4.8%)*

Dark Vader *(OG 1054, ABV 5.4%)*
Champion beer Ipswich Beer Festival 1999. Best in class Ipswich Beer Festival 2000.

LAKELAND

Lakeland Brewing Company, 1 Sepulchre Lane, Kendal, Cumbria, LA9 4NJ
Tel/Fax (01539) 734528

Brewing suspended in 2001 but owner Nigel Stevenson hopes to re-start.

LANGTON

Langton Brewery,
Bell Inn, Main Street,
East Langton, Market Harborough,
Leicestershire, LE16 7TW
Tel (01858) 545278
Fax (01858) 545748
Website www.thebellinn.co.uk
Tours by arrangement

Langton is run by two partners, Alistair
Chapman and Derek Hewitt, publican and
customer respectively of the Bell Inn.
Hewitt is a retired banker who brought his
business experience to underscore
Chapman's knowledge of the pub trade.
They installed an existing 20-barrel brewing
plant in outbuildings of the 17th century
Bell. They now brew 90 gallons a time of
Caudle Bitter (named after the range of
local hills) and Bowler, which celebrates the
Bell Inn's long association with Langton
Cricket Club, whose ground is opposite the
inn. A third beer was added in 2000. The
beers are available for take-away in nine-
gallon casks or 10-litre polypins.

Caudle Bitter (OG 1038, ABV 3.9%)
A session bitter, close to a pale ale in style.

Bowler Strong Ale
(OG 1048, ABV 4.8%)
A strong traditional ale with a deep red
colour and a hoppy nose.

Boxer Heavyweight (OG 1053, ABV 5.2%)

LARKINS

Larkins Brewery Ltd, Larkins Farm,
Chiddingstone, Edenbridge, Kent, TN8 7BB
Tel (01892) 870328
Fax (01892) 871141
Tours by arrangement Nov-Feb

⊠ Larkins Brewery was founded in 1986 by
the Dockerty family, farmers and hop
growers, who bought the Royal Tunbridge
Wells Brewery. The company moved to
Larkins Farm in 1987. Since then
production of three regular brews and a
Porter in the winter months have steadily
increased. Brews are made using only
Kentish hops, yeast and malt; no sugars or
brewing adjuncts are added to the beers.
Larkins owns one pub, the Rock at
Chiddingstone Heath, and supplies around
70 free houses within a radius of 20 miles.

Traditional Ale (OG 1035, ABV 3.4%)
Tawny in colour, a full-tasting hoppy ale
with plenty of character for its strength.

Chiddingstone (OG 1040, ABV 4%)
Named after the village where the brewery
is based, Chiddingstone is a mid-strength,
hoppy/fruity ale with a long, bitter-sweet
aftertaste.

Best (OG 1045, ABV 4.4%) ◣
Full-bodied, slightly fruity and unusually
bitter for its gravity.

Porter (OG 1052, ABV 5.2%) ◣
Each taste and smell of this potent black
winter beer (Nov-April) reveals another facet
of its character. An explosion of roasted
malt, bitter and fruity flavours leaves a
bitter-sweet aftertaste.

LEADMILL

Leadmill Brewery Co, 118 Nottingham Road,
Selston, Nottingham, Notts, NG16 6BX
Tel 01773 819280/07971 189915 (m)

Leadmill was established by Richard
Creighton in February 1999, originally
using an 18-gallon home-brewing plant. A
2-barrel plant was installed in August of
that year, enabling five brews to be made
each week. Beer is currently brewed in a
converted pigsty behind a 200-year-old
cottage but Richard hopes to move to bigger
premises and is looking to base his brewery
in a pub. Approximately 40 outlets are
supplied direct.

Ingot (ABV 3.6%)

Wild Weasel (ABV 3.9%)

Arc-Light (ABV 4.2%)

Rolling Thunder (ABV 4.5%)

Linebacker (ABV 4.6%)

Red River (ABV 4.8%)

Agent Orange (ABV 4.9%)

Niagara (ABV 5%)

Sidewinder (ABV 5%)

Apocalypse Now (ABV 5.2%)

LEATHERBRITCHES

Leatherbritches Brewery, Bentley Brook,
Fenny Bentley, Ashbourne,
Derbyshire, DE6 1LF
Tel (01335) 350278 Fax (01335) 350422
E-mail all@bentleybrookinn.co.uk
Website www.bentleybrookinn.co.uk

⊛ Leatherbritches Brewery is housed behind
the Bentley Brook Inn, just north of
Ashbourne on the A515. The inn is owned
by David and Jeanne Allingham, with
brewing conducted by David Corby.
Launched in 1994, the brewery now
produces 10 barrels a week and supplies
approximately 30-35 local outlets.
Leatherbritches no longer brews for the
Steamin' Billy Company (qv).

Goldings (OG 1036, ABV 3.6%)
A light hoppy session beer with a fruity
finish.

Ashbourne Ale (OG 1040, ABV 4%)
Bitter with fruity hints from fresh Goldings
hops with a crisp lasting taste.

Hairy Helmet (OG 1047, ABV 4.7%)

Bespoke (OG 1050, ABV 5%)
Mid-brown in colour, with a well-balanced sweet finish. Full bodied.

LEES

**J W Lees & Co (Brewers) Ltd,
Greengate Brewery, Middleton Junction,
Manchester, M24 2AX
Tel (0161) 643 2487
Fax (0161) 655 3731
Website www.jwlees.co.uk**
Tours by arrangement

☺ Family-owned brewery founded in 1828 by John Willie Lees and now employing sixth-generation family members. In 1995 Lees took on its first full-time cooper for almost 30 years (half its cask beer is still delivered in traditional oak casks). All the brewery's 175 pubs (most in north Manchester) serve real ale, which is also supplied to 150 other outlets direct. Seasonal beers: Archer Stout (March-April), Fudger Ale (May-June), Scorcher (July-Aug), Sloeberry Ale (Sept-Oct), MM (Nov-Dec).

GB Mild (OG 1032, ABV 3.5%) ◈
Malty and fruity in aroma. The same flavours are found in the taste, but do not dominate in a beer with a rounded and smooth character. Dry, malty aftertaste.

Bitter (OG 1037, ABV 4%) ◈
A pale beer with a malty, fruity aroma and a distinctive, malty, dry and slightly metallic taste. Clean, dry Lees finish.

Moonraker (OG 1073, ABV 7.5%) ⬡◈
A reddish-brown beer with a strong, malty, fruity aroma. The flavour is rich and sweet, with roast malt, and the finish is fruity yet dry. Available only in a handful of outlets.

LEITH HILL

⬡ **Leith Hill Brewery, c/o Plough Inn,
Coldharbour, nr Dorking,
Surrey, RH5 6HD
Tel (01306) 711793
Fax (01306) 710055
E-mail the_plough@btinternet.com
Website www.ploughinn.com**

Brewing started in a room at the side of the pub in 1996 and grew to a 1-barrel capacity. Brewing moved to a new, purpose-built brewery alongside the pub in August 2001 with a 2.5-barrel plant. New beers may be added.

Crooked Furrow (OG 1040, ABV 4%)
Well-rounded and fruity best bitter. English hops give a hint of cinnamon.

Tallywhacker (OG 1056, ABV 5.6%)
Strong dark ale with subtle overtones of barley.

LEYDEN

⬡ **Leyden Brewery, Lord Raglan, Nangreaves,
Bury, Lancs, BL9 6SP
Tel (0161) 764 6680**
Tours by arrangement

Brewery built by Brian Farnworth that started production in 1999. Additional fermenting vessels have been installed,

allowing a maximum production of 12 barrels a week. One pub is owned.

Nanny Flyer (ABV 3.8%)
A drinkable session bitter with an initial dryness, a hint of citrus, followed by a strong, malty finish.

Black Beard (ABV 3.9%)
A dark, creamy beer, brewed using oats and roasted malts.

Light Brigade (ABV 4.2%) ◈
Copper in colour with a citrus aroma. The flavour is a balance of malt, hops and fruit, with a bitter finish.

Raglan Sleeve (ABV 4.6%) ◈
Dark red/brown beer with a hoppy aroma and a dry, roasty, hoppy taste and finish.

Heavy Brigade (ABV 4.7%)
A traditional strong bitter beer, pale colour, with malt and a touch of bitterness coming through in the finish.

LICHFIELD

**Lichfield Brewery, John Thompson Inn,
Ingleby, Derbyshire, DE7 1HW
Tel (01332) 863033
Fax (01283) 712438**
Tours by arrangement

Lichfield Brewery moved to its present premises in 1998 and shares them with Lloyds Country Beers (qv). The beers are fermented in separate areas and have their own characteristics; in Lichfield's case, fruity and hoppy constitute the house style. The brewery continues to develop both its trading area and its beer range, with agencies or direct delivery. One-off brews supplement the regular and seasonal range, using an ever-wider selection of hops and malt blends. About 200 outlets are supplied. Seasonal/occasional beers: Steeplechase (ABV 3.7%, summer), Sheriff's Ride (ABV 4.2%, autumn), Resurrection (ABV 4.3%, spring), Happy New Beer (ABV 4.7%, New Year), Cavalier (OG 1047, ABV 4.7%), Hoppy Christmas (ABV 4.7%), Mincespired (ABV 5.8%, Christmas).

Inspired (OG 1040, ABV 4%) ◈
Dark brown malty beer with hops and some fruit aroma, and a bitter finish.

Steeplejack (OG 1045, ABV 4.5%) ◈
Pale brown, with a distinct aroma of malt and hops, tingles the palate and leaves a pleasant dry finish.

Gargoyle (OG 1050, ABV 5%)
Full-bodied and fruity, it has a powerful bitterness that belies its gravity.

LIDSTONES

**Lidstones Brewery, Coltsfoot Green,
Wickhambrook, Newmarket, Suffolk,
CB8 8UW
Tel (01440) 820232: brewery;
(01223) 701283: pub/fax
E-mail jane.fairhall@ntlworld.com**
Tours by arrangement

Lidstones was founded by Peter Fairhall in 1998. Formerly a partner in a law firm in Cambridge, he set up a 2-barrel plant in Wickhambrook. His sister Jane joined the business in 1999 to run sales and administration. In 2000 they took over the Kingston Arms in Cambridge and plan to install a brew plant in the cellar.

Rowley Mild *(ABV 3.4%)* ◀
Chocolate and toffee aromas lead into what, for its strength, is an impressively rich and flavoursome ale. The finish is pleasantly bitter-sweet.

Session Bitter *(ABV 3.7%)* ◀
Intensely aromatic, straw-coloured ale offering a superb balance of malt and hops on the tongue; an ideal session beer by any standards.

Lucky Punter *(ABV 4.1%)* ◀
Golden ale with a hint of banana on the nose. The taste is clean, crisp and moreishly hoppy, with grapefruit flavours also present.

Best Bitter *(ABV 4.3%)*
A light hoppy golden beer.

Colquhoun's Dark Mischief Stout
(ABV 4.5%) ◀
Less full-bodied than many stouts, this has a dry, burnt roast and coffee flavour, and a long, bitter follow-through.

Rawalpindi IPA *(ABV 5%)* ◀
Citrus flavours dominate both aroma and taste in this pale, smooth, refreshing beer; the aftertaste is quite dry.

Old Ale *(ABV 6.%)* ◀
Heavy, complex ale, mixing sweet and roasty flavours in intriguing fashion. The fruit-and-nut finish has some bitterness attached.

LINFIT

⚲ **Linfit Brewery, Sair Inn,**
139 Lane Top, Linthwaite, Huddersfield,
W Yorkshire, HD7 5SG
Tel (01484) 842370
Tours by arrangement

⊛ A 19th-century brew-pub that started brewing again in 1982, producing an impressive range of ales for sale at the pub and in the free trade as far away as Manchester (27 regular outlets). New plant installed in 1994 has almost doubled capacity. Occasional/seasonal beers: Smoke House Ale (ABV 5.3%), Springbok Bier (ABV 5.7%), Xmas Ale (ABV 8.6%), Ginger Beer (ABV 4.2%), Janet Street Porter (ABV 4.5%). Dark Mild and English Guineas Stout are suitable for vegetarians and vegans as isinglass finings are not used in their production.

Dark Mild *(OG 1032, ABV 3%)* ◀
Roast grain dominates this straightforward dark mild, which has some hops in the aroma and a slightly dry flavour. Malty finish.

Bitter *(OG 1035, ABV 3.7%)* ◀
A refreshing session beer. A dry-hopped aroma leads to a clean-tasting, hoppy bitterness, then a long, bitter finish with a hint of malt.

Cascade *(OG 1038, ABV 4%)*

Gold Medal *(OG 1040, ABV 4.2%)*

Special *(OG 1041, ABV 4.3%)* ◀
Dry-hopping provides the aroma for this rich and mellow bitter, which has a very soft profile and character: it fills the mouth with texture rather than taste. Clean, rounded finish.

Autumn Gold *(OG 1045, ABV 4.7%)* ◀
Straw-coloured best bitter with hop and fruit aromas, then the bitter-sweetness of autumn fruit in the taste and the finish.

English Guineas Stout
(OG 1050, ABV 5.3%) ◀
A fruity, roast aroma preludes a smooth, roasted barley, chocolatey flavour that is bitter but not too dry. Excellent appearance; good, bitter finish.

Old Eli *(OG 1050, ABV 5.3%)*
A well-balanced premium bitter with a dry-hopped aroma and a fruity, bitter finish.

Leadboiler *(OG 1060, ABV 6.6%)* ◀
Powerful malt, hop and fruit in good balance on the tongue, with a well-rounded bitter sweet finish.

Enoch's Hammer *(OG 1075, ABV 8%)* ◀
A straw-coloured beer with malt, hop and fruit aromas. Mouth-filling, smooth malt, hop and fruit flavours with a long, hoppy bitter finish. Dangerously drinkable.

LIVERPOOL

⚲ **Liverpool Brewing Company, The Brewery,**
21-23 Berry Street, Liverpool, L1 9DF
Tel (0151) 709 5055
Tours by arrangement

⊛ Brew-pub with a 5-barrel plant set up in 1990 to brew solely for the Black Horse & Rainbow pub, renamed The Brewery in 1996. Seasonal beers are available and bottle-conditioned beers are planned. Six pubs are owned with four serving cask-conditioned beer. Six outlets are supplied direct.

Berry Street Mild *(ABV 3.4%)*

Young Stallion *(OG 1038, ABV 3.6%)*

Red *(OG 1040, ABV 3.8%)*

Blondie *(OG 1044, ABV 4.1%)*

First Gold *(OG 1044, ABV 4.2%)*

Rocket *(OG 1045, ABV 4.3%)*

Berry Street Bitter *(ABV 4.5%)*

Devil in Disguise *(ABV 4.8%)*

Celebration *(OG 1050, ABV 4.8%)*

LLOYDS

Lloyds Country Beers Ltd, John Thompson Brewery, Ingleby, Derbyshire, DE73 1HW
Tel (01332) 863426
Tours by arrangement

⊠ Lloyds is the separate business set up to sell the beers brewed at the John Thompson Inn (qv) to the free trade. It supplies around 300 outlets nationwide. Demand for Vixen Porter has grown to such an extent that it has moved from winter to regular production, and is the base for several flavoured porters. Lloyds also brews for the High Peak Brewery until suitable premises are found for that company.

Derby Bitter or JTS XXX
(OG 1042, ABV 4.1%)
Full and fruity.

IPA (Ingleby Pale Ale)
(OG 1045, ABV 4.5%)

Scratching Dog *(OG 1045, ABV 4.5%)*

Vixen Velvet *(OG 1045, ABV 4.5%)*

Little Nipper *(OG 1048, ABV 4.7%)*

For High Peak:

Original Bitter *(ABV 4.2%)*

Original Gold *(ABV 4.3%)*

Original Porter *(ABV 4.5%)*

LORD RAGLAN*

◻ **Lord Raglan, High Street, Cefn-Coed,
Merthyr Tydfil, Mid-Glamorgan, CF48 2PN
Tel (01685) 721445**

Brewing started in January 2000. The plant, based in the pub, can produce just 1 barrel at a time. There are plans to move to bigger premises and to supply other outlets.

Ale *(ABV 4.1%)*

McGUINNESS

**Thomas McGuinness Brewing Co,
Cask & Feather, 1 Oldham Road,
Rochdale, Lancs, OL16 1UA
Tel (01706) 711476
Fax (01706) 669654
Website www.mcguinnessbrewery.com**
Tours by arrangement

McGuinness opened in 1991 and now averages 15-20 barrels a week. It supplies real ale to its own pub and several other outlets direct. Seasonal beer: Dark (ABV 4.6%).

Feather Plucker Mild *(ABV 3.4%)* ◆
A dark brown beer, with roast malt dominant in the aroma and taste, with hints of chocolate. Satisfying bitter and roast finish.

Best Bitter *(ABV 3.8%)*
Gold in colour with a hoppy aroma: a clean, refreshing beer with hop and fruit tastes and a hint of sweetness. Bitter aftertaste.

Special Reserve Bitter or SRB *(ABV 4%)* ◆
A tawny beer, sweet and malty, with underlying fruit and bitterness, and a bitter-sweet aftertaste.

Junction Bitter *(ABV 4.2%)* ◆
Mid-brown in colour, with a malty aroma. Maltiness is predominant throughout, with some hops and fruit in the taste and bitterness coming through in the finish.

Tommy Todd's Porter *(ABV 5%)* ⬚◆
A winter warmer, with a fruit and roast aroma, leading to a balance of malt and roast malt flavours, with some fruit. Not too sweet for its gravity.

McMULLEN

**McMullen & Sons Ltd, 26 Old Cross,
Hertford, SG14 1RD
Tel (01992) 584911
Fax (01992) 500729
Website www.breworld.com/mcmullen**
Tours by arrangement

⊗ Hertfordshire's oldest independent brewery, founded in 1827 by Peter McMullen. While the original brewery building of 1890 still stands, brewing is now undertaken in a new brewhouse built in 1984. Brewing 'liquor' (water) is still drawn from three deep artesian wells. Cask ale is served in all McMullen's 135 pubs in Hertfordshire, Essex and London (although all managed houses use cask breathers on all beers), and also supplies direct to 60 free trade outlets. Seasonal beers are brewed for a limited period under the banner of McMullen Special Reserve at ABV 5%. The award-winning Stronghart winter ale has not been brewed since 1997.

Original AK *(OG 1034, ABV 3.7%)* ◆
A pleasant mix of malt and hops leads to a distinctive, dry aftertaste that isn't always as pronounced as it used to be.

Country Best Bitter
(OG 1042, ABV 4.3%) ◆
A full-bodied beer with a well-balanced mix of malt, hops and fruit throughout.

Gladstone *(OG 1042, ABV 4.3%)* ◆
Amber-coloured beer. A mix of malt, hops and fruit in the aroma and taste lead to a dryish finish.

MALLARD

**Mallard Brewery, 15 Hartington Avenue,
Carlton, Nottingham, NG4 3NR
Tel/Fax (0115) 952 1289
E-mail phil@mallard-brewery.co.uk
Website www.mallard-brewery.co.uk**
Tours by arrangement (small groups)

⊗ Phil Mallard started brewing in 1973 as a home brewer with Boots beer kits, and by 1988 had graduated to a full mash and whole hop brew. In 1994, with the encouragement of his wife, Gill, they decided to try commercial brewing from a shed at the back of their house. He built and installed a 2-barrel plant and started brewing in 1995. The brewery is a mere nine square metres and contains a hot liquor tank, mash tun, copper, and three fermenters. The brewery was launched at the Nottingham Beer Festival in 1995. Since then production has risen from one barrel a week to between six or eight barrels, which is the plant's maximum. Phil has no plans at present to expand and now supplies around 40 outlets, of which seven are on a regular weekly basis. He has also launched a small-scale bottling enterprise and plans to produce bottled beers as limited editions supplied direct from the brewery by mail order. Seasonal beer: DA (ABV 5.8%, winter), Quismas Quacker (ABV 6%, Christmas). Bottle-conditioned beers: Owd Duck, Friar Duck, DA, Quismas Quacker, Duckling, Drake, Duckdown Stout, Spittin' Feathers, Waddlers Mild, Duck & Dive. Occasional beers: Owd Duck (ABV 4.8%), Duckdown Stout (ABV 4.6%), Spittin' Feathers (ABV 4.4%).

Waddlers Mild *(OG 1039, ABV 3.7%)*
A dark ruby mild with a fruity chocolate flavour in the mouth and a fruity finish.

Duck & Dive *(OG 1037, ABV 3.7%)*
A light single-hopped beer made from the hedgerow hop, First Gold. A bitter beer with a hoppy nose, good bitterness on the palate and a dry finish.

Best Bitter *(OG 1038, ABV 4%)* ◈
Golden brown, fruity and hoppy to the nose, with malt more apparent in the taste than anywhere else. The fruity hop carries through to a bitter, dry finish.

Duckling *(OG 1039, ABV 4.2%)*
A crisp refreshing bitter with a hint of honey and citrus flavour. Dry hopped.

Spittin' Feathers *(OG 1043, ABV 4.4%)*
A mellow, ruby bitter with a complex malt flavour of chocolate, toffee and coffee, complemented with a full and fruity/hoppy aftertaste.

Drake *(OG 1044, ABV 4.5%)*
A full-bodied premium bitter, with malt and hops on the palate, and a fruity finish.

Friar Duck *(OG 1047, ABV 5%)*
A pale full malt beer, hoppy with a hint of blackcurrant flavour.

MALTON

Malton Brewery Company Ltd, 12 Wheelgate, Malton, N Yorkshire, YO17 7HP
Tel (01653) 697580
Fax (01653) 691812
E-mail suddaby@crownhotel.plus.com
Tours by arrangement

☺ The Malton Brewery Company was founded in the stable block at the rear of the Crown Hotel, Wheelgate, Malton in 1984. The managing director is Neil Suddaby, who is also licensee of the hotel with Alan Brayshaw as brewer. Seasonal beers: Ryedale Champion (ABV 4.5%), Crown Bitter (ABV 4.5%), Auld Bob (ABV 6%), Pickwick's Porter (ABV 4.2%).

Double Chance *(OG 1038, ABV 3.8%)* ◈
A clean-tasting, amber bitter in which hops predominate. Little malt character, but hop and fruit flavours lead to a smooth, bitter finish.

Golden Chance *(OG 1039, ABV 4.2%)*
Golden coloured bitter with a complex hoppy finish. Two distinct varieties of hops combine with English malts to make this mid-strength bitter distinctive and quaffable.

Crown Inn Glory *(OG 1041, ABV 4.3%)*
Using Maris Otter malt and rye crystal, Bramling Cross, Challenger and Goldings hops to produce a slightly dry beer with a touch of bitterness and a fruity aroma.

Ryedale Champion *(OG 1044, ABV 4.5%)*
A combination of three different types of hops in this dark-coloured, biscuity-flavoured premium brew leads to an unusual satisfying finish.

Dog Breath *(OG 1049, ABV 4.9%)*
Strong, dark bitter, hoppy and rich.

Young Bob *(OG 1050, ABV 5.2%)*
Full-bodied, russet-coloured, deceptively strong bitter. Well hopped with a malty bouquet but with a dry, fruity aftertaste.

MALVERN HILLS

Malvern Hills Brewery Ltd, 15 West Malvern Road, Great Malvern, Worcestershire, WR14 4ND
Tel (01684) 560165

Fax (01684) 577336
E-mail MHB.ales@tesco.net
Website www.malvernhillsbrewery.co.uk

A 9-barrel capacity brewery opened in a former explosive store in a disused quarry in North Malvern. Local free trade and wholesalers are being supplied. A spring beer and a bottled beer are planned. Seasonal beer: Worcestershire Whym (ABV 4.2%).

Bitter *(OG 1039, ABV 3.9%)* ◈
A dainty blend of hops and malts leaves a strong bitter aftertaste.

Black Pear *(OG 1044, ABV 4.4%)* ◈
A complex array of flavours including an acidic fruitiness as well as a cereal maltiness make this an absorbing drink.

Dr Gully's Winter Ale
(OG 1052, ABV 5.2%) ◈
Rich, velvety malt flavours prevail in this classic winter warmer, leaving a warm satisfying aftertaste.

MANSFIELD

Mansfield Brewery PLC, Littleworth, Mansfield, Nottinghamshire, NG18 1AB. A subsidiary of Wolverhampton & Dudley Breweries.
Tel (01623) 625691
Fax (01623) 658620
Website www.mansfield-brewery.co.uk
Tours by arrangement

☺ Founded in 1855, Mansfield was bought by Wolverhampton & Dudley Breweries (qv) in 1999 and its future was placed in doubt as a struggle for ownership of the parent group intensified in 2001. A management buy-out collapsed in August 2001; the brewery will close, with its brands transferred to Banks's. Mansfield made a welcome return to cask ale production in 1982 after a break of 10 years. The purchase of Hull's North Country Brewery in 1985 and subsequent sizeable pub acquisitions have helped to bring Mansfield's award-winning ales, all fermented in traditional Yorkshire Squares, to a wider audience.

Dark Mild *(OG 1035, ABV 3.5%)* ◈
Chocolate malt on the nose leads to blackcurrant fruit on the taste, with hops finishing. The chocolate malt character continues throughout this ruby-black beer.

Riding Bitter *(OG 1035, ABV 3.6%)* ◈
Mid-brown and moderately bitter, it is dominated by an aromatic, fruity hop, but with malt always present.

Cask Ale *(OG 1038, ABV 3.9%)* ◈
This mid-brown bitter is well-balanced in taste but has hops to the fore on the nose and malt lingering in the aftertaste, although some bitterness is discernible.

For Scottish Courage:

Matthew Brown Lion Bitter
(OG 1034, ABV 3.5%)

Wilson's Original Bitter
(OG 1035, ABV 3.5%)

MARBLE

⌂ **Marble Brewery, 73 Rochdale Road, Manchester, M4 4HY**

Tel/Fax (0161) 610 1073
E-mail vance@marblebeers.co.uk
Website www.marblebeers.co.uk
Tours by arrangement

Opened in 1997, the brewery now produces beers made with organic malt and hops, and GM-free yeast. The beers are suitable for vegetarians and vegans: the brewery is registered with the Soil Association and the Vegetarian Society. There are plans to bottle Old Lag and Chocolate Heavy.

Chorlton-cum-Hazy *(OG 1038, ABV 3.8%)*
A classic dry northern bitter with a refreshing bitterness and light fruit character set in an organic malt base.

N/4 Bitter *(OG 1038, ABV 3.8%)* ◆
This golden amber beer has a shy nose with some hops and fruit, a fresh hoppy palate, and a short, dry aftertaste.

Cloudy Marble *(OG 1040, ABV 4%)* ◆
Amber in colour, with a hoppy/fruity nose. Hops, fruit and bitterness in the mouth, with quite a strong bitter finish.

Uncut Amber *(OG 1047, ABV 4.7%)* ◆
Red/brown beer with malt, coffee and fruit in the aroma. It has dark chocolate, malt and fruit on the palate, with a dry, roast finish.

The Old Lag *(OG 1050, ABV 5%)* ◆
Copper-coloured beer with a fruity and hoppy aroma. The flavour is a balance of malt, fruit and hops with a good bitter aftertaste.

Chocolate Heavy *(OG 1055, ABV 5.5%)* ◆
Black in colour; chocolate, roast malt and fruit nose. A smooth chocolatey, roasty bitter taste with hops and fruit also in evidence. Dry, roast, hoppy finish.

MARCHES

Marches Ales, Unit 6, Western Close, Southern Avenue Industrial Estate, Leominster, Herefordshire, HR6 0QD Tel (01568) 610063

⊗ Plans to expand the brewery in 2001 had to be put on hold as a result of foot-and-mouth disease in the locality, which meant that engineers could not get on to the site. The owners hoped that brewing would start again by the autumn of 2001.

MARSTON MOOR

Marston Moor Brewery, Crown House, Kirk Hammerton, York, YO26 8DD Tel/Fax (01423) 330341 E-mail marston.moor.brewery@ic24.net

☺ Small brewery set up in 1983: its beers are now brewed by Rudgate (qv).

Cromwell Bitter *(OG 1036-38, ABV 3.6%)* ◆
A golden beer with hops and fruit in strong evidence on the nose. Bitterness as well as fruit and hops dominate the taste and long aftertaste.

Prince Rupert Mild *(OG 1039-40, ABV 4%)*

Pilsener *(OG 1039-40, ABV 4%)*

Brewers Pride *(OG 1040-42, ABV 4.2%)* ◆
A light but somewhat thin, fruity beer, with a hoppy, bitter aftertaste.

Merriemaker *(OG 1044-46, ABV 4.5%)*

Brewers Droop *(OG 1048-50, ABV 5%)*
A pale, robust ale with hops and fruit notes in prominence. A long, bitter aftertaste.

Trooper *(OG 1048-50, ABV 5%)*

MARSTON'S

Marston, Thompson & Evershed PLC, The Brewery, Shobnall Road, Burton upon Trent, Staffs, DE14 2BW. A subsidiary of Wolverhampton & Dudley Breweries. Tel (01283) 531131 Fax (01283) 510378 Website www.breworld.com/marstons Shop 10-3 Mon-Fri; 9.30-12 Sat
Tours by arrangement, ring (01283) 507391

☺ Marston's was bought by Wolverhampton & Dudley Breweries in 1999, and in August 2001 W & D pledged to keep the brewery in full production. Marston's is the only brewery still using the Burton Union system of fermentation for Pedigree Bitter, with yeast propagated in the unions used for all other brews. Marston's reinforced its commitment to this method in 1992 with a £1 million investment in a new union room. Real ale is available throughout the Marston's estate, which stretches from Hampshire to Yorkshire. Marston's also enjoys a large free trade, thanks to many regional and national brewers. The programme of seasonal and occasional beers is uncertain at present.

Bitter *(OG 1038, ABV 4%)* ◆
An amber/tawny session beer that can often be sulphury in aroma and taste. At its best, a splendid, subtle balance of malt, hops and fruit follows a faintly hoppy aroma and develops into a balanced, dry aftertaste.

Pedigree *(OG 1043, ABV 4.5%)* ◆
Sulphurous aroma gives way to hops. Tastes hoppy and fruity, and leaves a bitter aftertaste. The classic Burton pale ale.

Owd Rodger *(OG 1080, ABV 7.6%)* ⬠◆
Strong, dark red, fruity barley wine. Sweet start with a liquorice character develops into fruit and hops, and finishes with a spicy, dry, lingering aftertaste. Now only brewed by special arrangement.

MASH

⬠ **Mash Ltd, 19/21 Great Portland Street, London, W1N 5DB Tel (0171) 637 5555 Fax (0171) 637 7333**

Brew-restaurant. The in-house brewery produces international beer styles on a rotation basis, including a Blackcurrant Porter, Scotch, IPA, Peach, Extra Stout and Pils. The beers are stored in cellar tanks using a CO2 system. Regular beer: Mash Wheat (ABV 5.2%).

MAULDONS

Mauldons Brewery Ltd, 7 Addison Road, Chilton Industrial Estate, Sudbury, Suffolk, CO10 2YW Tel/Fax (01787) 311055

E-mail sims@mauldons.co.uk
Website www.mauldons.co.uk
Tours by arrangement

☒ The company was bought by Steve and Alison Sims in 2000 from founder Peter Mauldon. Steve is a former sales manager with Adnams. Using traditional methods and quality materials, Mauldons supplies ales throughout East Anglia. There are plans to purchase a brew-pub. Seasonal beers: May Bee (ABV 3.7%, May), Bah Humbug (ABV 4.9%, Christmas), Christmas Reserve (ABV 6.6%), Midsummer Gold (ABV 4%), Mid Autumn Gold (ABV 4.2%), Midwinter Gold (ABV 4.5%), Cuckoo (ABV 4.3%), Three Lions (ABV 3.7%), Ploughmans (ABV 4.3%), Peggotty's Porter (ABV 4.1%), Eatanswill Old (ABV 4%). There is also a large number of occasional and one-off brews.

Moletrap Bitter (OG 1037.8, ABV 3.8%) ◥
A well-balanced session beer with a crisp, hoppy bitterness balancing sweet malt.

Dickens (OG 1039.8, ABV 4%)
A light-coloured bitter with a fine distinctive hop nose, and a refreshingly dry, fruity finish.

Pickwick (OG 1042, ABV 4.2%)
A best bitter with a rich rounded malt flavour with ripe aromas of hops and fruit. A bitter-sweet finish.

Suffolk Pride (OG 1048.8, ABV 4.8%) ◥
A full-bodied strong bitter. The malt and fruit in the aroma are reflected in the taste, and there is some hop character in the finish. Deep tawny/red in colour.

Black Adder (OG 1053.8, ABV 5.3%) ◥
A dark stout. Roast malt is strong in the aroma and taste, but malt, hop and bitterness provide an excellent balance and a lingering finish.

White Adder (OG 1053.8, ABV 5.3%) ◥
A pale brown, almost golden, strong ale. A warming, fruity flavour dominates and lingers into a dry, hoppy finish.

Suffolk Comfort (OG 1065.8, ABV 6.6%)
A clean, hoppy nose leads to a predominantly malty flavour in this full-bodied beer. Dry, hoppy aftertaste.

MAYPOLE

Maypole Brewery, North Laithes Farm, Wellow Road, Eakring, Newark, Notts, NG22 0AN
Tel (01623) 871690
Tours by prior arrangement on Friday evenings

☒ The brewery was set up in 1995 in an 18th-century converted farm building. Its name comes from the permanent giant maypole that is a feature of neighbouring Wellow. One beer, Lion's Pride (ABV 3.9%), is brewed just for the Olde Red Lion opposite the maypole. Several Maypole beers are sold under the Bees and Knees badge at the Beehive in Maplebeck, Notts. The brewery currently supplies around 40 outlets on an occasional basis, and also brews one-off beers for festivals and other events. Seasonal/occasional beers: May Day ABV 4.5%), Flanagans Stout (ABV 4.4%), Old Homewrecker (ABV 4.7%), Donner and Blitzed (ABV 5.1%, Christmas).

Mayfair (OG 1037, ABV 3.8%)
A golden-coloured beer with a bitter hop taste balanced by sweet maltiness, with a long bitter finish.

Lion's Pride (OG 1038, ABV 3.9%)
A tawny brown beer with a malty aroma and taste. Fruity hop bitterness comes through in the finish.

Celebration (OG 1040, ABV 4%) ◥
A ruddy-brown bitter in which malt dominates. Some fruity hop in the nose and taste, with an initial sweetness that dries into a bitter finish where the fruit and hops meet the malt.

Centenary Ale (OG 1041, ABV 4.2%)
A light-coloured bitter with a fruity nose and a dry aftertaste. There are hints of vanilla in this crisp, refreshing, full-bodied beer.

Loxley (OG 1041, ABV 4.2%)
A new golden ale launched to reflect the brewery's proximity to Robin Hood country. The Robin Hood (aka Sir Robin of Loxley) theme may be developed with further beers.

Mae West (OG 1044, ABV 4.6%)
A blonde, Belgian-style beer made with a single varietal hop. Citrus flavours predominate in the nose and taste. A deceptively drinkable beer for its strength.

Poleaxed (OG 1046, ABV 4.8%)
A tawny, smooth beer. Damsons come out in the nose and taste, which give way to a slightly burnt aftertaste. A full-bodied, warming beer.

MEANTIME

Meantime Brewing Co, 2 Penhall Road, Greenwich, London, SE7 8RX
Tel (020) 8293 1111
E-mail sales@mean-time.co.uk
Website www.mean-time.co.uk

A specialist brewery run by Alastair Hook, formerly of Freedom and Mash. He brews bespoke classic beer styles for customers with their own labels and concentrates on cold-fermented lagers and warm-fermented Bavarian-style wheat beers. He also produces bottle-conditioned beers for own-label sales. He plans his own range of classic lagers, such as a Vienna Red.

MIGHTY OAK

Mighty Oak Brewing Company Ltd, Units 14A & 14B, West Station Industrial Estate, Spital Road, Maldon, Essex, CM9 6TW
Tel (01621) 843713
E-mail moakbrew@aol.com
Tours for evening group visits only

☒ Founded in 1996 by former Ind Coope Romford brewer John Boyce, Mighty Oak has increased capacity three times in five years. In 2001, the brewery moved to its own premises in Maldon, doubling brewing capacity to 60 barrels a week. It is brewery policy not to sell via wholesalers, but beers are swapped with other independent brewers. Burntwood Bitter was Champion Beer of East Anglia in 1999, Champion Beer of Britain finalist 1999 and 2000. The brewery has some 200 customers in Essex, Suffolk, Herts, Kent, Wiltshire, Somerset and Gloucestershire. Seasonal beers: Brass Monkey (ABV 4.1%, Nov-March), Oscar Wilde Mild (ABV 3.7%, Jan, April-May, Aug-Sept, Nov), Ale Dancer (ABV 4.2%, April-June), Saffron Gold (ABV 4.3%, July-Oct), Spice (ABV 7%, winter).

IPA *(OG 1035, ABV 3.6%)*
Brewed using Maris Otter pale and crystal malts to produce a light amber beer that has a fullness of flavour unexpected in a beer of its strength. Golding hops produce a generous, but not overpowering, bitterness.

Burntwood Bitter *(OG 1040, ABV 4%)* 🍺
Full-flavoured tawny best bitter with malt and balancing hops, and a dryish finish.

Simply The Best *(OG 1043, ABV 4.4%)*
A tawny, full-bodied best bitter with a light balance of malt and hops, and a bitter-sweet finish.

Essex County Ale *(OG 1045, ABV 4.6%)*
Brewed using Maris Otter pale, crystal and chocolate malts to produce a rich copper-coloured premium beer. Well-balanced with a generous bitterness from Challenger and Progress hops following its underlying maltiness.

Mighty Oak Bitter *(OG 1047, ABV 4.8%)*
A rich, dark amber premium ale. Brewed with Maris Otter pale, crystal and chocolate malts, and Challenger and Fuggles hops, Mighty Oak has a balanced bitterness that does not dominate this full-flavoured, well-rounded ale.

MILK STREET

Milk Street Brewery, The Griffin,
25 Milk Street, Frome, BA11 3DB
Tel (01373) 467766
Website www.milkstreetbrewery.co.uk
Tours by arrangement

The brewery was commissioned in September 1999 and capacity is 20 barrels a week. Three beers are currently brewed with seasonal beers produced every two months. The brewery was designed by Rik Lyall using his experience gained as head brewer for Bunce's, Hop Back and Cotleigh breweries. 22 outlets are supplied direct.

Nature *(OG 1038, ABV 3.8%)*

Funky Monkey *(OG 1040, ABV 4%)*

Nick's *(OG 1044, ABV 4.4%)*

Zig-Zag *(OG 1045, ABV 4.5%)*

Beer *(OG 1050, ABV 5%)*

MILLERS THUMB

🏠 **Millers Thumb Brewing Co,**
t/a The Canal, 380 Bearsden Road,
Anniesland, Glasgow, G13 1EP
Tel (0141) 954 5333 Fax (0141) 954 5533
E-mail canal@bibbeat.co.uk
Website www.millersthumb.com
Shop open as bar. Tours by arrangement

American-style brew restaurant; the beers are filtered and carbonated. Seasonal beer: Molecatchers Ale (ABV 4.2%). Beers: Lighthouse Ale (ABV 3.2%), Black Canyon (ABV 3.9%), Red Brooster (ABV 4.1%), Thumb Blonde (ABV 4.5%), Independence Ale (ABV 4.8%), Woodcutters IPA (ABV 5.3%).

MILTON

Milton Brewery, Cambridge Ltd,
Unit 111, Norman Industrial Estate,
Cambridge Road, Milton, Cambs, CB4 6AT
Tel (01223) 226198 Fax (01223) 226199
E-mail enquiries@miltonbrewery.co.uk
Website www.miltonbrewery.co.uk
Tours by arrangement

Founded in 1999, the Milton Brewery grew rapidly and now supplies more than 100 pubs in Cambridge and beyond. It has a 15-barrel brew length; further expansion is envisaged, including the purchase of pubs. Seasonal beers: Pyramid (ABV 4.4%, May-July), Artemis (ABV 3.7%, July-Aug), Babylon (ABV 4.4%, Aug-Sept), Zeus (ABV 4.2%, Sept-Oct), Pharos (ABV 4.7%, Oct-Nov), Colossus (ABV 5.6%, Nov-Jan), Mammon (ABV 7%, December).

Minotaur *(OG 1035, ABV 3.3%)* 🍃
Rich and very full-bodied for its strength, a malty chocolateyness predominates, but vanilla and liquorice flavours also surface.

Jupiter *(OG 1037, ABV 3.5%)* 🍃
Golden session beer whose delicately hoppy flavour leads to a satisfying bitter finish.

Neptune *(OG 1039, ABV 3.8%)* 🍃
Delicious hop aromas introduce this well-balanced, nutty and refreshing copper-coloured ale. Good hoppy finish.

Pegasus *(OG 1043, ABV 4.1%)* 🍃
Hops dominate the first impression of this majestic ale, but the long, fruity/toffee finish shows that this is anything but a one-dimensional brew.

Electra *(OG 1046, ABV 4.5%)*
Golden colour, hoppy aroma, with a biscuity malt flavour, balanced by a strong and lasting bitterness.

Cyclops *(OG 1055, ABV 5.3%)*
Deep copper-coloured ale, with a rich hoppy aroma and full body; fruit and malt notes develop in the finish. Uses three different malts and four different hops.

MOLES

Moles Brewery (Cascade Drinks Ltd),
5 Merlin Way, Bowerhill, Melksham,
Wilts, SN12 6TJ
Tel (01225) 704734/708842
Fax (01225) 790770
E-mail cascade@cableinet.co.uk
Website molesbrewery.com
Shop 9-5. Tours by arrangement

⊗ Moles Brewery was built on the site of Cascade Drinks in 1982 (a drinks manufacturer and wholesaler) to brew cask-conditioned beer for local consumption, using Wiltshire grown and malted Maris Otter barley and choice Kent hops of the Fuggle and Golding varieties. In 1997 the brewery was expanded with a new brewhouse and 25-barrel brewing equipment. Thirteen pubs are owned, 12 serving cask beer. It currently supplies more than 100 free trade outlets direct. Seasonal beers: Barleymole (ABV 4.2%, summer), Molegrip (ABV 4.3%, autumn), Holy Moley (ABV 4.7, spring), Moel Moel (ABV 6%, winter).

Tap Bitter (*OG 1035, ABV 3.5%*)
A top-quality session bitter with a smooth, malty flavour and clean bitter finish.

Best Bitter (*OG 1040, ABV 4%*)
A well-balanced amber coloured bitter, clean, dry and malty with some bitterness and delicate floral hop flavour.

Landlords Choice (*OG 1045, ABV 4.5%*)
A dark, strong, smooth portery beer, with a rich fruity palate and malty finish.

Moles Molennium (*OG 1045, ABV 4.5%*)
Fruit, caramel and malty overtones in the aroma of this deep amber coloured ale, balanced by a pleasant bitterness.

MOONSTONE*

⚲ **Moonstone Brewery, Ministry of Ale, 9 Trafalgar Street, Burnley, Lancs, BB11 1TQ Tel (01282) 830909**

Small 2.5-barrel brewery based in the Ministry of Ale pub. The equipment was supplied by Moss Brew, which uses the site as a showplace for other potential customers. Brewing started in May 2001 and supplies only the pub at present, but there are plans to sell to other outlets.

Tiger's Eye (*ABV 3.8%*)

Dark (*4.8%*)

MOOR

Moor Beer Company, Little Whitley, Ashcott, Bridgwater, Somerset, TA7 9QW Tel/Fax (01458) 210050 E-mail moor-beer@talk21.com Website www.moorbeer.co.uk
Tours by arrangement

⊗ Based in a redundant workshop, Arthur and Annette Frampton started brewing on their former dairy farm in 1996. Their 10-barrel plant and its brews are now well-established in the West Country, with wholesalers taking the beer farther afield. Monthly specials are produced and 40 outlets are supplied direct. Bottle-conditioned beer: Old Freddy Walker (ABV 7.3%).

Withy Cutter (*OG 1041, ABV 3.8%*) ⬥
A lightly malty, pale brown beer with a moderate bitter finish.

Merlin's Magic (*OG 1044, ABV 4.3%*) ⬥
Dark amber-coloured, complex, full-bodied beer, with fruity notes.

Peat Porter (*OG 1045, ABV 4.5%*) ⬥
Dark brown/black beer with an initially fruity taste leading to roast malt taste with a little bitterness. A slightly sweet malty finish.

Summerland Gold (*OG 1052, ABV 5%*)
Straw-coloured beer with spicy hop aroma, malt with hints of vanilla on the palate, long fruit and hop finish.

Old Freddy Walker (*OG 1074, ABV 7.3%*) ⬥
Rich, dark, strong ale with a fruity complex taste, leaving a fruitcake finish.

MOORHOUSES

Moorhouses Brewery (Burnley) Ltd, 4 Moorhouse Street, Burnley, Lancs, BB11 5EN Tel (01282) 422864/416004 Fax (01282) 838493 E-mail moorhouses@moorhouses.fsbusiness.co.uk Website www.moorhouses.co.uk
Tours by arrangement

☺ Brewers of famous hop bitters from 1865, Moorhouses switched to cask beer production in 1978. A succession of owners failed to develop the company until it was taken over in 1985 by Bill Parkinson, since when it has grown substantially. A modern brewhouse was installed in 1988 and more fermenting vessels were added in 1991 to keep up with demand. The company owns six pubs, all serving cask-conditioned beer, and supplies real ale to around 200 free trade outlets. Two new 30-barrel fermenters and a 7.5 ton dray were added in 2000 to keep up with demand.

Black Cat (*OG 1036, ABV 3.4%*) ⬛⬥
An excellent dark, fruity ale. Smooth and well-balanced with fruity, chocolate and coffee flavours to complement the bitter roast character that lingers on in the aftertaste. Champion Beer of Britain 2000.

Premier Bitter (*OG 1036, ABV 3.7%*) ⬥
A clean and satisfying bitter aftertaste rounds off this consistent, well-balanced hoppy, amber session bitter.

Pride of Pendle (*OG 1040, ABV 4.1%*)
A fine balance of malt and hops give this beer a long, dry and extremely satisfying finish.

Pendle Witches Brew
(*OG 1050, ABV 5.1%*) ⬥
A faint malty nose leads into a rich, sweetish nutty flavour with a subtle hoppy bitterness. This develops into a delightful lasting bitter finish.

MORDUE

Mordue Brewery, Unit 21A, West Chirton North Industrial Estate, Shiremoor, Tyne & Wear, NE29 8SF Tel/Fax (0191) 2961879 E-mail garryfawson@ibm.net Website www.morduebrewery.com
Tours by arrangement

☺ The Mordue Brewery was the brainchild of home-brewers Garry Fawson and his younger brother Matthew, who lived in a house that was formerly the Mordue Brewery in the 18th century. The brothers leased a unit on an industrial estate, bought a 5-barrel plant, and brewed their first beer, Workie Ticket, which was launched at the 1995 Newcastle Beer Festival. It won the

Beer of the Festival award, and then went on to win the Champion Beer of Britain accolade at the Great British Beer Festival in 1997. By 1998, demand had outstripped capacity and the brewery moved to new premises with a 20-barrel plant. Bateman's distributes the beers in the south of England, while Caledonian looks after the north. There is a modest but thriving export business in the United States. Seasonal beers: Winter Tyne (ABV 4.7%), Spring Tyne (ABV 4.2%), Summer Tyne (ABV 3.6%), Autumn Tyne (ABV 4%), Wallsend Brown Ale (ABV 4.6%), Black Midden Stout (ABV 4.6%), Headmaster's Xmas Sermon (ABV 5%).

Five Bridge Bitter *(OG 1038, ABV 3.8%)* ◆
Golden brew, hoppy with a hint of fruit. The bitterness carries on in the aftertaste. A good session bitter.

Geordie Pride *(OG 1042, ABV 4.2%)* ◆
Amber beer, well-balanced and hoppy, with a long, bitter finish.

Workie Ticket *(OG 1045, ABV 4.5%)* ▯◆
Satisfying, complex beer with plenty of malt and hops; bitter finish. Mid-brown colour.

Radgie Gadgie *(OG 1048, ABV 4.8%)* ▯◆
Golden, easy-drinking strong bitter with plenty of fruit, malt and hops. The flavours extend into a long, satisfying finish; deceptively drinkable.

MORLAND

See Greene King.

MOULIN

▯ RTR Catering Ltd,
Moulin Hotel & Brewery, Kirkmichael Road, Pitlochry, Perthshire, PH16 5EW
Tel (01796) 472196 Fax (01796) 474098
E-mail hotel@moulin.u-net.com
Website www.moulin.u-net.com
Shop 12-3 daily. Tours by arrangement

The Moulin Brewery was the first brewery in Perthshire for over 50 years and was opened in 1995 during celebrations for the hotel's 300th anniversary. Moulin supplies the Moulin Inn across the road and three other outlets. Bottle-conditioned beer: Ale of Atholl (ABV 4.5%).

Light *(OG 1035, ABV 3.7%)* ◆
Thirst-quenching, straw-coloured session beer, with a light, hoppy, fruity balance ending with a gentle, hoppy sweetness.

Braveheart *(OG 1039, ABV 4%)* ◆
An amber bitter, with a delicate balance of malt and fruit and a Scottish-style sweetness.

Ale of Atholl *(OG 1043, ABV 4.5%)* ◆
A reddish, quaffable, malty ale, with a solid body and a mellow finish.

Old Remedial *(OG 1050.5, ABV 5.2%)* ◆
A distinctive and satisfying dark brown old ale, with roast malt to the fore and tannin in a robust taste.

NAGS HEAD

▯ Nags Head Inn, Abercych, Boncath, Pembrokeshire SA37 0HJ
Tel (01239) 841200

Pub-brewery producing just one brew on an occasional basis largely for its own consumption. Two outlets are supplied direct. Beer: Old Emrys (OG 1038-40, ABV 3.8-4%).

NETHERGATE

Nethergate Brewery Co Ltd, 11-13 High Street, Clare, Suffolk, CO10 8NY
Tel (01787) 277244 Fax (01787) 277123
E-mail orders@nethergate.co.uk
Tours by arrangement (trade and CAMRA groups)

▩ Small brewery producing award-winning beers, set up in 1986, which continues to use traditional methods and no additives. The Umbel beers are infused with coriander seeds, recalling an ancient brewing style. A single tied house and 300 free trade outlets are now supplied, mainly in East Anglia. Old Growler is now available in bottle-conditioned form. Seasonal/occasional beers: Vixen (ABV 4.3%, January), Golden Gate (ABV 4.5%, February), Black Pig (ABV 4%, March), Swift Ale (ABV 4.2%, April), Sheep's Eye (ABV 4.1%, June-July), Wild Fox (ABV 4.3%, August), Wild Rose (ABV 4.5%, September), Scutchers Ale (ABV 4.3%, October), Monk's Habit (ABV 4.2%, November), Winter Draught (ABV 4.8%, December).

Priory Mild *(OG 1036, ABV 3.5%)* ◆
Distinctive, full-flavoured, very dark mild. Pronounced lingering roast and dry hop aftertaste.

IPA *(OG 1036, ABV 3.5%)* ◆
This amber-coloured session bitter is clean, crisp and very drinkable. Plenty of malt and hoppy bitterness together with some fruit are pleasing to the palate. Bitterness lingers in a long dry aftertaste.

Umbel Ale *(OG 1039, ABV 3.8%)* ▨▯◆
Wort is percolated through coriander seeds to give a wonderful, warming, spicy fruit tang to both the taste and aroma. The hops are strong enough to make themselves known and a strong, bitter malt finish hits late.

Suffolk County Best Bitter *(OG 1039, ABV 4%)* ◆
Formerly Nethergate Bitter, Suffolk County retains the classic Nethergate taste but not so intensely bitter as previously. Still a fine balanced beer with plenty of hops and malt.

Golden Gate *(OG 1045, ABV 4.5%)*
A golden bitter using three hop varieties, giving it a fresh aroma and a hoppy finish. Malt and hops are balanced in the taste.

Augustinian Ale *(OG 1048, ABV 4.8%)* ◆
A pale, refreshing, complex best bitter. Fruity aroma leads to a bitter-sweet flavour and aftertaste with predominance of citrus tones.

Old Growler *(OG 1050, ABV 5%)* ▯◆
A complex and satisfying porter, smooth and distinctive. Sweetness, roast malt and fruit feature in the palate, with bitter chocolate lingering. The finish is powerfully hoppy.

Umbel Magna *(OG 1050, ABV 5%)* ▯◆
The addition of coriander to the Old Growler wort completes the original 1750s recipe for this distinctive dark beer. The powerful spiciness only adds to this porter's appeal.

NEWBY WYKE

Newby Wyke Brewery, Willoughby Arms, Station Road, Little Bytham, Lincolnshire, NG33 4RA
Tel (01780) 410276
Fax (01780) 410190
Tours by arrangement

The brewery, named after a Hull trawler skippered by brewer Rob March's grandfather, was set up in a converted garage at his home in Grantham. Brewing started in 1998 with a 2.5-barrel plant. Rob moved into purpose-built premises with a 10-barrel brewery and capacity for 30 barrels a week at the Willoughby Arms, Little Bytham in July 2001. Forty outlets are supplied direct. Stamford Gold (ABV 4.4%) is brewed regularly for the Green Man, Stamford; Lord Willoughby, named after another Hull trawler (ABV 4.8%), and Lord Ancaster (ABV 4.5%) are regular beers for the Willoughby Arms.

Sidewinder (*OG 1038, ABV 3.8%*)

Skipper Eddie's Ale (SEA)
(*OG 1039, ABV 4%*)

Slingshot (*OG 1041, ABV 4.2%*)

Slipway (*OG 1041, ABV 4.2%*)

Newby Wyke Bitter (*OG 1042, ABV 4.4%*)

Benvolio (*OG 1045, ABV 4.8%*)

White Squall (*OG 1045, ABV 4.8%*)

NORTH COTSWOLD

North Cotswold Brewery, Ditchford Farm, Moreton-in-Marsh, Glos, GL55 9RD
Tel (01608) 663947

Brothers David and Roger Tilbrook started brewing in 1999 on a 2.5-barrel plant, bought from the closed Viking Brewery. A new 10-barrel plant was installed in 2000. The brewery is in Warwickshire, despite the Gloucestershire postal address, on the estate of Lord Willoughby De Broke. Two mainstream beers are produced with other seasonals planned and 20 outlets are supplied direct. Seasonal beer: Solstice (ABV 3.7%, summer).

Genesis (*OG 1038, ABV 4%*)

Four Shires (*OG 1040, ABV 4.2%*)

NORTH YORKSHIRE

North Yorkshire Brewing Co, Pinchinthorpe Hall, Pinchinthorpe, Guisborough, N Yorkshire, TS14 8HG
Tel (01287) 630200
Fax (01287) 632000
Tours by arrangement

⊚ The brewery was founded in 1989 and moved in 1998 to Pinchinthorpe Hall, a moated, listed medieval monument near Guisborough that has its own spring water. The site also includes a hotel, restaurant and bistro. More than 100 free trade outlets are currently supplied. Seasonal beers: Love Muscle (ABV 4%, February), Honey Bunny (ABV 4.2%, April), Rocket Fuel (ABV 5%, November), Xmas Herbert (ABV 4.4%, December).

Prior's Ale (*OG 1036, ABV 3.6%*) ◆

Light, refreshing and surprisingly full-flavoured for a pale, low gravity beer, with a complex, bitter-sweet mixture of malt, hops and fruit carrying through into the aftertaste.

Best Bitter (*OG 1036, ABV 3.6%*)

Archbishop Lee's Ruby Ale
(*OG l040, ABV 4%*)
A full-bodied beer with a malty aroma and a balanced malt and hops taste, with vanilla notes.

Boro Best (*OG 1040, ABV 4%*)

Cereal Killer (*OG 1045, ABV 4.5%*)

Fools Gold (*OG 1046, ABV 4.6%*)

Golden Ale (*OG 1046, ABV 4.6%*) ◆
A well-hopped, lightly malted, golden premium bitter, using Styrian and Goldings hops.

Flying Herbert (*OG 1047, ABV 4.7%*)

Lord Lee's (*OG 1047, ABV 4.7%*) ◆
A refreshing, red/brown beer with a hoppy aroma. The flavour is a pleasant balance of roast malt and sweetness that predominates over hops. The malty, bitter finish develops slowly.

NORTHUMBERLAND

Northumberland Brewery Ltd, Earth Balance, West Sleekburn Farm, Bomarsund, Bedlington, Northumberland, NE22 7AD
Tel/Fax (01670) 822112
Shop 11-4 Mon-Fri; 12-5 Sat/Sun
Tours by arrangement

⊚ The Northumberland brewery, set up by business partners Derek Convery and Geoff Hudson, began production in 1996 at North Seaton Industrial Estate, Ashington. A year later, the brewery moved to the Earth Balance organic farm and visitor centre at West Sleekburn Farm, near Bedlington. The brewery employs environmentally-friendly processes, using renewable energy sources to brew the beer. The Cat and Sawdust brewery tap is integral to the project and has been enlarged by redesigning the brewery premises. The beers on sale in the pub are unfined, ie no fish finings are used, and are suitable for vegetarians. There's a folk club and community events at weekends. The brewery has an extensive free trade. Seasonal beers: Santa's Surprise (ABV 4.3%), Santa's Secret (ABV 4.7%).

Castles (*OG 1038, ABV 3.8%*)
A light and refreshing session bitter with a subtle malt and hop finish.

GNC (Great Northern Coalfield)
(*OG 1042, ABV 4.2%*)
A balanced malt character, smooth with a subtle hopped finish.

Secret Kingdom Ale
(*OG 1042, ABV 4.3%*)
A full-flavoured, dark malted ale, smooth and well-balanced with a hoppy finish.

Malnseam (*OG 1046, ABV 4.5%*)
Ruby-coloured, well-hopped, full-bodied malt flavours.

Sheepdog (*OG 1047, ABV 4.7%*)
A light, strong bitter, caramel flavoured with a hoppy finish.

Bomar Bitter (*OG 1049, ABV 5%*)
A light and fully hopped, easy-drinking strong bitter.

O'HANLON'S

O'Hanlon's Brewing Company Ltd, Great Barton Farm, Whimple, Devon, EX5 2NY.
Tel **(01404) 822412**
Fax **(01404) 833700**
Website **www.ohanlons.co.uk**
Tours by arrangement

⊠ The brewery was established in 1996 to supply John O'Hanlon's pub in Clerkenwell, London, but expanded to serve around 80 other outlets direct, with others taking the beers via wholesalers. In the summer of 2000, O'Hanlon's sold its pub and moved the brewery to the West Country. It still supplies O'Hanlon's pub in London as well as other free trade accounts. Seasonal beers: Maltsters Weiss (ABV 4%, spring/summer), Rye Beer (ABV 4.3%, autumn), Christmas Ale (ABV 4.3%, December).

Fire Fly (*OG 1035, ABV 3.6%*) ◆
Malty and fruity light bitter. Hints of orange in the taste.

Blakeley's Best (*OG 1040, ABV 4.2%*) ◆
Premium ale with complex flavours. Hoppy nose and finish are balanced by a fruity malt taste.

Dry Stout (*OG 1041, ABV 4.2%*) ◆
Dark brown with a hint of red. Roast malt dominates from start to finish with bitterness also present in the taste.

Myrica Ale (*OG 1039, ABV 4.2%*) ◆
The use of honey and bog myrtle for flavour produces a sweet, malty yellow beer with no noticeable bitterness.

Port Stout (*OG 1041, ABV 4.4%*) ▣
A black beer with a roast malt aroma that remains in the taste but gives way to hoppy bitterness in the aftertaste.

Red Ale (*OG 1044, ABV 4.5%*) ◆
A typical Irish red ale. Well balanced but fruity with a good, dry, hoppy finish.

OAKHAM

Oakham Ales, 80 Westgate, Peterborough, Cambs, PE1 2AA
Tel **(01733) 358300**
Fax **(01733) 310022**
Tours by arrangement (no charge to CAMRA members)

⊠ The future of Oakham Ales, one of the most successful craft breweries in Britain, is under threat as the local council has placed a compulsory purchase order on the site to make way for a shopping centre. Founded in 1993 on a Rutland trading estate, Oakham found new owners in 1995. The move to its present site in 1998 created Peterborough's first brewery for 80 years. It is housed behind the Brewery Tap, one of Europe's biggest brew-pubs, with viewing windows from the pub into the brewhouse; the Tap is a converted former unemployment office. Oakham has gone from a 10-barrel plant in 1993 to 35 barrels today. The year 2000 was the most successful in the brewery's history, gaining more than 30 CAMRA and industry awards, including two awards at the Great British Beer Festival, while White Dwarf was named Champion Beer of East Anglia. Oakham also supplies two other associated pubs, plus 60-100 free houses. Seasonal beers: Old Tosspot (ABV 5.2%, Dec-Feb), Black Hole Porter (ABV 5.5%, Jan-Feb), Harlequin (ABV 4.9%, March), Mompessons Gold (ABV 5%, March), Helterskelter (ABV 5%, June-Aug), Peterborough Beer Festival Special (strength varies, Aug-Sept), Five Leaves Left (ABV 4.5%, Oct-Nov), Cold Turkey (ABV 6.3, December).

Jeffrey Hudson Bitter or JHB
(*OG 1038, ABV 3.8%*) ▣▣◆
Impressive straw-coloured quaffing bitter with bold floral, grassy hop, grapefruit and kiwi fruit and a little sweetness followed by a long, dry aftertaste.

White Dwarf Wheat Beer
(*OG 1043, ABV 4.3%*) ▣▣
Full-bodied yellow-golden beer with a well-defined citrus hop, rounded off with a gentle underlying malty sweetness in the mouth but ending bone-dry with hops holding up well.

Bishops Farewell (*OG 1046, ABV 4.6%*) ◆
A well-rounded, full-bodied strong bitter, yellow in colour with a strong hoppy aroma joined by floral fruity flavours in the mouth with a grainy background and a dry, fruity finish.

OAKHILL

Oakhill Brewery, The Old Maltings, High Street, Oakhill, Radstock, Somerset, BA3 5BX
Tel **(01749) 840134**
Fax **(01749) 840531**
E-mail **gary@oakhillbrewery.co.uk**
Website **www.oakhillbrewery.co.uk**
Shop Informal, when brewery is open
Tours by arrangement Tue evening, £3.50 per person, max 25 people

⊠ Situated high in the Mendip Hills in Somerset, the brewery was set up by a farmer in 1984 in an old fermentation room of the original Oakhill Brewery (established in 1767 and burnt down in 1924). By the mid-1990s the brewery had outgrown its original premises and moved in 1997 to the old maltings building in Oakhill that had been newly renovated, with a brewing capacity of more than 300 barrels a week. It now supplies five tied houses and some 200 free trade outlets direct. It has signed a deal with the Innspired pub group (qv) that will offer Oakhill beers to Usher's pubs in the South-west.

XXX Mature *(ABV 3.7%)*
A slightly darker beer that replaced Bitter.

Best Bitter *(OG 1040, ABV 4%)* ◗
A clean-tasting, tangy bitter, with a good hop content and citrus fruit and malt balance. Dry finish; light hop aroma. Very quenching.

Black Magic Stout
(OG 1045, ABV 4.5%) ◗
A black/brown bitter stout with roast malt and a touch of fruit on the nose. Smooth roast malt and bitterness in the taste, with mellow coffee and chocolate.

Mendip Gold *(OG 1045, ABV 4.5%)*

Yeoman 1767 Strong Ale
(OG 1050, ABV 5%) ◗
A strong, pale brown, full-bodied bitter, with a floral hop palate and notable fruitiness. Dry, bitter, lasting finish.

Mendip Twister *(OG 1069, ABV 6.3%)*

OAKLEAF*

Oakleaf Brewing Co Ltd, Unit 7, Clarence Wharf Industrial Estate, Mumby Road, Gosport, Hants, PO12 1AJ
Tel (023) 92513 222
Website www.oakleafbrewing.co.uk

Dave Pickersgill opened his brewery in March 2000, taking over much of the business conducted by the former Winchester Arms company in Horndean. Oakleaf still supplies the Winchester Arms, the Hole in the Wall and other pubs in the Horndean, Portsmouth and Southsea area, but its main business is with Innspired, the pub company that owns the estate of the former Ushers of Trowbridge brewery.

Maypole Mild *(ABV 3.8%)*

Oakleaf Bitter *(ABV 3.8%)*

Nuptuale *(ABV 4.2%)*

Squirrel's Delight *(ABV 4.4%)*

Holehearted *(ABV 4.7%)*

Yodel Weiss *(ABV 5%)*

Blake's Gosport Bitter *(ABV 5.2%)*

India Pale Ale *(ABV 5.5%)*

OAKWELL

Oakwell Brewery, Pontefract Road, Barnsley, S Yorkshire,
Tel (01226) 296161
Fax (01226) 771457

☺ The brewery closed in 1970 shortly after being taken over by John Smiths of Tadcaster. Brewing recommenced in 1997 with plans for expansion on the original site. It supplies some 30 outlets direct. Barnsley Bitter should not be confused with the beer of the same name brewed by Barnsley Brewery (qv).

Barnsley Bitter *(OG 1036, ABV 3.8%)*

Old Tom *(OG 1036, ABV 3.8%)*

Old Tom Stout *(ABV 4%)*

ODCOMBE*

⌂ **Odcombe Ales, Masons Arms, 41 Lower Odcombe, Yeovil, Somerset, BA22 8TX**
Tel (01935) 862591

A brew-pub with a 1-barrel plant (on view to customers through a window in the pub) that started regular production in May 2001. The Masons Arms is the only outlet for the beers, but they will be made available to beer festivals.

Lower Odcombe Ale *(OG 1040.5, ABV 4%)*
Pale, dry bitter with a biscuity flavour.

Higher Odcombe Ale *(OG 1046, ABV 4.5%)*
A sweeter, stronger version of Lower Odcombe Ale.

OKELLS

Okell & Son Ltd, Kewaigue, Douglas, Isle of Man, IM2 1QG
Tel (01624) 661120
Fax (01624) 624253
E-mail okells@heronandbrearley.com
Website www.okells.co.uk
Tours by arrangement

☺ Founded in 1874 by Dr Okell and formerly trading as Isle of Man Breweries, this is the main brewery on the island, having taken over and closed the rival Castletown Brewery in 1986. The brewery moved in 1994 to a new, purpose-built plant at Kewaigue. All the beers are produced under the Manx Brewers' Act 1874 (permitted ingredients: water, malt, sugar and hops only). All of the company's 55 pubs sell real ale and more than 70 free trade outlets are also supplied direct. Occasional beers: Castletown Bitter (ABV 4%), Manx Cat (ABV 4%), Wheel Ale (ABV 4.2%), Spring Ram (ABV 4.2%), Poleaxed (ABV 4.2%), Autumn Dawn (ABV 4.2%), Chequered Flag (ABV 4.2%), Summer Storm (ABV 4.2%), Hoptunaa (ABV 4.2%), Olde Skipper (ABV 4.5%), St Nick (ABV 4.5%), Falcon Strong Ale (ABV 5%).

Mild *(OG 1034, ABV 3.4%)* ◗
A genuine, well-brewed mild ale, with a fine aroma of hops and crystal malt. Reddish-brown in colour, this beer has a full malt flavour with surprising bitter hop notes and a hint of blackcurrants and oranges. Full, malty finish.

Bitter *(OG 1035, ABV 3.7%)* ◗
A golden beer, malty and superbly hoppy in aroma, with a hint of honey. Rich and malty on the tongue, it has a wonderful, dry, malt and hop finish. A complex but rewarding beer.

Heart-Throb *(OG 1042, ABV 4.5%)*

OLD BEAR

⌂ **Old Bear Brewery, 6 Keighley Road, Cross Hills, Keighley, W Yorkshire, BD20 7RN**
Tel (01535) 632115
Tours by arrangement

☺ Brewery founded in 1993 by former Goose Eye Brewery owner Bryan Eastell, next to the Old Bear pub. Five other free trade outlets are also supplied. Occasional beers: Ursa Minor (ABV 4.6%), Ursa Major (ABV 5.8%), Summer Bear (ABV 3.9%).

Bitter *(OG 1038, ABV 3.9%)* ◆
A refreshing and easy-to-drink bitter. The balance of malt and hops gives way to a short, dry, bitter aftertaste.

OLD CANNON

Old Cannon Brewery Ltd, 86 Cannon Street, Bury St Edmunds, Suffolk, IP33 1JR
Tel (01284) 768769 Fax (01284) 701137
Website www.oldcannon.co.uk
E-mail rej@btinternet.com

St Edmunds Head pub opened in 1845 with its own brewery. Brewing ceased in 1917, and Greene King closed the pub in 1995. It re-opened in 1999 complete with unique state-of-the-art brewery housed in the bar area. Seasonal beers: Black Pig (ABV 5%, winter), Spring Ale (ABV 4.5%, temporary name), Summer Ale (ABV 4.2%, temporary name). An autumn ale will also be introduced.

Best Bitter *(OG 1040, ABV 3.8%)* ◆
An excellent session bitter brewed using Styrian Goldings, giving a crisp grapefruit aroma and taste. Very refreshing, full of flavour and extremely moreish.

Powder Monkey *(OG 1047, ABV 4.7%)*

Gunner's Daughter *(OG 1052, ABV 5.5%)* ◆
A well-balanced strong ale with a complexity of hop, fruit, sweetness and bitterness in the flavour, and a lingering pleasant hoppy, bitter aftertaste.

OLD CHIMNEYS

Old Chimneys Brewery, The Street, Market Weston, Diss, Norfolk, IP22 2NZ (office). Brewery: Hopton End Farm, Market Weston, Diss, Norfolk, IP22 2NX
Tel (01359) 221411
Tours by arrangement

⊗ A craft brewery opened in 1995 by former Vaux/Greene King/Broughton brewer Alan Thomson. In 2001 the brewery moved to larger premises in a converted farm building in the same village. Despite the postal address, the brewery is in Suffolk. The beers produced are mostly named after endangered local species. Four strong bottle-conditioned beers are also brewed. Old Chimneys currently supplies 50 outlets direct. Seasonal beers: Polecat Porter (ABV 4.2%, winter), Black Rat Stout (ABV 4.4%, winter), Golden Pheasant (ABV 4.7%, summer), Natterjack Premium Ale (ABV 5%, winter), Winter Cloving (ABV 7.2%, winter), Corn Cleavers Ale (ABV 4.3%, spring/summer). Bottle-conditioned beers: The Millers Ale (ABV 5%), Brimstone Lager (ABV 6.5%), Redshank Strong Ale (ABV 8.7%), Good King Henry Imperial Stout (ABV 9.6%).

Military Mild *(OG 1035, ABV 3.3%)* ◆
A rich, dark mild with good body for its gravity. Sweetish toffee and light roast bitterness dominate, leading to a moreish dry aftertaste.

Galingale *(OG 1041, ABV 3.9%)* ◆
This amber gold bitter has excellent body allied to a clean and refreshing character. Hops, malt and fruit combine to give a well-balanced, bitter-sweet flavour with hop in the early aftertaste, followed by a pleasing dry finish.

Great Raft Bitter *(OG 1043, ABV 4.2%)* ◆
Complex and satisfying for its gravity, this pale copper bitter is bursting with fruit throughout. Malt and hops add to the sweetish fruity flavour, which is nicely rounded off with hoppy bitterness in the aftertaste.

OLD COTTAGE*

Old Cottage Beer Co, Unit 3, Eccleshaw Industrial Estate, Hawkins Lane, Burton-on-Trent, Staffs, DE14 1PT
Tel (01283) 540969
E-mail oldcottage@euphony.net

Kevin Slater bought his brewing equipment from the former Old Cottage Brewery in Kendal and installed it in the Heritage Brewery in Burton. When the site was taken over, he was evicted and set up in a modern industrial unit.

Windrift *(OG 1043, ABV 4.3%)*

Stout *(OG 1048, ABV 4.8%)*
Black but not heavy! Full roast aroma with hints of liquorice and chocolate malt; the roast flavours linger to a bitter finish.

Cottage Pride *(OG 1048, ABV 4.8%)*

Old Comrades Special *(OG 1047, ABV 5%)*

Phoenix Ale *(OG 1050, ABV 5.2%)*

OLD KENT*

Old Kent Brewery Co, 11b Western Road, Borough Green, Sevenoaks, Kent, TN15 8AL
Tel (01732) 882111
Website www.okbc.co.uk

Sara Jane Anderson hails from Edinburgh and brewed with Old Forge, Cox's Yard and Valhalla before setting up on her own with a 5-barrel plant in a converted garage. She started brewing in August 2000 and has built up trade with pubs in Kent and London. Off sales are available at the brewery. In spite of her Scottish origins, Sara Jane has acclimatised to her new home and gives her names cricketing connections.

Fine Edge *(ABV 3.8%)*

Opener *(ABV 4.2%)*

Top Score *(ABV 4.6%)*

Full Pitch *(ABV 5%)*

Long Hop *(ABV 5%)*

OLD LAXEY

Old Laxey Brewing Co, Shore Hotel, Laxey, Isle of Man, IM4 7DA
Tel (01624) 861509/862451
E-mail shore@adusys.co.uk
Website www.welcome.to/shorehotel
Tours by arrangement

The brewery, designed and constructed by Peter Austin, the renowned 'father' of micro-brewing and founder of Ringwood Brewery, in Poole in 1997, has a 5-barrel plant that can be seen through a viewing window in the brewery bar. Twelve outlets are supplied direct.

Bosun Bitter *(OG 1038, ABV 3.8%)*
Crisp and fresh with a hoppy aftertaste.

OLD LUXTERS

Old Luxters Vineyard, Winery & Brewery, Hambleden, Henley-on-Thames, Oxon, RG9 6JW
Tel (01491) 638330
Fax (01491) 638645
E-mail enquiries@luxters.co.uk
Website www.luxters.co.uk
Shop 9-5 Mon-Fri; 11-5 Sat-Sun. Tours by arrangement

⊠ A brewery in Buckinghamshire (despite the postal address) set up in 1990 in a 17th-century barn by David Ealand, owner of Chiltern Valley Wines. Apart from the brewery and vineyard, there is a cellar shop and a converted barn used for private and corporate functions with in-house catering. The brewery supplies a few local free trade outlets and pubs further afield. Many brews are produced to order for other independent breweries, and own label bottle-conditioned ales are made on a regular basis for retail outlets and restaurants, such as Fortnum & Mason and Gilbey's. Bottle-conditioned beers: Barn Ale (ABV 5.4%), Dark Roast Ale (ABV 5%), Gold (ABV 5%).

Barn Ale Bitter (OG 1038, ABV 4%)
A fruity, aromatic, fairly hoppy, bitter beer.

Barn Ale Special
(OG 1042.5, ABV 4.5%) ◆
The original Barn Ale: predominantly malty, fruity and hoppy in taste and nose, and tawny/amber in colour. Fairly strong in flavour: the initial, sharp, malty and fruity taste leaves a dry, bitter-sweet, fruity aftertaste. It can be slightly sulphurous.

Dark Roast Ale (OG 1048, ABV 5%)

OLD MILL

Old Mill Brewery Ltd, Mill Street, Snaith, Goole, Yorkshire, DN14 9HU
Tel (01405) 861813
Fax (01405) 862789
Tours by arrangement

☺ A small craft brewery opened in 1983 in a 200-year-old former malt kiln and corn mill. A new brewhouse was installed in 1991 to increase the brew-length to 60 barrels, and the brewery is building its tied estate (now 17 houses). The innovation of selling beer in plastic, non-returnable handicasks has meant that the beer can now be found nationwide. Around 200 free trade outlets are supplied direct from the brewery. A bottling plant was installed in 1997. There are regular occasional and seasonal beers.

Traditional Mild (OG 1035, ABV 3.4%) ◆
A satisfying roast malt flavour dominates this easy-drinking, quality dark mild.

Nellie Dene (OG 1035, ABV 3.5%) ◆
A well-hopped, straw-coloured beer with hops throughout, slightly fruity in the middle, and a refreshing bitter finish. Lots of flavour for its strength.

Traditional Bitter (OG 1038, ABV 3.9%) ◆
The Old Mill character has returned to this beer, though bitterness remains at a premium. It has a malty nose and initial flavour, with hops hiding until the lingering finish.

Old Curiosity (OG 1044, ABV 4.5%)

Slightly sweet and malty to start with, with malt flavours all the way through. A good, well-roasted, balanced beer.

Bullion (OG 1045, ABV 4.7%) ◆
The malty and hoppy aroma is followed by a neat mix of hop and fruit tastes within an enveloping maltiness. Dark brown/amber in colour.

Blackjack (OG 1050, ABV 5%)

OLDE SWAN*

⌂ **Olde Swan Brewery, 89 Halesowen Road, Netherton, Dudley, West Midlands, DY2 9PY**
Tel (01384) 253075
Tours by arrangement

The welcome return of a once-famous and much-loved brew-pub, best known in the old days as 'Ma Pardoe's', after the matriarch who ruled it for years. The pub has been licensed since 1835 and the present brewery and pub were built in 1863. Brewing continued until 1988, and restarted in February 2001. The plant brews primarily for the on-site pub with some beer available to the trade. Seasonal beers are planned.

Light Mild/Olde Swan Original (ABV 3.5%)
A light golden beer with a remarkable likeness to the original Mrs Pardoe's celebrated 'home-brew'.

Dark Swan (ABV 3.9%)
A rich dark mild full of flavour.

Entire Swan (ABV 4.4%)
A premium bitter beer.

OLD WHEELTON

Old Wheelton Brewery, Dressers Arms, 9 Briers Brow, Wheelton, Chorley, Lancs, PR6 8HD
Tel (01254) 830041

Steve Turner worked in the commercial brewing industry, with Wilsons and John Smiths, before setting up his own 2-barrel brewery. Old Wheelton is part of the Marsden Inns group, which owns seven pubs in the North-west; the Dressers Arms plant supplies the other pubs with beer.

Big Frank's Bitter (ABV 3.8%)

Just a Flyer (ABV 4%)

Milk of Amnesia (ABV 4.2%)

OLDERSHAW

Oldershaw Brewery, 12 Harrowby Hall Estate, Grantham, Lincs, NG31 9HB
Tel (01476) 572135 (07801)
Fax (01476) 572193
E-mail goldbrew@lineone.net
Website www.oldershawbrewery.co.uk
Tours by arrangement

⊠ Experienced home-brewer Gary Oldershaw and his wife Diane set up the brewery at their home in 1997. Grantham's first brewery for 30 years, Oldershaw now supplies 60 local free houses. They concentrate on supplying outlets direct and are enjoying steady growth. A third fermenting vessel was added in 1999 to increase capacity to 20 barrels a week. The

Oldershaws planned to introduce some small-scale bottling by 2002, to include Old Boy, Yuletide, Royal Blonde and Grantham Stout. Seasonal beers: Sunnydaze (ABV 4%, summer wheat beer, May-Aug), Topers Tipple (ABV 4.5%, Nov-Feb), Yuletide (ABV 5.2%, Nov-Dec).

Harrowby Bitter (OG 1036, ABV 3.6%) ❧
Bitter and hoppy session beer, light brown in colour. Faint fruit and malt support the slow-dying hop character.

High Dyke (OG 1039, ABV 3.9%)
Golden and moderately bitter. A predominantly hoppy session beer.

Newton's Drop (OG 1041, ABV 4.1%) ❧
Balanced malt and hops but with a strong bitter, lingering taste in this mid-brown beer.

Ermine Ale (OG 1042, ABV 4.2%) ❧
Golden brown with a fruity hop the dominant feature on nose and taste giving a bitterness that lasts; malt plays a supporting role.

Caskade (OG 1042, ABV 4.2%)
Pale, golden beer brewed with American Cascade hops to give a distinctive floral, hoppy flavour and aroma, and a clean lasting finish.

Grantham Stout (OG 1043, ABV 4.3%)
Dark brown and smooth with rich roast malt flavour, supported by some fruit and bitterness. A long, moderately dry finish.

Ahtanum Gold (OG 1043, ABV 4.3%)
A gold-coloured, fruity, hoppy beer balanced with some maltiness. Moderately bitter.

Regal Blonde (OG 1043, ABV 4.4%) ❧
Straw coloured lager-style beer with a good malt/hop balance throughout; strong bitterness on the taste lingers.

Old Boy (OG 1047, ABV 4.8%) ❧
A full-bodied amber ale, fruity and bitter with a hop/fruit aroma. The malt that backs the taste dies in the long finish.

ORCHARD

Deltacloud Ltd, Orchard Brewery Bar, 15 Market Hill, Barnsley, S70 2PX Tel (01226) 288906/289312
Tours by arrangement

The Orchard Brewery Bar opened in December 1999. Eight pubs are owned, three serving cask-conditioned beer.

Bitter (ABV 3.9%)

Nortons Bitter (ABV 3.9%)

Tarn Bitter (ABV 3.9%)

Tyke Bitter (ABV 4.6%)

ORCHARD

Orchard Brewery, Little Acres, Silversides Lane, Scawby Brook, Brigg, Lincs DN2 9JP Tel (01652) 657174
Tours by arrangement

The brewery is a 2-barrel unit. It currently supplies only one outlet, the Queen's Arms in Brigg, though the beer is sometimes available via wholesalers.

Cobblers (ABV 4.2%)

ORGANIC

Organic Brewhouse, Unit 1, Higher Bochym Rural Workshops, Cury Cross Lanes, Nr Mullion, Helston, Cornwall, TR12 7AZ Tel (01326) 241555 E-mail a.hamer@btclick.com
Tours by arrangement

The brewery was set up by Andy Hamer in 2000 on the Lizard Peninsular, overlooking Goonhilly Downs. It is dedicated to brewing organic cask beers, using its own source of natural mineral water. Equipment is arranged as a mini 'tower' system (the brewing process flowing logically from floor to floor) and produces two regular beers, both also available in bottle-conditioned form. The brewery supplies several local outlets, and the beers occasionally head north with wholesalers. Lizard Point won its class at Cornwall Beer Festival in St Ives in 2000.

Lizard Point (OG 1038, ABV 4%)

Serpentine Dark Ale (OG 1042, ABV 4.5%)

ORKNEY

Orkney Brewery Ltd, Quoyloo, Stromness, Orkney, KW16 3LT Tel (01856) 841802 Fax (01856) 841754 E-mail beer@orkneybrewery.co.uk Website www.orkneybrewery.co.uk
Tours by arrangement

☻ Set up in 1988 in an old school building by former licensee Roger White, the brewery was completely modernised in 1995 with new buildings replacing a single cramped room. The brewery is run along strict ecological lines with its own water supply and unique effluent control system. The beers are available nationwide via wholesalers. Occasional beer: White Christmas (ABV 5%, December).

Raven Ale (OG 1038, ABV 3.8%) ❧
A pale brown beer in which fruit predominates. Roast is evident in the aroma and taste, and hop in the taste and aftertaste. Initially sweet, but with a satisfying dry, bitter aftertaste.

Northern Light (OG 1040, ABV 4%) ❧
A lager-coloured beer, hoppy and refreshing. Fruity hop notes can develop a true lager nose. A late copper hop that is intense without being cloying.

Dragonhead Stout (OG 1040, ABV 4%) ❧
A strong, dark malt aroma flows into the taste in this superb Scottish stout. The roast

741

malt continues to dominate the aftertaste, and blends with chocolate to develop a strong, dry finish. Hard to find.

Red MacGregor *(OG 1040, ABV 4%)* ◈
Smooth-tasting, full-bodied, tawny-red ale. A powerful smack of fruit and hop is a feature of this complex beer.

Dark Island *(OG 1045, ABV 4.6%)* ◈
Dark, beautifully balanced and full of roast, malt and fruit, and a hint of caramel. A sweetish taste leads to a long-lasting, roasted, slightly bitter finish. Full-bodied and deceptively drinkable. If beer was whisky, this would be it.

Skullsplitter *(OG 1080, ABV 8.5%)* ▥▣◈
An intense velvet malt nose with hints of apple, nutmeg and spice. Hops to the fore balanced by satiny smooth malt with fruity spicy edges leading to a long dry finish with a hint of nut.

OSSETT

Ossett Brewing Company t/a Ossett Brewery, Brewers Pride, Healey Road, Ossett, W Yorkshire WF5 8ND
Tel (01924) 261333
Tours by arrangement

Small brewery opened at the back of the Brewers Pride pub and run by former publican Bob Hunter and Bob Lawson, a brewer with more than 30 years' experience with Tetley in Leeds and Kelham Island in Sheffield. Occasional beers: Silver Fox (ABV 4.1%), Two Bobs (ABV 4.3%), Silver Link (ABV 4.6%), Warrior Bitter (ABV 4.8%) and Quick Silver (ABV 5%). Seasonal Beers: Summa Bobs (ABV 4.2%, summer), Ace of Spades Porter (ABV 4.5%, winter).

Special Bitter *(OG 1039.5, ABV 3.9%)*

Silver King *(OG 1041.5, ABV 4.3%)*

Dazzler *(OG 1044.5, ABV 4.5%)*

Excelsior *(OG 1051.5, ABV 5.2%)*

OTTER

Otter Brewery Ltd, Mathayes, Luppitt, Honiton, Devon, EX14 4SA
Tel (01404) 891285 Fax (01404) 891124
E-mail info@otterbrewery.com
Website www.otterbrewery.com
Tours by arrangement weekday evenings

⊗ Named after its position at the headsprings of the River Otter, the brewery began operation in 1990 under David McCaig, formerly of Whitbread. Steady growth over the following eight years has meant the need for a plant that can produce 30 barrels, with a capacity of 135 barrels a week. No further expansion is planned. The brewery also bottles its own beers. All beers are brewed with local spring water and its own yeast culture. 130 outlets are supplied direct. Seasonal beer: Otter Claus (ABV 5%, Christmas).

Bitter *(OG 1036, ABV 3.6%)* ▱◈
Well-balanced amber session bitter with a fruity nose and bitter taste and aftertaste.

Bright *(OG 1039, ABV 4.3%)* ◈
Fruit and hop aroma in a straw-coloured bitter with a strong bitter finish.

Ale *(OG 1043, ABV 4.5%)* ▤◈
Pale brown, pleasantly malty, moreish bitter, with a well-balanced, bitter-sweet, fruity finish.

Head *(OG 1054, ABV 5.8%)*
Fruity aroma and taste with a pleasant bitter finish. Dark brown and full-bodied.

OUTLAW

See Rooster's.

PACIFIC ORIENTAL

 ⚲ **Pacific Oriental, 1 Bishopsgate, London, EC2N 3AB**
Tel (020) 7621 9988

Pacific Oriental is a state-of-the-art boutique brewery based in the heart of the City of London. Brewing started in 1998 and the permanent brews are a Pilsner lager and a bitter with at least one other beer always on offer. These include a wheat beer, a golden ale and a red beer. The copper brewhouse is on full display at the front of the restaurant. The beers are filtered and served by mixed gas dispense. Beers: Bishops (ABV 4.5%), Pils (ABV 5%).

PACKHORSE

Packhorse Brewing Co Ltd, 5 Somers Road, Southsea, Portsmouth, Hampshire, PO5 4PR
Tel (01705) 750450

Packhorse Brewery was resurrected in Portsmouth from the former Ashford Brewery. It produces infusion mash, 100 per cent malt ales as opposed to the decoction lagers of the Ashford days. Seasonal beer: Rudolph's Revenge (ABV 7.9%).

Southern Star ASA *(ABV 3.5%)*

Best Bitter *(ABV 3.8%)*

Old Pompey *(ABV 4.8%)*

PALMER

JC & RH Palmer Ltd, Old Brewery, Bridport, Dorset, DT6 4JA
Tel (01308) 422396
Fax (01308) 421149
E-mail enquiries@palmersbrewery.com
Website www.palmersbrewery.com
Shop 9-6 Mon-Thu; 9-8 Fri-Sat
Tours by arrangement (01308) 427500

⊗ Palmers is Britain's only thatched brewery, founded in 1794, and situated by the sea in an idyllic location in West Dorset. The company is run by brothers John and Cleeves Palmer, great-grandsons of Robert Henry and John Cleeves Palmer, who bought the company in 1896. Its tenanted estate of 60 pubs all offer real ale. A further 100 free trade outlets are supplied direct, and Palmer's beers reach a wider audience throughout the south via wholesalers. Dorset Gold was added to the portfolio in 1999 and has been a great success. Occasional beer: Tally Ho! (ABV 5.5%). Bottle-conditioned beers: Palmers 200 and Tally Ho!

Bridport Bitter *(OG 1030, ABV 3.2%)* ◈
A light beer with a hoppy aroma, a bitter

hoppy taste with some malt, and a bitter aftertaste.

Dorset Gold *(OG 1036, ABV 3.7%)* ◆
Darker than might be expected, almost copper, with a light body that can become cloying. Hop and fruit dominate from the aroma right through to the dry, bitter finish.

IPA *(OG 1040, ABV 4.2%)* ◆
A deep copper beer that is hoppy and bitter throughout. Fruit and malt undertones give some balance in the aroma and taste, and there is a lingering bitter aftertaste.

200 Premium Ale *(OG 1052, ABV 5%)* ◆
Full-bodied, caramel sweetness and fruity aroma are balanced with a dry finish, not excessively bitter. A deep-copper ale, originally brewed to mark the brewery's 200th anniversary.

PARADISE*

2 Creamery Industrial Estate, Wrenbury Road, Wrenbury, Nantwich, Cheshire, CW5 8EX
Tel/Fax (01270) 780916

Paradise was founded by partners John Wood and Nick Platt, who traded as Paradise Plastics and turned to brewing when there was a recession in the plastics industry. The brewery is based in a former creamery. Seasonal beer: Rum Old Ale (ABV 6%).

Marbury Mild *(ABV 3.6%)*

Wrenbury Ale *(ABV 4%)*

Bitter *(ABV 4.2%)*

Wynbunbury Red *(ABV 4.5%)*

Premium Bitter *(ABV 4.5%)*

Dabbers Delight *(ABV 4.8%)*

Dabbers Gold *(ABV 5%)*

IPA *(ABV 5.6%)*

PARISH

⚑ **Parish Brewery, Courtyard of The Old Brewery Inn, High Street, Somerby, Leicestershire, LE14 2PZ**
Tel (01664) 454801 Fax (01664) 454777
Tours by arrangement

⊠ Parish started life at Burrough on the Hill in 1982 and moved to its present location after expanding to a 20-barrel plant in 1992. The Parish Brewery was one of the first brew-pubs to start up in the Midlands and is famous for brewing the strongest beer in the world, with an ABV of 23%, as listed in the Guinness Book of Records. It currently supplies 20 local outlets.

Mild *(OG 1038, ABV 3.7%)*

Parish Special Bitter or PSB *(OG 1040, ABV 3.9%)*

Farm Gold *(OG 1039, ABV 3.9%)*

Somerby Premium *(OG 1040, ABV 4%)*

Poachers Ale *(OG 1060, ABV 6%)*

Baz's Bonce Blower *(OG 1100, ABV 10-11%)*

PASSAGEWAY

Passageway Brewing Co, Unit G8, Queens Dock Commercial Centre, Norfolk Street, Liverpool, Merseyside, L1 0BG
Tel (0151) 708 0730 Fax (0151) 709 0925
Tours by arrangement

⊛ Adventurous brewery established in 1994 that experiments with continental beer styles. Yeast from a Belgian monastic brewery is used, and some water from St Arnold's Well in Belgium is added to the copper during each brew of St Arnold (named after Belgium's patron saint of brewers). 50 outlets are supplied direct.

Genuine Blonde Wheat Beer *(OG 1042, ABV 4.2%)* ◆
Naturally cloudy wheat beer with complex fruit and hoppy flavours and a distinctive aroma. Available in fined and unfined versions.

Czech Pils *(ABV 4.2%)*

German Pils *(ABV 4.2%)*

St Arnold *(OG 1050, ABV 5%)* ◆
Deep ruby in colour, this is a bitter and fruity beer, yet not sweet. Hop, roast malt, chocolate and liquorice flavours also fight for attention in the taste and dry aftertaste. A complex, heavy beer, reminiscent of a Belgian brown ale.

Dubbel *(OG 1060, ABV 6%)*

Tripel *(OG 1065, ABV 7%)*

PAYN

Payn Breweries Ltd, Unit 1 Eco Site, St Mary's Road, Ramsey, Huntingdon, Cambs, PE26 2SJ
Tel (01487) 710800
Fax (01487) 710900
E-mail sales@payn.co.uk
Website www.payn.co.uk
Tours by arrangement

Payn Breweries is an amalgamation of Nene, Leyland and Wincott breweries, and holds all the recipes from these companies. The new brewery was built in Ramsey in 1999, using most of the original equipment, and has a current capacity of 50 barrels a week. 200 plus outlets are supplied direct. Seasonal and occasional beers: Santa's Tipple (ABV 8%), Slated (ABV 3.6%, Christmas), St George's Day Bitter (ABV 3.8%).

Archers Rebuff *(OG 1035, ABV 3.5%)*
A balance of malt and hops with a dry bitter finish; rich chestnut colour.

Bullseye *(OG 1038, ABV 3.8%)*
An amber-coloured ale with a hop and fruity aroma. Well-balanced with a refreshingly smooth hop and malt flavour.

Fenland Gold *(OG 1042, ABV 4.2%)*
A light golden fruity ale with a fine balance of honey plus Fuggles and Goldings hops, which gives a gentle, bitter finish.

Fred's Favourite Fist Full
(OG 1042, ABV 4.2%)
A rich, nutty, clean-tasting brew, with a good balance of Fuggles, Goldings and a hint of Challenger hops; a smooth, well-rounded malty finish.

Ramsey Pride *(OG 1050, ABV 5%)*
A full malt brew with a strong body, and a rich fruit and hop flavour, with a remarkably smooth taste and a long, dry finish.

Strong Old Noll *(OG 1081, ABV 8%)*
A full flavour with a surprisingly smooth taste, with plenty of rich hop and barley flavour.

Ramsey Ruin *(OG 1320, ABV 13%)*
An exceptionally strong traditional English ale. Full hop flavour with a slightly sweet taste.

PEMBROKE

Pembroke Brewery Co, Unit 17, Kingswood Industrial Estate, London Road, Pembroke Dock, Pembrokeshire, SA71 4HN
Tel (01646) 682517
Fax (01646) 682008
Website
www.pembrokeshire.org/pembroke_brewery
Tours by arrangement

⊗ A brewery started in 1994 in former stables to the rear of the owner's house. It moved to new premises in June 2001. A tied house, the Station Inn, is in Pembroke Dock. The pub serves a new test brew each week and stages an annual beer festival. 10-15 outlets are supplied direct. Seasonal beers: Sound Whistle (ABV 3.8%, summer), Signal Failure (ABV 6%, winter).

The Darklin Mild *(OG 1035, ABV 3.5%)*

Two Cannons Extra *(OG 1036, ABV 3.6%)*

Dimond Lager *(OG 1041, ABV 4.1%)* ◆
A straw-coloured lager-style brew with a light hoppy aroma with sweetness balancing the bitterness to give a robust finish.

Main Street Bitter *(OG 1041, ABV 4.1%)*

Golden Hill Ale *(OG 1045, ABV 4.5%)*

Old Nobby Stout *(OG 1045, ABV 4.5%)* ◆
A drinkable stout with aroma of roast and caramel coming through on the palate. The slight bitterness gives way to sweetness in the finish.

Off the Rails *(OG 1051, ABV 5.1%)*

PHOENIX

Oak Brewing Co Ltd t/a Phoenix Brewery, Phoenix Brewery, Green Lane, Heywood, Greater Manchester, OL10 2EP
Tel (01706) 627009
E-mail phoenixbrewery@btclick.co.uk
Tours by arrangement

☺ A company established as Oak Brewery in 1982 at Ellesmere Port, it moved in 1991 to Heywood and changed its name in 1996 to Phoenix (after the original name of the brewery it occupies). It now supplies more than 450 free trade outlets mostly in the North-west and West Yorkshire. Seasonal beers: Black Shadow (ABV 4%, May), Whirlwind (ABV 4.1%, October), Jovian

(ABV 4.2%, February), Snowbound (ABV 4.3%, Nov-Feb), Spinning Jenny (ABV 4.3%, October), March Hare (ABV 4.4%, March), May Fly (ABV 4.4%, May), Christmas Kiss (ABV 4.5%, Nov-Dec), Midsummer Madness (ABV 4.5%, June-Aug), Tennis Elbow (ABV 4.5%, July), Sticky Wicket (ABV 4.7%, June-Sept), Struggling Monkey (ABV 4.7%, June), White Tornado (ABV 4.3%, Sept-Oct), Flashflood (ABV 4.1%, Sept-Xmas), Last Leaf (ABV 4.5%, Oct-Nov), Porter (ABV 5%, Nov-Jan), Humbug (ABV 7%, Oct-Jan; matured for six months), Golden Glow (ABV 6.5%, Xmas).

Bantam *(ABV 3.5%)* ◆
Light brown beer with a fruity aroma. Balance of malt, citrus fruit and hop in taste. Hoppy, bitter finish.

Monkey Town Mild *(ABV 3.9%)*

Best Bitter *(ABV 3.9%)*

Arizona *(ABV 4.1%)*

Pale Moonlight *(ABV 4.2%)*

Hopwood Bitter *(ABV 4.3%)* ◆
Amber beer with a hoppy, fruity nose and palate. Dry, hoppy finish.

White Monk *(ABV 4.5%)*

Old Oak *(ABV 4.5%)* ◆
A well-balanced, brown beer with a multitude of mellow fruit flavours. Malt and hops balance the strong fruitiness in the aroma and taste and the finish is malty, fruity and dry.

Thirsty Moon *(ABV 4.6%)* ◆
Fruity, malty aroma to this amber beer. Malt, fruit and bitter taste and a dry, hoppy finish.

Double Dagger *(ABV 5%)* ◆
A pale brown, malty brew, more pleasantly dry and light than its gravity would suggest. Moderately fruity throughout; a hoppy bitterness in the mouth balances the strong graininess.

Wobbly Bob *(ABV 6%)* ◆
A red/brown beer with a malty, fruity aroma. Strongly malty and fruity in flavour and quite hoppy, with the sweetness yielding to a dryness in the aftertaste.

PICKS

Picks Brewery, Willows Lane, Green Haworth, Accrington, Lancashire, BB5 3SJ
Tel (01254) 233194
Tours by arrangement

The brewery was originally sited in the cellar of the Red Lion pub in Green Haworth, but in 2000 it moved into a nearby industrial unit, converting 5-barrel beer tanks to make hot liquor tank, mash tun, copper, one fermenter and two conditioning tanks. Owner Steven Pickles has started supplying the free trade, with just a few local outlets. Six regular beers are produced and he plans to produce a real lager for the summer.

Moorgate Mild *(OG 1035, ABV 3.5%)*
A smooth, grainy, chocolate and coffee cream mild. Red-brown in colour, it is not oversweet, with a long, gently hopped aftertaste.

Pale Ale (OG 1036, ABV 3.7%)
Soft lemon and honey notes at the beginning, with a lingering bitter-dry end. A straw-coloured refreshing pint.

Bedlam Bitter (OG 1038, ABV 3.9%)
Complex sour and barley sugar flavours. Astringent throughout, pepper-dry at the end. A red-gold bitter.

Lions Main (OG 1041, ABV 4.2%)

Porter (OG 1042, ABV 4.5%)
Impenetrably dark beer, it has an immediate strong black coffee flavour, leading to a dry finish. A pronounced, teeth-coating maltiness throughout.

Lions Pride (OG 1049, ABV 4.9%)
A pale premium bitter, strong but sweet and deceptively easy-drinking. Golden in colour, it builds to a malty finish.

PICTISH

Pictish Brewing Company, Unit 9, Canalside Industrial Estate, Woodbine Street East, Rochdale, Lancs, OL16 5LB
Tel/Fax (01706) 522227
Tours by arrangement

Brewery established in 2000 by Richard Sutton, formerly senior brewer for the north with the Firkin Brewery until Punch Taverns took over the former Allied Domecq estate and closed the Firkin chain in 1999. The brewery supplies free trade outlets in the North-west direct. Seasonal beers: Summer Solstice (ABV 4.7%, May-Aug), Porter (4.4%, Nov-March). There are regular monthly specials.

Brewers Gold (OG 1038, ABV 3.8%) ◆
Yellow in colour, with a hoppy, fruity nose. Strong hop/fruit flavour with a dry, bitterness coming through in the aftertaste.

Celtic Warrior (OG 1042, ABV 4.2%)

PILGRIM

Pilgrim Ales, The Old Brewery, West Street, Reigate, Surrey, RH2 9BL
Tel (01737) 222651   Fax (01737) 225785
E-mail david@pilgrim.co.uk
Website www.pilgrim.co.uk

✪ Set up by Dave Roberts in 1982, and based in Reigate since 1985, Pilgrim has gradually increased its capacity and its beers have won both local and national awards, although sales are mostly concentrated in the Surrey area (around 60 outlets). Seasonal beers: Autumnal (ABV 4.5%, Sept-Oct), Excalibur (ABV 4.5%, March-May), Pudding (ABV 7.3%, Nov-Jan). Bottle-conditioned beers: Springbock (ABV 5.2%), Pudding (ABV 6.8%). The draught version of Springbock, originally cask-conditioned, is now a pressurised keg beer.

Surrey Bitter (OG 1037, ABV 3.7%) ◆
A clean, well-balanced session bitter. Hop flavour comes through in the finish.

Porter (OG 1040, ABV 4%) ◆
This porter, with a rich mouthfeel, has a good balance of dark malts, with berry fruit flavours declining to a short finish.

Progress (OG 1040, ABV 4%) ◆
Reddish-brown in colour, with a predominantly malty flavour and aroma, although hops are also evident in the taste.

Talisman (OG 1049, ABV 5%) ◆
A strong ale with a mid-brown colour, a fruity, malt flavour and a faint hoppiness.

PITFIELD

Pitfield Brewery, The Beer Shop, 14 Pitfield Street, London, N1 6EY
Tel (020) 7739 3701
Website www.pitfieldbeershop.co.uk
Shop 11-7 Mon-Fri; 10-4 Sat. Tours by arrangement

✪ The Beer Shop was founded in 1980 to supply real ale and international bottled beers. A 5-barrel brewery was installed to produce Pitfield Bitter. Dark Star was introduced in 1985 and in 1987 won the title of Best New Beer and was runner-up in the Champion Beer of Britain competition. The following year, it won the overall Champion Beer of Britain title; the beer has now been renamed Black Eagle. In the summer of 1996 The Beer Shop moved into larger premises, with the brewery in one building and the shop next door. In 2000, in response to the success of Eco Warrior, Pitfield converted all its beers to organic ingredients. Six outlets are supplied direct.

Original (OG 1037, ABV 3.7%) ◆
Bitterness balanced with sweetness producing a pleasant, hoppy/fruity bitter. Dry finish.

East Kent Goldings
(OG 1042, ABV 4.2%) ◆
Impressive, dryish and fruity yellow beer with a pleasant level of bitterness and a lingering citrus flavour. Some floral notes on the aroma.

Eco Warrior (OG 1045, ABV 4.5%) ◆
Yellow/gold ale with a smooth, rounded mouthfeel, balanced malt and hops and a bitter, dry aftertaste.

Hoxton Best Bitter (OG 1048, ABV 4.8%) ◆
Previously named Hoxton Heavy, a smooth, deceptively easy-drinking beer for the strength. Malt and fruit are well-balanced and pear notes persist in the dry aftertaste.

Black Eagle (OG 1050, ABV 5%) ◆
A light-drinking strong old ale, black with red hues, a lasting roast malt flavour and a malty, dryish aftertaste.

Shoreditch 1850 Porter
(OG 1050, ABV 5%)

PLASSEY

Plassey Brewery, The Plassey, Eyton, Wrexham, LL13 0SP
Tel (01978) 780922   Fax (01978) 781195
Website www.plasseybrewery.co.uk
Shop 1.30-5 Wed-Sun winter; 1.30-5 Tue-Sun summer
Tours by arrangement

Brewery founded in 1985 on the 250-acre Plassey Estate, which also incorporates a touring caravan park, craft centres, a golf course, three licensed outlets for Plassey's ales, and a brewery shop. 30 free trade outlets also take the beers. Seasonal beer: Ruddy Rudolph (ABV 4.5%, Christmas). Bottle-conditioned beer: Royal Welch Fusilier (ABV 4.5%).

Bitter *(OG 1041, ABV 4%)* ◆
Full-bodied and distinctive best bitter. Good balance of hops and fruit flavours with a lasting dry bitter aftertaste.

Royal Welch Fusilier
(OG 1046, ABV 4.5%) ▨

Welsh Stout *(OG 1046, ABV 4.6%)* ◆
A dry, roasty stout, sweetish; a long, dry finish.

Cwrw Tudno *(OG 1048, ABV 5%)* ▨▢◆
A mellow sweetish premium beer with classic Plassey flavours of fruit and hops.

Dragon's Breath *(OG 1060, ABV 6%)* ◆
A fruity, strong bitter, smooth and quite sweet, though not cloying, with an intense, fruity aroma. A dangerously drinkable winter warmer.

PLOUGH INN

⚲ Bodicote Brewery, The Plough, 9 High Street, Bodicote, Banbury, Oxon, OX15 4BZ
Tel (01295) 262327
E-mail bodicotebrewery@tinyworld.co.uk
Website
www.banbury-cross.co.uk/bodicotebrewery
Tours by arrangement

⊗ Brewery founded in 1982 at the Plough, which has been in the same hands since 1957. Two other outlets are also supplied with its full-mash beers. Two popular, week-long beer festivals are held each year in February and August. Seasonal beers: Three Goslings (ABV 3.9%, May-Oct), Old English Porter (ABV 4.4%, Oct-May).

Bodicote Bitter *(OG 1035, ABV 3.3%)*

No. 9 *(OG 1044, ABV 4.3%)*

Triple X *(OG 1060, ABV 6.3%)*

POINTS WEST*

Points West Brewery, Plymouth College of Further Education, Kings Road, Devonport, Plymouth, Devon, PL1 5QG
Tel (01752) 305890

The brewery was set up for catering students, but the beers are available commercially for pubs and beer festivals. Brewer/lecturer Roger Pengelly bought the 5-barrel plant from Bitter End in Cumbria, though the kit was actually made in France. As well as the two regular beers, brewed by Roger and his students, there are experimental brews: the kit can be tweaked to produce just one barrel.

HLB *(ABV 4.2%)*

Blackout Stout *(ABV 4.4%)*

POOLE

Brewhouse Brewery, 68 High Street, Poole, Dorset, BH15 1DA
Tel (01202) 682345
Tours by arrangement, limited to CAMRA members

Brewery established in 1980 by David Rawlins, who opened the Brewhouse pub in 1983. The brewery now has a capacity to brew about 1,000 barrels a year, and serves more than 15 outlets direct with a widespread free trade through wholesalers.

Seasonal/occasional beers: Pie-eyed Pudding (ABV 4.5%), Holes Bay Hog (ABV 4.5%).

Dolphin Best Bitter *(OG 1038, ABV 3.8%)*
The brewery's original session bitter: amber-coloured and well balanced.

Bosun Bitter *(OG 1045, ABV 4.6%)* .
The brewery's top-selling beer. A rich, amber-coloured beer with a smooth, crisp, powerful malty flavour and a pronounced hoppy aftertaste.

For Hogshead (on demand)

Hedgehog *(ABV 5.2%)*

PORTCHESTER*

Portchester Brewery, 6 Audret Close, Portchester, Fareham, Hants, PO16 9ER
Tel/Fax (01329) 512918
Website www.portchesterbrewery.co.uk

A tiny brewery, able to produce just nine gallons a time, set up in the garage of Gill Stone's home. After years of home-brewing, Gill was encouraged by her husband Graham (both are keen CAMRA members) to 'go commercial' in December 2000, as they were fed up with over-priced beer in pubs. Dr Graham Stone used his knowledge from his biology and physics doctorate to help Gill make the perfect pint. She is now supplying a few pubs and clubs in the locality, and hopes to upgrade to a 2-barrel plant; when she first started, she mashed in a converted top-loading washing machine, though it has since been replaced. The beers are named in honour of Portchester Castle.

Bastion *(ABV 3.8%)*

Caterpult *(ABV 4.8%)*

Battering Ram *(ABV 5%)*

PORTER

Porter Brewing Co Ltd, Rossendale Brewery, The Griffin Inn, 84-86 Hud Rake, Haslingden, Lancs, BB4 5AF
Tel/Fax (01706) 214021
Tours by arrangement

⊗ The Griffin Inn opened in 1994 and now has five tied houses. All five pubs sell a minimum of five house ales. All the pubs serve cask ale and a few other local outlets also take the beer. Occasional/seasonal beers: Timmy's Ginger Beer (ABV 4.2%, March and August), Stout (ABV 5.5%, Sept-Oct), Sleighed (ABV 6.5%, Dec-Jan), Celebration Ale (ABV 7.1%, July-Aug).

Dark Mild *(OG 1033, ABV 3.3%)*
A true dark mild, with a slight maltiness and a good hint of roast in the finish.

Floral Dance *(OG 1035, ABV 3.6%)*
Pale and fruity.

Bitter *(OG 1037, ABV 3.8%)* ◆
Unusually dark for a standard bitter, this beer has a dry and assertively bitter character that develops in the finish.

Railway Sleeper *(OG 1040, ABV 4.2%)*
Intensely bitter and hoppy.

Rossendale Ale *(OG 1041, ABV 4.2%)* ◆
A malty aroma leads to a complex, malt-dominated flavour supported by a dry, increasingly bitter finish.

Young Tom *(OG 1045, ABV 4.6%)*
Dark brown with chocolate flavour
dominant.

Porter *(OG 1050, ABV 5%)*
A rich beer with a slightly sweet, malty start,
counter-balanced with sharp bitterness and
a noticeable roast barley dominance.

Sunshine *(OG 1050, ABV 5.3%)*
An intensely hoppy and bitter golden ale,
full-bodied with some malt, a robust
mouthfeel and a lingering bitterness.

POTTON

**Potton Brewery Company,
10 Shannon Place, Potton, Sandy,
Beds, SG19 2PZ
Tel (01767) 261042
Website www.potton-brewery.co.uk**
Tours by arrangement

Run by Clive Towner and Robert Hearson,
both ex-managers of Greene King at
Biggleswade, they resurrected the Potton
Brewery Company name after it
disappeared as a result of a takeover in
1922. 100 outlets are supplied direct. Bottle-
conditioned beers: Butlers Ale (ABV 4.3%),
and Shambles. Potton also makes a draught
cider, Sam's Potton Mix (ABV 6%).

Potton No I *(OG 1037, ABV 3.2%)*

Shannon IPA *(OG 1035, ABV 3.6%)*

Phoenix *(OG 1040, ABV 3.8%)*

Shambles *(OG 1042, ABV 4.3%)*

Village Bike *(OG 1042, ABV 4.3%)*

Potton Gold *(ABV 4.8%)*

Pride of Potton *(OG 1057, ABV 6%)* ◆
Impressive, robust amber ale with a malty
aroma, malt and ripe fruit in the mouth,
and a fading sweetness.

PRINCETOWN

**Princetown Breweries Ltd, The Brewery,
Tavistock Road, Princetown,
Devon, PL20 6QF
Tel (01822) 890789
Fax (01822) 890798**
Tours by arrangement

⊗ A brewery established in 1994 by a former
Gibbs Mew and Hop Back brewer, capacity
has been increased to 45 barrels a week.
It supplies two hotels owned by a sister
company, the pub next door and 16 other
local outlets. Bottle-conditioned beer:
Jail Ale.

Dartmoor IPA *(OG 1039.5, ABV 4%)* ◆
Flowery hop aroma and taste with a bitter
aftertaste to this full-bodied, amber-
coloured beer.

Jail Ale *(OG 1047.5, ABV 4.8%)* ◆
Hops and fruit predominate in the flavour
of this mid-brown beer, which has a slightly
sweet aftertaste.

QUAY

**The Quay Brewery t/a Lapin Noir,
Brewers Quay, Hope Square,
Weymouth, Dorset, DT4 8TR
Tel (01305) 777515**
Shop 10-5.30 daily. Tours by arrangement

⊗ Brewery set up in summer 1996 in the
old Devenish and Groves brewery buildings,
10 years after the closure of Devenish. The
brewery is open to visitors as part of the
Timewalk attraction. A Victorian Tastings
Bar and shop opened in Easter 1997. Two
additional 5-barrel fermenters were added in
1998. 100 outlets take the beers. Seasonal
beers: Summer Knight (ABV 3.8%), Silent
Knight (ABV 5.9%, winter). Occasional beer:
Groves Oatmeal Stout (ABV 4.7%). There is
also a rotating monthly beer programme:
each beer is ABV 4%.

Weymouth Harbour Master
(OG 1036, ABV 3.6%) ◆
Well-balanced, nut-brown session beer,
sweetish, but not cloying, thanks to the dry
finish. May be badged by pubs as a house
beer.

Weymouth JD 1742
(OG 1038-42, ABV 4.2%) ◆
Clean-tasting, easy-drinking bitter. Well-
balanced with lingering bitterness after
moderate sweetness.

Weymouth Organic Gold *(ABV 4.7%)*

Old Rot *(OG 1048-50, ABV 5%)* ◆
Warming finish despite a rather light
caramel and malt taste. Hint of sulphur and
yeastiness throughout.

QUEEN'S HEAD

⛉ **Fat God's Brewery, Queen's Head,
Iron Cross, Evesham,
Worcs, WR11 5SH
Tel (01386) 871012
Fax (01386) 871362
E-mail fatgod@globalnet.co.uk
Website www.fatgodsbrewery.co.uk**

⊗ The pub has been operated by Andy and
Kym Miller since 1986 and the brewery was
installed in 1997. Brewing capacity was
doubled in 2001. Full-mash beers are
available direct from the brewery within a
50-mile radius. Seasonal beers: Merry Millers
Rusty Dusty (ABV 4%, autumn), Merry
Millers Summer Sensation (ABV 4.3%),
Merry Millers Spring Celebration (ABV
4.5%), Merry Millers Winter Wobbler (ABV
4.9%, Nov-Feb).

Fat God's Bitter
(OG 1036, ABV 3.6%) ✤
Balanced between maltiness and hoppiness, this mainly hoppy beer leaves a clean, dry aftertaste.

Morris Dancer *(OG 1039, ABV 3.9%)*

Porter of the Vale
(OG 1041, ABV 4.1%)

Thunder and Lightning
(OG 1042, ABV 4.3%) ✤
Malt is the main taste in this premium bitter. Hops are there in the mouth, but the final impression is one of malt.

RAILWAY TAVERN

◻ Famous Railway Tavern Brewing Co,
58 Station Road, Brightlingsea,
Essex, CO7 0DT
Tel (01206) 302581
Tours by arrangement

The brewery started life as a kitchen-sink affair, with Crab & Winkle Mild the staple brew. Crouch Vale Brewery obtained two fermenters from Vaux for the Railway Tavern and today two barrels are brewed every fortnight. It is hoped to increase this amount.

Crab & Winkle Mild
(OG 1040, ABV 3.7%)

Sprat & Oyster Bitter
(OG 1040, ABV 3.7%)

Bladderwrack Stout
(OG 1050, ABV 4.7%)

RAINBOW

◻ Rainbow Inn & Brewery,
73 Birmingham Road,
Allesley Village, Coventry,
W Midlands, CV5 9GT
Tel (024) 76402888
Fax (024) 76407415
Tours by arrangement

Pub brewery that started brewing in 1994 with a 2-barrel plant, upgraded to 4-barrels in 1996.

Piddlebrook *(OG 1037, ABV 3.8%)*

RANDALLS

RH Randall Ltd, St Julian's Avenue,
St Peter Port, Guernsey,
CI, GY1 3JG
Tel (01481) 720134
Shop 10-5 Mon-Sat. Tours by arrangement

⊠ The smaller of Guernsey's two breweries, it was purchased by RH Randall from Joseph Gullick in 1868. Successive generations have continued to run the business, except during the period of the German occupation, when it ceased brewing until after the war. Randalls owns 22 pubs (18 of which are tied) but only three serve real ale. Do not confuse with Randalls Vautier of Jersey, which no longer brews. Occasional beer: Stout (ABV 7%). Bottle-conditioned beers: Mild (ABV 3.4%), Bitter (ABV 5%).

Patois Ale *(OG 1046, ABV 5%)* ✤
Amber in colour, with a hoppy aroma. Bitter and hoppy both in the palate and finish.

RAT & RATCHET

◻ Rat & Ratchet Brewery,
40 Chapel Hill, Huddersfield,
W Yorkshire, HD1 3EB
Tel (01484) 516734
Website www.ratandratchet.co.uk
Tours by arrangement

An ale house where beer has been brewed since 1994 to supply the pub and occasional beer festivals. The brewing plant was upgraded to 3.5 barrels in 2000, the former plant having been sold to the new Anglo Dutch Brewery (qv) in Dewsbury. There is a rolling programme of beers using different versions of Rat. Seasonal beer: Winter Weser Weisse (ABV 4.5%)

White Mouse *(ABV 3.5%)* ✤
A very pale, hoppy bitter with a good balance of malt and fruity flavours, and a dry citrussy finish.

Silver Shrew *(ABV 3.7%)* ✤
Light pale, hoppy bitter with a delicate fruity aroma and taste.

Trap Tickler *(ABV 4.1%)* ✤
Straw-coloured pale bitter with an intense citrus flavour. Fruit and malt are evident throughout, leading to a dry, zesty and bitter finish.

Big Nipper *(ABV 4.5%)* ✤
Pale golden bitter with a good malt and hop balance, and fruity overtones throughout.

White Rat *(ABV 4.9%)*

RCH

RCH Brewery, West Hewish,
Weston-super-Mare,
Somerset, BS24 6RR
Tel (01934) 834447
Fax (01934) 834167
E-mail rchbrew@aol.com
Shop. Tours by arrangement

⊠ The brewery was originally installed by previous owners in the early 1980s behind the Royal Clarence Hotel at Burnham-on-Sea. But since 1993 brewing has taken place on a commercial basis in a former cider mill at West Hewish. A new 30-barrel plant was installed in 2000. RCH now supplies 100 outlets direct and the award-winning beers are available nationwide through its own wholesaling company, which also distributes beers from other small independent breweries. Bottle-conditioned beers: Pitchfork, Old Slug Porter, Firebox, Ale Mary (ABV 6%) 🍾.

Hewish IPA *(ABV 3.6%)* ✤
Light, hoppy bitter with some malt and fruit, though slightly less fruit in the finish. Floral, citrus hop aroma, pale brown/amber colour.

PG Steam *(ABV 3.9%)* 🗋✤
Amber-coloured, medium-bodied with a floral hop aroma with some fruit. Hoppy and bitter, with some malt, fruit and subtle sweetness. Finish is similar.

Pitchfork *(ABV 4.3%)* 🍾🗋✤
Floral citrus hop with pale malt. Yellow/gold in colour, hops predominate in a full-bodied taste, which is slightly sweet. Long finish — a class act.

Old Slug Porter *(ABV 4.5%)* 🗎✎
Chocolate, coffee, roast malt and hops with lots of body and dark fruits. A complex, rich stout, dark brown in colour.

East Street Cream *(ABV 5%)* 🗎✎
Superb premium ale, pale brown in colour, it is malty with chocolate hints, hoppy, fruity and bitter-sweet. All flavours vie for dominance in what is a notable and well-crafted ale.

Double Header *(ABV 6%)*

Firebox *(ABV 6%)* ✎
Mid-brown, it has a pleasant combination of malt, floral citrus hops and bitter-sweet fruit flavours. Full-bodied, smooth and full-flavoured.

READING LION

⚲ **Reading Lion Brewery, The Hop Leaf, 163-165 Southampton Street, Reading, Berks, RG1 2QZ**
Tel (0118) 931 4700
Tours by arrangement

⊠ A pub-brewery opened by Hop Back in 1995 at the Hop Leaf pub. It was Reading's first real ale brewery since Courage closed the old Simonds site in the late 1970s. The 5-barrel plant came from the Wyndham Arms in Salisbury, and beers are stored in both casks and cellar tanks (no blanket pressure). Beers are brewed only on an occasional basis. Beers: Hop Leaf Bitter (ABV 4.2%), Rye & Coriander (ABV 4.2%).

REBELLION

Rebellion Beer Company, Bencombe Farm, Marlow Bottom, Bucks, SL7 3LT
Tel/Fax (01628) 476594
E-mail tim@rebellionbeer.freeserve.co.uk
Website www.rebellionbeer.co.uk
Shop 8-6 Mon-Fri; 9-4 Sat
Tours by arrangement (CAMRA branches only)

⊠ Opened in 1993, Rebellion fills the gap left in Marlow by Whitbread, which shut down Wethereds in 1988. Rebellion moved to a new site in Marlow and increased brewing capacity from 50 to 200 barrels a week, when it bought a pilot brewery from Courage at Reading. The new brewery will now allow Rebellion to grow and produce a much wider range of beer styles. 160 outlets are supplied direct. Seasonal beers: Overdraft (ABV 4.3%, spring), Zebedee (ABV 4.7%, spring), Blonde Bombshell (4.3%, summer) 🍺, Red Oktober (ABV 4.7%, autumn), Roasted Nuts (ABV 4.6%, winter), Old Codger (ABV 5%, winter).

IPA *(OG 1039, ABV 3.7%)* ✎
Copper-coloured bitter, sweet and malty, with resinous and red apple flavours. Caramel and fruit decline to leave a dry, bitter and malty finish.

Smuggler *(OG 1042, ABV 4.1%)* ✎
A red-brown beer, well-bodied and bitter with an uncompromisingly dry, bitter finish.

Mutiny *(OG 1046, ABV 4.5%)* ✎
Tawny in colour, this full-bodied best bitter is predominantly fruity and moderately bitter with crystal malt continuing to a dry finish.

For Scanlons

Spike *(ABV 4.5%)*

RECTORY

Rectory Ales Ltd, Streat Hill Farm Outbuilding, Streat Hill, Streat, Hassocks, W Sussex, BN6 8RP
Tel/Fax (01273) 890570
E-mail sales@rectory-ales.co.uk
Tours by arrangement

⊠ Rectory was founded in 1995 by the Rector of Plumpton, the Rev Godfrey Broster, to generate funds for the maintenance of his three parish churches. 107 parishioners are shareholders. The brewing capacity is now 20 barrels a week. Some seasonal beers are produced. All outlets are supplied direct. Seasonal beer: Christmas Cheer (ABV 3.8%, December). Bottle-conditioned beer: Rector's Revenge (ABV 5.4%).

The Rector's Ale *(OG 1038, ABV 3.8%)*

Rector's Revenge *(OG 1054, ABV 5.4%)*
Copper-brown strong bitter with a complex aroma, becoming more hoppy in the mouth with a dry, bitter finish.

REDRUTH

Redruth Brewery (1742) Ltd, The Brewery, Redruth, Cornwall, TR15 1RB
Tel (01209) 212244
Fax (01209) 313793,
(01209) 210383 for orders
Website www.redruth-brewery.com
Shop noon-6 Mon-Fri; 10-4 Sat
Tours by arrangement

Since May 1995, Redruth Brewery (formerly Devenish) has been owned by the Hong Kong-based Dransfield Group. Cask-conditioned beer was re-established in 1998 after a break of nearly 10 years. It is still a large brewery with the capacity to increase barrelage significantly when required. Most of the activity centres on bottling and canning. There is no tied estate, with cask ale sold through the free trade in the South-west, although occasional contracts with J D Wetherspoon and The Beer Seller have given Redruth a higher national profile. More than 200 outlets are supplied in the South-west. Seasonal beers: Rudolph the Redruth Brain Beer (ABV 5.5%, Christmas). Occasional beers: Steam Brewed Bitter (ABV 5%, for Beer Seller), Crofty Cornish Bitter (ABV 3.6%), Miners Mild (ABV 3.6%).

Cornish Original *(OG 1042, ABV 4.1%)*
A cask ale based on an old traditional recipe. Amber in colour with a fruity flavour and a well-balanced hoppy character.

Cornish Rebellion *(OG 1049, ABV 4.8%)*
A full-flavoured, mid-brown beer with a strong hoppy aroma.

RED SHOOT

⚲ **Red Shoot Brewery, Toms Lane, Linwood, Ringwood, Hampshire, SP6 3RB**
Tel (01425) 475792
Website www.redshootinn.co.uk

The brewery, owned by Wadworth, was commissioned at Easter 1998 with Forest

Gold as the first brew. Tom's Tipple was introduced in 1998 as a winter brew and is now a permanent brand. Red Shoot would like to expand but the size of plant (2.5 barrels) makes this difficult, though some occasional beers are produced.

Forest Gold *(ABV 3.8%)*

Tom's Tipple *(ABV 4.8%)*

REEPHAM

Reepham Brewery, Unit 1, Collers Way, Reepham, Norwich, Norfolk, NR10 4SW
Tel (01603) 871091

⊗ A family-owned micro-brewery started by an ex-Watney research engineer and a retired architect in 1983. The purpose-built brewing plant was supplied by 'micro-brewing father' Peter Austin. Awards have been won for six years at the Norwich Beer Festivals, including Champion Beer twice with Velvet Sweet Stout. Some 20 outlets are supplied direct. Seasonal beers: Norfolk Wheaten (ABV 4.5%, summer); Brewhouse (ABV 5.5%, winter). Bottle-conditioned beer: Rapier Pale Ale.

Granary Bitter *(OG 1038, ABV 3.8%)* 🗂❖
A gold-coloured beer with a light hoppy aroma followed by a malty sweetish flavour with some smoke notes. A well-balanced beer with a long, moderately hoppy aftertaste.

Rapier Pale Ale *(OG 1042, ABV 4.3%)* 🗂❖
Wonderful golden brew with a distinct hoppy aroma. A soft, clean taste of malt and hops with chocolate hints continues to a long drawn-out finish with bitter-sweetness adding to the complexity.

Norfolk Wheaten *(OG 1045, ABV 4.5%)*
A straw-coloured, Continental-style wheat beer, with fruit and hops in the aroma. Light-bodied with a little sweetness and moderate bitterness. Clean-tasting and refreshing.

Velvet Sweet Stout
(OG 1045, ABV 4.5%) ❖
Coffee bean aroma and a beefy roast beginning. A sweetish black cherry flavour softens the initial bite of this mid-brown, filling stout. Finish slowly fades as all the flavours merge into a rich oaky blend.

Raspberry *(ABV 4.5%)* ❖
Raspberry hints befitting a fruit beer in both the nose and taste. A pale brown beer retaining a fruity sweet sparkle as the bitterness increases to the end.

RIDLEYS

T D Ridley & Sons Ltd, Hartford End Brewery, Chelmsford, Essex, CM3 1JZ
Tel (01371) 820316
Fax (01371) 821216
E mail innsight@ridleys.co.uk
Website www.ridleys.co.uk
Shop open for brewery trips only. Tours by arrangement

⊗ Ridleys was established by Thomas Dixon Ridley in 1842 and is still family run. It is currently expanding; as well as its main beers, Ridleys is establishing a range of 'event beers'. It also supplies 350 other outlets. Event and seasonal beers: Valentine

(ABV 3.9%, February), Hoppy Easter (ABV 4.3%, April), Fisherman's Whopper (ABV 4.3%, June), Santa's Secret (OG 1050, ABV 4.8%, December), Witchfinder Porter (ABV 4.3%, winter), Spectacular (ABV 4.6%, spring and summer), Blizzard (ABV 4.5%, January), Give Us A Try (ABV 4.1%, March), Maze Magic (ABV 4.1%, May), Time Out (ABV 4.3%, July), Two Halves (ABV 3.9%, August), Mer the End of Summer (ABV 4.1%, September), Chill Out (ABV 4.1%, November), Yule Cheer (ABV 4.6%, December).

IPA *(OG 1034, ABV 3.5%)* ❖
Well-balanced if under-powered tawny session bitter that is improving with the arrival of a new brewer.

Mild *(OG 1034, ABV 3.5%)* ❖
Darker, sweeter version of IPA; if you're lucky, a different mash, but more often an inferior 'paint job'.

ESX Best *(OG 1047, ABV 4.3%)* ❖
Astringent and bitter, with some fruit and malt in the balance.

Witchfinder Porter
(OG 1047, ABV 4.3%) ❖
At its best (late autumn), a fruity, full-bodied porter, with a juicy malt character and liquorice tones. The rest of the year, it's coloured ESX, albeit with the same pump clip.

Rumpus *(OG 1049, ABV 4.5%)* ❖
A sweet red beer, malty with a slightly hoppy edge to the finish.

Spectacular *(OG 1047, ABV 4.6%)* ❖
A pale, straw-coloured beer with a flowery nose. It has a delicate malty flavour and a rather bitter aftertaste.

Old Bob *(ABV 5.1%)* 🗂❖
A sweet, full-bodied beer, with a warming, malty character throughout.

RING O' BELLS*

Ring O' Bells Brewery, Pennygillam Way, Pennygillam Industrial Estate, Launceston, Cornwall, PL15 7ED
Tel (01566) 777787 Fax (01566) 777788
Tours by arrangement

Adrian Carne began brewing in 1998 in a 13th-century former brew-pub, the Ring O'Bells at North Hill, Cornwall. Due to demand for the beers, plans were made for a brand-new, 23-barrel plant in Launceston.

Production started in May 2001, with James Vincent, formerly of Ventonwyn Brewery, as assistant brewer. Plans are to concentrate on sales in Cornwall and Devon, with possible expansion into the London market. There are also plans to bottle the beers. Seasonal beer: Surf Boar (ABV 4%, summer).

Dark Boar (OG 1036, ABV 3.7%)
A malty, full-bodied beer.

Porkers Pride (OG 1036, ABV 3.8%)
A light, refreshing session ale that is well-balanced with a clean, hoppy finish.

Bodmin Boar (OG 1041, ARV 4 3%)
Full-flavoured, darkish premium ale, with a fine aroma and malty finish.

Stout Pig (OG 1044, ABV 4.4%)
A dark, rich, creamy stout.

Tipsy Trotters (OG 1048, ABV 5%)
Amber-coloured, full-bodied, malty beer, slightly fruity.

Barley Swine (OG 1085, ABV 9%)
Powerful beer, aged for several months.

RINGWOOD

**Ringwood Brewery Ltd,
Christchurch Road, Ringwood,
Hampshire, BH24 3AP
Tel (01425) 471177
Fax (01425) 480273
E-mail info@ringwoodbrewery.co.uk
Website www.ringwoodbrewery.co.uk**
Shop 9.30-5 Mon-Fri; 9.30-12 Sat
Tours by arrangement; individual visits every Wednesday at 3pm, but must book in advance

⊗ Ringwood, which celebrated 21 years of brewing in 1999, was set up in 1978 by legendary micro-brewery builder Peter Austin, and moved in 1986 to attractive 18th-century buildings, formerly part of the old Tunks Brewery. A new brewhouse was commissioned at the end of 1994, and a new fermenting room completed in 1995. The 21st anniversary was marked by commissioning a new copper and steam boiler. 500 outlets are supplied direct. Four pubs are owned, all serving cask-conditioned beer. Ringwood's impressive success, under managing director David Welsh, has moved the brewery out of the ranks of micro-brewers and it's now a small regional. In spite of talk of the decline in cask beer sales, Ringwood is once again facing problems of shortage of capacity. Bottle-conditioned beers: Fortyniner (ABV 4.9%), XXXX Porter (ABV 4.7%). Seasonal beers: Boon Doggle (ABV 3.9%, May-Sept), XXXX Porter (ABV 4.7%, Oct-March) ⌂.

Best Bitter
(OG 1038, ABV 3.8%) ◆
A well-balanced, golden brown beer. A malty and hoppy aroma leads through to a malty taste with some sweetness. Malty and bitter finish, with some fruit present.

True Glory (OG 1043, ABV 4.3%) ◆
A malty aroma leads to a hoppy taste with malt and fruit, followed by a malty, hoppy and fruity aftertaste. Copper-coloured.

Fortyniner (OG 1049, ABV 4.9%) ◆
Pale brown in colour. A malty and fruity aroma leads to a well-balanced taste of malt and hops. Fruity finish.

Old Thumper (OG 1056, ABV 5.6%) ◆
A mid-brown beer. A fruity aroma preludes a sweet, malty taste with some fruit. Surprisingly bitter aftertaste, with malt and fruit.

RIVERHEAD

⌂ **Riverhead Brewery Ltd, 2 Peel Street,
Marsden, Huddersfield,
W Yorkshire, HD7 6BR
Tel (01484) 841270
E-mail philip@riverheadbrewery.fsnet.co.uk**
Tours by arrangement

⊗ The Riverhead Brewery Tap is a brew-pub that opened in 1995 after its conversion from an old grocery store. The main beers are named after local reservoirs. It serves its own seven brews plus occasional specials such as Jazz Bitter (ABV 4%, for Marsden Jazz Festival), and Ruffled Feathers Bitter (ABV 4.2%, for Marsden Cuckoo Day). The brewery also supplies 10 local outlets on an occasional basis.

Sparth Mild (OG 1038, ABV 3.6%) ⌂◆
A light-bodied, dry mild, with a dark ruby colour. Fruity aroma with roasted flavour and a dry finish.

Butterley Bitter
(OG 1038, ABV 3.8%) ◆
A dry, amber-coloured, hoppy session beer.

Deer Hill Porter (OG 1040, ABV 4%)
A dark brown bitter with the characteristics of stout, but not as strong.

Cupwith Light Bitter
(OG 1042, ABV 4.2%)
A pale bitter with a distinctive bitter aftertaste.

Black Moss Stout
(OG 1043, ABV 4.3%) ◆
Roast malt and fruit aromas from a lightly-hopped dry stout with a chocolatey finish.

March Haigh Special Bitter
(OG 1046, ABV 4.6%)
A smooth, rounded flavour due to an interesting selection of hops.

Redbrook Premium Bitter
(OG 1055, ABV 5.5%) ◆
A rich and malty strong beer, with malt and fruit aroma and sweet, fruity aftertaste.

ROBINSON'S

**Frederic Robinson Ltd, Unicorn Brewery,
Stockport, Cheshire, SK1 1JJ
Tel (0161) 480 6571
Fax (0161) 476 6011
Website www.frederic-robinson.com**
Shop 9-5 Mon-Sat. Tours by arrangement

⊗ A major family brewery founded in 1838 in the Unicorn Inn and still run by the descendants of Frederic Robinson. The company moved to the present site in 1865. Robinson's bought Hartleys of Ulverston in 1982 and closed the brewery in 1991; only Hartleys XB is still brewed. The company supplies real ale to all its 400 tied houses in the North-west and North Wales, and to free trade outlets. It introduced a bi-monthly range of seasonal beers in mid-2000, which have met with increasing success.

Hatters Mild *(OG 1032, ABV 3.3%)* ✦
A light mild with a fruit and malt aroma, it has a refreshing, dry, malty flavour and aftertaste. A darkened version is available in a handful of outlets and badged Dark Mild.

Old Stockport Bitter
(OG 1034, ABV 3.5%) ✦
A beer with a refreshing taste of malt, hops and citrus fruit, a fruity aroma, and a short, dry finish.

Hartleys XB *(OG 1040, ABV 4%)* ✦
An overly sweet and malty bitter with a bitter citrus peel fruitiness and a hint of liquorice in the finish.

Best Bitter *(OG 1040, ABV 4.2%)* ✦
Amber beer with an aroma of citrus fruit, spices and earthy hop. Hoppy, bitter and quite fruity to taste with a short bitter finish.

Frederics *(OG 1049, ABV 5%)* ▢✦
A gold-coloured beer with an aroma of orange and a hint of spice. Citrus fruit and hops on the taste with a dry hoppy finish.

Old Tom *(OG 1079, ABV 8.5%)* ▢✦
A full-bodied, dark beer, it has malt, fruit and chocolate in the aroma. A delightfully complex range of flavours including dark chocolate, full maltiness, treacle toffee and fruits lead to a long, bitter-sweet aftertaste.

ROCKINGHAM

**Rockingham Ales, c/o 25 Wansford Road, Elton, Cambs, PE8 6RZ
Tel (01832) 280722**

A part-time micro-brewery established in 1997 and operating from a converted farm building near Blatherwyke, Northamptonshire (business address as above). The 2-barrel plant supplies half a dozen local outlets with beers on a rota basis, supplemented by special beers brewed to order. Seasonal beers: Fineshade (ABV 3.8%, autumn), Sanity Clause (ABV 4.3%, December), Old Herbaceous (ABV 4.5%, winter).

Forest Gold *(OG 1040, ABV 3.9%)*
A hoppy blonde ale with citrus flavours. Well-balanced and clean finishing.

Hop Devil *(OG 1040, ABV 3.9%)*
Up to six hop varieties give this light amber ale a bitter start and spicy finish.

Saxon Cross *(OG 1041, ABV 4.1%)*
A golden-red ale with nut and coffee aromas. Citrus hop flavours predominate.

A1 Amber Ale *(OG 1041, ABV 4%)*
A fruity, hoppy session beer that has blackcurrant undertones.

Fruits of the Forest *(OG 1043, ABV 4.2%)*
A complex, multi-layered beer in which summer fruits and several spices compete with a big hop presence.

ROOSTER'S

**Rooster's Brewing Co 20 Claro Business Centre, Claro Road, Harrogate, N Yorkshire, HG1 4BA
Tel/Fax (01423) 561861
E-mail seanf@roosters.co.uk
Website www.roosters.co.uk**

⊗ Rooster's Brewery was opened in 1993 by Sean and Alison Franklin. They now make a total of 40 barrels a week, but by the end of 2001 will have moved to new premises in Harrogate that will enable them to increase production. Under the Rooster's label they make seven regular beers while a subsidiary label, Outlaw Brewing Co, produces experimental beers. They change materials or process or both to make a new beer every two months. Sean Franklin is a devotee of hops and uses many varieties, including North American, in his brews. 70-80 outlets are supplied direct. Seasonal and occasional beers: Nector (ABV 5%, Christmas), Silver Lining (ABV 4.3%).

Special *(OG 1038, ABV 3.9%)* ▢✦
A yellow-coloured beer with an intense fruity/floral aroma, which is carried through the taste, where it is joined by a well-balanced bitter character.

Scorcher *(OG 1042, ABV 4.3%)* ▢✦
Golden aromatic and fruity, with balancing bitterness. The fruitiness is carried through into the aftertaste, where the bitterness tends to increase. A well-balanced beer.

Yankee *(OG 1042, ABV 4.3%)* ✦
A straw-coloured beer with a delicate, fruity aroma leading to a well-balanced taste of malt and hops with a slight evidence of sweetness, followed by a refreshing, fruity/bitter finish.

Oyster Stout *(OG 1042, ABV 4.3%)*
A soft, silky, seductive stout.

Cream *(OG 1045, ABV 4.7%)* ✦
A pale-coloured beer with a complex, floral bouquet leading to a well-balanced refreshing taste. Fruit lasts throughout and into the aftertaste.

Hooligan *(OG 1042, ABV 4.3%)*
A pale, aromatic premium bitter with aromas of tangerine. Moderately bitter.

ROTHER VALLEY

**Rother Valley Brewing Co, Station Road, Northiam, E Sussex, TN31 6QT
Tel (01797) 253535 Fax (01797) 253550**
Tours by arrangement

⊠ Rother Valley was established in Northiam in 1993 on a hop farm overlooking the river that marks the boundary between Kent and Sussex. It brews only with hops grown next to the brewery. Special beers are brewed to order and 55 outlets are supplied direct. Occasional/seasonal beers: Lighterman (ABV 3.5%, April-Sept), Wheat Beer (ABV 3.8%, occasional), Blues (ABV 5%, Oct-March), Hoppy Holly Daze (ABV varies, Christmas).

Level Best *(OG 1040, ABV 4%)* ✦
Full-bodied tawny session bitter with a malt and fruit aroma, malty taste and a dry, hoppy finish.

Spirit Level *(OG 1047, ABV 4.6%)* ✦
Tawny best bitter. Initial hoppy fruitiness leads to a well-balanced sweet mixture of flavours with a dry aftertaste.

RUDDLES

See Greene King.

RUDGATE

Rudgate Brewery Ltd, 2 Centre Park, Marston Business Park, Rudgate, Tockwith, York, YO26 7QF
Tel/Fax (01423) 358382
E-mail sales@rudgate-beers.co.uk
Website www.rudgate-beers.co.uk
Tours by arrangement

☺ Rudgate was founded in 1992 and is located in an old armoury building on the edge of a disused World War II airfield. It supplies 150 outlets with beers fermented in open square vessels and also brews for Marston Moor (qv). A range of seasonal beers has been launched. Awards: Beauty of Hops, English Ale Gold Medal 2000 and 1998, Silver 1999. Seasonal beer: Rudolf's Ruin (ABV 5.4%, Christmas).

Viking *(OG 1038, ABV 3.8%)* ◆
An initially warming and malty, full-bodied beer, with hops and fruit lingering into the aftertaste.

Battleaxe *(OG 1042, ABV 4.2%)* ◆
A well-hopped bitter with slightly sweet initial taste and light bitterness. Complex fruit character gives a memorable aftertaste.

Ruby Mild *(OG 1044, ABV 4.4%)*
Nutty rich ruby ale, stronger than usual for a mild.

RYBURN

⌂ **Ryburn Brewery, c/o Ram's Head, Wakefield Road, Sowerby Bridge, Halifax, W Yorkshire, HX6 2AZ**
Tel (01422) 835413/63355876

☺ Founded in 1989 in a former dye works, this brewery is now in its fourth home beneath its single tied house. Efforts are being concentrated on supplying the pub, with limited free trade sales.

Best Mild *(OG 1033, ABV 3.3%)* ◆
More akin to a thin, sweet stout than a dark mild, this dark brown beer has a 'rum and raisin' aroma, a slightly fruity, burnt taste and a short, dry finish.

Best Bitter *(OG 1038, ABV 3.6%)* ◆
A thin beer, initially sweet with some bitterness in the aftertaste.

Light *(OG 1042, ABV 4.4%)*

Rydale Bitter *(OG 1044, ABV 4.2%)* ◆
A lightly hopped, sweet bitter with a growing dry, bitter finish.

Old Stone Trough *(ABV 4.5%)*

Navigation Ale *(ABV 4.6%)*

Luddite *(OG 1048, ABV 5%)* ◆
This sweetish, black stout is dominated throughout by a roast maltiness. The finish is dry and quite bitter.

Stabbers *(OG 1052, ABV 5.2%)* ◆
A fruity sweetness competes with bitterness and malt, and leads to a dry aftertaste in this golden amber, strong bitter. There is some background sulphur throughout.

Coiners *(OG 1060, ABV 6%)* ◆
Fruit, a syrupy sweetness and some background bitterness characterise this strong bitter and develop into a short but increasingly dry finish.

SADDLEWORTH

⌂ **Saddleworth Brewery, Church Inn, Church Lane, Uppermill, Saddleworth, Greater Manchester, OL3 6LW**
Tel (01457) 820902
Fax (01457) 820831

☺ The brewery is in an old brewhouse that until four years ago had not brewed for more than 130 years. The copper is still fired by direct flame to give a fuller flavour to the beer. In 1999, a new fermentation room, barrelling room and cold room were added. The brew house has an additional copper and mash tun. Seasonal/occasional beers: Bert Corner (ABV 4.1%), Christmas Carol (ABV 7.4%).

Saddleworth More *(ABV 3.8%)*

Ayrtons Ale *(ABV 4.1%)*

Harvest Moon *(ABV 4.1%)*

Hop Smacker *(ABV 4.1%)*

Pete's Dragon *(ABV 4.6%)*

Shaft Bender *(ABV 5.4%)*

ST AUSTELL

St Austell Brewery Co Ltd, 63 Trevarthian Road, St Austell, Cornwall, PL25 4BY
Tel (01726) 74444
Fax (01726) 68965
E-mail adam.luck@staustellbrewery.co.uk
Website www.staustellbrewery.co.uk
Shop 9.30-4.30 Mon-Fri
Visitor centre and tours (01726) 66022

⊠ St Austell Brewery celebrated 150 years of brewing in 2001. Founded by Walter Hicks in 1851, the company is still family-owned and run, with Walter Hicks' great-great-grandson, James Staughton, at the helm as managing director since 2000. He leads a young team, with head brewer Roger Ryman, and there is a powerful commitment to cask beer. The beer range has been overhauled, with new branding and pump clips in pubs. Cask beer is available in all 150 licensed houses, as well as an increasing presence in the free trade throughout Devon, Cornwall and Somerset. An attractive visitor centre offers guided tours and souvenirs from the brewery. The brewery hosts its own Celtic Beer Festival late in the year. Bottle-conditioned beers: Clouded Yellow (ABV 5%), Hicks Strong Ale (ABV 5%). In 2001 a special commemorative bottle-conditioned beer was brewed, named 1851, with an ABV of 10.2%. The beer will improve with age.

Contact the brewery to see if any bottles are still available.

IPA *(ABV 3.4%)*
Copper/bronze in colour, the nose blossoms with fresh hops. The palate is clean and full-bodied with a hint of toffee caramel. The finish is short and crisp.

XXXX Mild
(OG 1037, ABV 3.6%) 🍺❦
Little aroma, but a strong, malty character. A caramel-sweetish flavour is followed by a good, lingering aftertaste that is sweet but with a fruity dryness.

Dartmoor Best Bitter
(OG 1037.5, ABV 3.9%)
A delicately hopped golden bitter. Originally brewed at the now-closed Ferguson Brewery in Plymouth, DBB was brewed by St Austell for Carlsberg-Tetley, but it is now owned by St Austell and is spearheading the Cornish company's increased presence in Devon.

Tinners Ale *(OG 1038, ABV 3.7%)* ❦
A deservedly popular, golden beer with an appetising malt aroma and a good balance of malt and hops in the flavour. Lasting finish.

Tribute *(ABV 4.2%)*
Pale amber in colour, full-bodied malt flavours are balanced by a fresh citrus nose.

Hicks Special Draught/HSD
(OG 1051, ABV 5%) ❦
An aromatic, fruity, hoppy bitter that is initially sweet and has an aftertaste of pronounced bitterness, but whose flavour is fully rounded. A good premium beer.

ST GEORGE'S

St George's Brewing Co Ltd, Bush Lane, Callow End, Worcester, WR2 4TF
Tel/Fax (01905) 831316
(07974) 563598 (m)
Tours by arrangement

St George's, situated halfway between Worcester and Malvern in an old bakehouse, started trading in 1998 and in 2000 was taken over by Brian McCluskie and David Butcher, who both took early retirement after long careers in the brewing industry. They have a strong commitment to traditional brewing and have revised the beer range, which they plan to expand.

Bitter *(OG 1038, ABV 3.7%)*
Light in colour with a pronounced, refreshing hoppy character.

Gold 2000 *(OG 1040, ABV 3.9%)*
A mellow beer using aromatic Goldings hops and a blend of specialist coloured malts.

Premium Bitter *(OG 1046, ABV 4.3%)* ❦
A fruity but unassertive bitter that allows the flavours of all its constituents to come through and be enjoyed.

Dragon *(OG 1046, ABV 4.4%)*
A North German-style cask-conditioned lager beer, deep brewed with lager malt, lager yeast and European hops. It has a great deal of character with a satisfying, hoppy finish.

Fire 2000 *(OG 1050, ABV 4.9%)*
754

A pungent, ruby-coloured strong ale using traditional English Fuggles and Brewers Gold hops. A satisfying malt character due to the blend of malts and roasted barley.

Supreme Bitter *(OG 1052, ABV 5%)*
Pale in colour with a full-bodied malt character balanced by bitter hops on the palate and finish.

ST PETER'S

St Peter's Brewery Co plc,
St Peter's Hall, St Peter South Elmham,
Bungay, Suffolk, NR35 1NQ
Tel (01986) 782322
Fax (01986) 782505
E-mail beers@stpetersbrewery.co.uk
Website www.stpetersbrewery.co.uk
Shop available 9-5
Tours by arrangement 12-4 Fri, Sat & Sun.

⊗ St Peter's Brewery was opened in 1996 in former dairy buildings at the ancient St Peter's Hall. The company has grown significantly over the past two years. It now has a bigger brew house, visitor centre, shop, restaurant and bar. It produces an extensive range of beers in cask and bottle (not bottle-conditioned) including fruit beers and a spiced ale. St Peter's Hall is a medieval manor house beside which is the deep bore hole that supplies water to the brew house. Forty-four outlets are supplied direct and three tied pubs all serve cask-conditioned beer. Cask ale is supplied direct to outlets in East Anglia and London, with nationwide delivery available. The company exports extensively. Seasonal beers: Winter Ale (ABV 5%), Cinnamon & Apple Spiced Ale (ABV 6.5%), Summer Ale (ABV 6.5%).

Best Bitter *(OG 1037, ABV 3.7%)*
Full-bodied ale with distinctive fruity caramel notes.

Mild *(OG 1038, ABV 3.8%)*
Sweetness balanced by bitter chocolate malt to produce a rare traditional mild.

Organic Best Bitter *(OG 1041, ABV 4.1)*
Organically-grown Chariot malted barley with organic Hallertau hops are used. The result is a full-bodied organic best bitter with a refreshing aftertaste.

Organic Ale *(OG 1045, ABV 4.5%)*
Light malted barley from Scotland with organic Target hops create a refreshing ale with a delicate character. Suitable for vegetarians.

Golden Ale *(OG 1047, ABV 4.7%)*
English Halcyon malts are used, with Goldings hops providing the bitterness and aroma. A distinctive light, golden ale similar in character to a full-bodied Czech lager.

Wheat Beer *(OG 1047, ABV 4.7%)*
A high proportion of premium wheat is used with modest amounts of Challenger and Goldings hop varieties to produce a light, smooth, clear and refreshing beer with a distinctive palate and a clean, crisp aftertaste.

Elderberry Fruit Beer *(OG 1047, ABV 4.7%)*
This refreshing beer has a wheat beer base complemented by the addition of elderberry. This rare example of an English

fruit beer has a delightfully floral fruit nose and refreshing dry finish.

Grapefruit Beer *(OG 1047, ABV 4.7%)*
The zesty/pithy grapefruit is in complete harmony with the hops and malt.

Spiced Lemon and Ginger Ale *(OG 1047, ABV 4.7%)*
A traditional English ale with a light citrus aroma and a delicate ginger aftertaste.

Suffolk Gold *(OG 1049, ABV 4.9%)*
Suffolk-grown First Gold hops provide the inspiration for this premium beer, which is brewed with Suffolk malt to produce a full-bodied ale with a lasting hop aroma.

Old Style Porter *(OG 1051, ABV 5.1%)*
A blend of a mature old ale with a younger light beer, as a true Porter should be. The marriage produces an extremely characterful brew that is dark in colour and complex in taste.

Honey Porter *(OG 1051, ABV 5.1%)*
Porter finished with honey for a unique aroma and taste.

Strong Ale *(OG 1051, ABV 5.1%)*
Challenger and Goldings hops act in perfect harmony with Suffolk malt and pure water. The first beer to be brewed at St. Peter's.

Cream Stout *(OG 1065, ABV 6.5%)*
Challenger and Fuggles hops plus a blend of four local barley malts create an aromatic, strong, dark chocolate cream stout with a satisfying bitter-sweet aftertaste.

SALAMANDER*

**Salamander Brewing Co,
Harry Street, Dudley Hill, Bradford,
W Yorkshire, BD4 9PH
Tel (01274) 652323**

Chris Bee and Daniel Gent launched their brewery in January 2001 in a former pie factory. Chris brewed at the Orange Brewery and the Yorkshire Grey brew-pubs in London, and Daniel honed his skills at Freedom, also in London. Their 10-barrel plant is made up of some vessels bought from Mitchells of Lancaster along with ex-dairy equipment. They have quickly established business with 150 outlets in the North and Midlands. Most of the beer names have salamander connections.

Owd Amos *(ABV 3.8%)*

Mudpuppy *(ABV 4.2%)*

Gent *(ABV 4.7%)*

Hellbender *(ABV 4.8%)*

Titus Tipple *(ABV 5.3%)*

Terry's Ruin *(ABV 10.8%)*

SALOPIAN

**Salopian Brewing Co Ltd, 67 Mytton Oak
Road, Shrewsbury, Shropshire, SY3 8UQ
Tel (01743) 248414
Fax (01743) 358866**
Shop 9-5 weekdays. Tours by arrangement

⊗ The brewery was opened in 1995 in an old dairy on the outskirts of Shrewsbury. Partners Wilf Nelson and brewer Martin Barry have developed cask sales locally and

nationally through wholesalers. The plant has been increased in size to 10 barrels. Bottle-conditioned beers are brewed at Brakspear, except for Minsterley and Gingersnap at Salopian. The brewery is actively seeking a brewery tap. Fifty-five outlets are supplied direct. Bottle-conditioned beers: Minsterley Ale (ABV 4.5%), Gingersnap (ABV 4.7%), Puzzle (ABV 4.8%), Entire Butt (ABV 4.8%) ⊗⊗.

Royal Mild *(OG 1035, ABV 3.5%)*

Shropshire Gold *(OG 1037, ABV 3.8%)*

Golden Thread *(OG 1048, ABV 5%)*

Ironbridge Stout *(OG 1050, ABV 5%)* ⊗

Proud Salopian *(OG 1044.5, ABV 4.5%)*

Heaven Sent *(OG 1044.5, ABV 4.5%)*

SARAH'S HOP HOUSE*

**Sarah's Hop House Brewery,
Railway Inn, 131 High Street, Golborne,
Warrington, Cheshire, WA3 3TG
Tel (01942) 713759**

Sarah Porter worked in the pub trade for 20 years, bought her own free house eight years ago, and decided to go the next mile and brew her own beer. She learnt the brewing skills by working with John Feeney at Bank Top. Her 5-barrel plant is situated in outbuildings behind the Railway Inn. She started brewing in February 2000 and now has 40-50 outlets in the locality plus pubs

nationwide supplied by wholesalers.

Hop House Bitter *(ABV 3.9%)* ⊗
An amber beer with a fruity nose. A nice balance of orange fruit and hops with malt and bitterness in the mouth and a satisfyingly bitter, fruity finish.

Black Mamba Mild *(ABV 4%)*
A roast malt and chocolate aroma complements the dark red/brown colour. Hints of treacle toffee join the roast malt and chocolate in the taste, before a dry roast finish.

Hop To It *(ABV 4.2%)* ⊗
Amber beer with a light citrus aroma. Bitter, malty palate with a bitter and very dry aftertaste.

Gordon's Amber Ale *(ABV 4.2%)*

Chocolate Stout *(ABV 4.7%)*
Dark red/brown beer with roast malt and chocolate on the aroma and flavour. Creamy, smooth palate and a fairly dry, roast aftertaste.

SAWBRIDGEWORTH*

**Sawbridgeworth Brewery, Gate Inn, 81 London Road, Sawbridgeworth, Herts, CM21 9JJ
Tel (01279) 722313**

Brew-pub run by former professional footballer Tommy Barnett (Tottenham Hotspur, Queen's Park Rangers and St Albans City) with equipment bought from Whitbread. Tommy started brewing in June 2000 and he supplies beer festivals as well as the Gate. 'Lynne Pearce' is named in honour of his favourite beer writer, the What's Brewing columnist who once wrote that she hoped a brewer would name a beer after her.

Brown Bomber *(ABV 3.7%)*

Selhurst Park Flyer *(ABV 3.7%)*

Teflon *(ABV 3.7%)*

Is It Yourself *(ABV 4.3%)*

Brooklands Express *(ABV 4.6%)*

Piledriver *(ABV 5%)*

Lynne Pearce *(ABV 5.2%)*

SCANLON'S

**Scanlon's Fine Ales, Rainbow Industrial Estate, Trout Road, Yiewsley, Middlesex, UB7 7XT
Tel (01895) 256270**

Scanlon's sells eight beers on a regular basis produced for the company by the following breweries:

Vale Brewery, Haddenham, Bucks:

Frays Mild *(OG 1036, ABV 3.6%)*

Colne Valley Bitter *(OG 1042, ABV 4.1%)*

Ealing Porter *(OG 1045, ABV 4.4%)*

Lord Ashford's Special Reserve
(OG 1052, ABV 5%)
A stout produced Dec-Jan.

O'Hanlon's Brewery:

Middlesex Gold *(OG 1039, ABV 3.8%)*

Elthorne White *(OG 1043, ABV 4.2%)*
A wheat beer produced March-Oct.

Brunel Premier Ale *(OG 1050, ABV 4.8%)*

Rebellion, Marlow, Bucks:

Spike *(OG 1046, ABV 4.5%)*

Elthorne White, Middlesex Gold, Ealing Porter and Colne Valley Bitter are also available in bottle-conditioned form.

SCATTOR ROCK

**Scattor Rock Brewery Ltd, Unit 5 Gidley's Meadow, Christow, Exeter, Devon, EX6 7QB
Tel/Fax (01647) 252120
E-mail keithscattorrock@aol.com
Website www.scattorrockbrewery.com**

Tours by arrangement

The brewery was set up in 1998 and is situated within the boundaries of the Dartmoor National Park, and named after a well-known local landmark. 60 plus outlets are supplied direct on a permanent or regular basis. Occasional beers: Quarryman Stout (ABV 4.9%), Scattor Brain (ABV 4.8%), Gidleys Bitter (ABV 4.4%), Completely and Utterly Brain Dead (ABV 9%). There is a seasonal beer available every month and branded as the 'Tor collection'.

Scatty Bitter *(OG 1040, ABV 3.8%)*

Teign Valley Tipple *(OG 1042, ABV 4%)*
A well-balanced tawny coloured beer with a hoppy aroma.

Skylark *(OG 1043, ABV 4.2%)*
A refreshing, light brown session ale.

Devonian *(OG 1045, ABV 4.5%)*
A strong, fruity, light-coloured ale.

Golden Valley *(OG 1046, ABV 4.6%)*
A golden refreshing ale.

Scat Tor Rockin Lager
(OG 1047, ABV 4.6%)
A natural cask-conditioned lager.

Valley Stomper *(OG 1051, ABV 5%)*
Light brown and deceptively drinkable.

SELBY

**Selby (Middlebrough) Brewery Ltd, 131 Millgate, Selby, N Yorkshire, YO8 3LL
Tel (01757) 702826**
Shop 10-2 and 6-10 Mon-Sat

☺ Old family brewery that resumed brewing in 1972 after a gap of 18 years but which is now mostly involved in wholesaling. Its beers, which are brewed on an occasional basis, are available, while stocks last (only in bulk) at the shop and not at the company's single pub. They are also sold as guest beers in the local free trade.

No. 1 *(OG 1040, ABV 4%)*

No. 3 *(OG 1040, ABV 4%)*

Old Tom *(OG 1065, ABV 6.5%)*

SHARDLOW

**Shardlow Brewing Company Ltd, The Old Brewery Stables, British Waterways Yard, Cavendish Bridge, Leicestershire, LE72 2HL
Tel/Fax (01332) 799188
E-mail
shardlowbrewery@netscapeonline.co.uk**
Tours by arrangement

⊗ The brewery opened in 1993 in the old kiln house of the original Cavendish Bridge Brewery (closed in the 1920s), and moved in 1996 to new premises, at the same site on the River Trent, opposite Shardlow Marina. The new brewery is situated on two floors of former stables that retain some original features. Shardlow supplies 40 free trade outlets and now has its own pub, the Blue Bell Inn in Melbourne, Derbyshire. It is hoped to offer beers in bottles by 2002.

Chancellors Revenge *(ABV 3.6%)*
A light-coloured, refreshing, full-flavoured and well-hopped session bitter.

Best Bitter *(ABV 3.9%)*
A well-balanced, amber-coloured, quaffable bitter.

Goldenhop *(ABV 4.1%)*
A golden bitter, dry hopped with Goldings for added flavour and aroma.

Kiln House *(ABV 4.1%)*

Narrowboat *(ABV 4.3%)*
A pale amber bitter, with a short, crisp hoppy aftertaste.

Old Stable Brew *(ABV 4.4%)*

Cavendish Gold *(ABV 4.5%)*
A premium pale bitter.

Reverend Eaton's *(ABV 4.5%)*
A smooth, medium-strong bitter, full of malt and hop flavours with a sweet aftertaste.

Mayfly *(ABV 4.8%)*

Whistle Stop *(OG 1050, ABV 5%)*
Maris Otter pale malt and two hops produce this smooth and surprisingly strong pale beer.

SHARP'S

Sharp's Brewery, Pityme Industrial Estate, Rock, Wadebridge, Cornwall, PL27 6NU
Tel (01208) 862121
Fax (01208) 863727
Tours by arrangement

⊗ Founded in 1994 in one industrial unit, the brewery has enjoyed rapid expansion and now occupies nearly half the estate. It supplies the free trade in Devon and Cornwall, and the beers are also widely available via wholesalers. Eden Ale won the Supreme Champion award at the 2000 Falmouth Beer Festival.

Cornish Coaster
(OG 1037, ABV 3.6%) ◣
A smooth, easy-drinking beer, golden in colour, with a fresh hop aroma and dry malt and hops in the mouth. The finish starts malty but becomes dry and hoppy.

Doom Bar Bitter
(OG 1040, ABV 4%) ◣
A rich, golden brown beer with a hint of barley. Dry malt and hops in the mouth. The malty finish becomes dry and hoppy. Fresh hop aroma.

Eden Ale *(OG 1043, ABV 4.4%)*
Brewed in celebration of Cornwall's Eden Project, it boasts a full and rounded flavour with a distinctively crisp and refreshing, dry hop finish.

Sharp's Own *(OG 1043, ABV 4.4%)* ◣
A deep golden brown beer with a delicate hops and malt aroma, and dry malt and hops in the mouth. Like the other beers, its finish starts malty but turns dry and hoppy.

Will's Resolve *(OG 1046, ABV 4.6%)*

Special *(OG 1052, ABV 5.2%)* ◣
Deep golden brown with a fresh hop aroma. Dry malt and hops in the mouth; the finish is malty but becomes dry and hoppy.

SHEPHERD NEAME

Shepherd Neame Ltd, 17 Court Street, Faversham, Kent, ME13 7AX
Tel (01795) 532206
Fax (01795) 538907
E-mail company@shepherd-neame.co.uk
Website www.shepherd-neame.co.uk
Shop 9-5 Mon-Fri. Tours by arrangement

⊗ Kent's major independent brewery is believed to be the oldest continuous brewer in the country since 1698, but records show brewing began on the site as far back as the 12th century. The same water source is still used today, steam engines are still usable, and the mash is produced in two teak tuns that date from 1910. A visitors' reception hall is housed in a restored medieval hall (tours by arrangement). In 2000, Shepherd Neame invested £2.2 million in a new brewhouse that boosted production to 200,000 barrels a year. The company has 390 tied houses in the South-east, nearly all selling cask ale, but tenants are encouraged to keep beers under blanket pressure if the cask is likely to be on sale for more than three days. More than 500 other outlets are also supplied direct. Seasonal beers: Early Bird (ABV 4.3%, spring), Late Red (ABV 4.5%, autumn), Goldings (ABV 4.7%, summer).

Master Brew Bitter *(ABV 3.7%)* ◣
A distinctive bitter, mid-brown in colour, with a hoppy aroma. Well-balanced, with a nicely aggressive bitter taste from its hops, it leaves a hoppy/bitter finish, tinged with sweetness.

Best Bitter *(ABV 4.1%)* ◣
Mid-brown, with less marked characteristics than the bitter. However, the nose is very well-balanced and the taste enjoys a malty, bitter smokiness. Malty, well-rounded finish. It also appears under the name Canterbury Jack.

Spitfire Premium Ale *(ABV 4.7%)*
A commemorative Battle of Britain brew for the RAF Benevolent Fund's appeal, now a permanent feature.

Bishops Finger *(ABV 5%)*
A cask-conditioned version of a famous bottled beer, introduced in cask in 1989.

SHOES

Shoes Brewery, Three Horseshoes Inn, Norton Canon, Hereford, HR4 7BH
Tel/Fax (01544) 318375

Landlord Frank Goodwin had long been a home brewer, but decided in 1994 to brew on a commercial basis for his pub. The beers are brewed from malt extract, stored in casks and dispensed under a blanket of mixed gas. Beers: Norton Ale (OG 1038, ABV 3.6%), Canon Bitter (OG 1040, ABV 4.1%). Limited edition only: Farriers 2000 (ABV 13.4%, unfiltered, bottle-conditioned).

SHRALEY BROOK

Shraley Brook Brewing Company, Studio 3, Townhouse Farm, Alsager Road, Audley, Stoke-on-Trent, Staffs, ST7 8JQ
Tel/Fax (01782) 723792
Tours by arrangement

Previously known as the Rising Sun Brewery, brewing was revived after a gap of two years using new recipes devised by three regulars of the pub. Naming of the beers has followed an English Civil War theme. Fifteen outlets are supplied direct. Occasional beers: Executioner (ABV 4.9%), Golden Sovereign (ABV 5.2%).

Charles' First Brew *(OG 1043, ABV 4.2%)*

SHUGBOROUGH

See Titanic.

SIX BELLS

Six Bells Brewery, Church Street, Bishop's Castle, Shropshire, SY9 5AA
Tel (01588) 638930
Website
bishops-castle.co.uk/SixBells/brewery
Tours by arrangement

⊗ Brewing started in 1997 with plant made from dairy equipment with a 5-barrel brew length. The brewery was upgraded in 1999 to expand to 20-barrel capacity and a bottling line. Six Bells has six regular outlets while a further 35 pubs take the beers as guest ales. Seasonal beers: Cloud Nine (ABV 4.2%, spring-Oct), Old Recumbent (ABV 5.2%, Oct-spring).

Big Nev's *(OG 1037, ABV 3.8%)*
A pale, fairly hoppy bitter.

Marathon Ale *(OG 1040, ABV 4%)*
Dark and malty.

Spring Forward *(OG 1047, ABV 4.6%)*
Originally a spring beer but now permanent: dry, hoppy and amber in colour.

Brew 101 *(OG 1048, ABV 4.8%)*

SKINNER'S

Skinner's Brewery, Riverside View, Newham, Truro, Cornwall, TR1 2SU
Tel (01872) 271885
Fax (01872) 271886
E-mail info@skinnersbrewery.com
Website www.skinnersbrewery.com
Tours by arrangement

⊗ A brewery founded in July 1997 by Steve and Sarah Skinner, formerly of the Tipsy Toad Brewery in Jersey. The beer names are based on Cornish folklore characters. The brewery has won many awards in its short life, including Supreme Champion at the SIBA Maltings Festival, Newton Abbot, in 1998, with Cornish Knocker. This was followed in 1999 with a repeat performance with Betty Stogs. Also in 1999 Who Put the Lights Out? won a gold medal in the National Beauty of Hops competition. Ice Blonde won Beer of the Festival at the Cotswold Festival in 2000. Skinner's owns one pub, the Skinner's Ale House in Newquay. Occasional beer: Jingle Knockers (ABV 5.5%, Christmas), Mild Oatmeal Stout (ABV 4%, April/May). Bottle-conditioned beers: Who Put the Lights Out? (ABV 5%), Cornish Knocker Ale (ABV 4.5%), Jingle Knockers (ABV 5.5%).

Coast Liner *(ABV 3.4%)*
A crisp, light brown, hoppy session bitter.

Spriggan Ale *(OG 1038, ABV 3.8%)* ⬧
A light golden, hoppy bitter. Well-balanced with a smooth bitter finish.

Betty Stogs Bitter *(ABV 4%)* ⬧
A pale amber, mid-strength bitter with hoppy overtones.

Cornish Knocker Ale
(OG 1044.5, ABV 4.5%) ⬧
A strong, clean-tasting golden ale. Distinctive flowery aroma with a lasting finish.

Figgy's Brew *(ABV 4.5%)* ⬧
A classic dark premium-strength bitter. Full-flavoured with a smooth finish.

Who Put the Lights Out? *(ABV 5%)*
Strong single hop amber ale first brewed to mark the solar eclipse in 1999.

Cornish Blonde Wheat Beer
(OG 1050, ABV 5%)

Ice Blonde *(OG 1050, ABV 5%)*
Wheat beer served at 4 degrees C.

SMILES

Smiles Brewing Co Ltd, Colston Yard, Colston Street, Bristol, BS1 5BD
Tel (01275) 375878. (0831) 599046 (m)
Fax (01275) 375076
E-mail info@smiles.co.uk or
mark.todd@smiles.co.uk
Website www.smiles.co.uk
Shop 8.30-7pm. Tours by arrangement

⊗ Smiles Brewing Co, founded in 1977, is a traditional tower brewery located in the heart of the city. The mainstream brands are complemented by monthly specials. The company sold 16 pubs to Young's; Smiles owns only its Brewery Tap. The brewery supplies more than 250 other outlets. The brewery has an e-store on the website where fresh beer and memorabilia can be purchased. Monthly beers: Bristol Porter (ABV 4.7%, January), Old Tosser (ABV 4.3%, February), March Hare (ABV 4%, March), April Fuel (ABV 4.8%, April), May Fly (ABV 4.5%, May), Zummer Vat Ale (ABV 4%, June), Maiden Leg Over (ABV 3.5%, July), Glorious 12th (ABV 3.8%, August), Wurz Ale Gone (ABV 4.1%, September), Old Russ Ale (ABV 4.4%, October), Roman Cand Ale (ABV 5.5%, November), Holly Hops (ABV 5%, December).

Original *(OG 1038, ABV 3.8%)* ⬧
Aroma of pale/crystal malt, fruit and floral hop, with similar, bigger taste. Good dry bitterness, with a finish less sweet and more dry. Amber-coloured, it is light, hoppy, dry and refreshing.

Best *(OG 1041, ABV 4.1%)* ⬧
Nicely balanced, mid-bodied and bitter-sweet ale, with malt, hops and fruit lasting throughout. Pale brown in colour.

Blond *(OG 1047, ABV 4.7%)* ⬧
Golden-amber coloured, with an aroma of pale malt, hop and fruit. Bigger tasting on malt, with some sweetness, but also bitter and dry. Less fruity and sweet in finish, more dry.

Heritage *(OG 1052, ABV 5.2%)* ⬧
Aroma of malt, chocolate and hops, this is a

medium to full-bodied, fruity ale, with a lasting, bitter-sweet finish. Red-brown in colour.

Imperial *(OG 1071, ABV 7.1%)*

SAMUEL SMITH

Samuel Smith Old Brewery (Tadcaster), High Street, Tadcaster, N Yorkshire, LS24 9SB Tel (01937) 832225 Fax (01937) 834673
Tours by arrangement

☺ Samuel Smith brews at Yorkshire's oldest brewery, which dates from 1758. Although related to the neighbouring John Smith's (now owned by Scottish Courage), who originally owned the old brewery, Samuel Smith's is a radically different company, still family-owned, and fiercely independent. Cask conditioned Old Brewery Bitter is brewed from well water without the use of adjuncts or any brewing aids and fermented in traditional Yorkshire Squares. All real ale is supplied in wooden casks made and repaired by the brewery's own cooper. Cask ale is sold in the majority of the 200 odd tied houses, although there is now only one cask brand, and the company has gone over to nitro-keg in a number of outlets, especially in London. While not bottle conditioned, Sam Smith's bottled beers, including Taddy Porter, Imperial Stout, and Organic Best Ale, are outstanding.

Old Brewery Bitter (OBB) *(OG 1040, ABV 4%)* ◆
Malt dominates the aroma, with an initial burst of malt, hops and fruit in the taste, which is sustained in the aftertaste.

SNOWDONIA

Snowdonia Parc Brewery, Snowdonia Park Hotel, Waunfawr, Caernarfon, Gwynedd, LL55 Tel (01286) 650409 Fax (01286) 650733
Tours by arrangement

Snowdonia started brewing in spring 1998 in a 2-barrel brew length brewhouse. The pub is the station master's house for the Welsh Highland Railway. Waunfawr station opened in summer 2000 and is now the railway terminus. The owners bought the Prince of Wales in Caernarfon, which is a second outlet for the brewery's beers. Seasonal beer: Haf (ABV 5%).

Welsh Highland Bitter *(ABV 5%)*

SPINNAKER

Spinnaker Ales Ltd, Unit 24, Winston Business Centre, Chartwell Road, Lancing, W Sussex, BN15 8TU Tel/Fax (01903) 851482 Website www.spinnakerales.co.uk

⊠ A brewery established in 1993, it increased its capacity in 1995 to around 55 barrels a week, some of which is taken by wholesalers, although up to 100 outlets are supplied direct. There was a change of ownership in 1999 and during the millennium year changed its trading name from Brewery on Sea to Spinnaker. Beers are

also brewed for East-West Ales, and the brewery often produces beers for special occasions. Seasonal beers: Big Fat Santa (ABV 4.2%, Nov-Dec) Shell Shock (ABV 4.3%, Easter), Leaf Thief (ABV 4.2%, autumn), Snow Belly (ABV 4.4%, Christmas), Whale Ale (ABV 4.4%, May), Valentine (ABV 4.6%, February), plus a large range of occasional and one-off beers.

Bitter *(OG 1036, ABV 3.5%)* ◆
A hoppy-tasting, smooth, basic ale.

Mild or **Lancing Special Dark** *(OG 1036, ABV 3.5%)*
Dark in colour and rich in flavour.

Golden Lite *(ABV 3.8%)*
Originally a summer brew, now brewed all year-round. Golden brown in colour and flavoursome.

Classic *(OG 1040, ABV 4%)* ◆
The brewery's first beer: copper-coloured, with hints of malt in the aroma, giving way to a fruity flavour.

Rain Dance *(ABV 4.4%)*
Pale with a cereal aroma.

Buzz *(OG 1045, ABV 4.5%)* ◆
An amber-coloured beer primed with honey, which dominates the aroma. An initial sweetness gives way to an intriguing flavour mix of malt, honey and hops. Hoppy aftertaste.

Special Crew *(OG 1050, ABV 5.5%)*
A full-bodied bitter that gains its flavour and copper colour from a mix of pale and crystal malts.

Ginger *(OG 1050, ABV 5.5%)*
Mid-brown in colour, the beer contains pure ginger, making it highly aromatic.

Riptide *(OG 1060, ABV 6.5%)*
A premium strong ale, fully fermented.

Tidal Wave *(OG 1065, ABV 7%)*
A dry-tasting, strong dark beer.

SPINNING DOG

⛿ Spinning Dog Brewery, the Victory, 88 St Owen's Street, Hereford, HR1 2QD Tel/Fax (01432) 342125/274998/0411 316013 E-mail jfkenyon@aol.com
Tours by arrangement

⊠ The brewery was built in a room of the Victory in 2000 by Jim Kenyon, following the purchase of the pub. Initially the brewery served only the pub, but is now supplying 30 other outlets in Herefordshire. As a result of the closure of Flannery's of Aberystwyth, Jim has taken on some of its beers. The brewery, with a 4-barrel brew length, can be seen from a window in the pub. Seasonal ale: Santa Paws (ABV 5.2%).

Muttleys Bark Mild *(OG 1035, ABV 3.5%)*
A dark, malty mild with a hint of bitterness and a touch of roast.

Chase Your Tail *(OG 1036, ABV 3.6%)*
A good session beer with an abundance of hops and bitterness. Dry, with citrus aftertaste.

Muttleys Mongrel *(OG 1039, ABV 3.9%)*
Brewed with a blend of three different hops to create a very hoppy ale.

Top Dog *(OG 1042, ABV 4.2%)*
A hoppy beer with both malt and fruit flavours, a hoppy aroma with a slight bitter, hoppy aftertaste.

Flannery's Oatmeal Stout
(OG 1044, ABV 4.4%)

Flannery's Harvest Moon
(OG 1045, ABV 4.5%)

Flannery's Rheidol Reserve
(OG 1048, ABV 4.8%)

Muttleys Revenge *(OG 1048, ABV 4.8%)*
A strong, smooth, premium hoppy beer, amber in colour. Full-bodied with a dry, citrus-like aftertaste.

SPINNING DOG BREWERY

CHASE YOUR TAIL

HEREFORD
OG. 1036ˮ

SP SPORTING ALES

SP Sporting Ales Ltd, Cantilever Lodge, Stoke Prior, Leominster, Herefordshire, HR6 0LG
Tel/Fax (01568) 760226

⊗ Small brewery that opened in 1996 and is now supplying more than 250 outlets. It was due to change ownership and address during 2001.

Winners *(ABV 3.5%)*

Dove's Delight *(OG 1040, ABV 4%)*

Joust Bootiful *(ABV 4.2%)*

Sting *(ABV 4.2%)*

Joust Perfic *(ABV 4.5%)*

Marathon *(ABV 5.1%)*

SPRINGHEAD

Springhead Brewery, Unit 3, Sutton Workshops, Old Great North Road, Sutton-on-Trent, Newark, Notts, NG23 6QS
Tel (01636) 821000 Fax (01636) 821150
E-mail springhead@compuserve.com
Website www.springhead.co.uk

⊗ Springhead started out as the country's smallest brewery but moved to larger premises in 1994. In 1997 brewing was temporarily halted but brewer Alan Gill succeeded in attracting new backers and re-launched the company in 1998, though he subsequently left to launch Broadstone in Retford (qv). Brewery tours available lunchtime or evenings by arrangement in the new visitor centre. Most of the beer names are associated with the English Civil War. Seasonal beers: Hersbrucker Wheat Beer (ABV 3.6%, March-Sept), Cromwell's

Hat (ABV 6%, Oct-March). Bottle-conditioned beers: Bitter, Roundhead's Gold, The Leveller, Roaring Meg, Cromwell's Hat.

Surrender *(OG 1035, ABV 3.6%)*
A burnished, copper-coloured bitter with a stunning combination of malt and hops. Long dry finish. Wonderfully refreshing.

Bitter *(OG 1040, ABV 4%)*
A clean-tasting, easy-drinking hoppy beer.

Puritans Porter *(OG 1040, ABV 4%)*
A porter, dark but not heavy. Smooth with a lingering finish of roasted barley.

Roundhead's Gold *(OG 1042, ABV 4.2%)*
Golden light, made with wild flower honey. Refreshing but not too sweet with the glorious aroma of Saaz hops.

Rupert's Ruin *(ABV 4.2%)*

Goodrich Castle *(OG 1044, ABV 4.4%)*
Brewed following a 17th-century recipe using rosemary. Pale ale, light on the palate with a bitter finish and a delicate flavour.

Sweet Lips *(ABV 4.6%)*
A light, smooth and refreshing beer with some grapefruit notes from American Cascade hops.

The Leveller *(OG 1046, ABV 4.8%)*
Dark, smoky, intense flavour with a toffee finish. Brewed in the style of Belgian Trappist ales.

Gardener's Tap *(ABV 5%)*

Roaring Meg *(OG 1052, ABV 5.5%)*
Smooth and sweet with a dry finish and citrus honey aroma.

STANWAY

Stanway Brewery, Stanway, Cheltenham, Glos, GL54 5PQ
Tel (01386) 584320
Website www.stanwaybrewery.co.uk

⊗ Small brewery founded in 1993 with a 5-barrel plant, which confines its sales to the Cotswolds area (around 25 outlets). Seasonal beers: Lords-a-Leaping (ABV 4.5%, Christmas), Cotteswold Gold (ABV 3.9%, summer).

Stanney Bitter *(OG 1042, ABV 4.5%)* ✎
A light, refreshing, amber-coloured beer, dominated by hops in the aroma, with a bitter taste and a hoppy, bitter finish.

STEAMIN' BILLY

Steamin' Billy Brewing Co Ltd, 5 The Oval, Oadby, Leics, LE2 5JB
Tel (0116) 271 2616/272 0852
Website www.steamin-billy.co.uk

In spite of the name, Steamin' Billy, owned by Barry and Liz Lount, doesn't brew. The beers on sale at the Vaults and the Cow & Plough in Leicester are brewed by Grainstore of Oakham, with the exception of the Mild, which is brewed by Belvoir of Old Dalby.

Grand Prix Mild *(ABV 3.6%)*

Country Bitter *(ABV 4%)*

Lazy Summer *(ABV 4%)*

Steamin' Billy Bitter *(ABV 4.3%)*

STONEHENGE

**Stonehenge Ales (Bunces Brewery),
The Old Mill, Mill Road,
Netheravon, Salisbury,
Wilts, SP4 9QB
Tel (01980) 670631
Fax (01980) 671187
E-mail stonehenge_ales@bigfoot.com
Website www.stonehengeales.co.uk**
Shop 9-5 Mon-Fri; 11-1 Sat. Tours by arrangement

⊗ A tower brewery, originally named
Bunce's Brewery after late founder
Tony Bunce, is housed in a listed building
on the River Avon. It was established in
1984, and sold to Danish master brewer Stig
Anker Andersen in 1993. Its cask-
conditioned beers are delivered to around
60 free trade outlets within a radius of 50
miles, and a number of wholesalers are also
supplied. Seasonal beers: Sign of Spring
(ABV 4.6%, March-April), Second to None
(ABV 4.6%, May-July), Stig Swig (ABV 5%,
Aug-Oct), Rudolph (ABV 5%, Nov-Jan).

Benchmark *(OG 1035, ABV 3.5%)* ⬥
A pleasant, bitter ale of remarkable
character. The taste is malty, the aroma
subtle and the long finish is dry on the
palate.

Pigswill *(OG 1040, ABV 4%)*
A beer first brewed for the Two Pigs pub at
Corsham, now more widely available.

Best Bitter *(OG 1042, ABV 4.1%)*
A complex malty and bitter beer with
noticeable fruit and a long, bitter aftertaste.

Heel Stone *(OG 1042, ABV 4.3%)*
Crisp, refreshing amber bitter with a
blackcurrant aroma and a dry, lingering and
bitter aftertaste.

Great Dane (cask-conditioned lager)
(OG 1044, ABV 4.6%)
Traditionally brewed, fermented and
lagered at low, controlled temperatures.
Only malt, lager hops, lager yeast and
brewing water are used. The result is a clean,
crisp and refreshing real premium lager
with a bitter aftertaste that lingers on.

Danish Dynamite *(OG 1050, ABV 5%)*
A light golden, slightly fruity, dry strong ale
with hop and bitter balance.

Old Smoky *(OG 1050, ABV 5%)* ⬥
A delightful, warming, dark bitter ale, with
a roasted malt taste and a hint of liquorice
surrounding a developing bitter flavour.

STORM

**Storm Brewing Co, Cheshire Bakeries,
Hulley Road, Macclesfield,
Cheshire, SK10 2LP
Tel (01625) 432978/615856**
Tours by arrangement

Storm started brewing in 1998 under the
guidance of Brian Rides of Wickwar
Brewery. Two partners, Hugh Thompson
and Dave Stebbings, brew five barrels a
week on a part-time basis. Storm currently
supplies approximately 30 outlets in the
Macclesfield area.

Beaufort's Ale *(OG 1036, ABV 3.8%)*
Golden brown, full-flavoured session beer
with a lingering hoppy taste.

Ale Force *(OG 1038, ABV 4.2%)* ⬥
Amber, smooth-tasting, complex beer that
balances malt, hop and fruit on the taste,
leading to a roasty, slightly sweet aftertaste.

Windgather *(OG 1043, ABV 4.5%)*
Pale brown, refreshing, clean-tasting best
bitter, complex and highly flavoured.

Storm Damage *(ABV 4.7%)*
A light-coloured, well-hopped beer with a
distinct fruitiness from start to finish.

STRAWBERRY BANK

**Strawberry Bank Brewery, Masons Arms,
Cartmel Fell, Grange-over-Sands,
Cumbria, LA11 6NW
Tel (0153 95) 68486
Fax (0153 95) 68780**
Tours by arrangement

☻ Strawberry Bank, at the rear of the
Masons Arms pub, now brews just Damson
Beer (ABV 6%) on an occasional basis.

SULWATH

**Sulwath Brewers Ltd, The Brewery,
209 King Street, Castle Douglas,
Dumfries & Galloway, DG7 1DT
Office: Strathmore,
14 Babbington Gardens, Hardthorn,
Dumfries, DG2 9JB
Tel (01556) 504525 Fax (01556) 504525
E-mail info@sulwathbrewers.co.uk
Website www.sulwathbrewers.co.uk**
Shop Mon-Sat. Tours by arrangement

☻ A small, privately-owned company that
started brewing in 1995. It sells cask ales
direct to the licensed trade and currently
has 53 outlets for draught, with a further 25
supermarkets and licensed shops for bottled
Criffel, Knockendoch and Galloway Gold
(lager); all brewery conditioned. Sulwath
moved from its original site at Southerness
to larger premises at Castle Douglas in 2000
to cope with increased business and
incorporate a small bottling plant on site.
A reception, shop and visitor centre
(capacity 50 people) is open for tours and
visitors Monday to Saturday.
Seasonal/occasional beers: The Black
Galloway (ABV 4.4%), John Paul Jones
(ABV 4%), Hawkhill Best (ABV 3.8%). All
the beers are suitable for vegetarians.

Cuil Hill *(OG 1039, ABV 3.6%)* ⬥
Distinctively fruity session ale with malt
and hop undertones. The taste is bitter-
sweet with a long-lasting dry finish.

Criffel *(OG 1043, ABV 4.6%)* ⬥
Full-bodied beer with a distinctive
bitterness. Fruit is to the fore of the taste,
with hop becoming increasingly dominant
in the taste and finish.

Knockendoch *(OG 1047, ABV 5%)* ⬥
Dark, copper-coloured, reflecting a roast
malt content, with bitterness from
Challenger hops.

Galloway Gold (cask-conditioned lager)
(OG 1048, ABV 5%) ⬥
A lager with full, refreshing taste. Best lager
and wheat malts with Continental hops are
used. There is a hint of citrus on the palate.

SUMMERSKILLS

Summerskills Brewery, 15 Pomphlett Farm Industrial Estate, Broxton Drive, Billacombe, Plymouth, Devon, PL9 7BG
Tel/Fax (01752) 481283

⊗ Originally established in a vineyard in 1983 at Bigbury-on-Sea, Summerskills moved to its present site two years later. National distribution via carefully vetted wholesalers ensures nationwide coverage for the company's prize-winning beers. Occasional/seasonal beers: Menacing Dennis (ABV 4.5%), Turkey's Delight (ABV 5.1%, Christmas).

Cellar Vee *(OG 1037, ABV 3.7%)*

Tamar *(OG 1037, ABV 3.7%)*
A tawny-coloured bitter with a fruity aroma, and a hop taste and finish.

Best Bitter *(OG 1042, ABV 4.3%)* ♦
A mid-brown beer, with plenty of malt and hops through the aroma, taste and finish. A good session beer.

Whistle Belly Vengeance
(OG 1046, ABV 4.7%) ♦
A red/brown beer with a beautiful malt and fruit taste and a pleasant, malty aftertaste.

Indiana's Bones *(OG 1055, ABV 5.6%)* ♦
A mid-brown beer with a good balance of fruit and malt in the aroma and taste, and a sweet, malty finish.

SUNSET

⌂ **Sunset Cider & Wine Ltd, The Leggers Inn, Stable Buildings, Savile Wharf, Mill Street East, Dewsbury, W Yorkshire, WF12 9BD**
Tel (01924) 502846
Tours by arrangement

The inn is based in an old converted hay loft in a canal basin. The brewery is situated under the pub and brews twice a week. Seasonal beer: Canal No 9 (ABV 6%, Christmas).

Canal No 5 *(OG 1038, OG 3.8%)* ♦
Amber-coloured bitter, moderately hopped with a low malty aroma and fruity taste. The finish is mellow.

Marriots Mild *(OG 1040, ABV 4%)*

Prospect Road *(ABV 4%)*

Golden Eye 700 *(OG 1042, ABV 4.2%)* ♦
Pale golden bitter, lightly hopped, with well-balanced fruity and malty character, and smooth finish.

Pharoes Curse *(OG 1046, ABV 4.6%)*

SUSSEX*

Sussex Brewery, Pett Road, Pett, E Sussex, TN35 4HB
Tel (01424) 813927 Fax (01424) 813928
Tours by arrangement

The 5-barrel brewery began life as the Pett Brewery Company, or Old Forge Brewery. It was rescued from liquidation by businessman Clive Soper and became Forge Brewery. In December 2000 the brewery was sold to Robert Chapman, one of the two original directors, and he is now the sole owner. Occasional/seasonal beers: Cuddles (ABV 4%), Summer Eclipse (ABV 4.6%).

Forge Bitter *(ABV 3.2%)*

Brothers Best *(ABV 3.9%)*
A hoppy, amber-coloured, session beer.

Old Black Pett *(ABV 4.6%)*

Pett Progress *(ABV 4.6%)*
Hoppy aroma, full body and a slightly bitter aftertaste.

SUTTON

Sutton Brewing Co,
31 Commercial Road, Coxside, Plymouth, Devon, PL4 0LE
Tel/Fax (01752) 205010
E-mail suttonbrewery@xsb42.force9.co.uk
Tours by arrangement

⊗ The brewery was built alongside the Thistle Park Tavern, near Plymouth's Sutton Harbour, in 1993. It went into production the following year to supply the pub and one other outlet. It now sells to more than 50 outlets in and around Plymouth, and is now expanding out of the South-west through wholesalers. A bigger plant and additional fermenters were installed in 1998 to cope with demand. Occasional/seasonal beers: Hopnosis (ABV 4.4%, summer), Plymouth Porter (ABV 5%, winter), Sleigh'd (ABV 5.5%, Christmas).

Plymouth/Dartmoor Pride
(OG 1039, ABV 3.8%)

XSB *(OG 1043, ABV 4.2%)* ♦
Amber nectar with a fruity nose and a bitter finish.

Wild Blonde *(ABV 1044, ABV 4.4%)*

Sutton Comfort *(OG 1045, ABV 4.5%)* ♦
Hoppy tasting mid-brown beer with a bitter hop finish underscored by malt and fruit.

Weetablitz *(OG 1045, ABV 4.4%)*

Jinja *(OG 1045, ABV 4.5%)*

Pandamonium *(OG 1048, ABV 4.8%)*
A dark brown beer with a distinct roast malt aroma, taste and finish.

Old Pedantic *(OG 1050, ABV 5%)*

Knickadroppa Glory *(OG 1056, ABV 5.5%)*

Bodmin Beast *(OG 1056, ABV 5.5%)*

SWALE

Swale Brewery, Little Telpits Farm, Grafty Green, Maidstone ME17 2AY
Tel (01795) 426871
E-mail swalebrewery@aol.com

⊗ Swale Brewery was opened by John Davidson in 1995 in Milton Regis, expanded and moved to new premises in Sittingbourne in 1997. He moved again in July 2001. Cask ales are brewed on a regular basis and are changed four times a year. Four bottle-conditioned beers are brewed all year. The brewery has a capacity of 80 barrels a week. 200 outlets are supplied direct. Seasonal beers: Mild (ABV 3.8%), Whitstable Oyster Stout (ABV 4.5%), Pickled Porter (ABV 5%), Mad Tom Courtney (ABV 5%), Cocklewarmer (ABV 5%, winter). Bottle-conditioned beers: Whitstable Oyster Stout, Indian Summer Ale, Kentish Gold (ABV 5%), Old Dick (ABV 5.2%).

Kentish Admiral (*OG 1038.5, ABV 3.5%*)
Russet-coloured, fresh clean flavour from
Kentish Admiral hops, giving a light, bitter
aroma and finish.

Kentish (*OG 1040, ABV 3.8%*)
A clean-tasting, light brown-coloured ale,
dry hopped with East Kent Goldings.

Indian Summer Ale (*OG 1043, ABV 4.2%*)
Pale ale rich in citrus grapefruit aroma and
flavour. Crisp bitter finish. Voted best
import of the year by Barley Corn magazine
(US) in 1999.

Bizarre (*OG 1048.5, ABV 4.8%*)

SWALED ALE

**Swaled Ale Brewery, West View, Gunnerside,
Richmond, N Yorkshire, DL11 6LD
Tel (01748) 886441**
Tours by arrangement

☒ Swaled was launched in 1995 by Fred
Bristow (with assistance from Buffy's
Brewery in Norfolk). Fred was frustrated by
the lack of local beer choice and his brewery
was set up as an indulgence rather than a
business to produce hand-crafted beers of a
quality seldom achieved by bigger brewers
handicapped by economic and commercial
constraints. Swaled is probably the smallest
micro-brewery to operate a tied house, the
King's Head at Gunnerside, acquired in
2000. The beers are named after local lead
mines. Seasonal beers: Hoppy Christmas
(ABV 4.4%, Christmas), Winter Warmer
(ABV 5.5%), Beidi Weiss Wheat Beer
(ABV 5.5%, summer/autumn), Hoppy Easter
(ABV 4.4%).

Priscilla Pale (*OG 1037-38, ABV 3.8%*)

Just Hopped By (*OG 1042-3, ABV 4.2%*)

Old Gang Bitter (*OG 1043-44, ABV 4.4%*)

Surrender Ale (*OG 1044-46, ABV 4.7%*)

SWAN*

⚲ **Swan on the Green, West Peckham,
Kent, ME18 5JW
Tel (01622) 812271
E-mail goodbeer@swan-on-the-green.co.uk**

A new pub brewery that opened in July
2000 on a site that dates back to 1526,
when an inn was first recorded. Over the
centuries it has been variously known as the
Millers Arms (when it included a bakery),
the Myllers Arms on the Greene, and
Honest Tom after landlord Thomas Oliver.
It became the Swan in 1852. The current
owner, Gordon Milligan, looked at micro-
breweries in the US and Britain, and picked
up brewing skills with Rob Jones at Dark
Star in Brighton, honing the skills on
courses with Brewlab at Sunderland
University. Gordon built his 2-barrel plant
himself and supplies just the pub with beer.
There are plans for an organic beer and a
2.6% ABV beer aimed at drivers. The pub
stages a 'green beer' festival in September,
offering beers made with hops harvested
straight from the hop fields.

Whooper Pale (*ABV 3.5%*)

Old Fashioned Mild (*ABV 3.5%*)

Ginger Swan (*ABV 3.6%*)

Stout (*ABV 4%*)

Trumpeter Best (*ABV 4%*)

Parliament Ale (*OG 1050, ABV 4.8%*)

SWANSEA

⚲ **Swansea Brewing Company, Joiners Arms,
50 Bishopston Road, Bishopston,
Swansea, SA3 3EJ. Office: 74 Hawthorne
Avenue, Uplands, Swansea, SA2 0LY
Tel (01792) 232658 brewery,
(01792) 290197 office**

☺ Opened in 1996, it was the first
commercial brewery in the Swansea area for
almost 30 years and is Swansea's only brew-
pub. It doubled its capacity within the first
year and now produces four regular beers
and occasional experimental ones. Three
regular outlets are supplied direct plus
various free trade outlets in the South Wales
area.

Deep Slade Dark (*OG 1034, ABV 4%*)

Bishopswood Bitter
(*OG 1038, ABV 4.3%*) 🍺❧
A pale brown bitter with a delicate aroma of
malt and an undertone of hops. A balanced
bitter taste with a hint of caramel and
sulphur leading on to a long, dry finish
with some fruitiness.

Three Cliffs Gold (*OG 1042, ABV 4.7%*)

Original Wood (*OG 1046, ABV 5.2%*)

SWEET WILLIAM*

⚲ **Sweet William Brewery, William IV,
816 High Road, Leyton, London, E10
Tel (020) 8556 2460**
Tours by arrangement

A new brew-pub that came on stream in
November 2000. The beers are currently
available only in the pub and a few selected
outlets.

East London Mild (*OG 1039, ABV 3.6%*)

Just William (*OG 1039, ABV 3.8%*)

William the Conqueror
(*OG 1045, ABV 4.4%*)

TALLY HO!

⚲ **Tally Ho! Country Inn & Brewery,
14 Market Street, Hatherleigh,
Devon, EX20 3JN**

Tel (01837) 810306 Fax (01837) 811079
E-mail tally.ho@virgin.net
Tours by arrangement

■ The Tally Ho! hotel has revived a 200-year-old tradition of brewing on the same site. Records show that ales were produced in 1790, when it was known as the New Inn Brewery. It was destroyed by fire in 1806 but was brewing again by 1824. The brewery finally closed in the early 1900s, when it could no longer compete with bigger commercial companies. The new brewery is based at the back of the Tally Ho! in what used to be the town's bakery. The 3.5-barrel plant, which can produce 260 gallons a week, can be viewed through a large picture window. The beers are full mash, using only English malts and hops, with no sugars, extracts or preservatives. The brewery was refurbished at the end of 2000 and early 2001. Bottle-conditioned beer: Midnight Madness (ABV 5.5%).

Potboilers Brew (OG 1036, ABV 3.5%)

Tarka's Tipple (OG 1042, ABV 4%)

Nutters (OG 1048, ABV 4.6%)

TAYLOR

Timothy Taylor & Co Ltd, Knowle Spring Brewery, Belina Street, Keighley, W Yorkshire, BD21 1AW
Tel (01535) 603139
Fax (01535) 691167
Website www.timothy-taylor.co.uk

◎ One of the classic brewers of pale ale, Timothy Taylor is an independent family-owned company established in 1858. It moved to the site of the Knowle Spring in 1863. Its prize-winning ales, which use Pennine spring water, are served in all 24 of the brewery's pubs as well as 400 other outlets. A new boiler and cask washer were installed in 1999 and the fermentation capacity was increased in 2000. While organic beers are not yet produced, none of the ales contains animal products. Seasonal beer: Ram Tam (ABV 4.3%, winter).

Golden Best (OG 1033, ABV 3.5%)
A clean-tasting and refreshing amber-coloured mild with fruit on the nose. Light hoppy taste, a bitter finish and background malt throughout. A good session beer.

Dark Mild (OG 1034, ABV 3.5%)
The hops of the underlying Golden Best combines with malt and a caramel sweetness and lead to a dry, bitter-sweet finish.

Porter (OG 1041, ABV 3.8%)
Sweetness and caramel can dominate this beer if it is served too young. However, when mature, the sweetness is balanced by fruity flavours and bitterness in the finish.

Best Bitter (OG 1038, ABV 4%)
Hops and a citrus fruitiness combine well with some biscuity malt in this drinkable bitter. Bitterness increases down the glass and lingers in the aftertaste.

Landlord (OG 1042, ABV 4.3%)
An increasingly dry, bitter finish complements the spicy, citrus hop character and complex fruitiness of this full-flavoured and well-balanced beer.

TEIGNWORTHY

Teignworthy Brewery, The Maltings, Teign Road, Newton Abbot, Devon, TQ12 4AA
Tel (01626) 332066
Fax (01626) 330153
E-mail john@teignworthy.freeserve.co.uk
Shop 10-5 weekdays at Tuckers Maltings

■ John and Rachel Lawton established Teignworthy Brewery in 1994. The 15-barrel plant produces an average of 25 barrels a week for outlets throughout Devon and Somerset. Based in the historic Tuckers Maltings, Teignworthy has first call on traditional, floor-malted grain. There are tours of the maltings and brewery every 45 minutes between Easter and the end of October. Tucker's shop stocks the full range of Teignworthy bottle-conditioned beers, and also has a mail order service. Seasonal/occasional ales: Making Ends Meet (ABV 3.8%), Strawberries & Cream (ABV 4.6%, Wimbledon period), Harvey's Ale (ABV 4.8%, April, May & October), Amy's Ale (ABV 4.8%, March, April & October), Maltster's Ale (ABV 5%), Full Moon (ABV 5.6%), Christmas Cracker (ABV 6%, Xmas). Bottle-conditioned beers: as cask beers.

Reel Ale (OG 1039.5, ABV 4%)
Clean, sharp-tasting bitter with lasting hoppiness; predominantly malty aroma.

Spring Tide (OG 1043.5, ABV 4.3%)
An excellent, full and well-rounded, mid-brown beer with a dry, bitter taste and aftertaste.

Old Moggie (OG 1044.5, ABV 4.4%)

Beachcomber (OG 1045.5, ABV 4.5%)
A pale brown beer with a light, refreshing fruit and hop nose, grapefruit taste and a dry, hoppy finish.

TEME VALLEY

☗ **Teme Valley Brewery, Talbot Inn, Knightwick, Worcs, WR6 5PH**
Tel (01886) 821235
Fax (01886) 821060
E-mail temevalley@aol.com
Website www.temevalley.co.uk
Tours by arrangement

The Teme Valley Brewery opened in 1997 behind the Talbot, with both brewery and inn owned by the farming and hop-growing Clift family. The brewery was the only privately-owned British brewery that grew and used its own hops, but in September 2000, after the hop harvest, Lulsley Court Estate was sold. The Clifts had grown hops at Lulsley Court since the late 19th century, had been heavily involved in the history of hop growing in the area, and were among the first to change to mechanical hop picking in 1947. Teme Valley will continue to feature English hops in all its beers and, when Lulsley Court varieties run out, will use other hops grown in the valley. With a 360-gallon weekly capacity, the brewery is on the smaller scale of micro plants, supplying the Talbot and 10 other pubs. Chris Gooch, the brewer, uses a full barley mash and ferments in traditional, open-topped fermenting vessels. Seasonal beers: The Hops Nouvelle is a range of single-hop varietal beers, using fresh, unkilned hops, Challenger, Earlybird Goldings, Fuggles, Mathon Goldings and Northdown: Spring Wot (ABV 4.7%, Jan-March), Fool's Gold (ABV 4.5%, April-May), The Dark Stranger (ABV 4.4%, June-Aug), Wassail (ABV 5.5%, Dec-Jan).

T'Other (OG 1035, ABV 3.5%) ◈
A powerfully pungent nose is not lived up to in the flavour with the fruity hops coming through in a very refreshing drink.

This (OG 1037, ABV 3.7%) ◈
A very subtle mixture of flavours and a contrasting aroma in this quaffing bitter.

That (OG 1041, ABV 4.1%) ◈
A well-balanced mixture of tastes with its floral hoppiness and rich malts.

THREE B'S

Three B's Brewery, Unit 19, Hamilton Street, Blackburn, Lancs, BB2 4AJ
Tel (01254) 208154
Tours by arrangement

Robert Bell designed and began building his 2-barrel brewery in 1997 and in October 1998 he obtained premises in Hamilton Street, Blackburn, to set up the brewery and complete the project. The first beers went on sale in 1999. 20 outlets are supplied direct.

Stoker's Slake (ABV 3.6%)
A traditional dark mild with roast malt aromas and creamy chocolate notes.

Bobbin's Bitter (ABV 3.8%)
Warm aromas of malt, Goldings hops and nuts; a full, fruity flavour with a light dry finish.

Tackler's Tipple (ABV 4.3%)
A best bitter with full hop flavour, biscuit tones on the tongue and a deep, dry finish. A darker coloured ale with a fascinating blend of hops and dark malt.

Pinch Noggin' (ABV 4.6%)
A luscious balance of malt, hops and fruit, with a lively, colourful spicy aroma of citrus fruit. A quenching golden beer.

Knocker Up (ABV 4.8%)
A porter with an exotic ebony texture and a deep, rich palate of roast barley and chocolate malt.

Shuttle Ale (ABV 5.2%)
A strong pale ale, light in colour with a balanced malt and hop flavour, and superb Goldings aroma, long dry finish and delicate fruit notes.

THREE TUNS

Three Tuns Brewing Co Ltd, Three Tuns Inn, Salop Street, Bishop's Castle, Shropshire, SY9 5BW
Tel (01588) 638797
Fax (01588) 638081
E-mail info@thethreetunsinn.co.uk
Website www.thethreetunsinn.co.uk
Shop open bar hours for sales of bottled beers
Tours by arrangement

⊗ Mystery surrounds the future of this renowned brew-pub. In June 2001, the Shropshire Star reported that pub and brewery were up for sale. This was denied by the owners, who said they had had the site valued when the brewery was being refurbished, but admitted they would sell if a buyer could meet the asking price of £450,000. The Three Tuns is a superb Victorian miniature tower brewery, built by John Roberts in 1899, though it's thought that brewing has taken place on the site since 1642. Much of the original 19th-century equipment is still used, along with the 17th-century timber-framed malt store next to the brewery. A museum of the History of Beer and Brewing is based next to the brewery. In late 2000 and early 2001, Hobson's brewed the beers while refurbishment work was carried out at the Three Tuns. By the summer of 2001, the Three Tuns was brewing twice a week, with plans to restore full-time brewing during the course of the year, unless the site is sold. Three Tuns' beers are used in the acclaimed dishes in the pub's restaurant. Seven outlets are supplied direct and beers are available via the website.
Occasional/seasonal beers: Reverend Glenn (ABV 4.5%, summer), Old Scrooge (ABV 6.7%, winter). Bottle-conditioned beer: Clerics' Cure (ABV 5%), Belfry (ABV 6.3%), Old Scrooge (ABV 6.7%).

Sextons Bitter (OG 1037, ABV 3.8%)
A well-hopped session bitter with a surprisingly malty finish.

XXX (OG 1042, ABV 4.3%)
A marriage of pure Maris Otter pale ale malt with Herefordshire Fuggles and Goldings. A golden pale ale with a surprisingly bitter finish.

Offa's Ale (OG 1048, ABV 4.9%)
A darker, strong bitter with good balance.

THWAITES

Daniel Thwaites Brewery PLC, PO Box 50, Star Brewery, Blackburn, Lancs, BB1 5BU
Tel (01254) 686868
Fax (01254) 681439
E-mail info@thwaites.co.uk
Website www.thwaites.co.uk
Tours by arrangement

⊛ One of the oldest family-run Lancashire firms, founded by excise officer Daniel Thwaites in 1807, and still brewing at the Star Brewery. It owns 390 tenanted pubs and 65 managed ones, with some 850 free trade accounts. Investment in technology has produced a modern brewhouse but Thwaites' commitment to cask ales is undiminished. Seasonal beers: Thoroughbred (ABV 4%, Sept-Oct), Good Health (ABV 4.9%, Nov-Dec), Swashbuckler (ABV 4.5%, Feb-April).

Best Mild (OG 1033, ABV 3.3%) ◈
A rich, dark mild presenting a smooth, malty flavour and a pleasant, slightly bitter finish.

Best Bitter (OG 1036, ABV 3.6%) ◈
A clean-tasting, refreshing session bitter, combining bitterness and biscuity flavours and with a lingering bitter finish.

Reward (ABV 4.2%) ◈

Daniel's Hammer (OG 1047, ABV 5%)

TIGERTOPS

Tigertops Brewery, 22 Oakes Street, Flanshaw Lane, Wakefield, W Yorkshire, WF2 9LN Tel (01924) 897728/716238
Tours by arrangement in August only

⊛ Tigertops was established in 1995 by Stuart Johnson, a former chairman of the Wakefield branch of CAMRA, and his wife, Lynda. The Johnsons also own the Foxfield Brewery in Cumbria. Barry 'Axeman' Smith, the brewer, produces Continental beer styles, using imported malts and yeasts. The brewery supplies mainly beer festivals and three or four other outlets. Seasonal beer: Marzen (ABV 5%, March).

Dark Mild Wheat *(OG 1036, ABV 3.6%)*
An unusual mild made primarily with wheat malt.

Axeman's Light *(OG 1035, ABV 3.6%)*
A hoppy pale ale.

Axeman's Block *(OG 1036, ABV 3.6%)*
A malty beer with a good hop finish.

Weiss Beer *(OG 1044, ABV 4.6%)*
A German-style wheat beer.

Bock *(OG 1058, ABV 6.4%)*
A fruity, full-bodied complex beer.

TINDALL

Tindall Ales Brewery, Thwaite Road, Ditchingham, Bungay, Suffolk, NR35 2EA Tel/Fax (01508) 518392
Tours by arrangement

Tindall Ales Brewery was established in 1998 and is situated on the edge of the medieval Tindall Wood. It is a family-run business with the main objective of producing a good quality, locally-produced ale for local real ale outlets. All the beers are made from best local malt and the finest Kentish hops. Seasonal beers: Lovers' Ale (ABV 4%), Christmas Cheer (ABV 4%), Summer Loving (ABV 3.6%), Autumn Brew (ABV 4%). All the beers are available in bottle-conditioned form.

Mild *(ABV 3.7%)*

Best Bitter *(ABV 3.7%)* ◆
Pale brown with a clean hoppy nose, a balanced, rounded feel, and lingering bitter finish. The malt, fruit and hops that vie with the initial bitterness slowly fade.

Resurrection *(ABV 3.8%)* ◆
The bitterness apparent in this amber/gold bitter continues long after the other flavours fade. Fruit and hops, dominant on the nose, continue into the first taste but do not linger to the somewhat dry end.

Alltime *(ABV 4%)* ◆
A malt-based best bitter. This amber-coloured bitter has a malty nose as a lead into a malty freshness that complements the sweet, fruity overtones. A long ending develops a filling hop and caramel feel.

Ditchingham Dam *(ABV 4.2%)*

Ale Extra *(ABV 4.5%)* ◆
A sweet, fruity ale with a distinct malt beginning. This fades as bitterness comes through to give a quick, dry finish. Amber in colour, with low malt notes in a gentle hoppy aroma.

TIPSY TOAD

⌂ **Tipsy Toad Brewery, St Peter's Village, Jersey, JE3 7AA Tel (01534) 485556 Fax (01534) 485559**
Tours by arrangement

⊗ A brew-pub launched in 1992 and taken over by Jersey Brewery in 1997. Jersey Brewery distributes the beers through its tied estate. Seasonal/rotating beers: Festive Toad (ABV 8%), Horny Toad (ABV 5%), Dixie's Wheat Beer (ABV 4%), Naomh Padraig's Porter (ABV 4.4%).

Tipsy Toad Ale *(OG 1038, ABV 3.8%)*

Jimmy's Bitter *(OG 1042, ABV 4.2%)*

TIRRIL

⌂ **Tirril Brewery, Queen's Head Inn, Tirril, Penrith, Cumbria, CA10 2JF Tel (01768) 863219 Fax (01768) 863243 E-mail brewery@queensheadinn.co.uk Website www.queensheadinn.co.uk**
Tours by arrangement (maximum four people at a time)

Tirril started brewing 100 years after J Siddle's Brewery was bought and closed in the village in 1899. The brew plant is working to its full capacity of 2.25 barrels a week, with usually two of the three beers available in the pub at any one time. There are plans to expand to a 10-barrel plant; if it can't be based on the pub premises, it will be in the village.

John Bewsher's Best Bitter *(OG 1037.5, ABV 3.8%)*
Lightly-hopped, pale brown coloured bitter. A popular session beer.

Charles Gough's Old Faithful *(OG 1039, ABV 4%)*
A light, golden, hoppy, aromatic bitter.

Thomas Slee's Academy Ale *(OG 1040.5, ABV 4.2%)*
A dark, full-bodied bitter, rich and malty.

TISBURY
See Heritage.

TITANIC
Titanic Brewery, Harvey Works, Lingard Street, Burslem, Stoke-on-Trent, Staffs, ST6 1ED

Tel (01782) 823447 Fax (01782) 812349
Tours by arrangement

☺ Named in honour of the Titanic's Captain Smith, who hailed from Stoke, the brewery was founded in 1985 and moved to larger premises in 1991, installing new brewing plant in 1995. In 1996 Titanic began brewing for demonstration purposes on the log-fired Victorian micro-brewery in the Staffordshire County Museum at Shugborough Hall. The company now supplies more than 200 free trade outlets, as well as two pubs of its own. For Shugborough Brewery: Coachman's Tipple (ABV 4.7%, Jan-Feb), Butler's Revenge (ABV 4.9%, March-April), Milady's Fancy (ABV 4.6%, May-June), Farmer's Half (ABV 4.8%, July-Aug), Gardener's Retreat (ABV 4.7%, Sept-Oct), Lordship's Own (ABV 5%, Nov-Dec). Shugborough brews are also available in bottle-conditioned form in the same periods. Titanic seasonal beers: Full Steam Ahead (ABV 4.4%, January), Rule Britannia (ABV 4.2%, February), Drop Anchor (ABV 4.4%, March), Night to Remember (ABV 4.3%, April), Stoker (ABV 4.5%, May), Golden Age (ABV 4.6%, June), Sundeck (ABV 4.3%, July), First Class (ABV 4.1%, August), Triple Screw (ABV 4.5%, September), Dog Watch (ABV 4.4%, October), RMS (ABV 4.2%, November), Eight Bells (ABV 4.5%, December), Iceberg wheat beer (ABV 4.1%, May-Aug), Summer Wreckage (ABV 6.6%).

Mild *(ABV 3.5%)*

Best Bitter *(OG 1036, ABV 3.5%)* ◀
A crisp, clean, refreshing pale gold bitter with a good balance of fruit, malt and hops. Bitter finish.

Lifeboat Ale *(OG 1040, ABV 4%)* ◀
A fruity and malty, dark red/brown beer, with a fruity finish.

Premium *(OG 1042, ABV 4.1%)* ◀
An impressive, well-balanced pale brown bitter with malt and fruit in the aroma, which develop into a full flavour and a dry, hoppy finish.

Stout *(OG 1046, ABV 4.5%)* ◀
A dark combination of malt and roast with some hops. Strongly flavoured and well-balanced.

White Star *(OG 1050, ABV 4.8%)* ◀
An amber ale with a fruity taste and long bitter-sweet, fruity aftertaste.

Captain Smith's *(OG 1054, ABV 5.2%)* ◀
A full-bodied, dark red/brown beer, hoppy and bitter with malt and roast malt flavours, and a long, bitter-sweet finish.

Wreckage *(ABV 7.2%)* ◀
This sweet malty winter ale has a port-like aroma and walnut aftertaste.

TOLLY COBBOLD

Tollemache & Cobbold Brewery Ltd, Cliff Road, Ipswich, Suffolk, IP3 0AZ
Tel (01473) 231723
Fax (01473) 261100
E-mail tolly.cobbold@btconnect.com
Website site www.tollycobbold.co.uk
Shop for brewery tours only. Tours by arrangement

⊠ Tolly Cobbold is one of the oldest brewing companies in the country, founded by Thomas Cobbold in 1723. After years of uncertainty under a succession of owners (Ellerman Shipping Lines, the Barclay Brothers and Brent Walker) the company has been independent for more than 10 years and has a small but growing pub estate of seven outlets and operates as a major wholesaler and contract distributor, supplying more than 700 product lines to the licensed trade in East Anglia. A new brewery was built in 1995 and the old Victorian tower brewery is used for fully-guided brewery tours for the public. The site has now become a major tourist attraction. 200 outlets are supplied direct. Seasonal beers are brewed throughout the year and include Poppy Pride (ABV 3.5%, Oct-Nov) and Old Strong (ABV 5%, winter).

Mild *(OG 1032.5, ABV 3.2%)* ◀
A tasty mild with fruit, malt and roast malt characters, and a pleasing aftertaste. It tends to lose complexity when forced through a sparkler.

Bitter *(OG 1035.5, ABV 3.5%)* ◀
A light, mid-brown malty beer lacking bitterness.

Original Best Bitter
(OG 1038.5, ABV 3.8%) ◀
A slightly stronger bitter with assertive hop character throughout. The finish is bitter, but with a good balancing maltiness. Disappointingly hard to find.

IPA *(OG 1040, ABV 4.2%)*
A best bitter, full of citrus fruit flavours and flowery hoppiness.

TOMINTOUL

Tomintoul Brewery, Mill of Auchriachan, Tomintoul, Ballindalloch, Banffshire, AB37 9EQ
Tel (01807) 580333
Fax (01807) 580358
E-mail aviemorebrewery@dial.pipex.com
Website www.tomintoul-brewery.com
Tours by arrangement

☺ The brewery opened in 1993 in an old watermill, in an area renowned for malt whisky and salmon. It is not currently brewing. Around 80 outlets are currently supplied and wholesalers take the beer to England and Northern Ireland. The company was bought by Aviemore Brewery (qv) in 2000, which brews the beers and handles sales and distribution.

TOWER*

Tower Brewery, The Old Water Tower, Walsitch Maltings, Glensyl Way, Burton-on-Trent, Staffs, DE14 1PZ
Tel (01283) 530695

John Mills worked as a brewer with Burton Bridge for 10 years before branching out on his own. He is based in the water tower of the former maltings attached to Thomas Salt's Brewery, once the second biggest brewery in Burton and in the vanguard of the pale ale revolution of the 19th century. The tower was empty for nearly eight years, and John had to clear out rubbish and pigeon droppings before he could install his 15-barrel equipment. He describes his system as a 'semi-tower brewery – there aren't enough floors for it to be a traditional tower brewery'. (A tower brewery, such as Harvey's and Hook Norton, is so arranged that the brewing process flows logically from floor to floor without the need for pumps.) John started brewing in April 2001 and has 70 regular outlets for his beers, which are brewed with floor-malted barley and English, New Zealand and Slovenian hops.

Bitter *(ABV 4.2%)*

Malty Towers *(ABV 4.4%)*

Walsitch Wobbler *(ABV 5.2%)*

TOWNES

◻ Townes Brewery, Speedwell Inn, Lowgates, Staveley, Chesterfield, Derbyshire, S43 3TT
Tel (01246) 472252
Tours by arrangement

▨ Townes Brewery started in 1994 in an old bakery on the outskirts of Chesterfield using a 5-barrel plant; it was the first brewery in the town for more than 40 years. After a period of steady progress, the Speedwell Inn at Staveley was bought and the plant was moved to the rear of the pub. Brewing at Staveley started in 1997 and, after a period of renovation, the pub opened a year later. It was the first brew-pub in North Derbyshire in the 20th century. It sells the full range of Townes Beers. There are plans to bottle the beers and to buy another tied house in the area. More than 20 outlets are supplied direct. Reciprocal deals with other micros are being extended. Seasonal beers: GMT (ABV 4.2%, winter), Speedwell Bitter (ABV 3.9%, winter), IPA (ABV 4.5%, summer), Sunshine (ABV 3.6%, summer).

Golden Bud *(OG 1038, ABV 3.8%)*

Best Lockoford Bitter
(OG 1040, ABV 4%)

Muffin Ale *(OG 1045, ABV 4.5%)*

TRAQUAIR

Traquair House Brewery Ltd, Innerleithen, Peeblesshire, EH44 6PP
Tel (01896) 830323
Fax (01896) 830639
E-mail enquiries@traquair.co.uk
Website www.traquair.co.uk
Shop and Brewery Museum 10.30-5.30 daily April-Oct
Tours by arrangement April-Sept

◉ The 18th-century brewhouse is based in one of the wings of the 1,000-years-old Traquair House, Scotland's oldest inhabited stately home, visited by Mary Queen of Scots and Prince Charles Edward Stuart. The brewhouse was rediscovered by the 20th Laird, the late Peter Maxwell Stuart, in 1965. He began brewing again using all the original equipment, which remained intact, despite having lain idle for more than 100 years. The brewery has been run by Peter's daughter, Catherine Maxwell Stuart, since his death in 1990. The Maxwell Stuarts are members of the Stuart clan. All the beers are oak-fermented and 60 per cent of

production is exported (mostly bottled Traquair House Ale and Jacobite Ale). Some five outlets take the cask beer. Seasonal beers: Stuart Ale (ABV 4.5%, summer), Bear Ale (ABV 5%, winter).

House Ale *(ABV 7.2%)*

Jacobite Ale *(ABV 8%)*

TRAVELLERS INN

◻ Travellers Inn Brewing Company, Tremerchion Road, Pen-y-Cefn, Caerwys, Flintshire, CH7 5BL
Tel (01352) 720251

Roy Morgan's Original Ale *(ABV 3.8%)*

TRIMDON

Trimdon Cask Ales, Unit 2c, Trimdon Grange Industrial Estate, Trimdon Grange, Co Durham, TS29 6PA
Tel (01429) 880967
Fax (01429) 882276

A small brewery that was launched in 1999. Brewing was suspended in 2001.

TRING

Tring Brewery Co Ltd, 81-82 Akeman Street, Tring, Herts, HP23 6AF
Tel (01442) 890721
Fax (01442) 890740
E-mail info@tringbrewery.com
Website www.tringbrewery.com
Tours by arrangement

▨ Tring Brewery was founded in 1992 and, after a break of more than 50 years, restored brewing to the West Hertfordshire town. The company was started by Andrew Shardlow, who had brewed with Devenish, Greene King and Ruddles, who has been joined by Andrew Jackson from Whitbread, who is now head brewer. A new range of beers has been developed for the 32-barrel plant, backed by contemporary marketing. Tring has leased the Two Brewers in Luton, which is run as a free house but always stocks two or three of the brewery's beers. The company plans to add five to 10 pubs in the next few years. The brewery supplies 60-100 outlets. As well as seasonal beers, there is a vast range of one-off specials. Seasonal beers: Cuckoo's Coming (ABV 4.5%, spring), Mother Haggy's Finest Summer Ale (ABV 3.7%), Reap the Rye (ABV 4.7%, autumn), Santa's Little Helper (ABV 4.8%).

Side Pocket for a Toad
(OG 1035, ABV 3.6%)
Unmistakable citrus notes from American

Cascade hops balanced with a floral aroma and crisp dry finish in a straw-coloured ale.

Jack O'Legs *(OG 1041, ABV 4.2%)*
A combination of four types of malt and two types of aroma hops provide a copper-coloured premium ale with full fruit and a distinctive hoppy bitterness.

Colley's Dog *(OG 1051, ABV 5.2%)*
Dark but not over-rich, strong yet drinkable, this premium ale has a long dry finish with overtones of malt and walnuts.

TRIPLE FFF

Triple fff Brewing Company, Unit 3, Old Magpie Works, Four Marks, Alton, Hampshire, GU34 2DN
Tel/Fax (01420) 561422
Website www.triplefff.co.uk

Established in 1997, and now under the sole proprietorship of Graham Trott, Triple fff has made steady progress. It has expanded from five to 18 barrel brew-lengths. Winner of 14 awards, the brewery supplies around 200 outlets, and also uses wholesalers to distribute outside its own delivery area. Seasonal beers: Apache Rose Peacock (ABV 4.2%), Goldffffinger (ABV 5.4%), Witches Promise (ABV 6%).

Alton's Pride *(ABV 3.8%)*
Quenching beer with a citrus tang from Pioneer hops and a toffee-caramel aroma.

Pressed Rat & Warthog *(ABV 3.8%)*
A dry, roasty dark brown mild with good body and a suggestion of blackcurrant. Moderately bitter, with a short dry and fruity finish.

After Glow *(ABV 4%)*
A superbly hoppy, award-winning bitter. Straw-coloured, with honey and citrus fruit on the nose, the beer is well-balanced, with a good body and an aromatic hoppy and fruity finish.

Moondance *(ABV 4.2%)*
An amber-coloured best bitter, wonderfully hopped, with a huge hop aroma, balanced by bittering hops and malt. Bitterness increases in the finish as the fruit declines.

Stairway to Heaven *(ABV 4.6%)*
An aroma of pale and crystal malts introduces this pale brown beer with a flavour of summer fruits. Well-balanced, with a dry and fruity finish.

Dazed and Confused *(ABV 4.6%)*
An aroma of pale and crystal malts introduces this pale brown beer with a flavour of summer fruits. Well-balanced, with a dry and fruity finish.

Comfortably Numb *(ABV 5%)*

Little Red Rooster *(ABV 5%)*

TRUEMAN'S

Sam Trueman's Brewery, Henley House, School Lane, Medmenham, Marlow, Bucks, SL7 2HJ
Tel (01491) 576100
Fax (01491) 571764
E-mail bar@crownandanchor.co.uk
Website www.crownandanchor.co.uk

Sam Trueman's beer was available through wholesalers throughout the country but, as a result of wholesalers not paying bills, the owners bought the Crown & Anchor in Marlow, where Best (cask) and Lager (unfiltered but pressurised) are always available, plus one of the other three brews, and guest ales. Sam Trueman's beers are now sold only at the pub. Bottle-conditioned beers: Percy's Downfall (ABV 8.2%) and No Name (ABV 6%). Seasonal beer: Percy's Downfall (ABV 8.2%).

Best *(OG 1036, ABV 3.5%)*

Tipple *(OG 1041, ABV 4.2%)*

Bees Knees *(OG 1043, ABV 4.3%)*

Gold *(OG 1050, ABV 5%)*

TURKEY*

Turkey Inn, Goose Eye, Oakworth, W Yorkshire, BO22 0PD
Tel (01535) 681339

A purpose-built brewhouse with walls four feet thick, it took three years to build, involving excavation of the hillside at the back of the pub. It opened in September 2000.

Turkey Bitter *(ABV 3.8%)*

Dow Cave *(ABV 4.3%)*

Lost John's *(ABV 4.8%)*

Black Shiver Stout *(ABV 4.2%)*

ULEY

Uley Brewery Ltd, The Old Brewery, Uley, Glos, GL11 5TB
Tel (01453) 860120
E-mail uley.beer@cwccom.net
Tours by arrangement

Brewing at Uley began in 1833 at Price's Brewery. After a long gap, the premises were restored and Uley Brewery opened in 1985. It serves 40-50 free trade outlets in the Cotswolds area. Seasonal beer: Pigor Mortis (ABV 6%, Nov-Dec).

Hogshead PA *(OG 1036, ABV 3.5%)*
A pale-coloured, hoppy session bitter with a good hop aroma and a full flavour for its strength, ending in a bitter-sweet aftertaste.

Uley Bitter *(OG 1040, ABV 4%)*
A copper-coloured beer with hops and fruit in the aroma and a malty, fruity taste, underscored by a hoppy bitterness. The finish is dry, with a balance of hops and malt.

Old Ric *(OG 1045, ABV 4.5%)*
A full-flavoured, hoppy bitter with some fruitiness and a smooth, balanced finish. Distinctively copper-coloured.

Old Spot Prize Ale *(OG 1050, ABV 5%)*
A distinctive full-bodied, red/brown ale with a fruity aroma, a malty, fruity taste, with a hoppy bitterness, and a strong, balanced aftertaste.

Pig's Ear Strong Beer *(OG 1050, ABV 5%)*
A pale-coloured beer, deceptively strong. Notably bitter in flavour, with a hoppy, fruity aroma and a bitter finish.

VALE

Vale Brewery Company, Thame Road, Haddenham, Bucks, HP17 8BY
Tel (01844) 290008
Fax (01844) 292505
E-mail valebrewery@yahoo.com.uk
Website www.valebrewery.co.uk
Tours by arrangement

⊗ After many years working for large regional breweries and allied industries, brothers Mark and Phil Stevens opened a small, purpose-built brewery in Haddenham. This revived brewing in a village where the last brewery closed at the end of World War II. The plant was expanded in November 1996 and now has a capacity of 40 barrels. All beer is traditionally brewed without adjuncts, chemicals, or preservatives. A bottling line has been added and the cask beers are also available in bottle-conditioned form. Around 200 local outlets take the beers. Seasonal beers: Hadda's Spring Gold (ABV 4.6%), Hadda's Summer Glory (ABV 4%), Hadda's Autumn Ale (ABV 4.5%), Hadda's Winter Solstice (ABV 4.1%), Good King Senseless (ABV 5.2%), Hadda's Headbanger (ABV 5%).

Black Swan Dark Mild *(ABV 3.3%)*

Notley Ale *(ABV 3.3%)* ◈
A refreshing copper-coloured session bitter with some malt in the aroma and taste, and an uncompromisingly dry finish.

Wychert Ale *(ABV 3.9%)*
A full-flavoured beer with nutty overtones.

Black Beauty Porter *(ABV 4.3%)*

Edgar's Golden Ale *(ABV 4.3%)* ◈
A golden, hoppy best bitter with some sweetness and a dry, bitter-sweet finish. An unpretentious and well-crafted beer.

Grumpling *(ABV 4.6%)*

VALHALLA

Valhalla Brewery, Shetland Refreshments Ltd, Baltasound, Unst, Shetland, ZE2 9DX
Tel/Fax (01957) 711658
Website www.valhallabrewery.co.uk
Tours by arrangement

Valhalla Brewery opened in 1997 on the island of Unst in the Shetland Isles, making it the most northerly brewery in Great Britain. It is run by husband and wife team Sonny and Sylvia Priest plus some part-timers. The latest acquisition was a bottling plant in 1999, which has greatly increased sales.

White Wife *(ABV 3.8%)* ◈
Predominantly malty aroma with hop and fruit, which remain on the palate. The aftertaste is increasingly bitter.

Auld Rock *(ABV 4.5%)*

Porter *(ABV 4.6%)*

VENTNOR

Ventnor Brewery Ltd, 119 High Street, Ventnor, Isle of Wight, PO38 1LY
Tel (01983) 856161
Fax (01983) 856404
Website www.ventnorbrewery.co.uk
Shop 9-5. Tours by arrangement

⊗ Ventnor Brewery has been brewing since the early 1840s. Using traditional recipes of malt, hops and the unique ingredient of St Boniface natural spring water, Ventnor Brewery continues the tradition of brewing high quality, hand-crafted cask and bottled ales for the island and beyond. More than 60 outlets are supplied direct. All the beers are available in bottle, all but SunFire are available bottle-conditioned. Seasonal ales are also available.

Golden *(OG 1040, ABV 4%)* ◈
Well-balanced, easy-drinking bitter with an interesting slight honey/yeasty aftertaste.

SunFire *(OG 1044, ABV 4.3%)* ◈
A generously and distinctively bittered amber beer that could be toned down if pulled through a sparkler.

Oyster Stout *(OG 1046, ABV 4.5%)* ◈
A thin stout/dark mild with real oysters in the brew.

Old Ruby *(ABV 4.7%)*

Wight Spirit *(OG 1050, ABV 5%)* ◈
Interesting pale, hoppy, strong bitter with a surprising reversal of flavours from taste to aftertaste.

Sandrock *(OG 1057, ABV 5.6%)*
Unique and excellent novelty beer brewed with smoked malt, destined for the Scotch whisky market, producing a smooth peaty malt flavour not dissimilar to a good malt whisky.

VERULAM

Verulam Brewery, 134 London Road, St Albans, Herts, AL1 1PQ
Tel (01727) 766702
Tours by arrangement

⊗ A brewery housed behind the Farmers Boy pub run by Viv and Tina Davies. There are monthly specials.

Special *(OG 1037, ABV 3.8%)* ◈
Well-balanced session beer with a dryish aftertaste.

IPA *(OG 1039, ABV 4%)* ◈
Impressive straw-coloured, very hoppy beer.

Farmers Joy *(OG 1043, ABV 4.5%)* ◈
A malty beer with overtones of sweetness.

WADWORTH

Wadworth & Co Ltd, Northgate Brewery, Devizes, Wilts, SN10 1JW
Tel (01380) 723361
Fax (01380) 724342
E-mail sales@wadworth.co.uk
Website www.wadworth.co.uk
Shop 9-7.30 Mon-Sat. Tours Trade visits mid-April to mid-October, open to public in September and during the Devizes Arts Festival in June.

⊗ A market town brewery set up in 1885 by Henry Wadworth and one of the few remaining breweries to sell beer locally in oak casks; the brewery still employs a cooper. Though solidly traditional, with its own dray horses, it continues to invest in the future and to expand, producing up to 2,000 barrels a week to supply a wide-ranging free trade in the South of England, as well as its own 250 pubs. All but two of the tied houses serve real ale and 6X remains one of the South's most famous beers, with national distribution through Interbrew. Wadworth also owns a brew-pub, the Red Shoot (qv). Seasonal beers: Old Timer (ABV 5.8%, Dec-Jan), Malt & Hops (ABV 4.5%, Sept-Oct), Blunderbuss (ABV 5%). Information about new seasonal beers for 2002: see website. Bottle-conditioned beer: Strongest Ale (OG 1097).

Henry's Original IPA
(OG 1035, ABV 3.6%) ◆
A golden brown-coloured beer with a gentle, malty and slightly hoppy aroma, a good balance of flavours, with maltiness gradually dominating, and then a long-lasting aftertaste to match, eventually becoming biscuity. A good session beer.

6X *(OG 1040, ABV 4.3%)* ◆
Copper-coloured ale with a malty and fruity nose and some balancing hop character. The flavour is similar, with some bitterness and a lingering malty, but bitter finish. Full-bodied and distinctive.

JCB *(ABV 4.7%)*

WARCOP

**Warcop Country Ales, 9 Nellive Park, St Brides, Wentloog, Gwent, NP1 9SE
Tel/Fax (01633) 680058**

Small brewery based in a converted milking parlour, with 30 outlets delivered direct and others supplied by two wholesalers. Seasonal beer: Red Hot Furnace (ABV 9%, Xmas).

Arc Light *(ABV 3.5%)*

Pitside *(ABV 3.7%)*

Pit Prop *(ABV 3.8%)*

Black and Amber *(ABV 4%)*

Casnewydd *(ABV 4%)*

Hilston Premier *(ABV 4%)*

Steelers *(ABV 4.2%)*

Furnace *(ABV 4.5%)*

Dockers *(ABV 5%)*

WARWICKSHIRE

**Warwickshire Beer Co Ltd, The Brewery, Queen Street, Cubbington, Leamington Spa, Warwickshire, CV32 7NA
Tel (01926) 450747 Fax (01926) 450763
E-mail warwickshirebeerco@yahoo.com
Website www.warwickshirebeerco.co.uk**
Shop 8-12 Sat (weekdays ring first)
Tours by arrangement

A 6-barrel plant opened in a former village bakery by Phil Page in 1999, it was commissioned by Warwick District Council to produce a commemorative bottled beer to celebrate the redevelopment of Warwick market place. Capacity was increased in 2000 to 26 barrels. In March 2001 it acquired its first pub, the Market Tavern in Atherstone. 80 outlets are supplied direct. Seasonal beer: Xmas Bare (ABV 4.9%).

Best Bitter *(OG 1039, ABV 3.9%)*
A golden brown session bitter flavoured with First Gold hops.

Lady Godiva *(OG 1042, ABV 4.2%)*
Blond, gentle, and full-bodied.

St Patricks *(OG 1044, ABV 4.4%)*
A rich porter brewed in the Irish tradition.

Falstaff *(OG 1044, ABV 4.4%)*
A mahogany-coloured bitter flavoured with Cascade and First Gold hops.

Castle *(OG 1046, ABV 4.6%)*
A premium full-bodied and malty bitter.

Golden Bear *(OG 1049, ABV 4.9%)*
Golden in colour with well-balanced bitterness and spicy/fruity notes.

King Maker *(OG 1055, ABV 5.5%)*
Its subtlety belies its strength with flavour dominated by Challenger hops.

TOMOS WATKIN

**Tomos Watkin Ltd, Phoenix Brewery, Unit 3, Century Park, Valley Way, Swansea Enterprise Park, Swansea, SA6 8RP
Tel (01792) 775333
Fax (01792) 775779
E-mail enquiries@tomoswatkin.com
Website www.tomoswatkin.com**
Shop 9-5. Tours by arrangement

◉ An aggressively expanding brewery that was established by Simon Buckley, formerly of Buckley's and Ushers, adopting the name of a Llandovery company that ceased production in 1928. Brewing started in 1995 and in 2000 the brewery moved from Llandeilo to Swansea to a bigger, custom-built brewhouse. In March 2001, Tomos Watkin bought the Swansea-based Tavern Wholesaling, which has become the brewery's distribution arm. This has increased the number of outlets supplied to 400. The number of tied houses stands at 10, with plans to expand to 50 over the next four years. The beer range is liable to change. The website, developed by Swansea University, is interactive and callers can view the brewing process. Seasonal beers: Canons Choice (ABV 4.5%, winter), Dewi Sant (ABV 4.2%, spring), Cwrw Haf (ABV 4.2%, summer), Owain Glyndwr (ABV 4.2%, autumn), Cwrw Santa (ABV 4.6%, winter). Cwrw Cayo (ABV 4%) is brewed for the Welsh Eisteddfod in early August, FBA (ABV 4.5%) is brewed exclusively for Wetherspoons.

Whoosh *(OG 1037.5, ABV 3.7%)*
Amber-coloured bitter; gentle hop and malt aroma lead on to a similar mix of flavours, with balancing bitterness.

BB *(OG 1040.5, ABV 4%)* ◆
Pale brown with a gentle aroma of malt and hops. Fruit and bitterness add to these in the taste, building to a bitter finish.

Merlin Double Stout
(OG 1043, ABV 4.2%)
A roast, malt and fruit aroma. A complex mix of flavours with roast, malt, hop and fruit. Increasing bitterness and a long finish make this a fine stout.

OSB *(OG 1045, ABV 4.5%)* ▽◆
A gentle aroma followed by a rounded taste of hops, fruit and malt, and a long, bitter finish make this a satisfying best bitter.

WAWNE

Wawne Brewery, Tickton Arms, Main Street, Tickton, Beverley, HU17 5TX. Office: 9 Mill Lane, Beverley, E Yorkshire, HU17 9JD
Tel (01482) 679876
Fax (01482) 886142
E-mail
wawne_brewery@microbrewery.fsnet.co.uk
Tours by appointment only

Set up in 1999 in a garage at Wawne, the brewery moved to outbuildings at the Tickton Arms, two miles east of Beverley, in 2000. The brewery produces special brews each month with three regular ales.

Monks Mild *(OG 1032, ABV 3.2%)* ◆
This dark mild assaults the drinker with rich, roasted malt flavours. Strong roasted coffee mixes with a good balance of fruit and hops. Tasty throughout, it has a dry, bitter finish. A gem.

Infringement Bitter *(OG 1038, ABV 3.8%)* ◆
Fresh and fruity, this golden/copper coloured beer mixes both bitterness and sweetness well. The hop flavours come through to give a dry and bitter aftertaste.

Waghen Bitter *(OG 1041, ABV 4.1%)* ◆
An easily drinkable premium beer, amber in colour with a crisp mix of floral hops and fruitiness. Full flavoured with a hint of caramel.

Melsa Bitter *(OG 1043, ABV 4.3%)*

WEATHEROAK

Weatheroak Ales, Coach & Horses Inn, Weatheroak Hill, Alvechurch, Birmingham, B48 7EA
Tel (0498) 773894 (m)
(0121) 445 4411 (eves)
E-mail weatheroakales@withybed.fsnet.co.uk
Tours by arrangement

The brewery was set up in 1997, in an outhouse of the Coach & Horses, by Dave and Pat Smith by arrangement with pub owners Phil and Sheila Meads. The first brew was produced in 1998. A real ale off-licence has been opened in nearby Alvechurch. Weatheroak supplies 40 outlets direct.

Light Oak *(ABV 3.6%)* ◆
The aroma is full of fruity hops that come out fully in the taste. A very dry bitter beer that has only a hint of malt flavours.

Weatheroak Ale *(ABV 4.1%)* ◆
Full of high alpha hops, this beer has a dry bitterness throughout.

Redwood *(ABV 4.7%)* ◆
The malts and hops have equal prominence in this well-balanced bitter that leaves you with a dry, clean aftertaste.

Triple Tee *(ABV 5.1%)* ◆
A richly malted bitter that is not over-powered by the bitterness of the hops.

WEETWOOD

Weetwood Ales Ltd, Weetwood Grange, Weetwood, Tarporley, Cheshire, CW6 0NQ
Tel/Fax (01829) 752377

⊗ The brewery was set up at an equestrian centre in 1993. In 1998, the 5-barrel plant was replaced by a 10-barrel kit. Around 100 regular customers are now supplied.

Best Bitter *(OG 1038.5, ABV 3.8%)* ◆
A clean, dry and malty bitter with little aroma. Bitterness dominates the finish.

Eastgate Ale *(OG 1043.5, ABV 4.2%)* ◆
Well-balanced, pale, refreshing beer with malty, fruity taste and short, dry finish.

Old Dog Bitter *(OG 1045, ABV 4.5%)* ◆
A fuller-bodied version of the bitter: fruitier, with a hint of sweetness.

Ambush Ale *(OG 1047.5, ABV 4.8%)*
Smooth, dark, amber-coloured beer with the fruity flavour balanced by the addition of Styrian Goldings hops.

Oasthouse Gold *(OG 1050, ABV 5%)* ◆
Sweet, golden beer with some light malt and hop flavours. Typical Weetwood sharp aftertaste. It is deceptively drinkable for a beer of this strength.

WELLS

Charles Wells Ltd, Eagle Brewery, Havelock Street, Bedford, MK40 4LU
Tel (01234) 272766 Fax (01234) 279000
E-mail postmaster@charleswells.co.uk
Website www.charleswells.co.uk
Tours by arrangement

⊗ The largest independent, family-owned brewery in the country established in 1876 and still run by descendants of the founder. The brewery has been on this site since 1976 and 290 of its 300 pubs serve cask ale, though about 50 per cent use cask breathers. Wells also supplies around 600 other outlets direct. A bottling line was added in 1996. Its export market of 23 countries earned it a Queen's Award for Export in 1997. In 2000 Charles Wells bought the John Bull Pub Company in Europe from Allied Domecq, giving it a dedicated estate of 28 franchised outlets from central to eastern Europe. The company runs 40 other retail outlets in Europe, mainly in Italy and Spain. In 2001 it launched cask-conditioned Bombardier in vented cans for supermarket sales. Seasonal beers: Josephine Grimbley (ABV 4.1%), Fargo (ABV 5%, winter).

Eagle IPA *(OG 1035, ABV 3.6%)* ◆
A refreshing, amber session bitter with pronounced citrus hop aroma and palate, faint malt in the mouth, and a lasting dry, bitter finish.

Bombardier Premium Bitter
(OG 1042, ABV 4.3%) ◆
Gentle citrus hop is balanced by traces of malt in the mouth, and this pale brown best bitter ends with a lasting dryness. Sulphur often dominates the aroma, particularly with younger casks.

WELTONS
See Hepworth.

WENTWORTH
Wentworth Brewery Ltd, The Powerhouse, Gun Park, Wentworth, Rotherham, S Yorkshire, S62 7TF
Tel (01226) 747070 Fax (01226) 747050
E-mail info@wentworthbrewery.com
Website www.wentworthbrewery.com
Tours by arrangement

Wentworth was built during the summer of 1999, using equipment from two defunct Sheffield breweries, Stones and Wards. Brewing started in August 1999 and the first brew, WPA, won Best Beer of the Festival at CAMRA's Sheffield festival. Wentworth has installed three 15-barrel fermenters, boosting production to 70 barrels. The owners plan to create a small tied estate, beginning with the purchase of a brewery tap. Approximately 40 outlets are supplied direct. Occasional beer: Gunpark Dark (ABV 3.4%, spring/summer). Bottle-conditioned beers: WPA, Oatmeal Stout, Rampant Gryphon.

Venture *(ABV 3.6%)* ◆
A session bitter with a rather bitter taste that dominates the aftertaste.

WPA *(ABV 4%)* ◆
An extremely well-hopped IPA-style beer that leads to some astringency. A very bitter beer. Champion Beer of South Yorkshire 2000.

Best Bitter *(ABV 4.3%)* ◆
A hoppy bitter beer with hints of citrus fruits. A bitter taste dominates the aftertaste.

Oatmeal Stout *(ABV 4.8%)* ◆
Bucketfuls of roast and chocolate malts with coffee overtones lead to a bitter aftertaste.

Gryphon *(ABV 5.1%)* ◆
A golden, clean-tasting, full-bodied strong bitter with a bitter-sweet taste and aftertaste.

Black Zac *(ABV 4.6%)*
A mellow, dark ruby red ale with chocolate and pale malts leading to a bitter taste, with a coffee finish.

Rampant Gryphon *(ABV 6.2%)* ◆
A strong, well-balanced golden ale with hints of fruit and sweetness but which retains a hoppy character.

WEST BERKSHIRE
West Berkshire Brewery Co Ltd, The Old Bakery, Yattendon, Thatcham, Berks, RG18 0UE
Tel (01635) 202968
Fax (01635) 202638
E-mail davemaggs@wbbrew.co.uk
Website www.wbbrew.co.uk
Tours strictly by arrangement only

⊠ A brewery established in 1998 by Dave and Helen Maggs in converted farm buildings in the grounds of the Pot Kiln pub, although the businesses are separate. Production started on a 5-barrel plant, but in 1999 a 25-barrel plant was added at a second site in Yattendon. The original plant remains at the Pot Kiln and will continue to brew the house beer, special brews, and will feed a new bottling plant. Alongside the new plant is the Yattendon Craft Gallery that sells the brewery's T-shirts, sweat shirts and mugs. More than 30 outlets take the beers regularly and they appear as guest ales in other pubs. Brick Kiln Bitter (ABV 4%) is only available at the Pot Kiln. Seasonal beers: Spiced Porter (ABV 4.7%, Christmas), Winter's Ale (ABV 4.6%, Christmas).

Skiff *(OG 1036, ABV 3.6%)* ◆
A pale brown session bitter with a good balance of malts and a pleasant hop aroma bouquet.

Mr Chubb's Lunchtime Bitter
(OG 1037, ABV 3.7%)

Maggs Magnificent Mild
(OG 1039, ABV 3.8%) ◆
An easy-to-drink southern mild with a good balance of malt and hops for the style. This dark red-brown beer has a short, dry finish.

Good Old Boy *(OG 1041, ABV 4%)* ◆
A well-balanced, fruity and hoppy beer with some sweetness in the finish.

Dr Hexter's Wedding Ale
(OG 1042, ABV 4.1%)
There are hints of grapefruit in this pale-coloured beer, with strong hop aromas and a long, bitter finish.

Dr Hexter's Healer
(OG 1050, ABV 5%) ◆
A full-bodied, vinous and sweet, end-of-the-evening beer that tastes stronger than it is. Tawny in colour, fruity and warming, with masses of malt and roast character.

Gold Star *(OG 1052, ABV 5.2%)* ◆
A pale brown beer, fruity and deceptively strong, with well-balanced fruit, malt and hops.

WEST YORKSHIRE
West Yorkshire Brewery, Victoria Buildings, Burnley Road, Luddendenfoot, Halifax, HX2 6AA
Tel (01422) 885930
Tours by arrangement

The brewery was bought in 2001 by the brewer Dave Sanders, following the collapse of the Drinks Link company, the former owner. Occasional beers: Mild & Dangerous (ABV 4.8%), Yorkshireman (ABV 4.1%), Night Porter (ABV 4.3%), Bedlam Hill (ABV 4.3%).

Baht'At *(OG 1038, ABV 3.8%)* ◆
Amber-coloured bitter with a hoppy and well-balanced malt and fruity character, and dry finish.

Beyond The Pale *(ABV 4%)* ✒
Pale golden bitter with an intensely citrus flavour that predominates the underlying biscuity malt and fruity character. The finish is long, dry and hoppy.

WHIM

**Whim Ales, Whim Farm, Hartington,
Nr Buxton, Derbyshire, SK17 0AX
Tel (01298) 84991
Fax (01298) 84702**

⊗ A brewery opened in 1993 in outbuildings at Whim Farm by Giles Litchfield who bought Broughton Brewery (qv) in 1995. Whim's beers are available in 50-70 outlets and the brewery's tied house, the Wilkes Head in Leek, Staffs. Some one-off brews are produced. Occasional/seasonal beers: Snow White (ABV 4.5%, a wheat beer), Special Ale (ABV 4.7%), Old Izaak (ABV 5%, winter), Black Christmas (ABV 6.5%, winter).

Arbor Light *(OG 1035, ABV 3.6%)*
Light-coloured bitter, sharp and clean with lots of hop character and a delicate light aroma.

Magic Mushroom Mild
(OG 1037, ABV 3.8%)
Ruby-black in colour, well-balanced with a complex mix of flavours and a sweet finish.

Hartington Bitter
(OG 1038, ABV 4%)
A light, golden-coloured, well-hopped session beer. A dry finish with a spicy, floral aroma.

Hartington IPA *(OG 1045, ABV 4.5%)*
Pale and light-coloured, smooth on the palate allowing malt to predominate. Slightly sweet finish combined with distinctive light hop bitterness. Well rounded.

WHITE

**White Brewing Company,
The 1066 Country Brewery,
Pebsham Farm Industrial Estate,
Pebsham Lane, Bexhill,
E Sussex, TN40 2RZ
Tel (01424) 731066**
Tours by arrangement

⊗ Brewery founded in May 1995 by husband-and-wife team David and Lesley White to serve local free trade outlets and some wholesalers, brewing five to 10 barrels a week. Seasonal beer: MM (ABV 4.9%, summer.) It appears under various labels, all with 'millennium' in the name.

1066 Country Bitter *(OG 1040, ABV 4%)*
Amber-gold in colour, a light, sweetish beer

with good malt and hop balance, and a bitter, refreshing finish.

White Dark *(ABV 4%)*

WHITE HART*

**White Hart, White Hart Lane,
Machen, Mid-Glamorgan, CF83 8QQ
Tel (01633) 441005**

A small plant supplying the White Hart only. But brewer Nick Davies is keen to 'go commercial' and plans to move to a farm in order to expand production. If the move takes place, the brewery will become known as Carter's, as Nick will be backed by the owner of the White Hart.

Fawn *(ABV 3.8%)*

Machen Bitter *(ABV 4.2%)*

T.U. *(ABV 5%)*

Gordon the Gofer *(ABV 5.2%)*

WHITEWATER

**Whitewater Brewing Co, 40 Tullyframe Road,
Kilkeel, Co Down,
N Ireland, BT34 4RZ
Tel/Fax 028417 69449
Website www.whitewaterbrewing.co.uk**
Tours by arrangement

⊛ Brewery founded in May 1996 on a farm outside Kilkeel with a 5-barrel brew length and 40-barrel conditioning capacity. It now supplies around 15 outlets in Northern Ireland, and other outlets throughout the British Isles via wholesalers, with beers that have already won beer festival prizes, including first at Belfast in 1996 and 1997. Seasonal/occasional beers: Cascade (ABV 4%), Solstice Pale (ABV 4%, summer), Mayflower (ABV 4.1%, summer), Bee's Endeavour (ABV 4.8%, summer), Knight Porter (ABV 5%, autumn/winter).

Best Bitter *(ABV 3.7%)*

Glen Ale *(ABV 4.2%)*

Mountain Ale *(ABV 4.2%)*

Stout *(ABV 4.3%)*

Belfast Special Bitter
(OG 1046, ABV 4.5%)

WICKED HATHERN

**Wicked Hathern Brewery Ltd, The Willows,
46 Derby Road, Hathern, Loughborough,
Leics, LE12 5LD
Tel/Fax (01509) 842585
E-mail Beer@Hathern.com
Website www.wicked-hathern.co.uk**
Tours by arrangement, cost £2.50 includes two free pints

The 2.5-barrel micro-brewery was set up by two drinking friends and their son and son-in-law. A member of Loughborough CAMRA designs their beers for them. Opened in 2000, the name derives from the comments by a 19th-century rector of Hathern who was appalled at the drunken brawling in the church. Hathern is a Saxon word for Hawthorn. The brewery supplies beers on a guest basis to local pubs and brews commissioned beers for special occasions. Seasonal beers: Doble's Dog (ABV

3.5%, autumn/winter), Hawthorn Gold (ABV 3.5%, spring/summer).

WHB (Wicked Hathern Bitter)
(OG 1038, ABV 3.8%)
A light-tasting session bitter with a dry palate and good hop aroma.

Cockfighter *(OG 1043, ABV 4.2%)*

Soar Head *(OG 1048, ABV 4.8%)*
A dark ruby bitter with a complex rich fruit taste and a mellow aroma.

WICKWAR

Wickwar Brewing Co, Arnolds Cooperage, The Old Cider Mill, Station Road, Wickwar, Glos, GL12 8NB
Tel/Fax (01454) 294168/299868
E-mail info@wickwarbrewing.co.uk
Website www.wickwarbrewing.co.uk
Shop 7.30-4.30 Mon-Fri. Tours by arrangement

⊠ The brewery was launched in 1990 by two Courage tenants, Brian Rides and Ray Penny, with the aim of providing guest ales for their three tenancies. The business proved so successful that they dropped the pubs to concentrate on supplying their other regular outlets (now totalling around 150). The brewery operates from the cooper's shop of the old Arnold, Perret & Co brewery and is currently brewing to capacity. Brian Rides has retired, but Ray Penny continues to run the company with an ambitious and adventurous team, led by head brewer Steve Mcdonald. They plan to move to bigger premises during 2002 so that production can increase to 25 barrels per brew. They also plan to buy pubs in order to create a small tied estate. Seasonal beers: Station Porter (ABV 6.1%, Oct-Dec) ⧇, Spring Ale (ABV 3.8%, March-May), Sunny Daze (ABV 4.2%, June-Aug). Bottle-conditioned beers: Old Arnold (ABV 4.8%), Station Porter (ABV 6.1%), Brand Oak Bitter (BOB) (ABV 4%).

Coopers WPA *(OG 1036.5, ABV 3.5%)* 🍺🍴
Golden-coloured, this well-balanced beer is light, refreshing, with hops, citrus fruit, apple/pear flavour and notable pale malt character. Bitter, dry finish. A crisp and quenching ale.

Brand Oak Bitter (BOB)
(OG 1038.5, ABV 4%) 🍴
Amber-coloured, this has a distinctive blend of hop, malt and apple/pear citrus fruits. The slightly sweet taste turns into a fine, dry bitterness, with a similar malty-lasting finish.

Cotswold Way *(OG 1040.5, ABV 4.2%)* 🍴
Amber-coloured, it has a pleasant aroma of pale malt, hop and fruit. Good dry bitterness in the taste with some sweetness. Similar though less sweet in the finish, with good hop content.

Old Arnold *(OG 1045, ABV 4.6%)*
Named after the founder of the original brewery (around 1800), this is a ruby-red ale, sweetish with malt and bitter overtones and Challenger hops providing rich fruitiness. It is brewed to a similar recipe used by Arnold in his Strong Old Beer.

Olde Merryford Ale
(OG 1048.5, ABV 4.8%) 🍴

Full-flavoured and well-balanced ale, with malt, hops and cherry fruit throughout. Amber/pale brown, it is slightly sweet, with a long-lasting, malty, dry, fruity and increasingly bitter finish.

WILLY'S

⧉ **Willy's Brewery Ltd, 17 High Cliff Road, Cleethorpes, Lincs, DN35 8RQ**
Tel (01472) 602145
Fax (01472) 603578
Tours by arrangement

⊛ Brewery opened in 1989 to provide beer for two outlets in Grimsby and Cleethorpes. It has a 5-barrel plant with maximum capacity of 15 barrels a week. The brewery can be viewed at any time from pub or street.

Original Bitter *(OG 1038, ABV 3.8%)* 🍴
A light brown 'sea air' beer with a fruity, tangy hop on the nose and taste, giving a strong bitterness tempered by the underlying malt.

Burcom Bitter *(OG 1044, ABV 4.2%)* 🍴
A dark ruby colour, sometimes known as Mariner's Gold, although the beer is dark ruby in colour. It is a smooth and creamy brew with a sweet chocolate-bar maltiness, giving way to an increasingly bitter finish.

Last Resort *(OG 1044, ABV 4.3%)*

Weiss Buoy *(OG 1045, ABV 4.5%)*
A cloudy wheat beer.

Coxswains Special Bitter
(OG 1050, ABV 4.9%)

Old Groyne *(OG 1060, ABV 6.2%)* 🍴
An initial sweet banana fruitiness blends with malt to give a vanilla quality to the taste and slightly bitter aftertaste. A copper-coloured beer reminiscent of a Belgian ale.

WINCHESTER

See Oak Leaf.

WOLF

**Wolf Brewery Ltd,
10 Maurice Gaymer Road, Attleborough, Norfolk, NR17 2QZ**
Tel (01953) 457775
Fax (01953) 457776
E-mail info@wolf-ales.co.uk
Website www.wolf-brewery.ltd.uk
Tours by arrangement

⊠ The brewery was founded by the former owner of the Reindeer Brewery in 1996, using a 20-barrel plant housed on the site of the old Gaymer's cider orchard. 200 outlets are supplied direct.

Golden Jackal *(OG 1039, ABV 3.7%)* 🍴
A singularly hoppy golden bitter with strong bitter overtones. This moves on to a quick dry finish that emphasises the bitterness.

Wolf In Sheeps Clothing 🍴
(OG 1039, ABV 3.7%)
A malty aroma with fruity undertones introduces this reddish-hued mild. Malt, with a bitter Bisto-like background that remains throughout, is the dominant flavour of this clean-tasting beer.

Wolf Bitter *(OG 1041, ABV 3.9%)* ◆
A gentle mingling of hops and malt in the aroma of this copper-coloured bitter. A first taste combines bitterness with a glowing fruity malt background. Hop notes are evident as the bitterness continues.

Coyote Bitter *(OG 1044, ABV 4.3%)* ❒◆
A pale brown bitter with light, fruit-enhanced hoppy vapours. A complex but well-balanced mix of hops and malt with more than a hint of citrus leads on to a crisp, well-hopped finale.

Newshound 2000 *(ABV 4.5%)* ◆
Amber malt provides rich colour, distinct nose and solid malty base. Old English Herald hops add balance and a refreshing bitterness. Slow-burning finish with a hint of caramel.

Woild Moild *(OG 1048, ABV 4.8%)* ◆
A big roast coffee bean aroma leads into a distinctively roasted barley base. A good balance of malt with a liquorice bitterness aids this dark-red mild towards a smoky, dark and long-lasting rich finish.

Granny Wouldn't Like It ❒◆
(OG 1049, ABV 4.8%)
A red-hued, full-bodied and fruity old style at odds with its delicate resinous nose. The richness continues to develop a bitter-sweet hoppiness that does not fade. Well-balanced and satisfying.

Timber Wolf *(OG 1060, ABV 5.8%)* ◆
A rich and warming winter ale. A solid currant bun aroma combines with a rich fruit and nut beginning to give this red-hued beer a sweet, spicy feel. A long, drawn-out bitter-sweet finale completes the experience.

WOLVERHAMPTON & DUDLEY

See Banks's, Camerons, Mansfield and Marston's.

WOOD

Wood Brewery Ltd, Wistanstow, Craven Arms, Shropshire, SY7 8DG
Tel (01588) 672523
Fax (01588) 673939
Tours by arrangement

⊠ The brewery was started in 1980 in buildings next to the Plough Inn. Several expansions of the premises have taken place and the Sam Powell Brewery and its beers were acquired in 1991. Production averages 60 barrels a week and future plans include increased fermentation capacity, more storage and a brewery visitor centre. 200 outlets are supplied direct. One pub is owned at present. Seasonal/occasional beers: Ironmasters (ABV 3.6%), Summer That! (ABV 3.9%), Hell For Leather (ABV 4%), Woodcutter (ABV 4.2%), Saturnalia (ABV 4.2%), Breast Stroke (ABV 4.3%), Governor's IPA (ABV 4.5%), Wheatear (ABV 4.5%), Holy Cow (ABV 4.5%), Natural Selection (ABV 4.6%), Get Knotted (ABV 4.7%), Hopping Mad (ABV 4.7%), Remembrance Ale (ABV 4.8%), Anniversary Ale (ABV 5%), Bonfire Brew (ABV 5.4%), Old Fireside (ABV 5.5%), Christmas Cracker (ABV 6%). Bottle-conditioned beers: Armada (ABV 4%), Hopping Mad (ABV 4.7%),

Shropshire Lad (ABV 5%), Christmas Cracker (ABV 6%). Other quarterly beers are produced under the Shropshire Heroes label.

Wallop *(OG 1034, ABV 3.4%)*

Sam Powell Original Bitter
(OG 1037, ABV 3.7%)

Parish Bitter *(OG 1040, ABV 4%)* ◆
A blend of malt and hops with a bitter aftertaste. Pale brown in colour.

Special Bitter *(OG 1042, ABV 4.2%)* ◆
A tawny brown bitter with malt, hops and some fruitiness.

Shropshire Lad *(OG 1045, ABV 4.5%)*

Sam Powell Old Sam
(OG 1046, ABV 4.6%)

Wonderful *(OG 1048, ABV 4.8%)* ◆
A mid-brown, fruity beer, with a roast and malt taste.

WOODBURY

Woodbury Brewery, Home Farm Cottage, Great Witley, Worcs, WR6 6JJ
Tel (01299) 896219
Tours by arrangement

The brewery stopped production early in 2001, but the owners hoped to restart if they could find someone willing to take on the brewing side.

WOODFORDE'S

**Woodforde's Norfolk Ales
(t/a Woodforde's Ltd), Broadland Brewery, Woodbastwick, Norwich, Norfolk, NR13 6SW**
Tel (01603) 720353
Fax (01603) 721806
E-mail info@woodfordes.co.uk
Website www.woodfordes.co.uk
Shop 10.30-3.30 Mon-Fri; 11.30-3.30 Sat-Sun May-Sept & Dec; closed Oct-April. Tours by arrangement

⊠ Founded in 1981 in Drayton near Norwich, Woodforde's moved to a converted farm complex, with greatly increased production capacity, in the picturesque Broadland village of Woodbastwick in 1989. It brews an extensive range of beers and runs three tied houses with some 250 other outlets supplied on a regular basis. Seasonal/occasional beers: Norkie (ABV 5%), Headcracker (ABV 7%). Bottle-conditioned beers: Wherry Best Bitter (ABV 3.8%), Great Eastern (ABV 4.3%), Nelson's Revenge (ABV 4.5%), Norfolk Nog (ABV 4.6%), Headcracker (ABV 7%) ❒, Norfolk Nips (ABV 8.5%). With the exception of Norfolk Nips, these are only sold at the visitor centre.

Mardler's *(OG 1035, ABV 3.5%)* ◆
A dark red mild with a soft malty aroma. Roast malt dominates throughout as the slightly sweet bitterness fades to a short, dry finish.

Kett's Rebellion
(OG 1036, ABV 3.6%) ◆
Brewed to celebrate the 450th anniversary of Kett's Rebellion, this moderately bitter session beer retains a hoppiness to the finish. Sweet caramel notes fade in the finish.

Wherry Best Bitter
(OG 1038, ABV 3.8%) 🍺🍷❧
Elderflower and hops are to the fore in the nose of this amber-coloured bitter. A hoppy backbone bolstered by a lemon fruit bitterness remain long after the initial, intensely bitter-sweet tones burst on the tongue.

Great Eastern *(OG 1043, ABV 4.3%)* ❧
Peppery hop notes introduce this clean-tasting bitter. A first taste brings together a combination of hop bitterness and a toffee-like sweetness. A long drawn-out dry hop finish ends this deep yellow beer.

Nelson's Revenge
(OG 1045, ABV 4.5%) 🍺❧
A dominant hop aroma with dried fruit undertones. A rich, fruit-cake feel with a creamy malt background give this full-bodied beer a warming disposition. A long citrus aftertaste with balanced hoppy airs.

Norfolk Nog *(OG 1049, ABV 4.6%)* 🍺❧
A riotous explosion of sultana sweetness, dark chocolate and charcoal greet the tongue. Consistent with its rich roast aroma, the flavours of this dark red old ale linger to a fittingly black cherry finale.

WOODHAMPTON

Woodhampton Brewing Co, Woodhampton, Aymestrey, Leominster, Herefordshire, HR6 9TA
Tel/Fax (01568) 770503
Tours by arrangement

⊗ Set up in 1996 in a converted barn at Woodhampton Farm by Steve Bowen of the Riverside Inn, Aymestrey, and Crawford Gibbons of Woodhampton Farm. Using spring water from a local hillside, the 5-barrel plant brews two or three times a week. It supplies around 30 outlets in the locality. Seasonal beer: Christmas Dark Stout.

Red Kite *(OG 1036, ABV 3.6%)*

Jack Snipe *(OG 1041, ABV 4.1%)*

Kingfisher Ale *(OG 1044, ABV 4.4%)*

WOODLANDS*

Woodlands Brewery, 27 Woodlands, Bishops Stortford, Herts, CM23 5BS
Tel (07949) 438353
E-mail woodlandsbrewery@yahoo.co.uk

Woodlands produces just 10 gallons at a time but new equipment, capable of making 2.5 barrels, has been acquired. The company is looking for a new site and hoped to be in place later in 2001.

Dark Wood *(ABV 3.5%)*

Bitter *(ABV 3.9%)*

Red Squirrel *(ABV 4.2%)*

WORFIELD

Worfield Brewing Co Ltd, Unit 1A The Bullring, Station Lane, off Hollybush Road, Bridgnorth, Shropshire, WV16 4AR
Tel (01746) 769606
Tours by arrangement

Set up in 1994 at the Davenport Arms, the plant of the Red Cross Brewery was purchased and the brewery relocated in 1998. It has relocated again to the above address, which is on the same water supply as the previous premises. Future plans include moving yet again to converted farm buildings to enable expansion and possibly bottling. The brewery sells beer wholesale to 23 free trade outlets. There are occasional special brews such as Hermitage Old Ale (ABV 8.8%).

JLK Pale Ale *(OG 1037, ABV 3.8%)*

Hopstone Bitter *(OG 1040, ABV 4%)*

Nailers ODJ *(OG 1041, ABV 4.2%)*

Shropshire Pride *(OG 1046, ABV 4.5%)*

Burcote Premium Pale
(OG 1050, ABV 4.9%)

Reynolds Redneck
(OG 1057, ABV 5.5%)

WYCHWOOD

Wychwood Brewery Co Ltd, Eagle Maltings, The Crofts, Corn St, Witney, Oxon, OX8 7AZ
Tel (01993) 702574
Fax (01993) 772553
E-mail rachael@wychwood.co.uk
Website www.wychwood.co.uk
Shop 9-5 Mon-Fri. On-line shopping on website
Tours only for CAMRA branch visits

⊗ Set up as Glenny Brewery in 1983, in the old maltings of the extinct Clinch Brewery, it moved to a modern site in the late 1980s and then back again to the Clinch site in 1994. The brewery now boasts a 110-barrel brew length with mash tun, Steel's masher and valentine tube all from Brains in Cardiff, steam boiler from Mitchells of Lancaster, and various fermenters all made to measure. Brewing capacity is now 40,000 barrels a year with production running at 25,000 barrels, 70 per cent of which is bottled. 30 pubs are now owned most called Hobgoblin, a mixture of freeholds and leased pubs. Seasonal beers: Goliath (ABV 3.7%, January), Romeo (ABV 4%, February), Dreamcatcher (ABV 4.3, March), Joker (ABV 4.1%, April), Alchemy Gold (ABV 4.4%, May), Oberon (ABV 4.2%, June), White Wych (ABV 4%, July), Bramling Cross (ABV 4.3%, August), Scarecrow (ABV 4.5%, September), She Devil (ABV 4.7%, October), Wickerman (ABV 4.4%, November), The Dogs Bollocks (ABV 5.2%, November), Santa Claus (ABV 5%, December).

Shires XXX *(OG 1036, ABV 3.7%)* ❧
A copper-coloured session beer with a fruity and malty aroma and admirable hop character. Good body for its strength. Fruit declines to a dry finish.

Fiddler's Elbow
(OG 1039, ABV 4.1%) ❧
A spicy amber beer, complex, with a spicy hop aroma and a suggestion of cinnamon. Easy to drink, with a crisp and refreshing finish.

Hobgoblin *(OG 1042, ABV 4.5%)* ❧
Powerful, full-bodied, copper-red, well-balanced brew. Strong in roasted malt, with a moderate, hoppy bitterness and a slight fruity character.

WYE VALLEY

Wye Valley Brewery Ltd, 69 St Owen Street, Hereford, HR1 2JQ
Tel 01432 342546 Fax 01432 266553
Website www.wyevalleybrewery.co.uk

⊗ The Wye Valley Brewery was launched in 1985 at the Nags Head in Canon Pyon, Herefordshire. It moved to the rear of the Barrels pub at the above address in 1986. A 22-barrel plant was installed in 1992 and a considerable expansion to the brewery was also undertaken. The beers are distributed locally on a weekly basis, and monthly to many parts of the country by the brewery's own transport. Seasonal beers: Dorothy Goodbody's Springtime Ale (ABV 4%), Dorothy Goodbody's Summertime Ale (ABV 4.2%), Dorothy Goodbody's Autumn Delight (ABV 4.4%), Dorothy Goodbody's Winter Tipple (ABV 4.7%), Dorothy Goodbody's Christmas Ale (ABV 6%).

Bitter (OG 1036, ABV 3.5%) ✦
A beer whose aroma gives little hint of the bitter hoppiness that follows right through to the aftertaste.

Dorothy Goodbody's Traditional Bitter
(OG 1038, ABV 3.8%)

Hereford Pale Ale
(OG 1040, ABV 4%) ✦
A pale, hoppy, malty brew with a hint of sweetness before a dry finish.

Butty Bach (OG 1046, ABV 4.5%)

Dorothy Goodbody's Wholesome Stout
(OG 1046, ABV 4.6%) ☐✦
A smooth and satisfying stout with a bitter edge to its roast flavours. The finish combines roast grain and malt.

Travellers Best (OG 1050, ABV 5%)

WYLAM*

Wylam Brewery Ltd, South Houghton Farm, Heddon on the Wall, Northumberland, NE15 0EZ
Tel (01661) 853377
E-mail john@wylambrew.co.uk
Website www.wylambrew.co.uk

Wylam Brewery was launched in the summer of 2000 by Robin Leighton and John Boyle. It is based on a farm close to the village of Wylam, where George Stephenson once lived. The brewery delivers to more than 40 local outlets. Occasional beer: Esquire Blackett Mild (ABV 3.2%). Bottle-conditioned beer: Flannel Hammer (ABV 9.5%).

Bitter (ABV 3.8%)

Heddonist (ABV 3.8%) ✦
A golden beer with a malty aroma; plenty of hops give a bitter-sweet finish.

Gold Tankard (ABV 4%)

Turbinia (ABV 4%) ☐✦
An easy-drinking bitter, full of flavour, some fruit mixing with the hops lead to a satisfying bitter finish.

Rocket (ABV 4.4%) ✦
A gold-coloured beer packed with flavour. Hops and malt come out in the flavour and lead to a smooth, bitter finish.

Landlord's Choice (ABV 4.8%)
Haugh (ABV 5.1%) ✦
A smooth velvet porter packed with flavour. Roast malt and a slight fruitiness provide a satisfying pint with a smooth finish.

WYRE PIDDLE

Wyre Piddle Brewery, Craycombe Farm, Fladbury, Nr Evesham, Worcs, WR10 2QS
Tel/Fax (01386) 860473

⊗ A brewery established in a converted stable by a former publican and master builder in 1992. Some 200 pubs in the Midlands take the beer. The brewery relocated and upgraded its equipment in 1997. It also brews for Green Dragon, Malvern: Dragon's Downfall (ABV 3.9%), Dragon's Revenge (ABV 4%). For Severn Valley Railway: Royal Piddle (ABV 4.2%). Seasonal beers: Piddle in the Sun (ABV 5.2%, summer), Yule Piddle (ABV 4.5%, Christmas). Bottle-conditioned beer: Piddle in the Hole (ABV 4.6%).

Piddle in the Hole
(OG 1039, ABV 3.9%) ✦
Copper-coloured and quite dry, with lots of hops and fruitiness throughout.

Piddle in the Wind (ABV 4.5%) ✦
This drink has a superb mix of flavours. A nice hoppy nose through to a lasting aftertaste makes it a good, all-round beer.

Piddle in the Dark (ABV 4.5%)
A rich ruby red bitter with a smooth flavour.

Piddle in the Snow (ABV 5.2%) ✦
A dry, strong taste all the way through draws your attention to the balance between malt and hops in the brew. A glorious way to end an evening's drinking.

YATES

Yates Brewery, Ghyll Farm, Westnewton, Carlisle, Cumbria, CA5 3NX
Tel/fax (016973) 21081
E-mail graeme@yatesbrewery.freeserve.co.uk
Tours by arrangement

⊕ Established in 1986 in range of outbuildings at Ghyll Farm, Westnewton, the brewery was bought in 1998 by Graeme and Caroline Baxter, who had previously owned High Force Brewery in Teesdale. More beers have been added to the range and direct distribution now includes Tyneside and Wearside, in addition to the traditional stronghold of the Lake District. 65 outlets are supplied direct. Seasonal beers: Spring Fever (ABV 4.7%), Summer Fever (ABV 3.9%), Autumn Fever (ABV 4%), Winter Fever (ABV 4%), Best Cellar (ABV 5.3%, winter).

Bitter (OG 1035, ABV 3.7%) ✦
Distinctive golden bitter, powerful hop and fruit aroma. Strong hop flavour with lingering bitterness.

No 3 (OG 1040, ABV 4.2%) ✦
A pale brown beer with a prominent butterscotch aroma. It has a strong roast and caramel taste with some maltiness. Full-bodied with a pleasant bitter taste.

XB (OG 1043, ABV 4.5%)
Premium (OG 1048, ABV 5.2%) ✎
A golden beer with hops and lingering fruity sweetness. Rising bitterness with some malt and good mouthfeel.

YATES*

**Yates Brewery, St Lawrence Inn, Undercliff Drive, St Lawrence, Ventnor, Isle of Wight, PO38 1XG
Tel (01983) 854689**

Dave Yates brewed with Hartridge on the island and installed a 5-barrel plant in part of the inn. He started in September 2000 and now supplies a number of outlets on the island as well as the St Lawrence. Seasonal beer: Xmas Pud (ABV 5%).

Undercliff Experience (ABV 4.1%)

Holy Joe (ABV 4.9%)

YORK

**York Brewery Company Ltd, 12 Toft Green, Micklegate, York, YO1 6JT
Tel (01904) 621162
Fax (01904) 621216
E-mail aw@yorkbrew.demon.co.uk
Website www.yorkbrew.demon.co.uk**
Shop 11-8 daily. Tours daily

⊛ York started production in 1996, the first brewery in the city for 40 years. A visitor centre, gift shop and bar were added in 1999. It is designed as a show brewery, with a gallery above the 20-barrel brew plant giving visitors a view of the fermenting and conditioning rooms. In 2000, York bought its first pub, the Last Drop inn, in Colliergate in the city. More than 400 pubs take the beers. Occasional/seasonal beers: Mildly Mad (ABV 3.3%), 100 Not Out (ABV 3.9%), Last Drop Bitter (ABV 4.5%), Bug Bitter (ABV 4.6%), Stocking Filler (ABV 4.8%).

Stonewall (ABV 3.7%) ✎
A light amber bitter with little maltiness but strong hop and fruit aromas and flavours. Clean-tasting, its hoppiness leads to a dry, bitter finish.

Brideshead Bitter (ABV 4%) ✎
Hoppy and fresh-tasting with some fruit and a citrus note. A good session ale with a slightly dry finish.

Yorkshire Terrier (ABV 4.2%) ◨✎
Refreshing and distinctive, well-balanced fruit and hops in the aroma and taste, with a background of malt. Hoppy bitterness

remains assertive in the aftertaste of this amber-gold brew.
Centurion's Ghost Ale (ABV 5%) ✎
Dark ruby in colour, full-tasting with mellow roast malt character balanced by bitterness that lingers into the aftertaste. Hops and fruit in the mouth.

YOUNG'S

**Young & Co's Brewery PLC, The Ram Brewery, High Street, Wandsworth, London, SW18 4JD
Tel (020) 8875 7000 Fax (020) 8875 7100
Website www.youngs.co.uk**
Shop 10-6, Mon-Sat. Daily tours of the brewery and stables (020) 8875 7005

⊠ Beer has been brewed continuously alongside the River Wandle since 1581, making it the oldest site in Britain for beer production. The present brewery was founded in 1675 and bought by Charles Young & Anthony Bainbridge in 1831; the business was continued by the Young family and, although it is a public company, it remains very much a family affair. The company brews award-winning beers in the traditional manner and also produces up to four seasonal beers. More than 1,000 free-trade outlets are supplied throughout Britain, concentrated in London and the South-east. Young's growing tied estate stands at more than 180 pubs. The brewery has outlawed pouring back spilt or unsold beer in its tied houses, and recommends the use of cask breathers only if its smallest casks cannot be consumed within three days. Bottle-conditioned beer: Special London Ale (ABV 6.4%) ◨▉.

Bitter (OG 1036, ABV 3.7%) ◨✎
A light-drinking bitter with a hoppy, malty nose and a dryish palate and finish, with hops predominating.

Triple A (OG 1040, ABV 4%) ✎
Creamy-textured dark amber beer with malty notes and a low aroma due to being served cold. Becomes cloying as it warms.

Special (OG 1046, ABV 4.6%) ✎
Smooth, fruity beer with a good malty/hoppy balance, and a fruity, bitter aftertaste with hoppy notes.

Waggle Dance (OG 1049, ABV 5%) ◨
Beer brewed with honey. The brand was bought from the Vaux/Swallow Group in the summer of 1999 and is available cask-conditioned and in bottle.

Winter Warmer (OG 1055, ABV 5%) ◨✎
Impressive ruby/black, smooth beer with a roast malt aroma, a sweet fruity flavour and finish, and caramel notes throughout.

ZERO DEGREES*

⌂ **Zero Degrees, 29-31 Montpelier Vale, Blackheath, London, SE3 0TJ
Tel (020) 8852 5619**

A bar and restaurant that started brewing in November 2000. It brews six regular beers and several one-off and occasional brews. The beers are stored in cellar tanks. Beers: Czech Pils, Pale Ale, Brown Ale, Wheat Ale, Raspberry Beer.

Global giants

Eight out of ten pints of beer brewed in Britain come from the groups listed below...

CARLSBERG-TETLEY

Carlsberg-Tetley Brewing Ltd, Bridge Street, Northampton, NN1 1PZ
Tel (01604) 668866

A wholly-owned subsidiary of Carlsberg of Copenhagen, Denmark. Carlsberg is an international giant best known for its pale lagers, though in Denmark it brews a large range of beers, including brown lagers and a porter-stout, all made by cold fermentation. In Britain its lagers are brewed at a dedicated plant in Northampton, while Tetley in Leeds also produces some Carlsberg products.

Carlsberg-Tetley Brewing Ltd, PO Box 142, The Brewery, Leeds, W Yorkshire, LS1 1QG
Tel (0113) 259 4595
Fax (0113) 259 4000
E-mail comms.website@carlsbergtetley.co.uk
Website www.carlsbergtetley.co.uk

Joshua Tetley founded his brewery in 1822, although brewing has taken place on the site since 1792. The brewery is now the biggest cask ale producer in the world (400,000 barrels annually), and the biggest brewer of cask mild, though nitro-keg and keg ales are also produced. All cask ale brewing uses traditional methods, including Yorkshire Square fermenters.

Tetley's Dark Mild
(OG 1031, ABV 3.2%) ◈
A reddish, mid-brown beer with a light malt and caramel aroma. A well-balanced taste of malt and caramel follows, with good bitterness and a satisfying finish.

Tetley's Mild *(OG 1034, ABV 3.3%)* ◈
A mid-brown beer with a light malt and caramel aroma. A well-balanced taste of malt and caramel follows, with good bitterness and a satisfying finish.

Ansells Mild *(OG 1035, ABV 3.4%)*

Ansells Best Bitter *(OG 1035, ABV 3.7%)*

Benskins Bitter *(OG 1035, ABV 3.7%)*

Friary Meux Bitter *(OG 1035, ABV 3.7%)*

Tetley's Cask Bitter
(OG 1035.5, ABV 3.7%) ◈
A variable, amber-coloured light, dry bitter with a slight malt and hop aroma, leading to a moderate bitterness with a hint of fruit, ending with a dry and bitter finish.

DBA or Ind Coope Burton Ale
(OG 1047, ABV 4.8%)
The beer is now a long way from Burton. Tetley uses Burton yeast and brews to the original recipe.

For former 'Greenalls' pubs, supplied by Scottish & Newcastle Retail and other wholesalers

Greenall's Mild *(OG 1034, ABV 3.3%)*
Greenall's Bitter *(OG 1036.5, ABV 3.8%)*

GUINNESS

Guinness Brewing GB, Park Royal Brewery, London, NW10 7RR
Tel (020) 8965 7700
Fax (020) 8963 5120

An Anglo-Irish giant that has world-wide brewing operations and distribution. In London it brews draught keg and pasteurised bottled stouts only.

INTERBREW

Interbrew UK Ltd, Porter Tun House, 500 Capability Green, Luton, Beds, LU1 3LS
A wholly-owned subsidiary of Interbrew of Leuven/Louvain, Belgium.
Tel (01582) 391166
Fax (01582) 397397
E-mail name.surname@interbrew.co.uk
Website www.boddingtons.com

Interbrew of Belgium is a major player in the European market with such lager brands as Stella Artois and Jupiler, and internationally with Labatt and Molson of Canada. It has some interest in ale brewing with the cask- and bottle-conditioned wheat beer, Hoegaarden, and the Abbey beer Leffe. It has a ruthless track record of closing plants and disposing of brands. In the summer of 2000 it bought both Bass's and Whitbread's brewing operations, giving it a 32 per cent market share. The British government told Interbrew to dispose of Bass, a decision that Interbrew is challenging in the courts. We list here all the breweries and their cask ales that are currently owned by Interbrew.

BASS

Bass Brewers, PO Box 217, Station Street, Burton-on-Trent, Staffs, DE14 1BG
Tel (01283) 511000
Fax (01283) 513873

Founded in 1777, Bass was once a proud ale

brewer but before its sale to Interbrew it had concentrated on nitro-keg, lager and alcopops. In 1999 Bass sold its Cardiff brewery to Brains and closed its Sheffield brewery. The Burton site includes the former neighbouring Ind Coope plant.

Bass Brewers

BIRMINGHAM
Bass Mitchells & Butlers, Cape Hill Brewery, PO Box 27, Smethwick, Birmingham, B16 0PQ
Tel (0121) 558 1481

M&B Brew XI (*OG 1039.5, ABV 3.8%*)
A sweet, malty beer with a hoppy, bitter aftertaste, now brewed by Brains in Cardiff.

M&B Mild
Brewed under contract by the Highgate Brewery, Walsall (qv).

BURTON
Bass Burton Brewery, 137 Station Street, Burton-on-Trent, Staffs, DE14 1JZ
Tel (01283) 511000
Worthington Dark, a famous dark mild brewed for the Cardiff and Welsh Valleys area, has been de-listed, following the sale of the Cardiff brewery to Brains and the transfer of the brands to Burton.

Stones Bitter (*OG 1037, ABV 3.7%*)

Hancock's HB (*OG 1038, ABV 3.6%*)
A pale brown, slightly malty beer whose initial sweetness is balanced by bitterness but lacks a noticeable finish. A consistent if inoffensive 'Welsh' beer.

Worthington Bitter (*OG 1038, ABV 3.6%*)
A pale brown bitter of thin and unremarkable character.

Draught Bass (*OG 1043.3, ABV 4.4%*)
Amber-coloured, sweetish with some malt but lacking any distinctive flavour.

MUSEUM BREWING CO
Bass Museum, Horninglow Street, Burton-on-Trent, Staffs, DE14 1YQ
Tel (0845) 6000598
Fax (01283) 513509
E-mail brewery@museum.brewers.bass.com
Website www.worthingtons.whiteshield.com
Shop (in Bass Museum) 9.30-4.30
Tours by arrangement

The Museum Brewing Co, based in the Bass Museum, is part of Bass/Interbrew but has a large degree of independence. It began brewing in 1994 and has a licence to recreate some of the older Bass beers that have been discontinued. The brewery dates from 1920 with some equipment going back to 1840. It has a maximum capacity of 60 barrels a week. Production is divided 50:50 between cask and bottled beers. As well as historic beers, the brewery produces seasonal brands and creates ales for CAMRA festivals.

Victoria Ale (*ABV 3.9%*)
Aroma of malt and fruit leads to a well-balanced beer with a bitter-sweet, almost dry aftertaste.

Nog Mild (*ABV 3.9%*)

Offilers Bitter (*ABV 4%*)
A medium-strength beer with moderate bitterness.

Joules Bitter (*ABV 4.1%*)
Malty with a bitter finish.

Massey's Bitter (*ABV 4.1%*)
Easy-drinking golden bitter with a hoppy bite.

Centennial (*ABV 4.3%*)
A light golden bitter, refreshing and aromatic. It is named after the American hop variety used for bittering.

Five Hides (*ABV 5%*)
Pale, flavoursome and refreshingly bitter from the use of American Willamette hops.

Masterpiece (*ABV 5.4%*)

Worthington White Shield (*ABV 5.6%*)

Wulfric (*ABV 5.5%*)
Bottle-conditioned beer brewed with ginger; winner of the Tesco Beer Challenge 2001.

P2 Imperial Stout (*ABV 8%*)
A black, sweetish, complex stout.

Bass No 1 Barley Wine (*ABV 10.5%*)
A dark ruby winter beer brewed in summer and fermented in casks for 12 months.

BODDINGTONS
Boddingtons Brewery, PO Box 23, Manchester, M60 3WB
Tel (0161) 828 2000
Fax (0161) 828 2213
Website www.boddingtons.com
Tours by arrangement

Established in 1778 and bought by Whitbread in 1989 when the Boddingtons company, which had already taken over and closed Oldham Brewery, decided to leave brewing and become a pub retailer. Production has grown from around 200,000 barrels a year when the company was independent to 800,000 barrels today. Following the closure of the Cheltenham Brewery, Flowers brands have been transferred to Manchester. The brewery now produces more nitro-keg 'Cream of Manchester' Boddingtons than the once-revered cask version.

Boddingtons Bitter
(OG 1035, ABV 3.8%) ◆
A golden straw-coloured beer in which the grainy malt, hop and bitter character can be spoiled by a cloying sweetness.

Flowers IPA *(OG 1035, ABV 3.6%)*

Flowers Original Bitter
(OG 1043, ABV 4.3%)

FELLOWS, MORTON & CLAYTON

Fellows, Morton & Clayton Brewhouse Company, 54 Canal Street, Nottingham, NG1 7EH
Tel (0115) 950 6795
Fax (0115) 953 9838

Pub that began brewing in 1980 and still uses malt extract. Beers: Fellows Bitter (ABV 3.8%), Post Haste (ABV 4.4%), Christmas Cracker (ABV 6%).

FROG & PARROT

Frog & Parrot Brewhouse, Division Street, Sheffield, S Yorkshire, S1 4GF
Tel (0114) 272 1280

Brew-pub launched in 1982. The beers are brewed from malt extract and stored in casks and are occasionally available in a few other pubs. Brewing is suspended during long students' vacations. Occasional/one-off brews. Beer: Roger & Out (ABV 12.5%).

LASS O'GOWRIE

Lass O'Gowrie Brewhouse, 36 Charles Street, Manchester, M1 7DB
Tel (0161) 273 6932
Tours by arrangement

Victorian pub that was revamped and reopened as a malt extract brew-pub in 1983. The brewery in the cellar is visible from the bar and the beer is now stored in casks. Occasional/one-off brews. Beers: Lass O'Gowrie (ABV 3.8%), Lass O'Gowrie (ABV 4.7%).

* Interbrew has been unable to say where Whitbread Trophy Bitter is brewed.

SCOTTISH COURAGE

Fountain House, 160 Dundee Street, Edinburgh, EH11 1DQ
Tel (0131) 656 5000
Fax (0131) 656 5217

Scottish Courage is Britain's second biggest brewing group with close to 30 per cent of the market. It joined the ranks of the global brewers in 2000 when it negotiated to buy Brasseries Kronenbourg and Alken Maes from the French group Danone; Kronenbourg is the biggest French beer brand and is exported internationally. Alken Maes is a major Belgian group that produces lagers and the Grimbergen abbey beers range. ScotCo also sells the Italian beer Peroni in the off-trade in Britain, and is interested in buying the Rome-based group if the ruling family is prepared to sell. Scottish & Newcastle was formed in 1960, a merger between Scottish Brewers (Younger and McEwan) and Newcastle Breweries. In 1995 it bought Courage from its Australian owners, Foster's. Since the merger that formed Scottish Courage, the group has rationalised by closing its breweries in Nottingham, Halifax and the historic Courage [George's] Brewery in Bristol, a dedicated cask ale plant. The remaining beers were transferred to John Smith's in Tadcaster. In June 2001, ScotCo sold 432 managed pubs to Enterprise Inns and 214 pubs to Robert Breare's Noble House for £360 million.

FOUNTAIN

Fountain Brewery, 159 Fountainbridge, Edinburgh, EH3 9YY
Tel (0131) 229 9377
Fax (0131) 228 9522

The once-legendary home of McEwan's and Younger's cask ales has now axed all its real ales save for one.

McEwan's 80/-
(OG 1042, ABV 4.2%)
Thin-bodied with a cloying metallic, caramel flavour. Once a classic, now bland and sweet with maltiness and fruit. Occasionally labelled Younger's IPA.

JOHN SMITH'S

Scottish Courage Brewing Ltd, John Smith's Brewery, Tadcaster, N Yorkshire, LS24 9SA
Tel (01937) 832091
Fax (01937) 833766
Tours by arrangement

The brewery was built in 1879 by a relative of Samuel Smith (qv). John Smith's became part of the Courage group in 1970. Major expansion has taken place since the formation of Scottish Courage, with 11 new fermenting vessels installed. However, traditional Yorkshire square fermenters have been replaced by conical vessels.

Webster's Green Label Best
(OG 1032, ABV 3.2%)

Webster's Yorkshire Bitter
(OG 1035, ABV 3.5%)

John Smith's Cask Bitter
(OG 1036, ABV 3.8%) ❦
A copper-coloured beer, well-balanced but with no dominating features. It has a short hoppy finish.

Courage Best Bitter *(OG 1038, ABV 4%)* ❦
Pale brown beer with hops throughout and a bitter aftertaste.

John Smith's Magnet
(OG 1040, ABV 4%) ❦
An almost ruby-coloured beer with a complex aroma of hops, malt and citrus fruit. Malt dominates the taste and aftertaste.

Courage Directors
(OG 1045, ABV 4.8%) ❦
Fruity, medium-bodied, pale brown beer with hoppy and yeasty notes throughout.

THEAKSTON
T&R Theakston Ltd, Wellgarth, Masham, Ripon, N Yorkshire, HG4 4YD
Tel (01765) 680000
Fax (01765) 689414
Shop April-Oct, open every day; Nov-Dec limited opening. Brewery tours (01765) 684333

Founded in 1827 and based on the present site since 1875, Theakston became part of S&N in 1987. More than £1 million has been invested in the brewery and in developing a museum of brewing, but most of Theakston's production now takes place in Newcastle (see below). The same pump clips are used for both Masham and Newcastle beers so the consumer is not told where the beers are sourced. The brewery still employs coopers. When production of Cool Cask is concentrated solely at Tyne, there will be capacity at Masham to produce a range of guest ales and seasonal brews. These could include the once-revered Younger's No 3.

Mild Ale *(OG 1035, ABV 3.6%)* ❦
A rich and smooth mild ale with a creamy body and a rounded liquorice taste. Dark ruby/amber in colour, with a mix of malt and fruit on the nose, and a dry, hoppy aftertaste.

Black Bull Bitter
(OG 1037, ABV 3.9%) ❦
A distinctively hoppy aroma leads to a bitter, hoppy taste with some fruitiness and a short bitter finish. Rather thin.

Cool Cask *(OG 1042, ABV 4.2%)*
Launched in 2000, distribution was at first restricted to the North of England. The beer is also brewed at the Tyne Brewery and all production is due to be concentrated there, and was due to be available nationally from the autumn of 2001. Cool Cask is served through special cellar and dispense equipment designed to deliver it to the bar at a temperature of 10° C.

XB *(OG 1044, ABV 4.6%)* ❦
A sweet-tasting bitter with background fruit and spicy hop. Some caramel character gives this ale a malty dominance.

Old Peculier
(OG 1057, ABV 5.7%) ❑❦
A full-bodied, dark brown, strong ale. Slightly malty but with hints of roast coffee. A smooth caramel overlay and a complex fruitiness lead to a bitter chocolate finish.

TYNE
Tyne Brewery, Gallowgate, Newcastle upon Tyne, Tyne & Wear, NE99 1RA
Tel (0191) 232 5091
Fax (0191) 261 2301

Home of Newcastle Breweries formed in 1890 from the amalgamation of five local companies. It brewed little cask ale in recent years until it took on the bulk of Theakston's production. See above for Theakston tasting notes.

Theakston Mild Ale
(OG 1035, ABV 3.6%)

Theakston Best Bitter
(OG 1036, 3.6%) ❦
A dry and metallic bitter with light hop character when fresh. Older samples lose character and end watery and pale.

Theakston Cool Cask
(OG 1042, ABV 4.2%)

Theakston XB *(OG 1044, ABV 4.6%)*

Theakston Old Peculier
(OG 1057, ABV 5.7%)

ORANGE
❑ **Orange Brewery, 37-39 Pimlico Road, London, SW1W 8NE**
Tel/Fax (020) 7730 5984

Pub-brewery opened in 1983 and refurbished in 1995. Check brewing is still in operation before visiting: following the closure of the in-house brewery at the Yorkshire Grey (see below) some doubt hangs over the future of brewing at the Orange. The full-mash brews are stored in cellar tanks under a blanket of CO2. Seasonal beers: Chelsea Blossom (ABV 3.7% March-June), SW19 (ABV 3.9%, to coincide with Wimbledon), Pimlico Porter (ABV 4.6% Nov-March), Donner & Blitzed (ABV 5%, December), Sloane Danger (ABV 6%, Nov-March), Spiritual Reunion (ABV 5.9% Nov-March). Regular beers: SW1 (ABV), SW2 (ABV 5%), Victoria Lager (ABV 5%) and SW1 (smooth, ABV 4%).

YORKSHIRE GREY
2-6 Theobalds Road, London, WC1X 8PN
Tel (020) 7405 8287
Fax (020) 7831 2359

Historic pub near London's legal heartland in the Inns of Court, High Holborn and Fleet Street. The brewery was extensively refurbished in 1995, but brewing ceased in June 2001 when the pub was sold to Enterprise Inns.

NEW BREWERIES

The following new breweries were notified to the Good Beer Guide as it went to press:

Doghouse Brewery, Scorrier, Cornwall.

The Lab, Lowes Arms, 301 Hyde Road, Denton, Greater Manchester.

Nathan's Fine Ales, Dovecote Brewery, Old Ale House, Top Street, Elston, Notts.

Nursery Brewery, Keynsham, Somerset.

Pub Groups

Pub groups are the new power in the land where beer retailing is concerned. They developed rapidly in the 1990s in the wake of the government's Beer Orders that required national brewers to give their tenants the right to buy guest beers free of the tie. Rather than improve pubgoers' choice, the brewers preferred to sell off most or all of their tenanted estates. As pub groups are not owned by brewers, they do not have to offer guest beers, and many focus on heavily-discounted national brands. The major developments in 2001 were the sale by the Whitbread pub division of its entire estate to Morgan Grenfell, the City of London bank that is a subsidiary of Deutsche Bank of Frankfurt, and the bid by Pubmaster for Wolverhampton & Dudley Breweries. The former Whitbread estate is now run under the name of Laurel Pub Company. In June 2001, Bass Leisure Retail changed its name to Six Continents, part of an agreement when Interbrew bought Bass Brewers.

AVEBURY

Avebury Taverns Ltd, Sterling House, 20 Station Road, Gerrards Cross, Bucks, SL9 8EL Tel (01753) 482600

Avebury operates 750 tenanted and leased pubs throughout England and Wales. All pubs trade as independent free houses with tenants able to choose 'market-leading brands' supplied by national, regional and local brewers. The choice includes more than 50 cask ales, and the group says it has a commitment to micro-brewers' products to satisfy local tastes.

BARRACUDA

Barracuda Group Ltd, Henley Road, Medmenham, Marlow, Bucks, SL7 2ER Tel (0845) 345 2528 Fax (0845) 345 2527

Barracuda is a new pub operator formed in July 2000. It has since bought 94 managed pubs in both the north of England from Enterprise Inns and the south of England as a result of taking over the Ambishus Pub Company. The main pub brands in Barracuda are the 20-strong Smith & Jones chain and the Barcentro chain. It takes its main cask beers from Adnams, Bass/Interbrew, Greene King, and Scottish Courage.

BASS

See Six Continents.

BURTONWOOD

Burtonwood Brewery plc, Bold Lane, Burtonwood, Warrington, WA5 4PJ Tel (01925) 225131

Brewing at the Burtonwood, Cheshire site is operated by Thomas Hardy Burtonwood, a joint venture formed in October 1998 between Burtonwood Brewery and Thomas Hardy Brewery of Dorchester. Burtonwood operates almost 500 pubs, the majority of which are traditional tenancies. Burtonwood's cask ales and a monthly changing cask beer from an independent brewer are made available to all Burtonwood tenancies. Fewer than half the Burtonwood estate stocks cask ale.

CAFE INNS

The company is now owned by Jennings of Cockermouth.

CATMERE

Catmere Ltd, Station Road, Scunthorpe, Lincs, DN15 6PY Tel (01724) 861703 Fax (01724) 861708

Catmere owns 10 pubs, nine managed, one tenanted, mostly in the free trade, but it plans to expand to 12 sites. Its guest ales are supplied by Bass/Interbrew, Courage and Wolverhampton & Dudley. One of its outlets, the Honest Lawyer, at Scunthorpe, offers regional and micro-brewery cask ales, changing on a daily basis.

TOM COBLEIGH

Tom Cobleigh, Spencer House, Cliftonville Road, Northampton, NN1 5BU Tel (01604) 745000

Established in 1992 with just two pubs, the estate has grown to 107 across England. The company was taken over by the Rank Group in 1996 but was bought by its management. Licensees choose beers from a head office range of national and regional ales, with Scottish Courage as the main supplier. A list of rotating guest beers is also offered. The tenanted estate of pubs was acquired in 1994 from Whitbread, though these are signed as belonging to the Nice Pub Company.

COMMER INNS

Commer Group Ltd, Commer House, Station Road, Tadcaster, N Yorkshire, LS24 9JF Fax (01937) 834236 E-mail commer@commer.co.uk Website www.commer.co.uk

A freehold-owned estate with 75 pubs run as tenancies from the north Midlands to the North-east. Supplies come from Bass/Interbrew, Carlsberg-Tetley, Scottish Courage and Whitbread/Interbrew. All cask ales on suppliers' lists are available to tenants.

CONQUEST INNS

Conquest Inns Ltd, 1st floor, 172 Bullsmoor Lane, Enfield, Mddx, EN1 4SE
Tel (01992) 717718
Fax (01992) 717788

Conquest Inns is a subsidiary of the Jersey Brewing Company and operates an estate, mainly tenanted, of 50 pubs. Most of the pubs are in the South-east, but the company plans to expand at the rate of 20 pubs a year. Beers come from Bass/Interbrew and Scottish Courage, and the company has no definitive policy on cask ale, leaving the choice to tenants.

CROWDED HOUSE

Crowded House Pub Company, 31 High Street North, Dunstable, Beds, LU6 1HX
Tel (01582) 471363

Formed with the purchase of 40 former Beefeater pub/restaurants from Whitbread for £36 million in 1998, Crowded House is now in receivership.

JT DAVIES

JT Davies & Sons Ltd, 7 Aberdeen Road, Croydon, Surrey, CR0 1EQ
Tel (020) 8681 3222
Fax (020) 8760 0390

Wine merchants now controlling 51 tenancies and leased houses in the South-east. Its main suppliers are Bass/Interbrew and Scottish Courage, with some beers from Fuller's and Harveys.

DAVY'S

Davy's, 59-63 Bermondsey Street, London, SE1 3XF
Tel (020) 7407 9670
Fax (020) 7407 5844

Wine merchants and shippers since 1870, Davy's has been opening wine bars/restaurants in the London area since 1965, taking previously unlicensed properties and creating a Dickensian, sawdust, nooks-and-crannies type of establishment. Its Davy's Old Wallop (ABV 4.8%) is a re-badged brew of undeclared origin (though Courage Directors fits the bill). This is usually served in pewter tankards or copper jugs. The company currently runs around 50 outlets, including a few pubs.

DEVONSHIRE

See Honeycombe.

ELDRIDGE POPE

Eldridge Pope & Co plc, Weymouth Avenue, Dorchester, ST1 1QT

Founded as the Green Dragon Brewery in 1837, Eldridge Pope divorced itself from brewing in 1996 when it split into two wings, the brewing side becoming known as Thomas Hardy Brewery (see Independents). The company now runs 188 pubs, 124 managed, the rest tenanted. It takes Eldridge Pope beers from Thomas Hardy and has supply agreements with Bass/Interbrew and Scottish Courage. See also Burtonwood.

ENTERPRISE INNS

Enterprise Inns plc, Cranmore Avenue, Shirley, Solihull, W Midlands, B90 4LE
Tel (0121) 733 7700
Fax (0121) 733 6447

Formed in 1991 with an initial acquisition of 372 pubs from Bass, the company has grown rapidly and is now one of the Big Three pub groups. Its estate of 2,600 incorporates pubs purchased through the acquisitions of John Labatt Retail, Discovery Inns, Gibbs Mew, Mayfair Taverns, Century Inns (Tap & Spile), and Swallow Inns. Enterprise added to this number by buying 439 former Whitbread pubs, and then in June 2001 bought 432 managed houses from Scottish & Newcastle, taking its estate to 3,400. Chief Executive Ted Tuppen said he planned to build an estate of 6,500. Enterprise believes that the leased and tenanted approach to operating pubs provides licensees with the opportunity to run their own pubs without the cost associated with buying it, though the company outraged many former S&N and Whitbread managers by 'encouraging' them to switch to tenancies. A range of cask beers from all the major brewers, as well as many of the regionals, is available through the Enterprise central distribution network.

FAMOUS

Famous Pub Company UK Ltd, Cranmore Avenue, Shirley, Solihull, W Midlands B90 4LE
Tel (0121) 733 7700
Fax (0121) 733 6447

Expanding pub company established with the purchase of 37 pubs from Whitbread in 1996. The company currently owns 45 tenanted pubs in London and the Home Counties. Famous is supplied by Whitbread/Interbrew. Some tenants are allowed a guest beer.

FITZGERALD

Sir John Fitzgerald Ltd, Cafe Royal Buildings, 8 Nelson Street, Newcastle upon Tyne, NE1 5AW
Tel (0191) 232 0664
Fax (0194) 261 4509

Long-established, family-owned property and pubs company. Its pubs convey a free house image, most offering a good choice of cask beers, including guest ales from smaller craft breweries. The 31 pubs are mainly in the North-east but there are also outlets in Edinburgh, Harrogate and London.

GRAND PUB COMPANY

See Unique.

GRAY

Gray & Sons (Chelmsford) Ltd, Rignals Lane, Galleywood, Chelmsford, Essex, CM2 8RE
Tel (01245) 475181
Fax (01245) 475182

Former Chelmsford brewery that ceased production in 1974 and which now supplies its 49 tied houses in Essex with a choice of cask beers from Adnams, Greene King and Mighty Oak. The tenants are also free to choose from a monthly guest list that features at least 10 different ales.

GREENALLS

Once-famous Warrington brewery that got out of brewing and has now even given up on pub owning, too, selling its estate to Inn Partnership, a subsidiary of Nomura.

HEAVITREE

Heavitree Brewery plc, Trood Lane, Matford, Exeter, EX2 8YP
Tel (01392) 217733
Fax (01392) 229939

A West Country brewery, established in 1790, which gave up production in 1970 to concentrate on running pubs. The current estate, which is mainly confined to Devon, stands at 112: 12 managed, and the rest tenanted or leased. The pubs are tied to beers from the Whitbread Cask Collection, with some products from Bass/Interbrew.

HONEYCOMBE

Honeycombe Leisure, Muldoons, 50 Water Lane, Ashton, Preston, Lancs, PR2 2NL
Tel (01772) 723764

This 25 year-old company bought the Devonshire Pub Co in 2000 and now has 89 managed houses. Beers are supplied by the nationals plus Burton Bridge, Eccleshall, Moorhouses, Phoenix and Timothy Taylor, and most micro-brewers in the North-west. It is one of the biggest sellers of Black Sheep, Moorhouses and Timothy Taylor in the north of England. Honeycombe also has its own micro-brewery based in Salford.

INN BUSINESS
See Punch.

INN PARTNERSHIP

Inn Partnership Ltd, Axis House, Tudor Road, Manor Park, Runcorn, Cheshire
Tel (01925) 651234
Fax (01925) 402560

Company owned by Nomura and bought from Greenalls in 1998. It has 1,200 pubs.

INNSPIRED

InnSpired Pubs & Taverns, Wiltshire Drive, Trowbridge, Wilts, BA14 0TT
Tel (01225) 763171
Website www.innspired.co.uk

InnSpired represents the remains of Ushers of Trowbridge, a famous West Country brewery founded in 1824. Ushers became part of Grand Metropolitan in 1960. The brewery passed into Courage's control, but a management buy-out restored its independence in 1991. In 1999 Ushers merged with the Alehouse Company of Southampton. With the involvement of the Alchemy group, it was always likely that the new owners would opt to concentrate on real estate and retailing. Brewing ceased early in 2000. InnSpired has an estate of more than 1,000 pubs. It bought 50 outlets in the North of England and plans to grow the estate to 2,000. 'Usher's' cask beers are brewed for InnSpired by Thomas Hardy of Dorchester; other brands, such as Manns Brown Ale and the Lowenbrau range of lagers, are brewed by Burtonwood. A separate company, Refresh UK, which operates from the same Trowbridge offices, has been set up to retail the Usher's brands. Under new tenancy agreements, InnSpired's landlords can offer a wide range of beers that often includes ales from specialist and local breweries.

INNTREPRENEUR

Inntrepreneur Pub Co Ltd, Suite 2, Pegasus House, Haddenham Aerodrome Industrial Estate, Haddenham, Bucks, HP17 8LJ
Tel (01844) 293500
Fax (01844) 293520

Inntrepreneur, with a 4,000-strong pub estate, was the pub-owning company formed by Courage (Foster's) and Grand Metropolitan as part of a pubs-for-breweries swap in 1991. It was bought by Nomura in 1997 and most of its pubs have been transferred to Nomura's Unique Pub Company (qv). Inntrepreneur now has an estate of 100 tenancies and around 600 leased outlets.

LAUREL

Laurel Pub Co, PO Box 888, Porz Avenue, Dunstable, Beds, LU5 5XA
Tel (01582) 844300

Laurel is the pub company run by Morgan Grenfell/Deutsche Bank, who bought the Whitbread pub estate in 2001. At present the estate is divided into Pub Partnerships, totalling 1,717 leased outlets, and Taverns, totalling 1,639 managed outlets, including Brewers Fayre, Kiln & Kettle, Hogshead, Peppers, Pitchers, Wayside Inns, Family Inns and Real Pub Co. Considerable rationalisation and sales are continuing, but Laurel plans to maintain the Hogshead group, which has played an important role in featuring beers from micro-brewers. Laurel is currently based in a Whitbread office and will move at some stage to new premises.

MACLAY

Maclay Group plc, Thistle Brewery, Alloa, FK10 1ED
Tel (01259) 723387
Fax (01259) 216511

Maclay, founded in 1830, stopped brewing in September 1999. It owns 35 pubs and its full range of cask ales is brewed under licence by Belhaven (qv).

McMANUS

McManus Taverns, Kingsthorpe Road, Northampton, NN2 6HT
Tel (01604) 713601

Company with 12 pubs in the East Midlands, Essex and Kent. Half serve cask beer mainly from ScotCo and Wadworth.

MAYFAIR TAVERNS

Mayfair Taverns Ltd, The Old Malt House, St John's Road, Banbury, Oxon, OX16 8HX Fax (01295) 278677

A company established with a management buy-out from Ascot Estates and the purchase of 251 Ascot pubs in 1996. Mayfair's pubs are spread throughout most of the country, as far north as Bradford and Manchester, and are either three-year tenancies or are leased on 20-year contracts. Beers are supplied entirely by Carlsberg-Tetley and Scottish Courage.

MERCURY

Mercury Management (UK) Ltd, Mercury House, Amber Business Village, Amington, Tamworth, Staffs, B77 4RP Tel (01827) 62345 Fax (01827) 64166 E-mail headoffice@mercurymanagement.co.uk Website www.mercurymanagement.co.uk

Mercury Management is the result of a 1999 buy-out of Mercury Taverns by Mark Butler and Kevin Thornton. They run 45 country pubs, and also operate 40 other premises: hotels, a holiday village, bars, pubs and workingmen's clubs. The estate is supplied mainly by Bass and Whitbread (Interbrew), but regional cask ales are supplied by The Beer Seller.

MILL HOUSE

Mill House Inns, Century House, Westcott Venture Park, Westcott, Bucks, HP18 0XB Tel (01296) 652600 Fax (01296) 652626

Mill House has 54 managed pubs nationwide, ranging from town bars to country pubs and family pub-diners. Its main supply agreement is with Bass/Interbrew.

MORRELLS

Morrells of Oxford Ltd, Ferry Hinksey Road, Oxford, OX2 OES Tel (01865) 727722 Fax (01865) 794262

Morrells of Oxford is a pub retailing company, all that remains of the once much-loved Oxford brewery that closed in 1998 following a boardroom split and the eviction of two members of the Morrell family. The 132 pubs are now owned by Michael Cannon, the retailer who closed the Devenish Brewery to run its pubs. Morrells beers are now brewed by Thomas Hardy of Dorchester, though the company promotes them as having 'the real taste of Oxford'.

NOBLE HOUSE

Noble House Pub Company, 4 Thamesside Centre, Kew Bridge, Brentford, Mddx TW8 OHF Tel (020) 8847 9100

A subsidiary of Noble House Leisure, which owns hotels and restaurants. The group is run by Robert Breare, who masterminded the exit from brewing by Ushers of Trowbridge to become the pub company InnSpired (qv). Mr Breare was interested in making a bid for Wolverhampton & Dudley in 2000, but withdrew to allow Pubmaster to make its own bid. Noble House owns 214 pubs bought from Scottish & Newcastle.

OLD ENGLISH

Old English Inns plc, Castle House, 21/23 Station Road, New Barnet, Herts, EN5 1PA Tel (020) 8275 3333 Fax (020) 8275 3334 E-mail enquiries@oldenlgish.co.uk Website www.oldenglish.co.uk

A company running 142 coaching inns and 53 pub/restaurants. All the pubs and inns are managed and extend across England from Lincolnshire southwards. All have restaurants and more than two thirds offer accommodation. All sell cask ale. Old English was bought by Greene King for £59 million in September 2001.

PHOENIX

Phoenix Inns Ltd, Pegasus House, Haddenham Aerodrome Industrial Estate, Haddenham, Bucks, HP17 8LJ Tel (01844) 293500

Operating from the same offices as Inntrepreneur, Phoenix is owned by Nomura and currently runs 500 tenancies.

PUB ESTATE

Pub Estate Company Ltd, 3-5 Ashfield Road, Chorley, Lancs, PR7 1LH Tel (01257) 238800 Fax (01257) 233918

A company established with the purchase of 230 pubs from Scottish & Newcastle, it currently has 335 pubs (28 managed, the rest tenanted or leased) based in the north of England and Scotland. The pubs offer beers from Bass/Interbrew, Carlsberg-Tetley, Scottish Courage and Whitbread/Interbrew, but some licensees have guest beer rights. The company's aim is to convert all pubs to three-year leases that would offer no guest beer entitlement and would mean all pubs being served by a favoured supplier, probably Scottish Courage.

PUBMASTER

**Pubmaster Ltd, Greenbank,
Hartlepool, TS24 7QS
Tel (01429) 266699 Fax (01429) 278457
Website www.pubmaster.co.uk**

Pubmaster was formed in 1991 to take over
the pub estate of Brent Walker, the property
group that also owned Cameron's and Tolly
Cobbold breweries in the 1980s. Following a
management buy-out in 1996, Pubmaster
continued to grow, with recent acquisitions
from Mercury Taverns, Devonshire Pub
Company and Swallow. Swallow, the
remant of the Vaux brewing group, sold 662
pubs to Pubmaster. In 2000, the initial
investors in the group sold their stake to
West LB (a German financial company),
First Principal Finance Group/Nomura of
Japan, Rotch Property Group, and St
Modwen Properties. Pubmaster is currently
operating more than 2,000 pubs and stocks
beers from Bass/Interbrew, Carlsberg-Tetley,
Whitbread/Interbrew and some
independents. Pubmaster launched an
unsuccessful bid for the 1,700-strong pub
estate of Wolverhampton & Dudley
Breweries in the summer of 2001.

PUNCH GROUP

Punch was formed in 1998 by a team led by
Hugh Osmond, founder of Pizza Express,
with the purchase of the Bass leased pub
estate. In 1999, Punch, with the backing of
Bass, bought Allied Domecq's pub estate. It
sold 550 former managed houses to Bass
and now owns some 5,000 pubs itself.
Punch claims its lessees are free to take
guest beers, but brewers who supply the
group are closely monitored and have to
offer substantial discounts to be accepted.
As a result, a number of small brewers have
lost their trade with Punch. One regional
brewer told the Guide that Punch 'screwed
us into the floorboards over discounts'. The
main cask ales sold by Punch are Tetley and
Worthington, with guest ales from a
number of regionals.

PUNCH RETAIL LTD
**107 Station Road, Burton-on-Trent,
Staffs, DE14 1BZ
Tel (01283) 545320
Website www.punch-retail.co.uk**

The managed side of the business, based in
the former offices of Allied Domecq. It
operates 1,046 pubs.

PUNCH PUB COMPANY
**Lincoln House, Wellington Crescent, Fradley
Park, Lichfield, Staffs, WS13 8RZ
Tel (01543) 443500
Fax (01543) 443502
Website www.punchpubs.co.uk**

Punch Pub Co, which includes the Inn
Business estate, is the tenanted and leased
division of the Punch Pub Company. It
owns some 4,000 pubs.

PYRAMID

**Pyramid Pub Co Ltd,
Suite H3, Steam Mill Business Centre,
Steam Mill Street, Chester, CH3 5AN
Tel (01244) 321171**

Manages 700 pubs owned by Royal Bank of
Scotland.

RANDALL VAUTIER

**Randall Vautier Ltd, PO Box 43,
Clare Street, St Helier,
Jersey, JE4 8NZ
Tel (01534) 887788
Fax (01534) 888350**

A brewery that ceased production in 1992.
It now runs 30 pubs on Jersey selling beers
from Bass/Interbrew, Scottish Courage,
Marston's and Whitbread/Interbrew. Not to
be confused with Randalls of Guernsey (see
Independents).

REGENT INNS

**Regent Inns PLC, 77 Muswell Hill,
London, N10 3PJ
Tel (020) 8375 3000
Fax (020) 8375 3001
Website www.regentinns.co.uk**

Founded in 1980, Regent owns 115
managed pubs in London and the Home
Counties, and is growing by 20 pubs a year.
Expansion into the Midlands and the north
is taking place. Most of the pubs are
unbranded, are allowed to retain their own
identities, and are not tied to any supplier.
Most pubs feature a wide range of national,
local and seasonal cask ales chosen by
managers. The company has contracts with
Bass/Interbrew, Scottish Courage and
Whitbread/Interbrew, plus half a dozen
regional breweries, but licensees can also
take beer from the Beer Seller wholesaler.
Branded pubs include Walkabout Inns and
Jongleurs.

RYAN

**Ryan Elizabeth Holdings plc,
Ryan Precinct, 33 Fore Street,
Ipswich, IP4 1JL
Tel (01473) 217458
Fax (01473) 258237**

The company's 54 pubs in East Anglia,
many bought from national brewers, are
mostly leased to individual operators on
35-year contracts, although eight are
managed. The pubs are generally free of the
tie but some have a tie to Bass/Interbrew.
A subsidiary company, Elizabeth Hotels,
operates independent bars/pubs in its
hotels with a local community focus,
offering four to five real ales and live
entertainment. The main beer supplier is
Bass/Interbrew but Adnams, Greene King,
Tolly Cobbold and Nethergate also supply
beers.

SCORPIO INNS

**Scorpio Inns Ltd, Commerce House,
Abbey Road, Torquay, TQ2 5PJ
Tel (01803) 296111
Fax (01803) 296202**

Formed in 1991, it now runs 111 pubs
(nearly all tenanted). These stock beers from
Interbrew's Bass and Whitbread, and are
located in South Wales, the Bristol and
Hereford areas, and along the M4 corridor
to Swindon.

SFI

SFI Group plc, SFI House, 165 Church Street East, Woking, Surrey, GU21 1HJ
Tel (01483) 227900
Fax (01483) 227903

Established in 1986, the SFI Group, formerly Surrey Free Inns, runs around 100 pubs and café bars in England, Scotland and Wales. The number is set to increase, with further acquisitions planned. Beers come from national brewers and a range of smaller regional brewers. Cask ale is a feature of the Litten Trees outlets. Not all the pubs are branded: around 20, such as the Ostrich Inn, at Colnbrook, near Heathrow, have kept their own identity. SFI bought the Slug & Lettuce group in 2000.

SIX CONTINENTS

Six Continents (formerly Bass Leisure Retail), Cape Hill, PO Box 27, Birmingham, B16 0PQ
Tel (0121) 558 1481
Fax (0121) 558 2515

Following the sale of its brewing interests to Interbrew, Bass had to change the name of its pubs division. In June 2001 it became Six Continents, to reflect its role as a leisure and retail company; it is one of the world's leading hoteliers through ownership of Holiday Inns. Six Continents runs more than 2,000 pubs, bars and restaurants and employs around 40,000 people. Its brands include Vintage Inns (traditional pubs), Ember Inns (local pubs), and Goose (traditional pubs offering good food and drink). All these outlets offer cask ales: Ember Inns always have one cask ale available and could have as many as four if the volume is sustainable. Ember Inns also hold Cask Ale Celebrations: the 2001 event featured more than 30 cask ales. Vintage Inns will always stock Draught Bass and one other cask beer, if the volume is sustainable. Goose pubs have the highest sales of cask ale. The company acquired 550 pubs from Allied Domecq in late 1999, the majority of which stock Tetley Bitter and Draught Bass. This acquisition has given the group some historic gems such as the Philharmonic in Liverpool, the Bear in Oxford, and several in London, including the Black Friar. Six Continents offers a selection of cask beers: as well as Draught Bass, Worthington Bitter, Stones, Hancocks, M&B Mild and Brew XI, a number of guest ales are also available, including Adnams, Highgate Bitter, Fuller's London Pride and Greene King Old Speckled Hen.

SLUG & LETTUCE

See SFI.

TYNEMILL

Tynemill Ltd, 2nd Floor, Victoria Hotel, Dovecote Lane, Beeston, Nottingham, NG9 1JG
Tel (0115) 925 3333
Fax (0115) 922 6741

Founded by former CAMRA chairman Chris Holmes, Tynemill has been established in the East Midlands for more than 20 years, and now owns 17 pubs. It has a 'pubs for everyone' philosophy, avoiding trends and gimmicks, and concentrating on quality cask ales and food in good surroundings, including public bars where space permits. It sold more than 1,500 different cask ales during 2000, thought to be more than anyone else in the industry. Managers have complete autonomy on guest beers they sell. During 2000, Tynemill entered into two joint ventures: the Mildly Mad Pub Co with York Brewery, to develop an estate in the York region, and with Breakthroughpoint in Nottingham. Tynemill is now the sole owner of the Castle Rock Brewery in Nottingham (qv). Regional and micro-brewers make up the bulk of Tynemill's products.

UNIQUE

Unique Pub Co Ltd, Mill House, Aylesbury Road, Thame, Oxon, OX9 3AT
Tel (01844) 262000
Fax (01844) 261332

Formed in 1998 by Nomura Principal Finance Group of Japan, Unique owns 734 tenanted and 2,479 leasehold pubs, the best of the Inntrepreneur and Phoenix estates. Through its wholly-owned supply company, SupplyLine Services, Unique pubs can access more than 200 drinks brands from national and a range of regional brewers including JW Lees, Shepherd Neame, Smiles and Young's. In 2000, Unique announced the launch of a pilot scheme with SIBA, the Society of Independent Brewers, to give Unique licensees in the North greater access to a wider range of cask ales from independent brewers. This scheme was set to expand during 2001.

WETHERSPOON

JD Wetherspoon plc, PO Box 616, Watford, WD1 1YN
Tel (01923) 477777
Fax (01923) 219810
Website www.jdwetherspoon.co.uk

Wetherspoon is a vigorous and independent pub retailer that currently owns more than 480 managed pubs, with rapid plans for expansion. No music is played in any of the pubs, all offer no-smoking areas, and food is served all day. Two standard beers from Scottish Courage are available to managers: Theakston Best Bitter and Courage Directors. Each pub also stocks regional ales from the likes of Cains, Fuller's, Greene King, Shepherd Neame and Wolverhampton & Dudley, plus at least two guest beers. There are usually two beer festivals a year, one in the spring, the other in the autumn, at which up to 30 micro-brewery beers are stocked over a four-day period. In 2000, Wetherspoon bought a small group of cafe bars known as Lloyds No 1. Cask beer has been introduced to all these outlets, which did not stock real ale before. Lloyds No 1 differs from Wetherspoon by offering contemporary background music. Wetherspoon joined the Cask Marque scheme in 2000 and now enjoys CM accreditation in more than 435 pubs.

WHARFEDALE

Wharfedale Taverns Ltd,
Highcliffe Court, Greenfold Lane,
Wetherby, W Yorkshire, LS22 6RG
Tel (01937) 580805
Fax (01937) 580806
E-mail wharfedale_taverns@compuserve.com

A company set up in 1993 by former Tetley employees to lease 90 pubs from that company, it currently owns 17 pubs, mainly in Yorkshire. It also runs 40 to 50 other houses with agreements from national brewers and pub companies. Fifty-five houses are managed and seven are tenanted. It is developing its Wharfedale Traditional Taverns concept: four houses are under this banner and all future acquisitions will fit into the concept. The main beers come from Carlsberg-Tetley; guest beers are from C-T's Tapster's Choice.

WHITBREAD

See Laurel.

WHITE ROSE

White Rose Inns plc,
Chantrell House,
1 Chantrell Court, The Calls,
Leeds, W Yorkshire, LS2 7HA
Tel (0113) 2461332
Fax (0113) 2461350

The group has 45 pubs: four managed houses and 41 tenancies in Yorkshire with supplies from Bass/Interbrew, Black Sheep, Carlsberg-Tetley, and its own micro-brewery, the Barge & Barrel Brewery, based at the Barge & Barrel at Elland (see Independents).

WILLIAMS

James Williams (Narberth),
7 Spring Gardens, Narberth,
Pembrokeshire, SA67 7BP
Tel (01834) 862200
Fax (01834) 862202

A privately-owned concern, founded in 1830 and operating 54 pubs in West and mid-Wales. Tenants are mainly supplied by Bass/Interbrew, Brains, Carlsberg-Tetley and Whitbread/Interbrew. A house ale, James Williams IPA, brewed by Brains, is also available. Regional brands are also supplied, including beers from Adnams, Banks, Bateman, Everards, Jennings and Shepherd Neame. The company has a regular, extensive guest cask beer policy.

WIZARD INNS

City Gate, 17 Victoria Street, St Albans,
Herts, AL1 3JJ
Tel (01727) 792200
Fax (01727) 792210

Former CAMRA national chairman Chris Hutt, also the ex-boss of Midsummer Inns and Unicorn Inns, purchased 30-40 former Phoenix Inns pubs to set up this new company. Nomura, the Japanese bank that owns Unique Pub company, has a £9.5 million stake. Wizard Inns operates traditional, unbranded pubs. All the pubs are managed and serve a selection of real ales.

YATES'S

Yates's Wine Lodges Ltd, Peter
Yates House, Manchester Road,
Bolton, BL3 2PY
Tel (01204) 373737
Fax (01204) 388383

Company founded in Oldham in 1884 by wine merchant Peter Yates, it now runs 95 managed pubs in locations from Scotland to London. Beers are mainly from Bass/Interbrew, Scottish Courage and Whitbread/Interbrew, with some regional ales also featured. Boddingtons Bitter is sold at one price nationwide but many branches do not serve real ale.

R.I.P.

The following breweries have closed, gone out of business, suspended operations, or merged with another company since the 2001 Guide was published:

Alchemy	Fiddlers	Man in the Moon
Berkeley	Flannery's	Mash & Air
Big Foot	Forge	Old Barn
Bishops London Bridge	Four Rivers	Old Pint Pot
Black Dog	Fromes Hill	Planets
Border	Hale & Hearty	Prince of Wales
Bridgewater	Hedgehog & Hogshead	Restalrig
Cock, Kingsthorpe	Henstridge	Tap & Tin
Deeping	Tom Hoskins	Tisbury
Duffield	Huddersfield/Kitchen	Welton's
Cranborne	Judges	Winchester
Falstaff	Kent Garden	Worldham
Farmers Arms	Machlachlans	Ventonwyn

The Beers Index

Over 2,000 beers are highlighted; they refer to beers in bold type in the Breweries section.

A

A1 Amber Ale Rockingham 752
A.T. Bob Heather 715
Abbot Ale Greene King 710
Acre Moss Amber Bryson's 684
Advent Ale Hogs Back 718
Aegir Ale DarkTribe 697
After Glow Triple fff 769
Agent Orange Leadmill 726
Agent X Altrincham 668
Ahtanum Gold Oldershaw 741
Albecore DarkTribe 697
Albert Ale Earl Soham 700
Albion Pale Ale Cox & Holbrook 694
Ale Extra Tindall 766
Ale Force Storm 761
Ale Mary Brandy Cask 682
Ale of Atholl Moulin 735
Ale to the Tsar Fernandes 703
Ale 2000 Bragdy Ceredigion 680
All Seasons Bitter Hanby 713
Alltime Tindall 766
Alton's Pride Triple fff 769
Ambeardextrous Beartown 674
Amber Ale Dolphin 698
Ambush Ale Weetwood 772
Amnesia Bragdy Ynys Môn 681
Anchor Street Porter Crouch Vale 695
Angel Ale Derwent Rose 698
Angel Hill Boggart Hole Clough 680
Ansells Best Bitter Carlsberg-Tetley 780
Ansells Mild Carlsberg-Tetley 780
Antonine Eglesbrech 700
Apache Kings Head 725
Apocalypse Now Leadmill 726
Arbor Light Whim 774
Arc Light Warcop 771
Arc-Light Leadmill 726
Archangel Abbeydale 667
Archbishop Lee's Ruby Ale North Yorkshire 736
Archers Rebuff Payn 743
Ariel Square Four Concertina 692
Arizona Phoenix 744
Armada Ale Harveys 715
Arms Park Ale Brains 681
Arrowhead Cannon Royall 688
Ashbourne Ale Leatherbritches 726
Asum Ale Evesham 702
Asum Gold Evesham 702
Atom Splitter City of Cambridge 690
Augustinian Ale Nethergate 735
Auld Alliance Fyfe 707
Auld Rock Valhalla 770
Autumn Gold Linfit 728
Avebury Ale Heritage 716
Aviator Flying Firkin (Dent) 698
Axeman's Block Tigertops 766
Axeman's Light Tigertops 766
Ayala's Angel Hesket Newmarket 716
Ayrtons Ale Saddleworth 753

B

Backwoods Bitter Cropton 695
Badger Stone Bitter Briscoe's 683
Balmy Mild Cropton 695
Bannock Burn Bridge of Allan 683
Bantam Phoenix 744
Barbus Barbus Butts 686
Barcud Coch Bragdy Ceredigion 680
Bargee Barge & Barrel 672
Barley Swine Ring O' Bells 751
Barmpot Goose Eye 709
Barn Ale Bitter Old Luxters 740
Barn Ale Special Old Luxters 740
Barn Owl Bitter Cotleigh 693
Barnsley Bitter Barnsley 673; Oakwell 738
Barnstablasta Barum 673
Barnstormer Bath 674; Frankton Bagby 705
Barochan Houston 721
Barrister's Bitter Church End 690
Barron's Hopsit Exe Valley 702
Barrows Bitter Bryson's 684
Bass No 1 Barley Wine Museum (Interbrew) 781

Bastion Portchester 746
Battering Ram Portchester 746
Battleaxe Rudgate 753
Baz's Bonce Blower Parish 743
BB Donnington 699; Tomos Watkin 772
Beach Boys Blencowe 679
Beachcomber Teignworthy 764
Beacon Bitter Everards 701
Bear Ass Beartown 674
Bearskinful Beartown 674
Beaufort's Ale Storm 761
Beastly Bitter Black Bull 677
Beaver Bitter Belvoir 676
Bedlam Bitter Picks 745
Beechwood Bitter Chiltern 690
Beer Milk Street 733
Bees Knees Bartrams 673; Trueman's 769
Beetroot Coles 692
Beggars Tipple Clearwater 691
Belfast Special Bitter Whitewater 774
Bellringer Abbey Ales 667
Ben Nevis Bridge of Allan 683
Benchmark Stonehenge 761
Bendigo Castle Rock 689
Bengal Tiger Concertina 692
Benskins Bitter Carlsberg-Tetley 780
Benvolio Newby Wyke 736
Beorma Beowulf 676
Berry Street Bitter Liverpool 728
Berry Street Mild Liverpool 728
Bespoke Leatherbritches 727
Best Boys Blencowe 679
Best Dark Ale Goacher's 708
Best Lockoford Bitter Townes 768
Betty Stogs Bitter Skinner's 758
Beyond The Pale West Yorkshire 774
Big Frank's Bitter Old Wheelton 740
Big Nev's Six Bells 758
Big Nipper Rat & Ratchet 748
Bill Monks Derwent 698
Billy Kings Head 725
Birthday Brew Bitter Caythorpe 689
Bishop Ridley's Ale Black Bull 677
Bishop's Tipple Refresh (Thomas Hardy) 714
Bishops Farewell Oakham 737
Bishops Finger Shepherd Neame 757
Bishop Ridley's Ale Black Bull 677
Bishopswood Bitter Swansea 763
Bizarre Swale 763
Black Adder Mauldons 732
Black and Amber Warcop 771
Black Bat B&T 671
Black Bear Beartown 675
Black Beard Leyden 727
Black Beastie Arundel 670
Black Beauty Porter Vale 770
Black Bishop Durham 700
Black Bull Bitter Black Bull 677; Theakston (Scottish Courage) 783
Black Bull Mild Blanchfields 678
Black Cat Moorhouses 734
Black Coombe Foxfield 705
Black Country Bitter Holden's 719
Black Country Mild Holden's 719
Black Cuillin Isle of Skye 723
Black Dog Mild Elgood's 701
Black Eagle Pitfield 745
Black Heart Stout Barnsley 673
Black Hoad Foxfield 705
Black Jack Stout Castle Rock 689
Black Knight Goff's 708
Black Magic Mild Hanby 713
Black Magic Stout Oakhill 738
Black Mamba Mild Sarah's Hop House 755
Black Mass Abbeydale 667
Black Moggy Mild Kemptown 725
Black Moss Stout Riverhead 751
Black Pear Malvern Hills 730
Black Porter Captain Cook 688
Black Shiver Stout Turkey 769
Black Stout Broadstone 683
Black Stump Barge & Barrel 672
Black Swan Dark Mild Vale 770
Black Velvet Durham 700
Black Widow Dark Horse 696
Black Witch Bragdy Ceredigion 680
Black Zac Wentworth 773
Blackguard Butts 686
Blackjack Old Mill 740
Blackmoor Stout Frome Valley 706
Blackout Big Lamp 677
Blackout Stout Points West 746
Blackwater Mild Crouch Vale 695
Bladderwrack Stout Railway Tavern 748
Blake's Gosport Bitter Oakleaf 738

Blakeley's Best O'Hanlon's 737
Blaven Isle of Skye 723
Blencathra Bitter Hesket Newmarket 716
Blodeuwedd Bragdy Ceredigion 680
Blond Smiles 758
Blonde Arran 669; Daleside 696
Blondie Liverpool 728
Bluebird Bitter Coniston 692; Coniston (Brakspear) 682
Boadicea Chariot Ale Iceni 722
Boathouse Bitter City of Cambridge 690
BOB Wickwar 775
Bobbin's Bitter Three B's 765
Bock Tigertops 766
Boddingtons Bitter Interbrew 782
Bodicote Bitter Plough Inn 746
Bodmin Beast Sutton 762
Bodmin Boar Ring O' Bells 751
Boggart Bitter Boggart Hole Clough 680
Boggart Brew Boggart Hole Clough 680
Bomar Bitter Northumberland 737
Bombardier Premium Bitter Wells 773
Bomber's Moon Boat 680
Boro Best North Yorkshire 736
Bosun Bitter Old Laxey 739; Poole 746
Bowler Strong Ale Langton 726
Boxer Heavyweight Langton 726
BPA Blackpool 678
Bramling Traditional City of Cambridge 691
Brand Oak Bitter Wickwar 775
Brandy Snapper Brandy Cask 682
Branoc Branscombe Vale 682
Braveheart Moulin 735
Braye Mild Guernsey 711
Breacais Highgate 717
Breakfast Barum 673
Brew Dolphin 698
Brew 101 Six Bells 758
Brewers Droop Marston Moor 731
Brewers Gold Crouch Vale 695; Pictish 745
Brewers Pride Marston Moor 731
Brewery Tap Chalk Hill 689
Brewhouse Bitter Dunn Plowman 699
Brideshead Bitter York 779
Bridge Bitter Burton Bridge 685
Bridge Street Bitter Green Dragon 710
Bridport Bitter Palmer 742
Brief Encounter Foxfield 705
Brigadier Bitter Hoskins & Oldfield 720
Bright Otter 742
Brighton Bitter Kemptown 725
Brindle Bullmastiff 685
Broadside Adnams 667
Bronte Goose Eye 709
Brooker's Bitter & Twisted Harviestoun 715
Brooklands Express Sawbridgeworth 756
Brothers Best Sussex 762
Brown Bomber Sawbridgeworth 756
Brunel Premier Ale Scanlon's (O'Hanlon's) 756
Brush Bitter Alcazar 668
Brydge Bitter Bank Top 671
Buccaneers Jollyboat 724
Buchanan's Best Bitter Federation 703
Buchanan's Original Federation 703
Buckley's Best Bitter Brains 681
Buckley's IPA Brains 681
Buckshot Cannon Royall 688
Buddy Confusing Bryn Celyn 684
Buddy Marvellous Bryn Celyn 684
Buddy's Delight Bryn Celyn 684
Bull Village Brewer (Hambleton) 712
Bull Best Bitter Blanchfields 678
Bullion Old Mill 740
Bullseye Payn 743
Burcom Bitter Willy's 775
Burcote Premium Pale Worfield 777
Burgh Bitter Fisherrow 704
Burglar Bill Clark's 691
Burnsall Classic Bitter Briscoe's 683
Burntwood Bitter Mighty Oak 733
Butcher's Best Crown 695
Butser Bitter Gale's 707
Butt Jumper Humpty Dumpty 722
Butterley Bitter Riverhead 751
Butty Bach Wye Valley 778
Buzz Spinnaker 759
BVB Branscombe Vale 682

C

Cairngorm Gold Aviemore 670
Cambridge Bitter Elgood's 701
Canal No 5 Sunset 762
Canary Green Jack 710
Canny Lad Durham 699

Captain Bill Bartrams Best Bitter Bartrams 673
Captain Smith's Titanic 767
Captain's Stout Bartrams 673
Cardinal Filo 704
Cascade Hanby 713; Linfit 728
Caskade Oldershaw 741
Casnewydd Warcop 771
Castle Arundel 670; Warwickshire 771
Castles Northumberland 737
Castletown Bitter Bushy's 686
Catbells Pale Ale Hesket Newmarket 716
Caterpult Portchester 746
Caudle Bitter Langton 726
Cauldron Snout High Force (Darwin) 717
Cavalier Clearwater 691
Cavendish Gold Shardlow 757
Celebration Liverpool 728; Maypole 732
Cellar Vee Summerskills 762
Celtic Gold Durham 699
Celtic Queen Iceni 722
Celtic Warrior Pictish 745
Centenary Ale Maypole 732
Centennial Museum (Interbrew) 781
Centurion Hadrian & Border 712
Centurion's Ghost Ale York 779
Cereal Killer North Yorkshire 736
Chainmaker Mild Enville 701
Challenger Barum 673
Champflower Ale Cottage 693
Champion Ale Badger 671
Chancellors Revenge Shardlow 757
Charles Gough's Old Faithful Tirril 766
Charles' First Brew Shraley Brook 758
Charter Ale Broadstone 683
Chase Your Tail Spinning Dog 759
Chaucer Ale Green Dragon 710
CHB Chalk Hill 689
Cherry Bomb Hanby 713
Chester's Strong & Ugly Barngates 672
Chevin Chaser Briscoe's 683
CHH Bryn Celyn 684
Chiddingstone Larkins 726
Chippy Best Henry's Butcher's Yard 715
Chiswick Bitter Fuller's 707
Chocolate Heavy Marble 731
Chocolate Stout Sarah's Hop House 755
Chorister Abbey Ales 667
Chorlton-cum-Hazy Marble 731
Christmas Noggin Hoskins & Oldfield 721
Churchill's Pride Archers 669
Classic Arundel 670; Castle Eden 688; Spinnaker 759
Claud Hamilton Humpty Dumpty 722
Cliff Hanger Bank Top 672
Cloghopper Holland 719
Cloudy Marble Marble 731
Club Bitter Concertina 692
Coachman's Best Bitter Coach House 692
Coal Porter Altrincham 668
Coast Liner Skinner's 758
Coast 2 Coast Derwent Rose 698
Coat O' Red John O'Gaunt 724
Cobblers Orchard 741
Cock o' t' North Halifax 712
Cocker Hoop Jennings 724
Cockersnoot Bitter End (Derwent) 677
Cockfighter Wicked Hathern 775
Codename Roz Fenland 703
Coiners Ryburn 753
Colley's Dog Tring 769
Colne Valley Bitter Scanlon's (Vale) 756
Colquhoun's Dark Mischief Stout Lidstones 728
Comfort Sutton 762
Comfortably Numb Triple fff 769
Coming of Age Brunswick 684
Conroy's Stout Derwent Rose 698
Constellation Brown Cow 684
Contraflow Ales of Kent 668
Cooking Bitter Grainstore 709
Cool Cask Theakston (Scottish Courage) 783
Coopers WPA Wickwar 775
Cornish Blonde Wheat Beer Skinner's 758
Cornish Coaster Sharp's 757
Cornish Knocker Ale Skinner's 758
Cornish Original Redruth 749
Cornish Rebellion Redruth 749
Cotswold Way Wickwar 775
Cottage Pride Old Cottage 739
Country Best Bitter McMullen 729
Country Bitter Steamin' Billy (Grainstore) 760
Country Bumpkin Country Life 694
County Pride Home County 719
Courage Best Bitter Scottish Courage 783
Courage Directors Scottish Courage 783
Coxswains Special Bitter Willy's 775

Falstaff Warwickshire 771
Farm Gold Parish 743
Farmers Joy Verulam 770
Farne Island Hadrian & Border 711
Fat God's Bitter Queen's Head 748
Fawn White Hart 774
Feather Plucker Mild McGuinness 729
Feb 59 Bryn Celyn 684
Fenland Gold Payn 743
Festival Ale Alewife 668; Burton Bridge 686;
    Clark's 691
Festival Mild Gale's 707
Fiddler's Elbow Wychwood 777; Donoghue 699
Figgy's Brew Skinner's 758
Fine Edge Old Kent 739
Fine Light Ale Goacher's 708
Fine Soft Day Iceni 722
Fire 2000 St George's 754
Fire Bellied Toad Frog Island 706
Fire Fly O'Hanlon's 737
Firebox RCH 749
First Gold Kings Head 725; Liverpool 728
First Out Black Dog 677
Fisherman Adnams 667
Five Bridge Bitter Mordue 735
Five Hides Museum (Interbrew) 781
Flannery's Harvest Moon Spinning Dog 760
Flannery's Oatmeal Stout Spinning Dog 760
Flannery's Rheidol Reserve Spinning Dog 760
Flashman's Clout Strong Ale Goldfinch 709
Flat Cap Bank Top 671
Fletcher's Ale Broadstone 683
Flintknapper's Mild Chalk Hill 689
Flintlock Best Bitter Coach House 692
Floral Dance Porter 746
Flotsam Hadrian & Border 711
Flowerface Bragdy Ceredigion 680
Flowers IPA Interbrew 782
Flowers Original Bitter Interbrew 782
Flying Herbert North Yorkshire 736
Fools Gold North Yorkshire 736
Forest Gold Red Shoot 750; Rockingham 752
Forest XB High Force (Darwin) 716
Forge Bitter Sussex 762
Formidable Ale Cains 687
Fortress Ale Beckett's 675
44 Special Blackawton 678
Fortyniner Ringwood 751
Founders Ale Refresh (Thomas Hardy) 714
4Bs Berrow 676
4K Mild Keltek 725
Four Shires North Cotswold 736
Fox Exmoor 702
Fox's Nob Highgate 717
Foxfield Flyer Foxfield 705
Fraoch Heather Ale Heather 715
Frays Mild Scanlon's (Vale) 746
Fred's Favourite Fist Full Payn 744
Frederics Robinson's 752
Freebooter Jollyboat 724
Friar Duck Mallard 730
Friary Meux Bitter Carlsberg-Tetley 780
Friggin in the Riggin Flagship 704
Fruiterer's Mild Cannon Royall 688
Fruits of the Forest Rockingham 752
Fuggle-Dee-Dum Goddards 708
Fuggles Special Dolphin 698
Full Ahead DarkTribe 697
The Full Malty Cottage Spring 693
Full Pitch Old Kent 739
Funky Monkey Milk Street 733
Furnace Warcop 771
Fursty Ferret Gribble Inn 711
Futtock Ale Flagship 704
Fyfe Fyre Fyfe 707

G

Galingale Old Chimneys 739
Galleon DarkTribe 697
Galloway Gold Sulwath 761
Gannet Mild Earl Soham 700
Gardener's Tap Springhead 760
Gargoyle Lichfield 727
Gauntlet Arundel 670
GB Gale's 707
GB Mild Lees 727
Ge It Sum Ommer Goldthorn 709
Gem Bitter Bath 674
Generation Hook Norton 720
Genesis North Cotswold 736
Gent Salamander 755
Genuine Blonde Wheat Beer Passageway 743
Geordie Pride Mordue 735
German Pils Passageway 743

GFB Hop Back 720
The Ghillie Broughton 684
Ghost Glentworth 707
Ghost on the Rim Anglo Dutch 668
Gilbert's First Brew Hop Back 720
Ginger Spinnaker 759
Ginger Beer Enville 701
Ginger Swan Swan 763
Ginger Tom Hoskins & Oldfield 721
Gingernut Premium Coach House 692
Gladiator Hadrian & Border 711
Gladstone McMullen 729
Glen Ale Whitewater 774
Glencoe Stout Bridge of Allan 683
Glory Barnsley 673
GNC Northumberland 737
Godfathers Itchen Valley 723
Gold Arundel 670; Broadstone 683; Bullmastiff 685;
    Butcombe 686; Exmoor 702; Iceni 722;
    Potton 747; Trueman's 769
Gold Beach Hart 714
Gold Digger Bank Top 671
Gold Dragon Bragdy Ceredigion 680
Gold Medal Linfit 728
Cold Star West Berkshire 773
Gold Star Ale Goacher's 708
Gold Tankard Wylam 778
Gold 2000 St George's 754
Golden Ventnor 770
Golden Ale North Yorkshire 736; St Peter's 754
Golden Arrow Cottage 693
Golden Bear Warwickshire 771
Golden Best Taylor 764
Golden Bitter Archers 669
Golden Blond Holland 719
Golden Braid Hopdaemon 720
Golden Brown Home County 719
Golden Bud Townes 768
Golden Chance Malton 730
Golden Delicious Burton Bridge 685
Golden Eagle Black Isle 677
Golden Eye 700 Sunset 762
Golden Gate Nethergate 735
Golden Glow Holden's 719
Golden Grale Beckett's 675
Golden Hill Ale Pembroke 744
Golden Honey Hanby 713
Golden Hornet Clark's 691
Golden Jackal Wolf 775
Golden Lance Keltek 725
Golden Lite Spinnaker 759
Golden Newt Elgood's 701
Golden Peace Cuckmere Haven 696
Golden Pig Country Life 694
Golden Promise Caledonian 687
Golden Smile Blackpool 678
Golden Thread Salopian 755
Golden Valley Scattor Rock 756
Goldenhop Shardlow 757
Goldfield Hambleton 712
Goldings Leatherbritches 726
Gone Fishing Green Jack 710
Good Old Boy West Berkshire 773
Goodrich Castle Springhead 760
Gordon the Gofer White Hart 774
Gordon's Amber Ale Sarah's Hop House 755
Gothic Enville 701
The Governor Hull 721
Graduate Morrells (Thomas Hardy) 714
Granary Bitter Reepham 750
Grand Prix Mild Steamin' Billy (Belvoir) 760
Grandad Tom's Porter Hoskins & Oldfield 721
Granny Wouldn't Like It Wolf 776
Grantham Stout Oldershaw 741
Grapefruit Beer St Peter's 755
Grass Hopper Green Jack 710
Gravediggers Church End 690
Great Cockup Porter Hesket Newmarket 716
Great Dane Stonehenge 761
Great Eastern Woodforde's 777
Great Northern Coalfield Northumberland 737
Great Raft Bitter Old Chimneys 739
Green Bullet Fernandes 703
Green Goddess Durham 699
Green Man Bartrams 673
Greenall's Bitter Carlsberg-Tetley 780
Greenall's Mild Carlsberg-Tetley 780
Greengrass Old Rogue Ale Daleside 696
Greenmantle Ale Broughton 683
Greyhound Strong Bitter Elgood's 701
Grizzly Ghost Anglo Dutch 668
Grozet Gooseberry Ale Heather 715
Grumpling Vale 770
Gryphon Wentworth 773
Gunner's Daughter Old Cannon 739

Light Brigade Leyden 727
Light Horse Bitter Caythorpe 689
Light Oak Weatheroak 772
Lightyear Glentworth 707
Lincolnshire Yella Belly Organic Bitter
  Bateman 674
Linebacker Leadmill 726
Lion Slayer Fyfe 707
Lion's Pride Maypole 732
Lionheart Hampshire 713
Lions Main Picks 745
Lions Pride Picks 745
Lip Smacker Holland 719
Liquor Mortis Blue Moon 679
Little Matty Hoskins & Oldfield 720
Little Nipper Lloyds 729
Little Red Rooster Triple fff 769
Little Sharpie Humpty Dumpty 722
Littondale Light Briscoe's 683
Lizard Point Organic 741
Logend Boggart Hole Clough 680
Lomond Gold Bridge of Allan 683
London Pride Fuller's 707
Long Hop Old Kent 739
Loosehead Happy Hooker 713
Lord Ashford's Special Reserve
  Scanlon's (Vale) 756
Lord Lee's North Yorkshire 736
Lord Rodney Porter Fernandes 703
Lorimers IPA Caledonian 687
Lost John's Turkey 769
Low House Bitter Earl Soham 700
Lower Odcombe Ale Odcombe 738
Loxley Maypole 732
Lucky Punter Lidstones 728
Luddite Ryburn 753
Lynne Pearce Sawbridgeworth 756

M

M&B Brew XI Interbrew 781
M&B Mild Interbrew (Highgate) 717
Machen Bitter White Hart 774
Mae West Maypole 732
Maggs Magnificent Mild West Berkshire 773
Magic Mushroom Mild Whim 774
Magik Keltek 725
Magus Durham 699
Maidstone Porter Goacher's 708
Main Street Bitter Pembroke 744
Mainbrace Bitter Jollyboat 724
Mainsail Crewkerne 694
Mainseam Northumberland 737
Malt Shovel Mild Fernandes 703
Malty Towers Towne 768
Man in the Boat Boat 680
Manannan's Cloak Bushy's 686
Marathon SP Sporting Ales 760
Marathon Ale Six Bells 758
Marbury Mild Paradise 743
March Haigh Special Bitter Riverhead 751
Mardler's Woodforde's 776
Marld Bartrams 673
Marquis Brewster's 682
Marriots Mild Sunset 762
Massey's Bitter Museum (Interbrew) 781
Master Brew Bitter Shepherd Neame 757
Masterpiece Museum (Interbrew) 781
Matins Abbeydale 667
Matthew Brown Lion Bitter Scottish Courage
  (Mansfield) 730
Mayfair Maypole 732
Mayfly Shardlow 757
Maypole Mild Oakleaf 738
McEwan's 80/- Scottish Courage 782
Medra Bragdy Ynys Môn 681
Melsa Bitter Wawne 772
Meltdown Dark Star 697
Mendip Gold Oakhill 738
Mendip Twister Oakhill 738
Mercian Shine Beowulf 676
Merlin Double Stout Tomos Watkin 772
Merlin's Ale Broughton 683
Merlin's Magic Moor 734
Merriemaker Marston Moor 731
Mickey Finn Hull 721
Middlesex Gold Scanlon's (O'Hanlon's) 756
Midhurst Mild Ballard's 671
Midnight Blinder Goldfinch 709
Midnight Sun Special Pale Ale Goldfinch 708
Mildew Green Dragon 709
Military Mild Old Chimneys 739
Milk of Amnesia Blue Moon 679;
  Old Wheelton 740
Millennium Ale Guernsey 711

Millennium City Durham 700
Millennium Mash Berrow 676
Millennium Premium Crouch Vale 695
Miller's Ale Bird in Hand 677
Minotaur Milton 733
Mirage Glentworth 707
Mistle Mild Brown Cow 684
Molennium Moles 734
Moletrap Bitter Mauldons 732
Molly Malone's Porter Hilden 717
Monkey Magic Eccleshall 700
Monkey Town Mild Phoenix 744
Monkey Wrench Daleside 696
Monkmans Slaughter Cropton 695
Monks Mild Wawne 772
Monty's Mild Brewster's 682
Moondance Triple fff 769
Moonraker Lees 727
Moonrunner Dark Horse 696
Moonshine Abbeydale 667
Moorgate Mild Picks 744
More Saddleworth 753
Morland Original Bitter Greene King 710
Morocco Ale Daleside 696
Morris Dancer Queen's Head 748
Mountain Ale Whitewater 774
Mr Chubb's Lunchtime Bitter West Berkshire 773
Mr Sheppard's Crook Exe Valley 702
Mudpuppy Salamander 755
Muffin Ale Townes 768
Murrays Summer Ale Caledonian 687
Mutineers Ale Derwent 698
Mutiny Rebellion 749
Muttleys Bark Mild Spinning Dog 759
Muttleys Mongrel Spinning Dog 759
Muttleys Revenge Spinning Dog 760
Mutton Clog Derwent Rose 698
Muzzle Loader Cannon Royall 688
My Better Half Franklin's 705
Myrica Ale O'Hanlon's 737

N

N/4 Bitter Marble 731
Nailers OBJ Worfield 777
Nailmaker Mild Enville 701
Nanny Flyer Leyden 727
Narrowboat Shardlow 757
Natterjack Frog Island 706
Nature Milk Street 733
Naughty Noughty Frome Valley 706
Navigation Ale Ryburn 753
Nellie Dene Old Mill 740
Nelson's Revenge Woodforde's 777
Nemesis Hart 714
Neptune Milton 733
Nessie's Monster Mash Tomintoul
  (Aviemore) 670
Nettle Coles 692
Nettlethrasher Barge & Barrel 672
NeueSchloss Durham 699
Nevisons Leap Boat 680
New Dawn Millennium Ale Alcazar 668
New Imperial Concertina 692
Newshound 2000 Wolf 776
Newton's Drop Oldershaw 741
Niagara Leadmill 726
Nick's Milk Street 733
Nightjar Daleside 696
Nightmare Hambleton 712
Nimmo's 4X Castle Eden 688
Nimmo's 3X Castle Eden 688
No-Eyed Deer Goose Eye 709
Noble Bitter Beowulf 676
Nog Mild Museum (Interbrew) 781
Nord Atlantic Humpty Dumpty 722
Norfolk Nog Woodforde's 777
Norfolk Wheaten Reepham 750
Norman's Conquest Cottage 693
Norman's Pride Corvedale 693
Northern Light Orkney 741
Northern Pride Hull 721
Nortons Bitter Orchard 741
Norwegian Blue Buffy's 685
Norwich Terrier Buffy's 685
Notley Ale Vale 770
Nottingham Pale Ale Castle Rock 689
No. 9 Plough 746
No I Potton 747
No. 1 Selby 756
No. 3 Selby 756
No 3 Yates 778
Nuptuale Oakleaf 738
Nut Brown Ale Fisherrow 704
Nutcracker Hanby 713

Priscilla Pale Swaled Ale *763*
Progress Pilgrim *745*
Prospect Road Sunset *762*
Proud Salopian Salopian *755*
PSB Parish *743*
Ptarmigan 80/- Harviestoun *715*
Puffer Ale Forth *705*
Pure Gold Itchen Valley *723*
Puritans Porter Springhead *760*

R

Radgie Gadgie Mordue *735*
Raging Bull Bitter Blanchfields *678*
Raglan Sleeve Leyden *727*
Rail Ale Beer Engine *675*
Railway Porter Brunswick *684*
Railway Sleeper Humpty Dumpty *722*;
    Porter *746*
Rain Dance Spinnaker *759*
Rainbow Chaser Hanby *713*
Rambrau Dent *697*
Rampant Gryphon Wentworth *773*
Rampart Hadrian & Border *712*
Rams Revenge Clark's *691*
Ramsbottom Strong Ale Dent *698*
Ramsey Pride Payn *744*
Ramsey Ruin Payn *744*
Rapier Pale Ale Reepham *750*
Raspberry Reepham *750*
Raspberry Wheat Iceni *722*
Rattler Boat *680*
Rave On Bryn Celyn *684*
Raven Ale Orkney *741*
Rawalpindi IPA Lidstones *728*
Real Mackay Far North *703*
The Rector's Ale Rectory *749*
Rector's Revenge Rectory *749*
Red Liverpool *728*
Red Ale Dark Star *697*; O'Hanlon's *737*
Red Cuillin Isle of Skye *723*
Red Dust Derwent Rose *698*
Red Gold Captain Cook *688*
Red Kite Black Isle *678*; Bragdy Ceredigion *680*;
    Woodhampton *777*
Red MacGregor Orkney *742*
Red Queen Bartrams *673*
Red River King *725*; Leadmill *726*
Red Squirrel Woodlands *777*
Redbrook Premium Bitter Riverhead *751*
Redwood Weatheroak *772*
Reel Ale Teignworthy *764*
Reg's Tipple Gribble Inn *711*
Regal Blonde Oldershaw *741*
Regatta Adnams *667*
Remus Cox & Holbrook *694*
Resurrection Tindall *766*
Rev James Original Ale Brains *681*
Revenge Keltek *725*
Reverend Eaton's Shardlow *757*
Reward Thwaites *765*
Reynolds Redneck Worfield *777*
Rhatas Black Dog *677*
Richmond Ale Darwin *697*
Ricketts 7X Hart *714*
Riding Bitter Mansfield *730*
Riggwelter Black Sheep *678*
Rip Snorter Hogs Back *718*
Riptide Spinnaker *759*
Roaring Meg Springhead *760*
Robin a Tiptoe John O'Gaunt *724*
Rocket Liverpool *728*; Wylam *778*
Roisin Dubh Iceni *722*
Rolling Thunder Leadmill *726*
Rope of Sand Fyfe *707*
Rossendale Ale Porter *746*
Roundhead's Gold Springhead *760*
Rowley Mild Lidstones *728*
Roy Morgan's Original Ale Travellers Inn *768*
Royal Mild Salopian *755*
Royal Oak Eldridge Pope (Thomas Hardy) *713*
Royal Welch Fusilier Plassey *746*
Ruby (1874) Mild Bushy's *686*
Ruby Mild Rudgate *753*
Ruddles Best Bitter Greene King *710*
Ruddles County Ale Greene King *710*
Rugby Special Frankton Bagby *705*
Rumpus Ridleys *750*
Rupert's Ruin Springhead *760*
Ruthven Brew Aviemore *670*
Rydale Bitter Ryburn *753*
Ryedale Champion Malton *730*

S

SA Brains *681*
Saddlers Best Bitter Highgate *717*
Saints Sinner Darwin *697*
Salem Porter Bateman *674*
Salsa Castle Rock *689*
Sam Powell Old Sam Wood *776*
Sam Powell Original Bitter Wood *776*
Samuel Cromptons Ale Bank Top *672*
Sanctuary Durham *700*
Sandrock Ventnor *770*
Sands Foxfield *705*
Sandy Hunter's Traditional Ale Belhaven *675*
SAS Crouch Vale *695*
Saxon Cross Rockingham *752*
SBA Donnington *699*
Scallywag Black Dog *677*
Scat Tor Rockin Lager Scattor Rock *756*
Scatty Bitter Scattor Rock *756*
Schiehallion Harviestoun *715*
Scorcher Rooster's *752*
Scoresby Stout Cropton *695*
Scottish Oatmeal Stout Broughton *683*
Scratching Dog Lloyds *729*
Scullion's Irish Hilden *718*
SEA Newby Wyke *736*
Sea of Tranquillity Blue Moon *679*
Second Brew Brunswick *684*
Secret Hop Corvedale *693*
Secret Kingdom Ale Northumberland *737*
Sedgley Surprise Sarah Hughes *721*
Selhurst Park Flyer Sawbridgeworth *756*
Serpentine Dark Ale Organic *741*
Session Bitter Lidstones *728*
Sextons Bitter Three Tuns *765*
Shaft Bender Saddleworth *753*
Shakemantle Ginger Ale Freeminer *706*
Shakespeare Special Bitter Fernandes *703*
Shambles Potton *747*
Shannon IPA Potton *747*
Sheepdog Northumberland *737*
Shefford Bitter B&T *670*
Shefford Dark Mild B&T *670*
Shefford Old Dark B&T *671*
Shefford Old Strong B&T *670*
Shefford Pale Ale B&T *670*
Shipwrecked Flagship *704*
Shire Bitter Hexhamshire *716*
Shires XXX Wychwood *777*
Shoemaker Frog Island *706*
Shoreditch 1850 Porter Pitfield *745*
Shot in the Dark Green Tye *711*
Shrimpers AVS (Daleside) *696*
Shropshire Gold Salopian *755*
Shropshire Lad Wood *776*
Shropshire Pride Worfield *777*
Shuttle Ale Three B's *765*
SID Kemptown *725*
Side Pocket for a Toad Tring *768*
Sidewinder Leadmill *726*; Newby Wyke *736*
Silver King Ossett *742*
Silver Shrew Rat & Ratchet *748*
Simpkiss Bitter Enville *701*
Simply The Best Mighty Oak *733*
Simpsons No. 4 Brown Cow *684*
Sir Roger's Porter Earl Soham *700*
6X Wadworth *771*
1646 Clearwater *691*
Skiddaw Special Bitter Hesket Newmarket *716*
Skiff West Berkshire *773*
Skinners Old Strong Bitter End (Derwent) *677*
Skipper Eddie's Ale Newby Wyke *736*
Skrimshander IPA Hopdaemon *720*
Skullsplitter Orkney *742*
Skylark Scattor Rock *756*
Slaters Bitter Eccleshall *700*
Slaters Original Eccleshall *700*
Slaters Premium Eccleshall *700*
Slaters Supreme Eccleshall *700*
Slaters Top Totty Eccleshall *700*
Sleeper Heavy Beer Engine *675*
Slingshot Newby Wyke *736*
Slipway Captain Cook *688*; Newby Wyke *736*
Smoke Stack Lightning Bank Top *672*
Smuggler Rebellion *749*
Smugglers Glory Ales of Kent *668*
Smugglers Mild Ales of Kent *668*
Snarlsberg Llager Bullmastiff *685*
Sneck Lifter Jennings *724*
Snowhite Castle Rock *689*
Soar Head Wicked Hathern *775*
SOD B&T *671*
Somerby Premium Parish *743*

Trotton Bitter Ballard's 671
True Glory Ringwood 751
Trumpeter Best Swan 763
Turbinia Wylam 778
Turnpike Harviestoun 715
Twin Screw DarkTribe 697
2B Arkells 669
Two Cannons Extra Pembroke 744
200 Premium Ale Palmer 743
Two Pints Cropton 695
2.5 Brakspear 681
2XS B&T 671
Twrogs Golden Summer Ale Coles 692
Tyke Bitter Orchard 741

U

Umbel Ale Nethergate 735
Umbel Magna Nethergate 735
Uncle Sam's Cropton 695
Uncle Stan Cox & Holbrook 694
Uncut Amber Marble 731
Undercliff Experience Yates 779
Up And Under Happy Hooker 713
Usher's Best Bitter Refresh (Thomas Hardy) 714

V

Vale Pale Ale Brewster's 682
Valley Stomper Scattor Rock 756
Vallum Bitter Hadrian & Border 711
Varsity Morrells (Thomas Hardy) 714
Velvet Sweet Stout Reepham 750
Venture Wentworth 773
Vicar's Ruin Church End 690
Victoria Ale Museum (Interbrew) 781
Victoria Bitter Earl Soham 700
Viking Rudgate 753
Village Bike Potton 747
Village Bitter Archers 669
Village Elder Cheriton 690
Vixen Velvet Lloyds 729
Vixen's Vice Alcazar 668
VPA Brewster's 682
Vulcan Bitter Featherstone 703

W

Waddlers Mild Mallard 729
Wages Blewitts 679
Waggle Dance Young's 779
Waghen Bitter Wawne 772
Wagtail Black Isle 678
Wakefield Pride Fernandes 704
Wallace IPA Maclay (Belhaven) 676
Wallop Country Life 694; Wood 776
Walsitch Wobbler Tower 768
Wammellers Wheat Bryson's 684
Wassail Ballard's 671
Wat Tyler Itchen Valley 723
Wealden Wonder Ales of Kent 668
Weather Ale Weatheroak 772
Webster's Green Label Best Scottish Courage 782
Webster's Yorkshire Bitter Scottish Courage 782
Wee Murdoch Aviemore 670
Wee Stoater Harviestoun 715
Weetablitz Sutton 762
Weiss Beer Tigertops 766
Weiss Buoy Willy's 775
Welsh Highland Bitter Snowdonia 759
Welsh Stout Plassey 746
Wem Special Hanby 713
Wennol Bragdy Ynys Môn 681
Weymouth Harbour Master Quay 747
Weymouth JD 1742 Quay 747
Weymouth Organic Gold Quay 747
Whap Wheasel Hexhamshire 716
Wharfedale Goose Eye 709
What the Fox's Hat Church End 690
WHB Wicked Hathern 775
Wheat-a-Bix Church End 690
Wheelbarrow Green Tye 711
Wherry Best Bitter Woodforde's 777
Whipping Golden Bitter Belvoir 676
Whispers Glentworth 707
Whistle Belly Vengeance Summerskills 762
Whistle Stop Shardlow 757
Whistling Joe Brandy Cask 682
Whitby Abbey Ale Black Dog 677
White Enville 701
White Adder Mauldons 732
White Bishop Durham 699
White Boar Village Brewer (Hambleton) 712
White Dolphin Hoskins & Oldfield 720
White Dwarf Wheat Beer Oakham 737

White Gold Durham 699
White Knight Goff's 708
White Monk Phoenix 744
White Mouse Rat & Ratchet 748
White Rat Rat & Ratchet 748
White Sapphire Durham 699
White Squall Newby Wyke 736
White Star Titanic 767
White Velvet Durham 699
White Wife Valhalla 770
Who Put the Lights Out? Skinner's 758
Whooper Pale Swan 763
Whoosh Tomos Watkin 772
Wichen Home County 719
Wight Spirit Ventnor 770
Wiglaf Beowulf 676
Wild Blonde Sutton 762
Wild Cat Tomintoul (Aviemore) 670
Wild Weasel Leadmill 726
Will's Resolve Sharp's 757
William the Conqueror Sweet William 763
Wilson's Original Bitter
 Scottish Courage (Mansfield) 730
Windgather Storm 761
Windrill Old Cottage 739
Winners SP Sporting Ales 760
Winter Brew Gale's 707
Winter Warmer Goddards 708; Young's 779
Witchfinder Porter Ridleys 750
Withy Cutter Moor 734
Wobbler Gribble Inn 711
Wobbly Bob Phoenix 744
Woild Moild Wolf 775
Wolf In Sheeps Clothing Wolf 775
Wolfhound Brown Cow 684
Wonderful Wood 776
Woodham IPA Bitter Crouch Vale 695
Workie Ticket Mordue 735
Worthington Bitter Interbrew 781
Worthington White Shield
 Museum (Interbrew) 781
WPA Wentworth 773
Wreckage Titanic 767
Wrenbury Ale Paradise 743
Wulfric Museum (Interbrew) 781
Wulfrun Gold Goldthorn 709
Wychert Ale Vale 770
Wykehams Glory Itchen Valley 723
Wynbunbury Red Paradise 743
Wynter Warmer Green Dragon 710

X

XB Bateman 674; Holden's 719; Theakston
 (Scottish Courage) 783; Yates 778
XL Bitter Burton Bridge 685
XSB Sutton 762
XTC Barum 673
XX Dark Mild Greene King 710
XXX Donnington 698; Three Tuns 765
XXX Mature Oakhill 738
XXXB Bateman 674
XXXX Hydes 722
XXXX Mild St Austell 754

Y

Yankee Rooster's 752
Yardstick Cambrinus 687
Yellow Hammer Black Isle 678
Yeoman 1767 Strong Ale Oakhill 738
Yodel Weiss Oakleaf 738
Yorkshire Grit Glentworth 707
Yorkshire Moors Bitter Cropton 695
Yorkshire Terrier York 779
Young Bob Malton 730
Young Pretender Isle of Skye 723
Young Stallion Liverpool 728
Young Tom Porter 747
Yr Hen Darw Du Bragdy Ceredigion 680
Ysbryd O'r Goeden Bragdy Ceredigion 680

Z

Zig-Zag Milk Street 733

Readers' recommendations

Suggestions for pubs to be included or excluded

All pubs are surveyed by local branches of the Campaign for Real Ale. If you would like to comment on a pub already featured, or any you think should be featured, please fill in the form below (or copy it), and send it to the address indicated. Your views will be passed on to the branch concerned. Please mark your envelope with the county where the pub is, which will help us to sort the suggestion efficiently.

Pub name:

Address:

Reason for recommendation/criticism:

Pub name:

Address:

Reason for recommendation/criticism:

Pub name:

Address:

Reason for recommendation/criticism:

Your name and address:

Please send to: [Name of county] Section, Good Beer Guide, 230 Hatfield Road, St Albans, Hertfordshire AL1 4LW

An offer for CAMRA members
GOOD BEER GUIDE
Annual Subscription

Being a CAMRA member brings many benefits, not least the big discount on the Good Beer Guide. *Now you can take advantage of an even bigger discount on the* Guide *by taking out an annual subscription.*

Simply fill in the form below and the Direct Debit form opposite (photocopies will do if you don't want to spoil your book), and send them to CAMRA at the usual St Albans address.

You will then receive the *Good Beer Guide* automatically every year. It will be posted to you before the official publication date and before any other postal sales are processed.

You won't have to bother with filling in cheques every year and you will receive the book at a lower price than other CAMRA members (the 2002 edition, for instance, was sold to annual subscribers at only £7.50).

So sign up now and be sure of receiving your copy early every year.

Note: This offer is open only to CAMRA members and is only available through using a Direct Debit instruction to a UK bank (use the form opposite, or copy it if you do not want to spoil your book). The offer is limited to one copy per member per year. Additional copies can be ordered separately at the CAMRA member's usual price. This offer applies to the 2002 *Guide* onwards.

Name

CAMRA Membership No.

Address and Post code

I wish to purchase the *Good Beer Guide* annually by Direct Debit and I have completed the Direct Debit instructions to my bank which are enclosed.

Signature   Date

Instruction to your bank or building society to pay by Direct Debit

Please fill in and send to the Campaign for Real Ale Limited, 230 Hatfield Road, St Albans, Herts AL1 4LW

Name and full postal address of your bank or building society

To the manager   Bank or building society

Address

Postcode

Name(s) of Account Holder(s)

Bank or building society account number

☐ ☐ ☐ ☐ ☐ ☐ ☐ ☐

Branch sort code

☐ ☐ ☐ ☐ ☐ ☐

Reference number

☐ ☐ ☐ ☐ ☐ ☐ ☐ ☐ ☐ ☐ ☐ ☐ ☐ ☐ ☐ ☐ ☐ ☐

Banks and building societies may not accept Direct Debit instructions for some types of account

Originator's identification number

9 2 6 1 2 9

For CAMRA official use only
This is not part of the instruction to your bank or building society

Membership number

Name

Postcode

Instruction to your bank or building society

Please pay CAMRA Direct Debits from the account detailed on this instruction subject to the safeguards assured by the Direct Debit Guarantee. I understand this instruction may remain with CAMRA and, if so, will be passed electronically to my bank/building society.

Signature(s)

Date

Postcode

Direct Debit
This Guarantee should be detached and retained by the payer.

The Direct Debit Guarantee
● This Guarantee is offered by all banks and building societies that take part in the Direct Debit Scheme. The efficiency and security of the scheme is monitored and protected by your own bank or building society.
● If the amounts to be paid or the payment dates change, CAMRA will notify you within ten working days in advance of your account being debited or as otherwise agreed.
● If an error is made by CAMRA or your bank or building society, you are guaranteed a full and immediate refund from our branch of the amount paid. You can cancel a Direct Debit at any time by writing to your bank or building society. Please also send a copy of your letter to CAMRA.

Join CAMRA
Free for three months!

- Has a pub near you been closed or ruined?
- Has your local brewery been taken over or its beers lost their flavour?
- Are you concerned about the price of a pint?

If you can answer 'yes' to any or all of these questions you are sure to benefit from becoming a member of CAMRA.

The Campaign for Real Ale is a voluntary organisation consisting of over 60,000 ordinary drinkers, run by an unpaid, elected National Executive and backed by a small core of professional executives. It speaks for drinkers everywhere in fighting to save pubs and breweries from closure, and in attempting to improve quality and to ensure pub standards are raised.

- As a member you can have your say about the issues which affect you. You can stand for election to office, attend the annual conference to speak and vote, and help organise local campaigns.
- You can help select pubs for the *Good Beer Guide*, help out at beer festivals and enjoy some excellent social activities.
- You can receive big discounts on the *Good Beer Guide* and other CAMRA books and products, free or reduced price admission to CAMRA beer festivals, plus the *What's Brewing* newspaper, delivered to your door each month. All new members receive the Members' Handbook as soon as they are registered.
- All this is available at the bargain price of just £14 per year (£17 per year for two people living at the same address).
- What's more you can even join for three months at no cost and see if you think it's worthwhile being a member.
- Fill in the application form below (or a photocopy of it) and the Direct Debit form on the previous page. If after three months you decide not to continue just write to CAMRA, cancel your membership and you will owe nothing.
Note: If you do not wish to take up the trial offer, but wish to join CAMRA anyway, fill in the application form and return it to us with a cheque for your first year's subscription. To pay by credit card, contact the Membership Secretary on (01727) 867201.
- Full annual membership £14
- Joint annual membership (two people at the same address) £17
- Life membership £168 (single)/£204 (joint)
- Under-26 membership £8 single/£11 joint.
Concessionary rates available on request.

Please delete as appropriate:
- ❏ I/We wish to take advantage of the trial membership, and have completed the instructions overleaf.
- ❏ I/We wish to become members of CAMRA
- ❏ I/We agree to abide by the memorandum and articles of association of the company.
- ❏ I/We enclose a cheque/PO for £   (payable to CAMRA)

NAME(S)

Address and Post Code

Date of birth

Signature(s)

To: CAMRA, 230 Hatfield Road, St Albans, Hertfordshire AL1 4LW